ALLE ZEIT WACH
1842

R.F. Schmidt G. Thews (Eds.)

Human Physiology

Second, Completely Revised Edition

Translated by Marguerite A. Biederman-Thorson

With 643 Figures, Most in Color

Springer-Verlag Berlin Heidelberg NewYork
London Paris Tokyo HongKong

Professor Dr. med. Robert F. Schmidt, Ph.D.
Physiologisches Institut der Universität
Röntgenring 9
D-8700 Würzburg, Fed. Rep. Germany

Professor Dr. Dr. Gerhard Thews
Physiologisches Institut der Universität
Saarstraße 21
D-6500 Mainz, Fed. Rep. Germany

Translation of „Physiologie des Menschen", 23. Auflage, 1987
ISBN 3-540-16685-8 Springer-Verlag Berlin Heidelberg New York
ISBN 0-387-16685-8 Springer-Verlag New York Heidelberg Berlin

ISBN 3-540-19432-0 Springer-Verlag Berlin Heidelberg New York
ISBN 0-387-19432-0 Springer-Verlag New York Heidelberg Berlin

Typsetting, printing and binding: Universitätsdruckerei H. Stürtz AG, Würzburg

2124/3145-543210

Preface to the Second Edition

This book first appeared in English in 1983, as a translation of the 20th Edition of the long-established German textbook *Physiologie des Menschen*. In this new English edition the text has been fundamentally "rejuvenated", to bring it up to date with the rapid advances in many areas of physiology and to incorporate many helpful suggestions from both readers and colleagues. In its scope and didactic goals, the book remains as we set forth in the Preface to the First Edition, which follows.

First, the content was substantially reorganized. The general aspects of cell physiology and intercellular communication, which underlie the functions of all organs, were extracted from the various chapters and brought together in a separate introductory section. We are most grateful to our colleague J. DUDEL for undertaking this task.

The second step was to make the text more concise in several places (for instance, the motor and somatovisceral systems previously occupied two chapters and have now been condensed into one). By these processes of condensation and distillation of the passages on general cell physiology, space was made for the necessary additions and expansions, with only a slight change in the overall length of the book.

The new chapters in the book, in sequential order, offer a separate discussion of "Nociception and Pain" (Chapter 10) and describe the physiology of the "Sexual Functions" (Chapter 32), "Reproduction and Pregnancy" (Chapter 33) and "Aging and Old Age" (Chapter 34). Several of the existing chapters were totally rewritten: "General Sensory Physiology" (Chapter 8), "Somatovisceral Sensory System" (Chapter 9), "Endocrinology" (Chapter 17), "Functions of the Alimentary Canal" (Chapter 29), "Function of the Kidneys" (Chapter 30) and "Water and Electrolyte Balance" (Chapter 31). All the other chapters were carefully revised, with attention to both content and presentation.

A few of the authors represented in the First English Edition have now withdrawn; we offer our sincere thanks for their previous collaboration. Furthermore, some of the authors who remain with us have developed their scientific work in new directions and left the old behind. As a result, some responsibilities have been redistributed in this new edition. Last but not least, we have been joined by a number of new colleagues. These welcome newcomers (in the order of their contributions) are M. WIESENDANGER, H. HANDWERKER, U. GRÜSSER-CORNEHLS, W. WUTTKE, W. JELKMANN, K. EWE, U. KARBACH, P. DEETJEN and R.K. ZAHN. We thank them both for their expertise and for their willingness to accept the constraints, temporal and otherwise, of our undertaking.

Of the many hundred illustrations in this textbook, many were newly drawn and others were improved or exchanged. We are very grateful to Mr. JÖRG KÜHN and the coworkers in his graphics studio in Heidelberg for taking over this task and executing it admirably. The synthesis of the old pictorial material with the new, and the realization of the – often quite diverse – ideas of the authors as a graphically uniform concept of high quality had to be achieved under stringent deadlines, as is so often the case in the production of books. These problems were solved with outstanding skill. The resulting illustrations should considerably assist the reader in penetrating even the most complex subjects treated in the text.

In the name of all the authors, we are again pleased to thank all who have helped with the preparation and production of this new edition.
Special thanks are due to our technical and secretarial staff for their untiring efforts; without them, it would hardly have been possible for any of the authors to complete their contributions on time. Dr. MARGUERITE BIEDERMAN-THORSON has again produced an outstanding translation. We greatly appreciate her capable and careful work. And we are equally indebted to Springer Verlag, in particular the staff of the Production Department under Mr. R. FISCHER, for excellent cooperation; their proficiency and attention to detail are obvious in the resulting book.

May 1989

R.F. SCHMIDT
G. THEWS

Preface to the First Edition

Human Physiology is the English version of a time-honored German textbook first published by HERMANN REIN in 1936. We undertook the preparation of a completely revised 20th edition with the intention of making the book accessible to a wide range of English-speaking readers. The subject-matter was therefore organized so as to correspond to the structuring of physiology courses in most countries of the world.

The book is directed primarily at students of medicine. Its aim is to enable them to understand living processes in the human organism, providing the basis for the scientific understanding of pathological changes. The material was chosen to give the reader not only the knowledge required for passing examinations, but also information necessary for a subsequent professional career. For this reason special attention was devoted to pathophysiological aspects.

We hope that the book will prove a useful reference on the present status of physiology for physicians in private and hospital practice as well as for its primary readership. The book should also serve biologists, biochemists, pharmacologists, pharmacists, and psychologists as a source of information on the physiological principles underlying their disciplines.

In order to facilitate quick reference, we have striven for clear organization, lucid presentation, the accentuation of key ideas, and instructive illustrations. For the sake of compactness we have dispensed with historical introductions, accounts of unproven hypotheses, and descriptions of specialized measuring techniques. The references provided at the end of each chapter are of two sorts: textbooks and handbooks providing interested readers with guidelines for further study, and selected original papers describing recent or little-known findings.

We would like to express our gratitude here to all those who assisted in the preparation and production of this textbook. Most of all we want to thank our coauthors for their willingness to take the ideas and wishes of the editors into consideration, thereby enhancing the book's clarity and balance. We are especially grateful to the staff of the Gay & Benz studios in Stuttgart for their excellent renderings of the illustrative material. We are particularly indebted to Dr. Marguerite Biederman-Thorson, Oxford, for her outstanding translation. Finally we would like to thank the publisher and his staff for their generous support in the preparation of this book.

August 1982

R.F. SCHMIDT
G. THEWS

Table of Contents

Part I. General Physiology of the Cell and of Intercellular Communication

Part II. Motor and Integrative Functions of the Nervous System; Muscle Physiology

Part III. General and Special Sensory Physiology

Part IV. Neuronal and Hormonal Regulatory Processes

Part V. Blood and the Circulatory System

Part VI. Respiration

Part VII. Energy Balance, Work, and Environment

Part VIII. Nutrition, Digestion and Excretion

Part X. Appendix

List of Authors

Professor Dr. H. Altner
Fachbereich Biologie der Universität,
Universitätsstraße 31
D-8400 Regensburg

Professor Dr. H. Antoni
Physiologisches Institut
der Universität,
Hermann-Herder-Straße 7
D-7800 Freiburg i.Br.

Professor Dr. J. Boeckh
Fachbereich Biologie
der Universität,
Universitätsstraße 31
D-8400 Regensburg

Professor Dr. K. Brück
Zentrum für Physiologie
am Klinikum
der Justus-Liebig-Universität,
Aulweg 129
D-6300 Gießen

Professor Dr. P. Deetjen
Physiologisches Institut
der Universität,
Fritz-Pegel-Straße 3
A-6010 Innsbruck

Professor Dr. J. Dudel
Physiologisches Institut der
Technischen Universität,
Biedersteiner Straße 29
D-8000 München 40

Professor Dr. K. Ewe
1. Medizinische Klinik
und Poliklinik,
Langenbeckstraße 1
D-6500 Mainz

Professor Dr. Dr. J. Grote
Physiologisches Institut I
der Universität,
Nußallee 11
D-5300 Bonn

Professor Dr. O.-J. Grüsser
Physiologisches Institut der Freien
Universität, Arnimallee 22
D-1000 Berlin 33

Professor Dr. Ursula Grüsser-Cornehls
Physiologisches Institut der Freien
Universität, Arnimallee 22
D-1000 Berlin 33

Professor Dr. H.O. Handwerker
Physiologisches Institut der
Universität, Universitätsstraße 17
D-8520 Erlangen

Professor Dr. W. Jänig
Physiologisches Institut der
Universität, Olshausenstraße 40–60
D-2300 Kiel

Professor Dr. W. Jelkmann
Physiologisches Institut der
Medizinischen Hochschule,
Ratzeburger Allee 160
D-2400 Lübeck

Professor Dr. U. Karbach
Medizinische Universitätsklinik
Innenstadt, Ziemssenstraße 1
D-8000 München

Professor Dr. R. Klinke
Zentrum der Physiologie,
Theodor-Stern-Kai 7
D-6000 Frankfurt 70

Professor Dr. J.C. Rüegg
II. Physiologisches Institut
der Universität,
Im Neuenheimer Feld 326
D-6900 Heidelberg

Professor Dr. R.F. Schmidt
Physiologisches Institut der
Universität, Röntgenring 9
D-8700 Würzburg

Professor Dr. Dr. G. Thews
Physiologisches Institut der Universität,
Saarstraße 21
D-6500 Mainz

Professor Dr. H.-V. Ulmer
Sportphysiologische Abteilung am
Fachbereich 26 der Universität,
Saarstraße 21
D-6500 Mainz

Professor Dr. Ch. Weiss
Physiologisches Institut der
Medizinischen Hochschule,
Ratzeburger Allee 160
D-2400 Lübeck

Professor Dr. M. Wiesendanger
Physiologisches Institut
der Universität,
Rue du Musée 5
CH-1700 Fribourg

Professor Dr. E. Witzleb
Institut für Angewandte Physiologie
und medizinische Klimatologie
der Universität,
Olshausenstraße 40/60
D-2300 Kiel

Professor Dr. W. Wuttke
Zentrum für Frauenheilkunde
der Universität
Abteilung für Klinische und
Experimentelle Endokrinologie,
Humboldt-Allee 19
D-3400 Göttingen

Professor Dr. R.K. Zahn
Institut für Physiologische Chemie
der Universität,
Saarstraße 21
D-6500 Mainz

Professor Dr. M. Zimmermann
II. Physiologisches Institut
der Universität,
Im Neuenheimer Feld 326
D-6900 Heidelberg

I
General Physiology of the Cell and of Intercellular Communication

1 Fundamentals of Cell Physiology

J. DUDEL

Subject matter of physiology. Physiology is the science of the functional mechanisms of living organisms. It is based on, and historically derived from, anatomy, the study of the large- and small-scale structure of organisms. Not until this century did biochemistry ("physiological chemistry") split off from physiology as a new discipline, leaving the physical processes in organisms as the subject of physiology. For example, physiologists examine the processes that maintain the identity of a living body during its exchanges with its surroundings and ensure its reproduction in subsequent generations; or they describe the manner in which information is received from the surroundings and converted into appropriate responses, by which the organism in turn influences its environment.

In a textbook of physiology it is taken for granted that the reader has a working knowledge of the structures, the function of which is to be described. Here, therefore, the discussion of each function is accompanied by only a brief indication of the underlying structures, so that the analysis of physiological relationships will be more readable. Similarly, details of the diverse chemical events that are coupled with the "physiological" events are left to textbooks of biochemistry. On the other hand, it has now become possible – in an increasing number of cases – to clarify macroscopically visible functional processes down to the molecular level. The distinction between physiology and biochemistry thus becomes only one aspect in a more general context: physiology is concerned chiefly with the relationship between functional processes and the performance of the organism as a whole.

We begin this exploration of human physiology by considering the **functions of cells**. These are the bricks of which organisms are built, and they are very similar in all the different animals. Cell function is rarely studied in human cells; amebas and the tissues of invertebrates, frogs, rats and other animals are most often used. A complete discussion of cell physiology is far beyond the scope of this book. Here we present only what seems necessary as a foundation for human physiology. The main topics are the mechanisms and control of the exchange of substances, both within a cell and between cells and their surroundings.

1.1 The Cell as a Compartment for Physiological Exchange Processes

Plasma membrane. Animal cells are enclosed by a plasma membrane (Fig. 1-1). Its structure, very similar to that of the many intracellular membranes, will be described in some detail. The basic matrix of the membranes consists of *lipids*, of which phosphatidylcholine is the most common. These lipids are composed of a hydrophilic head-group to which 2 long, hydrophobic hydrocarbon chains are attached. In water, such lipids spontaneously form a two-layered film, 4–5 nm thick, in which the hydrophilic heads of each layer point out toward the water, with the hydrophobic hydrocarbon chains packed next to one another to form a non-aqueous "oil phase". The cell membranes are lipid bilayers of this kind, containing glycolipids and cholesterol as well as phospholipids (Fig. 1-2). The glycolipids have a sugar in the hydrophilic head, an oligosac-

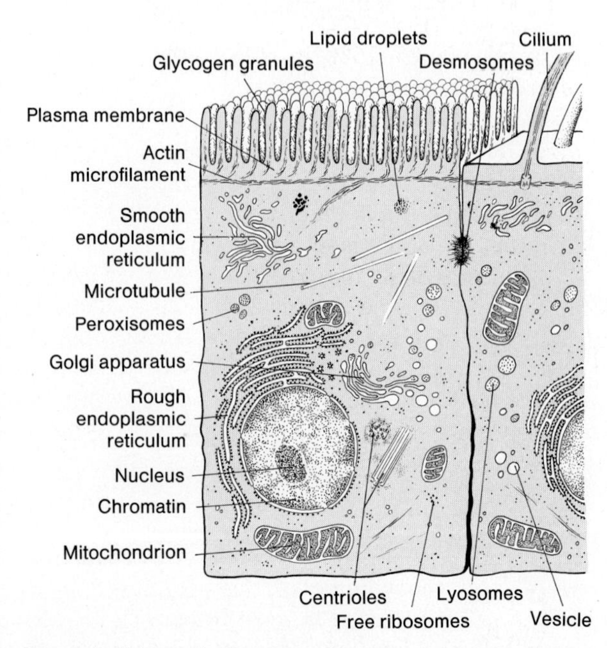

Fig. 1-1. Schematic drawing of a cell, showing the more important organelles

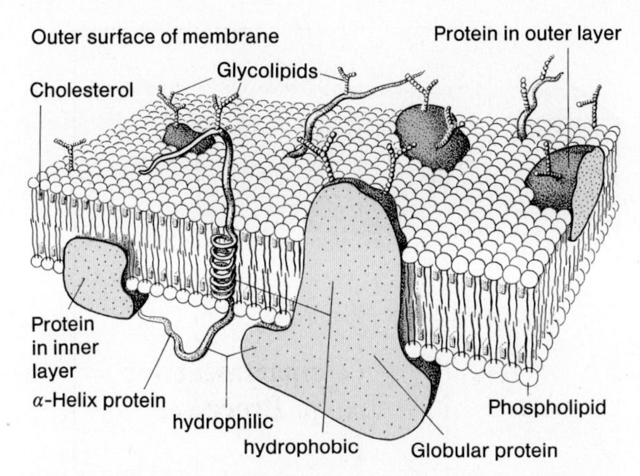

Fig. 1-2. Diagram of the plasma membrane. Embedded in a phospholipid bilayer are proteins, some of which extend all the way through the bilayer, while others are anchored only in the outer or the inner layer. [1, 10]

charide. They are always located on the outer surface of the plasma membrane, with the sugar projecting like a hair into the surroundings of the cell. Interspersed among the phospholipids, and about equal to them in number, are cholesterol molecules, which stabilize the lipid membrane. The various lipids are not scattered uniformly over the membrane; their distribution differs in the outer and inner layers, and even within a layer there are places where particular lipids are concentrated. This nonuniform distribution probably has some functional significance, though it is not yet understood.

The main functional elements embedded in the relatively inert lipid matrix of the membrane are **proteins** (Fig. 1-2). The amount of protein, by weight, is 25–75% in different membranes, but because proteins are much larger than the lipids, 50% by weight is equivalent to one protein molecule per 50 lipid molecules. Some proteins extend through the whole membrane, from outside to inside, and others are anchored only in the outer or inner layer. The proteins are regularly arranged so that their hydrophobic parts are within the lipid membrane, with the polar, hydrophilic groups on their outer surfaces directed toward the aqueous phase. Many proteins on the outside of the plasma membrane are glycoproteins; they bear hydrophilic sugar groups that project out into the surroundings of the cell.

Membrane systems of intracellular organelles. About half the volume of the cell is occupied by organelles enclosed in membranes. The membranes of the intracellular organelles have an area at least 10 times as large as that of the plasma membrane. The most extensive membrane system is the **endoplasmic reticulum**, an extremely convoluted space; large regions of the membrane are studded with ribosomes, so that it appears as rough endoplasmic reticulum (Fig. 1-1). *The Golgi apparatus* also consists of membrane-bounded lamellae, from which vesicles are split off (Fig. 1-1). The **lysosomes** and the **peroxisomes** are smaller specialized vesicles. In all these various cell organelles the membrane and the enclosed space are equipped with a specific set of enzymes, and in the interior particular metabolic products accumulate for use in the particular function of the organelle [1, 2, 5].

The *nucleus* and the *mitochondria* are special in that each of these organelles is enclosed in 2 membranes. The nucleus is responsible for kinetic control of metabolism; the much-folded inner membranes of the mitochondria are the site of oxidative metabolism – the production of energy-rich adenosine triphosphate (ATP) by the oxidation of pyruvic acid or fatty acids.

Cytoskeleton. The cytoplasm between the organelles is by no means amorphous. A cytoskeletal lattice runs through it. The cytoskeleton consists of microtubules, actin filaments and intermediary filaments (Fig. 1-1). The **microtubules** are are about 25 nm in outside diameter; they form as an orderly polymer, by the assembly of molecules of the protein tubulin. The **actin filaments**, contractile fibers below the membrane and in the interior of the cell, often participate in movement processes. The **intermediary filaments** are made of different chemical building blocks in different types of cell; they form diverse links between the two other elements of the cytoskeleton. The organelles and the plasma membrane are also joined to the cytoskeleton, which not only fixes the form of the cell and the position of the organelles, but is also the basis for changes of shape and for locomotion.

Cytosol. About half the volume of the cell is taken up by the cytosol. Because it consists of about 20% (by weight) of protein, it is more a gel than an aqueous solution. Small molecules are dissolved in the aqueous phase, among them inorganic and organic *ions*. The ions are exchanged between the cell and the surrounding phase, the extracellular space; these exchange processes will be treated in the next section. In the extracellular space the ion concentrations are kept constant with considerable precision, and the intracellular concentration of each ion also has a specific value, different from that outside the cell (Table

Table 1-1. Intra- and extracellular ion concentrations: muscle cell of a warm-blooded animal. A^- stands for "large intracellular anions"

Intracellular		Extracellular	
Na^+	12 mmol/l	Na^+	145 mmol/l
K^+	155 mmol/l	K^+	4 mmol/l
Ca^{2+}	10^{-8}–10^{-7} mol/l	Ca^{2+}	2 mmol/l
Cl^-	4 mmol/l	Other cations	5 mmol/l
HCO_3^-	8 mmol/l	Cl^-	120 mmol/l
A^-	155 mmol/l	HCO_3^-	27 mmol/l
Resting potential	−90 mv		

1-1). The most common cation in the external solution is Na^+; within the cell its concentration is more than ten times lower. Conversely, K^+ is the most abundant intracellular cation, and its concentration outside the cell is more than ten times lower. The largest extra- vs. intracellular gradient is that of Ca^{2+}, with a free concentration inside the cell at least 10,000 × smaller than outside. Not all the ions are dissolved in the cytosol; some are adsorbed on proteins or enclosed in organelles. In the case of Ca^{2+}, for instance, these bound ions are far more numerous than the free ions. Most of the proteins in the cytosol are enzymes, and here, with their aid, most processes of intermediary metabolism occur: glycolysis and gluconeogenesis, or the production and breakdown of amino acids, or the synthesis of proteins at ribosomes (Fig. 1-1). The cytosol also contains lipid droplets and glycogen granules as storage forms of important molecules.

1.2 Exchange of Substances between Cell and Surroundings

We have briefly described the structure of the cell as a basis for the consideration of cell physiology. The cell is by no means a static element, for there is a continual exchange of substances among the various intracellular regions and between these and the exterior. The structures of the cell are in dynamic equilibrium, and an interaction of the cells with the surroundings and with one another is a prerequisite for life, for a functioning organism. The fundamental mechanisms of this exchange are described here. In the following chapters these considerations will be applied directly to the nerve cell and its operation; but the same mechanisms also underlie the function of all other organs.

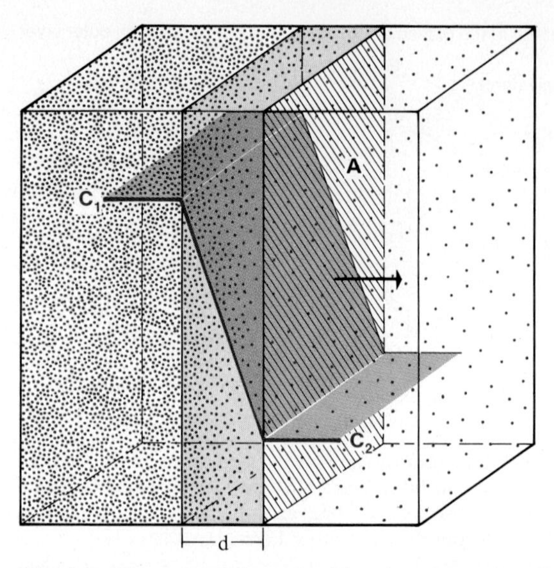

Fig. 1-3. Diagram of the quantities that determine diffusion. Two spaces are separated by a layer with thickness *d* and area *A*. c_1 high concentration of particles in the left space, c_2 low concentration in the right; *red surface* concentration gradient in the diffusion layer. Diffusion current dm/dt as in Eq. (1)

Diffusion. The simplest process by which materials change place is diffusion. In solutions (or gases) the atoms and molecules move freely, and concentration differences equilibrate by diffusion. Now consider two liquid- or gas-filled spaces (Fig. 1-3) in which a substance has the concentrations c_1 and c_2, separated by a layer with area *A* and thickness *d*. The flow of the substance m in time t is described by *Fick's first law of diffusion*:

$$\mathrm{dm/dt} = \mathrm{D}\frac{\mathrm{A}}{\mathrm{d}}(\mathrm{c}_1 - \mathrm{c}_2) = \mathrm{D}\frac{\mathrm{A}}{\mathrm{d}}\Delta\mathrm{c} \quad (1)$$

where *D* is the diffusion coefficient, which is constant for a given substance, solvent and temperature. More generally, for a concentration difference *dc* over the distance *dx*:

$$\mathrm{dm/dt} = -\mathrm{D} \cdot \mathrm{A} \cdot \mathrm{dc/dx}, \quad (2)$$

the flow over the cross section *A* being proportional to the concentration gradient *dc/dx*. The sign is negative because the concentration change in the x direction is negative.

Diffusion is the most important process by which most molecules in aqueous solution move over small distances. This also applies to movement within a cell, as long as diffusion is not impeded by membranes. Many substances can diffuse freely through the lipid membrane, espe-

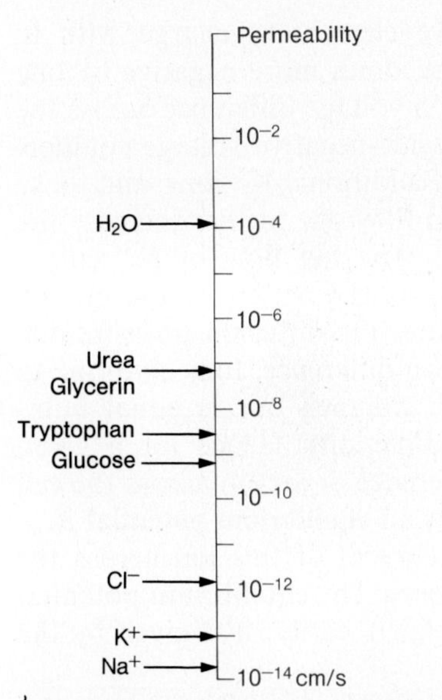

Fig. 1-4. Permeabilities of artificial lipid bilayers to various substances

cially water and dissolved gases like O_2 and CO_2. Lipid-soluble substances also diffuse well through the membrane; polar molecules do so if they are small enough, like ethanol and urea, but sugar can hardly pass through the lipid layers. On the other hand, the lipid layers are practically impermeable to charged molecules, even small inorganic ions. For non-electrolytes it is customary in writing the diffusion equation (1) to combine the characteristics of the membrane and the diffusing substance in a single term, the *permeability* P:

$$dm/dt = P \cdot A \cdot \Delta c \qquad (3)$$

The *permeabilities P of different molecules* passing through a *lipid membrane* are compared in Fig. 1-4.

Diffusion through pores in the membrane. The plasma membrane (and other cell membranes) is permeable not only to substances that diffuse through the lipid layers but also to many ions, sugars, amino acids and nucleotides. These substances cross the membrane through pores formed by *transport proteins* embedded in the membrane. Within such proteins is a water-filled channel, less than 1 nm in diameter, through which small molecules can diffuse. They move according to the concentration gradient and, if they carry a charge, movement through the channel is also influenced by the membrane potential. The membrane channels are relatively selective with respect to the kinds of molecules that can pass. For instance, there are potassium, sodium and calcium channels, each of which excludes almost all but its specific ion. This *selectivity* is achieved by charges or binding sites in the walls of the channels, which facilitate passage for the permeating molecules and prevent the permeation of other substances (Fig. 1-5A) [1, 3].

The behavior of the *membrane channels for ions* can be particularly well monitored because when ions move, the currents they generate can be measured for single channels. It has been shown that the channels alternate spontaneously, at a high frequency, between open and closed states. For a K^+ channel, current pulses about 2 pA (10^{-12} A) in amplitude, with a mean duration of a few milliseconds, have been measured (see Fig. 2-12, p. 29) [3]. During such a "channel opening", then, tens of thousands of ions flow. Rapid changes in the shape of proteins, in which they enter various conformational substates, have been found with X-ray and MÖSSBAUER radiation measurements and by measurement of nuclear magnetic resonance (NMR). Proteins are thus highly dynamic, pulsating structures, and a channel through the protein is not a rigid, water-filled pipe (Fig. 1-5A) but rather a water-filled labyrinth of rapidly moving molecule groups and charges. This dynamic character of the channel is reflected in the **energy profile of a channel** shown in Fig. 1-5B. Here the abscissa represents the length of the channel, from an external solution with the ion concentration c_o and the potential 0 to the internal solution with the concentration c_i and the potential E. The ordinate gives the energy level of the ion at the associated site in the channel; a peak signifies a barrier to permeation, which an ion needs much energy to overcome, and a valley indicates a relatively stable state, a binding. Despite the obstacle of the energy peaks, an ion can pass if the energy profile shifts spontaneously and cyclically within the channel; the ion can suddenly find itself on the opposite side of a peak and able to continue on. Depending on charge, size and hydration of the ion and on the opportunities for binding to wall structures, the energy profile through the channel will vary for different ions, which could explain the selectivity of the individual types of channel.

Diffusion equilibrium for ions. The diffusion of various ions through membrane channels should tend to eliminate the concentration differences between inside and outside. As Table 1-1 documents, however, the different internal and external concentrations persist; therefore there must

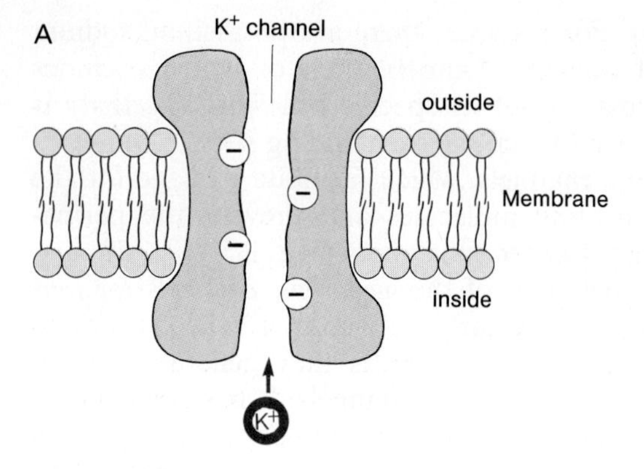

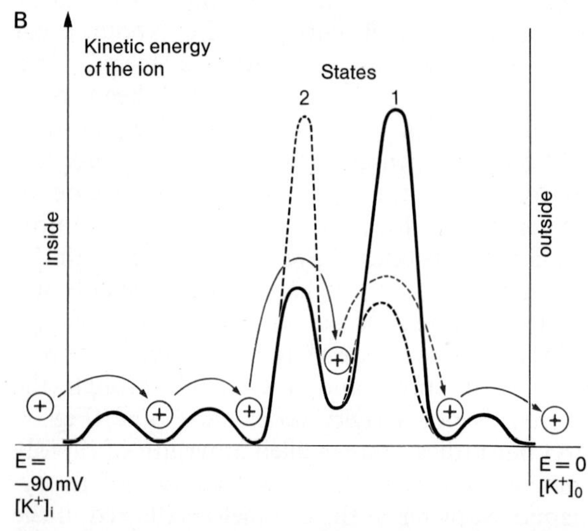

Fig. 1-5. A Diagram of a K^+ -channel protein embedded in the lipid bilayer of the plasma membrane. Four negative charges are fixed to the "wall" of the channel. **B** Schematic energy profile of a channel like that in **A**. The *ordinate* gives the amount of kinetic energy an ion needs to pass along the channel, and the *abscissa* represents the distance from inside to outside of the membrane. Energy minima correspond to sites at which the positive ion binds to the negative "fixed charges" in the channel wall. The energy maxima correspond to obstacles to diffusion within the channel. It is assumed that the conformation of the channel protein oscillates spontaneously, so that the energy profile is represented by the *continuous* and *dashed* lines in alternation; this oscillation greatly assists ions bound in front of the energy barrier in surmounting it. (Modified from [14])

be an **equilibrium** between diffusion and other processes of transport across the membrane. The next two sections are concerned with the way this equilibrium is set. In the case of ions, their charge affects the diffusion equilibrium. Diffusion of uncharged molecules is driven by the concentration difference dc, and when the concentrations are equal there is no net transport. Charged particles are additionally affected by an electrical field. For instance, if a K^+ ion flows out of the cell along its concentration gradient, it takes a positive elementary charge with it. The cell interior becomes more negative by one charge, producing a voltage difference across the membrane. The inside-negative voltage counteracts the outflow of additional K^+ ions, and those that do manage to flow out further increase the membrane charge. The net flow of K^+ comes to a stop as soon as the action of the electrical field compensates the diffusion pressure due to the concentration difference. Ions continue to move through the channel, but in equal numbers in the two directions. Hence for a given concentration difference of an ion across the cell membrane, there is an **equilibrium potential** E_{ion}, at which the net current of this ion across the membrane disappears. The equilibrium potential can be calculated fairly easily; it is given by the **Nernst equation**:

$$E_{ion} = \frac{R \cdot T}{z \cdot F} \cdot \ln \frac{\text{extracellular concentration of the ion}}{\text{intracellular concentration of the ion}}. \quad (4)$$

where R is the gas constant, T is the absolute temperature, z is the valence of the ion (negative for anions) and F is the Faraday constant. By combining the constants, at body temperature (T=310 K) we find for E_K:

$$E_K = -61 \text{ mV} \cdot \log \frac{[K^+]_i}{[K^+]_o}. \quad (5)$$

If $\frac{[K^+]_i}{[K^+]_o} = 39$ as in Table 1-1, then

$$E_K = -61\,\text{mV} \cdot \log 39 = -61\,\text{mV} \cdot 1.59 = -97\,\text{mV}.$$

Indeed, all cells have been found to have a *membrane potential*; in mammalian muscle cells it amounts to about −90 mV. Depending on the conditions and the relative ion concentrations, cells can have membrane potentials of −120 to −40 mV. For the cell in the above example (Table 1-1) the **resting potential** of −90 mV implies that the flow of K^+ ions through the membrane channels is approximately in equilibrium. This is not surprising, because in the resting membrane open K^+ channels are by far the most common; that is, the membrane is most permeable to K^+. But the membrane potential is also determined by the flows of other ions.

The ease with which particles can diffuse through the membrane is represented quantitatively in Eq. (3), for uncharged particles, by the permeability P. The **permeability of charged particles** has a slightly more complicated definition:

$$P = \frac{\mu \cdot R \cdot T}{d \cdot F} \qquad (6)$$

where μ is the mobility of the ion in the membrane, d is the thickness of the membrane, and R, T and F are the familiar thermodynamic constants. Permeabilities as so defined can be used to calculate the membrane potential E_m when K^+, $Na^+$and Cl^- ions are flowing simultaneously (with permeabilities P_K, P_{Na} and P_{Cl}). It is assumed that the potential falls off uniformly within the membrane – that is, field strength is constant. Then the *"constant-field" or Goldmann equation* applies [6, 12]:

$$E_m = \frac{RT}{F} \cdot \ln \frac{P_K[K^+]_o + P_{Na}[Na^+]_o + P_{Cl}[Cl^-]_i}{P_K[K^+]_i + P_{Na}[Na^+]_i + P_{Cl}[Cl^-]_o}. \qquad (7)$$

For most cell membranes P_K is about 30 times greater than P_{Na} (see also 1.3). The relative magnitude of P_{Cl} varies considerably; for many membranes P_{Cl} is small as compared with P_K, and for others (e.g., skeletal muscle) P_{Cl} is actually greater than P_K.

Active transport, Na pump. The preceding section described passive diffusion and the membrane potential it produces, for a given set of intra- and extracellular ion concentrations. However, the concentration within the cell is not automatically stabilized in this process, because the membrane potential is somewhat less negative than E_K and much more negative than E_{Na} (about +60 mV). By diffusion, the intracellular concentrations, at least those of K^+ and Na^+, would eventually approximate those outside the cell. The stability of the natural ion gradients is achieved by active transport processes: membrane proteins transport ions across the membrane against the concentration and/or electrical gradient, consuming metabolic energy to do so. The most important active transport process is the **Na-K pump**, present in practically all cell membranes, which moves Na^+ out of the cell and K^+ into it. It ensures that the intracellular concentration of Na^+ is low and that of K^+ high (Table 1-1). The Na^+ concentration gradient across the membrane has special functions, being employed for the electrical transmission of information (see Sec. 2.2) as well as to drive other active transport mechanisms and adjust

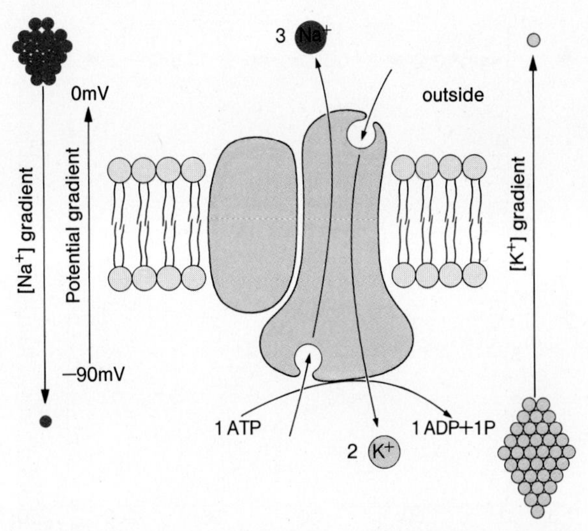

Fig. 1-6. Diagram of the Na-K pump, an ATPase in the lipid bilayer of the plasma membrane that in one pumping cycle removes 3 Na^+ from the cell, against the concentration and potential gradients, and brings in 2 K^+. In the process one ATP is split into ADP and phosphate P. The ATPase is shown as a dimer, with a large (functional) unit and a small unit; it is present in the membrane as a tetramer with 2 large and 2 small units

the volume of the cell (see below). Therefore it comes as no surprise that more than 1/3 of the energy consumption of cells is accounted for by the Na-K pump, and in some very active cells this pump uses up 70% of the energy [1, 11].

The Na-K transport protein is an ATPase. On the inside of the membrane it splits ATP into ADP and phosphate (Fig. 1-6). With the energy derived from one ATP it transports 3 Na^+ out of the cell, at the same time bringing 2 K^+ in; in each pumping cycle, then, it removes one positive charge from the cell. The Na-K pump is thus **electrogenic**, driving across the cell membrane an electric current that makes the membrane potential more negative, by about 10 mV. The protein performs this transport at a high rate: 150 to 600 Na^+ ions are expelled per second. Although the amino acid sequence of the transport protein is known, it is not yet clear how the complicated exchange transport is achieved. The process is best described in terms of the energy profiles associated with occupation of the protein by Na^+ and K^+ (Fig. 1-5B). Cyclic changes in these profiles, resulting from continual changes in conformation of the transport protein (an energy-consuming process), would produce a stoichiometric exchange of 2 K^+ for 3 Na^+.

The Na-K pump, like isolated Na^+- and K^+-dependent membrane ATPase, can be specifically inhibited by the cardiac glycoside ouabain (strophanthin). As a several-stage chemical re-

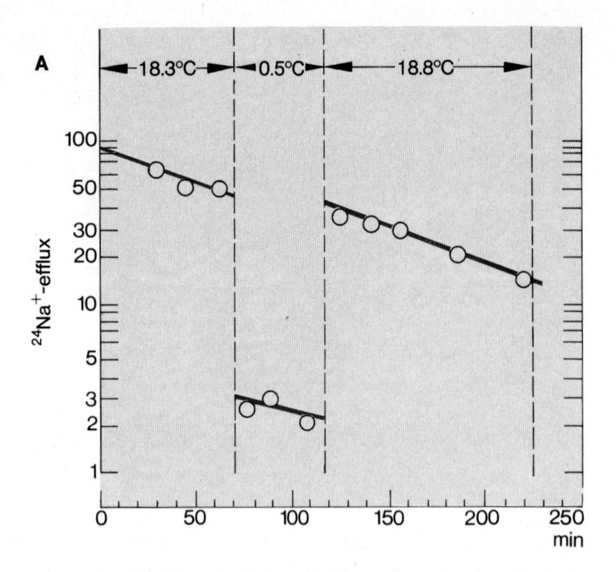

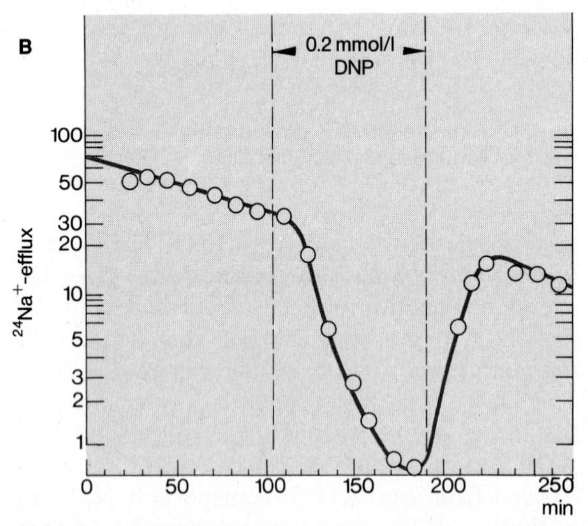

Fig. 1-7 A a. B. Demonstration of active Na^+ transport. *Ordinates:* Outflow of radioactive $^{24}Na^+$ from the cell, in counts per minute. *Abscissa:* Time since beginning of experiment. **A** The cell is cooled from 18.3 °C to 0.5 °C, and during the cold period Na^+ outflow is inhibited. **B** Inhibition of Na^+ outflow by 0.2 mmol/l dinitrophenol (DNP). (Modified from [13])

action, the Na-K pump is highly temperature-dependent, as illustrated in Fig. 1-7. Here the Na^+ outflow from muscle cells is plotted over time; for practical purposes, this is equivalent to the Na^+ outflow mediated by the Na-K pump, for the chance that a sodium ion would flow out of the cell passively against the steep concentration and potential gradients is extremely small. If the preparation is now cooled by about 18 °C, the Na^+ outflow decreases rapidly by a factor of 15; immediately after rewarming, it returns to the initial level. This reduction in Na^+ outflow is several times greater than would correspond to the temperature dependence of a diffusion

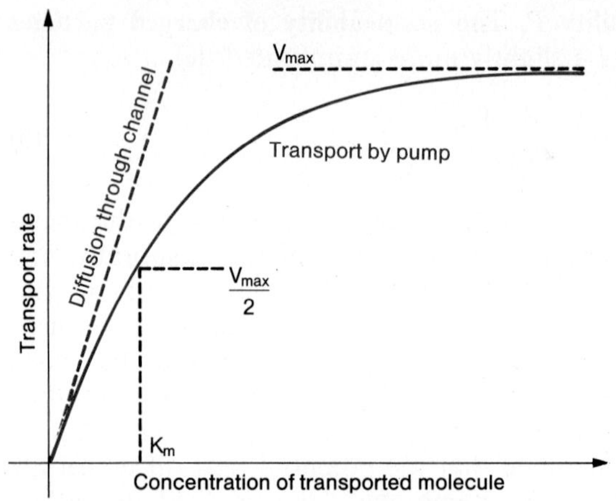

Fig. 1-8. Relation between the rate of transport of a molecule and its concentration (at the entrance to a channel or the binding site of a pump), for diffusion through a membrane channel and for transport by a pump. The latter saturates at high concentrations, with a maximal pumping rate V_{max}; the value on the abscissa corresponding to half the maximal pumping rate ($V_{max}/2$) is the apparent equilibrium concentration K_m

process or a simple chemical reaction. A similar effect is produced when the supply of metabolic energy is interrupted by poisoning with dinitrophenol (DNP) (Fig. 1-7B). This shows that the Na^+ outflow is driven by energy-dependent reactions, an active pump. Another characteristic of pumps, in addition to marked temperature and energy dependence, is that (like all chemical reactions) they reach a saturation level; that is, the pumping rate cannot increase indefinitely as the concentration of the molecules to be transported rises (Fig. 1-8). By contrast, the flow of passively diffusing substances increases in proportion to the concentration difference, as required by the law of diffusion (Eqs. 1 and 2).

Besides the Na-K pump, the plasma membrane contains at least one other, a *Ca pump*, which pumps Ca^{2+} out of the cell and helps to produce the extremely low intracellular Ca^{2+} concentration (Table 1-1). This pump is also present, in particularly high density, in the sarcoplasmic reticulum of the muscle cell, which concentrates Ca^{2+} by splitting ATP (see Chapter 4).

Effects of the Na-K pump on membrane potential and cell volume. Fig. 1-9 shows various membrane-current components together with the intracellular ion concentrations they serve to maintain. Through the K^+ channel there flows a net outward current of K^+, because the membrane potential is somewhat more positive than the K^+ equilibrium potential. Although the overall permeability of the Na^+ channels is much

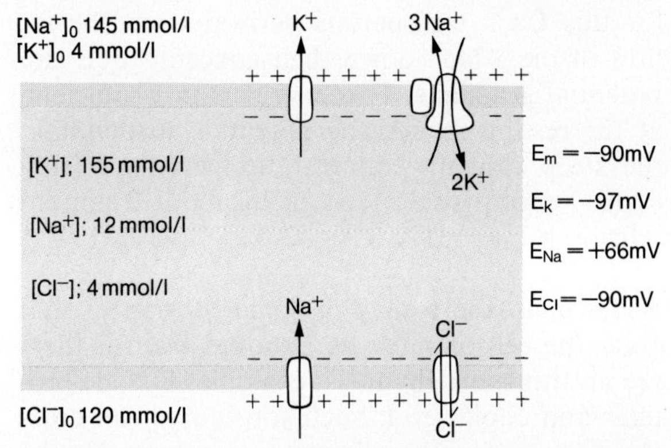

Fig. 1-9. Diagram showing the concentrations of Na^+, K^+ and Cl^- inside and outside the cell and the routes by which these ions cross the cell membrane, through specific ion channels or the Na-K pump. With the indicated concentration gradients, the equilibrium potentials E_{Na}, E_K and E_{Cl} are as shown, and the membrane potential is $E_m = -90$ mV

lower than that of the K^+ channels – or the Na^+ channels open much more rarely than the K^+ channels at the resting potential – about as much Na^+ flows into the cell as K^+ flows out, because the inward diffusion of Na^+ is driven by the large concentration gradient as well as by the potential. The Na-K pump provides ideal compensation of the passive diffusion currents, because it moves Na^+ out of the cell and K^+ into it. In doing so it is electrogenic, because of the net charge displacement, and at a normal pumping rate it makes the membrane potential about 10 mV more negative than it would be because of the passive ion flows (see Eq. 7). As a result, the potential approaches the K^+ equilibrium potential, which reduces the net K^+ current. The activity of the Na-K pump is regulated by the intracellular Na^+ concentration. The pumping rate slows when the concentration of Na^+ to be transported declines (Fig. 1-8), so that the pumping rate and Na^+ inflow balance one another out to give an intracellular Na^+ concentration of about 10 mmol/l.

To maintain an equilibrium between pump currents and passive membrane currents, far more Na-K-pump molecules are required than channel proteins for K^+ and Na^+. Each time such a channel opens, tens of thousands of ions pass through within a few milliseconds (see above), and as they usually open several times per second, the total is more than 10^5 ions/s. A single pump protein moves a few hundred Na^+/s. Therefore the plasma membrane must contain about 1,000 times more pump molecules than channel proteins. Measurements of the channel currents at rest have indicated about one K^+ and one Na^+ channel open per μm^2 of membrane; it follows that there must be about 1,000 Na-K-pump proteins in the same area. These would then be 34 nm apart on average; like the channel proteins, their diameter is 8–10 nm. The membrane thus contains quite a dense array of pump molecules [11].

Compensation of Na^+ inflow and K^+ outflow by the pump has another consequence, that the osmotic pressure in the cell remains stable and the **cell volume constant**. There is a high intracellular concentration of large anions, mostly proteins (A^- in Table 1-1). These cannot cross the membrane (or cross very slowly) and are therefore a fixed component within the cell. To balance the charge of these anions, an equal number of cations must be present. Because of the action of the Na-K pump, most of these are K^+. There could be an appreciable rise in the total intracellular ion concentration only if the anion concentration were to increase, which could occur by inflow of Cl^- along its concentration gradient (see Table 1-1). But the membrane potential counteracts Cl^- inflow. There is a net inward Cl^- current only until the Cl^- equilibrium potential is reached; this occurs when the gradient is about opposite to that of K^+, since chloride has a negative charge (see Eq. 4). Hence a low intracellular Cl^- concentration is established, corresponding to the low extracellular K^+ concentration. The result is a limitation on the total quantity of ions in the cell. If the membrane potential drops after blocking of the Na-K pump – e.g., by lack of oxygen – the Cl^- equilibrium potential is lowered and the intracellular Cl^- concentration rises accordingly. To restore charge balance K^+ ions also flow in; the total ion concentration in the cell rises, which raises the osmotic pressure, and water must enter the cell. The cell swells. Such swelling is observed in vivo in conditions of energy deficiency.

The Na^+ concentration gradient as a driving force for membrane transport. The significance of the Na-K pump for the cell is not limited to stabilization of the normal Na^+ and K^+ gradients across the membrane. The energy stored in the membrane gradient for Na^+ is often also used to drive the membrane transport of other substances. For example, Fig. 1-10 shows a **"symport"** of Na^+ and a sugar molecule in the cell. The transport protein in the membrane brings a sugar molecule into the cell, even against a concentration gradient, and at the same time a Na^+ flows in down its concentration and potential gradients, providing the energy for the **sugar transport**. This sugar transport is entirely dependent on the existence of a high Na^+ gradient; if the intracellular Na^+ concentration rises appreciably, sugar transport is halted. There are several such symport systems, for various sugars. The **transport of amino acids** into the cell is similar to the sugar transport in Fig. 1-10, also being

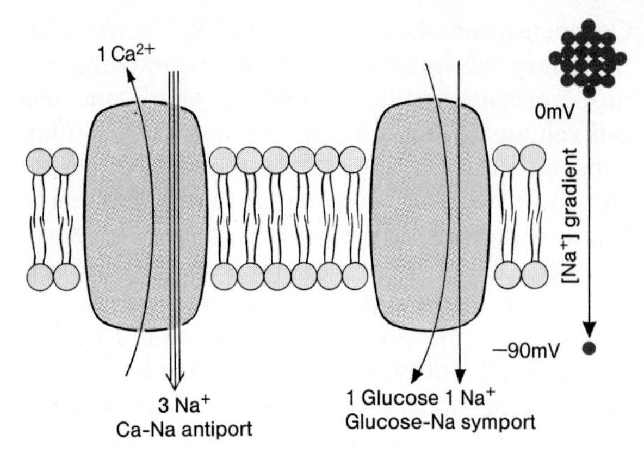

Fig. 1-10. Proteins embedded in the lipid bilayer of the membrane mediate a glucose-Na symport into the cell, as well as a Ca-Na antiport, in which the driving force is the Na^+ gradient across the cell membrane

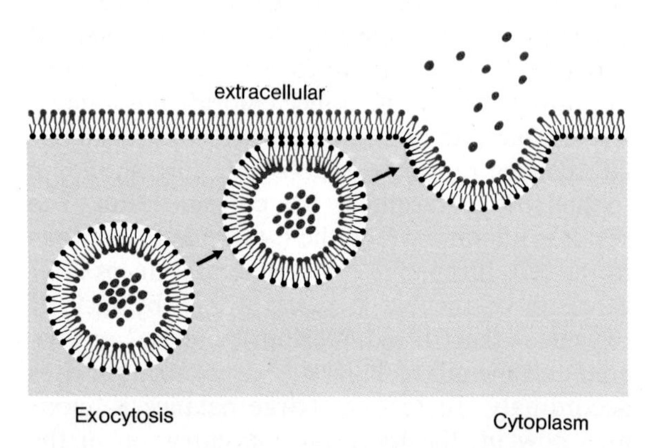

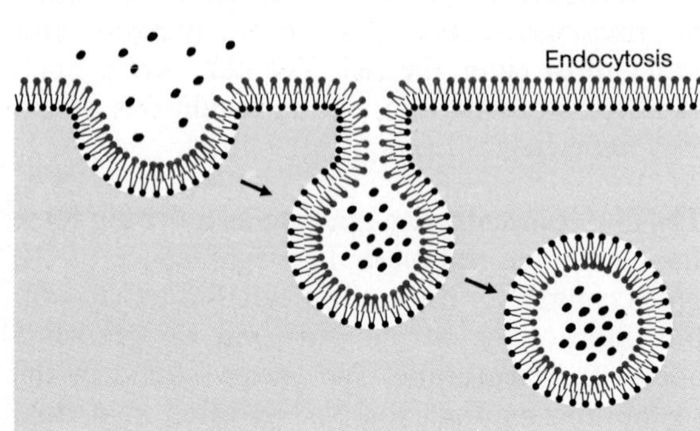

Fig. 1-11. Exocytosis and endocytosis. *Above:* An intracellular vesicle fuses with the lipid bilayer of the plasma membrane and empties into the extracellular space: exocytosis. *Below:* The plasma membrane invaginates in a small region and pinches off a vesicle filled with extracellular material: endocytosis

driven by Na^+ gradients; here there are at least 5 different symport systems, each specialized for a related group of amino acids.

Not only are there symport systems, there are also **"antiports"**. One of these, for instance, in each pumping cycle moves 1 Ca^{2+} out of the cell and allows 3 Na^+ in (Fig. 1-10). The energy for this **Ca^{2+} transport** is derived from the inflow of the 3 Na^+ down their concentration and potential gradients. This energy is just sufficient, at the resting membrane potential, to maintain the steep calcium concentration gradient from $< 10^{-7}$ mol/l inside the cell to about 2 mmol/l outside it.

Endo- and exocytosis. For some substances that enter the cell or must be removed from it there are no transport channels; examples include proteins and cholesterol. Such substances can cross the plasma membrane enclosed in **vesicles**, by endo- or exocytosis. Fig. 1-11 shows the principal mechanisms. In exocytosis certain organelles (see below) form vesicles filled with the substance to be expelled, such as a hormone or an enzyme with an extracellular action. When such vesicles reach the plasma membrane, their lipid membrane can fuse with the plasma membrane and open to discharge the contents of the vesicle into the external medium. In the opposite process, endocytosis, the plasma membrane invaginates to form a pit, which deepens and constricts to create an intracellular vesicle filled with extracellular fluid and some macromolecules. To produce these fusions and constrictions, contractile elements of the cytoskeleton operate together with the membranes themselves (see below). In endocytosis it is not always simply the external medium that is taken into the cell. Within the cell membrane, often arranged in specialized groups, there are specific receptors for macromolecules such as insulin or for antigens. After such molecules have bound to their receptors, endocytosis is elicited in the surrounding membrane region, so that the macromolecules are transported selectively (Fig. 1-12B).

Endo- and exocytosis proceed continually in all cells. The amount of cell membrane so converted is considerable; in one hour, a macrophage takes up as vesicles double the entire surface area of its plasma membrane. In most cells the turnover is lower, but even so a considerable "recycling" of the membranes must take place.

1.3 Exchange of Substances within the Cell

Endo- and exocytosis are processes that not only transport substances across the cell membrane but also exchange membranes, structural components of the cell itself. Other similar transport processes within the cell and at its organelles are the subject of this section.

Diffusion. Within the cytosol, of course, concentration differences are eliminated by diffusion, and the same is true of the fluids enclosed in organelles. Because of the high concentration of dissolved protein here, diffusion proceeds much more slowly than in water. The lipid membranes around the cell and in its organelles are themselves two-dimensional fluids, within which diffusion occurs. The lipids in the membrane bilayer diffuse within their own layer but rarely move from one layer to the other. The embedded proteins are also quite movable; they rotate about an axis vertical to the membrane, and diffuse laterally with very different diffusion constants, 2 to 10,000 times more slowly than the phospholipids. That is, while some proteins float fairly freely in the lipid layer and move almost as rapidly as the lipid molecules themselves, others are more firmly anchored, probably by binding to the cytoskeleton. There are "permanent" aggregations of special proteins in the membranes – e.g., at the pre- and postsynaptic structures of nerve cells (see p. 53). Freely movable proteins can be demonstrated by coupling them with a fluorescent dye, which can be induced to fluoresce by flashing light briefly onto a small spot of membrane. Such experiments have shown that within less than 1 min these proteins spread out uniformly over a region of membrane extending for about 10 μm.

Active transport at the membranes of organelles. The active transport processes that are so vital in the plasma membrane also occur within the cell, in the membranes of the organelles. The different organelles acquire their specific contents in part by internal synthesis and in part by active transport from the cytosol. One example of the latter has already been mentioned, the Ca^{2+} pump in the sarcoplasmic reticulum of muscle cells. It is particularly interesting that the principle of the ATP-driven pumps in the plasma membrane (see Fig. 1-6) is reversed in the case of ATP synthesis in the mitochondria. Here oxidative metabolism produces a steep H^+ gradient at the inner membranes. This gradient drives the pumping cycle of an active-transport molecule backwards: H^+ flows down the gradient through the membrane, and with the energy so released ATP is synthesized from ADP and phosphate. This ATP, in turn, provides energy at many sites in the cell – for active transport, among other things.

Transport in vesicles. The schematic drawing of a cell in Fig. 1-1 shows a large number of intracellular organelles and of vesicles associated with them. These organelles, and especially the vesicles, are in continual movement, transporting their contents to other organelles or to the plasma membrane. Vesicles may also migrate from the cell membrane to the organelles, as in endocytosis.

The process of **secretion of a protein** is illustrated in Fig. 1-12A. The protein is synthesized near the nucleus of the cell, at ribosomes associated with the rough endoplasmic reticulum. Having entered the endoplasmic reticulum, the protein is enclosed in transport vesicles that separate off and migrate to the Golgi complex. There they fuse with the cisternae of the Golgi apparatus, where the protein is modified (e.g., converted to a glycoprotein). At the edges of these cisternae transport vesicles are again pinched off; carrying the modified protein, these secretory vesicles move to the plasma membrane and release their contents by exocytosis.

Another example of a transport pathway within the cell is shown in Fig. 1-12B, a diagram of the **uptake of cholesterol** into the cell. While being transported in the blood, cholesterol is mostly bound to proteins as particles of **"low density lipoprotein" (LDL)**. Such particles bind to specific membrane regions that contain receptors for LDL. Then endocytosis occurs at these sites, and the LDL is transferred to the interior within "coated" vesicles. These vesicles fuse together to form endosomes, losing their "coat" in the process. The endosomes, in turn, fuse with primary lysosomes, which contain mainly hydrolytic enzymes, to form secondary, larger lysosomes. In these the cholesterol is liberated from the LDL particles; it diffuses into the cytosol, where it is available, for instance, for the synthesis of lipid membranes. The endosomes also pinch off LDL-free vesicles, which follow a separate pathway back to the plasma membrane and fuse with it, returning membrane material and probably also LDL receptors. From the time when the LDL particle is bound to the membrane, it takes 10–15 min until the cholesterol is released from the secondary lysosomes. Disturbances in the binding and uptake of LDL – that is, in the cell's supply of cholesterol – are an important factor in the pathogenesis of a disease of enormous clinical significance, atherosclerosis ("hardening" of the arteries).

There are many other transport pathways, similar to those shown in Figs. 1-11 and 1-12A, by which specific vesicles move through the cell. It

A Exocytosis of a protein

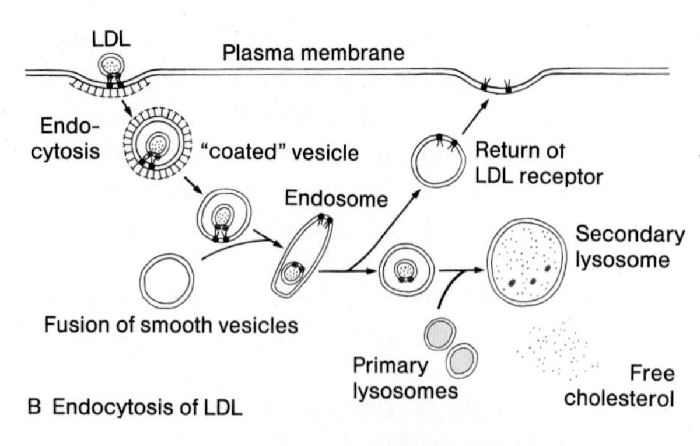

B Endocytosis of LDL

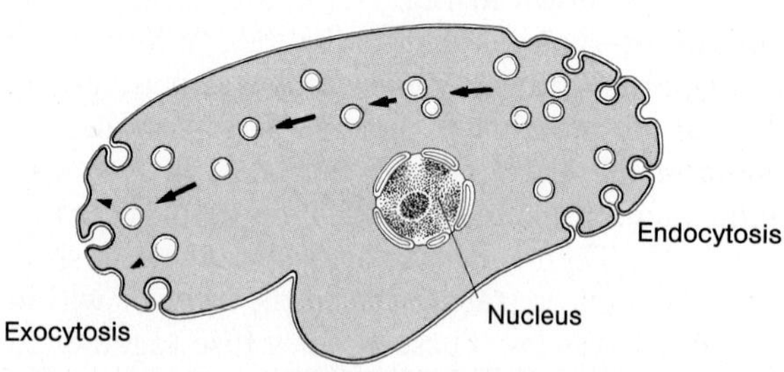

C Transcellular transport by endo/exocytosis

Fig. 1-12 A–C. Diagrams of processes involving exo- and endocytosis. **A** A protein is synthesized at the rough endoplasmic reticulum and transported in vesicles, by way of the Golgi apparatus, to the plasma membrane, where it is secreted by exocytosis. **B** Cholesterol bound to particles of LDL (low-density lipoprotein) binds to the plasma membrane, induces endocytosis in that part of the membrane, and is transported in vesicles to lysosomes, where it is released. **C** Extracellular material is taken in by endocytosis at the right-hand pole of a cell, transported through the cell in vesicles, and excreted again at the left pole by exocytosis

is not known how the vesicles are moved; probably elements of the cytoskeleton are involved. The vesicles could glide along microtubules, in which case the energy for the movement would have to be provided by an associated protein, an ATPase (see below). It is a complete mystery how the many different vesicles, moving past one another in all directions, are guided to their destinations. They must be marked in some way that is recognized by the transport system and converted into properly directed movement.

Transport by the creation and destruction of organelles. Endo- and exocytosis of vesicles have so far been considered from the viewpoint of transporting the vesicles' contents. Another aspect is that the orderly removal of plasma membrane at one end of the cell by endocytosis and addition of membrane at the other end by exocytosis can transport large areas of membrane (Fig. 1-12C), enabling the cell to form a new process, for instance, or to move.

Similar rearrangements are also typical of the cell skeleton, especially the microfilaments and microtubules (Fig. 1-1). The **microfilaments** consist primarily of the **protein F-actin**, which can assemble into fiber bundles by polymerization from the cytosol. The bundles are polarized; they often grow only at one end, by accumulating additional actin molecules, while the other end remains inert or is disassembled. Such polarized growth effectively displaces the microfilaments and can alter the structure of the microfilament lattice. The transition from the disorganized state, the sol, to the orderly gel state of the actin bundles can take place very rapidly, under the control of accessory proteins or of changes in ion concentration (see next section). There are also proteins that break the actin filaments into short fragments. The fine processes of many cells, the filopodia, contain a central actin bundle (see Fig. 1-1), and the diverse movements of the filopodia are probably caused by gel-sol transformations of the actin bundle.

The **microtubules** also typically undergo such transpositions. Their origin has a similar mechanism – the polymerization of tubulin from the cytosol, such that one end grows and the other does not change or is broken down. Hence the microtubule can move through the cytosol, by appropriate addition and removal of material.

Active movements in the cytoskeleton. Changes in cytoskeletal structure can be brought about by active movements, as well as by the rearrangements described above. In many of the cases in which microtubules and actin filaments move, the movements are produced by contractile proteins that link the filaments or tubules together and can displace them relative to one another. The proteins **myosin** and **dynein** are present in relatively high concentrations in the cytosol of all cells; these are the elements that convert energy into movement in specialized cells (muscles) and organelles (cilia). In muscle cells myosin

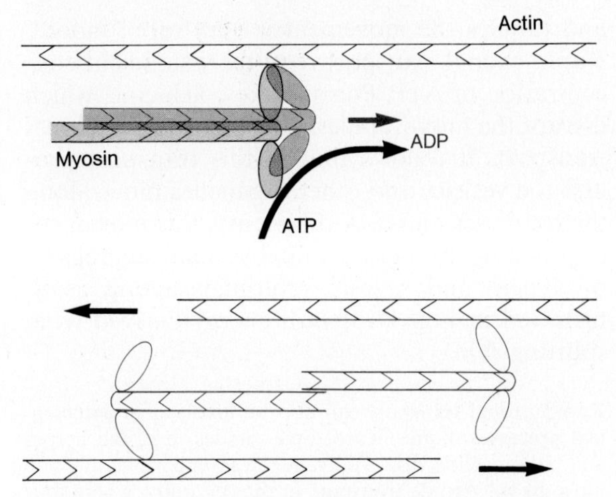

Fig. 1-13. Nonmuscular myosin-molecule aggregates, if suitably oriented, can bind to actin filaments of different polarities and, by splitting ATP, shift the actin filaments past one another

forms thick filaments arranged in parallel with the actin filaments. Myosin molecules attach by their "heads" to the actin filaments, split ATP and, with the energy so released, **shift the myosin along the actin**. Then the myosin detaches from the actin. Many such attachment-detachment cycles together produce the macroscopic **shortening of the muscle fibrils** (Chapter 4). Dynein plays a corresponding role in displacing microtubules during the movement of cilia (Fig. 1-1). In the cytoplasm of non-specialized cells, myosin and dynein do not form orderly fibers but, at most, small groups of molecules. Even as such small aggregates, however, they can shift actin filaments or tubules past one another. Fig. 1-13 illustrates this operation for an arrangement of two actin filaments polarized in different directions, to which two joined, oppositely polarized myosin molecules attach. Then the head groups of the myosins bend back toward the tails, splitting ATP in the process; the two actin filaments are shifted in opposite directions, and the myosins become detached. Displacements of this kind, in which the energy contained in ATP is converted to mechanical work, can change the shape of the cytoskeleton, and hence the cell, and also cause the transport of associated organelles.

Axonal Transport

Intracellular transport processes can be most impressively demonstrated in the axons of nerve cells. Here this **axonal transport** is considered in some detail, to illustrate events that probably occur in a similar way in most cells. Axons

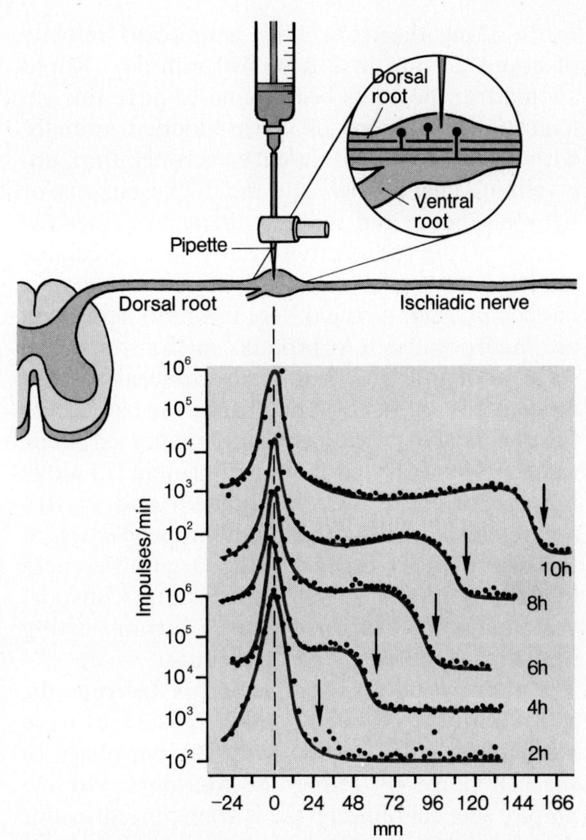

Fig. 1-14. Demonstration of rapid axonal transport in sensory fibers of the cat sciatic nerve. Tritium-labeled leucine is injected into a dorsal root ganglion and the radioactivity in the ganglion and the sensory fibers is measured 2, 4, 6, 8 and 10 h later (*below*). The *abscissa* gives the distance of the measurement sites along the nerve, starting with the dorsal root ganglion. The radioactivity is plotted on a logarithmic scale (shown only for the top and bottom curves) in counts per minute. The "wave" of increased radioactivity (*arrows*) moves at a velocity of 410 mm/day. (From [15])

only a few micrometers in diameter can have lengths of a meter or more, and for a protein to move from the nucleus to the end of the axon by diffusion would take years. It has long been known that when such an axon is greatly constricted at one spot, after a few hours the part of the axon proximal to the constriction expands. It looks as though a centrifugal flow within the axon has been blocked. This flow, **rapid axonal transport**, can be demonstrated by observing the movement of radioactive markers, as in the experiment of Fig. 1-14. Radioactively labelled leucine is injected into a dorsal root ganglion, and from the 2nd to the 10th hour the radioactivity in the sciatic nerve is measured as far as 166 mm peripheral to the cell bodies. There is a peak of radioactivity at the injection site, which hardly changes during the ten hours. But a wave of activity can be seen to advance along the axon, with a uniform velocity of about 34 mm in 2 h or 410 mm/day. Rapid axonal transport has been found to have this velocity in all neurons of warm-blooded animals, with no measurable differences between thin, unmyelinated nerve fibers and the thickest axons, or between motor and sensory fibers. Nor does the carrier of the radioactivity have an appreciable effect on transport velocity; various radioactive molecules, such as the different amino acids that are incorporated into proteins in the soma, can serve as markers. When the peripheral part of the nerve is analyzed to determine the carriers of the radioactivity that has been transported there, radioactivity is found mainly in protein fractions but also in transmitter substances and in free amino acids. Given the different properties of these substances, especially the large differences in size of the molecules, the constant transport velocity can be explained only by a transporting mechanism shared by all of them.

The above **rapid axonal transport is anterograde**, away from the cell body. Some substances have been found to be moved from the periphery to the cell body, by **retrograde transport**. For example, acetylcholinesterase is transported in this direction, at about half the velocity of rapid axonal transport. A labeling substance often used in neuroanatomy, horseradish peroxidase, is also moved by retrograde transport. Retrograde transport seems to play an important role in the regulation of protein synthesis in the cell body. A few days after transection of the axon, chromatolysis is evident in the cell body, which indicates a disturbance of protein synthesis. The time required for chromatolysis to appear is correlated with the duration of retrograde transport, from the site of the cut back to the cell body. This result suggests an explanation of the disturbance – that the supply of a substance from the periphery, a "signal substance" that regulates the rate of protein synthesis, has been interrupted.

The main "vehicles" used for rapid axonal transport are evidently **vesicles** and **organelles** such as mitochondria, which contain the materials to be transported. The transport of fairly large vesicles or mitochondria is barely visible through a microscope in vivo. Such a particle makes a brief, rapid movement in one direction, stops, often moves a bit backward or to the side, stops again, and then shoots some distance ahead in the preferred direction. 410 mm/d corresponds to about 5 μm/s average velocity in the anterograde direction; the velocity of the individual movements must therefore be still higher, and in comparison with the dimensions of the organelles, filaments and tubules the movement is very rapid indeed. Rapid axonal transport requires a sufficient concentration of ATP. Poisons like colchicine, which disrupt the microtubules, also block rapid axonal transport. It follows that in this transport process the vesicles and other organelles move along microtubules and actin filaments; this movement is probably brought about by small aggregates of dynein and myosin molecules acting as illustrated in Fig. 1-13, with energy derived from splitting ATP.

Rapid axonal transport can also be involved in **pathological processes**. Some neurotropic viruses (e.g., the herpes and poliomyelitis viruses) invade the axon peripherally and move by retrograde transport to the cell body, where they can multiply and exert their toxic effects. Tetanus toxin, a protein that can be produced by bacteria in skin wounds, is also taken up by nerve endings and transported to the cell body, where it triggers the muscle spasms characteristic of "lockjaw".

Toxic effects on axonal transport itself have also been observed – e.g., poisoning by the industrial solvent acrylamide. Moreover, it has been proposed that pathogenesis of the vitamin deficiency disease beriberi and of alcohol polyneuropathy involves impairment of rapid axonal transport.

In addition to rapid axonal transport, there are considerably **slower transport processes** within the cell. In an axon tubulin moves with a velocity of about 1 mm/d and actin is somewhat faster, moving up to 5 mm/d. Other proteins migrate along with these components of the cytoskeleton; for example, enzymes are evidently associated with actin or tubulin. The displacement velocity of tubulin and actin is roughly consistent with the growth rate found for the mechanism previously described, in which molecules are incorporated at the active end of the microtubule or microfilament. Therefore this mechanism could be the basis of slow axonal transport. The velocity of slow axonal transport is also approximately the same as that of axonal growth, which may indicate that construction of the cytoskeleton limits the rate at which the axon can grow.

To conclude this section, it should be emphasized that cells are by no means the static entities that they inevitably appear to be in, for instance, electron micrographs. The **plasma membrane** and especially the **organelles are in a state of constant rapid movement and reconstruction**, and it is only because of this that they can function. Furthermore, they are not simply chambers within which chemical reactions can occur, but **highly organized conglomerates of membranes and fibrils** at which reactions can occur in an optimally ordered sequence.

1.4 Control of Cell Functions

Maintenance of the individual cell as a functional unit is largely regulated by the nucleus; such mechanisms are a specific topic of cell biology and of biochemistry. On the other hand, cells must modify their functions according to environmental conditions and the needs of other cells in the organism; they must be subject to functional control. Here we consider briefly how such controlling influences act on the plasma membrane and how they can be conveyed to intracellular organelles.

Controlling Actions on the Cell Membrane

Membrane potential. In many cases changes in the membrane potential are used to control cell functions. The potential can change locally when (i) current from neighboring parts of the cell, or generated by another cell, flows through the membrane, (ii) extracellular ion concentrations (not uncommonly $[K^+]_o$) change, or (iii) ion channels through the membrane are opened. Membrane-potential shifts can affect the conformation of membrane proteins, and in particular can make channels open or close. As mentioned above, some membrane pumps depend on the membrane potential. Nerve cells are specialized for treating changes in the membrane potential as information, to be processed and passed on (see Chapter 2).

Extracellular control substances. The most important mechanisms for control by external influences are reactions of extracellular substances with specific receptors in the plasma membrane or within the cell. These substances include synaptic transmitters, which convey information from one nerve cell to another, local agents, and substances that circulate in the blood and reach all cells in the body, such as hormones and antigens in immune reactions. **Synaptic transmitters** are small molecules released from nerve endings at synapses; when they reach the plasma membrane of the immediately adjacent, postsynaptic cell, they trigger electrical signals or other control mechanisms. These are treated extensively in Chapter 3.

Local chemical agents are often released by specialized cells. Although they diffuse freely in the extracellular space, their action is limited to small groups of cells because they rapidly decompose, either spontaneously or by enzyme action. One example is the liberation of **histamine** by mast cells when they are stimulated by injury or immune reactions. The histamine causes smooth muscle cells in the vessels to relax, makes the vascular endothelium more permeable, and stimulates sensory nerve endings that mediate the "itch" sensation. Other local chemical agents are released by many cells. The **prostaglandins** are typical local agents; these are a group of about 20 fatty-acid derivatives. They are released continually from widely distributed cells but they act only locally, because they are soon split by phospholipases in the membrane. The various prostaglandins have a broad action spectrum: they can trigger contraction of smooth muscle cells, cause blood platelets (thrombocytes) to aggregate, or inhibit the corpora lutea of the ovary.
Other local agents serve as **growth factors.** The best known is that for sympathetic neurons (nerve growth factor, NGF), which is required for growth and survival of these neurons during development and also in cell culture. Evidently the target cells of this class of neurons release NGF, thereby ensuring that they are innervated by the right type of neuron. As the organs of the body are forming, it is often necessary for cells to find the way to other cells at a considerable distance. Accordingly, there must be a large number of specialized growth factors like NGF.
Hormones and **antigens** are carried in the blood to all the cells. The antigens elicit immune responses in cells that bear the specific antibody. However, antigens are usually foreign substances, not produced by the reacting organism, and will not be considered further here (but see Chapter 18). Some hormones such as insulin or thyroxine act on most cells, and others (e.g., the sex hormones) act only on particular cell types. The hormones are either peptides, the action of which is initiated when they bind to receptors in the cell membrane, or steroids and thyroxine, which diffuse through the lipid membrane and bind to intracellular receptors. Steroid hormones bind to chromatin in the nucleus, where they trigger the transcription of certain genes. The proteins so produced cause alterations in cell function, and these are the specific effect of the hormone. The release and actions of hormones are detailed in Chapter 17.

Intracellular Communication by "Second Messengers"

The control functions just described involve actions on the cell membrane. The information received there is usually concerned with producing reactions of organelles within the cell. It is conveyed to these organelles by various substances known as second messengers (with reference to the "first" messages brought to the cell from external sources). The study of second messengers is developing rapidly, and there is no guarantee that the present state of understanding is at all complete. Here we mention three well-established messengers, Ca^{2+}, cAMP and IP_3.

Calcium. The simplest intracellular messenger substance is the Ca^{2+} ion. Its free concentration in the resting cell is very low, 10^{-8} to 10^{-7} mol/l. It can enter the cell through specific membrane channels when they are opened – by changes in the membrane potential, for instance (see Chapter 2). The resulting elevated Ca^{2+} concentration enables important reactions in the cell such as the contraction of myofibrils, which is the basis of muscle contraction (see Chapter 4), or the release of vesicles containing transmitter substances from nerve endings (see Chapter 3). Both reactions require a Ca^{2+} concentration of about 10^{-5} mol/l. Ca^{2+} can also be released from intracellular stores, such as the endoplasmic reticulum, to exert its controlling influence. Release of Ca^{2+} from storage requires another messenger substance (e.g., see Fig. 1-16).

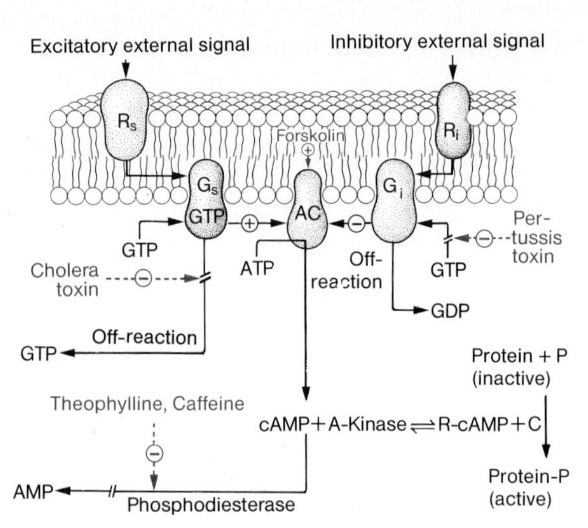

Fig. 1-15. Reaction chain involving the intracellular messenger cAMP (cyclic adenosine monophosphate). Excitatory or inhibitory external signals activate membrane receptors R_s or R_i. These control G proteins, which can react with intracellular GTP (guanosine triphosphate) and thereby stimulate or inhibit intracellular adenylate cyclase (AC). The amplifier enzyme AC converts adenosine triphosphate (ATP) into cAMP, which is eventually degraded to AMP by phosphodiesterase. Free cAMP diffuses into the cell and activates adenylate kinase (A-kinase), releasing its catalytic subunit C, which catalyzes the phosphorylation of intracellular proteins, the ultimate "action" of the extracellular stimulus. The diagram also shows drugs and toxins that promote (+) or inhibit (–) some of the reactions. (Modified from [8])

Cyclic adenosine monophosphate, cAMP. In recent years cyclic adenosine monophosphate (cAMP), a derivative of the general energy supplier ATP, has proved to be an important second messenger. The complicated chain of reactions shown in Fig. 1-15 begins with a receptor R_s in the outer surface of the plasma membrane, which can be a specific binding site for various transmitters and hormones. After binding to its "stimulus" molecule R_s changes its conformation; this change acts on a protein G_s in the inner surface, in such a way as to enable G_s to be activated by intracellular guanosine triphosphate (GTP). The activated protein G_s in turn stimulates an enzyme on the inside of the membrane, adenylate cyclase (AC), which catalyzes the conversion of intracellular ATP into cAMP. The water-soluble cAMP is the actual messenger that conveys the effect of stimulation of the extracellular receptor R_s to the interior of the cell.

In parallel with this stimulatory route involving R_s, it is possible for an inhibitory extracellular transmitter or hormone to bind to an inhibitory receptor R_i which, again by way of a GTP-activated protein G_i, inhibits AC and thus impedes the production of cAMP. When the messenger cAMP has diffused into the cell, it reacts with an adenylate kinase (A-kinase) so as to set free a catalytic subunit C, which *catalyzes the phosphorylation of proteins P*. This phosphorylation converts the proteins into the active form so that they can exert their specific controlling action (e.g., the degradation of glycogen). This complicated signaling system is extraordinarily effective, because the ultimate result is activation of an enzyme that can phosphorylate many proteins. That is, the regulatory signal is passed down the line with a large amplification factor. The external transmitter substances that bind to the receptors R_s or R_i, each specific to a particular receptor within these categories, form an extremely diverse group. Adrenalin binds to R_s or R_i to exert various kinds of control of glycogen and lipid metabolism, as well as to elicit stronger contractions of the heart muscle and other responses (see Chapter 19). By activating R_s, thyrotropin stimulates the thyroid gland to release the hormone thyroxine, and prostaglandin I inhibits the aggregation of blood platelets. Inhibitory effects mediated by R_i include those of adrenalin, which result in a reduced breakdown

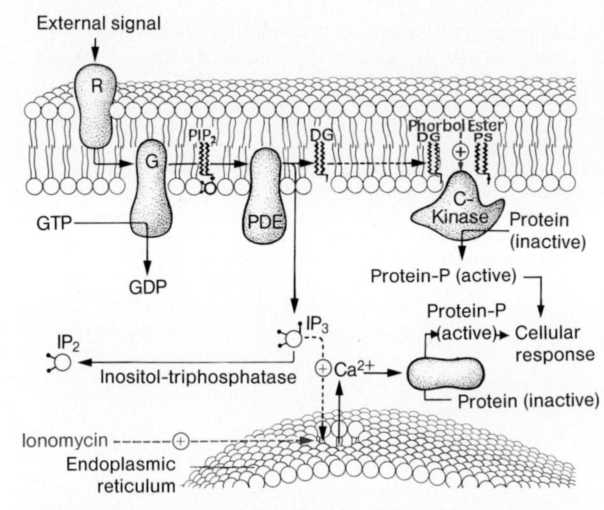

Fig. 1-16. Reaction chain involving the intracellular messenger IP_3 (inositol triphosphate). As in the cAMP system, the extracellular signal is mediated by a G protein; here it activates phosphodiesterase (PDE). The latter splits phosphatidylinosine diphosphate (PIP_2) in the plasma membrane into IP_3 and diacylglycerine (DG), and the IP_3 diffuses into the cytoplasm. There it releases Ca^{2+} from the endoplasmic reticulum, and the increase in $[Ca^{2+}]_i$ activates a protein kinase that phosphorylates, and thereby activates, an enzyme. The other product, DG, remains in the membrane and activates a C-kinase (cofactor phosphatidylserine, PS). This C-kinase also phosphorylates enzymes, mediating the specific action associated with stimulation of the external receptor R. The branches involving IP_3 and DG can be activated separately by ionomycin and phorbol esters, respectively. (Modified from [8, 9])

of lipids. The **cAMP system** is thus a **multifunctional intracellular control system,** which can be finely adjusted by stimulatory and inhibitory extracellular signal substances.

Phosphoinositol, IP_3. An intracellular second-messenger system that has only recently been discovered is the phosphoinositol system (Fig. 1-16). Here the inhibitory pathway is lacking, but this system resembles the cAMP system in that the effect of stimulating the receptor R is transmitted to a GTP-activated protein G in the inner surface of the membrane. In the next step a common membrane lipid, phosphatidylinositol (PI), having previously received two additional phosphate groups to become PIP_2, is split by the activated phosphodiesterase PDE into **inositol triphosphate** (IP_3) and the lipid **diacylglycerin** (DG). Inositol triphosphate, IP_3, is the water-soluble second messenger, which diffuses into the cytosol. It acts primarily by releasing Ca^{2+} from the endoplasmic reticulum. The Ca^{2+} in turn serves as a messenger, as described above; for example, it activates a Ca-dependent phosphokinase that phosphorylates enzymes. The lipid subunit DG (Fig. 1-16) also carries a signal, diffusing within the lipid phase of the plasma membrane to a C-kinase in the inner membrane surface, which it activates with the cofactor phosphatidylserine. The C-kinase then promotes the phosphorylation of proteins, converting them to an active form.

The IP_3 second-messenger system can also be driven by many external transmitters and hormones, including acetylcholine, serotonin, vasopressin and thyrotropin, and is as diverse in its intracellular actions as the cAMP system. It also seems to be activatable by light in visual receptors of the eye, and to play a central role in phototransduction (see Chapter 11). When the receptor of this system is first activated in the life of an organism, it is by spermatozoa; the effect is to enable IP_3 to participate in controlling the reactions accompanying fertilization of the egg.

The cAMP and IP_3-DG systems are both highly effective **biological amplifiers.** They convert the reaction between a transmitter and the external membrane receptor into the phosphorylation of many intracellular proteins, which then alter various functions of the cell. One remarkable aspect is that, as far as is known today, there are only two closely related control systems of this kind, systems that are used by a great variety of external messengers to control quite different intracellular processes. On the other hand, the various control systems, including that of Ca^{2+}, are intimately interlinked, which permits a finely graded control of cellular function.

1.5 References

Textbooks and Handbooks

1. Alberts, B., Bray, D., Lewis, J., Raff, M., Roberts, K., Watson, J.D.: Molecular Biology of the Cell. New York and London: Garland Publishing Inc. 1983
2. Czihak, G., Langer, H., Ziegler, H. (eds.): Biologie. Berlin, Heidelberg, New York: Springer 1983
3. Hille, B.: Ionic channels of excitable membranes. Sunderland, Mass.: Sinauer Assoc., 1984
4. Hoppe, W., Lohmann, W., Markl, H., Ziegler, H. (eds.): Biophysik. Berlin, Heidelberg, New York: Springer 1984
5. Jungermann, K., Möhler, H.: Biochemie. Berlin, Heidelberg, New York, Springer 1980
6. Kandel, E.R., Schwartz, J.H. (eds.): Principles of neural science. New York, Amsterdam, Oxford: Elsevier 1985
7. Schiebler, T.H., Schmidt, W.: Anatomie des Menschen. Berlin, Heidelberg, New York, Tokyo, Springer 1983

Original Papers and Reviews

8. BERRIDGE, M.J.: The molecular basis of communication within the cell. Sci. Amer. *253*, 124–134 (1985)
9. BERRIDGE, M.J., IRVINE, R.F.: Inositol triphosphate, a novel second messenger in cellular signal transduction. Nature *312*, 315–321 (1984)
10. BRETSCHER, M.S.: The molecules of the cell membrane. Sci. Amer. *253*, 124–134 (1985)
11. DAUT, J.: The living cell as an energy-transducing machine. A minimal model of myocardial metabolism. Biochim. et Biophys. Acta *895*, 41–62 (1987)
12. HODGKIN, A.L., KATZ, B.: The effect of sodium ions on the electrical activity of the giant axon of the squid. J. Physiol. (Lond.) *108*, 37–77 (1949)
13. HODGKIN, A.L., KEYNES, R.D.: Active transport of cations in giant axons from Sepia and Loligo. J. Physiol. (Lond.) *128*, 28–42 (1955)
14. LÄUGER, P.: Ionic channels with conformational substates. Biophys. J. *47*, 581–590 (1985)
15. OCHS, S., WORTH, R.M.: Exoplasmic transport in normal and pathologic systems. In: Physiology and Pathobiology of Axons. S.G. WAXMANN, Ed. New York: Raven Press 1978

2 Information Transfer by Electrical Excitation

J. DUDEL

There are two systems that transmit information over relatively long distances within the body: hormones and nerves. The principles of the release, distribution and action of hormones were mentioned in the preceding chapter and are detailed in Chapter 17. The nerves constitute a more rapid and more "individual" system. As a basis for later chapters concerned with particular functions of the nervous system, here we consider first the functional properties of single nerve cells (neurons), and then the principles of neuronal interactions (Chapter 3). It is characteristic of nerve cells that they function by means of changes in the membrane potential. We begin, therefore, with a closer look at the cell potentials.

2.1 Resting Potential

Measurement. Across the cell membrane of a neuron there is a potential difference, as in all other cells of the body (see p. 6). An arrangement for measuring this membrane potential is shown in Fig. 2-1. The sensor that detects the potential is a microelectrode, a glass capillary drawn out to a very fine tip (thinner than 1 μm) and filled with a conducting solution. The reference electrode in the extracellular space is a chlorided silver plate. Initially both electrodes are in the extracellular space (Fig. 2-1B, left) and there is no potential difference between them; the potential record in Fig. 2-1C shows the value zero for the "extracellular potential". Now the measurement electrode is advanced through the membrane into the cell (Fig. 2-1B, right), and the voltmeter indicates a stepwise change in potential to about –80 mV. This voltage is the **membrane potential.**

The membrane potential of nerve and muscle cells remains constant for long periods, if the cells are not activated by some external influence. The membrane potential of such resting cells is called the **resting potential** (Fig. 2-1C). In nerve and muscle cells the resting potential is always negative; its magnitude is constant and characteristic of each cell type. In warm-blooded animals it ranges from –55 to –100 mV except for smooth muscle cells, which have resting potentials as small as –30 mV.

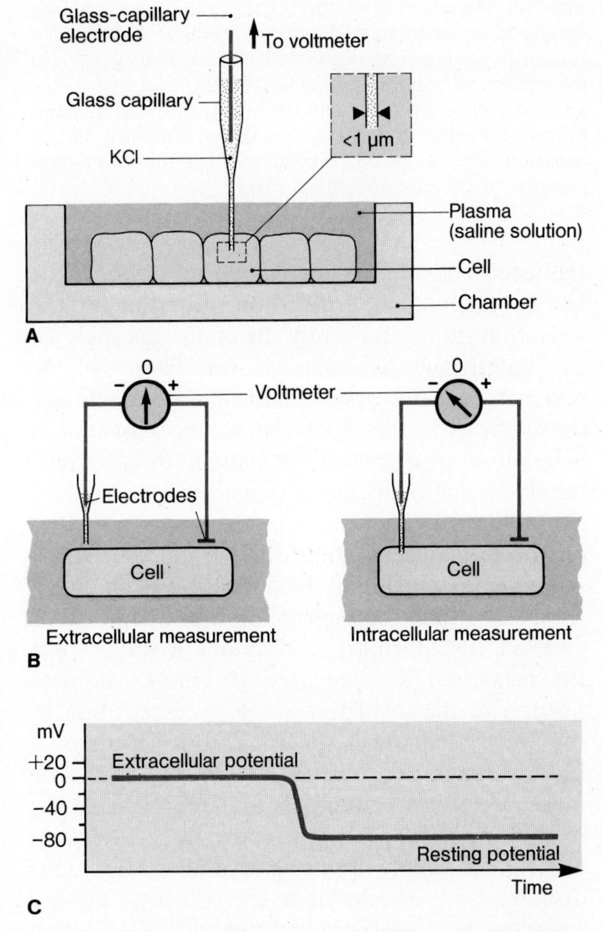

Fig. 2-1 A-C. Intracellular measurement of membrane potential. **A** The cell is placed in a chamber and the space around it filled with plasma (or saline solution). **B** *Left:* with recording and reference electrode both extracellular the voltmeter between the two registers zero. *Right:* with the recording electrode in the cell and the reference electrode outside, the voltmeter shows the resting potential. **C** The potential before and after the electrode penetrates the cell

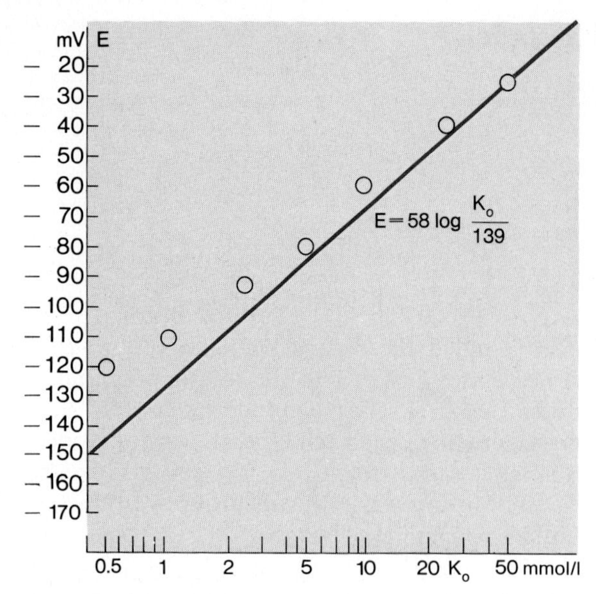

Fig. 2-2. Dependence of the resting potential of a frog muscle fiber (ordinate) on the extracellular K^+ concentration $[K^+]_o$ (abscissa, logarithmic scale). The *circles* give the membrane potentials measured for the indicated $[K^+]_o$, and the *straight line* is the relation between potassium equilibrium potential and $[K^+]_o$ calculated from the Nernst equation. The factor 58 takes account of the lower temperature of the frog. (Modified from [7])

Diffusion potential. As explained on pp. 6, 7, the resting potential is a diffusion potential for the ions that move passively through channels in the membrane (Chapter 1, Eq. 7, p. 7). At rest most of the open membrane channels are those for K^+; therefore *the resting potential is determined, to a first approximation, by the transmembrane concentration gradient of* K^+. Fig. 2-2 shows the dependence of the measured potential on the K^+ concentration outside the cell $[K^+]_o$. After the extracellular concentration is changed, for a short time the internal concentration is unaffected, and during this time one would expect the measured K^+ potential to change in proportion to the logarithm of $[K^+]_o$, according to the Nernst equation (p. 7). This K^+ potential, E_K, is shown by the red line in Fig. 2-2. The measured resting potentials are very close to E_K in the upper range, but for low $[K^+]_o$ they become increasingly less negative than E_K. This discrepancy is ascribable to the relatively greater significance of sodium permeability P_{Na} when $[K^+]_o$ is low (Chapter 1, Eq. 7, p. 7). The departure of the measured resting potentials from E_K disappears when the Na^+ flux is prevented – for example, by replacing the extracellular Na^+ with an impermeable cation such as choline. It follows that the normal resting potential is about 10 mV more positive than E_K.

Changes in the extracellular K^+ concentration. In the blood plasma, K^+ is ordinarily kept very close to its normal concentration of 4 mmol/l (see Table 1-1, p. 4). But many nerve cells do not exchange ions rapidly with the plasma, and for these $[K^+]_o$ can depart considerably from the normal value. Fig. 2-3 is a schematic drawing of a neuron in the CNS, which is separated from the nearest blood capillary by **glial cells.** Here the extracellular space is reduced to narrow clefts, about 15 nm wide. Peripheral axons are in a similar situation, being closely enveloped by Schwann cells. Although these interstitial spaces are entirely adequate for long-term equilibration of the external milieu by diffusion, during periods of intense neuronal activity the ion concentrations in the extracellular space can change considerably for a short time. During intense electrical activity Na^+ ions flow into the cell and K^+ ions flow out (see action potentials, p. 23, and excitatory postsynaptic potentials, p. 43). The high extracellular Na^+ concentration is not appreciably changed in the process, but *the* K^+ *concentration can increase considerably.* The extracellular K^+ concentration can be measured with microelectrodes filled with ion exchangers selective for K^+. When the nerve cells are very active the extracellular K^+ concentration rises from the normal 3–4 mmol/l to as much as 10 mmol/l [13]. As stated by the Nernst equation (see Fig. 2-2), these elevated extracellular K^+ concentrations cause considerable depolarization of the nerve cells. It may be that depolarization due to increased extracellular K^+ is one causative factor in the development of convulsive discharge in the brain, such as occurs in epileptic seizures [13]. After intense activity the active transport of K^+ can bring its extracellular concentration below normal, causing hyperpolarization of the nerve cells.

Another ion that can exhibit altered extracellular concentration in the CNS during neuronal activity is Ca^{2+}. The Ca^{2+} concentration, like that of K^+, can be measured with microelectrodes filled with a selective ion exchanger. When synaptic terminals are activated, Ca^{2+} flows into them (see Fig. 3-15, p. 54); accordingly, during high-frequency excitation of such terminals the extracellular Ca^{2+} concentration has been found to decrease. A low Ca^{2+} concentration results in an increase in neuronal excitability (see below, Fig. 2-10), which can produce pathological changes in the affected neurons [13].

Influence of the glia on the intercellular milieu. How do glial cells react to changes in the inter-

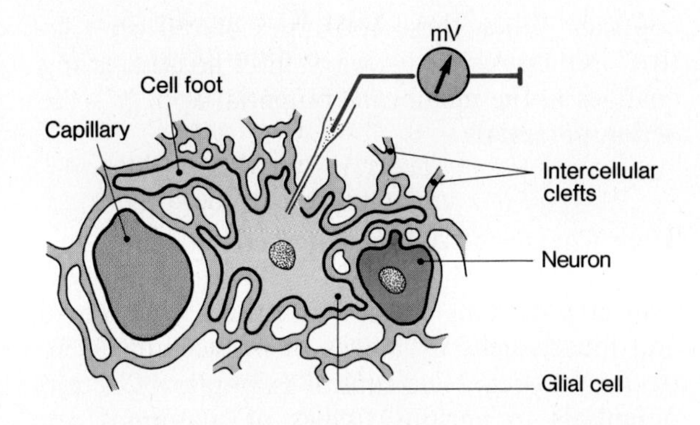

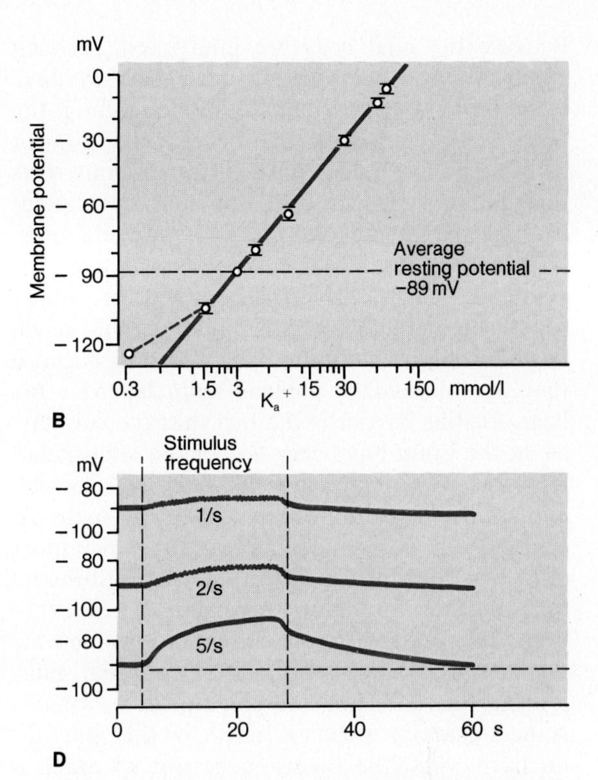

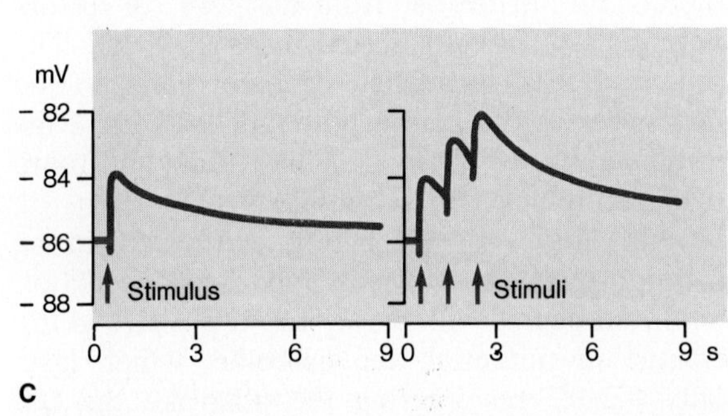

Fig. 2-3 A-D. Properties of the glial cells. **A** Schematic drawing of the relations among neurons, glia and capillaries at the electron-microscopic level. An astrocyte *(light red)*, penetrated by a microelectrode for the measurement of membrane potential, lies between a capillary and a neuron. All the cellular elements are separated from one another by intercellular clefts ca. 15 nm wide *(width exaggerated* in the diagram). **B** Dependence of the glial membrane potential (ordinate) on the extracellular K^+ concentration, $K_0{}^+$. The mean resting potential (RP) is −89mV. The data depart from the potential calculated by the Nernst equation only at $K_0{}^+ = 0.3$ mmol/l. **C** Depolarization of glial cells by activity of nearby neurons in the optic nerve of a salamander *(Necturus)*, elicited by 1 stimulus or 3 at intervals of 1 s (↑). **D** Depolarization of glial cells in the same preparation during series of stimuli lasting 20 s, within which the stimuli are repeated at rates of 1/s, 2/s and 5/s; the latter causes depolarization by almost 20 mV. Note in C and D that the time course of depolarization is much slower (seconds!) than that of the action potential. (Modified from [6])

stitial ion concentrations? Fig. 2-3A illustrates the measurement of the membrane potential of a glial cell, and in B the membrane potentials found for various extracellular K^+ concentrations are plotted. The data correspond to the curve for a K^+ electrode calculated from the Nernst equation more closely than was the case in the muscle cell (Fig. 2-2). That is, the predominance of K^+ permeability is even more pronounced in the glial-cell membrane. Accordingly, the glial cell also becomes depolarized when activity of the adjacent neurons causes the extracellular K^+ concentration to rise (Fig. 2-3C and D). When the K^+ concentration subsequently falls, glial-cell depolarization decreases with a time constant of several seconds. This decrease in the extracellular K^+ concentration is caused in part by the glia. The glial cells make electrical connections with one another by way of "gap junctions" (Fig. 3-20), as do epithelial and smooth muscle cells. When glial cells in a small region are depolarized owing to local increase in extracellular K^+ concentration, current flows between the depolarized and the non-depolarized cells. This electrical current causes K^+ to flow into the depolarized glial cells, decreasing the extracellular K^+ concentration. Because of the high K^+ permeability and the electrical connections of the glial cells, these cells act as a buffer with respect to increases in the extracellular K^+ concentration. There is no evidence of active uptake of K^+ into glial cells by means of an ion pump, although the glial cells probably take up transmitter substance actively at some synapses and thus limit the duration of its action [6].

Unlike nerve cells, glial cells are not excitable. They do have potential-dependent Na^+ and Ca^{2+} channels, but not in sufficient density to allow action potentials to occur (see p. 23). Some glial cells also have ion channels controlled by synaptic transmitters (see p. 57), but their function is not known.

Because the glial cells are interposed between capillaries and nerve cells (Fig. 2-3), they have been thought to participate in nourishing the nerve cells. However, the nerve cells do not seem to be dependent on transport of nutrients through the glia; diffusion of such substances through the intercellular clefts is quite adequate. Most neurons are less than 50 μm away from the nearest capillary. Nevertheless, there are many substances in the blood plasma that cannot reach the intercellular clefts and the neurons, because they are blocked by a **blood-brain barrier.** One basis for this barrier is the fact that the capillaries in the brain have very few of the endothelial fenestrae present in other capillary beds, which allow fairly large molecules to pass through. To emerge from a brain capillary, a substance must diffuse or be transported through the endothelial cells. Furthermore, after traversing the endothelium the substance must diffuse a considerable distance along the processes of the glial cells. During this diffusion, the glia can take up substances that are to be excluded, so that they do no harm. The glia seems to be not so much a supply line for the neurons as a means of protection and mechanical support.

Na-K pump. As explained in Section 1.2 (pp. 4–10), although the resting potential results to a great extent from the passive diffusion of K^+, the underlying transmembrane concentration gradients are not in themselves stable; they are produced by the Na-K pump in an energy-consuming process (Fig. 1-9). Production of the concentration gradients involves a net shift of charge; that is, the pump current is **electrogenic**, making the membrane potential more negative by 5–10 mV. Therefore, if the activity of the pump fluctuates, the resting potential can be changed by a few mV. If the pump is blocked by poisons or an energy deficit, this electrogenic component of the membrane potential is eliminated; the cell slowly takes up Na^+ and loses K^+, and the resting potential becomes progressively more positive (see p. 8).

2.2 The Action Potential

The function of nerve cells in the body is to receive information, to carry it to other parts of the system, to compare it with other information and finally to control the function of other cells. Muscle cells, under the control of nerves, contract. When these two types of cell are "active" in their respective ways, brief positive-going changes in the membrane potential appear – the **action potentials**.

Time Courses of Action Potentials

Action potentials can be recorded from nerve and muscle cells by means of intracellular electrodes (cf. Fig. 2-1). Typical examples of action potentials in various tissues of mammals are shown in Fig. 2-4. In all these action potentials there is an abrupt rise from the negative resting potential to a positive peak near +30 mV. The potential then returns at different rates to the resting level; the action potential lasts ca. 1 ms in nerves, ca. 10 ms in skeletal muscle and more than 200 ms in cardiac muscle.
Several phases of the action potential can be distinguished, as shown in Fig. 2-5. The action potential begins with a very rapid positive-going change in potential, the **upstroke,** which lasts only 0.2–0.5 ms. During the upstroke the cell membrane loses its normal charge or "polarization"; the upstroke is therefore also called the *depolarization phase*. As a rule, the depolarization crosses the zero line and the membrane potential becomes positive. This positive part of the action potential is called the **overshoot.** The phase following the peak, during which the original resting membrane voltage is restored, is called **repolarization.**

Afterpotentials. The last part of the repolarization phase is slowed in some types of action potential; the muscle action potential in Fig. 2-4 is a good example. About 1 ms after onset of the action potential there is a distinct inflec-

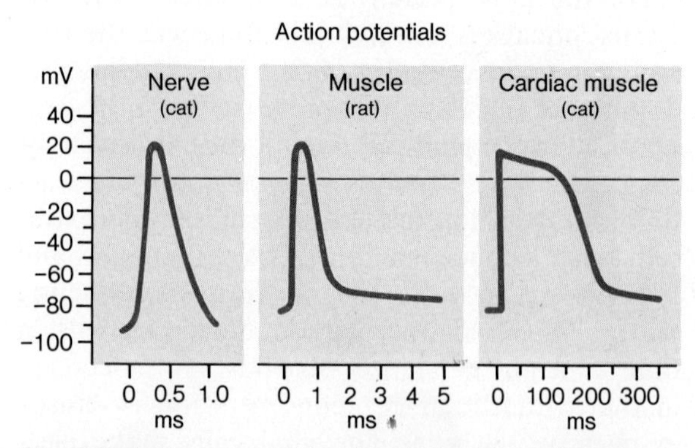

Fig. 2-4. Action potentials of various mammalian tissues, schematic. *Ordinate:* intracellular membrane potential; *abscisssa:* time since beginning of the action potential. The time scales of the different action potentials vary widely

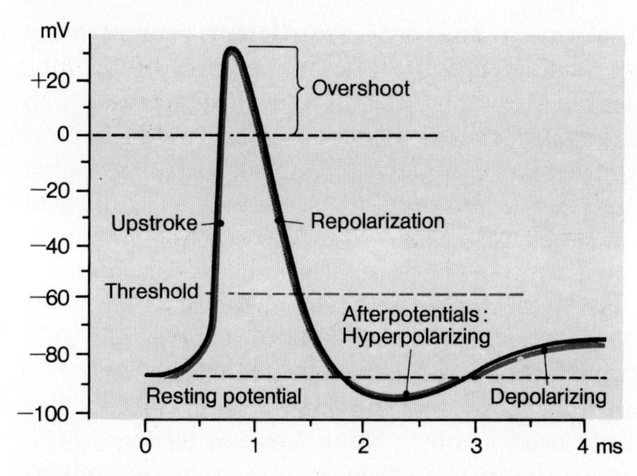

Fig. 2-5. Time course of a neuronal action potential subdivided to show the successive phases described in the text

tion of the repolarization curve; the following slowly changing potential is called the *depolarizing afterpotential.* In other tissues, such as nerve cells of the spinal cord, the repolarization curve rapidly crosses the resting potential, so that for some time the potential is more negative than the resting potential; this is called a *hyperpolarizing afterpotential* (cf. Fig. 2-5).

The Origin of the Action Potential

Threshold and excitability. How is the resting potential – otherwise kept so constant by the mechanisms just discussed – disturbed as much as to produce an action potential? Action potentials are always elicited when the membrane is *depolarized* from the resting potential to ca. −50 mV. The mechanisms that bring about this initial depolarization will be treated later (p. 33). The potential at which depolarization gives rise to an action potential is called the **threshold** (Fig. 2-5). At this threshold potential the membrane charge becomes unstable; it dissipates by an intrinsic mechanism which leads to a reversal of polarity – the rapid upstroke to the peak of the action potential. This state of automatic, progressive breakdown of the membrane charge is called **excitation**. Excitation usually lasts less than 1 ms. It is like an explosion, forceful but soon over. The depolarizing phase of the action potential in turn sets in motion processes that restore the resting membrane charge.

Cells in which action potentials can be elicited are called *excitable*. Excitability is a typical property of nerve and muscle cells. The time course of the action potential is constant and characteristic of each cell type. It is very little affected by the way or the frequency with which excitation is elicited. The fact that action potentials are so constant in shape has been called the *"all-or-none" law of excitation.*

Membrane conductance. During the action potential there is evidently a brief change in the permeability of the membrane to ions that determine the resting potential (Eq. 7, p. 7). When one is concerned with the electrical properties of a membrane, a useful measure of the permeability of the membrane to an ion is the membrane conductance g_{ion}. Conductance is given by the current I_{ion} divided by the driving voltage. At the equilibrium potential for the ion concerned, E_{ion} (see Nernst equation, 4, p. 6), the driving voltage and the net current are zero; therefore E_{ion} is the reference potential, and the departure of the membrane potential E from E_{ion} is the potential difference that drives the current I_{ion}. The conductance g_{ion} is then

$$g_{ion} = I_{ion}/(E - E_{ion}) \qquad (1)$$

We can now proceed to describe the ionic currents during the action potential in terms of the conductance for individual ions as so defined.

Ionic currents during the action potential. The resting potential, as shown in the previous section, is very close to the equilibrium potential of the K^+ ions, to which the membrane is most permeable at rest. If the interior of the cell becomes positive with respect to the extracellular space during the action potential, the membrane conductance for Na^+ (g_{Na}) must have increased, for only Na^+ has a positive equilibrium potential, at +60 mV, more positive than the peak of the action potential. This inference is confirmed by the experimental finding that action potentials can be triggered only when the extracellular Na^+ concentration is high. Should these extracellular sodium ions be lacking, there cannot be an increased inward sodium current no matter how much g_{Na} increases, and thus there can be no depolarization phase of the action potential. The basis of excitation, then, is an increase in the *membrane conductance for* Na^+, brought about by depolarization to threshold. However, the K^+ conductance of the membrane is also involved. If an increase in K^+ conductance is prevented by certain chemicals, such as tetraethylammonium, the action potential repolarizes much more slowly. This effect indicates that an increase in K^+ *conductance* is an important factor in repolarization of the membrane. The action potential is thus based on a cycle of Na^+ inflow into the cell and subsequent K^+ outflow.

Kinetics of Ionic Currents during Excitation

Membrane-current measurement. When the neuron is excited, the depolarization alters the conductance of the membrane for various ions, and these conductance changes in turn cause the potential to change. This complex process is analyzed by measuring the dependence of the different membrane conductances on the membrane potential. A stepwise potential change, from the baseline to a test potential, is imposed by injecting current into the cell with an electronically controlled amplifier. The current needed to maintain this **"voltage clamp"** is measured; it is the mirror image of the current generated by the cell membrane after imposition of the potential step [23. 24]. Fig. 2-6 illustrates the time course of the membrane current in these conditions for 2 nodes of Ranvier (see p. 39) of a frog nerve. Voltage steps of –60, –30, 0, +30 and +60 mV away from the starting potential elicit complex currents, the sum of Na^+ and K^+ current components. The components can be elegantly separated by eliminating them one at a time with a specific inhibitor substance.

In Fig. 2-6B tetraethylammonium (TEA) has been used to block the potassium currents [33]; hence the measured curves represent the **sodium currents**. These Na^+ currents are negative for test potentials below +40 mV; the Na^+ ions flow into the nerves. At +30 mV the Na^+ current is still negative but small, and at +60 mV, on the other side of the Na^+ equilibrium potential, its direc-

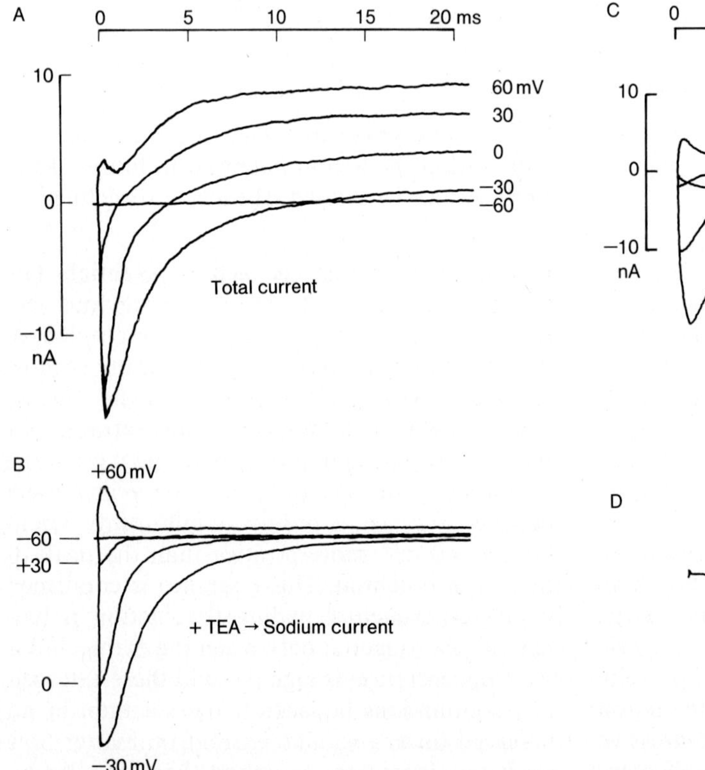

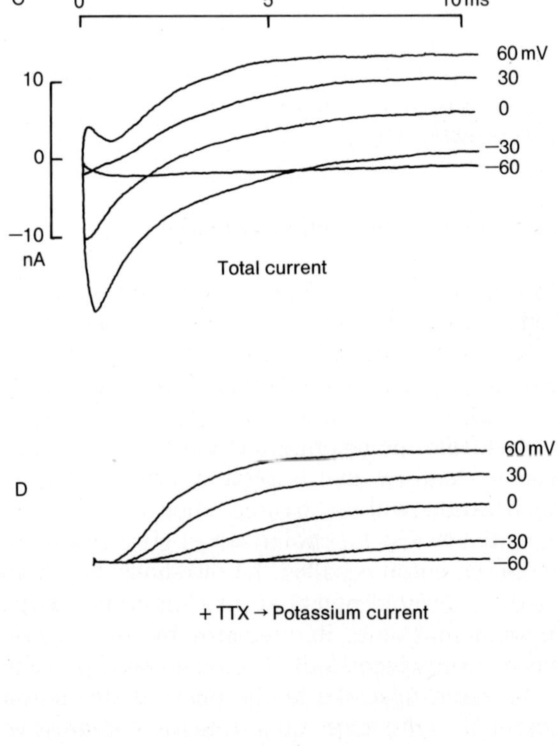

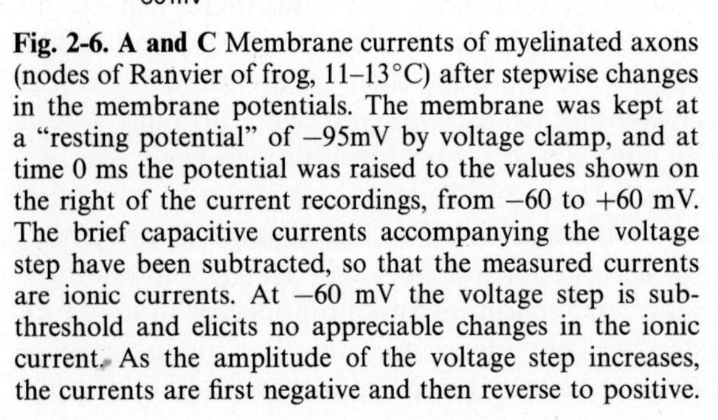

Fig. 2-6. A and C Membrane currents of myelinated axons (nodes of Ranvier of frog, 11–13 °C) after stepwise changes in the membrane potentials. The membrane was kept at a "resting potential" of –95mV by voltage clamp, and at time 0 ms the potential was raised to the values shown on the right of the current recordings, from –60 to +60 mV. The brief capacitive currents accompanying the voltage step have been subtracted, so that the measured currents are ionic currents. At –60 mV the voltage step is subthreshold and elicits no appreciable changes in the ionic current. As the amplitude of the voltage step increases, the currents are first negative and then reverse to positive. In **B** the preparation represented in **A** was subjected to the same voltage steps while the potassium currents were blocked by 6 mmol/l tetraethylammoniium (TEA), so that the currents are carried almost entirely by sodium; the Na^+ current changes polarity from negative to positive between +30 and +60 mV and flows for a shorter time as depolarization increases. In **D** the preparation shown in **C** was exposed to 0.3 µmol/l tetrodotoxin (TTX) to block the sodium current; hence the recording shows the potassium currents. These rise much more slowly than the sodium currents after depolarization and continue as long as depolarization is maintained. (Modified from [3])

tion has reversed. After each depolarizing step the Na^+ current very quickly reaches a maximum and then, if the depolarization is maintained, returns to zero. This **inactivation** of the Na^+ currents is slowest for small depolarizations and accelerates as the amplitude of depolarization increases: at +30 mV the Na^+ current has practically stopped in only 1 ms.
To complement the experiment of Fig. 2-6B, in D the Na^+ currents are blocked by tetrodotoxin (TTX) [35] to reveal the time courses of the **potassium currents**. These K^+ currents are positive over the whole range of test potentials; the equilibrium potential for K^+ is about −100 mV, so that at −60 mV to +60 mV K^+ flows out of the nerve. The K^+ currents increase about in proportion to the depolarization amplitude. Even with the largest depolarization there is a delay of about 0.5 ms before the current begins, and within about 5 ms it reaches a plateau that is maintained as long as the depolarization lasts. In contrast to the Na^+ current, then, the K^+ current in a neuron exhibits **no inactivation**. The other important difference between the K^+ and Na^+ currents is that the latter reach a maximum very soon after depolarization, whereas the **K^+ currents have a delayed onset** and then rise relatively slowly.

Na^+ and K^+ conductances during the action potential. The time course of membrane conductance for Na^+ and K^+ can be calculated by dividing the respective currents in Fig. 2-6 by the difference between the test potential and the equilibrium potential of the ion. Such data can also be obtained for small potential steps; for example, suppose that one knows the current produced by a small voltage step in the near-threshold region. This current flows into the membrane capacitance and through the membrane resistance, both of which are known values (see Figs. 2-16 and 2-17), thereby producing a small depolarization. This voltage in turn causes a calculable additional current, which leads to further depolarization. By proceeding with such small voltage and time steps, one can *reconstruct the course of the action potential* from the measured voltage dependences of the amplitudes and time courses of g_{Na} and g_K. Fig. 2-7 shows the action potential so derived, together with the time courses of g_{Na} and g_K. At the threshold g_{Na} rises sharply; it reaches its maximum before the peak of the action potential, because inactivation of the Na^+ current is beginning, and within 1 ms it returns to the resting level. On the other hand, g_K rises slowly, with some delay after depolarization

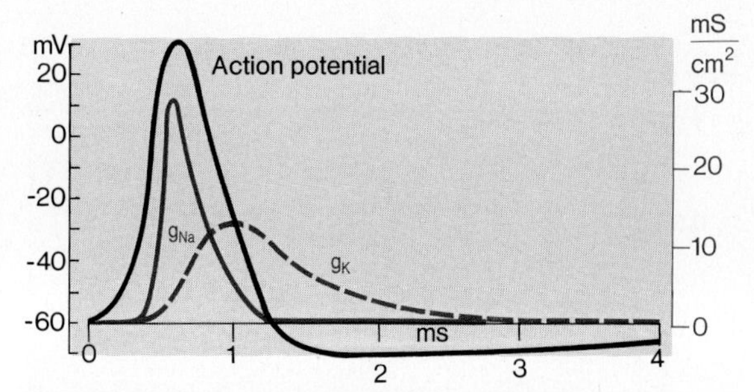

Fig. 2-7. Membrane conductances of the squid giant axon during the action potential. g_{Na} and g_K are calculated from series of depolarization steps like those in Fig. 2-6. (Modified from [16])

begins. It reaches its maximum late, when repolarization is half completed, and then declines again because depolarization is decreasing. That is, the increase in g_K accelerates the second phase of repolarization and causes the action potential in Fig. 2-7 to be followed by a hyperpolarizing afterpotential; while g_K is still above the resting value, the membrane potential moves away from the resting level, toward the negative potassium equilibrium potential E_K.

Inactivation of the Na^+ Current

Figure 2-6B showed that the Na^+ current in frog nerve fibers declines after about 0.5 ms even though depolarization is maintained. In warm-blooded animals, this time is still shorter at higher temperatures. The inactivation typical of the Na^+ current becomes more rapid as depolarization increases, so that the current falls back to zero more quickly. But this process by no means restores the resting state; if the membrane is briefly repolarized and depolarized again after complete inactivation has occurred, it is practically impossible to elicit a new Na^+ current. When the membrane is in this condition, the sodium system **cannot be activated**. Even after the resting potential has been established for some time, the Na^+ current can be only partially activated. The axon membrane must be hyperpolarized by 20–40 mV in order for depolarization from this starting potential to elicit the maximal Na^+ current, $I_{Na\,max}$ (Fig. 2-8). If the membrane potential is made 20 mV more positive than the resting potential for 10 ms or longer, depolarization from this baseline produces only a minimal Na^+ current. That is, prolonged depolarization can prevent excitation; cells with a potential more positive than −60 to −50 mV become inexcitable [3, 23]. Long-term depolarization can be

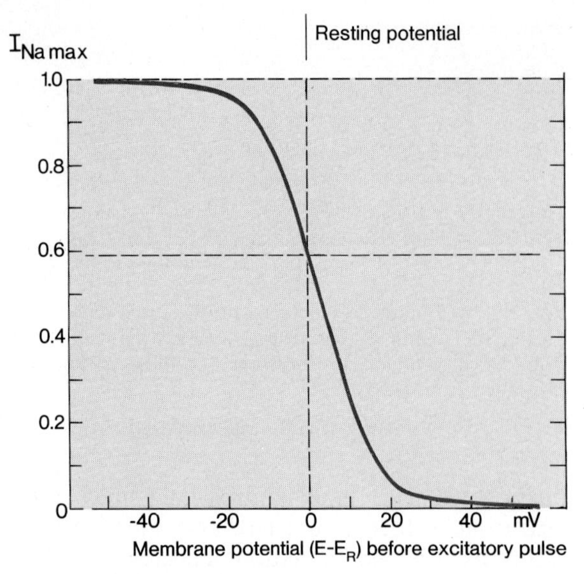

Fig. 2-8. Potential-dependence of sodium-system inactivation. Abscissa (E-E_R): departure of the membrane potential from the resting potential (−60mV). From each of these initial potentials the membrane was depolarized to −16mV, and the resulting maximal Na^+ current (I_{Namax}) is plotted as a fraction of the I_{Namax} corresponding to full activation of the sodium system (ordinate). (Modified from [15])

brought about by metabolic disturbances such as oxygen deficiency or by pharmacological influences, and are able to block the triggering of the excitatory process.

Refractory periods. As a further important consequence of Na^+-system inactivation, the membrane can become **refractory**. This phenomenon is illustrated in Fig. 2-9. If the membrane is depolarized immediately following an action potential, no excitation is induced at the threshold for the previous action potential or by any greater depolarization. This state of complete inexcitability, which in nerve cells lasts for ca. 1 ms, is called the **absolute refractory period**. It is followed by a **relative refractory period**, in which action potentials can be elicited by large depolarizations, though these potentials are of smaller than normal amplitude. Not until several ms have elapsed following an action potential does it become possible to elicit an action potential of normal amplitude by the normal threshold depolarization; the return to this condition marks the end of the *relative refractory period*. As mentioned above, refractoriness results from the inactivation of the Na^+ system during the preceding action potential. Although the membrane recovers from inactivation due to repolarization, this recovery is a gradual process requiring a few ms, and during this time the Na^+ system is not yet activatable, or activatable to only a limited extent. The **absolute refractory period limits the maximal frequency** with which action potentials can be triggered. If, as in Fig. 2-9, the absolute refractory period ends 2 ms after the onset of the action potential, the cell can be excited at a rate of at most 500/s. There are cells with still shorter refractory periods, so that in the extreme case excitation can be repeated at a rate as high as 1,000/s. In most cells, however, the maximal action potential frequency is less than 500/s.

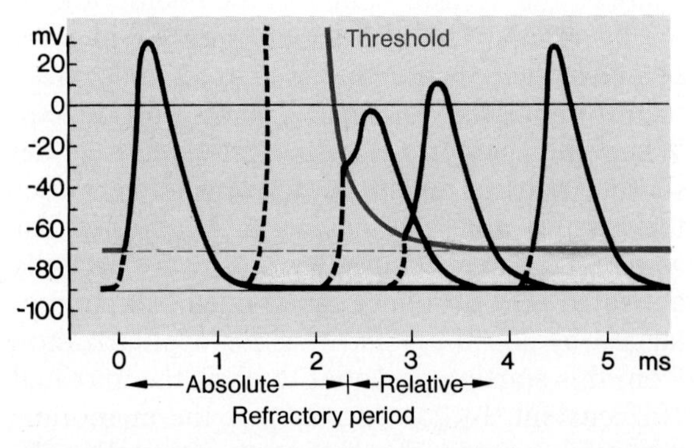

Fig. 2-9. Refractoriness following excitation. An action potential is elicited in a nerve of a mammal *(left)*, and further stimuli are applied at various times thereafter. The solid red line denotes the threshold potential and the dashed black lines, the depolarization of the fiber up to the threshold. In the absolute refractory period the fiber is inexcitable, and in the relative refractory period it is excited at a threshold higher than normal

Ionic Currents during the Afterpotentials

In many cells, the rapid depolarization of the action potential is followed by depolarizing or hyperpolarizing afterpotentials (Figs. 2-4 and 2-5). These afterpotentials have various causes; two of the more important types will be described briefly here.

A **brief hyperpolarizing afterpotential** immediately after repolarization is exhibited by many nerve cells and some cardiac-muscle cells (cf. Fig. 2-5). This afterpotential is an overshooting repolarization; when the repolarization phase reaches the resting potential g_K has not yet returned to its resting level (Fig. 2-7) and is thus higher with respect to g_{Na} than in resting conditions. Therefore the membrane potential approaches E_K more closely than when at rest. The resulting hyperpolarization fades away along with the increased g_K. This mechanism of brief hyperpolarization following an action potential participates in the development of repetitive excitation, and will be discussed again in that context (p. 40).

Prolonged **hyperpolarizing afterpotentials,** which summate when excitation is repeated at a high rate, are especially pronounced in the very thin nerve fibers of vertebrates, the Group IV fibers. These prolonged hyperpolarizing afterpotentials are produced by an **electrogenic Na^+ pump** (pp. 7–9), which removes from the cell the Na^+ that entered during excitation [28]. They disappear when pump activity is prevented by metabolic blocking agents such as DNP (cf. Fig. 1-7).

"Stabilization" of the resting potential by $[Ca^{2+}]_o$. The dependence of the Na^+ currents on the test potential illustrated in Fig. 2-6 can be influenced in a variety of ways. Blockade of a fraction of the Na^+ channels by tetrodotoxin or similar substances, as well as variation in density of the Na^+ channels in the membranes, changes only the amplitude and not the potential-dependence or time course of the Na^+ currents. The potential-dependence of the membrane currents is shifted in a characteristic manner by changes in the concentration of extracellular Ca^{2+}, $[Ca^{2+}]_o$. In Fig. 2-10 the maximal Na^+ permeability, P_{Na}, achieved at a given test potential (abscissa) is plotted for various $[Ca^{2+}]_o$. The curves for P_{Na}, plotted here on a logarithmic scale, rise as a straight line for a considerable distance and then saturate. Their parallel displacement along the abscissa demonstrates the effect of $[Ca^{2+}]_o$ on the potential-dependence of P_{Na}: with $[Ca^{2+}]_o$=0 large increases in P_{Na} are produced by small depolarizations, whereas with high $[Ca^{2+}]_o$ the membrane must be depolarized by 35 mV more to elicit the same Na^+ current. That is, reduction of $[Ca^{2+}]_o$ promotes the production of action potentials by depolarization. The effect of $[Ca^{2+}]_o$ on P_{Na} in Fig. 2-10 is complicated by another, acting in the same direction, on the potential-dependence of inactivation. The curves relating $I_{Na\,max}$ to the starting potential in Fig. 2-8 are shifted along the abscissa, just as in Fig.2-10, by changes in $[Ca^{2+}]_o$. The result is not only that for a given depolarization, lowering $[Ca^{2+}]_o$ produces a greater increase in P_{Na} (Fig. 2-10); there is also an absolute reduction of the maximal increase in I_{Na} that can be achieved (Fig. 2-8). The net effect, however is that *lowering $[Ca^{2+}]_o$* lowers the threshold for action-potential generation – that is, *raises excitability* – whereas an increase in $[Ca^{2+}]_o$ "stabilizes" the membrane potential. Distinct local changes in $[Ca^{2+}]_o$ are not uncommon in vivo; for instance, in the CNS as activity (especially of the synapses; see p. 54) increases, Ca^{2+} influx into the cells reduces $[Ca^{2+}]_o$ in the restricted interstitial spaces (Fig. 2-3); the cells become more excitable, which can trigger seizure-like discharge [13]. General reductions of $[Ca^{2+}]_o$ in the blood plasma produce the syndrome of **tetany**, in which uncontrollable excitation of the muscles leads to convulsions.

The striking parallel shifts in potential dependence of the Na^+ currents (and other membrane currents) due to $[Ca^{2+}]_o$ have an interesting physical basis. As indicated in the model of a Na^+ channel shown in Fig. 2-15, the outer side of the membrane bears fixed, mainly negative charges. These are parts of the phospho- and glycolipids, and of projections of the glycoproteins (Fig. 1-2, p. 3). They attract a cloud of ions to the membrane; as an order-of-magnitude estimate, about half the total membrane-potential gradient lies within this cloud, so that the channel proteins "feel" only about half of the potential difference measured between the inside and outside of the cell [3, 26]. Ca^{2+} ions react with the fixed charges in the surface of the plasma membrane and neutralize them. Therefore when $[Ca^{2+}]_o$ is high, the total external negative charge is reduced, and the negativity of the potential across the actual ion channels increases. In Fig. 2-10, for this reason, to achieve a given increase in P_{Na} about 20 mV more

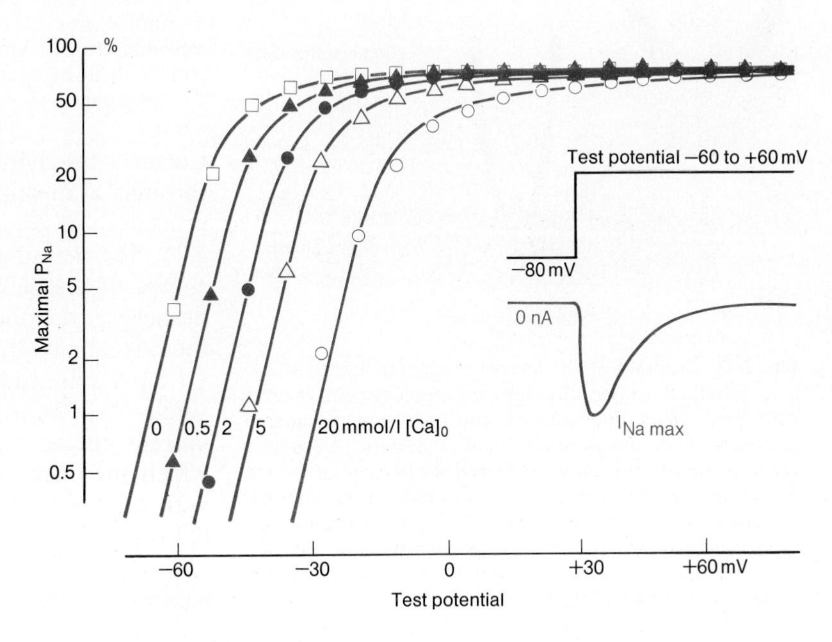

Fig. 2-10. Dependence of maximal Na^+ permeability, P_{Na}, on the magnitude of a stepwise depolarization. A node of Ranvier, initially with a membrane potential of −80mV, was depolarized to the test potentials indicated on the abscissa. The *inset* is a diagram of the depolarization to the test potential and the associated sodium current I_{Na}. Its maximum, $I_{Na\,max}$, is one determinant (along with the intra- and extracellular Na^+ concentrations and the membrane potentials) of the maximal P_{Na}, according to Eq. (7) (Chapter 1). The curves relating P_{Na} to potential are shifted along the abscissa, depending on the external Ca^{2+} concentration ($[Ca^{2+}]_o$ between 0 and 20 mmol/l). As $[Ca^{2+}]_o$ decreases, the threshold depolarization for eliciting a rise in P_{Na} is reduced; the excitability of the node of Ranvier increases. (Modified from [3])

depolarization is needed in the case of 20 mmol/l $[Ca^{2+}]_o$ than in that of 2 mmol/l $[Ca^{2+}]_o$. Conversely, decrease in $[Ca^{2+}]_o$ enhances the negative surface charge and shifts the potential- dependence curves toward reduced depolarization.

The effects on the superficial negative charge are mentioned here not only to explain how changes in $[Ca^{2+}]_o$ operate. Shifts of potential dependence very similar to those in Fig. 2-10 are also produced by changing the **extracellular pH**. Lowering the pH increases $[H^+]_o$ and reduces the negative charge at the membrane surface, and is thus analogous to increasing $[Ca^{2+}]_o$. By lowering the pH to 4.5, as by increasing $[Ca^{2+}]_o$ in Fig. 2-10, the activation of P_{Na} can be shifted by 25 mV. It is quite possible for the tissue pH to change, depending on the metabolic situation. The state of surface charge at the membrane can also influence the binding and action of ionized drugs, which are affected similarly by $[Ca^{2+}]_o$ and by pH [3, 26, 33].

2.3 Currents through Potential-Dependent Membrane Channels

Membrane patch clamp. So far we have been concerned with the currents and conductance changes of the whole membrane under depolarization. A few years ago a method was developed for measuring currents in patches of membrane as small as about 1 μm^2, which makes it possible to identify the molecular reactions of single channels as the basis of the potential- and time-dependence of the ionic currents. Fig. 2-11 illustrates the principle of the **"patch clamp"** [12, 24]. A glass pipette with an opening smaller than 1 μm in diameter is brought into contact with a cell membrane, and when suction is applied through the pipette a seal often forms; the electrical resistance between pipette and external solution jumps to more than 1 GΩ (10^9Ω). Consequently, the membrane patch is electrically isolated from its surroundings. The lumen of the pipette is connected to a clamp amplifier, which employs a control circuit to keep the voltage in the pipette at a set level. The current required to stabilize the voltage, the "clamp current", corresponds exactly to the current flowing through the membrane patch at each moment. The command voltage of the amplifier can be arbitrarily adjusted, so that the currents through the membrane patch can be measured for different membrane potentials or after stepwise changes in potential.

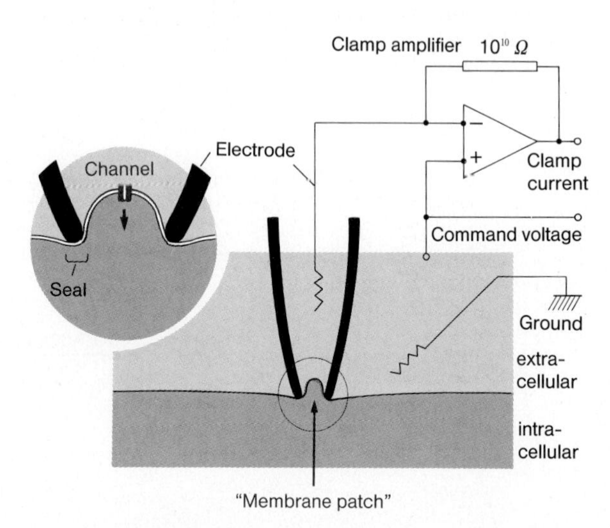

Fig. 2-11. Diagram of the membrane patch clamp. *Black:* a longitudinal section through the measurement pipette, with its ca. 1-μm-diameter opening on the membrane. If the electrode tip is absolutely dust-free and the cell surface is free of connective-tissue fibrils and the like, when suction is applied a seal can form, electrically isolating the channels in the patch of membrane within the pipette from the rest of the cell membrane (*inset*). The channel currents can then be measured with a "clamp amplifier" connected to the saline solution in the pipette. (Modified from [12, 24])

The gigaohm seal between pipette and membrane is so stable that when the pipette is withdrawn the membrane patch often tears away from the cell, remaining attached to the tip of the pipette. When this happens the measurements can be performed with a cell-free membrane patch, the former cytoplasmic surface of which can be rinsed with any desired solution. With skilled manipulation, the membrane patch can even be turned over on the pipette so that the outer surface of the membrane is exposed. Then the cytoplasmic surface is rinsed by the solution in the pipette, which must correspond approximately to an intracellular milieu, and various solutions can be made to flow past the outer surface; this "outside-out" configuration is very useful for testing the reactions of membrane channels to changes in the extracellular milieu or to transmitters or drugs with an extracellular action. A good seal between patch and pipette tip can be achieved only if both glass and membrane are absolutely clean. Connective-tissue fibrils can interfere with the seal, and it is usually necessary to remove them by applying enzymes such as collagenase to the membrane [12].

Currents through single Na^+ channels. Currents through a membrane patch, measured by the procedure of Fig. 2-11, are diagrammed in Fig. 2-12. Ten measurements of the Na^+ current are shown on the left, for each of which the membrane was depolarized for 14 ms. In each case there is maximally a single brief current pulse of −1.6 pA amplitude; this current flows through a single Na^+-channel protein. The duration of the current pulses, which represents the time during which the channel is open, varies considerably, with a probability distribution about a mean of 0.7 ms. The time when the opening occurs also varies, but if many single recordings are added together the net result is the time course of the

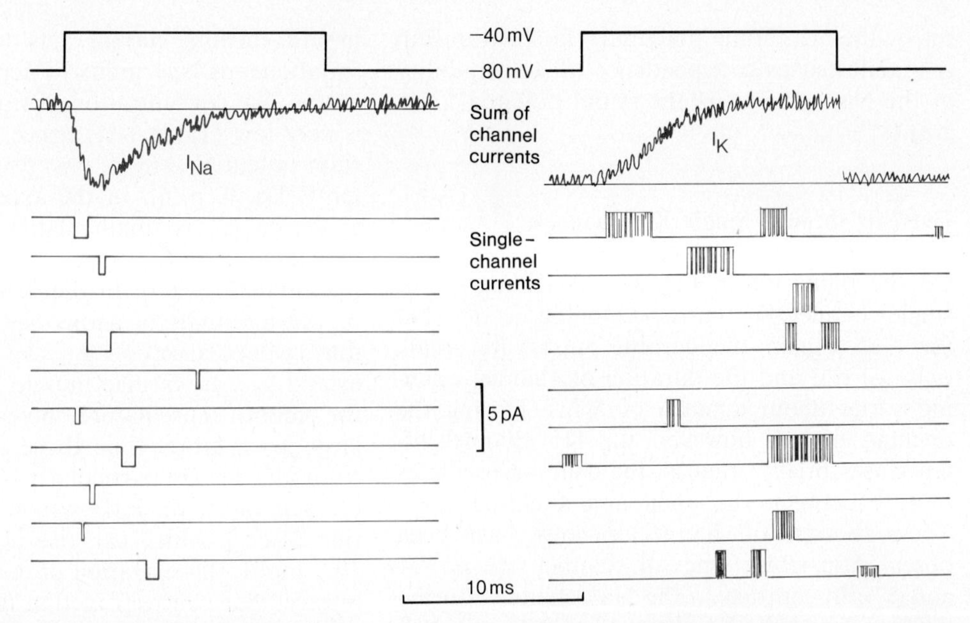

Fig. 2-12. Currents through sodium (*left*) and potassium (*right*) channels, schematic. The membrane potential was changed from –80 mV to –40 mV for 14 ms (*top*), in a patch clamp arrangement; the membrane currents measured in several repetitions of this depolarization are shown *below*. These single-channel currents can appear anytime during depolarization and have various durations. When many such recordings are added together, keeping the voltage steps in synchrony, the summed curves shown above in *red* result (I_{Na} and I_K). Their time course shows that the Na^+ channels are most likely to open shortly after the voltage step and that after about 1 ms opening is less frequent and finally stops altogether (inactivation). The K^+ channels on average delay opening until some time after the voltage step, but then have a mean frequency of opening that stays constant as long as the depolarization is maintained

current shown below the voltage-step record. It shows that **the probability of channel opening** rises sharply after depolarization, is greatest after 1.5 ms, and then decreases, becoming minimal 10 ms after the depolarizing step. This decrease in the probability of channel opening after depolarization corresponds to the **inactivation** of the Na^+ current [8, 31].

Hence the opening of the Na^+ channel following depolarization is not strictly deterministic; rather, there is an increased probability that a channel will be open, and once it has opened there is a certain probability that it will close again. The chemical reactions of molecules have this sort of "stochastic" behavior, and the various **channel states** "closed but activatable", "open", and "closed-inactivated" (and not activatable) can be related to one another by rate constants as is the case for chemical reactions. The simplest model that describes the behavior of the Na^+ channel incorporates these three states (Fig. 2-13). The transition **from closed-activatable to open** is promoted by **depolarization.** However, depolarization also accelerates the transition to the **inactivated state**, and it is for this reason that after a channel has opened it is rapidly inactivated and remains so, if it is not returned to the **closed-activatable state** by re- or hyperpolarization of the membrane. Furthermore, the equilibrium between the closed-activatable and closed-inactivated states is also

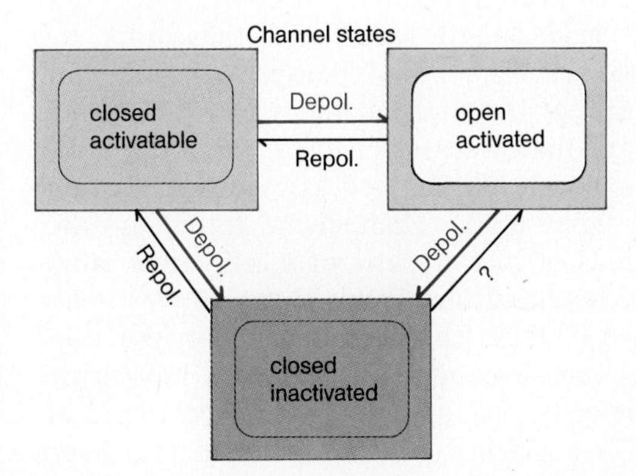

Fig. 2-13. Diagram of the states of the Na^+ channels. The state "closed-activatable" can be converted to the states "open-activated" or "closed-inactivated" by depolarization. When a channel is in the "open-activated" state, maintained depolarization promotes the transition into the "closed-inactivated" state. Only by repolarization can the channel eventually return to the "closed-activatable" state. (More realistic models include 3 "closed-activatable" and 4 "closed-inactivated" states in series [8])

set by the membrane potential; this relationship is manifested as a dependence of activatability of the Na^+ current on the initial potential (Fig. 2-8) [8].

Currents through Single K^+ Channels

On the right side in Fig. 2-12 is a diagram of single-channel K^+ currents analogous to that for Na^+. Again the current pulses are small, only +2 pA, and the duration of channel opening varies about a mean of 5 ms. During the opening period, however, the K^+ channel often closes briefly; that is, the channel oscillates rapidly between the open and a closed state. These "bursts" of channel openings have been observed in many types of channel (see pp. 31 and 57). In contrast to the Na^+ channel, during depolarization **the K^+ channel is not inactivated**; individual channels are continually opening and closing as long as depolarization is maintained. Accordingly, summation of the records gives a curve that rises to a constant level of K^+ current. That is, to describe the behavior of the K^+-channel currents in terms of the diagram in Fig. 2-13, no inactivated state is required, but rather two closed states in series, which produce the interruptions in the bursts [34] (see Ca^{2+} channel).

Fig. 2-12 illustrated the behavior of the K^+ channel typical of nerve fibers, characterized by a delayed voltage increase after depolarization, a marked increase in conductance when depolarized from the resting potential, and the absence of inactivation (cf. Fig. 2-6). **At least 5 other types of K^+ channels have been found**; they differ, for instance, in the relation between opening and potential, or they are inactivated (see Fig. 2-25, p. 41), or they are controlled by the intracellular Ca^{2+} concentration as well as by depolarization. These types of K^+ channel are found in various kinds of cell, or parts of a cell, either alone or in characteristic combinations. It is mainly because of these channels that action potential shapes vary, inasmuch as they affect repolarization velocity and afterpotentials (see Fig. 2-4). There is a marked contrast between the diversity of the K^+ channels and the uniformity of the Na^+ channels, which are rapidly activated by depolarization but then rapidly inactivated, in all excitable cells in the animal kingdom.

Currents through single Ca^{2+} channels. So far we have not mentioned that when a cell is depolarized, channels for Ca^{2+} also open. The resulting **inward calcium current** acts together with the simultaneous Na^+ influx to depolarize the membrane. The concentration of free Ca^{2+} in the cell is very low (Table 1-1); hence the Ca^{2+} equilibrium potential is more positive than E_{Na} (Chapter 1, Eq. 4, p. 6). In the axonal membrane of a neuron g_{Ca} is small relative to g_{Na}, which is why it could be neglected in analyzing the action potential (Fig. 2-7). In the dendrites of neurons or the terminals of axons (see p. 54), however, during depolarization g_{Ca} can rise so far as to exceed g_{Na}. In cardiac muscle, and still more in the smooth musculature, increases in g_{Ca} are as large as or larger than those of g_{Na}. These calcium influxes are particularly interesting because of their effect on intracellular Ca^{2+} concentration $[Ca^{2+}]_i$, which can rise from 10^{-7} mol/l to 10^{-6} mol/l; this elevation of $[Ca^{2+}]_i$ often has an intracellular control function (see p. 17 and Fig. 1-16). The opening of Ca^{2+} channels during depolarization and the intracellular consequences are very old phylogenetically, for they are found even in protozoans.

Currents through single Ca^{2+} channels in cardiac muscle cells (Fig. 2-14) are somewhat more complicated than the Na^+ and K^+ currents in Fig. 2-12. In a series of depolarizations, about 70% elicit relatively prolonged bursts of current pulses, each about 1 pA in amplitude, and during 30% of the depolarizations the channel remains closed. The individual openings within the bursts last about 1 ms on average, and the closures between them are only 0.2 ms long. The summed Ca^{2+} current during depolarization (bottom in Fig. 2-14) rises rapidly and is inactivated with a time constant of about 130 ms, the time course of the overall current being determined by the duration and frequency of the bursts. The channel kinetics can be described most simply (in accordance with Fig. 2-13) with the reaction formula

$$\text{closed 1} \overset{\text{depol.}}{\rightleftharpoons} \text{closed 2} \overset{\text{depol.}}{\rightleftharpoons} \text{open} \qquad (2)$$

in which the transitions between "closed 2" and "open" determine the duration and frequency of the individual openings, whereas the transitions between "closed 1" and "closed 2" are responsible for the frequency and duration of the bursts. The formula (Eq. 2) should be expanded to take account of an inactivated state as shown in Fig. 2-13 [32].

The records of activity of a Ca^{2+} channel in Fig. 2-14 also provide an example of the **modulation**

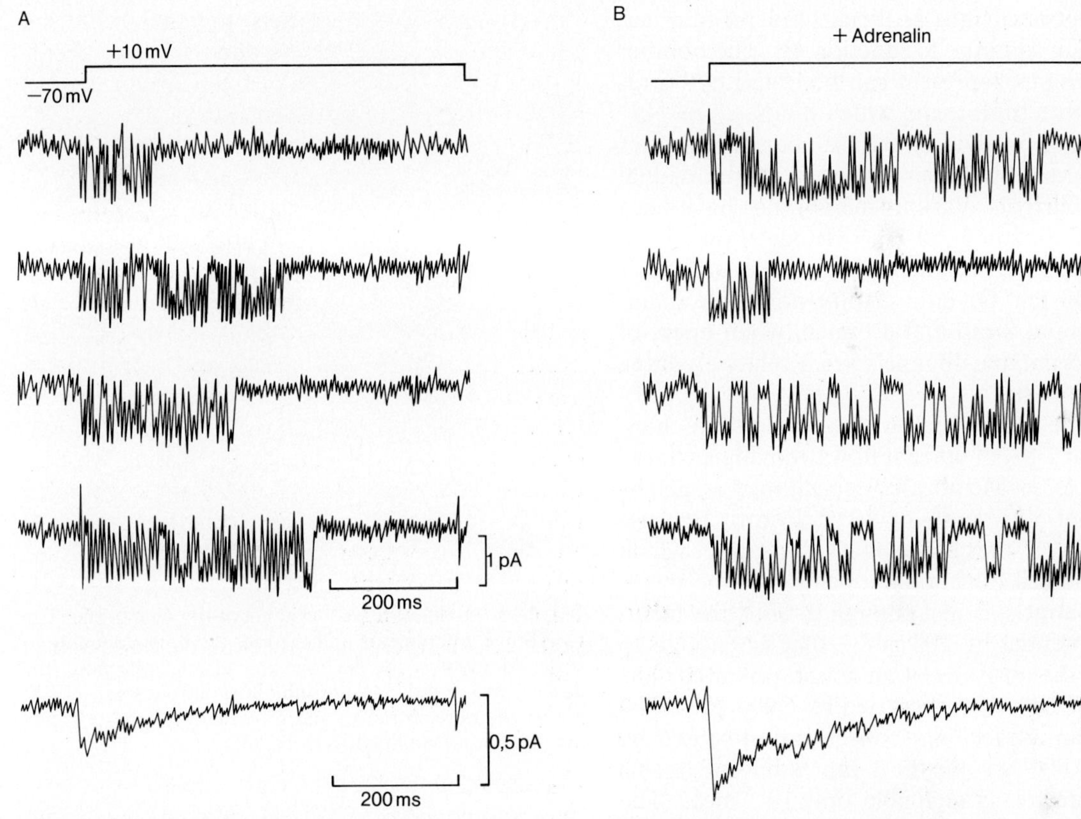

Fig. 2-14 A, B. Single calcium-channel currents in cardiac muscle cells. Top: the 600-ms depolarization from -70 to +10 mV produced by the patch clamp. Below it, 4 individual recordings of channel currents. Under normal conditions (**A**) 30% of the depolarizations produce no channel currents (not shown here). Bottom: the summed current, obtained by averaging many individual recordings, shows the inactivation of the Ca^{2+} current after depolarization. In the presence of 1 μmol/l adrenalin (**B**) the groups of single-channel openings last longer, and only 20% of the depolarizations fail to produce channel opening. The amplitude of the single-channel currents is unchanged by adrenalin, but the summed current (bottom) is considerably greater. (Modified from [32])

of channel activity by a hormone or a transmitter (see p. 57). **Adrenalin,** secreted by the adrenal cortex as an "ergotropic hormone", is carried to the heart in the bloodstream; one of its actions is to enhance heart contraction. It is also (with noradrenalin) released as a transmitter by sympathetic nerves to the heart, with the same effect (see p. 447). In the experiment of Fig. 2-14B, 10^{-6} mol/l adrenalin is applied to the cardiac muscle cell. Now in about 80% of the depolarizations single-channel activity was elicited, with an increase in the frequency of bursts. The brief openings and closings of the channels were as before. The summed curve (Fig. 2-14B, bottom) makes clear that **adrenalin increases the Ca^{2+} influx**. The effects of adrenalin on the Ca^{2+} channel can also be produced by perfusing the cardiac muscle cell with **cyclic adenosine monophosphate** (cAMP) or applying the catalytic subunit C of adenylate kinase. This finding demonstrates that adrenalin acts here by way of the second messenger cAMP, causing phosphorylation of enzymes by the catalytic subunit C as detailed in the discussion of Fig. 1-15 (p. 16) [19]. That is, adrenalin probably increases the Ca^{2+} current by initiating phosphorylation of the Ca^{2+} channel, which favors the transition from the state "closed 1" to "closed 2". The adrenalin effect shown in Fig. 2-14 is thus a prototype of the modulation of cell activity by hormones or transmitters.

There are, of course, also **Cl^- channels** through the membrane. These have not been much studied and will not be treated here.

Molecules of the Na^+ channel. The various channel proteins are quite similar to one another in structure and function; it has been suggested that they are all derived from the Ca^{2+} channel. Because the most thoroughly studied is the Na^+-channel molecule, we shall once again turn our attention to it. The Na^+ channel consists of a **glycoprotein** with a molecular weight of about 300,000. Its amino acid sequence has recently been worked out. Isolated molecules can be incorporated into artificial lipid membranes, where they continue to function [8]. The number of Na^+ channels present can be found by "titration" with tetrodotoxin, which binds to the Na^+ channels, or by dividing the Na^+ current per μm^2 of membrane by the amplitude of the individual channel currents. Various membranes have been found to contain **1–50 Na^+ channels/μm^2**. With 50 channels/μm^2 the mean channel separation is about 140 nm. Given a channel-molecule diameter of about 8 nm and a lumen, when open, of about 0.5 nm, the channels are a relatively large distance apart.

During the 1-ms opening of a single such channel, about 1 pA of current flows, moving a charge of 10^{-15}A · s. Membrane capacitance is generally about 1 $\mu F/cm^2$, or 10^{-14} $F/\mu m^2$. Because $1F = 1A \cdot s/V$, the charge of $10^{-15} A \cdot s/\mu m^2$, which enters the cell during **one** opening of the membrane channels, is just enough to shift the membrane potential by 100 mV – that is, enough to produce the upstroke of an action potential. The charge of 10^{-15}A · s is carried by 6,000 Na^+. The increase in intracellular concentration caused by adding 6,000 Na^+ to the 1 μm^3 adjacent to this membrane area is negligible, only 10^{-5} mol/l. The channel currents, then, are large enough to make action potentials possible but make no appreciable difference to the intracellular concentrations (with the exception of $[Ca^{2+}]_i$). The readjustment of the ionic gradients across the membrane by the Na-K-pump (see p. 8) is thus of no importance for the single action potential.

The Na^+-channel protein must be capable of quickly switching on a massive flow of Na^+ but must prevent the simultaneous influx of other ions, especially K^+, which is almost the same size. That is, the **Na^+ channels must be selective**. Anions are kept out by negative charges at the channel entrance, as indicated by the diagram in Fig. 2-15. Of the small cations, Li^+ moves through the Na^+ channel relatively well, but K^+ is almost completely excluded. The selectivity can be explained only by specific binding during passage through the channel, as discussed previously with reference to the energy level of binding along a channel (Fig. 1-5B, p. 6) [21].

In addition to being selective for Na^+, the Na^+ channel must be able to change its permeability rapidly when the membrane potential changes. Therefore the Na^+-channel molecule must contain charges that can be displaced by changes in field strength across the membrane. Displacement of these charges can be measured as a **"gating current"** [3, 9, 23] after complete blockade of the ion channels; the gating current indicates

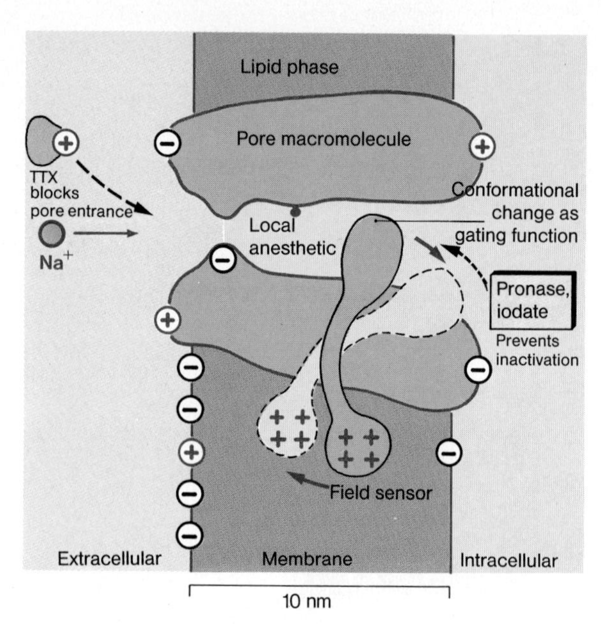

Fig. 2-15. Model of a Na^+ channel in the membrane. The membrane components and the ions are drawn roughly to scale. Along with the Na^+ passing through the pore, the *dashed arrows* indicate the inhibitors tetrodotoxin (TTX, blocks the pore entrance) and pronase or iodate (prevents inactivation). (Modified from [9, 14])

displacement of at least 4 charges per channel. These 4 charges are represented in the diagram of Fig. 2-15 as a "field sensor" that favors a change in conformation of the molecule that opens the channel. The open state is unstable and converts spontaneously to the closed-inactivated state. **Inactivation** is brought about by parts of the channel protein on the inner surface of the membrane. Substances with an intracellular action, such as iodate or pronase as well as specific toxins and drugs, can block inactivation.

Another form of Na^+-channel blockade is of medical interest. **Local anesthetics** are used to prevent excitation and its propagation in nerves, so that action potentials from "pain receptors" are not conducted to the CNS. The anesthetics are usually injected near the nerve to be blocked. However, the molecules bind only to the open channels, at a site between the selective pore entrance and the "gate" (Fig. 2-15) [25, 30]. The molecules of local anesthetics are too large to pass through the channel entrance on the outside of the membrane. They can enter the open channel only from inside or, if they are lipid-soluble, through the lipid membrane. The channel closures they cause are often only a few μs long, but repeated at high frequency; by chopping the single-channel current into many short sections, they make the Na^+ influx ineffective.

2.4 Electrotonus and Stimulus

Having discussed the molecular bases of excitation, we now return to the macroscopic behavior of nerve cells.
Excitation occurs when the membrane is depolarized to or beyond the threshold – a process also called **stimulation.** The stimulus as a rule is an imposed electric current that depolarizes the membrane as it flows through. Before considering the way in which stimuli elicit excitation, therefore, we shall first treat the depolarization of the membrane by electric current, beginning with voltage changes so small that they do not alter membrane conductance.

Electrotonus in the Case of Homogeneous Current Distribution

The simplest arrangement for the study of membrane responses to current flow is achieved with a spherical cell and intracellular electrodes for the application of current and recording of membrane potential (Fig. 2-16A). When a constant positive current is switched on (Fig. 2-16B), the inflowing positive charges progressively discharge the membrane capacitor and thus depolarize the membrane. Accordingly, the potential electrode records a rapid depolarization at the beginning of the current pulse. But the rate of depolarization very soon slows, for when the membrane potential shifts away from the resting potential the equilibrium of the ion fluxes is disturbed, and during depolarization more K^+ ions flow out of the cell. This countercurrent of positive ions through the membrane removes some of the charge introduced by the electric current, and discharge of the membrane capacitor is necessarily slowed. Eventually, at an increasingly slower rate, the depolarization reaches a final level at which the ion current through the membrane is equal to the electric current applied by the electrode; there is then no further discharge of the membrane capacitor (Fig. 2-16). The potential change caused by the current pulse is called an **electrotonic potential** or *electrotonus.* The final level, or the amplitude, of the electrotonic potential is proportional to the *membrane resistance* (the reciprocal of the membrane conductance) to the ion currents. The rate of rise of the electrotonic potential at the very beginning is determined only by the membrane capacitance; only *capacitive current* is flowing. When the countercurrent of ions begins to flow through the membrane, the potential begins to change exponentially, with the exponent $-t/\tau$. t is time, and the *membrane time constant* τ is the product of membrane resistance and membrane capacitance. τ ranges from 5 to 50 ms in different cells.

An exponential curve like that of electrotonus (or, for example, the decay in activity of a radioactive substance) is described by $e^{-t/\tau}$. τ is called the time constant because at time $t = \tau$ the exponent is -1. In such a curve, then, τ can be found by locating on the abscissa the time at which the amplitude has fallen to $e^{-1} = 1/e = 37\%$ of the starting value.

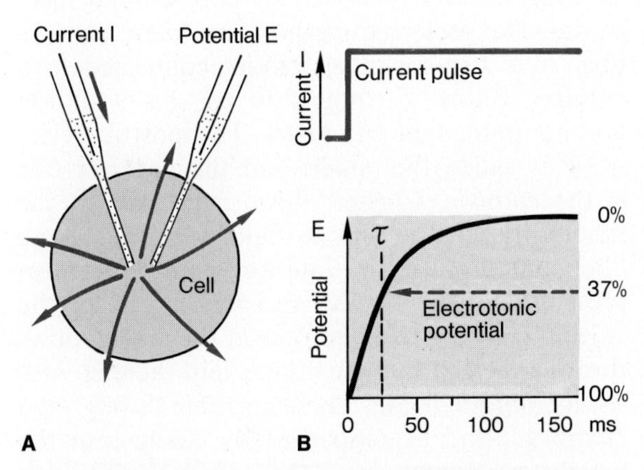

Fig. 2-16 A, B. Electrotonic potential of a spherical cell. **A** Intracellular electrodes measure the membrane potential E and inject a current I, which is distributed as shown by the red arrows. **B** Time course of a current pulse and the electrotonic potential measured simultaneously in the cell. The time constant τ of the electrotonic potential is established by the time at which the potential has approached to within 37% (1/e) of its final value

Electrotonus in Elongated Cells

Almost all nerve and muscle cells are very long as compared with their diameter; a nerve fiber, for example, with a diameter of only 1 μm can be a meter long. Current applied within such a cell will be very inhomogeneously distributed as it flows out, a marked departure from the situation illustrated in Fig. 2-16. Electrotonic potentials in an elongated muscle fiber are shown in Fig. 1-20, as they appear at the site of current injection (E_0) and at distances of 2.5 mm and 5 mm ($E_{2.5}$ and E_5). These curves differ in shape from that of Fig. 2-16; they are not simply exponential and they vary with distance. E_0, at the site of current injection, rises very rapidly, so that at a time corresponding to the membrane time constant τ it is within 16% of its final value (rather than the

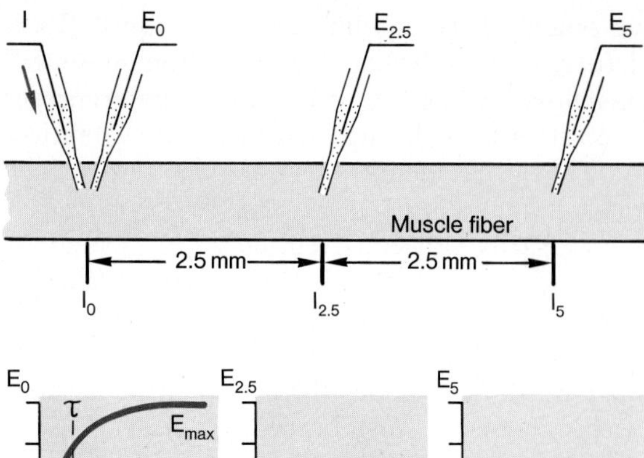

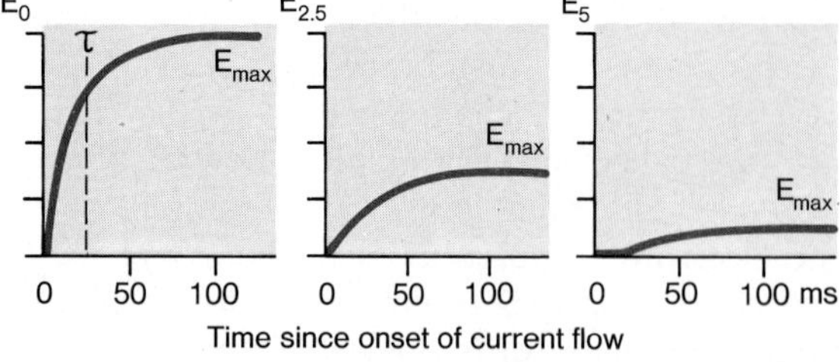

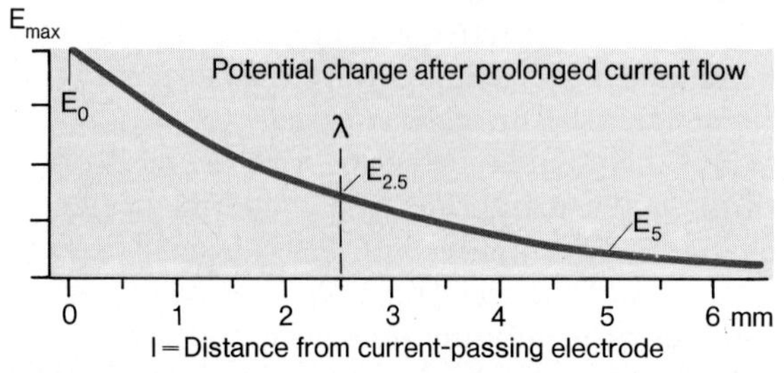

Fig. 2-17. Electrotonic potentials in an elongated cell. *Top:* Injection of current I into a muscle cell; the electrotonic potential is measured at distances of 0, 2.5 and 5 mm. *Middle:* Time courses of the electrotonic potentials at the three distances; each reaches a different final value E_{max}. *Bottom:* Relationship between E_{max} and distance from the site of current injection. The membrane length constant λ is equal to the distance at which E_{max} has fallen to 37% (1/e) of the amplitude at the site of current injection

37% in Fig. 2-16). This steeper slope is caused by the inhomogeneous current distribution; at first the membrane capacitor is discharged in a small region near the current source, and only then does current begin to flow through the interior of the cell, which has considerable longitudinal resistance, to more distant parts of the membrane. There, again, the membrane capacitor must be discharged before further current flow occurs, so that as distance from the current source increases, the time course of the electrotonic potential becomes progressively slower. In Fig. 2-17 there is a distinct delay before the onset of the electrotonic potential 5 mm away from the current electrode (E_5), and even after 120 ms the final value E_{max} has not been reached [17].

Even when the injected current has been flowing so long that a new charge distribution has been established, more current flows through the membrane near the point of injection than through areas further away, for at more distant points the current must overcome not only the membrane resistance but also the longitudinal resistance within the cell. The final value E_{max} of the electrotonic potential is plotted as a function of distance from the current electrode in the bottom graph of Fig. 2-17. E_{max} falls off exponentially with distance x, the exponent being $-x/\lambda$. The quantity λ is called the **membrane length constant**; in Fig. 2-17 it is 2.5 mm, and in other cells it ranges from 0.1 to 5 mm. The length constant λ is a measure of the distance over which electrotonic potentials can spread in elongated cells. At the distance 4 λ, for example, the amplitude of the electrotonic potential is only 2% of that near the current-injection site; thus in nerve fibers electrotonic potentials are measurable some centimeters, at most, from the site of origin.

It should be emphasized once again that this discussion of the effects of injected current applies only to potential changes so small that they do not change the ion conductance of the membrane. An electrotonic potential implies *passive* behavior of the membrane. Therefore if the polarity of the injected current is reversed, mirror-image electrotonic potentials result.

Membrane polarization by way of extracellular electrodes. The injection of current through an intracellular electrode, as illustrated in Figs. 2-16 and 2-17, creates a simple current-flow situation that assists the understanding of electrotonus. In medical research and in neurology, however, cells are usually polarized by extracellular electrodes. The preferred method is to place a nerve fiber over two metal electrodes connected to a voltage source. Current flow in this situation is diagrammed in Fig. 2-18. The positive electrode is called the *anode*, and the negative one is the *cathode*. Current flows from one to the other through the film of fluid adhering to the fiber, but because the interior of the fiber also presents a relatively low resistance, part of the current crosses the membrane at the anode, flows through the cell to the cathode, and there crosses the membrane again. These currents through the membrane are accompanied by changes in the membrane potential; at the anode the positive charges delivered to the outside of the membrane increase the charge on the membrane capacitor and thus increase the membrane potential. As a result, K^+ ions flow into the cell, carrying the current through the membrane. At the anode, then, the membrane becomes hyperpolarized. A

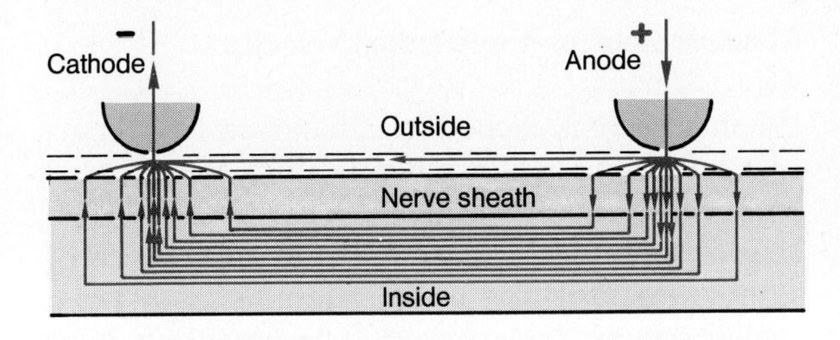

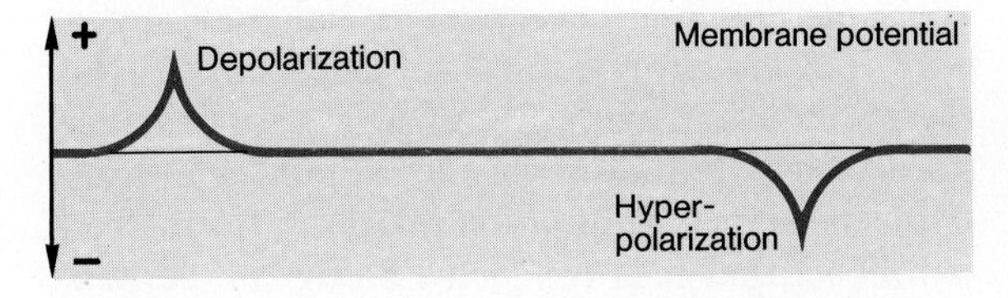

Fig. 2-18. Arrangement for extracellular application of current. Current flows from the anode to the cathode, both outside the nerve; part flows through the film of fluid on the surface of the nerve, and part flows through the nerve sheath and along the interior of the nerve fibers. The *curve below* shows the changes produced by the current in the membrane potential of a nerve fiber. (Modified from [20])

mirror-image change, a depolarization, occurs at the cathode. The voltage profile along the nerve fiber is shown in the lower part of Fig. 2-18. The voltage change is greatest at the site of the greatest current density, directly at the electrodes.
Usually when current is applied to nerve or muscle the intent is to depolarize and thus to stimulate the cell; the hyperpolarization at the anode is not particularly desired. In this case it is better to use an anode of large surface area or position it far from the nerve, so that the current density at the anode is less and the hyperpolarization of the cell, although more extensive, is of lower amplitude. The small-area electrode at which the lines of current and the polarization are concentrated is called the *stimulating electrode*, and the large-area electrode of opposite polarity is called the *reference electrode*.

Stimulus and Threshold

When a depolarizing electrotonic potential passes the threshold it elicits excitation. The current pulse that brings about this potential change is called the *stimulus*. Because of the membrane capacitance, the potential change induced by a current pulse occurs with some delay (Fig. 2-17). Therefore the threshold is usually reached a few ms after the stimulus current has been switched on. The stimulus must last long enough for the threshold to be reached; that is, the current pulse must be of adequate duration as well as adequate amplitude. Within limits, a very high stimulus amplitude can compensate for short duration.

Near-threshold stimuli. It often happens that the dendrites and somata of nerve cells are depolarized just barely to the threshold, so that very slight differences in intensity determine whether the information is passed on in the form of an action potential or not.
The action potential is triggered at the threshold because the depolarization has caused an increase in sodium conductance g_{Na}, and the resulting sodium influx becomes so great that the membrane automatically continues to depolarize. However, the Na^+ inflow elicited by depolarization does not begin abruptly at the *threshold potential*, but at potentials a few mV lower. This can be seen in the set of electrotonic potentials shown in Fig. 2-19, elicited by a uniformly incremented series of hyperpolarizing and depolarizing current pulses. Only the two smallest depolarizing electrotonic potentials are mirror images of the

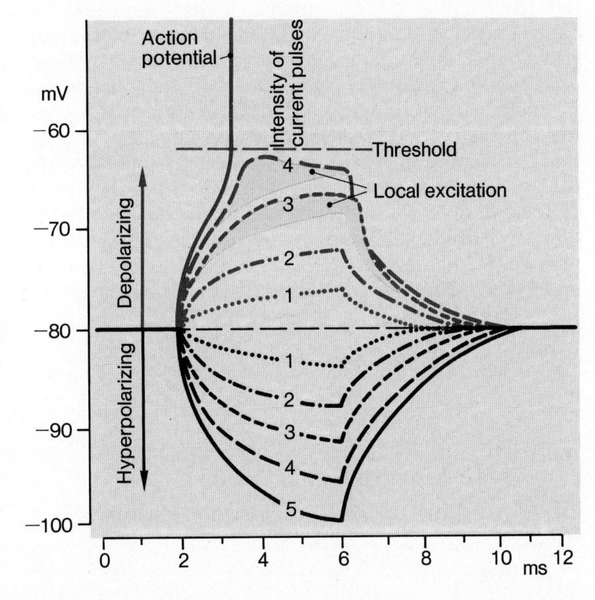

Fig. 2-19. Electrotonic potentials and local responses. Current pulses (4 ms in duration) of relative amplitudes 1, 2, 3, 4 and 5 in the hyperpolarizing direction produce proportional electrotonic potentials. With depolarizing currents of amplitudes 1 and 2, the potentials are mirror images of those with hyperpolarizing currents. The depolarizations produced by current amplitudes 3 and 4 exceed those of electrotonic potentials at levels beyond −70 mV, by amounts indicated by the red areas below the curves. The active depolarization, in excess of electrotonus, is called local excitation. The depolarizing current of amplitude 5 produces a depolarization that passes the threshold and triggers an action potential

hyperpolarizing potentials. The third and fourth depolarizations rise more rapidly and are larger than the corresponding hyperpolarizations, and the fifth depolarization is suprathreshold. The extra depolarization in the curves only slightly below threshold is shown by the red-shaded areas; it is called the **local response** and is caused by the increase in Na^+ conductance in this potential range. During such local responses the Na^+ inflow may very well exceed the K^+ outflow, but the Na^+ current is still not strong enough to depolarize the membrane as rapidly as necessary to trigger an action potential – that is, to overcome the slow inactivation near the threshold potential (see Fig. 2-6, −60 mV). The state of excitation is not fully developed, so that it remains a local phenomenon and is not propagated.

Electrical currents are of significance in neurophysiology apart from their use as stimuli to nerves; they can be applied to the skin for therapeutic purposes, and they are sometimes involved in accidents. Direct current acts as a stimulus chiefly when it is turned on and off, although strong currents can warm the tissue so much as to damage it, and if the voltage is too high sparks can be generated that cause deep skin wounds. Low-frequency alternating current (e.g., 50 Hz) has the same effects, with somewhat less tendency to generate sparks. It also stimulates excitable tissue at the frequency of the current alternation; such stimuli, especially if they arrive in the relative refractory period (vulnerable phase) of the myocardial action potential, can easily induce lethal fibrillation of the heart. For this reason, low-frequency a.c. is particularly dangerous. Alternating current at high frequencies (over 10 kHz) cannot depolarize a membrane to threshold during a half cycle, and the next half cycle eliminates the depolarization; as a result, such currents do not act as stimuli, but only warm the tissue. Therefore frequencies between 0.5 and 1 MHz can be used therapeutically in **diathermy**, for controlled local warming of tissue.

2.5 Propagation of the Action Potential

The role of the nerve fiber, and of the muscle-fiber membrane, is to disseminate information (or controlling signals) – to conduct excitation. To understand the mechanism underlying the conduction of excitation, we must consider the physiology of excitation discussed in Section 2.2 in the light of the laws governing longitudinal spread of currents and potentials (Sec. 2.3). We shall begin by describing the propagation of excitation in a nerve.

Measurement of Conduction Velocity

When a nerve is excited (e.g., by an electrical current pulse) the action potentials can be recorded with extracellular electrodes (Fig. 2-20). These action potentials appear not only at the site of stimulation, but also at considerable distances – a meter away, for example. The potentials have the *same amplitude* everywhere, but they appear with a *delay* proportional to the distance from the stimulus site. In a motor nerve, for instance, an action potential arrives at a point 1 m away from the site of stimulation in 10 ms, from which it follows that it is *conducted* along the nerve at a velocity of 100 m/s.

Fig. 2-20 illustrates the procedure of recording with extracellular electrodes. Two electrodes are placed in contact with the nerve fiber, which has been dissected free from the surrounding tissue over a certain distance and in this region is surrounded by an electrically insulating medium such as mineral oil or air. If a wave of excitation passes along the fiber from right to left, as it reaches Electrode 1 the surface of the fiber under this electrode loses its positive charge; this

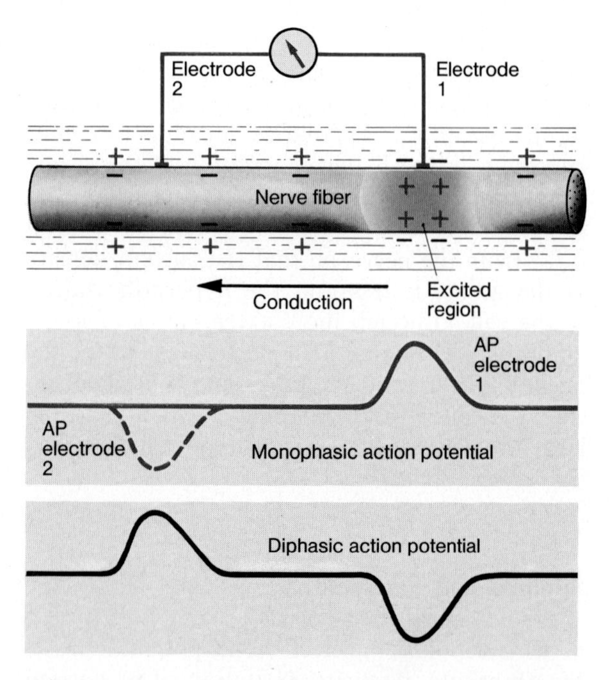

Fig. 2-20. The action potential as seen by extracellular electrodes. The potential is conducted from right to left *(above)*, and the excited region of the fiber has just reached Electrode 1; the recorded potential follows the continuous *red* curve *(middle line)*. When the action potential reaches Electrode 2, the potential change shown by the dashed red line is recorded. Each deflection in this red curve is a monophasic action potential. The two together constitute a diphasic action potential, plotted in the *lower* graph as a function of time

region becomes negative with respect to the region under Electrode 2, and the meter shows a positive voltage change corresponding approximately to the time course of the intracellular action potential. When the excitation reaches Electrode 2 the meter records a voltage change of reversed polarity, a negative action potential. Because the overall voltage change recorded with two electrodes has a positive and a negative component, it is called a *diphasic* action potential. From the time separating the positive and negative peaks and the distance between the recording electrodes the conduction velocity can be calculated. Usually the two phases of the action potential are not as distinctly separated as in Fig. 2-20. With a conduction velocity of 100 m/s and an action-potential duration of 1 ms, for example, the action potential occupies 100 mm of the nerve fiber (100m/s · 1ms), so that for complete separation of the phases of the diphasic action potential an exposed nerve 20 cm long would be required. This is usually impracticable, and therefore the two phases of the diphasic potential usually overlap.

It is also possible to record *monophasically* with extracellular electrodes. If the nerve is damaged, or depolarized by raising the K^+ concentration, in such a way as to prevent conduction of the action potential in Fig. 2-20 from Electrode 1 to Electrode 2, only the potential change shown in red is recorded – a monophasic action potential. Essentially monophasic potentials, though very small ones, can also be recorded by a single microelectrode next to the excited nerve or nerve cell; in this case the reference electrode must be far from the excited region, in the surrounding bath or in the animal. Such *"monopolar recording"* measures the voltage difference between the nearby extracellular solution and the "distant ground" produced by the local currents in the nerve fiber. The measured potential changes thus correspond to the time course of the membrane current during excitation (Fig. 2-22). For monopolar extracellular recording it is unnecessary to insulate the excited structure; this method is therefore particularly useful for studying the physiology of the CNS.

The compound action potential of a mixed nerve. A nerve in the leg, for example, contains fibers widely varying in function and diameter, and their conduction velocities also vary. When an electrode is placed in contact with the whole nerve and the nerve is stimulated at a certain distance from the recording site, the first action potentials it records are those of the most rapidly

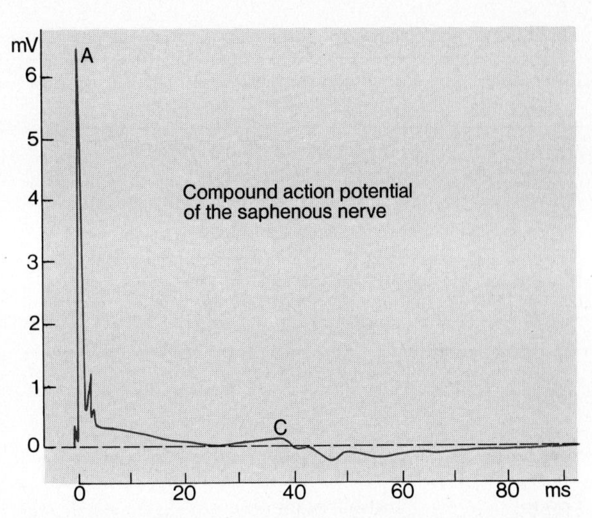

Fig. 2-21. Compound action potential of a mammalian nerve, measured with an extracellular electrode. All the fibers in the nerve were stimulated simultaneously at some distance from the recording site. The first action potentials to arrive are those of the most rapidly conducting fibers, the A-fibers; those of the slow C fibers appear about 38 ms later. The C-fiber deflection is followed by a prolonged hyperpolarizing afterpotential. The notches in the A-fiber deflection separate the activities of the α-, β-, γ- and δ-fiber subgroups. (Modified from [29])

conducting fibers, followed by various groups of potentials of other, slower fibers. That is, the action potential of such a nerve is compounded of a spectrum of fiber groups and conduction velocities (Fig. 2-21). The individual notches in this compound potential are associated with particular groups of fibers, listed in Table 2-1a together with their functions. This classification, by ERLANGER and GASSER [11], includes both motor and sensory fibers; the LLOYD/HUNT classification [22] shown in Table 2-1b, for sensory nerves, is also widely used.

Mechanism of Conduction

It is characteristic of the conducted action potential that excitation is complete at each point on the nerve fiber, so that the amplitude of the action potential is always the same. These all-or-none excitatory processes at different places in the membrane are coupled with one another by the mechanism of electrotonic spread of stimulus currents along the fiber. The Na^+ ions flowing inward at an excited membrane site act as a current source for a depolarizing electrotonic potential at a nearby, not yet excited site. When this depolarization reaches threshold it elicits excitation there. Thus the state of excitation propagates, by electrotonic coupling, from excited to not yet excited membrane areas.

Table 2-1a. The Erlanger/Gasser classification of nerve fibers

Fiber type	Function (examples)	Avg. fiber diameter (μm)	Avg. cond. velocity (m/s)
Aα	primary muscle-spindle afferents, motor to skeletal muscles	15	100 (70–120)
Aβ	cutaneous touch and pressure afferents	8	50 (30–70)
Aγ	motor to muscle spindles	5	20 (15–30)
Aδ	cutaneous temperature and pain afferents	< 3	15 (12–30)
B	sympathetic preganglionic	3	7 (3–15)
C	cutaneous pain afferents, sympathetic postganglionic	1 (unmyelinated)	1 (0.5–2)

Table 2-1b. The Lloyd/Hunt classification of nerve fibers

Group	Function (examples)	Avg. fiber diameter (μm)	Avg. cond. velocity (m/s)
I	primary muscle-spindle afferents and afferents from tendon organs	13	75 (70–120)
II	cutaneous mechanoreceptors	9	55 (25–70)
III	deep pressure sensors in muscle	3	11 (10–25)
IV	unmyelinated pain fibers	1	1

Note that there is a fundamental difference between the conduction of an action potential and the conduction of voltage pulses along a telegraph wire. In the wire current flows from one pole of a voltage source at one end of the wire to the other pole of a voltage source at the other end. The amplitude of the voltage pulse decreases with distance. In electrophysiological terms, the conduction in the telegraph wire is purely electrotonic. When an action potential is conducted the poles of the voltage sources in each region of the membrane are on the inside and the outside of the fiber, and the current is essentially a membrane current, perpendicular to the direction of propagation.

Membrane currents during the conducted action potential. Fig. 2-22 represents a "stop-action photo" of the voltage and current conditions along a nerve fiber as an action potential is conducted from right to left. The length of fiber occupied by the action potential depends on the conduction velocity; with a conduction velocity of 100 m/s and an action-potential duration of 1 ms, the length of the abscissa in Fig. 2-22 would correspond to 10 cm. The piece of fiber between the marker lines A and C is fully excited; the Na^+ inflow caused by the sharp increase in g_{Na} rapidly discharges the membrane capacitance, and after the peak the increased g_K and the resulting K^+ outflow initiate repolarization. Between A and C the inflow of positive charges predominates in the membrane current i_m; the excess positive charges flow away, as shown at the top of Fig. 2-22, through the interior of the fiber on both

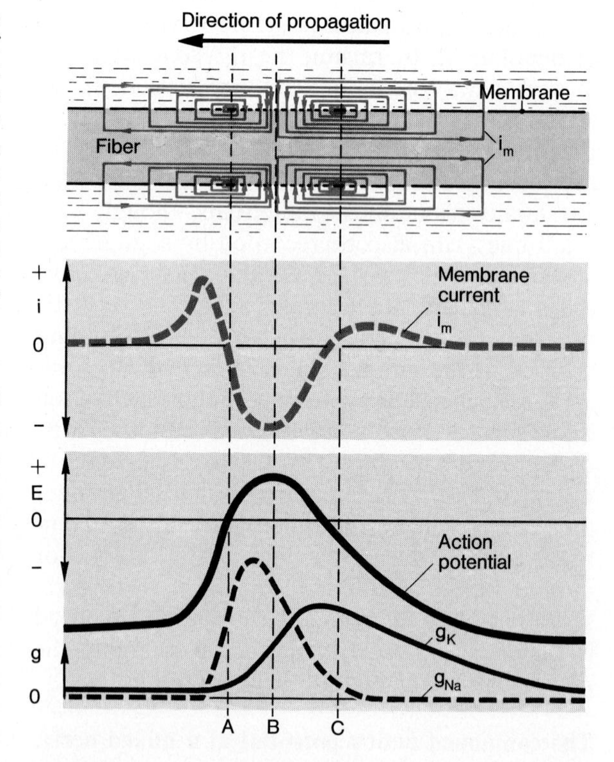

Fig. 2-22. Propagation of the action potential. The black curves show the time course of the action potential and of the associated membrane conductances g_{Na} and g_K. The red curve shows the membrane current i_m. The lines of current flow in and around the fiber are diagrammed at the top. The vertical dashed lines mark the times of maximal rate of rise (A), peak potential (B), and maximal rate of repolarization (C). (Modified from [27])

sides. This excess current is characteristic of the *conducted* action potential. In a non-conducted action potential at an isolated spot on the membrane, there is no net inward current at the peak of the action potential, for the Na^+ inflow equals the K^+ outflow. At the time of the peak of a conducted action potential the net inward ion flux is still about 80% of maximal; this current is required for the **electrotonic spread** along the fiber.

The part of the action potential critical for propagation is to the left of Line A in Fig. 2-22. In this region of the membrane the membrane current i_m flows outward and depolarizes the membrane **electrotonically**. The current source for the electrotonic depolarization is in the excited part of the membrane around B. The electrotonic depolarization at the beginning of the action potential reaches the threshold region just before Line A: g_{Na} increases, more Na^+ enters the cell and excitation results. The initial phase of the action potential is an electrotonic event, and the velocity of potential conduction thus depends on the fiber constants τ and λ, which describe the spread of electrotonic potentials.

At the end of the action potential, to the right of C in Fig. 2-22, there is also an outward current i_m that tends to depolarize the membrane. In the case of a conducted action potential this depolarization is prevented by the high g_K in this part of the membrane. But if g_K is relatively low or the effects of other depolarizing influences are added, the electrotonic membrane currents at the end of the action potential can cause new, so-called **repetitive excitation** (cf. Fig. 2-24).

It is because of the membrane current i_m that action potentials can be recorded with extracellular electrodes, for such electrodes measure the current density in the extracellular solution. Extracellular microelectrodes in the CNS record, from nerve cells and fibers, triphasic "spikes" proportional to the membrane current i_m in Fig. 2-22. i_m in turn, during a conducted action potential, is proportional to the second derivative of the intracellular potential with respect to time [16].

Factors determining conduction velocity. The conduction velocity of a nerve fiber can be found, by elaborate calculations, from the potential- and time-dependences of the ion currents and the conditions determining electrotonic spread – fiber diameter, membrane resistance and membrane capacitance. The result of such calculations closely matches the measured data [16], which confirms the applicability of the ionic theory of excitation and of electrotonus. Here we shall discuss only the qualitative factors affecting conduction velocity.

One of these is the *amplitude of the inward Na^+ current*, for the more current is available after excitatory discharging of the membrane, the more current can flow into adjacent, not yet excited regions and accelerate depolarization there. The inward Na^+ current can be reduced by decreasing the Na^+ concentration and by enhanced inactivation of the Na^+ system when the resting potential is depressed or under the influence of local anesthetics (cf. p. 32). Under all these conditions the conduction velocity of the action potential is *lowered*, and in the extreme case conduction is blocked.

The electrotonic spread of the membrane currents also has a fundamental effect on conduction velocity. Because the resistance and the capacitance of a unit area of membrane are nearly the same in all excitable cells, electrotonic spread is determined chiefly by the **fiber diameter**. The membrane area of a nerve fiber is proportional to its diameter, whereas the cross-sectional area of the fiber increases as the square of the diameter. Thus when the fiber diameter increases, the longitudinal resistance inside the fiber, determined by cross-sectional area, decreases with respect to the membrane resistance. The consequence is more extensive spread of the electro-

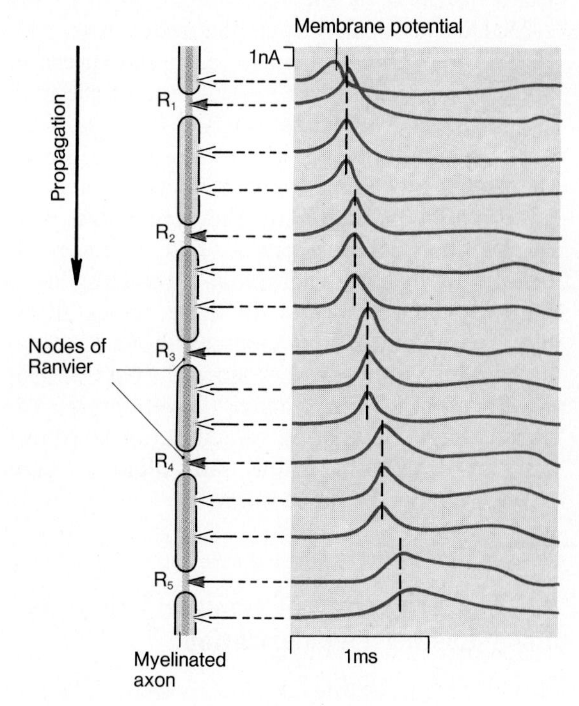

Fig. 2-23. Saltatory conduction. *Right:* time course of the membrane potential recorded at the points along the myelinated axon indicated by the arrows. R_1, R_2, R_3 ... are nodes of Ranvier. Propagation of the action potential *(from top to bottom)* is delayed only at the nodes. (Modified from [18])

tonic currents (increase in length constant λ) and accelerated conduction. Although the membrane capacitance also rises, in proportion to the membrane area, as diameter increases – which tends to reduce conduction velocity – the effect of the lower longitudinal resistance predominates. The net result is that the conduction velocity increases about as the square root of fiber diameter. This relationship is also evident in Table 2-1.

Conduction in myelinated axons. Because of their special structure, myelinated nerve fibers conduct action potentials especially rapidly. These fibers display a normal cell membrane only in very short segments, the nodes of Ranvier. In the internodal regions membranes are wound around the cell many layers thick, which greatly increases the membrane resistance. Therefore when the potential is changed practically no current flows through the membrane of the internodes, and an action potential at one node of Ranvier spreads to the adjacent nodes electrotonically and almost without decrement, through the internodes. The conduction time through the internodes is practically zero; the excitation leaps from one node to the next. This **saltatory conduction**, with no loss of time in the internodes, is well illustrated by the recordings shown in Fig. 2-23. Delays occur only at the nodes, where the electrotonic potential must reach the threshold and elicit excitation. The membrane of the node is specialized for excitation; the density of the Na^+ channels here is about 100 times greater than in unmyelinated nerve fibers. The acceleration of conduction by the myelinated parts of the fibers is considerable, and makes possible the many parallel rapidly-conducting nerve pathways in vertebrates. In these nerves all the fibers with conduction velocities above 3 m/s are myelinated; only the very slow C fibers (Group IV fibers) are unmyelinated. Invertebrates can achieve high conduction velocities, up to 10 m/s, only by developing a few unmyelinated "giant axons" almost 1 mm in diameter.

2.6 The Triggering of Impulse Volleys by Long-Lasting Depolarization

Only action potentials are conducted along nerve fibers; all the information to be transmitted over large distances by nerves must be represented by a "code", the frequency of action-potential discharge. The receptor membranes that receive sensory stimuli undergo slow, prolonged potential changes (receptor potentials; see p. 179), and the synaptic potentials of nerve cells (see p. 50) also add up to produce slow changes in the membrane potential. For the information contained in these slow potential changes to be transmitted by nerves, they must be encoded, converted to volleys of nerve impulses at a particular frequency.

Rhythmic impulse generation. Fig. 2-24 shows how a nerve cell responds when stimulus currents at 1 nA and 4 nA are switched on. The small current, 1 nA, causes a slow electrotonic depolarization toward the plateau indicated by the dashed line. But before this final level is reached, the depolarization crosses the threshold and elicits an action potential. Repolarization goes beyond the resting potential to give a hyperpolarizing phase, and then slow depolarization resumes; again, after about 0.5 s, the threshold is reached and another action potential is elicited. This cycle can repeat as long as the depolarizing current flows; the maintained depolarization is converted to a rhythmic volley of action potentials at about 2 Hz. When the current pulse is stronger, about 4 nA, basically the same thing happens as with 1 nA, except that the rate of rise and the amplitude of the maintained depolarization (dashed line) are greater

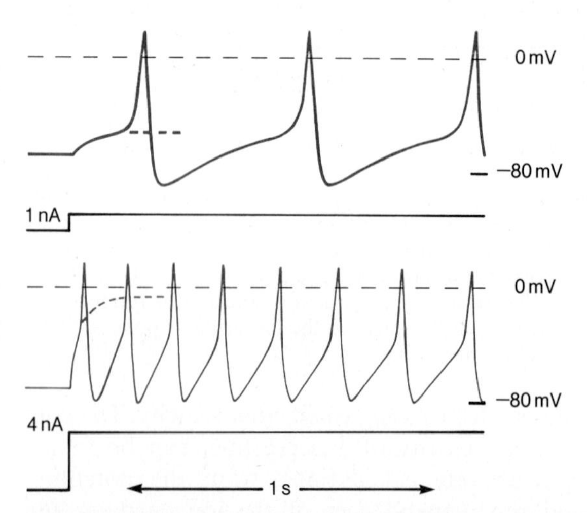

Fig. 2-24. Rhythmic pulse discharge elicited by a prolonged stimulus current. *Above:* A depolarizing 1-nA current into a neuron produces an electrotonic potential that would give a maintained depolarization of about 20 mV (*dashed*) if the threshold for triggering an action potential were not exceeded. The action potentials repeat rhythmically as long as the current flow continues. *Below:* A larger current generates an electrotonic potential that would reach almost 0 mV (*dashed*), except that a high-frequency series of action potentials is triggered.

and hence the frequency of the action potentials is higher, starting at 7 Hz and declining to 4 Hz. This slow reduction in frequency during a constant stimulus is typical and is called "adaptation" (see p. 182). The net effect in both cases is that the amplitude of the stimulus current (or of the maintained depolarization) is encoded as a corresponding action-potential frequency.

Mechanism of impulse-volley generation. Almost all excitable cells discharge volleys of action potentials in response to maintained depolarization within a certain range. The frequency is determined by the slope of the depolarization, which begins immediately after the point of maximal repolarization of the action potential. The rapid repolarization is brought about by the increasing K^+ current initiated, with a delay, by depolarization (see Figs. 2-7 and 2-12). When this current turns off after repolarization of the action potential, again with a delay, the membrane potential is caused to rise toward the final level of depolarization (dashed line). However, this delayed K^+ current, I_{KD}, helps to produce rhythmic action potentials only in a relatively small range of depolarization, and the frequency of these action potentials can change only to a small extent. The parts of the cell that must accomplish an effective encoding of depolarization into action-potential frequency usually incorporate another type of K^+ channel, which conducts the current I_{KA}. Fig. 2-25 shows the time courses of both K^+-current components. I_{KD} follows the de- and repolarization in the action potential with a delay. I_{KA} differs in that after it has been initiated by depolarization, it is rapidly inactivated, like the sodium current. I_{KA} cannot be activated again until the membrane has been briefly hyperpolarized; it is switched on when I_{KD} rapidly declines after maximal repolarization, and then I_{KA} prevents too-rapid depolarization and thus lowers the frequency of the impulse volley [10]. This mechanism broadens the range over which action-potential frequency can be altered by various levels of maintained depolarization.

High-frequency volleys of action potentials are often observed to decline in frequency and then stop altogether during a maintained stimulus, and to begin again after some time. That is, the volley is divided into bursts. The production of such bursts is assisted by still another type of K^+ channel. During the action potential Ca^{2+} flows into the cell (see p. 30), slightly raising the intracellular Ca^{2+} concentration, $[Ca^{2+}]_i$]. This increase in $[Ca^{2+}]_i$ activates a type of K^+ channel to produce a steadily increasing efflux of K^+, which enhances repolarization so that the impulse volley is eventually cut off. Then $[Ca^{2+}]_i$ returns to normal by means of the various transport processes (see p. 7), and the volley begins again.

The combined actions of various types of K^+ channel in this example shows how the special functions of certain cells and parts of cells are made possible by the diversity of ion channels. The presence of different Ca^{2+} channels also helps to provide a variety of forms of excitation.

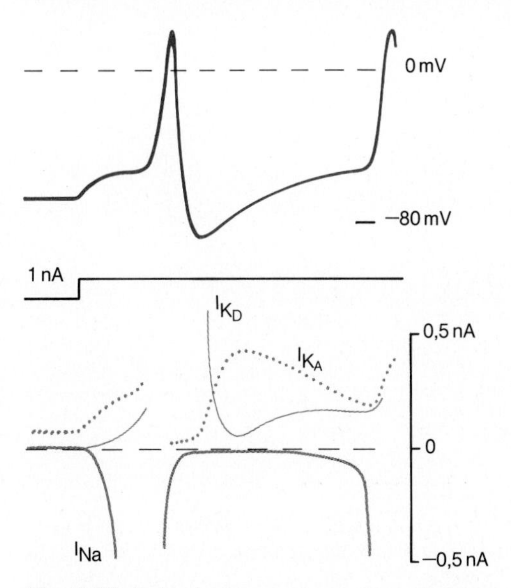

Fig. 2-25. Potassium-current components as a cause of rhythmic pulse discharge. *Above:* Action potentials triggered by a 1-nA current as in Fig. 2-24. *Below* are shown the current components produced by depolarization: the inward sodium current I_{Na}, the delayed, not inactivated outward potassium current I_{KD}, and the rapidly inactivated potassium current I_{KA}. (Modified from [10])

2.7 References

Textbooks and Handbooks

1. Alberts, B., Bray, D., Lewis, J., Raff, M., Roberts, K., Watson, J.D.: Molecular biology of the cell. New York and London: Garland Publishing Inc. 1983
2. Cooke, I., Lipkin, M.: Cellular Neurophysiology, a source book. New York: Holt, Rinehart and Winston 1972 (Collection of important original papers)
3. Hille, B.: Ionic channels of excitable membranes. Sunderland, Mass.: Sinauer Assoc., 1984
4. Hoppe, W., Lohmann, W., Markl, H., Ziegler, H. (eds.): Biophysik. Berlin, Heiderlberg, New York: Springer 1984
5. Kandel, E.R., Schwartz, J.H. (eds.): Principles of neural science. New York, Amsterdam, Oxford: Elsevier 1985
6. Kuffler, S.W., Nicholls, J.G., Martin, A.R.: From neuron to brain, Second Edition Sunderland, Mass., Sinauer Associates (1984)

Original Papers and Reviews

7. ADRIAN, R.H.: The effect of internal and external potassium concentration on the membrane potential of frog muscle. J. Physiol. (Lond.) 133, 631 (1956)
8. ALDRICH, R.W.: Voltage dependent gating of sodium channels: towards an integrating approach. Trends Neurosci. 9, 82–86 (1986)
9. ARMSTRONG, C.M.: Sodium channels and gating currents. Physiol. Rev. 61, 644–683 (1981)
10. CONNOR, J.A., STEVENS, C.F.: Inward and delayed outward membrane currents in isolated neural somata under voltage clamp. J. Physiol. (Lond.) 213, 1–19 (1971)
11. GASSER, H.S., GRUNDFEST, H.: Axon diameters in relation to the spike dimension and the conduction velocity in mammalian A-fibers. Amer. J. Physiol. 127, 393 (1939)
12. HAMILL, O.P., MARTY, A., NEHER, E., SAKMANN, B., SIGWORTH, F.J.: Improved patch clamp techniques for high resolution current recording from cells and cell-free membrane patches. Pflügers Arch. 391, 85–100 (1981)
13. HEINEMANN, U., LUX, D.: Ionic changes during experimentally induced epilepsies. In: Progress in Epilepsy, R.C. Rose, Ed., London: Pitman Medical, p. 87–102 (1983)
14. HILLE, B.: Ionic channels in excitable membranes. Biophys. J. 22, 283–294 (1978)
15. HODGKIN, A.L., HUXLEY, A.F.: The dual effect of membrane potential on sodium conductance in the giant axon of Loligo. J. Physiol. (Lond.) 116, 497 (1952)
16. HODGKIN, A.L., HUXLEY, A.F.: Quantitative description of membrane current and its application to conduction and excitation in nerve. J. Physiol. (Lond.) 117, 500 (1952)
17. HODGKIN, A.L., RUSHTON, W.A.H.: The electrical constants of crustacean nerve fibre. Proc. roy. Soc. B 133, 444 (1946)
18. HUXLEY, A.F., STÄMPFLI, R.: Evidence for saltatory conduction in peripheral myelinated nerve fibres. J. Physiol. (Lond.) 108, 315 (1949)
19. KAMEYAMA, M., HOFMANN, F., TRAUTWEIN, W.: On the mechanism of β-adrenergic regulation of the Ca channel in the guineapig heart. Pflügers Arch. 405, 285–293 (1985)
20. KATZ, B.: Electrical properties of the muscle fibre membrane. Proc. roy. Soc. B. 135, 506 (1948)
21. LÄUGER, P.: Ionic channels with conformational substates. Biophys. J. 47, 581–590 (1985)
22. LLOYD, D.P.C., CHANG, H.T.: Afferent fibres in muscle nerves. J. Neurophysiol. 11, 199 (1948)
23. MEVES, H.: Inactivation of the sodium permeability in squid giant nerve fibres. Prog. Biophys. Mol. Biol. 33, 207–230 (1978)
24. NEHER, E., SAKMANN, B., STEINBACH, J.H.: The extracellular patch clamp: A method for resolving currents through individual open channels in biological membranes. Pflügers Arch. 375, 219–228 (1978)
25. NEUMCKE, B., SCHWARZ, W., STÄMPFLI, R.: Block of Na channels in the membrane of myelinated nerve by benzocaine. Pflügers Arch. 390, 230–236 (1981)
26. NEUMCKE, B., STÄMPFLI, R.: Heterogeneity of external surface charges near sodium channels in the nodal membrane of frog nerve. Pflügers Arch. 401, 125–131 (1984)
27. NOBLE, D.: Applications of Hodgkin-Huxley equations to excitable tissues. Physiol. Rev. 46, 1 (1966)
28. RANG, H.P., RITCHIE, J.M.: Electrogenic sodium pump in mammalian non-myelinated nerve fibres and its activation by various external cations. J. Physiol. (Lond.) 196, 183 (1968)
29. RUCH, T.C., PATTON, H.D.: Physiology and Biophysics. Philadelphia: Saunders 1966
30. SCHWARZ, W., PALLADE, P.T., HILLE, B.: Local anesthetics: Effect of pH on use-dependent block of sodium channels in frog muscle. Biophys. J. 20, 343–368 (1977)
31. SIGWORTH, F.J., NEHER, E.: Single Na^+ channel currents observed in cultured red muscle cells. Nature (Lond.) 287, 447–449 (1980)
32. TRAUTWEIN, W., PELZER, D.: Voltage dependent gating of single calcium channels in cardiac cell membranes and its modulation by drugs. In: Calcium physiology, D. Marmé, Editor. Berlin, Heidelberg, New York, Toronto. Springer (in press) (1986)
33. ULBRICHT, W.: Kinetics of drug action and equilibrium results at the node of Ranvier. Physiol. Rev. 61, 785–828 (1981)
34. WHITE, M.W., BEZANILLA, B.: Activation of squid axon K^+ channel. Ionic and gating current studies. J. Gen. Physiol. 85, 539–554, (1985)
35. QUANDT, F.N., YEH, J.Z., NARAHASHI, T.: All or none block of single Na^+ channels by tetrodotoxin. Neurosci. Lett. 54, 77–83 (1985)

3 Transmission of Excitation from Cell to Cell

J. DUDEL

Within a nerve cell information is transferred by action potentials. It is passed from one cell to the next at morphologically specialized contact sites, the synapses. In neural and most other tissues (though not in many syncytia) the plasma membranes of adjacent cells do not fuse, and there is no direct communication between their interior spaces; therefore an action potential does not automatically proceed across a synapse. Special mechanisms are required for synaptic transmission. At **chemical synapses** a transmitter substance is used, and at **electrical synapses**, a particular current distribution. The chemical synapses are especially interesting because they enable very complex interactions of the cells and, from a medical viewpoint, because they are involved in specific pathological processes and there are certain drugs that act specifically upon them. Therefore we shall devote considerable attention to the chemical synapses.

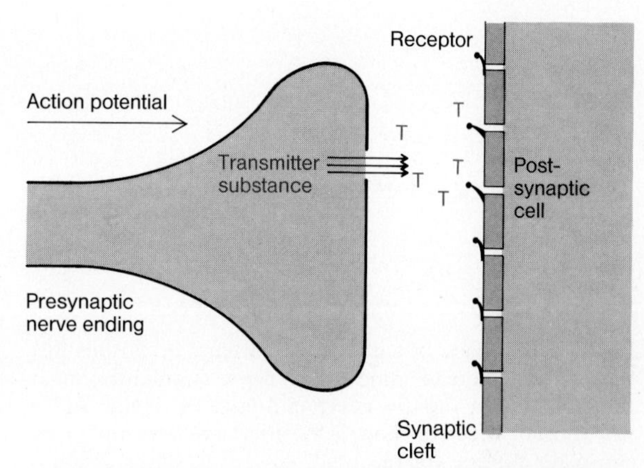

Fig. 3-1. Diagram of chemical synaptic transmission. The action potential in the nerve fiber depolarizes the presynaptic terminals. The result is release of a transmitter, T, which diffuses through the synaptic cleft and can bind to receptors in the membrane of the postsynaptic cell. The binding causes channels in the membrane to open, allowing specific ions to flow through, which changes the potential across the postsynaptic membrane

3.1 Chemical Synaptic Transmission

Figure 3-1 is a diagram to show the most important aspects of a chemical synapse. An action potential depolarizes the *"presynaptic"* terminal of a nerve cell, which causes the local release of a **"transmitter substance"** from the terminal into the **synaptic cleft** between the pre- and postsynaptic cells. The transmitter diffuses to the plasma membrane of the postsynaptic cell. There it encounters specific receptors to which it can bind, whereupon membrane channels open. The ionic currents flowing through them affect the *membrane potential* of the postsynaptic cell; for example, they depolarize it to the threshold and thus trigger an action potential.

This schematic outline of chemical synaptic transmission must be filled in with much more detail. First we consider the best-known synapse, the motor end plate.

Motor End Plate of the Muscle

The places where motor nerve fibers end on muscle fibers are visible under a magnifying glass; they are known as **"end plates"**. The morphological details of the motoneuron terminals and the postsynaptic region are shown in Fig. 3-13 and will be discussed later. When the motoneuron is stimulated and a microelectrode is inserted into the muscle fiber at the end plate (0 mm distance) (Fig. 3-2), one records an **end-plate potential**[1], a rapidly increasing depolarization that returns to the resting potential with a time constant of about 5 ms. This time constant corresponds approximately to that for discharge of the membrane capacitance (see Fig. 2-16, p. 33). When the microelectrode is inserted 1, 2 or 4 mm away from the end plate (Fig. 3-2), the mea-

[1] As this volume appears it is just half a century since the end-plate potential was discovered, by the now Emeritus Professors HANS SCHAEFER, currently at Heidelberg, and HERBERT GÖPFERT, currently at Freiburg [see Pflügers Arch 239:597-619 (1938), 242:364-381 (1939)].

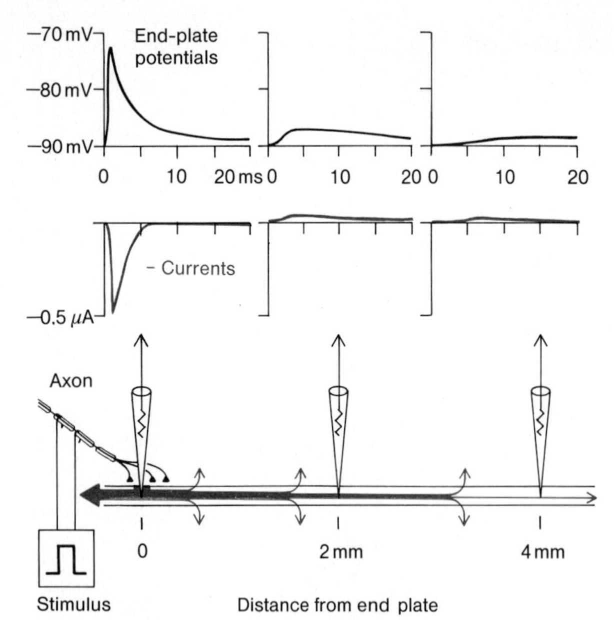

Fig. 3-2. End-plate potentials and currents at various distances from the end plate. After nerve stimulation, near the end plate a rapidly rising end-plate potential and a still shorter, negative (flow of positive ions into the fiber) end-plate current are recorded. At the distances 2 and 4 mm from the end plate the end-plate potentials are progressively smaller and more delayed, and the currents are positive. This shows that the end-plate current flows into the fiber only in the end-plate region, and that the potential change spreads out electrotonically over a few millimeters around the end plate

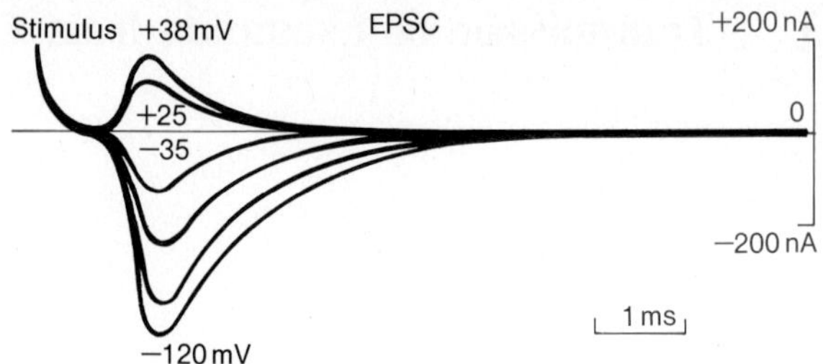

Fig. 3-3. Dependence of the end-plate current, or the "excitatory postsynaptic current", EPSC, on the membrane potential. A voltage clamp was used to keep the membrane potential constant at various levels, by regulation of an electrical current injected into the cell through a microelectrode. The EPSC is strongly negative at −120 mV clamp voltage, is reduced at clamp voltages of −90, −65 and −35 mV, and at +25 and +38 mV becomes increasingly positive. [3, 26]

sured end-plate potential becomes progressively smaller and extends over a longer time.

That is, the end-plate potential behaves like an *electrotonic potential* produced by applying a current pulse to the end plate (see Fig. 2-17).

The current pulse flowing into the muscle fiber during the end-plate potential, the **end-plate current**, can be measured by applying a voltage clamp (p. 24). In Fig. 3-2, inflow of the end-plate current is restricted to the region of the end plate; from there the current flows along the interior of the fiber, and beyond the end plate it flows back out of the fiber. To learn which ions carry the end-plate current one must measure its voltage-dependence, as in the experiment of Fig. 3-3. Here a voltage clamp is used to adjust the membrane potential to values between −120 mV and +38 mV. At about −10 mV the end-plate current reverses its direction. By varying the ionic concentrations it can be shown that this current is produced by a relatively unspecific *increase in the membrane conductance* for Na^+ and K^+, which results in an equilibrium potential of about −10 mV (Chapter 1, Eq. 7, p. 7). The end-plate current is much shorter than the end-plate potential (Fig. 3-2); the current dies out within a few milliseconds, and becomes shorter as depolarization increases (Fig. 3-3).

The end-plate potentials in Fig. 3-2 were made smaller than normal by lowering the extracellular Ca^{2+} concentration (see p. 54), so that they are subthreshold. Normally a single end-plate potential depolarizes by 30 mV or more and is well above threshold; that is, it triggers an action potential, which is conducted along the muscle fiber and causes the myofibrils to contract (see p. 66). When an action potential has been triggered, the *excitation has been transmitted from the motor axon to the muscle fiber* at this synapse.

The synaptic transmitter acetylcholine. According to the diagram of Fig. 3-1, at chemical synapses excitation is transmitted by a transmitter substance. At the end plate this substance is acetylcholine, one of the first transmitters to be discovered (it also used to be known as "vagus substance" for its action on the heart). Applied locally to the end plate, acetylcholine causes depolarization, but sensitivity to acetylcholine is limited to the immediate vicinity of the terminals [32].

Synaptic Inhibition

The motor end plate is the prototype of a synapse at which excitation is transmitted. At other excitatory synapses the correlate of the end-plate potential is called the "excitatory postsynaptic potential, EPSP". At least as common in the body as excitatory synapses are synapses at which inhibition is transmitted. The principle is illustrated

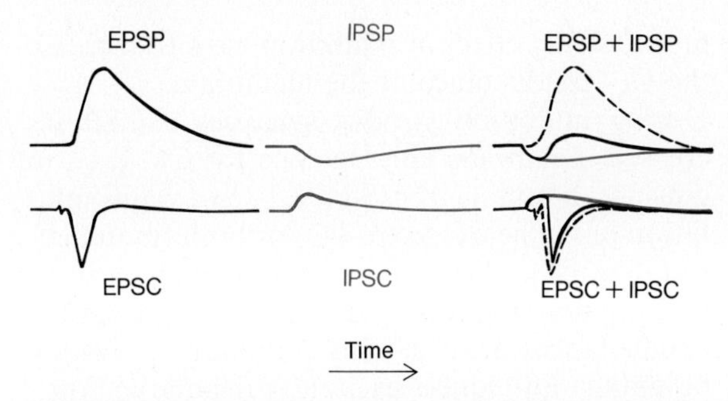

Fig. 3-4. Excitatory and inhibitory postsynaptic potentials (EPSP and IPSP, respectively) and currents (EPSC and IPSC). When superimposed, the EPSC and IPSC summate, but the EPSP and IPSP together give a smaller depolarization than would correspond to their sum. (Dudel in [4])

in Fig. 3-4. On the left an EPSP is shown together with the excitatory postsynaptic current (EPSC) (cf. Fig. 3-2). Activity of an inhibitory nerve fiber that communicates with the same postsynaptic cell as the excitatory fiber gives rise to an **inhibitory postsynaptic potential** (IPSP), usually a small hyperpolarization, with a corresponding outward current (IPSC). If excitation and inhibition occur at approximately the same time, the currents EPSC and IPSC summate; however, the resulting voltage change is much smaller than the sum EPSP+IPSP. Inhibition has greatly reduced the EPSP depolarization and diminished or prevented transmission of excitation at the synapse. *Inhibition is thus defined as the reduction or blockage of excitation.*

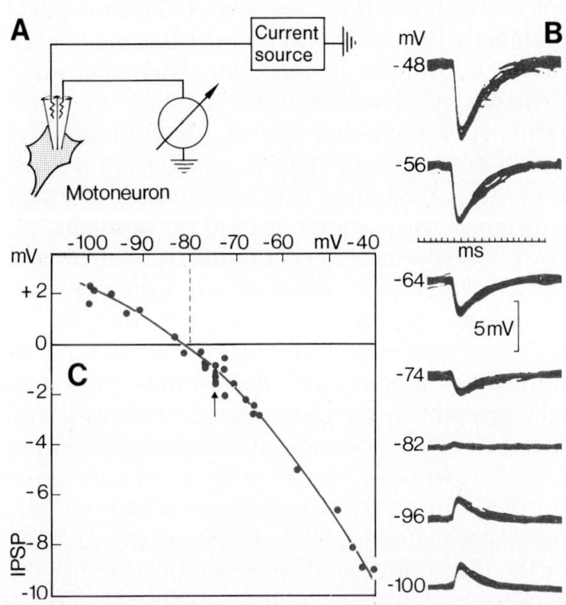

Fig. 3-5 A-C. Measurement of the equilibrium potential of inhibitory postsynaptic potentials. **A** Through one barrel of a double-barreled intracellular microelectrode the membrane potential of the motoneuron can be varied by current from an adjustable source. **B** Inhibitory postsynaptic potentials in a motoneuron to the semitendinosus muscle after stimulation of the quadriceps nerve with constant intensity. Amplitude and polarity of the resulting IPSP depend on the membrane potential. **C** Graph of the data from the complete series of measurements, some of which are represented in **B**. *Abscissa:* membrane potential. *Ordinate:* maximal amplitude of the IPSP. Hyperpolarizing IPSP's are plotted below the zero line, depolarizing above it. The equilibrium potential is at about −80 mV. The resting potential of the cell was −74 mV (*arrow* in **C**). From [2]

Equilibrium potential for inhibition. The ionic currents that flow during inhibition can be identified, again by injecting current to change the membrane potential. The result is shown in Fig. 3-5, for a motoneuron in the spinal cord. At the resting potential, −74 mV, the inhibitory potential (IPSP) is hyperpolarizing. As the membrane is progressively hyperpolarized, the polarity of the IPSP is found to reverse at about −82 mV. This reversal potential is influenced by the concentration gradients of K^+ and Cl^-; it follows that the IPSC is produced by an increase in the membrane conductance for K^+ and Cl^-.
How does increased membrane conductance inhibit excitation? The process can be explained most simply for electrotonic potentials. In the experiment of Fig. 3-6A a current pulse is injected into the cell, generating an electrotonic potential (see p. 33) with amplitude proportional to the membrane resistance. When an inhibitory synapse on this cell is activated, the IPSP normally hyperpolarizes the membrane by a few mV. Now, if the IPSP coincides with the electrotonic potential, the latter is very much reduced – indeed, practically eliminated – because the IPSP has lowered the membrane resistance. Fig. 3-6B shows the effect of inhibition for a wider range of membrane potentials. The membrane potential of one cell was plotted as a function of the injected current, producing a current-voltage relation. The control curve crosses the abscissa at −70 mV, the resting potential; positive currents depolarize the membrane from this level. High-frequency activity of the inhibitory synapse (simulated here by applying the inhibitory transmitter substance) shifts the current-voltage curve somewhat in the direction of hyperpolarization from the resting potential and also increases its slope, which corresponds to a decrease in the membrane resistance (voltage change per current change). The alteration of membrane resistance is the most important effect of inhibition. For instance, if under control conditions an EPSP or an action potential were to inject 0.1 μA into the

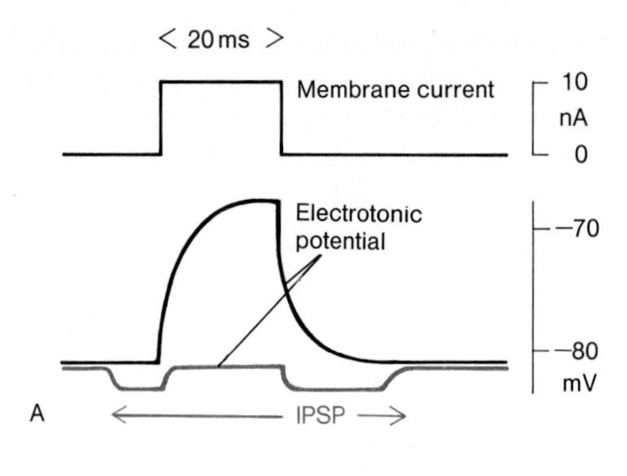

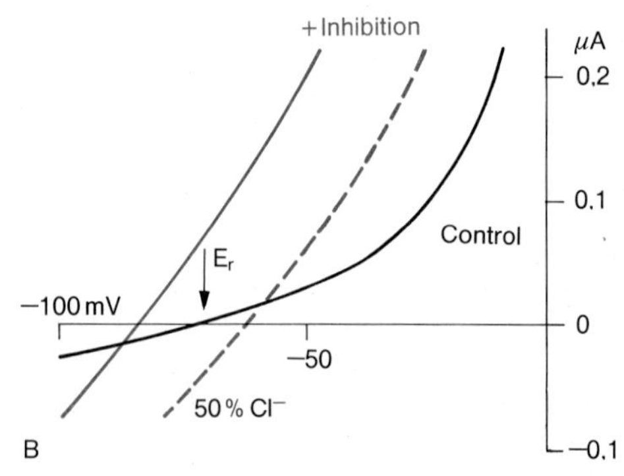

Fig. 3-6 A, B. Effect of inhibition on membrane currents. **A** A current pulse injected into a cell generates an electrotonic potential (black voltage trace). If the inhibiting nerve is activated with a stimulus series 40 ms in duration, a hyperpolarizing IPSP of the same duration is produced. When the electrotonic potential is applied during inhibition, it is much smaller than before (red voltage trace). **B** Relationship between membrane current (*ordinate*) and membrane voltage (*abscissa*) at rest (control); the intersection with the abscissa is the resting potential E_r. During inhibition (*red*), by application of a solution containing GABA, the membrane hyperpolarizes and the slope of the current-voltage curve (*continuous line*) increases; i.e., the resistance is lowered. When the chloride concentration in the bath solution is reduced to half, there is no noticeable change in the control curve, but inhibition depolarizes (dashed line). Data from a crustacean muscle with inhibitory GABAergic synapses. (DUDEL in [4])

cell, this current would depolarize the membrane to −25 mV. In the presence of inhibition the same 0.1-μA excitatory current would depolarize only to −60 mV, insufficient to trigger an action potential, as illustrated in Fig. 3-4 for the interaction of a single EPSP and IPSP. *The decrease in resistance short-circuits excitatory currents* and thereby prevents excitation. This effect is supplemented by the effect of hyperpolarization.

Fig. 3-6B also demonstrates the effect of reducing the extracellular Cl^- concentration. The control curve is hardly affected, but the current-voltage curve during inhibition is shifted to the right by almost 20 mV. A shift of 18 mV in this direction would be predicted by the Nernst equation (p. 6) if the only effect of inhibition were to increase the Cl^- conductance of the membrane.

During inhibition various synapses exhibit increased membrane conductance for Cl^- (e.g., in crustacean muscle, Fig. 3-6), K^+ (e.g., vagus inhibition of the heart; see p. 447) or both (motoneuron, Fig. 3-5). The equilibrium potentials of these ions are near the resting potential; increasing the conductances of these ions stabilizes the resting potential and reduces excitatory depolarization.

Synaptic Transmitters

We have already been introduced to one transmitter substance, acetylcholine. There are quite a number of other transmitters, the most important and best-known of which are listed in the top half of Fig. 3-7. The amino acid γ-aminobutyric acid is the most widespread inhibitory transmitter in the CNS; the even simpler amino acid **glycine** acts, for example, to inhibit the motoneuron (Fig. 3-5). The acidic amino acid **glutamate** is probably the most widespread excitatory transmitter in the CNS. **Adrenalin, noradrenalin** and **dopamine** form a family of transmitter substances that mediate excitation or inhibition both centrally and peripherally; together, they are called the "catecholamines". Another substance with similar actions is **serotonin** (5-hydroxytryptamine, 5HT), which together with the catecholamines constitutes the group of "monoamines". All these "classical" transmitters are small molecules that frequently appear in intermediary metabolism. Each binds to a specific receptor in the postsynaptic membrane and thereby increases membrane conductance, either for Na^+ (with K^+) so as to transmit excitation, or for K^+ or Cl^- so as to produce inhibition. The only specific step in this process is the reaction of the transmitter with the receptor; whether the result is excitation or inhibition depends only on the ion-channel properties of the receptor (see Fig. 3-18) and not on the transmitter substance itself.

Below the classical transmitters in Fig. 3-7 are listed a number of **peptide transmitters**. These substances act in the CNS or in the autonomic nervous system by mechanisms that are not yet well understood. It is likely that they are often synaptic **modulators**. That is, they do not directly change the conductance of the synaptic membranes, but rather influence the intensity and duration of the action of the classical transmitters, and they sometimes appear to be

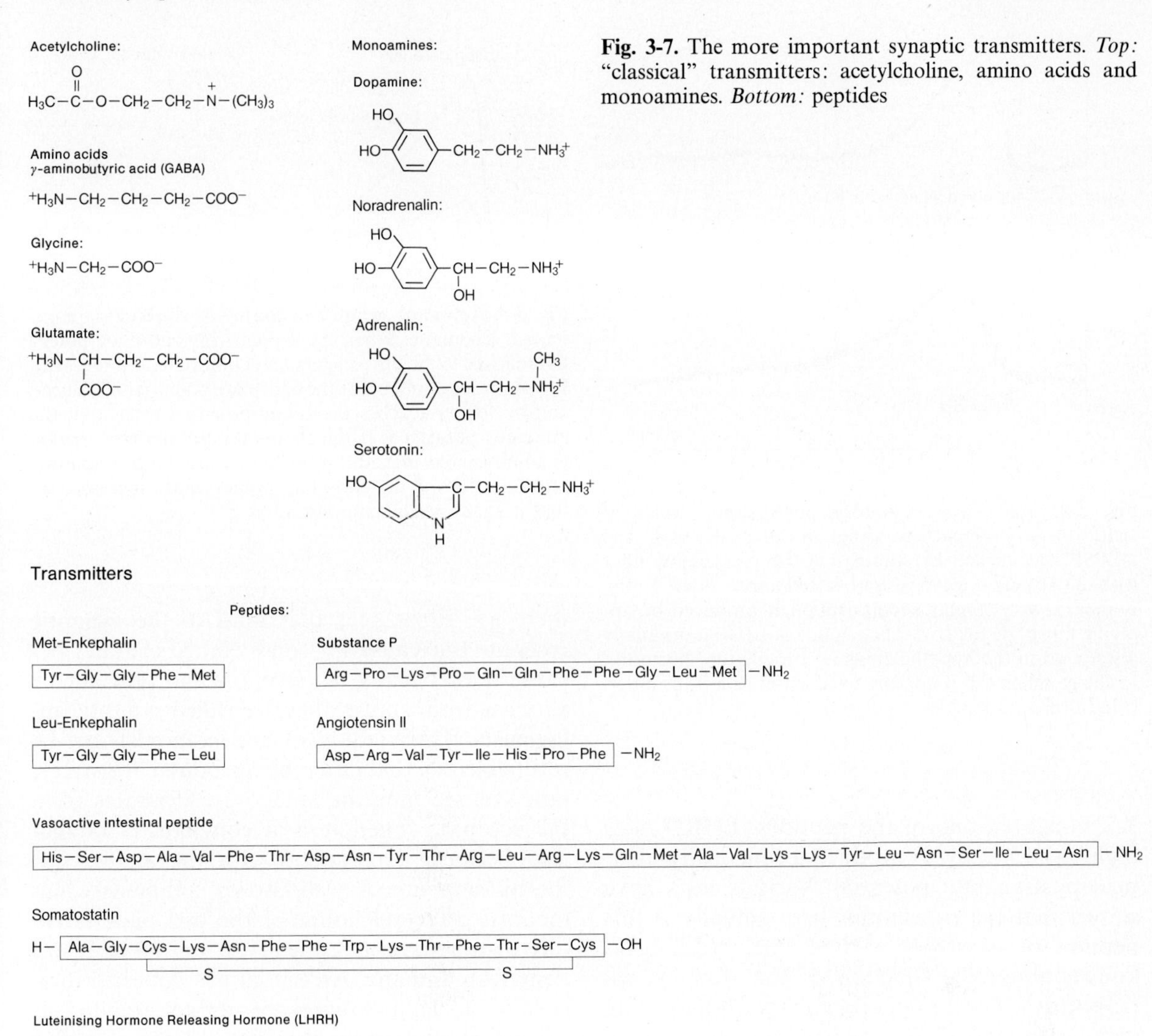

Fig. 3-7. The more important synaptic transmitters. *Top:* "classical" transmitters: acetylcholine, amino acids and monoamines. *Bottom:* peptides

released together with other transmitters. Fig. 3-7 shows representative examples selected from a large number of peptides currently under consideration. The enkephalins bind to morphine receptors; one of their actions is involved with the pain sensation. Substance P is another transmitter associated with pain, but it also causes smooth musculature to contract. Angiotensin II is a local hormone highly effective on blood vessels as well as in the CNS, and a similar substance is "vasoactive intestinal peptide". Somatostatin and LHRH (luteotropic-hormone-releasing hormone) participate in regulation of hormone release in the hypophysis (see Chapter 17) and also act at synapses [36].

For a long time it was thought that a nerve cell always releases only one transmitter at its terminals (Dale's Principle). In the autonomic nervous system, however, at least in embryonic cells, release of both acetylcholine and adrenalin from the same cell occurs. At the motor end plate adenosine triphosphate is released together with acetylcholine, and the former is probably also a transmitter. Often a synaptic terminal releases both a classical transmitter such as noradrenalin and a peptide that assists transmission. The details of such transmitter combinations, of **cotransmitters**, are still quite unclear, but the effects are probably usually a kind of **modulation**.

Slow autonomic synapse. A synaptic potential at a peptidergic synapse in a sympathetic ganglion is shown in Fig. 3-8. In this ganglion there are fast excitatory synapses at which acetylcholine is the transmitter. In addition, experiments with repeated stimulation of spinal-nerve fibers (e.g., 100 stimuli in 5 s as in Fig. 3-8) have revealed excitatory postsynaptic potentials that last for minutes and are not mediated by any of the classical transmitters shown at the top of Fig.

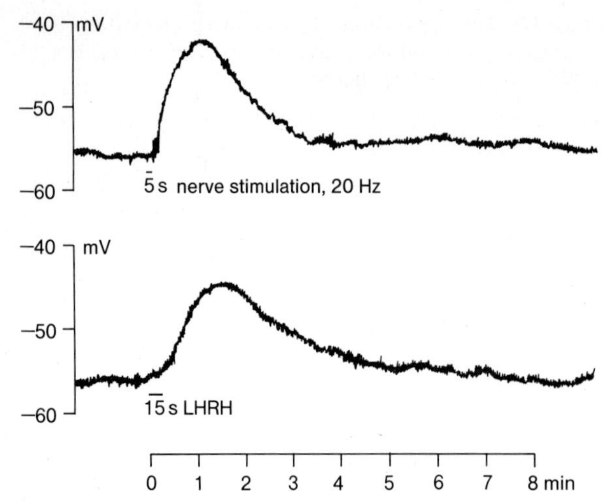

Fig. 3-8. *Top:* slow excitatory postsynaptic potential (ssEPSP) of a sympathetic ganglion cell in the frog. The ssEPSP was elicited by stimulating the presynaptic fiber with 20 stimuli/s for 5 s, and lasted more than 8 min. *Bottom:* a very similar depolarization is produced by applying a peptide for 15 s. The peptide is LHRH, originally discovered in the hypothalamus as a regulatory hormone. In the ganglion cell it appears to function as a transmitter. (Modified from [6, 22])

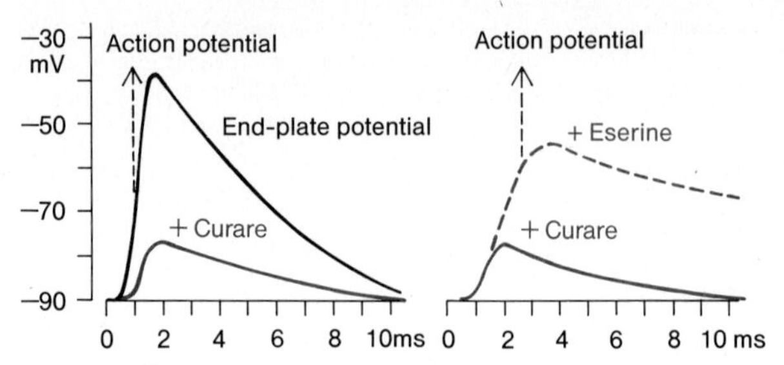

Fig. 3-9. Action of curare and eserine on the end-plate potential, schematic. When the depolarizing end-plate potential reaches -60 mV it triggers an action potential (*dashed*). In the presence of curare the end-plate potential is reduced and no longer reaches the action-potential threshold; the muscle is paralyzed. If the cholinesterase inhibitor eserine is administered in addition to the curare, both amplitude and duration of the end-plate potential are increased so that it again reaches the threshold

3-7. However, one of the peptides, **LHRH**, acts highly specifically to produce a practically identical postsynaptic potential. Various tests have shown that the transmitter here actually is this peptide or a closely related one. Nothing is known about the function of the slow synaptic potentials in the spinal ganglion; long-lasting depolarizations of this kind might well enhance the transmission of excitation at fast synapses, increasing their effectiveness for a relatively long time. As another example of **modulation**, Fig. 2-14 showed adrenalin extending the time during which a potential-dependent Ca^{2+} channel was open.

Agonists and antagonists of synaptic transmission. Each receptor in the postsynaptic membrane reacts with its own specific transmitter and, as a result, increases conductance for the corresponding ion. But the specificity for the transmitter is not absolute; practically all receptors will also bind to other substances. If binding is followed by the appropriate conductance change, so that the substance completely replaces the transmitter, such a substance is called an **agonist.** Agonists for acetylcholine at the end plate, for instance, are carbamylcholine or suberyldicholine [32]. Other substances, which bind with receptors but do not induce a conductance change as effectively, are called **partial agonists** [11]. Finally, there are substances that bind to the synaptic receptor but cause no conductance change; because these occupy the receptor and prevent the agonists from acting, they are called synaptic **antagonists.** The binding of an antagonist can be reversible, so that after being bound for a certain average time the antagonist separates from the receptor. Then it is a **competitive antagonist**, because it competes with the agonist for the binding site. A well-known competitive antagonist of acetylcholine at the end plate is **curare** (d-tubocurarine), the arrow poison of South American Indians. As the curare concentration rises it blocks a progressively larger fraction of the receptors, so that the effect of acetylcholine is attenuated because of the reduced number of receptors available [10]. Under curare the end-plate potential is smaller (Fig. 3-9), and if the dose is high enough the end-plate potential no longer reaches the action-potential threshold: the muscle is paralyzed. Curare and analogous substances are often used in anesthesia as **muscle relaxants**. During complete relaxation, of course, artificial respiration is necessary. Another form of muscle relaxation employs an acetylcholine agonist with a prolonged action, which produces maintained depolarization at the end plate. This *depolarizing muscle relaxant* inactivates the Na^+ channels of the muscle membrane (see p. 25) and thus prevents excitation of the muscle.

Although synaptic agonists and antagonists are often used in physiology to study the mechanisms of transmission, thorough examination of the interactions of the various agonists and antagonists is the province of **pharmacology**. Many important drugs are agonists or antagonists for synaptic receptors, and the physiologists' findings about transmitter mechanisms have frequently provided a basis for the development of new drugs. Agonists and antagonists are also used to characterize the binding sites of the receptors; from the relative effectiveness of appropriately altered analogs of the transmitters, one can draw inferences about structural properties of the binding sites. By determining the effectiveness of various agonists and antagonists one can also classify different types of receptors for certain transmitters such as acetylcholine and adrenalin (see Chapter 16).

Limiting the duration of transmitter action. Once a transmitter has diffused across the synaptic cleft (see Fig. 3-1), further diffusion out of the narrow cleft would only slowly reduce its concentration. But most transmitters act for a very brief time, at most for the duration of the synaptic currents (i.e., about 1 ms at the end plate); evidently something limits the time during which they can act. There are basically 2 mechanisms: *destruction* and *removal* of the transmitter. The end plate incorporates a very effective system for the decomposition of acetylcholine; associated with the postsynaptic membrane, in high concentration, is **cholinesterase**, an enzyme that splits acetylcholine into acetyl and choline (see also Fig. 3-13). A considerable fraction of the acetylcholine released is already split during diffusion across the synaptic cleft, before it reaches the receptors, and within a few ms practically all the ACh has been broken down by the cholinesterase. The synapse is then ready for a new transmission.

The significance of cholinesterase for transmission at the end plate becomes visible when the enzyme is blocked by a **cholinesterase inhibitor**. Fig. 3-9 shows the effect of one of these, **eserine**: the end-plate potential rises for a longer time than normal, reaching a greater amplitude, because acetylcholine can react with the receptors longer and in higher concentration [6]. In the case of Fig. 3-9 this is a "therapeutic" effect, because the eserine is applied to the curare-paralyzed muscle. The resulting enlargement of the end-plate potential permits it to reach the threshold for excitation, abolishing the paralysis. Similarly, cholinesterase inhibitors are used to counteract the muscle relaxation in anesthesia, as well as in diseases such as *myasthenia* (see below). On the other hand, people are sometimes poisoned by insecticides based on cholinesterase inhibitors, and some of the chemical weapons developed by the military are also cholinesterase inhibitors. The symptoms of such poisoning are convulsive effects of prolonged activation of cholinergic synapses, especially in the autonomic system.

At all the synapses that have been closely examined, the transmitter is either rapidly decomposed or removed from the synaptic cleft by transport mechanisms in the membranes of the adjacent cells. **Transport mechanisms** are especially important for adrenalin, noradrenalin, GABA and glutamate. At acetylcholinergic synapses it is not acetylcholine that is transported but the decomposition product choline. Some of these transport processes have the presynaptic terminal as their destination, which reduces the need for resynthesis of the transmitter. Like cholinesterase, the mechanisms by which transmitters are taken into the cells are targets for the action of many important drugs that influence synaptic transmission.

Myasthenia gravis. There is a global disturbance of neuromuscular end-plate function that is relatively well understood, myasthenia gravis [19]. Tone and contractions of the skeletal musculature are weak; for example, the patients cannot hold their eyelids up, or they can hardly walk. The reason is a decrease in density of subsynaptic acetylcholine receptors. The transmitter acetylcholine is released in normal amounts, but can bind to only a few receptors; as a result, the end-plate potential can become too small to reach threshold. The reduction in number of functional receptors is caused by an autoimmune response: the patients develop antibodies to their own acetylcholine receptors, which destroy the receptors or reduce their life span. These patients are very effectively helped by cholinesterase inhibitors (ambenonium, neostigmine, pyridostigmine), which allow the acetylcholine released at the synapses to act longer (Fig. 3-9, eserine) and hence depolarize the membrane sufficiently during the end-plate potential.

3.2 Interactions of Synapses

The motor end plate is an extreme type of synapse: as a rule, the muscle fiber has only one end plate, and each impulse in the motor axon generates a suprathreshold end-plate potential and hence a twitch of the muscle. At most synapses, especially in the CNS, the individual synaptic potentials are far below threshold, often smaller than 1 mV. In compensation, the postsynaptic cell bears many excitatory synapses, the effects of which summate, as well as inhibitory synapses, which counteract the excitation. The presynaptic elements usually come from many

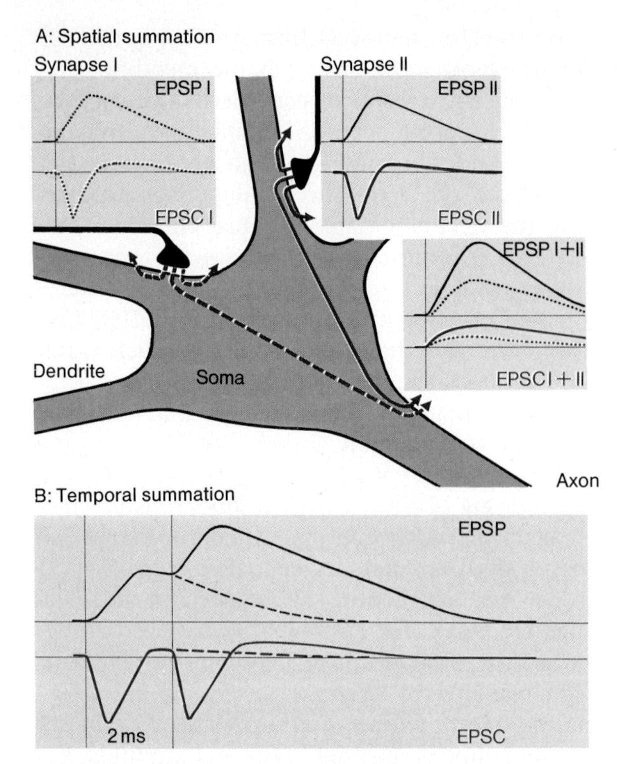

Fig. 3-10 A, B. Spatial and temporal summation of synaptic potentials. **A** Spatial summation. At 2 dendrites of a nerve cell simultaneous activation of terminals at synapses I and II produces excitatory synaptic currents and potentials, EPSCs and EPSPs. The currents propagate electrotonically, and where they exit through the membrane (e.g., at the axon hillock) they add to give a summed EPSP. **B** Temporal summation: at a single synapse one EPSP follows another at a short interval, 2 ms. The overlapping parts of the two EPSPs summate

different cells, the axons of which converge on the postsynaptic cell. The principles of this interaction of synapses of a single cell will now be presented briefly.

Synaptic summation. In Fig. 3-10A two of the thousands of excitatory synapses on a nerve cell have been drawn to demonstrate their interaction. At both synapses current, the EPSC, flows briefly into the cell and causes a local potential change, the EPSP (see Figs. 3-2 and 3-4). Part of the current leaves the cell at some distance from the synapses – for example, at the axon hillock, the place where the axon leaves the cell body (Fig. 3-10). The individual EPSP, an electrotonic potential, is somewhat smaller at a distance (e.g., 0.1 mm) from the synapse (Fig. 3-2). But the **currents** generated at the two simultaneously activated synapses summate, and together generate an enlarged EPSP. Because in this case what is summated is the simultaneous activation of spatially separated synapses, the process is also called **spatial summation**.
The summation of EPSPs naturally occurs at each place on the cell and follows the laws of electrotonic spread of potential changes. But the choice, in Fig. 3-10A, of the beginning of the efferent axon as the site of summation was not an arbitrary one. In most nerve cells the cell body and dendrites either cannot discharge action potentials or the threshold (e.g., to Ca^{2+} currents; see Fig. 2-14) is high. By contrast, the axon is readily excitable, so that as a rule action potentials are first triggered at the point of emergence of the axon. It is at this site, then, that summation of the potential changes determines whether the local synaptic potentials will give rise to propagated excitation.
Another form of synaptic summation is illustrated in Fig. 3-10B. Here we are concerned with the activity of immediately adjacent synapses, or even of a single synapse, when excitation is repeated at a short interval of up to a few ms. In this case the synaptic currents have practically finished by the time the second excitation begins. But the synaptic potentials have a longer time course, because after being charged by the synaptic current the membrane capacitance discharges with the time constant of electrotonus (see p. 33, Figs. 2-16 and 2-17). If a new synaptic current begins before discharge is complete, the depolarization it causes is added to the residual depolarization. This is called **temporal summation**. In a real nerve cell with many synapses and high-frequency activation, of course, spatial and temporal summation occur simultaneously, building up a fluctuating level of depolarization that determines the frequency of action-potential generation in the axon (see Fig. 2-24).
Summated synaptic potentials can exceed the threshold at the axon hillock and trigger action potentials. Often the activation of one "synaptic input" (i.e., a group of functionally identical synapses) alone is not sufficient to trigger an action potential. But if another synaptic activation is added, by spatial or temporal summation, the resulting EPSP is above threshold. Then it is said that one synaptic input has facilitated the other. In *spatial or temporal* **facilitation**, the result is more than the sum of the individual synaptic responses. A distinction must be made between this facilitation, a special case of summation, and true synaptic facilitation, a presynaptic event which will be described below (Fig. 3-16).

Postsynaptic inhibition. The synapses of a single cell can also interact to produce inhibition.

Figs. 3-4 and 3-6 showed that during inhibition excitatory synaptic potentials are short-circuited. The inhibitory synaptic potentials (IPSPs) often hyperpolarize the membrane as well, preventing depolarization to the action-potential threshold. The IPSPs and IPSCs of a nerve cell also summate temporally and spatially, with one another and with the EPSPs, and it is the complex sum of many EPSPs and IPSPs that ultimately determines the frequency of the action potentials in the axon. The spatial distribution of excitatory and inhibitory synapses can also be significant. Inhibitory synapses are often particularly numerous on the soma near the exit of the axon, where they can control how many of the EPSPs, which originate mainly on the dendrites, can have a depolarizing influence on the axon.

Presynaptic inhibition. As an extension of the above topic, the ways the different synapses on a cell interact, we turn now to a form of inhibition in which an axo-axonal synapse affects the release of transmitter from a terminal: *presynaptic inhibition.* Fig. 3-11 shows this kind of inhibition of a motoneuron. The motoneuron receives a major excitatory input from the muscle spindles, by way of Ia fibers (see Table 2-1, p. 38, and Chapter 5). The endings of interneurons make axo-axonal synapses with the endings of the Ia fibers. If these interneurons are excited a few ms before the Ia fibers, the EPSP that the Ia fibers produce in the motoneuron is inhibited (Fig. 3-11A and B). By stimulating the inhibitory interneuron at various times before occurrence of the Ia-fiber EPSP, one can see that the duration of presynaptic inhibition is some hundreds of milliseconds. The inhibitory effect and its time course are shown still more clearly when the compound action potential in the nerve containing the motor axons is taken as the measure of inhibition, rather than the EPSP (Fig. 3-11D). This presynaptic inhibition is evidently an effective control mechanism for spinal motor systems. It has the particular advantage that single synaptic inputs can be inhibited specifically, with no effect on the excitability of the cell as a whole. "Undesirable" information can be suppressed before it reaches the site of integration, the cell body of the neuron.

The inhibitory synapse on the endings of the Ia fibers is a chemical one with GABA as transmitter; it produces quite a large depolarization, called primary afferent depolarization (PAD). The PAD inactivates the excitatory Na^+ channels in the Ia-fiber terminals (see Fig. 2-8, p. 26) and thus prevents conduction of the action po-

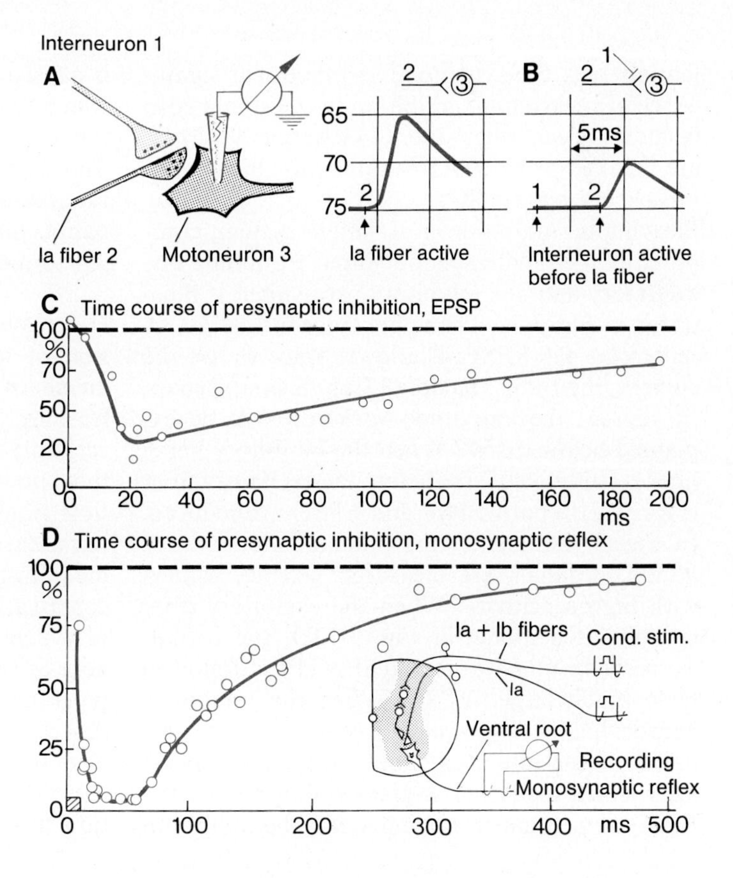

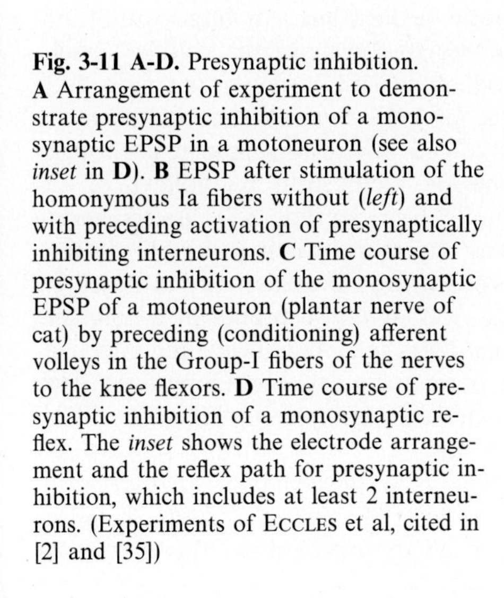

Fig. 3-11 A-D. Presynaptic inhibition. **A** Arrangement of experiment to demonstrate presynaptic inhibition of a monosynaptic EPSP in a motoneuron (see also *inset* in **D**). **B** EPSP after stimulation of the homonymous Ia fibers without (*left*) and with preceding activation of presynaptically inhibiting interneurons. **C** Time course of presynaptic inhibition of the monosynaptic EPSP of a motoneuron (plantar nerve of cat) by preceding (conditioning) afferent volleys in the Group-I fibers of the nerves to the knee flexors. **D** Time course of presynaptic inhibition of a monosynaptic reflex. The *inset* shows the electrode arrangement and the reflex path for presynaptic inhibition, which includes at least 2 interneurons. (Experiments of ECCLES et al, cited in [2] and [35])

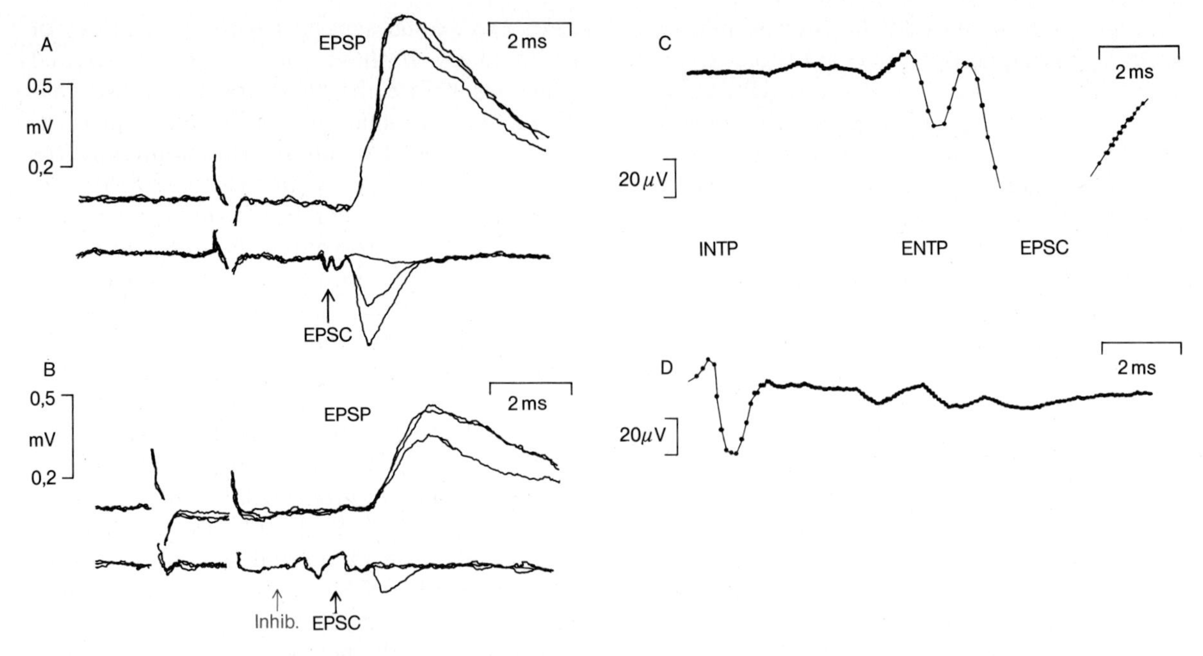

Fig. 3-12 A-D. Presynaptic inhibition in a crustacean muscle innervated by only one excitatory and one inhibitory nerve fiber. **A** Three intracellularly recorded EPSPs, superimposed and synchronized by the stimulus, and below them the local currents measured postsynaptically, EPSCs. The latter are composed of quanta (see below); in this case 0, 1 and 2 quanta are represented. **B** Recording at the same synapse as in A, with the inhibitory axon stimulated 2 ms before the excitatory axon, so that the EPSP and EPSC are reduced. *Black arrows:* extracellular recordings of the action potential in the terminal of the excitatory neuron (ENTP), *red arrow:* extracellular recordings of the action potential in the inhibitory terminal (INTP). **C** High-resolution recording (digitized), in another preparation, of the action potential in the excitatory terminal, ENTP, followed by the EPSC (cut off at the bottom). **D** When the inhibitory axon is stimulated before the excitatory axon, an INTP appears and the amplitude of the following ENTP is much reduced. The EPSC is almost completely blocked by this presynaptic inhibition. (Modified from [13, 15])

tentials past the synapse. The functional significance of presynaptic inhibition in the spinal cord becomes clear when the GABAergic synapses are blocked by the GABA antagonist bicucullin: muscle cramps result.

Presynaptic inhibition in a simple system, composed of a cell with synaptic input from only one excitatory and one inhibitory nerve fiber, is illustrated in Fig. 3-12. The upper trace in Fig. 3-12A represents the EPSP. The lower trace shows the current, the EPSC, recorded from a small synaptic region; the amplitude variation will be explained below (p. 54). When the inhibitory nerve fiber is stimulated 2 ms before the excitatory fiber (Fig. 3-12B), both EPSP and EPSC are reduced. In Fig. 3-12C and D the potential fluctuations at the terminals are measured (extracellularly) with high sensitivity. When the excitatory fiber is stimulated alone, in Fig. 3-12D, the triphasic nerve-terminal potential (ENTP) is followed by a much larger EPSC. When the inhibitory neuron has been stimulated previously, the terminal of the inhibitory fiber exhibits an INTP, after which the ENTP is greatly reduced and the EPSC almost entirely eliminated. The inhibition is caused by the release of GABA (see Fig. 3-7), which reacts with receptors in the excitatory terminal so as to increase its chloride conductance. That is, this presynaptic inhibition makes use, at the axo-axonal synapse, of the classical postsynaptic inhibitory mechanism illustrated in Figs. 3-4 to 3-6.

Heterosynaptic facilitation. An important function of the nervous system, the cellular mechanism of which is still largely unexplained, is **learning** (see p. 153). Synaptic mechanisms are certainly involved in learning, and it is thought that presynaptic facilitation by volleys of action potentials (see Section 3.3) assists short-term learning. Furthermore, it is very likely that medium-term learning processes are initiated by coactivation of 2 synaptic inputs in a cell, one of which *modulates* (e.g., facilitates) the effectiveness of the other for a relatively long time. Two types of such *heterosynaptic facilitation* will be described briefly.

The first type is a *postsynaptic facilitation* in neurons of sympathetic ganglia. Here, in addition to other synaptic potentials, there are slow

EPSPs mediated by acetylcholine. These sEPSPs can be from 5 to 100 ms long. (The peptidergic ssEPSPs of the same type of neuron, shown in Fig. 3-8, are even longer, lasting several minutes.) The ganglion cell also receives synaptic input from a dopaminergic neuron. The dopamine it releases does not itself affect ion conductances in the postsynaptic membrane. However, *for several hours it increases the amplitude of the sEPSP*, and thereby enhances the postsynaptic reaction to acetylcholine [23].
Another type of heterosynaptic facilitation has been found in mollusks and insects. Here the activation of serotonin-releasing nerve fibers results in the blockade of a K^+ channel in the membrane of presynaptic terminals. With the K^+ channels blocked, repolarization of the action potential is delayed (see Chapter 2); because the terminals remain depolarized longer, more transmitter is released. Hence this is a case of presynaptic facilitation, another example in which coactivation of two synapses increases the effectiveness of synaptic transmission [5].

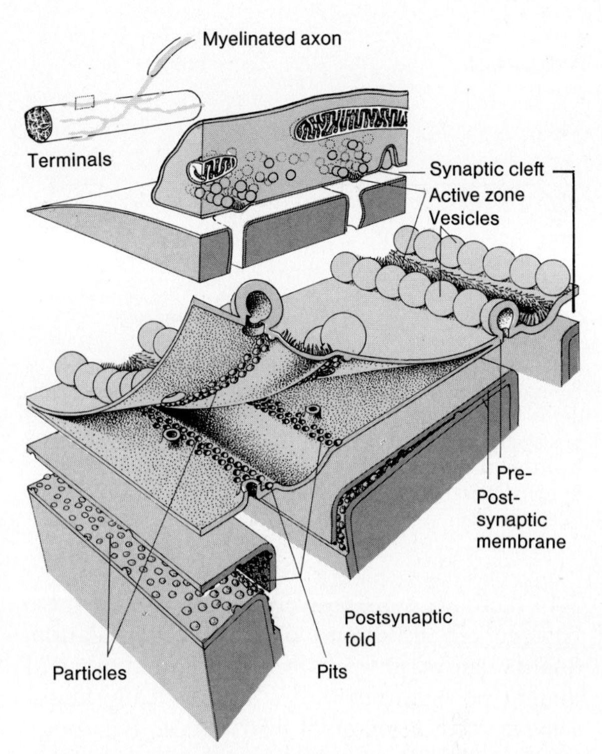

Fig. 3-13. Fine structure of the neuromuscular synapse. *Top left:* terminals on a muscle fiber; in the adjacent drawing the terminal region (*red*) is enlarged, together with the underlying folded muscle-fiber membrane. *Below*, further enlarged, the membrane of the presynaptic neuron (*red*) with the inner and outer layers partially separated, and under that (*black*) the corresponding layers of the underlying, subsynaptic muscle membrane. The label "particles" indicates acetylcholine receptors and cholinesterase molecules in the membrane. (Modified from [6])

3.3 Microphysiology of Chemical Synaptic Transmission

We have now mentioned the most important macroscopic processes at chemical synapses; each of these must be viewed as the sum of a great number of molecular processes. Many details of chemical synaptic transmission, like the membrane properties discussed in the preceding chapter, have been worked out at the molecular level – a considerable contribution to our understanding of synaptic mechanisms. As a first example, we return to a subject passed over before, the release of transmitter substances.

Release of Transmitter

Micromorphology of the end plate. The structural properties of the end plate that are known so far are illustrated, progressively enlarged, in Fig. 3-13. A striking feature on the presynaptic side is the clusters of "synaptic" **vesicles** in the motoneuron terminal. Opposite these, the postsynaptic membrane is deeply folded. Corresponding to each fold is an active zone of the presynaptic membrane, a groove in the inner surface with a row of vesicles running along either side. Some of these vesicles are found to be open to the exterior, toward the synaptic cleft. Hence the active zones and the associated vesicles must be an apparatus specialized for exocytosis (see p. 10), which discharges the contents of the vesicles into the synaptic cleft. With biochemical methods it has been shown that the vesicles contain high concentrations of acetylcholine, in addition to proteins and nucleotides. At the active zones, then, acetylcholine can be released from the motoneuron terminal in vesicle portions.

Quantization of the end-plate potential. Because the acetylcholine is released in approximately equal portions, corresponding to the volume of a vesicle, the postsynaptic current (the EPSC) must be composed of small subunits. These can be observed by using the patch-clamp method (see Fig. 2-11) to measure the synaptic currents in a part of the end plate a few μm long. When the motoneuron is stimulated, the EPSC amplitude is clearly an *integral multiple of a subunit*; in Fig.

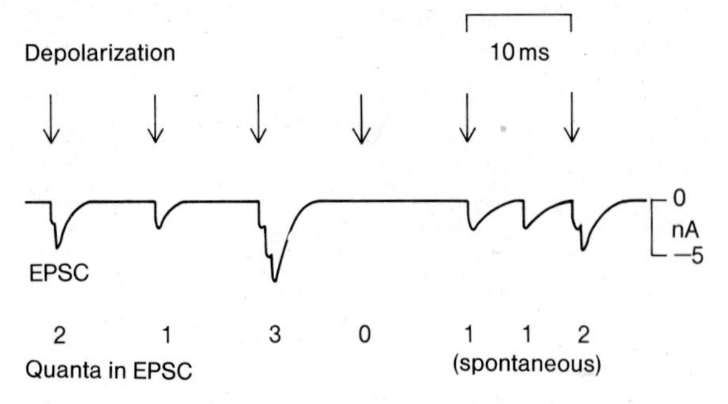

Fig. 3-14. Release of quanta of transmitter, manifest as "quantization" of the EPSC. At each *arrow* the nerve ending is briefly depolarized. The resulting EPSCs, measured postsynaptically, consist of 2, 1, 3 ... quanta, as indicated by the numbers below them. Between the EPSPs "evoked" by depolarization is a spontaneous EPSP with the same quantum size

3-14 there are consecutively 2, 1, 3, 0 ... of these *"quanta"*. In the absence of neuronal stimulation, quanta can occur *spontaneously*. The number of quanta per stimulus varies stochastically about a mean, with a binomial distribution. It is practically certain that one such current quantum corresponds to the acetylcholine content of one vesicle, which reaches the postsynaptic receptors by diffusion and causes ion channels to open. One vesicle contains some tens of thousands of acetylcholine molecules.

The presynaptic terminals at the end plate extend over more than 1 mm, and in response to one action potential in the motor axon the entire ending releases a few hundred quanta, not individually detectable in the summed response. But between the ca. 40-mV end-plate potentials (Fig. 3-2) one can detect spontaneous potential changes smaller than 1 mV, which are produced by spontaneous quantum release, by opening of a vesicle.

Transmitters are stored in and released from vesicles not only at the neuromuscular synapse but at all other known chemical synapses. The quantal currents in Fig. 3-12, for instance, were produced by the release of glutamate from vesicles. Vesicles can contain the various transmitters in Fig. 3-7, usually only one of them at any given synapse. But it is possible for vesicles to contain both a classical transmitter, such as GABA, and a peptide with a modulating action (see p. 47).

Release of transmitter quanta. An action potential in the presynaptic terminal causes the nearly synchronous (there is a small synaptic delay) release of quanta of transmitter, which produce a potential (e.g., an EPSP) in the postsynaptic membrane. The temporal relationships are shown in Fig. 3-15 for a squid giant synapse; here it is possible to measure the potential changes and currents both pre- and postsynaptically. In addition to the action potential and the synaptic currents and potential, Fig. 3-15A shows the Ca^{2+} influx into the presynaptic ending, which accompanies the Na^{+} and K^{+} currents during depolarization (see p. 30). This **inward Ca^{2+} current** plays a key role in quantum release. It has long been known that *when the extracellular Ca^{2+} concentration, $[Ca^{2+}]_o$, is greatly reduced, chemical synaptic transmission is impaired.* The effect varies approximately as the 4th power of $[Ca^{2+}]_o$ [12], which implies that quantum release is produced by the combination of 4 Ca^{2+} with an activator on the inside of the membrane. But the activator seems also to be potential-dependent; that is, even with a sufficiently high intracellular Ca^{2+} concentration the membrane must be depolarized for synchronized release of transmitter to occur [31]. The effect of depolarization on the activator can be thought of

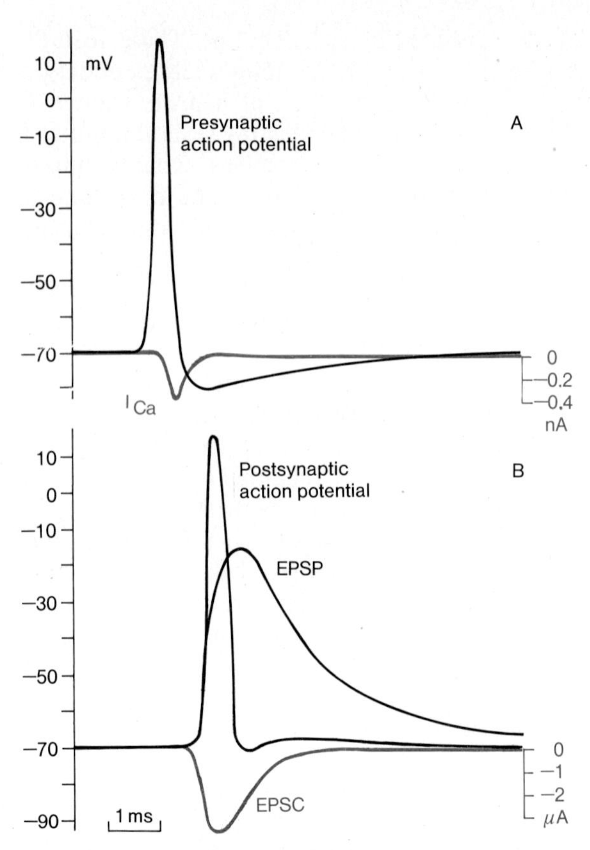

Fig. 3-15 A, B. Synaptic transmission at a squid giant synapse. **A** Presynaptic: time course of the action potential and the associated flow of Ca^{2+} into the nerve ending, I_{Ca}. **B** Postsynaptic: the postsynaptic current (EPSC, *red*), the postsynaptic potential (EPSP) and the action potential it triggers. (Modified from [24])

as resembling its effect on a channel molecule (Figs. 2-12 to 2-15). The presynaptic active zones with their vesicle-binding sites and membrane proteins ("particles") (Fig. 3-13) would thus be a device for the rapid control of exocytosis by depolarization and an increase in $[Ca^{2+}]_i$. The increased $[Ca^{2+}]_i$ could control contractile elements of the cytoskeleton (see p. 12, Fig. 1-13) or initiate the phosphorylation of enzymes (Fig. 1-16).

Synaptic facilitation. In the context of quantum release, we now turn to a synaptic mechanism similar in importance to *summation and inhibition*: synaptic **facilitation**. This process is illustrated in Fig. 3-16A. When one begins to stimulate a neuron terminal at a frequency of 20/s, the EPSP produced by the first stimulus is hardly visible, but as the series continues the EPSPs become progressively larger. That is, repeated activation increases the effectiveness of synaptic transmission. When the stimulus frequency is doubled (Fig. 3-16A, lower trace), the facilitating effect is greater. Moreover, because the EPSPs are so close together summation (Fig. 3-10) also occurs, raising the baseline from which the EPSPs begin.

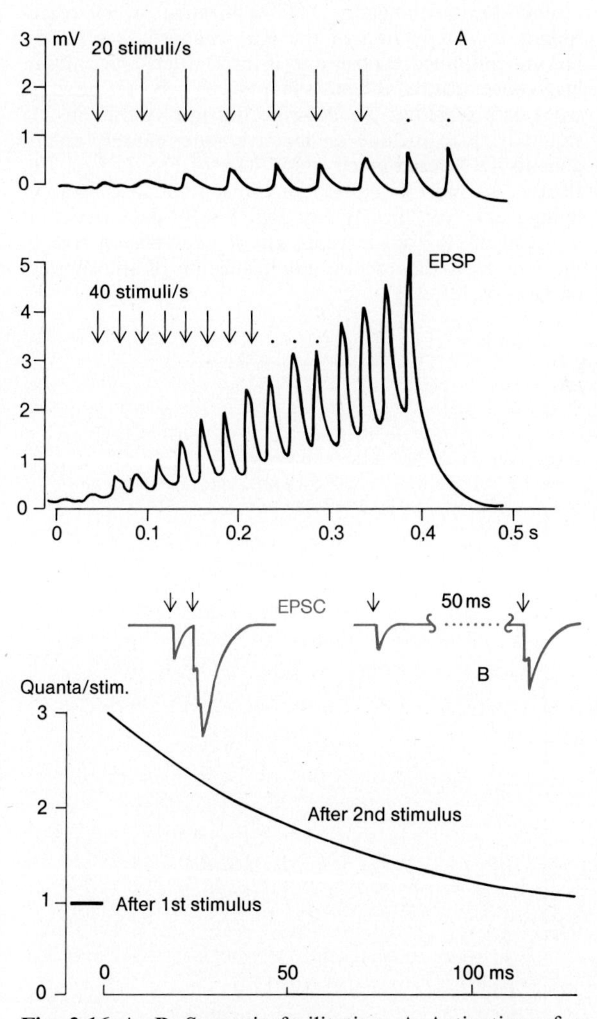

Fig. 3-16 A, B. Synaptic facilitation. **A** Activation of a presynaptic nerve fiber with 20 or 40 stimuli/s causes progressive enlargement of the EPSP, with partial temporal summation at 40/s. Facilitation within stimulus series is also called "tetanic potentiation". **B** When two stimuli are presented at various intervals (*abscissa*), the second EPSC is facilitated. Whereas the first EPSC on average consists of one quantum, a second after a short interval contains 3 quanta (see also *top left, red*), and after a longer interval, fewer quanta (e.g., *top right, red*, 50 ms interval)

Measurements of the synaptic currents show that the facilitated EPSCs are greater than the unfacilitated. As illustrated in Fig. 3-16B, during facilitation there is an increase in the average number of quanta released per stimulus. The facilitation is greatest when the second stimulus comes a few ms after the first, and attenuates with time constants of the order of 50 ms.

Because it increases the probability of release of transmitter quanta, this *facilitation is a presynaptic process*. Most authors consider it to be produced by **"residual calcium"**. While the terminal is depolarized, Ca^{2+} flows in and raises $[Ca^{2+}]_i$ (Fig. 3-15). The increased $[Ca^{2+}]_i$ is then returned to the resting level by transport and exchange processes. But as long as $[Ca^{2+}]_i$ remains above the resting level, at the next depolarization $[Ca^{2+}]_i$ begins to rise from an elevated baseline and therefore becomes greater than after the first depolarization. Because transmitter release is proportional to, e.g., the 4th power of $[Ca^{2+}]_i$, even very small relative increases in $[Ca^{2+}]_i$ produce considerable facilitation [20, 30].

Different synapses have different degrees of facilitation. Marked facilitation, as in Fig. 3-16, is particularly common at central synapses; here a single presynaptic action potential hardly causes one quantum to be released, whereas several impulses in rapid succession are much more effective. In facilitation the terminal has a form of "memory": for a few hundred ms it is affected by a preceding event. There are also synapses in which facilitation lasts for minutes. Synaptic facilitation is very probably the mechanism for a first step in short-term memory, from which longer-term memory processes can then develop (see Chapter 6).

When facilitation is brought about by relatively long series of action potentials, it is also called synaptic **potentiation**. The growth of the EPSP in the stimulus series of Fig. 3-16A is termed **tetanic potentiation**; the state of strong facilitation that persists after stimulation, and can last for several hours if stimulation was very prolonged, is **posttetanic potentiation**. It is likely that during such long series of stimuli the concentrations of other ions, such as Na^+, in the terminal increase along with $[Ca^{2+}]_i$. Another possible effect, mediated by an intracellular messenger, is to make vesicles available for transmitter release; that is, the *vesicles can be mobilized* [27].

Prolonged high-frequency excitation of the presynaptic endings can eventually produce the opposite of facilitation, **depression**. In this state, the number of transmitter quanta released per action potential is reduced. The actual causes are unclear; one possibility is that the supply of transmitter vesicles is used up. Furthermore, the endings usually branch before the synapses, and these branch points are weak spots for propagation of the action potential. The same amount of current that enters the fiber during excitation before the branch point must depolarize 2 fibers after it. During *high-frequency discharge*, therefore, it often happens that *the conduction of excitation into the branches is blocked*. These conduction blocks are also manifest as a depression of synaptic transmission. The depression caused by repeated activation of a synaptic pathway could also, in the form of **"habituation"** (a term borrowed from behavioral research, which means "becoming accustomed"), be a basis for processes of learning and memory.

Reaction of Transmitters with Postsynaptic Receptors

At the beginning of this chapter (Fig. 3-1) it was stated that a transmitter or agonist, A, reacts with a receptor, R, in the postsynaptic membrane and thereby causes a specific conductance change. This reaction is most simply described by the formula

$$R + nA \rightleftharpoons RA_n \rightleftharpoons (RA_n)^* \qquad (1)$$

where n is the number of agonist molecules that bind to a single receptor; the transition from RA_n to $(RA_n)^*$ represents the subsequent change in conductance or the *opening of a postsynaptic ion channel*. For many types of receptors n is greater than 1; for instance, it is about 2 at the end plate [32] and 4 or more at the glutamate synapses of Fig. 3-16A. When $n > 1$ the binding of the agonist to the receptor is **cooperative**, a condition in which the curve relating synaptic current I_s to agonist concentration (Fig. 3-17) rises very steeply. Above a "threshold concentration" of the agonist, glutamate in this case, the synaptic current increases very rapidly and saturates at about 3 times the threshold concentration. This large change in current over a narrow concentration range is necessary because the transmitters and some agonists also appear in the course of normal cell metabolism and are not uncommonly present, in low concentrations, in the interstitial fluid. The sharp transition from small to large current prevents low "noise levels" of the agonists from having an effect at the synapse; during the release of quanta, the concentrations in the synaptic cleft briefly reach the saturation range in Fig. 3-17.

Many reactions between transmitters and receptors also exhibit the phenomenon of **desensitization**, which corresponds to inactivation of the Na^+ channels (see p. 25). During continued exposure to a transmitter, especially in high concentration, the postsynaptic cell becomes progressively less sensitive. To describe desensitization, Eq. (1) would have to include an inactive state, entirely analogous to the "closed-inactivated" state of Fig. 2-13 (p. 29). Because at most synapses the transmitter concentration is high only very briefly (see Fig. 3-18B), desensitization is irrelevant to transmission, but it does play a role in the long-term therapeutic administration of transmitters or agonists [21, 32].

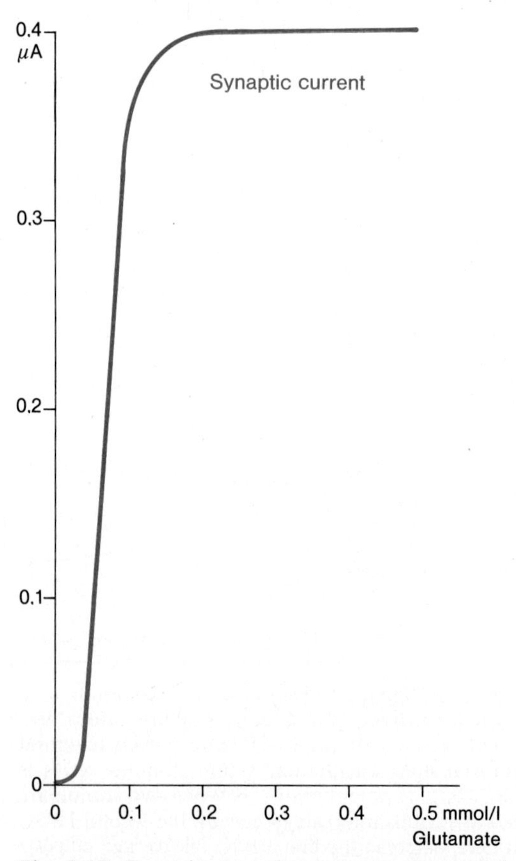

Fig. 3-17. Steep increase in postsynaptic current as the concentration of transmitter (glutamate, in this case) acting at the postsynaptic receptors rises. (Modified from [14])

Synaptic ion channels. So far we have been concerned only with specific conductance changes in the postsynaptic membrane, which occur when membrane receptors react with the transmitter. As discussed in Chapters 1 and 2, the conductance of the plasma membrane for ions is localized in channel proteins that allow specific ions to flow through an aqueous phase within the protein. As an example, a diagram of the protein of the Na^+ channel was presented (Fig. 2-15). The potential-dependence of the Na^+ channel is responsible for its gating function; similarly, in the channels of the chemical synapses the gate is opened by binding of the agonist to the receptor-channel complex. This macroprotein has been isolated for various receptor types, and for the acetylcholine receptor the complete amino acid sequence is known. The protein has a molecular weight of 258,000 and consists of 5 largely analogous subunits of about equal size, grouped around the central channel [29, 33]. For this channel, then, detailed discussions of the structure of the "channel wall" and of the agonist-binding site(s) in the subunits are possible [34]. The single-channel currents that produce the net synaptic current can also be resolved by patch-clamp recording (Fig. 3-18A), with the agonist in the lumen of the measurement electrode. The single-channel currents resemble those shown for Ca^{2+} in Fig. 2-14 (p. 31): the channel openings occur in groups, and there are long pauses between these "bursts". The different reaction steps in Eq. (1) reflect this grouping; the brief individual openings correspond to the reaction $RA_n \rightleftharpoons (RA_n)^*$, and the bursts are controlled by the reaction $R + nA \rightleftharpoons RA_n$ [11]. The single-channel current tends to be larger in the synaptic channels than in the potential-controlled channels. In the case of the glutamate-controlled channel, the channel current is −8 pA at the resting potential and increases in proportion to the distance of the membrane potential from the equilibrium potential (near 0 mV).

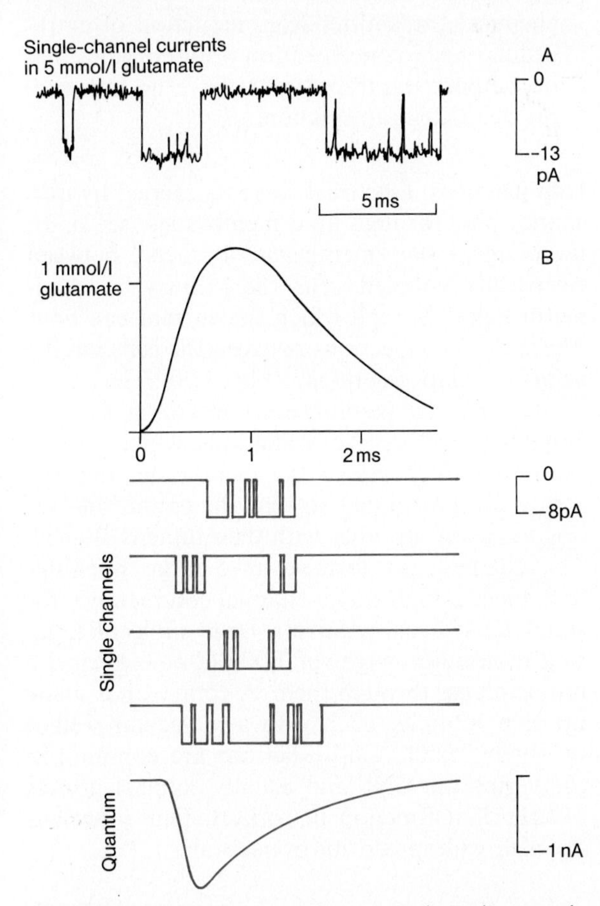

Fig. 3-18 A, B. Single-channel currents through transmitter-activated receptors. **A** Original recording with membrane patch clamp; the pipette contains 5 mmol/l glutamate. (Modified from [16]). **B** Diagram of transmission at a glutamatergic synapse. *Top:* time course of glutamate concentration after release of a "quantum" of glutamate from the presynaptic terminal (hypothetical). *Below it:* examples of the single-channel currents measured after such a glutamate pulse. *Bottom:* Sum of the single-channel currents: EPSC (one quantum)

Some of the synaptic channels that have been closely examined, particularly those controlled by acetylcholine and by glutamate (Fig. 3-18), have a more complex behavior [11, 16]. They have not just one open state with a particular conductance, but 2-4 such states, each with a different conductance. Furthermore, the grouping of open and closed times goes further in these channels than is described above and derivable from Eq. (1). To accommodate this, several additional states and reaction steps would have to be added to the formula. This complexity may be associated with the binding of several agonist molecules to subunits of the receptor-channel molecule.

The diagram in Fig. 3-18B summarizes the present view of the *time course of synaptic transmission at the single-channel level.* One quantum of transmitter (comprising tens of thousands of molecules) produces a transmitter concentration at the receptors that is high for a few ms and then rapidly diminishes. The initial rise in transmitter concentration increases the probability that channels will open, the openings being interrupted by brief closures. When the channel ultimately closes after a burst of openings, it usually does not reopen because after the mean duration of closure the transmitter concentration has become too low. The groups of channel openings summate to give a current quantum comprising several hundred single-channel currents. Because a quantum of transmitter almost always elicits only one burst of openings, the time constant of the decline of the synaptic current also nearly

corresponds to the mean duration of a burst of channel openings.
This molecular description of the transmitter mechanism concludes our discussion of chemical synaptic transmission. We now turn briefly to the electrical synaptic coupling of cells. This mechanism is not as closely related to the various pharmacological (and hence therapeutic) means of affecting the function of the nervous system and the control of other organs; but it may be that electrical synapses are about as common as chemical ones.

3.4 Electrical Synaptic Transmission

After the concept of chemical synaptic transmission had become generally accepted, between about 1930 and 1950, it came as a great surprise that synaptic transmission also occurs electrically [17]. The principle is shown in Fig. 3-19A. Two adjacent cells are in such close contact that the resistance to electrical current across the two cell membranes is of the same order of magnitude as that for currents through the remaining, exposed membrane area. If Cell 1 is excited, sodium current I_{Na} flows through the opened Na^+ channels into Cell 1. This current flows out of the cell through still unexcited parts of the membrane, and part of it crosses the membrane contacts and flows into Cell 2, which becomes depolarized. Of course, the depolarization is much less – say, 10% of the depolarization of Cell 1 (Fig. 3-19B). But this kind of electrically transmitted

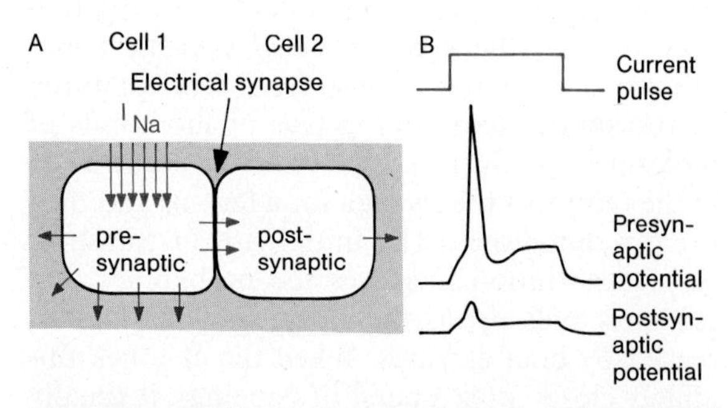

Fig. 3-19 A, B. Electrical synapse between Cell 1 and Cell 2. **A** Current distribution; *Cell 1* is excited and sodium current, I_{Na} flows in. There is a nexus (gap junction) betwen Cells 1 and 2. Part of the current entering Cell 1 flows through the nexus into Cell 2, which it depolarizes. **B** A current pulse (*red*) into the presynaptic cell generates an electrotonic potential which triggers an action potential in this cell. The potential that appears in the postsynaptic cell, having been conducted across the nexus, is a smaller reproduction of the presynaptic potential

depolarization can be above the threshold for triggering an action potential in Cell 2. Often it is subthreshold, and in this case Cell 2 can be excited only by summation with synaptic potentials produced by chemical or electrical transmission from other cells [8].
To recapitulate, the basic characteristics that distinguish chemical from electrical synaptic transmission are the following.

1. In *chemical* synaptic transmission the postsynaptic current is generated by the opening of channels in the *postsynaptic* membrane, and the current is driven by the ion gradients of the *postsynaptic cell.*
2. By contrast, in *electrical* synaptic transmission the *source of the postsynaptic current* is in the membrane of the *presynaptic cell.* There is no transmitter at electrical synapses, and all the factors that affect the release and action of a chemical transmitter (e.g., reduction of extracellular Ca^{2+} concentration or of enzymes that decompose the transmitter) have no influence on electrical transmission.

Gap junctions. Electrical currents carried by ions cannot pass through lipid membranes (see p. 3); therefore at the "membrane contacts" between electrically coupled cells there must be channel proteins through which the current can flow. These close connections between the cells are the **nexus** or "gap junctions" (Fig. 3-20). Here each of the two cell membranes contains a regular, closely-spaced array of **connexons**, which occupy the entire thickness of the membrane; the two arrays are positioned so that the connexons are oppposite one another with their lumens aligned. The channels so formed have large openings and hence a high single-channel conductance for small ions; even relatively large molecules, up to a molecular weight of 1,000 (diameter ca. 1.5 nm) can pass through them. A connexon is made up of 6 subunits, each with a molecular weight of about 25,000. Gap junctions are common in the vertebrate CNS and usually connect groups of cells that function in concert. Gap junctions are also widespread in invertebrates.

Functional syncytia. Cells in tissues other than the nervous system are also very frequently coupled by gap junctions [25]. In the context of transmission of excitation, those most worthy of mention are in the **heart muscle** and **smooth musculature**, in which the linkage by gap junctions creates a functional syncytium. In these tissues the excitation passes from cell to cell, with no vis-

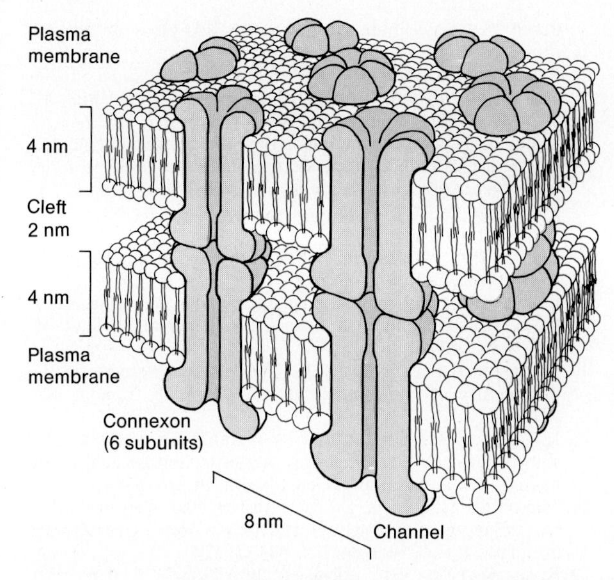

Fig. 3-20. Fine structure of a nexus (gap junction). Embedded in the membrane of the pre- and postsynaptic cells is a regular array of "connexons", exactly aligned with one another. There is a lumen within the connexon, so that each pair of opposed connexons provides a channel through which the two cells communicate. (Modified from [28])

ible pause or reduction in amplitude of the action potential at the cell boundaries (see Chapters 4 and 19). For these organs it is important that the gap junctions be controllable, and in fact *the channels close when the pH falls or the Ca^{2+} concentration rises.* As a result, closure always occurs when cells are injured or undergo severe metabolic deficiencies. This mechanism isolates the damaged places from the rest of the functional syncytium, so that in case of a cardiac infarct, for instance, spreading of the damage is restricted. In addition to these excitable tissues, there are many others – all epithelia, for instance, and the liver – in which cells are connected by gap junctions. For cells to be so connected is actually the original state; in small embryos all the cells are joined by gap junctions, and it is not until the organs differentiate that these intercellular connections are lost.

The role of the gap junctions in inexcitable cells is unclear. They enable the exchange of many small molecules, which could have significance in metabolism. Intracellular second messengers (see p. 15) could also diffuse through the gap junctions, carrying control signals for cellular processes through a tissue.
In view of the widespread occurrence of gap junctions, it seems curious that they are not more commonly employed in the nervous system for synaptic transmission. Evidently the more elaborate chemical synapses provide so much more specific and controllable intercellular communication that they have largely replaced the electrical synapses.

Inhibitory electrical synapses. The gap junction is by far the most common electrical synapse. But other mechanisms do exist; for example, inhibition can also be transmitted electrically. Here the action potential in specially arranged presynaptic fibers drives the local potential in the extracellular space around a postsynaptic axon so far positive that the action potential in the axon no longer reaches threshold and conduction is blocked [18].

Ephaptic transmission. There are various diseases in which axons are damaged. When an axon is transected not only does the peripheral piece degenerate; the proximal stump of the axon does so as well. Weeks later the axon regenerates in the peripheral nervous system, but when it first sprouts out it is unmyelinated. In **neuropathies** of various origins, too, axons lose their myelin sheaths, becoming *demyelinated.* Furthermore, there are *axonal neuropathies* in which the main symptom is probably impaired axonal transport (see p. 13).
Demyelinated axons are particularly subject to anomalous interactions. Impulses conducted in groups of nerve fibers induce excitation of other axons running in parallel. This "cross-talk" between neighboring axons is called **ephaptic transmission** [9]. When such anomalous action potentials are generated in sensory nerve fibers, the patient notices an anomalous sensation. **Paresthesias** of this kind can be agonizing, especially when nociceptive fibers (see p. 229) are involved and produce pain syndromes such as neuralgia, causalgia and neuroma pain. Cross-talk between axons can result not only from insufficient insulation (i.e., by myelin sheaths) but also from axonal hyperexcitability.

3.5 References

Textbooks and Handbooks

1. Cooke, I., Lipkin, M.: Cellular neurophysiology, a source book. New York: Holt, Rinehart and Winston (1972) (Collection of important original papers)
2. Eccles, J.C.: The physiology of synapses. Berlin-Göttingen-Heidelberg-New York: Springer (1964)
3. Hille, B.: Ionic channels of excitable membranes. Sunderland, Mass.: Sinauer Assoc., (1984)
4. Hoppe, W., Lohmann, W., Markl, H., Ziegler, H. (eds.): Biophysik. Berlin, Heidelberg, New York: Springer (1984)
5. Kandel, E.R., Schwartz, J.H. (eds.): Principles of neural science. New York, Amsterdam, Oxford: Elsevier (1985)

6. KUFFLER, S.W., NICHOLLS, J.G., MARTIN, A.R.: From neuron to brain, Second Edition Sunderland, Mass., Sinauer Associates (1984)
7. SCHIEBLER, T.H., SCHMIDT, W.: Lehrbuch der gesamten Anatomie des Menschen, 3rd Edition, Berlin-Heidelberg-New York-Tokyo, Springer Verlag (1983)

Original Papers and Reviews

8. BENNETT, M.L.V.: Electrical transmission: a functional analysis and comparison with chemical transmission. In: Cellular biology of neurons, Vol. 1, Sect. 1, Handbook of Physiology: The Nervous System. E.R. KANDEL ed., 357–416. Baltimore: Williams and Wilkins (1977)
9. BLUMBERG, H., JÄNIG, W.: Activation of fibers via experimentally produced stump neuromas of skin nerves: ephaptic transmission or retrograde sprouting? Experimental Neurology **76**, 468–482 (1982)
10. COLQUHOUN, D., DREYER, F., SHERIDAN, R.E.: The actions of tubocurarine at the frog neuromuscular junction. J. Physiol. (Lond.), **293**, 247–284 (1979)
11. COLQUHOUN, D., SAKMANN, B.: Fast events in single-channel currents activated by acetylcholine and its analogues at the frog muscle end-plate. J. Physiol. (Lond.), **369**, 501–557 (1985)
12. DODGE, F.A., RAHAMIMOFF, R.: Co-operative action of calcium ions in transmitter release at the neuromuscular junction. J. Physiol. (Lond.), **193**, 419–432 (1967)
13. DUDEL, J.: The mechanism of presynaptic inhibition at the crayfish neuromuscular junction. Pflügers Arch. **248**, 66–80 (1965)
14. DUDEL, J.: Dose-response curve of glutamate applied by superfusion to crayfish muscle synapses. Pflügers Arch. **368**, 49–54 (1977)
15. DUDEL, J. KUFFLER, S.W.: Presynaptic inhibition at the crayfish neuromuscular junction. J. Physiol. (Lond.), **155**, 543–562 (1961)
16. FRANKE, C., DUDEL, J.: High-resolution measurements of single-channel currents activated by glutamate in crayfish muscle. Neurosci. Lett., **59**, 241–246 (1985)
17. FURSHPAN, E.J., POTTER, D.: Transmission at the giant motor synapses of the crayfish. J. Physiol. (Lond.) **145**:289–325 (1959)
18. FURUKAWA, T., FURSHPAN, E.J.: Two inhibitory mechanisms in the Mauthner neurons of goldfish. J. Neurophysiol. **26**:140–176 (1963)
19. ITO, Y., MILEDI, R., VINCENT A., NEWSOM-DAVIS, J.: Acetylcholine receptors and end-plate electrophysiology in myasthenia gravis. Brain, **101**, 345–368 (1978)
20. KATZ, B., MILEDI, R.: The role of calcium in neuromuscular facilitation. J. Physiol. (Lond.), **195**, 481–492 (1968)
21. KATZ, B., THESLEFF, S.: A study of the 'desensitization' produced by acetylcholine at the motor end-plate. J. Physiol. (Lond.), **138**, 63–80 (1957)
22. KUFFLER, S.W.: Slow synaptic responses in autonomic ganglia and the pursuit of a peptidergic transmitter. J. Exp. Biol. **89**, 257–286 (1980)
23. LIBET, B.: Heterosynaptic interaction at a sympathetic neuron as a model for induction and storage of a postsynaptic memory trace. Neurobiology of Learning and Memory, G. LYNCH, J.L. MCGAUGH, N.M. WEINBERGER, editors, 405–430. New York, The Guilford Press (1984)
24. LLINÁS, R.R.: Calcium in synaptic transmission. Sci. Amer. **10**, 38–48 (1982)
25. LOEWENSTEIN, W.R.: Junctional intercellular communication: the cell-to-cell membrane channel. Physiological Reviews, **61**, 829–913 (1981)
26. MAGLEBY, K.L., STEVENS, C.F.: The effect of voltage on the time course of end-plate currents. J. Physiol. (Lond.), **223**, 151–171 (1972)
27. MAGLEBY, K.L., ZENGEL, J.E.: A quantitative description of stimulation-induced changes in transmitter release at the frog neuromuscular junction. J. Gen. Physiol. **80**, 613–638 (1982)
28. MAKOWSKI, L., CASPAR, D.L.D., PHILLIPS, W.C., GOODENOUGH, D.A.: Gap junction structures. II. Analysis of the X-ray diffraction data. J. Cell. Biol. **84**: 629–645 (1977)
29. NUMA, S., NODA, M., TAKAHASHI, H., TANABE, T., TOYOSATO, M., FURUTANI, Y., KIKYOTONI, S.: Molecular structure of the nicotinic acetylcholine receptor. Cold Spring Harbor Symposia Quant. Biol. XLVIII, 57–69 (1983)
30. PARNAS, H., DUDEL, J., PARNAS, I.: Neurotransmitter release and its facilitation in crayfish. 1. Saturation kinetics of release, and of entry and removal of calcium. Pflügers Arch. **393**:1–14 (1982)
31. PARNAS, H., DUDEL, J., PARNAS, I.: Neurotransmitter release and its facilitation in crayfish. VII. Another voltage dependent process beside Ca entry controls the time course of phasic release. Pflügers Arch. **406**:121–130 (1986)
32. PEPER, K., BRADLEY, R.J., DREYER, F.: The acetylcholine receptor at the neuromuscular junction. Physiol. Rev. **62**, 1271–1340 (1982)
33. POPOT, J.L., CHANGEUX, J.P.: Nicotinic receptor of acetylcholine: structure of an oligomeric integral membrane protein. Physiol. Rev. **64**, 1162–1239 (1984)
34. SAKMANN, B., METHFESSEL, C., MISHINA, M., TAKAHASHI, T., TAKAI, T., KURASAKI, M., FUKUDA, K., NUMA, S.: Role of acetylcholine receptor subunits in gating of the channel. Nature **318**: 538–543 (1985)
35. SCHMIDT, R.F.: Presynaptic inhibition in the vertebrate central nervous system. Ergebn. Physiol., 63, Springer Verlag, Berlin-Heidelberg-New York (1971)
36. WHITE, J.D., STEWART, K.D., KRAUSE, J.E., MCKELVY, J.F.: Biochemistry of peptide-secreting neurons. Physiol. Rev. **65**, 553–606 (1985)

II
Motor and Integrative Functions of the Nervous System; Muscle Physiology

4 Muscle

J.C. RÜEGG

It is only by contracting their muscles that people can interact with their environment. The movements so produced are required for the simplest manual tasks as well as to convey the most subtle thoughts and feelings – by speaking or writing, for instance, or by facial expression and gesture. These muscles constitute by far the most massive organ in the human body, accounting for 40-50% of its weight. Muscles are "machines" that contract by converting chemical energy directly into mechanical energy (work) and heat. The way the muscle machine operates – in particular, the mechanism of shortening and force development – can now be explained in considerable detail at the molecular level and on the basis of physical and chemical laws.

4.1 The Molecular Mechanism of Contraction

A gram of skeletal muscle contains about 100 mg of "contractile proteins." The way in which these proteins – **actin** (molecular weight 42,000) and **myosin** (molecular weight about 500,000) – interact during the elementary event in muscle contraction is described by the sliding-filament theory of HUXLEY and HANSON [11–14].

Sliding-Filament Theory

The contractile proteins actin and myosin form the thin and thick myofilaments in the myofibrils. They are arranged in parallel within the muscle cell, as shown in Fig. 4-1, a schematic drawing of a tiny part of a human muscle fiber. The drawing also shows one of the mitochondria (or sarcosomes) lying between the myofibrils, and part of the system of transverse and longitudinal tubules (the function of which is treated in Section 4.2). Myofibrils are contractile bundles of filaments about 1 μm in diameter; partitions called *Z-disks* subdivide them into many compartments ca. 2.5 μm long, the sarcomers.

The structure of the sarcomeres is illustrated, highly schematically, in Fig. 4-1. In the light microscope one sees a regular sequence of light and dark bands across the sarcomeres; according to HUXLEY and HANSON [11], this **cross-striation** of the myofibrils results from a particularly regular arrangement of the actin and myosin filaments. In the middle of each sarcomere lie some thousand *"thick" filaments* of myosin, each with a diameter of ca. 10 nm. At either end of the sarcomere are about 2,000 *"thin" (5 nm thick) filaments* of actin, attached to the Z-disks like the bristles of a brush. The bundle of regularly arrayed, 1.6-μm-long myosin filaments in the middle of the sarcomere appears in the light microscope as a dark stripe 1.6 μm wide; because it is birefringent in polarized light (i.e., anisotropic) it is called the A-band. On either side of the *A-bands* are regions containing only thin filaments,

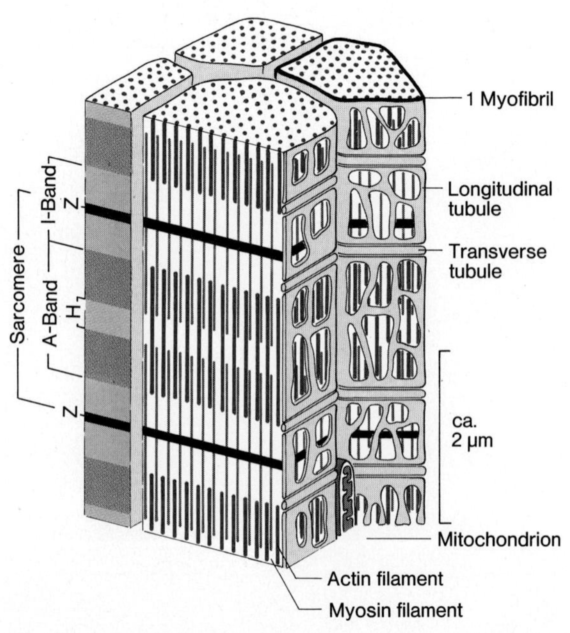

Fig. 4-1. Part of a human skeletal-muscle fiber, schematized from GARAMVÖLGYI

which therefore appear light; these isotropic *I-bands* extend to the Z-lines. It is this periodically repeated alternation of light and dark bands in countless sarcomeres that gives the myofibrils of cardiac and skeletal muscle fibers their striated appearance.
In the resting muscle the ends of the thick and thin filaments usually overlap only slightly at the boundary between the A-and I-bands. The zone of overlap in the A-band appears distinctly darker in the light microscope than the central zone, the *H-zone*, in which there are no actin filaments. Many electron micrographs of this zone reveal a very narrow, dark *M-line* in the middle of the sarcomere, a meshwork of supporting proteins that evidently holds the bundle of thick filaments together in the middle.

Shortening of the sarcomeres. The muscle shortens as a result of the shortening of countless sarcomeres connected "in series" in the myofibrils. By comparing the schematic structure of a sarcomere in two different functional states (Fig. 4-2), one can see how the striation and the myofilament arrangement change during contraction. During shortening the thin filaments of actin slide over the thick filaments of myosin, moving between them toward the middle of the bundle and of the sarcomere.
Fig. 4-2 illustrates a basic feature of the *sliding-filament theory* – that during the sliding process neither the myosin nor the actin filaments themselves shorten. This property gives rise to the light-microscope observation that the width of the A-bands (1.6 μm) remains constant during contraction, whereas the I- and H-bands become narrower.
Nor does the filament length change when the muscle is stretched. Rather, the bundle of thin filaments is pulled further out of the array of thick filaments, so that the amount of overlap decreases.
Now, how is the "opposed sliding" of the actin filaments in adjacent half sarcomeres brought about?

Operation of the cross-bridges. The myosin filament sends out transverse processes, the ca. 20-nm-long heads of about 150 myosin molecules; these form a bipolar array along the filament as shown in Fig. 4-3 A. During the contraction process each myosin head, or **cross-bridge,** can link the myosin filament to an adjacent actin filament (Fig. 4-3 A). By a tilting movement of the heads they join forces to "row" the actin filaments toward the middle of the sarcomere. The bipolar arrangement of the myosin molecules in the two halves of a sarcomere in itself makes possible the opposite direction (arrows) of sliding of the actin filaments in the left and right halves of the sarcomere.
A single rotational movement of the cross-bridges on an actin filament would shorten an individual sarcomere by only 2 × 10 nm, ca. 1% of its length. The sarcomeres of frog muscle fibrils during *isotonic contraction* shorten by as much as 0.4 μm, or 20% of their length, in a tenth of a second. To achieve this, the cross-bridges would have to perform the rowing motion just described not once in this time span, but 20 times. Only the

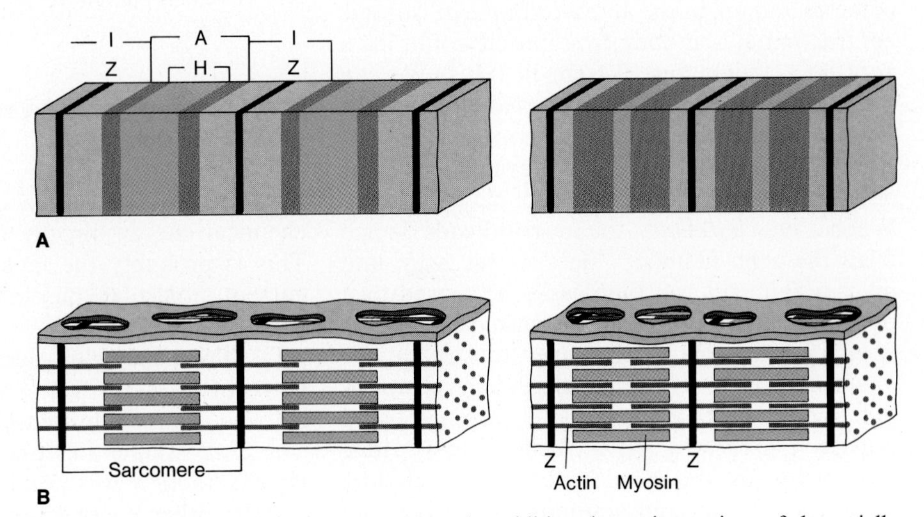

Fig. 4-2. **A** Banded structure of the myofibrils. *Left*, relaxed; *right*, contracted. **B** Arrangement of the myosin and the actin filaments in the relaxed and contracted sarcomere. Note the additive shortening actions of the serially arranged sarcomeres. (Modified from [11])

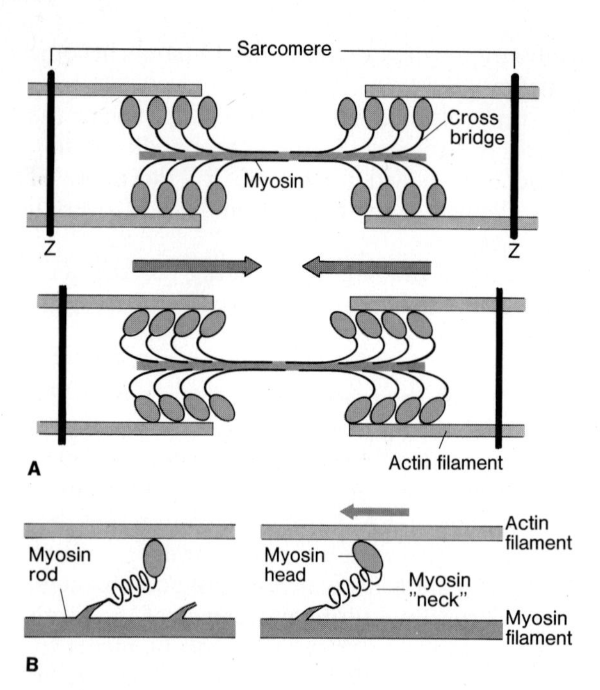

Fig. 4-3 A, B. Cross-bridge function. **A** Model of the way motion is produced: myosin filament with cross-bridges on adjacent actin filament; above before, below after the (actually asynchronous) "rowing strokes" of the bridges [2]. **B** Model [10] of force production by a cross-bridge; left before, right after a bridge "stroke". The cross-bridge corresponds chemically to the myosin subfragment "heavy meromyosin", which consists of subfragment I (myosin head) and subfragment II (myosin neck)

repeated release and reattachment of the myosin heads would eventually row or pull the actin filament to the middle of the sarcomere – rather as a long piece of rope is pulled in, hand over hand, by a team of men. Because the minimal shortenings of the myofibrils in a series of sarcomeres add up, in the above example of isotonic contraction a 2-cm-long frog muscle could lift a very light weight just 0.4 cm in 0.1 s. We can see that when the *rope-pulling principle* takes the form of countless sarcomeres connected in series, the repeated molecular movements of the cross-bridges result in a macroscopic movement. When a *muscle relaxes*, the myosin heads detach from the actin filaments. Because the actin and myosin filaments can then easily be moved past one another, the resistance of relaxed muscles to stretch is very low. A shortened muscle can be stretched back to its resting length by even a very light weight. During relaxation, then, lengthening is passive. Recently, the molecular cross-bridge movements just described have been detected by means of an X-ray diffraction method (roentgen small-angle scattering from contracted muscle at ms time resolution [14]).

The production of muscular force. Thanks to the elasticity of the cross-bridges, a sarcomere can develop force even if the filaments do not slide past one another – that is, under strictly isometric experimental conditions [10]. Fig. 4-3 B illustrates *isometric force production* by a cross-bridge. First the head of the myosin molecule (cross-bridge) attaches to the actin filament at right angles. Then it rotates about an angle of ca. 45°, perhaps because of the attraction of nearby attachment points on the myosin head and the actin filament. In so doing it acts like a miniature lever, to put the internal elastic structure of the cross-bridge (possibly the "neck" part between the myosin head and the myosin filament) under tension. The resulting elastic stretching amounts to only about 10 nm. The elastic pull exerted by a single cross-bridge is so slight that at least a billion cross-bridges connected "in parallel" would have to combine their spring forces to develop 1 mN of muscular force. Here the cross-bridges of the myosin filaments pull on the neighboring actin filaments with (additively) combined forces, like a team of men on a rope.
Even in isometric contraction the cross-bridges should not be regarded as being in an uninterrupted state of tension (this happens only in rigor mortis; see below). Rather, a single myosin head releases the actin filament after only a hundredth or tenth of a second; but the recovery pause is equally short, and is followed by renewed attachment to the actin filament. Despite the rhythmic alternation between cross-bridge attachment and detachment, at a frequency of something like 5–50 Hz, the force exerted by the muscle does not oscillate in physiological conditions (with the exception of oscillating insect muscles), because from a statistical viewpoint about the same number of cross-bridges are in the attached, tension-producing state at each moment.

Maintenance heat. A muscle maintaining a certain contractile tension under isometric conditions differs from a muscle shortening isotonically in that the former does no external work (for the product of force times distance is zero). But in each attach/detach cycle of the cross-bridges internal work is done to stretch the elastic cross-bridge structures, and this is degraded to heat upon detachment. The maintenance heat (or "internal work") during a given period of time is greater, the greater the number and the higher the stroke frequency of the rowing cross-bridges, as ATP is steadily consumed.

The Chemomechanical Energy Transformations

How can the muscle machine efficiently convert chemical energy directly to mechanical energy? This is probably the most burning question in current molecular muscle research.

ATP, direct source of energy for contraction. The correctness of this claim is no longer in doubt, since the hydrolytic splitting of ATP into adenosine diphosphate and phosphate during muscular contraction was demonstrated directly [15]. All the other energy-providing reactions in the muscle – for example, the aerobic and anaerobic breakdown of carbohydrates and the decompo-

Table 4-1. The direct and indirect energy sources in human skeletal muscle [2]

Energy source	Amount (μmol/g muscle)	Energy-providing reaction
Adenosine triphosphate (ATP)	5	ATP → ADP+P_i
Creatine phosphate (PC)	11	PC+ADP⇌ATP+C
Glucose units in glycogen	84	Anaerobic: breakdown *via* pyruvate lactate (glycosis)
		Aerobic: breakdown *via* pyruvate to CO_2 and H_2O
Triglycerides	10	Oxidation to CO_2 and H_2O

ADP=adenosine diphosphate, C=creatine, P_i = inorganic phosphate

sition of creatine phosphate – cannot be considered as direct sources of energy for the muscle machine; it is clear that they serve only to regenerate continually the real fuel of the machine, ATP. These metabolic processes are treated extensively in biochemical textbooks, so that a brief summary (Table 4-1) will suffice here. Only if the reconstitution of ATP is prevented by appropriate metabolic poisons can the rate of ATP consumption during a contraction be monitored directly [15]. Isolated frog muscles frozen very rapidly with liquid nitrogen at the peak of a stimulus-induced isotonic twitch contain on the average only 2.6 μmol ATP per gram wet weight, whereas unstimulated control muscles contain 2.9 μmol. Taking the place of the ATP that has been consumed is an equivalent amount (0.3 μmol) of the reaction products adenosine diphosphate and phosphate. Thus the 0.3 μmol ATP split during a twitch has provided the energy for the isotonic contraction and the heat produced in the process.

ATP is split hydrolytically and thus utilized energetically in the muscle by an *ATPase*, the enzyme *myosin* – a process activated by *actin*. Actin and myosin, of course, are the protein structures directly involved in the mechanical process of contraction, and ATP, with a single exception (rare nucleoside triphosphates), is the only substance in the muscle that can be utilized directly by the contractile proteins. WEBER and PORTZEHL succeeded in spinning gel-like contractile threads of actin and myosin *(actomyosin threads)*, which contract like living muscles with ATP and only ATP as the energy source [19]. This too is evidence that ATP is the direct source of energy for muscle contraction.

ATP consumption during contraction. Today we know that the myosin heads, which react with actin, themselves contain the catalytically active centers for the splitting of ATP. The ATPase of myosin is activated by actin in the presence of magnesium ions. Therefore under physiological ionic conditions – that is, in the presence of **magnesium ions** – ATP is always split to *liberate* ADP and phosphate only when the myosin head attaches to its activator actin. (Without actin the ADP that is formed is not liberated but rather blocks, for a matter of seconds, the catalytic center of the myosin and thus the continued splitting of ATP.) In each attach/detach cycle of a cross-bridge ATP is split once and only once (probably one molecule ATP per cross-bridge). This means that the more cross-bridges are active, the greater the rate of ATP splitting and the force of the muscle; therefore the ATP-splitting rate (or metabolic rate) and the force produced by the muscle are usually proportional to one another.

Muscles can contract more rapidly, the more rapidly their cross-bridges move – that is, the more rowing strokes they make per unit time. As a result, fast muscles consume more ATP (or energy) per unit time than slow muscles, and are less conservative of energy during tonic load-bearing. For a maintained postural function we therefore use chiefly the slow muscle fibers (type-I-fibers), rich in myoglobin, whereas the myoglobin-poor "white" muscle fibers (type-IIB) or the reddish type-IIA fibers are used for rapid movements.

Mode of action of ATP. The mechanism by which the energy donor ATP drives the rowing cross-bridges is the subject of intensive research [10, 13, 17]. Probably a molecule of ATP is bound to the cross-bridge when its "rowing stroke" is completed, and thus provides energy for the separation of the reaction partners actin and myosin. Almost immediately thereafter the myosin heads detach from the actin, and the ATP is split into the products ADP and phosphate. These products of ATP hydrolysis remain bound briefly to the catalytic center, a prerequisite for the next reattachment of the cross-bridge to the actin, and the subsequent force-generating "rowing stroke", during which the ADP and phosphate are liberated. Then a new molecule of ATP must bind to the cross-bridge before cross-bridge detachment and ATP hydrolysis can occur, beginning a new cycle. Only as long as ATP continues to be hydrolyzed – that is, as long as ATPase is activated – is cyclic cross-bridge activity possible, the repeated attachment and release of the bridges that produce muscle contraction. If the splitting of ATP is inhibited, the bridges cannot reattach, the resistance to stretch and the force of the muscle fibers fall to zero, and the muscle **relaxes**. After death the ATP level in the muscle cells falls; when it becomes lower than a criti-

Table 4-2. Action of ATP on the contractile structures in muscle fibers and the *actin-myosin interaction*

ATP:	absent	present but not split	present, split by ATPase
State of muscle fiber:	rigid	relaxed	contracted
Myosin cross-bridges:	attached to actin	detached from actin	alternately attached and detached
ATPase:	–	inhibited[a]	active[b]

[a] Ca^{2+} less than 10^{-7} mol/l
[b] Ca^{2+} ca. 10^{-6}–10^{-5} mol/l

cal limit the cross-bridges become permanently (until autolysis) attached to the actin filament. In this state the actin and myosin filaments are rigidly connected to one another; the muscle is in **rigor mortis**. The analysis of the conditions for the states of contraction, rigor and relaxation (Table 4-2) is based on studies of "isolated contractile systems" [19].

In order to analyze the role of ATP in contraction and relaxation, WEBER et al. [19] first removed all the intrinsic ATP from single muscle fibers (for example, by extraction with aqueous glycerol solutions, which make the cell membrane permeable to ATP). Such glycerol-extracted ATP-free fibers are in rigor, but when they are immersed in an ATP-containing solution they become soft and stretchable again. When ATPase activity is inhibited, however, extracted ATP-containing muscle fibers are always relaxed; they, like the above-mentioned artificial actomyosin threads, contract only when the ATPase is activated. Renewed ATPase inhibition again causes relaxation of the "fiber model."

4.2 The Regulation of Muscle Contraction

Muscles are ordinarily excited by the action potentials of the innervating motoneurons, which – via neuromuscular transmission at the end plates (cf. p. 43) – elicit muscle action potentials (indirect muscle stimulation). Muscle fibers can also be *stimulated directly*, but only under experimental conditions. For example, when an isolated frog muscle is stimulated by a single electrical pulse lasting ca. 1 ms, after ca. 1–2 ms a (conducted) *action potential* passes from the site of stimulation over the muscle fiber with a velocity of ca. 2 m/s; a few ms later the muscle fiber *twitches* (cf. Fig. 4-8). It is thus the action potential, or the excitation of the fiber membrane, that triggers contraction.

Table 4-3. Sequence of events in production of a twitch

1. Stimulation of muscle fiber
2. Action potential (membrane excitation)
3. Excitation-contraction coupling
   a. Conduction of excitation in T-system
   b. Release of calcium from the longitudinal system (Fig. 4-5)
   c. Action of calcium on myofibrils (Fig. 4-4)
4. Contraction of the myofibrils: cyclic cross-bridge activity

Excitation-Contraction Coupling

The transmission of the signal to contract, from the excited cell membrane to the myofibrils in the depths of the cell (excitation-contraction coupling), requires several sequential processes (Table 4-3) in which calcium ions play a key role [2a].

Site and mode of Ca^{2+} action. Intracellular injection of calcium ions causes contraction of the muscle fibers. However, intact living muscle fibers are less well suited for demonstration of direct calcium effect on the myofibrils than fibers with the external cell membrane removed or destroyed. This can be done mechanically by "skinning" them, by means of detergents, or by the glycerol-extraction procedure mentioned above. *Skinned or extracted fibers* contract only when immersed in an ATP-containing bath that also contains at least 10^{-6} mol/l *ionized calcium* to activate the ATPase. Under these conditions the cross-bridges of the myosin filaments, by continually splitting ATP, can react cyclically with the actin filaments. If the activating agent, the ionized calcium, is withdrawn (for example, by adding calcium-chelating substances) the myofibrils **relax,** because the interaction between cross-bridges and actin is prevented and therefore ATPase activity is inhibited (cf. Table 4-2). This relaxation effect is also completely reversible in experiments with extracted fibers. When the Ca^{2+} concentration is raised in steps from 10^{-7} mol/l to 10^{-5} mol/l, the extracted fibers respond with a graded increase in contractile force and in ATPase activity, both of which become maximal at concentrations of 10^{-6} to 10^{-5} mol/l.

The **mechanism** by which calcium ions activate the fiber can be better understood by considering the structure of the actin filaments (Fig. 4-4). About 1 μm long and 5–7 nm thick, the actin

filament consists of two chains of beadlike 5-nm-thick actin monomers twisted together. This structure is well illustrated by taking two strings of beads and winding them together into a "spiral" with 14 beads in each turn (Fig. 4-4A). At regular intervals of ca. 40 nm the actin chains bear spherical *troponin molecules,* and threads of *tropomyosin* run along the grooves between the two chains. Studies using the X-ray diffraction method (röntgen small-angle scattering) [13] have shown that in the absence of calcium ions – that is, in the relaxed state of myofibrils – the tropomyosin threads are positioned such as to block the attachment of myosin cross-bridges to the actin strands. Under the influence of the activating calcium ions the tropomyosin threads slip deeper into the grooves between the actin strands, exposing the sites of attachment of the myosin cross-bridges. As a result, the myosin bridges attach to the actin filaments (Fig. 4-4B), split ATP and develop muscular force.
These activation effects are elicited by an action of calcium on troponin, such that the latter functions as a sort of *"calcium switch"*. By binding with calcium ions the troponin molecule is deformed in such a way that it "pushes", figuratively speaking, the tropomyosin into the groove in the double strand of actin – into the "activated position."

Storage and release of calcium ions. Relaxed muscles contain over 1 μmol of calcium per gram wet weight. If the calcium salts were not locked away in special intracellular storage regions, the calcium-rich muscle fibers would be permanently contracted.
The structure of the intracellular systems for calcium storage varies somewhat in different muscles (for human skeletal muscle see Fig. 4-1; for frog muscle see Fig. 4-5). At many positions on the muscle cell the outer membrane is invaginated into the fiber along a line perpendicular to the long axis of the fiber, forming a tube; this *system of transverse tubules (T-system)* communicates with the extracellular space. The tubules (diameter 50 nm) usually surround the single myofibrils at the level of the Z-disks (frog muscle) or in the region of the I-bands (muscles of higher vertebrates).
Perpendicular to the transverse system – that is, parallel to the myofibrils – there is a *longitudinal system* of tubules (the actual *sarcoplasmic reticulum).* The vesicles at the ends of these tubules, the *terminal cisternae*, are closely apposed to the membranes of the transverse system, forming a *triad structure.* It is in these vesicles that the intracellular calcium is stored. In contrast to the transverse system, the longitudinal system does not communicate with the extracellular space. The membranes of the sarcoplasmic reticulum contain an ATP-driven calcium pump, which actively transports Ca^{2+} from the myoplasm to the interior of the longitudinal system, thereby reducing the myoplasmic Ca^{2+} concentration to about 10^{-7} mol/l in resting (relaxed) muscle.
Excitation-contraction coupling is brought about by the spread of the action potential along the membranes of the transverse system, to the interior of the cell. In this way the excitation rapidly invades the depths of the fiber, jumps across to the longitudinal system and ultimately causes the calcium ions stored in the terminal cisternae to be released into the intracellular fluid around the myofibrils, initiating a contraction (Fig. 4-5).
In a single twitch, contraction soon ceases (Fig. 4-8); **muscle relaxtion** occurs when the activating Ca^{2+} ions are returned by the calcium pump to the channel system of the sarcoplasmic reticulum [8]. The Ca^{2+} ions are removed until their concentration is reduced to about 10^{-7} mol/l. This reduction inhibits the actomyosin ATPase and the interaction of actin and myosin cross-bridges, which then detach (see Table 4–2).

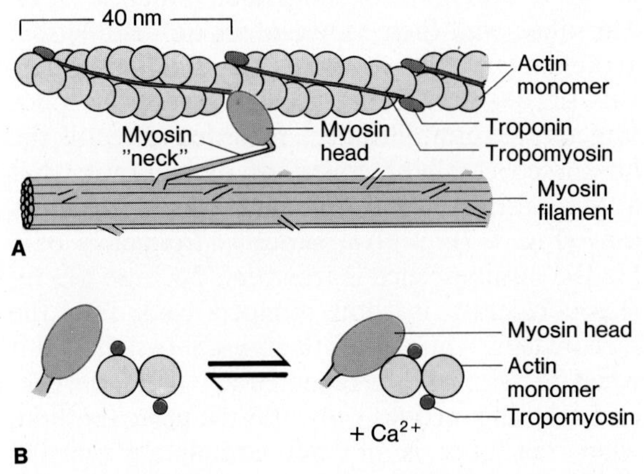

Fig. 4-4 A, B. Mode of action of the calcium ions during activation. **A** Actin filament and myosin filament in longitudinal section of fiber, **B** in cross-section. When calcium ions are bound by the troponin, tropomyosin slides into the groove between the two actin strands of the filament, exposing the site of cross-bridge attachment. (Modified from [13])

Spread of excitation to the interior of the fiber. This process is the first step in excitation-contraction coupling, as Huxley and Taylor [9] have shown (Fig. 4-6). By applying weak current pulses to a frog muscle fiber through a microelectrode they produced local depolarization of

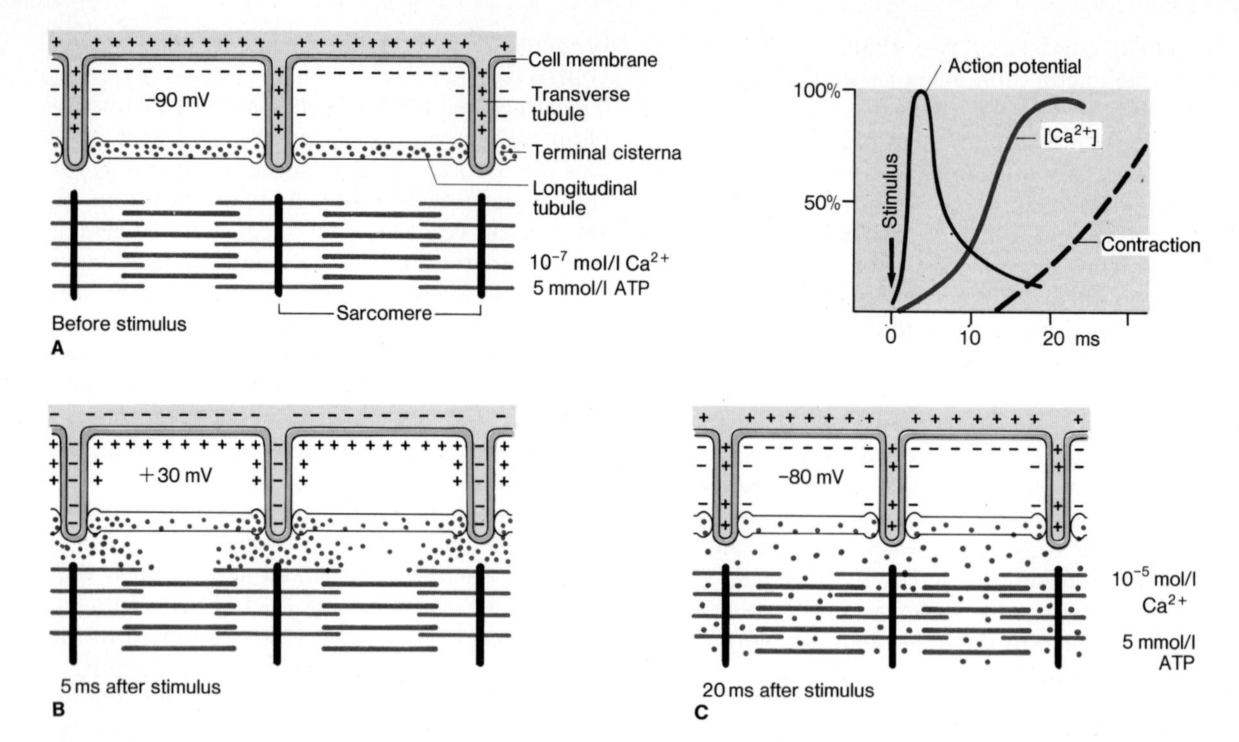

Fig. 4-5 A–C. Diagram of excitation-contraction coupling. **A** Relaxed muscle fiber with polarized cell membrane. The intracellular Ca^{2+} concentration is below 10^{-7} mol/l. **B** During the action potential the polarization of the cell membrane and the transverse-tubule membrane is reversed; Ca^{2+} ions begin to flow out of the terminal cisternae. **C** The intracellular Ca^{2+} concentration has reached ca. 10^{-5} mol/l at the end of the action potential; the sarcomeres of the myofibrils contract. Inset: The temporal sequence of events in excitation-contraction coupling during the "latency" and at the beginning of contraction, in the frog sartorius (0 °C)

an area of the membrane so small that only one transverse tubule (at the level of the Z-disks) was stimulated. The resulting local contraction (contracture) was limited to the superficial myofibrils in the two half sarcomeres adjacent to the tubule. As stimulus intensity was increased, the deeper myofibrils in the fiber were brought into action. Evidently the membranes of the transverse tubule system are particularly excitable by electric current, can conduct excitation, and constitute an important link in the process of signal transmission between the cell membrane and the calcium stores.

Only by the electrical transmission of signals along the transverse system can the rapid mobilization of the calcium stores deep in the fiber be ensured, and only in this way can the very brief *latency* between stimulus and contraction be explained. Diffusion of calcium ions from the external membrane to the centrally located fibrils in a muscle fiber 100 μm thick would take far longer than the observed stimulus-to-contraction latency, so that for *skeletal muscle fibers* such a mechanism can be ruled out on temporal grounds alone.

Calcium release in a single twitch. What is the evidence that calcium is released? BLINKS and his colleagues [4] isolated from certain luminous jellyfish the protein *aequorin*, which when reacting with calcium ions emits light, and injected it into an isolated skeletal muscle fiber. The fiber was then mounted in an "isometric" arrangement and stimulated electrically at intervals of 100 or 200 ms. A highly sensitive photometer (photomultiplier) recorded directly the luminescence (light emission) of aequorin that accompanied the intracellular release of calcium ions (Fig. 4-7). With a stimulus frequency of 5 Hz the luminescence is transient, because the released calcium is soon pumped back into the sarcoplasmic reticulum: the muscle twitches. But when the stimuli are repeated at 10 Hz the second stimulus arrives only 100 ms after the first, when the fiber is not yet completely relaxed. The second twitch is superimposed on the residual contraction from the first, the third twitch is superimposed on the preceding ones, and so on. **Summation** of individual twitches results in an increase in both the maximal tension of a contraction cycle and the amount of contraction

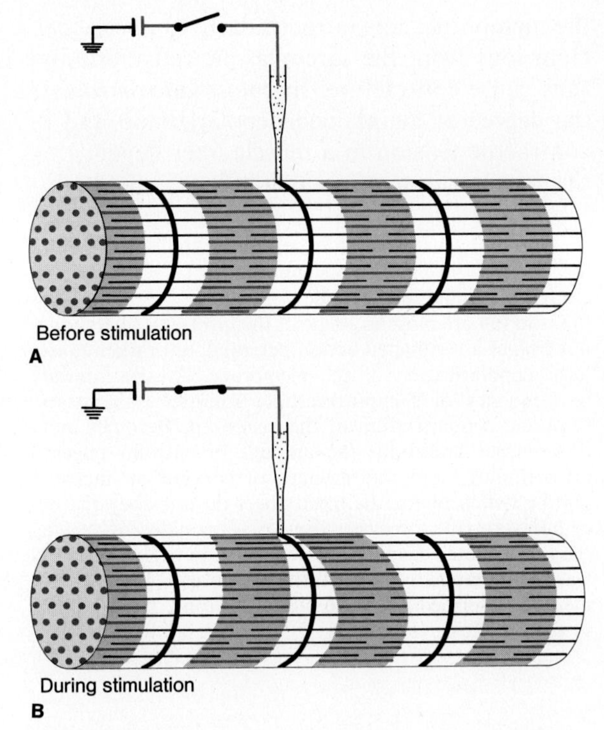

Fig. 4-6 A, B. Demonstration that the T-system can be activated locally. Modified from [9]. Weak local stimulation of striated muscle fiber of a frog (in the Z-disk region, immediately over a T-tubule) causes shortening of the adjacent I-bands under the microcathode. **A** Before, **B** during stimulation

remaining after each twitch in the series – even though (as the light emission indicates) the intracellular calcium level returns almost to the resting level after each twitch. The experiment of Fig. 4–7 makes it clear that the increase in total tension by the superposition of single twitches at intervals as short as 100 ms **cannot** be ascribed to an increase in the intracellular calcium-ion level.

Calcium release in tetanus. If the stimuli are repeated at a high rate, 20 Hz or more, the calcium-ion level remains high during the intervals because there is not enough time for the calcium pump to return all the calcium ions to the longitudinal system of the sarcoplasmic reticulum. In these conditions, as Fig. 4-7 shows, the individual twitches fuse (almost) completely. This state of maintained contraction, or **tetanus**, occurs whenever the interval between the stimuli (or action potentials in the cell membrane) is less than ca. 1/3 of the time required for a single twitch. Thus the fusion frequency is lower, the longer the duration of the single twitch; for this reason, it is temperature-dependent. The minimal time interval between successive effective stimuli in tetanus cannot be smaller than the **refractory period**, which corresponds roughly to the duration of an action potential.

All-or-none law. Single fast twitch fibers in skeletal muscle obey this law. That is, subthreshold stimuli trigger no action potential, and no calcium is released. But as soon as a particular *threshold* intensity is exceeded, a fully developed action potential is triggered and maximal calcium release ensues; the calcium ions give rise to a maximally strong twitch, which cannot be increased by raising the stimulus intensity (Fig. 4-8).
On the other hand, the contractile force of electrically stimulated whole muscles does depend on stimulus intensity. For example, a just-suprathreshold stimulus elicits an all-or-none re-

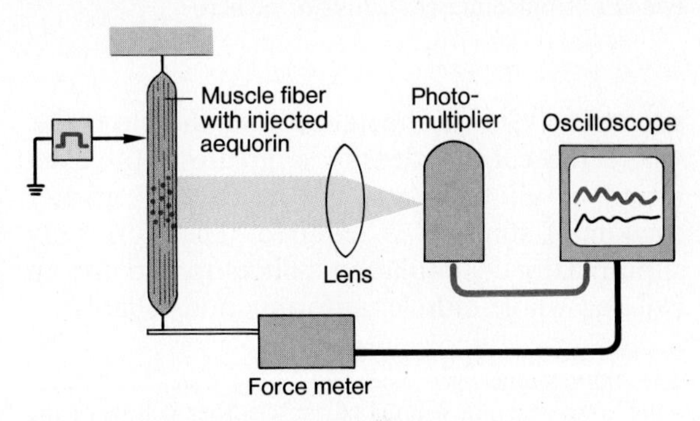

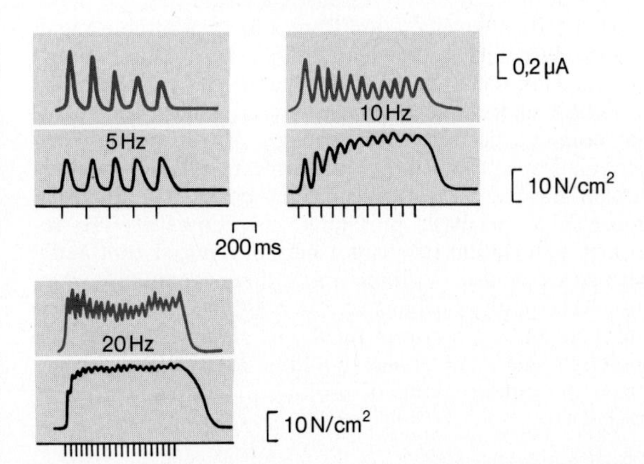

Fig. 4-7. Demonstration of intracellular calcium release in muscle fibers. Light emission *(red curves)* and isometric force development in an isolated muscle fiber of the clawed frog stimulated directly with 0.5 ms current pulses at frequencies of 5, 10 and 20 Hz (stimulus marks below graphs). Note the summation and fusion of the *single twitches* to (incomplete) *tetanus* as stimulus frequency is raised. Isometric force development calibrated in N/cm^2 muscle cross-section, light emission due to action of calcium calibrated in units of photomultiplier anodal current intensity. *Above:* experimental setup used by BLINKS et al. [4]

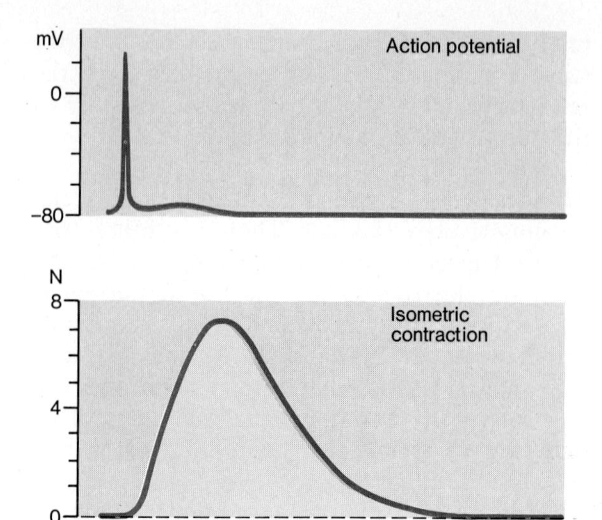

Fig. 4-8. Time course of action potential and isometric twitch in striated muscle (adductor pollicis)

sponse only in the fibers close to the electrode, where the current density is greatest; for excitation of all the fibers a considerably greater (maximal) stimulus is required. Therefore only supramaximal stimulation suffices to activate an isolated whole muscle uniformly and reliably.

The "all-or-none" law does **not** imply that the "all-or-none" response of a stimulated muscle fiber will be of the same size at all times. For example, a single stimulus delivered shortly after relaxation from a tetanus often elicits a far stronger single twitch than it did before "conditioning" by the tetanus. The cause of this **"posttetanic potentation"** is as little understood as the mechanism underlying **muscular fatigue,** a decrease in the strength of contraction when stimulation is repeated. In both cases the action potentials are of normal size. During oxygen deficiency, and even more after metabolic poisoning with iodine acetate, repeated stimulation results not only in reduced contractile strength but also in slower relaxation; eventually, when the ATP supply is exhausted, the poisoned muscle cannot relax at all – it becomes **rigid.** The states of **irreversible rigidity** *(rigor)* and *tetanus* should be strictly distinguished from the different kind of prolonged tension now to be discussed.

Contracture. Contracture is a reversible, non-propagated state of maintained contraction. It is distinguished from tetanus by the absence of a conducted action potential. The membrane potential may be *locally depolarized* to some extent for a prolonged period, as in potassium contracture, or it may be near the resting potential as in *caffeine contracture.* In unphysiologically high concentration (in the millimolar range) caffeine penetrates the muscle fibers and, without exciting the membrane, acts intracellularly to release calcium ions from the sarcoplasmic reticulum and thus cause contracture. In *potassium contracture* the degree of maintained depolarization and of contractile tension in a muscle fiber depends on the concentration of potassium ions in the bath.

In contrast to fast or slow twitch fibers, the *contraction of the "tonus fibers"* is *always* a contracture. Direct or indirect electrical stimulation of tonic striated muscle fibers (slow fibers in the eye muscles, some of the intrafusal fibers) does not trigger a conducted action potential, but rather causes local depolarization of the membrane. As the intensity or frequency of a suprathreshold stimulus is increased, the tonic depolarization of the membrane becomes more pronounced and both the amount of calcium released intracellularly and the strength of contraction increase. Unlike twitch fibers, the tonic fibers do not obey the all-or-none law; the force they develop is regulated by varying the intracellular calcium-ion concentration. This property was first demonstrated by ASHLEY, who used the aequorin method described above to study the tonic muscle fibers of the barnacle *Balanus.*

Regulation of Muscle Force in the Human Body

A motor unit consists of **one** motor neuron **and** the group of muscle fibers it innervates. Motor units vary widely in size. In the extrinsic eye muscles, for instance, a motoneuron supplies only ca. half a dozen muscle fibers. In other muscles the group of fibers supplied by one neuron is a great deal larger; the motor unit can often comprise between 500 and 1,000 fibers (Table 4-4). Because the all-or-none law applies to the individual fibers, the force produced by a motor unit in a single twitch varies only slightly; within the unit all the fibers are either stimulated and contracted or relaxed. But a change in *stimulus frequency* affects the force exerted. Because of the superposition and summation effects mentioned above, the force in complete tetanus (with a high rate of α-motoneuron discharge) is about twice that in an incompletely fused tetanus, at a lower rate of stimulation. Even with a very low impulse rate – for example, 5 to 10 per second – the low

Table 4-4. Large and small motor units

Muscle:	Lateral rectus of eye	Biceps of arm
Motor units/muscle	1,740	774
Muscle fibers/unit	13	750
Maximal force/unit (N)	0.001	0.5

total tension *(tonus)* of the muscle does not undulate, because in the various asynchronously active motor units the maxima of the twitches or incomplete tetani occur at different times.

Correlation between contractile force and action-potential frequency. When the rate of motoneuron discharge rises from 5 to 50 per second, the twitching or incompletely fused tetanus of the motor units is converted to a smooth, fused tetanus: as a result, the force of contraction is at least doubled. By inserting needle electrodes into motor units [3] one can record extracellularly the frequency of the muscle action potentials (Fig. 4-9). Such **electromyographic studies** have shown that the amount of muscle force voluntarily exerted is correlated with the frequency of the action potentials in the motor units, proving that force can be increased by raising the frequency of stimulation [3].

Recruitment of motor units. The force and contraction velocity (cf.p. 75) of a muscle can also be increased by the activation of more and more motor units (recruitment). Here the force can be more finely regulated, the smaller the size (and thus the force) of each motor unit. During a slight voluntary increase in muscle tension electromyographic recordings (with extracellular needle electrodes) show action potentials in only a few motor units: when the muscle is strongly tensed – after recruitment – very many units are firing. Accordingly, the integrated electrical activity of the muscle recorded by *surface electrodes* on the skin also increases progressively, the more powerfully the parts of the muscle beneath the skin contract.

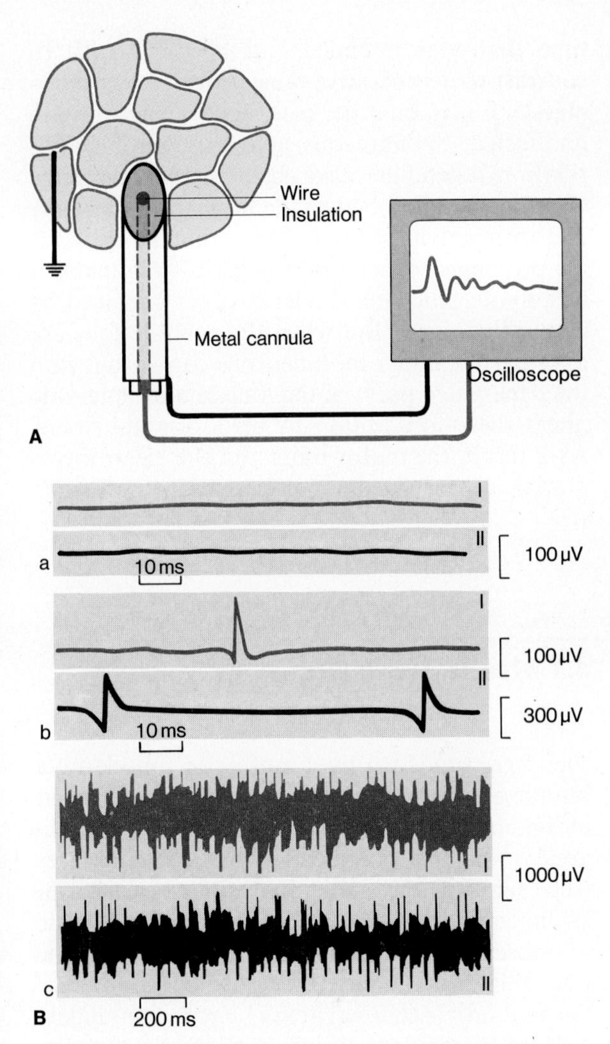

Fig. 4-9 A, B. Electromyography. **A** Extracellular recording technique, with concentric needle electrode inserted between the fibers of a motor unit in a muscle (extracellular). **B** Extracellular action potentials are recorded simultaneously from two different motor units (I and II) in a muscle, with two electrodes. a, relaxed muscle: b, weak voluntary contraction (note the asynchronous activity of the two motor units); c, maximal voluntary contraction. (Modified from [3])

Reflex tonus. Even when apparently at rest, some muscles exhibit a low level of electromyographically recordable activity. Because of the low-frequency reflexogenic periodic tensing of only a few motor units some (but not all) postural muscles are often in a state of involuntary tension, at a constant level owing to the asynchronous operation of the functional units. This *neurogenic "tonus"* can be modulated by the γ-fiber system of the muscle spindles (p. 90); during mental effort or excitement it is often involuntarily enhanced, and it vanishes completely only in a state of deep relaxation.

Clinical electromyography. In certain disorders involving muscle innervation (pp. 97, 111) passive movement or stretch of the muscles causes a reflexly increased tone, producing resistance to stretch. Accordingly, the electromyographically recorded muscle activity is increased during passive movement *(spasticity* or *rigidity)*. In diseases of the *myotonia* type the cell membranes of the musculature are so excitable that even the introduction of the needle electrode for electromyography triggers bursts of muscle impulses. When a muscle is voluntarily tensed after a period of rest there are prolonged afterdischarges in the hyperexcitable cell membrane (bursts of action potentials), so that the muscle contracts for a longer time than was intended and becomes stiff. In contrast to degenerative muscle disorders **dystrophies)**, in myotonia the contractile structures are unaffected. Spontaneous action potentials (fibrillation potentials) also occur in the first stage after denervation, before the **denervation atrophy** due to inactivity. Muscle fibers that atrophy after prolonged denervation (e.g., in poliomyelitis or amyotrophic lateral sclerosis), are replaced by connective tissue. But when the nerve lesions are only partial, intact motoneurons can sprout into the denervated parts of the muscle and innervate fibers there in addition to their original fibers. As a result, the motor units and the electromyographically recorded action potentials increase in size.

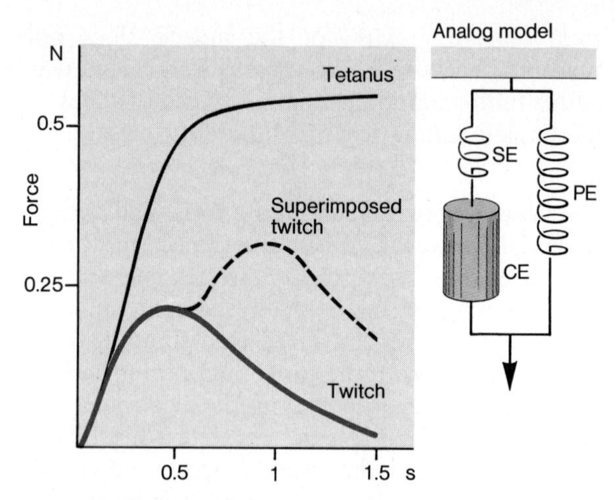

Fig. 4-10. Summation and fusion of single twitches during repeated stimulation (stimulus interval 500 ms for twitch superposition, 50 ms for smooth tetanus; frog muscle, 0 °C. Modified from [3]. Analog model of the muscle: CE contractile element; SE series elastic element; PE parallel elastic element

4.3 Muscle Mechanics

The *force* produced by a muscle or muscle-fiber bundle is the sum of the forces exerted by the individual fibers. The thicker a muscle, and the greater its "physiological" cross-sectional area (the sum of the individual fiber areas), the stronger the muscle is. For example, in cases of muscular *hypertrophy* the muscle force and fiber thickness increase by equivalent amounts.
Per unit cross-sectional area (1 cm^2), mammalian striated muscles usually develop maximal forces of more than 4 kgf (40 N), whereas those of frogs are capable of only ca. 30 N.
Muscular force does not only depend on activation unter central nervous control (see p. 70), but is also crucially affected by the external mechanical conditions under which the muscle is working.

Auxotonic and isometric contractions. In the human body the skeletal muscles transmit force to the skeleton by way of elastic, somewhat stretchable structures, the tendons. Therefore, the muscle *tends to shorten during force development* and thereby to stretch and develop tension in the elastic structures connecting the muscle to the skeleton. This kind of muscle contraction, in which the length of the muscle decreases at the same time as its force increases, is called **auxotonic contraction**. The maximal muscle force measured under auxotonic experimental conditions (with a stretchable elastic connection between muscle and force transducer) is called the *auxotonic contraction maximum.* It is considerably smaller than the contractile force developed by a muscle kept at a constant length – i.e., in **isometric contraction**. Experimentally, isometric contractions are studied by clamping the relaxed, resting muscle at its two ends so that the tension developed by the activated muscle is measured without allowing the muscle to shorten.
Even then, however, the contractile elements of the muscle fibers (myosin heads) can transmit force to the tendons or measuring device only by intramuscular structures which themselves are elastic. Some of these are within the cross-bridges [10] (cf. Fig. 4-3), and some in the actin filaments, the Z-disks and the attachment sites of the tendons. In a simplified model of this situation the muscle is a system of contractile elements (CE) and elastic elements (SE) in series with one another, represented by a mechanical analog in Fig. 4-10. During activation the contractile elements (auxotonically) shorten by ca. 1% and thus stretch the *series elastic elements;* it is this stretching that produces the measurable force.

Single twitch, superposition of twitches, tetanus. Under isometric conditions a single stimulus results in a rapid increase in contractile tension, which soon falls off again (isometric single twitch, Fig. 4-10; cf. p. 69 and Fig. 4-8). If the muscle is stimulated a second time before the twitch is over, the second twitch is superimposed on the first, so that the total tension is greater than that during the first twitch *(mechanical summation)*. When the stimuli recur at brief intervals the twitches fuse into tetanus (Fig.

4-10; cf. p. 69). There is as yet no generally accepted explanation of the fact that the tension achieved during tetanus or superposition of single twitches is much greater than the force of a single twitch. During the brief activation of the muscle at the beginning of a single twitch elastic tension develops in the cross-bridges between the actin and myosin filaments. But according to recent research the activation time does not suffice for all the cross-bridges to attach. During the longer period of activation permitted by repeated stimulation (e.g., in tetanus) additional attachments are possible. The number of cross-bridges attaching the actin to the myosin – and thus the force of the muscle – should, according to the sliding-filament theory, depend on the amount of overlap of thick and thin fibers, and therefore of course on the length of the sarcomere or muscle.

Isometric Contractile Force and Muscle Length

In the relaxed state a muscle held at the "resting length" by clamps at both ends does not exert any force on the holder. But if one end of the muscle is pulled out (Fig. 4-11) so as to stretch the fibers, passive tension develops in the muscle. That is, the resting muscle is elastic; but unlike a rubber band, its tension does not increase linearly with stretch. By plotting the measured force against imposed length in a rectangular coordinate system, one obtains a length-tension diagram of the resting muscle, the **resting tension curve.** It rises more steeply, the more the muscle is stretched (Curve *a* in Fig. 4-11). The modulus of elasticity of the resting muscle thus increases with stretch. This elasticity resides largely in stretchable structures in parallel with the contractile fibrils (hence the term *parallel elasticity),* such as the sarcolemma around the muscle fiber, the longitudinal system of the sarcoplasmic reticulum, and connective-tissue structures between the fibers. The myofibrils, by contrast, in the relaxed state offer practically no resistance to stretch; the actin and myosin filaments are not linked by cross-bridges and can be readily moved past one another.

Prestretching determines not only the amount of passive elastic tension in the resting muscle, but also the amount of additional force the muscle can develop at the given length when it is activated. The isometric increase in force during contraction is (additively) superimposed on the passive tension of the resting muscle; the peak

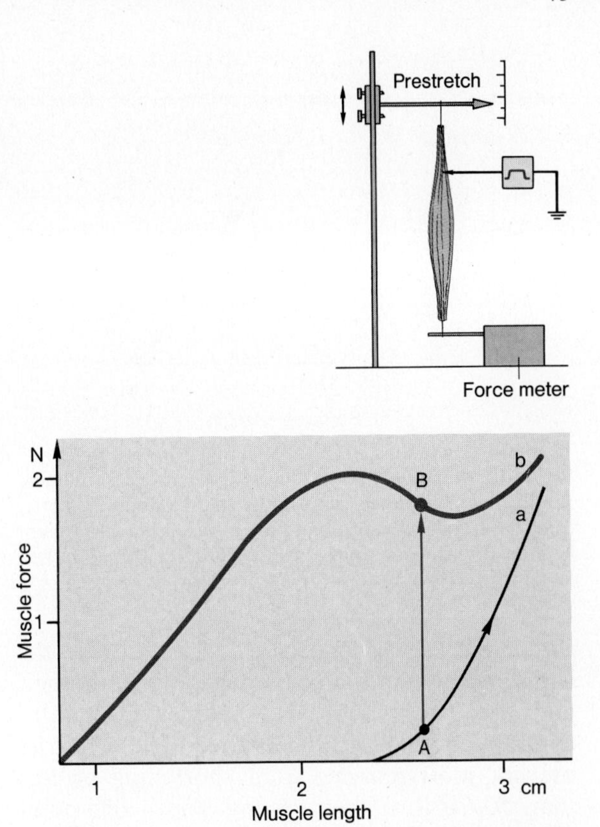

Fig. 4-11. Relation between force and muscle length, *a,* passive tension curve; *b,* curve of isometric maxima. The total force generated with a given prestretching (e.g., at B) is composed of the passive tension A and the active contractile force (B–A). *Above:* Arrangement for isometric experiment. Frog muscle at resting length (l_0 ca. 2.3 cm) is held between a force transducer (below) and a fixed point that can be moved up to stretch the muscle or down to release the stretch (below l_0). In this case a muscle shortens to a preset length before the isometric tension buildup begins

contraction under these conditions is the **isometric contraction maximum.** The passive elastic forces of the stretched longitudinal tubules and the sarcolemma are additively combined with the active contractile forces in the myofibrils because these structures are arranged in parallel, as illustrated by a mechanical analog model (Fig. 4-10, inset). The force-vs.-length diagram obtained by plotting the isometric contraction maxima measured at different muscle or sarcomere lengths against the length gives the **curve of isometric maxima** (Curve *b* in Fig. 4-11). To find the relationship between active contractile force and muscle or sarcomere length, we must subtract from this curve the passive tension curve. The curve so obtained (Fig. 4-12) has a characteristic maximum at about the resting length of the muscle, at which the sarcomere length is between 2.0 and 2.2 µm. At smaller muscle or

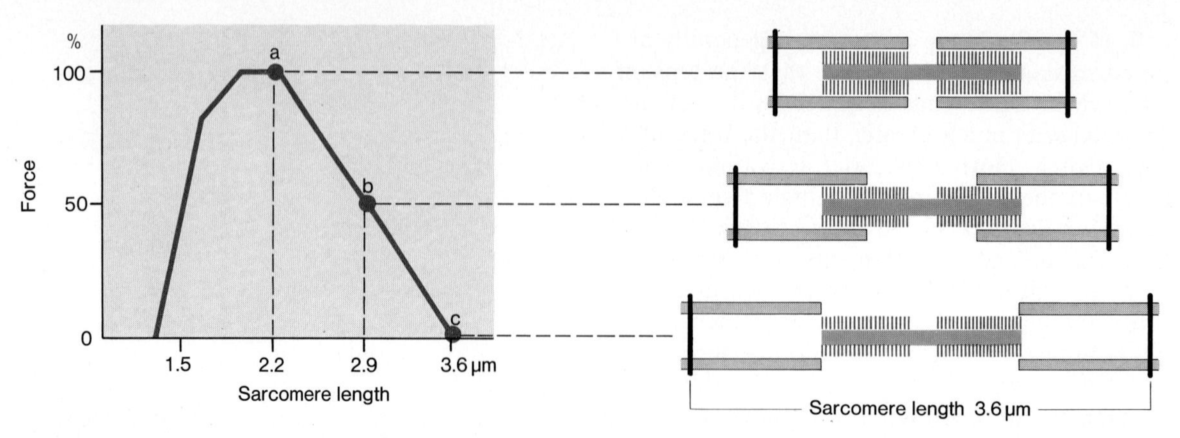

Fig. 4-12. Relation between contractile force, sarcomere length and filament overlap. *Left:* the maximal isometric force developed in tetanus with the muscle fiber at different lengths (indicated as sarcomere length on the abscissa); ordinate, force in percent of maximal force with muscle at resting length (sarcomere length 2.2 µm). *Right:* Overlap of myosin and actin filaments of a sarcomere at the lengths 2.2, 2.9 and 3.6 µm. (Modified from [7])

sarcomere lengths the force is less because the actin and myosin filaments impede one another, and because in shortened muscles excitation-contraction coupling is impaired. These factors prevent most muscles from shortening to less than 50–70% of their resting length (cf. point where the curve of isometric maxima in Fig. 4-11 intersects the abscissa). When muscle fibers are stretched to more than the resting length, contractile force decreases because the actin filaments are pulled out of the bundle of myosin filaments. With a sarcomere length of 2.9 µm, for example, the myofibrils can exert only ca. 50% of the maximal force, because each myosin filament overlaps the actin filaments by only half the normal distance, and only half of the myosin heads can attach to the actin. The dynamic resistance to stretch brought about by cross-bridge elasticity (HUXLEY's "immediate stiffness" [9]) is then also halved. With sarcomere lengths of more than 3.6 µm the resting tension curve and the curve of isometric maxima coincide (Fig. 4-11); at this length the myofibrils can no longer develop active force because the actin and myosin filaments no longer overlap at all. These mechanical experiments verify the prediction, at first entirely theoretical, that muscular force can be produced only by the interaction of actin and myosin filaments (in the sense of cross-bridge formation) [7].

Relation between Load and Shortening of the Muscle

Isotonic contraction is the shortening of a muscle under constant tension, or load. To record this shortening, an isolated resting muscle is suspended from a holder by one end. The other end is connected to a loaded lever (Fig. 4-13, inset), the tip of which moves by an amount proportional to the shortening of the muscle. The weight on the lever stretches the resting muscle passively. The relationship between the force pulling on the muscle (load) and the degree of muscle stretch can be represented in a length-tension diagram by the *resting tension curve (a* in Fig. 4-13; cf. also p. 73 and Fig. 4-11). When "tetanic" stimulation is applied to a loaded, prestretched muscle in the experimental arrangement of Fig. 4-13 (inset), it contracts **isotonically;** it maintains constant tension as it shortens, lifting the load and thereby doing mechanical work (load times distance). The amount of shortening (distance) is less, the greater the load. Thus the muscle length when contraction is maximal depends in a characteristic way on the previously applied load, as described by the curve of **isotonic maxima** (*e* in Fig. 4-13). To study the influence of the load on the distance it is lifted while eliminating the effect of differential prestretching, we use another form of contraction, as follows.

Afterloaded contraction. Prestretching of the muscle by its load can be prevented if the load is supported or the position of the lever fixed (set-screw in Fig. 4-13) prior to contraction. Then the tetanically stimulated muscle at first contracts isometrically, maintaining the initial length while developing enough tension to bear the load. Thereafter isotonic contraction lifts the load up from its support, with a force equivalent to the force of gravity on the load. In an afterloaded contraction the distance the load is

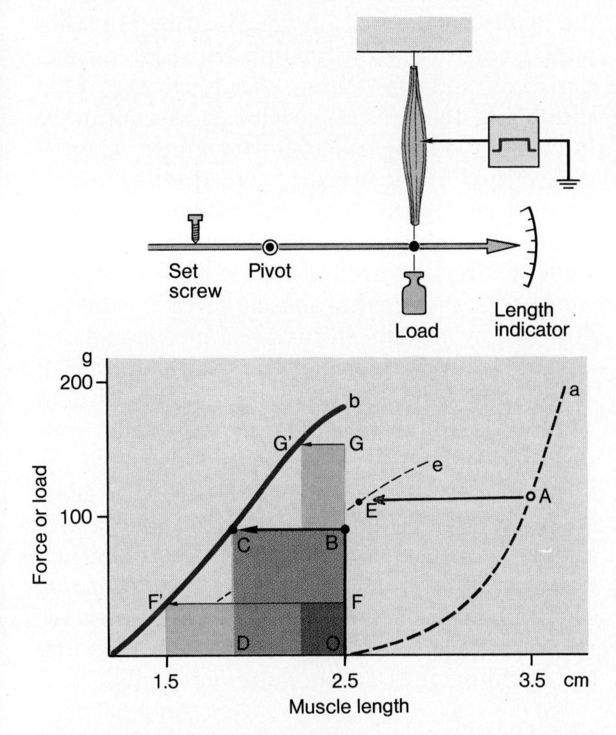

Fig. 4-13. Relation between load and shortening. Abscissa: muscle length; ordinate: muscle force or load (100 g load corresponds to a force of 1 N). Passive elongation of a resting frog muscle (starting length l_0 = 2.5 cm) as load is increased (resting tension curve *a*). OA: stretch caused by 120-g load. AE: isotonic contraction during tetanic stimulation of the muscle loaded with 120 g brings it to the length indicated by the curve of isotonic maxima *e*. OBC: isotonic afterloaded contraction in tetanus with 90-g load is composed of isometric tension buildup (OB) followed by an isotonic shortening phase, in which the load is lifted 0.6 cm (BC); the work done corresponds to the area OBCD. The gray shaded rectangles (OGG' and OFF') correspond to the muscle work done with loads of 160 and 30 g. 30-g load lifted the distance F–F'; 160-g load, G–G'. *b*, curve of isotonic afterloaded maxima. *Above:* Arrangement for measuring afterloaded contraction or (without set screw) isotonic contraction.

raised is greater, the smaller the load. Therefore a muscle is shorter at the time of peak contraction when lightly loaded than when the load is heavier. The "length-tension diagram" obtained by plotting these final lengths on the abscissa of a rectangular coordinate system, with the load (or muscle tension or force) on the ordinate, gives the curve of **afterloaded maxima** (Curve *b* in Fig. 4-13, which is distinctly above Curve *e* for the isotonic maxima, and nearly coincides with the curve of isometric maxima, *b* in Fig. 4-11). The approximate agreement between the isometric maxima and the afterloaded maxima is not accidental; during an afterloaded contraction the sarcomeres of a loaded muscle can of

Table 4-5. The effect of load on shortening distance and work performed

Load(g)	3	5	9
Shortening (cm)	0.5	0.36	0.12
Work (g·cm)	1.5	1.8	1.1
Duration of twitch (s)	0.55	0.48	0.4

Isotonic afterloaded twitches of a 3-cm-long frog sartorius at 0 ° C. Force of isometric twitch: 0.12 N (cf.[16])

course shorten only to the length at which the (isometrically possible) maximal muscle force is at least equal to the opposing force of the load. **The muscular work** done in a tetanic afterloaded contraction is the product of distance (muscle shortening) and load; it is given by the area of a rectangle in the length-tension diagram of Fig. 4-13 that has sides corresponding to the force component and the amount of shortening. It is evident in Fig. 4-13 that the work done with a moderate load (area OBCD) is greater than that with very large or small loads (gray areas); it is zero when the load equals the maximal isometric force and when the muscle shortens without a load.

The relationship between load and work during a single twitch is very similar (Table 4-5). In afterloaded twitches, however, the distance and work are less than in afterloaded tetani, because the period of activation in a twitch is too brief to allow as much muscle shortening as during tetanus.

Relation between Contraction Velocity and Force (Load)

In isotonic tetanic activation of a muscle not only the amount of shortening but also the rate of shortening depends on the load; the smaller the load, the greater the amount of shortening per unit time (Fig. 4-14, inset). An unloaded muscle shortens with the maximal velocity, depending on the type of muscle fibers.

The **maximal (unloaded) shortening velocity** of a sarcomere is the maximal rate at which the actin and myosin filaments can slide past one another. The more rapidly the cross-bridges split ATP and interact with actin, the higher the velocity of the elementary sliding process. Slow fibers (type-I fibers) like those in our postural muscles, contain a myosin with low ATPase activity and a different composition from the myosin with high ATPase activity in the fast fibers (type-IIA and IIB fibers; cf. p. 65) of muscles chiefly used for movement. Recent studies have shown that the fast fiber type can be transformed into the slow type; Buller and Eccles transected the motor nerve fibers of a slow and a fast muscle and exchanged the ends of the

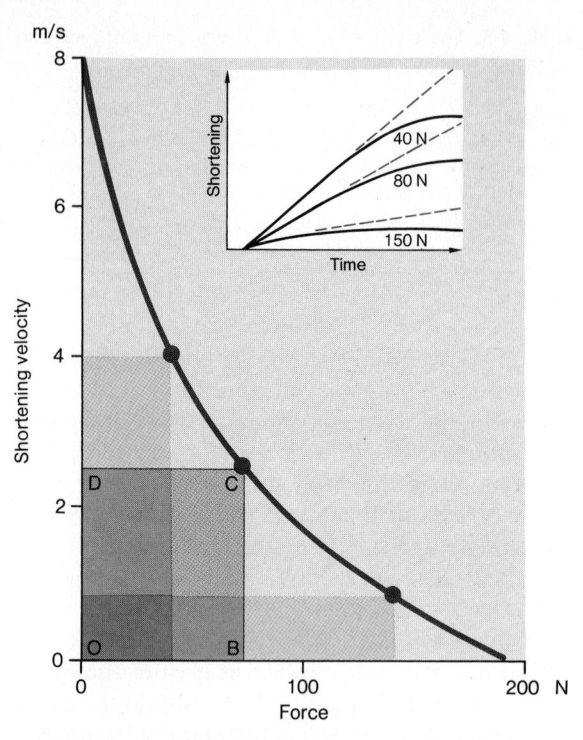

Fig. 4-14. Relation between force and contraction velocity. Ordinate: speed of shortening of a human arm muscle, in m/s. Abscissa: muscle load, expressed as the muscle force (in N) required to hold it. The area OBCD indicates the optimal mechanical power, at a contraction velocity 2.5 m/s. Light gray rectangles: power with loads of 4 and 14 kg. Modified from [20]. Inset: time course of the isotonic afterloaded contraction with loads of 4, 8 or 15 kg. Dashed lines indicate curve slope (= shortening velocity)

two nerves when reimplanting them in the muscles. After a few weeks, when this cross-innervation had become established, the originally fast muscle contracted slowly and the originally slow muscle rapidly. Because the shortenings of the sarcomeres in series in a myofibril add, for a given speed of sarcomere shortening a long muscle will contract more rapidly than a short muscle. For example, the sartorius of a frog contracts at a rate of 0.2 m/s (ca. 10 muscle lengths per second), each of the ca. 2-μm-long sarcomeres shortening to 1.6 μm in 20 ms. The much longer human arm muscles, by contrast, shorten at a rate of 8 m/s.

As shown in Fig. 4-14, contraction velocity decreases hyperbolically with increasing load (the HILL **force-velocity relation**), reaching ca. 1/5 of the maximal rate (achieved during unloaded shortening) when the relative muscle load is equivalent to half the maximal force that can be exerted under isometric conditions. If the load is just equal to the isometrically achievable force, the muscle does not shorten. With even greater loads it is stretched (braking action of muscles when walking downhill!).
Because the contractile force a muscle must exert during shortening is equivalent to the load, the load-velocity relation described by HILL implies a corresponding relation between contractile force and shortening speed. During rapid shortening the muscle develops less contractile force than during slow shortening or when it is stretched. This property explains the everyday experience that we can make very rapid "light" movements only if little force is required, when the muscles are not loaded (free to move); conversely, the greatest muscle force is achieved during slow movements, as when pushing a large object. Heavy weights can be lifted or shifted, if at all, only very slowly. This is not inconsistent with our ability to vary the rate of muscular contraction voluntarily. For example, when *all* the fibers of a muscle participate in lifting a given load, the *relative* load on the *individual* active muscle fiber is smaller, and therefore its contraction velocity is greater than when only a *fraction* of the fibers are active. We can thus increase the rate of muscle shortening under a given load by the recruitment of additional motor units.

Muscle power is the product of muscle force and shortening velocity. In the example of a human arm muscle illustrated in Fig. 4-14, the maximal power (200 W) is reached at a contraction velocity of 2.5 m/s. In this diagram power is represented by the area of a rectangle with sides corresponding to the force and velocity components. It is "graphically" demonstrated there that power is greater with moderate loads (area OBCD) or contraction rates than under extreme conditions (light gray rectangles). We apply this principle when we use appropriate gears while bicycling, or follow a zig-zag path up a mountain.

4.4 Muscle Energetics

Muscle heat and energy turnover. When a muscle is activated the elevated intracellular concentration of free calcium ions initiates contraction and the increased splitting of ATP; in the process, the metabolic rate of the muscle increases by a factor of 100 to 1,000. According to the first principle of thermodynamics (conservation of energy) the chemical energy converted in the muscle must equal the sum of mechanical energy (muscular work) and heat production. Even if no physically measurable muscle work is done – as during a maintained isometric tetanic contraction – there is a continual transformation of chemical energy to heat within the muscle **(maintenance heat),** at a rate proportional to the duration and tension of the contraction. Even when contraction is isometric the myosin cross-bridges are in continual cyclic activity, and the "internal" work associated with this ATP splitting and heat production is considerable. It is for this reason that motionless activities such as standing at attention are tiring. An additional amount of ATP is converted when a muscle lifts a load and thus does external work. The extra metabolism is then proportional to the work done (FENN effect).

Efficiency. Hydrolysis of one mole of ATP supplies ca. 48 kJ of energy. But only ca. 40–50% of this energy is converted to mechanical energy or work. The remaining 50–60% is dissipated as heat **(initial heat)** at the onset of and during the contraction of a muscle, which becomes somewhat warmer in the process. The elementary transformation in the myofibrils thus occurs with an efficiency of about 40–50%. During natural muscular activity, however, the mechanical efficiency is usually only ca. 20–30%, because during and after contraction "energy-wasting" recovery processes are occurring outside the myofibrils. These – for example, the activity of ion pumps and the oxidative regeneration of ATP – are associated with considerable heat production **(recovery heat).** The more work is done, the more heat is produced, with a higher consumption of energy sources (carbohydrate and fat) and of oxygen. This relationship, by the way, is the reason we become tired, sweaty and breathless when climbing a hill but not when coming down.

Energy metabolism. During steady, prolonged muscular activity ATP is regenerated **aerobically,** chiefly by way of **oxidative phosphorylation.** The energy required for synthesis derives from the oxidation of carbohydrates or fat. The system is stable, in a dynamic equilibrium, when the rate of ATP formation is just equal to the rate of ATP breakdown, so that the intracellular ATP level (ca. 5 mmol/l) and that of phosphocreatine (ca. 30 mmol/l) are constant. In the performance of endurance sports the rate of ATP splitting, which of course is coupled to the power output, is often 100 or even 1,000 times greater in the working muscles than when the muscles are at rest. A steady state, and thus long-term performance, can be achieved only if the rate of ATP resynthesis by oxidative phosphorylation can be increased to match the increased ATP consumption. The O_2 consumption of the muscle tissue is then up to 50–100 times as high as at rest, because to form one mole of ATP ca. 1/6 mole of O_2 is required. The rate of glycogen breakdown in the muscle is correspondingly elevated. Performance may be limited by the mitochondrial enzyme capacity, which determines the rate of oxidative breakdown of glucose; this capacity is fully exploited, for example, when a well-trained long-distance runner is running at a speed of 6 m/s [3].

The limit for long-term performance can be exceeded in the short term – for example, in the final spurt of a race – if *additional* glycogen is broken down **anaerobically,** in **glycolysis** (Table 2-1). In this reaction ATP formation occurs 2–3 times as rapidly, and the mechanical power produced by the muscle is 2–3 times as great as during (aerobically supported) long-term performance. The sprinter running only a short distance can go almost twice as fast (ca. 10 m/s) as the long-distance runner. 30 seconds is about the limit for this high performance, because the anaerobic energy reserves required to support the high rate of ATP formation are limited, and because glycolysis results in an accumulation of lactic acid in the cell fluid and in the blood; the end result is metabolic acidosis, which restricts performance capacity and causes **fatigue**. The intracellular pH changes associated with fatigue, and the accumulation of metabolites such as phosphate and ADP, can now be demonstrated in situ in cardiac and skeletal muscle by the nuclear magnetic resonance technique (NMR spectroscopy). Anaerobic processes are necessary for the short-term provision of energy, not only for brief peak physical exertion but also at the beginning of long-term muscular activity, because some time is required for oxidative metabolism (as well as glycolysis) to adjust to the increased demand. Therefore a steady state, in which just as much ATP is formed by oxidative phosphorylation per unit time as is split by ATPase, is reached only after 0.5–2 minutes.

Until this dynamic equilibrium is reached, ATP is regenerated from ADP and creatine phosphate by the Lohmann reaction (Table 4-1) so rapidly that its intracellular level stays practically constant:

$$\text{ADP} + \text{creatine phosphate} \rightleftharpoons \text{ATP} + \text{creatine}$$

While this reaction is proceeding, the intracellular *phosphocreatine* level falls until the aerobic formation of ATP has reached a rate high enough to meet the current requirement for ATP.

The pool of creatine phosphate is usually not replenished until the contraction is over, when the Lohmann reaction proceeds in the opposite direction; the ATP required is supplied by oxidative phosphorylation – that is, an oxygen-consuming reaction – during the first minutes of recovery. In a sense (according to HILL) this oxygen consumption amounts to repayment of an **oxygen debt;** according to WILKIE it corresponds approximately to the amount of energy the muscle has converted anaerobically at the beginning of or during its activity and has not yet repaid by aerobic energy-supplying processes [3]. The oxygen debt resulting entirely from (anaerobic) hydrolysis of creatine phosphate can be as great as 4 l; the glycolytic energy yield during extreme physical exertion (see above) increases the debt to as much as 20 l, for the lactate so formed and released into the bloodstream (up to 1.5 g/l) can be eliminated only by using up oxygen. Some of the lactate is oxidized in the myocardium and some (predominantly in the liver) is used for the neosynthesis of glycogen (see textbooks of biochemistry).

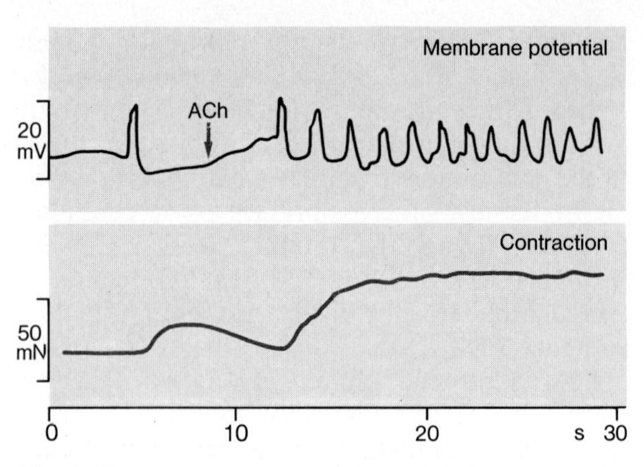

Fig. 4-15. A spontaneous action potential *(upper trace)* triggers a single twitch in the isolated tenia coli. Acetylcholine administration *(arrow)* raises the frequency of the action potentials; the single twitches fuse to a tetanus. *Lower trace (red):* time course of muscle tension. Cf. [5]

4.5 Smooth Muscle

Smooth muscle cells are spindle-shaped, ca. 50–400 μm long and 2–10 μm thick. Joined by special intercellular contacts (desmosomes), they form a network with intermeshed collagen fibers. Because the myosin and actin filaments are not regularly arranged, smooth muscle cells lack the striation typical of cardiac and skeletal muscle. Smooth muscle cells shorten by sliding of the myofilaments toward and over one another, but the rate of sliding and of ATP splitting is 100 to 1,000 times slower than in striated muscles. For this reason smooth muscles are especially well suited for prolonged maintained contraction, without fatigue and with little energy consumption. Their contractile tension per unit cross-sectional area of muscle is often as great as that of skeletal muscle (30–40 N/cm^2), and in the long term they can support as great a load. The energy consumed in the process, however, as measured by oxygen consumption, is smaller by a factor of 100–500 [18].

Myogenic activity of spontaneously active muscles. In many intestinal smooth muscles (e.g., the tenia coli) the single twitch elicited by an action potential lasts several seconds (Fig. 4-15). Therefore, when two twitches occur at an interval of less than 2 s they are superimposed, and at frequencies below 1 Hz they fuse to more or less complete tetanus (tetaniform "tonus") differing from that of striated muscle only in the low fusion frequency and the low frequency of the accompanying action potentials. The "tonus" is myogenic; unlike skeletal muscle, the smooth muscle of the intestine, ureter, stomach and uterus exhibits spontaneous tetaniform contractions after isolation and denervation, and even after the intramural ganglion cells are blocked. The action potentials, then, are not triggered by nerve impulses. In other words, they are not neurogenic but – as in the heart – myogenic in origin.

Myogenic excitation originates in pacemaker cells identical to the other muscle cells in structure but differing in their electrophysiological properties, as follows. Prepotentials or pacemaker potentials depolarize the membrane to threshold and thus elicit action potentials. Owing to the inflow of positive ions (mainly Ca^{2+}), the membrane is depolarized to the zero level and, for a few milliseconds, beyond it – to +20 mV. Repolarization is followed by another prepotential, which elicits a new action potential. The size of the interval between the pacemaker action potentials depends both on the rate of depolarization of the prepotentials and on the difference between the initial membrane potential and the threshold potential. In the experiment of Fig. 4-15 the pacemaker membrane potential is high (ca. −50 to −70 mV) and the "firing" rate is low. When *acetylcholine* is administered to this tenia coli preparation (large-intestine musculature; cf. p.

344) the pacemaker cells are depolarized to a near-threshold level and the action-potential frequency rises. The twitches they trigger fuse to an almost complete tetanus. The more frequent the action potentials, the more complete the tetanus and the stronger the contraction resulting from summation of the single twitches. Conversely, application of *noradrenalin* to the tenia coli hyperpolarizes the membrane, and thus lowers the action-potential frequency and the tonus. These are the mechanisms underlying the modulation of the spontaneous activity of the pacemakers by the autonomic nervous system and its transmitters (cf. p. 337).

The excitation spreads through the muscle by way of special **"gap junctions"** (nexus) between the cell membranes of adjacent muscle cells. These low-resistance contact regions allow the depolarization of an excited cell to be electrotonically transmitted to neighboring cells. As soon as the local current flowing through a nexus depolarizes the membrane to threshold an action potential results, which in turn excites other electrotonically coupled cells. In this way the activity spreads through the whole muscle at a rate of ca. 5–10 cm/s; the muscle behaves like a single functional unit, following almost synchronously the activity of its pacemaker.

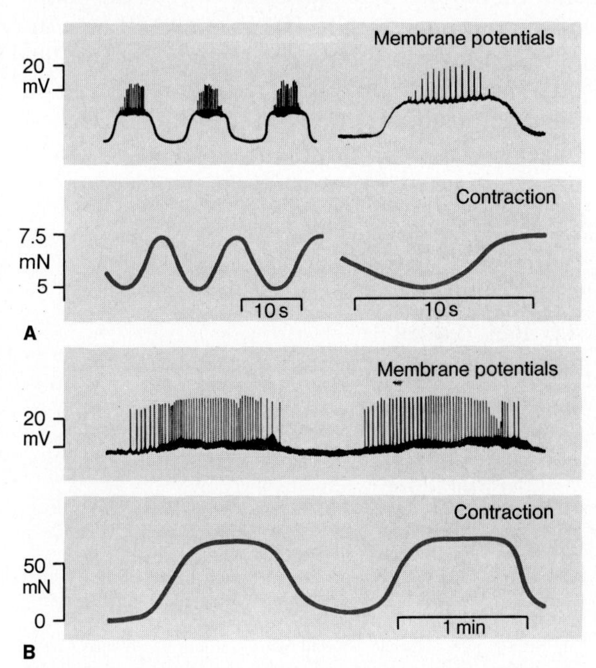

Fig. 4-16 A, B. Phasic rhythmic activity in smooth muscle. **A** Gastric-antrum musculature. Rhythmic depolarizations of the membrane potential with superimposed "spike bursts" *(upper trace)* cause fluctuations in tone *(lower trace)*. **B** Tenia coli; electrical activity *(above)* and rhythmic contractions *(below)*. (Modified from GOLENHOFEN [6])

Myogenic rhythms. Fluctuations of myogenic tonus with periods of seconds or minutes are brought about by spontaneous changes in the activity of the pacemaker cells. When the membrane of a pacemaker cell is depolarized for seconds or minutes at a time, it triggers a volley of action potentials that produces a tetanic contraction.

GOLENHOFEN [6] distinguishes between relatively brief, organ-specific rhythms and the longer *minute rhythms* ("slow waves"). In the smooth muscles of the gastric antrum (Fig. 4-16A) the slow wave is shorter and more conspicuous than in the tenia of the colon (Fig. 4-16 B). It is still unclear whether the slow oscillations of the membrane potential (depolarization waves) are caused by rhythmic activity of an electrogenic sodium pump.

Responses of smooth muscle to stretch. In contrast to the skeletal muscles, most smooth muscles in the stretch experiment often behave not like more or less elastic structures but like distinctly plastic or viscoelastic bodies. After an initial elastic rise in tension the smooth muscle exhibits plastic compliance; in this poststretching phase tension declines, rapidly at first and then ever more slowly (Fig. 4-17). Because of its *plasticity* the smooth muscle can be completely relaxed in both the shortened and the stretched state. Think, for example, of the urinary bladder, which, by yielding plastically as it fills, prevents an excessive rise in internal pressure.

In many cases strong stretching produces a *stretch-activated contraction* (Fig. 4-17), superimposed on the passive behavior just described. This contraction results from the increasing depolarization of the pacemaker cells as the muscle is stretched, which raises the frequency of the action potentials. As described above (p. 78), the increased discharge rate causes a stronger contraction. The stretch-activated contraction is significant with regard to *autoregulation* of the arterioles (p. 508) and the automatic emptying of the filled urinary bladder, when neural regulation is eliminated by destruction of the spinal cord.

Non-spontaneous smooth muscles. The smooth muscles of the arteries, like the muscles in the seminal ducts and iris and the ciliary muscles, usually exhibit little or no spontaneous activity. In contrast to the muscles of the intestine, their activity is often not myogenic but neurogenic in origin, elicited by the impulses in the autonomic nerve fibers that supply them. The differ-

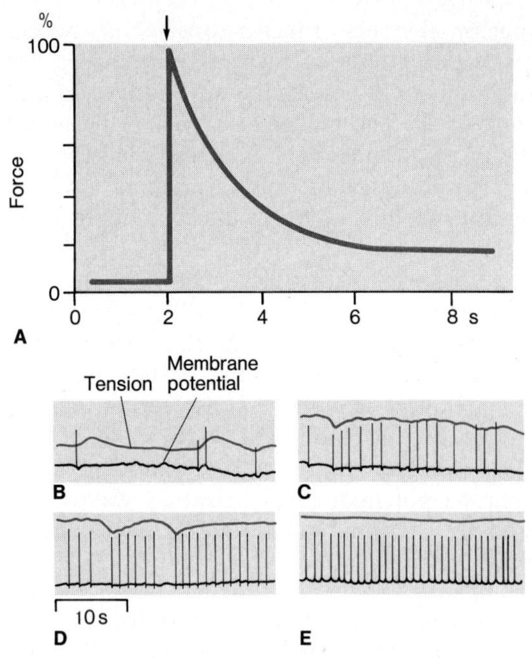

Fig. 4-17. A Viscoelastic behavior of a smooth muscle. When the muscle is stretched *(arrow)* its tension rises suddenly. As a result of plastic or viscoelastic compliance of the musculature, in the subsequent "poststretching" phase the muscle tension falls off quasi-exponentially. **B–E** Stretch-activated contraction of a smooth muscle. Recordings of membrane potential in a single cell (*black* traces) and force developed by a strip of tenia coli (*red* traces) before **(B)** and after **(C–E)** increasing passive stretch [5]. **B** Unstretched preparation; low-frequency action potentials followed by single twitches. **C–E** Stretching causes bursts of action potentials; the single twitches fuse to an incomplete tetanus **(C,D)** or complete tetanus **(E)**

ences are explained by structural properties. Although these muscle cells are electrically coupled by nexus, many of them make direct neuromuscular contact with the innervating nerve fibers (cf. p. 341). The transmitter substances released when a nerve impulse arrives can reach these effector cells by diffusion and activate them. In the muscle cells of seminal ducts or arterioles, for instance, they give rise to neurogenic prepotentials followed by action potentials, which elicit a tetaniform contraction. When directly applied to an isolated vessel muscle, noradrenalin produces a maintained contraction *(contracture):* the membrane of the cell – with the exception of the smooth muscles of the pulmonary and ear arteries – is depolarized throughout the time that noradrenalin acts.

Excitation-contraction coupling. Excitation of the smooth muscle cells causes either an *increased calcium-ion inflow* through potential-dependent **calcium channels** in the cell membrane or – mediated by the intracellular "second messenger" **inositol trisphosphate** – a release of calcium ions from the sarcoplasmic reticulum. In both cases the result is an increase in the sarcoplasmic Ca^{2+} concentration, which activates the contractile structures. Like cardiac and skeletal muscle, smooth muscles always relax when the intracellular calcium-ion concentration falls below about 10^{-7} mol/l. But they relax much more slowly, for the processes of uptake of calcium ions into the *sarcoplasmic reticulum* or removal through the cell membrane are slower. Removal of the Ca^{2+} results in splitting, by a phosphatase, of a functionally important phosphate group from a peptide chain of the myosin. The dephosphorylated myosin heads are incapable of forming cross-bridges to the actin. At the beginning of a contraction the calcium ions released from the sarcoplasmic reticulum activate, in conjunction with the calcium-binding protein **calmodulin,** a myosin kinase; this enzyme transfers a phosphate group from ATP to the myosin, thus setting off the actin-myosin interaction and the contraction. It is still unclear whether, in addition to this mechanism, control of smooth-muscle contractility involves other calcium switches, nor is it certain how intracellularly formed cyclic adenosine monophosphate (cAMP) or cyclic guanosine monophosphate (cGMP) lowers the tonus of smooth muscle cells. Possibly, cAMP may inhibit the myosin kinase or enhance calcium uptake into the sarcoplasmic reticulum. cGMP, on the other hand, may well be the intracellular messenger mediating relaxation of vascular smooth muscle induced by an endothelium-derived relaxing factor [3].

4.6 References

Textbooks and Handbooks

1. Hasselbach, W.: Muskel. In: Gauer, O.H., Kramer, K., Jung, R. (eds):Physiologie des Menschen. Vol. 4: Muskel. München-Berlin-Wien: Urban u. Schwarzenberg 1975
2. Peachey, L.D., Adrian, R.H. und Geiger S.R. (eds): Handbook of Physiology, Section 10: Skeletal Muscle, American Physiol. Soc. Bethesda 1983
2a. Rüegg, J.C. Calcium in Muscle Activation. Berlin-Heidelberg-New York: Springer 1986. Corrected, second printing 1988
3. Wilkie, D.R.: Muscle. Second edition, London: Edward Arnold Limited, 1976

Original Papers and Reviews

4. Blinks, J.R., Rüdel, R., Taylor, S.R.: Calcium transients in isolated amphibian skeletal muscle fibres: Detection with aequorin. J. Physiol. 277, 291–323 (1978)
5. Bülbring, E., Brading, A.F., Jones, A.W., Tomita, T.: Smooth Muscle, London: Edward Arnold 1970

6. Golenhofen, K.: Die myogene Basis der glattmuskulären Motorik. Klin. Wschr. *56*, 211–244 (1978)
7. Gordon, A.M., Huxley, A.F., Julian, F.J.: The variation in isometric tension with sarcomere length in vertebrate muscle fibres. J. Physiol. (Lond.) *184*, 170 (1966)
8. Hasselbach, W., Makinose, J.: Über den Mechanismus des Calciumtransports durch die Membranen des sarkoplasmatischen Reticulums. Biochem. Z. *339*, 94 (1963)
9. Huxley, A.F., Taylor, R.E.: Local activation of striated muscle fibres. J. Physiol. (Lond.) *144*, 426 (1958)
10. Huxley, A.F.: Muscular contraction. J. Physiol. *243*, 1–43 (1974)
11. Huxley, H.E., Hanson, J.: Changes in the cross-striation of muscle during contraction and stretch and their structural interpretation. Nature *173*, 973 (1954)
12. Huxley, H.E.: The mechanism of muscular contraction. Science *164*, 1356 (1969)
13. Huxley, H.E.: Structural changes in the actin and myosin containing filaments during contraction. Cold Spr. Harb. Symp. Quant. Biol. *37*, 361 (1973)
14. Huxley, H.E., Simmons, R.M., Faruki, A.R., Kress, M., Bordas, J., Koch, M.H.J.: Msec time resolved change in X-ray reflections from contracting muscle during rapid mechanical transients, recorded using synchrotron radiation. Proc. Natl. Acad. Sci., USA 78, 2297 (1981)
15. Infante, A.A., Davies, R.E.: Adenosintriphosphate breakdown during a single isotonic twitch of frog sartorious muscle. Biochem. Biophys. Res. Commun. *9*, 410 (1962)
16. Jewell, B.R., Wilkie, D.R.: The mechanical properties of relaxing muscle. J. Physiol. (Lond.) 152: 30–47, 1960
17. Mannherz, H.G. Schirmer, R.H.: Die Molekularbiologie der Bewegung. Chemie in unserer Zeit *6*, 165–202 (1970)
18. Rüegg, J.C.: Smooth muscle tone. Physiol. Rev. *51*, 201 (1971)
19. Weber, H.H., Portzehl, H.: The transference of the muscle energy in the contraction cycle. Progr. Biophys. Mol. Biol. *4*, 61 (1954)
20. Wilkie, D.R.: The relation between force and velocity in human muscle. J. Physiol. *110*, 249–280 (1950)

5 Motor Systems

R.F. SCHMIDT and M. WIESENDANGER

5.1 Neural Control of Posture and Movement: A Survey

Responsibility for the neural control of the skeletal musculature described in Chapter 4 – that is, for initiating and accomplishing all movements – lies with the **motor centers** of the CNS. These centers must ensure that the motoneurons to the musculature are excited and inhibited by precisely the right amount, so that the resulting muscle contractions produce the desired movement, no more and no less. But movements can be executed perfectly only if the initial posture of trunk and limbs is appropriate. The *neural control of the interplay of posture and movement and of their adequate coupling* is one of the most important functions of the motor centers.

Phenomenology of Motor Acts

Reflex-controlled movements [9]. When one pinches a hind foot of a decerebrate frog with intact spinal cord, the foot is pulled away. When a piece of filter paper soaked in acid is laid on the skin of the frog's back, it is soon pushed off by an accurate movement of the nearest hindleg. To denote such *automatic, repeatable and goal-directed responses of the organism to stimuli*, in 1771 the physiologist UNZER introduced the term **reflex**. Destruction of the spinal cord abolishes all reflexes. Therefore they can be ascribed to the activity of central nervous structures.

Stereotyped reactions are also frequently elicited in intact animals and in humans by stimuli from the environment (or within themselves), behavior that in the course of evolution or individual development has proved to be a particularly suitable response to such a stimulus. There are many familiar examples of these **innate** or **learned reflexes** (corneal, coughing, swallowing, withdrawal reflexes etc.). But most reflexes occur without our consciously noticing them. Examples include the reflexes by which food is propelled or processed in the stomach and intestines, and those that continually adjust blood flow and breathing to the body's needs.

Program-controlled (automatic) movements. Decerebrate dogs can make rhythmic movements, such as scratching the back with a hindpaw or walking movements, even after all sensory inflow is prevented from reaching the spinal cord by transection of the dorsal roots. It follows that movements cannot be organized entirely on the basis of reflexes. Breathing is another rhythmic process that continues under neural control even without any external stimuli. Such movement sequences, maintained by the CNS with no contribution from external stimuli, are called **"program-controlled"** or **automatic.** As demonstrated by the example of the spinal frog, even neuronal networks limited to the spinal cord (the *propriospinal system*) can supply many movement programs which, once initiated by a particular event, are then executed automatically.

Once the CNS had been found to be capable of stimulus-independent activities, the hypothesis that movements are basically controlled by programs rather than by reflexes rapidly gained ground; the **predominance of "program organization" in the CNS** became widely accepted. Breathing, walking and scratching are examples of innate (i.e., inherited) programs, to which many learned programs are added in the course of one's life. Among the latter are skills used in sport or work, such as gymnastic maneuvers or typing, which become nearly automatic after sufficient practice.

In psychology, the reflex theory of movement has given rise to the various stimulus-response theories of behavior, whereas the program theory supports interpretations that emphasize the stimulus-independent (spontaneous, voluntary, arbitrary) human acts. But little is gained by clinging to, or overemphasizing, one theory or the other. It seems that a combination of the two, in which **central programs can be influenced by sensory feedback,** provides the best framework for the data available at present, while leaving the way clear for further experiments.

Voluntary and involuntary movements. Especially in clinical parlance, the terms "voluntary" and "involuntary" are often used to describe movements. What is meant is that in the opinion of the observer and as reported by the patient, the movement was made intentionally or unintentionally. The observer's judgment is based on behavioral features and the patient's is based on subjective experience. As long as one keeps in mind the limits of these criteria, for practical purposes these words are justified in everyday clinical use and in discussing motor systems. But apart from such use by physicians or psychologists they are basically unacceptable, because in the natural sciences categories that can be established only by introspection are questionable. The same applies to the problem of consciousness and free will.

More or less automatic movements. Around the turn of the century the neurologist HUGHLINGS JACKSON suggested that all movements ("performances") could be arranged on a hierarchical scale, between the extremes **"least automatic"** and **"most automatic".** Today this ordering seems of **only limited usefulness.** On closer examination it turns out that movements "more automatic" in the Jacksonian sense (e.g., breathing or swallowing) are based largely on *innate, central patterns* (programs), whereas the "less" or "least automatic" are mostly *learned during life* (e.g., speaking or singing). However, the latter movements, once learned, are also nearly automatic in execution.

Postural and goal-directed functions. Another important consideration is that much of our muscular activity does not generate movement directed outward, into our surroundings, but rather serves to produce and maintain the body's **posture** and **orientation in space**. Without this postural control by the motor system we would collapse into helpless lumps on the ground – as the spectacle of a knocked-out boxer vividly illustrates.
In addition, the motor system controls all the **goal-directed** movements related to the world outside our bodies. Such movements are always accompanied by actions and reactions of the postural system, whether to prepare for a movement or to correct posture during and after the movement. The intimate interlinkage between the postural and goal-directed functions is a fundamental characteristic of the motor system. For didactic purposes, however, it is useful to consider them separately; as will become apparent in the discussion of the roles and central organization of the various "motor centers", some of them are concerned mainly with posture and others, mainly with goal-directed movements (see pp. 97 and 113).

Locations and Functions of Motor Centers

Hierarchy and partnership. The structures responsible for the neural control of posture and movement **("motor centers")** are distributed throughout the central nervous system, from the cerebral cortex to the spinal cord. Their **hierarchical order** is immediately evident; it can be interpreted as the result of progressive adaptation of the motor system to more complex tasks in the course of evolution. This phylogenetic development occurred not so much by reconstruction of existing motor systems as by superposition of additional control systems to achieve new kinds of performance. In parallel with this process, however, certain motor centers became highly specialized. The result is that the centers controlling motor activity not only serve as elements in a hierarchy but simultaneously, and increasingly, **operate in partnership**.
Figure 5-1 summarizes diagrammatically the **central** nervous flow of **activity** that governs posture and movement. For each set of motor centers in the left column, the right column shows the contribution it is thought to make to the ultimate motor action. To make this guide to initial orientation easier to follow, the hierarchical aspects are emphasized, and some of the higher motor

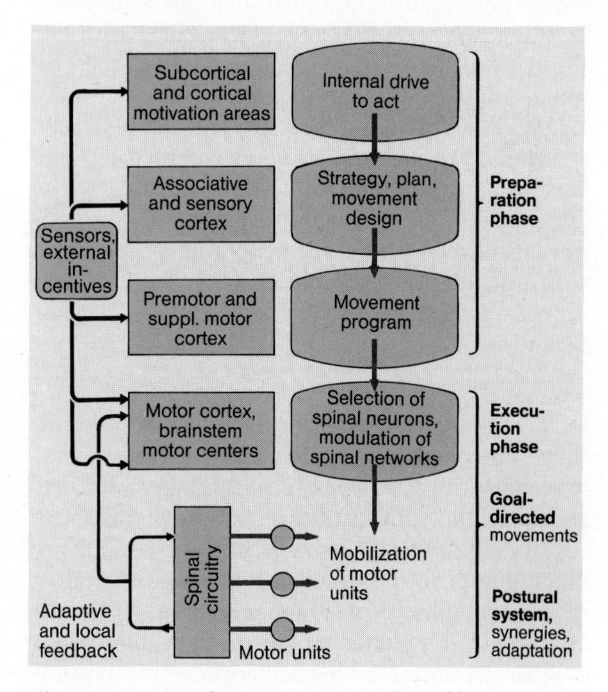

Fig. 5-1. Survey of motor systems. Hierarchical representation of the central nervous flow of excitation related to posture and movement. For simplicity, some higher motor centers (cerebellum, basal ganglia, motor thalamus) have been omitted. Their incorporation into the motor system is indicated in Fig. 5-2. (Extensive discussion in text)

centers (cerebellum, basal ganglia, motor thalamus) have been omitted for the sake of simplicity (their places in the motor system are discussed below in connection with Fig. 5-2). The brackets on the far right distinguish the preparation and execution phases of which most motor acts are composed; on the far left is a reminder that sensory inputs are of importance in all phases of motor activity (see below).

Spinal motor sytems. At the level of the spinal cord, the sensory afferents make a variety of connections with motoneurons, most by way of interneurons. The pattern of activation here determines whether movements will be promoted or inhibited. This circuitry, which constitutes the *reflex arcs* on which the **spinal reflexes** are based, is fixed anatomically. Nevertheless, its operation is governed to a great extent by other spinal or higher centers, which modulate differentially the ease with which signals can pass through the various reflex arcs.

The term "reflex" was originally derived from the notion that each reflex movement was stereotyped, appearing as a result of a sensory input (see above) as though the spinal cord had *reflected* it like a mirror. A much broader definition is now required, one that takes account of the central modulation and also includes inhibition. In this sense, a spinal reflex would be brought about by a change in neuronal activity elicited by spinal afferents that promotes or inhibits movements. The spinal reflexes amount to a **library of elementary postural and movement programs** that can be modified over a wide range to be integrated in an intended movement. The organism can draw upon these programs as required, with no need for the higher levels of the central nervous system to deal with the details of their execution.

Higher motor systems. This category includes all the supraspinal centers that are involved in motor control. Whereas postural functions and their coordination with goal-directed movement are controlled chiefly by structures in the brainstem, performance of the directed movements requires the participation of still higher centers. As shown in Fig. 5-1, the **drives to act** and the **movement designs** produced in the subcortical motivation areas and in the association cortex are subsequently converted to *movement programs*, which are passed on to the spinal cord and thence to the skeletal musculature for the actual execution of the movement.

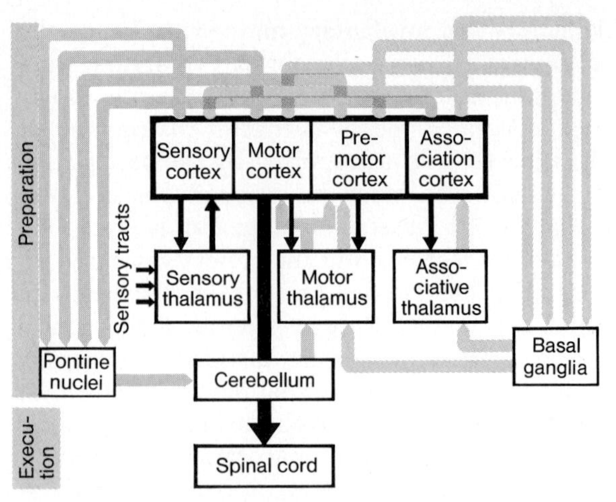

Fig. 5-2. Survey of the flow paths of excitation in the motor system, including the centers not shown in Fig. 5-1. In this representation the aspect of partnership in the operation of the various higher motor centers is brought out by arranging them horizontally (cf. Fig. 5-1), and emphasis is placed on the significance of the internal loops, especially those through the basal ganglia and the cerebellum, in the preparation of a movement

In Fig. 5-2 the flow diagram of Fig. 5-1 is expanded to show the motor centers that were previously omitted and, at the same time, to bring out more clearly the **partnership of motor centers** within the hierarchy. The associative, premotor and motor cortical areas, shown in the left column of Fig. 5-1, here are arranged horizontally from right to left, indicating that they are interconnected, and the sensory cortex is added on the left. The pink and gray flow paths in the figure show that in parallel with the corticocortical information processing there are massive cortex-to-cortex loops by way of extracortical structures, in one case the pontine nuclei and the cerebellum, and in the other the basal ganglia. The cerebellar loop and one of the two loops through the basal ganglia (the *"motor"* loop) also pass through motor nuclei of the thalamus; the other (*"complex"*) loop through the basal ganglia runs to the association cortex (for details see Figs. 5-20, 5-22 and 5-23 and the relevant sections of the text).

Movements that **accompany** other motor patterns, such as swinging of the arms during walking or the expressions and gestures associated with speaking, in many cases are controlled by deeper brain structures, so that involvement of the motor cortex is not absolutely required. Disappearance of such accompanying movements is characteristic of certain pathological states – for example, the Parkinson syndrome (p. 111).

The system controlling **gaze direction** is discussed separately, beginning on p. 237).

Coupling of sensory and motor systems. It should already be clear from Figs. 5-1 and 5-2 that sensory information and motor actions are intricately intermeshed. For movements to be carried out in a functionally appropriate way, all the structures involved in their production require and receive information from the periphery as to the momentary position of the body and the progress of the intended movement. Furthermore, certain kinds of sensory information – for example, from vision and touch – can be acquired only with the assistance of differentiated motor acts. In both cases some of the sensory input reaches the motor system by a short local route (e.g., spinal reflexes), but part is also carried through long reflex loops that are quite likely to include cortical structures (see p. 116).

5.2 Sensors for Motor Functions: Muscle Spindles and Tendon Organs

Morphological Aspects

Structure of the muscle spindles [25]. Practically every muscle contains **stretch receptors (or sensors)**, called **muscle spindles** because of their shape. Their structure is shown schematically in Fig. 5-3A. A capsule of connective tissue encloses a number of muscle fibers that are thinner and shorter than the ordinary muscle fibers. The fibers in the capsule are called **intrafusal muscle fibers**; the ordinary fibers, which make up most of the muscle and are responsible for the work it performs, are the **extrafusal muscle fibers**. The difference in size is quite conspicuous; the intrafusal fibers are about 15-30 μm in diameter and 4-7 mm long, whereas the extrafusal fibers have diameters of the order of 50 to 100 μm and lengths ranging from a few millimeters to many centimeters or decimeters (see also pp. 62ff.). At each end the muscle spindle is attached to the connective-tissue sheath (perimysium) of an extrafusal fiber bundle, by way of tendonlike strands of connective tissue 0.5–1 mm long.

Afferent innervation. The main **sensory innervation** of these stretch receptors is provided by afferent fibers that wind several times around the centers of the intrafusal fibers, forming **annulospiral endings** (Fig. 5-3A). These afferents are thick, myelinated fibers (diameter about 13 μm) called **Ia fibers** (see also Table 2-1, p. 38). Each spindle receives only a single Ia fiber, which branches to form several annulospiral endings (also called **primary muscle-spindle endings**).

Many, though not all muscle spindles also have a **second sensory innervation**. The afferent fibers with these stretch-sensitive endings are thinner than those with annulospiral endings (Group-II fibers, diameter ca. 9 μm; see Table 2-1, p. 38). Just as the latter are called primary endings because of their Ia innervation, the receptor structures innervated by **Group-II fibers** are called **secondary muscle-spindle endings.** Their form is similar to that of the primary

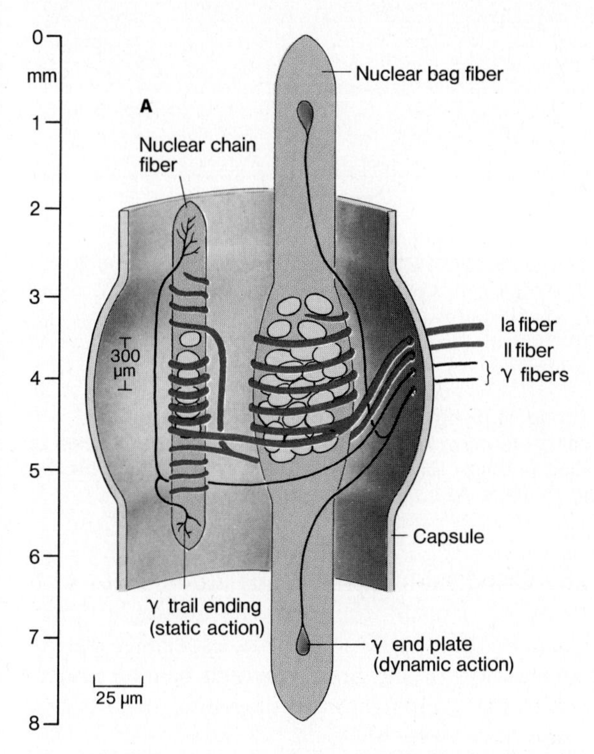

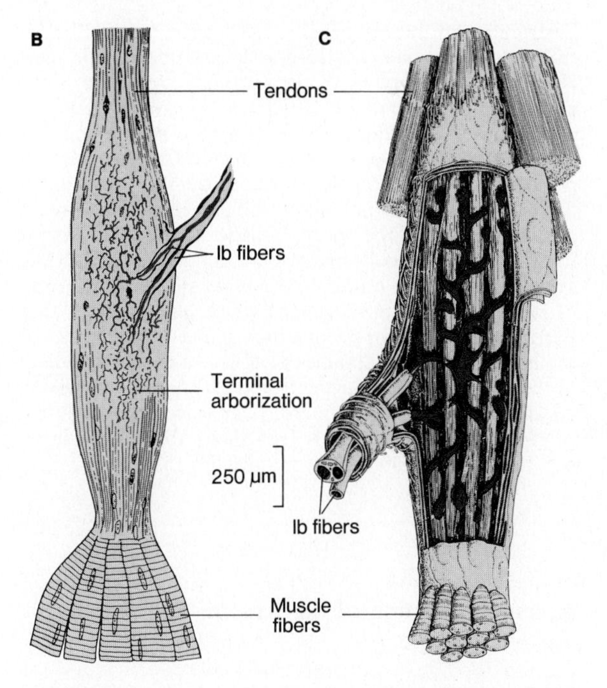

Fig. 5-3 A-C. Structure of muscle spindles and tendon organs. **A** Schematic drawing of the main components of a muscle spindle, a composite of many histological and physiological data, especially those of BARKER, BOYD, MATTHEWS and their coworkers [15, 25]. To gain a rough idea of the dimensions of the spindle, note the differing longitudinal and transverse scales. **B** Drawing of a Golgi tendon organ as seen in the light microscope, by RAMON Y CAJAL (1906). **C** Reconstruction of the terminal arborization *(red)* of a Ib fiber inside a tendon spindle (from R.V. KRISTIC: Die Gewebe des Menschen und der Säugetiere. Berlin-Heidelberg-New York: Springer 1978)

endings but not nearly as regular; often they are described as spiral, but sometimes as resembling a flower spray.

Efferent innervation. In addition to their sensory innervation, the intrafusal muscle fibers have a **motor innervation** just as the extrafusal fibers do; however, the motor axons of the intrafusal fibers are thinner than normal. Normal motor axons are usually termed Aα fibers, or α (alpha) fibers for short. The motor axons of the intrafusal musculature are called Aγ fibers, shortened to γ (gamma) fibers. (The diameter of the α fibers is 9–21 μm, and that of the γ fibers is 2–8 μm; see Table 2-1, p. 38. The diameters of the muscle fibers supplied by these two kinds of motoneurons are proportional to the diameters of the nerve fibers. The reason for this relationship is unknown.) The structures by which the γ motor axons synapse with the intrafusal muscle fibers resemble end plates and are usually located toward the ends of the muscle fibers (Fig. 5-3A). There are two morphological types of intrafusal fibers (nuclear bag and nuclear chain fibers, Fig. 5-3A), of γ motoneurons, and of intrafusal end-plate formations (γ end plates and γ trail endings, Fig. 5-3A). The physiological significance of these differences is becoming increasingly clear, but will not be discussed here (for further information see [25]).

Structure of the tendon organs. All the muscles of terrestrial vertebrates are also equipped with sense organs in the tendons, near the junction with the muscles. These **tendon organs** (or *Golgi tendon organs;* Fig. 5-3B,C) consist of the tendon fascicles of about 10 extrafusal muscle fibers enclosed in a connective-tissue capsule and supplied by one or two thick myelinated nerve fibers (diameter 10–20 μm). The afferent nerve fibers are called **Ib fibers.** After entering the capsule they divide into thinner branches, eventually becoming unmyelinated, and form highly ramified endings among the tendon fascicles (Fig. 5-3B,C; for details see [15]).

Distribution of muscle spindles and tendon organs. Practically all mammalian striated muscles contain **muscle spindles.** There are none in the extraocular muscles of some animals, such as the rabbit, cat, dog and horse, but humans and many other mammals have numerous muscle spindles in these muscles as well. The number of muscle spindles per muscle depends on the muscle's size and function. In humans it varies from about 40 spindles in the small hand muscles to 500 in the triceps muscle of the arm, with a total of about 20,000 spindles for all the muscles. The **spindle density**, the number of muscle spindles per gram of muscle tissue, is particularly high in small muscles that participate in fine movements, such as the small muscles of the hands (up to 130 spindles/g); it is less than 1 spindle/g in the large muscles near the trunk. The **number of tendon organs** per muscle has not been extensively investigated. A general rule of thumb is that there are 50-80 tendon organs for every 100 muscle spindles [1, 15, 25].

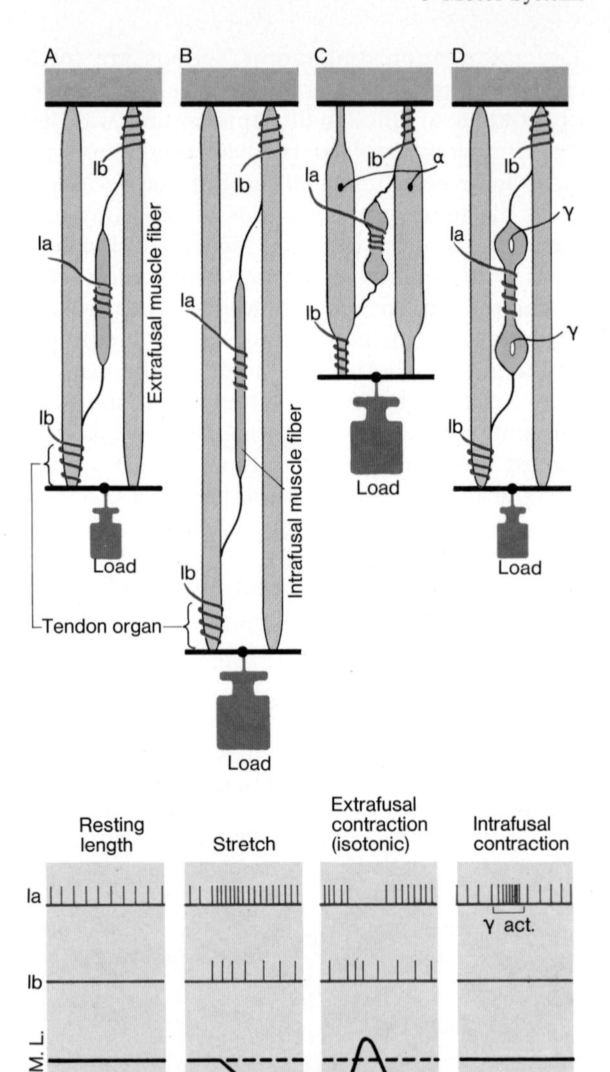

Fig. 5-4. Schematic drawing of the positions and the discharge patterns of the muscle spindles and the Golgi tendon organs in the muscle at rest **(A)** and their changes in shape under passive stretch **(B)**, during isotonic contraction of the extrafusal muscle fibers **(C)** and during contraction of the intrafusal muscle fibers alone **(D**, γ act.). The combination of (B) and (D) causes especially strong activation of the muscle-spindle afferents. Ia, discharge patterns of the primary muscle-spindle afferents in their Ia fibers. Ib, discharge patterns of the tendon organs, in Ib fibers. M.L., muscle length

Receptor Function of the Muscle Spindles and Tendon Organs

Position and discharge pattern. In terms of their adequate stimulus, muscle spindles and tendon organs are both **stretch receptors.** However, their arrangement in the muscle differs (Fig. 5-4); the muscle spindles lie in **parallel** with the extrafusal fibers, and the tendon organs are **in series** with them. As a result, there are characteristic differences in the discharge pattern, especially during contraction of the muscle, which can be understood by comparing the diagrams of the two receptors in Fig. 5-4.

When a muscle is stretched to about its resting length (Fig. 5-4A) most of the primary muscle-spindle endings (those of Ia fibers) discharge, whereas the tendon organs (supplied by Ib fibers) as a rule are silent. During **stretching** (Fig. 5-4B)

the discharge rate of the Ia fibers increases, and the tendon organs also begin to discharge. **Isotonic contraction** of the extrafusal musculature (Fig. 5-4C) decreases the tension in the muscle spindle, so that the discharge of the receptor ceases. The tendon organ, however, remains stretched and its discharge rate actually increases transiently during the contraction, because the acceleration of the load briefly stretches the tendon organ still more.
These findings imply that the **muscle spindles** measure primarily the **length** of the muscle, whereas the **tendon organs** measure primarily the **tension**. It would therefore be expected that during *isometric contraction* the discharge rate of the tendon organs would greatly increase, whereas that of the muscle spindles would remain about the same. (The role of the muscle receptors in the sense of effort is discussed on p. 207).

Action of the fusimotor nerve fibers. One way to excite the muscle spindle is, as described above, to stretch the muscle; because the extrafusal fibers and the intrafusal fibers lie in parallel, this procedure stretches both of them, activating the stretch receptor (cf. Fig. 5-4A,B). There is a second way to excite the primary muscle-spindle endings – by contraction of the intrafusal muscle fibers via the γ motoneurons (Fig. 5-4D). The contractile force exerted by the intrafusal muscle fibers is too small to change the length or tension of a muscle as a whole, even if all the intrafusal fibers in the muscle contract simultaneously. However, the intrafusal contraction **stretches the central part of the intrafusal fibers** (Fig. 5-4D), thus inducing excitation of the primary muscle spindle ending and its afferents, just as when the whole muscle is stretched.
These two means of spindle activation, *stretching the muscle* and *intrafusal contraction*, can have additive effects. On the other hand, intrafusal contraction can more or less compensate the action of extrafusal contraction, so that even during shortening of the muscle the spindles can continue to function as length sensors. In other words, *intrafusal prestretching* of the stretch receptor can serve to avoid silencing during active shortening of the muscle, thus preserving the receptor's ability to signal small perturbations.

Secondary muscle-spindle endings. The secondary endings, with Group-II afferent fibers, are also **stretch receptors**, with thresholds higher than those of primary spindle endings. This threshold can also be shifted by contraction of the intrafusal muscle fibers. The function of the secondary endings in spinal reflexes is less well understood than that of primary endings. They signal mainly length rather than length changes.

5.3 Spinal Motor Reflexes

Elements of a reflex arc; reflex time. The general definition of reflexes has been presented above (see pp. 82 and 84). The **reflex arc** comprises the afferents, central neurons and motoneurons consecutively activated during the reflex. All **sensors** participate in reflexes of some kind, so that their afferent fibers serve as the **afferent pathway** in the reflex arc concerned. The number of **central neurons** in a reflex arc is always greater than one except for the monosynaptic stretch reflex (see below). The **efferent pathway** is provided by either motor axons or the postganglionic fibers of the autonomic nervous system, and the **effectors** are the skeletal musculature or the smooth musculature, the heart, and the glands.
The time between onset of a stimulus and action of the effector is called the **reflex time.** In most cases it is determined chiefly by the *conduction time* in the afferent and efferent pathways and in the central parts of the reflex arc (the conduction velocities of human nerve fibers are all somewhat smaller than those given in Table 2-1, p. 38, for the cat [18]). To this are added the times required for (i) the transformation of a stimulus into a conducted impulse at the receptor, (ii) transmission across synapses at central neurons (synapse time), (iii) transmission from the efferent pathway to the effector (e.g., endplate potential) and (iv) activation of the effector by excitation of the membrane (e.g., excitation-contraction coupling).

Reflex Arc with Primary Muscle-Spindle Afferents

Stretch reflex elicited by muscle stretch. The *Ia fibers* of the muscle spindles make excitatory synapses with homonymous α motoneurons (that is, the motoneurons to their own muscles). **Activation of the primary muscle-spindle endings** by stretching the muscle must therefore cause **excitation of the homonymous motoneurons**. An experiment to illustrate this is diagrammed in Fig. 5-5. The muscle is stretched briefly by tapping the recording lever lightly with a hammer; after a short latency the muscle contracts, as shown by the recording at the lower left. This reflex involves only one synapse, between the Ia fibers and the homonymous motoneuron, and therefore is called the **monosynaptic stretch reflex** of the musculature. (The term **myotatic reflex** is also commonly used for the stretch reflex.) The

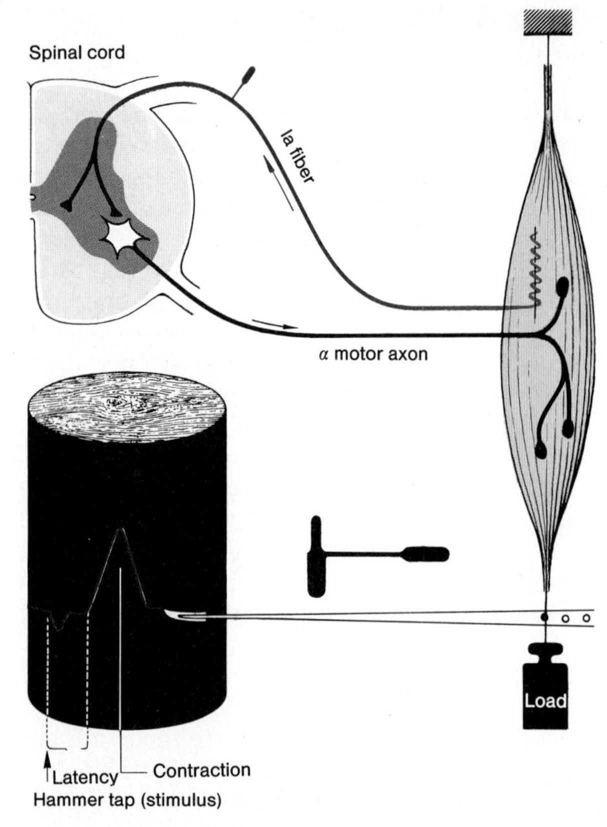

Fig. 5-5. Reflex arc of the monosynaptic stretch reflex. A lever is connected to the muscle in such a way that its tip traces out an amplified record of the muscle length; a light tap with a hammer on the lever (downward deflection in the record) after a brief latency produces contraction of the muscle. The reflex arc underlying this reflex is diagrammed, from the muscle spindles via the Ia fibers to the motoneurons and back to the muscle

monosynaptic stretch reflex is the simplest example of a complete reflex arc (see also the other examples in Figs. 5-7 and 5-8).

The best-known example of a monosynaptic stretch reflex is the **patellar tendon** ("knee-jerk") **reflex:** the quadriceps muscle is stretched briefly by striking its tendon below the patella. After a short latency there is a twitch of the muscle which causes the freely hanging lower leg to be raised. The expression "tendon reflex" is thus misleading; here, as in the other "tendon reflexes", a monosynaptic muscle-stretch reflex is involved. Clinically important examples of such reflex tests include the following. *Head:* stretching the muscle that closes the mouth by tapping the chin (masseter reflex); *arm:* stretching the biceps muscle by tapping its tendon at the elbow; *leg:* stretching the triceps surae in the lower leg by tapping the calcaneal tendon (Achilles-tendon reflex). Monosynaptic stretch reflexes elicited by tapping a tendon are also given the clinical designation **T-reflexes.**
Systematic testing of the stretch reflexes is of special significance in that the reflex arcs pass through different spinal segments, so that disturbances in individual reflexes can provide evidence as to the level of a pathological process in the spinal cord. On the whole, there is great variation in the **magnitude of a stretch reflex,** which depends heavily on the activity in other (facilitatory or inhibitory) inputs to the neurons involved (see below). Except in extreme cases, therefore, the feature of clinical significance is less the *vigor* of the reflex than the question whether there is a difference between the reflexes on the two sides, or whether certain reflexes stand out as abnormal when compared with the overall reflex behavior.

Facilitation of T-reflexes. Weak patellar-tendon and other T-reflexes of the lower limbs can often be elicited more readily when the patient is told to hook his hands together in front of his chest and try to pull them apart, or to press the hand of a third person **(Jendrassik's maneuver).** The exertions required by these actions cause a facilitatory activation of the motoneurons in the lumbar cord.
By a similar mechanism, T-reflexes can be facilitated by a slight background activity of the motoneurons (slight tensing of the muscle to be tested).

Induction of H-reflexes. In both the laboratory and neurological practice the human monosynaptic stretch reflex can also be induced by electrical stimulation of the Ia afferents of a muscle nerve. This form of the monosynaptic stretch reflex is called the **H-reflex** (after PAUL HOFFMANN). Usually the H-reflex is elicited by electrical stimulation of the popliteal nerve, and the response is recorded electromyographically by surface (cutaneous) or intramuscular (needle) electrodes from the triceps surae muscle, in particular the soleus component (Fig. 5-6). Because the Ia fibers have the lowest threshold of all nerve fibers, with weak stimuli (20–30 V in Fig. 5-6C) at first only the reflex response (H wave) appears, with a latency of 30–35 ms. With stronger stimuli (from 35 V on in Fig. 5-6B, C) there is progressively greater excitation of α-motoneurons as well, which activate the muscle with a latency of 5–10 ms (M waves in Fig. 5-6B, C). As the stimulus intensity continues to increase, both responses at first become progressively larger; then, while the M response proceeds to increase to the maximum, the H response becomes steadily smaller. When the M response is maximal the H response is almost completely suppressed (stimulus intensity $\geq$ 95 V in Fig. 5-6B, C).

Three factors are responsible for the *decrease in the H-response as stimulus intensity increases.* 1. Progressively more Ib fibers from the Golgi tendon organs are excited, in addition to the Ia fibers. The Ib fibers inhibit the associated (homonymous) motoneurons (cf. Fig. 5-10, p. 92). 2. Stimulation of the α motor axons generates not only orthodromic action potentials, which produce the M-response, but also antidromic impulses. The latter activate the reflex path of Renshaw inhibition (see p. 94). 3. The antidromic action potentials in the α motor axons also invade the soma and dendrites of the motoneurons, where they come into collision with the excitatory events triggered by the Ia fibers. It can happen either that a motoneuronal impulse triggered by way of the (more rapidly conducting) Ia fibers encounters an antidromic

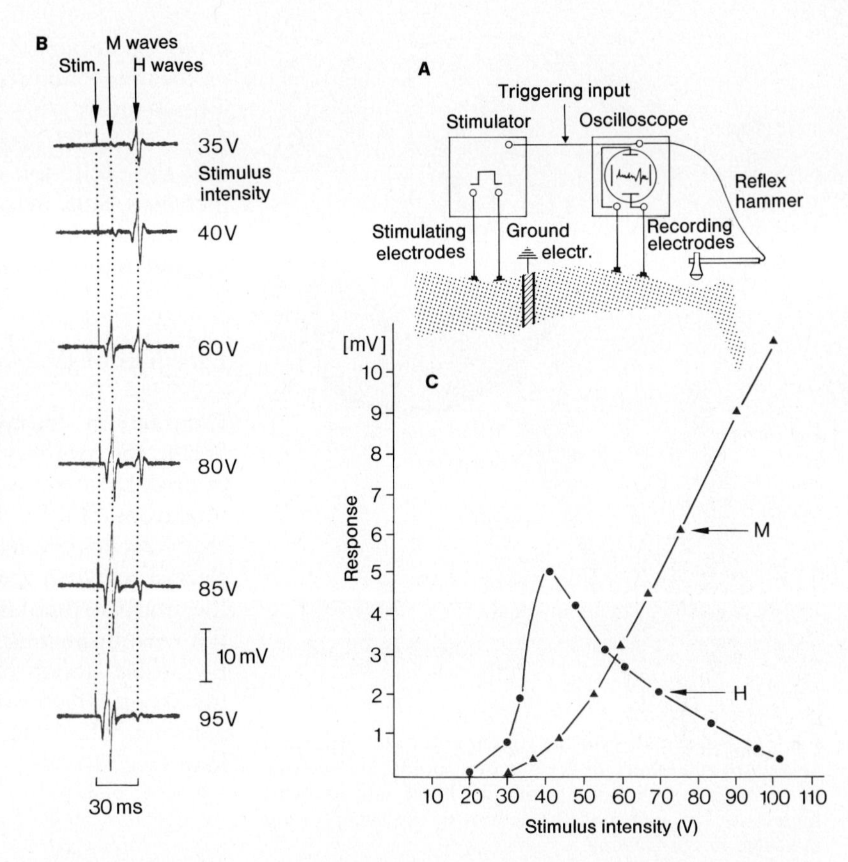

Fig. 5-6 A-C. Production and recording of H- and T-reflexes in humans. **A** Arrangement of the apparatus. To initiate a T-reflex of the triceps surae, the tendon is tapped with reflex hammer equipped with a contact switch. Closure of the switch triggers the oscilloscope beam, which displays the electromyographically recorded response. The H-reflexes are elicited by stimulating the popliteal nerve through the skin with 1-ms square pulses. Again, the stimulus is used to synchronize the sweep of the oscilloscope beam. **B** H and M responses as stimulus intensity is increased. **C** Amplitudes of the H and M responses *(ordinate)* plotted as a function of stimulus intensity *(abscissa)*. Healthy subject. (B,C) from HOPF and STRUPPLER: Elektromyographie. Stuttgart: Thieme 1974)

impulse and the two extinguish one another, or that the antidromic impulse makes the motoneuron refractory just at the time that the Ia excitation occurs. Of these factors, the third is by far the most important.

Silent period. After a T- or H-reflex the sustained activity of the muscle falls off sharply for a brief period (100–500 ms). At least four factors combine to produce this **post-reflex silent period.** 1. The synchronous reflex contraction relieves the tension on the muscle spindles and thus reduces or stops the tonic, excitatory afferent drive from primary muscle-spindle endings (cf. Fig. 5-4C). 2. The reflex contraction activates Golgi tendon organs, which have an inhibitory action on the associated motoneurons (cf. Fig. 5-10). 3. The synchronous excitation of motoneurons causes a transitory enhancement of Renshaw inhibition (cf. Fig. 5-12). 4. The hyperpolarizing afterpotentials following the action potentials in the motoneurons participating in the reflex reduce their excitability temporarily.

Stretch reflex for the control of muscle length. The *physiological significance of the monosynaptic reflex arc* goes far beyond its usefulness in diagnosis. It can be regarded primarily as a control mechanism for the regulation of muscle length. That is, stretching the muscle causes activation of the muscle spindles, monosynaptic excitation of the motoneurons, and contraction – a shortening of the muscle that counteracts the stretching. This *reflex maintenance of muscle length* is particularly important with regard to the preservation of **maintained tone** in postural muscles. For example, while standing upright, whenever the knee joint bends even so slightly that the bending is neither seen nor felt, the associated stretching of the quadriceps muscle enhances the activity in the primary muscle-spindle endings. As a result, the α motoneurons to the quadriceps are additionally activated (by a "patellar tendon reflex"; cf. Fig. 5-7) and the tone of the muscle is increased, instantly counteracting the incipient bending. Conversely, excessive contraction of the muscle reduces the stimulus to its stretch receptors. Their discharge rate, the excitatory input to the motoneurons, is diminished, and the muscle tone decreases. By means of this control circuit, then, the **length of the muscle** is kept constant.

Reciprocal antagonist inhibition by Ia afferents. The Ia fibers do not only have monosynaptic excitatory connections with homonymous motoneurons, to form the reflex arcs of the stretch reflex. They also make **inhibitory** connections with the antagonistic motoneurons (Fig. 5-7). The inhibitory reflex arc includes a central interneuron and hence is **disynaptic;** that is, there are two central synapses, one (excitatory) between the Ia fibers and the interneurons, and a second (inhibitory) between the axons of the interneurons and the motoneurons. These are the shortest inhibitory reflex arcs that are known,

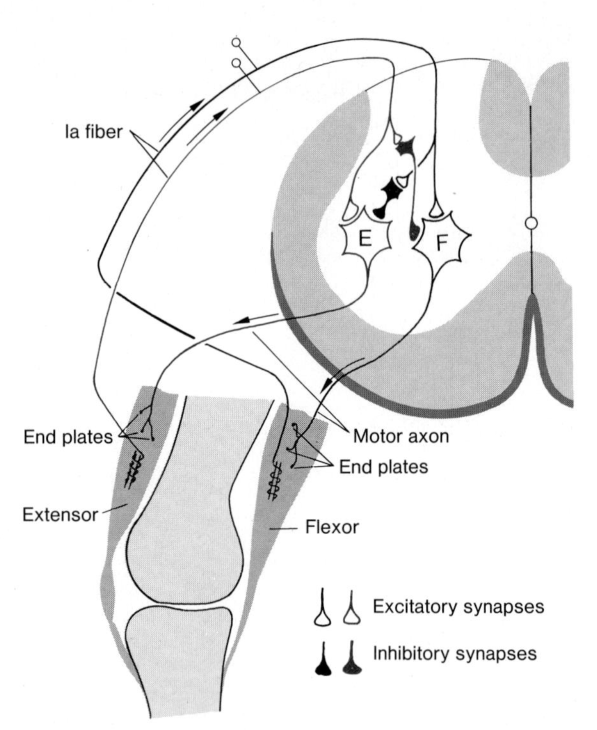

Fig. 5-7. Reflex paths for the stretch reflex and reciprocal antagonist inhibition. F, flexor motoneurons; E, extensor motoneurons of the knee joint. The flexor and extensor muscles of this joint and the actions of the synapses are indicated in the drawing

and for this reason the inhibition has been called **direct inhibition.** But the term **reciprocal antagonist inhibition** is preferable, as it makes clear that the motoneurons to each of a pair of antagonistic muscles (e.g., the flexor and extensor muscles at a given joint) can be inhibited during activation of the other member of the pair, by way of this reflex arc [6].

From a **functional** point of view, reciprocal antagonist inhibition reinforces the effect of Ia-fiber activity in producing or promoting contraction of one of the muscles acting at a joint, by simultaneously reducing the excitatory output to the muscle that would oppose that contraction. Because that muscle, in turn, has Ia fibers correspondingly connected to its antagonist, the system comprises **4 reflex arcs** altogether (Fig. 5-7). When activated by passive (externally imposed) changes in joint position, these reflexes work together to oppose the change, to **keep the initial muscle length constant.** For instance, if the influence of gravity causes the knee joint in Fig. 5-7 to begin to bend, stretching of the muscle spindles of the extensor *(first)* increases the excitation of the extensor motoneurons and *(second)* increases the inhibition of the flexor motoneurons. Moreover, the lessening of muscle-spindle stretch in the flexor reduces both *(third)* the homonymous excitation of the flexor motoneurons and *(fourth)* the reciprocal inhibition of the extensor motoneurons (this kind of "removal of inhibition" is called **disinhibition).** The net result is that the excitation of the extensor motoneurons increases and that of the flexor motoneurons decreases. Together, the reflex arcs constitute a **length-control system** for the muscle.

Functions of the γ-Spindle Loop

Contractions initiated by intrafusal activation. When the primary muscle-spindle endings are excited by intrafusal contraction via the γ motoneurons (Fig. 5-4D), the Ia-fiber activity directly excites the motoneurons to the same muscle just as when the muscle is stretched. That is, the muscle spindles can initiate contractions of the extrafusal musculature as a result of either (i) muscle stretch or (ii) activation of the γ motor axons, which causes the intrafusal muscles to contract. The latter route is called the **γ-spindle loop** (Fig. 5-8A).

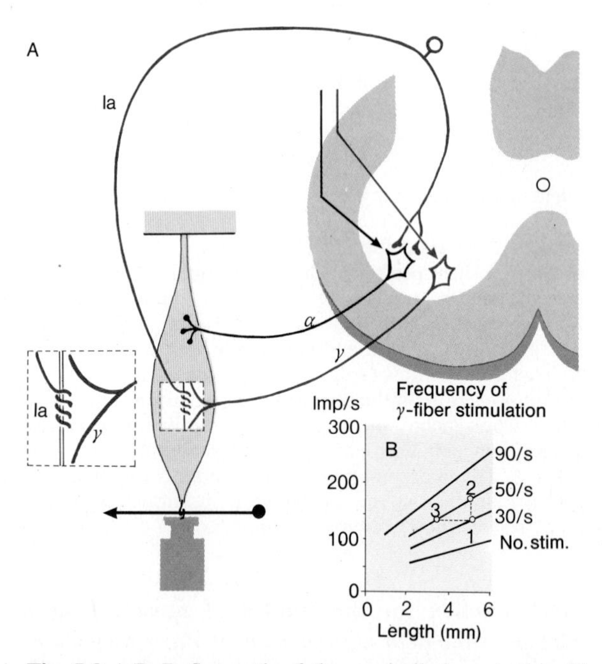

Fig. 5-8 A,B. Reflex path of the γ-spindle loop (*red* in **A**) and the influence of fusimotor activity on the discharge rate of a primary muscle-spindle ending (ordinate in **B**). With supraspinal activation of the γ loop there is usually a simultaneous descending activation of the associated (homonymous) α motoneurons (α-γ coactivation, indicated by the red and black descending pathways). The responses in **B** were those of a spindle in the soleus muscle of a cat; its resting length was increased as indicated on the abscissa and the frequency of fusimotor stimulation was changed as shown at the right. [**B** modified from A. Crowe and P.B.C. Matthews, J. Physiol. (Lond.) 174, 109 (1964)]

An advantage of *direct activation of the α motoneurons* by supraspinal centers is that the latency is short, but it has the disadvantage that the delicate balance of the length-control system that operates by way of the stretch reflex is initially upset. As a result, the stretching of the spindles in the affected muscle may become insufficient (subthreshold) or excessive (saturation). By contrast, *activation of the γ loop* brings about shortening of the muscle with little or no change in the discharge rate of the muscle-spindle afferents.

Fig. 5-8B is a graph of the relation between muscle length (abscissa) and discharge rate of a primary spindle afferent (ordinate) for different stimulus frequencies (0, 30, 50, 90 Hz) of the associated γ fiber. For example, if the frequency of the γ discharge rises from 30 to 50 Hz, the afferent discharge is represented by the shift from Point 1 to Point 2. The original afferent discharge rate is restored by shortening the muscle to Point 3. Thus the γ efferents allow the muscle length to change without continual changing of the discharge rate of the muscle-spindle receptors.
In this example, then, contraction of the intrafusal muscle fibers is followed by enhanced contraction of the extrafusal muscle fibers, until the original discharge rate of the primary spindle afferents is reached once again. The γ-spindle loop, incorporating a stretch-reflex arc, in this case is a **servomechanism** in which the controlled variable *muscle length* follows the controlling variable *muscle-spindle length.*

Alpha-gamma coactivation during movements. Originally it was thought that during goal-directed movements **direct excitation of the α motoneurons** (Fig. 5-8A) was used chiefly when speed was of greatest importance, while **activation of the γ-spindle loop** was used for particularly smooth and finely graded movements. It has since been shown that although as a rule extrafusal contraction is associated with an increase in spindle discharge (and thus intrafusal contraction), this increase *does not precede* the movement, as would be required if the movement were elicited by the γ motoneurons, but rather *follows it with a slight delay* (Fig. 5-9). Under these conditions the α and γ motoneurons are evidently activated simultaneously; the activity in the spindle afferents, however, because of the lower conduction velocity of the γ fibers and the time required for intrafusal contraction, is delayed with respect to the electromyographically recorded activity (EMG) [52]. This α-γ coactivation is also termed α-γ **linkage.** The main *role of the γ innervation* is therefore probably to prevent relaxation of the muscle spindle during extrafusal contraction, in order to ensure that the accuracy of the muscle spindle as a sensor – and thus the stabilizing action of the stretch reflex – is preserved even dur-

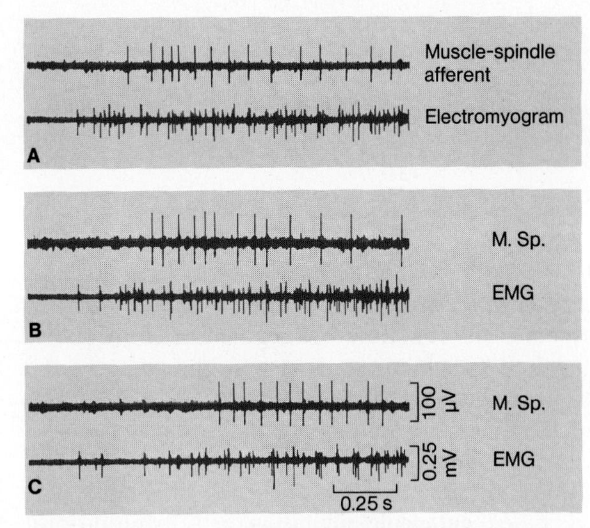

Fig. 5-9 A-C. α-γ coactivation during active finger movement by a human subject. The finger was bent three times **(A, B, C)**. The upper oscilloscope trace in each pair shows the activity of a muscle-spindle afferent (M.Sp.) from the flexor digitorum longus muscle, and the lower shows the electromyogram (EMG) of the same muscle, recorded with needle electrodes, as a measure of its α motor activity. From [52]

ing movement. In addition, the increased spindle activity produced by activity of the γ motoneurons serves to assist the movement in progress [4, 15, 52] in a manner analogous to the power-assisted steering or braking in an automobile – with the simultaneous effect that the sensor in the control system (the primary muscle-spindle ending) is kept within a favorable measurement range. Therefore the best way to describe the **role of the γ loop** is as a **servomechanism to assist movements.**

Reflex Arcs of Secondary Muscle-Spindle Afferents

The central connections of the Group-II afferents from muscle spindles are considerably different from those of the Ia afferents. Apart from the now well-established monosynaptic excitation of homonymous motoneurons – the extent and functional significance of which, however, cannot yet be evaluated – the segmental reflex circuitry of the secondary spindle afferents to a great extent resembles that of the afferents that can elicit the flexor reflex (p. 93). The implication is that regardless of their muscle of origin, under certain conditions they exert an excitatory influence on all the flexors of the limb involved, and an inhibitory influence on all the extensors. Thus their action is not limited, as is that of the

Ia afferents in most cases, to the synergists and antagonists acting at the same joint; rather, it extends to the control of movement of the entire limb [36].

Motor Reflex Arcs with Tendon-Organ Afferents

Segmental connections of the Ib fibers. With respect to its function, the segmental connectivity of the Ib fibers appears, at first glance, to be the mirror image of that of the Ia fibers. As Fig. 5-10 shows, the tendon organs have *di- or trisynaptic inhibitory* connections with their homonymous and agonistic motoneurons (this inhibition is called **autogenic inhibition** = self-inhibition), and *disynaptic excitatory* connections with antagonistic motoneurons [6]. Note, however, that this connectivity has not been observed in all cases. In particular, the excitatory actions of the flexor Ib fibers on extensor motoneurons have often failed to appear, or appeared only under certain conditions; evidently supraspinal control plays a major role here. Moreover, the expression *autogenic inhibition* encompasses only part of the function of Ib afferents, for they influence not only the motoneurons of synergistic and antagonistic muscles, but also motoneurons to muscles that act at other joints [6].

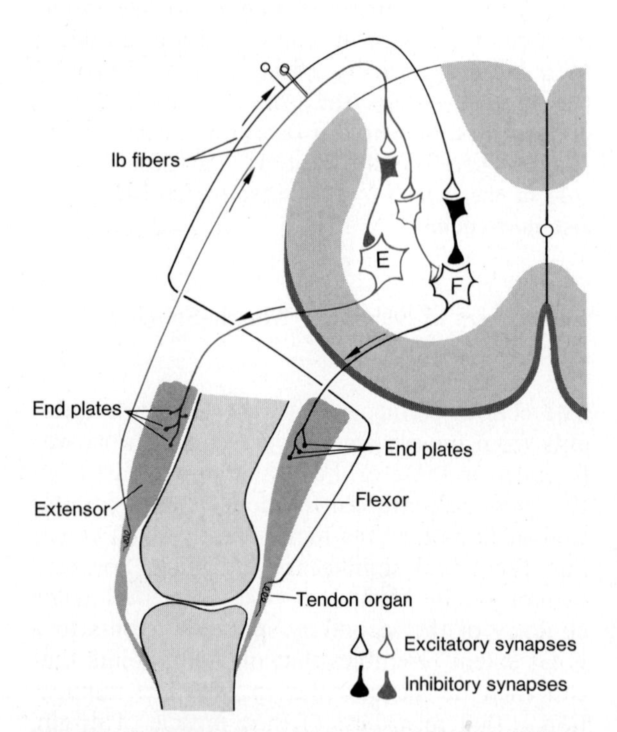

Fig. 5-10. Segmental connectivity of the Ib fibers from the tendon organs in a muscle. Representation analogous to Fig. 5-7. The excitatory connection of the flexor Ib fibers to the extensor motoneuron E has been omitted, because a corresponding reflex action is not routinely observed

Functions of the tendon organs. Because the tendon organs measure the tension in the muscle (p. 87), an increase in muscle tension owing to extrafusal contraction causes an inhibition of the homonymous motoneurons, by way of the activation of Ib afferents. Conversely, a decrease in muscle tone causes *disinhibition* (reduction of inhibition) and thus an activation of homonymous motoneurons. In other words: the reflex arc of the tendon organs is organized in such a way that it can serve to keep the **tension of the muscle constant.**

Every muscle, then, has two feedback systems (control circuits): a **length-control system** with the muscle spindles as sensors, and a **tension-control system** with the tendon organs as sensors. The action of the length-control system is essentially restricted to a single muscle and its antagonist, whereas the tension-control system of the Ib afferents contributes to the control of muscle tone in the whole limb.

From the standpoint of **control-systems technology** it is not immediately obvious why a tension-control system should be necessary in addition to a length-control system. In an ideal length-control circuit the force developed by the muscle would always be proportional to the efferent discharge of the α motoneurons, and a tension-control system would be superfluous. But we also know from Chapter 4 that the force developed by a muscle depends on other factors as well – the amount of prestretching, the contraction velocity, and the degree of muscular fatigue. The departure of muscle tension from the desired value due to these factors is measured by the tendon organs and corrected by way of the tension-control system.

When the external load on a muscle is changed, it is physically impossible to keep both the length and the tension of the muscle constant. If the load increases, the muscle either becomes longer or must increase its tension in order to keep its length constant. In this (common) situation, then, the length-control and tension-control systems work against one another rather than together. According to Houk [33], this conflict could be resolved if neither the length nor the tension of the muscle is kept constant as an individual variable, but rather the **muscle stiffness,** defined as the ratio of tension change to length change. The experimental analysis of this suggestion is currently underway.

In decerebrate animals and in **patients with spasticity**, rapid passive stretching of the muscle causes (by way of the stretch reflex) increasing muscle tension, until a state of extreme stretch is reached in which the muscle tone suddenly falls off. This abrupt drop in muscle tension, called the **"clasp-knife phenomenon,"** has been ascribed to the inhibitory action of the Golgi tendon organs [15]. It had been concluded that the role of the autogenic inhibition consisted in protecting the muscle from an increase in tension so great that it might cause tearing of the muscle or tendon. But because the tendon organs discharge and exert their influence in response to even a minimal rise in tension due to muscle contraction, it is doubtful that this "protective reflex" represents an important function of the tendon organs.

Polysynaptic Reflexes

With the exception of the monosynaptic stretch reflex and the disynaptic inhibitory reflex arc of the Ib fibers, all reflexes are mediated by arcs including a series of two or more central neurons. That is, they are **polysynaptic.** Furthermore, the sensor in a polysynaptic reflex is often located in a different part of the body from the effector. Reflexes of this kind include **autonomic reflexes** [45], the arcs of which terminate in the effectors of the autonomic nervous system (see p. 346), and **polysynaptic somatic reflexes,** with skeletal muscles as effectors. The latter play a major role in all sorts of movements – during feeding, for example, and particularly in escaping from harmful stimuli *(protective reflexes).*

Characteristics of polysynaptic reflexes. As an example to illustrate the features of polysynaptic reflexes, consider the cough reflex, a typical protective reflex. We know that a slight "tickle" or "scratchy" feeling in the throat causes one to cough, not immediately but after a little while. The delay is associated with the fact that in polysynaptic reflexes subthreshold stimuli can summate to give a suprathreshold stimulus. This **summation** is a central phenomenon; it occurs at interneurons and motoneurons in the reflex arc, and not at the peripheral sensors. The unpleasant subjective sensations (tickle, scratchiness) preceding the cough are a clear sign that the sensors that will eventually trigger the reflex are already excited.
As the stimulus intensity increases, the time between the onset of the stimulus (tickling) and the reflex response (coughing) becomes shorter. In other words, the **reflex time** in a polysynaptic reflex **depends on the stimulus intensity:** the stronger the stimulus, the sooner the reflex begins. The reflex time is reduced because when the responding sensors are more numerous and more active, the central neurons in the reflex arc reach suprathreshold excitation more rapidly; that is, the reduction is caused mainly by temporal and spatial facilitation.
The response can also vary in intensity – from a slight clearing of the throat to prolonged, violent coughing – again depending on the stimulus intensity. This increase in response as stimulus intensity increases is also a typical feature of polysynaptic motor reflexes. It is based on the progressive involvement of previously unused muscle groups, a phenomenon called **irradiation**.

The **plasticity of the reflex response** in polysynaptic reflexes with spatially separated sensors and effectors is evident in a number of other characteristics of these reflexes, including local sign, habituation, sensitization and conditioning. The term **local sign** denotes a property exemplified by the response to painful stimulation of a leg; the flexor muscles of the hip, knee and ankle contract to different degrees, *depending on the site of stimulation.* **Habituation** is a *reduction* of the reflex response when a stimulus that is neither painful nor harmful (e.g., stroking the skin of the abdomen) is frequently repeated at the *same site* and the *same intensity.* The weakening of the response occurs even though the excitability of the sensors, motoneurons and skeletal muscles involved in the reflex is unaltered [24, 41]. A change in the stimulus site or in some stimulus parameter (especially a higher intensity) causes the response to return to normal, an effect called **dishabituation**. The original response is also restored by allowing a fairly long interval without stimulation. The habituation of polysynaptic reflexes is probably based on synaptic depression (p. 56), at least in invertebrates.
Repeated *painful stimuli* can produce **sensitization.** Here the threshold of the reflex is lowered, the reflex time is shortened, the receptive field is enlarged and the reflex irradiates [31]. **Conditioning** comprises the various *long-term changes in the reflex response* brought about by the capacity of polysynaptic reflexes for adaptation and learning. For example, in an experiment designed so that a painful stimulus could be stopped only by making a movement *toward* the stimulus, it proved possible to reverse the normal flexor reflex response [30]. Note, however, that the term **conditioning** is also used in a somewhat different sense, to denote procedures by which behavior is altered (p. 155).

Flexor reflex and crossed extensor reflex. If a hindpaw of a spinal animal is painfully stimulated (by pinching, strong electrical stimuli, heat), the stimulated leg is pulled away by bending (flexion) of the ankle, knee and hip joints. Painful stimulation of the forepaw causes an equivalent **flexor reflex** of the foreleg. The receptors responsible for this reflex are in the skin. The movement they initiate evidently serves to pull the limb away from the vicinity of the painful (and hence harmful) stimulus, so that this is a typical *protective reflex*. Its characteristics, together with the fact that it occurs in a spinal animal, identify it as having a spinal, polysynaptic reflex arc (Fig. 5-11).

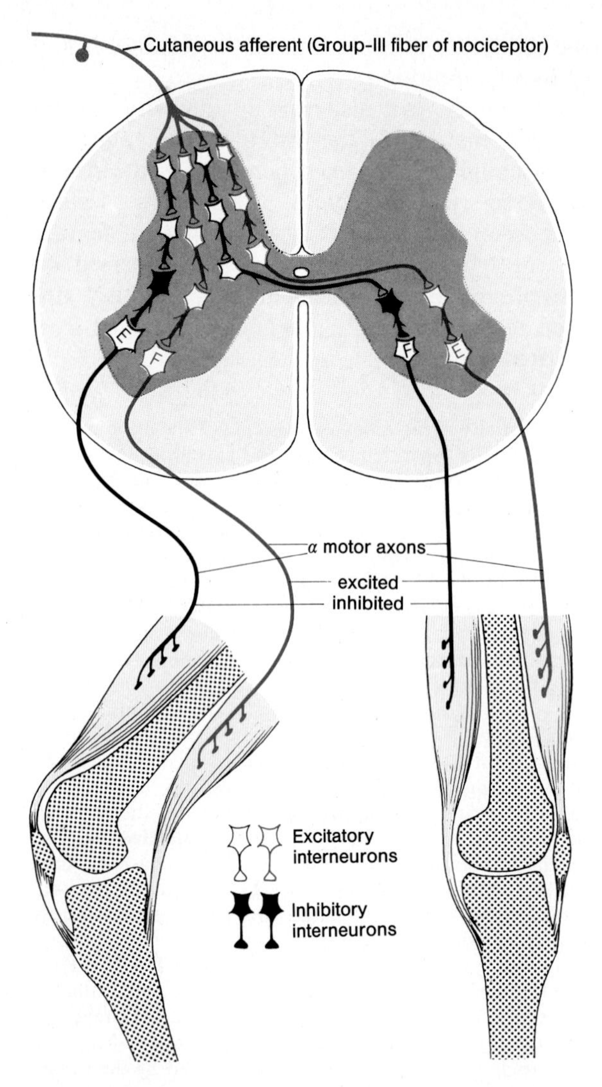

Fig. 5-11. Intrasegmental connectivity of an afferent fiber from a nociceptor in the skin of the foot. The Group-III afferent fiber and the reflex paths for the ipsilateral flexor reflex and the contralateral extensor reflex are shown in *red.* E, extensor motoneurons; F, flexor motoneurons

The flexor reflex of one hind or fore limb is often accompanied by extension of the opposite (contralateral) limb, especially with painful stimulation. The contralateral response is called a **crossed extensor reflex**, because the afferent activity in the nociceptive fibers crosses to the contralateral side of the spinal cord in order to induce the extension there. Altogether, then, as Fig. 5-11 shows, painful stimulation of a limb activates four motor reflex arcs at the segmental level: on the ipsilateral side the flexors are excited and the extensors inhibited, and on the contralateral side the opposite occurs.

Not everyone has the opportunity to study the flexor reflex, the crossed extensor reflex and the associated reciprocal inhibition in a spinal animal in the laboratory. But the flexor reflex can also be observed without spinalization, in domestic animals (dogs, cats etc.) during the first few days of life, as well as in human infants. At this early age the higher motor centers are not yet fully mature, so that the simple spinal reflex activity is not yet integrated in complex motor behavior. Overt flexor reflexes nevertheless also occur in adults – e.g., when pulling the hand away from a hot object, or raising a bare foot that has stepped on a sharp stone.

Flexor-reflex afferents. Very diverse flexor reflexes can be elicited by electrical stimulation of all nerves, especially if the stimulus intensity is above the threshold of Group-III and -IV afferents. For this reason these afferents have been classified as **flexor-reflex afferents** [27]. This concept has been widely adopted. However, the receptor afferents named above also make *reciprocal* connections with the same motoneurons in the same limb – that is, excitatory connections with extensor motoneurons, and inhibitory with flexor motoneurons. Thus each of these afferents has an excitatory and an inhibitory reflex route to each group of motoneurons. Which of the two paths is used depends on the controlling inputs from higher motor centers, and probably also on the momentary position and state of movement of the limb [12].

Role of the Group-III and -IV afferents from the muscles. Unlike the Group-I and -II muscle afferents, the chief functions of which are in the realm of motor control, the Group-III and -IV muscle afferents (which account for well over half of all afferent fibers in muscle nerves) have important additional functions. Some of them are responsible for muscular pain [15]. Others act on the autonomic nervous system in such a way as to participate in the control of blood flow through the muscle.

Role of the joint afferents. The joint nerves also contain mainly fine afferent nerve fibers of Groups III and IV, along with a smaller number of Group-II afferents. All these afferents seem to make only a small contribution to the conscious perception of the position and movements of the joints. It may be that their chief functions are nociception (i.e., signaling joint pain) and the reflex inhibition of movements that threaten to take the joint out of its normal working range.

Recurrent inhibition and presynaptic inhibition in spinal motor systems. As Fig. 5-12 shows, within the spinal cord the motoneurons send out collaterals to interneurons, the axons of which in turn have inhibitory synapses on motoneurons. This inhibitory circuit is called **Renshaw inhibition** after its discoverer, and the inhibitory interneurons are **Renshaw cells.** This is a typical example of **feedback inhibition**, because the interneurons inhibit the same cells by which they themselves are excited. Renshaw inhibition evidently serves to prevent an uncontrolled oscillation of motoneuronal activity. In particular, it appears to *limit the discharge rate of static motoneurons producing*

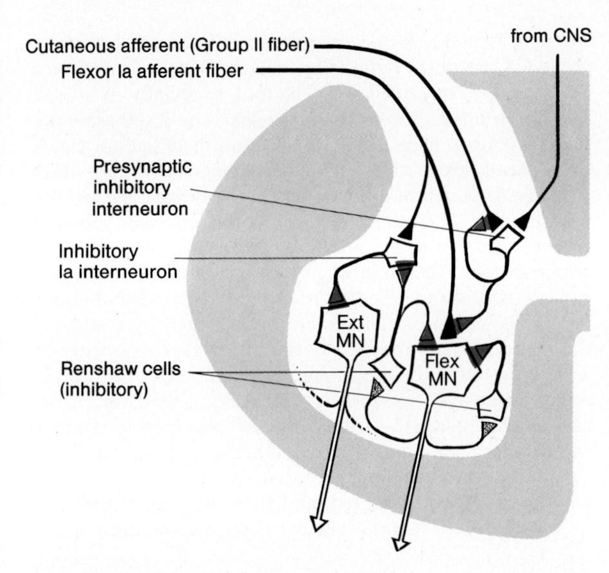

Fig. 5-12. Recurrent Renshaw inhibition and presynaptic inhibition in spinal motor reflex arcs

isometric contractions. It has been suggested that pathologically increased muscle tone *(spasticity)* is caused by a diminished frequency-limiting action of the Renshaw cells.

The synaptic mechanism of **presynaptic inhibition** and the possible effects it can have were discussed in Chapter 3 (p. 51). An additional aspect is illustrated in Fig. 5-12; that is, primary afferents are particularly often under presynaptic control, in the form of **feedback inhibition** in some cases but in others as **feed-forward inhibition**. In the latter, a primary afferent fiber (in Fig. 5-12, the flexor Ia afferent) is inhibited without having previously been excited. The cutaneous afferents as a whole seem to be under greater spinal and descending presynaptic control than the muscle afferents. It should be noted, however, that very few details are known as yet about the specific functions of presynaptic inhibition in spinal reflex activity [46, 47].

Cross connections between segmental reflex arcs. The reflex circuits described so far are not strictly separated from one another. Even at the segmental level there is *extensive convergence* of signals from other sources onto interneurons in the reflex arcs. An example is shown in Fig. 5-12, where interneurons for reciprocal antagonist inhibition (Ia inhibitory interneurons) are inhibited by Renshaw cells. In addition, these neurons receive inputs – some inhibitory, some excitatory – from other (flexor reflex) afferents and from higher motor centers. The full functional significance of these inputs remains to be discovered, but certain possibilities come readily to mind. For example, suppression of antagonist inhibition would seem to be useful when a joint is to be stabilized by simultaneous contraction of agonists and antagonists.

The Propriospinal System and the Capabilities of the Isolated Spinal Cord

Intersegmental reflex connections. In addition to the segmental reflex arcs discussed so far, the spinal cord comprises ascending or descending *intersegmental reflex pathways.* The interneurons of the intersegmental reflex pathways are **propriospinal neurons,** with their cell bodies in the gray matter of the spinal cord. Their axons run for various distances up and down in the white matter as **propriospinal tracts,** never leaving the spinal cord. Degeneration experiments (in which parts of the cord were completely isolated) have shown that the majority of spinal nerve cells are propriospinal neurons. Some of them form **independently functional groups** that are responsible for the automatic movements mentioned at the beginning of the chapter **(spinal-cord automatisms).** The intersegmental reflexes and the spinal-cord automatisms assist in the **coordination of movements** initiated at various levels in the spinal cord – in particular, the coordination between fore and hind limbs and that of neck and limb movements [12, 20]. The afferent impulses for these intersegmental reflexes seem to come mainly from the secondary muscle-spindle endings, the cutaneous receptors, and other flexor-reflex afferents and not from Ia and Ib fibers.

By way of these reflexes and automatisms, the spinal cord is capable of *executing complex movements and adjusting them to one another,* when an appropriate signal is received from the periphery or from higher parts of the central nervous system. We refer to this as the **integrative function** of the spinal cord, keeping in mind that in the higher vertebrates – mammals in particular – the higher levels of the central nervous system have increasingly taken control of the spinal functions (the process of **encephalization**).

Spinal locomotion. As has been noted, the basic pattern of locomotion – that is, the progression of a person or animal through the surroundings by means of coordinated limb movements – is programmed at the level of the spinal cord [12, 50]. Painful stimulation of one limb of a spinal animal leads to reflex movements of all four limbs, and if the stimulation is prolonged these can develop into a rhythmic flexion and extension of the three unstimulated limbs. If such an animal is held with its feet on a treadmill, under certain conditions it can carry out coordinated walking movements that closely resemble those of a freely walking animal. These walking movements can be maintained by the spinal cord alone, with no feedback of information from the receptors activated by the movement.

In a spinal animal anesthetized and paralyzed with curare, under certain conditions rhythmically alternating volleys of impulses can be recorded from extensor and flexor motoneurons, which correspond roughly to those discharged in freely walking animals. Because they occur without actual movement, they are called *fictive locomotion.* Fictive locomotion is generated by as yet unidentified **locomotor centers** in the spinal cord. There appears to be one such center associated with each limb. The coordination of the centers with one another is achieved by the propriospinal systems and by tracts that cross the cord within individual segments.
Humans are also thought to have spinal locomotor centers. For example, the **stepping reflex of the newborn** is regarded as a manifestation of the locomotor centers activated by stimuli to the skin. As the central nervous system matures, however, these centers are evidently brought under such strong supraspinal control that in an older person they cannot become independently active. It is probably because of this development that it has not yet been possible to elicit coordinated locomotion in human *paraplegics* (see below).

The above phenomena are examples, at the level of the spinal cord, of the **program-controlled (automatic)** behavior discussed at the beginning of the chapter. The higher motor centers comprise far more of these *stimulus-independent movement programs*, some innate and others established by a learning process (cycling, for example). Not only is the operation of the spinal and supraspinal movement programs independent of external stimuli, they can also be executed with *no sensory feedback* (see p. 82).

Paraplegia. The question of the extent to which movements can be accomplished by reflexes in the isolated human spinal cord is of great practical significance, in view of the facts that accidental *spinal transection* (especially in automobile accidents) is becoming increasingly common, and that modern methods of intensive care make it increasingly likely that these patients can be brought through the acute stage and rehabilitated to live a useful and tolerable life.
In cases of complete **paraplegia** (usually with the cord severed in the thoracic region, T_2 to T_{12}) there is (i) an immediate and permanent *paralysis of all voluntary movement* in the muscles supplied by spinal segments caudal to the injury; (ii) *conscious sensations* associated with the region supplied by the separated spinal segments are also *lost* forever; and (iii) all motor and autonomic reflexes in the affected parts of the body are initially extinguished *(complete areflexia).*
The **motor reflexes** recover in the subsequent weeks and months. Given correct care, recovery follows a fundamental pattern discernible despite many individual differences. There are four stages: (i) **Complete areflexia** usually lasts 4–6 weeks. It is followed by a period lasting 2 weeks to several months, in which (ii) **small reflex movements** of the toes, especially the great toe, can be observed. In the next stage (iii) **flexor reflexes** become steadily more pronounced – first those of the toe (Babinski's sign) and ankle joints, whereas later flexor movements of the knee and hip joints appear. *Mass flexor reflexes* are in some cases accompanied by *crossed extensor reflexes.* The foot, especially its sole, is by far the most sensitive *reflexogenic zone* for these complex responses; even gentle tactile stimuli suffice to trigger widespread flexor reflexes. In the *chronic stage* (iv), which is reached after 6 months or more, the flexor reflexes also predominate as a rule. Now, however, stronger **extensor reflexes** can also occur, and may give rise to prolonged *extensor spasms.* The latter can be so intense that the patient can actually stand briefly without support **("spinal standing").** The extensor reflexes are best elicited by stretching the flexor muscles (especially the hip flexors) suddenly by a small amount. In this stage, then, the excitability of all reflex pathways is evidently increased. Departures from this clinical picture – especially the presence of marked extensor reflexes and elevated muscle tone shortly after the injury – are usually a sign that the spinal cord has not been completely transected, and thus that the prospect of motor and sensory improvement is correspondingly better [18, 34, 41].
The changes in and recovery of the autonomic reflexes (evacuation of the bladder and rectum, in particular) are discussed on p. 347; for further aspects of motor rehabilitation see Section 5.8.

Spinal shock. The reversible motor and autonomic areflexia following spinal-cord transection is called **spinal shock**. In experiments on animals functional blockage, by local cooling or anesthesia, also brings on spinal shock. Once the reflexes have returned following an initial transection, a second transection below the first does not produce spinal shock. Therefore the decisive factor in spinal-shock induction is the loss of the connection to the rest of the central nervous system.
Hardly anything is known about the **causes of spinal shock** or about the mechanisms by which the reflexes are restored. Transection of the descending pathways eliminates many excitatory inputs to spinal neurons, and it may be that inhibitory spinal interneurons are disinhibited. Both effects would strongly suppress activity in the reflex arcs, which would be manifest clinically as areflexia. For the present, it remains an open question which mechanisms are responsible for the return of certain spinal functions, and why the recovery period lasts many months in humans (the duration of spinal shock is only a few minutes in frogs, hours in carnivores, days or weeks in monkeys, and weeks to months in the anthropoid apes).

5.4 Motor Centers in the Brainstem

Hierarchical position of the brainstem centers; methods of study. In the introduction to this chapter it was noted that the coordination of motoneuronal activity is brought about by motor centers. It is the responsibility of these centers, in cerebral cortex and brainstem, to generate a finely graded spatial and temporal pattern of excitation in populations of motoneurons, such that an appropriate movement is carried out together with the necessary postural adjustments (Fig. 5-1). In mammals, and especially in primates, the cerebral cortex exerts a dominant influence in motor control. To what extent can the **brainstem centers** operate independently, and is it justified to consider them separately from the cerebral cortex?

This question can be answered from a phylogenetic viewpoint. In the lower vertebrates a remarkable degree of independence has been demonstrated; with the brainstem centers intact, forebrain lesions cause relatively slight motor disturbances. As cerebral evolution progresses, the situation changes. In mammals – and outstandingly in the primates – the brainstem motor centers exert their control on spinal networks in harmonious subordination to the cerebral cortex. Thus, forebrain lesions lead to more severe motor deficits in these animals.

The classical method of studying the function of the brainstem centers is to *remove superordinate parts of the brain*, so that whatever capacity the brainstem motor centers may possess for independent function will be revealed; in particular, their **role in regulating posture and muscle tone** has been analyzed. At the beginning of this century animals were prepared in this way, with lesions at various levels of the brainstem, and the results of these experiments are still relevant to the disturbances of postural functions and of muscle tone common in human pathology [14, 19, 20, 21].

This technique has certain limitations, however. Interpretation of the role of a part of the brain on the basis of motor deficits is problematic for two main reasons. First, the *motor centers are elements in a system that can be disrupted as a whole when only a part has been destroyed;* its function derives from the interaction and coordination of many centers arranged hierarchically and in parallel. Second, allowance must be made for the fact that an acute lesion is followed by *long-term processes of reorganization in the CNS* (see Section 5.8). Nevertheless, if these limitations are taken into account, careful and quantitative observation of lesion deficits can provide valuable hints as to the role played by a given brainstem center in a particular motor function.

The findings now to be described show that the brainstem centers are indeed fundamentally involved in the **control of body posture**, though in an animal with forebrain removed this control is no longer integrated into the control of goal-directed movements. The influence of the brainstem centers is exerted by way of **descending fibers to the spinal cord**, about which much has been learned from anatomical studies and electrophysiological (stimulation and recording) experiments. Recently interest has been directed chiefly toward the complex event of **upright standing and walking** in humans and to the way in which the brainstem governs **program-controlled automatisms.**

The Decerebrate Preparation and Decerebrate Rigidity

The metabolic requirements of the cerebrum (the cortex in particular), and also of the basal ganglia and the thalamus, are higher than those of the deeper brainstem centers. Therefore even brief anoxia (e.g., because of temporary cardiac arrest) can selectively and irreversibly damage the forebrain. The vital circulatory and respiratory centers of the brainstem often remain intact in such cases, enabling the patient to survive in a purely "vegetative" state. All intellectual abilities, including speech and voluntary movements, are lost; the patient is **brain dead** (it would be more correct to speak of *forebrain death*). The brain damage is often followed immediately by severe stiffening of the muscles, especially the extensors and the neck muscles. This well-known phenomenon in human pathology was the point of departure for detailed investigation in animal models.

Decerebrate rigidity. In classical **decerebration** (transection 1 in Fig. 5-13) the rostral half of the midbrain and still further rostral parts of the brain are removed. Immediately after this operation a massive muscular stiffness develops, especially in the muscles that serve to oppose gravity. This elevated muscle tone, called **decerebrate rigidity**, is manifest in a strong resistance to stretching. The *reflex nature* of the rigidity is evident in the fact that it is diminished or vanishes altogether when the dorsal roots are transected (which interrupts the reflex arc). The immediate appearance of rigidity is interpreted as a disinhibition phenomenon; that is, the superordinate motor centers in cerebellum and cerebrum are thought normally to act as a brake on the brainstem centers. The animal can be set up on its legs, which support it because of the extreme tone of the extensor muscles, so that it stands in a caricature of the normal posture; but there is no fine regulation at all, and the slightest disturbance causes it to fall over.

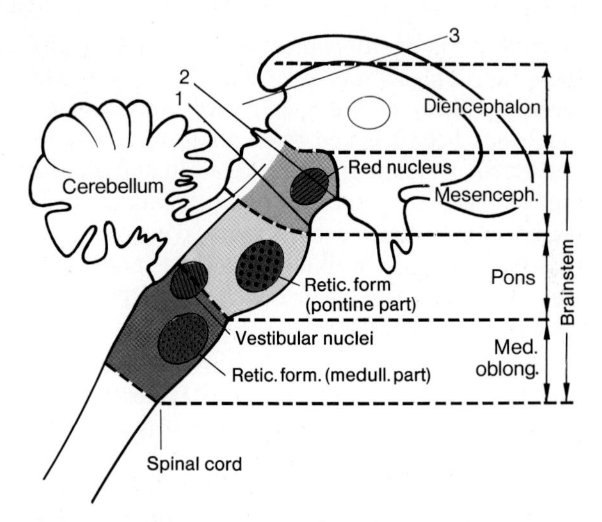

Fig. 5-13. Schematic survey of the positions of the motor centers in the brainstem – medulla oblongata, pons and mesencephalon (midbrain). When communication with the parts of the brain above the indicated three levels of section is interrupted, the result is a decerebrate animal (1), a midbrain animal (2) and a thalamic animal (3). Further discussion in text

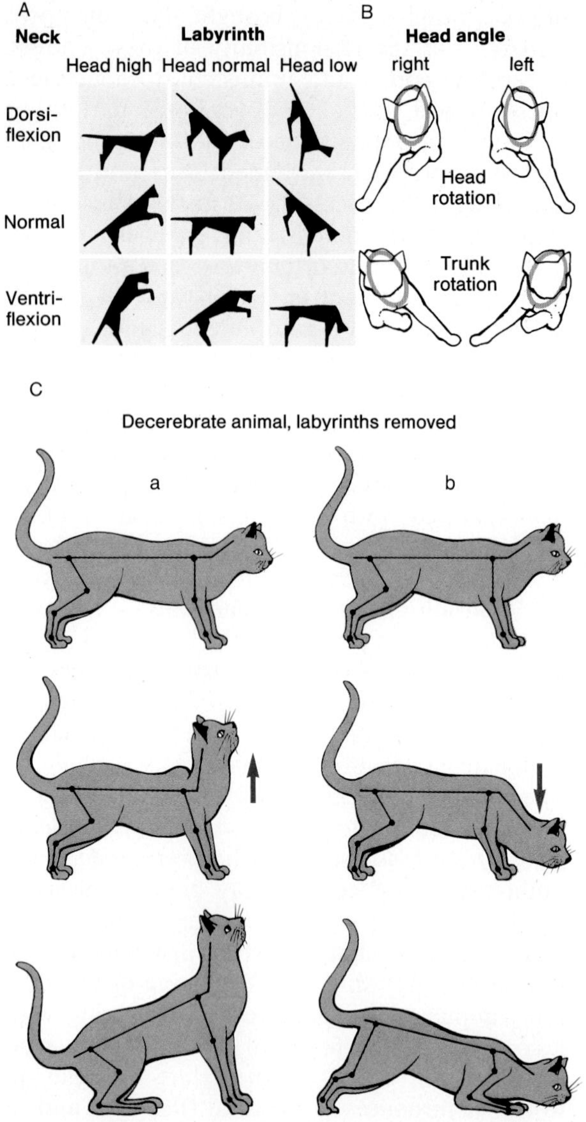

Fig. 5-14. A Tonic neck and labyrinth reflexes and their combined effects: the main body axes of a quadruped as seen from the side. From [20]. **B** Comparison of the effects on the limb positions of rotation of the head *(top)* and of the trunk with head stabilized *(bottom)*. From [20]. The angle of the trunk is shown by the *red* outline. **C** Tonic neck reflexes of a cat with no vestibular apparatus. Passive bending of the neck to raise the head (*red arrow* in a) reduces the extensor tone in the hindlimbs and increases the extensor tone in the forelimbs. The opposite effects are produced by pushing the head down (*red arrow* in b)

Motor patterns following other cerebral lesions. In the **midbrain animal** the whole midbrain remains intact (transection 2 in Fig. 5-13). Motor performance is not as severely impaired as in the decerebrate case; the animal can stand up by itself and the rigidity is less pronounced. The improved motor control is ascribed to the *red nucleus,* which remains intact in this preparation. In the **thalamic animal** (transection 3 in Fig. 5-13) the diencephalon is also retained. The main use of this preparation is in studies of locomotion, because rhythmic stepping movements either occur spontaneously or can easily be induced. The locomotor patterns are like those of an automaton, however, with none of the elegance of the normal gait. Finally, after extensive **decortication** which leaves the basal ganglia intact, the movement repertoire is preserved remarkably well – in rodents and carnivores, at least. Again, however, the movement sequences have an automatic quality. In many cases locomotion is extremely persistent, so that the animal tries to proceed even against obstacles.

Does the diencephalon also function in higher motor control? As mentioned in Section 16.5, complex movement sequences can be elicited in the waking animal by repetitive electrical stimulation of the diencephalon. These are typical behavior patterns, indistinguishable from the normal innate (instinctive) behavior. For instance, when a small area of the hypothalamus is stimulated, the response is **attack behavior with all the accompanying autonomic reactions** (pupil dilation, piloerection, elevated blood pressure and pulse rate), in the absence of any external reason for such an attack. The neural mechanisms of such responses are unknown. But it seems unlikely to be a matter of activating an "attack program" stored in a special "attack center". A conceivable alternative is that when the artificial stimulus reaches a certain threshold, it activates transmitter systems that in turn "trigger" subcortical or cortical mechanisms.

Static and statokinetic reflexes [14, 19]. Animals with forebrain lesions, particularly thalamic animals, exhibit, in exaggerated form, a number of **postural and righting reflexes**. These enable the animal to respond to certain stimuli by *correcting the distribution of tone in the musculature* (reflexes to maintain a certain body posture) or to return its body to the *normal orientation* (righting reflexes). **Static reflexes** occur in the resting position, and **statokinetic reflexes** are associated with changes in position. The former ensure that parts of the body (e.g., the head) are kept stably in place, and the latter adjust the limb positions when the orientation of the body changes.

The postural reflexes involve chiefly the musculature of the trunk and the proximal parts of the limbs. The signals that initiate them, by oligo- and polysynaptic routes, originate in the *afferents from the neck musculature and the labyrinth* – hence the term **tonic neck and labyrinth reflexes.** The two kinds of afference cooperate in triggering the reflexes. Recent electrophysiological studies have shown that the reflex adjustments of posture are brought about by **multisensory convergence**, to which *cutaneous and visual afferents* also contribute.

The drawings in Fig. 5-14 show how overall posture is adjusted as the angles of head and trunk are changed. Such adjustments are automatic reactions that take place similarly in humans; although we are completely unconscious of them, they are incorporated into the voluntary motor system so as to assist the movements. Whereas at first it was important to understand the properties of the basic reflexes in a "reduced preparation", today the emphasis is more on the ways in which *postural motor patterns are employed as a background to purposeful, goal-directed movements* ([23] and NASHNER in [22]).

It is important, especially where these tonic postural reflexes are concerned, that the reflex concept not be restricted to an utterly inflexible automaticity, in which a sensory input inevitably elicits a motor reaction. A reflex is actually a subtle regulatory process, which can be set and to a great extent controlled by higher centers in the voluntary motor system. The machine-like aspect of tonic postural reflexes is manifest only under special circumstances, as in an infant (with a still immature cerebrum) or in patients with cerebral disorders.

Problems Associated with the Erect Stance of Humans and its Modification during Movements

That humans can walk upright, standing on feet with a relatively small surface area, is in itself a marvel of regulation, considering that breathing and all sorts of active manipulation and trunk movement cause continual shifting of the body's center of gravity, which must be actively compensated. Electromyographic analyses in human subjects have shown that every such "disturbance" (e.g., the elevation of the thorax during inspiration) does indeed set off a chain of reactions of the trunk and leg muscles, called **postural synergies.** These synergies are often studied by observing a subject standing on a movable platform, by means of which the feet can suddenly be tilted downward or upward (as happens during skiing). In the clinical examination of neurological patients, this "platform paradigm" has proved extremely valuable for the quantitative analysis of impaired postural function **(posturography)**.

The electromyographically measurable activity patterns of the leg and trunk muscles in response to platform movements have the characteristics of reflexes. The largest and functionally most important components appear with a latency of 100–150 ms, a long reflex time that indicates complex processing in the CNS involving supraspinal structures. *The synergic reaction always has a stabilizing effect*, to prevent the subject from falling forward or backward.

The magnitude of the individual reflex responses changes when the same test is repeated several times, so that gradually the stabilizing effect is optimized. This *"context-dependent" adaptation* requires the involvement of higher motor centers such as the cerebellum; it is based on a complex processing of information from proprioceptive, vestibular and visual afferents, the details of which are still unknown. In any case, it seems clear that the postural motor system is also hierarchically organized as diagrammed in Fig. 5-1: the **local reflex mechanisms** are subordinate to **long functional loops** including supraspinal centers. The *"long-loop reflexes"* also operate automatically, but their magnitude and effects are adjusted to the current situation.

The example of breathing shows that **postural compensation** is made necessary not only by disturbances of external origin but also by **one's own movements.** Posturographic analysis of the compensatory adjustments to goal-directed movements has produced the interesting result that these do not appear after the delay characteristic of reflexes but rather are simultaneous or even **anticipatory**, preceding the intended movement. An impressive (and easily demonstrated) example is illustrated in Fig. 5-15. The subject is instructed to support a weight with his arm while keeping his eyes closed. In the situation shown

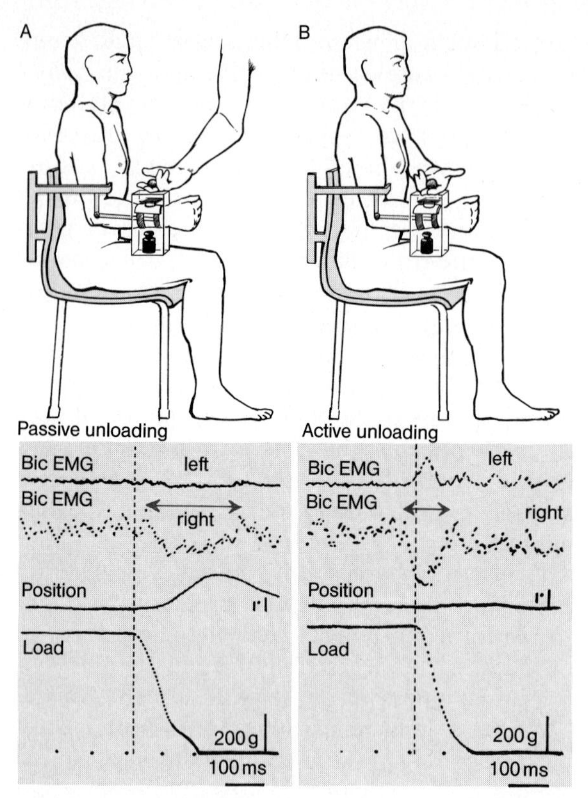

Fig. 5-15. Comparison of a passive **(A)** and an active **(B)** unloading reaction. *Above:* the subject supports a load with his arm, and the angle at the elbow is monitored by the potentiometer P. The weight of the load is measured with a force transducer. *Below:* recordings, from top to bottom, of the rectified left and right biceps electromyograms (Bic EMG), the position of the forearm (in angular degrees), and the load acting on the forearm. The load is removed ten times in succession and the recorded data are averaged by computer. The *red arrows* mark the interval in which EMG activity is reduced. With the passive unloading in A, this reduction occurs by a reflex, but when the load is actively removed as in B, the reduction is anticipatory (nearly simultaneous with the contraction of the left biceps). From HUGON, MASSION and WIESENDANGER (1982): Pflügers Arch. 393, 292

in A, when the experimenter suddenly removes the load, the subject's arm makes an upward movement that cannot be voluntarily prevented. The electromyogram reveals a decrease in biceps activity, but only after a delay of about 60 ms. In this case the **external** disturbance has triggered the classical **"unloading reflex".** Because it takes some time for the biceps activity to be reflexly reduced, there is a transient small destabilization of the forearm. In the experiment shown in B, the subject himself removes the load, and the forearm remains stable. As the electromyogram shows, the reason is that the motoneuronal message to reduce its activity is received by the biceps **before** the load is raised, at about the same time as it is grasped by the other hand.

Such **anticipatory postural synergies** have been confirmed in many experiments. From the results of electromyographic analyses of the human postural motor system, then, one can draw the general conclusion that *compensatory mechanisms can be both reflex- and program-controlled.*

Hierarchical Influences on Program-Controlled Automatisms: Locomotion and Chewing

Automatisms are elements (subprograms) of the motor system that are under the influence of higher motor centers. Two examples will serve to illustrate this point ([50, 12] and LUSCHEI and GOLDBERG in [2]). As was mentioned in Section 5.3, the spinal cord of mammals, very probably including humans, contains **"stepping generators".** However, these spinal networks provide only **stereotyped stepping rhythms,** which can be modified in various ways by supraspinal centers to suit the terrain and other circumstances. A cat in an open field must continually alter its **goal-directed locomotion** according to the tactile, olfactory, visual and acoustic situation; a **"stalking" program** must instantly be switched to a **"pouncing" program.** In humans, the supraspinal driver of the spinal stepping generators has to be especially well developed, as does the overall control by the cerebrum. When the supraspinal influences are eliminated, as in a paraplegic with completely transected spinal cord, a person can no longer make stepping movements (though a lower mammal still can). There are very few experimental data concerning the role of the cerebral cortex in locomotion. More is known about a **locomotor center in the brainstem** that extends from the diencephalon to the midbrain. This "locomotor strip" appears to promote locomotor activity in general; minimal electrical stimulation here either induces walking rhythms or intensifies and accelerates ongoing locomotion. The same effects are produced by systemic administration of catecholamines, which suggests noradrenergic transmission from the brainstem centers.

Proprioceptive and cutaneous stimuli also influence locomotion; indeed, stepping rhythms can be **induced and sustained** by such stimuli. But feedback from the peripheral sensors is not a prerequisite for locomotion, because locomotor activity has been observed even after all sensory input to the spinal cord has been interrupted (deafferentation). The rhythmic sensory feedback during walking can also be eliminated by paralyzing the animal with curare, so that **execution of the movements is prevented.** Nevertheless, electrical stimulation in the locomotor strip still initiates rhythmic discharge patterns that can be recorded in the muscle nerves. This response is called **"fictive" locomotion** (see also Section 5.3).

Chewing is another rhythmic automatism. Normally triggered by the oral intake of solid food, it can also be initiated voluntarily, like locomotion. Even **decerebrate animals** routinely execute **rhythmic chewing movements** when food is placed in their mouths. Chewing rhythms can be elicited, most readily in rodents, by electrical stimulation in a discrete region of the brainstem *("chewing center")*. In humans the brainstem centers for chewing movements seem to be controlled primarily by the frontal and temporal cerebral cortex. Patients with extensive lesions in these cortical regions not uncommonly exhibit chewing automatisms (that is, chew spontaneously in an inappropriate context). In normal people **lip-smacking automatisms** occasionally appear during sleep, perhaps because when a person is asleep the subordinate pattern generators are released from control by the cerebral cortex.

The Brainstem Motor Centers as the Origin of Descending Pathways, and Cortical Influences upon Them

The magnocellular part of the red nucleus (nucleus ruber), the vestibular nuclei, the median parts of the reticular formation and the tectum of the midbrain serve as **brainstem motor centers**, *controlling the spinal motor elements* by way of descending fiber systems (see especially KUYPERS in [2]). In many mammals the rubrospinal pathway still plays an important role, with a function resembling that of the pyramidal tract, but in humans this system is retained only in rudimentary form and is relatively insignificant. The remaining descending pathways make a major contribution to the **control of postural functions.** This supraspinal influence is always present (i.e., it is tonic); accordingly, it must promote activity mainly in the groups of muscles that counteract gravity – the extensors and the trunk muscles. A fraction of the descending fibers, the medial vestibulospinal tract in particular, runs only as far as the cervical cord. These fibers act on the neck muscles, changing the position of the head on the basis of information from the vestibular apparatus.

The **tone-enhancing action of the brainstem motor centers** is also evident in a brain-stimulation experiment, as follows. When the lateral parts of the brainstem of an animal with decerebrate rigidity are stimulated electrically, the muscle tone increases further; when the medial parts are stimulated, the rigidity disappears as long as the stimulus continues. However, no clear association between these excitatory and inhibitory centers and particular tract systems has yet been discerned. Recent microelectrophysiological studies have shown that activity patterns in vestibulo- and reticulospinal fibers spread over several segments. It can be inferred that **postural synergies** are called up by way of the extensive arborizations of these descending fibers. The target neurons of the descending pathways are predominantly interneurons, but direct (i.e., monosynaptic) connections to α and γ motoneurons have also been demonstrated.
The hierarchy continues beyond the motor centers in the brainstem, for these are in turn **subordinate to the cerebral cortex.** Indeed, there is a certain parallelism between the direct connection of cortex to spinal cord, by way of the pyramidal tract (see Section 5.7) and the indirect control the cortex exerts by way of the brainstem centers. The latter, then, are not independent controllers of postural motor functions. Because the cortex evidently exerts a considerable part of its influence on the spinal cord by way of motor centers in the brainstem, these low centers must also subserve goal-directed movements. This conclusion is clearly supported by experiments on animals in which the pyramidal tract has been interrupted [53]; they retain goal-directed motor patterns to an astonishing degree (see also Section 5.7).

The indirect systems (e.g., the corticorubrospinal system as well as the basal ganglia) were once collectively called the **"extrapyramidal system"**. Because it has caused some confusion, this term **should now be avoided**. For a long time the basal ganglia, like the brainstem centers discussed above, were thought to act as an intermediate relay station for the systems projecting from cortex to spinal cord. The clinical custom of using "extrapyramidal disorders" as a synonym for disorders of the basal ganglia still persists. Although, as we shall see in Section 5.6, opinion about the position of the basal ganglia in the motor system has changed profoundly, the label "extrapyramidal system" has remained firmly attached to the basal ganglia. Therefore it is recommended that the term **non-pyramidal system** be used for the indirect pathways from the cerebral cortex through the brainstem motor centers to the spinal cord.

The discovery of new descending tract systems. In recent years new neuroanatomical methods have been developed and widely applied, including axoplasmic flow methods to reveal neuronal connections, and histochemical and immunofluorescence procedures to demonstrate specific transmitter systems. As a result, a number of additional descending systems have been identified. There are already important indications that the **descending noradrenergic system** from the *locus coeruleus* (possibly together with a small number of dopaminergic fibers) acts as a **modulating element** in the control of spinal motor mechanisms. As has been mentioned, locomotor patterns and stereotyped chewing motions can be elicited by the artificial administration of catecholamines. Both electrical stimulation in the locus coeruleus and the local application of minute amounts of noradrenalin can strongly modulate spinal reflexes. Similar effects have been reported for **descending serotonergic fibers** that originate in the *raphe nuclei* of the caudal brainstem.

Other **neurons with descending connections to the spinal cord** have been discovered in the dorsal-column nuclei, the interstitial nucleus of Cajal, and nuclei in the hypothalamus. The functional significance of all these non-classical descending fiber systems is not at all clear. In addition to a direct influence on spinal motor mechanisms, possibilities to be considered are the *control of autonomic mechanisms* and the centrifugal *control of somatosensory transmission* (see Section 9.12).

5.5 Cerebellum

Survey of the role of the cerebellum in the motor system. Much of what is known about cerebellar function is derived from the observations of clinical neurologists. Patients with cerebellar lesions (e.g., tumors or inflammatory foci in multiple sclerosis) are not paralyzed, nor are their sensations impaired, although the cerebellum receives mainly sensory signals and projects to motor centers. Instead, cerebellar symptomatology is characterized by abnormalities in the details of evolving movements and by disruption of the normally perfect coupling of movement and posture. By virtue of its role in sensorimotor integration, then, the cerebellum serves an important **function in motor coordination.**

Cerebellar symptoms depend on the **site of the lesion**, as follows. *Medial* lesions cause disturbances of postural motor patterns as well as oculomotor disturbances, whereas *lateral* lesions affect chiefly goal-directed movements and speech.

The *functional duality* observed clinically is paralleled by a *structural and phylogenetic duality.* As a simplification, it can be said that the phylogenetically older, medial elements receive spinal, vestibular and visual signals and are closely related to the motor apparatus (motor centers in spinal cord and brainstem), whereas the phylogenetically younger, lateral elements (hemispheres) primarily receive information from the cerebral cortex, to which they in turn are linked by ascending pathways. From these neurological and anatomical relationships it has been concluded that the **medial** parts of the cerebellum function mainly to **control and correct** the execution of ongoing movements. By contrast, the **hemispheres** are more involved in the preparation phase, in the **programming** of movements. Furthermore, long-term changes in cerebellar signal transmission have been discovered. This cerebellar plasticity is thought to play a role in long-term **motor adaptation** and in **motor learning.**

Microcircuitry and Neuronal Operations

"Crystalline" fine structure of the cerebellar cortex. Experimental research on the cerebellum has provided a great deal of information about fine-structural linkage, and its function, in both cortex and nuclei. The surface of the cerebellar cortex is made very large by its extensive folding (**folia**, Fig. 5-16); unfolded, it would measure 17 cm × 120 cm. All the individual folia are identical in fine structure, with the neural elements

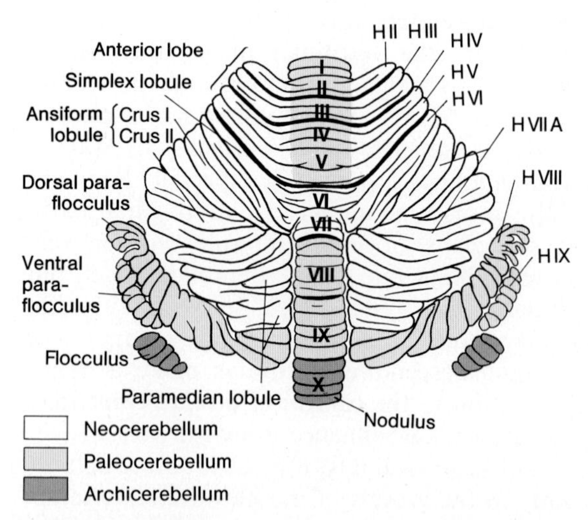

Fig. 5-16. Subdivisions of the primate cerebellar cortex (monkey). The anterior lobe is "opened out" and shown in the same plane as the posterior lobe. The lobules are identified by Roman numerals (I-IX), and the associated parts of the hemispheres are labelled HII-HIX. The phylogenetic subdivisions are distinguished by colors. The cerebellar cortex is folded in a characteristic way, producing many folia. From [10]

arranged so regularly as to resemble a crystal. This regularity is an advantage for physiological studies, in that functional principles can be generalized to the entire cerebellum.

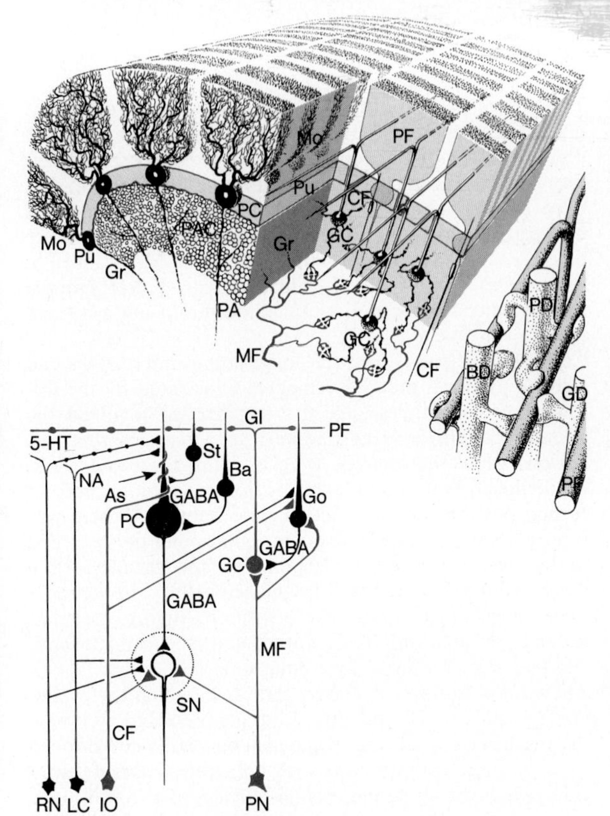

Fig. 5-17. Neuronal organization of the cerebellar cortex. *Upper left:* Transverse section of folium, to show the molecular layer *(Mo)*, the Purkinje-cell layer *(Pu)* and the granular layer *(Gr)*. The planes of the conspicuous Purkinje dendrites are in the transverse plane of the folium. The Purkinje cell *(PC)* has an axon *(PA)* that runs into the white matter of the cerebellum and sends back collaterals *(PAC)*. The Purkinje cells form a regular array both across and along the folium. The granule cells *(GC)* receive synaptic input from the mossy fibers *(MF)* and have T-shaped axons that run along the folium as parallel fibers *(PF)*, forming many synaptic contacts with the dendrites of the Golgi cells *(GD)*, basket cells *(BD)* and Purkinje cells *(PD)*. These contacts with the dendritic spines are shown enlarged on the right. *Below:* The main synapses in the folium, with inputs by way of the mossy fibers *(MF)* and the parallel fibers *(PF)*, the climbing fibers *(CF)* from the inferior olive *(IO)*, the serotonergic fibers from the raphe nuclei *(RN)* and the noradrenergic fibers from the locus coeruleus *(LC)*. The Purkinje cells *(PC)* are the only output elements in the cerebellar cortex. The stellate cells *(St)*, basket cells *(Ba)* and Golgi cells *(Go)* are local interneurons. All cells shown in *black* are GABAergic and have an inhibitory action. Excitatory transmitters are aspartate *(As)* and probably also glutamate *(Gl)*. The cerebellar cortex also includes large amounts of serotonin *(5-HT)* and noradrenalin *(NA)*. The target neurons of the Purkinje cells are in the intracerebellar nuclei and the vestibular nuclear complex *(SN)*. Modified from [7, 13]

In a unique example of concentrated collaboration, during the 1960's ECCLES, ITO and SZENTÁGOTHAI [7] and their colleagues worked out the basic features of the functional connections and the nature of the transmitter substances in the cerebellar network. Figure 5-17 is a simplified illustration to show the laminar structure of the folium, the regular palisade-like arrangement of the dendritic arborizations of Purkinje cells, through which parallel fibers run at right angles, and the transmitters at various points in the microcircuitry. Above the layer occupied by the **Purkinje-cell somata** (ca. 15 million in humans) is the **molecular layer**, consisting of the dense network of Purkinje-cell and Golgi-cell dendrites and the axons of the parallel fibers. Scattered through this neuropil are the cell bodies of interneurons (stellate cells, basket cells). Below the Purkinje-cell layer is the **granular layer**, characterized by the very numerous granule cells (over 2 million per mm^3!) and also containing the cell bodies of the Golgi interneurons.

Each individual Purkinje cell is reached by one climbing fiber, and each climbing fiber supplies 10-15 Purkinje cells by way of collaterals from its trunk. The climbing fiber twines around the dendritic tree of the Purkinje cell, forming many excitatory synapses there. With this arrangement, synaptic transmission is extraordinarily reliable. The *mossy fibers* make synaptic contact with dendrites of the *granule cells.* Mossy fibers have extensive terminal arborizatons, so that by way of this **divergent connectivity** they can excite a great number of cells in the cerebellar cortex.

The axons of the granule cells are T-shaped, dividing into two *parallel fibers* that run along the folium in opposite directions. It has been calculated that over 200,000 parallel fibers run at right angles through each Purkinje-cell dendritic tree. That is, there is also an enormous **convergence** of mossy fibers onto cells in the cerebellar cortex.

Finally, the cerebellar cortex also receives inputs from *noradrenergic* fibers originating in the locus coeruleus and *serotonergic* fibers from the raphe nuclei of the brainstem; the significance of these is still unclear.

The *Purkinje neurons* are the *output channels* of the cerebellar cortex. They have an inhibitory action on the cerebellar and vestibular nuclei. At a number of points in this basic input-output circuit, transmission can be inhibited by various *interneurons* (Golgi, basket and stellate cells). The Purkinje cells have a resting discharge, which tonically inhibits the target neurons in the cerebellar and vestibular nuclei. Against this background, increased Purkinje-cell activity due to excitatory inputs from the mossy-fiber and climbing-fiber system **deepens the inhibition,** and a reduction of Purkinje-cell activity due to the inhibitory interneurons causes **disinhibition** of the target neurons. The combination of (i) a continuous high resting level of activity of the neurons in the output nuclei of the cerebellum and (ii) numerous inhibitory phenomena within the cerebellar cortex creates a pattern of excitation in the nuclear output neurons with a delicately adjustable temporal and spatial structure and allows contrast development.

Modular fractionation of the cerebellar cortex into longitudinal microstrips. Despite the uniformity of its fine structure, in functional terms the cerebellar cortex has been found to consist of longitudinally organized modular units based on **specific input and output relationships.** Anatomical and microelectrophysiological studies, in particular, have shown that the climbing fibers from the **individual sections of the inferior olive** have a strictly topological projection to the cerebellar cortex, where they form **longitudinal strips** [13]. These strips in turn project topologically to **longitudinal columns in the underlying cerebellar nuclei.** The mossy-fiber system, by contrast, has wider projections and can control several microzones of the cerebellar cortex.

According to a recent hypothesis, the distinct operations of the cerebellum take place within the microzones just described [13]. The hypothesis grew out of the observation that a **microzone in the flocculus** is responsible for the adaptive gain control of the **vestibulo-ocular reflex.** As further explained in Sections 11.7 and 12.1, turning of the head induces an automatic counterrotation of the eyes. This vestibulo-ocular reflex serves to *stabilize the foveal image* on the retina, and must therefore be extremely precisely coupled to the process of vision. The microzone in the flocculus is well provided with information by which to adjust this reflex, for it receives signals from the vestibular afferents by way of the mossy-fiber system as well as visual input by way of climbing fibers; furthermore, this microstrip inhibits the vestibulo-ocular reflex by way of its projection to the vestibular nucleus [13].

Cerebellar plasticity, motor adaptation and motor learning. The role of the cerebellum in motor adaptation has been demonstrated experimentally. When vision is disturbed (e.g., by placing prisms in front of the eyes), the abovementioned compensatory eye movement as a reflex response to head-turning is no longer consistent with the visual information reaching the brain. The consequence is that the subject initially has great difficulty in moving correctly while wearing the prism glasses. Astonishingly, however, within a few days he learns to adjust to the abnormal visual input. Quantitative measurements revealed a distinct *change in the gain of the vestibuloocular reflex*, a **long-term adaptation.** Ablation experiments have shown that motor adaptation in the vestibulo-ocular reflex is critically dependent on the cerebellum.

The neural mechanism of such an adaptive process has not yet been explained. However, prolonged changes in the discharge rate of Purkinje cells have been observed after the excitatory input from the climbing-fiber system has been blocked [39], indicating that long-term interactions between the climbing-fiber and mossy-fiber systems are possible. The idea was first suggested by D. Marr and J.S. Albus. After some initial failures, experimental support for the Marr-Albus model has made promising advances [13].

Cerebellar plasticity and the longitudinal microzones can also be useful in **motor learning**, as illustrated by the following two examples. The first experiment involved the operant conditioning of monkeys in a reaction-time situation; while the animals were learning the motor task, cerebellocerebral signal transmission was monitored. It turned out that as the reaction time improved, there was a progressive increase in the compound potential recorded in the cerebral cortex in response to the visual starting signal, which was mediated by the cerebellum. In the same experimental situation monkeys with preexisting cerebellar lesions exhibited only rudimentary motor learning, even if training was continued for a long time [43].

The second example concerns rabbits in which the eyelid-closing reflex was tested. Such blinking is elicited by touching the cornea lightly, but it can also be readily conditioned by combining this stimulus with an acoustic signal; eventually the tone alone induces lid closure, as a conditioned reflex. The *paradigm of classical conditioning* by the method of Pavlov (see Section 6.5, p. 153) can be regarded as a *simple model of motor learning*. Circumscribed regions of the cerebellum and of the inferior olive were found to be necessary for both establishment and retention of the reflex [38].

Somatotopic arrangement of the cerebellum [13]. The cerebellum receives massive inputs from *ascending spinal tracts* and from *trigeminal afferents*. A rough somatotopic arrangement of these somatosensory projections was first found by the method of evoked potentials. It was only recently that the **complex microorganization** was worked out from single-cell recordings. When the somatosensory **mossy-fiber projections** at the level of the **granule layer** were examined, small regions of the ipsilateral body surface were found to be represented in **discrete, sharply delimited projection foci** (the fractionated somatotopy). A remarkable feature was the presence of multiple, sometimes widely separated foci with identical or similar representations. Figure 5-18 shows examples of **discrete receptive fields of Purkinje cells** located close to one another in a folium

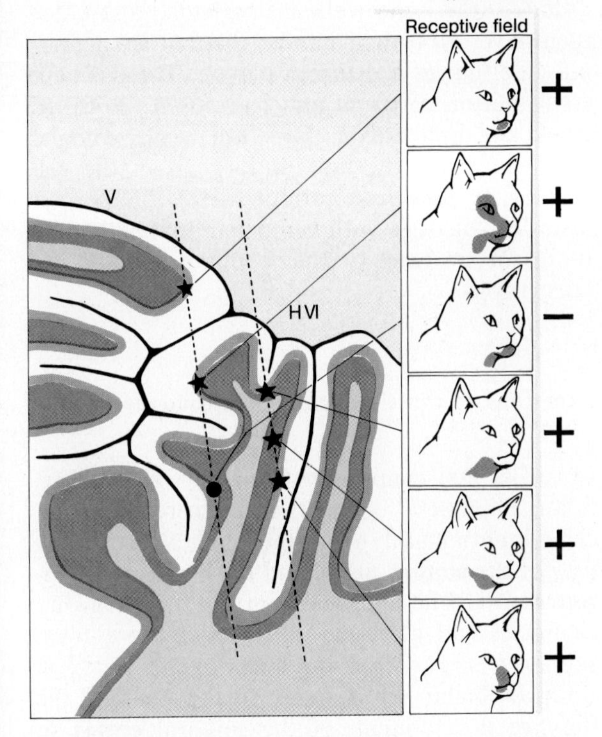

Fig. 5-18. Small receptive fields of 6 Purkinje cells, the activity of which was recorded in two microelectrode penetrations (lobules V and HVI). The characteristic action-potential response indicated that these cells were activated by the climbing-fiber system. All but one of the cells also responded to electrical stimulation of the contralateral cerebral cortex (facial area SI). From T.S. MILES and M. WIESENDANGER: J. Physiol. (Lond.) 245:425 (1975)

and excited **by way of climbing fibers**. As a rule, Purkinje cells are also influenced by the corresponding somatotopic areas of the contralateral cerebral cortex.

On the motor side, however, there is no discernible somatotopic organization. Focal cerebellar lesions are manifest in **motor deficits** primarily on the **ipsilateral side of the body,** but they are usually not limited to particular parts of the body. Instead, they seem to affect particular control systems – for oculomotor functions, balance, speech and so on – depending on the site of the lesion. This aspect will be discussed further in the following section.

Many new experimental findings that have only been touched on here are of considerable theoretical interest. In the following, however, because of their relevance to medicine, cerebral function is treated from the viewpoint of the effects of lesions.

Function of the Medial Elements of the Cerebellum

We shall take as a working hypothesis the **general functional principle of the medial elements** of the cerebellum diagrammed in Fig. 5-19. This diagram is based on both the neural connections and the clinically observed deficits [10]. The basic idea is that *the cerebellum is on a side circuit with respect to the main cortex-spinal cord axis.* On one hand it receives sensory feedback, an **afference copy**, and on the other it also receives an **efference copy** from the motor centers; in technical terms the former signals the current state of the controlled variable and the latter is a representation of the set point, the desired state. By setting the one against the other *(comparator function)* the cerebellar cortex can calculate an *error signal,* which is transmitted to the motor centers by way of the output nuclei. In so doing, the cerebellum can continually correct both intentional movements and automatisms.

Elements and connections. The various elements in the medial division of the cerebellum are shown by the dark outline on the left of Fig. 5-20 (see also Fig. 5-16). The phylogenetically oldest part *(archicerebellum)* is composed of the flocculus and the nodulus; it is dominated by vestibular inputs *(vestibulocerebellum).* Other old structures are the vermal parts of the anterior lobe,

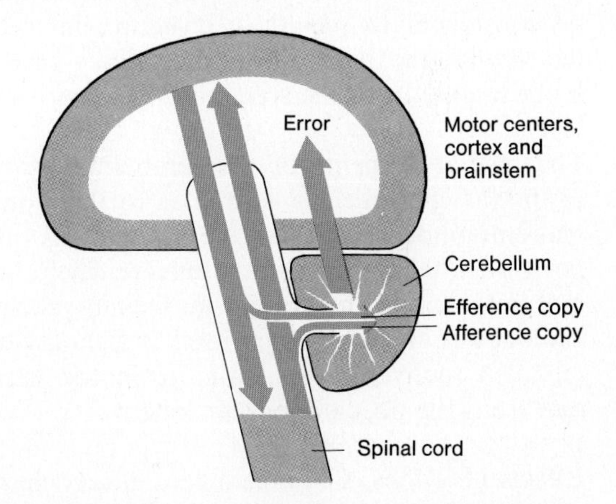

Fig. 5-19. Simplified functional diagram of the medial parts of the cerebellum. By way of collaterals, these receive an efference copy of command signals sent from the motor centers along descending motor pathways to the spinal cord. On the other hand, the cerebellum also receives a sensory afference copy by way of collaterals from ascending pathways. According to the hypothesis illustrated here, the cerebellum can calculate departures from the set point (errors) by comparing the two inputs. The result is signaled to the motor centers, so that the motor program can be continually corrected after a movement has been initiated

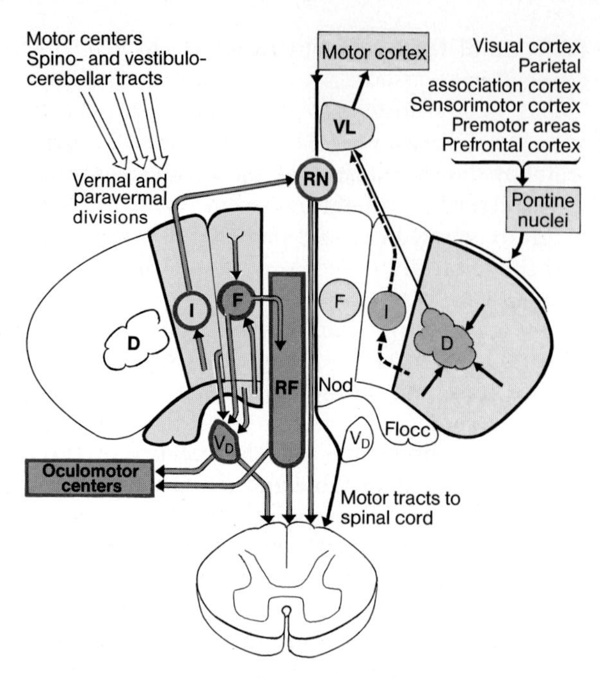

Fig. 5-20. The main connections of the medial *(left)* and lateral *(right)* parts of the cerebellum. The former project chiefly to the motor centers in the brainstem, and the latter project to the motor cortex by way of the thalamus (VL). Further explanation in text. Flocc, Nod, flocculus and nodulus; F, fastigial nucleus; I, nucleus interpositus; D, dentate nucleus; RN, red nucleus; RF, reticular formation; V_D, Deiters' nucleus

the pyramids, the uvula and the paraflocculus *(paleocerebellum)*. The medial division can also be considered to include a structure lateral to the vermis, the pars intermedia, which receives input mainly from the spinal cord *(spinocerebellum)*.

The medial elements of the cerebellum project to the fastigial nucleus as well as to the globose and emboliform nuclei (in the cat, nucleus interpositus), which in turn communicate chiefly with motor centers in the brainstem. Deiters' nucleus, a vestibular nucleus which itself is a motor center, also receives direct input from the vermis and from the flocculonodular lobe.

Effects of lesions. The preeminent effects characterizing lesions of the **vestibulocerebellum and the vermis** are *disturbances of equilibrium* similar to those associated with damage to the vestibular apparatus. The patients often suffer from vertigo and nausea, with vomiting. Objective *oculomotor disturbances*, in which the eyeballs turn spontaneously from side to side (oscillating nystagmus), are also typical. When the **vermis and paravermal divisions** are damaged, the patient has difficulty in standing and walking. These symptoms are especially pronounced in the dark (when the visually mediated corrections are eliminated). In order to stand and walk the patients must brace themselves with their hands; the gait is staggering, like that of a drunken person. The deficient coordination of trunk and leg muscles is called **trunk and gait ataxia.** The Italian physiologist L. Luciani was the first, at the end of the last century, to carry out careful studies of the gait disorders of dogs with cerebellar lesions and to represent graphically the stepping patterns of ataxic dogs.

Functions of the Cerebellar Hemispheres

Elements and connections (on the right in Fig. 5-20). The lateral elements in the cerebellum receive inputs mainly from the **cerebral cortex**, by way of the **pontine nuclei** and the **nuclei of the inferior olive**. The neurons from the former group of nuclei end as **mossy fibers**, and those from the latter end as **climbing fibers** in the cortex of both cerebellar hemispheres. In parallel with the massive development of the cerebral cortex in humans, the pontine and olivary nuclei are also well developed. The most important inputs to the *pontine nuclei* come from the visual cortex, the parietal association areas, the sensorimotor cortex, and the premotor and prefrontal association cortex. The term **pontocerebellum** reflects the dominance of the linkage between the pontine nuclei and the cerebellar hemispheres. The *inferior olive* receives projections from motor and premotor cortical areas (and perhaps from additional parts of the cortex in humans) as well as afferents from subcortical motor centers (by way of the central tegmental tract).

The Purkinje cells of the hemispheres project through the lateral *dentate nuclei* to motor nuclei of the *thalamus* and on to the *motor areas of the cortex*. By both input routes, the hemispheres clearly receive information from those cortical areas that are activated in the *preparation phase* and hence are involved in the **"programming" of movements** (see also Fig. 5-2).

Effects of lesions. The most prominent consequences of lesions in the hemispheres are defective *initiation of movements* and disturbed *coordination* during the execution of a movement. These effects can be explained by the loss of information from the cerebral cortex (see above). When the patient reaches for an object, the symptoms are dramatically obvious; the hand shakes,

making ever-wider sweeps. This **intention tremor** is tested clinically by having the patient point to his nose with his eyes closed.
The tremor is accompanied by a marked **dysmetria**, failure to reach the object accurately because the distance has been incorrectly programmed. Complex movement sequences for which widely separated groups of muscles are normally activated in a particular sequence *(synergies)* become disorderly in those with cerebellar defects. For instance, if the patient tries to tilt his head back while standing up, he risks falling backward, because he cannot balance by bending his knees as a normal person does. Patients also have *difficulty in rapidly stopping a movement.* When one arm is held out horizontally and a load is suddenly placed on it or removed, the arm makes transient overshooting oscillations before settling into a stable position. This instability is called the **rebound phenomenon.** Even without an external disturbance the patient has trouble keeping the outstretched arm in a stable position; when he closes his eyes, it gradually sinks down.
Severe problems are encountered when the patient tries to "change programs" rapidly – for example, to alternate between pronation and supination of the hand in rapid succession. The movements become irregular and are executed slowly **(adiadochokinesia)**. The coordination of the speech muscles, so important for the articulation of words, is also disrupted **(dysarthria)**. Speech becomes slow, expressionless, monotonous. A major contribution was made by the British neurologist GORDON HOLMES [32], who carried out detailed studies of casualties from the First World War who had sustained circumscribed, mostly unilateral cerebellar lesions. He succeeded in describing the symptoms objectively, by measuring reaction times to document the retarded initiation and execution of movements and by making impressive photographs in which impaired coordination was demonstrated by the traces of lights attached to the limbs (Fig. 5-21).

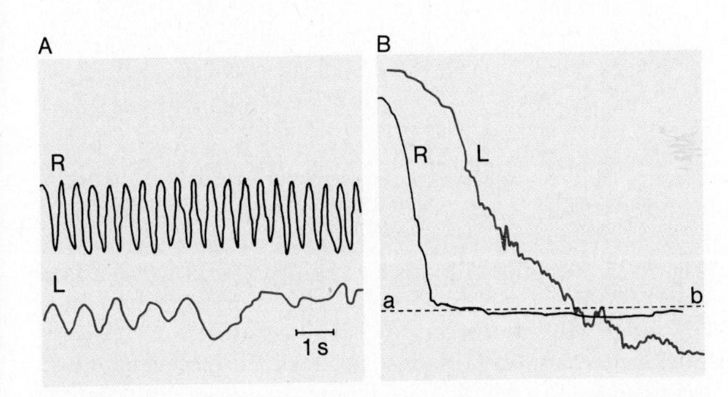

Fig. 5-21. A Recordings (light traces) to demonstrate adiadochokinesis in a patient with unilateral cerebellar lesion on the left. The alternating hand movement is regular and rapid on the right (R), and irregular and slower on the **left** (L). **B** The patient is instructed to make a forceful pulling movement (against springs) with both arms at the start signal, and when the position *a-b* is reached to maintain that position. The movement with the left arm begins after a delay, is irregular and overshoots the target. Modified from G. HOLMES [32]

5.6 Basal Ganglia

The place of the basal ganglia in the motor system. In general, pathological changes in the basal ganglia produce severe, dramatic deficits in voluntary movement. The best-known example is the restriction of voluntary movements (akinesia) in Parkinson's disease. The information currently available about the basal ganglia indicates that they play an important role in the *translation of the design for an action (preparation phase) into the required selection programs (execution phase)*, as diagrammed in Fig. 5-1. This large complex of nuclei is located below the cerebral cortex, in the depths of the cerebrum. With their massive cortical input, the basal ganglia serve as integra-

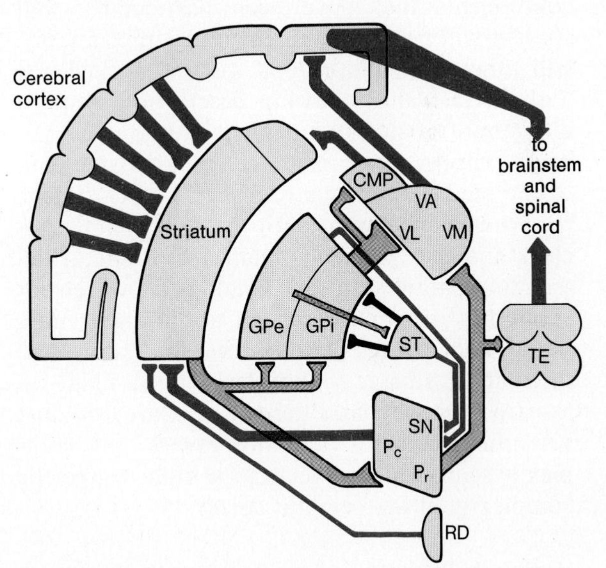

Fig. 5-22. The main connections of the basal ganglia. Excitatory actions are shown in *red*, inhibitory actions in *black*. GP, globus pallidus; e, external part; i, internal part; SN, substantia nigra; c, pars compacta; r, pars reticulata; ST, subthalamic nucleus; TE, tectum of the midbrain; VA ventralis anterior nucleus of the thalamus; VL, ventrolateral nucleus of the thalamus; VM, ventromedial nucleus of the thalamus; CMP central medial and parafascicular nuclei of the thalamus; RD, dorsal raphe nucleus. From S. KITAI in [2]

tion centers for a great variety of corticofugal excitation patterns. On the output side, the basal ganglia are coupled to the frontal cortex by way of thalamic nuclei. The general arrangement of this loop, from the cortex through the basal ganglia and back to the cortex, is diagrammed in Fig. 5-2 (along with a similar loop by way of the cerebellum).

The components of the basal ganglia and their connections (Fig. 5-22). The input structure of the basal ganglia is the **striatum**; it is divided into two parts, the *putamen* and the *caudate nucleus* (not shown in Fig. 5-22), by the fibers of the internal capsule. From the striatum information flows to thalamic nuclei by way of either the **pallidum (globus pallidus)** or the **pars reticulata** of the **substantia nigra** (there is also a small collateral connection to the tectum). The discovery that Parkinson's disease is caused by a deficit in the dopamine system led to the demonstration of dopamine-producing neurons in the **pars compacta** of the substantia nigra. The axons of these cells project to the striatum and are largely responsible for the normal function of the basal ganglia. Finally, the diagram of Fig. 5-22 emphasizes the fact that many of the connections are inhibitory.

In the following paragraphs some of the loop components that have been particularly well studied will be described. In future, presumably, still other functional loops will be worked out [24]. In fact, the following description omits a number of anatomical connections that are already known – for instance, the massive link to the medial thalamus (CMP in Fig. 5-22), the reciprocal connections with the subthalamic nucleus and the (probably small and indirect) descending pathway to the spinal cord. As yet not enough is known for certain about their functional significance. Despite the remarkable and fascinating advances that have been made in research on the basal ganglia, we are still just beginning to understand this exceedingly complex system, which reflects to a high degree the complexity of the cerebral cortex.

Information Flow in Parallel Functional Loops; Transmitter Systems of the Basal Ganglia

The **most important input** of information to the basal ganglia comes from the cerebral cortex. It is likely that all parts of the cortex are represented in the **corticostriate projection**, though the contribution of the frontal lobes is particularly great. The projection is strictly topographic. The transmitter of the corticostriate neurons appears to be the amino acid **glutamate**. As shown in Fig. 5-22, the basal ganglia communicate with the thalamus by way of two inhibitory neurons in series; their transmitter is **GABA**. This arrangement is found in both the route through the pallidum and that through the substantia nigra. The neurons of these output structures are known to to have a high level of background activity. Therefore it appears that the cortically induced excitation patterns in the thalamus will take the form of **disinhibition**, a mechanism frequently encountered in the CNS. Detailed studies of the localization of the corticofugal neurons and of their connections within the neuronal circuit of the basal ganglia have given rise to the *concept of multiple, separate functional loops in parallel* (Fig. 5-23; see CARPENTER in [2], KITAI in [2] and [24]).

The skeletomotor loop. This loop receives input from the premotor, motor and somatosensory cortical areas. The main information flow path is through the putamen, the inner segment of the pallidum or the caudolateral pars reticulata of the substantia nigra, then through thalamic

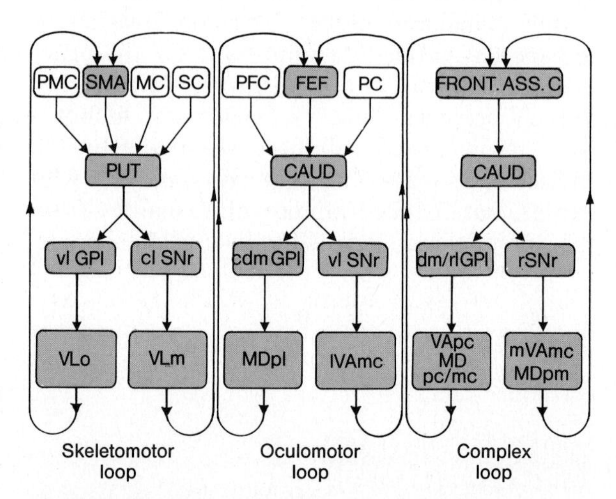

Fig. 5-23. Functional loops through the basal ganglia (see text). PMC, premotor cortex; SMA, supplementary motor area; MC, motor cortex; SC, somatosensory cortex; PUT, putamen; GPI, inner segment of the globus pallidus; SNr, substantia nigra, pars reticulata; VLo, oral part of the ventrolateral nucleus (thalamus); VLm, median part of the ventrolateral nucleus (thalamus); PFC, prefrontal association cortex; FEF frontal eye field (area 8); PC, parietal association cortex (area 7); CAUD, caudate nucleus; MD medial dorsal nucleus (thalamus). VA ventralis anterior nucleus: mc, magnocellular part; pc, parvocellular part; cdm, caudal- dorsomedial; cl, caudal-lateral; dm, dorsomedial; l, lateral; m, medial; pl, paralamellar; pm, posteromedial; r, rostral; rl, rostrolateral; vl, ventrolateral. Modified from [24]

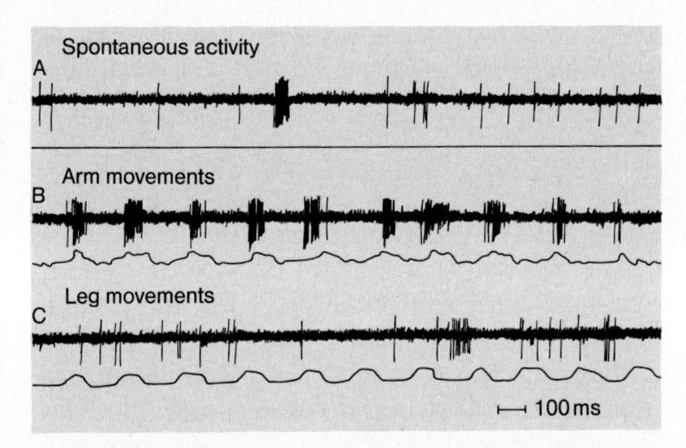

Fig. 5-24 A-C. Activity of a cell in the inner segment of the pallidum, recorded in a monkey during a behavioral task requiring specific movements. The activity is clearly correlated with arm movements **(B)** and not with leg movements **(C)**. The level of spontaneous activity in the pallidum is fairly high even in the absence of movement **(A)**. From DeLong and Georgopoulos in [2]

motor nuclei and back to area 6 of the cerebral cortex (Fig. 5-23, left). Single-cell recordings in the putamen and pallidum of monkeys that had learned to execute standardized movements revealed unequivocal correlations between these movements and the activity of certain neurons. A clear topographic organization was found; that is, activity in a given region was always correlated only with quite specific movements of particular parts of the body (Fig. 5-24). Furthermore, the activity was often most closely correlated with a particular movement parameter – the force, for instance, or the amplitude or direction of the movement. Evidently, then, the neurons of the motor loop in putamen and pallidum are used to control the parameters of movements. Single-cell recordings have also shown that the route from the striatum through the lateral parts of the reticular zone to a special section of the thalamic motor nuclei is involved mainly with **control of face and mouth movements.**

The oculomotor loop (Fig. 5-23, middle). This loop is anatomically distinct from the skeletomotor loop and seems to be specialized for the control of eye movements. The input comes from cortical areas known to control **gaze direction**: the *frontal eye field* (area 8 of Brodmann) and the caudal parts of area 7 in the parietal cortex (see also Fig. 5-26). The flow path proceeds through the caudate nucleus to a dorsomedial sector of the inner part of the pallidum, or to the ventrolateral pars reticulata of the substantia nigra. The next station is in thalamic nuclei that in turn project back to the frontal eye field. It should also be mentioned that the axons of the reticulata neurons of the substantia nigra bifurcate, sending a branch to the superior colliculus, which is also known to be involved in eye movements. Figure 5-25 shows a positive correlation between the activity of a reticulata cell and a gaze saccade. The discharge rate is suddenly reduced **before** the saccade, an effect of the inhibitory striatonigral connection. This interruption in the inhibitory output of the substantia nigra produces a phasic activation at the next station, the thalamus or superior colliculus. The strict spatial separation of the skeletomotor and oculomotor loops is evident, for example, in the finding that the activity of a neuron in the reticular zone is correlated either with eye movements or with orofacial movements, but never with both.

Complex loops (Fig. 5-23, right). There is already anatomical evidence of a number of "complex" loops originating in the association areas and returning to frontal association areas (dorsolateral prefrontal cortex, lateral orbitofrontal cortex, anterior cingulum) by way of thalamic association nuclei. There is a marked phylogenetic increase in the size and significance of these cortical, striatal and thalamic structures, so that in humans they have become more massive than the motor loops. However, hardly any experimental research has been devoted to the function of these loops. We do know – from single-cell recordings in the relevant cortical areas and from ablation

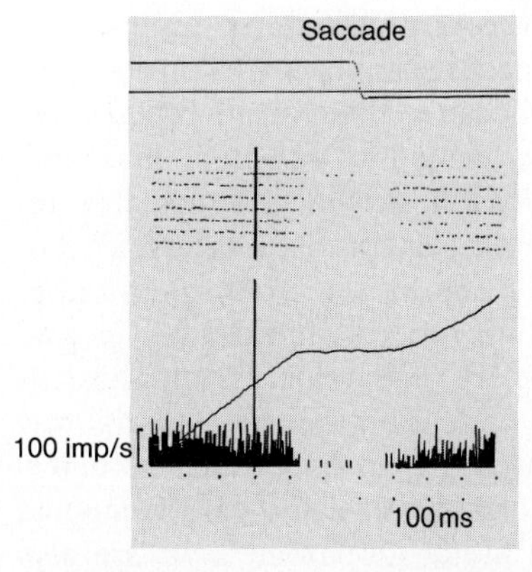

Fig. 5-25. Activity of a cell in the pars reticulata of the substantia nigra (monkey), correlated with saccades of the eyes. At the vertical line a light spot is turned on. The monkey is trained to make a saccade to this new fixation point. About 100 ms after the appearance of the light and barely 200 ms before the beginning of the saccade, the activity of the cell is almost completely suppressed (gaps in the sequential dot patterns and in the histogram; plateau in the cumulative distribution curve). This suppression of neuronal activity will produce disinhibition (activation) of the target neurons in thalamus and tectum. From O. Hikosaka and R.H. Wurtz: J. Neurophysiol. 49 (1983)

experiments, as well as from clinical observations of patients with lesions in the frontal lobe and the limbic system – that these cortical regions are responsible for "higher" (complex) brain functions. As detailed in Chapters 6 and 17, these associative systems play a role in *general drive* and in the control of *individual drives* such as hunger and sexuality. They are also involved in the control of *motivation*, in the *choice of strategies* and in *cognitive performance*. On the other hand, all these complex functions may also be disturbed in patients with diseases of the basal ganglia. It follows that the manifestation of these complex functions and their incorporation into normal motor activity are fundamentally dependent on the basal ganglia.

The links between motor and complex functional loops in the basal ganglia. Given that the individual functional loops are separate from one another in the basal ganglia, how and where are the neuronal substrates for the cognitive and motivational components of motor activity conjoined with the details of the motor commands? This is a difficult question, and at present any answer must be speculative. At least we can say, in view of the separation within the basal ganglia, that this synthesis occurs not in the basal ganglia themselves but rather at a cortical level. **Area 6** seems to be a good candidate, because it is the most important target structure of the motor loop and also receives inputs from the frontal association field.

Modulation of information transfer in the functional loops of the basal ganglia. Flow of information along the main path described above, in multiple, parallel transstriatal functional loops, can be promoted or inhibited by modulation systems. These mechanisms are of considerable clinical interest, because the overall function of the basal ganglia evidently depends on a delicate balance between the facilitatory and inhibitory modulation systems (see below, Pathophysiology of the Basal Ganglia). A number of demonstrated or potential modulation systems are known; the **dopamine system** has received particular attention because of its role in Parkinson's disease. The dopaminergic **nigrostriatal pathway** originates in the **pars compacta** of the substantia nigra. Dopamine cells are also found scattered or in groups outside the substantia nigra, but only in nearby regions.

The very slender axons have many branches and supply the entire striatum in a relatively diffuse way (i.e., with no clear topographic organization). Along the extensively diverging arborization there are many minute swellings, visible in the light microscope, called varicosities. In electron micrographs these can be identified as presynaptic elements. The neurons from the pars compacta have a rather regular discharge, at a rate of about 1 Hz. Every second, then, the impulse in a single dopamine cell will release dopamine from countless synapses distributed over a large region of the striatum.

Being so diffusely arranged, the dopamine system is not suitable for the transmission of detailed, topographically organized information. Instead it can be seen as a kind of "irrigation system" that *modulates* transmission in the main channel. Recent results have in fact shown that the dopamine released in the striatum **modulates glutaminergic corticostriatal transmission,** though it is not entirely clear whether the dopamine produces inhibition, facilitation or both. The ascending dopaminergic fibers from the mesencephalon project not only to the striatum but also to limbic structures and to the prefrontal cortex.

A similar modulating influence may be exerted in the basal ganglia by **serotonergic fibers from the raphe nuclei and noradrenergic fibers from the locus coeruleus**, as well as fibers with unknown transmitters from the **intralaminar nuclei** of the thalamus and fibers from the **amygdala**, all of which also project to the striatum. Finally, it must be mentioned that the basal ganglia contain a large number of **local neurons** (interneurons), which also act to modulate information flow in the transstriatal loops. These include the **cholinergic neurons** of the striatum and diverse **peptidergic neurons**, which have recently been discovered.

Modular and Longitudinal Organization in the Striatum

Transmitter compartments. For a long time the striatum appeared to be a large, homogeneous mass of cells. Not until recently was the modular nature of this structure discovered ([49, 29] and DeLong and Georgopoulos in [2]). The endings of the two large afferent fiber systems from the cortex and the intralaminar nuclei of the thalamus form small, sharply delimited foci in the striatum. Anatomical experiments in which the various fiber systems were differentially stained have shown that within the caudate nucleus agglomerations of endings from the frontal association cortex intermingle with those from the temporal association cortex, as in a puzzle. The histochemical picture is similar, with the different transmitters (glutamate, GABA, acetylcholine, various peptides) represented in small, well-defined areas. Today these foci are regarded as independent **compartments** or **micromodules**. Finally, even in striatal sections with the cell bodies stained by traditional methods (Nissl stain) one can discern small, elongated **islands** of high cell density, surrounded by a **matrix** in which the cells are loosely packed.

An attempt to find the *relation of these cellular compartments to the various transmitter systems* is well under way. It can already be stated that compartmentalization into functionally different groups of neurons is a *general organizational principle of the striatum.* There seems to be only one exception, the dopamine system; these fibers, with their varicosities, branch diffusely throughout the striatum. In *young* animals, however, at first the arriving dopaminergic fibers are arranged in dopamine islands or **striosomes**.

Topographic relations between the cerebral cortex and the striatum. Here, again, clear results have only recently been obtained. They reveal a topographic ordering in **longitudinal columns** that extend through the whole striatum. For example, the projections of the frontal and temporal association cortex are arranged in this way. By high-resolution microelectrophysiological sampling, somatotopically arranged longitudinal columns have been discovered within the skeletomotor loop. It seems, for instance, that in an *arm column* signals from the premotor, motor and somatosensory areas of the cortex are brought together. The common denominator of the neurons in such a longitudinal column is their similar somatotopic properties.

Functional interpretation of the micromodular organization of the basal ganglia. The extraordinarily complex parceling of the basal ganglia, established by the criteria of transmitters and topography, is unquestionably of crucial functional significance, and it will surely give rise to new working hypotheses. The convergence of various cortical fields onto an "arm column" within the motor loop, described above, is evidently a structural correlate of the process of sensorimotor integration by which an arm movement is executed.

Pathophysiology of the Basal Ganglia

The severe motor symptoms that accompany basal-ganglia disorders can be categorized as *minus* and *plus symptoms.* The first category is that of **akinesia** (literally, absence of movement); the second includes **rigidity** (elevated muscle tone), **ballism** (involuntary flinging movements), **athetosis** (sinuous movements), **chorea** (rapid jerks) and **tremor** (trembling). The symptoms in the second category are signs of overexcitability of the motor system, which is interpreted as the consequence of disinhibition. The current approach is to try to understand the symptoms in terms of the deficient or excessive function of transmitter systems.

Deficiency in the dopamine system and Parkinson's disease [37]. The **triad of symptoms** characteristic of Parkinson's disease, the most common disorder of the basal ganglia, consists of **rigidity, tremor and akinesia**. The muscular hypertonia is such that the tonic (but not the phasic) stretch reflexes are increased; accordingly, even slow stretching encounters a waxy resistance, which often gives way periodically *(cogwheel phenomenon).* There are conspicuous coarse trembling movements of the fingers, and sometimes also of the lips and other parts of the body.

The akinesia is manifest in a number of symptoms. The patient has problems with starting and stopping a movement, and on occasion the voluntary motor system can essentially "freeze up". It becomes extremely difficult to do two things at the same time. The face is expressionless, like a mask, and the modulation of speech is diminished; while walking, the patient fails to swing the arms as normal, takes short steps and is usually bent forward.

The **motor defects in parkinsonism** can be **analyzed quantitatively** from electromyographic data electronically averaged, which enables a more precise evaluation of the pathophysiological mechanisms and of the effects of therapy. As would be expected, the *reaction times* are often lengthened, mainly because movements are carried out more slowly. Disturbances in the *anticipatory adjustment of posture* for intended movements have also been observed. The Parkinson's patient has great difficulty in *tracking* a moving light with a finger, especially when the changes of direction are unpredictable. When the target changes direction regularly (e.g., moves sinusoidally) the patient follows it with a delay, whereas a healthy person plans the tracking movements in advance. It is often impossible for a Parkinson's patient to make two or more movements (e.g., closing a fist and bending the arm) *simultaneously.* It appears as though each individual movement is completed before the next component is initiated. To generalize, the **deficient planning of movement** can be regarded as a fundamental defect in Parkinson's patients.

In a doctoral dissertation in 1919 (by TRETIAKOF) the first mention was made of a loss of the normal dark color of the substantia nigra in fresh sections of the brains of deceased Parkinson's patients. This lead was followed up,

and it was eventually established that the **dopamine cells of the substantia nigra degenerate** in this disease. (The blackness of the substantia nigra is produced by the pigment melanin, a side product of dopamine synthesis which is stored in the dopamine cells of pars compacta.) Following the death of the dopamine cells, there is a *sharp decrease in the dopamine content of the striatum.* This discovery had far-reaching consequences; once it was known that the loss of dopaminergic innervation in the striatum was causally related to the symptoms of Parkinson's disease, spectacularly successful substitution **therapy** became possible. Dopamine could not be administered directly, because it does not pass the blood-brain barrier. The way out of this difficulty was to use its precursor in the synthesis pathway, **L-dopa (levodopa)**, which can pass from the blood into the brain. Usually a decarboxylase inhibitor is given at the same time, to prevent the L-dopa from being converted to dopamine in the peripheral tissues (the inhibitor does not pass the blood-brain barrier). Therefore the entire dose of L-dopa is reserved for the brain, where it is decarboxylated to form dopamine. Fortunately, the main improvement is in the akinesia, which had previously been essentially uncontrollable; the lesser problems of rigidity and tremor are not as much affected by dopamine. Evidently, then, there is a *causal relationship between dopamine deficiency and akinesia.* After some years the L-dopa treatment becomes less effective, probably due to secondary changes in the dopamine receptors. Therefore it is important to continue study of the still unsolved aspects of parkinsonism in animal models.
Occasionally addicts consuming synthetic drugs develop severe Parkinson's symptoms, which have been found to be due to contamination of the drugs with a pyridine derivative (N-methyl-4-phenyl-1,2,3,6-tetrahydropyridine= **MPTP**) [35]. A metabolite of this substance appears to be *neurotoxic* and act preferentially on the *dopamine neurons* of the substantia nigra. MPTP can also be used to produce Parkinson-like symptoms experimentally in animals (e.g., mice), which is of great importance to research on the remaining problems of Parkinson's disease. Dopamine antagonists such as phenothiazine derivatives and haloperidol (substances that play a role in psychopharmacology) can have undesirable Parkinson-like symptoms as side effects.

Even before the L-dopa era, interestingly, a degree of therapeutic success was achieved with **acetylcholine antagonists** (derivatives of atropine). Now it is thought that in the absence of the dopamine system the cholinergic neurons are disinhibited. According to this theory, there is normally a precisely adjusted equilibrium between the two transmitter systems.

Hypofunction of GABAergic and cholinergic systems; chorea and ballism. The condition called **chorea**, first described by HUNTINGTON, is a hereditary degenerative disease of the basal ganglia, characterized by involuntary spasmodic twitches. Postmortem examination has shown a severe *loss of cells in the striatum.* The main cells affected appear to be the **GABA**-*producing* striatopallidal and striatonigral neurons and the local *cholinergic* cells. Without inhibition by the striatonigral neurons, overshooting activity of the dopamine cells can result. In any case, this is another example of disequilibrium, here involving dopamine, acetylcholine and GABA.
In **hemiballism** there are violent, involuntary flinging movements on one side of the body, usually as a result of unilateral vascular damage in the subthalamic nucleus. Because this nucleus projects to the pallidum by way of **GABA**ergic neurons, it seems likely that the flinging movements are caused by **disinhibition of the pallidum.** However, attempts to treat the disease by administration of **GABA** or its agonists have not been successful.

5.7 Motor Fields of the Cerebral Cortex

Historical introduction. It was already known in ancient times that disorders in one half of the brain could cause impaired voluntary movement on the opposite side of the body. The pyramidal decussation at the transition to the spinal cord was discovered in the 18th Century, and then it was demonstrated that there is a continuous fiber tract leading from the cortex through the pyramids to the spinal cord. These findings led, in the 19th Century, to the concept of the pyramidal-tract system as the morphological correlate of the voluntary motor system. Supporting evidence was provided by the *strokes (apoplexy)* often suffered by older people as a result of a sudden disturbance of blood circulation through the brain. The typical symptom is paralysis on the side opposite to the lesion, and at autopsy, in most cases, degeneration of the pyramidal tract is found.
From clinical observations by the great English neurologist HUGHLINGS JACKSON the important concept of **somatotopy** emerged, as the topographic relationship between the cerebral cortex and individual groups of skeletal muscles was recognized. JACKSON was the first to point out that an epileptic attack often begins with isolated twitches. For example, first the thumb twitches and after a few seconds the convulsions spread to the hand, then to the arm and finally to the whole side of the body. His interpretation was that such an attack is initiated by a focal irritation in the cortex, and that the seizure is first apparent in the musculature controlled by this region; as the pathological excitation gradually spreads out over the cortex, the convulsions become correspondingly generalized. This sensible interpretation has since been fully confirmed, in that such patients have indeed been found to have pathological foci in the contralateral central region of the cerebral cortex. In our example, the focal abnormality (e.g., a brain tumor) would be located in the thumb area of the precentral region.
Shortly after JACKSON's work there were demonstrations in many clinical laboratories that the precentral region of the cerebral cortex is "electrically excitable" and that particular muscle groups on the opposite side of the body are topographically associated with the stimulus sites. Today, of course, we know that the whole brain is electrically excitable; but at the end of the 19th Century muscle twitches

were the only directly visible sign that the electrical stimulus had been effective. Instead of speaking of an "excitable cerebral cortex", therefore, we now use the terms **motor cortex** or **motor cortical field**. Originally based on the brain-stimulation experiments and the consequences of lesions (paralysis of voluntary movement), the definition of these terms was subsequently extended to include anatomical criteria – in particular, *cytoarchitectonics* (the architecture of the cell layers) and the fiber connections from the motor nuclei of the thalamus.
The brain-stimulation experiment marked the actual beginning of modern brain research. The combined efforts of researchers in various fields and clinical neurologists proved so fruitful that in the first quarter of the 20th Century interdisciplinary institutes for the study of the brain were founded. Here, with refined brain-stimulation methods, lesion techniques and structural analyses, motor **cortical maps** were worked out for the brains of several mammalian species. The maps of BRODMANN and of the VOGTS (a husband-and-wife team), with numbered cytoarchitectonic and stimulus-response fields, are still widely used as references for the functional organization of the cerebral cortex (see Figs. 6-3 to 6-5, beginning on p. 127, and Fig. 5-26). The literature has been thoroughly surveyed by CREUTZFELDT [3] and WIESENDANGER [53].

The Cortical Map of Motor Responses to Electrical Stimuli, and the Definition of the Motor Cortex

An example of a cortical map of the responses to electrical stimulation is shown in Fig. 5-26. Clearly, motor responses can be elicited by repetitive stimuli in large regions of the cerebral cortex, but there are great differences in the mean threshold and in the pattern of the response. The motor cortex in the strict sense, the **primary motor area**, is the region in which twitches of muscles in small groups are elicited (e.g., thumb twitches synchronous with the stimulus), at the lowest threshold intensity. This area coincides approximately with the precentral gyrus (including the anterior wall of the central sulcus), and with the cytoarchitectonic area 4 of BRODMANN. The cortex is especially thick here; the inner granular layer is absent, and the 5th layer contains conspicuously large pyramidal cells, the giant cells of BETZ (hence the alternative term *area agranularis gigantopyramidalis* for the primary motor area).
Repetitive stimulation of the cortical surface in the postcentral areas 1, 2, 3 and 5 and in the frontal area 6 also elicits motor responses if it is maintained for seconds, but the stimulus intensity must be high and the responses are usually complex. For example, typical responses triggered from area 6 include rotation of the trunk and eyes, and raising of the contralateral arm; similar movements can occur in humans during an epileptic attack when the focus lies in area 6. The complex effects of stimulation in area 6 are evidently produced by massive spatial and temporal summation of the excitation, in which complex multisynaptic neuronal chains are activated. Area 6 is a **secondary motor field**, consisting of a medial part, the **supplementary motor area**, and a lateral part, the **premotor cortex** (see Fig. 5-26).
As an alternative to the earlier verbal description of the motor responses, WOOLSEY tried to represent them by drawings called **"figurines"** [57]. As shown in Fig. 5-27A, the drawing of the part of the body that is caused to twitch is placed at the cortical site of the stimulus (note the overlapping motor representation). A further simplification is to superimpose an outline of the whole body on the cortex in the appropriate orientation (Fig. 5-27B). This popular way of symbolizing somatotopy in the form of a small monkey, a **"simiusculus"**, makes it easy to remember the basic (highly simplified) features, including the fact that the various parts of the body are not represented in proportion to their size. A particularly large volume of cortex is occupied by representations of the face, hand and foot muscles.
This disproportionality gives impressive evidence that *those parts of the body with the greatest degrees of freedom of movement require correspondingly great cortical control.* Motor cortical maps of the human brain have been constructed from data obtained in neurosurgical operations [16], and the **motor homunculus** (Fig. 5-27C) proves to be an even more extreme caricature, with gigantic hands as a correlate of the human skill in manipulation (see also the *sensory homunculus* in Fig. 9-24, p. 217).

Motor Cortex and Motor Behavior

Activation of neurons in the motor cortex during learned movements [8]. Important as they have been, anatomical studies and stimulus-response and lesion experiments have always provided only indirect evidence of the functional implication of the motor cerebral cortex in the control of movement. There was a new breakthrough when the methods of experimental psychology were combined with the painless recording of the activity of single neurons by microelectrodes. In these studies natural, learned movements can be directly correlated with the activity of the CNS. In a classical experiment of this type, the

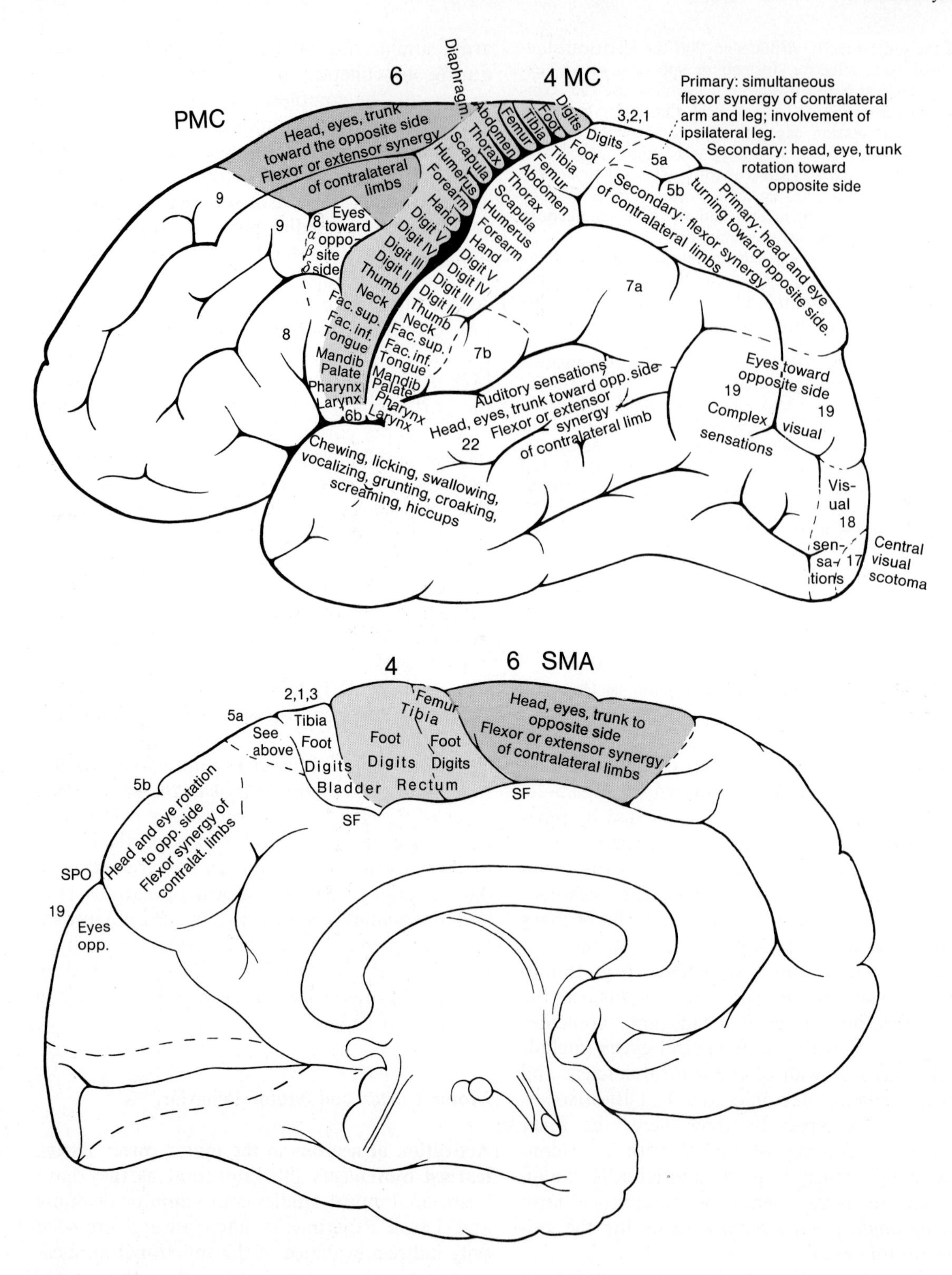

Fig. 5-26. Map of the human brain, based on motor responses to repetitive electrical stimulation (50 Hz) of the surface of the brain of patients during neurosurgery. The effects of stimulation are entered at the corresponding stimulus sites in the diagram of the brain surface. PMC, premotor cortex or lateral area 6; MC, motor cortex or area 4 (corresponds roughly to the precentral gyrus); SMA, supplementary motor area or medial area 6. Whereas the responses to stimuli in the motor cortex were discrete and elicited at low thresholds, stimuli in area 6 as well as in the posterior areas elicited only complex movements, and high intensities were required. From O. FOERSTER [28]

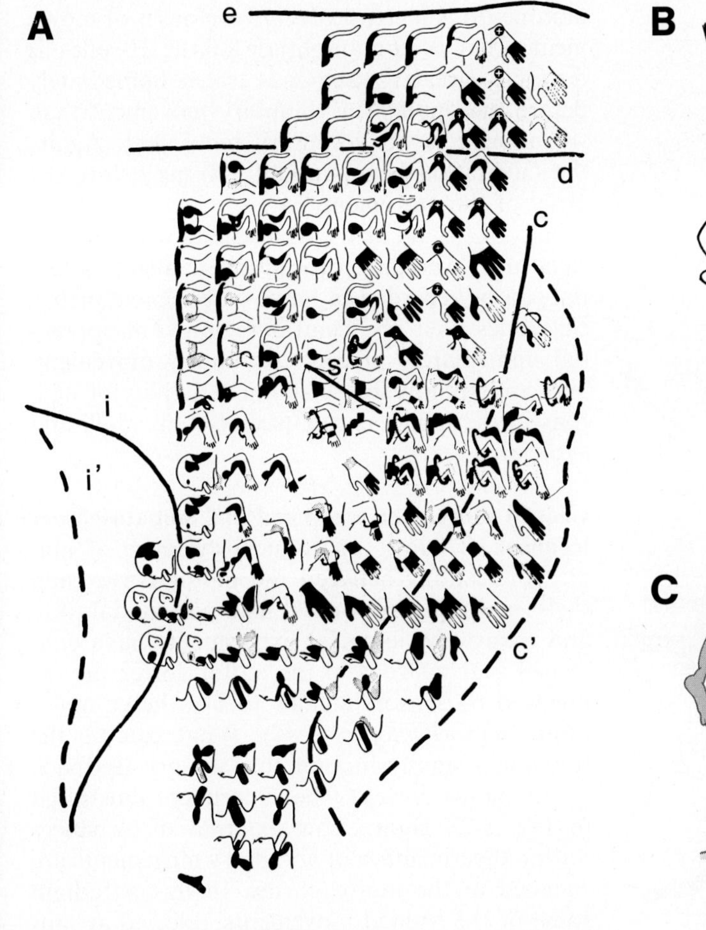

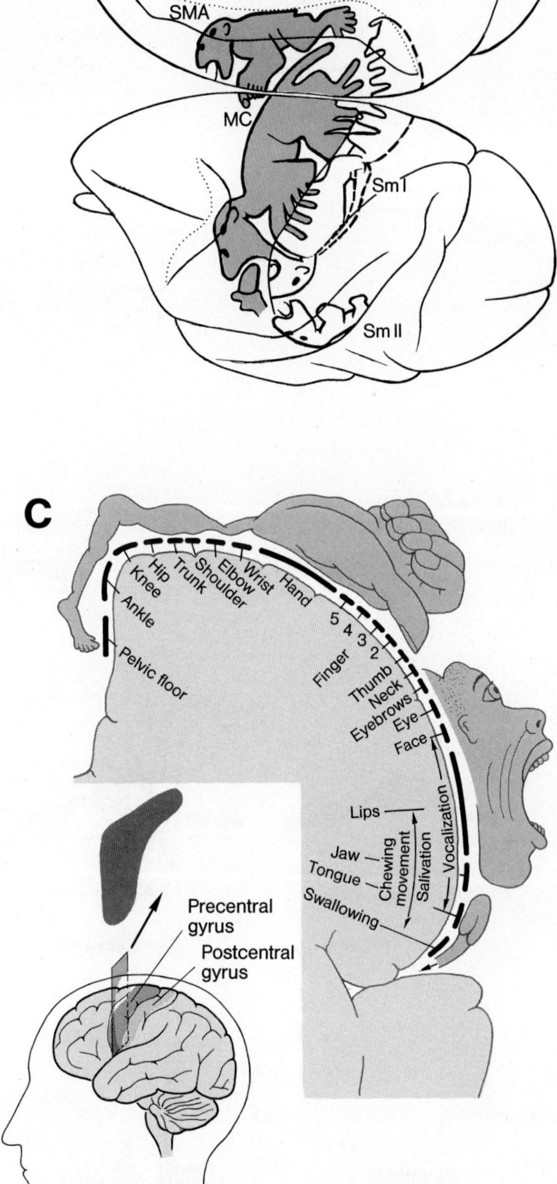

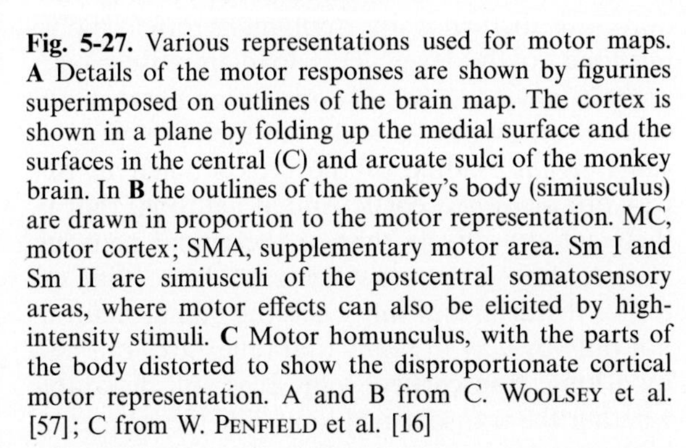

Fig. 5-27. Various representations used for motor maps. **A** Details of the motor responses are shown by figurines superimposed on outlines of the brain map. The cortex is shown in a plane by folding up the medial surface and the surfaces in the central (C) and arcuate sulci of the monkey brain. In **B** the outlines of the monkey's body (simiusculus) are drawn in proportion to the motor representation. MC, motor cortex; SMA, supplementary motor area. Sm I and Sm II are simiusculi of the postcentral somatosensory areas, where motor effects can also be elicited by high-intensity stimuli. **C** Motor homunculus, with the parts of the body distorted to show the disproportionate cortical motor representation. A and B from C. WOOLSEY et al. [57]; C from W. PENFIELD et al. [16]

impulses of neurons in the motor cortex of a monkey are recorded while the animal makes reproducible arm movements in order to obtain a reward of food (Fig. 5-28).

To what extent does a single cell encode a particular movement? What is the relative timing of cortical activity, electromyographic activity and the onset of movement? Figure 5-28 shows that such questions can be answered experimentally (though the conclusions must always be based on results from a population of neurons). Basically, such experiments show that the neuronal activity in the motor "arm area" of the precentral gyrus *precedes the arm movement* (by 50–100 ms) and the phasic activation dies out again shortly after the beginning of the movement. Such correlations are very often *directionally specific.*

The long delay between the beginning of neuronal activity in the cortex and the beginning of the movement shows that *considerable temporal summation at the spinal level is necessary for the recruitment of the motor units.* In humans the H-reflex (see 5.2) can be used to demonstrate indirectly that the excitability of the spinal

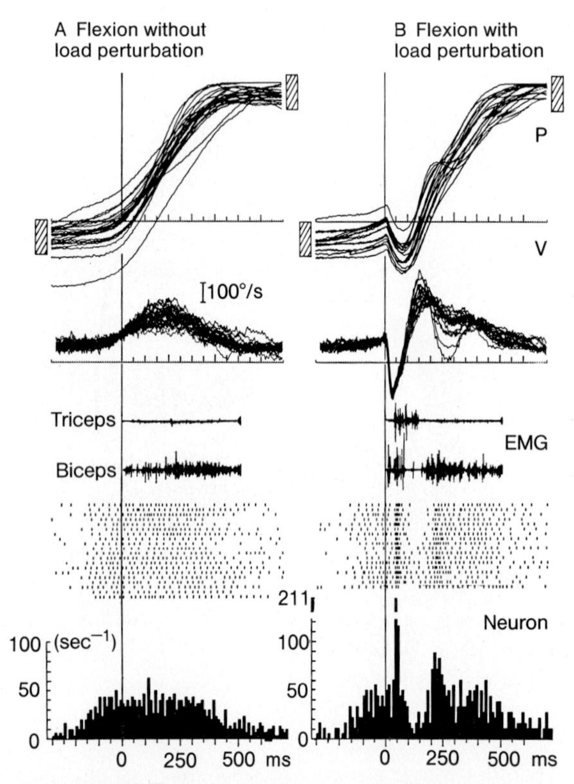

Fig. 5-28 A,B. Activity pattern of a cell in the motor cortex, recorded during execution of a motor task. *Top:* experimental paradigm with a monkey that has learned to carry out flexion and extension movements for a food reward. Occasionally a torque motor is engaged to provide a brief load pulse at the beginning of the movement. The computer evaluation treats undisturbed flexion movements **(A)** separately from those disturbed by the load pulse **(B)**. From top to bottom: position signal of the movement (P), velocity of movement (V), electromyogram (EMG), dot patterns (in which each discharge of the cortical cell is represented by a dot), and time histogram in which the discharges are summed. Time 0 coincides with the beginning of the self-initiated movement. The neuron in this case already increased its discharge about 150 ms before the onset of movement. The disturbed movements (B) were rapidly corrected (see mechanical and EMG signals); in the time histogram and in the dot patterns the extra activity of the cell in response to the disturbance is clearly visible (two peaks at about 40 ms and 220 ms). This transcortical reaction will have an effect at the spinal level by way of the corticospinal neurons ("long-loop" reflexes). From B. CONRAD, K. MATSUNAMI, J. MEYER-LOHMANN, M. WIESENDANGER and V.B. BROOKS: Brain Res. 71:507 (1974)

motoneurons increases *before* the onset of movement. That is, the amplitude of the H-reflex is distinctly greater when it is tested immediately before the onset of a voluntary movement than when there is no voluntary movement. Again, the facilitation begins about 100 ms before the onset of the movement.

Finally, it should be mentioned that with modern electronic averaging procedures a **motor potential** can be recorded in humans, by epicutaneous electrodes over the central region. This potential immediately precedes voluntary movement, and corresponds to the summed activity of neurons in the motor cortex (see also Fig. 5-30 and associated text).

Central movement command and somatosensory feedback. There is anatomical evidence of ample connections between the motor cortex and the somatosensory cortical field just caudal to it, and many physiological experiments have confirmed that neurons in the motor cortex are influenced by sensory signals (hence the common term *"sensorimotor cortex"*). What can be the functional significance of this sensory feedback to the motor cortex? The experiment illustrated in Fig. 5-28 shows how external disturbances during the execution of voluntary movements are signaled to the motor cortex. In this paradigm some of the trained movements, selected at random, are disturbed by applying a brief opposing load to the lever. This load impulse causes a *short-latency, reflex-like discharge burst* in the cortical cell, which is added to the *"central command signal"*. Some of the cells studied in this way are identified corticospinal neurons; that is, their activity affects that of the spinal neurons. This finding gives convincing evidence that external disturbances influence the spinal neurons not only by way of segmental reflex arcs but also by a long, **transcortical loop**. It is still debatable whether the transcortical loop, like the segmental loop, serves to "intercept" and compensate for the disturbance [56].

Corticofugal Control

The pyramidal tract [53, 17]. The motoneurons in the nuclei of the cranial nerves and in the spinal cord receive inputs by way of the corticobulbar and corticospinal fibers in the pyramidal tract. The spinal neurons are also indirectly connected to the motor cortex by way of the motor centers of the brainstem (see Section 5.4). *Experimental transection of the pyramidal tract* in the monkey by no means prevents all voluntary movement. On the contrary, at first glance the general mobility of the monkey seems to be only slightly disturbed; it climbs around in the cage and reaches for pieces of food. But when detailed records of the movements are made, it becomes apparent that the **fine motor patterns, especially those of the hand, are abnormal** (Fig. 5-29). The movements are *slowed*, during grasping all the *fingers are closed together*, and the animal has great difficulty with the *precision grip* – e.g., in using the thumb and index finger to pick raisins out of a small well in the feeding board and place them in its mouth. These fine digital movements are thought to depend on direct connections between the cortex and motoneurons. This **monosynaptic corticomotoneuronal system**, a component of the pyramidal tract, first evolved in primates and is maximally developed in humans. Furthermore, it affects chiefly the distal muscles, which underlines their significance in the extraordinary manual dexterity of humans.

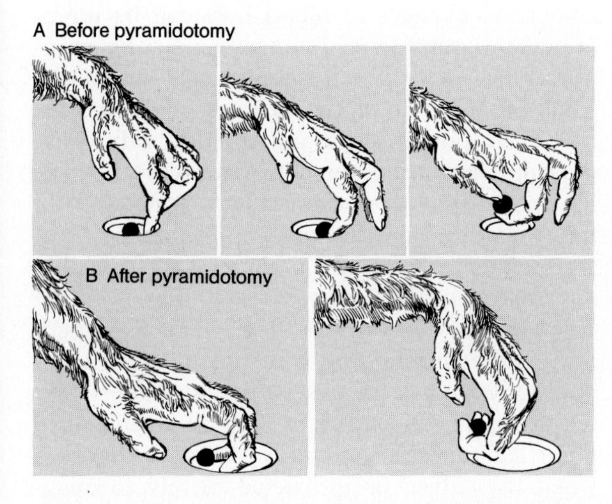

Fig. 5-29. Precise positioning of thumb and forefinger (precision grip) when a normal monkey grips a small object. **B** After transection of the pyramidal tract in the medulla oblongata, the monkey can grasp the object only by scooping it up with all fingers. (Data of E. CHAPMAN and M. WIESENDANGER)

When a stimulating current of less than 10 μA is passed through an intracortical microelectrode, it excites a region of the cortex with a radius of about 90 μm, containing about 30 cells. Such minimal excitation zones in the cortex can activate only a few motor units in a single muscle or in muscles very close to one another. It has now been discovered that for a given set of target motoneurons there are several of these **efferent microzones**, scattered over a relatively large region of the motor cortex and interspersed among efferent microzones that drive other motoneurons. Apparently, then, the motor program calls on a number of microzones in various combinations, depending on the movement.

The **pyramidal tract** to a great extent (and even exclusively, in nonprimates) **controls the motoneurons by way of other spinal neurons**. It can be shown experimentally that impulses from a large number of segmental afferents, cutaneous and proprioceptive, converge on single local interneurons together with impulses from descending tract systems. The implication is that cortical control is exerted in part by *mobilization of segmental reflex circuits*. It was of considerable theoretical interest when *propriospinal neurons* in the upper cervical cord were found to be influenced monosynaptically by the pyramidal tract and other descending tracts. The propriospinal neurons form a complex network extending over several segments. As discussed in Section 5.4, this arrangement permits the cortex to initiate and modulate *spinally organized movement synergies*.
Furthermore, many pyramidal-tract neurons in the postcentral somatosensory areas have fibers that terminate predominantly in the dorsal horn. This component of the pyramidal tract is probably responsible for the demonstrated corticofugal modulation of somatosensory transmission (see also Section 9.12, p. 219).

Supraspinal feedback circuits. Descending connections to supraspinal centers are very numerous in primates, far exceeding the spinal projection. The main targets are the motor thalamus (the ventrolateral nuclear complex), the putamen, the pontine nuclei and other nuclei in the caudal brainstem. Functionally, these descending projections can be regarded as components of internal feedback circuits through which **efference copies** of the motor commands can be transmitted. Although not much is known as yet about these circuits, it seems likely that at higher phylogenetic levels the cortical control of movement becomes increasingly dependent on internal feedback loops (see also 5.5 and 5.6).

Higher Motor Functions of Area 6

Immediately rostral to area 4 is BRODMANN's area 6, including the **medial supplementary motor cortex** and the **lateral premotor cortex** (Fig. 5-26). These were once regarded as additional motor fields or as parts of the primary motor cortex in which the trunk musculature was represented, but opinion has changed in recent years. Although the notion that area 6 also functions in parallel with area 4 cannot be discarded, recent findings (particularly in humans) provide clear evidence of a *hierarchically superordinate position of area 6*. This interpretation is supported by the analysis of deficits resulting from lesions in area 6, by the recording of readiness potentials (Fig. 5-30) and by the local changes in cerebral metabolism during the execution of movements (Fig. 5-31). In some cases direct recordings from cells in area 6 corroborate its superordinate role in the sense of a motor association field [8, 54, 55].

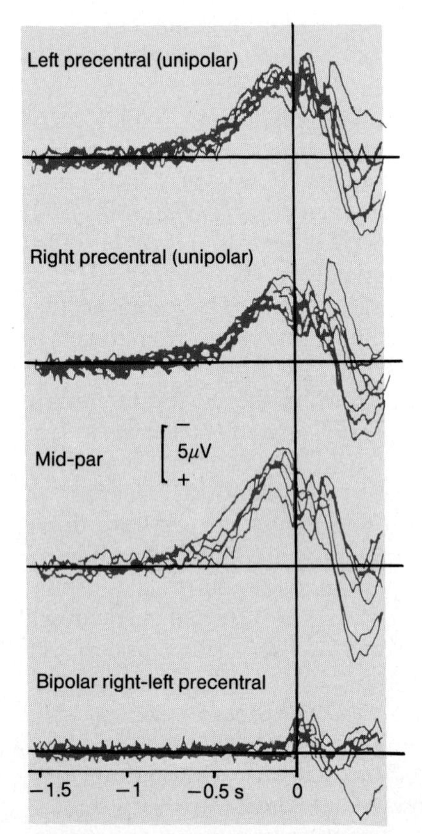

Fig. 5-30. Readiness potentials (recorded from the scalp) of a human making voluntary movements of the index finger. Each individual curve is a mean of the curves recorded in the same individual on different days (1,000 movements per day). The first detectable beginning of movement is taken as time 0. The readiness potential begins about 800 ms before the movement; it is bilateral and widespread over precentral and parietal regions. The "premotion positivity" begins ca. 90 ms before the movement and is followed immediately by the motor potential, which can be clearly seen only in the lowest (bipolar) recording. This motor potential is limited to the precentral gyrus contralateral to the movement and begins 50-100 ms before the movement. The potentials that appear during the movement are evoked by sensory (reafferent) signals. From [26]

Readiness potential [26]. When a subject by his own iniative (i.e., not in response to a sensory stimulus) repeats a finger movement many times, electronic averaging of recordings from scalp electrodes shows that a slowly rising, surface-negative potential develops about 1 s **before** the beginning of the movement. This **readiness potential** (Fig. 5-30) appears on both sides over large areas of the skull, but is maximal over the vertex – that is, approximately over the supplementary motor cortex. From this observation it was concluded that the supplementary motor cortex plays a particularly important role in the neural organization of the **planning of movement**. However, similar experiments in monkeys have shown that potentials preceding a movement also occur in the frontal, parietal and limbic association cortex.

Metabolic measurements. In another approach to the localization of cerebral processes associated with voluntary movement, the **local changes in cortical blood flow** are measured (see Fig. 6-14 and text, p. 137). As might be expected from electrophysiological observations, the metabolic rate in certain parts of the cortex rises while a voluntary movement is being made, and the associated changes in blood flow can be represented by computerized images on a color monitor. First, there is a local increase within the somatotopic area of the primary motor cortex that corresponds to the part of the body being moved. Depending on the nature of the motor act, additional activation can be detected in the frontal and parietal association cortex. Most conspicuous, however, is a bilateral focus medial and rostral to the motor cortex – that is, in the **supplementary motor area** (Fig. 5-31). A particularly interesting finding was that this frontomedial activation is greatest with movements that require close concentration (finger movements in a particular sequence) and can even be observed when the subject is instructed merely to imagine the movement sequence (in which case the primary motor cortex is not activated). This observation again indicates that the supplementary motor area is concerned **more with the planning than with the execution** of movements [42].

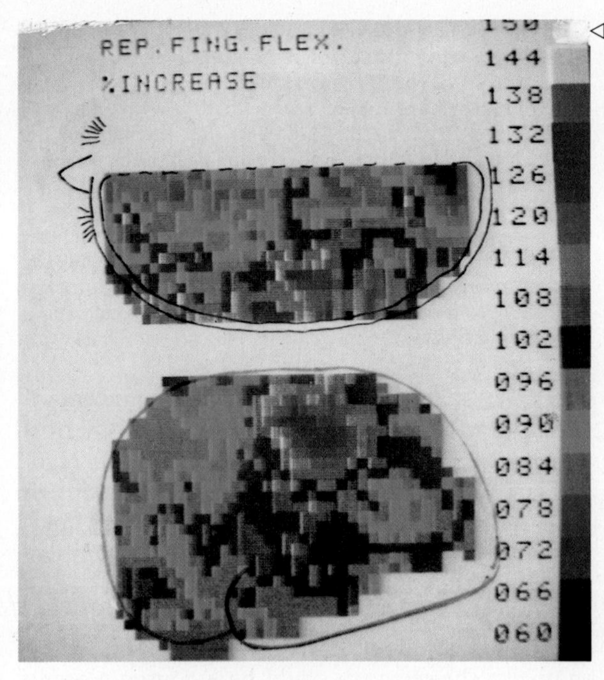

A

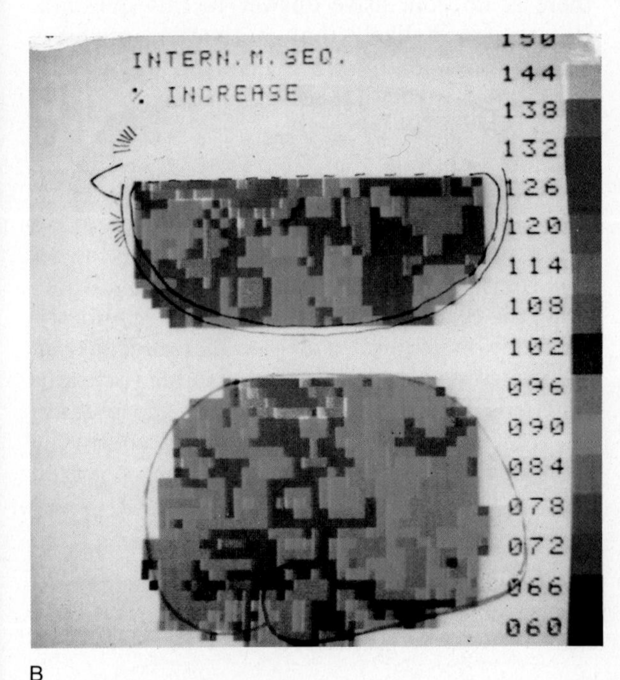

B

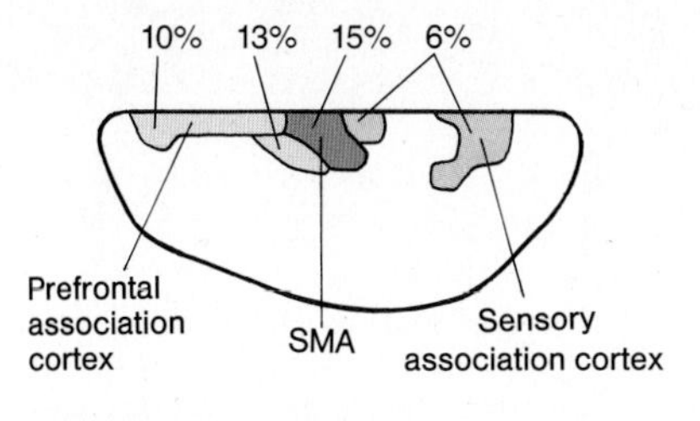

C

◁ **Fig. 5-31.** Measurements of regional blood flow through the human brain during various motor activities. The left hemisphere is shown from the side and from above. The percent changes from the resting blood flow are given by a color code *(right)*. In **A** a rapid, repetitive finger movement is executed; accordingly, there is metabolic activation in the area of the contralateral motor cortex in which the hand is represented. This relatively simple and stereotyped movement is not associated with activation of the SMA. By contrast, in **B** simply imagining a complex finger movement, without executing it, causes bilateral activation of the SMA (only the contralateral side is shown here). The percentages are given numerically in **C**. From ROLAND et al. [42]

Inferences from lesions. Similar conclusions can be drawn from the motor deficits resulting from area-6 lesions. **Lesions of the premotor cortex** cause errors in postural adaptation. After experimental ablation monkeys have difficulty executing a complex movement pattern in the correct temporal sequence, especially when the movements are visually directed. **Medial lesions including the supplementary motor area** in humans produce a striking poverty of movement. Spontaneous speech is also greatly impoverished, although the patient can repeat what is spoken by others quite normally; this, too, indicates a higher function of area 6. In ablation experiments on monkeys disturbances of bimanual coordination have been observed. The anatomical finding that a major fraction of the output from the basal ganglia via the thalamus terminates in the supplementary motor area is of particular interest, in view of the general deterioration of the voluntary motor system in certain disorders of the basal ganglia (see also 5.6).

Discharge patterns of single neurons in area 6 (see contributions of BRINKMAN and PORTER and of TANJI and KURATA in [5]). As in the motor cortex, the activation of area-6 neurons precedes the movement. It is not entirely clear whether, on average, the discharge of neurons in area 6 precedes the discharge of those in area 4, but it is certain that the correlations of discharge with movement are more diverse in area 6. For instance, correlations with movements of the contralateral as well as the ipsilateral hand have been observed. It is striking that the area-6 neurons often encode sensory "instruction signals". This property was established by the reaction-time paradigm, in which, during a specifically timed preparation phase, the animal was given a sensory signal as an instruction for the movement to be executed (e.g., green lamp for movement to the right, red lamp for movement to the left). The activity of neurons in area 6 was frequently better correlated with the instruction signal than with the onset of movement.

5.8 Functional Restitution after Lesions in the Motor System

Recovery from Acute Lesions

Sudden damage to motor structures in the brain and spinal cord often results from traffic accidents or from acute circulatory disturbances. Typical and dramatic examples include bilateral paralysis of the legs *(paraplegia)* or even of all four limbs *(quadriplegia)* due to spinal-cord injury, and paralysis on one side *(hemiplegia)* due to vascular obstruction or bleeding in the internal capsule. In both cases the lines of communication from the supraspinal motor centers to the spinal cord are interrupted. Fortunately, in time many patients show some recovery of motor function. To conclude this chapter on motor systems, the possible mechanisms of recovery will briefly be discussed. A detailed understanding would undoubtedly be of great clinical significance, but the process of rehabilitation is very complex and in many respects it remains obscure [53].

Usually the first result of the lesion is flaccid paralysis with hyporeflexia. Even the visceral reflexes are initially absent in most cases. This condition invariably follows spinal transection **(spinal shock)**, but a similar state can also be associated with supraspinal lesions. Not until several weeks have passed does it become possible to elicit spinal reflexes. If the descending pathways are not completely interrupted, the ability to make voluntary movements also returns, though at first only the proximal muscle groups can be moved, weakly and by a great effort of will. Gradually the reflexes become more vigorous, and the force and extent of the voluntary movements increase. Mobility can continue to improve over months or even years; ordinarily the fine movements of the hands recover the least successfully. In the chronic stage, the reflexes become overactive. **Spasticity** is often manifest in a great increase in the phasic stretch reflex. As a sign of a pyramidal-tract lesion, stroking the sole of the foot causes a reflex spreading of the toes and dorsiflexion of the big toe ("Babinski positive").

The German neurosurgeon O. FOERSTER described an extraordinary case of functional restitution that is particularly interesting because at autopsy the pyramidal tract was found to have totally degenerated. This patient was said to have relearned the skill of writing, holding the pen normally with thumb and fingers and guiding it perfectly [28]. Astounding recovery has also been observed in monkeys after ablation of the motor cortex or transection of the pyramidal tract in the brainstem. Within 1–3 months the animals appear to move almost normally. Only by close scrutiny and measurement can one detect an awkwardness of the hands when grasping small objects and a general slowing of the movements [53, 17].

Recovery by learning or structural reorganization? Long-term studies in which the motor performance of individual patients undergoing regular training is measured produce learning curves like those found for healthy people. This finding raises the question whether the functional rehabilitation amounts simply to **motor learning,** employing the remaining neural structures for new movement strategies or "tricks". Alternatively, the recovery could be a consequence of **structural reorganization** (see below). At present there is no conclusive answer to this question. It seems most likely that motivation, intensive practice and learning are involved along with processes of structural reorganization.

Structural Aspects of Recovery

It is a common assumption that when one structure is lost, another structure with a similar function can take over for it, operating **vicariously**. This notion requires a degree of **redundancy** in the structures. In the cat, for example, vicarious functions have been described for the pyramidal tract and the corticorubrospinal tract; in the monkey the postcentral cortex has been reported

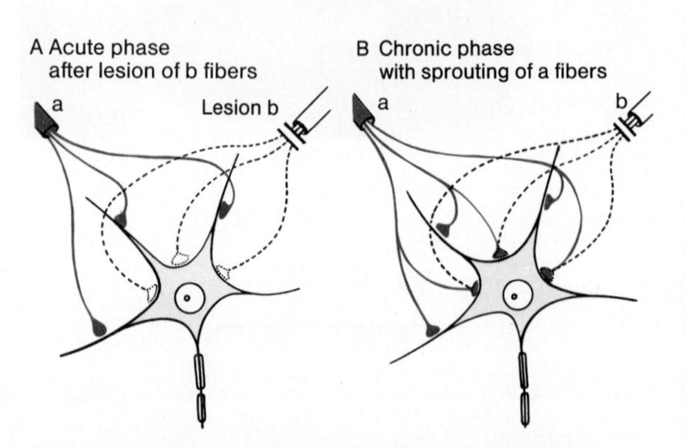

Fig. 5-32 A,B. Local sprouting after partial deafferentation. In the chronic phase **(B)**, several weeks after **A**, new terminals grow out from the intact fibers **(a)** and occupy the free synaptic contact sites

to take over some of the functions of the motor cortex [44]. When the pyramidal tract is interrupted, the ipsilateral corticospinal connections could act vicariously for the destroyed crossed fibers. But in all these cases proof of the vicarious action is difficult and indirect.

It is known that nerve cells in the CNS of adult mammals cannot regenerate. It remains a puzzle why transected axons of peripheral nerves can grow out again and reinnervate muscle fibers, whereas central axons cannot grow out over very long distances after they have been cut. However, a **local sprouting** of the lesioned fibers, with the formation of **new synapses**, has been observed (Fig. 5-32) [51]. In the first observation of this process, new terminals were formed after partial transection of the dorsal roots proximal to the ganglia. These new endings appear to grow out from intact fibers and to occupy the membrane sites that had been left vacant. It has also been reported that after deafferentation sprouting from descending fibers occurs, though the segmental afferents have high priority in the reoccupation process. An increased segmental input resulting from such sprouting could play some role in hyperreflexia, which is also a gradually developing phenomenon. The sprouting process is disorderly, however, which suggests that it might not necessarily produce a functional improvement. Another reason for caution in considering sprouting as a basic factor in functional recovery is that some of the reports of sprouting in the spinal cord have been challenged after the application of more recent anatomical methods.

An interesting **model for the sprouting process** is the red nucleus, with its two main inputs from the cortex and the cerebellum (nucleus interpositus). Intracellular recordings of the synaptic potentials here have shown that the cortical afferents terminate at a distance from the soma, whereas the endings of the cerebellar afferents are near the soma. After the cerebellar afferents have been irreversibly interrupted, the cortical afferents terminate progressively closer to the soma; that is, the synapses are rearranged so that as the cerebellar synapses degenerate, the free space is occupied by the sprouting corticorubral endings. It is as though the degenerating synapses stimulate the new formation of terminals and the empty membrane sites attract the sprouting fibers (Fig. 5-32).

Restitution processes in the immature brain. When the brain, especially the cerebral cortex, is damaged in early childhood, in general the consequences are less severe than those of comparable damage to the adult brain. This applies to the motor systems as well as to speech (cf. p. 153). Newborn monkeys with lesions of the motor cortex differ hardly at all from intact monkeys during the first year of life. The ability to grip with thumb and fingers develops only after 6–9 months in monkeys; in the animals with lesions this specific function of the motor cortex and pyramidal tract does not develop at all [40]. In the hamster, if the pyramidal tract is transected shortly after birth the overall mobility of the animal appears to develop quite normally. Histological examination of the brains of these animals revealed an interesting phenomenon: there was a new, "aberrant" bundle of the pyramidal tract, which had formed rostral to the old lesion and taken an anomalous route to the spinal cord. It could even be demonstrated that the descending fibers made synaptic contact with the spinal neurons. Does this mean that the young brain is capable of forming new connections even over long distances? Although the findings in the hamster suggest so, there is another interpretation. We know that many of the connections in the immature brain disappear during the maturation process. For example, there are *"exuberant" callosal connections*, a large proportion of which are later eliminated; the immature rodent brain contains neurons in the visual cortex that project as far as the spinal cord but eventually are eliminated. It could be, then, that lesions **inhibit the regression processes** and that the fibers that would normally have been eliminated can vicariously take over the function of the destroyed fibers. Even with this interpretation, though, the principle remains that the immature brain has a greater **plasticity**, more opportunity for rearranging its "circuit diagram" than the mature brain.

Molecular aspects. A few days after denervation the individual fibers in a muscle develop conspicuous spontaneous activity, evident as *fibrillation.* The muscle-fiber membrane becomes overexcitable and its responsiveness to acetylcholine extends progressively from the end plate over the entire length of the fiber. Similar events occur in the CNS. The **supersensitivity of denervated structures** appears to be a general principle. It is of great clinical importance that neurons in the striatum have been shown to respond more strongly to dopamine after loss of the dopaminergic innervation (in Parkinson's disease) [48]. The development of supersensitivity in a receptor can be ascribed to phenomena at the molecular level (Fig. 5-33). Abnormalities of the receptors for aminergic transmitters have recently been dis-

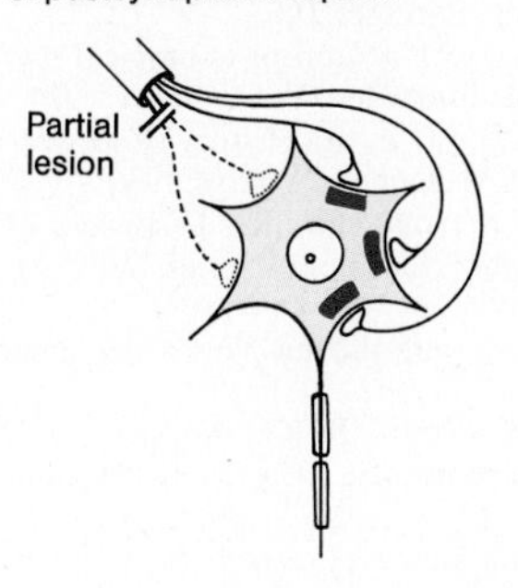

Fig. 5-33. After degeneration of presynaptic terminals the postsynaptic receptors *(red)* develop supersensitivity, so that they have abnormally large reactions to the transmitter. The result is a compensatory enhancement of synaptic transmission

cussed as possible factors in certain neurological and psychiatric disorders.

Prospects. One of the main current goals of basic research is to learn just what **conditions of the milieu** are favorable to **regeneration processes.** Subjects of interest include the phenomenon of receptor supersensitivity, the formation and degeneration of synapses, the participation of the glia in regeneration and the search for substances that control the growth of neurons.
A highly topical line of research involves the **transplantation into the striatum** of tissue that contains catecholamine-producing cells. Such experiments may provide an alternative to the administration of L-dopa in the treatment of Parkinson's disease. Another very promising experimental approach is to explore the possibility of assisting regeneration in the CNS by implanting pieces of peripheral nerve to guide the new growth.

5.9 References

Textbooks and Handbooks

1. BOYD, J.A., DAVEY, M.R.: Composition of Peripheral Nerves. Edinburgh, London: Livingstone 1968
2. BROOKS, V.B. (Ed.): Handbook of Physiology, Section I, The Nervous System, Vol. 2, Parts 1 and 2: Motor Control. Bethesda: Amer. Physiol. Soc. 1981
3. CREUTZFELDT, O.D.: Cortex cerebri, Leistung, strukturelle und funktionelle Organisation der Hirnrinde. Heidelberg: Springer 1983
4. DESMEDT, J.E. (Ed.): Cerebral Motor Control in Man: Long Loop Mechanisms. Basel: Karger 1978
5. DESMEDT, J.E. (Ed.): Motor Control Mechanisms in Health and Disease. Adv. Neurol. Vol. 39, New York: Raven Press 1983
6. ECCLES, J.C.: The Inhibitory Pathways of the Central Nervous System. The Sherrington Lectures IX. Springfield/III.: Ch.C. Thomas 1969
7. ECCLES, J.C., ITO, M., SZENTÁGOTHAI, J.: The Cerebellum as a Neuronal Machine. Heidelberg: Springer 1967
8. EVARTS, E.V., SHINODA, U., WISE, S.P.: Neurophysiological Approaches to Higher Brain Functions. New York: Wiley 1984
9. FEARING, F.: Reflex Action. A Study in the History of Physiological Psychology. Baltimore: William & Wilkins 1930
10. GILMAN, S., BLOEDEL, J.R., LECHTENBERG, R.: Disorders of the Cerebellum, Contemporary Neurology Series, Vol. 21, Philadelphia: Davis 1981
11. GRANIT, R.: The Basis of Motor Control. New York: Academic Press 1970
12. HERMAN, R.M., GRILLNER, S., STEIN, P.S.G., STUART, D.G. (Eds.): Neural Control of Locomotion. New York: Plenum Press 1976
13. ITO, M.: The Cerebellum and Neural Control. New York: Raven Press 1984
14. MAGNUS, R.: Körperstellung. Berlin: Springer 1924
15. MATTHEWS, P.B.C.: Mammalian Muscle Receptors and their Central Actions. London: Arnold 1972
16. PENFIELD, W., RASMUSSEN, T.: The Cerebral Cortex of Man. New York: McMillan 1950
17. PHILLIPS, C.G., PORTER, R.: Corticospinal Neurones. Their Role in Movement. Monographs of the Physiol. Soc. No. 34, London: Academic Press 1977
18. POECK, K.: Neurologie, 6. Aufl. Heidelberg: Springer 1982
19. RADEMAKER, G.G.J.: Das Stehen. Berlin: Springer 1931
20. ROBERTS, T.D.M.: Neurophysiology of Postural Mechanisms, 2nd Ed. London: Butterworth 1978
21. SHERRINGTON, C.S.: The Integrative Action of the Nervous System. New Haven: Yale University Press, 2nd Ed. 1947. Reprinted 1961 (1906)
22. TOWE, A.L. and LUSCHEI, E. (Eds.): Handbook of Behavioral Neurobiology, Vol. 5: Motor Coordination. New York: Plenum 1981
23. WHITING, H.T.A. (Eds.): Human Motor Actions. Amsterdam: North Holland 1984

Original Papers and Reviews

24. ALEXANDER, G.E., DELONG, M.R., STRICK, P.L.: Parallel organization of functionally segregated circuits linking basal ganglia and cortex. Ann. Rev. Neurosci. *9*, 357 (1986)
25. BOYD, J.A.: Muscle spindles and stretch reflexes. In Scientific Basis of Clinical Neurology (Eds. M. SWASH, C. KENNARD) S. 74–97. London: Churchill Livingstone 1985
26. DEECKE, L., GRÖZINGER, B., KORNHUBER, H.H.: Voluntary finger movement in man: cerebral potentials and theory. Biol. Cybernetics *23*, 99 (1976)
27. ECCLES, R.M., LUNDBERG, A.: Synaptic actions in motoneurones by afferents which may evoke the flexion reflex. Arch. ital. Biol. *97*, 199 (1959)
28. FOERSTER, O.: Motorische Felder und Bahnen. In: BUMKE, O., FOERSTER, O. (Eds.) Handbuch der Neurologie, Band 6, Berlin: Springer 1936
29. GRAYBIEL, A.M.: Neurochemically specified subsystems in the basal ganglia. In: EVERED, D., O'CONNOR, M. (Eds.) Functions of the basal ganglia. CIBA Foundation Symp. 107, London: Pitman 1984
30. HAGBARTH, K.E., FINER, B.L.: The plasticity of human withdrawal reflexes to noxious stimuli in lower limbs. Progr. Brain Res. I, 65–78 (1963)
31. HAGBARTH, K.E., KUGELBERG, E.: Plasticity of human abdominal skin reflex. Brain *81*, 305–319 (1958)
32. HOLMES, G.: Selected Papers (Ed. C.G. Phillips) London: Oxford University Press 1979
33. HOUK, J.C.: Regulation of stiffness by skeletomotor reflexes. Ann. Rev. Physiol. *41*, 99 (1979)
34. KUHN, R.A.: Functional capacity of the isolated human spinal cord. Brain *73*, 1 (1950)
35. LANGSTON, J.W.: MPTP and Parkinson's disease. Trends Neurosci. *8*, 79 (1985)
36. LUNDBERG, A., MALMGREN, K., SCHOMBURG, E.D.: Comments on reflex actions evoked by electrical stimulation of group II muscle afferents. Brain Res. *122*, 551 (1977)
37. MARSDEN, C.D.: Which motor disorder in Parkinson's disease indicates the true motor function of the basal ganglia? In: EVERED, D., O'CONNOR, M. (Eds.) Functions of the basal ganglia. CIBA Foundation Symp. 107, London: Pitman p. 225, 1984
38. MCCORMICK, D.A., STEINMETZ, J.E., THOMPSON, R.F.: Lesions of the inferior olivary complex cause extinction of the classically conditioned eyeblink response. Brain Res. *359*, 120 (1985)
39. MONTAROLO, P.G., PALESTINI, M., STRATA, P.: The inhibitory effect of the olivo-cerebellar input to the cerebellar Purkinje cells in the rat. J. Physiol (Lond.) *332*, 187 (1982)
40. PASSINGHAM, R.E., PERRY, V.H., WILKINSON, F.: The long-term effects of removal of sensorimotor cortex in infant and adult Rhesus monkeys. Brain *106*, 675 (1983)
41. PUCHALA, E., WINDLE, W.F.: The possibility of structural and functional restitution after spinal cord injury. A review. Experimental Neurology *55*, 1 (1977)
42. ROLAND, P.E., LARSEN, B., LASSEN, N.A., SKINHØJ, J.E.: Supplementary motor area and other cortical areas in organization of voluntary movements in man. J. Neurophysiol. *43*, 118 (1980)
43. SASAKI, K., GEMBA, H.: Development and change of cortical field potentials during learning processes of visually initiated movements in the monkey. Exp. Brain Res. *48*, 429 (1982)

44. SASAKI, K., GEMBA, H.: Compensatory motor function of the somatosensory cortex for the motor cortex temporarily impaired by cooling in the monkey. Exp. Brain Res. *55,* 60 (1984)
45. SATO, A., SCHMIDT, R.F.: Somatosympathetic reflexes: afferent fibers, central pathways, discharge characteristics. Physiol. Rev. *53,* 916 (1973)
46. SCHMIDT, R.F.: Presynaptic inhibition in the vertebrate central nervous system. Ergebn. Physiol. *63,* 20 (1971)
47. SCHMIDT, R.F.: Control of the access of afferent activity to somatosensory pathways. In: Handb. of Sensory Physiology. Vol. II, Somatosensory System (Ed. A. IGGO), p. 151. Heidelberg: Springer 1973
48. SCHULTZ, W.: Depletion of dopamine in the striatum as an experimental model of parkinsonism: direct effects and adaptive mechanisms.. Progr. Neurobiol. *18,* 121 (1982)
49. SELEMON, L.D., GOLDMAN-RAKIC, P.S.: Longitudinal topography and interdigitation of cortico-striatal projections in the Rhesus monkey. J. Neurosci. *5,* 776 (1982)
50. SHIK, M.L., ORLOVSKY, G.N.: Neurophysiology of locomotor automatism. Physiol. Rev. *56,* 465 (1976)
51. TSUKAHARA, N.: Synaptic plasticity in the mammalian nervous system. Ann. Rev. Neurosci *4,* 351 (1981)
52. VALLBO, A.B.: Muscle spindle response at the onset of isometric voluntary contractions in man. Time difference between fusimotor and skeletomotor effects. J. Physiol. (Lond.) *218,* 405 (1971)
53. WIESENDANGER, M.: The pyramidal tract: its structure and function. In: Handbook Behav. Neurobiol. Vol. 5. Motor Coordination (Eds. A.L. TOWE, E.S. LUSCHEI) New York: Plenum 1981
54. WIESENDANGER, M.: Organization of secondary motor areas of cerebral cortex. In: Handbook of Physiology, Section 1. The Nervous System, Vol. II, Motor Control, Part 2 (Ed. V.B. BROOKS) Bethesda, Md.: Amer. Physiol. Soc. 1981
55. WIESENDANGER, M.: Recent developments in studies of the supplementary motor area of primates. Rev. Physiol. Biochem. Pharmacol *103,* 1 (1986)
56. WIESENDANGER, M., MILES, T.S.: Ascending pathways of low-threshold muscle afferents to the cerebral cortex and its possible role in motor control. Physiol. Rev. *62,* 1234 (1982)
57. WOOLSEY, C.N., SETTLAGE, P.H., MEYER, D.R., SENCER, W., PINTO-HAMUY, T., TRAVIS, H.M.: Patterns of localization in precentral and "supplementary" motor areas and their relation to the concept of a premotor area. Proc. Assoc. Res. nerv. Ment. Dis. Vol. 30 (1950)

6 Integrative Functions of the Central Nervous System

R.F. Schmidt

6.1 Definition and Localization of Integrative Functions

The term "integrative" as applied to the CNS denotes those functions that are not directly involved in the processing of sensory inputs or in the activity of the motor and autonomic centers. The main mechanisms in this category are those underlying the sleeping/waking cycle, consciousness, language, thinking (understanding, reason), memory (including learning), motivation (drives) and emotion (feelings). The structures subserving these integrative functions are located chiefly (but not exclusively) in two large parts of the telencephalon, the **limbic system** and the **neocortex**. The first of these is treated in the chapter on autonomic functions, where the neurophysiological bases of motivation and emotion are also described (Section 16.6, Limbic System and Behavior, beginning on p. 362). Here we are concerned with the neocortex and the neurophysiological mechanisms underlying the other integrative functions mentioned above.

Functional Topography of the Neocortex

Cerebral localization versus holistic views. Attempts to assign sensory, motor and higher mental functions to particular cortical areas were already being made in the last century. The **phrenology** of F.J. Gall, in the early 1800's, was based on the idea that a person's mental and moral characteristics could be deduced from careful measurement of the skull, because they were situated in particular regions of the brain surface. However, there was no adequate scientific foundation for his theses. A series of later observations rapidly provided considerable evidence of a **specific function of particular cortical areas**. Examples include (i) Pierre Broca's demonstration of the motor speech center in 1865, (ii) the discovery of the primary motor cortex by G.T. Fritsch and E. Hitzig in 1870, and (iii) the description of the sensory speech center by C. Wernicke in 1874 (references in [10]). In the first half of this century detailed subdivision of the human cortex was proposed by several authors, on the basis of thorough examination of the neurological and psychological deficits caused by local lesions of the cortex in humans (due to disease or gunshot wounds). A historically noteworthy example is the map produced by K. Kleist [24, 52], illustrated in Fig. 6-1.
From the very beginning, there was some disagreement with this highly discrete localization of individual mental functions. For example, Lashley [54] found that when he ablated various part of the rat cortex, the deficits depended more on the size of the lesion than on its site. These results led him to postulate an **"equipotentiality"** of all sections of the brain, implying that practically any section could take over the functions of another. Today, this holistic view and those related to it must be considered just as obsolete as the notion of a strictly localized functional specialization [4, 10, 12, 21].

Boundaries of the association cortex. The currently accepted *subdivision of the cerebral cortex into sensory, motor and association areas* is shown in Fig. 6-2. The **unspecific** or **association areas** in this scheme are the regions to which no predominantly sensory or motor function can be assigned (for discussion of the latter areas see the relevant sections in Chapters 5 and 8-12). In humans the unspecific areas occupy a large part of the cerebral cortex. The term *association cortex* derives from the early idea that sensory and motor areas were "associated" with one another by way of corticocortical connections through this region, which would simultaneously serve as the seat of the highest mental functions (cf. Fig. 6-1).
But the original categorization, in which all cortical fields that were not primarily motor or sensory were regarded as unspecific and assigned to the association cortex, has proved to be oversimplified. As can be seen in Fig. 6-2, secondary and even higher sensory and motor fields have since been isolated from the "unspecific" cortex. The only subdivisions now considered as **unspecific** or **association cortex in the narrow sense**

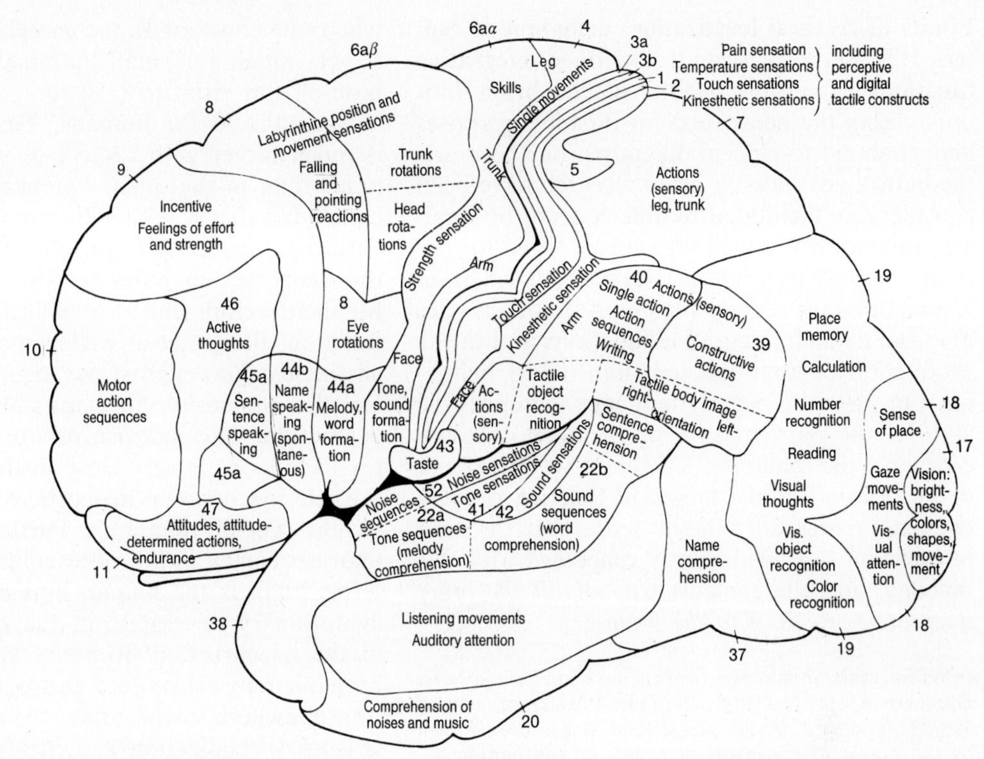

Fig. 6-1. Subdivision of the lateral cerebral cortex into function fields, as proposed by KLEIST [24, 52]. The *numbers* denote the cytoarchitectonic fields of BRODMANN (see Fig. 6-4). The map is still correct in its basic features, but it oversimplifies in showing a circumscribed localization of complex integrative functions now known to be more broadly based

are (i) the parietal-temporal-occipital association cortex, (ii) the prefrontal association cortex and (iii) the limbic association cortex. As a simplified description of their functions, each is particularly significant for a different class of integrative processes, the first for higher sensory functions and language (see p. 147), the second for higher motor functions (see p. 118) and the third for memory and the emotional (affective) aspects of behavior (see p. 362).

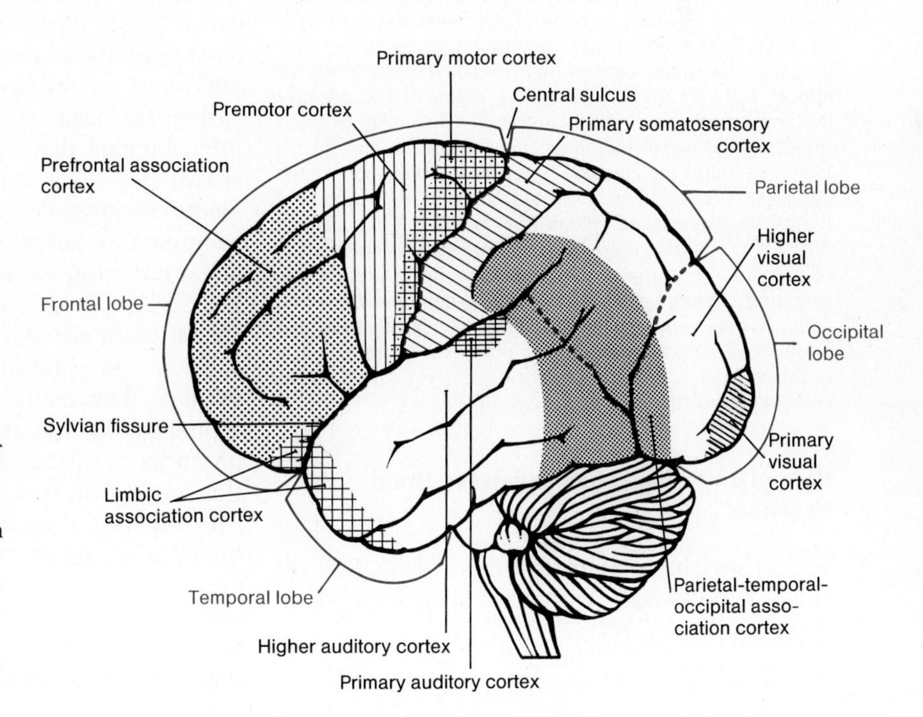

Fig. 6-2. The four components of the cerebral cortex (frontal, temporal, parietal and occipital cortex) as seen from the side. Within them are the primary motor and sensory regions, the higher-order (second, third, etc.) motor and sensory regions and the regions of association (unspecific) cortex. Discussion in text

Limits of cerebral localization, definition of centers. It is useful to assign well-defined integrative functions to certain regions of the brain (not only within the neocortex) for didactic purposes and as an aid to clinical diagnosis. Furthermore, theoretical advances in brain research have been considerably facilitated by this concept of localized functions. But it should not be taken too literally, because as a rule several parts of the brain – sometimes far removed from one another – are involved in such integrative functions and in the production of goal-directed (non-reflex) behavior. For instance, orderly language is impossible without the participation of the diencephalon, especially the thalamus. Therefore we can speak of **localization of the language function** or of a **language center** only in the sense that the area in question is **predominantly concerned with this function**, and the same is true of *all the other integrative processes of the brain.*

In recent years animal experiments have increasingly cast doubt on the classical subdivision into sensory, motor and association cortex. In the rat, at least, it has been shown by the horseradish peroxidase technique (retrograde axonal transport of a dye from the site of injection) that *all* the cortical areas that have been examined receive either visual, auditory or somatovisceral afferents from the thalamus, to which they also send outputs [47]. No room was found for association fields between the sensory areas. These anatomical studies were supported by experiments in which animals were found to be neither blind nor deaf after destruction of the corresponding primary projection areas; it was also shown that agnosias (inability to interpret particular sensory stimuli or to relate to one's surroundings) cannot be produced by lesions of the association fields *alone*. The concept of the primary motor area must also be qualified in view of the facts that axons descending from almost the entire cortex pass to the anterior horns of the spinal cord (which makes the whole cortex appear to be "motor") and that a lesion of the primary motor areas produces hardly any motor deficit, apart from the deterioration of fine finger movements (see p. 117).
However useful the classical functional subdivision of the cortex still seems, then, it would come as no surprise if it were to be replaced by another in the not too distant future. For instance, there might be a **chemical demarcation** of individual brain regions. Chemical criteria are already revealing a distinct general structural principle in the CNS, which does not conform to the phylogenetically established boundaries but rather combines older and younger parts of the brain in functionally uniform, clearly distinguishable systems; for further discussion see [4].

Role of Encephalization in Higher Brain Functions

Within vertebrate animals, brain weight **E** is related to body weight **P** approximately by a power function of the form

$$E = K \cdot P^{2/3}$$

where the constant **K**, the **encephalization factor**, is very small for small mammals (0.06 for the mouse), has risen to 0.30 for chimpanzees and is almost 1.00 for humans. That is, the brain is much larger with respect to the body in humans than in the other vertebrates. It has been concluded that a relatively large brain, together with the apparently disproportionate increase in the neocortex in humans, was the prerequisite for the development of specifically human brain functions (language as well as mental, moral and aesthetic achievements; see, e.g., [10]).
But this conclusion does not stand up to critical evaluation. The increase in size of the neocortex in humans is very close to that predicted by the relation between neocortical and total brain weight over all mammals. Furthermore, the human neocortex is no more enlarged, in relative terms, than is the human limbic system. As an evolutionary development, the relative increase in the neocortex in primates, and especially in humans, may be more a consequence of reduction elsewhere in the brain – due to decreasing sensory specialization (e.g., deterioration of the sense of smell) and a need for fewer motor response patterns – in combination with development of the neocortex into a **system for multisensory representation of the environment.** In this case, language appears to be a special case of sensory integration, requiring a system for the exact temporal control and storage of tones such as is provided by the neocortex (references in [4]).
The progressive **encephalization** in vertebrates, carnivores in particular, is ascribed by evolutionary biologists to the interaction between hunter and prey, as follows. Under selection pressure carnivores need efficient strategies for locating prey animals that are scarce in both time and space, and their sensory systems and neuronal analyzers have developed accordingly. The development of language may have little to do with advanced encephalization, because language appeared in *Homo sapiens* only recently, about 40,000 years ago (the present brain weight of ca. 1,400 g was reached about 200,000 years ago). Perhaps, then, language is only a late result of encephalization. But the development of language probably contributed to the marked lateralization of cortical functions (see p. 147).
The superior thinking and learning abilities of humans, as compared with all other organisms, are also not based on the development of special nerve cells such as "speech neurons" or "memory neurons". Instead, it is highly probable that they depend entirely on a **quantitative** change,

an **increase in the number of neuronal aggregates available for information processing.** Much of this increase occurs in the neocortex, which thereby seems to become particularly responsible for the *higher speed of information processing* in learning and recall from memory, for instance, and in speaking and understanding speech. From this viewpoint, the neuronal circuitry in the cerebral cortex and the way it communicates with other cortical and deeper areas of the brain deserve special attention.

6.2 General Physiology of the Cerebral Cortex

Functional Histology of the Cerebral Cortex

General arrangement of the cortex, cortical layers. The cerebral cortex consists of multilayered, much-folded neuronal tissue with a *total surface area* (both hemispheres) of about 2,200 cm^2 (corresponding to a square measuring 47 cm × 47 cm). Its *thickness* varies in different parts of the cerebrum, between 1.3 and 4.5 mm. Its volume is 600 cm^3. It is composed of **10^9 to 10^{10} neurons** plus a large but unknown number of glial cells [6, 58]. Within the cortex, layers in which cell bodies predominate alternate with others made up chiefly of axons, so that the freshly cut cortex has a striated appearance. In the typical cortex **6 layers** can be distinguished on the basis of the shape and arrangement of the cells; some of the layers can be subdivided into two or more sublayers (Figs. 6-3, 6-5).

More than 90% of the cerebral cortex is of this *basic 6-layered type,* which in phylogeny first appears with the mammals and therefore is called **neocortex;** because of its structure it is also called **isocortex.** The phylogenetically older **allocortex** has a basically 3-layered structure. Located deep in the temporal lobe, it is not visible from outside the brain. It includes the *archipallium* (fascia dentata, Ammon's horn, subiculum), the *paleopallium* (prepiriform region, periamygdalar region, entorhinal region) and the *cortical derivatives* claustrum and amygdala [6, 10, 21].
The layers in the **isocortex,** counting from the surface down, are as follows (Fig. 6-3, 6-5).

I. Molecular layer (plexiform layer). Fibers are abundant here, but there are few cells. The fibers form a dense plexus tangential to the surface.

II. External granular layer. Here small neurons varying widely in shape are closely packed, with small pyramidal cells (named for their shape) among them. The predominant orientation of the nerve fibers is tangential to the surface.

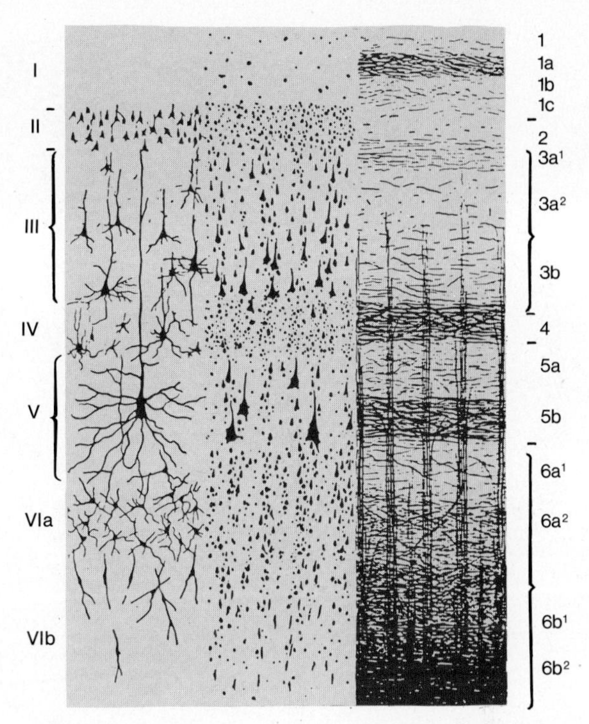

Fig. 6-3. Semidiagrammatic representation of the layered structure of the cerebral cortex. *Left:* the most important types of nerve cell in the various layers (Golgi impregnation). *Middle:* neuron somata (Nissl stain). *Right:* general arrangement of fibers, from a myelin-sheath preparation. The layers are numbered from the surface down; two common numbering systems are shown. Layers described in the text. (Modified from BRODMANN and VOGT)

III. External pyramidal layer. The chief elements here are pyramidal cells of intermediate size, with the larger cells in the deeper parts of the layers.

IV. Internal granular layer. A loose array of small neurons (stellate cells) of various sizes penetrated by bundles of densely packed fibers tangential to the surface.

V. Internal pyramidal layer. Basically composed of medium-sized and large pyramidal cells, especially large in the precentral gyrus (Betz's giant pyramidal cells). Like all pyramidal cells these have long apical dendrites, extending as far as the molecular layer, whereas the basal dendrites spread out more or less tangential to the surface.

VI. Fusiform-cell layer. Predominantly spindle-shaped neurons. The inner part of this layer (VI b) merges with the white matter.

Cortical maps. Although the basic structural pattern of the isocortex is uniform, there can be considerable local variation. On the basis of cortical **cytoarchitectonics** alone – that is, the density, arrangement and shape of the neurons – Brodmann subdivided the cerebral cortex into about 50 areas (Fig. 6-4). Other maps are still more detailed (VON ECONOMO and VOGT [6]). To a certain extent these histologically defined areas match

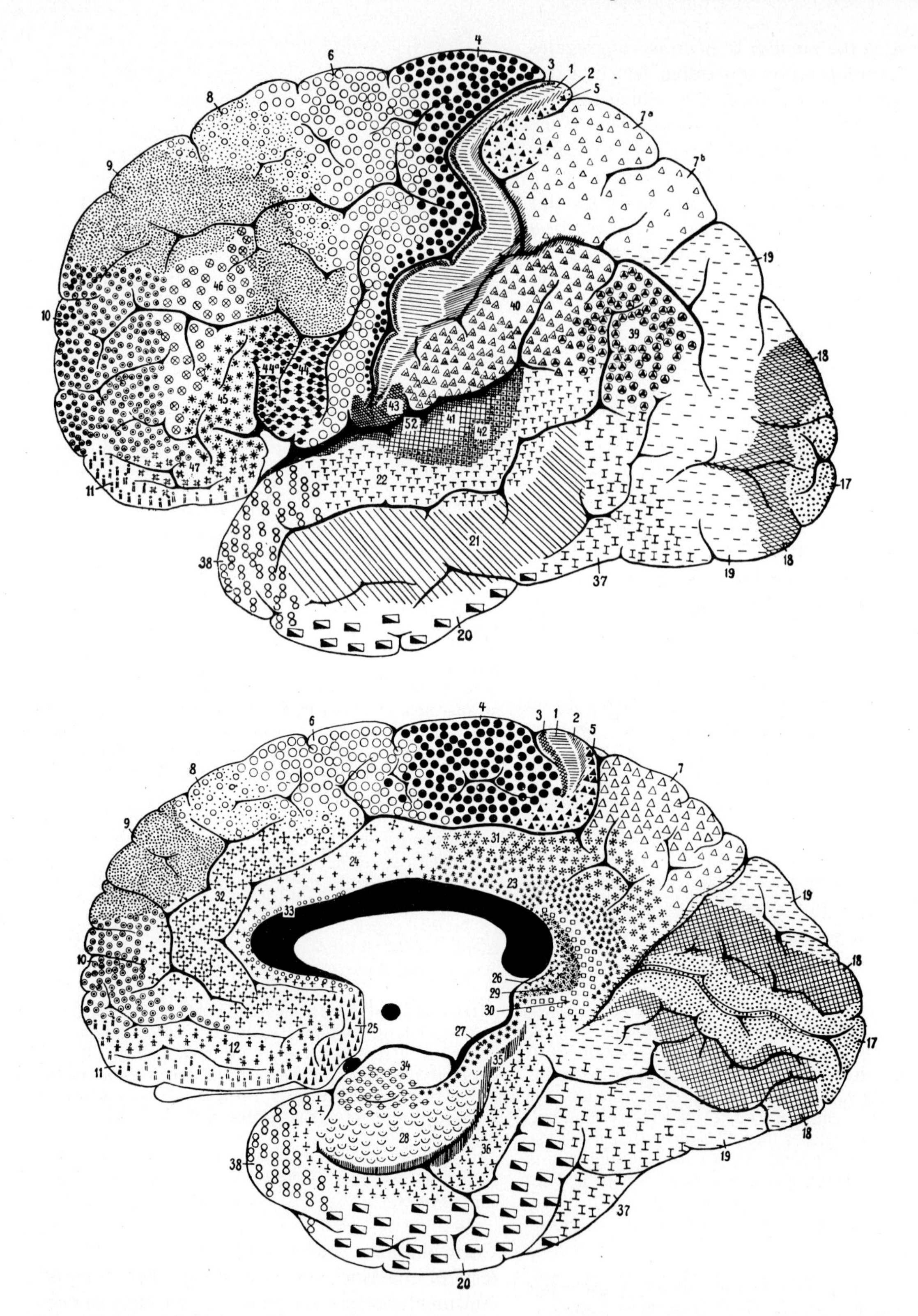

Fig. 6-4. Map of Brodmann's cytoarchitectonic fields in the human cortex. The various fields (areas) are identified by numbers and distinguished in the map by different symbols. The map was first published in 1909

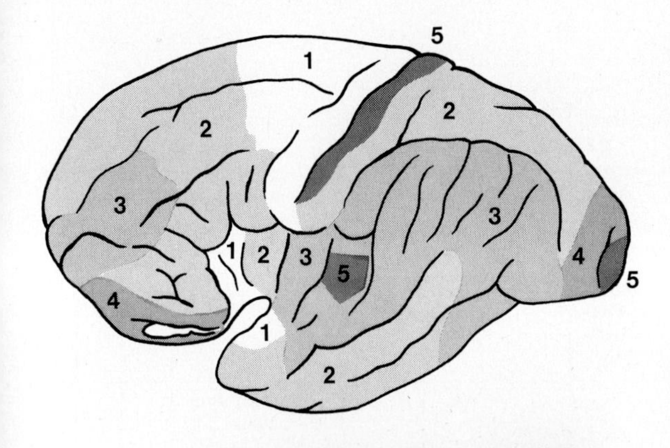

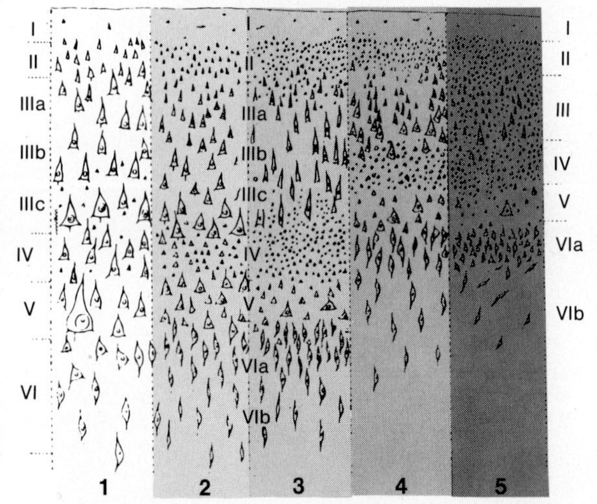

Fig. 6-5. Basic types of neocortical cytoarchitectonics *(bottom)* and their distribution in the cerebral cortex *(top)*. 2, 3, 4 homotypical cortex; 1,5 heterotypical cortex, of which 1 is agranular and 5 granular. The data were first published in 1927 by Von Economo. He stated specifically that the transitions from one type of cortex to another are gradual. The regions labelled "2" in the frontal cortex are now called dysgranular, as is the anterior half of the cingulate gyrus (not visible here)

the areas to which particular functions are ascribed on the basis of physiological experiments and clinical observations (see Sec. 6.1). Examples will be presented with reference to Fig. 6-5.

Differences in the arrangement of the nerve fibers – that is, **myeloarchitectonics** – have also been represented in cortical maps. On the whole, these are consistent with the cytoarchitectonic maps. Other features of cortical structure also vary in ways that can be used to characterize the different areas of cortex; these include the structure of the vascular system **(angioarchitectonics),** the arrangement, nature and shape of the glial cells **(gliarchitectonics),** and the chemical substances such as enzymes and transmitters found in the cells **(chemoarchitectonics)** [6, 10].

Homotypical and heterotypical isocortex. Von Economo grouped the cytoarchitectonic cortical areas into *five basic types* (Fig. 6-5). The types 2, 3 and 4 in the lower diagram of the figure contain (to varying extents) all 6 layers, and therefore are called **homotypical.** By contrast, in mature cortex of types 1 and 5 fewer than 6 layers are clearly identifiable; the cortex is **heterotypical.** In the *heterotypical cortex* of type 1 there are no distinct granular layers (II and V), whereas in type 5 these layers are especially conspicuous, and the pyramidal-cell layers (III and IV) are very poorly developed. Therefore type 1 is called **agranular cortex** and type 5, **granular cortex** or **koniocortex** (Greek *konios* = dusty, from the dark band of granular cells in layer IV).

Agranular cortex is found particularly in regions where *cortical efferents* originate, for example, in the precentral gyrus and rostral to it (Fig. 6-5). It can thus be regarded as the **prototype of the motor cortex.** Conversely, the **granular** or koniocortex is found especially in areas in which the major sensory pathways terminate. It can therefore be classified as the **prototype of the sensory cortex.** The *unspecific cortex* comprises the various forms of **homotypical cortex.** There are gradual transitions between the different types of cortex. The parts of the frontal cortex labeled "2" in Fig. 6-5 and the anterior half of the cingulate gyrus are now thought to be better classified as heterotypic cortex and are called **dysgranular.**

Fiber connections in the neocortex. The afferent and efferent connections of the cerebral cortex, in turn, can be assigned to a few basic types. The **cortical efferents** (corticofugal fibers) serve (i) as **projection fibers** to subcortical structures (for example, the corticospinal tract and corticopontine and corticothalamic pathways), (ii) as **association fibers,** passing to neighboring and more distant cortical areas in the *same hemisphere,* and (iii) as **commissural fibers,** providing a link to cortical areas in the *contralateral hemisphere.* The great majority of commissural fibers cross in the corpus callosum (cf. p. 148). They are very numerous; for example, in humans a total of 200 million has been estimated (100 million in each direction).
The **cortical afferents** (corticopetal fibers) comprise both the *association and commisural fibers* from other parts of the cortex, mentioned above, and the **thalamocortical fibers,** the dominant if not **only afferents from subcortical structures.**

Cortical neurons and the circuits they form. The cortex contains a great number of very diverse neurons (cf. Figs. 6-3 and 6-5, bottom), but they can all be assigned to *two main types*, the **pyramidal cells** and the **stellate cells**. The former are so called because of the pyramidal shape of the cell body (Fig. 6-6). Their special feature is that their axons leave the cortex and terminate in other cortical or non-cortical structures (see below). The stellate cells are also named for their shape (Fig. 6-6A,C). Their axons terminate within the cortex; that is, they are *cortical interneurons.*
The **connections of the cortical neurons** to one another and to the afferents that enter the cortex conform to the basic pattern illustrated in Fig. 6-6, with certain modifications in the differ-

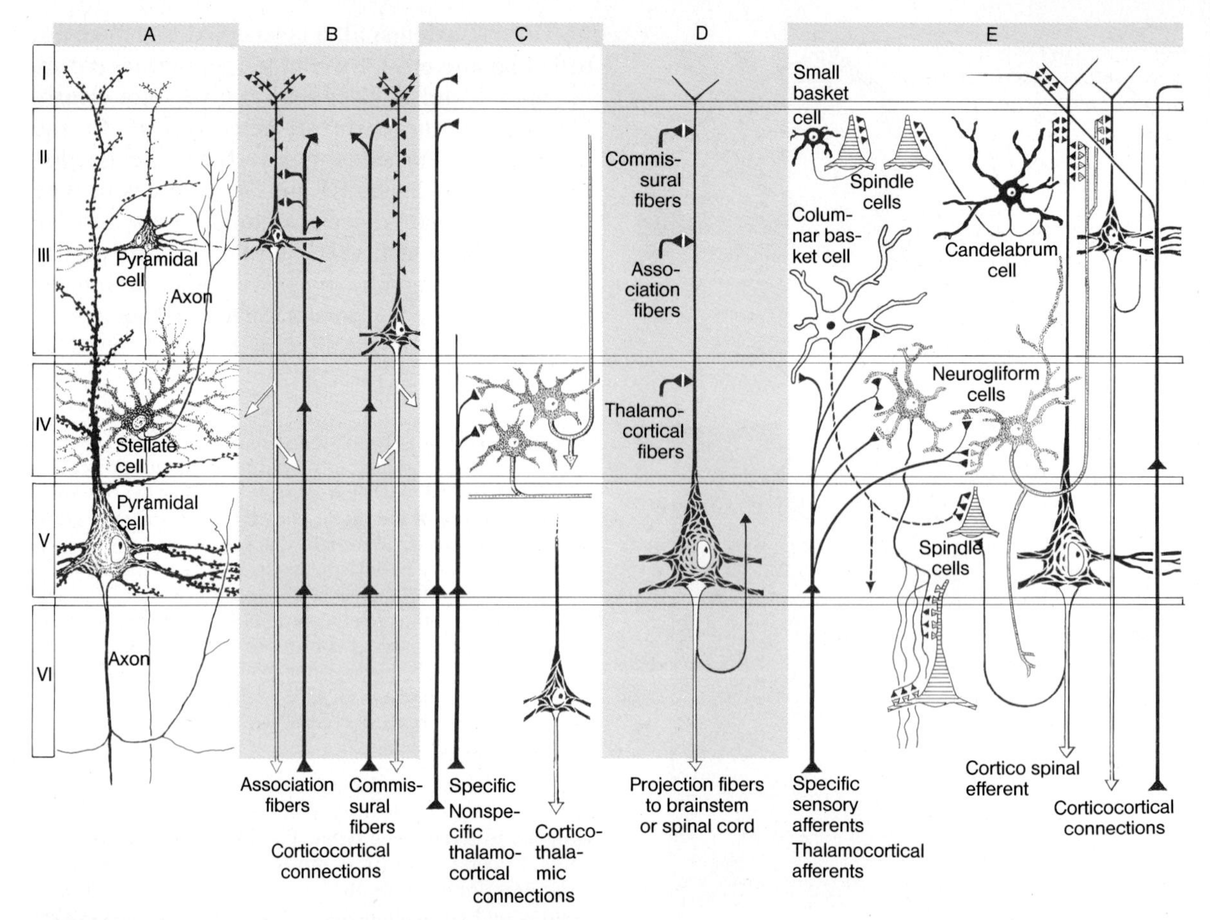

Fig. 6-6. Cortical neurons, their intracortical circuits and their afferent and efferent connections. Highly simplified and schematic drawings on a background indicating the cortical layers. **A** Position and appearance of the two main types of cortical neurons. **B** Input-output relations of corticocortical connections (association and commissural fibers). **C** Characteristics of thalamocortical (nonspecific and specific) and corticothalamic connections. **D** Synaptic input zones of a pyramidal cell, the axon of which projects to subthalamic regions (brainstem, spinal cord). **E** Summary of the cortical circuitry (based on several publications of J. Szentágothai, redrawn and highly simplified; **B-D** from the findings of many authors)

ent cortical areas [12, 21]. *Layer I* is occupied mainly by the apical dendrites of the pyramidal cells and axons of stellate cells, which run tangential to the surface. These axons mediate **local, intracortical communication** among neurons very close to one another. *Layers II and III* (Fig. 6-6B) contain small pyramidal cells, the axons of which pass to other cortical areas; axons from other cortical areas enter the same layers as afferents. That is, layers II and III serve for **intercortical information transfer.** The main input to *layer IV* (Fig. 6-6C) is provided by specific thalamic afferents, which terminate there on many stellate cells and in some cases directly on pyramidal cells (Fig. 6-6D). The information arriving from the thalamus is distributed from layer IV to other layers. Information flow from the cortex back to the thalamus is mediated primarily by neurons of *layer VI* (Fig. 6-6C). Layers IV and VI, then, are responsible for the **thalamocortical and corticothalamic information exchange.** The nonspecific thalamocortical fibers also terminate in layers I and II (left in Fig. 6-6C; for definition of specific and nonspecific see Fig. 9-22 and associated text, beginning on p. 214). Finally, *layer V* contains especially large pyramidal cells (called giant cells of BETZ in the motor cortex; Fig. 6-6D), the axons of which run to deeper regions of the brain such as the basal ganglia, the brainstem and the spinal cord. These long descending pathways, the most typical example of which is the corticospinal tract (pyramidal tract, p. 117), thus subserve the **transfer of information to the subthalamic parts of the brain.**

With respect to the **direction of information processing** in the cortex, inferences can be drawn from the afferent and efferent neuronal elements shown in Fig. 6-6A-D and their connections to the local circuits (Fig. 6-6E). Put in simplified terms, the basic orientation of the chain of elements processing particular kinds of information is **perpendicular to the cortical surface**. This situation is also reflected in the *concepts of histological and functional cortical columnar modules*, which we encountered in the previous chapter as they are manifest in the motor cortex (microzones, p. 117) and will meet again in the discussion of the somatosensory cortex (columns, p. 217) [12, 21].

The long **apical dendrites** of the pyramidal cells, perpendicular to the cortical surface, are particularly well suited to receive information from a great variety of afferents and interneurons. Most of these axodendritic synapses seem to be *excitatory synapses*. The **basal dendrites** near the axon, on the other hand, also bear many *inhibitory synapses*; this is a strategic site for inputs to control the flow of excitation out of the cortex.
As far as the stellate cells (Fig. 6-6A,C) are concerned, their actions are excitatory in some cases, inhibitory in others. The axons of the **excitatory stellate cells** in general run **perpendicular** to the surface of the cortex, parallel to the apical dendrites of the pyramidal cells, with which they make many synaptic contacts. The axons of the **inhibitory stellate cells** are **horizontal,** parallel to the surface. Their inhibitory synapses form a "basketlike" enclosure around the parts of the pyramidal cells near the axon, and for this reason the stellate cells are also called *basket cells*. One of their functions could be to shield an active cortical column from its surroundings by **pericolumnar inhibition**.
Not all of the **transmitter substances of the cortical neurons** are known as yet. The pyramidal cells apparently use an (excitatory) amino acid, perhaps glutamate or aspartate. Some of the excitatory stellate cells contain neuropeptides (CCK, VIP; see p. 47), and there are indications that the basket cells use GABA as a transmitter. Given the great number of stellate cells, it is likely that other transmitters are also employed here. Many of the afferent fibers use the monoamines noradrenalin or dopamine, and others use acetylcholine.

Electrophysiological Correlates of Cortical Activity

Biophysical properties of cortical neurons. The cortical neurons resemble other neurons in their biophysical properties. The **resting potentials** of pyramidal cells are −50 to −80 mV and the **action potentials** have an amplitude of 60–100 mV and a duration of 0.5–2 ms. The action potentials originate at the *axon hillock* of the cell and are not only conducted peripherally but also spread out over the soma and at least the proximal dendrites. Because the action potential is not followed by an appreciable afterpotential, the *pyramidal cells can discharge at frequencies up to 100 Hz.*

Although the axon hillock is the main site at which pyramidal action potentials are generated, it has been shown that there are additional sites in the dendritic trees that can give rise to **"fast prepotentials"** and **slow dendritic action potentials**. The former can be blocked by tetrodotoxin ("Na-channel inhibitor") and the latter by Mg ("Ca-channel inhibitor"). Such **dendritic generating sites** are also found in the dendritic trees of the cerebellar Purkinje cells, but not in those of spinal motoneurons. In the Purkinje cells, as in the pyramidal cells of the neo- and allocortex, their function is to amplify the excitatory synaptic activity at the dendrites and conduct it actively to the main generating site at the axon hillock [10, 21].

Synaptic activity of cortical neurons. As compared with motoneuronal postsynaptic potentials (cf. Figs. 3-10 and 3-11, pp. 50,51), the cortical potentials are all longer in duration. **Excitatory postsynaptic potentials** often have a rise time of several milliseconds and a decay time of 10–30 ms, whereas **inhibitory postsynaptic potentials** usually last still longer, 70–150 ms. Often records from a given neuron reveal excitatory postsynaptic potentials differing in rise time; these probably arise in synaptic structures at different distances from the recording electrode. Inhibitory postsynaptic potentials are less common than excitatory potentials in the spontaneously active cortex, and those that occur are of smaller amplitude. By contrast, after the activation of corticopetal sensory pathways large, long-lasting inhibitory postsynaptic potentials are frequently

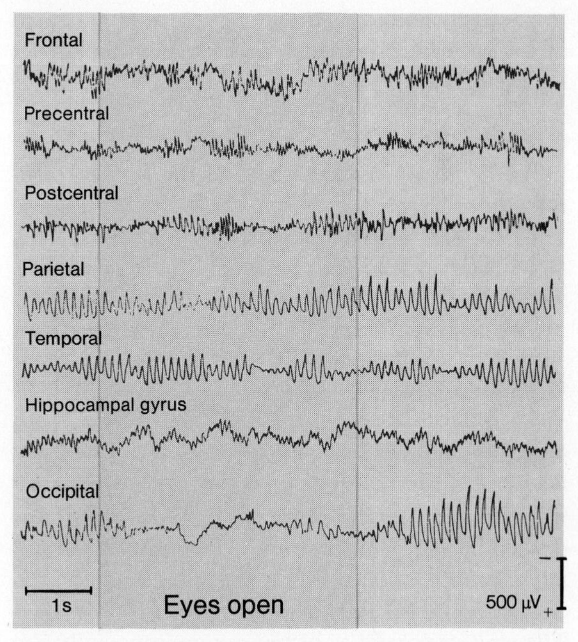

Fig. 6-7. Electrocorticograms of a resting, waking human, recorded from the indicated cortical areas with bipolar silver-chloride brush electrodes. The basic α rhythm predominates in the occipital and temporal cortex and all the parietal cortex except for the postcentral gyrus. More rapid activity is found in the more frontal regions, with a relatively pure β rhythm in the precentral gyrus. The occipital α rhythm is blocked by opening the eyes (cf. also Fig. 6-11). (From Penfield and Jasper [28])

recorded, either in isolation or following excitatory synaptic potentials. The frequency of the **cortical impulse activity elicited by postsynaptic potentials** is low, even in waking animals. It is usually below 10 Hz, and not uncommonly below 1 Hz; the resting potentials of cortical cells usually fluctuate in the range 3–10 mV below threshold [45].

Electrocorticograms. When one records between two electrodes laid on the surface of the cerebral cortex, or between one such electrode and a reference electrode some distance away (e.g., on the earlobe), in humans (Fig. 6-7) and other vertebrates continuous *potential fluctuations* are observed, called the **electrocorticogram (ECoG).** Their frequencies are between 1 and 50 Hz, and their amplitudes are of the order of 100 μV or more (Fig. 6-7).

Under normal conditions **frequency and amplitude of the ECoG** depend fundamentally on the species of animal, the recording site (Fig. 6-7) and the degree of wakefulness. In **humans** in the awake but relaxed state the predominant activity is waves at 8–13 Hz, most pronounced over the occipital cortex; these are called **α waves.** When the eyes are opened (see the bottom trace in Fig. 6-7) the α waves disappear **(α blockade)** and are replaced by higher-frequency **β waves** (14–30 Hz) of lower amplitude. (For further phenomenological details see p. 135).

Origin of the ECoG. The ECoG essentially reflects the **postsynaptic activity of the cortical neurons,** not the conducted impulse activity of these cells nor the activity of cortical glial cells. This conclusion is derived from many experiments in which the ECoG was recorded from cortical neurons with intracellular and extracellular electrodes simultaneously.

Simplifying matters, we can say that a *positive potential fluctuation* on the cortical surface is caused either by excitatory postsynaptic potentials in the deeper layers of the cortex or by inhibitory postsynaptic potentials in the superficial layers; conversely, a *negative potential fluctuation* is elicited by synaptic activity of the opposite kind at the various depths [10, 25, 45].

The *rhythmic activity of the cortex,* especially the α rhythm, is induced largely by the activity of deeper structures, especially the **thalamus** (Fig. 6-8). Unilateral ablation of the thalamus or deafferentation of the cortex (to isolate an area of cortex) causes the α waves to disappear ipsilaterally (Fig. 6-8A, B). On the other hand, decortication leaves the rhythmic activity of the thalamus practically unchanged. Intrathalamic recordings indicate the existence of multiple **thalamic pacemakers** (Fig. 6-8C), which by way of appropriate excitatory and inhibitory connections are capable of initiating and sustaining rhythmic activity. Their activity in turn is modified by thalamopetal influences. **Reticular structures** in particular have a *rhythm-generating (synchronizing)* and *rhythm-inhibiting (desynchronizing)* action on the thala-

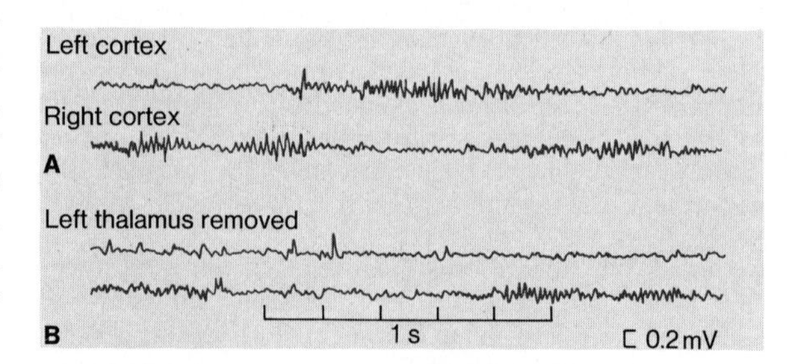

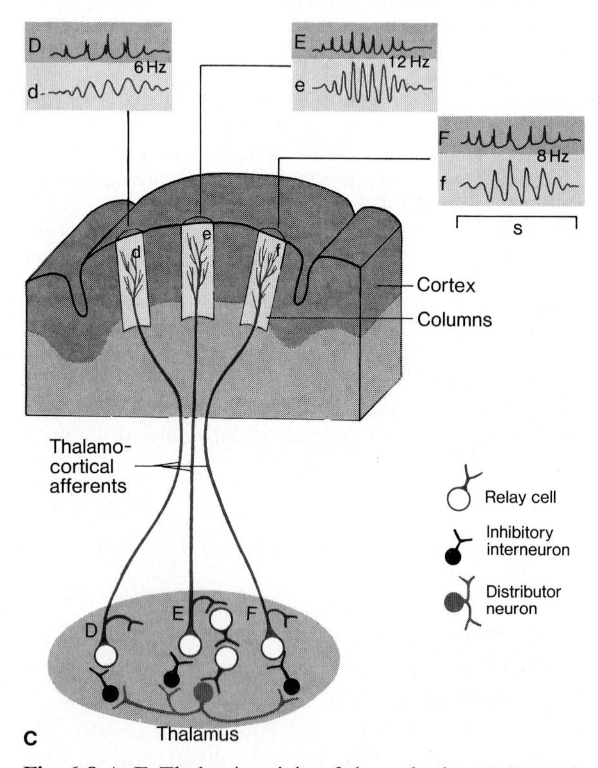

Fig. 6-8 A–F. Thalamic origin of the α rhythm. **A** Records of the electrocorticogram from the left and right motor cortex of the cat. **B** Like **A,** except that the left thalamus has been removed by suction. The rhythmic basic activity (α spindles under barbiturate anesthesia) has disappeared on the left but is unchanged on the right. **C** Model of the connections of thalamic pacemaker areas with the cortex (projection of D, E, F to d, e, f) and with one another. The individual areas are linked to one another by "distributor neurons." The duration and intensity of the inhibitory feedback within the individual pacemaker groups determines the basic rhythm of thalamic discharge (D, E, F, upper records) and of the electrocorticograms d, e, f thus induced (lower records). (Modified from Andersen and Andersson [1])

mus, as described in greater detail in the discussion of the sleeping/waking cycle, Section 6.3 [1, 10].

Event-related potentials, ERPs. In addition to the spontaneous activity of the cortex, there are characteristic potential fluctuations that tend to appear after psychological, motor and sensory events. As a rule these potentials are of such small amplitude that they become visible only when successive records are summated. They are called **event-related potentials, ERPs** [25]. Examples of ERPs have already been mentioned in Chapter 5: the *expectancy potential*, the *readiness potential* and *premotor positivity*. The events to which these are related occur during the preparation for and execution of goal-directed movement (Fig. 5-30). The potential changes that appear in the CNS in response to the stimulation of receptors (sensors), of peripheral nerves, of sensory tracts or nuclei or of other sensory structures (e.g., cortical areas) are called **evoked potentials, EPs** [40].

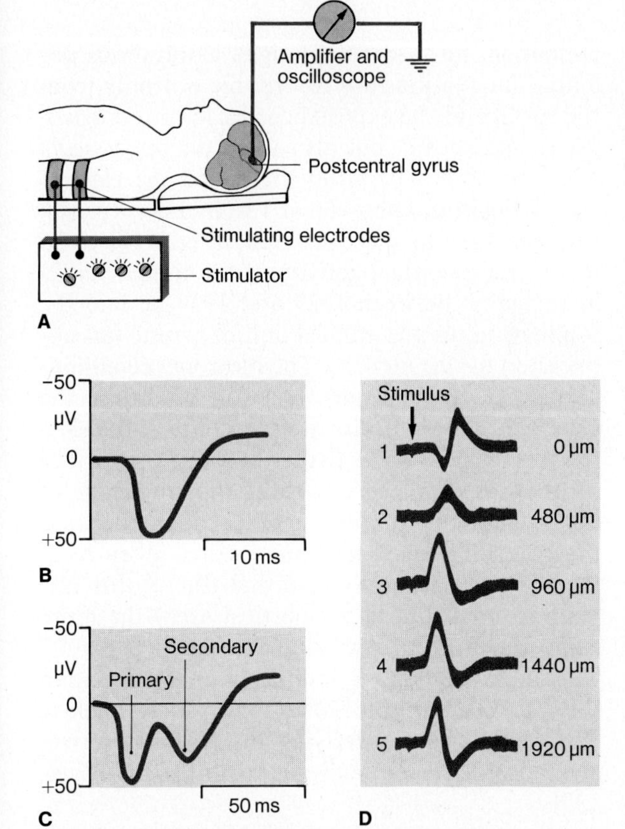

Fig. 6-9 A–D. Cortical evoked potentials recorded in human **(A–C)** and the cat **(D)**. **A** Experimental arrangement. Instead of the electrical skin stimulus chosen here other stimulus modalities (mechanical, thermal) could be used. Recording is done with an EEG electrode on the scalp. **B** Primary evoked potential from the associated projection area in the postcentral gyrus. **C** Primary evoked and secondary evoked potential. Note the different time scales in **B** and **C. D** Cortical evoked potential recorded with a microelectrode. As the microelectrode is advanced to the indicated depths below the surface of the cortex (record 1, 0 μm) in steps of 480 μm (records 2–5), the potential changes polarity and latency. [B–D modified from T.T. RUCH et al.: Neurophysiology, 2nd ed., W.B. Saunders: Philadelphia and London 1965]

After stimulation of peripheral somatic nerves or sensors slow, positive-negative potential deflections can be recorded from the sensorimotor areas of the cortex (SI, SII). These **somatic evoked potentials, SEPs**, are illustrated in Fig. 6-9. The first, positive potential change, the **primary evoked potential,** occurs only in a narrowly circumscribed region of the cortex, the cortical projection field of the point stimulated (e.g., when a cutaneous nerve is stimulated, there is a primary evoked potential in the somatotopically corresponding area of the postcentral gyrus). The subsequent late response, which lasts distinctly longer (Fig. 6-9C, D), is called the **secondary evoked potential.** This potential is found in an extensive cortical region.

With regard to the **mechanism of origin of evoked potentials,** there is general agreement that they, like the waves of the electrocorticogram, basically reflect the *synaptic activity* rather than the impulse activity of neurons. For example, the change in an evoked potential observed as a microelectrode is advanced from the cortical surface to deeper layers (Fig. 6-9D) – that is, the disappearance of the initial positive component in favor of an initial negativity with short latency – shows that the neurons of the internal granular layer (layer IV) in particular are depolarized during this time (owing to excitation by afferent input), as would be expected from the discussion on p. 131.

The main value of EP measurement for clinical diagnosis is that it can be applied to test the intactness of peripheral sensory and subcortical pathways. As an example, consider the *auditory evoked potential*, **AEP**, illustrated in Fig. 6-10. Six distinct positive peaks are visible in this summated potential, each of them corresponding to activity in one of the consecutive stations of the auditory pathway (cf. Fig. 12-13), as follows. Wave I is assigned to activity in the auditory nerve; wave II indicates activity in the cochlear nucleus and wave III, that in the superior olive. Waves IV and V are thought to reflect activity in the lateral lentiform nuclei and the inferior colliculi. Wave VI is presumably generated at the thalamic level. Not until this short-latency **"brainstem AEP"** has been completed do the later EPs associated with the cortex appear (details of these will not be described here).

Like the SEP (Fig. 6-9) and the AEP (Fig. 6-10), *visual evoked potentials*, **VEPs,** can be recorded

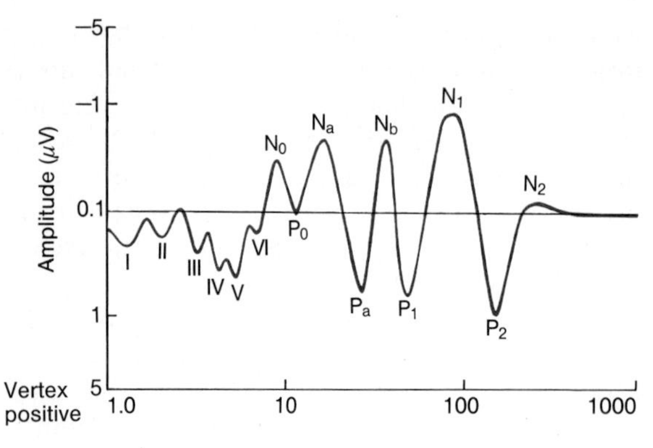

Fig. 6-10. Schematic representation of an auditory evoked potential (AEP) with logarithmic time axis. The peaks **I–VI** are generated between the cochlear nerve and the lateral geniculate body, relatively far away from the recording site and the skull surface. Hence these peaks are also called "far-field potentials". Peak VI is not prominent in recordings from the vertex. The peaks labeled N (negative) and P (positive) probably represent activity in thalamic nuclei, the auditory cortex and association areas. (From [25], based on PICTON et al., J. Electroenc. Clin. Neurophysiol. *36*, 179, 1974)

and evaluated for diagnostic purposes. These are more complicated and variable in structure than the SEP and AEP, because the eye receives, and sends on to the primary and secondary projection areas, more information (luminance, color, pattern, contrast etc.). For tests in the contexts of neurology, ophthalmology and psychophysiology, VEPs are triggered mainly by flashes of light but also by checkerboard and striped patterns [4, 25, 40].

Cortical DC potentials. Normally a maintained potential difference can be measured between the cortical surface and the white matter below it, or between the surface and a distant reference electrode; it amounts to several millivolts (surface negative). This **cortical DC or steady potential,** however, also exhibits *fluctuations,* though their frequency is considerably lower than that of the ECoG. For example, when one falls asleep the cortical surface becomes more positive; conversely, both arousal reactions and increases in activity of an already wakeful animal are accompanied by increased surface negativity. Local or general convulsive discharge and disturbances of the respiratory-gas supply (O_2 deficiency, CO_2 excess) also cause characteristic changes in the DC potential, the time course and polarity of which can be used for prognoses about the reversibility of cortical damage. Unfortunately, **clinical-diagnostic application** of these findings is nearly impossible, for the many sources of error (primarily electrode potentials of unknown origin) make the routine recording of DC potentials impracticable [10, 35, 45].

As to the **origin of the cortical DC potentials,** there is as yet no consistent interpretation. It seems certain that the negative DC shifts result primarily from depolarization of the apical dendrites in layers I and II, due to the activity of nonspecific thalamic afferents. Glial cells make an indirect contribution to the duration and amplitude of these potentials, though they do not themselves produce postsynaptic potentials. Potential differences at the blood-brain barrier and at the meninges can be ruled out as generators of the DC potentials.

The Electroencephalogram (EEG)

Definition, mechanism of origin. Continuous potential fluctuations are recordable not only from the surface of the exposed cortex (electrocorticogram; see above), but also from the *intact scalp* over the skull. The latter are called the **electroencephalogram,** abbreviated **EEG.** HANS BERGER was the first to discover that it is possible to record the electrical activity of the human brain in this way. Between 1929 and 1938 he laid the foundation for the clinical and experimental application of this method. The **recording conditions** correspond basically to those for recording the electrocorticogram. However, because of the electrical resistance of the tissues between the surface of the brain and the electrodes the amplitude of the potential fluctuations is reduced, and because the recording electrodes are further away from the potential generators (so that the recording is from a somewhat larger cortical area) the more rapid potential fluctuations are "averaged out." Therefore the EEG is smaller in amplitude than the ECoG, and somewhat lower in frequency. The **mechanisms underlying the EEG,** however, are those discussed with regard to the ECoG (p. 132).

Recording and interpreting the EEG. The recording of the EEG is a routine procedure used internationally for neurological diagnosis. To enable comparison, therefore, the positions of the recording electrodes (Fig. 6-11 B, left) and the recording conditions (paper speed, time constants and filters in the amplifier system) have been **extensively standardized**. The EEG is recorded either with a **bipolar** arrangement, between two recording electrodes placed on the skull, or with a **monopolar** arrangement, between a *recording* electrode on the scalp and a distant *reference* electrode (on the earlobe, for instance; Fig. 6-11). The record is **interpreted** primarily on the basis of the frequency, amplitude, shape and distribution of the waves contained in the EEG, and in the proportions of the different kinds of waves. This analysis can be done "by hand" or with the assistance of analog and digital devices. An example is given in Fig. 6-12. For further details the reader is referred to the literature [10, 25].

Forms of the EEG; diagnostic significance. In the discussion of the ECoG (Fig. 6-7) mention was made of the fact that in a *healthy adult* resting with eyes closed the **basic α rhythm** (alpha waves, 8–13 Hz, averaging 10 Hz) predominates and is especially prominent in the occipital area (*synchronized EEG,* Fig. 6-11). When the eyes are opened or other sensory stimuli impinge, the α waves vanish **(alpha blockade)** and higher-frequency **β waves** (beta waves, 14–30 Hz, averaging 20 Hz) of smaller amplitude appear; the EEG becomes *desynchronized* (Fig. 6-11). Other, distinctly slower waves of larger amplitude have been identified (Fig. 6-13, left) – for example, the **ϑ waves** (theta waves, 4–7 Hz, averaging 6 Hz) and the **δ waves** (delta waves, 0.3–3.5 Hz, averaging 3 Hz) – but they are not normally observed in a *waking adult.* The EEG of *children and adolescents,* by contrast, is slower and more irregular, exhibiting δ waves even in the waking state. Otherwise, slow waves are observed in a healthy person only during sleep (see p. 141).

Even today the EEG remains the only available method for the *continuous quantification of neuronal processes in the intact human brain.* All the other procedures (see pp. 136 – 138) either do not provide continuous measurement and/or are so expensive and technically demanding that they can

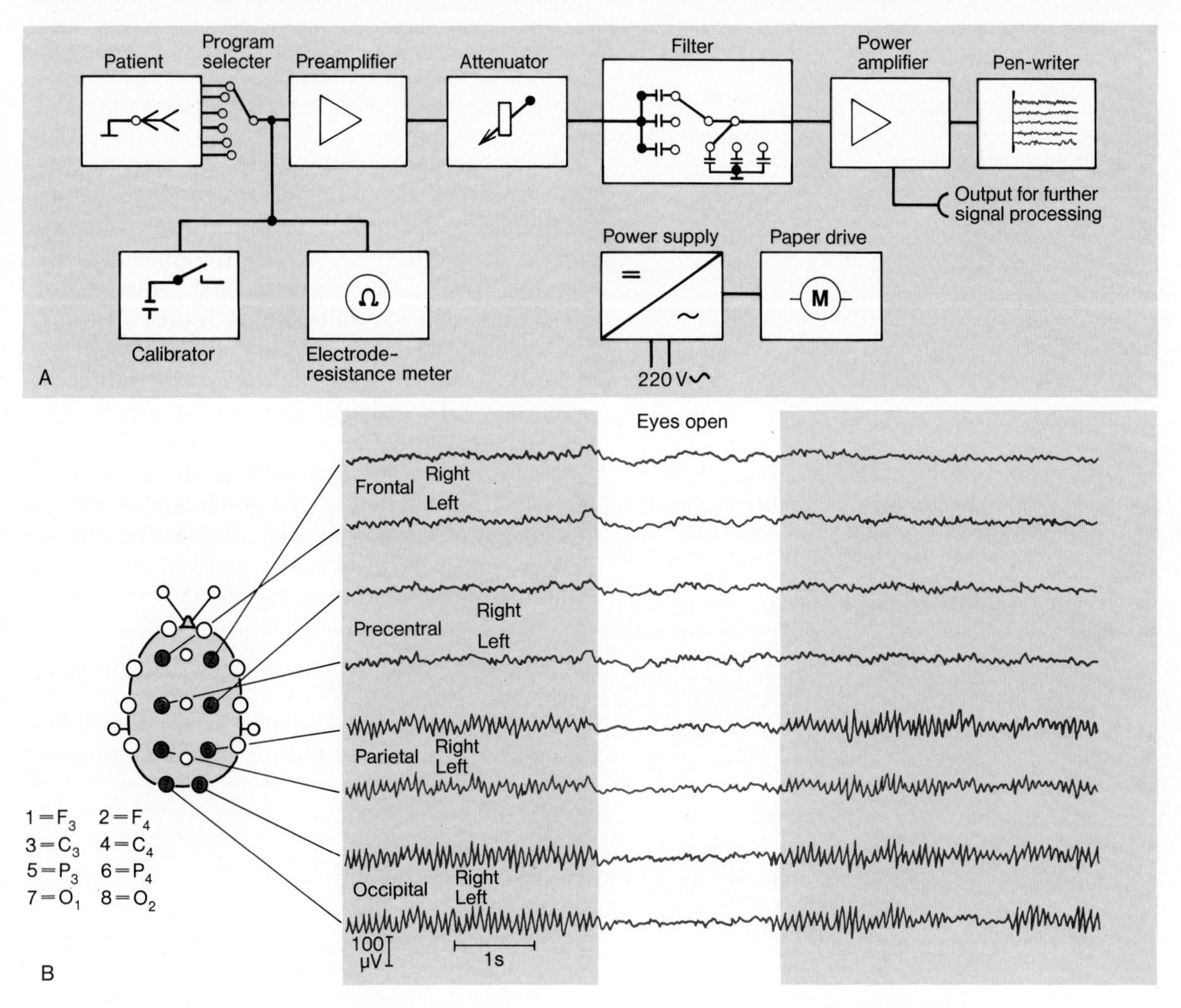

Fig. 6-11. A Block diagram of an electroencephalograph; an instrument has up to 16 recording channels in parallel, only one of which is shown here. **B** Normal EEG of a resting, waking human. Simultaneous eight-channel monopolar recording from the indicated sites on the skull. Opening the eyes blocks the α rhythm. Compare with Fig. 6-7. (Modified from RICHARD JUNG)

be applied to only a few questions in a few places. Therefore the EEG, including the event-related potentials, still offers the *most important means of access to human information processing and behavior-controlling mechanisms* for both **psychophysiological research and clinical practice.** Providing unproblematic long-term records with high temporal resolution, it permits analysis of the dynamic relationships between cerebral activity and behavior. Questions once approachable only by way of animal experiments can now be investigated in humans, without impeding or endangering the subject [4, 25, 35, 40].

With regard to the **clinical significance of the EEG,** only a few examples will be given here [30]. The records on the right in Fig. 6-13 illustrate a number of **seizure potentials** such as appear in epileptics, in particular. Other general changes, such as *slowing and irregularity in the recorded curves,* accompany diffuse organic brain diseases or follow cerebral trauma or metabolic intoxication (coma). Tumors, too, often produce (local) changes in the EEG. It should also be noted that many medications, especially psychoactive drugs, affect the EEG. A general extinction of the EEG **(isoelectric or flat EEG)** is increasingly being taken as a *criterion for death* in cases of doubt. That is, when modern methods of resuscitation succeed in overcoming an interruption of circulation and breathing, but the patient neither regains consciousness nor begins to breathe spontaneously, one suspects that the cerebral cortex and brainstem have been irreversibly damaged by the ischemia (deficient blood supply). This state of **brain death** is distinguished not only by the symptoms just described (flat EEG, unconsciousness, no spontaneous breathing) but also by the absence of a light response and the mydriasis (dilation) of the pupils and by areflexia, atony and unresponsiveness.

Cortex and brainstem have *low ischemia tolerance.* The maximal duration of ischemia that can be survived – the **resuscitation** or **structure-maintenance limit** – is only 3–8 min in the case of the cortex and 7–10 min for the brainstem. In other organs the resuscitation limit is considerably longer. For instance, given a normal body temperature, it is 20 minutes for the myocardium, and 150 minutes for the kidney. Therefore these organs can be kept alive by resuscitation techniques even after brain death has occurred, so that in certain circumstances, especially when the brain death is the consequence of an accident to a healthy young person, they can be used for **organ transplants.**

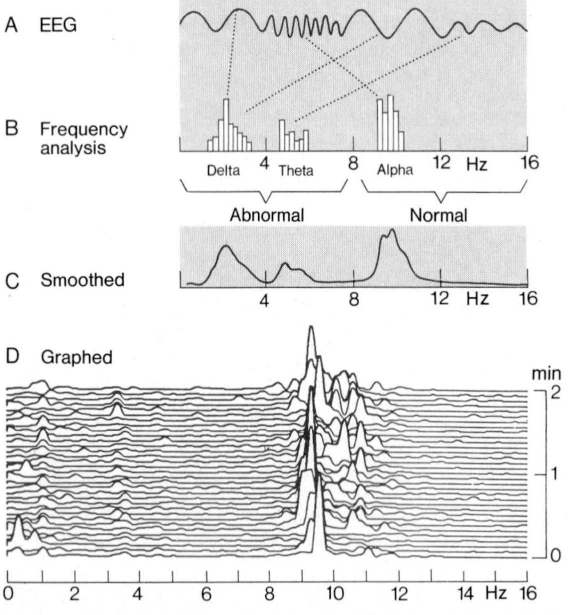

Fig. 6-12 A–D Computer-assisted analysis of the EEG. Four-second-long sections of an EEG record **(A)** are broken down electronically into their frequency components (Fourier analysis, **B**) and after smoothing **(C)** are displayed in sequence from bottom to top **(D).** The resulting picture of an "EEG landscape" gives a graphic impression of both the frequency components in the record (plotted from left to right; **D** represents the α rhythm of a normal subject), and their variation in time (from bottom to top). (From BICKFORD, R.: J. Altered States Consciousness 1, 49, 1973)

Magnetencephalography, MEG. Because any movement of electrical charges produces a magnetic field, the brain generates weak magnetic fields in addition to the electric fields recorded in the EEG. The magnetic fields (flux density less than one ten-millionth of the earth's magnetic field) can be demonstrated by means of highly sensitive detectors filled with liquid helium (SQUID: superconducting quantum interference devices). The advantage of this elaborate procedure as compared with the EEG lies in its considerably **better spatial resolution of the site of origin of cortical activity** (due to the absence of cross-talk from adjacent regions). At present the method is used only for research purposes.

Cerebral Activity, Metabolism and Blood Flow

The brain consumes about 50 ml O_2 per minute, roughly 20% of the total oxygen requirement of

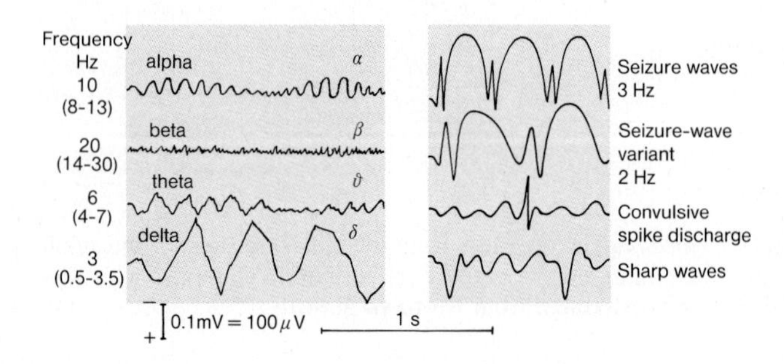

Fig. 6-13. Main forms of the EEG. *Left:* the different types of wave that can appear in a healthy person. Discussion in text. *Right:* examples of seizure potentials, as recorded primarily from epileptics. The characteristic sequence of rapid and slow fluctuations is called a "spike-and-wave" complex. (Modified from RICHARD JUNG)

a resting person. Accordingly, the brain must be provided with around 15% of the cardiac output at rest, although it accounts for only 2.5% of the total body weight. But the rate of perfusion is by no means uniform in all parts of the brain. For one thing, far less blood flows through the white matter than through the cerebral cortex; for another, even the different parts of the cortex almost always receive at least slightly different amounts of blood. At rest (Fig. 6-14 A, B), with a typical α-wave EEG, *much more blood flows through the frontal regions than through the other cortical areas.* Slightly painful stimulation of the skin (C) causes the perfusion maxima to shift to the region of the parietal cortex – that is, to the primary sensory area. (At the same time there is a slight increase in overall blood flow through the brain.) The perfusion pattern changes in the same direction, even more distinctly, when the contralateral hand is actively opened and closed (D). Reading aloud (E) results in a Z-shaped distribution of perfusion maxima, extending into the visual regions of the occipital lobe [50].

The regional changes in blood flow appear to be predominantly under **metabolic control.** "Metabolic" maps obtained by monitoring the uptake of radioactive glucose into the brain cells correspond to a great extent with the "blood-flow maps." The implication is that any regionally elevated neuronal activity, whether sensory, motor, or based on a form of thinking, is accompanied by enhanced metabolic activity of the neurons; the metabolites released in the process cause local vasodilation and thus increased blood flow.

Clinical experience reveals that in unconscious or comatose patients, or those with high-grade dementia or schizophrenia, the sensory, motor or mental deficits in each case are accompanied by decreases in both overall blood flow and in perfusion of the relevant regions [50]. Blood flow measurements can therefore be expected to acquire increasing clinical significance, especially if it proves possible to refine their resolution and to monitor parts of the brain below the surface as well.

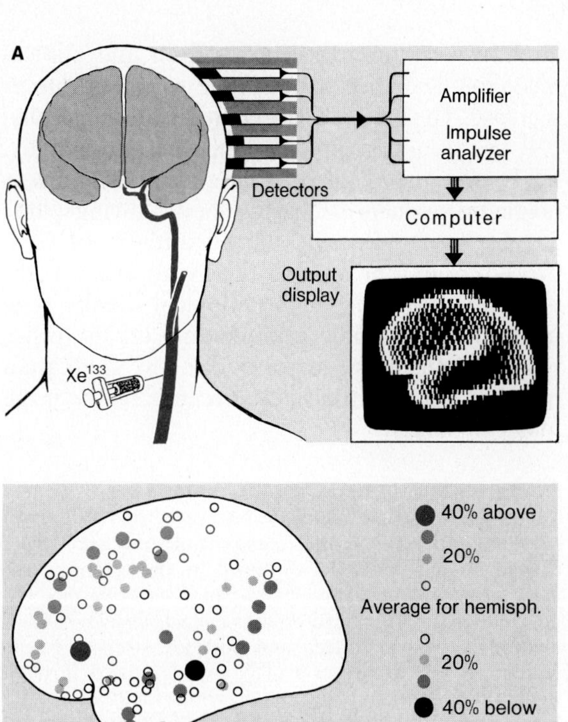

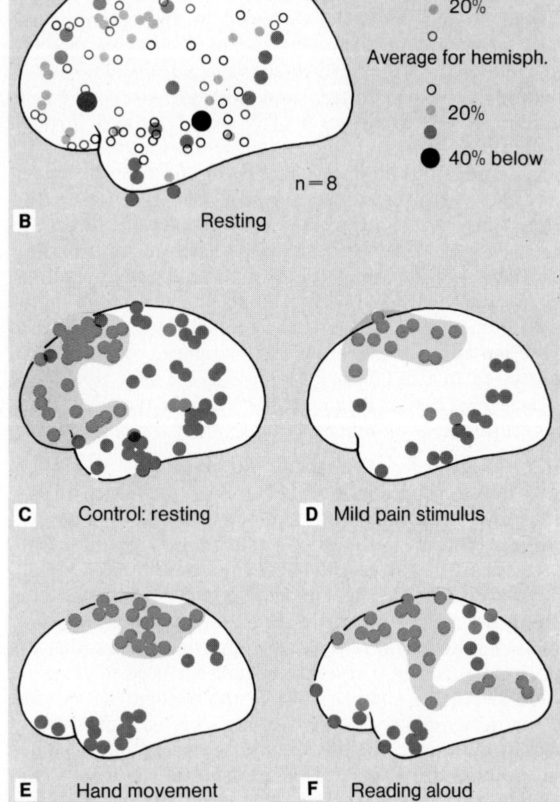

Fig. 6-14 A–F. Measurement of regional blood flow by means of intraarterial injection of ^{133}Xe into the internal carotid artery (N.A. LASSEN and D.H. INGVAR). The uptake and washing out of this gas in the different regions of the brain is monitored with Geiger counters (as many as 245) mounted on the side of the head. With the help of a computer the blood flow is calculated and represented numerically or graphically. **A** Diagram to illustrate the method. **B** Flow through the dominant hemisphere at rest. Means of 8 subjects. Deviation from the mean is indicated by the symbols shown on the right. **C** like **B,** except that only those areas are shown that have blood flow at least 20% above or below the mean. **D–F** Change in regional blood flow during the indicated cerebral activities, represented as in **C.** Measurement by D.H. INGVAR et al. (From [50])

Imaging Procedures for the Representation of Brain Structures and Activities

In recent years the above-mentioned procedures for revealing cerebral activity (EEG, measurement of blood flow by the xenon method) have been supplemented by procedures in which an image of the brain is obtained. A major factor in their invention and further development has been the availability of computers for processing large amounts of data. These imaging procedures are already very important in research and clinical medicine, and their significance will continue to increase. The first is X-ray **computed tomography, CT,** the second is **positron-emission tomography, PET,** and the third is tomography by **nuclear magnetic resonance, NMR**. The following paragraphs briefly describe the advantages of each procedure in representing the living brain, without going into the methodological details. The method of **ultrasonic examination**, on the other hand, is much less useful within the skull than in other parts of the body, because of the large mass of bone.

CT. Because brain tissue absorbs X rays approximately uniformly throughout, until a few years ago radiological examination of the brain was possible only after injection of air into the space occupied by the cerebrospinal fluid *(pneumoencephalography)* or of a contrast medium into one of the large head arteries *(angiography)*. Neither method is without danger, and both are stressful to the patient. In CT a fine beam of X rays is passed through the brain and the source is rotated about the head in a selected plane; the radiation emerging on the opposite side of the head is measured with a scintillation counter. In this way, X-ray images are obtained from several directions for each region of tissue. Elaborate computer programs are then used to calculate, from these many recordings, the radiation density of the tissue at each point in the measurement plane. The result is a **high-contrast image of a section** through the brain in that plane, with a spatial resolution of 0.5–1 mm for a layer 2–13 mm thick. The radiation exposure is no greater than is required for a conventional X-ray image.

PET. This procedure employs radioisotopes of biologically important atoms (^{18}F, ^{15}O, ^{13}N, ^{11}C), which release positrons. After traveling a short distance (2–8 mm) each positron collides with an electron. In this reaction both particles are destroyed and two γ rays are emitted at an angle of exactly 180°. The γ rays are intercepted by photodetectors arranged around the head, and a point is registered only when two detectors exactly opposite one another are hit simultaneously. These data, again, are used to calculate a cross-sectional image in which the elementary variable is the decay density of the isotope; this is a measure of activity differences in the volume being examined. When the isotopes are incorporated into substances such as water, glucose, amino acids or other biologically interesting molecules, they can be used to measure the **distribution of these substances in the brain** (e.g., the above-mentioned "metabolic map" of glucose consumption by brain cells). The PET procedure has a spatial resolution of 4–8 mm and a temporal resolution of 1 s. Because the isotopes it requires have only a short half life, the cyclotron used to produce them must be located in the immediate vicinity, and the procedure is very costly.

NMR. Nuclear magnetic resonance has long been a common means of spectroscopic analysis in physics and chemistry, used to clarify the structure of molecules. When it is applied for medical diagnosis, additional spatial information is needed for reconstruction of a sectional image, because not only the presence but also the origin of the detected signal must be known. It was only recently that the necessary techniques were developed. The physical bases of NMR are complex and involve the fact that atomic nuclei rotate (that is, they exhibit a torque impulse or spin) and in so doing, because of the protons within them, generate a magnetic field with its two poles on the axis of rotation of the nucleus. Normally the axes of rotation of various molecules are oriented in all directions at random, but an externally imposed magnetic field influences their directions as the earth's magnetism does a compass needle. In favorable circumstances this effect produces resonance of the atomic nuclei, which causes them to emit electromagnetic radiation. The **occurrence and decay of this resonance radiation** are recorded; they are the **actual measurement signal**. The nucleus of the hydrogen atom, a component of the water and many other molecules in the body, is a particularly good resonator. In medical NMR, therefore, the resonance of hydrogen is measured. Images can be produced in any desired plane of section. At present the layer thickness ranges from 5 to 10 mm, and within an image details are discernible at about 1 mm. On the other hand, the temporal resolution is still poor, 10–20 s. The contrast is equivalent to that in CT and can surely be increased. It remains uncertain whether the applied magnetic fields could be dangerous to health above a certain magnitude. The devices now being used for diagnosis have a field strength of 0.2 tesla, and that of experimental devices can be 2.3 tesla (50,000 times the strength of the earth's magnetic field) or more. Magnetic fields of < 2 tesla are currently considered harmless.

6.3 Waking and Sleeping

Circadian Periodicity as the Basis of the Waking/Sleeping Rhythm

The circadian oscillator. Nearly all living beings, from protozoans to humans, undergo rhythmical changes in the state of their organs and functions. These changes are often coupled to the 24-hour periodicity associated with the earth's rotation (but in some cases to the tides, the phases of the moon or the annual cycle), so that it has frequently been concluded that animal and human diurnal rhythms are a passive response of the organism to environmental periodicity. Many experiments, however, have shown unequivocally that this rhythmicity continues even *after all environmental factors have been excluded.* The period of such a **free-running rhythm** is often shorter or longer than 24 h, a further indication that the cause of the rhythm lies not in the environment, but rather in endogenous processes (of unknown nature, summarized in the term "biological clock"). The endogenous periodicity thus corresponds only approximately *(circa)* to the natural duration of a day *(dies)*, which has given rise to the adjective **circadian.** A free-running circadian rhythm does not die out for a long time (weeks, months); that is, it behaves like a self-excited oscillator. Normally the periodicity of this oscillator is **synchronized** with the 24-h cycle by external **entraining signals ("Zeitgeber")** such as the alternation between light and darkness or social factors [3, 7, 38, 42].

Circadian periodicity in humans. More than 100 parameters of human organs and functions have been found to change cyclically with a 24-h period [42]. Body temperature, for example, is known to vary between a minimum in the early morning and a maximum, about 1–1.5 °C higher, in the evening. But the most impressive diurnal fluctuation is the **waking/sleeping cycle.** It comes as no surprise, then, that the many adjustments of the organism normally associated with the onset of sleep – for instance, the fall in body temperature, heart rate and respiratory rate (see Fig. 6-17) – have been thought to be *causally* related to sleep. Many experiments have shown, however, that the diurnal rhythmicity of these and many other vegetative and physiological parameters is retained even during *sleep deprivation.* From these and other experiments it has been concluded that humans (and other highly organized metazoans) possesses **a considerable number of circadian oscillators** of somewhat different periods. These are synchronized with one another to some extent, and can also be entrained by external signals.

Clear evidence of the **independent periodicity of autonomic rhythms** is provided by *studies of shift workers.* In these people, for example, the rhythms of body temperature and other parameters do not change phase even when night work is continued for a long time, although the curve may be *distorted* by the night work. Evidently **social contacts** and **knowledge of the time of day** are more effective Zeitgeber for the phase of the circadian oscillators than the working rhythm and the resulting waking/sleeping behavior. One of the consequences of this conflict situation is that performance capacity continues to reach a minimum in the hours after midnight despite the demands of the job, so that mistakes and accidents are more frequent at this time (cf. p. 659).

Humans shut off from the environment (during experiments in underground bunkers or caves) also exhibit a **circadian periodicity,** with a cycle duration in most cases somewhat longer than 24 hours (Fig. 6-15A). Here, again, differences in cycle length and the relative independence of individual oscillators can be demonstrated. For example, in Fig. 5-15A the maxima of body temperature (upward-pointing triangles) occur just before the onset of sleep in the entrained cycle; during the first two days in free-running conditions this phase relation persists, but then there is a clear phase shift. This result suggests that the sleeping and temperature cycles are coupled to one another, their phase shift depending on the prevailing circumstances and in particular on the period of the system as a whole. In extreme cases, when the free-running waking/sleeping rhythm has an especially long period (in a few cases 48-hour cycles, or *bicircadian rhythms,* have been observed [38, 42]), autonomic variables such as temperature become completely uncoupled **(internal desynchronization)** and continue to run with the original period of ca. 25 hours. In other words, the "temperature clock" is evidently less

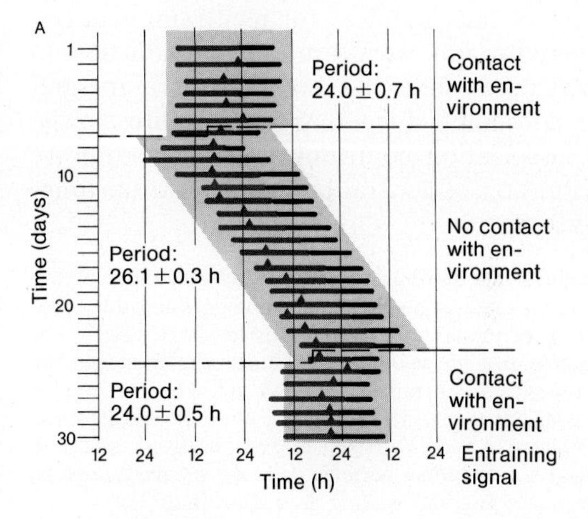

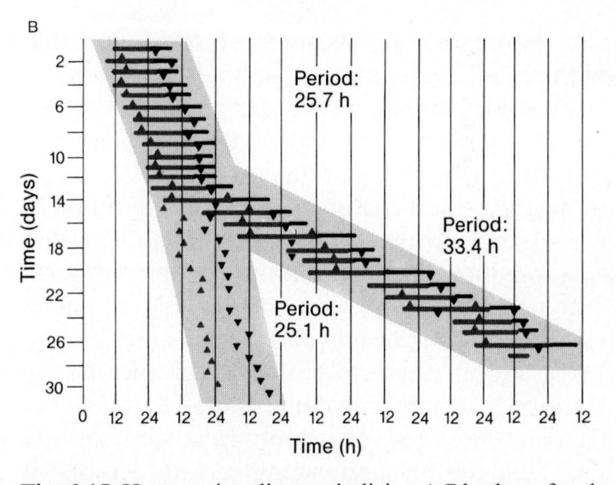

Fig. 6-15. Human circadian periodicity. **A** Rhythm of waking *(red parts of bars)* and sleeping *(black parts)* of a subject in an isolation chamber with open door (social Zeitgeber) and in isolation (without Zeitgeber). The *triangles* indicate the time when body temperature is maximal. With the door open, the period was exactly 24 h (mean daily deviation ±0.7 or ±0.5 h), but in isolation it rose to 26.1±0.3 h. **B** Activity rhythm of a subject isolated in a bunker, in whom on Day 15 the temperature rhythm (maxima, *upward-pointing red triangles;* minima, *downward black triangles)* became uncoupled from the waking/sleeping rhythm, continuing with a period of 25.1 h. At this time, for unknown reasons, the waking/sleeping (activity) rhythm suddenly changed to a period of 33.4 h. (Measurements by Prof. J. Aschoff and coworkers)

flexible; unable to match the new, extremely long period of the "activity clock", it detaches itself from the sleeping/waking rhythm.

If the **rhythm of the external Zeitgeber is shifted once** – for example, shortened by a flight to the east or lengthened by a westward flight – the circadian systems require about 1 day per time zone (1-h shift) to regain their normal phase relation to the Zeitgeber ("jet lag"). Reentrainment proceeds more rapidly after flights to the west than after flights to the east (i.e., the internal rhythm is more easily resynchronized after a phase delay than after a phase advance). Furthermore, the individual systems differ in the amount of time required for reentrainment. Social activity and work are rapidly adjusted to the Zeitgeber shift, but body temperature and other autonomic functions follow more slowly. This dissociation contributes to the temporary deterioration of general performance after long-distance flights.

The **ratio of the duration of activity and rest times** within a circadian cycle is not kept constant. Remarkably, prolongation of the activity phase leads to shortening of the subsequent rest phase – that is, the average circadian period is kept as constant as possible (cf. Fig. 6-15). This finding is contrary to what would be expected on the basis of a fatigue hypothesis (sleep as recuperation), and is a sign that the **circadian periodicity is the primary process,** to which sleeping and waking are subordinate [14].

The **biological significance of the circadian rhythms** of humans and animals has tended to be underestimated. For instance, physicians should take more account of the daily fluctuations of nearly all organ functions when deciding on diagnosis and therapy. Circadian rhythmicity is evidently inherited, and should be regarded as a phylogenetic adaptation to the temporal structure of our environment. Having an **internal copy of the schedule of environmental events,** the organism can adjust itself **in advance** to the changes in environmental conditions to be expected at any time. The resulting advantages extend from simply performing certain actions at suitable times of the day to actually measuring time by means of the "internal clock"; the latter ability is required, for example, by animals that orient by using the sun as a compass. Seen in this light, the **waking/sleeping rhythm** is not the cause, but rather one of the *side effects of endogeneous circadian periodicity.* An explanation of the nature of these endogenous oscillators, which is just beginning to emerge [3, 7, 33, 38, 42], will also bring us closer to an understanding of the mechanisms underlying waking/sleeping behavior.

The pacemakers for the circadian rhythm are within the CNS. At present two regions are thought to be the most important oscillator sites, the **suprachiasmatic nucleus, SCN,** in the ventral hypothalamus and a region in the **ventromedial nucleus of the hypothalamus, VMH.** The former seems to be responsible chiefly for regulating the activity cycle (sleeping/waking rhythm) and the latter, for the temperature and feeding rhythms (including the glucose level and the corticoid levels in the plasma). The SCN receives abundant inputs from the visual system and is synchronized with the VMH by close reciprocal connections [3, 5, 33; see also p. 357].

Phenomenology of Waking and Sleeping

Human waking/sleeping behavior. Whereas a person who is awake is in active contact with the environment – for example, responds to stimuli with adequate actions – in sleep the contact with the environment is very much restricted. It is not entirely eliminated, however, for stimuli, especially those with a particular significance, can wake the sleeper. For example, the whimpering of an infant awakens its mother, though considerably louder traffic noise does not. Nevertheless, the traffic noise, like all noise, is detrimental to sleep, affecting its depth and the sequence of sleep stages, and thus impairs well-being in general. Therefore all disturbing environmental stimuli should be kept away from the bedroom.

Neither waking nor sleeping is a homogeneous state of consciousness. Just as in the waking state the amount of attention directed outward can vary considerably, there are distinct **stages of sleep.** The simplest and oldest measure of the **depth of sleep** is the *intensity of a stimulus* sufficient for awakening. The deeper the sleep, the higher the awaken threshold.

Practically the only measure of depth of sleep in use today is the **EEG.** Four or five stages of sleep can be distinguished on the basis of the EEG pattern, and there is widespread agreement on standard criteria for them [25, 32, 46, 55]. As shown in Fig. 6-16, in a state of **relaxed wakefulness** the dominant pattern is an α rhythm with rising and falling amplitude. In **stage A** this rhythm begins to disintegrate, so that the α waves are increasingly separated by a baseline with very small ϑ waves. This stage marks the *transition from waking to sleeping.* Many authors count it as waking rather than as a separate stage. **Stage B** (falling asleep and the lightest level of sleep) is characterized by ϑ waves. At the end of stage B large "vertex sharp waves" (duration 3–5 s) can be recorded over the precentral region of the brain; these are forerunners

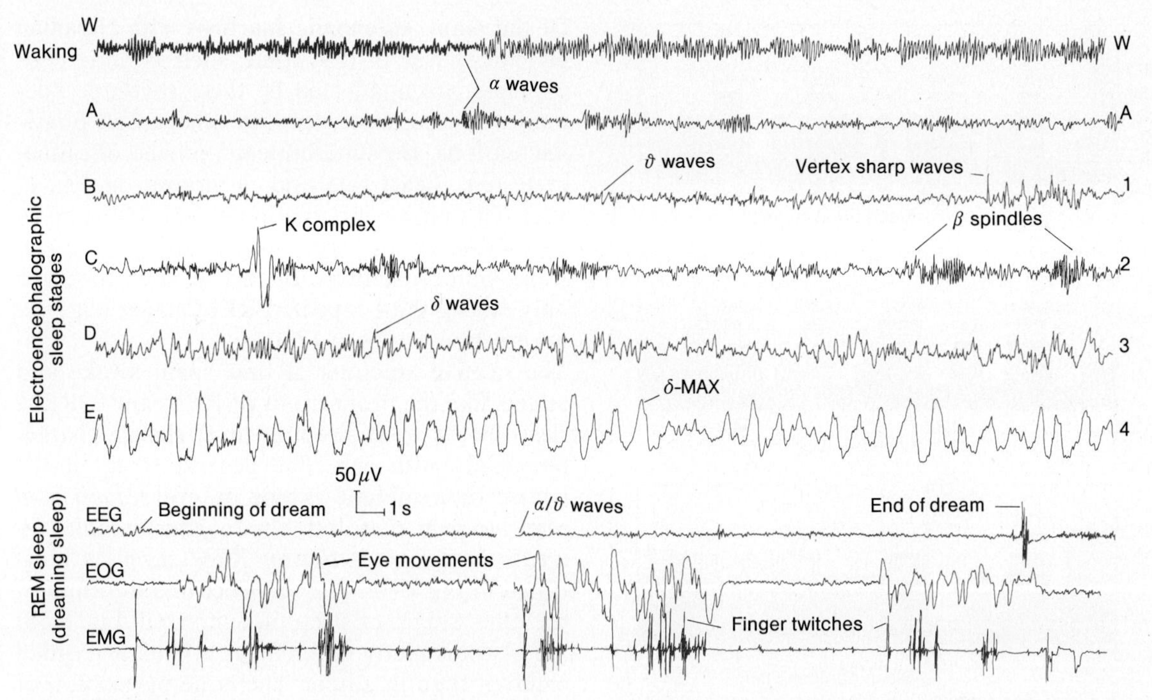

Fig. 6-16. Classification of the stages of human sleep on the basis of the EEG. The first 6 recordings are labeled on the *left* according to LOOMIS et al. [55] and on the *right* according to KLEITMAN and his coworkers [23]; see also [32]. *Stage W:* Relaxed waking. *Stage A:* Transition from waking to falling asleep. Many authors consider this stage to be part of stage W. *Stage B or 1:* Falling asleep and the lightest sleep. The vertex sharp waves at the end of the recording are considered to mark the "physiological moment" of falling asleep. *Stage C or 2:* Light sleep. *Stage D or 3:* Intermediate sleep. *Stage E or 4:* Deep sleep. In the 3 traces at the bottom the EEG, the electro-oculogram (EOG) and the electromyogram of an index finger (EMG) are recorded synchronously during REM (dreaming) sleep. The REM phases typically occur at the end of each sleep cycle (see Fig. 6-17). They cannot be assigned to any of the "classical" sleep stages, but constitute a stage of their own. Further details in text. (From U.J. JOVANOVIĆ: Methodik und Theorie der Hypnose. Stuttgart: Fischer 1986)

of **stage C** (light sleep). Once these vertex sharp waves have appeared, the sleeper can no longer differentiate small external stimuli. During the lightest sleep β spindles ("sleep spindles") and K complexes are the characteristic signs of bioelectrical brain activity. In **stage D** (intermediate sleep) rapid δ waves (3.0–3.5 Hz) are recorded. In **stage E,** the stage of deep sleep, the EEG is slow (synchronized), with a pattern composed almost entirely of maximally slowed δ waves (0.7–1.2 Hz) upon which small α waves are occasionally superimposed.

Usually a sleeper passes through another, special stage before waking up; this stage is characterized by desynchronized waves in the EEG (resembling stage B) and by *bursts of rapid eye movement*. The latter are visible to an observer through the closed lids of the sleeper and can be recorded by electro-oculographic methods (see EOG in Fig. 6-16). The rapid eye movements are so typical of this stage that it is called the **REM stage** [23, 46]. The rest of the musculature is practically atonic during REM sleep, as it is in deep sleep, except that during the REM bursts brief twitches (e.g., of the facial or finger muscles) may occur (EMG in Fig. 6-16).

The *awakening threshold* is about as high in REM sleep as in deep sleep, even though the EEG resembles that during the waking or transition-to-sleep stages – hence the synonyms **paradoxical sleep** and **desynchronized sleep** for REM sleep. Often all the other stages of sleep are lumped together as **NREM sleep** (non-REM sleep), also called *synchronized sleep* or *SW (slow-wave) sleep.* This dichotomy is further justified by the finding that dreams evidently occur mainly during REM sleep (see below).

A sleeper **passes through the successive stages of sleep several times** during a night, 3–5 times on average (Fig. 6-17). In general the maximal depth of sleep reached during each cycle decreases toward morning, so that at this time stage E disappears or is very brief. In normal sleep REM stages recur about every 1.5 hours. Their duration averages 20 min and increases in the course of the night (Fig. 6-17).

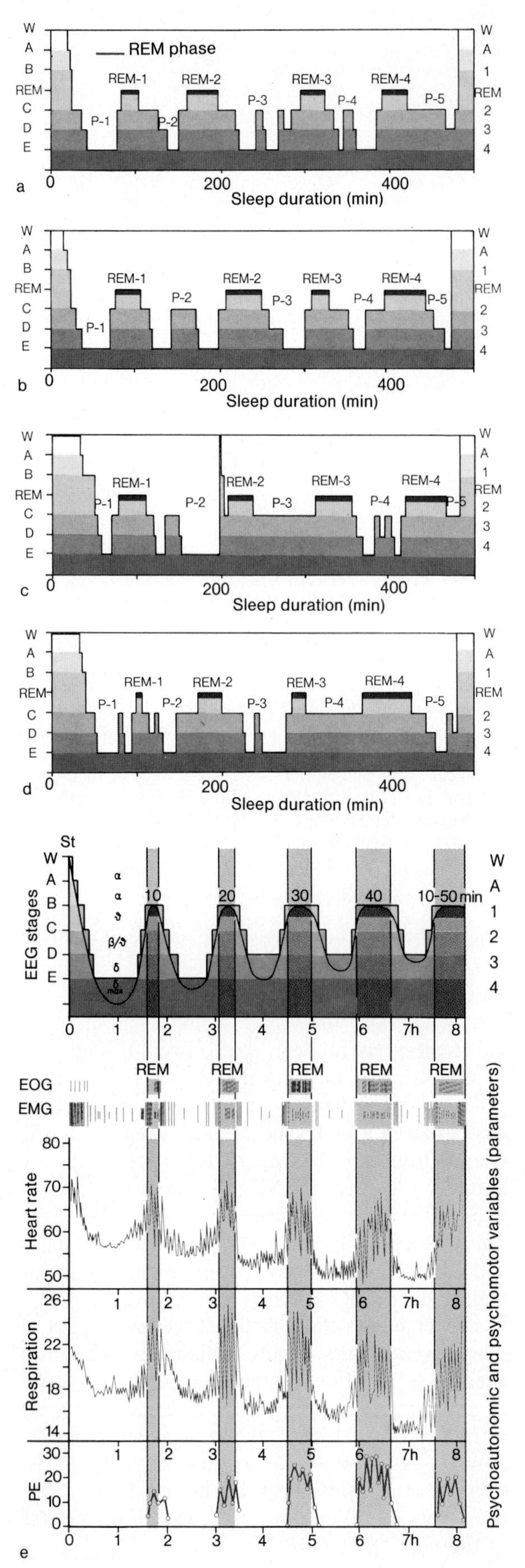

Of the many **autonomic functions with circadian periodicity** (see p. 139) some, such as body temperature, are unaffected by these rhythmic fluctuations in depth of sleep; in other cases, phasic fluctuations are superimposed on the circadian cycle (e.g., heart rate and respiration in Fig. 6-17e). This phasic modulation is especially apparent whenever the cycle passes through a REM stage. Some reactions, in fact, can be observed only during these repeated REM stages (e.g., penis erection in Fig. 6-17e).

The relative amounts of time spent awake and asleep, like the proportions of REM and NREM sleep in the total sleeping time, **change characteristically with age.** The general trend in the course of a lifetime is not only a *reduction in total sleeping time* but also a considerable *decrease in the proportion of REM sleep*, as illustrated in Fig. 6-18. The sequence and duration of the other stages of sleep (not shown in Fig. 6-18) are also distinctly different in infants and small children than in adults. The large proportion of REM sleep in very young children has suggested that these periods of elevated neuronal activity (desynchronized EEG like that during attentiveness; see, e.g., α blockade in Figs. 6-7 and 6-11) are important for the ontogenetic development of the CNS. That is, in these individuals, exposed to very few external stimuli, "dreaming" provides internal stimulation as a substitute for the external input that is lacking.

Sleep and dreams [2, 9, 20, 23, 61]. When children and adults are awakened during or immediately

◁

Fig. 6-17. Sequence of sleep stages and associated changes in certain autonomic variables during a night, in humans. **a-d** Sleeping rhythm of a healthy 28-year-old man in 4 consecutive nights, based on analysis of continuous EEG recordings. Classification as in Fig. 6-16. During each night the level of sleep passes through 4-5 cycles (P-1 to P-5); 3–5 cycles are normal. Each cycle begins with the end of the preceding REM phase and ends with the end of the next REM phase, except for P-1 (beginning when the subject falls asleep) and P-5 (ending when he wakes up). (From U.J. Jovanović: Methodik und Theorie der Hypnose. Stuttgart: Fischer 1986). **e** Diagram showing the average values of certain psychoautonomic and psychomotor parameters during the sleep cycles; sleep stages as in a-d and Fig. 6-16. For technical reasons the REM stages are shown at the level of stage B or 1, although actually they are a separate stage (see text). EOG: electro-oculogram. REM: eye movements during sleep; a few slow movements accompany falling asleep. EMG: electromyogram of the neck muscles. Activity indicated by vertical lines. Heart rate: beats per min. Respiration: breaths per min. PE: penis erection (relative strength). (From: Jovanović [20])

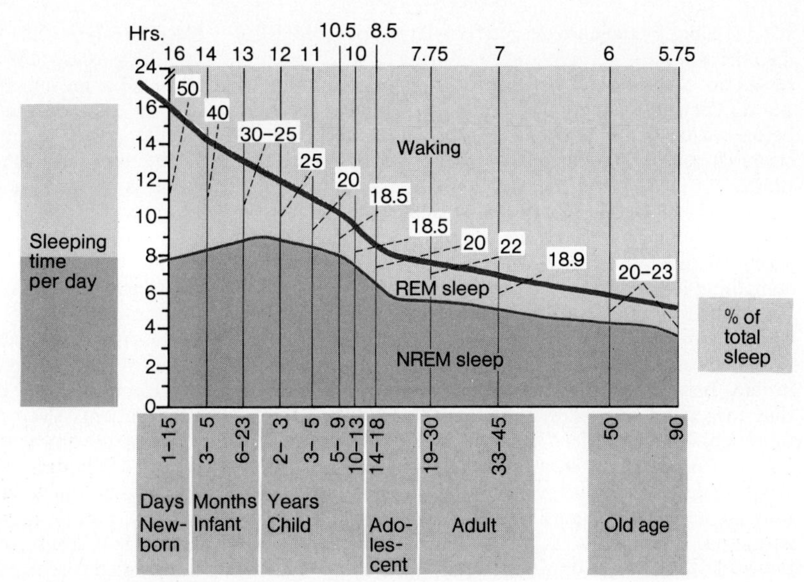

Fig. 6-18. Waking and sleeping times and the proportions of NREM and REM sleep during a human lifetime. Apart from the reduction in total sleeping time, the most notable change is the marked reduction in the duration of REM sleep during the early years.
(From ROFFWARG et al. [60])

after a REM stage they report considerably more often that they have just been dreaming than when they are awakened from NREM sleep. All who have done such experiments found a high percentage (60–90%) of **dream reports on waking from REM sleep,** whereas the percentage of dream reports on waking from NREM sleep was distinctly lower on average in the different studies and had a greater range of variation (1–74%). It therefore seems certain that dreams very often or usually occur during REM sleep. During NREM sleep there are other signs of mental activity, such as *talking, sleepwalking* and the *"night terror"* of children [27].

The **dreams reported** by people awakened from REM sleep are distinctly more lively, visual and emotional than those reported after NREM sleep. The content of NREM dreaming tends to be more abstract and "thought-like" (cognitive). The reports after REM sleep are not as conceptual and verbalization is more difficult; the dream content is "sensory" (pictures, odors, tones), the dream seems more real and has a greater power to keep the sleeper under its spell [4].
There are considerable **differences in the content of dreams** during the **first and second halves of the night.** Early dreams are more closely related to reality, having to do with events of the preceding day; the dreams in the latter part of the night are less related to everyday life. Toward morning dreams are increasingly bizarre and emotionally intense. People remember only the dreams during a REM episode after which (within 5 min) they were awakened, or the last dream before they wake up. It is because the dreams toward the end of the night are normally the most clearly recalled that dream life seems so unreal to us. The dreams earlier in the night contain quite reasonable and coherent material (references in [4]).

Dreams can be **influenced by preceding events.** For example, water deprivation (thirst) increases the duration and intensitiy of the REM phases and the dreams experienced during them. A similar effect seems to appear when one watches an exciting movie or television play before going to bed. Moreover, when one is awakened each time a REM period begins and thus **deprived of REM sleep,** the REM phases in subsequent undisturbed sleep are longer and deeper, and dreaming is more intense – a sort of "catching up" effect. In these experiments it was noted that even when people or animals were deprived of REM sleep for a long time there were **no long-lasting physical or mental consequences** of the lack of REM sleep and thus of dreams, as various authors had at first expected [2, 27, 60, 61].
External stimuli during REM sleep, especially acoustic stimuli, are occasionally incorporated into dreams. In the sleep laboratory such stimuli can be used as **time markers for the dream reports.** Their incorporation into dreams provides especially good support for the inference that the dreams actually do occur during the REM periods.
REM sleep appears to offer especially good conditions for dreaming. It is **by no means a consequence of visual dreaming,** for typical REM eye movements also occur under conditions in which there have been no preceding complex visual experiences – for example, in the unborn and, as mentioned above, the newborn (including newborn animals before the eyelids have opened).

Sleep, dream and memory. A number of devices or techniques have been advertised as enabling people to acquire knowledge effortlessly by learning while they sleep. Unfortunately, when material to be learned is presented during sleep it is **not retained** unless α activity appears in the EEG (i.e., the subject is actually awake) during or after the presentation. Similarly, of the diverse forms of brain activity during sleep, all that can be remembered is the final dream before awaking (see above) – another indication that the sleeping brain is less capable of learning than the waking brain.

On the other hand, it is correct that **sleeping facilitates the consolidation of material to be learned.** Something learned shortly before falling asleep is recalled better 8 h later than something learned in the morning. There are several possible reasons, and so far it is not clear which applies. For one thing, during the day there are many distracting events, not present at night, that can interfere with the consolidation process between learning and recall. Another possibility is that forgetting is a passive process that simply operates more slowly during sleep than in the waking brain. It is also conceivable that sleep, especially the "active" REM sleep, makes a positive contribution to consolidation, if only by removing "superfluous" items from the memory. In animal experiments, at least, there is close correlation between the REM proportion of the total sleep and the amount of material that is retained (references in [4]).

Sleep disorders [2, 20, 27]. Some forms of disturbed sleep affect those in the vicinity as well as (or more than) the sleeper. One of these is **snoring,** sound production by a sleeping (usually supine) person while breathing with mouth open and tongue sunk back into the throat. Snoring is occasionally followed by **sleep apnea** (spontaneous interruption of breathing), which may be lethal. Another such disturbance is **grinding of the teeth** during sleep; this can eventually wear the teeth down and damage the supporting tissue. The cause is unknown. Perhaps it is a phylogenetically old behavior pattern, corresponding to the teeth-sharpening movements observed in animals. Some also regard **talking in one's sleep** as a disorder. It is harmless, however, and (as mentioned above) is better considered as the manifestation of a certain kind of mental activity.

Sleepwalking (somnambulism), too, is neither a pathological symptom nor – apart from occasional accidents – is it harmful. It can happen to people at any age, but is most common in children and young people. The eyes of the sleepwalker are open, gazing straight ahead – apparently into emptiness. No attention is paid to the surroundings. The movements are stiff and awkward. Sleepwalking, as mentioned above, usually occurs when the person has been in deep sleep, and is therefore not the motor expression of a dream. It seems to be a special form of waking, in which the conversion of sensory stimuli into activity is basically intact but the consciousness is excluded.

Bed-wetting (enuresis), which happens to about 10% of all children above the age of two, practically always occurs during NREM sleep. Accordingly, when the children are awakened immediately thereafter they are confused and disoriented and can say nothing about having dreamed. The causes of bed-wetting are unknown; both physiological and psychological factors are under discussion. Another phenomenon of childhood sleep, found predominantly between the third and the eight years of life and only rarely after puberty, is **pavor nocturnus** ("night terror"). Suddenly, during sleep, the child sits up and begins to scream, appearing to stare at someone or something with eyes wide open. The face is pale and covered with sweat, and breathing is difficult. After a short time the child wakes up, recognizes its surroundings and, reassured, goes back to sleep. Adults can experience something similar with **nightmares.** A special variant of these is the **sleep paralysis** that occasionally occurs when waking up or falling asleep; for a short time it is absolutely impossible to make a movement. Often it happens when the person is fully conscious, and it tends to be more surprising than terrifying. But it can also be accompanied by startling or frightening hallucinations, such as the impression that a stone is lying or a person crouching on one's chest. As soon as the "paralyzed" person is spoken to or touched all symptoms vanish.

About 15% of all adults complain of **insomnia;** that is, they have the impression that they cannot sleep, or not long enough. This subjective sleep deficiency does not necessarily mean that the affected person objectively sleeps too little and suffers impaired health as a result of lack of sleep. In sleep laboratories it has been shown that such patients sleep more than they realize. Moreover, in experiments on the **effects of sleep deprivation** it has turned out that although, as would be expected, transient physical and psychological changes occur when sleep is prevented entirely, partial sleep deprivation – for example, only five and a half hours of sleep per night for many weeks – causes slight or no detectable change in the performance and well-being of the subject. In other words, as long as the insomnia does not involve distinct shortening of total sleep duration for a long period, our present knowledge suggests that the condition does not necessarily represent a threat to health. The **pharmacological treatment of insomnia** should therefore be appropriately **restrained.**

Waking/sleeping behavior of animals. Like humans, all the other **mammals** exhibit a form of sleeping behavior, in which NREM stages can be clearly distinguished from REM stages. **Phylogenetically,** *REM sleep is a relatively recent development.* Fish and reptiles have no REM sleep. In birds the phases of REM sleep are very brief (seconds), amounting to less than 1% of the total sleeping time. By contrast, all mammals spend a considerable fraction of their sleeping time in REM sleep. It is striking that hunting species (human, cat, dog) have distinctly more REM sleep (about 20% of the total on the average) than those that are hunted (rabbits and ruminants average 5–10%). The late appearance of REM sleep in phylogeny, however, is not recapitulated in **ontogeny.** On the contrary, like humans (cf. Fig. 6-18) other newborn mammals spend a larger proportion of their total sleeping time in REM sleep than they do later in life. Thus whereas REM sleep is a feature only of highly developed brains it may, as mentioned with regard to Fig. 6-18, be of (still unknown) significance to the ontogenetic development of these brains.

Mechanisms of Waking and Sleeping

In the preceding section the sleeping/waking rhythm was presented as one aspect of circadian periodicity. Sleep is also, as we have seen in this section, a highly structured phenomenon in itself, with two main components – NREM and REM sleep – that alternate rhythmically several times in the course of a night (Figs. 6-16, 6-17). A theory of sleeping and waking, then, must be based on (or evolve from) a theory of circadian periodicity, and it should provide satisfactory answers to at least the following questions about sleep: (i) Why must we sleep? (ii) How does sleep begin? (iii) Why and how does it end? (iv)

What mechanisms are responsible for the various stages of sleep and for the periodic transition from one stage to another?
The transition from waking to sleeping could occur in two ways. First, the mechanisms that underlie the waking state could gradually become "fatigued". From this point of view, sleep would be a passive event, the consequence of a decrease in wakefulness. Alternatively, the mechanisms responsible for waking could be actively inhibited. In this case sleep-promoting neural mechanisms would build up while one is awake and, eventually, actively terminate the waking state. Sleep research in this century has intensively pursued both lines of thought, and until recently the prevailing opinion was that sleep is initiated passively; but no final decision is yet in view. The current state of research is sketched briefly in the following paragraphs.

Deafferentation theory of sleep. In the late 1930's F. BREMER observed that the EEG of a cat brain separated from the medulla (*encephale isolé* = isolated brain; Fig. 6-19A, top) and allowed to recover from the shock of the operation exhibited a rhythmic alternation between the typical synchronized sleeping and desynchronized waking patterns. During the waking EEG the pupils were dilated and the eyes followed moving objects; during the sleeping EEG the pupils were constricted. If the cut was higher, at the level of the corpora quadrigemina (*cerveau isolé* = isolated forebrain; Fig. 6-19A, bottom), so that all sensory stimuli except sight and smell were eliminated, only a synchronized sleeping EEG was recorded. These findings supported the old notion that the activity of the CNS is induced and controlled primarily by sensory stimuli (simple reflex concept). BREMER concluded that the waking state requires at least some minimal level of cortical activity, maintained by sensory input, whereas sleep is fundamentally a condition induced and maintained by a reduction or diminished effectiveness of sensory input, a kind of **deafferentation.** His experiments came to be regarded as the crucial evidence for the notion that sleep induction is **basically a passive phenomenon** (see above).

From its inception, the deafferentation theory faced opposition. The objection was raised that in time the chronic cerveau isolé preparation does develop a sleeping/waking rhythm. In humans, furthermore, sensory deprivation (in

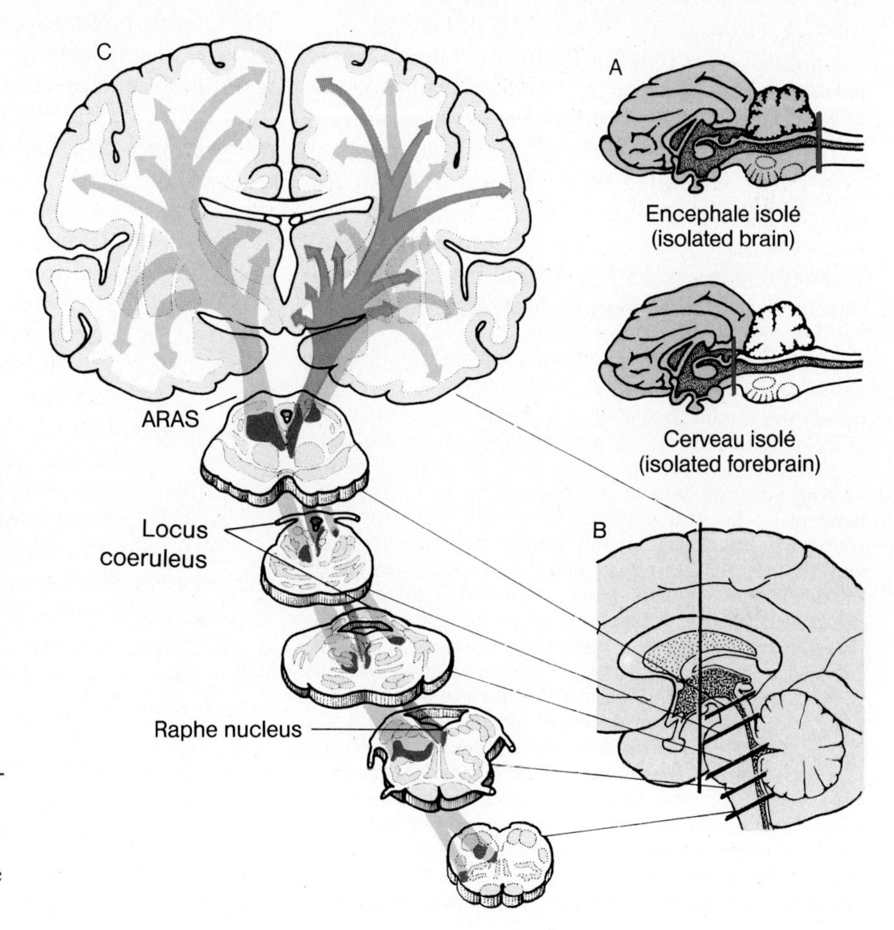

Fig. 6-19. Routes and cerebral projections of 3 major (nonspecific) inputs from the brainstem. **A** Level of section to produce an encephale isolé (isolated brain) and cerveau isolé (isolated forebrain). **B** Levels of the brainstem cross sections shown in **C** and of the frontal section through the hemispheres. In these sections the origin and course of the ascending reticular activating system (ARAS) are shown on the *left*, and the position of the raphe nucleus and locus coeruleus and the projections of the fibers originating there are shown on the *right*. (Based on [37])

sleeping chambers where all auditory, visual and proprioceptive stimuli are completely excluded) causes a progressive decrease in the duration of sleep during the period of isolation, and patients with traumatic quadriplegia also sleep for varying amounts of time. Finally, the concept that descending cortical tone causes wakefulness also seems incorrect, because a sleeping/waking rhythm is also found in *organisms without the tel- and diencephalon*, such as anencephalic human infants and chronically decerebrate mammals.

Reticular theory of waking and sleeping. The reticular formation of the brainstem comprises a large number of diffusely arranged neurons, the axons of which extend to almost all regions of the cerebrum except the neocortex (Fig. 6-19C, left half of brain). Its role in waking/sleeping behavior was investigated in the late 1940's by G. MORUZZI and H. W. MAGOUN. They found that sleeping cats could be immediately awakened **(arousal)** by high-frequency electrical stimulation of the reticular formation. Conversely, lesions in this region produced permanent (comalike) sleep, whereas when only the sensory tracts passing through the brainstem were cut, no such effect resulted. These discoveries led to a reinterpretation of BREMER's experiments. The reticular formation was regarded as having a unitary function, to maintain the level of excitation necessary for the waking state by sending out an ascending stream of activating impulses. This function is expressed by the term *ascending reticular activating system*, abbreviated **ARAS.** This system remains intact in the encephale isolé preparation but is separated from the forebrain in the cerveau isolé preparation. Hence waking results from the activity of the ARAS, and sleep ensues when the activity of the ARAS declines, either passively or due to extraneous influences.

The ascending pathways belonging to the ARAS are called **nonspecific projections** to distinguish them from the classical sensory specific projections. *Relatively large fluctuations* in the amount of ascending reticular activation are thought to be responsible for the transition from sleeping to the waking state and back. These fluctuations in turn are dependent on the sensory input to the reticular formation (by way of collaterals of the specific pathways on their way through the brainstem; here the theory is related to the deafferentation theory) and on the activity of descending pathways from cortex and subcortical structures, so that there is a reciprocal connection between brain and brainstem. During the waking phase *smaller fluctuations* in ARAS activity are thought to be responsible for subtle behavioral changes (e.g., degree of attentiveness).

The notion that the reticular formation is the crucial arousal center is contradicted by a number of findings. First, electrical stimulation of the reticular formation can elicit sleeping reactions as well as arousal, depending on the site and frequency of the stimulus and on the initial state of the animal. It would follow that both a sleeping and a waking center are present; it appears that the more caudal parts of the reticular formation have an inhibitory influence on the rostral parts. Second, the neuronal activity of the reticular formation during sleep, especially REM sleep, is not less than in the waking state (as the reticular theory postulates) but is only organized differently. Third, as mentioned above, even the cerveau isolé, which lacks a reticular formation, exhibits a sleeping/waking rhythm. Responsibility for this rhythm seems to reside mainly in diencephalic structures (parts of the medial thalamus and the anterior hypothalamus). The reticular formation is therefore not solely responsible for waking and sleeping.

Serotonergic theory of sleep. In the upper part of the brainstem are two regions, the **raphe nuclei** and the **locus coeruleus**, the neurons of which project as extensively as those of the reticular formation, reaching large parts of the CNS (Fig. 6-19C, right). The transmitter of the raphe neurons is **serotonin (5-HT),** and that of the coeruleus neurons is **noradrenalin** (for biochemistry see p. 46). In the late 1960's a number of observations led M. JOUVET [51] to the conclusion that these two neuron systems, the raphe nuclei in particular, play a fundamental role in inducing sleep. Destruction of the raphe nuclei of the cat causes total insomnia for several days; during the following few weeks, sleep behavior becomes normal again. Partial loss of sleep can also be produced by blocking the synthesis of 5-HT (with p-chlorophenylalanine). This insomnia can be corrected by administering 5-hydroxytryptophan, the precursor of serotonin (the latter does not cross the blood-brain barrier). Bilateral destruction of the loci coerulei completely abolishes REM sleep but has no effect on NREM sleep. If the stores of serotonin and noradrenalin are exhausted simultaneously by the administration of reserpine, insomnia results, as would be expected. But in this case the subsequent administration of 5-hydroxytryptophan restores only NREM sleep, not REM sleep.

It was concluded from these findings that the **release of serotonin** causes active inhibition of the arousal systems and hence **induces sleep,** NREM sleep always appearing first. Later there is a transition to REM sleep, which can occur only with the participation of the locus coeruleus (its activity is responsible for the general muscular atonia and the rapid eye movements). In parallel with these effects, activity of the locus coeruleus inhibits the activity of the raphe nuclei and thereby initiates awakening.

Unfortunately, this theory is no longer tenable in its original form. There is now evidence that the **raphe neurons are most active**, releasing the most serotonin, **in arousal** rather than in sleep. Furthermore, REM activation seems to be due less to the neurons of the nucleus coeruleus than to those of the more diffusely distributed **nucleus subcoeruleus**. But it does not follow that serotonin plays no role in sleep. Indeed, recent experiments (which will not be described here) indicate that serotonin serves both as a neurotransmitter in the process of arousal and as a **"sleep hormone"** while one is awake, promoting the synthesis or release of "sleep substances" or "sleep factors" that in turn induce sleep [5, 14].

Endogenous sleep factors. It is an obvious fact that when people have been awake for a long time, they feel an irresistible need to sleep. Consequently, at a very early stage research was directed toward the idea that tiredness and sleep are caused primarily by the periodic accumulation, depletion or specific production of metabolites (sleep factors) that circulate in the blood; during sleep, the waking concentrations of these substances would be restored by elimination or metabolic processes. In the last two decades this idea has been revived by developments in neurochemistry [19], especially with regard to the neuropeptides. Attempts have been made to detect such factors, either after a period of sleep deprivation or during sleep. The former approach is based on the expectation that **sleep factor(s)** would **accumulate during the waking state** until their concentration becomes high enough to induce sleep; the latter postulates that **sleep-promoting substances are produced or released during sleep.**
Both approaches can claim some experimental success. With the first, for example, a small glucopeptide **(Factor S)** has been isolated from the urine or cerebrospinal fluid of humans and animals, which induces NREM sleep when it is injected into other animals. A **REM-sleep factor** also seems to exist. With the second approach, a nonapeptide was found (and has since been synthesized) that induces deep sleep (**DSIP:** delta sleep inducing peptide). But for neither these nor a number of other "sleep substances" that have been found in both kinds of experiment is it known what role they play in the physiological control of sleep [5, 14, 59]. Moreover, these peptides often act as sleep inducers only in certain species, and sleep can also be promoted by many other substances.

Biological functions of sleep. There is still no satisfactory answer to the question of why we must sleep. The various suggestions made so far, which are not necessarily mutually exclusive, remain unproved. In any case, the most popular idea of the role of sleep – that it **serves for recovery** – has very little experimental support (for instance, severe physical exertion causes one to fall asleep more rapidly but does not change the duration of sleep). It is also unclear why some people manage with extremely little sleep while others must sleep for a long time in order to feel rested. Finally, there is no explanation for the existence of two such different sleep stages as REM and NREM sleep, or for their repeated alternation during a night (see above).

6.4 Neurophysiological Correlates of Consciousness and Speech

The most impressive change in the state of our bodies in everyday experience is the return of **consciousness** when we awaken from sleep (or from anesthesia, coma or severe concussion). This state of consciousness with all its shadings, which can only be experienced introspectively and which is the essential feature of our existence, has been the object of many attempts at interpretation by both physiologists and psychologists, some of them very contradictory and still in flux [11, 15, 31, 36, 41, 62]. The physiologist can contribute to this discussion by establishing the boundary conditions, from the *viewpoint of the natural sciences,* that determine whether consciousness is possible or not.

Phylogeny of consciousness. Whereas it can hardly be doubted that higher vertebrates (birds, mammals) with a *highly differentiated nervous system* exhibit one or several characteristics of conscious behavior, animals with *very simple nervous systems* display such behavior patterns, if at all, only in isolated instances and in a sketchy form. Consciousness is thus *bound to complex neuronal structures* and **cannot exist apart from these structures.** But as the previous considerations may already have made clear, it is impossible to draw a sharp dividing line between animals with consciousness and those without. Rather, consciousness seems to develop roughly in parallel with the phylogenetic development of the nervous system. In other words, the animal kingdom comprises **many gradations and extremely varied forms of consciousness,** the human consciousness without doubt being by far the most differentiated form.
This view – that **consciousness presupposes a correspondingly differentiated nervous system** – suggests that during phylogeny consciousness of one form or another always evolves when simpler forms of neuronal activity (e.g., reflexes) no longer suffice to direct and control the organism. If this is so, the emergence of consciousness is an *important step in evolution,* absolutely required for the optimal adaptation of higher organisms to their environment [8, 31].

Functional and Structural Prerequisites for Consciousness; Role of the Hemispheres

As far as *human consciousness* is concerned, only very simple and on the whole *entirely inadequate*

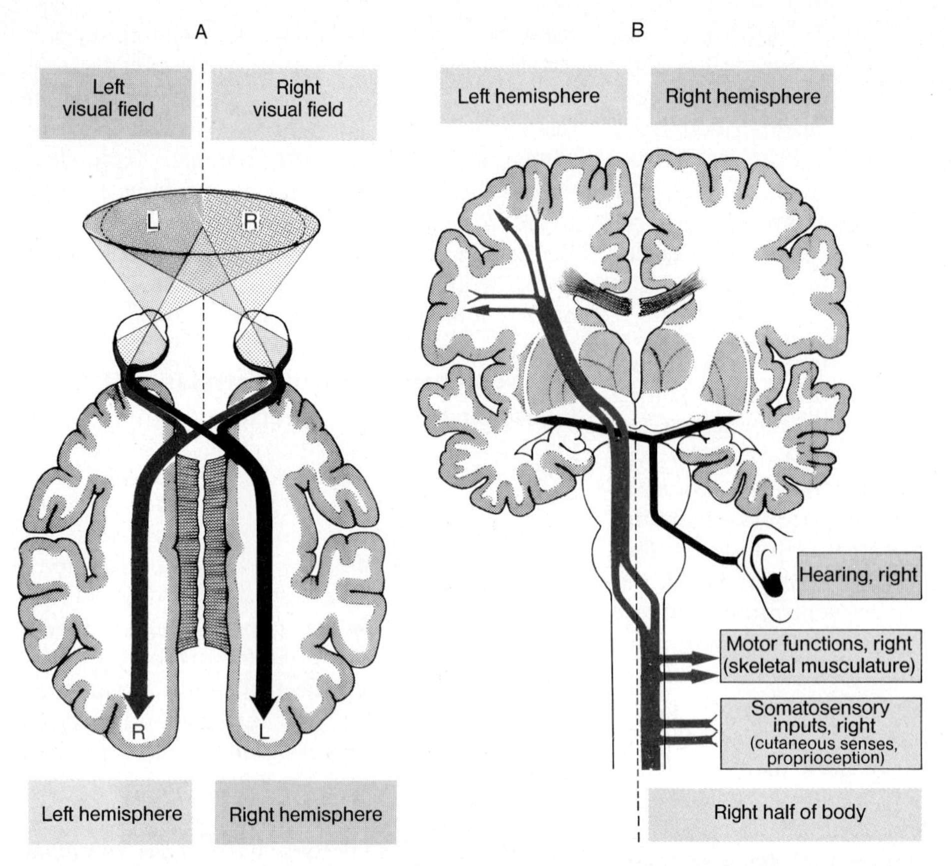

Fig. 6-20. Somatosensory, motor, visual and auditory connections in split-brain patients. **A** View from above, **B** frontal view. The left hemisphere has somatosensory (afferent) and motor (efferent) connections only to the right half of the body and the right hemisphere only to the left half. The right field of view (of each eye!) projects to the visual cortex of the left hemisphere, and vice versa. By contrast, each ear projects to the auditory cortex of both hemispheres, even in split-brain patients

statements can be made about the **functional prerequisites,** that is, the associated neuronal activity. Consciousness evidently requires an **intermediate activity level** in the central nervous structures involved, as represented, for example, by a desynchronized waking EEG. Too little neuronal activity, as in anesthesia or coma, is incompatible with consciousness, and so is excessive neuronal activity like that in an epileptic seizure (EEG with spikes and waves; cf. Fig. 6-13) or under electroshock. It also seems certain that consciousness is possible only in the **interplay of cortical and subcortical structures;** each of these structures is incapable of creating consciousness by itself. The ascending reticular activating system (ARAS), as would be expected in view of its role in sleeping/waking behavior (p. 146), probably occupies a key position in this regard [8, 15].

Important insights into the **structural prerequisites** of consciousness have recently been provided by studies of patients in whom the corpus callosum and anterior commissure have been surgically transected in order to ameliorate otherwise uncontrollable epileptic seizures, or at least to restrict them to one half of the brain. The transection of the *commissural fibers* in these **split-brain patients** breaks all connections between the two cerebral hemispheres, leaving each to its own devices, so to speak. Because many ascending and descending pathways cross the midline, the postoperative situation is as follows (Fig. 6-20). The left half of the patient's cerebrum has the motor and somatosensory responsibility for the right side of the body, and the right half of the cerebrum is responsible for the left side. Due to the special form of decussation of the optic nerves in the chiasm, the right half of the visual field projects to the left hemisphere and the left half, to the right. The central auditory pathway is partly crossed and partly uncrossed, so that each hemisphere receives input from both the ipsilateral and the contralateral ear. (The corpus callosum is no longer completely transected in these operations, since partial transection has been found to serve the purpose as well.)

Split-brain patients are **inconspicuous in everyday**

life, and their intellect appears unchanged. At most one can detect a reduction in spontaneous activity on the left side of the body (of right-handed people) and an absence or attenuation of responses to stimuli (e.g., pushing) on that side. With psychological tests, however, R. Sperry and his colleagues revealed **considerable differences in the operation** of the two halves of the brain, the existence of which is also documented by many other clinical and experimental findings [11, 15, 16, 17, 39, 62].

With the experimental set-up shown in Fig. 6-21 separate visual signals (flashes of light, objects, writing) can be presented to the two halves of the visual field. In addition, the right or left hand can be used for tactile exploration or for writing without visual control. Visual and tactile sensory stimuli on the right are conveyed *only to the left half of the brain* (left hemisphere) in this situation, and vice versa. The most important results of these experiments are as follows.

When an object (e.g., a key or pencil) is projected into the **right half of the visual field,** the split-brain patient can *name* it or *pick it out* from other objects with the *right hand*. When words are projected into this half of the visual field he can *read* them aloud, *write them down* and again pick out the appropriate object with the right hand. When an object is placed in his *right hand* the results are consistent with the above; the patient can *name* the object and *write* its name down. In other words, the patient in these situations does not differ from a normal experimental subject.

When an object is projected into the **left half of the visual field** the split-brain patient **cannot name it.** But he is able to pick it out from other objects with the *left hand* when he is asked to do so. Even then, however, after a successful search, he cannot name the object, nor can he name it when it is placed in his **left hand.** He is unable to read aloud words projected into the left half of the visual field. But if the word is the name of an everyday object he can select the object with his left hand (Fig. 6-21). Again, even after having successfully located it, he cannot name it. In this situation, then, the patient can carry out certain tasks but he cannot express what he is doing verbally or in writing even on request.

The most important **conclusion** from these results is the following. With regard to *language and speech* the performance of the **left hemisphere alone** is indistinguishable from that of the two coupled hemispheres, either from the subjective viewpoint of the patient or by the objective observable behavior. Therefore it (or parts of it, see below) is to be regarded as the decisive neuronal substrate for language and speech *in the normal brains as well* [11, 17, 39]. The **right hemisphere alone** cannot express itself verbally or in writing, but what it can achieve is remarkable. For example, it is capable of visual and tactile form recognition, abstraction and a degree of speech comprehension (oral commands are carried out and simple words read: cf. Fig. 6-21). Some patients can even write or copy simple short words. (It remains an open question whether this understanding of speech was present preoperatively or was learned postoperatively). In some respects, as in the identification of faces (Fig. 6-22) and in regard to spatial conceptualization and certain musical tasks, the right hemisphere actually seems superior to the left. (The significance of these findings with respect to the mind-body problem, in particular the philosophical positions of monistic identity theories and dualistic interac-

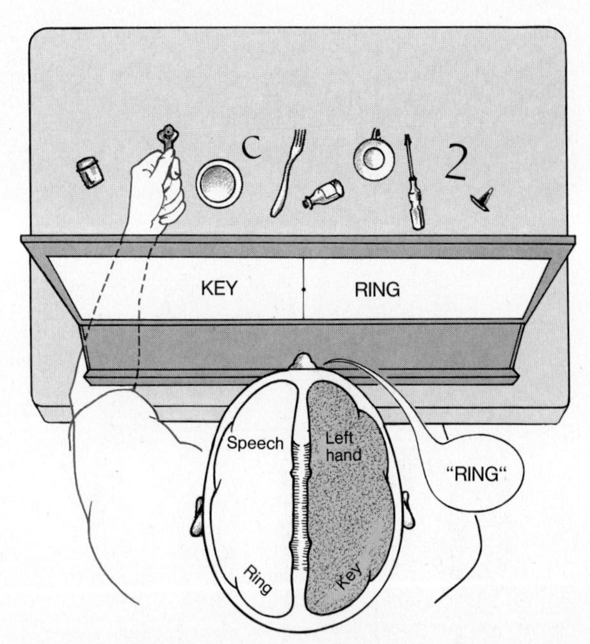

Fig. 6-21. Behavior of a split-brain patient during a test by Roger Sperry and his coworkers. The patient sits in front of an opaque milk-glass screen onto which objects or written words can be projected in the left, right or both halves of the visual field. The patient is told to fixate a point in the middle of the screen; the visual stimuli are presented briefly (0.1s) so that a change in gaze direction., which would bring the stimulus into the other visual field, is prevented. In the test illustrated the patient reports (by way of his left, speaking hemisphere) that he has read the word RING in the right field of view. He denies having seen the word KEY in the left field, and he cannot name any object placed in his left hand. But he can use his left hand to select the correct object, though he says he has no knowledge of the object. If asked to name the object he has selected, the speaking hemisphere calls it "RING." (Modified from SPERRY in [38])

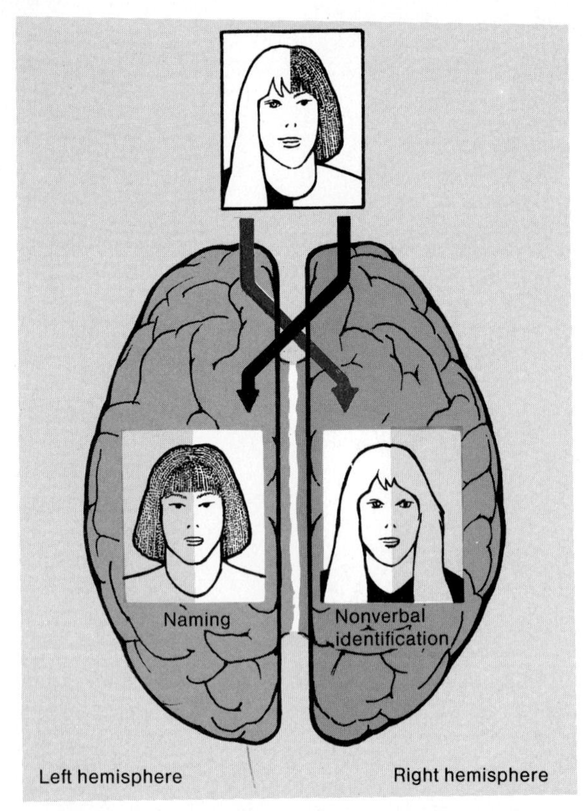

Fig. 6-22. The identification of faces by the left and right hemispheres of a split-brain patient. When the arrangement of Fig. 6-21 is used to present "composite portraits" as visual stimuli, each hemisphere supplements the half-face it sees to form a complete face, about which the other hemisphere knows nothing. When verbal identification of the face is required, as expected the left hemisphere dominates. In all other, nonverbal tests the right hemisphere is far superior to the left. Such tests include operations with complex geometrical figures that cannot be described verbally. (Modified from SPERRY et al. in [38])

tionism, is discussed extensively by us elsewhere [4]).

It should be noted that there is normally a continuous exchange of information between the right and left hemispheres, in which the left hemisphere seems to serve mainly as a **"cause interpreter"**. That is, constellations of excitation from all parts of the neocortex and subcortical regions are examined here to determine what has caused them, with the goal of *reducing cognitive dissonance*. In other words, when there is a mismatch between one's visible motor or invisible emotional or autonomic reactions and one's cognitive expectations, the left hemisphere constructs theories about the causes of these reactions until *consonance* is achieved; the beliefs or attitudes on which expectation was based are altered or reorganized so that there are no contradictions with the actual behavior [16].

Hemispheric dysfunctions. In clinical observations, patients with lesions of the *right* hemisphere are often found to be in emotionally indifferent or euphorically disinhibited states, whereas those with *left*-hemisphere lesions exhibit *"catastrophe reactions"* with deep depression, even when speech functions are not affected (see below). It has been shown neurophysiologically that a lesion on one side produces overexcitation of the other side, by disinhibition. Emotional expression is impaired by anterior cortical lesions, whereas posterior lesions alter emotional recognition and discrimination. Patients with a right parietal lesion often deny the existence and consequences of the disease and/or affective components **(sensory and emotional neglect)**, and their emotional expression is either poor or inappropriately disinhibited. In **depressive disorders** there is abnormally high activity in the right frontal EEG, and in **manias** the elevated activity is in the left frontal region [4].

Neurophysiological Aspects of Language and Speech

Lateralization of language and speech. Most of our knowledge about the neurophysiology of language and speech is based on *clinical observations*. So far the greatest amount of information has been derived from studies in which speech disturbances could be correlated with the post-mortem neuropathological determination of the underlying brain damage. But brain surgery, especially in combination with electrical stimulation of the exposed brain of a waking patient, and other methods of study have made valuable contributions. For example, the therapeutic transection of commissural fibers (split-brain operation; see above) has shown that as a rule only the **left hemisphere** contains the regions necessary for language and speech. This had already been inferred from considerably older clinical-neuropathological findings, and it was for this reason that the left hemisphere was called the **dominant hemisphere.** The dominance of the left hemisphere over the right was assumed to extend to other functions, because motor skills are also distinctly lateralized, most people being *right-handed*. It was concluded further that the cortical speech and language areas of *left-handed* people would as a rule be found on the right.

Neither generalization is correct. It is true that the speech and language areas of right-handers are practically always on the left, but some left-handers also have them on the left, while in others they are on the right or bilateral [17, 29, 34, 39, 44]. Moreover, because it is becoming ever clearer (mainly through the studies of split-brain patients) that in some respects the right hemisphere is superior to the left, it is more appropriate to speak of a *mutually complementary* **specialization of the two hemispheres** in which the left as a rule is **language-dominant.**

Speech and language areas. BROCA, over a hundred years ago, was the first to observe that lesions of the lower part of the third frontal gyrus on the left caused a *failure of speech* (aphasia) such that although speech is still understood

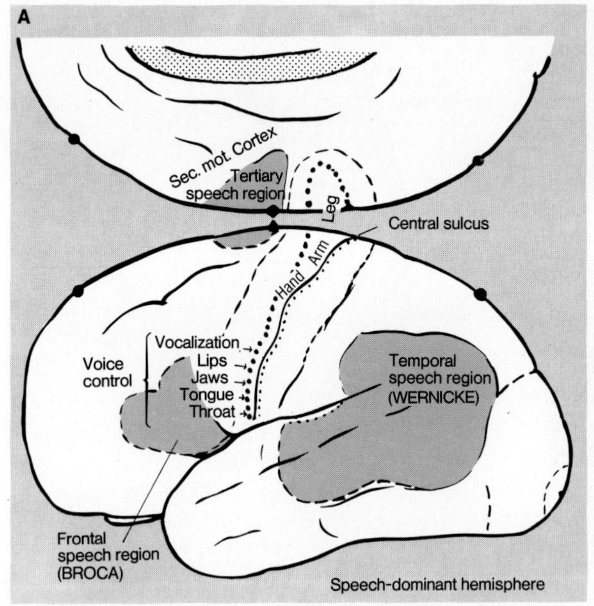

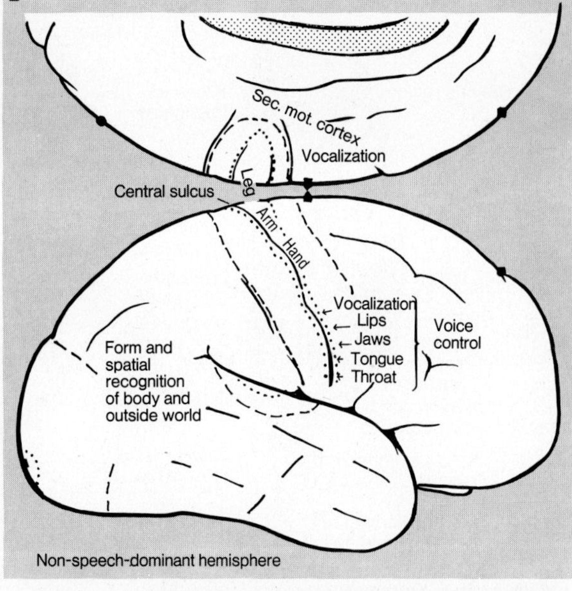

Fig. 6-23. Language and speech areas *(red)* in the language-dominant *(left)* hemisphere **(A)** and the corresponding areas of the non-language-dominant *(right)* hemisphere **(B)**, as established by electrical stimulation of the exposed cortex of adult patients by PENFIELD and his coworkers. Control of the vocal muscles is localized bilaterally in the precentral gyri. Unlike the rest of the body, each half of the face is represented bilaterally. The temporal language region is probably less extensive than shown in A, particularly in the temporal lobe. Wernicke's and Broca's regions are connected by the arcuate fasciculus (see Fig. 6-24). (Modified from PENFIELD and ROBERTS [29])

the patients say hardly anything spontaneously. On command, hesitantly and with great effort, they can produce short sentences, reduced to the most essential nouns, verbs and adjectives (telegraphic speech). This form of aphasia is called **motor aphasia,** and the associated area of the brain is called **Broca's speech region.** As Fig. 6-23A shows, this area is immediately in front of the parts of the motor cortex that control the muscles of the face, jaws, tongue, palate and throat – the muscles necessary for *articulation.* But the motor aphasia that results from damage to *Broca's region* is not ascribable to paralysis of these muscles. Even direct damage to the facial region of the precentral gyrus (Fig. 6-23A, B; cf. Fig. 5-26) causes only slight contralateral deficits, because the facial musculature is represented bilaterally in the cortex and a unilateral deficit can be compensated by the opposite side.

Soon after BROCA'S discovery WERNICKE described another type of aphasia, in which the *understanding of language* is severely impaired but the spontaneous speaking by the patient is fluent, though distorted. This **sensory aphasia** is strikingly well correlated with damage to the temporal lobes, especially in the posterior part of the first temporal gyrus, in the immediate vicinity of the auditory cortex (**Wernicke's speech region,** Fig. 6-23A).

The speech regions described by BROCA and WERNICKE were approximately confirmed by the experiments of PENFIELD and his coworkers, in which the exposed cortex was stimulated (Fig. 6-23). Electrical stimulation of these areas and of a third area overlapping roughly with the secondary motor area (MII) induces aphasia for the duration of stimulation. Words or sentences are never elicited by stimulation of these regions. This effect is distinct from that obtained by stimulation of the lateral precentral gyrus (dots in Fig. 6-23), in which stimulation on either side elicits *vocalization* (as a rule, vocal exclamations) [28, 29]. These findings also imply that the *language functions are lateralized to one hemisphere* whereas the cortical areas responsible for articulation, the execution of speech, are bilateral (Fig. 6-23A, B). In fact, the "prosodic" aspects of speech (accentuation, intonation) seem to depend primarily on processes in the right hemisphere.

Accordingly, neurosurgical observations show that unilateral **removal of the speech-related parts of the precentral gyrus** never produces aphasia but rather, as just mentioned, often causes only astonishingly slight disturbances of speech. By contrast, when the **speech regions are removed** the result is aphasia of varying duration. The aphasic disturbance following removal of the third speech region (overlapping with MII) persists for some weeks. Removal of Broca's area brings about a more long-lasting aphasia, though even in an adult there is an improvement after

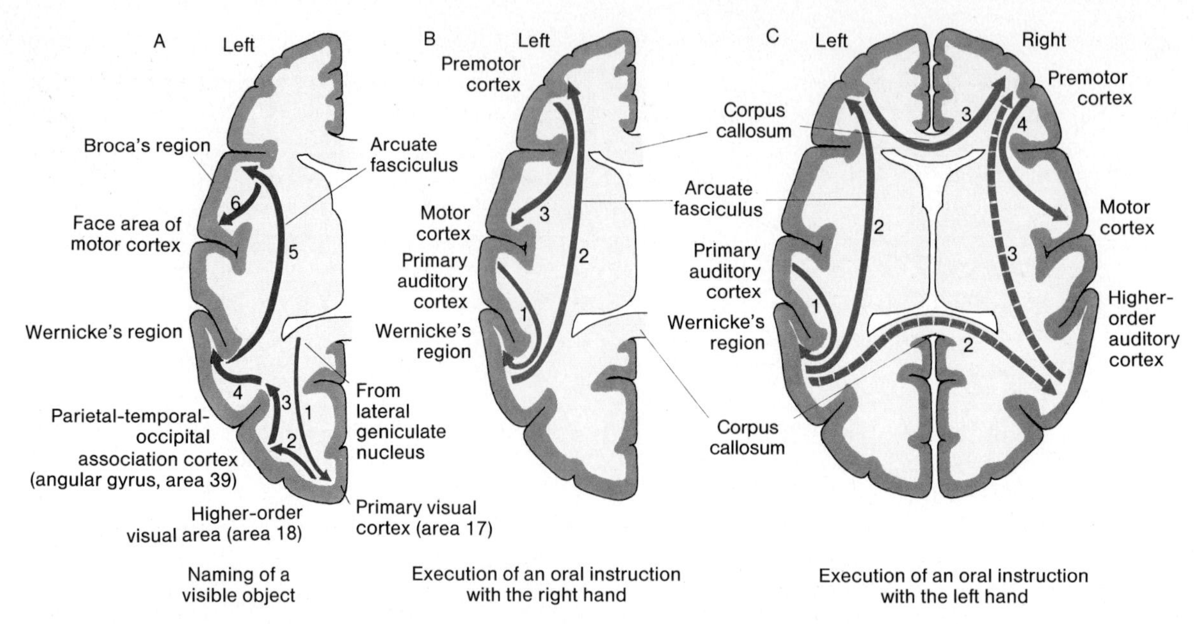

Fig. 6-24 A–C. Steps in neuronal information processing underlying a vocal response to visual or auditory instructions, according to the models of Wernicke and Geschwind (see text). Schematic horizontal sections through a human brain at the level of the corpus callosum. **A** Sequence of information processing *(arrows 1-6)* in visual identification and naming of an object. **B** Sequence involved in responding to an oral command to lift the *right* hand. **C** Sequence involved in responding to an oral command to lift the *left* hand. Transmission from the premotor area of the left cortex to that on the right is by way of the corpus callosum *(arrow 3)*. There may be an additional transcallosal connection between Wernicke's region on the left and the higher auditory cortex on the right, from which the information is conducted to the premotor cortex *(dashed arrows 2 and 3)*. If the command had been presented visually, the "auditory" *arrow 1* in B and C would be replaced by *arrows 1–4* from A. (Modified from MAYEUS and KANDEL in [21])

months or years. Removal of the temporal speech region, however, produces permanent aphasia. The *temporal speech region,* viewed in this light, is the *primary* region [15, 17, 28, 29].

Wernicke-Geschwind model of language. WERNICKE's concepts of the way the various cortical areas in the dominant hemisphere work together, later made more precise by GESCHWIND (see [4, 17, 21]), provide a framework within which important correlations can be established between the different forms of aphasia observed by clinicians and psychologists and the location of the associated neural deficits in the brain. For instance, Fig. 6-24A illustrates the steps in neuronal information processing by which one names an object that is seen. The **visual information** is first transmitted from the retina through the visual pathway (Fig. 11-27, p. 258) to the primary visual cortex (area 17; cf. Fig. 6-4), then to higher visual areas (area 18) and finally to the adjacent association cortex (area 39; cf. Figs. 6-2 and 6-4), where **shape recognition** occurs. The shape information is then transferred to the Wernicke region (area 22) for (receptive) **word-finding**. From there it is conducted through the *arcuate fasciculus* to Broca's region, where the (expressive) **forming of speech** is accomplished. In the final step, the information about the form of the words to be spoken is used for **articulation**, having been transferred to the areas of the motor cortex responsible for vocalization. If the subject had received an acoustic signal requiring a verbal response, the route of information flow would be comparable, except that Wernicke's region would be activated by way of the auditory rather than the visual centers (cf. Fig. 6-24B,C). In the light of this model, the language disorders associated with **sensory** and **motor aphasia** described above are immediately comprehensible. In the former case, when receptive word-finding in Wernicke's region fails, the information required for speech to be formulated is unavailable. And with a lesion in Broca's area the ability to formulate speech is lost. Interruption of the arcuate fasciculus produces **conduction aphasia,** which resembles sensory aphasia. If both Broca's and Wernicke's areas are damaged (both are in the region supplied by the medial cerebral artery) the result is **global aphasia,** in which expressive as well as receptive functions are severely impaired. Finally, disturbances in the temporal-parietal association cortex can cause **amnesic aphasia,** in which disturbances of *word-finding ability* predominate. The patient replaces the word he is looking for with a filler word ("the whatsit") or by a more general category ("bird" instead of pigeon) or by circumlocution ("to write with" instead of pencil). For a more detailed description of the symptomatology of the various aphasias and for more recent attempts to characterize aphasias more precisely and to classify them, the reader is referred to the literature [30, 34, 38].

Disturbances of language-related abilities – *reading, writing* and *arithmetic* – appear as side effects of aphasia; sometimes they are the chief symptoms, in which case they are called **alexia, agraphia,** and **acalculia,** respectively. Whereas alexia is more in the category of sensory aphasia, agraphia indicates a disturbance of expressive speech function.

Aphasia as a consequence of gradual (e.g., arteriosclerosis) or sudden (e.g., stroke; p. 120) damage to the speech and language areas **isolates the patient from his social environment.** He cannot communicate with other people as he once could, and they in turn are usually not able to detect (especially with aphasia of slow onset) that the speech difficulty is not the result of altered personality structure but rather is due to damage in the parts of the brain responsible for language and speech. In other words, many aphasics are regarded by people around them as *behaviorally disturbed or schizophrenic.* Particularly in the sensory aphasias a layman cannot readily discern that the obvious failure to understand speech, together with the uninhibited but more or less incoherent spontaneous speech, is not evidence of a disturbed mind. These patients suffer doubly and triply: from their aphasia, from the false interpretation of the nature of their illness, and from the lack (or incorrectness) of treatment.

Ontogenetic aspects. Once a child has learned to speak, destruction of the speech region in the left hemisphere causes complete aphasia. But after about a year the child begins to speak again. Now language and speech are represented in the corresponding regions of the right hemisphere (cf. Fig. 6-23). This **transfer of language dominance** from the left hemisphere to the right is possible only up to the tenth year of life, at the latest [38]. The original ability to establish the language center in either hemisphere is lost at this age, probably for two reasons. First, the development of the *basic neuronal patterns* necessary for language (which are also employed for later learning of a second language) is no longer possible. Second, the corresponding regions of the *non-language-dominant hemisphere* at this time have already taken on other tasks, in particular that of spatial orientation and consciousness of the dimension of the body itself and its relationship to the surroundings (Fig. 6-23B). However, the plasticity of the brain exacts a price: patients whose right hemisphere has had to take over the task of language and speech in addition to the nonverbal functions just cited, because the left hemisphere was damaged in childhood, all have lower general intelligence and poorer language abilities than a comparable sample of normal people [38].

Language and action. The close link between language and motor actions is also made evident by the Wernicke-Geschwind model. For example, Fig. 6-24B shows the steps in neuronal information processing when a person is instructed verbally to lift the *right* hand. After the **verbal command has been received** by the auditory centers, the information is passed on to Wernicke's region for **interpretation** and thence via the arcuate fasciculus to the left associative premotor cortex, where a **design for the action** is worked out. Finally, the design is sent to the arm region of the left primary motor cortex for **execution of the movement**.

An entirely comparable sequence occurs when the instruction is to lift the *left* hand (Fig. 6-24C). Here, though, it is necessary for the information to travel across the corpus callosum to the right premotor cortex and from there to the right arm area of the motor cortex. That is, language and motor actions are intimately connected, and according to the information pathways shown in Fig. 6-24B,C the **left hemisphere is dominant** not only for language but **also for motor actions** (the left premotor cortex is involved in every movement design, whether it is executed on the right or left side of the body).

Motor apraxia. Given the sequence of information processing shown in Fig. 6-24, it is not surprising that aphasias are often accompanied by disturbances of motor activity. For one thing, these disturbances result from a deficient understanding of verbal instructions (especially in sensory aphasia); for another, they are also influenced by the fact that the **production of a design for the action** is incomplete when there is a lesion of the left or right premotor association cortices or the connections between them. The resulting disorders in the sequential arrangement of individual movements to form complex actions, while elementary mobility is preserved, are called **motor apraxias.** As can also be understood on the basis of Fig. 6-24, the nature and degree of the various forms of apraxia depend very much on the location and extent of the cerebral lesion. For details see the literature [21, 30].

6.5 Plasticity, Learning, Memory

Forms of Learning and Memory

Biological significance and extent of information storage. The intake, storage and retrieval of information are general properties of neuronal networks. Their *biological significance* as the basis of **adaptation of individual behavior to the environment** can hardly be overestimated. Without learning and memory neither the individual nor its species could survive, for successes could not be repeated by planning and failures could not be intentionally avoided. Accordingly, much attention has been directed to these phenomena in recent decades by neurobiologists. It has been shown that we store only a *small part* of the events of which we are conscious, and these are only a small fraction of all our sensory inputs. It is also certain that we forget most of the information that once was stored. Both these mechanisms, *selection* and *forgetting*, protect us from being inundated with data, which would be just as detrimental as the lack of learning and memory.

At present we can make only a rough estimate of the **storage capacity of the human brain.** Comparisons between the storage capacity necessary for learning languages (4–$5 \cdot 10^7$ bits) and the number of neurons in the associated temporal areas ($3 \cdot 10^8$) indicate that about *10 neurons* are required to store *one bit of information*. Extrapolation of this result to the entire human cortex gives a total storage capacity of about $3 \cdot 10^8$ bits. This storage capacity would suffice for the permanent storage of about 1% of the information flowing through our consciousness, a value obtained from cybernetic considerations as follows [53]. The **information flow through consciousness** from the entire sensory system is less than 50 bits $\cdot$ s^{-1} under all conditions. For example, it is 40 bits $\cdot$ s^{-1} for quiet reading, 12 bits $\cdot$ s^{-1} for mental calculation, and 3 bits $\cdot$ s^{-1} for counting. Assuming an average value of 20 bits $\cdot$ s^{-1}, the total information flow in 70 years of 16-hour days is about $3 \cdot 10^{10}$ bits, a hundred times more than the available storage capacity as derived above. From all this material, **one percent** must be selected for **long-term storage.** It seems evident that the information selected will be primarily that most important to the individual for one reason or another.

Uptake (learning) and storage (in memory) of information by the nervous system have been more thoroughly studied in recent decades than the problem of retrieval from storage (remembering). For the first two processes, therefore, the underlying mechanisms are beginning to be revealed, at least in outline. On the other hand, most of the processes underlying retrieval remain obscure, and we can say little about them here.

Habituation and sensitization (non-associative learning). In animals and humans, a new stimulus – for example, a loud and unexpected sound – elicits a number of somatic and autonomic reactions such as looking toward the stimulus source, elevated muscle tone, a change in heart rate, and desynchronization of the EEG. Together, these constitute an **orienting response.** If a stimulus that turns out to have no significance for the organism is repeated several times, the orienting response soon disappears. For instance, someone living on a loud city street eventually becomes accustomed to the constant noise of traffic at night and is no longer awakened by it. This form of accommodation to a repeated stimulus that the organism recognizes as unimportant is called **habituation.**

Habituation is not only the simplest but probably also the **most widespread form of learning** in humans and animals. By habituation we learn to ignore stimuli with no novelty value or no further significance, so that we can turn our attention to more important events. Habituation is always stimulus-specific (on a background of traffic noise, either an unusual sound or an unusual silence will wake one up). And it is not a matter of fatigue, but rather an independent adjustment process in the nervous system. Furthermore, habituation should not be confused with *adaptation*, the increase in threshold of a sense organ exposed to continuous stimulation.

The opposite learning process can also be exhibited in animals and humans, an **increase in a physiological or behavioral reaction to stimuli** after presentation of a particularly intense or noxious stimulus. This process is called **sensitization**. In the traffic-noise situation described above, if an unaccustomed noise occurs (e.g., the squealing of tires when brakes are applied suddenly, followed by the sound of one car crashing into another) we find ourselves more attentive to the normal traffic noises for a while. Sensitization is a stimulus- and situation-specific, simple but independent learning process in the nervous system, which in many of its features is the mirror image of habituation (see also p. 93; further details and references in [4]).

Behavioral memory and knowledge memory. Going beyond the simple processes of habituation and sensitization, research on memory has employed two different approaches to the phenomena of learning and retention. In one they have been studied by **conditioning** (classical and operant), and in the other they are regarded as a **cognitive process.** The former produces a **behavioral memory** and the latter, a **knowledge memory** [36]. One reason for the distinction is methodological: whereas learning and retention by animals are more readily predictable by the principles of conditioning, in experiments on humans the acquisition, retention and recall of knowledge and skills are more precisely explained by cognitive principles. But the different methods tend to channel their users into different theoretical positions: whereas the behavioristically oriented conditioning researchers want to explain even complex learning processes (such as the acquisition of language) by the rules of conditioning, cognitive memory researchers believe that additional principles are necessary to understand how knowledge is acquired (references in [4]).

Associative and non-associative learning. The conditioning procedures, described in more detail below, are often called **associative learning**, because the central process consists of forming an association between stimuli (S) and responses

(R), as distinct from the (cognitive) acquisition of knowledge. This distinction is probably misleading inasmuch as associations may well also play a major role in cognitive learning. On the other hand, habituation and sensitization are clearly "non-associative", because they are simply a function of stimulus intensity and of the temporal sequence of stimuli, and do not involve a *close temporal pairing* (association) of stimuli.

Behavioral Memory (Learning by Conditioning)

Classical conditioning. In any animal, regardless of its prior history, painful stimulation of the foot causes the leg to be withdrawn by bending at all its joints. This *flexor reflex* is an example of an *unconditioned reflex*, an innate response based on fixed connections in the chain of neurons from the receptor (sensor) to the effector. Of still more interest in everyday life are the *acquired* or *conditioned reflexes*, in which the functional connections between the excited sensors and the patterns of activity in effector organs become established by learning processes.

The acquisition of conditioned reflexes by many animals can be followed in the laboratory. The original procedure of this sort is the **classical conditioning** developed by PAVLOV. First an *unconditioned* reflex (UR) is triggered – e.g., the flow of saliva in a dog when food (the unconditioned stimulus, US) is presented. Then a second stimulus (CS) to which the animal does not ordinarily respond – e.g., the sound of a bell – is presented shortly before the unconditioned stimulus. If this association of unconditioned (US) and conditioned (CS) stimuli is repeated several times, eventually the CS alone triggers the reflex response; even if no food is presented, the dog's saliva will flow after the bell sounds (cf. Fig. 29-23). In classical conditioning, then, the association of the adequate stimulus (US) for an unconditioned reflex (UR) with a neutral test stimulus (CS) converts the latter to the effective stimulus for a *conditioned reflex* (CR). The situation can be formulated briefly as follows: By practice, the sequence **CS → US → UR** becomes **CS → CR** (further details in [4]).

Imprinting is a special form of associative learning based on an innate predilection for particular stimulus-response combinations at a certain time during an organism's development. A vivid example is given by Konrad Lorenz's young greylag geese; during a short period soon after hatching they will learn to follow a human if the natural conditioning stimulus, the mother goose, is not present.

Operant conditioning. In classical conditioning the conditioned reflex is learned passively. An

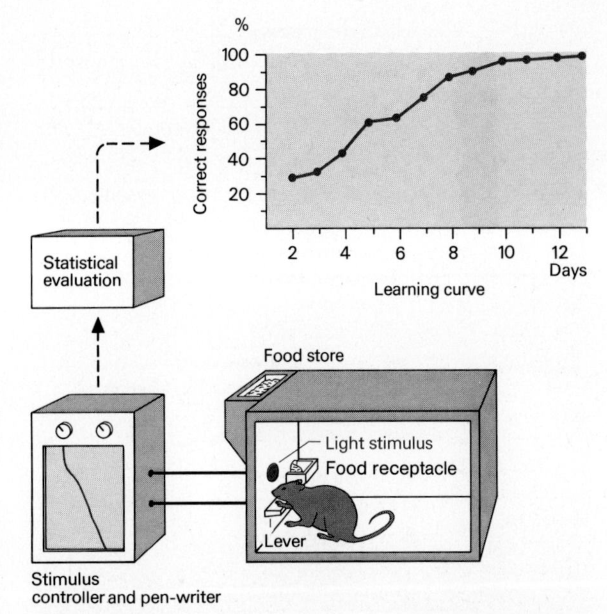

Fig. 6-25. Operant conditioning in the "Skinner box." When the controlling element turns on the stimulus (here a light) the animal can press the bar and is automatically rewarded with food. The stimuli and the resulting behavior are plotted by the pen recorder as a learning curve. *Abscissa:* days since the beginning of the learning experiment; *ordinate:* percentage of correct responses to the test stimulus

animal can acquire new behavior *actively* during **instrumental** or **operant conditioning.** Here the *response* to be learned is followed immediately by a rewarding or punishing stimulus (Fig. 6-25). The result is positive or negative **reinforcement** of the behavior. That is, the behavior itself *operates* on the situation, increasing the positive or decreasing the negative stimuli – hence the term **operant** or **instrumental learning** (references in [4, 37]).

In animal experiments conditioning is often done by *apparatus* that automatically presents the stimulus, records the response and supplies the reward in accordance with preset criteria. These devices are called **Skinner boxes** after the pioneer of operant conditioning, who designed the prototypes (Fig. 6-25).

Many forms of human and animal behavior are acquired and maintained or inhibited by the principles of operant conditioning. Classical conditioning plays less of a role in the acquisition of **motor responses**, but is involved in the development of **autonomic** reactions.

There are some similarities between instrumental and classical conditioning; for instance, the optimal time interval between the critical events is 500 ms in both cases. But there are also differences, in view of which a **common physiological basis of the two processes appears unlikely.**

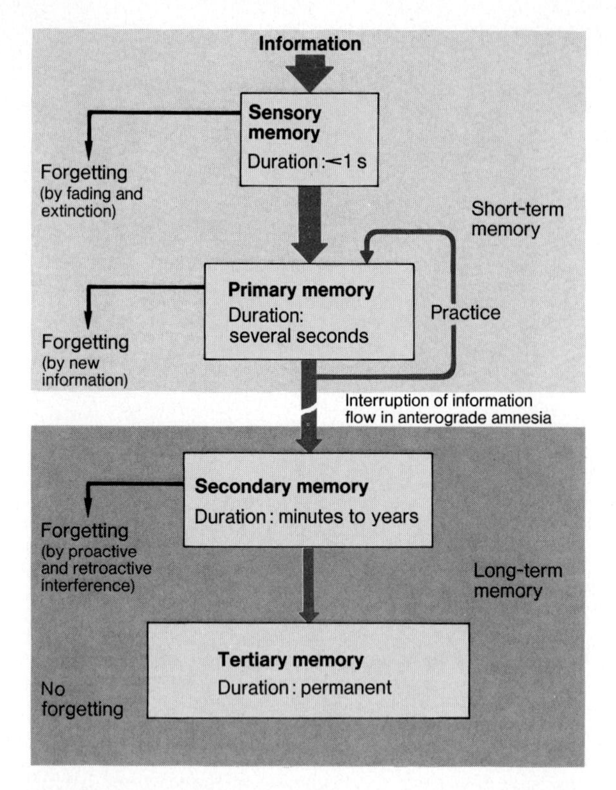

Fig. 6-26. Diagram of the information flow from the sensory to the secondary memory, by way of the primary memory. In the primary memory, the material to be remembered is either repeated (practiced) or forgotten. Some of the material that has been practiced is then transferred to the secondary memory. However, practice is not indispensible for transfer from primary to secondary memory, nor does it guarantee such transfer. (Modified from WAUGH and NORMAN [38])

Operant conditioning is possible only with the more highly developed organisms (e.g., it is very difficult to cause fish to learn by punishment), and it requires more complex neural networks than does classical conditioning; in mammals, presumably, it requires an intact neocortex.

Learning in the autonomic nervous system. Since PAVLOV's time it has been known that the activity of effectors of the autonomic nervous system (heart, smooth musculature, glands) can also be changed by way of **classical conditioning**. It was long thought that this very restricted form of learning was the only form of which the autonomic nervous system is capable. But application of the technique of **operant conditioning** has shown that even in the autonomic nervous system far more extensive learning is possible. For example, in experiments on animals it has been possible to produce long-term changes in heart rate, the tone of the intestinal musculature, the excretion of urine and the blood flow through the wall of the stomach.

The greatest difficulty encountered in studying the behavioral changes induced by operant learning in the autonomic nervous system is that the most easily measurable responses (e.g., heart rate) can also be affected **indirectly by way of the skeletal musculature** – that is, by changes in muscular work, muscle tone or diaphragm contraction. The same is true of more subtle indirect influences, such as the general degree of wakefulness and attentiveness of the experimental animal. It has not always been possible to rule out such indirect factors conclusively. Although in many experiments learning occurred in the autonomic nervous system even *after the skeletal musculature had been paralyzed with curare,* there has been some criticism of the results [4].

Attempts have also been made to influence autonomic processes *in humans* by the technique of operant conditioning. For example, if the subject of such an experiment is allowed to monitor his own heartbeat or its frequency by visual or audible signals, in general small changes in heart rate in the desired direction can serve as a reward and as an incentive to achieve larger changes. Such **biofeedback arrangements** are regarded as a promising therapeutic approach, by which disease processes in the organism can be ameliorated without the use of drugs. Successes have been reported, for example, in the treatment of disturbed heart rhythms, muscle cramps, migraine and difficulty in falling asleep (for control of EEG frequency see p. 136). But here, even more than in animal experiments, it should be kept in mind that many indirect (especially muscular) influences can participate in changing the autonomic parameter under study. Such effects are also indicated by the encouraging results obtained with biofeedback in the treatment of diseases and muscular paralysis ("neuromuscular reeducation").

Knowledge Memory (Cognitive Learning)

Memory research was founded in 1885 by the German psychologist H. EBBINGHAUS, who tested the ability of people to reproduce nonsense syllables. His results have been undisputed for 100 years, although the theoretical interpretation has changed. EBBINGHAUS himself made a distinction between *memory span* and *natural memory,* now called **short-term** and **long-term memory** (Fig. 6-26). Information in the short-term memory – for instance, a telephone number one has just looked up – is soon forgotten unless it is transferred to the long-term memory by *practice.* Once in the latter it remains available for reference after quite a long time; the memory trace it has formed, the **engram,** is reinforced every time it is used. This fixing of the engram, so that an item

Table 6-1. Survey of human memory processes. (Modified from ERVIN and ANDERS [48]).

	Sensory memory	Primary memory	Secondary memory	Tertiary memory
Capacity	Limited by the information transmitted from receptor	Small	Very large	Very large
Duration	Fractions of a second	Several seconds	Several minutes to several years	Permanent
Entry into storage	Automatic during perception	Verbalization	Practice	Very frequent practice
Organization	Representation of the physical stimulus	Temporal ordering	Semantic and by spatiotemporal relations (Gestalt learning)	?
Access to storage	Limited only by speed of readout	Very rapid access	Slow access	Very rapid access
Types of information	Sensory	Verbal (among others?)	All forms	All forms
Types of forgetting	Fading and extinction	New information replaces old	Interference, proactive and retroactive	Possibly no forgetting

of memory becomes progressively less likely to be lost, is called **consolidation.**

The following description of the human memory processes takes into account the concept of short- and long-term memory, extending it to correspond to the current state of our knowledge. These more recent findings include (i) the differential treatment of verbally and nonverbally coded material, (ii) a **sensory memory** preceding the short-term memory, and (iii) the possibility of special memory mechanisms for the storage and retrieval of especially well consolidated material [18, 22, 43, 48, 63]. These processes are summarized in Table 6-1.

Sensory memory. Sensory stimuli are first stored automatically, for a few hundred milliseconds, in a *sensory memory,* where they are encoded for the short-term store(s) and their most important features are extracted. Forgetting begins immediately after the information is acquired. The stored information can also be actively extinguished, or written over by information taken up shortly thereafter (Table 6-1, Fig. 6-26).

The experimental findings from which the existence of a sensory *(echoic* for auditory stimuli, *iconic* for visual) memory has been inferred are predominantly in the realm of vision. When a large number of stimuli (e.g., 12 letters) are presented for a very short time (e.g., 50 ms), during the following 0.5–1 s the subject can often reproduce up to 80% of them, like visual afterimages. But after a few seconds the reproduction rate falls to 20%. Tests in which the stimuli are presented in sequence have shown that the information not only "fades" passively but can also be actively "overwritten" by new information. These and other findings have implied the existence of a large-capacity sensory storage facility in the primary sensory systems (including the primary cortical projection areas), which keeps the sensory impressions stable for seconds to allow encoding and feature extraction as well as the activation of attentiveness systems.

The transfer of information from the short-lived sensory record to a more permanent memory can occur in two ways. One is by verbal coding of the sensory data, which the available experimental results indicate is the most common in adults. The other is a nonverbal way about which little is known, which must be used by small children and animals and also serves for the uptake of memory items that are difficult or impossible to express verbally.

Primary memory (Table 6-1). This memory serves for the **temporary storage of verbally coded materials.** Its capacity is smaller than that of the sensory memory. The information is stored in the order of its arrival time. Forgetting occurs when the stored information is replaced by new items. Because the organism is continually processing information, the average duration of stay in the primary memory is short, only a matter of seconds. The **primary memory** corresponds roughly to the *short-term memory* mentioned above. *Nonverbally coded material* is not stored by the primary memory. It is transferred from the sensory memory to the secondary memory (see below) either directly or by way of an intermediate storage mechanism of its own.
Transfer from the *primary memory* into the more permanent *secondary memory* is facilitated by **practice** – that is, attentive repetition and the corresponding circulation of the information in the primary memory (Fig. 6-26). The probability of transfer to the secondary memory depends on the duration of this practice.

Secondary memory (Table 6-1). This memory is a large long-term storage system. Only if it is stored there does information remain available for retrieval after a long time. So far there have been no well-founded estimates of its capacity or of the duration of stay of the stored material. The information is stored according to its "significance." This *organizational difference* from the primary memory is clear in the nature of the mistakes that can occur during retrieval from storage. In the primary memory these usually amount to the confusion of phonetically similar sounds such as p and b, whereas in the secondary memory words of similar significance are confused. The two stores also differ in *speed of access;* retrieval from the primary memory is rapid and from the secondary memory, slow (searching through a large store takes more time).
Forgetting in the secondary memory appears to be based largely on interference with the learning process by other things learned previously or subsequently. In the first case the term **proactive inhibition** is used and in the latter, **retroactive inhibition.** Proactive inhibition seems to be the more important factor, since a greater amount of previously learned material is available. Viewed in this way, the blame for most of our forgetting must be placed on what we have learned before [48].

Tertiary memory (Table 6-1 and Fig. 6-26). There are engrams – for example, one's own name, the ability to read and write or other skills employed daily – that as a result of years of practice are essentially *never forgotten,* even if through disease or injury the entire remaining content of memory is more or less erased. These engrams are also distinguished by *extremely short access times.* They may be stored in a particular form of memory, the **tertiary memory** [48], but it is also possible that they are simply very well consolidated engrams in the secondary memory. The **long-term memory** mentioned above corresponds to the secondary plus (if it exists) the tertiary memory.

Procedural and declarative long-term memory. Neurobiological theories based on animal experiments, as a rule, postulate a unitary long-term memory. On the other hand, studies in cognitive psychology suggest that there are at least two fundamentally different forms of long-term memory (apart from the above-mentioned possibility of distinct secondary and tertiary memories). That is, we must make a distinction between the fact that we "know something" (procedural) and the fact that we "know that we know it" (declarative). The modification of behavior when a skill is learned is procedural; the ability to state when and how the information was aquired is declarative. Hence procedural memory "contains" a detailed representation of the actions, and declarative memory stores the verbally encoded rules for its execution. The declarative memory seems to be subdivided into an **episodic** and a **semantic memory;** the time at which one has learned something (episodic) is forgotten much more frequently than verbally or visually encoded knowledge [4].

Disturbances of Memory

Anterograde amnesia. The inability to learn newly acquired information – that is, to store it permanently where it is accessible for reference – is called **anterograde amnesia.** In the clinic this syndrome is called the *amnestic syndrome* or *Korsakoff's disease.* The patients (often chronic alcoholics) have nearly normal secondary and tertiary memory with respect to the time before the illness, and the primary memory is also functional. But they *cannot transfer information from the primary to the secondary memory.* Clinically, this situation is rather imprecisely called the loss of **"recent memory"** with retention of **"established (remote) memory."**

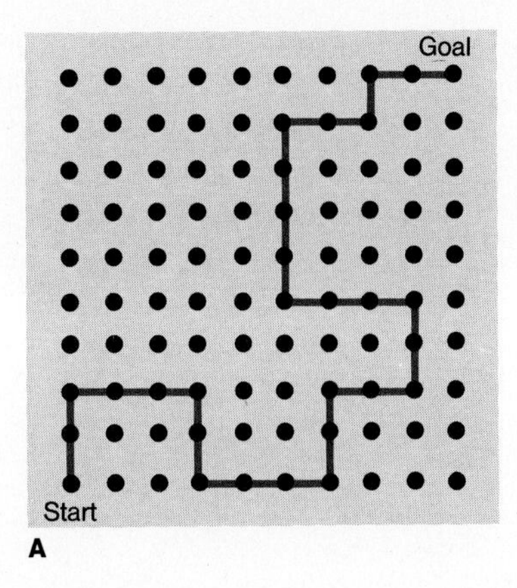

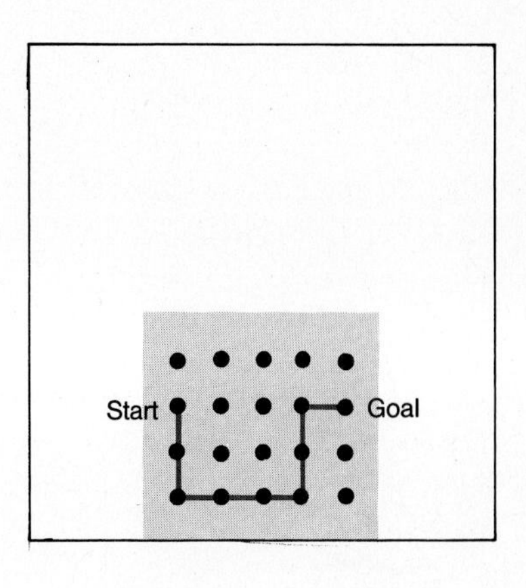

A

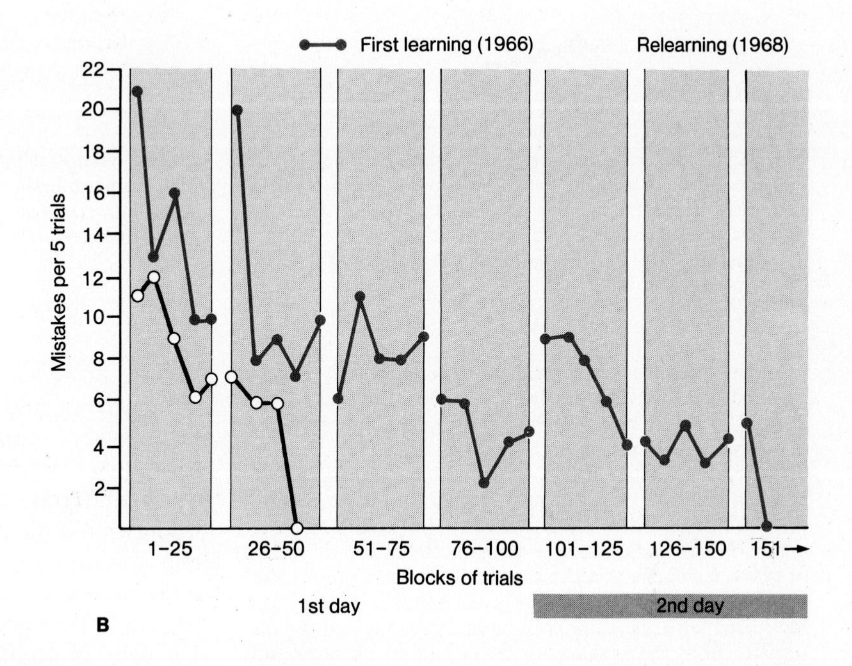

B

Fig. 6-27. Learning in a peg maze. **A** The *black circles* symbolize metal pegs on a wooden board. The normal pegboard is shown on the left and a smaller one on the right. The subject must discover the correct path from start to goal *(red)* and remember it. When an incorrect peg is touched a click sounds. A normal subject can learn to perform the task without mistakes three times in a row in twenty trials or less. Even highly intelligent patients with anterograde amnesia cannot solve the problem. **B** Learning by a patient with anterograde amnesia, using the small board. Even this simple task was learned only after 155 trials *(red line)*. When the test was repeated two years later some retention was evident, but the patient could not remember having ever performed the task. (From MILNER [57])

Pathological-anatomical and neurosurgical observations indicate that anterograde amnesia is caused in particular by bilateral damage to or removal of the *hippocampus and the structures associated with it.* These structures apparently play a key role in the *recoding and transfer* of information from the primary to the secondary memory. Because this process is also coupled with the *selection* of information for permanent storage, it must be assumed that the hippocampus and other limbic structures are especially involved in this activity [57].

The thorough study, over two decades, of the intelligent patient H.M., who suffered **anterograde amnesia** following bilateral removal of the median parts of the temporal lobes [57], showed that he could retain **simple material** (e.g., the number 584) for at least 15 minutes **by constant repetition** (in his primary memory). But if his attention was diverted only briefly the information was immediately lost forever. Tasks that exceeded the capacity of the primary memory – for example, finding and remembering the way through a peg maze with 28 steps from start to goal (Fig. 6-27A) – could not be performed successfully even after many hundred trials. Not until the task was made much simpler (Fig. 6-27B) could it be solved despite the patient's inability to remember the preceding practice session or the task itself.

Anterograde amnesia appears to be particularly severe where declarative (i.e., usually verbal) tasks are concerned, and **less pronounced for procedural learning** (usually nonverbal). For example, the patient H.M. achieved practically normal performance in learning certain continuous motor tasks (Fig. 6-28). But even here, when *repeating the task he could never remember* having practiced it before. This, then, is a kind of learning in which no feeling of familiarity with the learned material develops. The inference that **in anterograde amnesia the declarative memory is most severely affected** is supported by the results of experiments employing classical and operant conditioning and others in which shape recognition is tested. In these experiments, as long

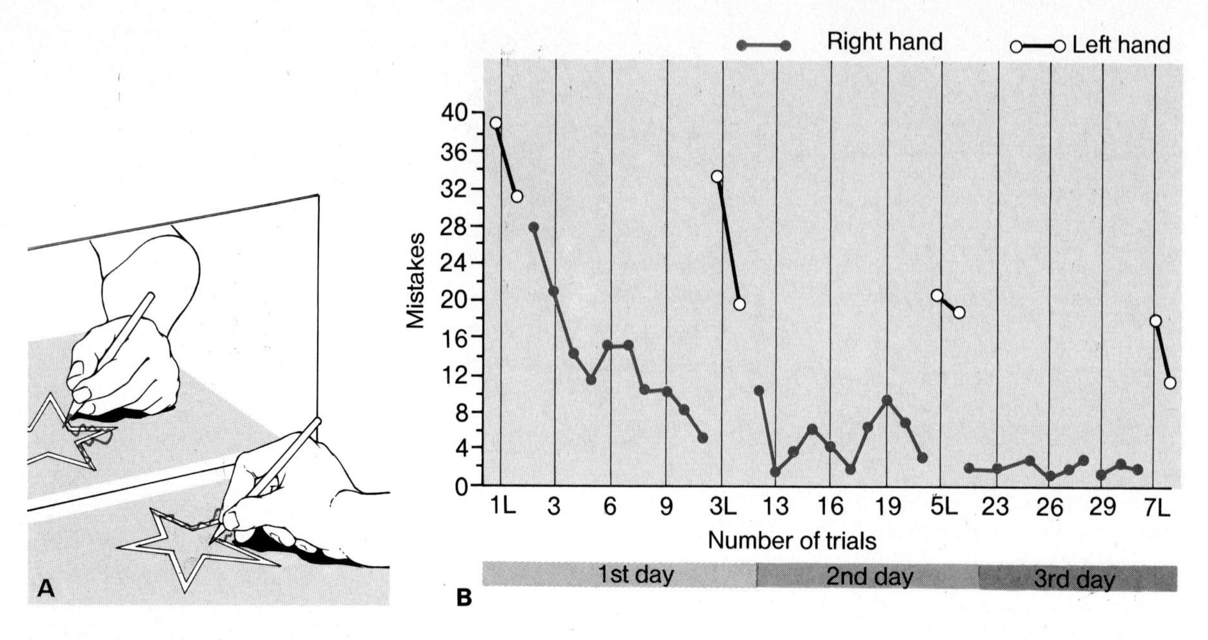

Fig. 6-28 A, B. Learning of a motor program. The subject sees the star in **A** and the pencil he is holding in a mirror, and must trace the star in the space between the two outlines (try it yourself!). Crossing either outline counts as a mistake. The learning curves in **B** were produced by the same patient as in Fig. 6-27. This patient, with marked anterograde amnesia, learned the task just as rapidly as a normal subject. Again, however, he could not remember ever having performed the task. (From MILNER [57])

as no intentional act of searching (an active search process in the declarative memory) was required, the results were normal or nearly normal – but again *without the patients' remembering that they have learned anything* [48].

So far, unfortunately, *experimental lesions in animals have never produced a syndrome* comparable to human anterograde amnesia. Three main causes of this failure come to mind. (i) The disturbance in humans is limited to verbal or verbalizable material, so that it cannot become evident in animals. (ii) The experiments on animals done so far have used tests that cannot monitor accurately enough the transfer from the primary to the secondary memory. (iii) The role of the hippocampus and associated structures has changed during phylogeny (together with the development of speech?).

Retrograde amnesia. The inability to retrieve items stored in memory in the time before normal brain function was impaired is called **retrograde amnesia.** Well-known examples of its possible causes are mechanical shocks (concussion), stroke (apoplexy), electroshock (therapeutic or by accident) and anesthesia. All are associated with fairly generalized disruption of brain function, and it is not yet known which particular structural and functional disturbances give rise to retrograde amnesia.

In any case, the event that produces retrograde amnesia erases the content of the *primary memory*. Initially more less large parts of the secondary memory are also lost, further back into the past the more severe the damage was. It is striking, however, that the forgotten time span later narrows and in some cases shrinks so far that no gap remains. Moreover, special techniques (e.g., hypnosis) can be used to recall forgotten materials to memory. These and other findings make it seem likely that **retrograde amnesia** amounts mainly to **interference with access to the secondary memory** and less to a loss of the content of memory. The *tertiary* memory, as a rule, is unaffected even in severe cases of retrograde amnesia [48].

Animal experiments relevant to retrograde amnesia have so far had results just as unsatisfactory as those designed to study anterograde amnesia. Among other techniques, these experiments employ general electroshock, local electrical stimulation (e.g., of the amygdala), rapid anesthesia, partial or complete *functional decortication* by temporary application of isotonic KCl solution to the cerebral cortex (which causes local massive depolarization spreading into the surroundings, and thus inexcitability of the cortical neurons, called *"spreading depression"*), intense cooling of cortical areas, and the application of cholinesterase and protein-synthesis inhibitors. The aim in each case has been to produce retrograde amnesia or to disturb the process of consolidation; the results are extraordinarily inconsistent.

Hysterical amnesia. Very rarely patients with complete loss of memory are encountered who cannot remember who they are and what they have done prior to this moment in their lives. In these cases one is dealing with an *exclusively functional* mental disturbance quite unlike the amnesias discussed so far. It is described by the term **hysterical amnesia.** The disorder is distinguished from the primarily organic amnesias (caused by damage to brain tissue) by three characteristics: (i) all personal data are forgotten, including even the person's own name; (ii) the amnesia is global in nature and entirely unaffected by key stimuli (for example, returning the patient to his former surroundings or to the company of relatives; and (iii) the inability to remember past events persists even though new information can be remembered well.

Neuronal Mechanisms of Plasticity and of the Engram

Learning and memory are the most obvious signs of the life-long **modifiability and plasticity** of the nervous system. One of the central problems of neurobiology is the search for the structural, physiological and biochemical bases of this plasticity. However, the various forms of neuronal plasticity are not equivalent to the various forms of memory, because **plasticity is only a prerequisite** for learning, retention and recall. Its different forms are utilized in very diverse ways in learning and in the formation of an engram. Unfortunately, our understanding of these processes remains quite incomplete, and the following description of them is correspondingly brief. Extensive literature is available for further study [4, 21, 26, 43, 49, 64].

Habituation and sensitization. We now know that these two mechanisms are probably based on **depression or facilitation of synaptic transmission** [21]. Brief habituation and sensitization involve functional changes at the synapses, a reduction or enhancement of the release of presynaptic transmitter. Details of these events can be found in the discussions of synaptic potentiation and depression in Chapter 3 (p. 55). For long-term habituation and sensitization (as for other learning processes, see below) the functional changes may be followed by structural alteration of the synapses, such as a *decrease or increase in the number and size of the presynaptic active zones* [21].

Changes in synaptic efficiency due to use and non-use have long been regarded as one of the essential **bases of neuronal plasticity**. In particular, it has been possible to observe *posttetanic potentiation* at certain *excitatory* synapses (e.g., in the hippocampus) for many hours, and it can probably persist considerably longer. At an early stage it was recognized that this process may well reflect changes in the nervous system associated with formation of the structural engram [11, 31]. It is consistent with this view that in the spinal cord, where only relatively brief posttetanic potentiation is found, no permanent learning has been observed. Further support is provided by the fact that when synapses are not used, their ability to function declines. For instance, in the visual cortex of mice dendritic synapses unused from birth (because the eye was removed or the animal raised in darkness) show histological and functional signs of degeneration.

However, the relation between use/non-use of synapses and their efficiency must not be viewed too simply. Because the nervous system is continually active throughout life, the eventual result of the cumulative activity would be considerable hypertrophy of all the synapses. To get around this difficulty, hypotheses have been proposed to account for the plasticity of central synapses in highly developed nervous systems. For example, in the cerebellum only the **simultaneous activation of the synapses of mossy and climbing fibers** on a Purkinje cell is thought to induce a synaptic learning process in the mossy-fiber synapses.

Engrams of the behavioral memory. At present, the neuronal mechanisms underlying learning in **classical and operant conditioning** are probably best understood as a mixture of the abovementioned processes affecting single neurons or synapses and the events in groups of neurons to be described below. Studies of classical conditioning in simple nervous systems (e.g., the sea slug *Aplysia*) have demonstrated that presynaptic facilitation is involved in the learning process [21]. Here, however, conditioning is possible only if the conditioned stimulus is one that in itself elicits a response (in a behavioral experiment, by contrast, the conditioning stimulus is by definition one to which the animal is unresponsive until the association with the unconditioned stimulus is established). The *Aplysia* experiments show that associative learning can be ascribable to the activity of a few neurons; on the other hand, it also reveals the limitations of purely cellular models of learning. In any case, many learning processes that produce engrams in the behavioral memory cannot be explained without invoking complex neuronal networks [4].

Engrams of the knowledge memory. The simplest and most intuitively appealing idea about the **neuronal basis of cognitive learning** is that information is initially stored in the form of an orderly spatiotemporal pattern of **reverberating excitation**. This *dynamic engram* subsequently brings about **structural changes at the synapses involved** (consolidation to a *structural engram*). The content of memory can then be retrieved by corresponding activation of these synapses.

The *concept of reverberating excitation* is consistent with the subjective experience that we must *practice* material to be learned – that is, let it pass repeatedly through our consciousness – in order eventually to retain it. Morphological and, in particular, electrophysiological findings indicate at least the possibility of such reverberation. For example, it has been shown in operant-conditioning experiments that when the task has been learned, there are well-defined changes in the EEG (e.g., in the amplitude of evoked potentials) [4].

Efforts to **localize the engram** in the mammalian brain have produced two basic results, which are only seemingly contradictory. One is that almost *all regions of the brain*, subcortical and cortical, have a *potential memory function*, and that the memory trace is not laid down in a spatially circumscribed area. This feature is most clearly manifest in the fact that even in the presence of extensive cerebral lesions humans and animals can still perform surprising feats of learning and memory (examples in [64]). Second, it is becoming increasingly clear that *different memory processes* require different, *clearly distinguishable brain regions* (see above description of the patient H.M.), and that a particular learning process involves only a finite and specific population of neurons, leaving nearby neurons unaffected (examples in [64]). Even though a memory trace may appear to extend over a large region of the brain, then, its substrate is evidently highly specific.

Neurochemical Mechanisms of Plasticity and of the Engram

Since the coding of **genetic memory** in deoxyribonucleic acid (DNA) has been discovered, and the study of **immunological memory** has been similarly successful, there has been an incentive to look for molecular changes underlying **neuronal memory** that could be considered the basis of the engram. In particular, the observations of structural alteration of neurons during the development of engrams suggest a crucial **role of protein biosynthesis in consolidation,** the transfer of an evanescent memory trace (in short-term memory) into the long-term memory. The evidence in favor of this hypothesis has now become convincing. But the detailed mechanisms are still unclear, as are the biological bases of the *persistence of a memory trace for years.*

At first, many experiments were concerned with the question whether learning can bring about **changes in the ribonucleic acids** (RNA) of neurons and glial cells. Changes were actually found in the sequences of the 4 bases of RNA, but these changes proved to be largely *unspecific consequences of activity and the stress of the experiment.* Furthermore, **cannibalism experiments** in which "educated" animals (or their CNS) were fed to "uneducated" individuals have not been reproducible in either flatworms (*Planaria*) or fish and mammals (references in [4]).

A more successful approach has been to **inhibit protein biosynthesis** (by means of the antibiotics puromycin, cycloheximide or anisomycin) in order to interfere with the formation of a structural engram in the cell or cell membrane. By this method, for example, the protein synthesis that usually begins in the mouse brain a few minutes after the start of a training session, and lasts for many hours, can be blocked; at the same time, permanent learning is prevented.

The results reported in several hundred publications in this area give a relatively uniform picture (references in [4]): 80–90% of cerebral protein synthesis can be temporarily blocked without causing gross behavioral deficits in any respect apart from memory. The most pronounced amnesia is achieved when protein synthesis is inhibited shortly before the beginning of a training session, so that there is **no protein synthesis during training.** Even weeks after training has been completed, recall remains deficient. Performance of a task in itself is not influenced by blocking of protein synthesis, which has no effect on previously learned material. The implication is that *protein synthesis is necessary only for a critical consolidation phase during and shortly after training.* After this time no new protein synthesis is required to ensure long-term storage (in the secondary and tertiary memory, see above).

The inhibition of protein synthesis does not interfere with the short-term memory, at least not in animal experiments. This is another important argument for a **different mode of operation of short-term and long-term memory**. The mechanism by which information is converted from one form to the other is still unclear.

As an argument against specificity of the above effects, it has been proposed that the antibiotics, by inhibiting corticosteroid production in the adrenal cortex, reduce the activation of the brain and in this way cause memory problems. Similarly, the interference with memory has been ascribed to a disturbance of the catecholamine level in the brain. Both of these objections have been largely ruled out by experiments (references in [4]). Despite the significance of the catecholamines in arousal, motivation and emotion, their role in learning and memory is considered negligible.

In the last analysis, whatever enthusiastic claims have been made, it is still not possible to achieve a direct, specific **improvement of intelligence and of learning and memory performance by pharmacological means.** Many substances have been suggested for this purpose – primarily glutamic acid (glutamate), cholinergic agonists and antagonists, strychnine, picrotoxin, tetrazole, caffeine and ribonucleic acid – but none has been proved to be effective.

6.6 Functions of the Frontal Lobes

In Section 6.1 it was explained that the **prefrontal association cortex** of the frontal lobe, together with the **limbic association cortex** (also partly located in the frontal lobe), must be regarded as association cortex in the strict sense, and that the only other region in this category is the *parietal-temporal-occipital association cortex* (cf. Fig. 6-2). The first two are thought to have special functions in the motor system, in memory and in the affective aspects of behavior. This section is concerned with the findings, from clinical-pathological observations and animal experiments, on which this interpretation is based (see also p. 363).

Connections of the frontal lobe [13]. The prefrontal cortex in the narrow sense comprises the areas 9 to 12 on the dorsal and lateral surfaces of the frontal lobe (see Fig. 6-4, p. 128) plus areas 13 and 14 on the orbital surface. The afferents to the prefrontal cortex come mainly from the **dorsomedial nucleus**, one of the *nonspecific* nuclei of the thalamus (see Fig. 9-22, p. 214). The prefrontal cortex also has extensive reciprocal connections with various parts of the limbic system, including the cingulate gyrus, the hippocampus, the amygdala and the hypothalamus. Therefore it, together with the limbic association cortex, has also been regarded as the **neocortical part of the limbic system**, with its dorsal components linked more to the hippocampus and the ventral components, more to the amygdala. Given that the limbic system plays a special role in the species-specific behavior of an organism (drives, motivation; cf. p. 364), these anatomical connections in themselves suggest that one of the functions of the prefrontal cortex is the *learned control* of innate behavior patterns.

Inferences from Frontal-Lobe Lesions in Humans

Patients with frontal-lobe lesions have normal scores on most of the standard *intelligence tests*. Often, however, they exhibit subtle personality changes, rather hard to describe, such as the *lack of motivation* and the *absence of firm intentions and plans based on foresight*. Moreover, they are often unreliable, crude or tactless, frivolous or irascible; as a result, despite their normal "intelligence," they can become embroiled in social conflicts (for example, while at work) [13, 15, 30].

In *tests with tasks involving movement*, these patients are inclined to persist in a motor act they have begun, even when the rules of play have long since demanded that they do something else. In the task illustrated in Fig. 6-29 the patients are told, after each drawing, which geometric figure they should draw next. Although they understand this instruction (and can repeat it if asked), they frequently proceed to draw again a figure already drawn one or more times [56]. Such persistence in what has been begun is called **perseveration.**

Perseveration is often accompanied by a *dissociation between verbal and other motor reactions*. For instance, if such a frontal-lobe patient is asked

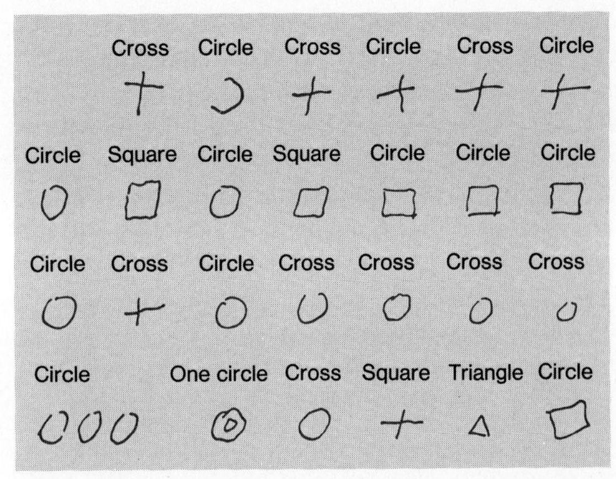

Fig. 6-29. Perseveration in the performance of motor tasks by four patients with frontal-lobe damage. Each line shows the patient's drawings in red, and above them the instructions given by the examiner. The first, second and fourth patients had tumors of the left frontal lobe, and the third had an abscess in the right frontal lobe. (From LURIA [56])

to press a button with the left hand when given a green signal and with the right hand when the signal is red, he will follow this instruction a few times and then begin to respond to both signals with one hand only or with either at random. Asked to repeat the instruction, he can do so correctly, but he does not correct his mistake. It appears as though the verbal instruction is not conveyed to the motor areas responsible for the movement of the hands. (Similar disparities are occasionally seen in everyday life – for example, when a person says "left" but turns to the right.) The tendency to perseveration is also reflected in learning experiments in which the patient has difficulty distinguishing a stimulus in a series from those that preceded it. Their behavior gives the impression that the preceding memory trace cannot make room for the next rapidly enough – that their problem is an *enhanced proactive inhibition* (cf. p. 158 and Table 6-1).

When tested with peg mazes (Fig. 6-27) these patients also make far more than the average number of mistakes made by normal people or patients with other kinds of brain damage. In particular, they tend to carry on regardless of their mistakes, or to jump diagonally from peg to peg though this is prohibited by the rules. Here, again, they are conscious of their mistakes, but they are incapable of bringing their impulsive actions under control.

Frontal-lobe patients, then, find it difficult to change their behavior when the circumstances require it. The effectiveness of external constraints appears to be weakened, and when several external and internal motivations are in competition it is hard for the patient to change from one to another rapidly and appropriately. This conclusion from observations of behavior is consistent with that drawn above, in the context of the anatomical connections – that the prefrontal cortex is involved in the **learned control of inborn behavior patterns** and in **harmonizing external and internal motivations.**

Psychosurgery. In behavioral studies on chimpanzees (see below) it was noticed that animals that previously became enraged at their mistakes began to accept them calmly after the connections between frontal lobe and thalamus had been cut. A rather hasty application of these findings to humans by MONIZ led to the performance of such operations on neuropsychiatric patients in the period 1940–1950. These **prefrontal lobotomies** or **leukotomies** were meant to treat mental disorders and intractable pain; in the latter case it was thought that the pain continued to be sensed but that its affective elements were considerably reduced.
Prefrontal leukotomy was always controversial and has since become obsolete – that is, unnecessary and no longer justified – owing to the introduction of effective psychoactive drugs. But its original acceptance as therapy marked the beginning of **psychosurgery,** the deliberate attempt to *affect human behavior by the destruction or removal of brain tissue.* In a broader sense electroshock treatments, long-term therapy with psychoactive drugs, and the insertion of electrodes into the brain should also be regarded as psychosurgery, because these procedures can also produce permanent alterations of brain tissue.
In view of the extent of our ignorance about the way the brain works and the functions of its individual components, the grounds for using psychosurgical procedures today are more empirical than theoretical. For example, **amygdalotomy** is used as a last resort to control aggressive behavior, though grave misgivings are expressed about such profound interference with personality. It should never be performed without painstaking examination of the individual case. There must be firm proof that despite the utmost effort none of the conventional psychiatric treatments have helped the patient for whom the operation is being considered, and that in the present state of knowledge there is a fair chance that limited psychosurgical intervention will succeed in improving his condition without causing any fundamental personality change.

Frontal-Lobe Symptoms in Animal Experiments

The systematic study of the effects of frontal-lobe lesions on the behavior of chimpanzees and other mammals has so far had two main results [13]: (i) like humans, the animals show a strong tendency to **perseverate,** and (ii) they perform *tasks with delayed reinforcement considerably more poorly* (see below).
Many test arrangements have revealed the *tendency to perseveration* – for example, arrangements in which alternate switches are to be pressed in response to light signals. As in the experiments on humans described above (Fig. 6-29), rather than alternating, the animal continues for a long time to give the response first chosen. The *interpretation of this behavior* is analogous to that for humans (see above).
In the simplest case of a **delayed-reinforcement task,** a reward (e.g., a nut) is placed under one of two overturned cups while the animal is watching, and then an opaque screen is let down between the cups and the animal. After a predetermined time has elapsed the screen is raised again and the animal can look for the reward under one of the cups. Normal chimpanzees can readily solve this problem after a minute's delay, but animals with frontal-lobe lesions fail after a delay of only five seconds. One might well suspect that the difficulty lies in an impairment of (short-term) memory, but experiments have not supported this view. If the animal is kept in the dark during the waiting period, its performance improves, indicating that the stimuli to which it is exposed in the light during the delay crowd out the information about the position of the reward. That is, the animals suffer from **enhanced retroactive inhibition** (cf. p. 158 and Table 6-1), and find it difficult to pay enough attention to the crucial stimuli. This thesis of **increased distractability** of animals with prefrontal lobectomies is supported by still other evidence: the animals are usually hyperactive and hyperreactive; small doses of sedatives, such as barbiturates, have positive effects like that of darkening the room during the waiting period; and in tests with many stimuli or choice situations the results are particularly bad.
In general, all these findings can be summarized in the hypothesis that the prefrontal cortex is of major significance in the **development of behavioral strategies.** An inability to work out such strategies becomes especially clear whenever it is necessary to change behavior rapidly, and when there is a delay between the presentation of the problem and its solution, so that the additional input of information during this time must be appropriately incorporated into the behavioral strategy.

6.7 References

Textbooks and Handbooks

1. ANDERSEN, P., ANDERSSON, S.A.: Physiological Basis of the Alpha Rhythm. New York: Appleton-Century-Crofts 1968
2. ARKIN, A.M., ANTROBUS, J.S., ELLMANN, S.J. (Eds.): The Mind in Sleep. Psychology and Psychophysiology. Hillsdahle, New Jersey: Lawrence Erlbaum Assoc. 1978
3. ASCHOFF, J., DAAN, S., GROOS, G.A.: Vertebrate Circadian Systems. Structure and Physiology. Berlin: Springer 1982
4. BIRBAUMER, N., SCHMIDT, R.F.: Biologische Psychologie. Berlin-Heidelberg-New York: Springer (in press)
5. BORBÉLY, A., VALATX, J.L. (Ed.): Sleep Mechanisms. Berlin: Springer 1984

6. Brodal, A.: Neurological Anatomy in Relation to Clinical Medicine, 3rd ed. New York, London, Toronto: Oxford University Press 1981
7. Bünning, E.: Die physiologische Uhr. Circadian Rhythmik und Biochronometrie. 3. Aufl. Berlin-Heidelberg-New York: Springer 1977
8. Buser, P.A., Rougeul-Buser, A. (Eds.): Cerebral Correlates of Conscious Experience. Amsterdam, New York, Oxford: Elsevier 1978
9. Cohen, D.B.: Sleep and Dreaming: Origins, Nature and Functions. Oxford: Pergamon Press 1979
10. Creutzfeldt, O.D.: Cortex Cerebri. Leistung, strukturelle und funktionelle Organisation der Hirnrinde. Berlin: Springer 1983
11. Eccles, J.C.; The Understanding of the Brain. New York, St. Louis, San Francisco, Düsseldorf: McGraw-Hill 1973
12. Evarts, E.V., Shinoda, Y., Wise, S.P.: Neurophysiological Approaches to Higher Brain Functions. New York: J. Wiley 1984
13. Fuster, J.M.: The Prefrontal Cortex. New York: Raven Press 1982
14. Ganten, D., Pfaff, D. (Ed.): Sleep. Clinical and Experimental Aspects. Berlin: Springer 1982
15. Gazzaniga, M.S. (Ed.): Neuropsychology. Handbook of Behavioral Neurobiology, Volume 2. New York, London: Plenum Press 1979
16. Gazzaniga, M.S.: The Social Brain. New York: Basic Books 1985
17. Geschwind, N., Galabarda, A. (Eds.): Cerebral Dominance: The Biological Foundations. Harvard: Harvard Univ. Press 1984
18. Hoffmann, J.: Das aktive Gedächtnis. Berlin-Heidelberg-New York: Springer 1983
19. Hucho, F.: Einführung in die Neurochemie. Weinheim: Verlag Chemie 1982
20. Jovanović, U.J.: Normal Sleep in Man. Stuttgart: Hippokrates 1971
21. Kandel, E.R., Schwartz, J.H. (Eds.): Principles of Neural Science. 2nd Ed. New York: Elsevier 1985
22. Kintsch, W.: Gedächtnis und Kognition. Berlin-Heidelberg-New York: Springer 1982
23. Kleitman, N.: Sleep and Wakefulness. Chicago: University Press 1963, revised ed. 1972
24. Kleist, K.: Gehirnpathologie. Leipzig: J.A. Barth 1934
25. Lutzenberger, W., Elbert, Th., Rockstroh, B., Birbaumer, N.: Das EEG. Psychophysiologie und Methodik von Spontan-EEG und ereigniskorrelierten Potentialen. Berlin: Springer 1985
26. Marler, P., Terrace, H.S. (Ed.): The Biology of Learning. Berlin: Springer 1984
27. Mendelson, W.B., Gillin, J.Ch., Wyatt, R.J.: Human Sleep and its Disorders. New York and London: Plenum Press 1977
28. Penfield, W., Jasper, H.: Epilepsy and the Functional Anatomy of the Human Brain. Boston: Little, Brown and Company 1954
29. Penfield, W., Roberts, L.: Speech and Brain Mechanisms. Princeton/N.J.: Princeton University Press 1959
30. Poeck, K.: Neurologie, 6. Aufl. Berlin-Heidelberg-New York: Springer 1982
31. Popper, K., Eccles, J.C.: The Self and its Brain. Berlin-Heidelberg-New York: Springer 1978
32. Rechtschaffen, A., Kales, A. (Eds.): A Manual of Standardized Terminology. Techniques and Scoring System for Sleep Stages of Human Subjects. Washington (D.C.).: Publ. Health Service, U.S. Government Printing Office 1968
33. Redfern, P.H., Campbell, I.C., Davies, J.A., Martin, K.F. (Eds.): Circadian Rhythms in the Central Nervous System. Weinheim: VCH 1985
34. Reinvang, I.: Aphasia and Brain Organization. New York: Plenum Press 1985
35. Rockstroh, B., Elbert, Th., Birbaumer, N., Lutzenberger, W.: Slow Brain Potentials and Behavior. München: Urban & Schwarzenberg 1982
36. Rohracher, H.: Die Arbeitsweise des Gehirns und die psychischen Vorgänge. München: Barth 1967
37. Rosenzweig, M.R., Leimann, A.L.: Physiological Psychology. Lexington, Mass.: D.C. Heath 1982
38. Schmitt, F.O., Worden, F.G. (Eds.): The Neurosciences, Third Study Program. Cambridge/Mass. and London: The MIT press 1974
39. Springer, S.P., Deutsch, G.: Left Brain, Right Brain, 2nd Ed. New York: Freeman 1985
40. Stöhr, M., Dichgans, J., Diener, H.C., Büttner, U.W.: Evozierte Potentiale. Berlin: Springer 1982
41. Werth, R.: Bewußtsein. Psychologische, neurobiologische und wissenschaftstheoretische Aspekte. Berlin: Springer 1983
42. Wever, R.A.: The Circadian System of Man. Berlin-Heidelberg-New York: Springer 1979
43. Woody, C.D.: Memory, Learning, and Higher Function. A Cellular View. Berlin: Springer 1982
44. Zülch, K.J., Creutzfeld, O., Galbraith, G.C. (Eds.): Cerebral Localization. Berlin-Heidelberg-New York: Springer 1975

Original Papers and Reviews

45. Creutzfeldt, O.: The neuronal generation of the EEG. In: Handbook of Electroencephalography and Clinical Neurophysiology, 2/C. (A. Remond). Amsterdam. Elsevier Scientific Publishing 1974
46. Dement, W., Kleitman, N.: Cyclic variations in EEG during sleep and their relation to eye movements, body mobility and dreaming. Electroencephalogr. Clin. Neurophysiol. *9*, 673–690, 1957
47. Diamond, I.T.: The subdivision of neocortex: A proposal to revise the traditional view of sensory, motor and association areas. In: Progress in Psychobiology and Physiological Psychology, ed. J. Sprague and A.N. Epstein, Vol. 8, pp. 1–44. New York: Academic Press 1979
48. Ervin, F.R., Anders, T.R.: Normal and pathological memory: data and a conceptual scheme. In: The Neurosciences, Second Study Program (Hrsg. F.O. Schmitt), p. 163. New York: Rockefeller University Press 1970
49. Gould, J.L.: The biology of learning. Ann. Rev. Psychol. *37*, 163–193 (1986)
50. Ingvar, D.H.: Functional landscapes of the dominant hemisphere. Brain Research *107*, 181 (1976)
51. Jouvet, M.: The role of monoamines and acetylcholine-containing neurons in the regulation of the sleep-waking cycle. Ergebn. Physiol. *64*, 166 (1972)
52. Kleist, K.: Die Lokalisation im Großhirn und ihre Entwicklung. Psychiat. Neurol. *137*, 289–309 (1959)
53. Küpfmüller, K.: Grundlagen der Informationstheorie und Kybernetik. In: Physiologie des Menschen (Eds. O.H. Gauer, K. Kramer, R. Jung), 2. Aufl. Band 10, S. 209. München, Berlin, Wien: Urban & Schwarzenberg 1974
54. Lashley, K.S.: In search of the engram. Symp. Soc. Exp. Biol. *4*, 454–482, 1950
55. Loomis, A.L., Harvey, E.N., Hobart, G.: Electrical potentials of the human brain. J exp. Psychol. *19*, 249–279 (1936)
56. Luria, A.R.: The functional organization of the brain. In: Physiological Psychology. Readings from SCIENTIFIC AMERICAN, p. 406. San Francisco: Freeman 1971
57. Milner, B.: Memory and the medial temporal regions of the brain. In: Biology of Memory (Eds. K.H. Pribram, D.E. Broadbent), p. 29, New York and London: Academic Press 1970
58. Pakkenberg, H.: The number of nerve cells in the cerebral cortex of man. J. comp. Neurol. *128*, 17 (1966)
59. Pappenheimer, J.R., Koski, G., Fencl, V., Karnovsky, M.L., Krueger, J.: Extraction of Sleep-Promoting Factor S From Cerebrospinal Fluid and From Brains of Sleep-Deprived Animals. J. Neurophysiol. *38*, 1299 (1975)
60. Roffwarg, H.P., Muzio, J.N., Dement, W.C.: Ontogenetic development of the human sleep-dream cycle. Science *152*, 604 (1966)
61. Snyder, F., Scott, J.: The psychophysiology of sleep. In: Handbook of Psychophysiology (Eds. N.S. Greenfield, R.A. Sternbach). New York: Holt 1972
62. Sperry, R.: A modified concept of consciousness. Physiol. Rev. *76*, 532 (1969)
63. Waugh, N.C., Norman, D.A.: Primary memory. Psychol. Rev. *72*, 89–104 (1965)
64. Woody, C.D.: Understanding the cellular basis of memory and learning. Ann. Rev. Psychol. *37*, 433–493 (1986)

7 The Nervous System in the Context of Information Theory

M. ZIMMERMANN

Because of functional resemblances between the nervous system and man-made communication systems – in particular, the analogy between a nerve fiber and a cable over which information is transmitted – a number of authors have approached the nervous system from the viewpoint of the communications engineer, primarily by applying information theory [6, 7, 8, 10]. The latter, together with control-systems theory (Chapter 15), constitutes the branch of science called cybernetics [1, 2, 3, 5, 9]. This chapter first presents an introduction to the fundamentals of information theory and the measurement of information content. This method is then applied to examples drawn from neurophysiology and psychophysics, to describe quantitatively the performance and limits of biological information transfer.

7.1 Introduction to Information Theory

Information theory provides a quantitative measure of the **information content** of a message and a means of describing the characteristics of information-transmitting systems [5, 11, 14, 15]. Every transmission of information involves the following components (Fig. 7-1): information source, transmitter, transmission channel, receiver, and user, plus a source of disturbance (which, in this example, affects the transmission channel). This fundamental concept of information theory can be applied to all kinds of **information transfer**, in man-made or biological systems. Below each component diagrammed in Fig. 7-1 are listed technological (verbal transmission by telex or telephone) and neurophysiological examples.

The items of information in neurophysiology are concerned, for instance, with the quality, intensity, location, spatial extent and duration of a stimulus to a sense organ. In the nerve fibers they are transmitted as a train of action potentials (nerve impulses).

Information: symbols and coding. Messages are composed of and transmitted by means of symbols (e.g., letters, numerals, Morse signals) selected in particular combinations by the information source (Fig. 7-1). Only a few letters suffice to form the many words and sentences with which we convey verbal information. Usually the symbols provided by the information

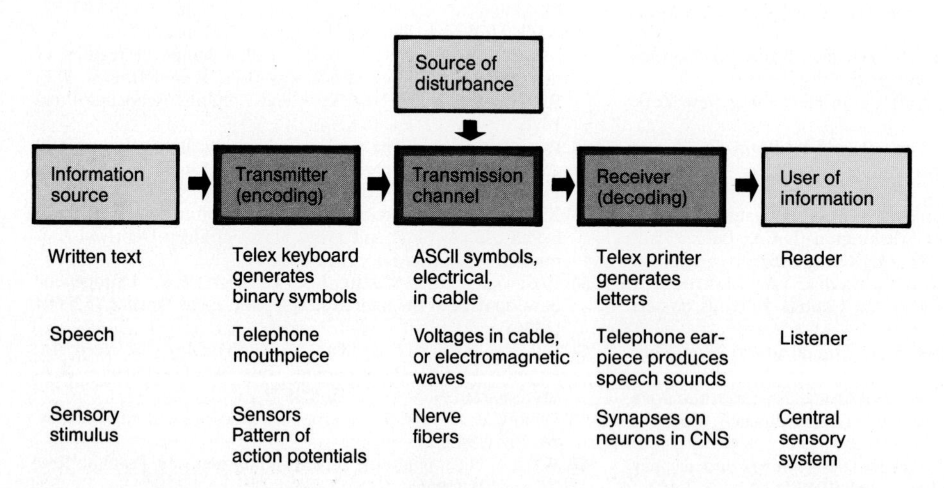

Fig. 7-1. Fundamental concept of information theory *(above)*, with examples of components of this information chain in technical and biological systems *(below)*

Morse alphabet

A .–
B –...
C –.–.
D –..
E .
F ..–.
G ––.
H ....

S ...
O –––
S ...

Fig. 7-2. Part of the Morse alphabet, as an example of coding. In the Morse code, the letters are represented by combinations of short symbols (dots) and long symbols (dashes). The symbols can be transmitted in various physical forms: lights, sounds, or electrical pulses of different durations. On the *right*, the signal for emergencies at sea (SOS) is shown in Morse code

source are encoded in the transmitter, converted to other symbols more suitable for transmission in the particular channel that will be used (e.g., frequency-modulated electromagnetic waves for VHF radio, trains of action potentials in the nervous system). Encoding is the unambiguous assignment of each member of one set of symbols to a member of another set. Examples include the assignment of a Morse symbol to each letter of the alphabet (Fig. 7-2) and the transformation of pressure on the skin into the discharge rate of a mechanoreceptor (SA receptor, see Fig. 7-5). In the receiver the transmitted information is **decoded** and passed on to the user in the original form. One of the tasks of information theory is to specify the coding procedures that are optimal for transmission in a particular channel and minimize the loss of information caused by disturbances.

Measurement of Quantity of Information

When the term **information** is used in information theory, it refers strictly to a **measurable**, mathematically formulatable aspect of a message [6, 7, 8]. The following example illustrates how one arrives at this concept of information.
When one of a fair pair of dice is thrown, one of six equally likely numbers comes up. The probability of each – which is all the player knows before the throw – is $p = 1/6$. Thus each time the player throws, he removes the same amount of **uncertainty**; each throw has the same measurable information content. More generally, *information is the quantifiable reduction of uncertainty about an event.*
It is easy to see that the less common an event is – that is, the smaller the **probability p** of its occurrence – the greater is the reduction of uncertainty when it does occur. Therefore the information content I can usefully be expressed in terms of the reciprocal of this probability, $1/p$. It also makes sense to stipulate that when an event is certain to occur, so that the probability $p = 1$, the information content $I = 0$. Accordingly, the **measurable information content I** of a message is defined as follows:

$$I = \log_2 \frac{1}{p} = \mathrm{ld} \frac{1}{p} \quad (1)$$

Here ld stands for **dual logarithm**, the logarithm to the base 2 ($\mathrm{ld} = \log_2$).
With this formula it is possible to find a numerical value for the information content of each throw in a game of dice: $I = \mathrm{ld}\ 1/(1/6) = \mathrm{ld}6 = 2.58$ bits. The **unit "bit"** will be explained in the next section.

Because pocket calculators usually have no program for the dual logarithm, we use a conversion formula:

$\mathrm{ld}\ n = \log_{10} n / \log_{10} 2 = 3.32 \cdot \log_{10} n.$

In general, the probability of occurrence of each symbol in a set of n possible symbols (or states of the information source) is $p = 1/n$. Hence Eq. (1) can be transformed into

$$I = \mathrm{ld}\ n \quad (2)$$

That is, the information content I of a message is the dual logarithm of the number n of all symbols or possible states of the information source. We shall apply this relation to neurophysiology below (pp. 168f.).

Symbols with unequal probability of occurrence. In deriving the measure of information (Eq. 2) we made the simplifying assumption that all n states of the information source occur with the same probability, $p = 1/n$ – as is true, for instance, of fair dice. But usually the individual symbols or states of an information source are not equally likely to occur. For example, in an English text "e" is the most common letter, and "z" occurs relatively rarely. Although unequal probability is the general case, we shall not consider it further in this introduction to the measure of information.
The **significance of an item of information** to the user is irrelevant in this quantitative concept of information. In a game of dice, for example, a number may mean different things to a player, depending on many factors (the nature of the game, the rules, previous experience, the other players). These aspects, which are ignored by information theory, are termed **semantic information.**

Binary and non-binary symbols; the bit. In the simplest case, information can be transmitted with a set of only 2 symbols, called **binary sym-**

bols (e.g., 0 and 1). With these, the information source can signal a *decision between two alternatives* (e.g., yes/no). Binary systems are particularly convenient from a technical viewpoint (light/dark, switch position on/off, magnetization large/small, etc.). This is one of the reasons why the information content of the binary symbol, I = ld 2 = 1, has been chosen as the unit of information; the **elementary unit of information**, the amount transmitted by a single binary symbol, is **one bit.**

A bit is a very small amount of information. If relatively long messages are to be transmitted with binary symbols, **words** must be formed by stringing several symbols together. The word length (the number of binary symbols per word) is a direct measure, in bits, of the information transmitted. The number of words that can be constructed with 2 binary digits is $2^2 = 4$, as follows: 00, 01, 10, 11. With 3 symbols $2^3 = 8$ word combinations are possible: 000, 001, 010, 011, 100, 101, 110, 111. With m binary symbols per word there are $n = 2^m$ possible combinations; that is, we can send $n = 2^m$ different signals, each with an information content of m bits.

Information content can be determined as discussed above when **any arbitrary symbols** serve as carriers of information, for any set of symbols can be represented by words made up of binary symbols. To obtain an unequivocal association (coding) of a set of n symbols with a set of binary words, the latter must have an average word length of m = ld n binary symbols. Think of some examples to illustrate this situation – for instance, the encoding in binary words of the letters A to H or the numbers 1 to 16.
Now, if an arbitrary symbol can be replaced by a binary word, then one may say that it has the same information content (in bits) as the corresponding binary word. The average information content I of a symbol in a set of n symbols is therefore I = ld n. This is Eq. (2), which was derived above from the definition of information content.

In this introduction to the basic concepts of information theory we have simplified matters considerably, particularly in assuming equal probability of occurrence for all the symbols in a set. More precise and extensive treatments of information theory can be found in the specialized literature.

Redundancy. During coding, transmission and decoding, **disturbances** of information transmission can occur (Fig. 7-1). For example, the mains electricity can introduce 50- or 60-Hz hum in a tape recording, telephone signals can be attenuated by defective cable insulation, and a television picture can be distorted if the signal from a distant transmitter is too weak. In such cases a measurable amount of information is lost. In communications technology the methods available for protecting information from disturbing influences make use of the concept of **redundancy**. As an illustration of this notion, consider an example from the field of linguistics. Try to decipher the following incomplete text (missing letters replaced by dots):

T.. i..orm.t..n c..t.nt .f
a m.ss.g. i. me.s.r.bl.

It is possible to understand what this sentence is saying even though 44% of the letters are missing. That is, written language contains **more symbols** than are necessary for the meaning to be detected. This excess of symbols is redundancy; it is measurable in bits.

Calculations based on the frequency of occurrence of the 26 letters of the alphabet in English texts have shown that the mean information content approaches an upper limit of only 1.5 bits per letter. Theoretically, neglecting the differences in probability of occurrence, the average information content of each of the 26 letters in the alphabet is ld 26 = 4.7 bits; therefore the redundancy in this case averages 4.7 bits - 1.5 bits = 3.2 bits per letter.

The advantages of this apparent waste of symbols become clear when the **transmission channel is disturbed** – for instance, with a bad telephone connection, noisy radio reception, or messy handwriting. Here the redundancy in a language ensures that a text can be recognized when only a fraction of the symbols are identifiable. Information theory provides a quantitative treatment of the fact that *information transmission is the more secure against disturbance, the greater the redundancy built into the coding*. Some simple methods of introducing redundancy are to transmit signals through many channels in parallel, to transmit each symbol several times in succession, or to add extra "parity bits" to a signal in binary code. The principle of redundancy is also realized in the nervous system.

7.2 Information Theory in Sensory Physiology

The concept illustrated in Fig. 7-1, previously treated in general, will now be applied to information transfer in the nervous system [5, 11, 14, 15]. As a suitable example, consider a receptor (sensor) with its afferent nerve fiber. Here information is encoded as a **train of nerve impulses** and transmitted in this form. The information source (see Fig. 7-1) consists of the environmental stimuli, the transmitters are the receptor cells in a sense organ, the transmission channel is the nerve fibers, the receiver is a set of central neurons, and the user is the central nervous system as a whole.

The physically measurable parameters of stimuli (e.g., intensity of pressure on the skin, location of a stimulus on the peripheral sensory surface, wavelengths of light and sound stimuli) are items of information. In many sensors the information "stimulus intensity" is encoded as the information "mean frequency of nerve impulses". This kind of code, comparable to the **frequency modulation** used in communications devices, is found in sensors of all modalities; muscle spindles, pressure receptors in the skin, chemoreceptors on the tongue, and photoreceptors of the retina all signal the intensity of their adequate stimulus by the mean frequency of the impulses in their fibers. *The frequency of nerve impulses is a universal information carrier.*

Because the afferent fibers of particular sensory receptors usually are connected to specific associated neuronal systems in the CNS, the information signalled by an impulse train is unambiguous and is interpreted appropriately. For example, Ia afferents terminate on homonymous motoneurons, mechanosensitive cutaneous afferents project to the postcentral gyrus, where they form a "map" of the body surface, and thermoreceptors send their signals to the temperature controller in the hypothalamus.

Information transmission in an ideal sensor (receptor). In what sense do the impulse trains discharged by a receptor exhibit distinct states, the information content of which can be calculated? Consider the **coding of stimulus intensity.** If a receptor is able to generate only two levels of response to a stimulus, either one impulse or none, then it can provide information about two levels of stimulus intensity; no action potential = stimulus intensity below threshold, one action potential = stimulus intensity above threshold. If a stimulus can elicit a maximum of N impulses in the afferent fiber, in theory the receptor can signal N+1 **different intensity levels** to an impulse counter in the CNS.

This situation is illustrated in Fig. 7-3. Because the impulse count N in the afferent fiber must be an integer, a plot of N vs. stimulus intensity S gives a staircase curve. In an **ideal receptor,** which responds to a maintained stimulus by discharging impulses at a constant rate, the impulse count N is the product of the impulse frequency f and the observation time t : $N = f \cdot t$. The number of distinguishable stimulus-intensity levels in the nerve-fiber discharge is thus

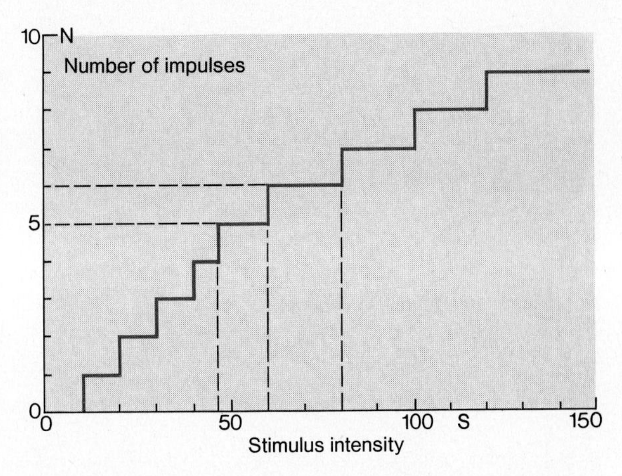

Fig. 7-3. Encoding of stimulus intensity S in nerve impulses. While a receptor (sensor) is exposed to an adequate stimulus of a certain duration, an integral number N of action potentials is generated in the afferent fiber *(ordinate)*. Therefore the curve relating response to stimulus intensity *(abscissa)* is a staircase function

$$N + 1 = f_m \cdot t + 1 \qquad (3)$$

where f_m is the maximal impulse frequency of the receptor. In the case of a receptor with spontaneous discharge (in the absence of a detectable external stimulus) at the frequency f_0, in Eq. (3) and all the following equations f_m should be replaced by $f_m - f_0$.

The size of the set of symbols available here is given by the number of distinguishable states of the discharge in the afferent nerve fiber. Hence the information content, with respect to stimulus intensity, in the example of Fig. 7-3 is $I = \text{ld}\,(N+1) = \text{ld}\,10 = 3.3$ bits. In general, for a receptor with stimulus-intensity-dependent discharge the maximal frequency f_m is the **information content** *re* **stimulus intensity** [11]

$$I = \text{ld}\,(f_m \cdot t + 1) \qquad (4)$$

This relationship is illustrated in Fig. 7-4. Clearly, the information content I rises with both f_m and t. The maximal frequency f_m is an invariant property of a receptor. By extending the observation or evaluation time t, on the other hand, the information content with respect to the intensity of a prolonged constant stimulus can be increased. In practice, the time available for evaluation of afferent discharge seems to be limited by central-

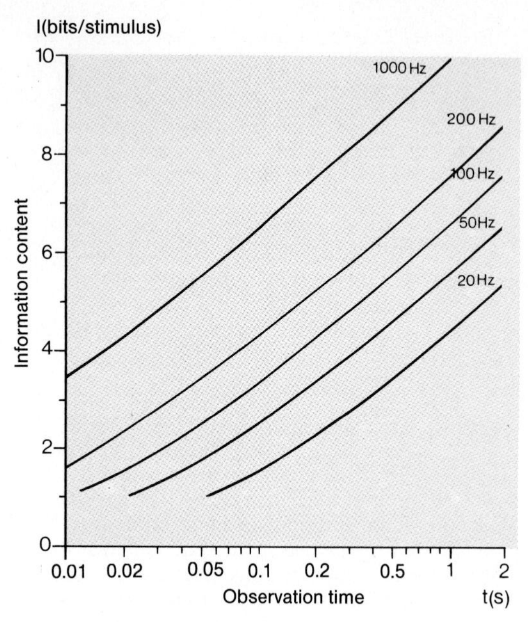

Fig. 7-4. Information content I in bits/stimulus *(ordinate)* of an ideal receptor (sensor) as a function of observation time t *(abscissa)* in seconds. The parameter distinguishing the curves is the maximal discharge frequency f_m of the sensor, calculated by Eq. (4). The *red shaded* region indicates the information content determined experimentally for mechanosensitive cutaneous sensors as a function of t. (Based on the author's own observations of SA receptors in the cat and on [14, 15])

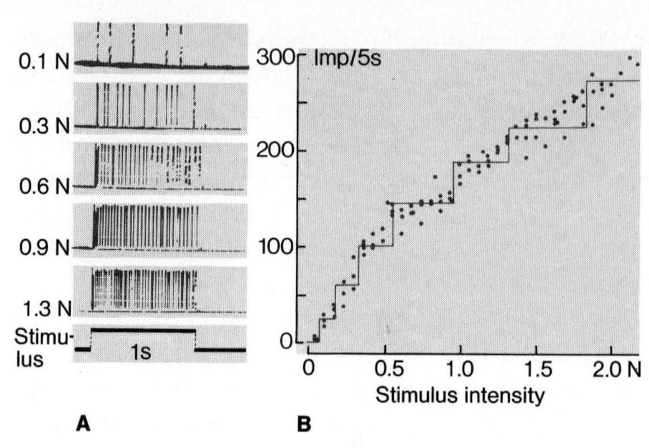

Fig. 7-5 A, B. Noise associated with coding by a real sensor (receptor). **A** Original recording of the discharge of an SA receptor in the sole of the cat's paw in response to force stimuli 1 s in duration (intensity in newtons, N). **B** Discharge rates (impulses per 5 s, *ordinate*) measured in many recordings like those in **A**, as a function of stimulus intensity *(abscissa)*. The staircase curve drawn through the scattered data shows approximately the number of stimulus intensity steps that can be distinguished in the discharge of the receptor

nervous "time constants". From studies of real receptors [15] and from psychophysical experiments [13] it is possible to estimate the extent to which an increase in observation time t can increase the information content *re* stimulus intensity (see below).

Transmission of information in a real sensor (receptor). So far we have been considering an ideal receptor, one that responds to a stimulus at constant intensity with a regular discharge at a constant frequency. Biological receptors do not behave in this way.

In experiments, when a receptor is stimulated repeatedly at the same intensity, the impulse frequency of the response is usually variable. In Fig. 7-5 the carrier of the information "stimulus intensity" is the impulse frequency of the SA sensor; the scatter of the dots shows a stochastic (random) fluctuation in impulse frequency, for no apparent reason. In communications technology, fluctuations of the information carrier in general are called **noise**. They always diminish the ability of a channel to transmit information and thus amount to a source of **disturbance** (see Fig. 7-1).

To estimate how much information is lost due to noise in the coding process, consider the experimentally measured coding relationship graphed in Fig. 7-5B. Each point represents the result of a single measurement like those in (A), but with an observation time of 5 s. The number of distinguishable states can be estimated by drawing a staircase curve through the field of dots; there are 8 steps (the first at 0 impulses), so that the amount of information that can be conveyed about stimulus intensity is ld 8 = 3 bits per stimulus.

The rationale for this graphic method of finding information content is as follows. Two stimulus intensities can be reliably distinguished if all the impulse counts associated with one of them (ordinate in Fig. 7-5B) are different from those associated with the other. The "worst case", which represents the minimum discriminability available, is given by the staircase curve with the greatest step height that can be drawn in the experimentally measured field of dots.

If our receptor were to behave like an **ideal frequency modulator** (an ideal receptor, without noise), under the conditions of the experiment in Fig. 7-5B about 300 steps of stimulus intensity would be discriminable, and the information content would be 8.2 bits per stimulus (Eq. 4). In this example of a real receptor, then, for each stimulus 8.2 bits − 3 bits = 5.2 bits are lost due to noise.

The largest values of information content per stimulus known so far in sensory receptors were obtained with muscle spindles: primary (Ia) endings can transmit 4.8 bits per 1-s stimulus, and secondary (II) endings actually transmit 6.3 bits.

Departures from the ideal receptor (sensor) are also found when the observation time t is varied. As t is increased, the information content of an ideal sensor rises continuously, as illustrated by the curves corresponding to Eq. (4) in Fig. 7-4. However, the information content of real receptors cannot be increased indefinitely by lengthening the observation time [15]. The shaded area in Fig. 7-4 represents the range within which the information content per stimulus varies with observation time as measured experimentally in slowly adapting mechanosensors. The cutaneous SA receptors in this example have essentially reached the maximum (3 bits/stimulus) after about 1 s. Thus, although many receptors can discharge at frequencies of several hundred Hz, they evidently perform no better in this regard than an ideal sensor with a maximal discharge frequency around 10 Hz.

Redundancy in the nervous system. One effective way of using redundancy to protect against information losses due to noise consists in transmitting the information over two or more channels in **parallel.** This possibility is realized in the nervous system. In the periphery the density of the receptors is usually so high that even punctate stimuli excite several nerve fibers. The information content of the combined discharge of all the activated sensory fibers is greater than that of a single fiber, as the relative noise levels (i.e., the relative stochastic fluctuations of the impulse discharge) decrease with increasing discharge rate [12, 13]. In general, *redundancy by transmission in parallel fibers compensates for disturbance (noise) of coding in the sensor.*

The extent to which the information content of such parallel transmissions is actually utilized depends on the nature of the central nervous processing. For instance, on the assumption that the evaluation of stimulus intensity is based simply on summation of the activity in all the afferent fibers activated by the stimulus, the information available can be calculated from the **variability of the summed discharge,** by the method illustrated in Fig. 7-5B. In the process of summation the total number of impulses increases approximately linearly with the number of afferent fibers, but there is a smaller increase in the variability of discharge (noise) – the width of the band of uncertainty occupied by the dots in Fig. 7-5B – as the number of fibers increases. Therefore a greater number of steps can be drawn (as in Fig. 7-5B) through the data points obtained from a set of simultaneously responding afferents; accordingly, the information content of the summed discharge is greater than that of the discharge of a single afferent fiber.

Redundancy is achieved by parallel transmission in the central nervous system as well. But here new factors enter. Because of convergence and divergence in synaptic relay stations, the parallel channels may be cross-connected. It has been demonstrated by information theory that such an arrangement provides additional redundancy compared to simple parallel-fiber transmission.

Under these conditions, however, there would have to be an enormous spatial diffusion of the excitation in the CNS (see Chapter 8) and hence a loss of information about the site of the stimulus. Lateral inhibition (see Chapter 8, Fig. 8-7) can be regarded as a means of counteracting this loss of spatial acuity in the central mapping of a stimulus. In a more general interpretation, we can consider lateral inhibition as a mechanism for the adaptation of central nervous processing to different tasks. Depending on the degree of lateral inhibition, the map of the periphery that is produced in the CNS will preserve either more information about stimulus intensity or more about the location of the stimulus.

7.3 Measurement of Information in Psychology

The quantitative concept of information is also employed in experimental psychology, especially in psychophysics (see Chapter 8) [4, 12, 13]. Here we shall give some examples of such applications, emphasizing the relationships between the neurophysiological and psychophysical data so obtained. In the latter experiments, people can **subjectively estimate** the intensity of a stimulus (such as light to the eyes, or pressure on the skin) and express it in some way – for instance, on a numerical scale (see Chapters 8 and 10, Fig. 8-14). When such estimates are repeated and plotted as a function of the objective stimulus intensities, the resulting graph corresponds to Fig. 7-5B, with the number on the ordinate representing the subjective estimate instead of the receptor discharge. The information content can be found from the scatter of the data in the same way as before, though in this psychophysical experiment we are dealing with information at the level of **conscious perception**. For example, when a subject was asked to estimate the intensity of a pressure stimulus to the skin, an information content of about 3 bits per stimulus was found; this value is about the same as that for a single pressure sensor (see Fig. 7-5B).

When an area of 1 cm^2 on the hand is stimulated by mechanical pressure, about 20 afferent fibers from slowly adapting (SA) receptors are excited. In the psychophysical experiment with this stimulus about 3 bits of information regarding stimulus intensity can be consciously extracted. Evidently, then, in this psychophysical experiment only a small fraction of the information in the afferent nerve fibers is evaluated to give the subjective perception of intensity. As far as this very special psychophysical question about the intensity of a stimulus is concerned, the remaining neuronal information would be considered redundant.

In interpreting this result, one should not ignore the fact that the discharge in the population of SA fibers also conveys information about the size, shape, location and surface properties of the pressure stimulus; all of these can be evaluated consciously or unconsciously and examined in psychophysical experiments. Studies of the ability of human subjects to detect the **location** of a touch stimulus to the body surface have shown that more than 200 different skin areas can be distinguished; the psychophysically measured information about the site of stimulation is therefore about 8 bits (= ld 256) per stimulus.
In another kind of experiment, two stimuli are presented consecutively to determine the smallest **intensity difference** that can be detected. In psychophysical experiments of this kind, with cold stimuli to the skin, temperature differences of 0.05°C were perceived [13]. Comparison of the psychophysical and neurophysiological information values of cold stimuli, as above, showed that the subjective discrimination of these cold stimuli required the use of the information contained in the summed discharge of all the afferents from cold receptors (see Fig. 9-13) in the stimulated skin area. For this task, all the available neuronal information is evaluated to produce the perception.

Neuronal and psychophysical information flow. We now consider how the overall sensory-neurophysiological information compares with psychophysical information. For this purpose, the performance of our information-transfer systems is characterized by the **maximal information flow** in bits/s, which is also called channel capacity.
The **channel capacity** of a mechanosensor (see Fig. 7-5), for example, is found experimentally by raising the repetition rate in a series of stimuli, simultaneously shortening the individual stimuli. For stimulus durations below about 1 s, the information content of the individual stimulus decreases (see Fig. 7-4), but because there are more stimuli per unit time there is usually an increase in information flow. Table 7-1 shows the channel capacities of all the receptors in various sense organs, estimated from the total number of afferent fibers and the channel capacity of each fiber. Next to these are the corresponding values for **psychophysical channel capacity**, the maximal information flow at the level of conscious perception. In the psychophysical experiments from which the latter were taken, the measurement of capacity for the visual system was based on reading, and for the auditory system, on hearing speech.
As we know from personal experience, our full **conscious attention** can be directed to only one sense organ at a time. Therefore it is impossible for more than one of the values for maximal psychophysical information flow listed on the right in Table 7-1 to apply at any given time. It follows that the maximal information flow in conscious sensory perception is 40 bits/s, many orders of magnitude below that in the sensors (on the left in Table 7-1). *What we perceive at any moment, therefore, is limited to an extremely small compartment in the stream of information about our surroundings flowing in from the sense organs.*

Table 7-1. Comparison of neuronal information flow with the information flow for conscious perception, in five sensory systems. On the *left* are the estimated numbers of sensors and afferents in each system and an estimate of the maximal overall information flow (channel capacity). On the *right* side are the corresponding values for the maximal information flow available at the level of consciousness, the channel capacities derived from psychophysical experiments; here estimates are indicated by (?).

Sensory system	No. of sensors	No. of afferents	Total channel capacity (bits/s)	CNS	Psychophysical channel capacity (bits/s)
Eyes	$2 \cdot 10^8$	$2 \cdot 10^6$	10^7	Processing in Central Nervous System	40
Ears	$3 \cdot 10^4$	$2 \cdot 10^4$	10^5		30
Skin	10^7	10^6	10^6		5
Taste	$3 \cdot 10^7$	10^3	10^3		1 (?)
Smell	$7 \cdot 10^7$	10^5	10^5		1 (?)

7.4 References

Textbooks and Handbooks

1. ERISMANN, T.H.: Grundprobleme der Kybernetik. Berlin-Heidelberg-New York: Springer 1972
2. FLECHTNER, H.-J.: Grundbegriffe der Kybernetik. Eine Einführung, Stuttgart: Wissenschaftl. Verl. Ges. 1966
3. FRANK, H.: Kybernetik, Brücke zwischen den Wissenschaften. Frankfurt: Umschau-Verlag 1970
4. GARNER, V.R.: Uncertainty and Structure as Psychological Concepts. New York: John Wiley 1962
5. KEIDEL, W.D.: Einführung in die biologische Kybernetik. Darmstadt: Wissenschaftliche Buchgesellschaft 1985
6. SAMPSON, J.R.: Adaptive Information Processing, An Introductory Survey. Heidelberg: Springer 1976

7. Pierce, J.R.: An Introduction to Information Theory: Symbols, Signals and Noise. Mineola, N.Y.: Dover Pubns. Inc. 1980
8. Reza, F.M.: An Introduction to Information Theory. New York: McGraw-Hill 1961
9. Shannon, C.E., Weaver, W.: The Mathematical Theory of Communication. Urbana: The University of Illinois Press 1949
10. Wiener, N.: Cybernetics. Paris, New York: Freymann 1948

Original Papers and Reviews

11. Grüsser, O.-J.: Informationstheorie und die Signalverarbeitung in den Sinnesorganen und im Nervensystem. Naturwissenschaften *59*, 436 (1972)
12. Darian-Smith, I.: The sense of touch: performance and peripheral neural processes. In: Handbook of Physiology, Sect. 1: The Nervous System (Eds. Brookhart, J.D., Mountcastle, V.B.), p. 739. Baltimore: William & Wilkins 1984
13. Darian-Smith, I.: Thermal sensibility. In: Handbook of Physiology, Sect. 1: The Nervous System (Eds. Brookhart, J.D., Mountcastle, V.B.), p. 879. Baltimore: William & Wilkins 1984
14. Walloe, L.: On the transmission of information through sensory neurons. Biophys. J. *10*, 745 (1970)
15. Werner, G., Mountcastle, V.B.: Neural activity in mechanoreceptive cutaneous afferents: stimulus-response relations, Weber functions and information transmission. J. Neurophysiol. *28*, 359 (1965)

III
General and Special Sensory Physiology

8 General Sensory Physiology

H. O. Handwerker

8.1 Subject Matter of General Sensory Physiology

The "general" branch of sensory physiology is concerned with the basic principles underlying sensory abilities – both the operation of the individual **sensory systems** and the subjective **perceptions** that result. The two require different research strategies. When the operation of sensory systems is examined by making physicochemical measurements, we speak of objective sensory physiology; when subjective perceptions are studied with psychological methods and the results applied to the analysis of sensory functions, this approach is called subjective sensory physiology.

Objective and Subjective Sensory Physiology

Of the multitude of environmental factors impinging on our bodies, some (but by no means all) are able to affect our sense organs. In this context such factors are called **sensory stimuli**. These stimuli cause receptor cells to generate potentials that activate afferent sensory nerve fibers. The impulses discharged by many afferent nerve fibers are conducted to sensory centers in the brain, where they are processed. The chain of physicochemical events leading up to this point can be observed and analyzed by the methods used to study other physiological events. This area of research is called **objective sensory physiology.** Because the sense organs of humans and animals are organized on similar fundamental principles, certain general rules of objective sensory physiology can be formulated.

A sensory stimulus often gives rise to a subjective sensory impression. Sensory impressions are the elements of **sensations.** For example, electromagnetic oscillations with the wavelength 400 nm elicit the sensory impression "blue". A person who says "I see a blue area within which are round white areas of various sizes" is describing such a sensation. Normally we immediately attempt to interpret our sensations by fitting them into what we have previously experienced and learned; the sensation becomes a **perception.** The sensation "I see a blue area ..." might correspond to the perception "There are clouds in the sky." The effect of experience on perception goes still further: where a meteorologist sees stratocumuli, an illustrator of children's books might see the clouds as woolly sheep. Perceptions are influenced by many mental factors, such as one's mood. Our perceptions, of which we are conscious directly without the aid of measuring instruments, appear to us as something entirely different from the receptor potentials and action potentials recorded by the methods of objective sensory physiology. When we draw upon subjective sensations and perceptions to determine what our sense organs can accomplish, we are in the area of **subjective sensory physiology.**

The "picture puzzle" shown in Fig. 8-1 gives a vivid illustration of the fact that a perception is not simply like a photographic representation of the surroundings provided by the sense organs. The object in Fig. 8-1 can be seen as either a hare's head or a duck's head. If you look at the picture for some time, the two perceptions often alternate, although there has apparently been no change in the information mediated by the eyes. Furthermore, we cannot see the hare and the duck simultaneously, even though we

Fig. 8-1. The "hareduck", a two-way picture designed by Jastrow, first published around 1900. (From [6])

know that the picture is ambiguous. Perception is evidently given structure and made unambiguous by active, integrative processes in the brain [6].

Since the last century sensory physiologists have been concerned primarily with the quantitative relation between stimulus magnitude and the magnitude of subjective sensation. This field of research, called **psychophysics** (see pp. 186 ff.), belongs equally to sensory physiology and experimental psychology – or, more precisely, **perception psychology.** Recently, however, for many sensory systems it has been possible to unite physiological measurements of the performance of sense organs with the measurement of the associated sensations, so that the two realms can be compared directly. Such studies are assigned to the area of **psychophysiology,** and in this book they are discussed under the heading **integrative sensory physiology.**

Figure 8-2 shows a rough diagram of the mapping of each sensory level onto the next. Here the black arrows signify "induces" or "leads to". The dashed red arrow marks the transition from the physical to the mental dimension. Can one interpret the "leads to" as a causal connection at this point?

Mind-body problem. Over the centuries, philosophers have developed various theories regarding the nature of mind and its relation to the body. Today two basic positions dominate. According to one, the complex cerebral processes following a sensory stimulus are identical to the subjective sensations; the two are simply different dimensions or ways of considering a single phenomenon, the function of the brain. This is the **monist viewpoint.** For monists, the dashed arrow in Fig. 8-2 does not represent a causal link, and should be replaced by an equals sign.

From the other, **dualist** point of view, the brain is the complicated instrument of an independent mind (or soul). The dashed arrow in Fig. 8-2 then does represent a causal link; brain processes act upon the mind – and vice versa.

How such causal interactions of brain and mind can take place is beyond our knowing. The mind-body problem is a philosophical problem, which cannot be solved by the methods of the natural sciences [11]. That this is so is evident in our inability to think of an experiment that would refute ("falsify", in the sense of POPPER [22]) either the monist or the dualist view. Neurophysiologists and psychologists have also occupied themselves with philosophical considerations directed to the mind-body problem [12, 23].

Parapsychology. Can parapsychology provide an empirical solution to the mind-body problem? Parapsychologists are concerned with the empirical demonstration of phenomena such as telepathy and precognition (clairvoyance). These phenomena are subsumed under **ESP** (extrasensory perception), and various experiments have been devised to demonstrate them. If ESP existed, that would of course be a strong argument in favor of a body-independent mind, which contains extrasensory information. Nevertheless, not all dualists believe in ESP.

Parapsychological studies have not so far produced a proof of the existence of ESP phenomena that convinces skeptics [14]. The difficulty is probably not that the parapsychologists, as outsiders, have been treated unfairly by the "scientific establishment" (as they sometimes believe themselves), but rather that their scientific methods are not adequate to document ESP phenomena, primarily for two reasons. First, such ESP phenomena as may exist evidently occur only rarely, under poorly controlled conditions, and are not reproducible. Errors of statistical interpretation are often made here; for example, when a dice-player succeeds in throwing "6" three times in succession, he has presumably been lucky and has not demonstrated ESP ability. There is little point in calculating afterward that the probability of this event is only $1/6 \cdot 1/6 \cdot 1/6$, or less than 0.5%, because once an event has occurred its probability is irrelevant. The event would constitute a proof of the player's extraordinary ability only if he had said in advance that he would throw this sequence of sixes. If he

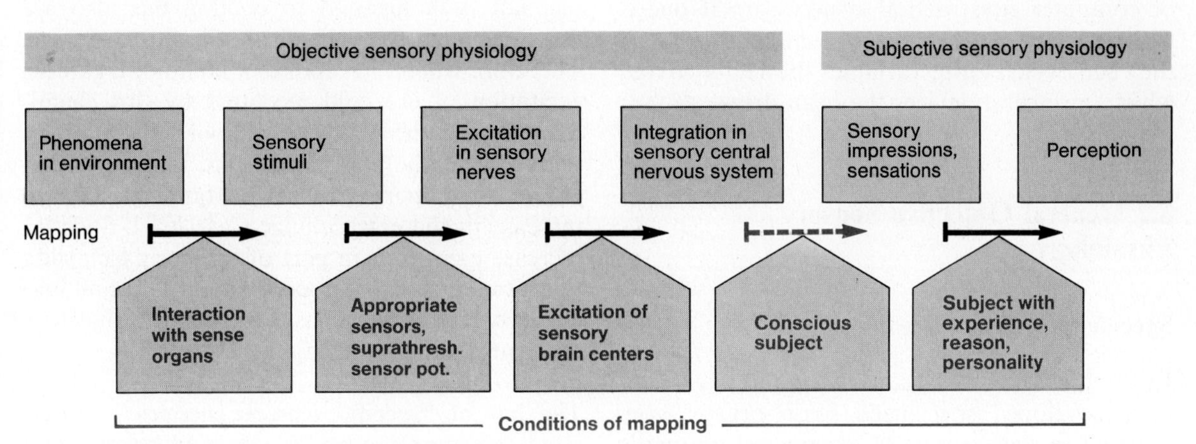

Fig. 8-2. Diagram of the mapping relationships in sensory physiology. The *boxes* represent basic phenomena of sensory physiology, and the *arrows* between them denote "leads to" or "induces", under the conditions listed below each arrow. The *dashed arrow* is at the transition from physiological to mental processes

could do so, of course, the next step would be to look for a trick. And here lies the second reason for the difficulty: parapsychology presents a fascinating history of illusions, which have ensnared even seemingly critical scientists [14]. Those with a "talent" for ESP often like to excuse themselves from strictly controlled experiments on the grounds that such situations diminish their extrasensory powers. Experiments in this area demand very precise controls, great skill at detecting trickery, and a thorough knowledge of the techniques of professional magicians, which is uncommon among scientists.

Independent validity of physiological and psychological rules. One might think that a monist standpoint with respect to the mind-body problem would make it superfluous to divide sensory physiology into subjective and objective approaches. But this is not the case. Regardless of whether processes ascribable to the mind are fundamentally "identical" to the brain functions or not, each dimension – the physical and the mental – has its own distinct set of rules and relationships, and hence its own concepts and terminology. This independence of different dimensions can be illustrated by the example of a computer. A complete, exact knowledge of its construction, the hardware, does not in itself convey a thorough understanding of the functional laws of a "higher" computer language such as BASIC, and certainly no understanding of the functional laws and content of particular programs that can run on this computer. It is presumably no more likely that complete knowledge of the anatomy and physiology of the brain could explain the behavior of a human being.
Nevertheless, as detailed in Section 8.4, on "integrative sensory physiology", the mental dimension is based on and determined by the dimension of brain functions. It is from objective sensory physiology that we learn the boundary conditions for perception. Similarly, knowledge of computer construction is necessary if one is to know how large programs can be, how fast they run, which input variables they refer to and which peripheral devices they can drive.

8.2 General Objective Sensory Physiology

Specificity of Sense Organs

In the course of evolution all animal organisms have developed specialized sense organs, constructed in such a way as to respond optimally to particular stimuli. It is usually easy to discover, by observing the responses of the organism, what the optimal stimulus for a sense organ is. Most commonly, it proves to be the stimulus requiring minimal energy to excite that organ. We call the form of stimulation that elicits optimal response of a sense organ the **adequate stimulus** for the organ. For example, the rods and cones of the retina can be excited by rubbing the eyeball strongly with a finger, as is evident when such massage produces visual impressions. However, the optimal (and hence adequate) stimuli are electromagnetic oscillations with wavelengths between 400 and 800 nm. The specificity of a sense organ is greater, the more likely it is to be excited, under physiological conditions, only by adequate stimuli.

Structure of sense organs as a cause of specificity. In many sense organs it is not only the properties of the receptor cells that determine which stimulus is adequate, but also the macroscopic structure of the organ. For instance, the adequate stimulus for the receptors in the vestibular organ and those in the inner ear, which are hair cells in both cases, is a flow of endolymph that deflects the hairs and thereby excites the cells. But the structure of the inner ear ensures that here the endolymph flow occurs when mechanical oscillations at frequencies of 20-20,000 Hz reach the cochlea, whereas in the vestibular organ the endolymph is displaced when the position of the head changes.

Responses of sense organs to stimuli of different kinds. When chemical stimuli are taken into consideration as well as physical stimuli, it is not always simple to discover the adequate stimulus for a sense organ from a purely formal consideration of energy requirements. The cold receptors in the mucosa of mouth and nose, for example, not only respond to cooling but also are quite sensitive to a chemical stimulus, menthol. Therefore when one smokes a menthol cigarette, excitation of the cold receptors by this chemical produces the sensation of cool smoke. Warm receptors in the skin, which are excited by increases in temperature, are also quite sensitive to increase in the extracellular Ca^{2+} level. Such an increase can occur in part of the body following injection of a calcium-containing solution into an associated artery; as a result, the injection will cause a local sensation of warmth.

The law of "specific sensory energies", formulated 150 years ago by JOHANNES MÜLLER, states that the nature of a sensation is determined not by the stimulus but by the sense organ that is

stimulated. The examples above offer evidence of its validity. This law is an important rule of subjective sensory physiology.
With regard to objective sensory physiology, it follows that the central processing of the excitation originating in a sense organ is a crucial determinant of that organ's specificity. For example, warm receptors in the skin are responsible for thermoreception and thermoregulation mainly because of their central connections.

Categorization of the senses. The diverse sense organs in the body can be classified in three large groups, as follows.
(i) The first things we think of when we hear the word "senses" are the organs and sensors that receive stimuli from our surroundings. These sensors (receptors) are all in the category of **exteroceptors.**
(ii) Other sense organs detect muscle length, the stretching of tendons, the angles at joints and other parameters of position and movement of the body; these are the **proprioceptors.** The vestibular organ is also assigned to this group of sense organs.
(iii) Finally, the visceral nerves mediate sensory information from the region of the internal organs. These afferents are called **interoceptors**.
Much – perhaps most – of the information sent to the CNS by interoceptors and proprioceptors rarely or never reaches our consciousness. For instance, we are unconscious of the signals from the *baroreceptors* in the carotid sinus, which continuously monitor the arterial blood pressure. For a long time there was disagreement as to whether the impulses from the muscle spindles reach the conscious level. The resolution was eventually provided by McCLOSKEY [20], in an experiment on himself in which a muscle was exposed surgically and stimulated in a manner adequate for *primary (Ia) muscle-spindle afferents.* The result demonstrated conclusively that an increase in the discharge rate of muscle-spindle afferents, in isolation, produces a sensation of a change in position in the affected limb.

The Transduction Process

In every sense organ there are "receptors", excitation of which initiates the sensory process. Unfortunately, the term has recently become somewhat ambiguous. Originally a receptor was understood to be a sense cell, but today the same term is used by molecular biologists to denote complexes of molecules in cell membranes that react specifically with other molecules, such as hormones. And even in the context of sensory physiology, the term "receptor" is not unambiguous, because anatomists and physiologists use it somewhat differently. Anatomists consider a receptor to be a morphologically characterizable cell, whereas sensory physiologists view a receptor as the part of the membrane of a sensory cell or nerve ending that is specialized for the reception of stimuli. We shall adopt the term **sensor** for this "sensory-physiological receptor" and define it as the cell or part of a cell that is responsible for the transduction of stimuli into neural excitation. Sensors are often the peripheral axonal or dendritic endings of afferent nerve fibers. On the other hand, in some sense organs the afferent nerve endings are connected to specialized, nonneural sense cells (e.g., the hair cells in the cochlea). In the retina, finally, there are sense cells of neural origin, the rods and cones, to which the term "sensor" as defined here also applies.

The sensor potential. The sensors "translate" the energy of the stimulus into a change in permeability of the sensor membrane, in a process called *transduction.* The permeability change causes a potential change, the "receptor potential". Because receptor potentials generate action potentials in the afferent nerve fibers, they have also been termed **generator potentials.** Here we shall call these potentials **sensor potentials.**

Definition of the sensor. The above definition can now be reworded in terms of potentials: the sensor is a cell, or section of the membrane of a cell, that develops sensor potentials which are encoded in the associated afferents as trains of action potentials. In those sensors in the skin, viscera and muscles, the function of which has been elucidated, the sensor potentials are found in the endings of the afferent nerve fibers. These endings themselves are therefore the sites of transduction. They may take the form of naked nerve endings, lying free in the tissue, or they may be embedded in specialized structures such as corpuscles or muscle spindles.
The potential changes produced by stimulation of various sensors can be recorded with intracellular microelectrodes. Three examples of sensors in which the generator potentials have been measured are shown in Fig. 8-3. In two of these cases, the muscle spindle and the Pacinian corpuscle (PC sensor), the sensor is the axon terminal; in the other it is a separate cell, the hair cell. The sensor potential in the latter is thought to excite

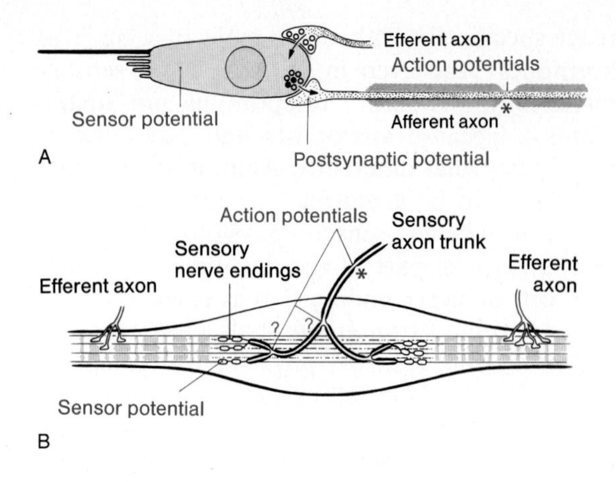

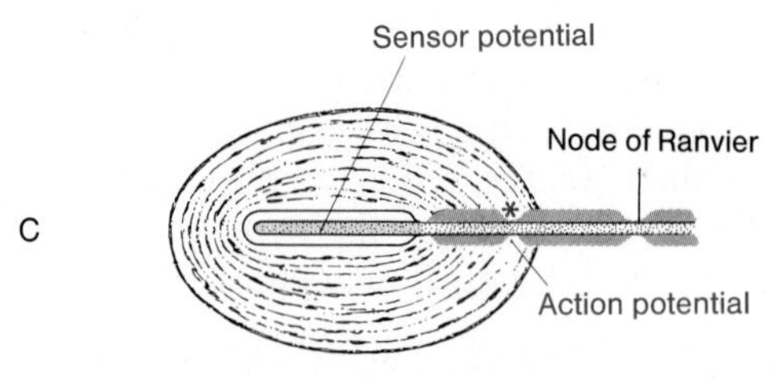

Sensor potential

Node of Ranvier

C

Action potential

Fig. 8-3 A-C. Various types of sensors. **A** Hair cell in the cochlea or the vestibular organ. **B** Muscle spindle of the frog. **C** Pacinian corpuscle. The *asterisks* mark the points at which transformation from generator potential to action potential is thought to occur. (A modified from FLOCK in [2])

the afferent axon by way of a synaptic mechanism, the transmitter of which is not yet known (see also Chapter 12).

The nature of the molecular mechanisms underlying transduction of the stimulus into a sensor potential within the sensor membrane is not entirely understood in most cases. One reason is that the receptive sites on the cell membranes are usually very small and often relatively inaccessible. In principle, transduction involves the opening of membrane channels to allow currents of ions to flow through the membrane, driven by extra-/intracellular concentration differences. The membrane channels are controlled by special molecular complexes that are altered by the stimulus. In chemoreceptors, the binding of receptive membrane molecules to the stimulus substance influences a molecule that opens ion channels. In mechanoreceptors, stretching of the membrane could influence the channel size so as to allow the entry of ionic currents. The sensor potentials in all these sensors are depolarizing. In the photoreceptors of the retina, the rods and cones, an ionic current flows chiefly in the dark; it is blocked when light acts on the disk membranes of the outer segments of the sensors. Here a hyperpolarizing sensor potential is produced.

Properties of sensor potentials in afferent nerve endings:

1. They are produced *in the nerve ending itself*, not in the cells surrounding the nerve endings, which are part of the structure of the sense organ. This property is well demonstrated by the PC sensor (Fig. 8-4), the axon of which remains excitable by mechanical stimuli even when the surrounding onion-like structure is removed. Further proximal, where the action potentials are generated and conducted away, the axon membrane is much less sensitive to mechanical influences.

The equilibrium potential of the PC-sensor membrane is about 0 mV. The implication is that the permeability change induced by a mechanical stimulus is not restricted to the Na^+ channels.

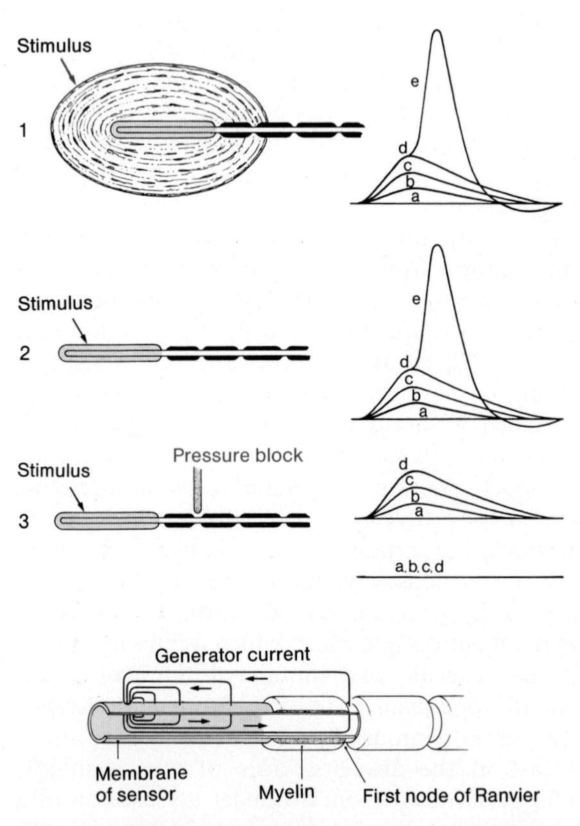

Fig. 8-4. Generator potentials and action potentials of a PC sensor (Pacinian corpuscle). **1** Weak stimulation of an isolated PC sensor at the site marked with an *arrow* induces sensor potentials (generator potentials), the amplitude of which encodes the stimulus intensity *(a-d)*. Suprathreshold sensor potentials trigger action potentials *(e)*. **2** Even after the layers surrounding the sensor have been removed, sensor potentials can be produced by mechanical stimulation. **3** Pressure exerted at the 1st node of Ranvier of the afferent axon blocks the production of action potentials, but does not affect the sensor potential. Below: Triggering of action potentials at the first node by electrotonic spread of the generator potential. (Modified from LOEWENSTEIN, [19])

Recordings from Pacinian corpuscles in vitro have shown that when all the Na^+ is removed from the surrounding solution, the sensor potential is reduced to about 1/3 of the control size but not eliminated. Additional evidence is that the Na^+ channels involved in the sensor potential are fairly insensitive to tetrodotoxin (TTX), quite unlike the Na^+ channels at the nodes of Ranvier of the axon, which are responsible for producing the action potential. It is possible for the sensor potential of a PC sensor to persist even when conduction of the action potentials in the afferent fiber has been blocked with TTX.

2. The sensor potential is a *graded response.* Most sensors are depolarized (or hyperpolarized, in the case of rods and cones) to different degrees by stimuli of different intensity. Although the amplitude of the sensor potential reflects the magnitude of the stimulus, the stimulus is not the source of energy for this potential change. As explained above, the sole action of the stimulus is to control ionic currents through the membrane.

The receptive membranes of many sensors are extremely sensitive to their adequate stimuli. In some cases their sensitivity seems to reach the theoretical limit. For instance, the hair cells of the cochlea are excited by a movement no greater than the diameter of a hydrogen atom. Even one photon can trigger sufficiently large currents through the membrane of a single rod in the retina that the resulting generator potential has a measurable effect on the activity of retinal ganglion cells associated with that rod. That is, transduction involves an amplification process.

3. The sensor potential is a *local potential,* which spreads over the membrane electrotonically and is not actively conducted.

4. Sensor potentials can undergo *spatial and temporal summation.* When two weak stimuli are applied simultaneously to the PC sensor, for example, they can elicit a suprathreshold depolarization. And when two weak stimuli occur in such rapid succession that the second sensor potential is added to the first, suprathreshold depolarization can result.

Altogether, then, sensor potentials have many properties in common with the local synaptic currents of central neurons.

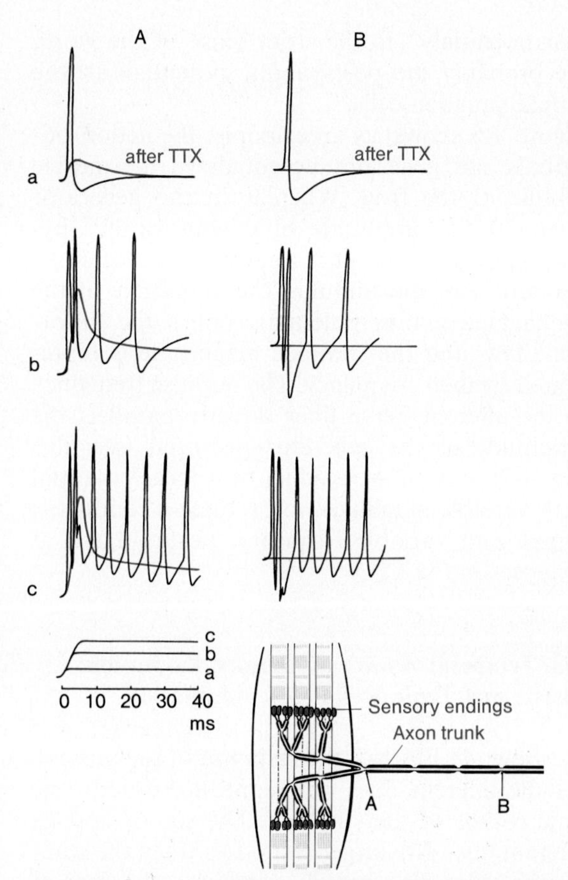

Fig. 8-5 A, B. Generator potentials and trains of action potentials in a frog muscle spindle, and the effect of tetrodotoxin on them. **Top**: recordings from the afferent axon trunk near the sensory nerve endings *(A)* and further proximal *(B)* for various degrees of muscle stretching *(a, b, c,* time course of stimulus at bottom left). The *black curves* indicate action potentials; in **A** they are superimposed on sensor potentials, but in **B**, a recording further away from the sensors, the sensor potential is not visible. *Black* recordings under normal conditions, *red* after action potentials are blocked with tetrodotoxin (TTX). The rate of depolarization and the action-potential frequency are functions of the amplitude of depolarization of the sensor potential. **Bottom**: sketch of the middle region of a frog muscle spindle, showing the recording sites *A* and *B*. (Modified from OTTOSON and SHEPHERD in [2])

Transformation of Generator Potentials into Trains of Action Potentials

As the next step in the excitation of the sensors, the generator or sensor potential gives rise to a sequence of action potentials. This **transformation** ordinarily takes place at the first node of Ranvier in the afferent nerve fiber. Some afferents are unmyelinated (e.g., nociceptors and warm fibers); the exact site of transformation in these is unknown. The generator potential must spread electrotonically to the site of action-potential generation, just as the synaptic potentials in the soma of a motoneuron spread to the axon hillock (see p. 50). In some sense cells, such as the hair cells of the inner ear and the photoreceptors of the retina, synaptic processes are probably interposed between the sensor potentials and the action potentials. Here the "gener-

ator potentials", in the strict sense of the word, are probably the postsynaptic potentials in the retinal ganglion cells.
Figure 8-5 shows, as an example, the action potentials and generator potentials in the muscle spindle of the frog. Whereas in the generator potential the amplitude of depolarization (hyperpolarization, in photoreceptors) reflects the magnitude of the stimulus, the amplitude of the propagated action potentials obeys the all-or-none law, and the stimulus magnitude is represented by their frequency. The impulse frequency in the afferent nerve fiber directly parallels the amplitude of the generator potential (see also Fig. 8-2). A similar **recoding** of a local potential with variable **amplitude**, to produce a conducted signal with variable **frequency**, occurs again at synapses in the CNS.

The Temporal Aspect of Sensory Excitation: Phasic and Tonic Responses, Adaptation

As shown in Fig. 8-5, the response of the muscle-spindle afferent does not reproduce exactly the time course of the stimulus. The sensor and its afferent fiber give larger responses when the stimulus is increasing rapidly, signaling the rate of change of the stimulus. This aspect of the response is called the **dynamic** or **phasic** or **differential** response – the latter because the rate of change (velocity, v) is given by the first derivative of length with respect to time: $dL/dt = v$.
On the other hand, if the response of a sensor is largely independent of the rate of change of the stimulus, it is called **tonic** or **static** or **proportional.** In most sensors, even a tonic response slowly declines when a constant stimulus is maintained for a long time. This decrease in excitation is called **adaptation.**
The sensor shown in Fig. 8-5 is a **PD sensor**, a sensor with both differential and proportional characteristics. The various sensors and afferents differ greatly in their phasic and tonic sensitivity.

The causes of differences in the adaptation rates of different sensors. The PC sensor acts as an acceleration detector because of its extremely rapid adaptation, which is enabled by the onion-like layering of the structure that surrounds it. This extraordinarly compact structure acts as a mechanical high-pass filter, which shields the receptive ending (the sensor) from continuous pressure and transmits only the high-frequency components of mechanical stimuli.
However, the various sensors do not all differ in adaptation rate for the same reason. Furthermore, these differences are not always based on the structure of the sensors; the rate of adaptation can also be determined by the process in which the generator potential is transformed into a train of action potentials. For example, when the first node of Ranvier of a PC afferent is depolarized with a long current pulse, only a brief response is elicited, 1-2 action potentials. When the same experiment is performed with the first node of Ranvier of a frog muscle spindle afferent, the prolonged depolarization generates a long-lasting series of action potentials. The rate of adaptation of an afferent nerve fiber is ultimately determined in the conducting membrane, at the stage of recoding from generator potential to action potentials.

The most common type of adaptation. With regard to information transfer in sensory systems, it should be noted that the frequency of occurrence of the various types of adaptation is not uniform. Although there are some afferents with extremely rapid adaptation (e.g., PC afferents) and others with extremely slow adaptation (e.g., secondary muscle-spindle afferents), most afferents have the **PD characteristic** illustrated in Fig. 8-5. These inform the nervous system about stimulus magnitude (proportional component of the response) but emphasize, by discharging impulses at a higher frequency (in the differential component), the rapid changes in the stimulus which are particularly important for regulatory processes (reflexes). In most sensory channels, this preferential transmission of information about rapid changes in a stimulus is further amplified during transmission to higher neurons in the CNS.

The Spatial Aspect of Sensory Excitation; Receptive Fields

A sensor in the skin is excited by those stimuli that affect the skin immediately overlying the sensor. The afferent nerve fiber from this sensor can have several branches, each innervating a different sensor. A single afferent nerve fiber can therefore be stimulated within a larger area; the size of its **receptive field** depends on the degree of arborization. To distinguish these receptive fields from those of central neurons, we call them **primary receptive fields** (see Fig. 8-6).
The primary afferent nerve fibers converge onto central sensory neurons, with various numbers of afferents per central neuron. As a result, the

receptive fields of the central neurons can be larger than the primary fields of the afferents.
The size of the receptive fields of primary and higher sensory neurons has a characteristic spatial distribution for most sensory modalities. For example, the receptive fields of many cutaneous afferents in the fingertip are smaller than those in the skin of the forearm or the trunk. At higher levels this difference is more pronounced. In the somatosensory projection field of the cortex, the "fingertip" neurons have much smaller receptive fields than the "trunk" neurons. The same is true of the retina; the receptive fields of ganglion cells connected to foveal sensors are smaller than those innervated by sensors in the periphery of the retina. In regions with high **innervation density** there is a finer spatial resolution of stimuli (see also Chapters 9 and 11).

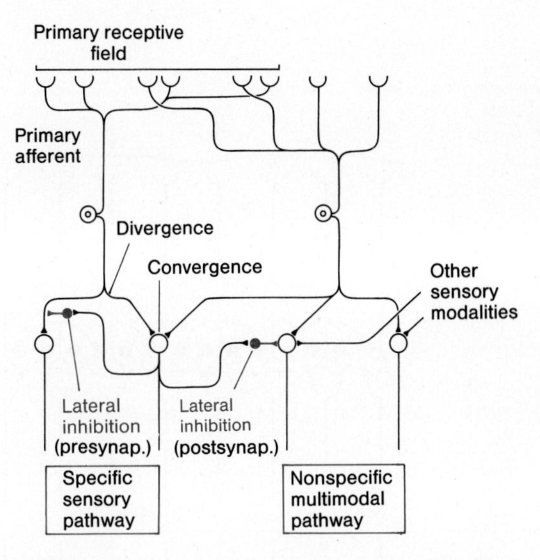

Fig. 8-6. Schematic drawing of a sensory system. (Modified from [5])

Sensory Systems in the CNS: Specific and Nonspecific Pathways

After entering the spinal cord or the brain, the primary afferent nerve fibers synapse with secondary sensory neurons. The axons of the latter run together, as **sensory tracts,** to higher nuclei. In each sensory system, typically, this ascending pathway passes through several such sensory centers. For all the senses apart from olfaction, the highest centers are a nuclear region in the thalamus and its cortical projection area. A sensory pathway, then, consists of a series of central neurons connected to one another by synapses and excited sequentially by discharge initiated at the corresponding sensors. All the neuronal connections within such a sensory pathway plus the inhibitory systems associated with it together form a **sensory system.**
The diagram in Fig. 8-6 illustrates some characteristic features of a sensory system. The primary afferents ordinarily branch in the target organ to innervate several sensors, forming a **primary receptive field.** They also branch at their central ends, making synaptic contacts with several sensory neurons. This branching is called **divergence.** Conversely, each secondary sensory neuron makes synaptic contact with several primary afferents; that is, **convergence** also occurs. The same intricate connectivity is also present in the higher sensory centers. Therefore, although a sensory pathway can be regarded as a chain of neurons *in series*, it is also true – because of convergence and divergence – that the sensory information is transmitted simultaneously over many channels *in parallel.* This parallel transmission is probably the most important source of the extraordinary reliability of sensory systems. Loss of an occasional neuron due to disease or aging can be tolerated; only if large numbers of neural elements are affected does the function of these systems deteriorate.

The significance of inhibitory synapses. The interconnections in the sensory pathways are not limited to excitatory synapses. Various forms of **inhibition** are also employed in sensory systems. In the next section the function of inhibition for the extraction of information is described. It also serves other purposes, as follows.

1. It is used to prevent an unrestricted spread of excitation through the neural network. When inhibition by way of the glycinergic synapses is blocked by the glycine antagonist strychnine, the resulting breakdown of orderly transfer of information in the CNS leads to convulsions and death.
2. Higher sensory neurons very often send out collaterals to interneurons that inhibit sensory neurons at a lower level in the same pathway. This **feedback inhibition** adjusts the gain in the sensory pathway. The same purpose is probably also served by the "primary afferent depolarization" (PAD) in the somatosensory system (see p. 51).
3. Finally, higher non-sensory brain centers can act through descending inhibitory pathways **(descending inhibition)** to block transmission in sensory systems (p. 219). One of the functions of these inhibitory mechanisms is to shut out certain items of sensory information when the attention is being focussed on others.

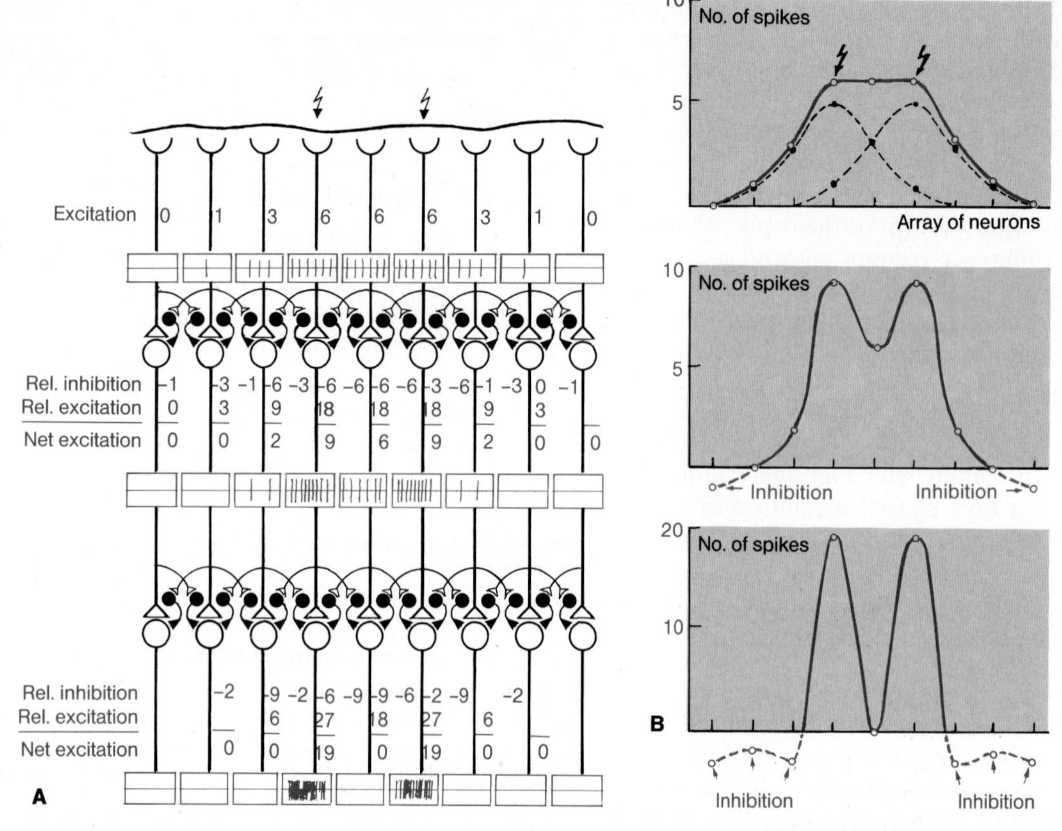

Fig. 8-7 A, B. A simple model of a sensory system, to illustrate lateral inhibition. **A** The two arrows symbolize two stimuli a small distance apart, applied simultaneously. The *black* structures represent the matrix of the sensory system. The *numbers* and the *boxes* containing trains of action potentials in red indicate the relative levels of excitation. It is assumed that at each synaptic relay level excitation is amplified threefold, whereas attenuation in the collaterals and inhibitory interneurons produces lateral inhibition equal to the input without amplification. The resulting net excitation is found by subtraction of the inhibition values from the excitation values (see also text). **B** Graphs of net excitation over the array, at three levels in the matrix of sensory cells

Nonspecific systems. The neurons to which information is transmitted by a sensory system are not all specific (i.e., associated with only the one modality). All sensory systems also make connections with neuron groups and pathways that receive signals from several sensory systems – multimodal or **nonspecific neuron groups** and pathways. One important nonspecific system extends through the reticular nuclear regions in the brainstem and thalamus. It is likely that the specific (unimodal) sensory pathways transmit precise information about stimuli (they communicate what is happening), while the nonspecific pathways are responsible for sensory integration and for the modifications of behavior demanded by the stimuli (they communicate the significance of what is happening). Often the behavioral modification consists of activation and redirection of attention. To mediate these effects appears to be an important function of the ascending reticular activating system (ARAS) (see also p. 146).

Extraction of Distinguishing Characteristics of Sensory Information

The receptive fields of primary afferent neurons are determined by the terminal arborization of the axon – i.e., by the distribution and number of the sensors to which the axon is connected. The afferent fiber is excited by stimuli anywhere in the receptive field. As a rule, however, the *receptive fields of central neurons* are more complex. Many of these neurons are excited by stimuli in the center of their receptive field but inhibited by those in a surrounding area, the size and shape of which can vary in different neurons. Inhibitory surrounds result from connections between primary afferents and interneurons with inhibitory

synapses on the secondary neurons. Because the inhibition is exerted "sideways", originating in neurons in the same sensory pathway as the excitatory neurons, it is called **lateral inhibition.**
The complex receptive fields of central sensory neurons serve to bring out particular aspects of the sensory information (feature extraction). One major task here is **contrast enhancement;** it is most clearly demonstrated in the visual system and in cutaneous mechanoreception. The ultimate result of this emphasis on contrast is that the eyes inform us less about absolute brightness levels but more accurately about differences in brightness in a scene and hence about the boundaries of its individual elements.

Contrast enhancement by lateral inhibition. The diagram of a sensory system in Fig. 8-7 is greatly simplified in that it omits the convergence and divergence discussed in the previous section. The arrows indicate two punctate stimuli a small distance apart, applied simultaneously to an array of sensors. The resulting distribution of excitation in the array is such that the two stimuli cannot be detected as separate. But with the parameters of lateral inhibition assumed in the model, in two steps of synaptic transmission complete separation of the simultaneous stimuli is achieved.

To simulate lateral inhibition, the afferent neurons in Fig. 8-7 are indirectly interconnected with neighboring secondary neurons; each of them excites interneurons (black cell bodies in the diagram) by way of axon collaterals, and each interneuron inhibits the neighboring secondary neuron (white cell bodies). The degree of inhibition of course depends on the degree to which the interneurons are excited, which depends on the level of excitation in the primary afferent. It is assumed in the model that at each synapse between a primary afferent and its secondary neuron there is a synaptic amplification factor of 3; the inhibition by way of the interneurons (one excitatory and one inhibitory synapse in series) is assumed to have an overall amplification factor of −1. As is ordinarily the case in postsynaptic inhibition, the inhibitory influences (IPSPs) are subtracted from excitatory ones (EPSPs). At the next level of synaptic transmission this process is repeated with the same transmission factors. In Fig. 8-7 the levels of excitation and inhibition produced in the model are indicated numerically. The resulting net excitation can be interpreted, for example, as "number of action potentials", as illustrated by the hypothetical recordings from the axons shown in the red boxes. The changes that are found from level to level in this matrix can easily be calculated from the assumptions given above.

Complex feature extraction by higher sensory neurons. Contrast enhancement is not all that is accomplished by information extraction in higher sensory neurons. In the projection and association areas of the cortex individual neurons extract considerably more complicated information from the sensory excitation. For instance, there are neurons in the somatosensory system that encode the velocity and direction of movement of a stimulus over the skin. The visual cortex contains simple and complex cells (see p. 261) that represent particular features of the geometry and movement of visual stimuli. Details of the organization of the various cortical sensory projection areas are discussed in the chapters concerned with those sensory systems. Here, in the context of general sensory physiology, the main point is simply that our central sensory systems – especially the cortical systems – perform an analysis of the incoming information and provide the conscious perception process with **extracts** or **abstractions** of the sensory information.

8.3 General Subjective Sensory Physiology

Basic Dimensions of Sensations

At the beginning of the chapter, subjective sensory physiology was defined as the area of research concerned with the relationship between the physicochemical world of *stimuli* and the subjective world of *sensations* and *perceptions*.
Sensations are traditionally considered to have four basic dimensions, the *intensity dimension*, the *quality dimension*, the *temporal dimension* and the dimension of *spatial extent*. In some senses the latter is more a *dimension of location;* in the case of hearing and olfaction, it refers to the ability to localize sounds or odors. In other senses, such as taste, there is no spatial dimension.
We shall discuss primarily the first two dimensions listed above, beginning with the *quality dimension*. This dimension describes the fact that sensations are fundamentally different in nature. "Seeing" is something entirely different from "hearing". Complexes such as seeing, hearing, smelling and tasting are termed **sensory modalities.** Each sensory modality in turn comprises various **qualities.** The color red is one quality of the vision modality, and the color green is another.
In classical medicine five senses were distinguished: sight, hearing, taste, smell and touch. We now recognize several additional modalities (for instance, the senses of temperature and balance). The number of senses available to humans will always be a matter of interpretation.

We should also bear in mind that other vertebrate species have sense organs that we lack. For instance, the pit organ of snakes contains sensitive infrared sensors with which they detect the body warmth of their prey. Some fish have a sense organ for electric fields, which allows them to detect the currents associated with muscular activity of prey hidden in the sandy bottom. Human technology is capable of constructing similar artificial sense organs, but for us to use them their output must be converted to visible (or, less commonly, audible) signals.

The five classical human senses are all in the category of exteroception (see p. 179). Proprioceptors and interoceptors were not known to exist until physiologists discovered them.
Particular difficulties are encountered in classifying pain and other unpleasant sensations such as itch. Pain is a sensory modality, and perhaps itch can be considered a quality of that modality. But pain differs from other senses in that it is found in all realms of sensation: interoception, proprioception and exteroception. Nociceptors, the sensors that mediate pain, occupy a special position among the cutaneous receptors (all of which are exteroceptors) because the information they provide is not about the external world but rather about injury to one's own body. That is, pain is a body-related modality. A detailed discussion of pain physiology is presented elsewhere in this book (Chapter 10, beginning p. 223).
It was for the quality dimension that JOHANNES MÜLLER (1837) formulated the **law of specific sensory energies** mentioned above: the modality of a sensation depends not on the stimulus but on the organ that is stimulated (see p. 178).
Sensory modalities cannot be compared with one another by direct measurements. At the level of qualities, however, one can make such measurements. By slowly changing the frequency of a tone, one can find a **threshold**, a difference in frequency sufficient that there is an audible change in the quality of the tone. Similarly, by changing the frequency of electromagnetic oscillations one can change the color of a light. Here, again, it is possible to determine a threshold, the smallest change in frequency for which a different color is seen.

The Intensity Dimension: Absolute Thresholds and Differential Thresholds

The **intensity dimension** of sensation has been most thoroughly studied with the methods of **psychophysics.** His interest in learning whether the intensity of sensations can be quantified led G.T. FECHNER to devise, around 1850, the first useful technique for the quantitative measurement of subjective experience. He arrived at the first psychophysical law that attempts to describe the quantitative relation between the physical intensity dimension (ϕ) and the subjective dimension of strength of sensation (ψ). Until then DESCARTES' (1596-1650) doctrine that measurements are impossible in the subjective sphere ("res cogitans") was generally accepted. The sensory **threshold** is a central concept in psychophysics.
The **absolute threshold** (stimulus limen) was defined as the smallest stimulus that is just capable of producing a particular sensation. Some authors would restrict the term "absolute threshold" to the lowest threshold obtainable with optimal stimulus configuration and adaptation. Elsewhere in this book threshold values are given for hearing as a function of sound frequency (p. 287) and for vision as a function of adaptation time (p. 256).

Differential thresholds. In the range of suprathreshold stimuli another kind of threshold can be defined, the "just noticeable difference" **(j.n.d.).** This is the amount by which one stimulus must differ from another in order for the difference to be sensed. E.H. WEBER (1834), in experiments on the sense of force, was the first to show that for two weights to be distinguished, they must differ by a larger amount if both are heavy than if both are light. Figure 8-8A shows the relation between the weight (force) of the first object presented and the just noticeable increase in weight. In the intermediate range of stimuli the relation is linear; that is, the same fraction of the initial weight must be added to it in order to exceed the differential threshold. The change in stimulus intensity that can just be detected ($\Delta\phi$) is a constant fraction (c) of the initial stimulus intensity (ϕ). Weber's law is expressed by the equation

$$\frac{\Delta\phi}{\phi} = c; \quad \Delta\phi = c \cdot \phi \qquad (1)$$

According to this law, $\Delta\phi/\phi$ is constant for all stimulus intensities. The rule does in fact apply over a wide range of stimulus intensities for many sensory modalities. However, when the absolute threshold is approached, the **Weber fraction** ($\Delta\phi/\phi$) tends to increase. The relation between the Weber fraction and stimulus intensity is shown in Fig. 8-8B for the loudness of tones. It is evident that in this case Weber's law begins to apply only when the stimulus reaches 40 dB above the absolute threshold, because the

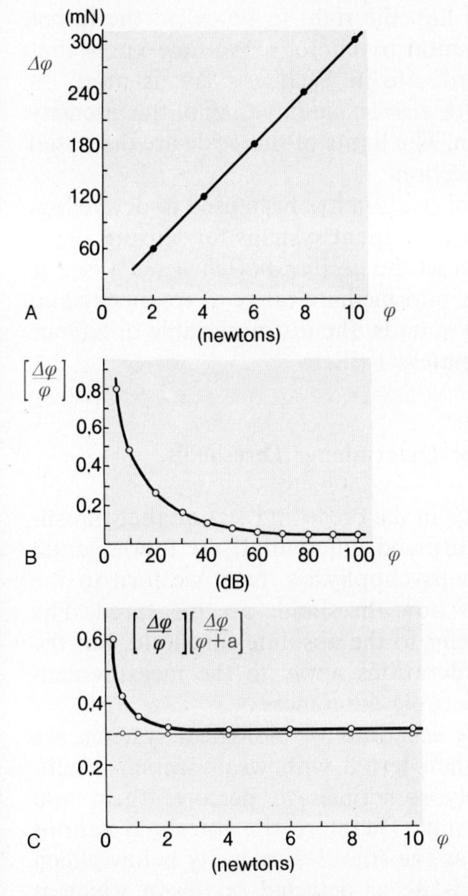

Fig. 8-8 A-C. The Weber fraction and Weber's law. **A** Relation between initial stimulus magnitude (ϕ) and the increase ($\Delta\phi$) required to exceed the differential threshold, for the sense of force. **B** Dependence of the Weber fraction ($\Delta\phi/\phi$) on the intensity of the initial stimulus, for auditory stimuli. Only for stimuli more than 40 dB above the absolute threshold is the Weber fraction a constant. **C** Correction of the Weber fraction by the constant "a". The corrected law (Eq. 2) also applies to near-threshold stimuli. (A and B modified from [1])

Weber fraction remains constant from this intensity on. Similar curves are obtained for other modalities.

The Weber fraction is a useful measure of the relative sensitivity of sensory systems. Although it is impossible to use physical dimensions to compare the sensitivity of the eye to light intensities with the sensitivity of the ear to sound pressure levels, the Weber fractions for the two modalities can be compared with one another, because they are dimensionless. In such experiments discrimination of light intensities by the eye is found to be somewhat better than that of sound intensities by the ear.

Weber's law (Eq. 1) can be reformulated as follows, to obtain a better fit to the experimental data:

$$\frac{\Delta\phi}{(\phi + \mathrm{a})} = \mathrm{c}; \quad \Delta\phi = \mathrm{c} \cdot (\phi + \mathrm{a}) \tag{2}$$

where a is a constant, usually with a small numerical value. When the stimulus intensity (ϕ) is fairly large, the term "a" becomes negligible, and Weber's law in its original form is sufficiently precise (see Fig. 8-8C).

In one sense the constant "a" is simply a correction factor added to the formula to make it more consistent with experimental findings. However, "a" has also been interpreted as the "noise" in the sensory channel. In neurophysiological terms, "noise" can be considered to be the spontaneous activity of sensory neurons, particularly those at higher levels – impulses discharged when no stimulus is acting on the sense organ. This spontaneous activity must probably be added to the activity in response to the stimulus and therefore also affects the magnitude of the increase required to produce a just noticeably larger signal in the CNS. The spontaneous activity is small in comparison to the response to strong stimuli but it affects the quantity ($\Delta\phi/\phi$) when the stimulus is weak.

According to this neurophysiological interpretation, the absolute threshold would be the stimulus intensity just sufficient to produce in a sensory system excitation distinguishably greater than the spontaneous activity in that system. This interpretation is employed in certain psychophysical theories (e.g., in the "sensory decision theory" discussed below). In the section on integrative sensory physiology we return to the question whether spontaneous activity does in fact have a crucial influence on the threshold.

FECHNER's Psychophysics

Apart from determining thresholds, can one measure sensations in the subjective dimension? FECHNER had the idea of using the differential thresholds to define a **scale of intensity of sensation** (ψ). Zero on such a scale is the absolute threshold, the next stronger sensation is greater by precisely one just noticeable difference, the next by another j.n.d., and so on. Because each step corresponds to the smallest possible increase in sensation, the j.n.d. is the basic unit of sensation intensity. In Fig. 8-9 sensation intensity on FECHNER's scale is plotted as a function of stimulus intensity. This relation between ψ and ϕ is described by an equation known as **Fechner's psy-**

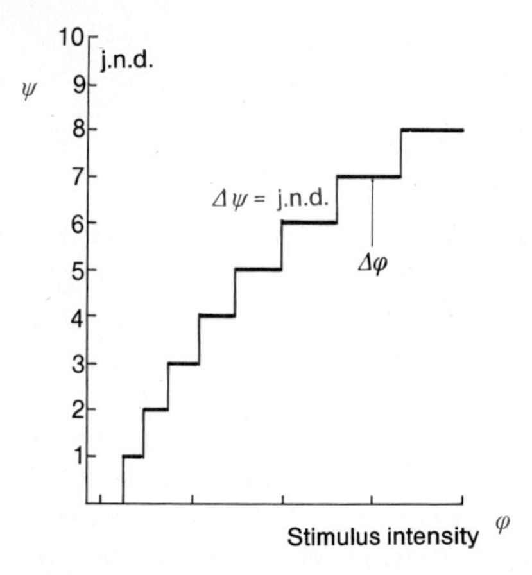

Fig. 8-9. Diagram of Fechner's law. *Abscissa,* stimulus intensity; *ordinate,* cumulative differential thresholds

chophysical law. Because the stimulus increases by successive additions of $\Delta\phi/\phi$, the resulting curve is logarithmic (see Fig. 8-9); hence the law says that for a linear increase in sensation intensity (ψ) there is a logarithmic increase in stimulus intensity (ϕ). When the psychophysical function in Fig. 8-9 is replotted in linear-logarithmic coordinates, the curve becomes a straight line (see Fig. 8-13). Fechner's law is expressed by the equation

$$\psi = k \cdot \log(\phi/\phi_0) \quad (3)$$

where ψ is the intensity of sensation, k is a constant, ϕ is the stimulus intensity and ϕ_0 is the stimulus intensity at the absolute threshold.
This psychophysical law is based on two major assumptions:

a. Fechner's law holds only to the extent that Weber's law is correct. It was shown in the preceding section that the Weber fraction is not constant for very low stimulus intensities. The validity of Fechner's law is necessarily limited to stimulus intensities to which Weber's law applies.
b. It is also assumed that the j.n.d.'s are all the same basic units of increasing sensation intensity – that the sensation elicited by a threshold change in a weak stimulus is the same as that elicited by a threshold change in a strong stimulus. When considering Stevens' law we shall see that this assumption of FECHNER's is incorrect, and as a result the validity of his "law" is severely restricted. In view of this finding, it would be better to refer to the **Fechner psychophysical relation.**

FECHNER performed a great service by defining the first useful scale of "sensation intensity"; it has earned him the right to be called the father of experimental psychology. We now know that the "ψ" ordinate in Fechner's law is more an expression of *discriminability* than of the intensity of sensation. The limits of this scale are discussed in a later section.
The Fechner relation has been used to derive logarithmic measurement systems for sensory physiology, such as the *decibel and phon scale* (see p. 287). In the intermediate range of frequency and intensity of sounds, the just noticeable difference is approximately 1 dB.

Methods for Determining Thresholds

It was shown in the preceding section that thresholds (absolute and differential) are fundamental concepts in psychophysics. Now we turn to the question of how thresholds are measured. The examples refer to the absolute threshold, but the same considerations apply to the measurement of just noticeable differences.
Because the reactions of biological systems are variable, when tested with weak stimuli a subject is likely sometimes to perceive them and sometimes not. Therefore the threshold cannot be defined as the stimulus intensity below which a stimulus is never detected or above which it is always detected. Instead, the stimulus must be presented several times, after which a statistical procedure is applied to the results to estimate the "true", mean threshold. There are several techniques for determining threshold, some of which go back as far as FECHNER.
One classical method is the **method of limits.** Here the initial stimulus is far from the presumed threshold. For instance, the intensity is first made so high that the subject perceives the stimulus easily and then reduced until the stimulus becomes subthreshold. Then the test begins again, this time with a very weak stimulus which is increased until the threshold is reached. These ascending and descending sequences are repeated several times and the mean of the resulting threshold values is taken as an estimate of the true threshold. The stimulus intensity can be recorded automatically on a strip chart, so that to graph the fluctuations of the threshold over time one need only draw a line connecting the endpoints of the stimulus-curve segments.

Subjective sensory physiology and behavioral experiments on animals. The method of limits, like other procedures for threshold measurement, can also be used in animal experiments. An example

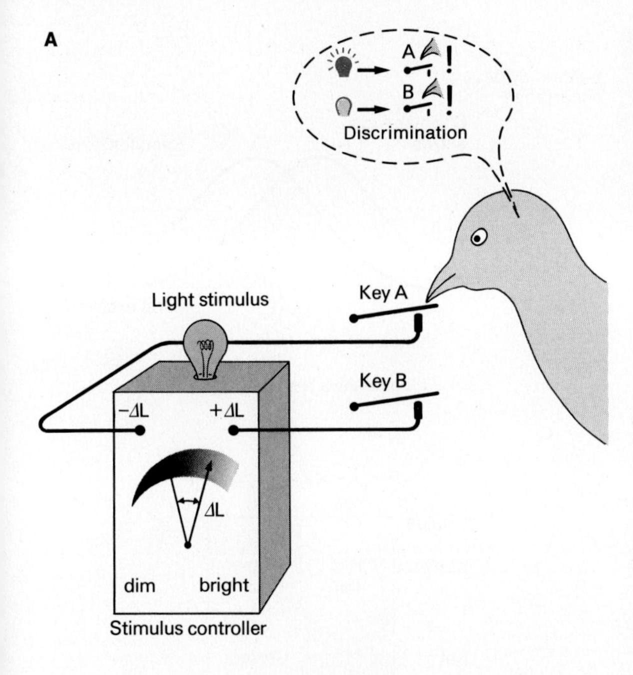

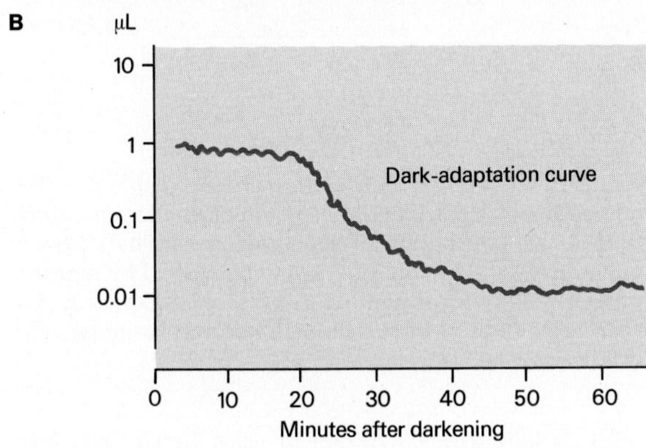

Fig. 8-10 A, B. Measurement of visual threshold of a pigeon in a behavioral experiment. **A** Diagram of the experimental arrangement: the pigeon pecks Key A when it sees light, and as a result the light intensity is reduced. Pecking of Key B, when no light is visible, increases the intensity of the next stimulus. **B** Gradual decrease in the threshold intensity after the bright background lighting is turned off; the *curve* is the dark-adaptation curve of the pigeon. (Modified from [8, 9])

is illustrated in Fig. 8-10. Here a pigeon has been conditioned (see Chapter 6) to obtain a food reward by pecking Key A when it sees a light and Key B when no light is visible. Key A reduces the stimulus intensity and Key B increases it. The pigeon's behavior produces curves of ascending and descending light intensity, the reversal points of which give a measure of the visual threshold. When the threshold is measured continuously in this way after the test cage has been darkened, a dark-adaptation curve is produced (see p. 256) which resembles that of humans. This example shows quite clearly that the methods of subjective sensory physiology can be applied to behavioral experiments on animals.

Such animal experiments are mentioned here in the context of subjective sensory physiology because the methods so closely resemble those used in psychophysical experiments on humans. One can of course also take the view that the measured behavior expresses the animal's subjective sensations – which need not imply that the conscious experiences of animals are comparable to those of humans.

In a modification of the method of limits, the subject adjusts the stimulus himself (e.g., by turning a knob), raising the intensity until he detects the stimulus or lowering it until he no longer does so. The advantage of this **method of adjustment** is that the subject can play a more active role than in other psychophysical procedures, which counteracts fatigue due to boredom. The disadvantage is that the time course of stimulation cannot be kept constant.

The psychometric function. A much more elaborate procedure, but one that produces cleaner results, is to present a series of different stimuli in randomized order. This is called the **method of constant stimuli.** The stimuli are selected so that the weakest is so small that it is hardly ever detected and the largest so large that it almost always is. For each stimulus the subject reports whether he has seen it or not, and the percentage of stimuli detected at each intensity is recorded. Figure 8-11 shows examples of the results so obtained. The dots represent the relative frequencies of detection measured for stimuli at

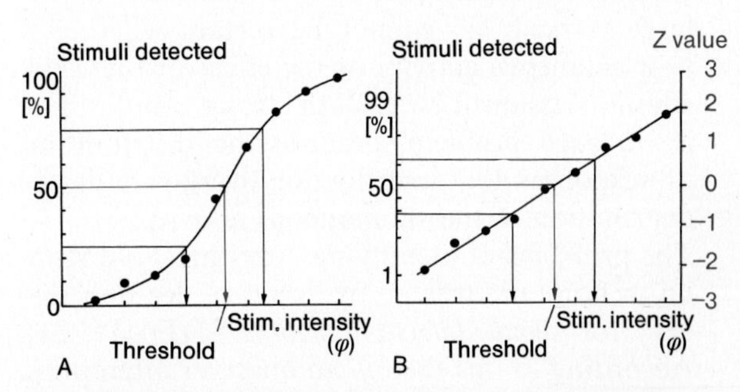

Fig. 8-11 A, B. Psychometric function found when threshold intensity is measured by random presentation of stimuli (method of "constant stimuli"). The threshold is defined as the *point* on the curve corresponding to detection of 50% of the stimuli. **A** Representation of the relative frequency of hits *(ordinate)* as a function of stimulus intensity *(abscissa)*. **B** Often the sigmoid psychometric functions correspond to the integral of a normal distribution (ogive). When the relative frequencies of hits are transformed into Z values (e.g., on probability paper), the psychometric function becomes a straight line. (Modified from [1])

different intensities; for most subjects, the curve through the dots, the **psychometric function,** is sigmoid. The threshold is defined as the stimulus magnitude for which 50% of the stimuli are detected. In the example in Fig. 8-11 the threshold does not coincide with any of the stimuli tested but is an interpolated point on the curve.

The sigmoid psychometric function often matches closely the cumulative form of the normal distribution (the integral of the Gaussian distribution). This curve is called an **ogive.** In such cases, when the relative frequencies of detection of randomly presented stimuli are plotted as probabilities (the Z values on the right ordinate), the data fall approximately on a straight line (Fig. 8-11B). This axis transformation is easily done with "probability paper". The fact that the psychometric function often conforms to an ogive is of theoretical interest; it indicates that a statistical process underlies the fluctuations in perception (see also next section).

Statistical Analysis of Thresholds, Sensory Decision Theory

In a previous section we hypothetically defined the absolute threshold as the stimulus intensity that produces neural excitation in a sensory channel just noticeably greater than the spontaneous activity in the channel. On the assumption that the fluctuations in this spontaneous activity can be described by a normal distribution and that the variations in the response to a weak (constant, repeated) stimulus are also normally distributed, frequency distributions like those shown schematically in Fig. 8-12A are obtained. It is evident in this diagram that an observer who experiences neural excitation at the level marked "a" cannot be certain whether it is spontaneous activity or the effect of the weak stimulus assumed here. With strong stimuli there is no such problem, because the distributions of responses to these do not overlap with the distribution of the spontaneous activity.
The problems of identifying near-threshold stimuli in noise are treated by **"sensory decision theory"** (or *signal detection theory*; SDT) [15, 21]. According to this theory, an observer attempting to separate a weak signal from noise must make a decision. This *decision* could, for example, consist in regarding all levels of neural excitation in this system that are greater than "b" as due to a stimulus, and all lower levels as spontaneous activity. The dividing line fixed by this decision is called the *criterion* or *bias*. In the example illustrated in Fig. 8-12A, there can be no decision that will eliminate error; in the cases corresponding to the (uniformly) red shaded area in the diagram

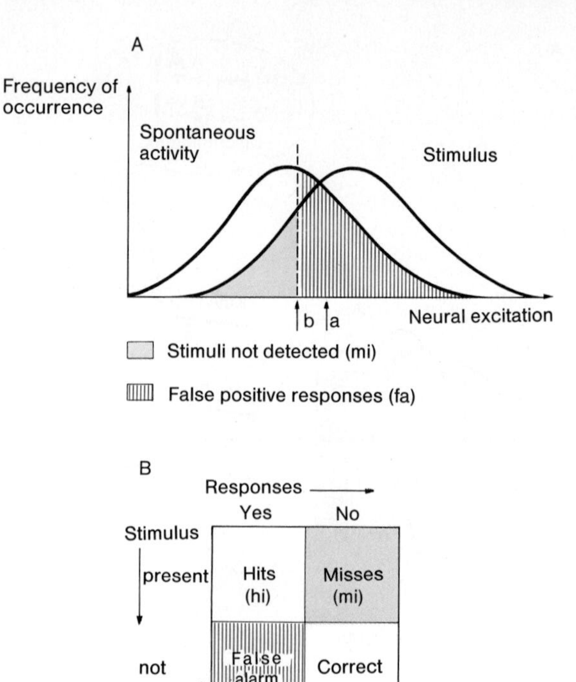

Fig. 8-12 A, B. Diagrams of near-threshold stimulus situations in sensory decision theory. **A** Schematic representation of the distribution of spontaneous activity ("noise") in a sensory system and of the activity elicited by repeated presentation of a constant near-threshold stimulus. **B** Possible combinations of correct and incorrect responses. For details see text

stimuli will not be detected, and in the hatched area to the right of the criterion, spontaneous activity will be erroneously considered to be a response to a stimulus.
In Fig. 8-12B the four possible combinations are diagrammed. In this situation there are two correct response combinations: *"hit"* and *"correct rejection"*. There are also two incorrect combinations: *"false alarm"* and *"miss"*. The probabilities of occurrence of these types of response to weak stimuli are not independent of one another. For the two kinds of correct answers, the relation is inversely proportional: the more hits, the fewer correct rejections. The same is true of the incorrect answers: the more misses, the fewer false alarms. This can be visualized by shifting the criterion in Fig. 8-12A; the sizes of the two shaded areas change in inverse proportion.
Sensory decision theory (SDT) has transformed the threshold concept. It shows that threshold measurements are determined by two factors, **sensory selectivity** and the **criterion** fixed by a decision process. Finding a value for selectivity

corresponds most closely to finding a threshold value. Possible ways in which sensory physiologists can investigate separately the selectivity of a sensory system and the decision-making processes (of humans or animals) have been described [15, 21].

The realization that in uncertain stimulus situations decision criteria determine sensory responses has implications far beyond the realm of sensory physiology. In such general approaches noise is defined as the sum of the uncertainty factors. Medical diagnosis offers an example. The uncertain, visual impression that the skin of a patient has a yellowish tinge will lead the doctor to diagnose jaundice or not, depending on the degree of yellow discoloration at which his decision criterion has been set. The criterion of course depends on the doctor's experience – that is, on an intuitive estimate of probability. But its setting should also depend on the consequences of the decision. If the suspected disease is a serious one and if the tests needed to confirm it are not too drastic, the doctor will prefer to risk a "false alarm" rather than a "miss". If the material and immaterial costs of the decision are distributed otherwise, the criterion should be shifted accordingly. That is, medical decisions involve not only probability considerations but also evaluation of the consequences and ethical judgments.

Stevens' Psychophysics

For a hundred years there was essentially no opposition to FECHNER's assumption that sensation intensity could be scaled in units of differential threshold (j.n.d.). Then STEVENS showed that the j.n.d. is not a constant unit; for instance, a tone 20 j.n.d. steps above the absolute threshold is estimated to be more than twice as loud as a tone at the same frequency 10 j.n.d. steps above threshold. It follows that a just noticeable difference in intensity does not produce the same difference in strength of sensation for all initial intensities. STEVENS concluded that another kind of sensation scale must be constructed in order to find "the" psychophysical law. In these attempts to scale sensation directly, the concept of threshold no longer has a significant place.

Before we consider STEVENS' psychophysical law, another case should be described that seems to provide impressive support of FECHNER. For more than 2,000 years astronomers have observed and classified the stars. About 150 B.C. the Greek astronomer HIPPARCHOS introduced a quantitative scale of stellar brightness, which is still in use today. The brightest stars belong to the first class, the next brightest to the second, and so on down to the sixth class, which can barely be seen with the naked eye. For many centuries astronomers estimated the brightness of stars according to this six-point scale, until photometric devices became available. The classification of stars is thus a gigantic psychophysical experiment that has been in progress

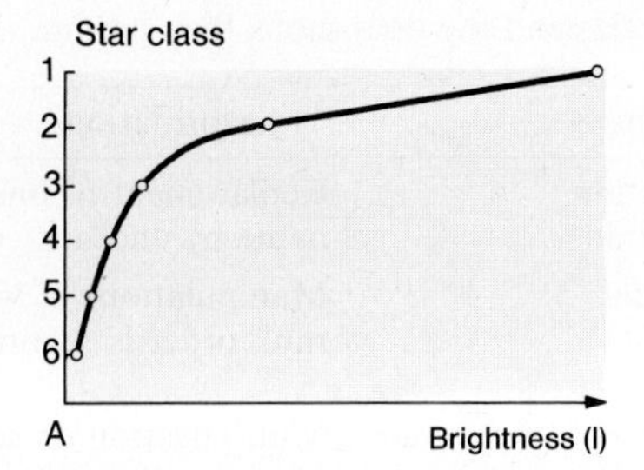

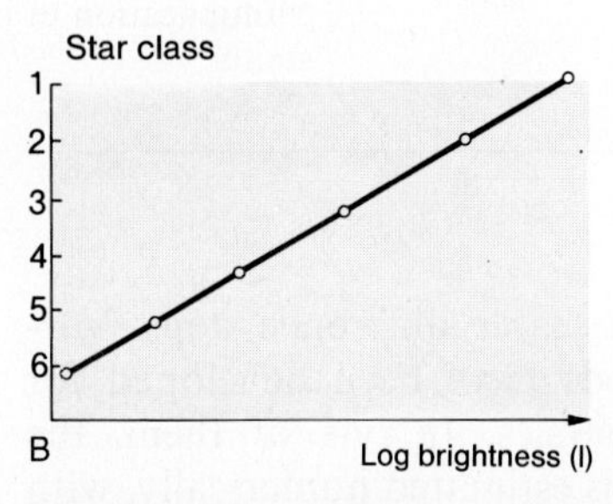

Fig. 8-13. Mean brightness of the stars in different classes, with linear **(A)** and logarithmic **(B)** scales for brightness on the *abscissa*. (Data of JASTROW, from [24])

for hundreds of years. Toward the end of the last century, when scientists compared the old scale with the measured brightness data, they found an approximately logarithmic relation – which could have been predicted from Fechner's law. This relation is graphed in Fig. 8-13. Today stars are classified according to their photometric brightness, but a logarithmic scale (magnitude) is still ordinarily used. Fechner's law applies in this case because the astronomers were not trying to estimate their **sensation intensity**; their six-point scale was intended only to meet the criterion of **discriminability**. The crucial thing was that a star in the first class is discriminably brighter than one in the second class, and so on. It is irrelevant how large a difference there is in our sensations of brightness when comparing a star with another in a different class.

Fechner's law is therefore applicable when the subjective scale is defined as a *scale of discriminability*. It must be noted that this scale counts only as an **ordinal scale;** multiplications (e.g., statements such as "twice as bright") are impossible in it. On the other hand, STEVENS' scale is meant to be a **ratio scale,** the values in which can be multiplied – a necessary property for statistical measures such as the arithmetic mean and the standard deviation. Table 8-1 shows the mathematical operations that are possible with the various kinds of scale. The scales are listed in ascending order, such that the statistical operations permitted in the lower types can also be used in the higher, but not the reverse.

In STEVENS' psychophysics the subject is asked to estimate the intensity of his sensations directly; it is not found indirectly by counting the

Table 8-1. Kinds of scales and the operations they permit. (Modified from [24])

Scale	Operations	Transformations	Statistic	Example
Nominal	Identification, classification	Replacement of one class name by another	Number of cases, modal value	Numbers given to the players on a team
Ordinal	Rank order	Manipulations in which rank order is retained	Median, percentile, rank correlation	Examination grades, ranking in a sport
Interval	Measurement of separations or differences	Multiplication or addition of constants	Arithmetic mean, standard deviation	Temperature, °C
Rational	Ratios, fractions, multiples	Multiplication of constants	Geometric mean	Temperature, K

number of just noticeable difference steps. Various scaling methods have been developed for this **direct psychophysics.** In one of them, the sensation intensity is estimated numerically, with "0" taken as the absolute threshold and another number agreed upon to represent the sensation elicited by a standard stimulus (the modulus). It is important that the scale is not divided into discrete steps but allows continuous gradation; the subject uses concepts like "half or twice as intense" and picks a number to correspond to these. This method of measuring sensation intensity is based on the principle of proportional ordering. The results obtained with such ratio scales led STEVENS to propose that the relation between strength of sensation (ψ) and stimulus intensity (ϕ) is described by a power function. According to Stevens' law,

$$\psi = k \cdot (\phi - \phi_0)^a \quad (4)$$

where ψ again is the sensation intensity, k is a constant dependent on the scaling of the stimulus, ϕ is the stimulus intensity and ϕ_0 is the stimulus intensity at the absolute threshold. The exponent a depends on the sensory modality and the conditions of stimulation; it determines the shape of the curve in a plot of ψ as a function of ϕ. For example, if the exponent is 1, the relation is linear. If the exponent is greater than 1, the strength of sensation increases more rapidly than the stimulus intensity (curve concave upward), and if it is less than 1, the reverse occurs.

When plotted in a logarithmic coordinate system, a power function is a straight line.

$$\log \psi = \log k + a \cdot \log(\phi - \phi_0) \quad (5)$$

One can see from Eq. (5) that in the case of a power function the data must fall on a straight line when plotted in the coordinates $\log(\phi - \phi_0)$ and $\log(\psi)$. The slope of this line (the tangent of the angle to the abscissa) is given by the exponent a.

Power functions found by STEVENS for various modalities and qualities are shown in Fig. 8-14. These coefficients are undoubtedly dependent on the conditions of stimulation; furthermore, there is considerable scatter among different subjects. But in spite of their dependence on stimulus configuration and context, to a certain degree these exponents are also characteristic of the various sensory channels. The differences in exponent magnitude can be explained by the fact that in different sensory systems the extent of the range of stimulus intensities can vary; light intensity covers four decades, whereas the range for the sense of warmth is one decade at most. The ranges of sensation intensity presumably do not

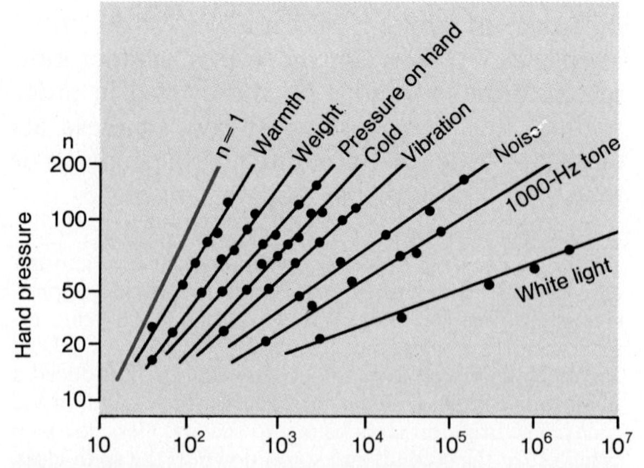

Fig. 8-14. Intensity of sensation as a function of stimulus intensity, as determined by cross-modality intensity comparison (force on a hand dynamometer matched to sensation intensity, ordinate). The exponents of the different power functions are given in Table 8-2. After[9]

vary so widely; it may be that all modalities are represented in "sensation-intensity dimensions" of similar magnitude. In that case, the exponent for perception of brightness would have to be smaller than that for the temperature sense.

Cross-modality comparison of intensity. In direct psychophysics the intensity of a stimulus of one modality can be represented in another modality. For instance, the brightness of a light or the loudness of a tone can be expressed by the force exerted when the hand presses a dynamometer. This procedure, called cross-modality matching, reveals an additional relationship among the exponents of the Stevens functions. Consider the following example. When the loudness of a tone is estimated directly on a ratio scale, the exponent is found to be about 0.6, and the exponent for hand force on the ratio scale is about 1.7. When sound intensity is represented by pressure exerted with the hand, the resulting power function has the exponent 0.35. Multiplication of this exponent for the cross-modality matching by the exponent for hand force gives approximately the exponent for loudness. That is, the exponent for a cross-modality comparison is approximately equal to the ratio of the exponents for the two modalities being compared.

$$a_r/a_p = a_i; \quad a_r = a_p \cdot a_i \qquad (6)$$

where a_r and a_p are exponents measured directly with a ratio scale (a_r for the modality to be tested and a_p for the modality by which the intensity estimate is to be represented) and a_i is the exponent found in the cross-modality intensity comparison.

In Table 8-2 the exponents of the curves in Fig. 8-14 are listed together with the corresponding exponents for estimation on ratio scales. Division of the latter by the former gives an average value of 1.65, close to the exponent found for hand pressure by direct estimation. Such measurements are not very precise, however, and there is considerable interindividual variation.

Visual analog scale. Another kind of cross-modality intensity comparison has come into wide use in determining Stevens functions: the representation of estimated stimulus intensity by linear distances. The visual analog scale was developed from this comparison. In this procedure the stimulus intensity is reported as a distance along a (usually 10-cm) line. Because the exponent measured directly for distance estimation is approximately 1, estimates on visual analog scales give about the same exponents as the method of numerical estimation described at the beginning of this section.

8.4 Integrative Sensory Physiology

So far in this chapter the discussion has been in terms of two separate compartments, "objective" and "subjective" sensory physiology. The two deal with different topics, one with the *functions of sensory systems,* and the other with *subjective perceptions.* At the outset it was noted that these two compartments either interact with one another (dualist standpoint) or are different manifestations of the same sensing brain (monist standpoint). Therefore advances in sensory physiology can never be entirely satisfactory if they are limited to only one compartment; the two must ultimately be set in relation to one another.

Table 8-2. The exponents of Stevens' power functions found for various stimuli in cross-modality intensity comparisons (a_i) and by estimation on ratio scales (a_r). (Modified from [24])

Form of stimulus	Stimulus range	Measured exponent		a_r/a_i
		Ratio scale a_r	Force comparison a_i	
Temperature (warm)	2–14.5°C above neutral temp.	1.6	0.96	1.67
Weight of objects	0.28–4.8 N	1.45	0.79	1.83
Pressure on hand surface	2.5–25 N	1.1	0.67	1.64
Temperature (cold)	3.3–30.6°C below neutral temp.	1.0	0.6	1.67
60-Hz vibration	17–47 dB *re* threshold	0.95	0.56	1.70
Loudness of noise	55–95 dB *re* 0.0002 dyn/cm^2	0.6	0.41	1.46
Loudness of 1000-Hz tone	47–87 dB *re* 0.0002 dyn/cm^2	0.6	0.35	1.71
Brightness (white light)	56–96 dB *re* 10^{-10} lambert	0.33	0.21	1.57
Force of hand on dynamometer		1.7		

Integrative approaches to sensory physiology can have various points of departure:
(i) **concepts** shared by both areas of research,
(ii) **perceptual phenomena** for which neurophysiological correlates are sought, and finally
(iii) **neurophysiological functional complexes** for which the effects on perception are to be found.
In this chapter we can give only one example of this important integrative aspect of sensory physiology. We return to a concept central to both the objective and subjective realms, the concept of the **threshold.** In the section on subjective sensory physiology a hypothesis for the absolute threshold was introduced that has its origin in the area of neurophysiology and hence in objective sensory physiology. According to this hypothesis, the threshold is exceeded when the excitation in a sensory channel is discriminably above the level of spontaneous activity in that channel (see p. 187). To test this hypothesis is a typical problem in integrative sensory physiology. The ogive form of the psychometric function (Fig. 8-11) shows that a statistical process does indeed play a role in the perception of weak stimuli. Does it involve the spontaneous activity of neurons in the CNS or, instead, the variability of function of sensors in the periphery of the body?
One possible means of deciding between these two hypotheses is the method of **microneurography,** in which the activity of primary afferents in the peripheral nerves of human subjects is recorded [17, 18]. For instance, by plotting the frequency of occurrence of responses of a rapidly adapting mechanoreceptor in the skin of the palm (RA sensor, see p. 198) to weak, controlled tactile stimuli one obtains a sigmoid threshold curve that resembles the "psychometric function" of sensation (Fig. 8-15). From this ogive an absolute threshold can be derived for this type of sensor. Furthermore, the fact that both curves have the same S shape demonstrates that part, at least, of the scatter in psychometric threshold measurements can be ascribed to the sensors themselves. With microneurography, the neural and subjective functions can be determined simultaneously in the same subject. When such an experiment is performed with an RA sensor in the fingertip, the two functions nearly coincide; in this case, then, spontaneous activity of central neurons seems not to contribute to the variability of the sensation threshold. The result is quite different when the responses of RA sensors in the palm, which are about as sensitive as those in the fingertips, are compared with the corresponding sensation thresholds. Here the psychometric function for sensation threshold is shifted to the right, indicating that an additional loss of information occurs in the CNS, either during synaptic transmission or because of the increase in overall spontaneous activity.
Even when the mechanical stimulus is applied to a small area of the fingertip or palm, several RA sensors will be excited. Since the fingertips are among the most important organs of touch, while the palm is not, the density of these sensors is greater in the fingertip than in the palm (Fig. 8-15). Similarly, the fingertips are represented by larger groups of neurons in the somatosensory projection area of the cortex. It follows that the information from these parts of the body is transmitted by more parallel channels, which can compensate for the loss of information in transmission across central synapses.

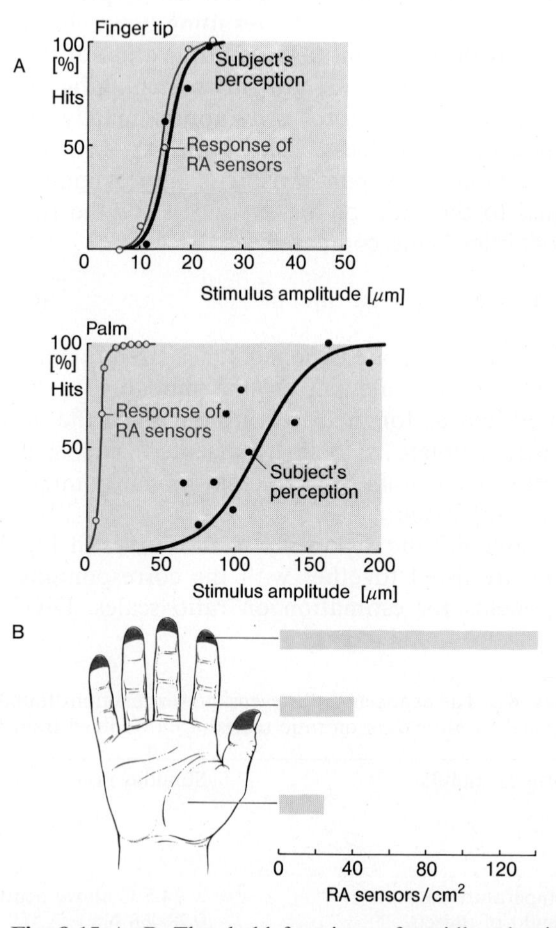

Fig. 8-15 A, B. Threshold functions of rapidly adapting mechanoreceptors in the skin (RA sensors) and psychometric functions. **A** Psychophysical threshold measurements were taken and the responses of skin afferents recorded simultaneously in a microneurographic experiment. **B** Innervation density of the RA sensors at various places on the hand surface. (Data of VALLBO and JOHANSSON, from [18])

In microneurographic studies of human cutaneous nociceptors with unmyelinated afferents, it has been shown that when a large area is stimulated the ability of a single sensor to respond differentially to heat stimuli is about as great as the ability of the subject to sense these stimuli as painful to different degrees [16], whereas with a laser beam incident on a small area the subjects do not discriminate as well as their nociceptors [10]. These findings, again, indicate compensation of central nervous information losses by parallel transmission.
In summary, comparison of the thresholds of afferent nerve fibers with sensation thresholds shows that in the *sensory systems with the best discrimination ability* there is *practically no loss of information* during processing in the CNS. Probably the neural processes associated with focussing of attention (see p. 183) also reduce information losses in individual sensory channels.

8.5 References

Textbooks and Handbooks

1. Gescheider, G.A.: Psychophysics: method and theory. New York: John Wiley & Sons 1976
2. Handbook of Sensory Physiology, Vol. I.: Principles of Receptor Physiology (Ed. W.R. Loewenstein). Berlin-Heidelberg-New York: Springer 1971
3. Hensel, H.: Allgemeine Sinnesphysiologie, Hautsinne, Geschmack, Geruch. Berlin-Heidelberg-New York: Springer 1966
4. Keidel, W.D.: Sinnesphysiologie, Teil I: Allgemeine Sinnesphysiologie, Visuelles System. Berlin-Heidelberg-New York: Springer 1971
5. Shepherd, G.M.: Neurobiology. New York-Oxford: Oxford University Press 1983

Original Papers and Reviews

6. Attneave, F.: Multistability in perception, Scientific American, Dec. 1971, S. 63–71
7. V. Bekesy, G.: Mach band type lateral inhibition in different sense organs. J. gen. Physiol. *50*, 519 (1967)
8. Blough, D.S.: Dark adaptation in the pigeon. J. comp. Physiol. Psychol. *49*, 425 (1956)
9. Blough, D.S., Yager, D.: Visual psychophysics in animals. In: Handbook of Sensory Physiology, Vol. VII/4: Visual Psychophysics (Eds. D. Jameson, L.M., Hurvich). Berlin-Heidelberg-New York: Springer 1972
10. Bromm, B., Jahnke, M.T., Treede, R.-D.: Response of human cutaneous afferents to CO_2 laser stimuli causing pain. Exp. Brain Res. *55*, 158–167 (1984)
11. Churchland, P.S.: Neurophilosophy. Toward unified science of the mind-brain., The MIT Press, Cambridge, Massachusetts, 1986
12. Eccles, J.C.: The wonder of being human. Our brain and our mind. New York-London: The Free Press (1984)
13. Fiorentini, A.: Mach-band phenomena. In: Handbook of Sensory Physiology. Vol. VII/4: Visual Psychophysics (Eds. D. Jameson, L.M. Hurvich). Berlin-Heidelberg-New York: Springer 1972
14. Gardner, M.: Science good, bad and bogus. Oxford University Press, Oxford, 1983
15. Green, D.M., Swets, J.A.: Signal detection theory and psychophysics. New York: John Wiley & Sons (Pb.) 1966
16. Gybels, J., Handwerker, H.O., Van Hees, J.: A comparison between the discharges of human nociceptive nerve fibres and the subject's ratings of his sensations. J. Physiol. *292*, 193–206 (1979)
17. Hagbarth, K.E., Vallbo, A.B.: Mechanoreceptor activity recorded percutaneously with semimicroelectrodes in human peripheral nerves. Acta Physiol. Scand. *69*, 121–122 (1967)
18. Handwerker, H.O. (Ed.): Nerve fiber discharges and sensations. Hum. Neurobiol. *3* (1984)
19. Loewenstein, W.R.: Biological transducers. Scientific American *203*, 99–108 (1960)
20. McCloskey, D.I., Cross, M.J., Honner, R., Potter, E.K.: Sensory effects of pulling or vibrating exposed tendons in man. Brain *106*, 21–38 (1983)
21. McNicol, D.: A primer of signal detection theory. London: George Allen & Unwin. Pb. 1972
22. Popper, K.R.: The logic of scientific discovery. New York-Hagerstown-San Francisco-London: Ind Harper Torchbooks ed., Harper and Row Pb (1968)
23. Popper, K.R., Eccles, J.C.: The self and its brain. Berlin-Heidelberg-New York: Springer International (1977)
24. Stevens, S.S.: Psychophysics. New York-London-Sydney-Toronto: John Wiley 1975

9 The Somatovisceral Sensory System

M. ZIMMERMANN

The sensory system discussed in this chapter encompasses cutaneous sensibility, the sensibility of the internal organs (visceroception or interoception) and the deep sensibility of muscles and joints (proprioception). The sensations mediated by the **skin** provide a link with the outside world. With the *sense of touch* we learn about the three-dimensional aspects of our surroundings; with the *temperature sense* we perceive warmth and cold; with the *sense of pain* (Chapter 10, p. 223ff.) we recognize potentially dangerous stimuli. **Visceroception** enables us to perceive something of our interior state – for instance, feelings of fullness, shortness of breath or heart pains. By **proprioception** we keep track of the positions and movements of our joints. However, not all of the sensory information from these sources is consciously perceived; it is also required for many regulatory processes of which we are unconscious. Proprioception and the tactile sense participate in *motor coordination* (see Chapter 5), temperature information is used in the *automatic regulation of body temperature* (see Chapter 25), breathing is controlled on the basis of information about the gas content of the blood, and painful stimuli elicit *protective responses* (see Chapter 5). It is by integration of the diverse items of sensory information from the skin and the joints that we create the subjective impression of our body as a whole, the **body image**. In this process, visceroception seems to play only a minor role.

The capabilities of the somatovisceral senses are comparable with those for any other sensory modality. They used to be called the "lower senses", to indicate the lack of complicated specialized sense organs, but in the light of current knowledge this term is misleading and no longer useful.

9.1 Psychophysics of Cutaneous Mechanoreception

The sensitivity of the cutaneous innervation to mechanical stimuli can be measured by the reports of human subjects. For instance, the methods of psychophysics (see Chapter 8) can be used to find the absolute threshold, the subjective intensity, and the spatial resolution of tactile perceptions. These results can then be related to the events in the nervous system revealed by neurophysiological experiments [36, 38]. Such measurements are also of clinical significance, inasmuch as departures from the norm can indicate neurological disorders [20].

Thresholds and Subjective Intensity of Touch Stimuli

The **absolute threshold** to a tactile stimulus can be measured with calibrated hairs, a method introduced in psychophysics in the 19th century by the German physiologist MAX VON FREY (Fig. 9-1A). In modern stimulators precise movements of a stylus are generated electromagnetically (Fig. 9-1B). The latter produce skin deformation of graded intensity with variable time course – for instance, brief single pulses or periodic movements with sinusoidal time course (vibration stimuli).

The thresholds of perception found with von Frey hairs and with vibration stimuli (200 Hz) produced by an electromagnetic stimulator are shown for various parts of the body in Table 9-1. At the fingertips, vibration with an amplitude less than 1 μm is perceived. There is remarkable variation in the relative sensitivities of the different body regions. Furthermore, different results are obtained with different stimuli (Table 9-1); the explanation of this discrepancy is that near-threshold vibration stimulates different kinds of mechanosensors (-receptors) than are stimulated by the von Frey hairs.

Psychophysical intensity function. With suprathreshold mechanical stimuli to the skin, the relation between **intensity of sensation** and stimulus intensity can be measured, by the methods described in Chapter 8. An example of such experiments is illustrated in Fig. 9-2. The subjec-

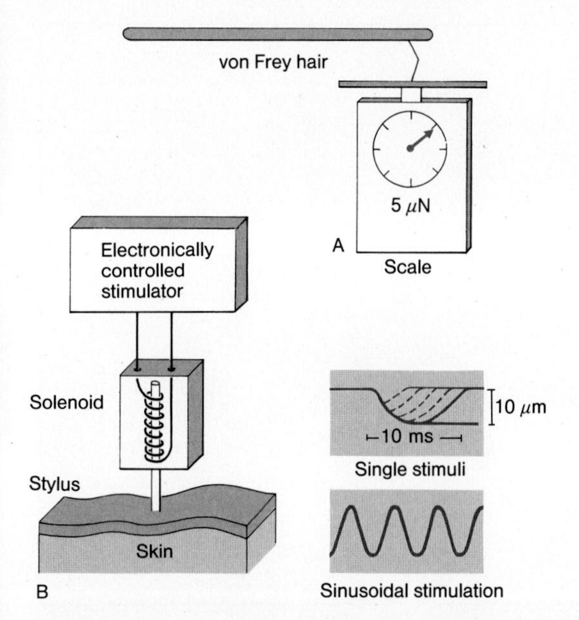

Fig. 9-1 A, B. Measurement of skin sensitivity. **A** With a set of von Frey hairs of different thicknesses the touch threshold of the skin can be measured. The results are quantified by calibrating, with a sensitive scale, the force that just causes the hair to bend. **B** Electromechanical device to apply precise mechanical stimuli to the skin. The flow of current through a coil in a magnetic field causes the coil to move by a specific amount (as with the moving coil in a loudspeaker). Arbitrarily selected electrical waveforms are converted into movements of the stylus

Table 9-1. Perception thresholds for mechanical stimulation of human skin

Place on body	Point stimulation[a] with von Frey hairs (mg)	Stimulation of area (1cm^2) with vibrator[b] at 200 Hz (μm)
Nose	5.3	4.7
Forehead	7.8	4.2
Fingertip	36	0.07
Hand (palmar)	77	0.07
Upper arm	34	2.2
Sole of foot	164	0.45
Calf	112	5.6
Hip (ventral)	66	2.8
Chest	42	1.7
Abdomen	21	5.2
Shoulder	26	1.4

[a] Data for point stimulation from Weinstein [11]
[b] Data for vibration stimulation from Wilska, Acta Physiol. Scand. *31*, 285,1954.

tively experienced (estimated) stimulus intensity is plotted as a function of amplitude of the pressure stimulus for two subjects (A and B). The ability to perceive different stimulus intensities probably is based on the transfer characteristics of the afferent systems. There are considerable

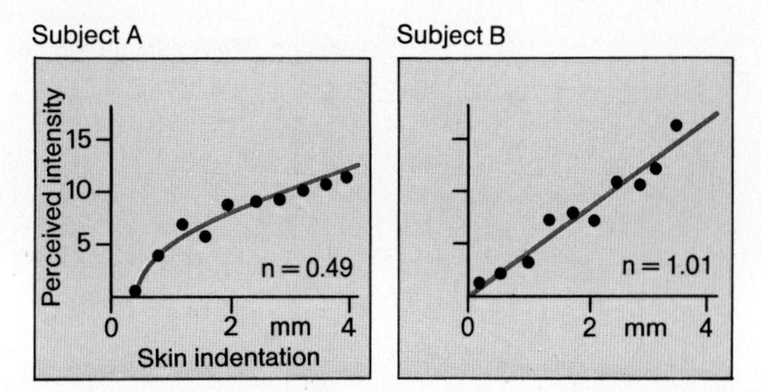

Fig. 9-2. Psychophysical experiments to estimate stimulus intensity. The subject expresses the perceived intensity of a pressure stimulus on the palm, here 1 s in duration, as a number on an arbitrary scale *(ordinate)*. The objective stimulus intensity *(abscissa)* was varied in random sequence. The curves *(red)* are power functions fitted to the data, with the exponents *n* shown in the diagrams. (Modified from Knibestöl and Vallbo, from [25])

interindividual differences in the psychophysical estimates of intensity, manifest as differences in the exponents of the power functions fitted to the data (see p. 191).

The result can be influenced by the experimental conditions as well as by the instructions given to the subject. Comparisons with neurophysiological studies give no evidence that these differences are caused by interindividual variability in the afferent systems.

Spatial Resolution of Tactile Stimuli

There are various tests requiring the recognition of spatial details of tactile stimuli that can be applied to obtain a *measure of spatial resolution.* One that is often used involves a pair of compasses, the two tips of which are placed on the skin simultaneously (Fig. 9-3A) to determine the **two-point threshold** [11]. The subject must decide, without looking, whether one or two points have been touched. With an assistant you can try this experiment on yourself, to find the smallest distance apart the two points can be while still being perceived as spatially separate. For example, when the points of the compasses are less than 5 cm apart, on the back the two stimuli are usually perceived as a single stimulus point. You will find that the two-point threshold is not the same everywhere on the skin (Fig. 9-3B). This difference results from the nature of the innervation of the various skin areas and the associated connectivity of the afferent nerve fibers in the CNS (see p. 211).

Clinical tests of the sense of touch [20]. For routine clinical testing the skin is touched lightly (e.g., with cotton wadding) and the patient is asked about the kind of sen-

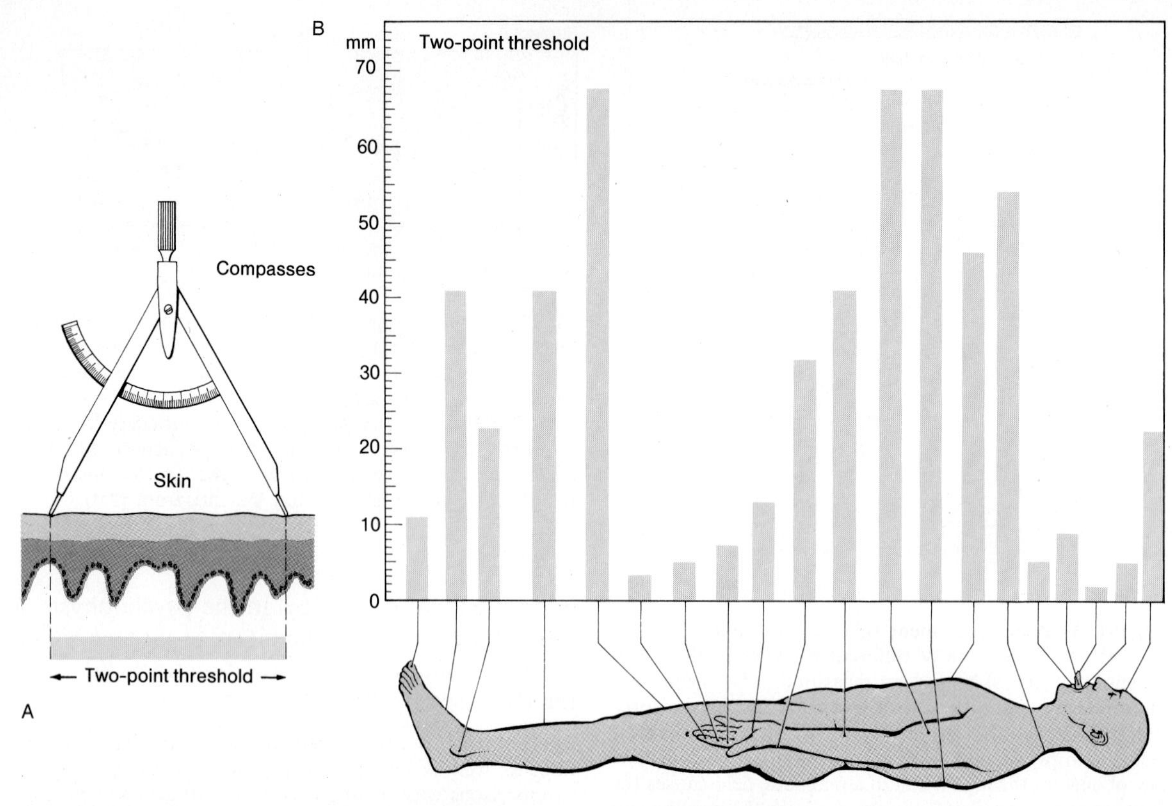

Fig. 9-3 A, B. Two-point threshold of the skin. **A** A pair of compasses is touched to the skin repeatedly, with the tips different distances apart. The two-point threshold is the smallest tip separation for which the subject can tell that there are two stimulus points. **B** Variation of the two-point threshold of the skin over the human body. (Presentation adopted from [22], data from E.H. WEBER, Archiv für Anatomie, Physiologie und wissenschaftliche Medizin, 1835, p. 152)

sation and the location of the stimulus. Spatial resolution is evaluated by the recognition of numbers or letters written on the skin, in various sizes, with a blunt probe.

The sensation of vibration is examined accurately with an electromagnetic vibrator that operates like the device shown in Fig. 9-1B. The physician tests both the absolute threshold for a sensation of vibration (see Table 9-1) and the difference threshold for changes in vibration frequency. In cases of polyneuropathy, for example, the perception of vibration stimuli is impaired.

9.2 Cutaneous Mechanosensors

From studies in humans and animals, the physiological function and histological structure of mechanosensitive receptors (mechanosensors) in the skin are well understood, and the two have been found to be correlated. In mammalian skin there are only a few basic types of sensitive mechanosensors, discussed in the following paragraphs [2, 9, 16, 25, 27, 36, 38].

Types of Low-Threshold Mechanosensors in the Skin

Neurophysiological experiments have shown that the hairless skin of rats, cats, monkeys and humans contains 3 basic types of sensitive mechanosensors with Group II (Aβ) afferents. They are called SA, RA and PC receptors or sensors. **SA** stands for **slowly adapting**; when exposed to a long-lasting mechanical stimulus (pressure; e.g., the weight of the body on the sole of the foot) such a sensor sends a continuous train of action potentials along its afferent fiber. Similarly, **RA** is a **rapidly adapting** mechanosensor, which responds only to mechanical stimuli varying in time. PC is an abbreviation of Pacinian corpuscle, a histologically identified structure that functions as a **very rapidly adapting** mechanosensor. These abbreviations are used internationally in the scientific literature.

Neurophysiological studies of these sensors can be carried out with anesthetized animals or waking human volunteers (Fig. 9-4). The impulses in the afferent fiber are recorded

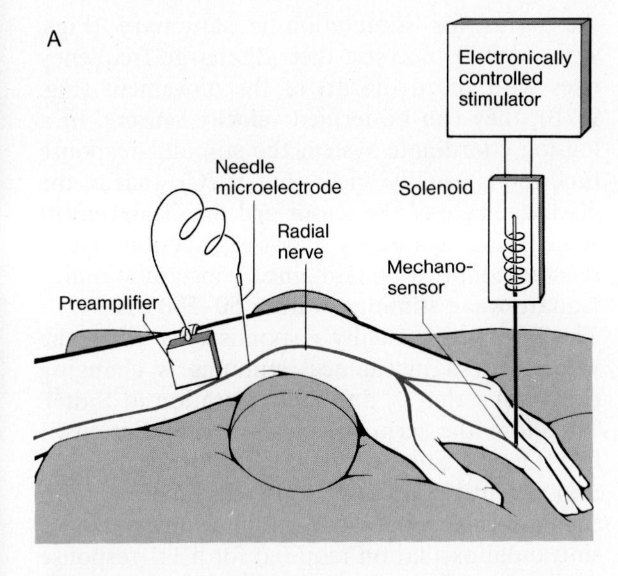

Fig. 9-4 A, B. Microneurography of human nerves. **A** The tip of a microelectrode (made, e.g., of tungsten) is inserted percutaneously into a cutaneous nerve (e.g., radial nerve) of a waking subject. Action potentials of single nerve fibers can be recorded by way of an amplifier. The discharge in response to stimulation with an electromechanical stimulator (see Fig. 9-1B) provides a quantitative characterization of the mechanosensitive sensors in the skin. **B** Responses of an SA sensor in the skin to 1-s stimuli at different intensities (N = newton). (**A** modified from HANDWERKER in [39])

and their relationship to specific mechanical stimuli to the skin is analyzed. In animal experiments a cutaneous nerve (e.g., the plantar nerve of the hind paw) is exposed and divided, under a dissecting microscope, into progressively finer filaments until the activity of a single fiber can be identified in the response to electrical stimulation of the nerve. Single-fiber activity is characterized by "all-or-none" action potentials. With human subjects, a metal microelectrode with tip diameter about 1 μm is inserted through the skin into a nerve – for example, the radial nerve near the wrist (Fig. 9-4A). When action potentials of uniform size are elicited by electrical or natural stimulation of the skin, a single-fiber response is being recorded.

Sensors for degree of indentation, velocity and acceleration. The functional properties of the types of sensors listed above can be characterized by applying mechanical stimuli with a ramp waveform (Fig. 9-5); these can be produced with an electromagnetic stimulator (Fig. 9-1B) [38]. The

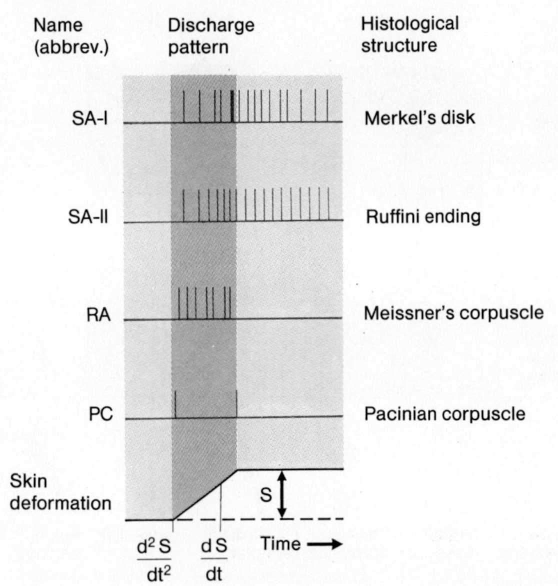

Fig. 9-5. Stimulus-response behavior of mechanosensors in the hairless skin of primates. The four types of sensitive mechanosensors have characteristic discharge patterns in response to a ramp deformation of the skin. The histological structure associated with each is given on the right (see Fig. 9-6). The time course of the ramp deformation generated with an electromechanical stimulator (see Fig. 9-1B), with depth of skin indentation S, is shown below the discharge patterns

stylus is moved from its starting position so that it presses the skin inward with constant velocity for a certain distances, and remains there. Such a stimulus comprises a phase of constant velocity (dS/dt, the first derivative of deformation S with respect to time) followed by a plateau phase, with constant skin deformation (S). At the transitions between movement and immobility of the stylus, where the velocity changes, there are accelerations (d^2S/dt^2, the second derivative of distance S with respect to time).

Only the SA sensors respond during the plateau phase, and their impulse frequency indicates the degree of skin indentation (or the force or pressure). By contrast, the RA sensors fire only when the stylus is moving; they respond to the velocity of skin deformation. The PC sensors usually discharge only when the velocity of skin deformation changes and therefore, to a first approximation, can be regarded as acceleration sensors.

Histology of the cutaneous mechanosensors. In animal experiments, histological examination following the neurophysiological measurement has revealed the morphological substrate of the recorded responses (Fig. 9-6). In the hairless (glabrous) skin of primates, the SA-I sensor has been found to correspond to the **Merkel's** disk, the SA-II sensor to the **Ruffini** ending, the RA sensor to the **Meissner's** corpuscle, and the PC sensor to the **Pacinian**

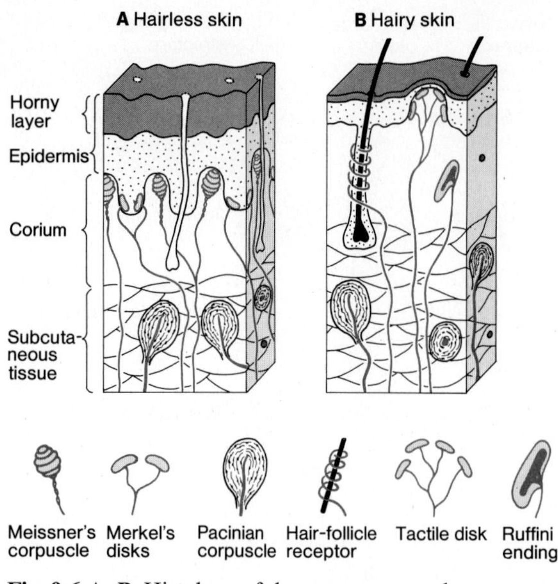

Fig. 9-6 A, B. Histology of the cutaneous mechanosensors. Position and structure of the various types of mechanosensors in hairless **(A)** and hairy **(B)** skin are shown schematically. For details see text

corpuscle. In the hairy skin (Fig. 9-6B) the SA-I sensors are also Merkel's disks, but here they are grouped below characteristic wartlike skin elevations about 0.5 mm in diameter, the Pinkus-Iggo tactile corpuscles. The SA-II sensors here, again, are Ruffini corpuscles. There are no Meissner's corpuscles in hairy skin; instead there is a conspicuous sensory innervation of the roots of the hairs, the hair-follicle sensors.

Coding of Stimulus Information in Mechanosensors

As the amplitude of skin deformation increases, the discharge frequency of the SA sensors rises (Fig. 9-4B); that is, they are sensors for force or pressure stimuli to the skin, or **intensity sensors**. In a double-logarithmic coordinate system (e.g., Fig. 9-7C) the **relation between stimulus intensity I and discharge rate E** in general is often represented by a straight line, which indicates that this relation is a **power function**, with the formula $\mathbf{E = const \cdot I^n}$. Because they continue to respond as long as the skin is deformed (Fig. 9-4B), the SA sensors also signal the **duration** of a skin indentation. In more detailed studies the SA sensors were divided into two classes, SA-I and SA-II [2, 9]. The SA-I sensors respond best to deformation perpendicular to the skin surface, whereas the SA-II sensors are more responsive to stretching the skin.

The RA and hair-follicle sensors respond only when the skin or a hair is moved, and not when the stylus for stimulation is stationary (Figs. 9-5 and 9-7). Because their discharge frequency rises with speed (dS/dt) of the movement (Fig. 9-7B), they can be termed **velocity sensors.** In a log-log coordinate system the stimulus-response function is usually linear (Fig. 9-7C); that is, the **discharge rate of the sensor and the displacement velocity** are related by a power function. These sensors adapt to a maintained constant stimulus (square-wave stimulus) within 50–500 ms.

The PC sensor usually responds only when the velocity of a mechanical stimulus is changing (Fig. 9-5) – that is, during acceleration (d^2S/dt^2). Therefore the term **acceleration sensor** is justified. During sine-wave stimulation (Fig. 9-8) action potentials are discharged in synchrony with each stimulus cycle; the minimal amplitude of sinusoidal oscillation required for a 1:1 response decreases sharply as the oscillation frequency rises (Fig. 9-8C), which indicates that the acceleration of the skin displacement is the adequate stimulus. Threshold is minimum for frequencies around 200 Hz and rises again with higher frequencies. The PC sensor can also be called a **vibration sensor.**

Sensors like the SA sensors, which signal primarily the intensity of a stimulus rather than its change in time, have been called **proportional sensors** (P sensors) by analogy with technical sensors. The corresponding term for sensors that respond like RA sensors is **differential sensors** (D sensors). Sensors with both static and dynamic response components are PD sensors.

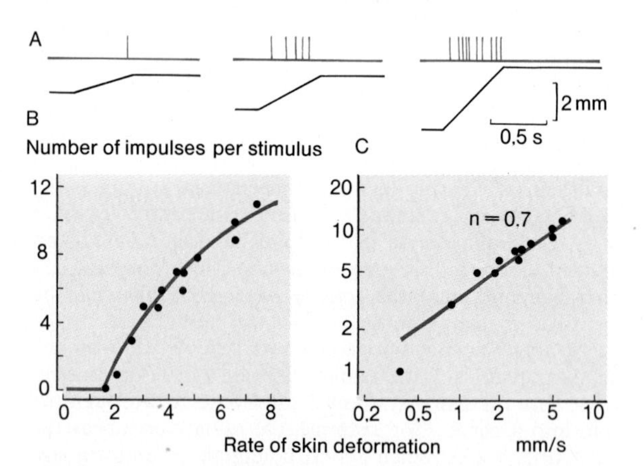

Fig. 9-7 A–C. The RA sensor, a velocity sensor. **A** Discharge pattern of an RA sensor in the skin of a cat *(above)* in response to skin deformation at various rates *(below)* produced by an electromechanical stimulator (see Fig. 9-1B). **B** Number of action potentials as a function of the rate of skin deformation. **C** Like B, but in a double-logarithmic coordinate system. Here the threshold rate of indentation, 1.6 mm/s, was subtracted on the abscissa. The exponent *n* of the power function was found from the slope of the line fitted to the data. (From [38])

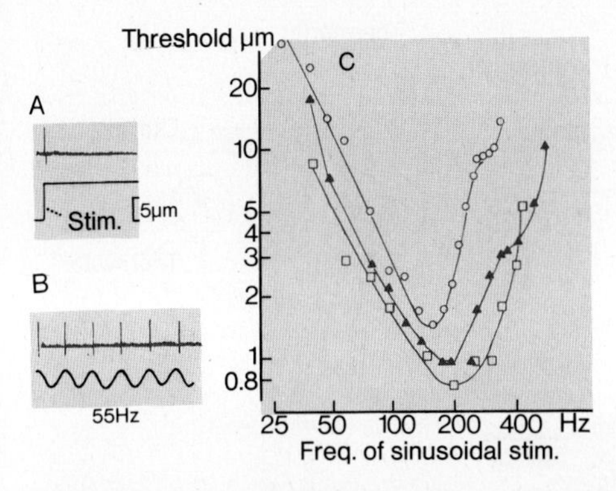

Fig. 9-8 A–C. Responses of PC sensors to mechanical stimulation of the skin. **A** Single impulse in response to a square-wave stimulus. **B** Repetitive response, one impulse for each cycle of a sine-wave stimulus. **C** Threshold stimulus intensities *(ordinate)* of 3 PC sensors in the cat's paw, as a function of the frequency of the sinusoidal mechanical stimulus *(abscissa)*. Coordinate scales are logarithmic. (Modified from JÄNIG, SCHMIDT and ZIMMERMANN, Exp. Brain Res. *6*, 100, 1968)

With three basic types of mechanosensors, then, various aspects of a stimulus are encoded and transmitted to the CNS: *intensity* or *amplitude* (S), *velocity* (dS/dt) and *acceleration* (d^2S/dt^2) of skin deformation. It is likely that when the stimuli are complex, like those that arise during **tactile exploration** with actively moving fingers [2, 5, 27], all three types of mechanosensors in the skin are excited, and that the perception of tactile events is based on the evaluation and synthesis of the signals from all of them by the CNS.

Receptive Fields and Innervation Density of Mechanosensors

The area within which a stimulus of given intensity can excite a mechanosensitive afferent fiber is called the fiber's **receptive field**. It corresponds approximately to the anatomical extent of all the fiber's endings. For example, one afferent fiber supplies 2-3 tactile corpuscles in the hairy skin, and all of the 30-50 Merkel's disks in each corpuscle are innervated by a fiber collateral. The spread of such branches is much greater in the case of the hair-follicle sensors, for each afferent fiber can supply many hair follicles and each follicle is innervated by several afferent fibers. In humans the receptive fields of the RA and SA-I afferents in the hairless skin are the smallest, 12 mm^2 on average, with only slight differences between the fingertips and the palm [36]. The receptive fields of the SA-II and PC afferents are larger by about a factor of 10.

Which properties of the sensors determine the **spatial resolution** measured by the **two-point threshold**? Various studies have provided evidence that the size of the receptive field is not crucial; the decisive feature is the **innervation density**, (i.e., the number of afferent fibers per cm^2 of skin surface). VALLBO and coworkers made microneurographic measurements in humans and concluded from their results that only the density of the RA and SA-I afferents at various places on the hand corresponded to the spatial resolution in those places (Fig. 9-9). From the observation that people are most successful in identifying objects by touch when they move their fingers, it may be concluded that the RA sensors (Meissner's corpuscles) make a major contribution here [2, 25, 36].

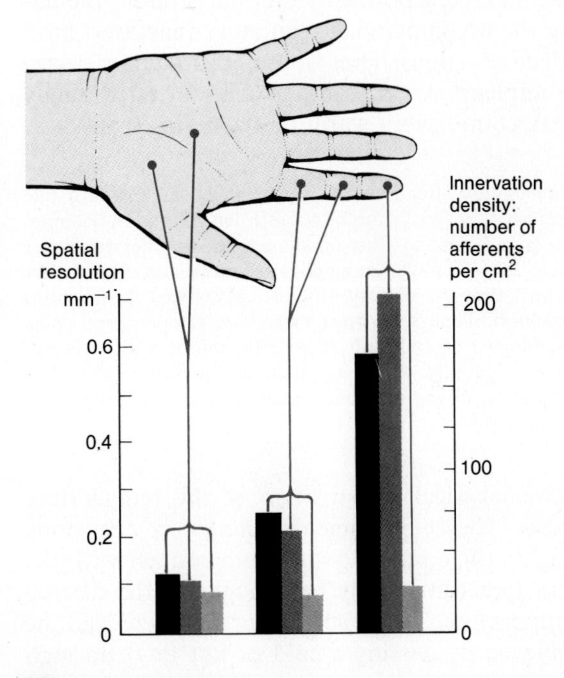

Fig. 9-9. Innervation density of mechanosensors and spatial resolution of tactile sensation. For various regions of the human hand, the bars show the innervation densities *(right ordinate)* of afferent fibers from RA and SA-I sensors and those from PC and SA-II sensors, and the spatial resolutions in those regions *(left ordinate)*. The innervation density was determined from a large number of microneurographic experiments on humans (see Fig. 9-4A). The spatial resolution was calculated as the reciprocal of the two-point threshold (in mm; see Fig. 9-3). (From [36])

9.3 Psychophysics of Thermoreception

There are two qualities of **thermoreception** (the temperature sense) in the skin, the **sense of cold** and the **sense of warmth** [6, 11, 12, 25]. It has been known for some time that there are *specific cold and warm points* on the human skin, at each of which only cold or only warm sensations can be elicited. *Cold points* are more numerous than *warm points*. For example, on the palm there are 1-5 cold points per cm^2 but only 0.4 warm points. The greatest densities are found in the region most sensitive to temperature, the face; here we have 16-19 cold points per cm^2, and the sensitivity to warmth cannot be resolved as single sensory points. The temperature sensitivity of the skin does not only give rise to conscious sensations; in warm-blooded animals it is also involved in processes of **body-temperature regulation** of which one is unconscious (see Chapter 25). The perceptions of thermal stimuli, including the accompanying regulatory reactions, have **affective** actions. That is, they can seem pleasant or unpleasant: one can feel chilly or refreshingly cool, comfortably warm or sweltering.

Immediately after entering a warm (ca. 33 °C) bath one feels a distinct sensation of warmth, but this soon becomes less intense. On the other hand, on a hot summer day water at ca. 28 °C in a swimming pool at first feels cool, but after a short time the sensation of cold gives way to a neutral sensation. That is, in an intermediate temperature range warming or cooling only transiently causes a sensation of warmth or cold. Evidently there is an almost complete **adaptation** of the temperature sensation to the new skin temperature.

Psychophysical investigation of the temperature sense. These experiments employ a thermode (Fig. 9-10), a metallic surface in contact with the skin that can rapidly be brought to the desired temperature. This temperature change can be achieved by passing a cold or hot fluid through the thermode or by using a Peltier element, the temperature of which depends on the electrical current flowing through it.
There is a range of temperatures in which, if the thermal stimulus remains constant, we have no sensation of warmth or cold; that is, in this **neutral zone** the temperature sensation has adapted. Above or below the neutral zone maintained thermal sensations are produced even by a constant temperature (one can feel cold feet for hours). The upper and lower limits of the neutral zone, for a skin area of 15 cm^2, are 36 °C and 30 °C, respectively (Fig. 9-11).

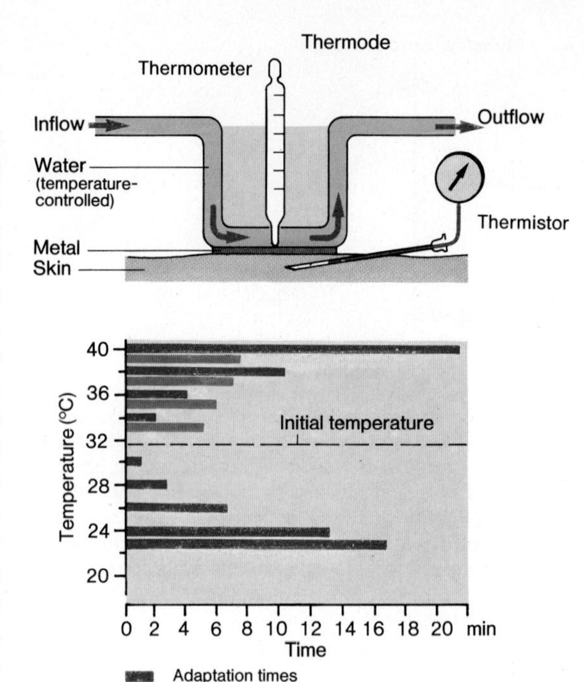

Fig. 9-10. Thermode for psychophysical study of the temperature sense. The metal surface in contact with the skin can have various sizes (e.g., 2 cm^2); it is kept at a selected temperature by fluid circulating past it from a thermostat. The temperature can be changed by switching the thermode to a second thermostat. The temperature distribution within the skin and its time course can be monitored by an intracutaneous thermistor

Permanent warm and cold sensations. The long-lasting sensations of warmth experienced with constant skin temperatures above 36 °C are more intense, the higher the skin temperature. At temperatures around 45 °C the sensation of warmth gives way to a painful **heat sensation.** When large areas are cooled to temperatures below 30 °C, there is a long-lasting cold sensation; cold pain is felt with skin temperatures of 17 °C or less.

Dynamic temperature sensations. The temperature sensations experienced while the skin temperature is changing are basically determined by three parameters – the initial temperature of the skin, the rate of temperature change, and the size of the skin area affected by the stimulus.
The influence of the **initial temperature** on the threshold for a sensation of warmth or cold is shown in Fig. 9-11. At low skin temperatures – for example, 28 °C – the threshold for a warmth sensation is high (i.e., a large temperature change is required) and that for a cold sensation is low. When the initial temperature (abscissa) is higher, the warm thresholds decrease and the cold thresholds rise.

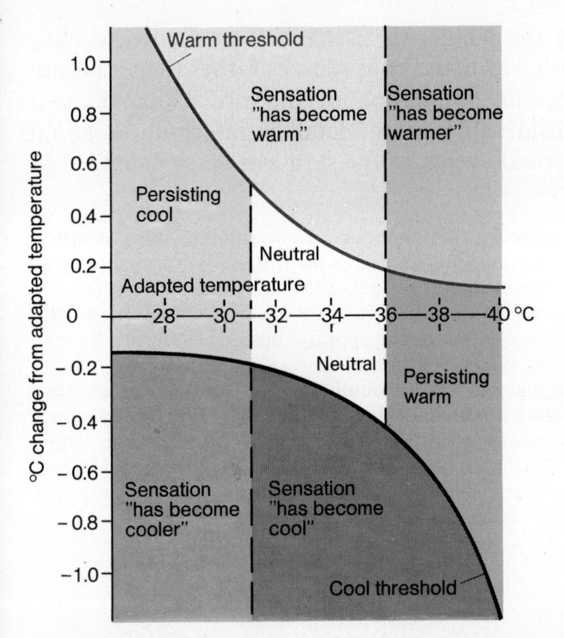

Fig. 9-11. Psychophysics of the temperature sense. The *curves* show the thresholds for the sensation of warmth or cold. Starting from the temperature shown on the *abscissa,* to which the skin had been adapted for some time, the skin temperature must be changed by various amounts *(ordinate)* to elicit a warm or cold sensation. The rate of temperature change for these measurements was at least 6 °C/min. The quality of sensation is indicated for each of the variously shaded fields. (Modified from KENSHALO in [25])

In other words: a cool skin (at 28 °C, say) must be cooled further only slightly, by less than 0.2 °C, to convert the maintained cold sensation into the sensation "has become colder". But the same skin must be warmed by almost 1 °C before a sensation of warmth occurs. Correspondingly, if the initial temperature is 38 °C a slight warming (< 0.2 °C) elicits the sensation "has become warmer", whereas the skin must be cooled by around 0.8 °C to produce a cold sensation.
A final conclusion to be drawn from Fig. 9-11 is that the change to a given skin temperature can produce sensations of **either warmth or cold**, depending on the starting temperature. You can easily convince yourself of this phenomenon with **Weber's three-bowl experiment**: fill one bowl with cold, one with lukewarm, and the last with warm water and then put one hand in the cold water and the other in the warm water. Now if you move both hands to the bowl with the lukewarm water, you will have a clear sensation of warmth in one hand and of cold in the other.

If the **rate of temperature change** is greater than about 5 °C/min, there is little effect on the warm and cold thresholds, but when the temperature changes more slowly, both thresholds increase steadily. For example, when the skin is cooled by 0.4 °C/min, from a starting temperature of 33.5 °C, it takes 11 min for a cold sensation to be felt; by that time the temperature has fallen by 4.4 °C. *When cooling is very slow,* then, a person may not notice that *large regions of skin have become quite cold* (with concomitant loss of heat from the body), especially if his attention is distracted by other things. It is conceivable that this factor is involved when one **catches a cold.**

9.4 Thermosensors

In mammals and many other species the presence of **specific thermosensors** (thermoreceptors) has been established conclusively. There are **warm and cold sensors**, both insensitive to non-thermal stimuli [2, 6, 7, 9, 11, 12, 13, 25, 30]. Cold sensors are usually supplied by Group III (Aδ) fibers, and warm sensors, by Group IV (C) fibers. Histologically, cold sensors have been found to have a special structure at their endings, whereas no histological specialization has yet been found for warm sensors – they must be in the category of free nerve endings.

Responses at constant skin temperature. Figure 9-12 shows the discharge rates of thermosensors as a function of the steady-state skin temperature. The **static discharge frequency of the warm sensors** increases from ca. 30 °C to ca. 43 °C, and then falls off sharply; in the region of the threshold for heat pain (ca. 45 °C) warm sensors are usually inexcitable. The discharge frequency of **cold sensors** rises as the temperature decreases from between 33 °C and 40 °C, reaching a maxi-

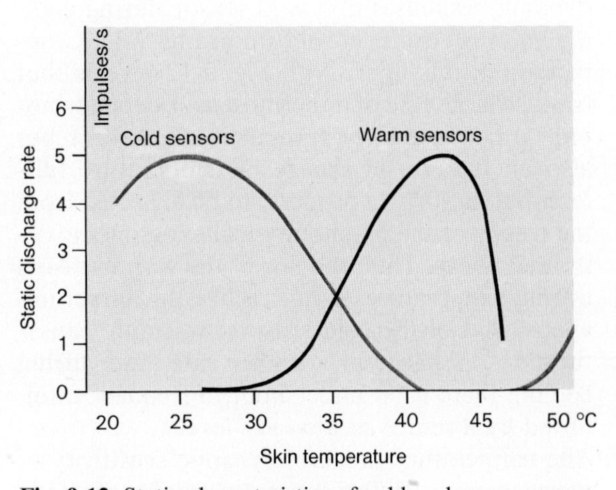

Fig. 9-12. Static characteristics of cold and warm sensors in monkey skin. The *curves* show the mean discharge frequency in several afferents of each population of sensors, as a function of the maintained skin temperature. The discharge of cold sensors rises again at temperatures above 45 °C. The data are from recordings of single fibers in anesthetized animals. (Modified from KENSHALO in [25])

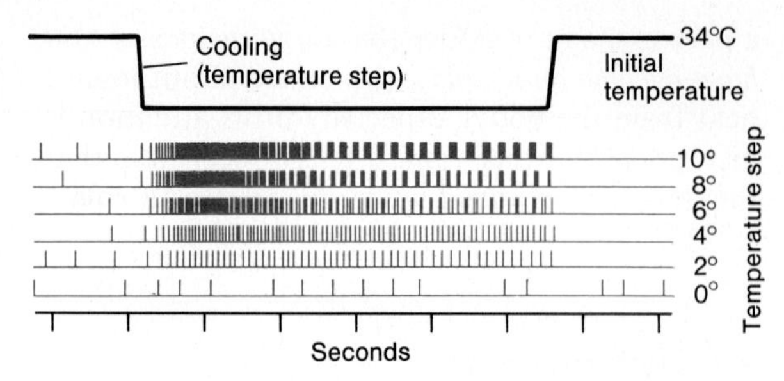

Fig. 9-13. Responses of a cold sensor in the monkey hand to transient reduction of skin temperature. The cooling steps were of different sizes, always with an initial and final temperature of 34 °C. Recordings from a single fiber in the median nerve of an anesthetized monkey. (From DARIAN-SMITH, JOHNSON and DYKES: J. Neurophysiol, *36*, 325, 1973)

mum at between 17 °C and 26 °C, depending on the individual sensor. Because of this maximum, every discharge frequency is associated with two temperatures, but the CNS can nevertheless correctly identify cold in the range below 17 °C; how this is done is still unknown [7]. It may be that the dynamic responses of the cold sensors are involved here, because even in the temperature range below the maximum of the static characteristic, cooling transiently increases the discharge rate. It has also been suggested that temperatures below the maximum of steady-state responsiveness can be identified by the occurrence of *grouped impulses* at low temperatures (Fig. 9-13).

Responses during change of skin temperature. The dynamic responses of a cold sensor during cooling and rewarming are shown in Fig. 9-13. Comparison of this figure with Fig. 9-12 reveals that the discharge rate of a thermosensor depends not only on temperature (proportional sensor) but also on the **rate of change** of temperature (differential sensor) – a property to be expected from the results of the psychophysical experiments described above. The behavior of the warm sensors during temperature changes is like the mirror image of that of the cold sensors; warming causes them to discharge at a higher rate, and during cooling there is an undershoot in frequency, followed by a return to a steady level.
The temperature range of **dynamic sensitivity** of thermosensors differs from the range of static sensitivity. For instance, when the skin is cooled in the temperature range below the maximum of static discharge of a cold sensor (Fig. 9-12), there is a dynamic increase in its discharge rate even though the static discharge is reduced.

On the whole, then, it is advantageous to have both warm and cold sensors rather than a homogeneous population of thermosensors, because considerably more detailed information about thermal events at the skin can be signaled to the CNS.

Nonspecific thermosensors. In mammals some sensitive mechanosensors, in particular the SA-II sensors, are also excited by cooling [7, 9, 12]. Perhaps their behavior explains why the colder of two otherwise identical weights placed on the hand appears heavier than the warmer weight (Weber's illusion).
Very intense warm stimuli (e.g., too-hot bath water) often produce a **paradoxical cold sensation.** It is probably caused because the cold sensors, which normally are silent above 40 °C (Fig. 9-12), when rapidly warmed above 45 °C discharge transiently, behaving like heat-sensitive nociceptors (see Chapter 10).

9.5 Visceral Sensibility

The spinal nerves and some of the cranial nerves contain afferents from the internal organs (see Figs. 9-19 and 9-20). The main peripheral nerves in which these visceral afferents run are the vagus, the splanchnic and the pelvic nerves. The efferent fibers in these nerves belong to the parasympathetic and sympathetic systems, but the afferent fibers cannot be assigned to those systems.
The information carried by the visceral afferents is used chiefly for automatic **regulatory processes** governing circulation, respiration, digestion and electrolyte and water balance. These control functions, of which we are largely unconscious, are discussed in other chapters of this book.
To some extent, activity of the visceral afferents also gives rise to **conscious perceptions** (Fig. 9-14). These may be *sensations mediated directly* by the visceral afferents or may be brought about *indirectly by reflex actions* initiated by the visceral afferents. Evidently the visceral afferents affect conscious sensation more strongly, the greater our ability to counteract disturbances in these regulatory systems by conscious behavioral responses. Intense, potentially injurious stimuli to the internal organs are perceived as **pain** (see Chapter 10); when insufficient food or water has been consumed, the activities in visceral afferents (e.g., glucose sensors and osmosensors) produce the "general" sensations **hunger** and **thirst** (see Chapter 14); and fullness of the bladder eventually induces us to urinate. Between these concrete

perceptions and the completely unconscious regulatory actions of the viscerosensors, the visceral afferents also give rise to **unspecific** pleasant or unpleasant **feelings**. These feelings generally determine one's **degree of well-being** and usually strongly affect one's emotional situation.

Cardiovascular system. The sensors involved in the regulation of blood pressure and blood volume are mechanosensors in the aorta and carotid artery and in the atria of the heart (see Chapter 20). We are not conscious of the continuous activity of these sensors. In some special situations, however, we can detect the activity of the heart – for instance, during severe physical or mental strain. These *perceptions of the beating heart* are probably also mediated by the sensitive mechanosensors in skin and muscles, excited by the considerable changes in shape and position of the heart and the pulse waves in the arteries. This would be an example of *indirect perception* of the activity of visceral afferents by way of their reflex actions.

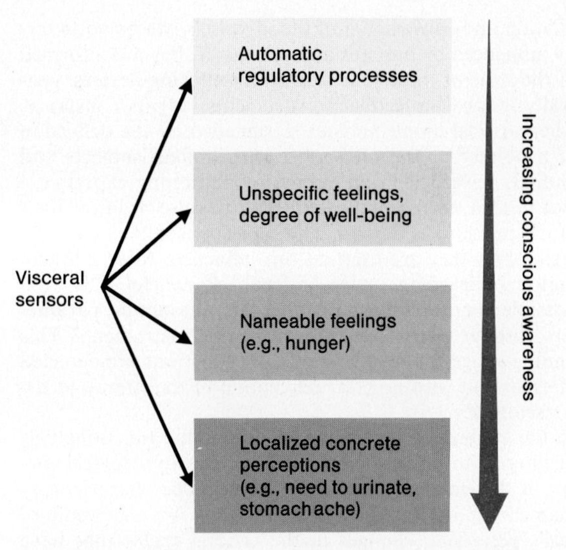

Fig. 9-14. Levels of visceroception. The activity of viscerosensors (sensors in the internal organs) contributes to various functional systems, reaching various levels of conscious perception. Regulatory processes of which we are unconscious can be perceived indirectly by way of effects of the regulation

Pulmonary system. The afferents that control breathing are primarily chemosensors in the arterial system and probably also in the brain, which are excited by decreasing O_2 partial pressure and increasing CO_2 partial pressure. The activity of these sensors, again, is in general not perceived. Only when the CO_2 partial pressure rises sharply and/or in case of obstruction of the airways (e.g., asthma) does one feel **short of breath.** The decrease in O_2 partial pressure caused by a lack of oxygen in the inspired air (e.g., when one climbs a high mountain or the pressure in an aircraft cabin falls) is not detected, even if it is sufficient to induce semiconsciousness. Hence it is not very likely that the chemosensors that test the bloodstream induce directly the feeling of shortness of breath; more probably, what one perceives is a deficiency in the motor execution of the respiratory program. The rhythmic movements of breathing are consciously perceived, probably by excitation of the many sensitive mechanosensors in the thoracic skeletomuscular apparatus and skin.

Gastrointestinal system. In its embryological origin, the gastrointestinal tract is part of the body surface. There is also a functional correspondence in that, while processing the ingested food, the stomach and intestines are exposed to many stimuli that originated outside the body. It is not surprising that mechanical, thermal and chemical stimuli in the gastrointestinal system are perceived more than those in other internal organs [8]. Stretch stimuli are particularly clearly perceived, as has been shown experimentally by blowing up an inserted balloon by way of a catheter. Stretching the stomach in this way causes a **feeling of fullness** or **satiety,** while stretching the intestine makes one feel bloated (as by intestinal gases). In such balloon experiments the stimuli are sometimes erroneously localized in the **Head's zones** on the body surface (see Fig. 9-18 and p. 210). Intense stimulation of the gastrointestinal system by stretching or ischemia is perceived as pain, especially when the situation elicits contracture of the smooth musculature (colic pain; see Chapter 10).

Thermal and chemical stimuli are detected mostly in the region of the esophagus and in the rectum. According to reports from the days when abdominal operations were carried out on unanesthetized patients, touching and manipulation of gastrointestinal structures are not consciously perceived.

Renal system. People are also not conscious of any sensations from the region of the kidneys and ureters, apart from pain. But if the urinary bladder is filled sufficiently to stretch it, one perceives an urge to urinate, which enables voluntary urination to occur (see also the discussion of micturition and defecation in Chapter 16, beginning p. 350).

Experimental biofeedback of visceral functions; theories of emotion. Visceral functions such as blood pressure or the dilation and constriction of blood vessels can be voluntarily influenced by humans and animals if they are informed of the state of these functions by monitoring devices, generally termed biofeedback instruments [14]. For instance, when arterial blood pressure is signalled by the deflection of a pointer or the pitch of a tone, human subjects and animals rewarded in an operant-conditioning experiment (see p. 155) learn, in repeated trials, to raise or lower their blood pressure as desired. The subjects usually cannot describe how they are exerting this influence. After a longer period of learning under biofeedback control it is even possible for the subject to alter his autonomic parameters without reference to the measuring instruments. This finding suggests that the regulatory functions are detected after all, but with no clear perception of the stimuli at the conscious level.

In the context of perception of autonomic functions it is of interest to reconsider an early **psychophysiological theory of the emotions.** According to the *James-Lange theory* (named for its founders), the emotions are the result of one's perceiving changes in the visceral realm that have been brought about by an external stimulus. For example, fear of a bear would be induced because the sight of the wild animal causes changes in blood pressure, heart rate, gastric-juice secretion and so on, which are signaled to the CNS by the visceroceptors, thereby endowing the perceptual situation with emotional overtones. Other emotions (happiness, sadness, rage) would be brought about similarly, by afferent information as to various states of "internal agitation" (i.e., autonomic responses).

There are many indications that the basic mechanism by which emotions are produced need not involve this peripheral loop; for instance, even paraplegics with transections high in the spinal cord have been found to have normal emotional responses. That visceral afferents may contribute to our emotional state, however, has not been ruled out.

9.6 Proprioception

The sense by which we perceive the *posture and movement of our own body* is called proprioception (also, deep or kinesthetic sensibility). Posture is determined by the angle at each joint, which is adjusted either passively, by external forces, or actively by muscular contraction. The sensors that mediate proprioception are located not only in the joints but also in the muscles, tendons and skin. Inputs from the vestibular organ are combined with these to determine the position of the body in the field of gravity. All these propriosensors are also involved in our various conscious and unconscious motor activities (see Chapter 5). This section is concerned chiefly with the proprioceptive signals of which we are conscious.

Qualities of Proprioception

Sense of posture. Even with eyes closed we are well aware of the angles at our joints and, therefore, of the positions of the parts of the body relative to one another. This ability can easily be demonstrated by simple experiments performed with closed eyes. When a limb on one side is put in any position (e.g., an elbow is bent), whether passively or by your own movement, you can match that position very accurately with the limb on the other side. Furthermore, when asked to point to a particular site on the body, we can do so with little error.

Sense of movement. When the position of a joint is changed, we perceive both the direction and the velocity of this movement. The amplitude threshold for perception of joint movements depends on the angular velocity.

We can perceive smaller changes in angle with the proximal than with the distal joints. The perception threshold for a movement of the shoulder joint is 0.2-0.4° for a velocity of 0.3°/s; the threshold for movement of a finger joint is 1.0-1.3° for a velocity of 12.5°/s. There is practically no difference between the thresholds for active and for passive movement.

Sense of force. It is by this sense that we perceive the degree of muscular force necessary to carry out a movement or maintain a joint position (e.g., under different gravitational loadings). With the sense of force we can estimate the weights of objects fairly well by lifting them in a hand. When comparing two weights by lifting them at the same time, one in each hand, we can perceive differences as small as 3-10%. But if the weights to be compared are placed on the hands while they are resting on a support, the estimates – now evidently based on afferent information from cutaneous sensors – are considerably less accurate.

Sensors for Proprioception

Conscious perceptions of joint positions and movements seem to be provided by various sensitive mechanosensors in combination: joint sensors, muscle spindles, tendon sensors and sensors in the skin. It is consistent with this notion that the somatosensory nucleus of the thalamus (the ventro-basal complex) and the somatosensory cortex SI (see Sections 9.10 and 9.11) receive neuronal information from all the above types of sensors [15, 31, 32]. In recent years there has been some controversy about the relative contributions of the different sensor types to perception.

For a long time the **joint sensors** were thought to be predominant in proprioception. These are sensitive mechanosensors in the joint capsules, which encode different joint positions or joint movements. However, their presumed special role in proprioception was contested when patients with artificial joints were found to perceive the joint positions almost as well as normal. More recent psychophysical experiments on the perception of joint positions and movements have reinforced the hypothesis that the **muscle spindles** make the most important contribution. By applying vibration to muscles and tendons, a stimulus that activates primarily the muscle spindles and tendon sensors, baffling illusions of joint movement can be produced [32, 35].

The conclusion to be drawn from the many psychophysical investigations and clinical observations is that to achieve proprioception the CNS utilizes **all the available neural information** (Fig. 9-15). It seems clear that afferent signals from muscle spindles, tendon organs, and sensors in the joints and skin [34] are integrated to give the complex perceptions of body posture and movement. Probably efferent motor information – for instance, movement commands from the motor cortex – are also involved as an **efference copy** in this integration process.

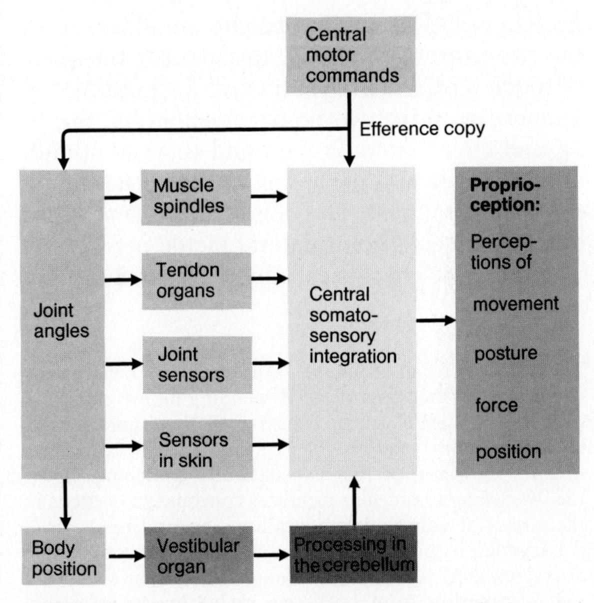

Fig. 9-15. Proprioception. Summary of the afferent and efferent systems that combine to give the proprioceptive sensations of which we are conscious. When perception of, for example, movement of a joint persists after one component of the system has been eliminated, it does not necessarily follow that this component normally makes no contribution to the conscious perception, according to the principle of redundancy in the nervous system (see Chapter 7)

9.7 Functional and Anatomical Survey of the Central Somatosensory System

The central processing of the signals from the peripheral sensors can be considered in terms of three functional levels: the *afferent, integrative* and *efferent* subsystems. The **afferent** or **sensory** level of the central somatovisceral system has been located in the spinal cord, brainstem, thalamus and cortex. Various pathways are employed, allowing parallel processing in separate lines for different functions. The peripheral sensory surface (the set of all sensors outside the CNS) projects to the thalamus and cortex in such a way that there is an orderly mapping of the periphery onto parts of the CNS, a **somatotopic arrangement.** The next stations of central neural processing are at the integrative and efferent levels. The association and limbic systems have predominantly **integrative** functions. One of the most important responsibilities of these systems is to assemble signals from several sensory systems plus information that has been stored in memory. The motor and autonomic systems have **efferent** functions. The complex interactions of these functional subsystems must be viewed as the basis of behavior. Our behavior in response to sensory stimuli consists of perceptions and reactions with five components: *cognitive* (involving conscious recognition), *affective* (related to the emotions), *motivational* (related to drives), *motor* and *autonomic.*

Dichotomy in the ascending central somatovisceral system. The afferent nerve fibers from the trunk and limbs enter the spinal cord by way of the spinal nerves, and those from the face enter the brainstem in the trigeminal nerve. The signals from the sensors are employed in the spinal cord and brainstem in various ways, for motor and autonomic reflexes, and they are also sent on to the brain in ascending fiber systems. Figure 9-16 is a greatly simplified diagram for general orientation.

There are two dominant **systems of ascending tracts** for somatosensory information, which differ anatomically and functionally. They are

- the **dorsal-column** or **lemniscal system**
- the **anterolateral-funiculus system.**

The main connections in both systems serve to link each side of the body with the opposite (contralateral) half of the brain. Functionally, the dorsal-column system is associated with cutaneous mechanoreception and proprioception, and the anterolateral-funiculus system primar-

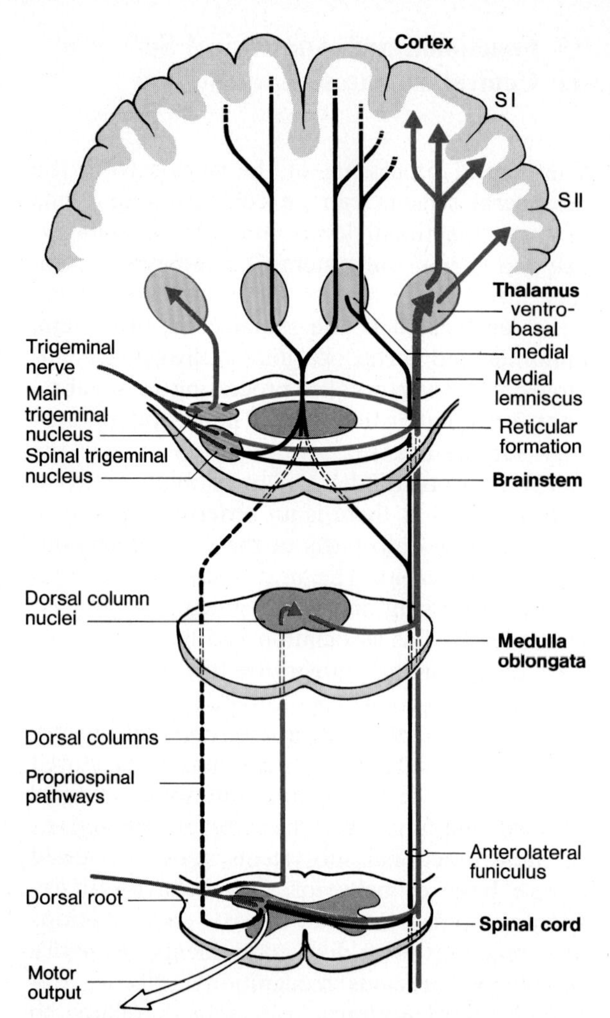

Fig. 9-16. Anatomical arrangement of the main functional elements in the somatosensory system (diagrammatic). *Red:* Tracts and nuclei of the dorsal-column system. *Black:* Tracts and nuclei of the anterolateral-funiculus system. The *red arrows* denote somatotopic mapping, topographically ordered projections of a peripheral sensory surface onto the associated region of the CNS. *SI, SII:* First and second somatosensory projection areas of the cortex

ily subserves thermoreception and nociception. Although additional ascending pathways for somatosensory information have been identified in the spinal cord, it is useful to retain the subdivision based on the two dominant tract systems.

Effects of spinal-cord injury. When the spinal cord is transected on one side only (e.g., in an accident), the interruption of tracts in the white matter causes characteristic neurological deficits, the **Brown-Séquard syndrome** (Fig. 9-17A). It consists of sensory impairments on both sides of the body below the lesion, with paralysis of voluntary movement on the side of the lesion

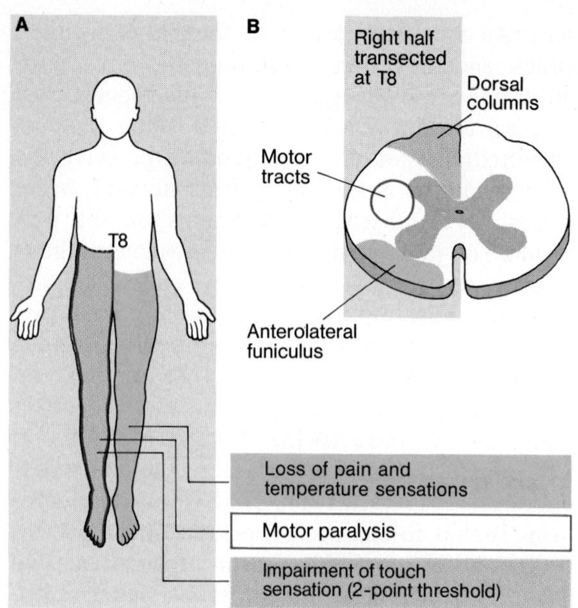

Fig. 9-17 A, B. Deficits following unilateral transection of the spinal cord (Brown-Séquard syndrome). **A** Transection of the right side in segment T8 results in ipsilateral motor paralysis and impairment of the sense of touch (marked increase in the two-point threshold), and contralateral abolition of sensations of pain and temperature. **B** Cross section of the cord at the level of segment T8, showing the three spinal pathways, interruption of which causes the deficits listed in **A**

(ipsilateral). The **sensory deficits** are different on the two sides of the body; ipsilaterally the sense of touch is affected (as indicated, for example, by an increase in the two-point threshold; cf. Fig. 9-3), and contralaterally pain and thermal stimuli are no longer well perceived. On the other hand, the ipsilateral pain and temperature sensations are normal, as is contralateral tactile perception. Therefore the effect is called a **dissociated sensory deficit** [20].

These effects result from the transection of tracts in the white matter. Blocking of the descending motor pathways (e.g., the *pyramidal tract*) causes ipsilateral paralysis of voluntary motor actions, blocking of the *dorsal column* impairs the sense of touch ipsilaterally, and blocking of the *anterolateral funiculus* produces contralateral deficits in the senses of pain and temperature. Sensory inputs from a particular region of skin run on different sides in the dorsal column and anterior funiculus, but in the brain the information from both sensory pathways is mainly contralateral to the side of the body where it originated.

The Dorsal-Column System

The name of this system (shown in red in Fig. 9-16) reflects the fact that the sensory signals are transmitted in the dorsal column (or funiculus), a massive bundle of fibers in the dorsal white matter of the spinal cord. It consists of direct collaterals of thick myelinated afferent fibers (Groups I and II) of the spinal nerves. An alternative name is **lemniscal system**, because above the spinal cord the signals are conducted in the *medial lemniscus*. This ascending somatosensory subsystem connects the spinal and trigeminal mechanoreceptive afferents to two anatomically and neurophysiologically distinct regions of the parietal cortex, the first somatosensory area SI and the second somatosensory area SII (see also Fig. 9-22).

The **afferents in the dorsal-column system** come from the low-threshold cutaneous mechanosensors (i.e., the SA, RA and PC sensors), the muscle spindles, the tendon sensors and the joint sensors. Conduction in this ascending pathway is rapid, for it contains only three synaptic relays. It consists of the following main sections (Fig. 9-16): dorsal columns of the spinal cord, dorsal-column nuclei of the medulla oblongata (1st synapse), medial lemniscus, decussation (crossing to the opposite side), ventrobasal nucleus of the thalamus (2nd synapse), Areas SI and SII of the cortex (3rd synapse). The trigeminal collaterals synapse in the main trigeminal nucleus of the brainstem, which corresponds to the dorsal-column nuclei. After decussation the pathway continues in the medial lemniscus to the thalamus.

The **somatotopic** organization mentioned above is a special characteristic of the dorsal-column system: the topographic relations of the various regions of the skin, the peripheral sensory surface, are roughly preserved in all the central relay stations. This situation amounts to a (geometrically distorted) *mapping* or **projection** like that found in the visual and auditory systems. Details are discussed below (see p. 216).

The dorsal-column system is especially highly developed in primates – that is, monkeys, apes and humans. It is the anatomical substrate of **tactile sensations** (the sense of touch) and **proprioception**, all the (conscious and unconscious) abilities that require discrimination of the spatial and temporal details of a mechanical stimulus to the body.

The signals from the skin, muscles and joints that are transmitted in the dorsal column provide important information about the **execution of movements,** especially those of tactile exploration. Patients with dorsal-column injury therefore have a greatly reduced ability to identify objects by active touch, for instance, or recognize numbers written on the skin. The two-point threshold is raised.

The Anterolateral-Funiculus System

This system is shown in black in Fig. 9-16. The anterolateral funiculus comprises a number of tracts in the ventral white matter of the spinal cord that contain ascending fibers of spinal neurons with cell bodies in the gray matter, primarily in the dorsal horn. The trigeminal axons corresponding to the anterolateral funiculus arise from neurons in the spinal trigeminal nucleus (Figs. 9-16 and 9-20). The afferent inputs to the anterolateral funiculus carried in the *spinal* and *trigeminal nerves* come from **thermosensors** and **nociceptors**, as well as from low-threshold mechanosensors, mainly those in the skin.

The ascending axons join the anterolateral tract contralateral to the site of their cell body and the entry of their afferent fibers into the spinal cord. Because there are two main destinations, in the **reticular formation** and other brainstem areas and in the **thalamus,** a distinction is made between the *spinoreticular tract* and the *spinothalamic tract*. The information they transmit appears eventually to reach many parts of the brain, chiefly by **polysynaptic, slowly conducting** routes. However, there is no clear somatotopic organization, nor is there any well-defined projection to the cortex comparable with that in the dorsal-column system. The anterolateral-funiculus system is regarded as the anatomical substrate of **thermal sensations** and **pain.** In addition, it is considered to be part of the nonspecific system discussed below.

This categorization of the anterolateral-funiculus system does not include a phylogenetically recent component, the **neospinothalamic tract** (light red in Fig. 9-16). This tract, well developed in primates, transmits information from cutaneous mechanosensors by way of the ventrobasal nucleus of the thalamus to the Areas SI and SII of the somatosensory cortex; for this reason, some researchers consider it as **functionally part of the lemniscal system.**

Other ascending pathways. Three long tracts (not shown in Fig. 9-16) will be mentioned only briefly here; their role in the somatosensory system is not clear. The two **spinocerebellar tracts** carry mechanosensory information from skin, muscles and joints to the cerebellum. Functionally, they belong to the motor system (see p. 102). The **spinocervical tract**, which occupies a dorsolateral position, is most prominent in carnivores (e.g., cats), where it is thought to be the functional equivalent of the **neospinothalamic tract** (see above), which is not well developed here. Because of its supraspinal connections (e.g., to the somatosensory cortical area SI), it is assigned to the lemniscal system [9]. The dorsal columns also include, in addition to the collaterals of myelinated afferents, axons of neurons in the gray matter of the spinal cord, most of which are excited by strong, potentially harmful stimuli. Little is known about either the destinations in the brain or the functions of this **postsynaptic dorsal column pathway**.

The pathway that has been least studied consists of a series of short elements in the spinal cord, the **intersegmental (propriospinal) connections** represented by the dashed black line in Fig. 9-16. The results of bilateral hemisections at different segmental levels in experimental animals indicate that this *polysynaptic* pathway is diffusely distributed over the cross section of the spinal cord, and that as it ascends there are multiple crossings to the opposite side and back again. This pathway is thought primarily to subserve nociception and pain; its existence could explain the observation that even after *bilateral cordotomy* sensations of pain persist or recur.

The Nonspecific System

Since about 1950 the concept of the *nonspecific system* has become widely accepted in neurophysiology [1, 18, 22, 24]. It is the alternative to the specific systems in various sensory modalities, which can be clearly defined anatomically and physiologically; in the somatosensory modality, the dorsal-column system is the specific system. The nonspecific system has been considered to mediate a number of **generalized reactions** observed in animal experiments, such as

- arousal reactions,
- influences on the EEG,
- the sleeping/waking rhythm,
- affective behavioral reactions,
- blood-pressure reactions.

Such reactions can be elicited both by sensory stimuli (especially pain stimuli) and by electrical stimulation in the *reticular formation* of the brainstem and the *medial thalamic regions.* These central regions have therefore been regarded as the site of the nonspecific system, supplied with sensory information mainly by the anterolateral tracts.

The many studies of this phylogenetically old part of the brain indicate that many vital integrative and regulatory processes take place here, processes manifest in functions of the spinal cord (e.g., sympathetic responses) as well as the cerebrum (e.g., alertness). However, there is insufficient evidence of the existence of a homogeneous nonspecific system. Indeed, as data on the physiological, anatomical and biochemical differentiation of these brain regions have accumulated [17], the concept of a nonspecific system is becoming less and less tenable. We shall return to it again in discussing the brainstem reticular formation (see p. 213).

9.8 The Transfer of Somatovisceral Information in the Spinal Cord

The dermatome. The afferents from skin, muscles, joints and viscera enter the spinal cord by way of the dorsal roots. There is an orderly spatial *(topological)* arrangement along the cord (Fig. 9-18); the cutaneous afferents in each dorsal root innervate a circumscribed region of skin called a **dermatome.** There is considerable overlap of adjacent dermatomes, owing to the rearrangement of fiber bundles that occurs as the fibers grow into the periphery, which is most pronounced in the brachial and lumbosacral plexuses. A peripheral nerve contains fibers from several adjacent dorsal roots, and each dorsal root contains fibers from various nerves. Whereas transection of a peripheral nerve causes a sensory deficit in a restricted area, *transection of a single dorsal root tends rather to thin out the innervation* of an area without causing a marked deficit.

In the skeletal musculature, **myotomes are the equivalent of dermatomes.** The **Head's zone** of an internal organ consists of the dermatomes associated with the same spinal-cord segments that supply the organ. The neuronal organization of the two sets of afferents is such that *referred pain* can be produced (p. 231).

Functional Properties of the Spinal Somatovisceral System

The somatovisceral afferents make synaptic connections with neurons in the *posterior* or *dorsal horn* of the spinal cord (Fig. 9-19). Some of the thick myelinated afferents (Groups I and II) also send out branches, called collaterals, that ascend in the dorsal column (see p. 208). The **dorsal horn,** considered as a neuronal processing station, has **four outputs:** (i) long tracts ascending to the brain, mainly those in the anterolateral funiculus (see p. 209), (ii) and (iii) ascending and descending propriospinal connections to adjacent segments, and (iv) segmental connections to the motoneurons and to sympathetic neurons (participation in spinal motor and autonomic reflexes). Probably, however, an individual neuron will not make all four kinds of connections.

Within the ascending tracts, the axons coming from a particular segment run side by side. This produces a **somatotopic layering** (Fig. 9-19); the axons originating in progressively higher segments always join the existing tract on the side

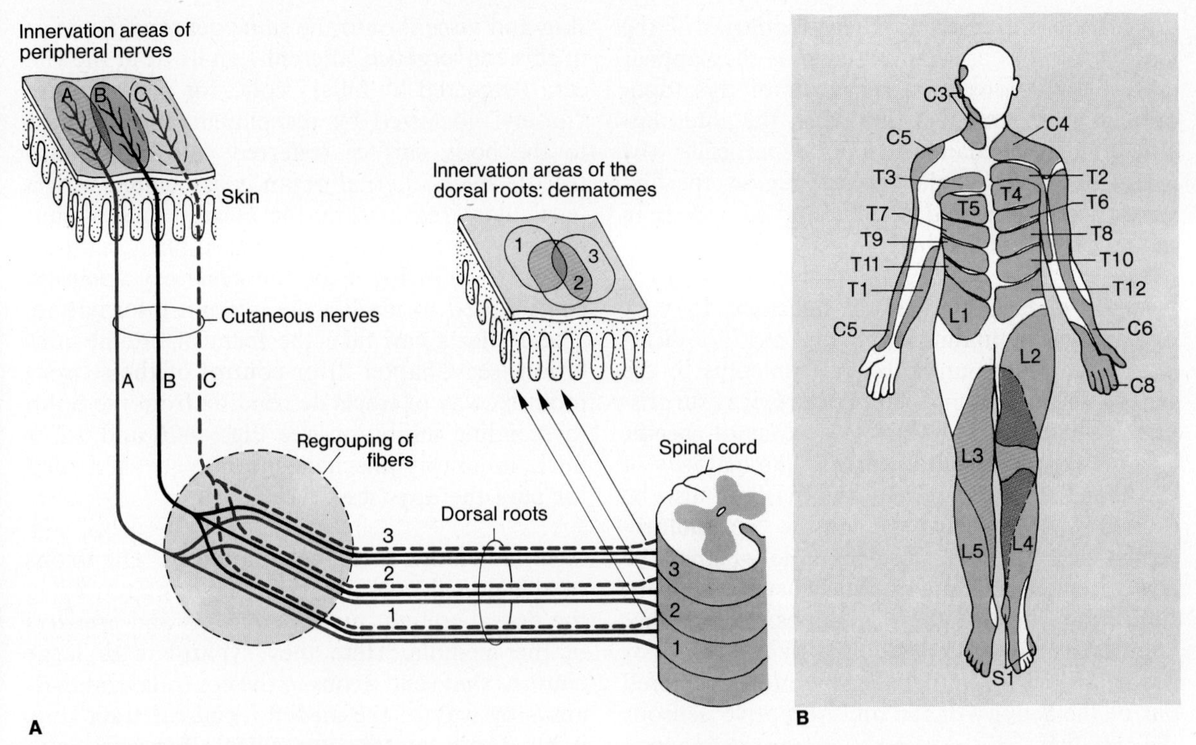

Fig. 9-18 A, B. Regions innervated by cutaneous nerves and dorsal roots. **A** The cutaneous nerves (A, B, C) innervate sharply delimited regions with little overlap. Because the peripheral nerve fibers are redistributed among the spinal nerves, the cutaneous innervation areas of the dorsal roots (dermatomes 1, 2, 3) are less well defined and have greater overlap. **B** The cutaneous innervation areas of the dorsal roots (i.e., the dermatomes) of successive segments of the spinal cord are shown on alternating sides of the body. To clarify the extent to which adjacent dermatomes overlap, L3 (lumbar 3) is shown on both legs. (Modified from FOERSTER, O., in LEWIS, T.: Pain. New York, Macmillan, 1942)

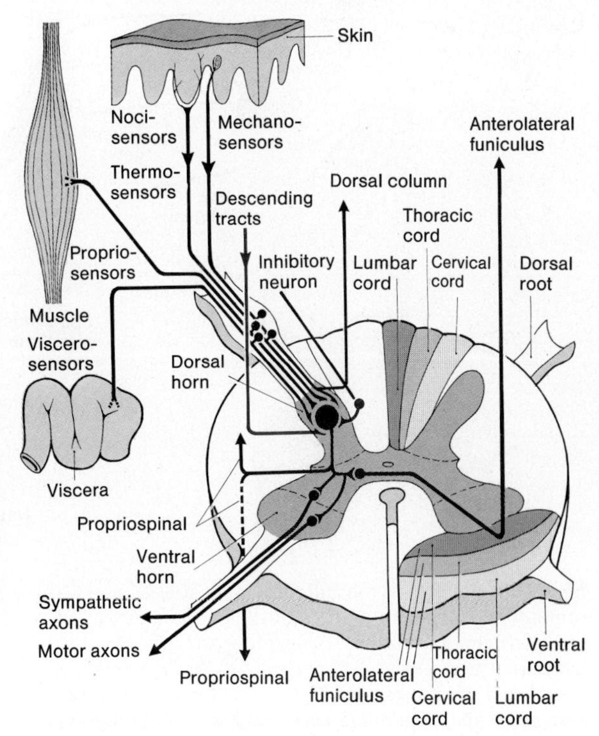

Fig. 9-19. Connections of cutaneous and visceral afferents in the spinal cord. Entering through the dorsal roots, the afferents synapse with dorsal horn neurons which pass the information on to spinal segmental efferents, to adjacent segments (propriospinal fibers) and to ascending tracts (e.g., anterolateral funiculus). Collaterals of Groups I and II afferents ascend in the dorsal column of the white matter directly to the medulla oblongata. Two inhibitory influences on the dorsal horn neuron, shown in *red,* are exerted by way of pathways descending from the brain or by spinal inhibitory interneurons. On the *right* the topographic segregation of the ascending fibers from different parts of the spinal cord is shown (schematically) as it appears in the cervical white matter

toward the gray matter. The boundaries of the various bundles are not as sharp as they appear in Fig. 9-19, however. One result of this topographic arrangement is that when the anterolateral funiculus is damaged only superficially (by injury or tumor) in the cervical region, the first sensory deficits would be expected to appear in the lower half of the body.

Neurons of the anterolateral funiculus. In view of the clinical findings (see Fig. 9-17) indicating a role of the anterolateral funiculus in the sensations of pain and temperature, it is surprising that it contains only a few axons of **specific noci-** or **thermosensitive neurons.** The majority of the axons are those of neurons that can also be excited by light mechanical stimuli – i.e., **multireceptive neurons.** It is still debatable whether the few specific noci- and thermosensitive neurons suffice to transmit these qualities, or whether additional information required by the brain for the sensations of pain and temperature is filtered out of the activity of the multireceptive neurons [13, 23, 39].

A significant feature of the relay station in the dorsal horn is the **convergence** of afferents from skin and viscera onto the same neurons. Because of this convergence, afferent signals from the viscera (triggered by biliary colic, for instance) are "falsely" localized by the patient and ascribed to the body surface (referred pain, see Chapter 10). Each internal organ is associated with a particular area of skin, the **Head's zone** of that organ. Another feature of dorsal-horn circuitry shown (red) in Fig. 9-19, the **inhibitory synapses,** can be used to modify the afferent information. These effects can take the form of lateral inhibition (see Chapter 8) or control of the sensory input by way of tracts descending from the brain (descending inhibition, see Figs. 9-26 and 9-27). Such inhibitory mechanisms may be activated for pain therapy (see Chapter 10).

Neurons of the dorsal-column nuclei. The axons of the dorsal column terminate ipsilaterally in the dorsal-column nuclei (*cuneatus* and *gracilis*) in the medulla. Here they synapse with large neurons that send axons to the contralateral thalamus by way of the **medial lemniscal tract** (Fig. 9-20). These neurons are called *relay neurons* to distinguish them from *interneurons* with axons that do not leave the dorsal-column nuclei. The

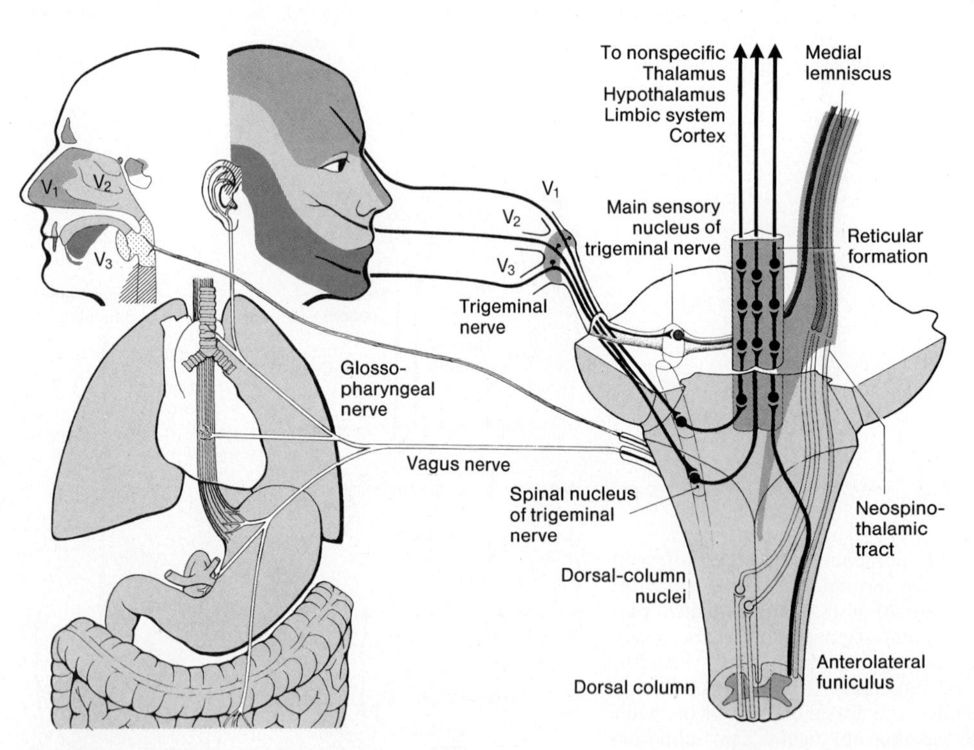

Fig. 9-20. Survey of the afferents and structures of the somatovisceral system in the brainstem (*right:* dorsal view of brainstem, schematic). It comprises the afferents in the trigeminal nerve (with 3 branches V_1, V_2, V_3) and in the vagus and glossopharyngeal nerves, the central afferent system of the trigeminal nerve and its ascending pathways, the reticular formation (*gray*) and the tracts coming from the spinal cord, the dorsal columns (*red*) and the anterolateral funiculus (*black*). The central course of the afferents in the glossopharyngeal and vagus nerves is not shown

processing of afferent information in synaptic transmission to the **relay neurons** has the following characteristics:

- Preservation of sensor specificity; only afferents of the same sensor type converge on a neuron.
- Large safety factor in synaptic transmission; even single impulses in an afferent fiber can cause postsynaptic impulse discharge.
- Small receptive fields.
- Somatotopic organization; there is an orderly spatial representation of the skin.
- Afferent inhibition (lateral inhibition, p. 185).
- Descending control inputs, from the cerebral cortex in particular (see Fig. 9-26).

These properties are also characteristic of the subsequent relay stations in the lemniscal system, and are responsible for the quality and discrimination ability of sensations mediated by the information transmitted here.

9.9 Somatosensory Functions of the Brainstem

The brainstem, consisting of the *medulla oblongata, pons* and *midbrain* (cf. Fig. 5-13), is the origin (or destination) of most of the cranial nerves. It is crowded with distinct nuclei having predominantly sensory, motor or regulatory functions, between which all the ascending and descending pathways linking the brain to the spinal cord, as well as cerebrum to cerebellum, must find their way. In this section the afferent system for somatosensory input from the head is discussed, along with the reticular formation – the latter being a main constituent of the nonspecific system.

The Trigeminal Nerve and Its Central Connections

The head is innervated by 12 pairs of **cranial nerves**, most of which join the central nervous system in the brain stem and the diencephalon. The fifth cranial nerve, called the *trigeminal nerve* because of its three branches, carries afferents from the face and mouth region (Fig. 9-20). It innervates the skin, teeth, oral mucosa, tongue and cornea. The seventh cranial nerve *(facial)* also, to a lesser extent, contains somatosensory afferents from the head. Cranial nerves IX *(glossopharyngeal)* and X *(vagus)* contain visceral afferents from the organs of circulation, respiration and digestion. The somatovisceral afferents, then, are distributed among the spinal nerves and cranial nerves V, VII, IX and X.

Sensory trigeminal nuclei and ascending pathways. The afferents of the trigeminal nerve synapse in the nucleus of the spinal tract and the principal sensory nucleus (Fig. 9-20). The **nucleus of the spinal tract** corresponds functionally to the dorsal horn of the spinal cord. Here mechanoreceptive, thermoreceptive and nociceptive information is transferred to axons that carry it to the reticular formation and the thalamus, like the fibers in the spinal anterolateral funiculus that carry information from the spinal cord. All the afferents that terminate in the **principal sensory nucleus,** which corresponds to the dorsal-column nuclei, are from low-threshold mechanosensors. The postsynaptic axons cross to the other side and pass to the thalamus in the *medial lemniscal tract.*

In the brainstem, the information supplied by the trigeminal afferents is integrated into motor reflexes of the head musculature and into numerous autonomic reflexes. Especially in mammals, the *trigeminal system performs vital functions* – in tactile exploration of the environment, feeding, sound production and so on. It is already well developed at birth and carries the sensory signals that initiate feeding behavior. The trigeminal system provides the infant with its first sensory experience of its surroundings.

The Reticular Formation

The reticular formation, an elongated structure within the brainstem (Fig. 9-20), is an important **integration region of the nonspecific system** (see p. 210). The many afferent and efferent connections of this region are summarized in Fig. 9-21. The somatovisceral afferents arrive by way of the spinoreticular tract of the anterolateral funiculus, probably also by propriospinal (polysynaptic) pathways, and by corresponding pathways from the nucleus of the spinal trigeminal tract. The reticular formation also receives afferent input from the other cranial nerves. There are also many diverse efferent connections: descending to the spinal cord and ascending by way of the nonspecific thalamic nuclei to the cortex, the hypothalamus and the limbic system [1, 9, 16, 18, 24].

The diversity of the afferent connections and the unspecificity of the system are also evident at the level of the single

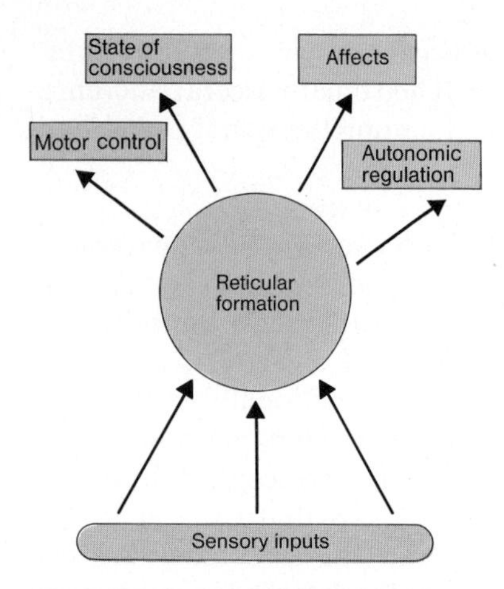

Fig. 9-21. Survey of the contributions of the brainstem reticular formation to various functional systems

reticular neuron. Microelectrode recordings have revealed the following features:
- Multimodal convergence: the convergence of several afferents of different origins onto a single neuron.
- Large receptive fields, often bilateral on the body surface.
- Long latency of the response to peripheral stimulation, due to polysynaptic conduction.
- Low response reproducibility: unpredictable fluctuations in the number of action potentials when a given stimulus is repeated.
- Temporal facilitation with multiple stimulation.

All these properties are opposite to those of neurons in the specific nuclei – for example, the dorsal-column nuclei (see p. 212) or the ventrobasal nucleus of the thalamus (see p. 215).

The various **functions of the reticular formation** are not yet completely understood. As diagrammed in Fig. 9-21, it is thought to participate in a number of processes that can be summarized as follows:
- Control of the excitability of the cortex: level of consciousness, sleeping/waking rhythm (key term: ascending reticular activating system, ARAS; see p. 146).
- Mediation of the affective-emotional aspects of sensory stimuli, especially painful stimuli, by transmission of the afferent information to the limbic system.
- Motor control functions, particularly those related to the so-called vital reflexes (circulatory, respiratory, swallowing, coughing and sneezing reflexes) requiring the coordination of several afferent and efferent systems.
- Involvement in the control of postural and goal-directed movement (see p. 97).

This list corroborates the impossibility of drawing sharp lines in the reticular formation to distinguish the central sensory and integrative systems (see p. 208). On the other hand, it has recently become evident that several regions within the reticular formation can be defined on the basis of their anatomical, functional and chemical properties (e.g., the serotonergic raphe nuclei and the noradrenergic locus coeruleus). It is to be expected that as our knowledge of the reticular formation expands, the concept of the nonspecific system can be revised.

9.10 Thalamus

The thalamus is interpreted as the gateway and distributing station by which all afferent systems gain access to the phylogenetically younger cerebral structures, which make possible conscious sensations and consciously goal-directed behavior (see also Chapter 6.4, p. 147ff.).

Anatomical and Functional Survey

In the diagrammatic summary of Fig. 9-22, the right thalamus is subdivided into several functionally and/or anatomically distinguishable nu-

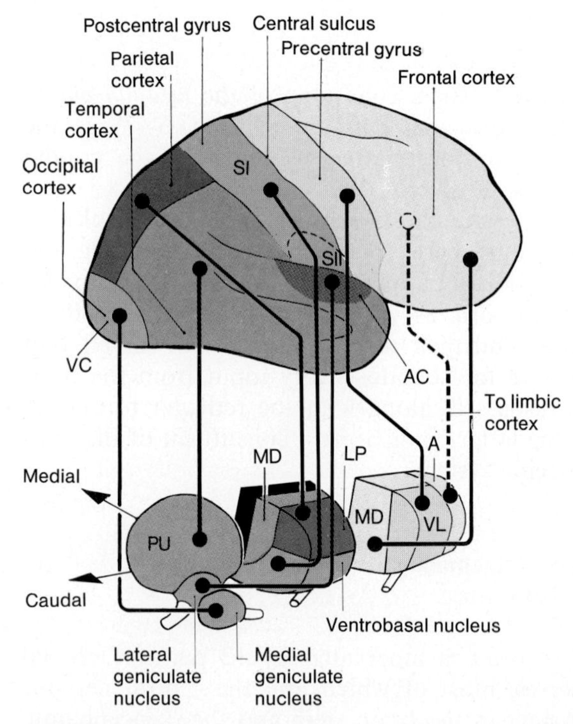

Fig. 9-22. Thalamus of the right half of the brain (highly diagrammatic). The anatomical and functional linkage between thalamic nuclei and areas of the right cortex is indicated by lines and color correspondence. Functional subdivisions of the thalamic nuclei: specific sensory nuclei *(dark red);* motor nuclei *(light red);* association nuclei (various *shades of gray);* nonspecific nuclei *(black).* PU, pulvinar; LP, nucleus lateralis posterior; MD, nucleus medialis dorsalis; VL, nucleus ventralis lateralis; A, nucleus anterior

clei, which are connected to particular cortical areas. For general orientation, we can separate the thalamic nuclei into four functional classes, as follows:

- Specific relay and processing nuclei for the cutaneous sense organs, the eye, and the ear (dark red in Fig. 9-22),
- Nuclei with predominantly motor functions (light red),
- Nuclei with associative functions (various shades of gray),
- Nonspecific nuclei (black), with no discrete cortical target areas.

Thalamic relay nuclei for the sense organs. These relay and processing stations (dark red in Fig. 9-22) project to the cortical area concerned with their particular sensory modality and, in turn, are subject to controlling influences (excitatory and inhibitory) from the same cortical region (cf. Fig. 9-26). The specific nuclei for the visual and auditory systems, the *lateral geniculate body (LGB)* and *medial geniculate body* (*MGB*), respectively, are treated together with their cortical projections in Chapters 11 and 12. The somatosensory nucleus of the thalamus is the **ventrobasal nucleus (VB);** the associated cortical areas SI and SII are situated on the parietal lobe (see also Figs. 6-2 to 6-5). The afferent pathway is the medial lemniscus.

Nonspecific nuclei. This category (black in Fig. 9-22) includes the medial regions bordering on the third ventricle as well as the intralaminar nuclei (not shown in Fig. 9-22). These are the higher-level processing and distribution stations for the afferent information that converges on the reticular formation in the brainstem (see Figs. 9-16 and 9-20). The inputs from the spinal cord arrive directly in the paleospinothalamic tract and indirectly by way of the spinoreticular tract (Fig. 9-20).

Experiments in which the nonspecific nuclei of animals are stimulated have shown that they exert modulating influences on practically all cortical areas and also make connections with the hypothalamus and limbic system [17, 24]. These functional connections are diffuse, in contrast to the circumscribed cortical projections of the other thalamic nuclei (Fig. 9-22).

Motor nuclei. The most important of these (light red in Fig. 9-21) is the ventrolateral nucleus (VL), which links the cerebellum and the basal ganglia to the motor cortex (see Chapter 5). Surgical lesions at appropriate positions in the VL can alleviate motor disorders (e.g., in Parkinson's disease).

Associative nuclei. These parts of the thalamus (various gray shades in Fig. 9-22) are connected to the cortex but cannot be assigned to a particular sensory system. They participate in the **integrative functions** of the brain. Three representatives of the group (PU, MD, LP) are shown, each of which is related chiefly to one of the major association areas of the cortex.

The Specific Thalamic Nucleus of the Somatosensory System

Because of its anatomical position (see Fig. 9-22), this second station in the lemniscal system

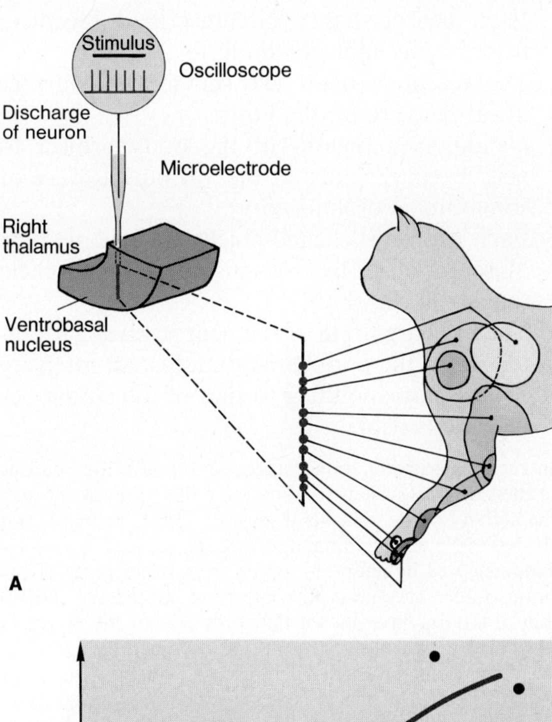

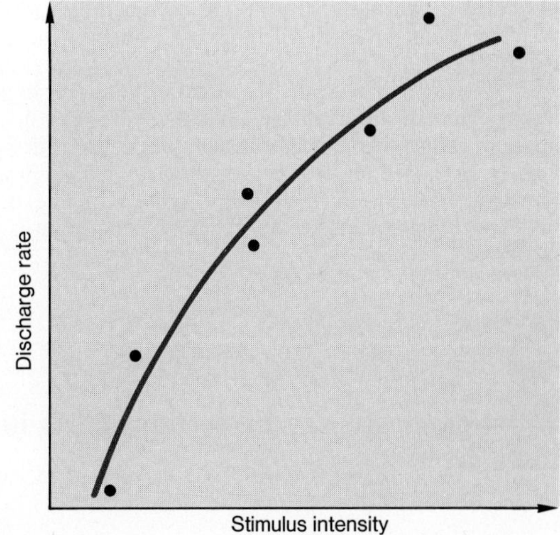

Fig. 9-23. Receptive fields of neurons in the ventrobasal nucleus of the thalamus. A microelectrode advanced through the thalamus of an anesthetized cat encountered 10 neurons responsive to mechanical stimulation of the skin. The receptive fields of the neurons were on the left foreleg, as shown. (Modified from MOUNTCASTLE and POGGIO, Bull. Johns Hopkins Hosp. *106*, 266, 1960)

is called the **ventrobasal nucleus** *(VB)* or *ventrobasal complex*. It is subdivided into the *VPL (ventral posterolateral nucleus)* and *VPM (ventral posteromedial nucleus)*. The neuronal representation of the body is in the VPL, and that of the face is in the VPM. The main pathway leading to the VPL is the **medial lemniscal tract,** and that to the VPM is the **trigeminothalamic tract,** which comes from the principal sensory nucleus of the trigeminal nerve.

In experiments on anesthetized animals, the VB neurons were found to have the following functional characteristics (Fig. 9-23):

- Each neuron has a circumscribed receptive field for mechanical stimuli to the skin.
- The receptive fields are smaller, the further distal they are on the limbs.
- Neighboring regions of the body project to neighboring regions of the VB (an instance of somatotopic organization).
- Each neuron is excited chiefly by a single type of sensor (e.g., by SA sensors or hair-follicle sensors in the skin).
- The discharge rate of the neuron rises with intensity of the peripheral stimulus, an intensity coding corresponding to that of the cutaneous mechanosensors.

In such experiments on anesthetized animals, the neurons of the lemniscal system are found to reflect quite accurately the activity of the peripheral sensors. This is probably not the case in a waking animal, where the sensory inputs are supplemented by neuronal inputs from other parts of the brain; under anesthesia, the latter are suppressed. Histological studies have shown that only 8% of the synapses on the relay neurons of the VB are occupied by terminals of fibers from the medial lemniscus; evidently the great majority (92%) of the synapses mediate other (excitatory and inhibitory) influences [37]. Because few **recordings in waking animals** are available (that is, neurophysiological measurements of single neurons with microelectrodes previously implanted under anesthesia), our understanding of the ways sensory information is processed in the thalamus and other somatosensory regions of the brain is still incomplete.

9.11 Somatosensory Projection Areas in the Cortex

The ventrobasal complex of the thalamus is connected, by both ascending and descending axons, with the two cortical regions called SI and SII (first and second somatosensory area) (Fig. 9-22). **SI** is located on the **postcentral gyrus,** immediately posterior to the central sulcus, a deep furrow lying transversely on the cerebral hemisphere. **SII** is on the upper wall of the lateral sulcus, which separates the parietal and temporal lobes. SI, phylogenetically younger than SII, is of great significance in the higher mammals (especially primates); it mediates all those functions of the somatosensory system that depend on good spatial and temporal discrimination of stimuli. Some of these functions can be tested by the two-point threshold of the skin, for example (see Fig. 9-3).

Topographic Organization of the Somatosensory Cortex

The **somatotopic** representation of the periphery of the body on one side in the contralateral SI is remarkably detailed and has been thoroughly investigated. The entire body surface is mapped onto the cortex, and there are actually **multiple projections** of the hand in primates [2, 10, 16, 33]. There is a similar, though less clear-cut, mapping in SII, where it is partially bilateral. There are several methods of studying the somatotopic organization of the sensory cortex: in humans, local electrical stimulation of the cortex has been used during brain surgery to evoke sensations localized to the corresponding body sites [9], or local cortical blood flow can be measured with radioactive xenon [23] during stimulation of the skin. In animals, analysis of evoked potentials and recording from single neurons have been performed to map the cortical representation of the periphery of the body.

Electrical stimulation of the human cortex. Some neurosurgical operations require local electrical stimulation of the cortex while the patient is awake (with local anesthetization of the incision site). The sensations elicited by such stimuli were perceived as originating in the periphery. By systematic sampling of SI in this way, the symbolic diagram shown in Fig. 9-24 has been constructed. This "somatosensory homunculus" is a conspicuously distorted mapping of the peripheral sensory surface, in which the finger and mouth regions, in particular, are disproportionately large. These are the regions that have a particularly dense innervation in humans, and psychophysical experiments have shown them to be characterized by excellent spatial discrimination – that is, low two-point thresholds (see Fig. 9-3, p. 198). These two findings are evidently causally related, and the relationship also applies to other sensory systems: the more sensors

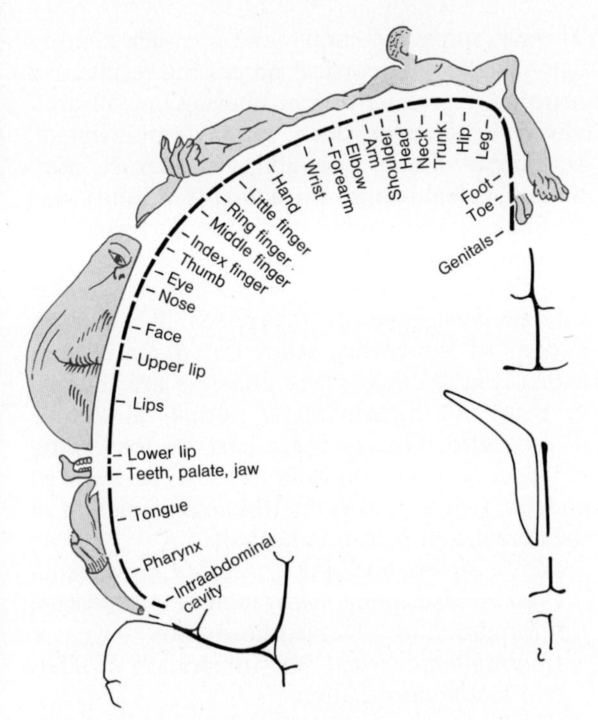

Fig. 9-24. Somatotopic organization of the human somatosensory cortex SI. The symbols drawn over the brain cross section (at the level of the postcentral gyrus) and the associated labels show the spatial representation of the body surface on the cortex, as found by local electrical stimulation of the brains of waking patients. (From [19])

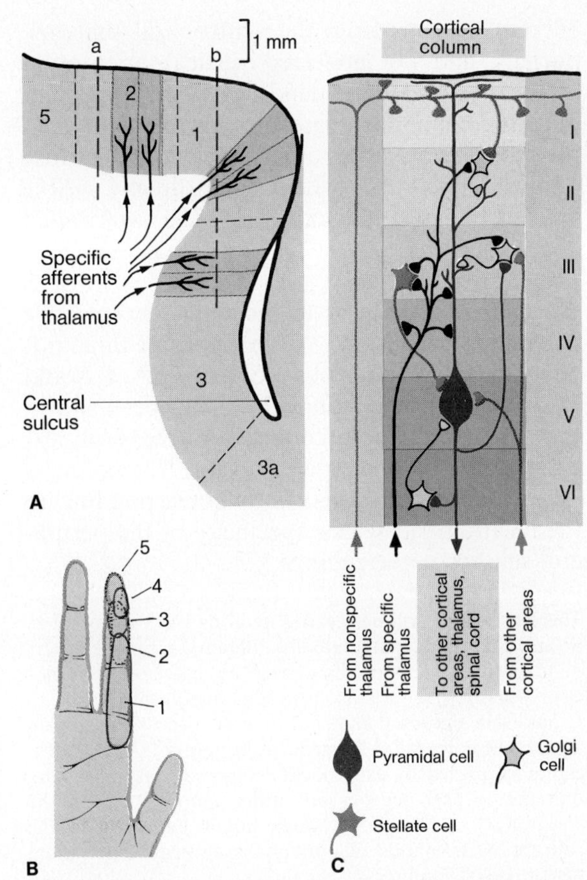

Fig. 9-25 A–C. Columnar arrangement of cortical neurons. **A** Sagittal section through the postcentral gyrus. In each of the cytoarchitectonic areas 1, 2 and 3 (BRODMANN's classification; see p. 128) two adjacent columns are shown. The lines *a* and *b* show two possible directions of microelectrode penetration in animal experiments, one parallel to the columns and one transverse. **B** Receptive fields (monkey hand) of 5 neurons encountered as the electrode advanced in a direction as indicated by line *a*. **C** The column, a functional element in the cortex. That the neurons within a column have related functions can be partially explained by anatomical considerations; the dendrites of the pyramidal cells are limited in lateral extent, as are the terminals of specific thalamocortical afferents, and these limitations coincide with column width

and central neurons there are per mm^2 of sensory surface, the better is the **spatial resolution** of stimuli to the sense organ.

Evoked potentials. By exposing the cortex of an experimental animal, one can record evoked potentials in response to peripheral stimulation – the summed activity of populations of neurons (see Fig. 6-9, p. 133). After a brief latency (conduction in the dorsal-column system) the **primary evoked potential** appears. Its amplitude, for stimulation at a given peripheral site, is maximal in a circumscribed area of SI (and SII). Thus the somatotopic representation can be mapped by systematically plotting the potential maxima associated with various stimulus sites, and these maps correspond to those obtained by local stimulation of the human cortex (Fig. 9-24). The largest cortical projections are those of **specialized sensory surfaces:** in the rat, for instance, most of SI is occupied by the projection of the vibrissae (tactile hairs on the snout). The vibrissae are probably more important than the visual system to the rat, as a means of identifying the animal's surroundings.

Information Processing in the Neurons of the Somatosensory Cortex

Columns of cortical neurons. When a microelectrode is advanced perpendicular to the surface of the postcentral gyrus (Line a in Fig. 9-25A), the neurons successively encountered often have identical or broadly overlapping receptive fields (Fig. 9-25B). When advanced at an angle to the surface (Line b) it encounters neurons with adjacent but distinctly separated receptive fields (corresponding to the somatotopic arrangement). It has been deduced from these and other findings that the sensory cortex, like the motor cortex (see Chapter 5, p. 117), is organized in functional units, **columns** of neurons perpendicular to the surface; six columns are diagrammed in Fig. 9-25A. These columns (0.2–0.5 mm in diameter) are based on two anatomical features, the limited horizontal extent of the terminals of afferent neurons from the ventrobasal thalamic nucleus, and the preferred vertical orientation of the pyramidal-cell dendrites (Fig. 9-25C). In mice the columnar aggregates corresponding to the vibrissae are especially conspicuous; because of their appearance when made directly visible with histological methods they have been called "barrels".

Receptor specificity of the columns. By selective adequate stimulation – for example, of three different types of cutaneous receptors (SA, RA and PC sensors; see Section 9.2) – it has been shown that the neurons in a column are frequently excitable only by one type of sensor. The columns are evidently functional units corresponding to the location and sensor specificity of the peripheral sensory nerve endings.

Thermosensitive and **nociceptive** neurons are also found in SI and SII, though they are less numerous, by 1-2 orders of magnitude, than mechanoreceptive neurons. It is not clear whether they are also arranged in columns.
It has been proposed that information processing in and among the columns is **hierarchical** in nature. This hypothesis is supported by experimental observations suggesting that the cortical neurons are either simple ("low in the hierarchy") or complex ("higher in the hierarchy"). The concept has been most elaborately developed for the visual system (see Chapter 11).

Simple and complex neurons. The discharge characteristics of simple cortical neurons match quite closely those of the associated sensor types. For instance, SI has been found to include simple neurons that behave like RA sensors. Cortical neurons that respond to peripheral stimuli with discharge patterns not directly resembling those of the associated sensors are called **complex neurons.** This term therefore covers a variety of neurons. Among them are neurons that respond specifically to stimuli moving linearly over the skin surface, with a maximal response to movement in a particular direction. Such neurons have been found in SI and SII, and in the association areas of the parietal cortex (BRODMANN's areas 5 and 7) [3].

The **thermosensitive cortical neurons** found in the monkey are also complex neurons. Unlike peripheral thermosensors (see Section 9.4), they respond either only to changes in skin temperature or only to the steady-state temperature. Furthermore, thermosensitive cortical neurons do not have the peak response at temperatures around 26 °C that is characteristic of cold sensors (Fig. 9-12). Another kind of complex thermosensitive neuron has been found in the rat cortex. Here the discharge rate jumps between maximal and minimal when the temperature of the skin in the receptive fields is changed by ca. 2 °C (threshold detector) [7].

These examples of simple and complex neurons demonstrate that cortical processing results in a neuronal representation or filtering out of information concerning widely varying parameters of peripheral stimuli. This ability to extract information, called **feature extraction** [2, 23] has been particularly thoroughly studied in the visual cortex (see Chapter 11, p. 259).

Efferent connections of SI. Area SI, like all other regions of the cortex, sends out many efferent axons (Fig. 9-25C). These efferents are thought to carry information about peripheral stimuli, in processed form, to other parts of the central nervous system. Connections exist between SI and the following regions (the main function of the connection is also indicated):
- *Motor cortex:* feedback control of movement
- *Parietal association fields:* integration of visual information and tactile information
- *Contralateral SI and SII:* Integration of bilateral tactile information
- *Thalamus, dorsal-column nuclei, spinal cord:* efferent control of the afferent information flow (see Section 9.12, p. 219)

Cortical area SII. This area, considerably smaller than SI, lies at the lateral end of the postcentral gyrus, in the upper wall of the sylvian fissure. Here the somatotopic representation of the body surface is bilateral. The neuronal columns usually have receptive fields on both sides of the body, often symmetrically positioned. SII is thought to play a special role in the sensory and motor coordination of the two sides of the body (e.g., grasping or exploring with both hands) [2].

The Somatosensory Cortex and Perception

Many findings indicate that SI is essential for precise tactile discrimination and conscious perception of events on the skin surface, with high resolution of intensive, spatial and temporal details. On the other hand, excitation of SI does not necessarily produce conscious perception; for example, peripheral stimulation elicits primary evoked potentials in an anesthetized or sleeping person, who has no conscious perception of them.

Stimulation of the human cortex. As described above (p. 216), local electrical stimulation of SI or SII in a waking patient gives rise to perceptions that often seem identical to those produced by adequate stimuli at the periphery. Perceptions also resulted from stimulation of SII and the visual and auditory projection regions (see Fig. 9-22), but nowhere else in the cortex. Near-threshold punctate stimuli to SI were described as "similar to natural stimulation". The range of experiences reported during electrical cortex stimulation included simple receptor-specific sensations (vibration, warmth, cold) as well as sensations of moving stimuli on the skin or of joint movements. Pain sensations were rarely reported [9].

Cortical ablation. When parts of the human cortex in SI are damaged by injury or surgically removed, perceptual deficits result. Stimuli to the skin can still be perceived as such, but the ability to recognize **spatial details** is reduced. The severity of the deficits depends on the extent of the cortical lesion and gradually recedes as time goes by. This improvement is thought to result from a capacity of other cortical regions (e.g., area 5 of the parietal cortex, adjacent to SI) to take over the functions of SI [2, 9].

Correlations between somatosensory neurophysiology and psychophysics. Recently research has been directed toward establishing a quantitative relation between perception and the states of activation of single neurons or populations of neurons. The results often permit conclusions about the **neuronal bases of perception.**
In one such experiment, an electric vibrator (cf. Fig. 9-1) was used to produce sinusoidal mechanical deformation of the skin of a monkey's hand at various frequencies and amplitudes. The threshold for detection (perception) of this stimulus was determined by operant conditioning (see Fig. 6-25). The monkeys were equipped with a microelectrode (implanted previously under anesthesia) so that the electrophysiological activity of neurons in SI could be recorded simultaneously; for instance, their threshold to the mechanical stimulus could be measured. A quantitative agreement was found between the neuronal and perceptual thresholds. One conclusion to be drawn is that these SI neurons are involved in the processes by which mechanical stimuli to the skin are perceived.

9.12 Control of Afferent Input in the Somatosensory System

At all levels of the CNS, afferent information can be influenced and changed *(modulated)*. These effects can be produced by reciprocal inhibition among the afferents (afferent inhibition) as well as by **centrifugal** or **descending inhibition.** Several examples of afferent inhibition have been discussed elsewhere: *autogenic inhibition* and *antagonist inhibition* in spinal motor systems (see Chapter 5), and *lateral inhibition* in many sensory systems (see Chapter 8). The following section is concerned with functions of *descending inhibition* in the somatosensory system [9, 23].

Centrifugal Control of Afferent Information

Sensory systems must not be regarded as one-way streets over which information travels from the periphery to the cortex; rather, the intermediate processing of such information involves a number of (excitatory or inhibitory) influences of central origin, conducted in the opposite direction. The diagram in Fig. 9-26A shows **descending** inhibitory pathways of the somatosensory system (drawn in red) that originate in the cortex and brainstem.

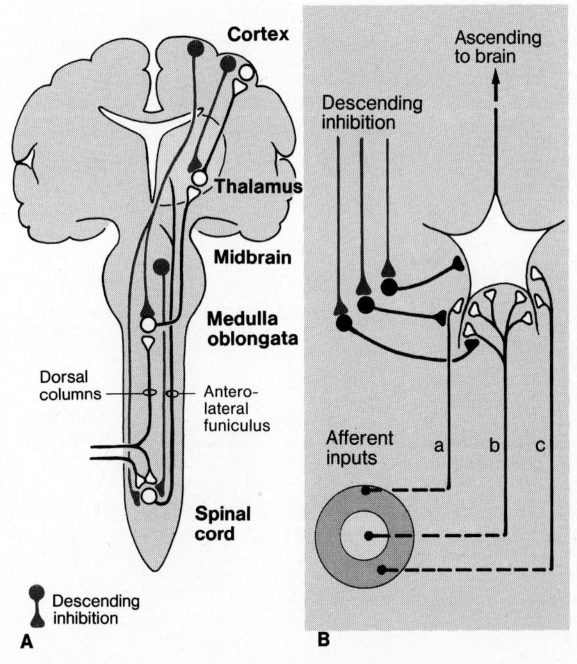

Fig. 9-26 A, B. Centrifugal control in the somatosensory system. **A** The afferent information can be modulated at a synaptic relay by descending inhibition (inhibitory pathways and synapses shown in *red*). **B** Example of functions of descending inhibition. Descending inhibition at synapses through which the activity of afferents *(a, b, c)* is transmitted to a central somatosensory neuron can change the size of the neuron's receptive field, if the afferents from the peripheral region of the receptive field (a, c) are more strongly inhibited than those from the center (b)

What can these systems of descending inhibition achieve? The known or suspected functional influences on afferent information flow can be summarized as follows [9, 23]:

- The threshold for afferent synaptic transmission is raised by descending inhibition. One result is the *suppression of trivial information* (e.g., maintained stimulation by clothing).
- The size of the receptive field of a central neuron is reduced as the degree of descending inhibition increases (Fig. 9-26B).
- Change in the modality of a neuron onto which various types of afferents converge (Fig. 9-26B, a, b).
- Control of sensitivity, or range-setting, of afferent information transmission. An example is discussed in the following section.

Control of Sensitivity of Afferent Transmission by Descending Inhibition

Fig. 9-27 shows how the afferent information from cutaneous receptors can be inhibited at neurons in the spinal cord, by electrical stimulation in the midbrain. The inhibition is mediated by a descending pathway and can act either pre- or postsynaptically. Both nociceptive and non-nociceptive signals are inhibited. In this example the sensory stimulus is skin temperature at noxious levels; its intensity is encoded approximately linearly in the discharge rate of the spinal neurons (Fig. 9-27C). Stimulation in the midbrain inhibits the discharge of the spinal neuron (Fig. 9-27B), so that the slope of the curve representing **intensity coding** is reduced (Fig. 9-27C). Here the

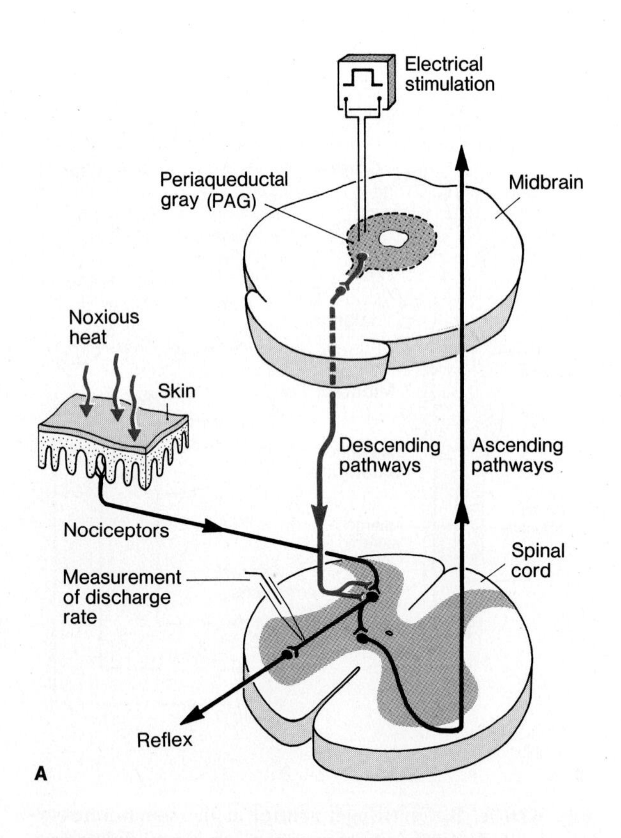

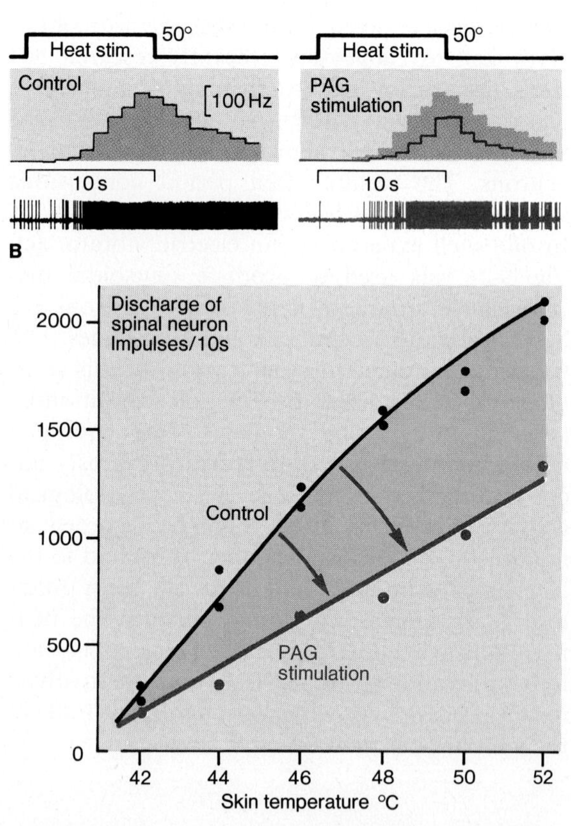

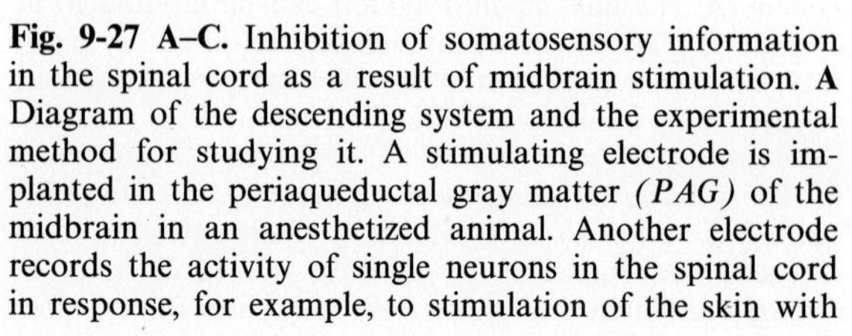
Fig. 9-27 A–C. Inhibition of somatosensory information in the spinal cord as a result of midbrain stimulation. **A** Diagram of the descending system and the experimental method for studying it. A stimulating electrode is implanted in the periaqueductal gray matter *(PAG)* of the midbrain in an anesthetized animal. Another electrode records the activity of single neurons in the spinal cord in response, for example, to stimulation of the skin with noxious heat or to controlled touch stimuli. **B** Response of a spinal neuron to heat stimulation of the skin before *(left)* and during *(right)* electrical stimulation in the PAG. **C** Relation between discharge rate of the spinal neuron *(ordinate)* and intensity of the heat stimulus (skin temperature, *abscissa)* before *(black curve)* and during *(red curve)* stimulation in the PAG. (Modified from CARSTENS, YOKOTA and ZIMMMERMANN, J. Neurophysiol. *42,* 558, 1979)

descending inhibition can be regarded as a mechanism for **sensitivity adjustment** or **gain control** of afferent transmission; the responses to stimuli at all intensities are diminished by the same factor, depending on the degree of descending inhibition.

We do not yet know much about the way such inhibitory systems are activated naturally. One of their functions is thought to be assisting attentive behavior. It has been suggested that in some cases the information ascending from the spinal cord can itself activate the descending inhibition. This would be a case of *recurrent inhibition (feedback inhibition)*, differing from spinal segmental recurrent (Renshaw) inhibition (Fig. 5-12) in that a supraspinal loop is involved. In this special case of feedback inhibition the effect may amount to **automatic range-setting:** the slope of the characteristic curve (Fig. 9-27C) – or the gain of afferent transmission – is determined by the intensity of the afferent neuronal information itself. This mechanism is comparable, for example, to the automatic gain control in the input amplifier of a cassette recorder.

Influences of motor systems on afferent information. Motor centers can also exert a considerable centrifugal influence on the signals from sensors. Consider the control of the muscle spindle by the γ-fiber system, the position control of the eyes by the oculomotor system, the scanning movements of the fingers during tactile examination, and the changes of muscle tone in the middle-ear apparatus. These qualify as mechanisms of centrifugal modification of the sensory channels. From these examples it should be evident that the CNS is involved in perception not only as the passive receiver of peripheral information but as an active participant, influencing and controlling the flow of information in a variety of ways [5].

9.13 References

Textbooks and Handbooks

1. BRODAL, A.: Neurological Anatomy in Relation to Clinical Medicine. 3rd Ed. New York-London-Toronto: Oxford University Press 1981
2. BROOKHART, J.D., MOUNTCASTLE, V.B. (eds.): The Nervous System. Handbook of Physiology, Sect. 1. Baltimore: Williams & Wilkins 1984
3. FULTON, J.F.: Physiology of the nervous system. London-New York-Toronto: Oxford University Press 1943
4. GAUER, O.H., KRAMER, K., JUNG, R. (Hrsg.): Physiologie des Menschen, Bd. 11: Somatische Sensibilität, Geruch und Geschmack. München-Berlin-Wien: Urban & Schwarzenberg 1972
5. GORDON, G. (ed.): Active Touch. Oxford-New York-Toronto-Sydney-Paris-Frankfurt: Pergamon Press 1978
6. HENSEL, H.: Allgemeine Sinnesphysiologie. Hautsinne, Geschmack, Geruch, pp. 1–345. Berlin-Heidelberg-New York: Springer 1966
7. HENSEL, H.: Thermoreception and Temperature Regulation. London-New York-Toronto-Sydney-San Francisco: Academic Press 1981
8. HOLZEL, R., WHITEHEAD, W.E. (eds.): Psychophysiology of the Gastrointestinal Tract. New York: Plenum Press 1983
9. IGGO, A. (ed.): Somatosensory System. Handbook of Sensory Physiology, Vol. 2. Berlin-Heidelberg-New York: Springer 1973
10. KANDEL, E.R., SCHWARTZ, J.H. (eds.): Principles of Neural Science. 2nd Ed. New York-Amsterdam-Oxford: Elsevier 1985
11. KENSHALO, D.R. (ed.): The Skin Senses. Springfield: Thomas 1968
12. KENSHALO, D.R. (ed.): Sensory Functions of the Skin of Humans. New York-London: Plenum Press 1979
13. KORNHUBER, H.H. (ed.): The Somatosensory System. Stuttgart: Thieme Verlag 1975
14. LEGEWIE, H., NUSSELT, L. (Hrsg.): Biofeedback-Therapie, Fortschritte der Klinischen Psychologie, Bd. 6. München-Berlin-Wien: Urban & Schwarzenberg 1975
15. MATTHEWS, P.B.C.: Mammalian Muscle Receptors and their Central Actions. London: Edward Arnold Publishers Ltd. 1972
16. MOUNTCASTLE, V.B. (ed.): Medical Physiology, Vol. 1: 15th Ed. Saint Louis: Mosby 1984
17. NIEUWENHUYS, R.: Chemoarchitecture of the Brain. Berlin-Heidelberg-New York-Tokyo: Springer 1985
18. NIEUWENHUYS, R., VOOGD, J., VAN HUIJZEN, C.: The Human Central Nervous System. Berlin-Heidelberg-New York: Springer 1978
19. PENFIELD, W., RASSMUSSEN, T.: The cerebral cortex of man. New York: Macmillan 1950
20. POECK, K.: Neurologie. 6. Auflage. Berlin-Heidelberg-New York: Springer 1982
21. ROWE, M., WILLIS, W.D., Jr. (eds): Development, Organization, and Processing in Somatosensory Pathways. New York: Alan R. Liss 1985
22. RUCH, T., PATTON, H.D. (eds.): Physiology and Biophysics. The brain and neural function. Philadelphia-London-Toronto: W.B. Saunders Co. 1979
23. VON EULER, C., FRANZEN, O., LINDBLOM, U., OTTOSON, D. (eds.): Somatosensory Mechanisms. London: Macmillan Press 1984
24. WILLIAMS, P.L., WARWICK, R. (eds.): Functional Neuroanatomy of Man. Edinburgh-London-New York: Churchill Livingstone 1975
25. ZOTTERMAN, Y. (ed.): Sensory Functions of the Skin in Primates. Oxford: Pergamon Press 1976

Original Papers and Reviews

26. BOIVIE, J., PERL, E.R.: Neuronal substrates of somatic sensation. In: International Review of Physiology, Vol. 3. Neurophysiology I (ed. C.C. HUNT). p. 303. London: Butterworths 1975
27. DARIAN-SMITH, I.: Touch in primates. Ann. Rev. Psychol. *33*, 155 (1982)
28. FOERSTER, O.: Symptomatologie der Erkrankungen des Rükkenmarks und seiner Wurzeln. In: Handbuch der Neurologie (Hrsg. O. BUMKE, O. FOERSTER), Bd. *5*, S. 1. Berlin: Springer 1936
29. GORDON, G. (ed.): Somatic and Visceral Sensory Mechanism. British Medical Bulletin *33*, 89 (1977)
30. HENSEL, H.: Thermoreceptors. Ann. Rev. Physiol. *36*, 233 (1974)
31. MATTHEWS, P.B.C.: Where does Sherrington's "muscular sense" originate? Muscles, joints, corollary discharges? Ann. Rev. Physiol. *5*, 189–218 (1983)
32. MCCLOSKEY, D.I.: Kinesthetic sensibility. Physiol. Rev. *58*, 763 (1978)
33. MERZENICH, M.M., KAAS, J.H.: Principles of organization of sensory-perceptual systems in mammals. Progr. Psychobiol. Physiol. Psychol. *9*, 1 (1980)
34. MOBERG, E.: The role of cutaneous afferents in position sense, kinaesthesia and motor function of the hand. Brain *106*, 1–19 (1983)

35. ROLL, J.P., VEDEL, J.P.: Kinaesthetic role of muscle afferents in man, studied by tendon vibration and microneurography. Exp. Brain Res. *47*, 177–190 (1982)
36. VALLBO, A.B., JOHANSSON, R.S.: Properties of cutaneous mechanoreceptors in the human hand related to touch sensation. Human Neurobiol. *3*, 3 (1984)
37. WELKER, W.I.: Principles of organization of the ventrobasal complex in mammals. Brain Behav. Evol. *7*, 253 (1973)
38. ZIMMERMANN, M.: Mechanoreceptors of the glabrous skin and tactile acuity. In: Studies in Neurophysiology presented to A.K. MCINTYRE (Ed. R. PORTER). pp. 267. Cambridge: Cambridge University Press 1978
39. ZIMMERMANN, M., HANDWERKER, H.O. (Hrsg.): Schmerz. Konzepte und ärztliches Handeln. Berlin-Heidelberg-New York-Tokyo: Springer 1984

10 Nociception and Pain

R.F. Schmidt

Unlike the other sensory modalities, pain contributes little to our knowledge of our surroundings. Rather, it informs us about threats to our bodies, from outside or within them. In so doing it *protects us from permanent damage*, and is thus indispensable for a normal life. If we were not warned by pain, during the most ordinary everyday activities we would often injure ourselves and soon be severely maimed.

Pain, therefore, increases our chances of survival, and in this respect it is like the other senses. In many of its *physiological* features, too, it is entirely comparable to the other senses. But it is also set apart from them by a broad spectrum of special features. To provide optimal care of a patient in pain, one must understand these special properties of the pain sense.

Definition of pain. Of the many attempts that have been made to characterize pain accurately and concisely (see review in [8]), we choose here the formulation published a few years ago by an international committee of experts (quoted from Pain 6, 248–252, 1979):

PAIN An unpleasant sensory and emotional experience associated with actual or potential tissue damage, or described in terms of such damage.

This definition expresses the fact that pain as a rule is *more than a pure sensation*, since the sensory experience is accompanied by a usually *unpleasant affective experience* (see Components of Pain below, and Fig. 10-2). It also makes clear that pain is felt when body tissue is stimulated so strongly that there is danger of its destruction. Furthermore, as stated in the last part of the definition, although all pains are experienced as being associated with tissue destruction or the risk thereof, it is *entirely irrelevant to the pain experience* whether such damage actually occurs. This brief definition thus refers to several of the important peculiarities of pain, though by no means all of them.

In the following sections we first consider the various qualities and components of pain and the ways they are evaluated and measured (10.1), then turn to the neurophysiology of pain (10.2) and some pathophysiological aspects (10.3), and finally cast a glance at the endogenous pain-control systems and the physiological mechanisms underlying the most important procedures for alleviating pain (10.4).

10.1 The Characterization of Pain

Pain Qualities

The *modality* pain can be categorized in terms of a number of *qualities* based on the *site of origin* of the pain. These are shown in the red boxes in Fig. 10-1. The first dichotomy is that between the qualities **somatic** and **visceral** pain.

Somatic pain. If somatic pain originates in the *skin* it is called **superficial pain**; if it comes from

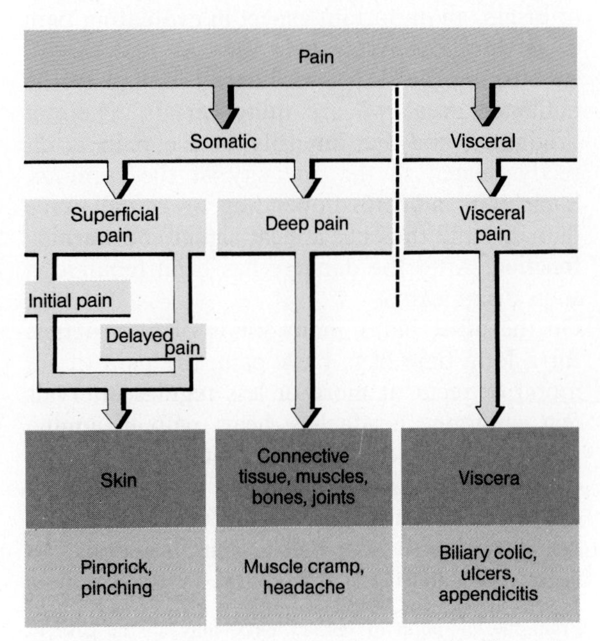

Fig. 10-1. Qualities of pain *(red background)*. The region of origin of each quality is indicated *(gray background)*, with examples of specific forms of pain. Discussed in text

the muscles, bones, joints or connective tissue it is called **deep pain.** Superficial and deep pain are thus (sub)qualities of somatic pain.
The *superficial pain* produced by *piercing the skin* with a needle is "bright" in character, a readily localizable sensation that fades away rapidly when the stimulus stops. This **initial pain** is often followed by a **delayed pain** with a latency of 0.5-1.0 s. The delayed pain has a dull (burning) character, is more difficult to localize and dies out more slowly; it can also be easily elicited by squeezing an interdigital fold.

Deep pain. Pain from the *skeletal muscles, bones, joints and connective tissue* is called **deep pain**. Like superficial pain, deep pain is a category of somatic pain. Examples include the acute, subacute and chronic *joint pains* which are among the most common forms of pain in humans. Deep pain is dull and hard to localize as a rule, and it tends to radiate into the surroundings [6].

Visceral pain. As diagrammed in Fig. 10-1, visceral pain is a major quality distinct from somatic pain and its (sub)qualities. Visceral pain can be caused by rapid, severe stretching of the hollow organs in the abdomen (e.g., the gallbladder or the renal pelvis). Spasms or strong contractions of the viscera are also painful, especially when they are associated with inadequate blood flow (ischemia).

Acute and chronic pains. In addition to the site of origin, an important aspect in evaluating pain is its duration. **Acute pain** such as that caused by burning the skin is ordinarily limited to the damaged area; we are quite certain where it originates, and the intensity of the pain is directly related to the intensity of the stimulus. Such pain indicates impending or actual tissue damage, and thus has a clear **signal and warning function.** After the damage has been repaired it soon disappears.
On the other hand, many kinds of pain persist for a long time (e.g., back pain, the pain of tumors) or recur at more or less regular intervals (e.g., migraine headaches, heart pain in angina pectoris). These forms of pain, **persistent and recurrent pain,** together are called **chronic pain**. In general pain is not regarded as "chronic" until it has lasted more than half a year; however, this is not an obligatory, well-founded convention.

From the viewpoint of sensory physiology, in the case of chronic pain there is often no straightforward relation between the degree of organic damage and the intensity of the pain. Indeed, eventually the pain experience can become dissociated from the original underlying disorder. Because of this tendency to become *"independent"*, **chronic pain** can appear as a **separate, individual syndrome** quite distinct from acute pain [9, 10, 11, 13].
Usually no physiological function can be ascribed to chronic pain. In this sense much chronic pain is "pointless" and should be alleviated. But one should not ignore the fact that chronic pain can have a clear **social function** which, in certain cases at least, contraindicates the treatment of the pain (e.g., when treatment would seriously threaten to disrupt the social structure within which the one suffering the pain is living) [10, 11, 18].
In some cases no peripheral organic cause at all can be found for a chronic pain. Given positive psychiatric criteria, the term **psychogenic pain** applies. On rare occasions psychogenic pain may be a **hallucination**, such as also occur in other sensory modalities. But it is more commonly a matter of **conversion neurosis.** A striking and typical feature of conversion-neurotic pain is that the function of the affected organ is in no way impaired – even when the patient complains of the most violent pain. The patient does not realize that he is expressing a mental conflict, which he cannot resolve or manage otherwise, as a physical phenomenon, in this case pain [11].

Itch. Itch is a quality of cutaneous sensation about which not enough is known. It is mentioned here because it is *at least related to pain*, and it may be a special form of the pain sensation elicited in particular stimulus conditions. This interpretation is supported by the fact that a sequence of itch stimuli at high intensity leads to sensations of pain; moreover, an interruption of the nociceptive pathway in the anterolateral funiculus is accompanied by a loss of itch sensation, whereas a disturbance of the senses of pressure and touch (transmitted in the dorsal columns) leaves the itch sensation unaffected. It has also been shown that the skin is sensitive to itch only at discrete points, and that these **itch points** correspond to the *pain points* (cf. Fig. 10-4).

But other considerations suggest that **itch is a sensation independent of pain,** which may have receptors of its own. For example, the sensation of itch can be elicited only in the outermost layers of the epidermis, whereas pain is produced in the deeper layers of the skin as well. It is also possible, using suitable techniques, to generate all degrees of itch without pain and vice versa. Finally, it appears to be a prerequisite for the occurrence of an itching sensation that a chemical substance, perhaps **histamine,** be released. An intradermal histamine injection elicits severe itching, and in skin injuries that lead to itching histamine is set free in the skin.

Components of Pain

Sensory component. When a hand is dipped into water at over 45 °C, **nociceptors in the skin** are excited (for the definition of nociceptors see 10.2). Their afferent impulses mediate informa-

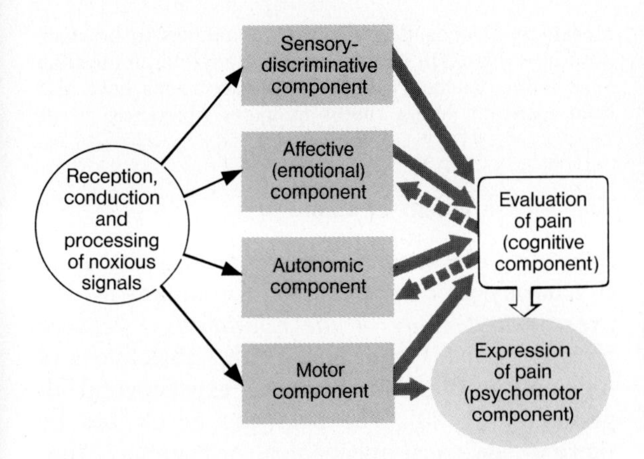

Fig. 10-2. Diagram of the components of pain activated by noxious signals. The contributions of the sensory, affective and autonomic components to the evaluation (cognitive component) and expression (psychomotor component) of the pain vary, depending on the nature of the pain. The outcome of the evaluation process in turn influences the magnitude of the affective and autonomic components *(dashed arrows)*. The diagram also applies to pain not induced by way of nociceptors or neuralgic excitation

tion about the *site* of the heat stimulus, its *onset*, its *intensity* (which depends on the water temperature) and its *end*, as soon as the hand is withdrawn from the water. We are just as conscious of this information as a **sensation** as we are of other sensory impressions, such as when the hand is immersed in lukewarm or cool water to generate a sensation of warmth or cold. This aspect of pain is called its **sensory** or **sensory-discriminative component** (Fig. 10-2).

Affective component. To remain with the example of temperature, when we bathe in water at 25 °C on a very hot summer day we do not only sense a cold stimulus to the skin; at the same time, the cooling produces a pleasant feeling of refreshment. On a cold winter day, however, the same bath would be sensed as unpleasantly cool. That is, a sensory impression can elicit *feelings of pleasure or displeasure, depending on the starting conditions and other circumstances.* This is true of practically all sensory modalities – vision, hearing, smell or taste. Pain is an exception. The affects or emotions it elicits are almost exclusively unpleasant; it disturbs our well-being, it hurts. This aspect of pain is its **affective** or **emotional component.**

Autonomic component. Immersing one's hand in hot water not only produces pain but also causes dilation of the vessels in the skin and hence increased blood flow, as can be seen by the reddening of the skin. Conversely, immersion in ice water constricts the vessels, with a corresponding decrease in blood flow. In both cases, as a rule, the blood pressure and heart rate rise, the pupils dilate and there is a change in the breathing rhythm. These reactions to the painful stimulation are *reflexes mediated by the autonomic nervous system*; that is, pain has an **autonomic component.** This component can be very prominent, especially in the case of **visceral pain**; in biliary colic, for example, it may take the form of nausea and vomiting, sweating, and a drop in blood pressure.

Motor component. Finally, it is a familiar experience that when a hand unintentionally makes contact with hot water, it is jerked back long before we become conscious of heat pain so that we could have responded voluntarily. This **motor component** of the pain appears as an *escape or protection reflex* in many contexts. It is particularly important with regard to noxious stimuli of external origin, but even deep pain and visceral pain can be found to have motor components – for example, in the form of *muscular tension.* In a broader sense still other behavioral manifestations of pain, resulting from the evaluation of the pain (see below), can be regarded as motor or, better, **psychomotor components** of the pain (Fig. 10-2, lower right).

Usually **all the components of pain** appear together, although their magnitudes vary. However, the central pathways they employ are in part quite distinct, and very different parts of the nervous system participate in producing them. For example, thalamocortical elements underlie the sensory component, responsibility for the affective component resides mainly in limbic structures, and the autonomic and motor systems are also involved. For this reason the pain components are **basically only loosely interrelated,** and it is entirely possible for them to **appear in isolation.** For example, a sleeping person may pull his hand away from a painful stimulus even though he has no conscious sensation of the pain, and chronically decerebrate animals can be observed to give motor and autonomic responses to pain (pseudoaffective responses [31]) just like those of intact animals, even though they have no forebrain.

The Evaluation and Expression of Pain

In the **evaluation** of pain – for example, as *mild, unpleasant, disturbing, violent* or *intolerable* – the various components contribute to different degrees (Fig. 10-2, right). For instance, in the case of superficial pain the sensory component usually predominates, in visceral pain the autonomic component will play a major role, and in chronic pain the affective component often decisively influences the evaluation.

A crucial factor in the evaluation of pain is **comparison of the existing pain with the kinds of pain encountered in the past**, the consequences of which are known. That is, present pain is measured against the previous experiences of pain stored in the short- and long-term memory, and evaluated in the light of these experiences. This evaluation, then, can be regarded as the *recognizing* or **cognitive component** of pain. Depending on the outcome of this cognitive process, the pain will be **expressed** in various ways (*psychomotor component*), by gesture, groans, demands for painkilling drugs, and so on. The cognitive judgment probably also influences the degree of the affective and autonomic components (dashed arrows from right to left in Fig. 10-2); that is, these components are not only weighted in the evaluation of pain, but in turn depend on the result of that evaluation. We suffer more from a pain that we think will have an "important" effect on our well-being than from one (equally intense) that we regard as ordinary and unthreatening.

A number of other factors, which can be mentioned only briefly here, also enter into the evaluation of pain and the resulting expressions. For example, the degree to which a patient complains of pain depends greatly on the *current social situation*, his *family background and upbringing*, and his *ethnic origins*. The behavior of an Apache warrior being martyred at the stake would be entirely different, with regard to the expression of pain, from that of a Southern Italian housewife with biliary colic – even if both are suffering pain at the same intensity.

Furthermore, the *circumstances in which a pain arises* often decisively affect the evaluation. It is well known that soldiers wounded in action need far less treatment with painkillers than is required for comparable injuries in civilian life. Apparently the anticipation of being sent home and the feeling of good fortune at having survived the battle at all considerably reduce the perception of pain and cause it to be evaluated as less severe.

Contrary to expectation, however, only *slight correlations* were found between *pain behavior and long-term personality traits* (e.g., in a comparison between extroverts and introverts). From an analysis of personality variables, it is essentially impossible to predict how the person will respond to pain [18].

Finally, it should also be pointed out that appropriate behavior and emotionally **normal responses to painful stimuli** are apparently to a large extent not innate but **must be learned** by the young organism at an early stage in its development. If such experiences are missed in early childhood, the responses are very hard to learn later. Young dogs prevented from encountering harmful stimuli for the first 8 months of their lives were found to be incapable of responding suitably to pain, and subsequently learned to respond only slowly and incompletely. They would sniff repeatedly at open flames and allow needles to be stuck deep into their skin without showing anything more than local reflex twitches. Comparable observations have also been made of young rhesus monkeys (references in [8, 11]).

The Measurement of Pain

Subjective algesimetry. The classical methods of psychophysics can be applied to humans for the *experimental study of the relationships between noxious stimulus and pain.* Both subjective and objective tests are used in this **experimental algesimetry** [3, 20]. The pain can be elicited by thermal, electrical, mechanical or chemical stimuli. In *subjective* algesimetry measurements are made of (i) the **pain threshold**, the stimulus intensity just high enough to produce a pain sensation, (ii) the **pain intensity** (expressed verbally or by some other signal), and (iii) the **pain-tolerance threshold**, the stimulus intensity at which the subject demands that stimulation be stopped.

Adaptation to pain. In addition to the intensity of pain, the most important aspect clinically is

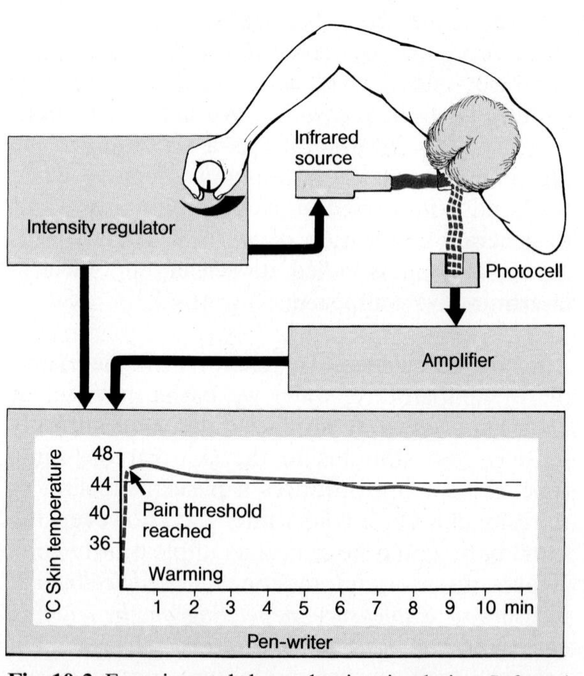

Fig. 10-3. Experimental thermal pain stimulation. Infrared rays warm a blackened area of skin on the subject's forehead. The skin temperature is monitored by a radiation sensor (photocell) and recorded on a pen-writer. [Modified from HARDY: J. appl. Physiol. *5*, 725 (1953)]. The *red curve* shows dependence of the pain threshold (average values) on duration of the heat stimulus. The subjects are required throughout the experiment to regulate the intensity of the radiation themselves, to a level such that the temperature of the forehead is just felt to be painful. The initial overshooting of skin temperature, beyond the pain threshold, is caused by the inertia of the equipment. [Modified from GREENE and HARDY: J. appl. Physiol. *17*, 693 (1962)]

whether the pain sensation adapts. Subjective experience tends to indicate a **lack of adaptation** (headaches and toothaches can last for hours). When the pain produced by a prolonged heat stimulus is **measured experimentally** (Fig. 10-3), there is no evidence of adaptation to the pain. In fact, the pain threshold actually decreases slightly in time, indicating that the prolonged heat stimulus causes **sensitization** of the nociceptors in the irradiated skin area. (On the other hand, *habituation* to repeated nociceptive stimuli is ordinarily observed in everyday life.)

Objective algesimetry. As applied to humans, objective algesimetry is concerned mainly with the measurement of motor and autonomic reactions to pain and with the recording of evoked potentials from the cerebral cortex (the term "objective" means simply that variables recorded by the observer are measured, rather than "subjective" reports of the person being tested). Often various methods are employed simultaneously (e.g., recording of evoked potentials while pupil diameter is monitored as a measure of sympathetic tone), and subjective methods can be combined with the objective tests **(multidimensional algesimetry)**. Experimental algesimetry is a rapidly expanding field of research, which can be expected to provide fundamental information about the nature of pain [3, 20].

Clinical algesimetry. At the subjective level, one approach in clinical algesimetry is to apply **methods of ratio estimation**; for example, the patient is asked at different times to express the degree of his pain on a simple visual analog scale, ranging from no pain to unbearable pain. Another is to ask lists of questions such as the widely used McGill Pain Questionnaire developed by the Canadian psychologist RONALD MELZACK (see [8]). Finally, clinical pain intensity can also be related to an experimental pain. For example, to determine the **tourniquet pain quotient** the patient compares the intensity of his pain to that of experimentally induced ischemic muscle pain [10].

10.2 Neurophysiology of Pain

Theories of Pain

Specificity theory of pain. Present-day hypotheses about the *origin of pain in tissues* are based on the idea that **pain is an independent sensation** with its own specialized neural apparatus of sensors, conduction pathways and centers. According to this concept, which has a solid experimental foundation, all humans and practically all animals possess special sensors (sensory receptors) with such a high threshold that they can be excited only by stimuli that are injuring or threatening to injure the surrounding tissue. The sensors responsive to these "noxious" stimuli (Latin *noxa* = damage) are called **nociceptors**, and the neuronal structures they activate are the **nociceptive system**. Accordingly, the *reception, conduction and central nervous processing* of noxious signals together are termed **nociception**, in order to make a clear distinction between these "objective" neuronal processes and the "subjective" sensation of pain.

From this viewpoint, the "specificity theory of pain" is merely a **specificity theory of nociception.** This is but one example of the confusion of the terms *nociception* and *pain* that is sometimes still encountered. Care should be taken to distinguish them, to prevent the nociceptive neuronal structures and the electrical and chemical processes by which they operate from being implicitly regarded as equivalent to the subjective world of experienced pain.

One of the first experimental supports of the specificity theory was the finding, illustrated in Fig. 10-4, that pain sensitivity is not uniformly distributed over the skin; as is also found for mechano- and thermoperception, pain stimuli are perceived only at discrete **pain points.** These are *distinctly more numerous* than pressure points (a ratio of 9:1 in Fig. 10-4). Because the cold and warm points on the skin are still less numerous than the pressure points, the ratio of pain points to these is even greater than 9:1. For this reason alone it seemed likely that nociception is medi-

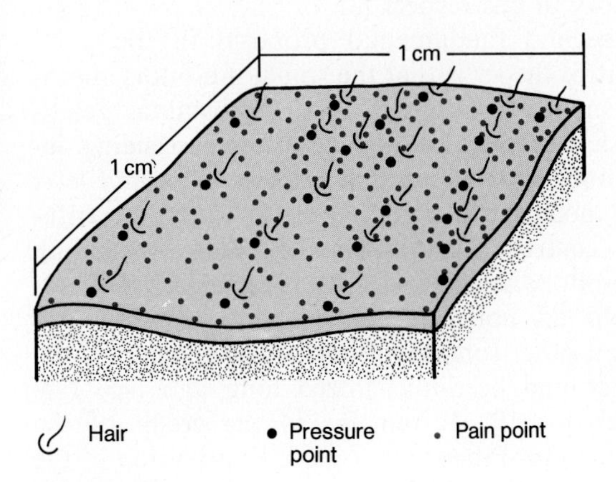

Fig. 10-4. Pain and pressure points on the human skin. The locations of the pain points were determined with von Frey hairs. [From STRUGHOLD: Z. Biol. *80*, 376 (1924)]

ated by separate sensors, specialized nociceptors, rather than by way of mechano- or thermoreceptors (as would be required by the intensity and pattern theories described below).

Intensity and pattern theories of nociception. For a long time these theories competed with the specificity theory. Their appeal lay in the fact that noxious stimuli are so diverse (that is, there is no single adequate stimulus), which appeared inconsistent with the existence of specialized nociceptors. Pain was thought to occur whenever the low-threshold mechano- and thermoreceptors were stimulated at an intensity above a certain level. According to the **intensity theory**, nociceptive stimuli would elicit especially **high-frequency bursts of impulses** in the low-threshold sensors, whereas the **pattern theory** proposed **special impulse patterns** differing from those in response to harmless stimuli. Their seeming simplicity, in requiring no special neuronal structures for nociception, was the main attraction of these theories. (Today they no longer seem so simple, since it is now regarded as a considerably greater problem to encode varied sensory information in a single neural network than to handle it in separate systems.)

Gate-control theory. Proposed in 1965 by MELZACK and WALL [22], the gate-control theory for the **spinal processing of nociceptive information** postulated, as one of its fundamental points, that the centripetal dorsal-horn neurons of the nociceptive system are inhibited by the excitation of *thick non-nociceptive* afferents (gate closed) and activated by excitation of *thin nociceptive* afferents (gate open). This inhibition was said to be generated in the **substantia gelatinosa** of the dorsal horn in the spinal cord and – this was the critical point of the theory – to be exerted exclusively by a **presynaptic inhibitory mechanism** acting on the *thin nociceptive* afferents. This hypothesis could not be confirmed experimentally; indeed, its basic postulates have been refuted [26, 27]. Therefore its authors had to modify the theory in this respect [8].

A second fundamental proposal in the gate-control theory is that the spinal inhibitory mechanisms of nociception in the substantia gelatinosa can also be activated by **descending inhibitory systems**, so that *even at the spinal level* the nociceptive information is under **centrifugal control.** The existence of such descending inhibitory systems is now regarded as well established, not only in the nociceptive but also in all other somatosensory systems; some of the latter had been recognized long ago (see Fig. 9-26, p. 219). It remains to the credit of the gate-control theory that it called attention to the considerable **modulation** of *nociceptive* inputs in the spinal cord, at as low a level as the first central neurons, by *local* and *descending* influences [14, 27, 30].

Transduction and Transformation in Nociceptors

Modality and structure of the nociceptors. Most of the nociceptors found so far in the human skin respond to **mechanical** (e.g., pinprick, pinching) as well as to **thermal** (heat, cold) and **chemical** (e.g., bradykinin, prostaglandin) stimuli (Fig. 10-5A-I). That is, these nociceptors are **multimodal.** Multimodal nociceptors also appear to predominate in the skeletal musculature, tendons and joint tissue [5, 23]. The latter, however, have been studied almost exclusively in animals, in which **unimodal** nociceptors such as heat receptors are more common than in humans. Histologically, the nociceptors are **free** or, more precisely, **noncorpuscular nerve endings**. Very little research has been devoted to their ultrastructural localization in the tissue and their relations to the surrounding perineural structures. As far as is known, nociceptive endings seem to be located mainly in the adventitia of small blood and lymph ves-

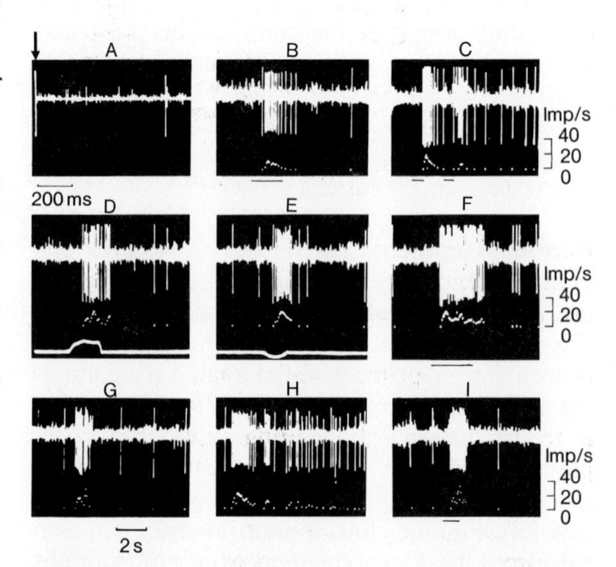

Fig. 10-5. Responses of a single multimodal nociceptor in a waking human. The impulse discharge was recorded with a transcutaneous metal microelectrode in contact with the peroneal nerve at the level of the knee, while the skin was stimulated in its receptive field on the big toe. **A** Response to a single electrical stimulus. **B** Stimulation with a von Frey hair calibrated at 2 g, which gives rise to a tickling sensation 2 s after its onset. **C** Repeated firm stroking of the receptive field with a thin stick causes slight pain. **S** Stimulation with a rod (weight 15 g) is sensed as pressure. **E** 5-g pressure with a pointed rod produces slight pain. **F** A pinprick evokes initial and delayed pain. **G** Application of itching powder to the receptive field causes burning itch. **H** Contact with a stinging nettle leads to pain followed by itch. **I** A hot thermode produces sharp pain at first, which later acquires a burning quality. [From: TOREBJÖRK, H.E., Acta Physiol. Scand. *92*, 374, (1974)]

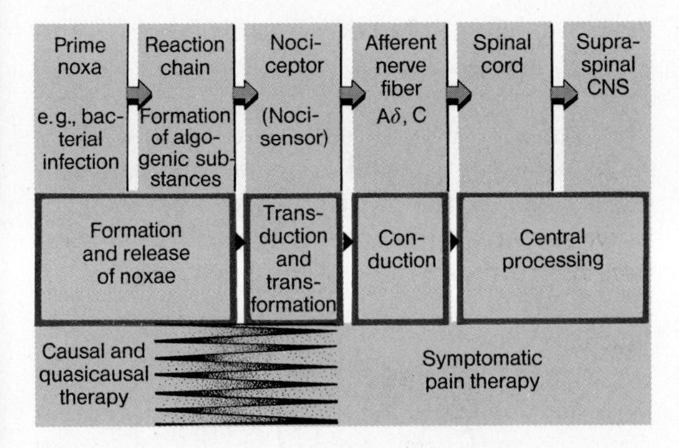

Fig. 10-6. Survey of the structures and substrates involved in nociceptor pains. At the *top* is the sequence of stages in the production of pain, and in the *middle* are the processing steps involved. At the *bottom* it is indicated that causal and quasicausal therapy of pains due to nociceptor excitation is possible only in the peripheral tissue

sels, next to the vessel lumen, and also in the connective-tissue spaces and, surprisingly, in the endoneurium itself [17].

These remarks *by no means imply* that all noncorpuscular nerve endings serve as nociceptors. In all tissues – certainly in the skin, skeletal muscles, tendons, joints, myocardium and other viscera – there are many **non-nociceptive** sensory units with **noncorpuscular nerve endings**. These are specifically sensitive to low-intensity mechanical or thermal stimuli and to non-noxious chemical stimuli, and their activity does not produce pain (see, e.g., [23, 24]).

Excitation of nociceptors. The structures and substrates involved in the excitation of nociceptors are summarized diagrammatically in Fig. 10-6. The chain of events always begins with the appearance of a "prime noxa", an agent that threatens to disrupt normal tissue function. The prime noxa can be bacteria invading a joint, for example, or a factor such as inadequate blood flow through the heart musculature or the release of a (hypothetical) migraine factor. Violent mechanical forces, heat and severe cold can also act as prime noxae.
In some cases the prime noxa stimulates and may activate nociceptors directly, as happens during imposition of a strong mechanical force. But it is probably much more common for them to be activated by way of a *chain of cell and tissue reactions* ending with the release of one or more substances (e.g., prostaglandins, bradykinin, serotonin etc. in the case of joint inflammation) that then serve as **noxae in the strict sense**, exciting and sensitizing the nociceptors. The **generator** or **receptor potentials** induced by the noxae in the **transduction areas** of the nociceptors cannot be observed directly by electrophysiological methods, because the endings are so fine. The subsequent step of **transformation**, however, produces **action potentials** that can be recorded in the associated nerve fibers in humans and animals, as shown in Fig. 10-5.

Sensitization and desensitization. The *threshold of the nociceptors* to noxious stimuli is neither uniform among all nociceptors nor constant in a given nociceptor. Healthy tissue contains nociceptors with widely varying thresholds to noxious stimuli, some of them so high that the nociceptors cannot be excited in an experiment ("sleeping" nociceptors). But if the tissue has undergone pathological alteration (e.g., by inflammation), all the **nociceptors are sensitized**; that is, their thresholds are lowered, in some cases so far that even normally non-noxious stimuli now excite the nociceptors. Even the "sleeping" nociceptors are "awakened" [24, 25]. Sensitization is probably brought about by *algesic substances* such as prostaglandins, but the details of the mechanism are unknown. The opposite effect, a threshold elevation or **desensitization of nociceptors,** can also be observed. Some analgesics apparently act at the periphery, raising the nociceptor threshold to noxious stimuli.

Peripheral Conduction of Noxious Signals

Essentially only two types of nerve fibers are candidates for the peripheral conduction of noxious signals, the **thin myelinated** (Group III or Aδ) and **unmyelinated** (Group IV or C) fibers. The conduction velocities of the former are mostly between 2.5 and 20 m/s, and those of the latter are below 2.5 m/s (average 1 m/s; cf. Table 2-1, p. 38). The *Group-IV fibers are much more numerous* than the Group-III fibers.
By **graded electrical stimulation of cutaneous nerves** in humans it has been shown directly that excitation of the thick (low-threshold) myelinated afferents (Group II) does not produce pain sensations, whereas excitation of the (high-threshold) Group-III and -IV afferents does. It appears that in the case of **superficial skin pain** the initial pain (see p. 224) is transmitted by *Group-III fibers* and the delayed pain, by *Group-IV fibers.*

This inference is supported by the following findings. (i) When conduction in a nerve is blocked by **mechanical pressure,** the thick fibers are affected first and the thin fibers somewhat later. As long as only the Group-II fibers are blocked, both qualities of superficial pain persist. But as soon as the Group-III fibers are blocked, the initial pain disappears, leaving only the delayed pain. (ii) When a nerve is blocked with a **local anesthetic** (e.g., Novocain) to which the Group-IV fibers are more sensitive than the Group-III fibers, the reverse phenomenon is observed; the dull, delayed pain disappears before the bright, initial pain. (iii) **Electrical stimulation** of exposed cutaneous nerves at intensities such that Group-III fibers are excited produces sharp pain sensations. But if the **myelinated fibers are blocked** and a stimulus intensity appropriate to Group IV is used, the result is a dull burning pain, subjectively so unpleasant that it is described as difficult to endure. The difference in latency of the two pain sensations is evidently due primarily to the different conduction velocites of the two types of fibers.

In the **skeletal muscles,** the **joints** and other deep tissues, as well, the *nociceptors* seem to be supplied almost entirely by fibers of Groups III and IV [5, 23, 24]. Most of the afferent fibers from the viscera are unmyelinated. It is not yet known which of them serve for *visceral reflex regulation* and which are involved in *visceral pain.*

Central Conduction and Processing

In the spinal cord the nociceptive afferents terminate on neurons in the **dorsal horn.** These are the cells of origin of the **anterolateral-column tracts** (spinothalamic etc.) described in detail in the preceding chapter. These tracts ascend toward the brainstem, where they combine with the nociceptive afferents from the head region, mostly coming from the **trigeminal nerve**, on the way to the **thalamus** (Fig. 10-7, left half; see also Fig. 9-20). For information about the mode of operation of these ascending systems, their further centripetal projections and the involvement of the reticular formation, thalamus and cerebral cortex in the processing of nociceptive signals, see the relevant sections of the preceding chapter [14, 30].

Here we refer to the **participation of the cerebral cortex in nociception and pain**, in particular its sensory-discriminative and cognitive components, only to mention that in the first half of this century the prevailing view, based on clinical and experimental findings, was that the cortex was not absolutely necessary for the production of conscious pain sensations. Instead, the *thalamus* was regarded as the *crucial center for conscious sensations of pain.* Subsequent careful observations, particularly of people who sustained brain injuries in the Second World War, have necessitated a *revision of this view.* Damage to certain cortical areas in the depths of the parietal part of the central sulcus was found to produce a permanent contralateral insensitivity to pain. In some cases only part of the contralateral side was affected (e.g., an arm or a leg), but in others the entire half of the body became insensitive to pain. It has since been possible to corroborate these findings experimentally, in that local electrical stimulation of these brain areas in humans elicits pain. We can now conclude that **pain sensations**, like all the other sensory impressions of which we are conscious, are **impossible without the collaboration of the cerebral cortex** [29].

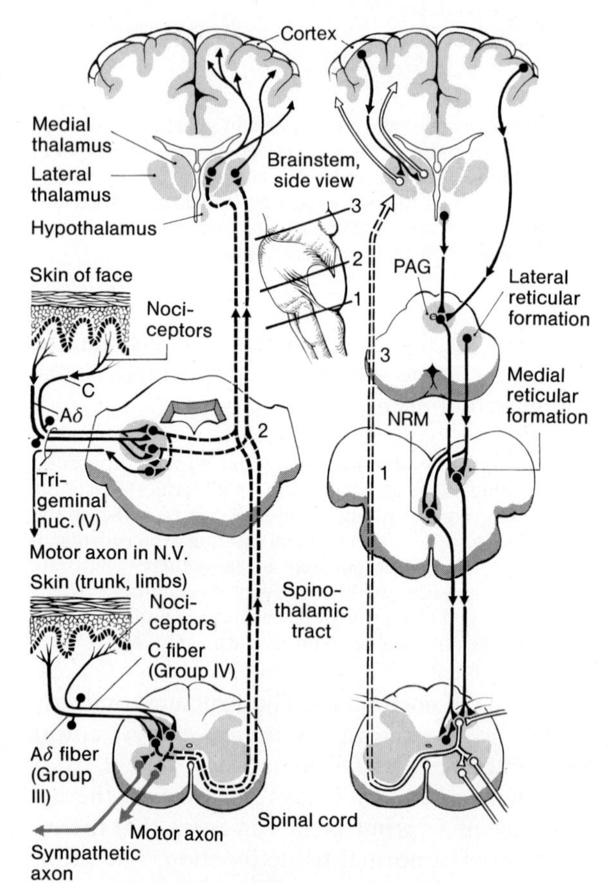

Fig. 10-7. Schematic illustration to show the courses of the ascending nociceptive pathways *(left)* and of the descending tract systems by which the nociceptive input is modulated *(right)*. Of the ascending systems, only the spinothalamic tract and the trigeminothalamic inputs that join it are shown. Other tracts involved in the ascending conduction of nociceptive information (e.g., the spinoreticular and spinocervical tracts) have been omitted for simplicity. The specific thalamocortical tracts originate in the lateral thalamus and terminate mainly in the somatosensory cortex. The efferents from the medial thalamic nuclei are more diffuse, projecting not only to extensive areas of the frontal cortex but also to subcortical structures, especially the limbic system (not shown here; the massive reticular inputs to these nuclei are also not shown). The descending systems exert their influence chiefly at the spinal level (or on the corresponding trigeminal structures, not shown). The central *inset* shows a side view of the brainstem, with the levels of section: 1 cranial edge of the inferior olive, 2 middle of the pons, 3 lower mesencephalon. PAG periaqueductal gray; NRM Nucleus raphe magnus (based on the experimental results of many authors)

10.3 Pathophysiology of Nociception and Pain

Pain that appears as a consequence of the excitation of nociceptors is the normal, physiological form of pain. But pain can also be produced by excitation of the nociceptive systems at more proximal sites (consider the example of psychogenic pain, mentioned on p. 224). It should also be kept in mind that the sensitivity of nociceptors can be shifted over a wide range by the processes of sensitization and desensitization (p. 229) and that such shifts, as well as central adjustments of sensitivity, can considerably alter the resulting pain experience. These phenomena, together with the transmission of pain in healthy parts of the body, are the subject of this section.

Projected and Neuralgic Pain

Projected pain. This pain is the *simplest illustration* of the fact that not all kinds of pain originate in the nociceptors. For example, everyone knows that a sharp blow to the elbow can stimulate the ulnar nerve and give rise to unpleasant sensations in the region it supplies (Fig. 10-8). Evidently the discharge in the afferent nerve fibers generated at the elbow is **projected** by our consciousness into the region containing the sensory endings of these fibers, because normally it is in these sensors that such discharge originates. We find it difficult to interpret the resulting sensations (tingling and the like), because the impulse patterns produced by direct mechanical stimulation of the nerve fibers are not normally encountered.

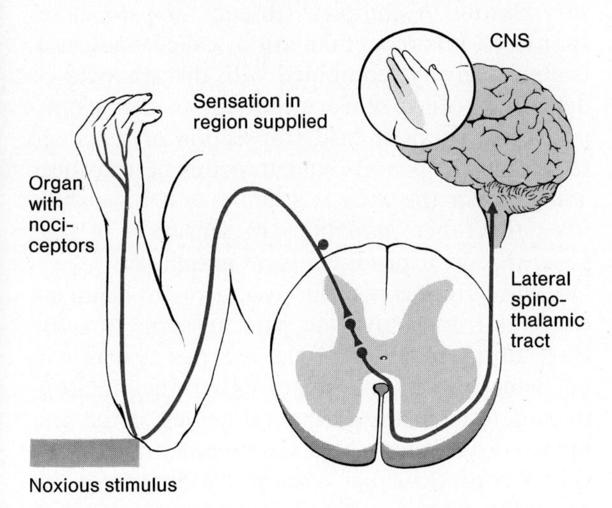

Fig. 10-8. Origin of projected pain (schematic). Discussed in text

Projected sensations can in principle occur in all sensory modalities, but only **projected pain** is clinically significant. Often, for example, such pain is produced by compression of a spinal nerve due to an acute intervertebral-disk syndrome. The mechanical stimulus generates centripetal impulses in nociceptive fibers, and the associated sensations of pain are projected into the region supplied by the stimulated spinal nerve. (There may, of course, also be pain in the region of the disk itself.) In the case of projected pain, then, the site at which the noxious agent acts is not that at which the pain is sensed.

Neuralgia. Far more serious than acute projected pain of this type is projected pain produced by *continuous irritation of a nerve or a dorsal root.* Such chronic nerve damage causes **"spontaneous" pain** that often comes in waves or attacks. Usually, as would be expected for projected pain, these are restricted to the region supplied by the affected nerve or root. Only this kind of pain, resulting from **pathological impulse generation in nociceptive fibers** (not in the nociceptors), should be called **neuralgia** or **neuralgic pain**.

The membrane of the nociceptive afferent fibers normally serves only to conduct impulses generated in the sensory endings. The mechanism by which it becomes capable of **regenerative impulse production** due to prolonged pulling or pressure (and perhaps by the action of chemical substances that accumulate in association with inflammation or tissue damage) is unclear. Pathophysiologically, it could be a matter of the incorporation of regenerative membrane, the unmasking of preexisting regenerative membrane, or a process of reconstruction within the axon or in the perineural tissue. It may be that regenerative impulse production is brought about by several factors.

Causalgia. For unknown reasons, nerve injury (especially when due to gunshot wounds) can give rise to a special form of neuralgia – chronic, tormenting *pain in the region supplied by the injured nerve*, accompanied by *vascular and trophic disturbances* in the affected region. This complex of systems is called **causalgia** [7]. The impairments of blood flow and tissue nutrition indicate an **involvement of the sympathetic nervous system.**

Referred Pain

Nociceptive stimulation of the viscera often produces a sensation of pain not (or not only) in the affected organ but rather (also) in distant, superficial parts of the body. Such pain is called **referred pain.** As a rule, the referral is to the parts of the periphery supplied by the same segment of the spinal cord as the affected internal tissue. That is, with respect to the skin surface, the pain is referred within the associated *dermatome* (cf.

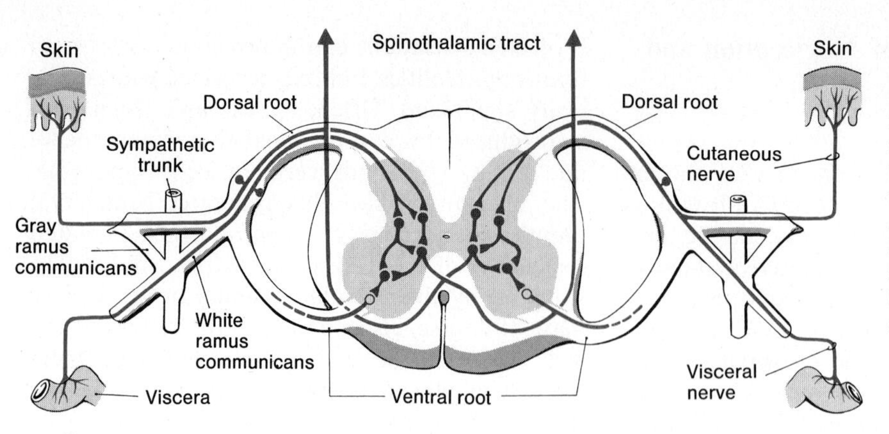

Fig. 10-9. Routes by which referred pain originates. *Left:* some of the nociceptive afferents from the viscera terminate in the dorsal horn on the same neurons as nociceptive afferents from the skin. *Right:* in some cases branches of the same nociceptive afferent nerve fiber can supply both superficial and deep tissue

Fig. 9-18, p. 211). Because the relationship between dermatomes and internal organs is known, referred pain is often an important aid to diagnosis.

The **production of referred pain** probably occurs as illustrated in Fig. 10-9. One factor is the convergence of nociceptive afferents from the skin and those from deep tissues onto the same cells of origin of the ascending nociceptive tracts (left half of picture). Another is branching of primary nociceptive afferents in the spinal nerves to form two or more collaterals, so that a given fiber can innervate both superficial and deep structures. In either case, excitation of the central nociceptive neurons is interpreted as pain in the periphery, probably because this interpretation has usually been **appropriate in previous experience**.

Another consequence of the central convergence and divergence of nociceptive afferents illustrated in Fig. 10-9 is that **hyperpathia** or **hyperesthesia** (see below) of the skin may develop in the affected dermatome. The reason is that the excitability of the spinal interneurons is increased by the nociceptive impulses from the deep tissues, so that a stimulus to the skin causes greater than normal central activity. Finally, it should be kept in mind that neuralgic pain can also give the impression of referred pain or occur together with a referred component.

Abnormally High or Low Pain Sensitivity

The entire nociceptive system is characterized by considerable plasticity, resulting partly from the fact that the sensitivity of the **nociceptors** can be altered over a wide range (e.g., by inflammatory processes; see above). Another factor is the extensive **central divergence and convergence of the nociceptive system**, which has just been described as a cause of referred pain. Pain sensitivity can be either *enhanced* or *reduced*, and these effects can appear alone or in combination with other changes in sensitivity. The terminology reflects this complexity, as follows.

In the condition called **allodynia** pain is caused by *non-noxious* stimulation of normal skin; for instance, the nociceptors become so highly sensitized that even an ordinary mechanical or thermal stimulus to the skin gives rise to sensations of pain. This state is distinct from **hyperalgesia**, in which one becomes oversensitive to *noxious* stimuli. **Hyperesthesia** is an oversensitivity of the *mechano- and thermoperceptive* systems to nonnoxious stimuli. In each case it must be specified which modality has become hyperesthetic, and for which forms of stimuli. **Hyperpathia** is a pain syndrome characterized by an increased response with delayed onset and an afterresponse that outlasts the stimulus; it is especially clearly apparent when the stimulation is repetitive. Hyperpathia can be combined with hypo-, hyper- or dysesthesia.

In **hypoalgesia** sensitivity to *noxious* stimuli is reduced. Hypoalgesia is usually a component of **hypoesthesia**, a reduced sensitivity to somatosensory stimuli. A complete absence of pain in response to noxious stimulation, called **analgesia**, is almost always combined with disturbances or deficits in other sensory modalities. For example, in the simplest case, transection or blockage (e.g., with Novocain) of a cutaneous nerve causes analgesia in the area it supplies but also abolishes the other modalities of sensation in that area; that is, it produces local **anesthesia**.

Occasionally people are found with **complete congenital insensitivity to pain**. In some of these cases no clear defect of the nervous system can be detected, and in others either the nociceptive afferents in the peripheral nerves or the first higher-order neurons in the dorsal horn of the spinal cord (Lissauer's tract) are absent. In all cases the symptoms are the same: the patients do not perceive injurious stimuli as such. Typically, therefore, from earliest childhood they are constantly being seriously hurt or hurting themselves. As a rule, these mutilations result in an early death [11].

Central pain. Functional disturbances or defects in the spinal and supraspinal nociceptive systems can lead to enhanced excitability and even spontaneous activity in these structures, which can cause severe pain. Familiar examples of such **central pain** include the pain of **anesthesia dolorosa** after dorsal roots have been torn out, the **phantom pain** following amputations [12] and the **thalamic pain** associated with diseases of the sensory ventral nuclei of the thalamus.

10.4 Endogenous and Exogenous Inhibition of Pain

Pain-Control Systems within the Body

There are apparently a number of possibilities available to the human body by which to reduce the activity of its central nociceptive systems. The way these **endogenous pain-control systems** operate has recently become clearer due to two fundamental discoveries. One is the finding of **opiate receptors** and the associated **ligands** produced by the body itself *(endorphins, enkephalins, dynorphin)*. The other is the discovery of supraspinal areas in which **electrical stimulation produces analgesia**. As discussed below, the two phenomena may be closely related to one another (references in [11, 13, 16, 21, 30]).

Endorphins, enkephalins, dynorphin. Opiates are substances that inhibit the sensation of pain without appreciably affecting the other sensory modalities. The action of the opiates is so well targeted because of the existence of **specific opiate receptors** on the neurons of the nociceptive system. At least four subtypes of these are known; they differ in their sensitivity profile for opiates and for the various endogenous ligands [21].
The endogenous ligands, such as the pentapeptides **methionine- and leucine-enkephalin**, can be released by certain kinds of stimulation of the nervous system. Acting on the opiate receptors, they *produce analgesia.* Administration of the opiate antagonist **naloxone** inhibits this action, and peptidases break down the ligands in vivo. *Methionine-enkephalin* is a component of the polypeptide **beta-endorphin**; *leucine-enkephalin* is contained in the polypeptide **dynorphin**. Both polypeptides also act as analgesics, and dynorphin in particular is distinctly more effective than the enkephalins.

Descending inhibitory systems (Fig. 10-7, right half). Electrical stimulation of the whole brain can produce anesthesia and analgesia (**"electronarcosis"**). However, the effect seems to originate only in *circumscribed sites within the periventricular gray matter*, because in animal experiments local electrical stimulation in these areas causes deep analgesia, called **stimulation-produced analgesia, SPA.** It appears that the *nucleus raphe magnus* and the *nucleus paragigantocellularis* (or *magnocellularis*) in the reticular formation are particularly important sites, because direct *descending tracts* lead from these nuclei to the spinal cord. It may be that activity in these tracts inhibits the transmission of nociceptive information in the dorsal horn.
Like electrical stimulation, microinjection of *morphine into the periventricular gray matter* causes distinct analgesia, indicating a **close link between SPA and opiate analgesia**. Other structures closely correlated with SPA, such as the reticular formation (see above), are also clearly opiate-sensitive. Therefore it is likely that the analgesic effects of SPA and of the exogenous and endogenous opiates are mediated by the same neuronal systems.
The most interesting consequence of this conclusion is that one of the most crucial sites for inhibition of the nociceptive signals – not only for SPA but also for opiate analgesia – must lie in the **dorsal horn of the spinal cord**. Apparently the analgesic actions originating in the brainstem are mediated by several descending tract systems (Fig. 10-7, right). These seem to employ **monoaminergic transmitters**, in particular *serotonin, noradrenalin and dopamine.*

Sites of Action of Exogenous Pain Inhibition; Pain Therapy

The alleviation of pain is one of the fundamental tasks of the physician. If the condition causing the pain can be eliminated, the pain will disappear as well. But if this course is not possible, symptomatic treatment of the pain is indicated (cf. Fig. 10-6). The **most important procedures for the treatment of pain** are summarized in Fig. 10-10. The pharmacological procedures (1–4) serve either to prevent the reception (1) and conduc-

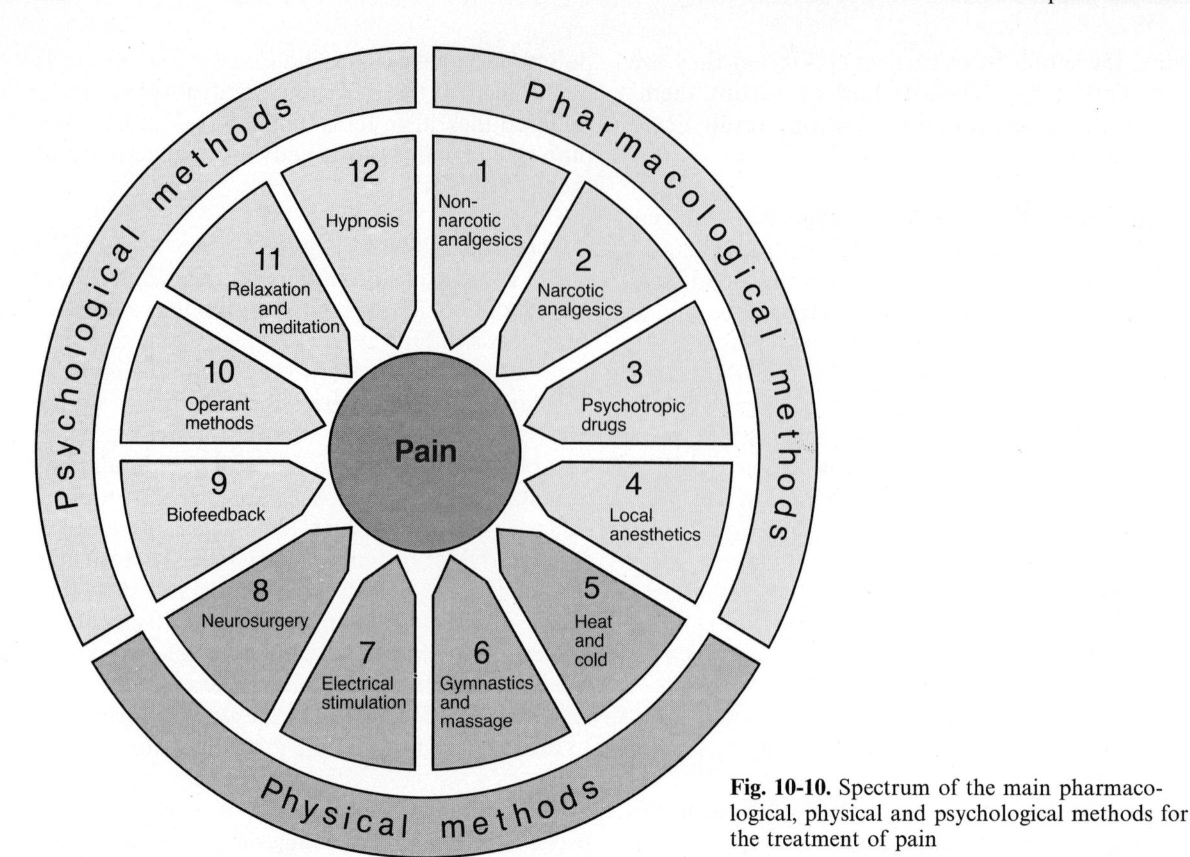

Fig. 10-10. Spectrum of the main pharmacological, physical and psychological methods for the treatment of pain

tion (4) of noxious signals or to inhibit central processing (2) and diminish affective participation in the pain event (2, 3). The physical procedures (5-8) act against pain by extremely diverse routes and at quite different sites. A third category includes the psychological procedures for coming to terms with the pain (9-12), which in general can be described as "coping strategies". The following paragraphs briefly describe the *modes of action of the treatments* in these various categories, in the same order as in Fig. 10-10 [1, 2, 9, 11, 13, 15, 16].

Pharmacological treatment of pain. Under the rubric **non-narcotic analgesics** (1 in Fig. 10-10) are a number of substances that reduce pain without abolishing (narcosis) or appreciably restricting consciousness [15, 19]. The best-known of these analgesics are derivatives of salicylic acid, and by far the most commonly used of these is *acetylsalicylic acid*. The **narcotic analgesics** (2 in Fig. 10-10) are substances that are capable of alleviating even the most severe pain but as a side effect have such a strong sedating, even somniferous action that at high concentrations they can induce a narcotic state. The oldest representative of this category is **morphine**, a constituent of opium (hence the terms **opiate** or **opioids** for all substances comparable to morphine). Their analgesic action depends on their binding to the **opiate receptors** described at the beginning of this section, which *activates the endogenous pain-control system* [15, 21, 32].

Of the medications classified as **psychotropic** (3 in Fig. 10-10) because of their marked effects on mental state, the *tranquilizers* are used not only to treat pain but also to resolve or diminish states of anxiety, tension and agitation. The *antidepressants* are used primarily to treat endogenous depression. Because such depressives often complain of pain and because, conversely, chronic pain often leads to a depressive state, in these cases antidepressants can be used with considerable hope of success.

Local anesthesia (4 in Fig. 10-10) can be produced by **nerve blocking** or by **infiltration anesthesia**. On mucous membranes a local anesthetic can be applied **topically** by spraying or brushing it onto the surface. When a small area of skin is to be anesthetized briefly it can be sprayed with ethyl chloride, which evaporates rapidly and thus cools the skin so deeply that the receptors are inactivated.

In the treatment of pain in a well-defined region, nerve block can bring considerable relief temporarily (for a few hours). In rare cases the pain is relieved for longer than would be expected from the duration of action of the local anesthetic on the nerve. Local anesthesia can also have a positive influence on the disease process itself; when used for this purpose, it is called **therapeutic local anesthesia** [2, 11, 16].

Physical treatment of pain (5 to 8 in Fig. 10-10). This category includes procedures with extremely diverse actions, ranging from the application of heat or cold through massage and gymnastics to electrical stimulation and neurosurgery. Some of them have been used to treat pain for centuries or even millennia. A very ancient physical treatment is also the simplest, **rest and immobilization**; it is often very helpful in pain therapy.

Heat is probably the physical treatment in most frequent use. Although locally applied heat warms only the superficial layer of the skin, circulation of the blood through deeper organs can be increased reflexly. It is also possible to heat deeper tissues directly by **diathermy** (high-frequency electromagnetic irradiation). Heat application is most effective on pain caused or exacerbated by insufficient blood flow. Other kinds of pain (e.g., in acute inflammatory processes) are associated with dilation of the vessels, and these can be counteracted by the application of **cold**. Cold also slows the development of inflammation, by reducing both blood flow and the local metabolic rate.
Therapeutic exercises are used mainly to promote healing of joints, muscles, tendons, ligaments and bones. Therefore the contribution of such therapy to the relief of pain is usually indirect, and the same is true of the various forms of **massage** (6 in Fig. 10-10).

The use of **electrical stimulation as pain therapy** (7 in Fig. 10-10) is based on the observation that pain is often distinctly reduced by other, simultaneous sensory stimuli such as rubbing, scratching, or warmth or cold (see above). In all these cases of *"masking"* or *"counterirritation"* the stream of nerve impulses from the nociceptors continues as before, but its conduction to the relay stations in the CNS is inhibited at some point – either in the spinal cord or at higher levels, such as the brainstem or thalamus. The mechanism of this **afferent inhibition** is not understood in all details [14, 27, 30].

The electrical stimulus is usually applied through the skin, in the method called **TENS (transcutaneous electrical nerve stimulation)**. A variant of this method is **dorsal-column stimulation**, for which the electrodes are surgically implanted in the vertebral canal. The intention is to achieve especially intense stimulation of the afferent fiber bundles in the dorsal column of the spinal cord and hence especially strong afferent inhibition. A third approach is to attempt direct activation of the afferent inhibitory centers in the brain, and especially in the brainstem, by implanted electrodes. This **electrical brain stimulation** is an application of the stimulation-produced analgesia (SPA) mentioned at the beginning of this section.

Acupuncture is also regarded by some as a method that produces analgesia by way of *afferent inhibition.* This interpretation may apply to intense **electroacupuncture** in neuroanatomically defined stimulus areas, which apparently has an analgesic action that goes beyond placebo effects. But for **classical acupuncture** and its variants (e.g., **ear acupuncture**) there are still no indications of a primary neurobiological mechanism of action [11, 28].

All the **neurosurgical measures for pain relief** known at present (8 in Fig. 10-10) are basically methods of last resort [4, 11, 13]. The one with the greatest practical significance is transection of the anterolateral funiculus of the spinal cord **(cordotomy)**, by which conduction of nociceptive signals from the contralateral half of the body is prevented. It can be quite successful in alleviating severe chronic pain, such as pain in the region of the true pelvis, for short to intermediate periods (weeks to months). Surgery in the brain itself – e.g., in the thalamus *(thalamotomy)*, the cingulate gyrus of the limbic system *(cingulotomy)* or the connections to the frontal lobe *(leukotomy)* – has proved to give entirely unsatisfactory results and is now hardly ever attempted.

Psychological methods of pain management. Psychological variables are a central factor in many pains, particularly those with no clear peripheral cause. Accordingly, **psychological therapy** plays a large role in these cases. But there are also many situations in which pain associated with organic disorders responds better to psychological than to somatic treatment. Important examples of procedures in this category are shown in Fig. 10-10 under 9 to 12 [1, 9, 10, 11, 13, 18].

10.5 References

Textbooks and Handbooks

1. BARBER, J., ADRIAN, C. (Eds.): Psychological approaches to the management of pain. New York: Brunner/Mazel 1982
2. BONICA, J.J.: The management of pain. Philadelphia: Lea & Febiger 1953, reprinted 1980
3. BROMM, B. (Ed.): Pain measurement in man. Amsterdam: Elsevier 1984
4. FOERSTER, O.: Die Leitungsbahnen des Schmerzgefühls und die chirurgische Behandlung der Schmerzzustände. Berlin: Urban & Schwarzenberg 1927
5. KNIFFKI, K.-D.: Muskuläre Nociception. Weinheim: edition medizin 1986
6. LEWIS, TH.: Pain. London: Macmillan 1942, reprinted 1981
7. LIVINGSTON, W.K.: Pain mechanisms. A physiological interpretation of causalgia and its related states. New York: Plenum Press 1943, reprinted 1976

8. MELZACK, R., WALL, P.D.: The challenge of pain. New York: Basic Books 1983
9. MILTNER, W., BIRBAUMER, N., GERBER, W.-D.: Verhaltensmedizin. Heidelberg: Springer 1986
10. STERNBACH, R.A.: Schmerzpatienten. Krankheitsursachen und Behandlung. Heidelberg: Verlag für Medizin 1983
11. SCHMIDT, R.F., STRUPPLER, A.: Der Schmerz. Ursachen, Diagnose, Therapie. 2. Aufl. München: Piper (Serie Piper Bd 241) 1983
12. SIEGFRIED, J., ZIMMERMANN, M. (Eds.): Phantom and stump pain. Heidelberg: Springer 1981
13. WALL, P.D., MELZACK, R. (Eds.): Textbooks of pain. Edinburgh: Churchill Livingstone 1984
14. WILLIS, W.D.: The pain system. Basel: Karger 1985
15. WÖRZ, R. (Ed.): Pharmakotherapie bei Schmerz. Weinheim: edition medizin 1986
16. ZIMMERMANN, M., HANDWERKER, H.O.: Schmerz. Konzepte und ärztliches Handeln. Heidelberg: Springer 1984

Original Papers and Reviews

17. ANDRES, K.H., DÜRING, M. v., SCHMIDT, R.F.: Sensory innervation of the Achilles tendon. Anatomy and Embryology *172,* 145 (1985)
18. BIRBAUMER, N.: Psychologische Analyse und Behandlung von Schmerzzuständen. In: (16)
19. BRUNE, K., DIETZEL, K., MÖLLER, N.: Pharmakologie des Schmerzes. In: (16)
20. HANDWERKER, H.: Experimentelle Schmerzanalyse beim Menschen. In: (16)
21. HERZ, A.: Biochemie und Pharmakologie des Schmerzgeschehens. In: (16)
22. MELZACK, R., WALL, P.D.: Pain mechanisms: a new theory. Science *150,* 971 (1975)
23. MENSE, S.: Slowly conducting afferent fibers from deep tissue: Neurobiological properties and central nervous actions. Progress in Sensory Physiology *6,* 139 (1986)
24. SCHAIBLE, H.-G., SCHMIDT, R.F.: Mechanosensibility of joint receptors with fine afferent fibers. Exp. Brain Res. Suppl. *9,* 284 (1984)
25. SCHAIBLE, H.-G., SCHMIDT, R.F.: Effects of an experimental arthritis on the sensory properties of fine articular afferent units. J. Neurophysiol. *54,* 1109 (1985)
26. SCHMIDT, R.F.: Die Gate-control-Theorie des Schmerzes: eine unwahrscheinliche Hypothese. In: JANZEN, R. et al. (Eds.): Schmerz. Stuttgart: Thieme (1972)
27. SCHMIDT, R.F.: Control of the access of afferent activity to somatosensory systems. In: Handbook of Sensory Physiology, Vol. 2, Somatosensory Systems. A. IGGO (Ed.), pp 151–206. Heidelberg: Springer (1973)
28. SCHMIDT, R.F.: Neurobiologische Aspekte der Akupunktur und ihre Konsequenzen. Deutsches Ärzteblatt *82,* 413 (1985)
29. SWEET, W.H.: Cerebral localization of pain. In: R.A. THOMPSON, J.R. GREEN (Eds.): New perspectives in cerebral localization, pp 205–242. New York: Raven (1982)
30. WILLIS, W.D.: Control of nociceptive transmission in the spinal cord. Progress in Sensory Physiology *3,* 1–159 (1982)
31. WOODWORTH, R.S., SHERRINGTON, C.S.: A pseudaffective reflex and its spinal path. J. Physiol. (Lond) *31,* 234 (1904)
32. ZENZ, M.: Schmerztherapie mit Opiaten. In: (16)

11 The Sense of Sight

O.-J. GRÜSSER and U. GRÜSSER-CORNEHLS

11.1 Seeing, Looking, Gazing

The philosopher and physicist J.F. FRIES of Jena, one of the few Kantians in the age of Romanticism, in 1818 published a "Handbook of Psychological Anthropology" in which he wrote: "Where the knowledge of Nature is concerned, humans are instructed by their eyes. Vision alone leads us beyond the surface of the earth, out to the stars, and on earth itself this sense provides us with most of our perceptions of things, from the greatest distances and with the greatest ease of comprehension ... The seeing person apprehends all the life of nature about him by light and color; the eye is our world sense *(Weltsinn)*."
In this chapter we consider the physiological basis of this "world sense".
What one perceives by vision is the result of an interaction of sensory and motor functions of the eye and the CNS, because both voluntary and involuntary movements of eyes, head and body cause the images of the surroundings on the retinas of the eyes to be displaced every 200–600 ms. Our brain produces a *unified* and *continuous* picture of the stationary surroundings from a series of *discontinuous* retinal images, which are slightly different in the two eyes (for reasons of optical geometry) and change from one fixation period to the next. Despite the shifting of the retinal images, we see the extrapersonal space that surrounds us, and the objects in it, as motionless and with stable directionality – i.e., within a fixed system of coordinates.
The movements by which an attentive observer directs his gaze position the eye so that the image of the object of current interest coincides with the place on the retina where vision is most acute. If the object is large enough, the gaze is redirected to "sample" it by small, jerky eye movements (**saccades**). These active motor components of the sense of sight find expression in terms such as "survey", "scan", "peer", "glance" and so on. Only when we are lost in thought and uninterested in our surroundings can we find ourselves "staring into space".

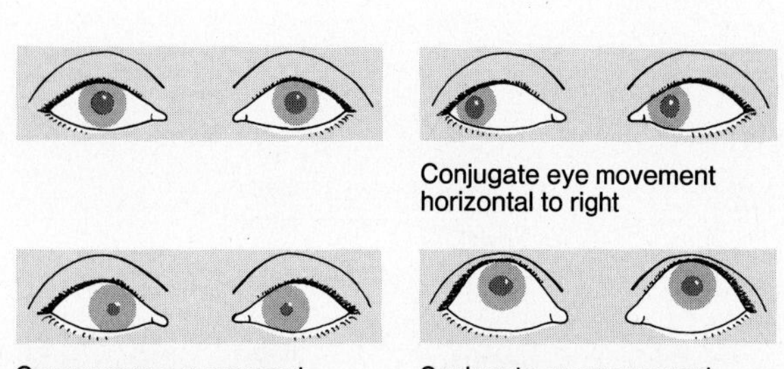

Fig. 11-1. Conjugate eye movements and vergence movements

The Binocular Coordination of Eye Movements

The human eye is moved by 6 external eye muscles, innervated by 3 cranial nerves, the **oculomotor, trochlear** and **abducens** (see textbooks of anatomy). To examine the binocular coordination of gaze-directing movements, the subject's head is kept motionless and the position of the fixation point altered. Two classes of motor programs can be distinguished in this way, as follows (Fig. 11-1).
(i) **Conjugate eye movements,** in which the eyes move together with respect to the coordinates of the extrapersonal space – upward, downward, or to the left or right. The eyelids are raised when one looks up, and lowered when one looks down.
(ii) **Vergence movements,** in which the movement of one eye is approximately the mirror image of that of the other, relative to the *head coordinates.* When the fixation point is moved from far away to a closer position, the two eyes make a **convergence movement**. A **divergence movement** accompanies shifting of the gaze from a nearby object to a distant point; the visual axes of the eyes move apart until, in viewing something at a great distance, they are parallel to one another.
If the subject's head is tilted to one side, careful observation will reveal the third class of eye movements:
(iii) **Cyclorotatory movements** of both eyes in the same direction, in the frontoparallel plane. **Symmetrical** cyclorotatory eye movements accompany fairly large convergence movements; as a rule they are no larger than 10° (see p. 282 [1, 2]).

The Temporal Properties and Dynamics of Eye Movements

Saccades. When we gaze freely about us, our eyes move from one fixation point to the next in quick (10–80 ms duration) jerks called saccades (Fig.

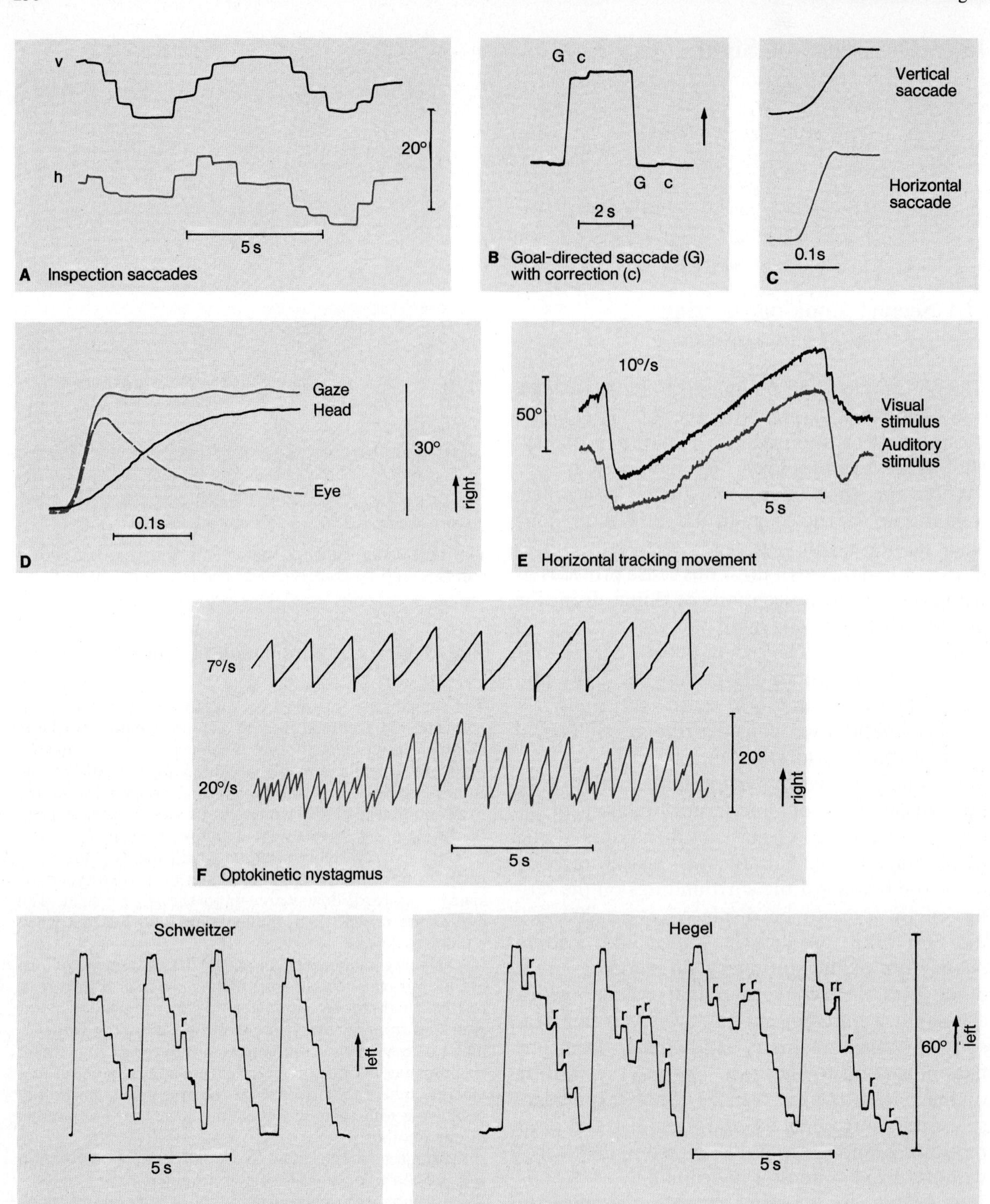

Fig. 11-2 A–H. Electro-oculographic recordings of eye movements in man. **A** Horizontal saccades when subject looks around freely. **B** Large goal-directed horizontal saccade (G) with small corrective saccade (c). **C** Horizontal and slower vertical saccades. **D** Eye and head movement recorded when a rhesus monkey reflexly shifts its gaze to a small light stimulus appearing suddenly in the right visual field (modified from E. BIZZI, Scientific American, October 1974). **E** Horizontal pursuit movements in tracking stimuli in a dark room: a small (0.2° diameter) horizontally moving light spot or a small loudspeaker moving at the same speed while emitting white noise. **F** Horizontal optokinetic nystagmus elicited by a moving pattern of stripes. **G** Horizontal eye movements in reading a text simple in both style and content (ALBERT SCHWEITZER's "Aus meiner Kindheit und Jugendzeit") and **(H)** a simply written text with difficult content (G.F. HEGEL's "Einführung in die Philosophie"). During reading of the conceptually more difficult text regression saccades *(r)* from right to left occur much more frequently, and the total number of saccades per line is greater while the speed of reading declines. (Modified from GHAZARIAN and GRÜSSER, unpublished, 1977)

11-2, A-C). A saccade may cover only a few minutes of arc ("microsaccade") or, by a voluntary command, be larger than 90°. When the gaze is shifted less than 10° from the resting position of the eyes in the head (looking straight ahead horizontally), it is done mainly by movements of the eyes. For larger shifts (e.g., from 60° below left to 40° above right) the saccades of the eyes are always accompanied by **head movements** unless the latter are actively suppressed. The nerves to the eye muscles and those to the neck muscles begin to discharge at about the same time, but because the mass of the head is larger it moves somewhat later and more slowly than the eyes. As a result, in a **directed** head and eye movement there is first a saccade toward the object to be viewed; then the head follows, while the eyes move slowly back with respect to the head, so that in this phase the direction of gaze is kept constant in space (Fig. 11-2D). The angular velocity of the eyes during saccades increases with amplitude of the saccade, reaching about 500°/s during large saccades (> 60°).

Fixation periods. When one looks freely around in a well structured visual environment, the saccades are separated by periods of fixation lasting 0.2–0.6 s (Fig. 11-2A). With some practice and good voluntary concentration one can suppress saccades for several seconds, but unless this effort is made, the fixation point shifts slightly even during the fixation periods. Several factors produce this shift; some eye tremor is always present, and there are short slow "drifts" and small involuntary microsaccades. The frequency components of these fine movements are mainly between 20 and 150 Hz, and their amplitudes are of the order of minutes of arc.

Smooth pursuit movements. Moving objects are followed visually by means of **smooth pursuit movements.** The angular velocity of these eye movements corresponds approximately to that of the object being fixated, as long as it moves no more rapidly than 60–80°/s. In this case the image of the fixated object is kept within an area covering 2° about the center of the fovea centralis. During a pursuit movement small corrective saccades compensate for the discrepancy between image position and the middle of the fovea that is produced whenever the angular velocity of the eye movement does not match the object velocity. With object velocities above 80°/s the eye does not move as rapidly as the object, which is then followed by a combination of pursuit eye movements, large corrective saccades and head movements. As an example, observe the way spectators at a tennis match or automobile race watch the proceedings.

Smooth eye movements also occur when a motionless object is fixated with the eyes while one's head or body is moving. You can observe this in a mirror, as follows. Fixate the pupil of one of your eyes and then turn your head slowly to the right, left, up or down. The eyes move uniformly in the orbits, maintaining the same orientation in space.
Pursuit movements of the eyes can also be elicited in the dark, by auditory or tactile stimuli (Fig. 11-2E), but these smooth eye movements are less precise and are often interrupted by saccades, because of the lack of visual feedback.

Optokinetic nystagmus. A periodic alternation between slow pursuit movements and saccades is called **nystagmus.** Nystagmus occurs, for instance, when a person riding in a train fixates an object outside it. Both eyes then make smooth conjugate eye movements in the direction of the *apparent movement* of the surroundings – opposite to the direction in which the train is traveling – at an angular velocity that depends on the velocity of the train and the distance of the fixated object. When the object disappears from the field of view, a saccade in the **reverse direction** brings the eye to a new fixation point, which is then maintained for some time by initiation of another slow phase of nystagmus. In the laboratory and in clinical examinations, this sort of **optokinetic nystagmus (OKN**, Fig. 11-2F) is usually elicited by moving a striped pattern. In such studies the variable parameters are the angular velocity and the direction of movement of the striped pattern. The angular velocity of the slow phase of the OKN is higher when the subject is attentively following the pattern (gaze nystagmus) than when he is looking at it "passively". Even when one is not paying visual attention, pattern movement induces reflex OKN (stare nystagmus). The eye-movement velocity during gaze nystagmus is almost as high as the pattern velocity, within the limits given for pursuit movements. In stare nystagmus the angular velocity of the eye is distinctly lower than that of the stimulus pattern. **Quantitative** measurements of OKN provide quantitative indications of impaired optomotor function, resulting from disturbances in the brain-stem gaze-control system, cerebellar lesions, lesions in the region of the parietal lobe of the cerebral cortex, and changes in the vestibular system [1, 6, 19, 21, 30, 53, 54].

Eye Movements in Viewing Complex Stimulus Patterns

As one surveys a visually well-structured region, saccadic eye movements in all directions occur. When the viewing distance is altered, vergence movements are superimposed on the saccades. Figure 11-3 shows a two-dimensional record of the **eye positions** of a subject viewing a photograph of a face. The preferred fixation points are along *contours* and at the *interruptions or intersections of contours.* Furthermore, one's **interest** in the object affects the frequency with which a

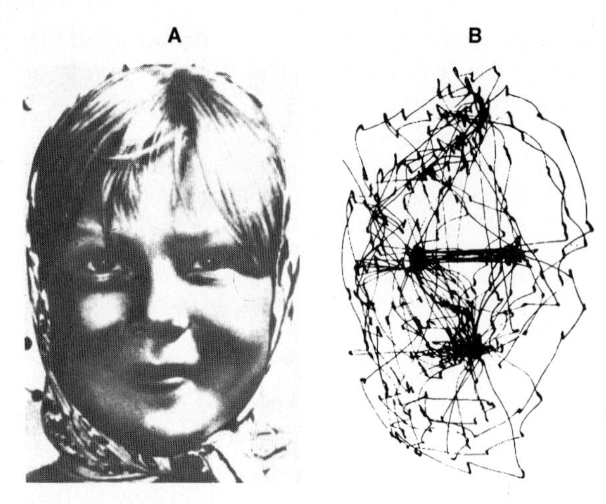

Fig. 11-3 A,B. Two-dimensional plot of eye movements during viewing of a face **(B)**. The subject looked at the photograph **(A)** for several minutes. (Modified from [32])

particular visual structure is fixated. When looking at a face, one fixates the eyes and mouth more often than the other parts. As a rule, the gaze is directed to the right half of the face almost twice as often as to the left. That is, optomotor control is determined not only by the formal structural properties of the stimulus pattern but also by the **significance** of the visual signals to the observer and his current interest in them [32].

Eye movements in reading. A particularly regular form of eye movement occurs during reading: when the text is printed according to the occidental convention, the fixation point moves along the lines in rapid saccades from left to right. Between the saccades there are fixation periods lasting 0.2–0.6 s (Fig. 11-2G,H). When the reader's fixation point has reached the end of a line, the eyes usually return to the beginning of the next line with *a single saccade toward the left*. The amplitude and frequency of the reading saccades depend on the format of the text (size, subdivisions, system of capitalization), but are also influenced by the reader's *understanding* of the text. If the style of writing is unclear or the content difficult to comprehend, *regression saccades* often occur (Fig. 11-2H); these are saccades opposed to the normal direction of reading. The eye movements of a child learning to read also show many regression saccades, and they are common in children and adults who have difficulty in comprehending written words and in correct orthography (*congenital dyslexia*). In reading Arabian or Hebrew texts, of course, the direction of the saccades is the opposite of that for occidental texts, and Japanese or Chinese texts written in the traditional vertical columns are read with a sequence of saccades from top to bottom.

The Neuronal Control of Eye Movements

During slow pursuit movements, saccades and fixation periods, the motor programs for the two eyes are normally well coordinated, under the control of oculomotor centers in the brainstem. The nerve cells responsible for the **horizontal movements** are mainly located in the **paramedian pontine reticular formation** (PPRF), and those directing the vertical movements are in the **mesencephalic reticular formation** (MRF). Their axons pass from these regions to the neurons in the eye-muscle nuclei (abducens, oculomotor and trochlear nuclei) and the motoneurons of the upper cervical cord, so that the movements of eyes and head can be adjusted to one another. The state of excitation of the oculomotor centers is controlled by various visual regions in the brain – the superior colliculi, secondary visual cortex, parietal integration cortex (chiefly area 7) and frontal eye field (see p. 128). The nerve cells in the vestibular nuclei, flocculus and paraflocculus of the cerebellum also make connections with the PPRF and the MRF. The neuronal mechanisms by which direction of gaze is controlled have been quite well worked out from microelectrode recordings of the activity of single neurons in the eye-muscle nuclei and the gaze motor centers of the PPRF and MRF. These results can be used to interpret the disturbances of gaze control and of other eye movements that result from brainstem lesions. Lesions in the region of the PPRF impede horizontal rotation of the eyes toward the side of the lesion, whereas those in the region of the MRF prevent vertical gaze-shifting movements of both eyes (further details in the first edition of this book; for summaries see [53, 54]).

11.2 Light and the Eye

Electromagnetic radiation at wavelengths between 400 and about 750 nm is perceived by humans as **light**. The light source most important to us is the sun. In a rainbow, we see the yellowish-white light of the sun separated into its components, the spectrum of wavelengths; the long-wavelength components appear red to us, and the short-wavelength components blue-violet (Fig. 11-4). The term **monochromatic light** is applied to radiation in any very narrow band within this spectrum.

Most objects in our surroundings absorb or reflect different amounts of light, depending on its wavelength. If an object has a **spectral reflectance** nonuniformly distributed over the visible spectrum, its surface appears **colored** to us. The difference in mean luminance of adjacent structures determines their physical contrast (C);

$C = (I_b - I_d)/(I_b + I_d)$, where I_b is the luminance of the brighter structure and I_d, that of the darker. Vision depends primarily on the perception of **light-dark contrasts** and, for surfaces with nonuniform spectral reflectance, on the perception of **color contrasts**. By means of color contrast we can distinguish from one another objects that have no average physical contrast.

The **mean luminance** of the natural human environment varies widely: about 10^{-6} cd·m^{-2} (cd = candela) under an overcast night sky, 10^{-3} cd·m^{-2} in starlight with no moon, 10^{-1} cd·m^{-2} on a clear night with full moon, and as much as 10^7 cd·m^{-2} in bright sunshine with brightly reflecting surfaces (e.g., fields of snow). The visual system adjusts to this great range of intensities by various **adaptation processes**, discussed on p. 255. They enable vision within a large relative energy range, about 1:10^{11}. The range over which one must adapt under constant illumination, however, is considerably smaller, about 1:40; this represents the variation in mean reflectance of the surfaces of most of the things one sees, excluding mirrorlike surfaces [9, 13, 22, 25].

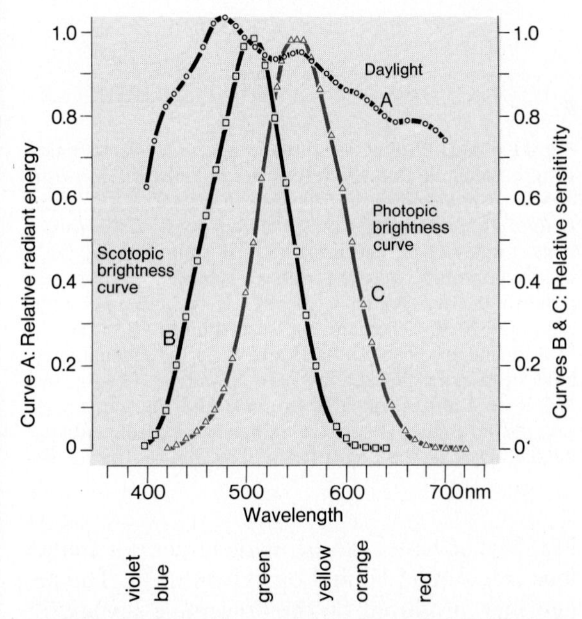

Fig. 11-4. Spectrum of sunlight on the earth's surface (A) and spectral sensitivity of the human visual system (B, C). Curve A was obtained by measuring the relative energy of daylight under a cloudless sky in the visible region of the electromagnetic radiation. The scotopic (B) and photopic (C) brightness curves are the means of measurements on many observers with normal vision (standard curves of the International Color Society), as follows. First the relative energy required to produce the sensation "equally bright" with various monochromatic light stimuli was measured. The results were then normalized by setting the energy value for the most effective wavelength (500 nm for scotopic vision, 555 nm for photopic vision) equal to 1. Curves B and C thus represent the reciprocal of the relative radiant energy

Seeing without physical light. We can perceive light and visual structures even when no physical light is falling onto the retina from the surroundings – when we are in **complete darkness.** A person who has been in a dark room for some time sees an "intrinsic light" (*Eigengrau*); the visual field is full of "light nebulae", rapidly flashing dots of light and indistinct moving structures of various shades of gray. Eidetically predisposed people soon begin to see colored patterns, faces or figures, and some recognize scenes as in a picture. These **imaginary visual phenomena** were described by ARISTOTLE, who also reported correctly that they are more common in adolescents and children than in adults. They are *not* pathological symptoms, though they occur more frequently during high fever. The famous physiologist JOHANNES MÜLLER made a thorough study of them (1826).
Light is also perceived when the retina or the afferent visual system is excited by **inadequate stimuli** (see p. 178). For instance, pressing lightly with a finger on the outside of the eye in darkness causes one to see **pressure phosphenes** (see p. 257). **Electrical phosphenes** are produced when the retina, the optic nerve or the afferent visual system is stimulated electrically. **Migraine phosphenes**, usually perceived as jagged, bright, fluttering bands, are caused by excitation of the nerve cells in the primary visual cortex, due to a temporary, local disturbance in the regulation of the sodium and potassium content of the extracellular space around them. Usually this is a sign of locally impaired circulation. Finally, every reader will be familiar with the **scenic visual hallucinations** experienced during dreaming. The perception of these visual images is characterized by rapid saccadic eye movements, with which we look at the dream pictures (REM phase of sleep; see p. 143). **Pathological visual hallucinations** can occur as part of endogenous or symptomatic psychoses. Scenic visual hallucinations are particularly common in alcoholic delirium (Korsakoff's psychosis); here the perception of the hallucinated objects and events is closely interlinked with that of "real" things.

The Eye and Its Dioptric Apparatus

The dioptric apparatus. The optical system of the eye is a not-exactly-centered, compound lens system that casts an inverted, reduced image of the environment onto the retina. The **dioptric apparatus** consists of the transparent **cornea**, the anterior and posterior **chambers filled with aqueous humor**, the **iris**, which encloses the **pupil**, the **lens**, surrounded by a transparent **lens capsule**, and the **vitreous body**, which occupies most of the space within the eyeball (Fig. 11-5). The vitreous body is a clear gel composed of extracellular fluid containing collagen and hyaluronic acid in colloidal solution. At the back of the eye, its inner surface is lined by the **retina**. The space between the retina and the firm sclera that encloses the eyeball is filled by a vascular network, the choroid layer. At the posterior pole of the human eye, there is a small pit in the retina. This **fovea centralis** is the place where vision is most acute in daylight [26].

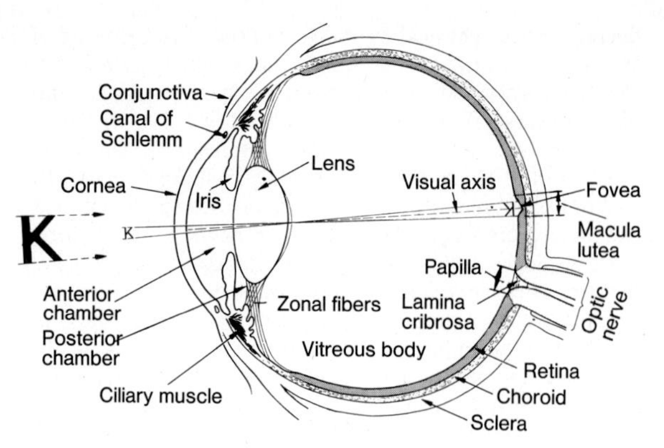

Fig. 11-5. Horizontal section through the right eye (diagrammatic)

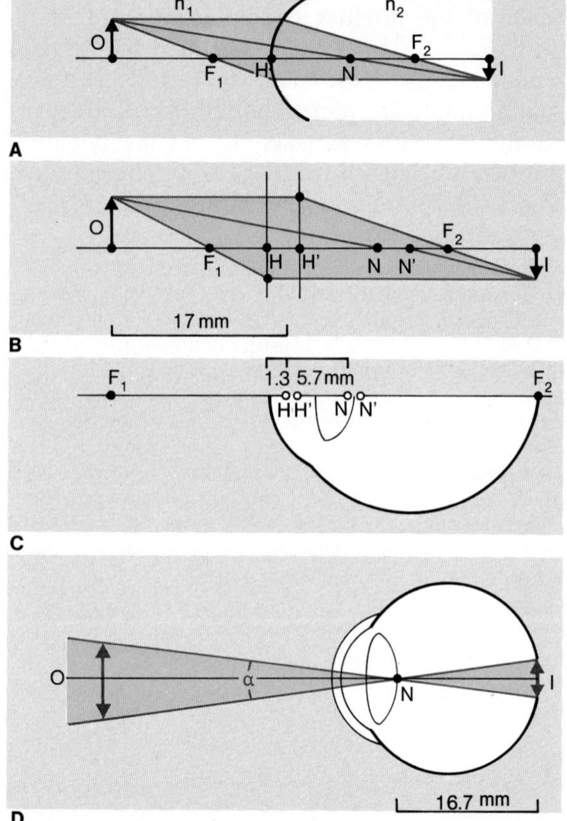

Fig. 11-6 A–D. Production of an image by a simple optical system, schematic and reduced eye. **A** Paths of rays from object to image in a simple optical system. F_1, F_2, focal points; H, principal point; N, nodal point; O, object; I, image; index of refraction $n_2 > n_1$. **B** Simplified ray paths in a compound, centered optical system that has been reduced to two principal planes H, H' and two nodal points N, N'. **C** Schematic eye according to GULLSTRAND. **D** Reduced eye. The points H and H' in the schematic eye have been superimposed, as have N and N'. The distance N-I is 16.7 mm. From this distance and the angle α the size of the image (I) on the retina can be calculated: 1 degree of arc at the object (O) $\approx$ 0.29 mm on the retina

Tears. The outer surface of the cornea is covered by a thin film of tears, which improves the optical properties of its surface structure. The tears are produced continually in small amounts by the lacrimal glands, and are distributed uniformly over the cornea and conjunctiva by the movements of the eyelids. Some of the tear fluid evaporates into the air, and the remainder flows through the nasolacrimal ducts into the nasal cavity. The tears protect the cornea and conjunctiva from drying out, and simultaneously act as a lubricant between the eyeball and lids. When a foreign body comes between the lids and the eye, it stimulates the mechanoreceptors in the cornea and conjunctiva, with axons in the *trigeminal nerve*, causing a reflex increase in tear secretion. The purpose of tear production in this case is to rinse the object out of the eye, with the help of more frequent blinking. Tears taste salty; in composition they correspond approximately to an ultrafiltrate of plasma. In addition they contain enzymes that act against pathogenic organisms, protecting the eye to some extent from infection. In humans, as everyone knows, tear secretion also serves to express emotion, when one cries.
The secretion of tears is also increased by the stimulation of mechanoreceptors and nociceptors in the nasal epithelia, by strong olfactory or taste stimuli, toothache or stimuli in the region of larynx and pharynx that cause coughing; it is controlled by the efferent autonomic nervous system (see p. 336). **Parasympathetic** neurons of the **pterygopalatine ganglion** activate tear secretion. The preganglionic axons reach this ganglion by way of the **greater petrosal nerve**; the somata of these cells lie in the pontine region of the brainstem. These neurons are excited by hypothalamic and limbic systems as well as by signals from neurons in the sensory trigeminal nucleus (reflex activation). The **sympathetic innervation** of the lacrimal glands mainly inhibits secretion; it is controlled by neurons in the upper thoracic cord, which send signals to the glands by way of neurons in the **superior cervical ganglion** and sympathetic nerve fibers running along the cerebral arteries.

The Production of an Image on the Retina

Foundations of physical optics. The simplest optical system is the **camera obscura**, a device in which a small aperture creates a reversed image. The image is sharp only if the aperture is very small, so that the intensity of the image is very low. The aperture can be made larger if a convex lens is mounted behind or in front of it. The image then produced on the "receptive surface" is reversed and reduced. This principle is realized in the imaging of the surroundings on the retina by the compound optical system of the eye: the air-cornea interface acts as a lens in front of the aperture (pupil, adjusted by the iris), and there is a biconvex lens behind the aperture (Fig. 11-6) [9, 12, 22, 26].

Refraction and focal length. When a ray of light strikes an interface between two transparent media of different refractive index (n), it is bent by an amount depending on the angle of incidence (Fig. 11-6A). All the rays parallel to the optical axis of a spherically curved interface (the line through the principal point H in Fig. 11-6A; see below) are bent in such a way as to converge at the focal points (F_1, F_2). The **refractive power** of the system depends on the radius of curvature r of the interface and the refractive indices (n_1, n_2) of the two media. When parallel rays from the medium with smaller refractive index (n_1) pass through the interface they converge at focal point F_2 in the medium with greater index. The **focal length** "behind" the lens (f_2, the distance H-F_2) is

$$f_2 = \frac{n_2 \cdot r}{n_2 - n_1} \text{ [m]} \tag{1}$$

When parallel rays cross the interface in the opposite direction they converge at F_1, so that the focal length "in front" of the lens is

$$f_1 = \frac{n_1 \cdot r}{n_2 - n_1} \text{ [m]} \tag{2}$$

These equations are strictly valid only for a small (Gaussian) area about the optical axis. The **optical axis** is the line connecting the focal points F_1 and F_2, and the principal point H is the point at which this line intersects the interface. The **nodal point** N is the center of the sphere of which the interface is a part. The refractive power RP of the interface is defined as

$$RP = \frac{1}{f} \text{ [D]} \tag{3}$$

When the focal length f is given in meters, the unit of refractive power is the **diopter** (D).
The refractive power RP_l of a lens with two refractive surfaces can be calculated by Gullstrand's formula, as follows:

$$RP_l = RP_f + RP_b - \frac{d}{n} \cdot RP_f \cdot RP_b \text{ [D]} \tag{4}$$

where RP_f is the refractive power of the front surface of the lens and RP_b that of the back surface, d is the distance between the two refractive surfaces in meters, and n is the refractive index of the medium between the refractive surfaces.

Image formation. A spherical lens with focal length f, given an object d_o meters away, produces an image of that object d_i meters away on the opposite side of the lens. If the lens is surrounded on all sides by the same optical medium, it holds that

$$\frac{1}{f} = \frac{1}{d_o} + \frac{1}{d_i} \tag{5}$$

If the object is at infinity, or at a sufficiently great distance, then $1/d_o \rightarrow 0$, so that the image distance d_i is equal to the focal length f of the lens. Focal length can thus be found by measuring the image distance for infinitely distant objects.

Image formation by the dioptric apparatus of the eye. The data required for calculating image formation in the eye are summarized in Table 11-1. The air-cornea interface, according to Eq. (2), has the **object-side focal length** f_c

$$f_c = \frac{n_a \cdot r_1}{n_c - n_a} = \frac{7.7}{0.376} \approx 20.5 \text{ [mm]} \tag{6}$$

Table 11-1. Schematic eye (Modified from GULLSTRAND)

Indices of refraction:		
Air, n_a	= 1.00	
Cornea, n_c	= 1.376	
Aqueous humor and vitreous body, n_h	= 1.336	
Lens, n_l	= 1.414 (unaccommodated, U)	
Lens	= 1.424 (accommodated, A)	
	Radius of curvature (mm)	**Distance from pole of cornea (mm)**
Front corneal surface	7.7	0
Back corneal surface	6.8	0.5
Front lens surface	10.0 (U)	5.6 (U)
Front lens surface	5.3 (A, max)	5.2 (A, max)
Back lens surface	–6.0 (U)	7.2
Back lens surface	–5.3 (A, max)	7.2
Retina		24.4
1st principal point H		1.35
2nd principal point H′		1.60
Anterior nodal point N		7.05
Posterior nodal Point N′		7.30
Image-side focal length		22.78 (U)
Object-side focal length		−17.05 (U)

where n_a and n_c are the refractive indices of air and cornea, respectively. The refractive power RP_{ac} of the front surface of the cornea is thus 1/0.0205 = 48.8 D. The interface between cornea and aqueous humor causes the light rays to diverge, because $n_h < n_c$ (Table 11-1). From Eqs. (1) and (3) we find that the refractive power RP_{ch} of this interface is –5.9 D. Gullstrand's formula (Eq. 4) can now be used to calculate the total refractive power RP_{co} of the system air-cornea-aqueous humor from RP_{ac}, RP_{ch} and d = 0.5 mm: RP_{co} = 43 D. The *image-side focal length* f_{co} of the whole cornea system is found by Eqs. (1) and (3):

$$f_{co} = \frac{n_h}{RP_{co}} = \frac{1.336}{43} \approx 31 \text{ [mm]} \tag{7}$$

The lens. To obtain a sharp image on the fovea, 24.4 mm from the pole of the cornea, the *additional refractive power* of the lens of the eye is required. This biconvex lens consists of several lamelliform layers, differing in both radius of curvature and refractive index; the latter increases progressively from the *periphery to the core* of the lens. That is, the lens is optically inhomogeneous. The experimentally determined **total index** given in Table 11-1 is greater than the individual indices of the lens layers. The refractive power RP_l of the lens in its flattest state was found by GULLSTRAND to average 19.1 D.
Total refractive index of the eye. From the refractive power of the cornea RP_{co} and that of the lens RP_l, the total refractive power RP_e of the dioptric apparatus of the eye can be calculated, using Gullstrand's formula (Eq. 4, with d = 5.6 mm and n = n_h = 1.336). RP_e is found to be 58.6 D. The image-side focal length f_i of the whole dioptric apparatus – the critical parameter of image formation in the eye – is thus

$$f_i = \frac{n_h}{RP_e} = \frac{1.336}{58.6} \text{ [m]} = 22.8 \text{ [mm]} \tag{8}$$

The schematic eye. The diagrammatic representation of the imaging process in a *compound optical system* is facilitated by determining the **cardinal points** (for details see textbooks of physical optics). In this schematization of the optical system the effects at all optical interfaces are represented by two principal planes (H, H'), two nodal points (N and N') and two focal points (F_1, F_2; Fig. 11-6B). GULLSTRAND determined the values listed in Table 11-1 for the human eye (Fig. 11-6C). The distance from the pole of the cornea to the posterior principal point (1.60 mm) and the image-side focal length f_i of the eye (22.8 mm) together give the cornea-to-fovea distance (24.4 mm).

The reduced eye. A further simplification is the reduced eye (Fig. 11-6D), in which H coincides with H' and N with N'. In the reduced eye the distance from the nodal point N to the retina is 16.67 mm. From this value and the visual angle α subtended by the object the size of the image on the retina can be estimated.

Regulatory Process in the Dioptric Apparatus

The refractive power of the lens and the diameter of the pupil can be altered by neurally controlled smooth muscles.

Pupil responses. Normally both pupils are round and of equal size. The mean pupil diameter decreases with advancing age.

Light response. When the ambient illumination is constant, the amount of light entering the eye per unit time is proportional to the *area of the pupil.* Reflexes cause the pupils to become larger, the lower the ambient light intensity. When a person in daylight closes his eyelids for 10–20 s, the pupils enlarge; when he opens them again, the pupils become smaller. This **light response** can be further differentiated by separately illuminating the two eyes (Fig. 11-7). When one eye is illuminated, within 0.3–0.8 s its own pupil constricts **(direct light response)**, and that of the unilluminated eye constricts as well **(consensual light response)**. The light response is clearly a useful regulatory mechanism, for it reduces the amount of light incident on the retina when the surrounding light intensity is high (e.g., in bright sunlight), and in dim light increases the light reaching the retina, by pupil dilation. The sensors in this negative-feedback **control circuit** are the retinal receptors, and the controlled variable is pupil diameter. In young people the diameter of the pupil can vary from 1.5 to ca. 8 mm, changing the relative amount of light entering the eye by a factor of about 30. In comparison to the range of mean environmental luminance discussed on p. 241, however, the regulation provided by change in pupil diameter is slight.

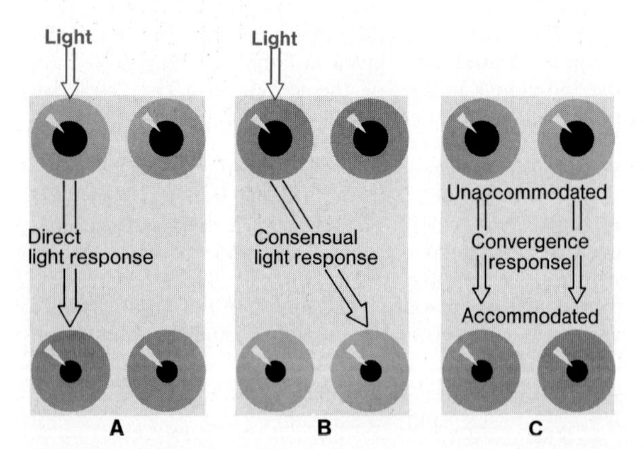

Fig. 11-7. Diagram of the pupil responses (direct and consensual light responses and accommodation response). The arrows symbolize illumination of one eye

Near-vision response (convergence response). The diameter of the human pupil also depends on the *distance* of the object fixated. When an experimental subject initially looking into the distance shifts his gaze to an object 30 cm away, his pupils become constricted. Because the visual axes of the two eyes converge, as a rule, when one looks at a nearby object (cf. p. 237), this pupil constriction is also called the **convergence response.** This adjustment of the pupil to a near object is accompanied by an increase in the refractive power of the lens (discussed below). As in a camera when the aperture is reduced, the *depth of focus* in the eye increases when the pupil constricts.

Function and innervation of the pupillomotor muscles (Fig. 11-8). The pupil responses are brought about by two smooth-muscle systems in the iris. By contraction of the annular *sphincter muscle* in the iris the pupil becomes smaller **(miosis)**, whereas contraction of the *dilator muscle*, with fibers arranged radially in the iris, widens it **(mydriasis)**. The sphincter muscle is innervated by parasympathetic nerve fibers arising in the ciliary ganglion, behind the eye. The preganglionic fibers originate in *pupillomotor neurons* in the Edinger-Westphal nucleus, the "autonomic" part of the oculomotor nucleus in the brainstem, and pass to the orbit along with the other fibers in the oculomotor nerve. The state of activity of the pupillomotor neurons in the Edinger-Westphal nucleus is controlled by nerve cells in the pretectal region (Fig. 11-8). Axons from the ganglion-cell layer of the retina and from the visual cortex (areas 18 and 19) terminate in this region. The dilator muscle, on the other hand, is innervated by sympathetic nerve fibers that are excited by neurons in the **ciliospinal center** of the spinal cord, at the level of the 8th cervical segment and the 1st to 2nd thoracic segments. Axons from the ciliospinal center run in the cervical sympathetic chain to the superior cervical ganglion, where they synapse with the postganglionic neurons; their axons pass to the orbit along the *internal carotid* and *ophthalmic arteries*, and run in the ciliary nerve to the eye. The state of activation of the ciliospinal center depends on the general level of autonomic tone.

Clinical significance of the pupil response. The diameter of the pupils and the pupil responses are important diagnostic signs, for they can indicate lesions of the retina and the optic nerve as well as lesions in the brainstem (oculomotor region), the cervical cord, or the regions through

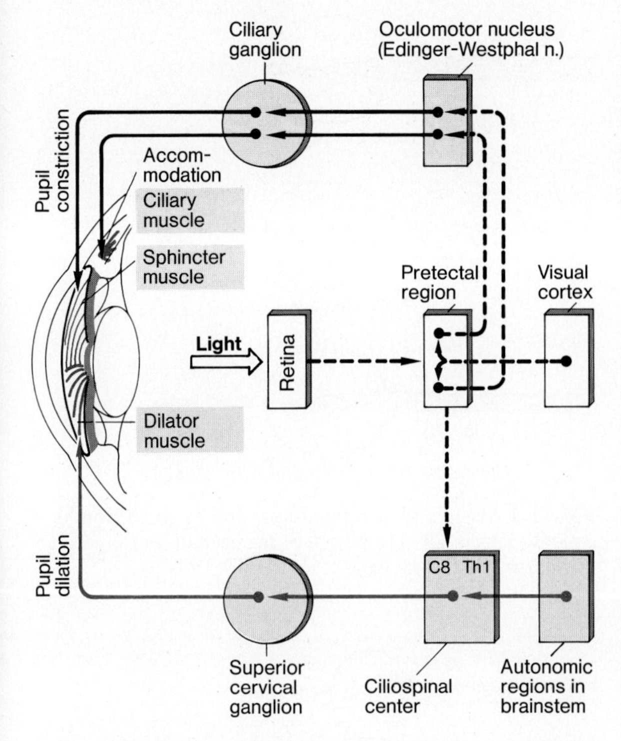

Fig. 11-8. Diagram of innervation of iris musculature and ciliary muscle. The neurons of the efferent sympathetic nervous system are shown in *red*, and those of the efferent parasympathetic nervous system in *black*

which the pre- and postganglionic pupillomotor fibers run (deep neck region, sphenoid bone and orbit). The autonomic innervation of the iris muscles also accounts for the dependence of pupil size on age, psychological factors, attentiveness and degree of fatigue [12, 30].

Accommodation. In the human eye adjustment of the refractive power of the dioptric apparatus to the distance of the fixated object **(accommodation)** is brought about by changing the curvature of the lens, its *front surface* in particular. The amount of curvature depends on the elasticity of the lens and on the forces acting on the lens capsule. The passive elastic forces of the ciliary apparatus, the choroid and the sclera are imposed upon the lens capsule by the fibers of the **ciliary (Zinn's) zonule**. The mechanical tension of the sclera in turn depends on the intraocular pressure, the chief source of this tension (cf. p. 248). When the tension in the zonule fibers increases, the lens is stretched and thus flattened. The influence of these passive elastic forces on the lens is modified by the ciliary muscle, which encircles the lens (Figs. 11-5, 11-8). The smooth muscle fibers of this muscle are oriented radially, circularly and meridionally and are supplied by autonomic, chiefly parasympathetic nerve fibers. When the ciliary muscle contracts it reduces the elastic force exerted on the lens by the zonule fibers, so that the tension in the lens capsule is less. The front surface of the lens, in particular, becomes more strongly curved, and the refractive power of the lens increases; it is in a state of **accommodation.** When the ciliary muscle relaxes, the lens is **unaccommodated**; when least curved its refractive power is lowest. In this state a normal eye forms a sharp image on the retina of objects at an infinite distance (far point = ∞).

Range of accommodation. The increase in refractive power (in diopters) as the focus is changed from the far point to the near point is called the **range of accommodation**. It is greatest in the young, 14 diopters at most. It follows from Eqs. (3) and (5) that such an eye, when maximally accommodated, can bring objects at a distance of 1/14 m = 0.07 m = 7 cm into sharp focus on the retina. With advancing age the lens becomes progressively less elastic owing to water loss, so that its ability to change refractive power and thus its accommodation amplitude are reduced. The near point gradually moves away from the eye, so that older people with otherwise normal eyes need reading glasses **(presbyopia)**.

Neural control of accommodation. The preganglionic parasympathetic axons (cf. p. 333) of the accommodation system, like those of the pupillomotor system, originate in cells of the Edinger-Westphal nucleus and pass to the ciliary ganglion. The adequate stimulus for a change in accommodation is a **blurred image** on the retina. This property of the stimulus pattern is presumably detected by neurons in the foveal projection region of the visual cortex (area 18), a region that makes connections with the Edinger-Westphal nucleus (Fig. 11-8).
The peripheral autonomic synapses at the ciliary muscle and muscles in the iris, like other synapses in the autonomic nervous system, can be influenced by drugs. If an **atropine** solution is dripped into the connective-tissue sac behind the eyelid, it diffuses to the iris and the ciliary body and blocks signal transmission at the parasympathetic synapses, so that the lens becomes unaccommodated and the pupil expands. **Neostigmine**, a cholinesterase inhibitor (cf. p. 49), on the other hand, causes constriction of the pupils and accommodation [12, 20, 26, 30].

Optical Defects and Refractive Anomalies

The lens system in a modern camera can produce a considerably better image than the dioptric apparatus of the eye. The physicist and physiologist Hermann v. Helmholtz (1821–1894) once wrote that if he should receive an optical instrument so carelessly constructed as the eye, he would send it back to the maker. The "physiological" deficiencies in focussing by the eye discussed here, however, are largely compensated by neuronal contrast mechanisms (cf. p. 255).

Astigmatism. The corneal surface is not rotationally symmetric about the optical axis, for the vertical curvature is usually somewhat greater than the horizontal curvature. As Eq. (1) indicates, this discrepancy results in an angle-dependent difference in refractive power *(astigmatism* or *astigmia)*. If the difference is no greater than 0.5 D, the condition is called "physiological" astigmatism.

Spherical aberration. The cornea and the lens of the eye, like all simple lenses, have shorter focal lengths in the peripheral regions than in the central part around the optical axis. The resulting *spherical aberration* causes blurring of the image. The smaller the pupils, the more the peripheral rays are excluded and the less distortion is caused by spherical aberration.

Chromatic aberration and accommodation. As do all simple lenses, the dioptric apparatus refracts short-wavelength light more strongly than long-wavelength light *(chromatic aberration)*. Therefore greater accommodation is required for sharp focussing of the red parts of an object than for the blue parts. It is because of this difference that blue objects appear to be further away than red ones at the same objective distance. The builders of Gothic churches often exploited this physiological illusion in their stained-glass windows, by making the background blue and the figures other colors, so that one sees an apparent spatial separation between figures and background.

Stray light and clouding of the dioptric apparatus. The lens and the vitreous body contain structural proteins and macromolecular substances in colloidal solution. Therefore a slight *diffuse dispersion* of the light occurs in the dioptric apparatus. But this *stray light* impairs visual perception only with very bright stimuli (cf. p. 256). Even in the healthy eye there are *cloudy areas in the vitreous body*, visible against a white wall as small disks or irregularly shaped small gray spots. When the eye moves they seem to flit like gnats across the light background. In older people the water content of the lens can decline so greatly that the structure of the remaining material becomes condensed, making the lens opaque *(senile cataract)*. Removal of the lens enables these patients to see normally when they are fitted with spectacles having a strong convex lens (ca. + 13 D for long-distance vision).

Myopia. The total refractive power of the dioptric apparatus of a normal, unaccommodated eye is 58.6 diopters (cf. p. 243). With this refractive power an infinitely distant object is focussed sharply on the retina when the distance between the pole of the cornea and the fovea is 24.4 mm. If the axial length of the eyeball is greater, distant objects cannot be seen sharply because the plane of focus is *in front* of the fovea **(nearsightedness, myopia)**. A nearsighted person must wear glasses with concave lenses (negative refractive power) to see sharply at a distance (Fig. 11-9).

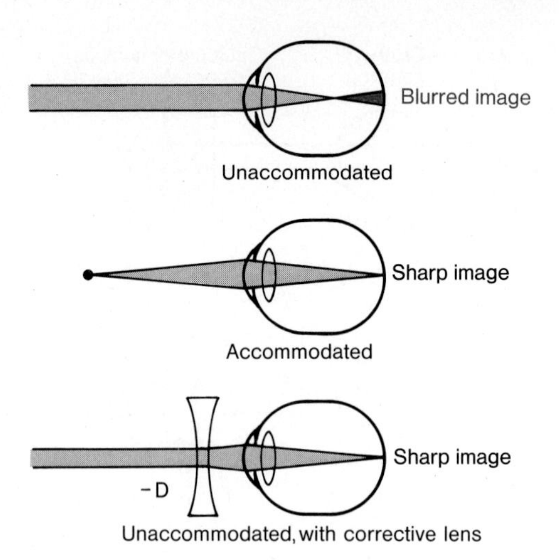

Fig. 11-9. Myopia (nearsightedness) and its correction by a concave lens (–D). The length of the eyeball is exaggerated for clarity ("axial myopia")

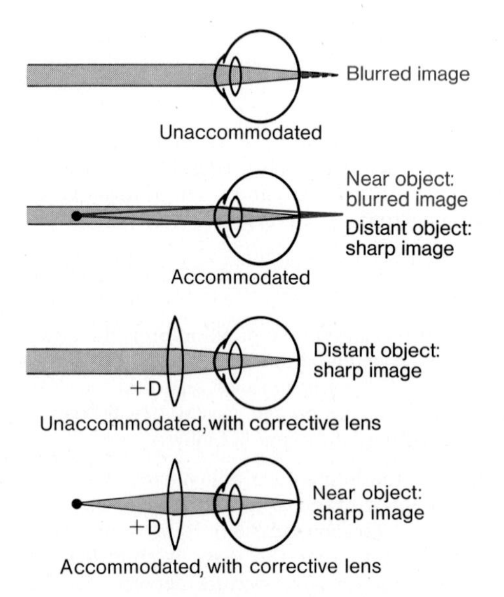

Fig 11-10. Hypermetropia (farsightedness) and its correction by a convex lens (+D)

Hypermetropia. If the axial length is too short for the refractive power of the dioptric apparatus, a condition of "farsightedness" **(hyperopia** or **hypermetropia)** exists. The hypermetropic person can see distant objects clearly by accommodating, but his accommodation range is not sufficient to allow sharp focussing of nearby objects. Convex lenses (positive refractive power) are required to compensate this defect (Fig. 11-10) [12, 23, 26].

Measurement of Refractive Errors and Prescription of Corrective Lenses

The refraction of the dioptric apparatus can be measured by either *objective* or *subjective* methods. The objective procedures (retinoscopy, infrared technique) are in the province of ophthalmology. Here we consider briefly the **subjective** procedures.

Subjective measurement of refraction. The vision-testing charts described on p. 265 can be used to determine refraction subjectively. The patient views a chart monocularly from a distance of 6 m. With a nearsighted patient, lenses of progressively increasing – D values are placed in front of the eye until visual acuity becomes optimal. The refractive power of the lens giving this result is about equivalent to the refractive error. A hypermetropic patient, as a rule, can see optimally at a distance without a corrective lens. In this case convex lenses (+ D) are placed in front of the eye until acuity deteriorates. Then, once the near point has been determined, the degree of hypermetropia can be determined from the diopter number of the lens.

Spectacles. The corrective lens and the eye together form a compound optical system to which Eq. (4) applies. If a corneal contact lens is worn instead of spectacles with *concave lenses*, the term d in Eq. (4) becomes smaller – that is, the refractive power of the *corneal contact lens* can be somewhat lower than that of the lens in a pair of glasses. When fitting spectacles care must be taken to ensure that (when the patient looks straight ahead) the optical axes of eye and corrective lens coincide. To this end, the distance between the right and left pupils (56 –70mm) must be measured and the frame of the lenses selected correspondingly.
The *size* of the retinal image depends on the strength of the corrective lens. If the refraction or the left eye is not identical to that of the right, complete correction produces images of different sizes on the retinas, which can impair **binocular vision** (cf. p. 268). In this case a compromise must be found between optimal correction and undisturbed binocular vision. The difference in refractive power of the two lenses should not exceed 3 D.
Pronounced "regular" **astigmatism,** in which there is a systematic variation in curvature along different meridians of the cornea, can be corrected by a **cylindrical** lens. "Irregular" astigmatism is produced by irregular deformations of the cornea, and is better compensated by contact lenses.

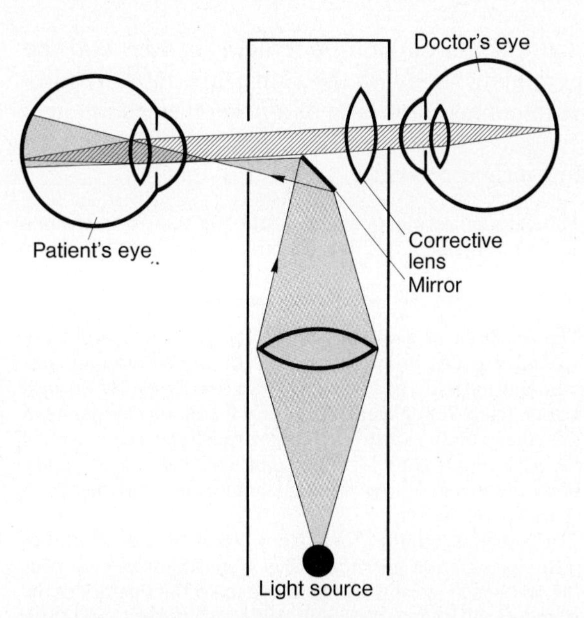

Fig. 11-11. Highly simplified diagram of the use of the direct ophthalmoscope (upright image)

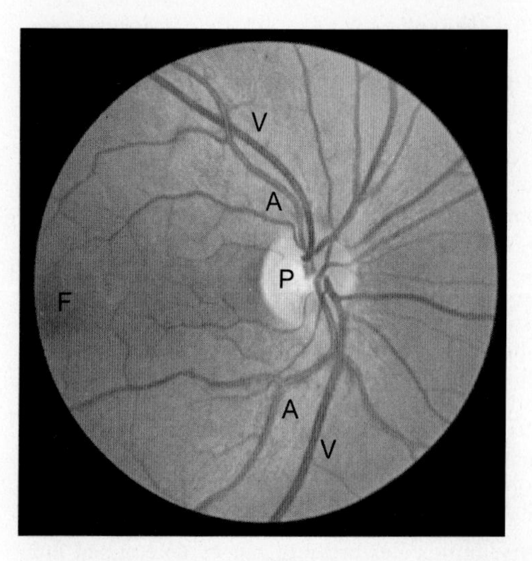

Fig. 11-12. Fundus of the eye (part of the right retina) as seen in the direct ophthalmoscope. A, branches of the central artery of the retina; V, branches of the central veins of the retina; P, papilla of the optic nerve; F, fovea centralis. (From W. Leydhecker, Grundriß der Augenheilkunde, 20th Ed., 1979)

Examination of the Interior of the Eye with the Ophthalmoscope

When an animal in the dark looks into the headlights of a car, the driver can see the animal's eyes "glowing", because the light is reflected from the eyeground (fundus oculi). The technique of **ophthalmoscopy** takes advantage of this reflection of light. A simplified diagram of the paths of the entrant and reflected rays is shown in Fig. 11-11. The examiner must relax his eye as though looking into the distance in order to see the retina clearly; refractive errors of his own or the patient's eye must be corrected by lenses. An example of what one sees under these conditions is shown in Fig. 11-12. The **papilla**, the retina **vessels** and the inner surface of the retina appear in an upright image enlarged about 15 times, because the dioptric apparatus acts as a magnifying lens.
To see a **reversed image** of the retina the physician uses an indirect ophthalmoscope at a distance of ca. 80 cm. The parallel rays of light emerging from the patient's eye are focussed by a convex lens of +13 to +15 D, to give a reversed, real image of the retina. The physician accommodates to this image. In this method the image is magnified only about 4 x, but the advantage is

that a larger part of the retina is in view and the peripheral areas of the retina are more readily visible than in the case of a non-reversed image.

Intraocular Pressure

The external shape of the eye and the relative positions of the components of the dioptric apparatus are nearly constant. This stability is provided by the firm **sclera** and the constancy of the **intraocular pressure**.

The secretion of aqueous humor. The pressure within the eyeball depends primarily on the amount of aqueous humor continuously produced and drained away. By *ultrafiltration* (cf. p. 738) plasma fluid from the blood capillaries in the ciliary body moves into the extracellular space within the ciliary body (Fig. 11-5); the epithelial cells of the ciliary body then **secrete** it, as aqueous humor, into the posterior chamber of the eye.
The aqueous humor flows from the posterior chamber into the anterior chamber, and from there passes over the trabecular meshwork at the edge of the chamber (the iridocorneal angle), through Schlemm's canal, and into the venous system. The intraocular pressure is constant when the amount of aqueous humor drained off through Schlemm's canal per unit time exactly equals that produced by the ciliary body. When the production rate is normal but the outflow is restricted, the intraocular pressure rises. A pathological increase in intraocular pressure is called **glaucoma**. In chronic glaucoma (glaucoma simplex) the mechanically weakest part of the wall of the eye – the lamina cribrosa – bulges **outward,** damaging the blood supply of the optic nerve fibers. In an attack of **acute glaucoma** ("narrow-angle glaucoma") the iridocorneal angle becomes blocked, the intraocular pressure rises sharply and blood flow through the retina is impaired. As a consequence of the reduced blood flow, the retina can suffer temporary or permanent damage, with blindness.
The elastic forces in the iris are transmitted to the iridocorneal angle (Fig. 11-5) in such a way that when the iris is stretched (the pupil constricted) the trabecular meshwork and Schlemm's canal are expanded. For this reason drugs that cause pupil constriction increase the rate of aqueous-humor outflow, and those that expand the pupil (e.g. atropine) reduce it. Thus when glaucoma is suspected, pupil-dilating medications are to be strictly avoided.

Tonometry. Intraocular pressure can be determined indirectly by measuring the degree to which the cornea is indented by a stylus of specified diameter and weight **(impression tonometry)** or by measuring the force required to flatten a small area of the corneal surface **(applanation tonometry)**. The intraocular pressure is considered to be pathologically high when it is above 20 mm Hg (2.66 kPa) in repeated measurements. In an attack of acute glaucoma it can exceed 60 mm Hg (8 kPa) [30, 37].

11.3 Signal Reception and Processing in the Retina

During embryonic development the retina is formed by evagination of the floor of the diencephalon; it is therefore **part of the brain.** In the vertebrate eye the layer containing the receptor cells (rods and cones) is furthest from the vitreous body, in close mechanical and functional contact with the **cells of the pigment epithelium**; these in turn are adjacent to the vascular system of the choroid, so that they are an important route for the receptor-cell metabolites. The receptors are separated from the vitreous body by the layers of horizontal cells, bipolar cells, amacrines and ganglion cells (Fig. 11-13). **The mechanically weakest part of the retina** is the boundary between the pigment epithelium and the outer segments of the photoreceptors; the retina can easily become detached here. *In a detached region of the retina the outer segments of the receptors degenerate.* Vision is no longer possible with this part of the retina. If therapeutic measures are taken to restore permanent contact with the pigment epithelium before it is too late, the outer segments **regenerate** and vision, too, can be restored.

The Duplicity Theory of Vision

Adjustment to the widely varying environmental light levels is assisted by the presence of two retinal receptor systems with different absolute thresholds (**duplicity theory**). At twilight and by starlight one sees with the **rods** of the retina (**scotopic** vision), and by day with the **cones** (**photopic** vision). In scotopic vision no colors are perceived. Though the objects seen on a clear night are colorless, they differ in brightness. In photopic vision both the color and the brightness of an object can be discriminated. The spectral sensitivity of the eye has a maximum at about 500 nm for scotopic vision, and at 555 nm for photopic vision (Fig. 11-4). The transition between scotopic and photopic vision is called mesopic vision; in the mesopic region limited color vision is possible [12].

The Transduction Process in Vision

Structure of the photoreceptors. In the human eye the receptor layer consists of ca. 120 million rods and 6 million cones (Fig. 11-13). The receptor density (number of receptors per unit area) is highest in the middle of the fovea in the case of the cones, whereas the rod density is greatest in the parafoveal region. There are no rods in the fovea centralis. Rods and cones are similar in structure in that each has an outer segment consisting of about a thousand membranous disks (rods) or infoldings of the membrane (cones). The outer segment is joined to the remainder of the cell by a narrow cilium (Fig. 11-14A,B). Seen in cross section, the outer segments of the photoreceptors form a regular mosaic pattern. In the middle of the fovea the diameter of the cone outer segments is about 2 μm, which corresponds to a visual angle of about 0.4 minutes

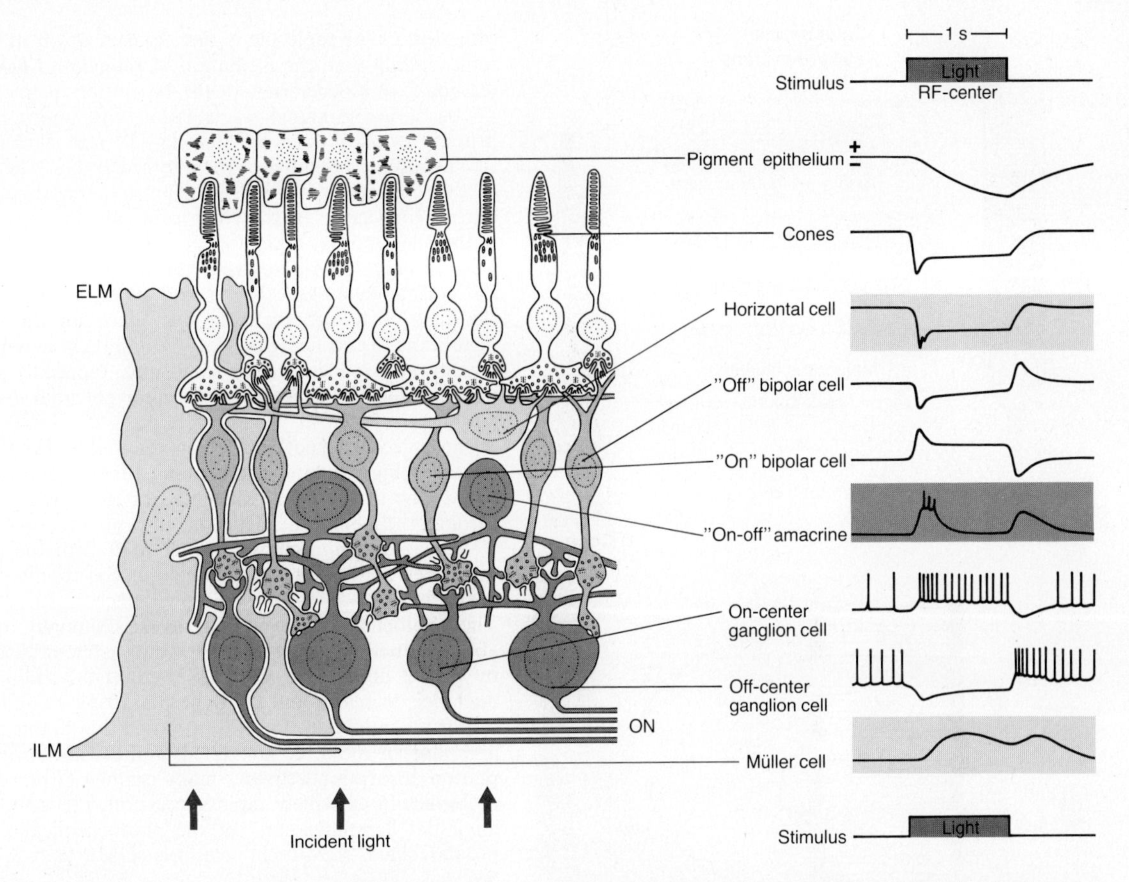

Fig.11-13. Structure of the primate retina [redrawn schematically from an illustration by BOYCOTT and DOWLING, Proc. Roy. Soc. (Lond.) *166*, 80 (1966)] and diagram of the responses of single neurons in the retina to a light stimulus [GRÜSSER, Fortschr. Ophthalmol. *80*, 502 (1983)]. ELM: external limiting membrane; ILM: internal limiting membrane; ON: axons of the optic nerve. Horizontal cells make additional contacts with bipolars that are not shown

of arc. The diameter of the cone outer segments increases from the fovea to the periphery of the retina.

Visual pigments. The molecules of the visual pigments are very regularly embedded in the lipid bilayer of the membranous disks of the outer segments (Fig. 11-14). A solution of the visual pigment of the rods (rhodopsin, or "visual purple") prepared in the dark looks red, because rhodopsin absorbs green and blue light especially strongly. This property can be measured exactly by determining the **spectral absorption curve** of the visual pigment. Rhodopsin has 2 absorption maxima, one in the visible region at about 500 nm and the other in the ultraviolet, at about 350 nm.

The absorption curves of the visual pigments of single photoreceptors have been measured by **microspectrophotometry**. Under microscopic control a very small pencil of light is projected through the isolated outer segments of the photoreceptors in a piece of retina excised during surgery, and highly sensitive photocells are used to measure the light absorbed at different wavelengths (Fig. 11-15). The results are as follows:

(i) The visual pigments of the rods and cones have different spectral absorption curves.

(ii) The absorption curve for the rods corresponds to that of rhodopsin, and closely approximates the spectral sensitivity of scotopic vision (Fig. 11-4). Rhodopsin consists of a glycoprotein (opsin) and a chromophore group, 11-cis-retinal, the aldehyde of Vitamin A (retinol).

(iii) There are **3 types of cones** differing in their visual pigments (Fig. 11-15).

Bleaching and regeneration of the visual pigments following light absorption. The **transduction process** in vision begins with the absorption of a photon in the π-electron region of the conjugated double bonds of the rhodopsin molecule. As a result, the molecule is raised to a higher energy level and oscillates more strongly. With a probability ("quantum efficiency") of 0.5–0.65, **stereoisomerization** of the 11-cis-retinal occurs, a transition from the 11-cis form to the all-

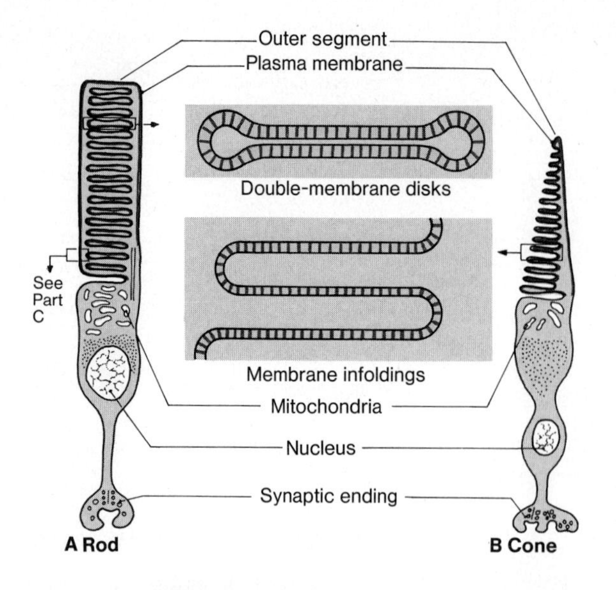

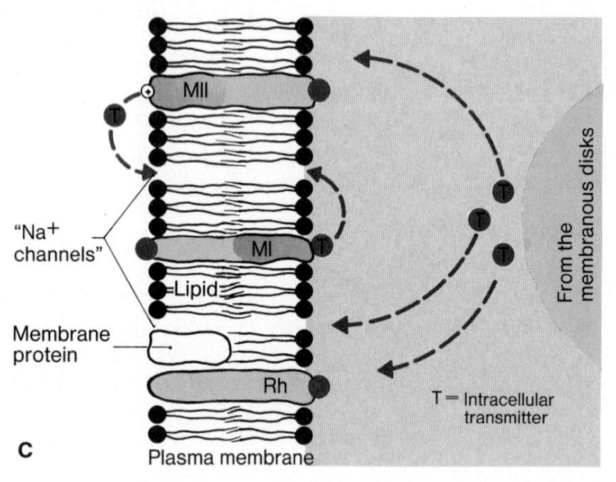

Fig. 11-14 A–C. Diagram of the stucture of a rod **(A)** and a cone **(B)** in the vertebrate retina, with enlarged diagrams of the membrane of the disks in the outer segments of the rods, and of the membranous infoldings in the outer segments of the cones. Diagram of the structure of the disk or plasma membrane of photoreceptors **(C)**. MI, metarhodopsin I; MII, metarhodopsin II

trans form. The molecule is then broken down in several steps, ending with the formation of **retinol** and **opsin** (see textbooks of biochemistry or the 1st edition of this book). To be of use in signal transmission, this photochemical primary process must be "converted" into a change in the membrane potential of the photoreceptors. The details of this conversion are still in debate. In one hypothesis, during conversion of the rhodopsin calcium ions bound in the membranous disks are "activated". These Ca^{2+} ions were thought to diffuse from the membranous disks to the plasma membrane of the rod outer segments or, in the case of the cones, from one place on the plasma membrane to another (Fig. 11-14C), and there to **reduce** the membrane conductance for small ions, especially sodium ions, producing the **secondary receptor potential** discussed below.

A more recent hypothesis is based on the idea that the relatively high sodium conductance of the outer-segment membrane in the dark, which causes the "dark current" through the membrane, depends on an interaction of cyclic 3′-5′-guanidinemonophosphate (cGMP) with the protein molecules at the sodium channels of the receptor membrane. cGMP causes the sodium channels to stay "open". The photochemical primary process is thought to bring about reduction of the cGMP within a few milliseconds, by way of an enzyme chain. As a result the sodium conductance decreases and the hyperpolarizing secondary receptor potential appears. It is proposed that in this process a rhodopsin molecule converted to metarhodopsin II by photon absorption activates many enzyme ("transducin") molecules in extremely rapid succession; this amounts to an initial "amplification" of the photochemical primary process, since "transducin" controls cGMP [4, 5, 8, 34, 46, 53, 56a].

The primary receptor potential of photoreceptors and the photochemical components of light-dark adaptation. The conformational change of the rhodopsin molecules causes an electrical potential with very short latency (< 1 ms), the **primary receptor potential** (*early receptor potential*, ERP; Fig. 11-16). It has various components, which can be isolated by cooling the retina by different amounts. When the visual pigment has been broken down to retinol and opsin, rhodopsin is resynthesized in a chain of energy-consuming, enzyme-catalyzed reactions. With a constant photon flux onto the retina, an *equilibrium* is reached between the light-induced bleaching of the visual pigment and its enzymatically controlled regeneration. This *dynamic* equi-

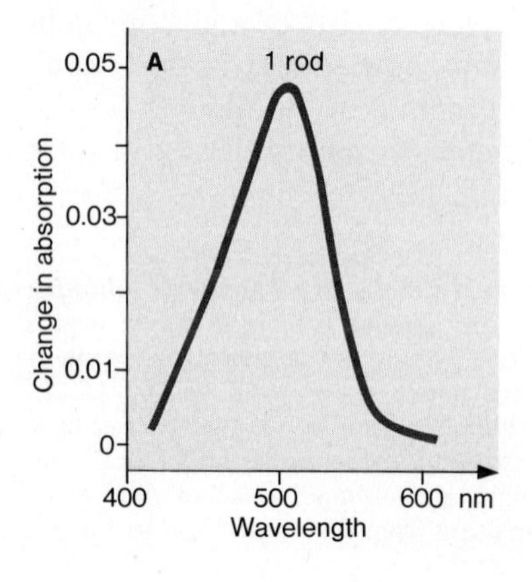

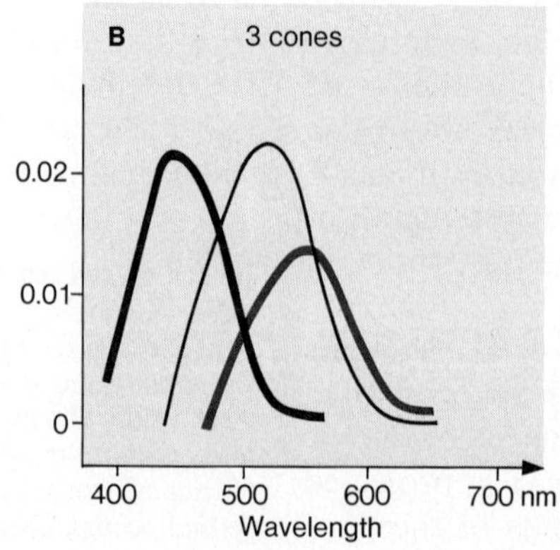

Fig. 11-15. Results of microspectrophotometric measurements of the spectral absorption of single receptors in the human retina (specimens from operations). The curves represent difference spectra (i.e., the difference in spectral absorption before and after bleaching). Three types of cone can be distinguished. [Schematized from BROWN and WALD, Science *144*, 45 (1964)]

librium is shifted to higher rhodopsin concentrations, the less light is incident on the retina. This is the *photochemical part* of a process familiar to everyone, the *dark adaptation* of the eye (see pp. 265–266). During dark adaptation, the amplitude of the ERPs elicited by constant-intensity light stimuli rises, because there is a greater probability that the incident photons will strike unbleached rhodopsin molecules [8].

The secondary receptor potential. Whereas the ERP is produced by a synchronous change in conformation of the visual-pigment molecules, the secondary receptor potential (*late receptor potential,* LRP) – which is not directly coupled to the ERP – is a change in the membrane potential of the photoreceptors. This membrane potential, −25 to −40 mV in the dark, is **hyperpolarized** under illumination. The amplitude of this receptor potential increases with the intensity of the light stimulus (Fig. 11-17). The secondary receptor potential of the rods rises more slowly than that of the cones; that is, the rod system has a greater temporal inertia than the cone system (p. 257). The difference in spectral sensitivity of the secondary receptor potentials of the various types of cones (Fig. 11-18) confirms the results of microspectrophotometry and supports the **trichromatic theory of color vision** (p. 269) – i.e., there are three cone types, with different spectral sensitivities. The spectral sensitivity of the receptor potentials of the rods corresponds approximately to the spectral absorption curve of rhodopsin, with a maximum at ca. 500 nm.
The receptor potential of vertebrate photoreceptors differs from those of all other receptors in that the adequate stimulus (light) produces hyperpolarization rather than depolarization.
The amplitude A of the secondary receptor potential is related to stimulus intensity I_s (number of photons incident per unit time and area on the retina) as follows (Fig. 11-17 B,C):

$$A = \frac{\alpha I_s}{1 + k \cdot I_s} \text{ [mV]} \tag{9}$$

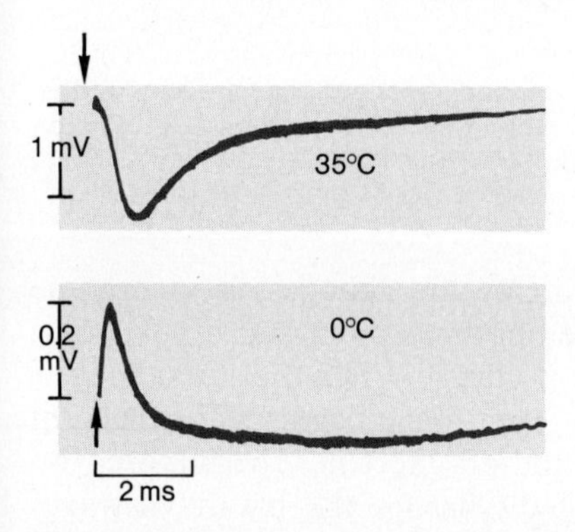

Fig. 11-16. Early receptor potential (ERP) of the ground squirrel, recorded at two different temperatures (modified from PAK and EBREY: J. gen. Physiol. *49* (1966)). The amplitude of the various components of the ERP rises about in proportion to the logarithm of the light-flash intensity over 2–3 $\log_{10}$ units. The brief light flashes are indicated by arrows

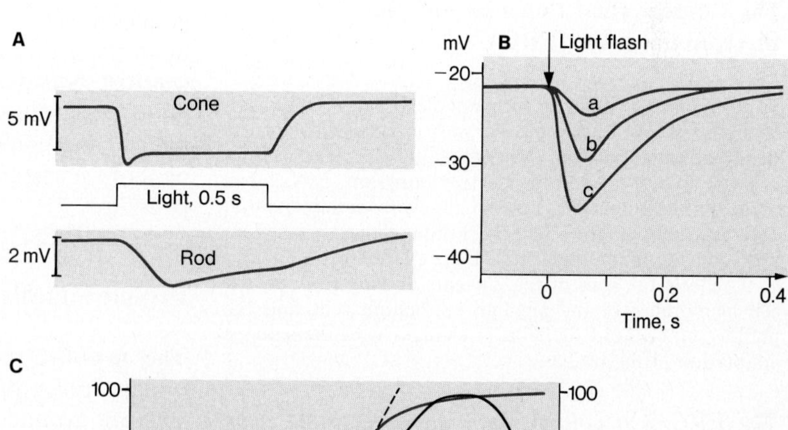

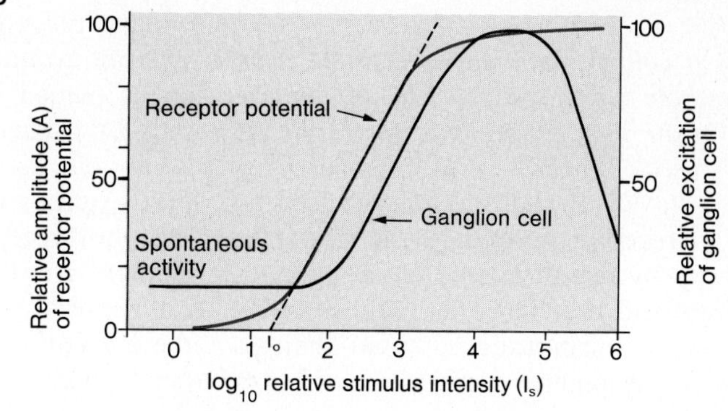

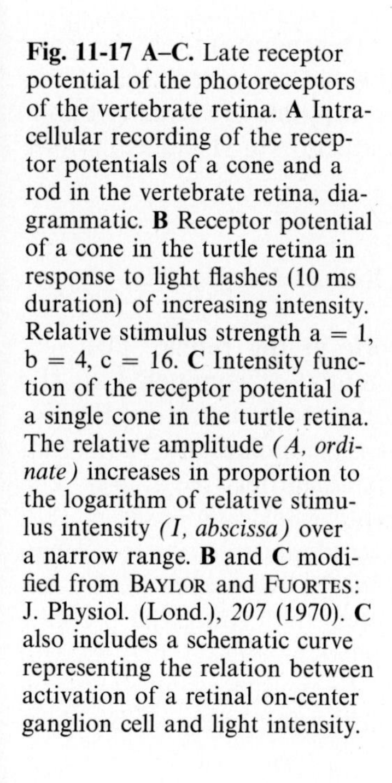

Fig. 11-17 A–C. Late receptor potential of the photoreceptors of the vertebrate retina. **A** Intracellular recording of the receptor potentials of a cone and a rod in the vertebrate retina, diagrammatic. **B** Receptor potential of a cone in the turtle retina in response to light flashes (10 ms duration) of increasing intensity. Relative stimulus strength a = 1, b = 4, c = 16. **C** Intensity function of the receptor potential of a single cone in the turtle retina. The relative amplitude *(A, ordinate)* increases in proportion to the logarithm of relative stimulus intensity *(I, abscissa)* over a narrow range. **B** and **C** modified from BAYLOR and FUORTES: J. Physiol. (Lond.), *207* (1970). **C** also includes a schematic curve representing the relation between activation of a retinal on-center ganglion cell and light intensity.

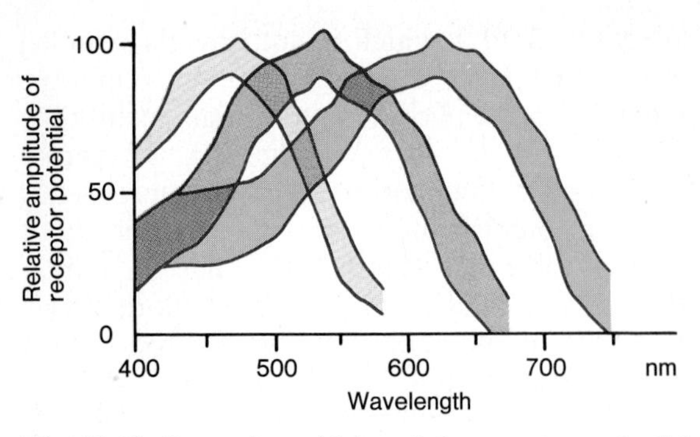

Fig. 11-18. Spectral sensitivity of the receptor potentials of the fish retina. Means (with standard deviation) of measurements from three different classes of cones are shown (Modified from [61])

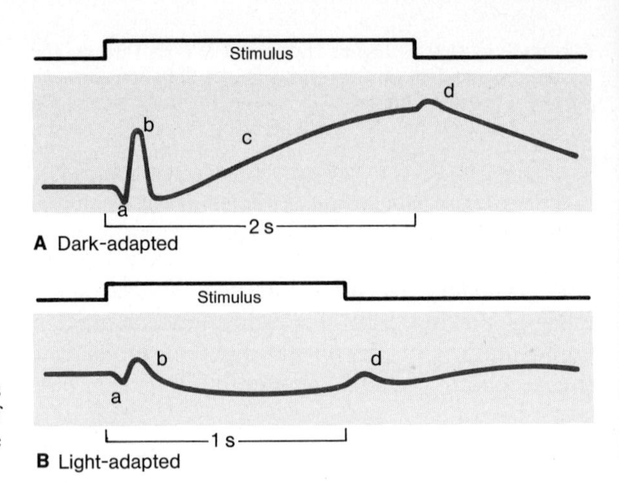

Fig. 11-19. Electroretinograms of the human retina. Schematized from recordings of HANITZSCH et al. [Vision Res. *6*, 245 (1966)]

For the intermediate intensity range, this hyperbolic equation ("Hering's law") can be approximated by a logarithmic function that is known as the **Weber-Fechner law** in sensory physiology (see p. 186):

$$A = k^* \log I_s/I_o \ [mV] \qquad (10)$$

where I_o is a **threshold stimulus intensity** dependent on the state of excitation. The constants α, k and k^* in Eqs. (9) and (10) change as a function of the wavelength of monochromatic light; this relation corresponds approximately to the spectral sensitivity of the receptor potentials (Fig. 11-18) [8, 36].

The Corneoretinal Potential and the Electroretinogram (ERG)

Two functionally different forms of electrical potential can be recorded from the whole eye with macroelectrodes: the **steady potential** between the cornea and the retina (retina negative to cornea) and the **electroretinogram** (ERG). The corneoretinal potential is derived largely from the potential difference between the sclera side of the pigment epithelium cells and the inner segments of the photoreceptors; that is, it reflects the sum of the currents flowing through the cell membranes of the pigment epithelium cells and the photoreceptors, and therefore it changes with the state of adaptation of the retina.

The ERG is a voltage fluctuation recorded from the eye as a whole, which is elicited by an increase or decrease in the light falling onto the retina. It consists of several "waves": a, b, c, and d (Fig. 11-19). The a-wave is thought to be produced by summation of receptor potentials, the slower b-wave primarily by membrane-potential changes in the bipolars and the glial cells (Müller cells), and the c-wave by membrane-potential changes in the cells of the pigment epithelium. The d-wave is the sum of the changes in membrane potential of the photoreceptors and bipolar cells at "light off" (off-effect). When the stimulus lasts more than 0.3 s, the c-wave begins while the light is still on and the off-effect is superimposed on it. With brief light flashes the b- and d-waves coincide [8, 10].

A **pattern-reversal ERG** is measured when the eye is seeing a pattern in which light and dark are periodically exchanged (e.g., by reversing the light and dark squares of a checkerboard pattern on a TV screen). The mean luminance of such a stimulus is constant; therefore the pattern-reversal ERG is mainly produced by the retinal ganglion cells, the neuronal elements with a particularly strong response to *contrast changes* and *contrast boundaries*. Degeneration of the ganglion cells causes the pattern-reversal ERG to vanish; the clinical symptoms are usually blindness or an extreme reduction in visual acuity (see p. 265).

Receptive Fields of Retinal Neurons

The neuronal network in the retina. The secondary receptor potential is conducted to the synaptic contacts of the receptors, where the signal is passed on to the bipolar and horizontal cells by a chemical transmitter (see p. 43). The latter cells have **receptive fields** (RF; see p. 182) that extend over several photoreceptors. When the photoreceptors in the **RF-center** of the **on-bipolars** are illuminated, they cause the bipolar-cell membrane to *depolarize* (Fig. 11-13). Around the RF-center is the **RF-periphery**; illumination here causes hyperpolarization of the on-bipolars.

This *hyperpolarization* is brought about indirectly, by way of the contacts between horizontal cells and bipolars or by a feedback loop between horizontal cells and cone synaptic vesicles.

Horizontal cells, as a rule, have a relatively extensive receptive field. They are functionally connected with one another. Some of them, the *L-horizontal cells*, are hyperpolarized by light in their RF regardless of its spectral composition. Other horizontal cells are either depolarized or hyperpolarized by light, depending on its location in the visible spectrum (color-specific *red-green* or *blue-yellow horizontal cells*; p. 273).

The **off-bipolar cells** are hyperpolarized by light in their RF-center and depolarized by light in the RF-periphery (Fig. 11-13). *The retina contains approximately equal numbers of on- and off-bipolars.* The functional organization of the bipolar-cell layer is based on the two most important principles of neuronal signal processing for vision:

(i) Excitation of the photoreceptors by photons is signalled to the CNS by two separate neuronal "channels": the **on-system**, activated when the light stimulus in the RF-center is stronger than that in the surround or than the preceding stimulus in the center, and the **off-system**, activated by a reduction in illumination.

(ii) The receptive fields of many bipolar cells are organized **antagonistically**; that is, **opposite reactions** are elicited by light stimuli, depending on whether they are in the center or periphery of the RF. This spatial organization of the RF is produced in two ways: by the convergence of signals from several receptors onto a single bipolar cell, and by indirect (inhibitory) signals from the RF-periphery that reach the bipolars by way of the horizontal cells (lateral inhibition, p. 185).

This principle of **signal convergence** plus **lateral inhibition** is repeated at the next level of retinal signal processing (ganglion cells, amacrines; Fig. 11-13). As a rule, several on-bipolars ("direct" excitation) and off-bipolars ("direct" inhibition) converge onto one on-center ganglion cell, whereas considerably more bipolar cells are indirectly connected to a ganglion cell by way of their contacts with the amacrines, forming the **RF-periphery** of this ganglion cell (lateral on-inhibition, lateral off-excitation). The off-center ganglion cells receive excitatory inputs from the off-bipolars, direct inhibitory inputs from the on-bipolars (RF-center) and "lateral" inhibitory contacts from the off-amacrines and, finally, lateral excitation from amacrines excited by on-bipolars [11, 17, 18, 33, 49].

Classes of Retinal Ganglion Cells

Three major classes of retinal ganglion cells have been found in the mammalian retina, by stimulation with **achromatic** light. Two of these have been mentioned above; their receptive fields are antagonistically organized. The **on-center ganglion cells** become depolarized in response to illumination of the RF-center, and at the axon hillock this depolarization is converted to a train of action potentials (all-or-none law, see p. 23; Figs. 11-13, 11-20). On the other hand, both illumination of the RF-periphery and "light off" in the RF-center cause **hyperpolarization** of the membrane potential and hence a transient inhibition of neuronal activity. When center and periphery of the RF are illuminated **simultaneously**, the response to the center dominates; however, the activation is less than that caused by illuminating the RF-center alone, because the excitation from the center and the inhibition from the periphery summate (Fig. 11-20).

The receptive fields of the **off-center ganglion cells** are functionally opposite to those of the on-center ganglion cells; illumination in the center causes "direct" inhibition, and reduction of the light in the center causes "off-activation". Illumination of the RF-periphery produces lateral

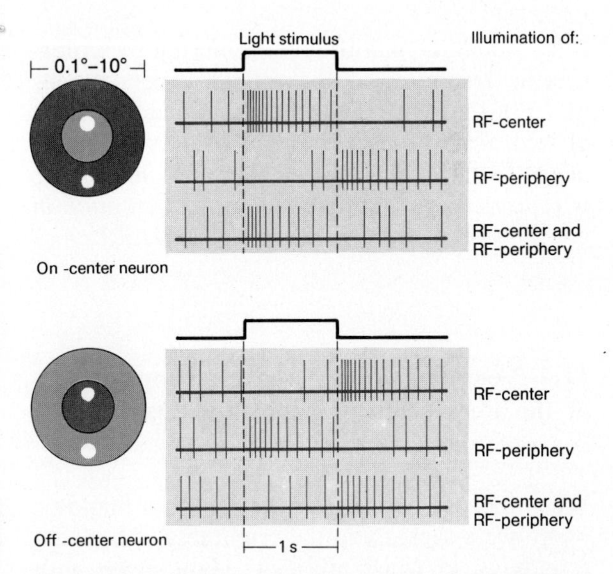

Fig. 11-20. Functional organization of receptive fields of the ganglion cells in the mammalian retina. For analysis of the receptive fields spots of light (shown in *white*) are projected into either the RF-center or the RF-periphery. Light stimuli elicit different responses of the on-center and off-center neurons. When both parts of the receptive field are illuminated simultaneously, the excitatory and inhibitory processes associated with illumination of the center and periphery summate. However, the response elicited by stimulation of the RF-center predominates

activation, whereas "light off" in the periphery results in a transient "lateral" inhibition of the neuronal discharge rate. During simultaneous illumination of center and periphery these effects summate, with the inhibition and off-activation associated with the center dominating, as a rule (Fig. 11-20).
The **on-off ganglion cells** usually give a brief on-response to a stationary light stimulus and a brief off-response to a reduction in light intensity. This class of ganglion cells includes, e.g., the **movement-sensitive neurons**, which are particularly responsive to a light-dark edge that moves through the receptive field; the degree of activation depends on the angular velocity of the stimulus.

Another classification of ganglion cells is based on the **conduction velocity** of their axons. Most of the larger ganglion cells, which have relatively thick, myelinated axons that conduct at high velocity (see p. 38), give a brief *"phasic"* response to illumination of the receptive field (neurons of Latency Class I, or **Y-neurons**). The smaller and much more numerous ganglion cells with somewhat thinner myelinated axons usually respond with *"tonic"* excitation or inhibition to a light in the RF-center (neurons of Latency Class II, or **X-neurons**). Among the X and Y neurons, on-center and off-center ganglion cells are about equally common. Finally, the retina contains ganglion cells with thin, only slightly myelinated axons (Latency Class III, or **W-neurons**); movement-sensitive neurons of the on-off system are predominantly in this class.

It is evident, even without considering the color-specific responses of the retinal ganglion cells (p. 273), that the retina is a complicated system of neurons. *Within the retina itself, the optical image that excites the receptors in the input layer is converted to a multiple pattern of excitation in ganglion cells of different types* [10, 49, 52].

11.4 Neurophysiology and Psychophysics of the Perception of Light and Dark

When a cloud passes over the sun on a fine day, we notice a decrease in the brightness of our surroundings, to which we soon **adapt**. Even with a hundredfold change in the light intensity, the perceived relative lightness or darkness and the colors of the surrounding objects change only slightly. In photopic vision contrast and color vision are relatively independent of mean luminance; that is to say, the appearance of an object is determined by the reflectance of its surfaces and not by the absolute intensity of the light reflected from it. This mechanism is important for the phenomenal constancy of our visual world.
When a circumscribed area of the retina in a **constant** state of adaptation is illuminated, there is an approximately logarithmic relation between the perceived **subjective brightness** of the light spot and its **luminance** (Eqs. 9, 10). Microelectrode recordings have demonstrated that the same relation applies to the discharge rate of the on-center neurons (Fig. 11-17C). The discharge rate of off-center neurons is also approximately a function of the logarithm of the preceding negative intensity step, at "light off". *In general there is a linear correlation between subjective brightness and the mean discharge rate of neurons in the on-system, and between subjective darkness and the mean discharge rate of neurons in the off-system.* With this simple **correlation rule** for neuronal activation and perception, a number of elementary phenomena in vision can be explained.

Neurophysiological Basis of Simultaneous Contrast

We now come to the first example of correlation between visual perception and the activation of neurons in the on- and off-systems. A gray field on a white background appears darker than the same field on a black background (Fig. 11-21). Along the light-dark boundary the light part seems somewhat lighter and the dark part, somewhat darker than the areas further from the boundary (border contrast, Mach band). The functional organization of the RF of retinal ganglion cells offers an explanation of this simple example of simultaneous contrast, as illustrated in Fig. 11-22. Simultaneous contrast is an important mechanism, which provides partial functional compensation of the physiological errors of the dioptric apparatus described on p. 245–246, and thereby improves visual acuity [35].

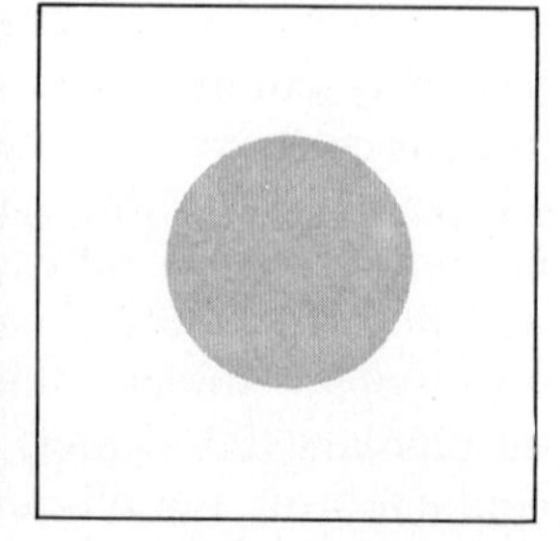

Fig. 11-21. Patterns demonstrating visual simultaneous contrast

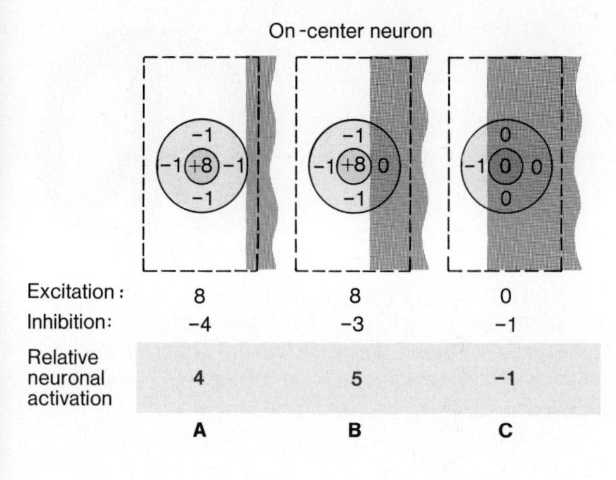

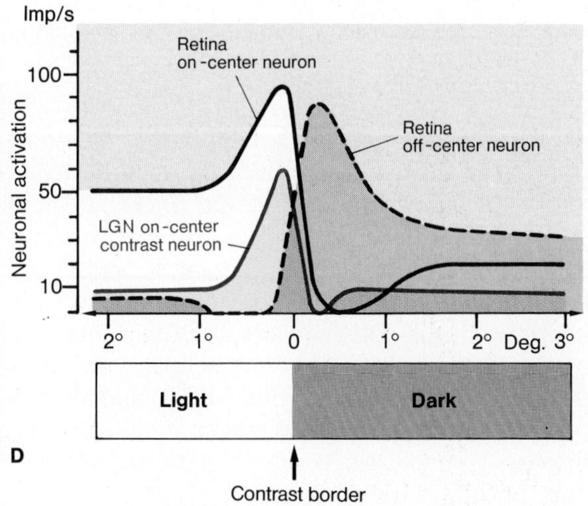

Fig. 11-22 A–D. Diagram of the mechanisms underlying simultaneous contrast. **A–C** The activation of an on-center neuron depends on the position of a light/dark boundary within the RF. The maximal activation is produced at Position **B**, where the light/dark boundary coincides with the boundary between RF-center and RF-periphery. The numbers indicate relative excitation, neglecting spontaneous discharge. **D** Dependence of the activation of visual neurons on the position of a light/dark boundary in the receptive field (abscissa). The schematized curves represent the responses of retinal on-center and off-center neurons and of on-center contrast neurons in the lateral geniculate nucleus.

The Change in Visual Acuity and in Organization of the Receptive Fields When Environmental Luminance Changes

Everyone knows from experience that visual acuity decreases from the center of the field of view to the periphery, and that it is much worse in scotopic vision than in photopic vision. *Within the photopic region visual acuity decreases when the mean luminance of the surroundings is reduced:*

You can read this small print only if you fixate it directly while enough light is falling on the book.

The dependence of contrast perception and visual acuity upon mean luminance can be explained by a change in the RF-organization of retinal ganglion cells (Fig. 11-23). The threshold of the direct excitatory process (excitation by way of the RF-center) is evidently at a lower light intensity than that of the lateral inhibitory processes, but the efficacy of the latter increases more rapidly than that of the excitatory processes as luminance increases. When the spatial organization of the RF is constructed as the sum of the excitatory and inhibitory processes, as in Fig. 11-23, one finds that the diameter of the functional RF-center becomes smaller when the mean luminance increases. From the ratio of the numbers of receptors and ganglion cells (on average about 125:1) it is evident that the average **signal convergence** from the receptor layer to the ganglion cells is quite pronounced. For the region of the fovea centralis, however, there is considerably less convergence. The adjustment of signal convergence and lateral inhibition in the fovea region in optimal lighting permits a degree of visual acuity here that is very close to the theoretical limit set by the spatial mosaic of the cone array – 0.5 minutes of arc, which corresponds roughly to the diameter of the outer segments of the foveal cones.
A decrease in visual acuity is not the only disadvantage of inadequate lighting – of a book one is reading, or of a workroom. Because of the *apparent* blurring of the image, reflexes to improve accommodation are triggered (p. 245), and are of course ineffective. When such demands are continually made upon the accommodation system, headaches can easily result. It is therefore worthwhile to ensure appropriate lighting of the workplace, avoiding intermittent light sources.

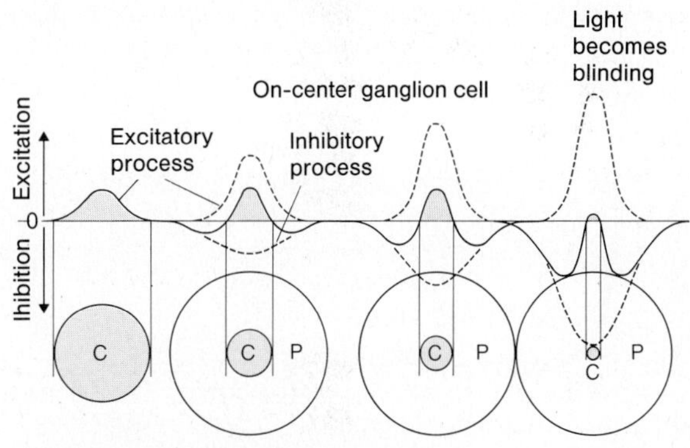

Fig 11-23. The spatial organization of the receptive field of an "on" ganglion cell can be explained by superposition of the spatial distributions of an excitatory and an inhibitory process. The excitation has a lower threshold than the inhibition. As luminance is raised in the above-threshold region, if inhibition increases more than excitation the result is a functional reduction of the RF-center. With very strong lights, which are perceived as dazzling, inhibition predominates; the light response of the "on" ganglion cell is inhibited and visual shape perception is impaired. In optimal light adaptation the RF-center is smallest and hence visual acuity is greatest [from GRÜSSER, Fortschr. Ophthalmol. *80*, 502 (1983)]

Light-Dark Adaptation, Afterimages, Effects of Glare

When the average ambient illumination changes, the sensitivity of the eyes adjusts to the altered conditions. At night, a person who steps outdoors from a brightly lit room at first cannot see the objects in his dark surroundings, but after a while he can at least discern their outlines.

During **dark adaptation** there is a slow increase in the **absolute sensitivity** of the visual system, but in the dark-adapted state visual acuity is always considerably less than in daylight vision. The time course of dark adaptation can be found by repeated measurements of the threshold light intensity (Fig. 11-24). The slow rate of adaptation is well matched to the gradual dimming of the ambient light during the evening twilight. As dark adaptation proceeds, the rod system becomes considerably more sensitive than the cone system. After a long time (> 45 min) in complete darkness the **absolute threshold** of vision becomes as low as ca. 1-4 photons per receptor per second. Under scotopic conditions of adaptation one can see weak light stimuli better with the parafoveal retina than with the fovea. Therefore a dim star is visible only when its image falls onto the parafoveal region of the retina; it "disappears" when one tries to fixate it.

In animals well adapted to nocturnal life the sensitivity of the dark-adapted retina is increased 5- to 20-fold by a layer of reflecting cells (the **tapetum lucidum**) between the pigment epithelium cells and the blood vessels of the choroid. The tapetum reflects the photons that pass through the receptor layer back to the receptors. Its pigment is yellowish-green, which causes the green glow of the eyes of cats and foxes in the beam from automobile headlights.

The inverse of dark adaptation, called **light adaptation**, is considerably more rapid. When a dark-adapted person enters a brightly lit room, his visual system adjusts to the new ambient illumination within a few seconds. If there is a very large change in illumination, the eyes may be temporarily **dazzled**, with a reduction in form perception [8, 13, 16, 25].

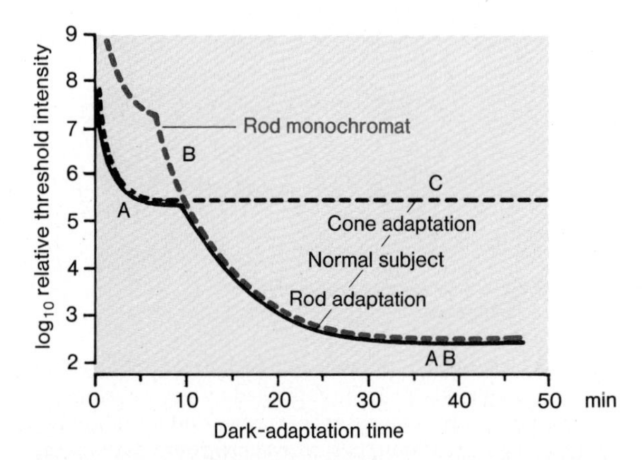

Fig. 11-24. Human dark-adaptation curve. (A) Curve of the means for 9 normal subjects. (B) Dark-adaptation curve of a completely color-blind person, measured for the part of the retina 8° above the fovea centralis. (C) Dark-adaptation curve for the cone system of a subject with normal color vision (fovea, red light stimulus). For curve (B) the time axis (abscissa) should be shifted to the right by 2 min. (A and B drawn from data of E. AUERBACH, Vision Research Laboratory, Jerusalem, 1973)

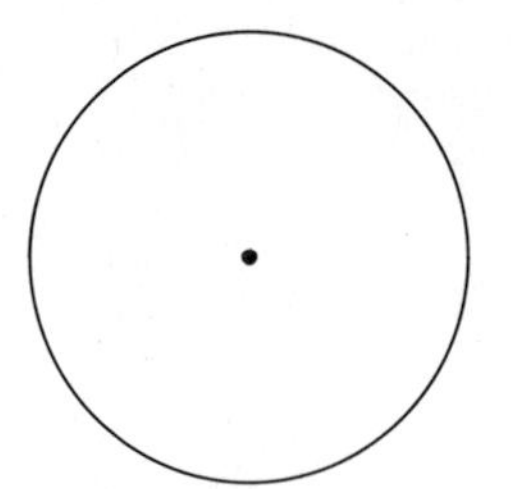

Fig. 11-25. Patterns to demonstrate afterimage production. When one fixates the center of the geometric figure on the right for ca. 30 s and then looks at the center of the circle on the left, one sees a negative afterimage of the right-hand figure

Mechanisms of light-dark adaptation. In addition to the shifted equilibrium between bleached and unbleached pigment in the photoreceptors (p. 250), light/dark adaptation also involves crucial neuronal mechanisms. Vision is "switched" from the cone system to the rod system by the horizontal cells. Furthermore, the functional size of the RF centers of retinal neurons increases during dark adaptation (Fig. 11-23), and the dependence of **pupil size** on mean ambient intensity, discussed on p. 244, is also a neuronal component of light/dark adaptation.

Local adaptation and afterimages. Local adaptation occurs when circumscribed areas on the retina are illuminated at different intensities, even though the **average** ambient luminance is constant. After the center of the geometrical pattern in Fig. 11-25 has been fixated for ca. 30 s, if the gaze is shifted to a white or gray background a **negative afterimage** appears for several seconds. In the negative afterimage what was light in the original pattern appears dark, and what was dark appears light. Those parts of the retina on which the image of the dark parts of the pattern lay have become more sensitive than the nearby regions corresponding to the light parts of the image during the fixation period.

Afterimages persist for a long time when a retinal area has been illuminated strongly or for a sufficiently long period. Local adaptation to **colored stimulus patterns** produces afterimages in the **complementary color** (see p. 271):

"As I entered an inn toward evening, and a buxom maid with a dazzling white face, black hair and scarlet bodice came into my room and stood at a little distance from me, I gazed at her intently in the half-light. Then when she

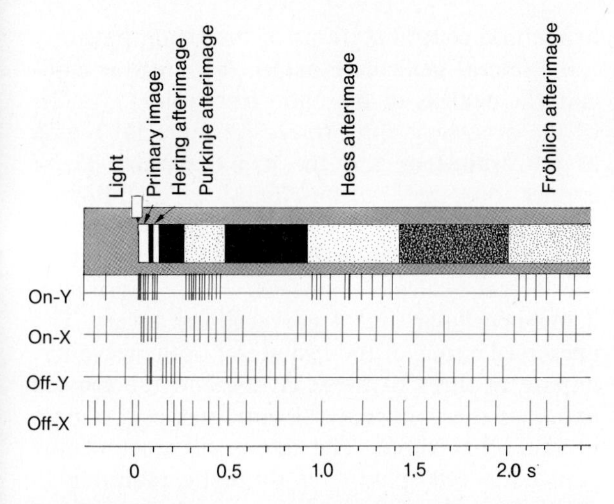

Fig. 11-26. Diagram to illustrate the correlation between the phasic afterimages that follow brief light flashes and the neuronal activity of retinal ganglion cells. The on-center neurons (On-Y and On-X) are activated during the primary image and the periodic bright afterimages, and the off-center cells discharge during the dark phases between the afterimages. (Modified from [51])

moved away I saw on the white wall opposite me a black face surrounded by a bright glow, and the clothing of the completely distinct figure appeared a beautiful sea-green" (Goethe, *Zur Farbenlehre*, I, 52).

After exposure to brief flashes of light one perceives a rapid succession of positive (light) **periodic afterimages** separated by negative (dark) periods. The periodicity of the afterimages can be observed particularly well by watching a narrow, moving bar of light. Activation of the on-center and off-center ganglion cells in the retina is closely correlated with the afterimage periodicity (Fig. 11-26). Periodic activation is brought about in part by signal feedback within the retina, by way of the **interplexiform cells** (Fig. 11-13) [51].

Effects of glare. Sudden strong illumination of the retina – for example, by the headlights of an oncoming car at night – can cause a positive afterimage so intense that one is **dazzled**; form vision is temporarily disrupted. Sudden dazzling triggers a **reflex lid closure** by a pathway connecting the retina to subcortical visual centers and the neurons of the facial nucleus. Severe dazzling increases tear secretion (p. 242).

Pressure Phosphenes

When a person in complete darkness deforms his eyeball by pressing a finger against it from the side, at first there is a sensation of light shining in the part of the visual field opposite the pressure site; as deformation continues, this perceived light spreads gradually over the retina, becoming mixed with moving **light nebulae** and dotted with small, bright, stationary light points. This is a monocular pressure phosphene produced by retinal deformation. Observation of these pressure phosphenes is the oldest known experiment in sensory physiology. It was first described in the 5th Century B.C., by the pre-Socratic philosopher and physician ALCMAEON of Croton. Pressure phosphenes probably arise as follows. Deformation of the eyeball stretches the horizontal cells in the retina, raising the sodium conductance of their cell membrane and hence depolarizing the horizontal cells. By way of the contacts between the horizontal and bipolar cells, the on-bipolars are thereby depolarized and the off-bipolars are hyperpolarized. As a result, the ganglion cells of the on-system are activated and those of the off-system are inhibited. In accordance with the above-mentioned correlation rule, one sees light [49].

The Temporal Properties of Transmission in the Retina

In the age of films, television and computer monitors the temporal transmission aspects of visual perception play an important role, because all these devices produce visual patterns by flashing pictures or lines of light in rapid succession; i.e., the stimuli are intermittent. The term **flicker-fusion frequency** (or critical flicker frequency, CFF) is used for the lowest frequency at which intermittent light stimuli *no longer appear to flicker*. In the range of *scotopic intensities (rod vision)* the maximal CFF is 22-25 stimuli per second. In the *photopic range* the CFF increases about in proportion to the logarithm of luminance, of the degree of modulation, and of the area stimulated, to a maximum of 80 stimuli per second. The flicker-fusion frequency of retinal ganglion cells is governed by the same laws as the subjective flicker-fusion frequency. Intermittent light stimuli in the frequency range 5-15 kHz cause particularly strong activation of retinal nerve cells and cells in the primary visual cortex. Therefore in some epileptic patients flickering light can trigger convulsions [10, 17, 18].

Many modern light sources (fluorescent lamps, television screens, computer monitors) produce intermittent light stimuli (50–120 Hz) that can cause flickering excitation of the retina when the eyes **simultaneously** move over the light source. Especially when prolonged work at a computer monitor is to be done, it is an urgent requirement that the images appear on the screen at a rate well above 100 per second; because of the saccadic shifts of the retinal image, intermittent illumination of the retina causes an **apparent** loss of acuity. The futile attempts of the accommodation system to correct this apparent error can cause headaches after one has been looking at the screen for some hours.

11.5 Signal Processing in the Central Visual System

The Central Visual Pathway

Visual information is carried to the brain by the axons of the retinal ganglion cells, which form the optic nerves. The human optic nerve consists of about 1 million myelinated, poorly myelinated and unmyelinated axons. The optic nerves of the two eyes coalesce at the base of the skull, forming the **optic chiasm** (Fig. 11-27); here the nerve fibers from the nasal half of each retina cross to the opposite side. The fibers from the temporal half of each retina continue ipsilaterally, together with the crossed axons from the contralateral optic nerve, as the **optic tract.** The optic tract leads

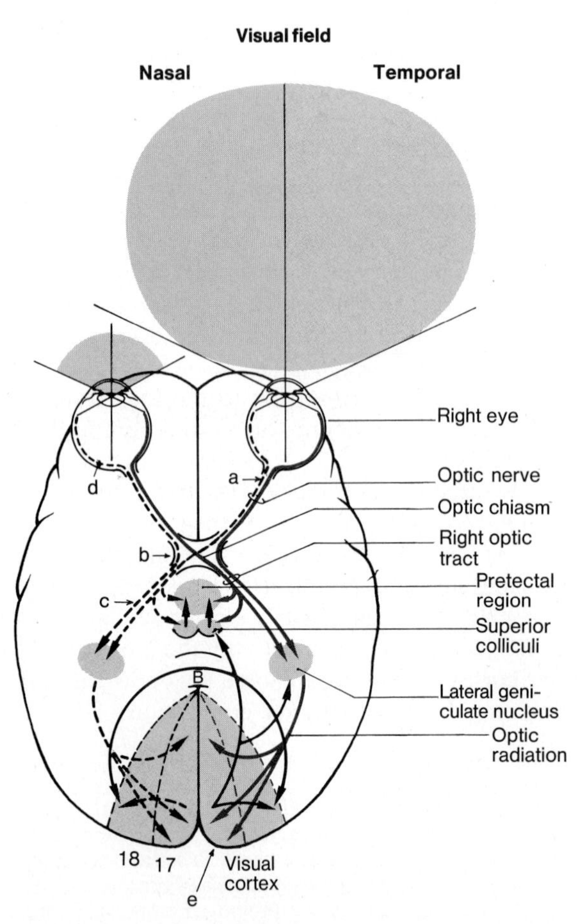

Fig. 11-27. Diagram of the visual pathway in the human brain. The efferent connections between the visual cortex and subcortical structures are shown on the right side. The visual-cortex areas on the left and right halves of the brain are connected with one another by axons running through the corpus callosum (CC). The arrows labelled with letters indicate possible sites of lesions producing the visual-field deficits shown in Fig. 11-35

to the first central stations of the visual pathway – the **lateral geniculate nuclei**, the **superior colliculi**, the **nucleus of the optic tract** (NOT), nuclei of the **accessory optic tract,** the **pretectal region of the brainstem** and the **hypothalamus.** These connections serve various functions, as follows.

(i) The most important and massive projection of the retina in humans is that linking it to the **lateral geniculate nucleus**, which consists of **2 magnocellular** and **4 parvocellular** layers. The **uncrossed** axons of the ipsilateral optic nerve terminate in three of these layers, and the **crossed** axons of the contralateral optic nerve terminate in the other three. The axons of most of the geniculate cells pass over the **optic radiation** to the nerve cells of the *primary visual cortex* (area 17 or V1 of the occipital cerebral cortex). This area is connected to the *secondary visual cortex* (area V2), the *tertiary visual cortex* (areas V3, V3a) and the *visual integration regions* in the occipitoparietal or occipitotemporal cerebral cortex; the latter are discussed below. *The projection of the visual pathway in the LGN functions in the recognition of objects, in color and movement vision, and in stereoscopic depth perception.*

(ii) The connection between retina and **hypothalamus** serves to couple the day/night alternation with the endogenous, *circadian rhythm or the sleeping/waking rhythm* (see p. 138) and to control part of the endocrine system (see p. 371). By way of connections from the hypothalamus to the epiphysis, the retina also influences skin pigmentation.

(iii) Some of the connections between the retina and the **pretectal region** serve to regulate pupil size (see p. 244).

(iv) Optic-nerve axons end on nerve cells in the *pretectal nuclei* of the *"accessory optic tract"*. The latter communicate with the gaze-control centers in the brainstem, mainly to direct the **vertical eye movements** and the **vergence movements.**

(v) The projection of the retina into the **superior colliculi** serves to control reflex eye movements by saccades. The axons of the neurons in the superior colliculi pass to the optomotor centers in the brainstem and in the visual part of the pulvinar. Visual signals passing through these thalamic stations eventually reach the *parietal visual association regions* (p. 263).

(vi) Retinal ganglion cells with axons that end on neurons in the **nucleus of the optic tract** (NOT) are predominantly movement-specific (on-off-neurons). Neurons of the NOT make connections with the vestibular nuclei of the brainstem and the inferior olive. By this route, the visual movement signals reach the central vestibular system and, by way of the olivocerebellar climbing fibers (see p. 103), the cerebellum. Both projections are involved in optomotor control, especially in horizontal OKN (p. 239). The indirect projection of the retina into the vestibular nuclei also serves for perception of one's own movement in space during locomotion [6, 17–19, 21, 60].

The Retinotopic Organization of the Visual Pathway

The principle of topological organization in the CNS, already familiar to you in the somatosensory and motor systems (see p. 216), is also realized in the neuronal representation of the retina in the brain. The afferent and much of the central visual system is characterized by **"retinotopic" organization.** Just as a certain geographical region is represented on a map, one's surroundings (or their image on the retina) are represented in a systematic way in the spatial pattern of excitation of the neurons in the cortical visual areas. In contrast to a map – with a scale, say, of 1:100,000, so that 1 cm on the map corresponds to 1 km in nature – the retinotopic projection of the retina onto the central visual system is *nonlinear: the small area of the fovea centralis is projected into a much larger region of the visual cortex than is an area of equal size in the periphery of the retina.* However, a more or less linear topological projection is obtained by considering not area but rather the *density of the cone array or of the ganglion cells in the retina,* for these decrease from the fovea to the periphery. The number of retinal ganglion cells that connect with a cortical column (cells arranged perpendicular to the surface of the brain) 1 mm^2 in diameter, for instance, is about the same for all regions of the retina. Because the foveal region has a high ganglion-cell density, the projection from the fovea occupies a relatively large part of area V1 [17, 18, 54, 56].

Signal Processing in the Lateral Geniculate Nucleus (LGN)

The lateral-geniculate neurons, like the ganglion cells in the retina, mostly have concentrically organized receptive fields. The classes of neurons in the LGN are similar to those in the retina. In some of the LGN neurons the mechanisms of simultaneous contrast are distinctly enhanced (*"contrast neurons"*); others transmit predominantly the local light/dark values in the visual stimulus pattern (*"light-dark neurons"*) or are characterized by color-specific receptive fields. The *parvocellular geniculate layers* consist chiefly of neurons with *color-specific receptive fields* (see p. 273), and the *magnocellular* layers contain neurons with contrast- and movement-sensitive receptive fields. Not only axons of the optic nerve terminate on the LGN neurons; they also receive numerous synapses from axon terminals having *cells of origin in the brainstem.* It is by these nonvisual synapses that the *degree of wakefulness, spatially directed attentiveness* and the associated *eye movements* are thought to influence visual signal processing in the LGN.

Signal Processing in the Primary Visual Cortex (V1, Area 17)

The various properties of a visual stimulus pattern – for instance, *color, contrast and movement* – are signaled *simultaneously* to the primary visual cortex (V1) by different afferent neuron systems. The axons of the optic radiation form synapses mainly on the nerve cells of the cytoarchitectonic layers IVa-c, though a few axonal collaterals run to nerve cells in the other layers (Fig. 11-28). Microelectrode recordings from the visual cortex in cats and monkeys have shown that the neurons

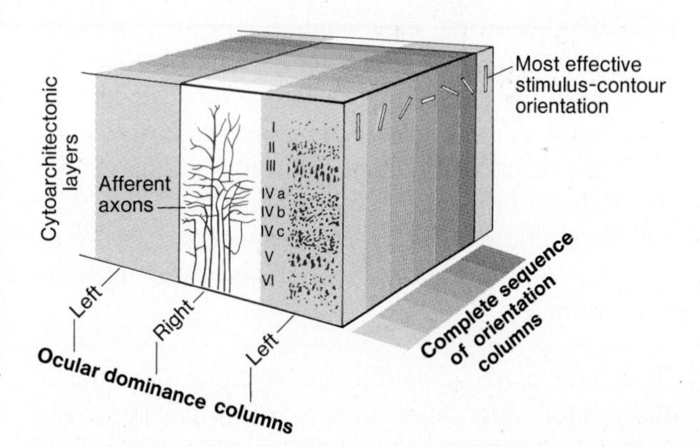

Fig. 11-28. Diagram of the "horizontal cytoarchitectonic layers" (I-VI), the ocular-dominance columns and the orientation columns in the visual cortex (area 17 = V1) of the rhesus monkey (schematized from HUBEL and WIESEL [56] and LIVINGSTON and HUBEL [57]). Within the ocular-dominance columns the orientation columns are repeated in sequence; only one complete sequence is represented here. Between the columns of nerve cells with receptive fields in which there is a preferred contour orientation, there are larger regions, also in the form of columns, in which the nerve cells have receptive fields with no preferred orientation of stimulus contours. These nerve cells respond to diffuse light stimuli, and one of their functions is color-specific signal transmission; their receptive fields are concentrically organized

of the "granular" layers IVa, b and c have predominantly **"simple"** receptive fields. They are either concentrically organized, like the receptive fields of the LGN, or they consist of on- and off-zones arranged in parallel (Fig. 11-29A). In area V1 of primates there are additional regions, within which the nerve cells of all layers contain a large amount of cytochrome oxidase and have simple, mostly concentric receptive fields. These neurons respond very well to large, diffuse light stimuli and are predominantly **color-specific** (Fig. 11-28; red-green system and blue-yellow system, see p. 273). Outside the cytochrome-oxidase-rich "blobs" the nerve cells in layers I-III and V respond particularly well to contours in certain orientations.

One aspect of functional organization, then, is the **arrangement of cells in layers parallel to the surface**. The visual cortex, like other cortical regions, also exemplifies a second *principle of geometric organization, perpendicular* to the brain surface, as follows.

(i) The receptive fields of neurons within a "cortical column" are all located in the same part of the retina. The neurons within a cortical column are coupled to one another by **interneurons**. Neurons in immediately adjacent columns have receptive fields that only partially overlap.

(ii) The neurons in a **column** about 1 mm in diameter are mainly activated either by signals from the left eye or by those from the right eye (**"ocular-dominance columns"**). In the transition zones between adjacent ocular-dominance columns are neurons that are about equally strongly activated from the left and the right eye (**binocular integration**).

(iii) The ocular-dominance columns are subdivided into "orientation columns" (Fig. 11-28). The nerve cells within such a column all have receptive fields with similar functional "axial orientations"; that is, they respond best to light/dark contours with the same spatial orientation. The RFs of neurons in adjacent "orientation columns" usually differ in preferred orientation by only about 30 degrees of arc.

(iv) There are columns containing neurons with no orientation-specific receptive fields, which nevertheless usually give color-specific responses [11, 54-57].

Examples of "Signal Selection" by Neurons of the Visual Cortex

The receptive fields of some of the neurons in areas V1 and V2 of the occipital cortex are organized on principles different from those we have encountered in the ganglion-cell layer of the retina and in the LGN neurons. Some of the

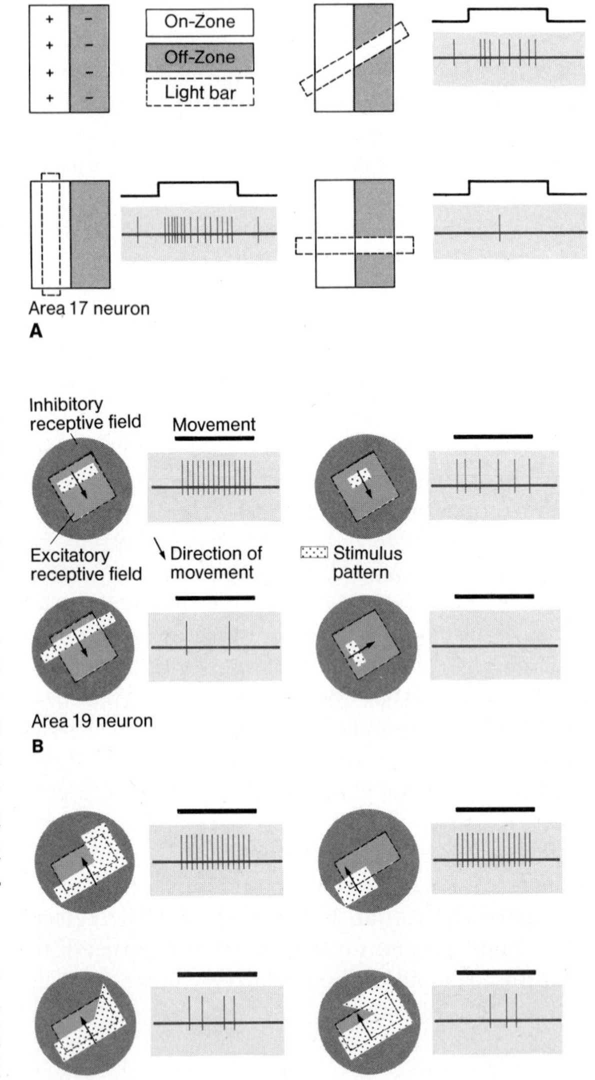

Fig. 11-29 A–C. Discharge patterns of single neurons in the visual cortex. **A** Neuron with *simple* receptive field, on- and off-zones arranged in parallel. **B** Neuron with complex receptive field. The greatest activation is produced by a moving, tilted bar of light of limited extent. **C** Neuron with hypercomplex receptive field. Maximal activation is elicited by two contrast boundaries meeting at right angles. The stimulus patterns in each case are shown in *white*. In **B** and **C** the arrows show the direction of movement of the stimulus patterns. (Schematized from data of HUBEL and WIESEL)

cortical neurons have concentric receptive fields and hence still respond to diffuse light stimuli, but many visual neurons in the cortex have receptive fields with **on- and off-zones** arranged in parallel (Fig. 11-29A). Diffuse illumination of the entire receptive field produces only a slight change, as a rule, in the spontaneous activity of these neurons.

On the other hand, if a bar of light with the "correct" orientation and position is projected into the receptive field, this stimulus triggers a strong response (Fig. 11-29A). When the bar of light is perpendicular to this *optimal direction*, as a rule the nerve cell does not respond. Because the parallel on- and off-zones in the RF can be mapped relatively simply by projecting small dots of light onto the retina, these are called **"simple receptive fields".** The arrangement of the on- and off-zones explains why these neurons give especially strong responses to light/dark contours in a *particular orientation* (Fig. 11-29A).

Other neurons of the primary and secondary visual cortex have **"complex" receptive fields**. Small dots of light projected into the RF usually do not elicit much activity of these neurons, whereas light/dark contours of a certain size and in a particular orientation are especially effective stimuli, as are interruptions of contours and corners (Fig. 11- 29B,C). The part of the RF in which a "correct" stimulus pattern activates the neuron is called the **excitatory receptive field (ERF)**. Usually the ERF is surrounded by a region in which light/dark patterns can only produce **inhibition (inhibitory receptive field, IRF).**

The cortical neurons with complex receptive fields are much more strongly activated by *moving patterns* or a rapid *alternation of patterns* than by a stationary pattern visible for a few seconds. Neuronal activation is also partially dependent on the *direction of movement* of the pattern. Movement- and direction-sensitivity of cortical visual neurons equip the neuronal system to deal with a crucial problem – that a "cerebral picture" of the stationary visual world must be established during brief fixation periods, between saccades that shift the position of the image of the surroundings over the retina (pp. 238f.).

Binocular summation. *Under normal conditions, when fixating an object in our surroundings with two eyes we see it as single.* It is therefore not surprising that some of the neurons in the visual cortex are excited by signals from both eyes. There are different neuronal mechanisms for binocular integration.

(i) Greater excitation may be produced by binocular than by monocular stimulation (binocular summation), with some of the neurons being activated only when the ERFs in the left and right retinas are excited *simultaneously*. When the optimal orientation of the light/dark contour differs somewhat in the ERFs of the left and right eyes, *binocular stimulation* is most effective when a contour is tilted at an angle to the frontoparallel plane and is imaged in the receptive fields of both eyes. This finding indicates that these neurons have a function in **stereoscopic depth perception** (p. 267).

(ii) Some of the neurons in area V1 are activated by stimulating one retina and inhibited by stimulating the other (binocular inhibition). This mechanism, found even in some neurons of the LGN (where the binocular inhibition is transmitted by interneurons from one geniculate layer to another), is the neuronal basis of "binocular rivalry". Binocular inhibition is thought to play an important role in the fine adjustment of eye-axis position for binocular vision.

The Visual Areas of the Cerebral Cortex outside the Primary Visual Cortex (Extrastriate Visual Cortex)

In recent years, systematic microelectrode recordings in the cerebral cortex of the rhesus monkey have confirmed an earlier suspicion, based on clinical observations of patients with brain lesions, that area V1 is not the only cortical visual region. In the monkey, extensive areas in the occipital, occipitoparietal and temporal cortex are also involved in visual signal processing (Fig. 11-30). Whereas in humans the **striate area** (V1) is located predominantly on the medial surface of the occipital cortex (Fig. 11-27 and Fig. 6-4, p. 128), in the monkey it occupies a large part of the lateral occipital surface. Near the **lunate sulcus** it merges with area V2 (area 18) in the temporal and parietal directions; area V2 in turn is bounded temporally and parietally by the visual areas V3, V3a and V4. These 4 different "extrastriate" cortical visual fields represent a *specialization of neuronal signal processing according to different qualities of vision.* Nerve cells in area V2 respond preferentially to *contours in certain orientations* and to *interruptions of contour.* This region evidently serves for visual pattern recognition. On the other hand, neurons in **area V4** have predominantly **color-specific** receptive fields. Damage to this region in the human brain causes a *cortical color-vision deficit.* Bilateral destruction of a considerable part of the "extrastriate" visual fields lying outside area V1 results in *object agnosia*; patients with this condition can "see" objects but cannot identify them by sight, though they can do so by other senses (e.g., touch). The RF of nerve cells in **area V3** and other visual integration areas, the regions called MT and MST (the cortex along the superior temporal sulcus), have a marked *movement sen-*

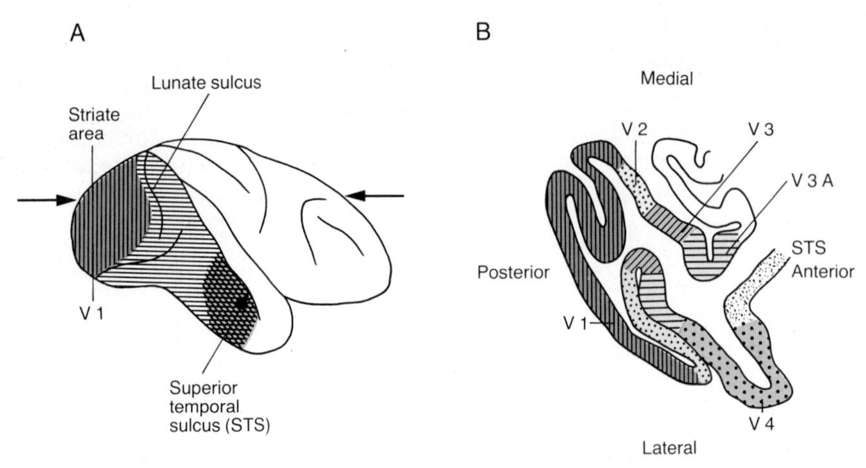

Fig. 11-30. A The distribution of the visual areas in the cerebral cortex of a rhesus monkey. Area V1 (or 17) occupies a large part of the outer occipital surface. The *horizontally hatched* region comprises the parts of the visual cortical areas V2, V3, V4, MT and MST that are visible on the surface. In these visual areas there is a regular retinocortical projection ("retinotopic" representation), which is not present in the visual regions of the **inferior temporal gyrus** (*cross-hatching*). The latter contain nerve cells responsive only to very complex visual stimuli. For example, in the depths of the superior temporal sulcus, near the *tip of the pointer*, there are cells that respond preferentially to faces or face-like configurations. **B** Horizontal cross section through the occipital cortex of the rhesus monkey at the level of the *arrow* in **(A)**. The various cortical areas are identified by different symbols. Modified from [64]. STS: cortex region in the vicinity of the superior temporal sulcus

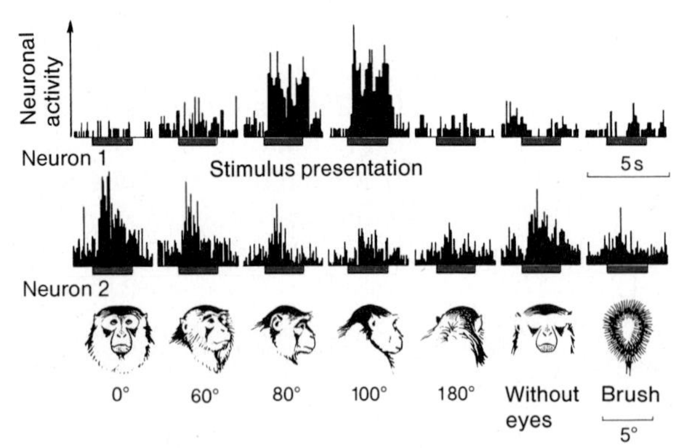

Fig. 11-31. Mean discharge rate *(ordinate)* of 2 nerve cells (Neuron 1, Neuron 2) in the "face-specific" cortical region, in the depths of the superior temporal sulcus (see Fig. 11-30). The pictures in the bottom row were presented to the waking animal for 2.5 s each *(red horizontal bars)*. Neuron 1 is maximally activated when the stimulus, which subtends about 5°, is a monkey profile; Neuron 2 is maximally activated when the monkey face is seen from the front. When a horizontal portion over the eye region is obliterated from the face, there is relatively little change in the response. A brush, on the other hand, produces only weak neuronal activation. (Modified from [40])

sitivity. Some of these movement-specific visual neurons respond only to movements of objects along the Z axis – that is, movements toward the eyes or away from them. There is only a gross retinotopic organization in the MT and MST regions, because many nerve cells here have very large RFs (up to 30°). Bilateral destruction of this cortical region interferes with the visual perception of motion [42–45].

In the **visual integration regions** of the **inferior temporal gyrus**, again, only a gross retinotopic organization can be found. In these cortical regions there are neurons that respond only to very complex visual patterns; in some cases their response depends on visual learning processes and the current motivation of the experimental animal.

A visual integration region that in the monkey is located deep in the cortex, around the **superior temporal sulcus**, consists of nerve cells most readily activated by *faces* or *face-like* stimulus configurations (Fig. 11-31). Some of these "face-specific" visual neurons are maximally excited by a face shown in *profile*, while others respond to the *frontal view* of a face. Among the regions to which face-specific nerve cells project are parts of the **amygdaloid nucleus** that also contain populations of face-specific neurons. It may be that the latter, in a region belonging to the limbic system (p. 363), evaluate information about the *emotional components* of faces and expressive facial movements. In humans the "face-specific" visual integration region lies at the basal boundary between the occipital and temporal lobes. A bilateral lesion of this region – which can occur when circulation through branches of the *posterior cerebral artery* is impaired – produces the symptoms of **prosopagnosia**. These patients can no longer recognize faces or facial expressions, although they have no difficulty in perceiving other objects and can immediately recognize familiar people by other identifying features, such as their voices or typical movements [40, 50, 59a].

Eye Movements and the Activation of Cortical Visual Neurons

As was mentioned at the beginning of this chapter (p. 240), visual perception is closely coupled to eye and head movements that change the direction of gaze. It is not surprising, then, that there are many different connections between the cortical visual fields and the gaze centers in the brainstem. For instance, area V2 projects into the superior colliculi, from which the gaze-directing neurons in the PPRF and MRF are controlled (p. 240). The extrastriate visual fields are linked to the prefrontal cortical regions that are responsible for voluntary control of eye movements (area 8) and for hand-mouth coordination. These regions in turn, like **area 7 of the parietal cortex** (discussed below), are connected to the **gaze centers of the brainstem** and also back to the occipital visual fields of the cortex. For the afferent projections of movement-specific visual signals in area 7, the pathway from the retina by way of neurons in the superior colliculi (p. 258) plays an important role. The neurons of the superior colliculus send signals to the pulvinar of the thalamus, from which they proceed to the extrastriate cortical visual fields and area 7 of the parietal lobe. These connections also subserve the integration of gaze movements and visual perception.

The Neuronal Representation of Extrapersonal Space

The coordinates and the spatial arrangement of objects in our surroundings appear unchanged to us even when their image on the retina is shifted by active movements of eyes, head or body. Moreover, at least in the part of the extrapersonal space that is within reach, the objects have multimodal properties; a teacup is perceived as such when you see it, touch it or drink from it. Major lesions in the parietal lobe of the human cerebral cortex disrupt or abolish the perception of objects in space. As a rule, this deficit is restricted to the half of the extrapersonal space contralateral to the brain lesion (unilateral **visual neglect**). It is usually accompanied by a disturbance of the voluntary gaze movements toward the contralateral side. The function of the parietal fields of the cerebral cortex has been studied by recording with microelectrodes chronically implanted in the brain of the rhesus monkey. In **area 7** of the parietal cortex there are neurons that can be activated by both visual and tactile stimuli. Neuronal activation is in part *dependent on the eye movements*, though it also depends on interest and on the part of the surroundings to which the animal is paying attention (Fig. 11-32). Evidently in area 7 the representation of extrapersonal space is independent of the retinotopic projection. The visual regions of the pulvinar, which project into area 7, are also involved in these complex functions [15, 39, 48, 58, 59].

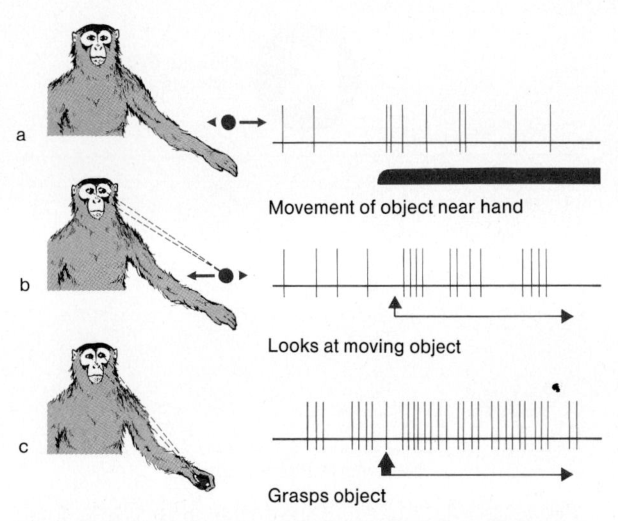

Fig. 11-32 A–C. Diagram of the response of a neuron in area 7 of the waking rhesus monkey. **A** An object (e.g., a nut) within reach of the hand is moved, and the movement activates the neuron (increases its discharge rate). **B** The animal looks at the object, and the discharge rate rises further. **C** When the animal reaches for the object, the neuron is very strongly activated [47]

11.6 Practical and Clinical Applications of Visual Physiology

Neurophysiological Bases of Form Perception

A good sketch conveys the "essence" of a complex object with a few strokes, by extracting it from all the nonessential details and internal structures. The visual neuronal networks in the cerebral cortex perform this kind of "extraction". The neuronal operations that make certain fea-

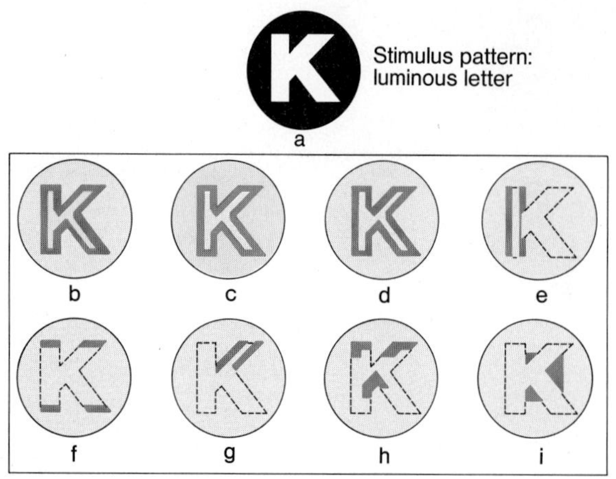

Fig. 11-33 a–i. Diagram of the excitation elicited by a luminous letter K (cf. Fig. 11-5) in various neuronal layers of the retina and in the central nervous system. **a** Image of the luminous letter on the retina, and spatial pattern of excitation in the receptor layer of the retina. **b** and **c** Pattern of excitation in the output layer of the retina (ganglion cells). In **b** to **i** the excitation is denoted by red bars. **b** On-center neurons, **c** off-center neurons. **d** Pattern of excitation in the neurons of the lateral geniculate nucleus and of layer IV of the visual cortex with concentric RF. The contours of the luminous letter elicit excitation of the nerve cells. **e** to **i** Pattern of excitation in various neuron layers and different nerve-cell classes in the primary, secondary and tertiary visual cortex. These nerve cells are stimulated only by contours in certain orientations, with certain interruptions of angle or contour. The illustration greatly simplifies the neurobiological situation; the spatial distribution of excitation in the various nerve-cell layers of the cerebral cortex is not a linear transformation of the stimulus pattern

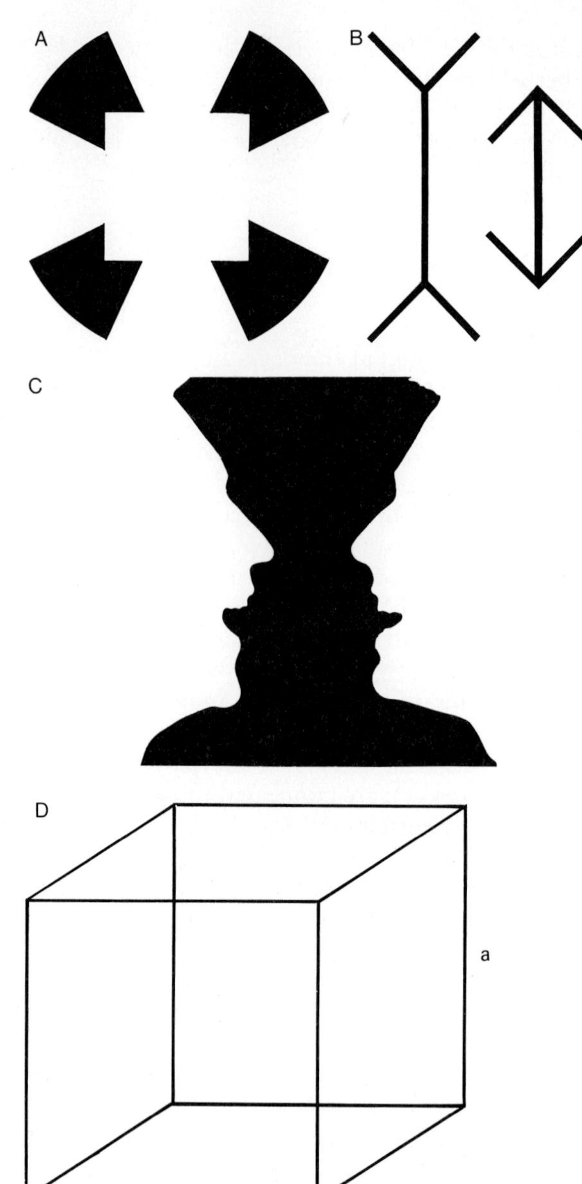

Fig. 11-34. A Example of visual shape completion *(white square)*. **B** Müller/Lyer illusion; the objective lengths of the two vertical lines are equal. **C** Pattern to demonstrate *alternation of figure and background*. The viewer sees either a black "candlestick" on a white background or two smiling profiles on a black background (negative of a silhouette). **D** Necker cube. When viewed for a long time, its depth relations change; the back edges "jump" forward and the front edges, back. This alternation cannot be suppressed

tures stand out – contours with a certain orientation or length, interruptions or angles in a contour – can be regarded as the first step in a feature-abstraction process. Each network comprising a particular class of neurons with complex receptive fields represents, by the spatial pattern of excitation within the network, a different feature of the stimulus pattern. In the simplified example of Fig. 11-33 this situation is illustrated by the stimulus pattern "K". *It is still not known what neuronal mechanisms integrate these multiple neuronal representations in the visual cortex, so that a single object (in this case, the letter K) is perceived.*

Optical illusions. Some familiar optical illusions can be explained by the organization of the receptive fields of cortical visual neurons. For example, an observer viewing Fig. 11-34A without preconceptions sees a white square on a darker background. Microelectrode recordings have shown that area V2 includes neurons with complex receptive fields that respond to "apparent contours". It seems likely, then, that perception of the apparent contours in Fig. 11-34A derives from the receptive-field organization of such cortical nerve cells.

The Müller-Lyer illusion, shown in Fig. 11-34B, probably also results from the organization of complex receptive fields of cortical neurons. As mentioned above, activation of some of these neurons depends on the angle between two contours – an important determinant of the effectiveness of the Müller-Lyer illusion. Optical illusions are usually isolated phenomena in form perception, which can give the sensory physiologist an indication of the operations by which signals are processed in the visual centers of the brain.

Figure and background in form perception. One is able to see shapes when figures stand out against a "background". The distinction between figure and background can be ambiguous under certain conditions, as illustrated in Fig. 11-34C; here one sees either the silhouette of a black goblet (or candlestick) on a white background or two white faces in profile, smiling at one another against a black background. It is impossible to perceive the black figure and the white profiles **simultaneously** as shapes. If one continues to gaze at the picture, one cannot prevent figure and background from alternating, presumably because of an adaptation process in the visual system outside area V1. The same is true of the spatial ambivalence in the "Necker cube" shown in Fig. 11-34D. When one looks at this cube for some time, with one eye or both, its orientation seems to alternate; edge "a" switches from the front to the back. One can cause the Necker cube to "jump" voluntarily, but a change cannot be suppressed for more than a few seconds.

Constancy of shape and size. As a rule we see the things in our surroundings unchanged in shape and size, even though the angle subtended on the retina and the shape of the image change. For example, when a boy cycles past he always seems the same size, regardless of distance. The wheels of the bicycle are still perceived as circular even when their images on the retina have become narrow ellipses. In the phenomenon of **shape and size constancy**, experience certainly helps to determine **how** we see our environment. Experience also affects our perception of depth in extrapersonal space. The region directly within reach and the space beyond it that is close enough for interactions with ourselves are "euclidian"; that is, equal metric distances are perceived to be equal in all directions. But this does not apply to more distant space, as most readers will be able to confirm from their own experience. When one looks down from a tower 100–150 m high, the people and cars at the base of the tower look like small toy figures. But when the same objects are viewed from a distance of 150 m horizontally, they retain their "correct" size. The nonlinear distortion of the far visual distance is also the reason for the so-called moon illusion: the moon or sun appear much smaller near the zenith than on the horizon. The noneuclidian distortion of visually perceived space in these examples is said to change after one has worked for some time on high scaffolding. When the parieto-occipital cortex is damaged, the mechanisms for size constancy can be impaired, in which case objects may appear abnormally small **(micropsia)**, too large **(macropsia)** or distorted **(dysmorphopsia)** [9, 12, 13, 30].

Measurement of Visual Acuity

The image of an object fixated with the eyes in the normal position is projected onto the fovea centralis of each eye, and in photopic vision this is the place where visual acuity is greatest; acuity decreases from the fovea to the periphery of the retina (Fig. 11-35). In scotopic vision acuity is greatest in the parafoveal region. At the site where the optic nerve leaves the eye, visual acuity is null ("blind spot", Fig. 11-4).

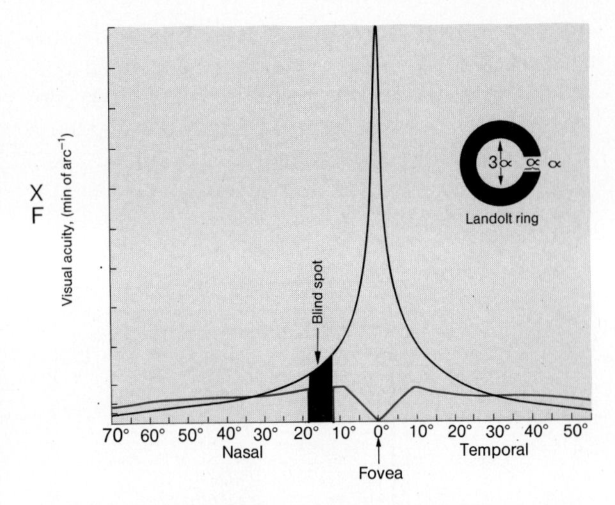

Fig. 11-35. Dependence of visual acuity *(ordinate)* on position in the visual field *(abscissa)*. *Black curve:* photopic vision, *red curve:* scotopic vision. Visual acuity was measured with the Landolt ring (inset). This figure can be used to demonstrate the blind spot, by viewing the cross F monocularly with the right eye from a distance of ca. 32 cm. Then the Landolt ring falls in the blind spot and is no longer seen

In a clinical examination the **"visus" (V, visual acuity at the point of greatest acuity)**, is ordinarily measured by instructing the patient to fixate a standardized target. The most common measure in North America and parts of Europe is the Snellen fraction:

$$V = d/D \quad (11)$$

where d is the distance at which a symbol can be discriminated, and D is the distance at which that symbol subtends one minute of arc. The symbols in this case are letters in a Snellen chart. In practice, the chart is set at a standard distance from the patient, usually 20 feet, and D is calculated from the size of the smallest letters the patient can read. For people with normal vision D is the same as the test distance, so that the Snellen fraction is 20/20.

An alternative procedure is to determine the angular extent α of the gap in a Landolt ring (inset, Fig. 11-35) that is just detectable by the subject. The visus is then given by $V = 1/\alpha$ and has units of (minutes of arc)$^{-1}$. The visus for normal acuity (discrimination of a target subtending 1 minute of arc) is thus 1/minute of arc. When visus is measured after refractive errors have been corrected with glasses, the result is called **visus cum correctione**, and that measured without glasses is called **visus sine correctione** [20, 25, 26].

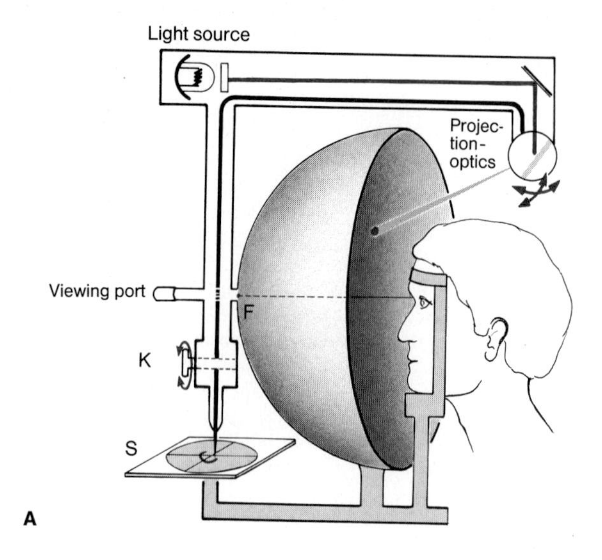

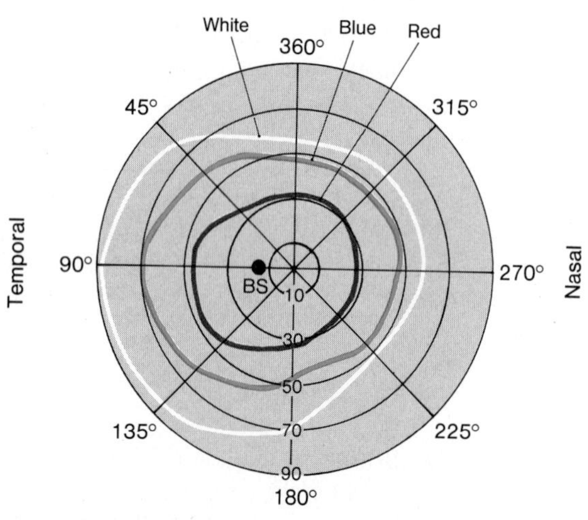

B Visual field of the left eye

Fig. 11-36. A Perimeter apparatus, diagrammatic. The field of view **B** is measured monocularly. The eye of the patient is positioned at the center of the perimeter hemisphere. The patient fixates a point at the pole of the perimeter. The examining physician checks his fixation by looking through the viewing port and moves a light spot over the perimeter surface by adjusting the projection optics with the knob K. The light spot can have various sizes, luminances and colors. The subject makes a signal as soon as he sees the light spot, and its position at this time is recorded on a card on the stage S. **B** Result of a measurement of the normal visual-field boundaries with white, blue and red light. BS, blind spot. The fixation point is the center of the concentric circles, which demark distance from the fixation point (in degrees of arc)

Measurement of the Visual Field and of Visual-Field Defects by Perimetry

The **monocular visual field** is the part of the visual environment perceptible with one *motionless eye*. The total visual field comprises all points in space that can be perceived with *both* (motionless) eyes. *Within the total visual field is a region that can be seen with both eyes*, the **binocular visual field,** on either side of which is a region visible by only one eye, the monocular crescent. Even with the head motionless, of course, a region greater than the "total" visual field can be brought into view by eye movements (field of gaze).

A visual field defect is the loss of visual sensation in one part of the visual field; when a visual field defect is surrounded by normal visual field, it is called a **scotoma.** Visual field defects can be caused by damage to either the retina or the central visual system. The boundaries of the normal or abnormal visual field are mapped and the locations of scotomas identified by means of **perimetry** (Figs. 11-36, 11-37). For precise perimetry the state of adaptation and the size, intensity and spectral composition of the stimulus light must be exactly defined. From the nature of a scotoma the physician can deduce the site of damage within the visual pathway – assuming, of course, that he knows the anatomical relationships discussed on p. 258. In ordinary measurements (gaze straight ahead) the visual field is limited on its nasal side by the nose. For the nasal boundary of the visual field to be measured precisely, the subject would have to turn his gaze away from the standard position, toward the side. The visual field in the light-adapted state is greater for light/dark perception than for color perception (Fig. 11-36). The functional "color blindness" of the outer periphery of the visual field is caused by the scarcity of cones in this part of the retina [3, 24, 30].

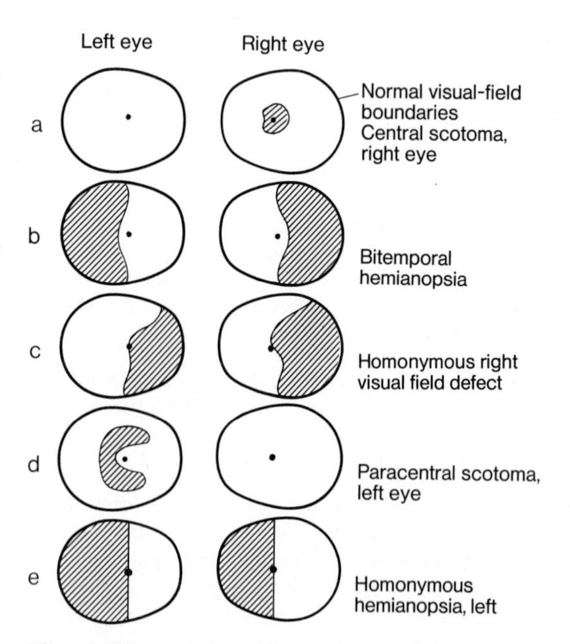

Fig. 11-37 a–e. Typical visual-field defects, diagrammatic. Possible sites of origin of the defects are **a** right retina (fovea centralis) or right optic nerve, **b** optic chiasm, **c** left optic tract or left central visual system, **d** left retina or left optic nerve, **e** right optic tract or right central visual system. The locations of these lesions are shown in Fig. 11-27

Electrophysiological Studies of the Visual System

The function of the visual system can be tested objectively, at retinal or central levels, by electrophysiological measurements. Recording of the **electroretinogram** was mentioned on p. 252; another important objective test of the afferent visual system is provided by the **visual evoked potentials** (VEP) of the electroencephalogram (EEG, p. 134) recorded by electrodes on the scalp above the brain. These potentials are revealed by summing the responses to several light stimuli. A flash of diffuse white light with a large area produces the simple VEP, the waves and latencies of which change depending on the luminance and spectral composition of the stimulus (Fig. 11-38A). The **pattern-reversal VEP** is measured with *light and dark stripes* or *checkerboard patterns* as stimuli, the light and dark areas being periodically exchanged (Fig. 11-38B). When visual patterns of various configurations are alternated aperiodically, the VEP provides an objective measure of more complex visual processing in the CNS (Fig. 11-38C,D). In multiple sclerosis, one of the most common neurological diseases, the latencies and amplitudes of the waves of the simple pattern-reversal VEP are altered, because this disease usually involves damage to the axons of the optic nerve (optic neuritis). Therefore measurement of the VEP is an important aid to diagnosis in clinical neurology and neuro-ophthalmology [28].

Depth Perception

While walking through a well-structured landscape, provided that one has normal binocular vision, one perceives its features as being arranged at various distances and can even estimate fairly accurately the relative distances of the objects. This impression of spatial depth is brought about in part by binocular stereoscopic vision, but *monocular* mechanisms are also involved: *differences in size of familiar objects, occlusion by interposition, shadows, perspective shortening* and in particular *the parallactic shifts of objects with respect to one another* that accompany movement of the head. That objects are perceived in three dimensions by means of **binocular stereoscopy** is particularly important when they are within reach or not much further away. Because the eyes are situated at different places on the head, the optical geometry causes an object fairly close to the observer to be imaged differently on the two retinas. The larger and closer the objects, the greater the **horizontal disparity**.

That the images of an object on the two retinas differ can be easily demonstrated by the following experiment. Holding your arm out horizontally in front of you, look at the thumb monocularly with the left and right eye in alternation. With each change of eye the thumb appears to shift rapidly with respect to the background; that is,

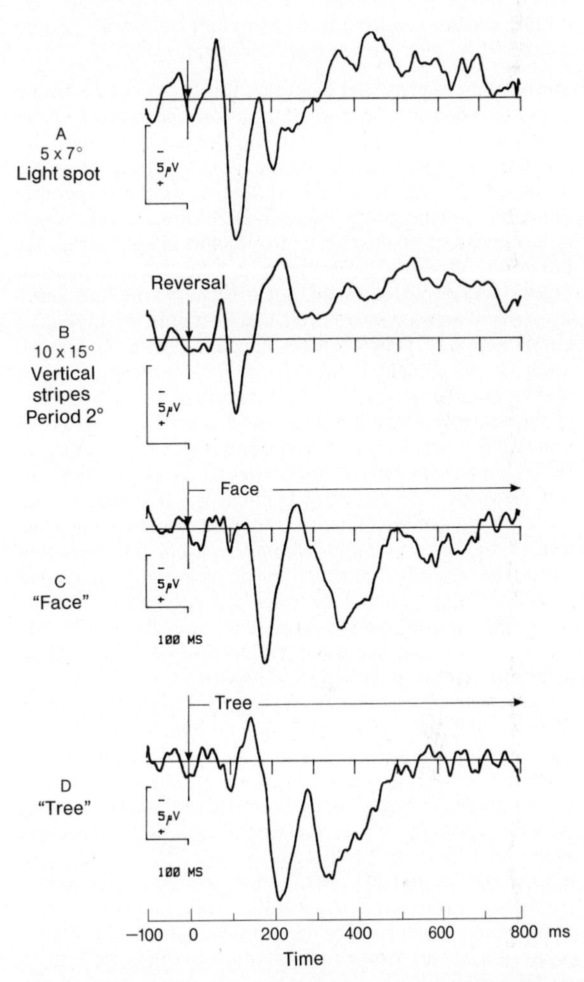

Fig. 11-38 A–D. Visual evoked potentials recorded from the occipital region of the skull surface of a human subject. Each curve is the mean response to 40 stimuli. **A** Response to a diffuse light flash 20 ms in duration that illuminated an area of 5° × 7° in the binocular visual field. Simple evoked potential. **B** Pattern-reversal potential. The subject saw a pattern of vertical stripes in which, at the *arrow*, the white stripes changed to black and the black stripes, to white. The mean luminance of the stimulus field (field size 10° × 15°, stripe period 2°) was unchanged. **C** Evoked potential elicited by a change in shape *(arrow)*. A drawing of a face was presented after a drawing of a tree or a chair. **D** At the *arrow* a drawing of a tree was presented after one of a face or chair. The shape-dependent evoked potentials in C and D differ in waveform; the greatest voltage difference between the two curves occurs at 220 ms (Measurements by K. Bötzel, Berlin)

the images of the thumb seen with the left and right eyes cover different objects behind them. The further the other objects in view are from the thumb, the larger is the thumb's displacement relative to them. The geometry of horizontal disparity is illustrated in Fig. 11-39. When both eyes are fixating a point at a finite distance, all objects on the circle defined by the nodal points of the optical systems of the two eyes plus the fixation point are imaged on **corresponding sites on the retina.** All objects inside or outside this circle, the **horopter circle**, are imaged on non-corresponding sites, and if the horizontal disparity (sum of the angles α and β in Fig. 11-39) is great enough, **double images** are produced. The spatial separation of the double images resulting from horizontal disparity can be measured by reference to the "cyclopean eye".

Horizontal disparity and binocular fusion. As stated above, with the head in the normal position the images of an object at a finite distance from the eye are projected onto the right and left retinas in different positions, and the quantitative measure of this difference is the horizontal disparity. A binocularly viewed three-dimensional object is perceived to "fall apart" into **double images** when the horizontal disparity has exceeded a certain limit. There is a considerable range of tolerance between the horizontal disparity 0 (object at infinity) and the limit of binocular depth vision, at which double images appear. This tolerance can be explained by the size of the receptive fields of binocularly activated cortical neurons, as follows: The spatial extent of the ERF of such neurons in areas V1 and V2 is considerably larger than the visual acuity of the corresponding place on the retina. Some of the cortical neurons have receptive fields in the two retinas that correspond exactly; therefore these are most strongly activated by objects in the horopter region. On the other hand, the receptive fields of some binocularly activated cortical neurons do not coincide precisely on the retina; these cells are optimally activated by an object a certain distance away from the horopter, which therefore produces a certain amount of horizontal disparity.
Stereoscopic depth perception plays a role in the practice of medicine, especially in surgery and most importantly for microsurgical operations in which a binocular microscope is used. Physicians who lack normal binocular vision are hampered in performing microsurgery, and should try to avoid choosing this area of specialization. Stereoscopic vision can easily be tested by having the subject view binocularly separated patterns that look like random distributions of dots to each eye alone. Only a person capable of binocular correlation of the individual dots, with appropriate horizontal disparity, can perceive shape and depth in the pattern [12, 13, 14, 16, 25].

Visual Movement Perception and the Viewer's Own Movement

Depth perception at distances beyond one's immediate vicinity is based mainly on the parallactic shifts of images on the retina that occur when one moves through space. During uniform forward motion – such as riding in a car or taking off and landing in an airplane – the image displacements on the retina follow a simple rule: *The closer the objects in the field of view, the greater their angular velocity.* This perceived flow of movement can be simulated by appropriate filmed or computer-generated picture sequences. When a person who is not moving views a wide-angle film of this kind, he feels as though he is moving in the direction opposite to that of the optical signal flow (**vection**). One's *apparent own motion* can have linear or rotational components (**linear** and **circular vection**, respectively). Examples of such perceived motion include the sensations experienced in a flight or driving simulator as well as the sensation of movement when riding in a vehicle at constant velocity. The truer to nature the parallactic shifts in the picture sequence – that is, the better the pictures simulate the three-dimensionality of visually perceived space – the more natural the apparent movement induced. Vection is brought about by the connections between the retina and the vestibular nuclei and by the interaction of the central visual system with the vestibular regions of the cerebral cortex.

Strabismus

When a fixated object is projected onto the fovea in only one eye, and onto a parafoveal region in the other, the condition is called squint or *strabismus.* If the two optical axes diverge sufficiently, double images are perceived. This happens, for instance, when paralysis of an eye muscle prevents coordinated movement of the two eyes. Such patients see double images whenever an eye movement involving the affected muscle is attempted. Accurate description of the double images and their relative positions (crossed or uncrossed, Fig. 11-39) is an important aid to diagnosis, by which the ophthalmologist can determine which of the extraocular muscles is paralyzed. *You can easily observe double images by fixating a nearby object binocularly and then displacing one eye slightly with your finger.*

When binocular eye movements are uncoordinated in infancy (congenital squint), **strabismic amblyopia** usually develops in one eye; finely structured visual stimuli are seen only with the fovea of the other eye. This deficit is not caused by impaired retinal function but by a functional change in the visual cortex: processing of the signals from the amblyopic eye by cortical neurons is reduced or abolished. Amblyopia also occurs when a young child is prevented from seeing with one eye for a long period (e.g., because of ptosis, a congenital drooping of the upper eyelid).
The most common cause of strabismic amblyopia in children is **hypermetropia** (see p. 246). The young patients must accommodate more strongly to sharpen the image of an object on the retina (see p. 245). Because of the *coupling of accommodation and convergence* in vision at close range, the eyes of a hypermetropic child converge more than is

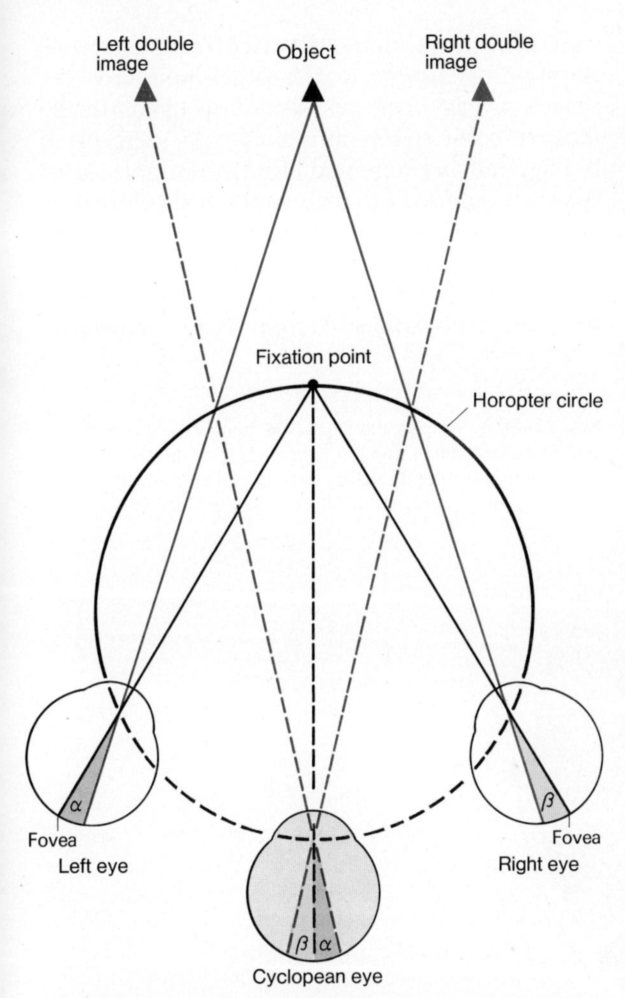

Fig. 11-39. Diagram of binocular vision and the construction of the cyclopean eye. When an object is outside the horopter its image is projected to the right of the fovea in the left eye and to the left of the fovea in the right eye. In this case, binocular viewing gives an uncrossed double image, the position of which can be found by mapping the retinas of the left and right eyes onto the imagined retina of the cyclopean eye

appropriate to the distance of the object, so that it is on the optical axis of only one of the eyes. The binocular inhibitory mechanisms mentioned above (p. 261) suppress the signals that reach the visual cortex from the other eye. If the hypermetropia is not corrected by lenses and the strabismus treated in time, the **strabismic amblyopia** that eventually results can no longer be cured, since the synaptic contacts of the geniculate afferents associated with the affected eye are functionally uncoupled from the cortical binocular neurons.
Squinting can also be caused by a *disturbance of optomotor coordination* in the brainstem; again, strabismic amblyopia develops. Treatment of squint in children – whether with corrective lenses, exercises or surgical correction – should be carried out before age 2 or 3, because afterward the "sensitive phase" during which the cortical neuronal mechanisms of binocular vision become established is completed, and therapy of strabismic amplyopia usually becomes ineffective. Later corrective surgery is only of cosmetic value.

11.7 Color Vision

Colors and the Measurement of Color

The phenomenon of color vision makes it especially clear that perception depends not only on the stimulus and the receptors, but also on processing within the nervous system. In the psychophysics of color perception two major color categories are distinguished, the **chromatic** valencies, (red, orange, blue etc.) and the **achromatic** valencies, the shades of gray on a scale ranging from the deepest black to the brightest white. In the visible **spectrum** of sunlight (e.g., in a rainbow) the various regions seem to be differently colored, giving a continuum of color sensation from violet through blue, green, yellow, orange to red. But this observation does not imply that the color sensation is determined only by the wavelength λ of a monochromatic light stimulus. For one thing, we can perceive hues that are not present in the spectrum of sunlight, the **purple colors** between red and blue; for another, all the color sensations in the visible light spectrum can be obtained by mixing other wavelengths. *Colors obtained by spectral mixing cannot be distinguished from pure spectral colors.*
The laws of color vision describe the **phenomenological structure** of color perception, the "color space" within which a person with normal color vision can perceive about 7 million different color valencies, including both the small category of achromatic and the very large class of chromatic valencies. The chromatic valencies of the surface colors of objects are characterized by three phenomenological attributes: **hue, saturation** and **lightness.** In the case of luminous color stimuli (e.g., a colored light source) the dimension "lightness" is replaced by the luminance (brightness).
The **hues** form a natural unlimited continuum, the **color circle**, with the sequence red, yellow, green, blue, purple and back to red (Fig 11-40A). Ideally, hues are "pure" colors. A hue can be "mixed" with an achromatic valency to give different shades of color; for instance, pure red gives pink when mixed with white, and brown when mixed with black. The **saturation** of a shade is measure of the relative amounts of its chromatic and achromatic components, and its **lightness** is determined by the position of the achromatic component on the gray scale.
All the perceptible color valencies can be represented in a three-dimensional **color solid**, in which the relative positions of the colors can

be specified with metric precision or only represented qualitatively. Figure 11/40B shows an early, non-metric representation, the **color sphere** of the German painter PHILIPP OTTO RUNGE (1810). Each color valency is represented by a particular place on or in the color sphere. The equatorial cross section of the sphere represents the pure colors of the color circle at the periphery, and toward the center these are increasingly mixed with gray. The center of the sphere is a neutral gray; along the axis, from one pole through the center to the other pole, are the shades of gray from white to deep black. In the modern color spaces, in which color perception is metrically represented, Runge's simple color sphere is deformed to a non-spherical color solid. The aim of these metric color systems is an unambiguous **description** of the color perception of normal observers; they do not provide a physiological **explanation** of color vision. However,

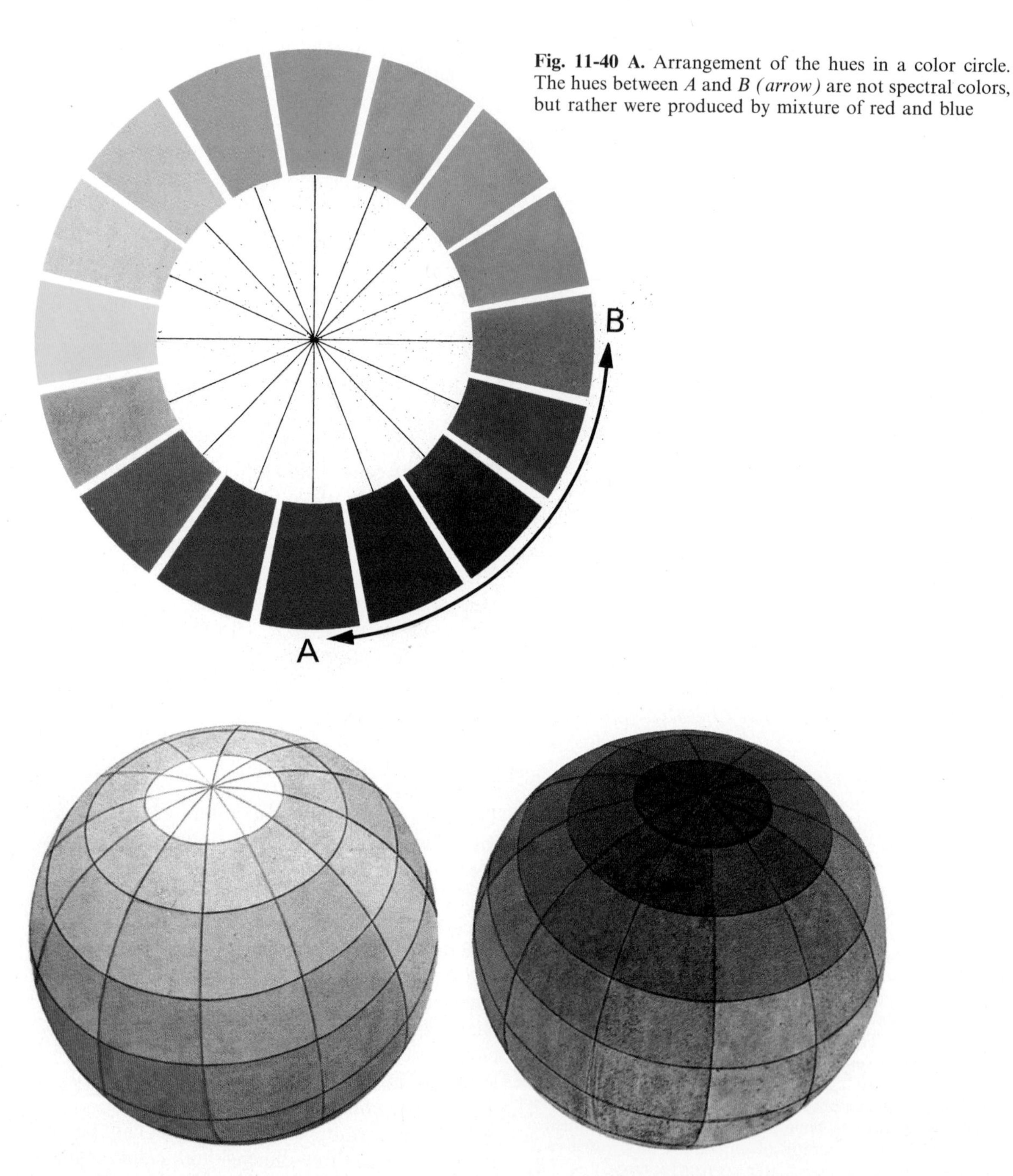

Fig. 11-40 A. Arrangement of the hues in a color circle. The hues between *A* and *B (arrow)* are not spectral colors, but rather were produced by mixture of red and blue

Fig. 11-40 B. The color sphere of PH. O. RUNGE (1810), a non-metric representation of color space

when a comprehensive physiological therory of color vision is put forward, it will have to account for the structure of metric, psychophysical color systems.

Color constancy. It is important in everyday life that in natural ambient illumination the perception of surface colors is relatively independent of the spectral composition of the light. For this independence to prevail, the objects seen must be illuminated by light comprising a large range of the visible spectrum. We experience color constancy because what we perceive as color is predominantly the **spectral reflectance** of objects. It enables us to recognize objects in the natural environment under various lighting conditions. But there are limits to color constancy; for instance, compare the contrast between the brown of a fir tree's trunk and the deep green of its needles on a gray, rainy day with the much stronger color contrast when the fir is viewed in the reddish light of the setting sun on a summer evening. In artificial light, which comprises only part of the visible spectrum, the colors of patterned material look different than in daylight – a point to be remembered when one is buying clothes.

Color mixtures. We know from everyday experience that when *paints of various hues are mixed*, the resulting color is of a different hue. But the effects of mixing paint are quite distinct from those of combining light in different parts of the spectrum. An **additive color mixture** is produced when *light of different wavelengths falls onto the same spot on the retina* (Fig. 11-41). If the individual light sources are monochromatic, the additive mixture can result in hues corresponding to another part of the spectrum or to the nonspectral region between red and blue (purple). The description of color relationships embodied in the color solid is based in part on a systematic

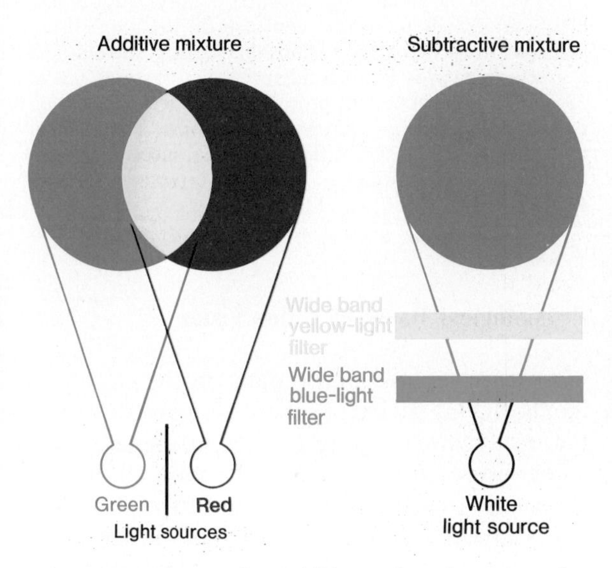

Fig. 11-41. Diagram of an additive and a subtractive color mixture

study of additive color-mixture equations. These equations are also used in tests of **color-vision deficits** (see p. 274). An instrument for making such tests is the **anomaloscope**; with it, for example, spectral yellow ($\lambda = 589$ nm) is projected onto one half of a circle and a mixture of spectral red ($\lambda = 671$ nm) and green ($\lambda = 546$ nm) is projected onto the other half (Fig. 11-41). The subject must adjust the proportions of red and green to give a mixture with a yellow color indistinguishable from the spectral yellow. The result is represented by the color-mixture equation

$$\text{a(red 671)} + \text{b(green 546)} \cong \text{c(yellow 589)} \qquad (12)$$

where the symbol $\cong$ signifies *equivalence of sensation* and has no mathematical significance. A person with normal color vision would set the coefficient of the red component at about 40, and that of the green component at 33 relative units (that of the yellow component being 100). When two monochromatic light stimuli, one between 430 nm and 555 nm and the other between 492 nm and 660 nm, are mixed additively, it is always possible to obtain white by adjusting the proportions. But if a monochromatic light above 660 nm is mixed with one below 430 nm, there is no proportion that will give white; rather, one obtains purple hues not present in the spectrum (Figs. 11-40, 11-43).

The color white. For every hue in the color circle there is another hue that can be additively mixed with it to produce the color white. The constants (weighting factors a and b) of this color-mixing equation

$$\text{a}\{F_1\} + \text{b}\{F_2\} \cong \text{c(white)} \qquad (13)$$

depend on the definition of white. The hues in any pair F_1, F_2 that satisfies Eq. (12) are called **complementary colors.**

Subtractive color mixing. Subtractive color mixing differs from additive color mixing in that it is a purely physical process. When white light is sent through a broad-band yellow filter followed by a broad-band blue filter, the resulting subtractive color mixture is **green**, because only the green part of the spectrum is passed by **both** filters (Fig. 11-41). A painter who mixes pigments is producing a subtractive color mixture, because the individual pigment granules act as chromatic broad-band filters.

Trichromacy. In the case of normal color vision, any given hue (F_4) can be produced by additive mixing of three suitably chosen hues (F_1 – F_3). This situation is described by the unique and sufficient sensation equation

$$a\{F_1\} + b\{F_2\} + c\{F_3\} \cong d\{F_4\} \quad (14)$$

By international convention the primary colors F_1, F_2 and F_3 chosen for construction of the modern metric color systems are spectral colors with the wavelengths 700 nm (red), 546 nm (green) and 435 nm (blue), respectively. For additive mixing to give the color white, the weighting factors a, b, c of these primary colors are related as

$$a + b + c = d = 1 \quad (15)$$

The results of experiments in sensory physiology based on Eqs. (11) through (14) can be represented geometrically by the chromaticity diagram shown in Fig. 11-42 ("color triangle"). The shades of gray included in the **color solids** are omitted in this diagram, so that the three-dimensional representation is reduced to two dimensions. The color resulting from mixture of any two colors in the chromaticity diagram lies on a straight line between the two. Pairs of **complementary colors** can be found with this diagram by drawing straight lines through the "white point" (E) [9, 12, 13, 16, 31, 33].

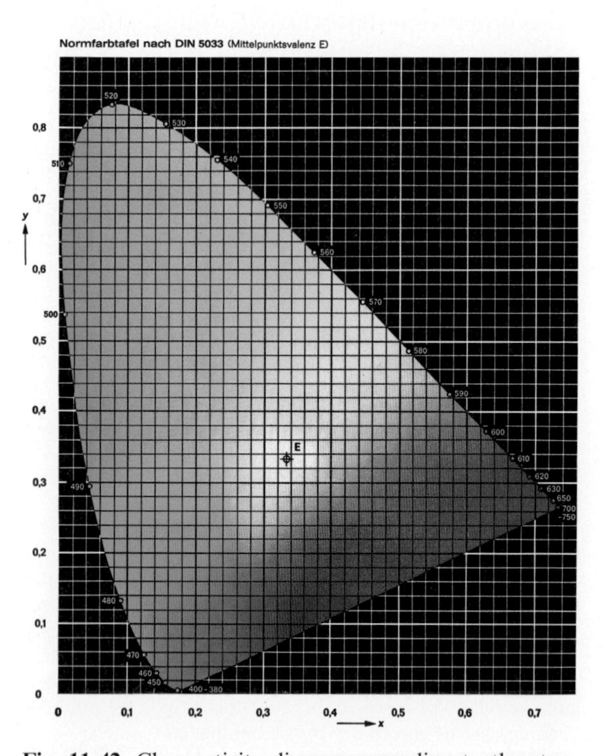

Fig. 11-42. Chromaticity diagram according to the standard DIN 5033. The white region surrounds the point E. The base of the "color triangle" is made up of the purple hues. The additive mixed colors composed of two arbitrary colors A and B lie on the line connecting A and B. Complementary colors are on lines through the point E

Theories of color vision. In the following paragraphs the two most important theories of color vision are described. Once there were vigorous disputes between their supporters, but today the two are regarded as complementary theoretical interpretations of color vision. Each applies "correctly" to a different level of the afferent visual system and has been adequately confirmed by direct physiological measurements. A synthesis of these rival theories was proposed 80 years ago by JOHANNES VON KRIES in his **zone therory**.

The trichromatic theory of color vision. This theory, credited to YOUNG, MAXWELL and VON HELMHOLTZ, proposes that three different types of cones act as **independent** receiver systems in photopic vision. The signals from these three cone types are analyzed in combination in two neuronal systems, a **brightness system** and a **color system**. The trichromatic theory is supported by the way colors are perceived at the lower limit of photopic sensitivity; here only the three hues red, green and blue can be discriminated. Direct measurements of the spectral absorption of the photopigments in single cones and of the receptor potentials of these cones in the retinas of animals with color vision (see pp. 250f.) have provided objective confirmation of the three-receptor hypothesis for color vision.

The opponent-process theory. The polarized arrangement of hues in the color circle is associated with the second line of thought. MACH and HERING proposed that the chromatic valencies are based on four **primary colors** *(Urfarben)*, red, yellow, green and blue. According to HERING, these are coupled by two physiological processes, each antagonistically organized: the green-red process and the yellow-blue process. A third opponent process was required for the achromatic complementary colors black and white. The term "opponent colors" *(Gegenfarben)* was derived from the polarized nature of color perception; that is, there is no "greenish red" and no "bluish yellow". The opponent-process theory is supported by observations of the chromatic simultaneous contrast and successive contrast phenomena. For example, a gray area surrounded by a luminous green ring appears slightly red because of chromatic simultaneous contrast; if the ring disappears, the observer sees a glowing red ring surrounding a greenish interior (chromatic successive contrast, see p. 256). HERING's opponent-process theory requires antagonistic, color-specific neuronal mechanisms. The level of the visual system at which these neuronal mechanisms are located appears to differ in different vertebrates [5, 8, 9, 12, 13, 16, 31].

Physiological Bases of Color Vision

Microspectrophotometric data on the cone pigments and microelectrode recordings of the membrane potential of single cones in animals with color vision confirm the predictions of the trichromatic theory of color vision: there are three major groups of cones, which differ in their spectral absorption (see Fig. 11-15). The antagonistic reactions demanded by the opponent-process

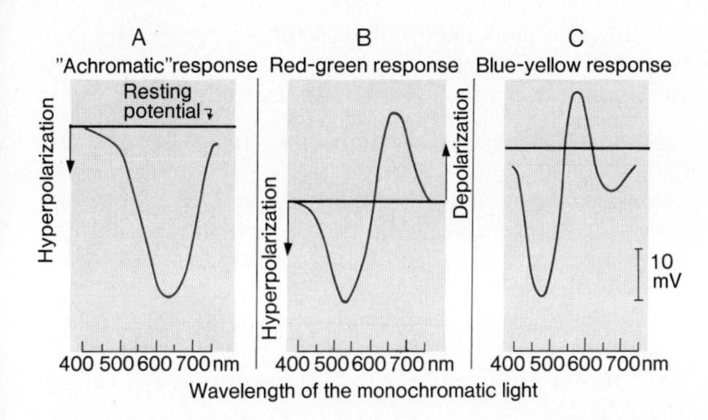

Fig. 11-43 A–C. Dependence of the membrane potential of three different horizontal cells in the fish retina on the wavelength of monochromatic light stimuli (abscissa). The wavelength of monochromatic light stimuli of equal energy is changed slowly. **A** Horizontal cell that responded with hyperpolarization in all regions of the spectrum. **B** Red-green horizontal cell; green light causes hyperpolarization and red light, depolarization. **C** Yellow-blue horizontal cell. The level of the resting membrane potential is shown by a black line in each graph. The amplitude of hyperpolarization is plotted below this line, and that of depolarization above it. [Modified from SPEKREIJSE and NORTON: J. gen. Physiol *56* (1970)]

theory can also be found in the retina, in the spectral responses of neurons in the horizontal- and bipolar-cell layers, as a result of spatial interaction of the signals from the different types of cones. The curves in Fig. 11-43A–C are derived from measurements of the responses of horizontal cells in the retina of fish that have been shown, by behavioral tests, to have good color vision. There are three classes of horizontal cells. One class is hyperpolarized by light, regardless of its wavelength *(L-type)*; the two others exhibit *red-green* and *blue-yellow antagonism*, respectively (Fig. 11-43B,C). Color-antagonistic horizontal cells are hyperpolarized when the eye is stimulated with monochromatic light from one part of the spectrum and depolarized by light from another part. In mammals with color vision, a similar color-specific organization is found in some of the on-center and off-center bipolars, in some ganglion cells and in the neurons of the lateral geniculate nucleus. In the retina there are neurons activated by red light and inhibited by green light in the receptive field (**simple opponent cells**). Figure 11-44 shows a further development of the opponent-color principle, as applied to the organization of the receptive field. Here both the RF-center and the RF-periphery give opposite responses to different colors (**double opponent cells**). Neurons of this kind can be found in the lateral geniculate nucleus or the primary visual cortex of primates with color vision. As an example of the responses of such neurons, if red light in the RF-center activates a neuron and green light inhibits it, in the RF-periphery the opposite will occur. This double-opponent organization of the receptive field explains the phenomenon of simultaneous color contrast. Color-specific neuronal signals are processed primarily in those regions of area V1 that have no orientation-specific receptive fields, "blob-regions" (Fig. 11-28). The color-specific neurons of the primary visual cortex are particularly sensitive to the boundaries between different colors. Further color-specific cortical processing occurs mainly in **area V4**, to which the axons of neurons in V1 project. Area V4 has been shown to include nerve cells with a high degree of color specificity, which are activated by stimuli within a relatively narrow range of hues. The receptive fields of some of these neurons are subdivided into bands with different color specificity, so that color contrasts are particularly effective stimulus patterns. The implications of the data now available on the color-specific responses of neurons in the afferent and central visual system of primates are still under discussion, but the following picture is beginning to emerge:

(i) The validity of the trichromatic color theory at the level of the cones is not in doubt.

(ii) A simple opponent-color mechanism is present at an early stage – in the retina.

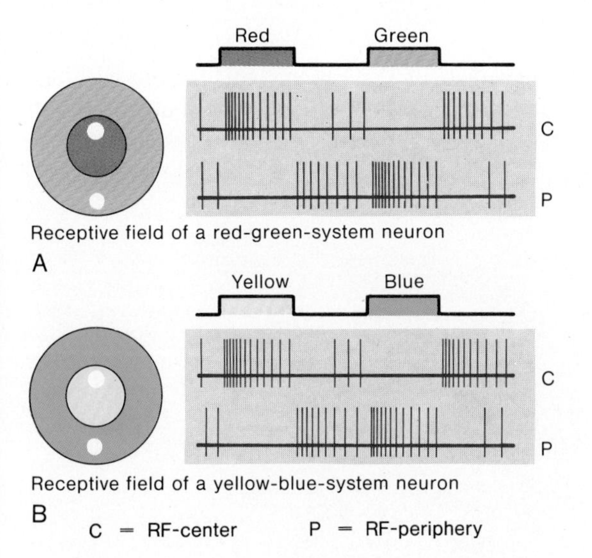

Fig. 11-44 A,B. Simplified diagram of the spatial organization of 2 receptive fields in either the ganglion-cell layer of the retina or the lateral geniculate nucleus of a mammal with color vision. **A** Nerve cell of the red-green system. **B** Nerve cell of the yellow-blue system. In color-specific receptive fields there is an antagonistic organization of RF-center and RF-periphery

(iii) The stage of color-specific signal-processing at which neurons with a double-opponent mechanism (Fig. 11-44) are present is still debatable.

(iv) It seems certain that in the extrastriate visual regions, especially area V4, rather than a simple opponent-color system there is a more complex processing of the color signals, with relative color constancy [8, 13, 16].

Defects of Color Vision

The pathological changes that impair color perception can affect the visual pigments, signal processing in the photoreceptors or at higher levels, or the spectral transmittance of the dioptric apparatus. Very rarely, color vision is disturbed as a result of cortical lesions. In the "peripheral" color-vision disturbances of genetic origin discussed below, both eyes are almost always affected, though there are rare cases of typical color-vision impairment in only one eye. The latter individuals can describe the subjective perceptions of disturbed color vision, because they can compare the different sensations they experience with the right and left eyes. There are two major classes of peripheral color-vision impairment, the **trichromatic** and the **dichromatic disorders of color vision**.

Anomalies of trichromatic vision. The mildest forms of color-vision impairment are the **anomalies**, which as a rule are *inherited as a recessive trait carried by the X chromosome.* Therefore males with these anomalies are much more numerous than females. Anomalous trichromats can distinguish fewer color valencies than people with normal color vision. Like normal trichromats, they require three primary valencies (as in Eq. 13) to describe completely the colors they see, but the weighting factors a, b, and c in Eq. 13 are abnormal. There are three categories of color anomaly. **Protanomalous** and **deuteranomalous** people cannot distinguish unsaturated red and green from one another. When tested in the anomaloscope, the protanomalous adds more red to the mixture than normal, and the deuteranomalous adds more green. In the very rare cases of tritanomaly, the yellow-blue system is disturbed.

Dichromats. Most forms of dichromatopsia are also inherited as recessive X-chromosomal traits. Dichromats can match all the hues they see by mixing only **two** spectral colors (in analogy with the process of Eq. 13). *The number of discriminable color valencies is therefore very much smaller for dichromats than for trichromats.* In **protanopes** and **deuteranopes** the red-green system is disturbed, presumably because of deficiencies both in the pigments of the red and green cones and in the connections among the retinal neurons. The photopic spectral brightness curve of protanopes has a maximum at about **520 nm**, and that of deuteranopes peaks at about **580 nm**. The protanope confuses certain red hues with black, dark gray and brown and in some cases, like the deuteranope, with green. To the protanope, the spectrum of sunlight appears achromatic between 480 and 490 nm; the achromatic range for the deuteranope is 495–500 nm. The very uncommon tritanopes confuse yellow with blue; the blue-violet end of the spectrum appears to them in black and shades of gray, and they also see an achromatic band in the spectrum between 565 and 575 nm. In both dichromats and anomalous trichromats, as a rule, scotopic vision is normal.

Cortical disturbances of color vision. An extensive lesion of the extrastriate visual cortex (area V4) can also impair color perception. Such patients sort surface colors into groups in an abnormal way; that is, the categorical organization of their color perceptions seems to be distorted. These cortical disturbances of color perception are to be distinguished from the difficulty in naming colors (**color anomia)** that may be experienced by patients with lesions in the region of the **angular** and **circumflex gyri** of the left hemisphere.

Total color blindness. Fewer than 0.01% of the population are completely color-blind. These *monochromats* see the world approximately as someone with normal color vision sees it in a black-and-white film – in various shades of gray. Monochromats usually have insufficient light adaptation in the photopic region and are dazzled by relatively dim light; therefore they discern shapes very poorly in daylight, which produces the symptom of *photophobia.* Even in normal daylight, monochromats wear very dark glasses. Their visual acuity in the fovea region is reduced to less than 0.1 (minute of arc)$^{-1}$. There is usually no histologically detectable abnormality in the cones of the monochromat retina. Because monochromats have the normal spectral brightness curve in the scotopic region (Fig. 11-1), it is thought that their cones contain rhodopsin as the visual pigment; their dark-adaptation curves (Fig. 11-24, p. 256) are consistent with this inference.

Disturbances of the rod system. People with abnormal rod systems perceive colors normally but their capacity for dark adaptation is severely re-

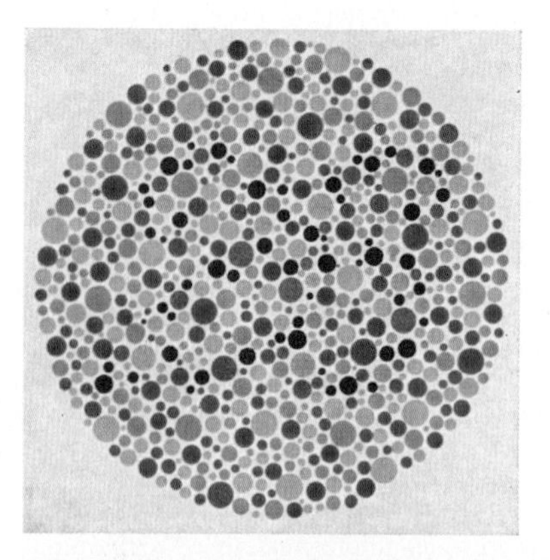

Fig. 11-45. Example from the series of "pseudo-isochromatic" charts of ISHIHARA. A person with normal color vision perceives the number 26, whereas the protanope sees "6" and the deuteranope, "2"

stricted. The cause of this "night blindness" or *nyctalopia* can be a dietary deficiency of Vitamin A_1, the precursor of retinal (see p. 249).

Diagnosis of abnormal color vision. Because color-vision disturbances are carried by the X chromosome, they are much more common in men than in women. About 0.9% of the male population are protanomalous, 1.1% are protanopic, 3–4% are deuteranomalous and 1.5% are deuteranopic. Tritanomaly and tritanopia are extremely rare. About 0.3% of the female population are deuteranomalous, and 0.005% are protanomalous.

Because normal trichromatic color vision is essential for many professions (e.g., pilots, locomotive drivers, fashion designers), all children should be tested for color vision before they begin training for a particular kind of work. One simple test uses the "pseudo-isochromatic" charts of ISHIHARA (Fig. 11-45). These charts show areas covered with spots of different sizes and colors arranged to form letters or numbers. Spots of different colors are at the *same lightness levels.* People with disturbed color vision cannot see some of the numbers, depending on the colors that form them. By testing a sufficient number of hue combinations, with several Ishihara charts, color-vision impairment can be detected quite reliably. Precise diagnosis of disturbances in color vision is possible by color-mixing tests based on Eqs. (12) through (14).

11.8 References

Textbooks and Handbooks

1. BAKER, R., BERTHOZ, A. (eds.): Control of gaze by brain stem neurons. Amsterdam-New York: Elsevier (1977)
2. BING, R., BRÜCKNER, R.: Gehirn und Auge. Grundriß der Ophthalmo-Neurologie, 3rd Ed. Basel: Schwabe 1954
3. CAJAL, R.S.: Die Retina der Wirbeltiere. Wiesbaden: Bergmann (1894)
4. DARTNALL, H.J.A. (ed.): Photochemistry of vision. Handbook of Sensory Physiology, Bd. VII/1, Berlin-Heidelberg-New York: Springer 1972
5. DAVSON, V.: The Eye. 4 vols. London: Academic Press 1962
6. DICHGANS, J., BIZZI, E. (eds.): Cerebral control of eye movements and motion perception. Basel: Karger 1972
7. DRUJAN, B.D.S., LAUFER, M. (eds.): The S-potentials, New York, Liss (1982)
8. FUORTES, M.G.F. (eds.): Physiology of photoreceptor organs. Handbook of Sensory Physiology, Vol. VII/2. Berlin-Heidelberg-New York: Springer 1972
9. GRAHAM, C.H. (ed.): Vision and visual perception. New York-London. Sidney: J.Wiley 1965
10. GRANIT, R.: Receptors and sensory perception. New Haven: Yale University Press 1955
11. GRÜSSER, O.-J., KLINKE, R. (eds.): Zeichenerkennung durch biologische und technische Systeme. Berlin-Heidelberg-New York: Springer 1971
12. HELMHOLTZ, H. VON: Handbuch der Physiologischen Optik, 2nd Ed. Hamburg, Leipzig: L. Voss 1896
13. HERING, E.: Grundzüge der Lehre vom Lichtsinn. Berlin: Springer 1920
14. HOFMANN, F.B.: Die Lehre vom Raumsinn des Auges (1920). Berlin-Heidelberg-New York: Springer 1970 (Reprint)
15. HYVÄRINEN, J.: The parietal cortex of monkey and man. Berlin-Heidelberg-New York: Springer 1982
16. JAMESON, D., HURVICH, L.M. (eds.): Visual Psychophysics. Handbook of Sensory Physiology Vol. VII/4. Berlin-Heidelberg-New York: Springer 1972
17. JUNG, R. (ed.): Central processing of visual information. A: Integrative function and comparative data. Handbook of Sensory Physiology, Vol. VII/3A. Berlin-Heidelberg-New York: Springer 1973
18. JUNG, R. (ed.): Central processing of visual information. B. Visual centers in the brain. Handbook of Sensory Physiology, Vol VII/3B. Berlin-Heidelberg-New York: Springer 1973
19. KOMMERELL, G. (ed.): Augenbewegungsstörungen. Neurophysiologie und Klinik. München: J.F. Bergmann (1978)
20. LANDOLT, E.: Die Untersuchung der Refraction und der Akkommodation. In: Graefe-Saemisch's Handbuch der gesamten Augenheilkunde, 3rd Ed., Untersuchungsmethoden, Vol. 1. Berlin: Springer 1930
21. LENNERSTRAND, G., BACH-Y-RITA, P.: Basic mechanisms of ocular motility and their clinical implications. Oxford: Pergamon Press, 1975
22. LINKSZ, A.: Physiology of the eye. Vol. I: Optics. Vol. II: Vision. New York: Gruner und Stratton 1950–1952
23. MÜTZE, K., NEHRLING, B., REUTTER, J.: Brillenglasbestimmung. Zürich: Verlag für Augenheilkunde und Optik 1972
24. POLYAK, S.: The vertebrate visual system. Chicago: University of Chicago Press 1957
25. SCHOBER, H.: Das Sehen, Vol. 2, 2nd Ed. Leipzig-Fachbuchverlag 1958
26. SIEBECK, R.: Optik des menschlichen Auges. Berlin-Göttingen-Heidelberg: Springer 1960
27. SPIEGEL, I.M. (ed.): Readings in the study of visually perceived movement. New York: Harper and Row 1965
28. STÖHR, M., DICHGANS, J., DIENER, H.C., BUETTNER, U.W.: Evozierte Potentiale. Berlin-Heidelberg-New York, Springer 1982
29. WALLS, G.L.: The vertebrate eye and its adaptive radiation. New York, London: Hafner 1963
30. WALSH, F.B., HOYT, W.F.: Clinical neuroophthalmology, 3rd Ed. Baltimore: William and Wilkins 1969
31. WRIGHT, W.D.: The measurement of colour, 3rd Ed. London: Hilger und Watts 1964
32. YARBUS, A.L.: Eye movements and vision. New York: Plenum Press 1967
33. ZRENNER, E.: Neurophysiological aspects of colour vision in primates. Berlin-Heidelberg-New York: Springer 1983

Original Papers and Reviews

34. ALTMAN, J.: New visions in photoreception. Nature *313*, 264–265 (1985)
35. BAUMGARTNER, G., HAKAS, P.: Die Neurophysiologie des simultanen Helligkeitskontrastes. Pflüg. Arch. ges. Physiol. *274* 489 (1962)
36. BAYLOR, D.A., FUORTES, M.G.F.: Electrical responses of single cones in the retina of the turtle. J. Physiol. (Lond.) *207*, 77 (1970)
37. BILL, A.: Uveoscleral drainage of aqueous humour in human eyes. Exp. Eye Res, *12*, 275 (1971)
38. BOYCOTT, B.B., WÄSSLE, H.: The morphological types of ganglion cells of the domestic cats' retina. J. Physiol. (Lond.), *240*, 397 (1974)
39. COLLEWIJN, H.M., CURIO, G., GRÜSSER, O.-J.: Spatially selective visual attention and generation of eye pursuit movement. Experiments with Sigma movement. Human Neurobiology *1*, 129 (1982)

40. DESIMONE, R., ALBRIGHT, T.D., GROSS, C., BRUCE, C.: Stimulus selective properties of inferior temporal neurons in the macaque. J. Neurosciences *4*, 2051 (1984)
41. DIE, G. VAN, COLLEWIJN, H.: Optokinetic nystagmus in man. Role of central and peripheral retina and occurrence of asymmetries. Human Neurobiol. *1*, 111 (1982)
42. ESSEN, D.C. VAN: Visual areas of the mammalian cerebral cortex. Ann. Rev. Neurosciences *2*, 227 (1979)
43. ESSEN, D.C. VAN, MOUNSELL, J.H.R., BIXBY, J.L.: The middle temporal visual area in the macaque: myeloarchitecture connections, functional properties and topographic organization. J. Comp. Neurol. *199*, 293 (1981)
44. ESSEN, D.C. VAN, NEWSOME, W.T., BIXBY, J.L.: The pattern of intrahemispheric connections and its relationship to extrastriate visual areas in the macaque monkey. J. Neuroscience *2*, 265 (1982)
45. ESSEN, D.C. VAN, ZEKI, S.M.: The topographic organization of Rhesus monkey prestriate cortex. J. Physiol. *277*, 193 (1978)
46. FESENKO, E.E., KOLESNIKOV, S.S., LYBARSKY, A.L.: Induction by cyclic GMP of cationic conductance in plasma membrane of retinal rod outer segment. Nature *313*, 310 (1985)
47. GRÜSSER, O.-J.: Grundlagen der neuronalen Informationsverarbeitung in den Sinnesorganen und im Gehirn. Informatik-Fachberichte Bd. 16, 234. Berlin-Heidelberg-New York: Springer 1978
48. GRÜSSER, O.-J.: Multimodal structure of the extrapersonal space. In: HEIN, A., JEANNEROD, M.: Spatially oriented behaviour. New York-Berlin-Heidelberg-Tokyo: Springer 1982, p. 328
49. GRÜSSER, O.-J.: Die funktionelle Organisation der Säugetiernetzhaut – physiologische und pathophysiologische Aspekte. Fortschr. Ophthalmol. *80*, 502 (1983)
50. GRÜSSER, O.-J.: Face recognition within the region of neurobiology and beyond it. Human Neurobiol. *3*, 183 (1984)
51. GRÜSSER, O.-J., GRÜSSER-CORNEHLS, U.: Periodische Aktivierungsphasen visueller Neurone nach kurzen Lichtreizen verschiedener Dauer. Pflüg. Arch ges. Physiol. *275*, 292 (1962)
52. GRÜSSER, O.-J., GRÜSSER-CORNEHLS, U.: Neurophysiologie des Bewegungssehens. Bewegungsempfindliche und richtungsspezifische Neurone im visuellen System. Ergebn. Physiol. *61*, 178 (1969)
53. HAGINS, W.A., PENN, R.D., YOSHIKAMI, S.: Dark current and photocurrent in retinal rods. Biophys. J. *10*, 380 (1970)
53a. HENN, V., BÜTTNER-ENNEVER, J.A., HEPP, K. The primate oculomotor system I. and II. Human Neurobiol. *1*, 77 and 87 (1982)
54. HUBEL, D.H., WIESEL, T.N.: Receptive fields and functional architecture of monkey striate cortex. J. Physiol. (Lond.) *195*, 215 (1968)
55. HUBEL, D.H., WIESEL, T.N.: Cell sensitive to binocular depth in area 18 of the macaque monkey cortex. Nature *225*, 41 (1970)
56. HUBEL, D.H., WIESEL, T.N.: Functional architecture of macaque visual cortex. Proc. Roy. Soc. (Lond.) B *198*, 1 (1977)
56a. LAMB, T.D. Transduction in vertebrate photoreceptors: the roles of cyclic GMP and calcium. Trends in Neurosciences *9*, 224 (1986)
57. LIVINGSTON, M.S., HUBEL, D.H.: Anatomy and physiology of a color system in the primate visual cortex. J. Neurosci. *4*, 309 (1984)
58. LYNCH, J.C.: The functional organization of posterior parietal association cortex. Behavior and Brain Science *3*, 485 (1980)
59. LYNCH, J.C., MOUNTCASTLE, V.B., TALBOT, W.H., YIN, T.C.T.: Parietal lobe mechanisms for directed visual attention. J. Neurophysiol. *40*, 362 (1977)
59a. PERETT, D.I., ROLLS, E.T., KAAN, W. Visual neurons responsive to faces in the monkey temporal cortex. Exp. Brain Res. *47*, 329 (1982)
60. SCHILLER, P.H.: The role of the monkey superior colliculi in eye movement and vision. Invest. Ophthal. *11*, 451 (1972)
61. TOMITA, T.: Electrical activity of vertebrate photoreceptors. Quart. Rev. Biophys. *3*, 179 (1970)
62. WILD, H.M., BUTLER, S.R., CARDEN KULIKOWSKI, J.J.: Primate cortical area V4 important for colour constancy but not wavelength discrimination. Nature *313*, 133 (1985)
63. WURTZ, R.H., GOLDBERG, M.E.: The primate superior colliculus and the shift of visual attention. Invest. Ophthal. *11*, 441 (1972)
64. ZEKI, S.M.: Functional specialization in the visual cortex of Rhesus monkey. Nature *274*, 423 (1978)
65. ZEKI, S.M.: Uniformity and diversity of structure and function in Rhesus monkey prestriate visual cortex. J. Physiol. (Lond.) *277*, 273 (1978)

12 Physiology of the Sense of Equilibrium, Hearing and Speech

R. KLINKE

This chapter is concerned with the physiology of two phylogenetically related sense organs. Not only are the organs of **equilibrium** and **hearing** close together anatomically, lying side by side in the petrous bone to form the **inner ear;** they are also derived from the same structure in evolution. Because in man the most important means of communication, speech, is mediated by the auditory organ, the **physiology of speech** is also treated in this chapter.

Speech requires hearing. On the other hand, verbal communication is the most important means of education. Thus deafness, or even only a hearing deficit, is the most serious threat to the mental development of the child. Comparative psychological investigations have shown that deafness causes more severe mental deficits than blindness. Thus one may conclude that hearing is the most important sense for a human being.

12.1 Physiology of the Sense of Equilibrium

Physiology of the Peripheral Sensory Apparatus

Introductory comments on anatomy. The vestibular organ is one part of the **membranous labyrinth,** which constitutes the inner ear; the other part is the organ of hearing (Fig. 12-1). The membranous labyrinth is filled with a fluid, the **endolymph**, and surrounded by another fluid called the **perilymph** (their compositions are given on p. 286). There are two morphological subunits of the vestibular organ – the **macula organs** *(macula utriculi* and *macula sacculi),* also called **statolith organs,** and the **semicircular canals** *(horizontal* plus *anterior* and *posterior vertical* canals). In the region of the maculae, and in the semicircular canals near the ampullae, there is a sensory epithelium within which the receptors are embedded. The sensory epithelium is covered by a gelatinous mass made up largely of *mucopolysaccharides.* In the macula organs this mass lies over the sensory cells like a pillow, and contains calcium-carbonate deposits in the form of minute **calcite crystals,** called otoconia. Because of these stony inclusions it is called the **otolith membrane.** In the semicircular canals the gelatinous mass is more a sheet-like membrane. This structure, the **cupula,** contains no crystals.

The receptors and the adequate stimulus. In the sensory epithelia of the maculae and semicircular canals there are receptor cells of two morphologically different types [8], which evidently do not differ appreciably in their physiological properties.

Both have submicroscopic hairs **(cilia)** on the free surface, and for this reason are called hair cells (Fig. 12-2). In the electron microscope it is possible to distinguish the **stereocilia,** of which each receptor cell bears about 60–80, from the **kinocilium;** each receptor has one kinocilium. The receptors are secondary sensory cells; that is,

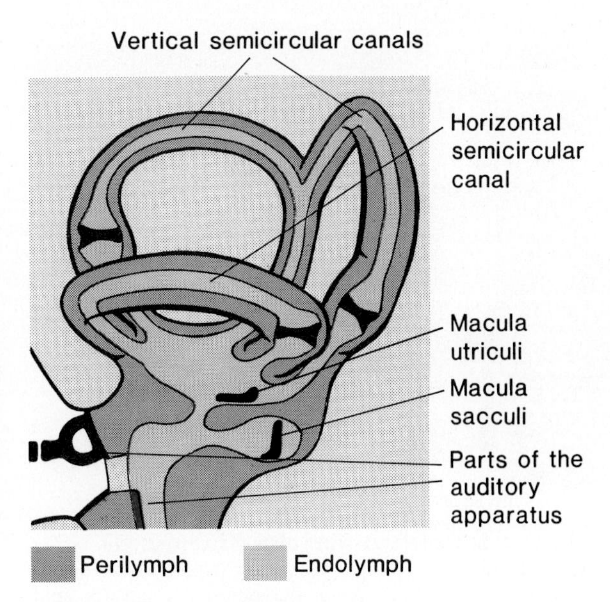

Fig. 12-1. Diagram of the vestibular labyrinth. The lymph spaces are in communication with those of the cochlear labyrinth.

they have no neural processes of their own, but are innervated by afferent fibers from the nerve cells in the **vestibular ganglion,** which together form the vestibular nerve. Efferent nerve fibers also terminate on the receptor cells. The afferent fibers transmit information about the state of excitation of the receptors to the CNS. The efferent fibers change the sensitivity of the receptors, but the significance of this influence is not yet entirely clear [37].

Recordings from single afferent fibers in the vestibular nerve reveal a relatively high, regular **resting activity** – neuronal discharges produced in the absence of external stimuli. If the gelatinous structure is experimentally displaced with respect to the sensory epithelium, the background activity is increased or decreased, depending on the direction of displacement. The change is brought about as follows: The cilia extend deeply into the mass, so that when it moves with respect to the sensory epithelium they are bent. This shearing of the bundle of cilia is the adequate stimulus to the receptor. When the direction of shear is toward the kinocilium (Fig. 12-2) the associated afferent nerve fiber is activated – that is, its discharge rate increases. If the bundle is bent in the opposite direction the discharge rate is reduced [8]. Shear in a direction perpendicular to this axis is ineffective. The information is transmitted from the receptor cell to the afferent nerve ending by way of a receptor potential and an as yet unidentified synaptic transmitter [38]. The crucial point here is that *shearing* (bending) of the cilia is the adequate stimulus for the vestibular receptors, which increases or decreases the activity in the afferent nerve depending on the direction of shear. Thus there is a receptor-cell **orientation,** morphological with respect to the arrangement of the cilia and functional with respect to the effect on their activity.

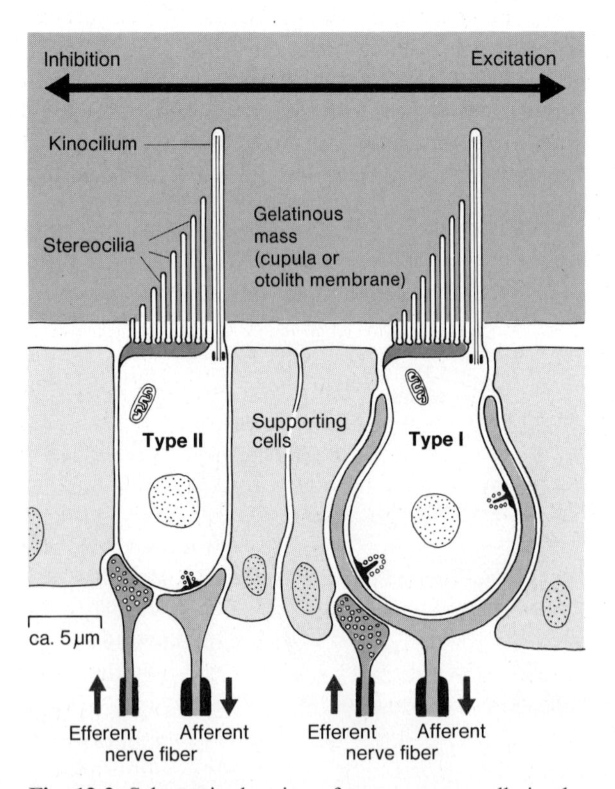

Fig. 12-2. Schematic drawing of two receptor cells in the sensory epithelium of the vestibular organ, with the associated nerve fibers. When the bundle of cilia is bent toward the kinocilium the discharge rate in the afferent nerve increases, and when the cilia are bent away from the kinocilium it is reduced

The natural stimuli to the macula organs. As we have seen, the cilia of the receptor cells project into the otolith membrane. Because of the calcite crystals it contains, the otolith membrane has a considerably higher specific gravity (ca. 2.2) than the endolymph (ca. 1) filling the rest of the interior of the utricle or saccule. Because of this difference in density, the ubiquitous **gravitational acceleration** exerts stronger forces on the otolith membrane than on the endolymph. Whenever the sensory epithelium of the macula utriculi or the macula sacculi is not exactly horizontal, therefore, the **force of gravity** will cause the entire otolith membrane to slide down for a very small distance over the sensory epithelium. (Imagine what would happen to the gelatinous mass colored red in Fig. 12-2 if it were heavy and you tilted the book, holding it vertically, to one side. The red-shaded region above the sensory and supporting cells would slide downward at an angle). This small displacement of the otolith membrane exerts a shear force on the cilia – the adequate stimulus for the receptors [8]). When the body is erect with the head held normally, the macula utriculi is about horizontal, so that the otolith membrane applies no shear force to the underlying sensory epithelium. But when the head is tilted the macula utriculi is tipped at an angle, the cilia are bent and the receptors are stimulated. Depending on the direction in which the head is inclined, the discharge rate in the afferent nerve fibers will either increase or decrease. The situation is in principle the same in the macula sacculi, but it is roughly vertical when the head is in the normal position (cf. Fig. 12-1). Thus for every position of the skull in space each otolith membrane has a certain position with respect to the underlying sensory epithelium. As a result, each head position is associated with a certain constellation of excitation in the nerve fibers. Because two populations of sensory cells are arrayed within the sensory epithelium of a macula with their cilia in opposite orientations, it is not possible to say in general that a particular inclination of the head will activate the nerve fibers [8, 26]. On the contrary, for every angle of head tilt some fibers are activated and others inhibited. There is no position in which the activity of all the nerve fibers can drop to zero.

The central components of the vestibular system evaluate the pattern of excitation in the vestibular nerve [3, 21, 26], so as to inform the organism about the position of the skull in space. To provide this information is the most important task of the macula organs. Gravitational acceleration is only one, special form of translational acceleration, and of course the maculae will also respond to any other translational acceleration. But the acceleration due to gravity is so strong that in its presence other linear accelerations encountered in daily life (e.g., when a car begins to move) play a subordinate role for the vestibular system, and they may even be interpreted incorrectly by the CNS (see p. 281).

The natural stimuli to the semicircular canals. The second possible kind of adequate stimulus to the vestibular-receptor cilia is realized in the semicircular canals (Fig. 12-3). Even though the actual shape of the canals in the body is not a perfect circle (Fig. 12-1), in principle they operate as closed circular channels filled with endolymph. In the region of the ampulla the outer wall is lined with sensory epithelium (Fig. 12-3). Here the cupula, deeply penetrated by the cilia of the receptor cells, projects into the endolymph. Lacking mineral inclusions, the cupula in a semicircular canal is of **exactly the same density** as the endolymph. Translational or gravitational acceleration therefore does not affect the organ; when the body is accelerated in a straight line, and when the head occupies various positions in the earth's gravitational field, the semicircular canal, cupula and cilia remain in the same position with respect to one another. The effect of **angular** (rotational) **acceleration** is different. When the skull is rotated away from a resting position, the semicircular canals of course rotate with it, but because of its inertia the endolymph within them does not. Therefore the pressure is different on the two sides of the cupula, and as a result the cupula, which is fused to the canal wall to make a water-tight seal [26], is deflected in the opposite direction like a loosely suspended membrane (Fig. 12-3). This deflection exerts a shear force on the cilia and thus changes the activity in the afferent nerve. In the horizontal canals all the receptors are oriented such that the kinocilium is toward the utricle. Therefore the activity in the afferent fibers is increased when the cupula is deflected toward the utricle *(utriculopetally)*. In the left horizontal semicircular canal, this happens during rotation to the left. In the vertical canals a *utriculofugal* deflection of the cupula (away from the utricle) activates the nerve fibers. Again, the activity of these fibers is evaluated in the CNS. From the discharge pattern in the afferent nerves of the total two × three canals, the brain extracts the information as to the angular acceleration acting on the skull. Because the head can be rotated about all three spatial axes – nodded forward or backward (pitch), tilted to right or left (roll), and turned about the long axis of the body (yaw) – it is necessary to have at least three semicircular canals. As required, they lie in planes approximately perpendicular to one another. During rotation about any diagonal axis, more than one of the semicircular canals are affected by the stimulus. The brain performs a vectorial analysis of the information to find the actual axis of rotation. In clinical examination (see p. 282) it is important to know that the "horizontal" semicircular canal is not exactly horizontal; its front edge is raised by about 30 degrees.

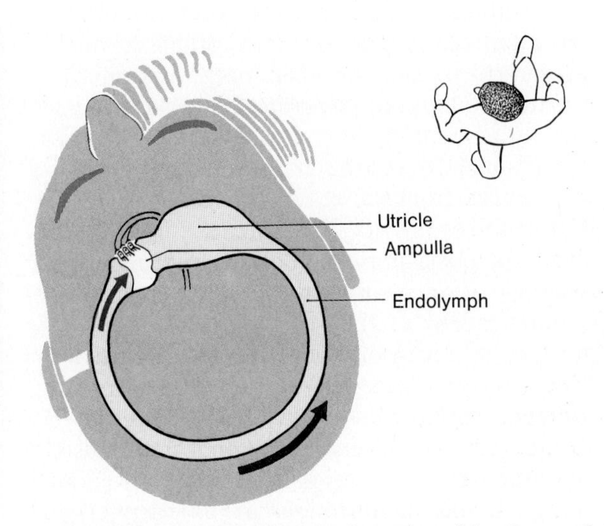

Fig. 12-3. Diagram of the left horizontal semicircular canal, seen from above. Except for the swelling that indicates a utricle, other parts of the labyrinth are not shown. Angular acceleration in the direction of the *black arrow* (imagine that you are turning the book counterclockwise) deflects the cupula as shown by the *red arrow*.

Peculiarities of cupular mechanics. First consider what happens to the cupula during a brief an-

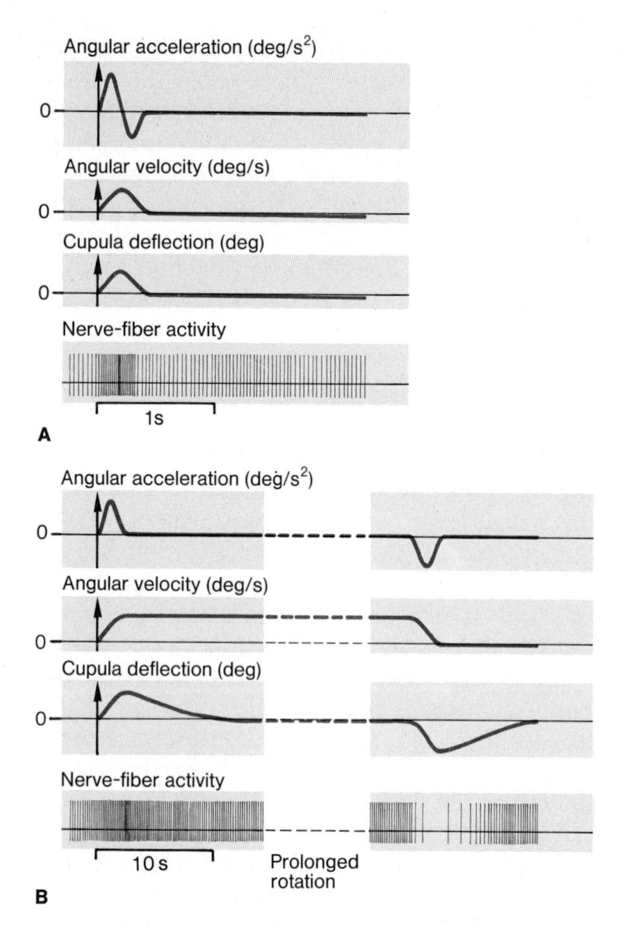

Fig. 12-4 A, B. Deflection of the cupula and activity in an afferent nerve fiber, with **A** brief rotation (e.g., turning the head) and **B** prolonged rotational movement (e.g., rotating chair). Note different time scales in **A** and **B**

gular acceleration, as occurs in daily life when we turn our heads. It is evident in Fig. 12-4 A that the deflection of the cupula does not correspond to the angular acceleration but rather to the momentary angular velocity. Accordingly, the change in neuronal discharge rate as compared with the spontaneous rate approximates the change in angular velocity rather than the change in acceleration, even though the forces causing deflection of the cupula are forces of acceleration. By the time this brief movement is over the cupula has returned to the starting position and the afferent nerve fiber is again discharging at the resting rate. Fig. 12-4 B shows the fundamentally different behavior during prolonged rotation (for example, on a revolving chair). The initial acceleration builds up to a constant angular velocity, which is maintained for a long time. The cupula is deflected at first; during the phase of uniform rotation it slowly returns to the resting position. A rapid interruption of the constant-velocity rotation again deflects the cupula, now in the opposite direction; because of its inertia, the endolymph tends to remain in motion, and the resulting pressure differences on the two sides of the cupula cause a deflection, which apart from its direction has the same characteristics as at the onset of movement. A relatively long time (10–30 s) is required for the cupula to return to its resting postion.

The difference between the responses of the cupula to short and to long stimuli arises from the mechanical properties of the system cupula-endolymph, which behaves – though only to a first approximation – like a highly damped torsion pendulum [26]. But it should always be kept in mind that the forces leading to cupula deflection are **always exclusively** forces of acceleration, even though during the brief angular accelerations most common under physiological conditions the deflection of the cupula is proportional to angular velocity rather than angular acceleration.

The deflections of the cupula under physiological conditions are very small [41]. On the other hand, the receptors are extremely sensitive. When the body of an experimental animal is very quickly rotated by only 0.005 degrees, the cupular deflection is of about the same order of magnitude, but even this stimulus is well above threshold for the receptor cells in the canals [32].

The Central Vestibular System

The primary afferent nerve fibers in the vestibular nerve terminate chiefly in the region of the vestibular nuclei, in the medulla oblongata. On each side there are four different nuclei, distinct from one another both anatomically and functionally: the *superior* (BEKHTEREV's), *medial* (SCHWALBE's), *lateral* (DEITER's) and *inferior* (ROLLER's) vestibular nuclei. The inputs to these nuclei from the vestibular receptors do not in themselves provide unambiguous information about the position of the body in space, because the angle of the head, movable at the neck joints, is independent of that of the trunk. The CNS must know the position of the head relative to the trunk and take it into account in determining the position of the body as a whole. Therefore the vestibular nuclei receive additional neuronal inputs *from the neck receptors* (muscles and joints) [3, 21]. If these connections are interrupted experimentally, the resulting disturbances of equilibrium resemble those following destruction of a labyrinth (cf. p. 283). Somatosensory inputs from other joints (arm, leg) and visual inputs are also present.

The fibers leaving the vestibular nuclei make connections in other parts of the central nervous system that enable the reflexes necessary to maintain balance. These pathways are as follows [3, 21]:

a. The **vestibulospinal tract,** which ultimately influences γ-motoneurons of the extensors in particular, though some of the fibers go to α-motoneurons.
b. Connections to the **motoneurons of the cervical cord,** corresponding in principle to the vestibulospinal tract.
c. Connections to the **oculomotor nuclei** (see p. 240), which mediate the eye movements elicited by vestibular activity. These fibers run in the medial longitudinal fasciculus.
d. Tracts to the **vestibular nuclei on the opposite side,** by means of which the inputs from the two sides can be processed jointly.
e. Connections to the **cerebellum,** the archicerebellum in particular (see below).
f. Connections to the **reticular formation,** by way of which the reticulospinal tract is influenced; the latter is yet another (polysynaptic) route to the α-and γ-motoneurons.
g. Tracts via the **thalamus** to the **postcentral gyrus** of the cortex, which subserve the conscious processing of vestibular inputs and thus conscious orientation in space.
h. Fibers to the **hypothalamus;** these fibers are chiefly involved in the production of kinetoses (motion sicknesses; cf. p. 283).

Its many neuronal connections, of which only the most important have been listed above, enable the vestibular system to play a central role in generating the motor outputs for posture and direction of gaze. Here an upright **stance** and **gait** are guaranteed primarily by the macula organs, whereas the semicircular canals are chiefly involved in adjusting the **direction of gaze.** It is the afferents from the semicircular canals, acting together with optokinetic mechanisms (see p. 244), that maintain visual contact with the surroundings during head movements. When the head is rotated or nodded, the eye moves in the opposite direction so as to keep the image on the retina stable (see statokinetic reflexes). The horizontal compensatory eye movements are controlled by the horizontal semicircular canal, and the vertical movements by the anterior vertical canal; torsion of the eye is controlled mainy by the posterior vertical canal.

The other main part of the CNS involved in the postural and gazing movements is the cerebellum, which receives some primary vestibular afferents (so-called direct sensory cerebellar pathway) in addition to the secondary vestibular neurons mentioned above. Both the primary and the secondary vestibular afferents (in mammals) terminate as mossy fibers (cf. p. 103) on the granule cells of the nodulus and flocculus (archicerebellum) and in parts of the uvula and paraflocculus (which belong to the paleocerebellum). The granule cells excite the Purkinje cells in these regions, and the axons of these Purkinje cells project back into the vestibular-nucleus region. The control circuit thus established regulates the fine tuning of the vestibular reflexes. When the cerebellum becomes nonfunctional owing to disease these reflexes are disinhibited, with symptoms such as increased or spontaneous nystagmus (cf. below and the section on oculomotor regulation, p. 240) and disequilibrium, manifest by a tendency to fall, a straddling walk, and overshooting movements, especially in walking. These symptoms are part of the syndrome called *cerebellar ataxia.*

The discharge patterns of the neurons in the vestibular-nucleus region are as diverse as their anatomical connections, so that details are outside the present scope. The interested reader is referred to the specialized literature [3, 10, 21].

The Vestibular Reflexes; Clinical Tests

Static and statokinetic reflexes. Equilibrium is maintained reflexly, without the primary participation of consciousness. The reflexes involved are subdivided into two groups, **static** and **statokinetic** reflexes [3, 10]. The vestibular receptors and somatosensory inputs, especially those from proprioceptors in the neck region, are responsible for reflexes in both groups. The **static reflexes** bring about particular positions of the individual limbs with respect to one another, or of the body in space – *postural and attitudinal reflexes,* respectively. The vestibular inputs for the static reflexes are the macula organs. A static reflex easily visible in cats, because of their vertical pupils, is **compensatory rolling of the eyes,** which appears when the head is turned about the long axis of the body (e.g., left ear down). The pupils keep very close to the vertical position, the eye rolling in a direction opposite to that of head rotation, and remain so as long as the head is in the abnormal position. This reflex is also present in man. The **statokinetic reflexes** are responses to movement stimuli that in themselves take the form of movements. They can be elicited by the semicircular canals and the macula organs. These reflexes are treated in greater detail on p. 98; examples include the twisting of a cat's body during a fall, so that it will land on its feet, and the movements one makes to recover from a stumble.

One statokinetic reflex, **vestibular nystagmus,** deserves further discussion because of its special clinical importance. As mentioned previously, various eye movements are elicited by the vestibular system; this particular form of eye movement is observed at the beginning of a rotational movement more extensive than the usual brief head movements. In vestibular nystagmus the eyes turn **against** the direction of rotation so as to maintain the original direction of gaze. Before the eyes have reached the limit of their movement range they are suddenly flicked back **in** the direction of rotation so that the gaze is directed at a new region in space. This rapid phase is followed by another **slow** movement against the direction of rotation.

The slow phase of nystagmus is initiated by the vestibular system, whereas the rapid restoring movement is brought about by the prepontine reticular formation (see p. 240).

When the body is turned about the vertical axis the horizontal semicircular canals are essentially the only part of the organ affected. Therefore deflection of the cupulae of the two horizontal canals produces **horizontal nystagmus.** The direction of the two (quick and slow) nystagmus components depends on the direction of rotation and thus on the direction of cupular deflection. If the body were to be turned about a horizontal axis (e.g., an axis through the two ears or sagitally through the forehead), the two vertical semicircular canals would be stimulated. Accordingly, a vertical or rotatory nystagmus would be produced. By convention, the direction of nystagmus (which, of course, has components in both directions) is defined as the direction **of the quick phase.** That is, in a "right nystagmus" the quick phase is to the right.

During passive rotation two factors tend to elicit nystagmus – the stimulation of the vestibular apparatus, and the movement of the visual field with respect to the subject. The vestibular nystagmus and the "optokinetic" nystagmus elicited by visual input act synergistically. The neuronal connections involved are discussed on p. 240.

Diagnostic significance of nystagmus. Nystagmus is used clinically as a *test of vestibular function*, usually in the form of **"postrotatory"** nystagmus. The subject is seated on a rotating chair and turned at a constant speed for a long time. Then the movement is suddenly stopped. Fig. 12-4 shows the behavior of the cupula when such maintained rotation is interrupted. The stop causes a deflection of the cupula in the direction opposite to that in which it was deflected at the onset of movement, and this deflection elicits a nystagmus. The term *postrotatory nystagmus* is used for the nystagmus associated with the cessation of prolonged uniform motion. The direction of postrotatory nystagmus can be deduced from the record of cupular deflection; it must be **opposite** to the direction of the previous motion. Records of the eye movements resemble those of optokinetic nystagmus (cf. Fig. 11-2, p. 238). Such records are called **nystagmograms.**

In testing postrotatory nystagmus it is important to eliminate the possibility of **visual fixation,** for in optomotor reactions visual inputs predominate over vestibular inputs and under some conditions could suppress nystagmus. For this reason the patient wears glasses with very strong convex lenses and a built-in light source *(Frenzel's spectacles).* These make the patient myopic and unable to fixate, while allowing the physician to observe easily the movement of the eyes. Glasses to prevent visual fixation are also necessary for clinical tests for the presence of **spontaneous nystagmus** – the first, simplest and most important procedure in the clinical examination of vestibular function.

Another clinical procedure to elicit vestibular nystagmus is **thermal stimulation** of the horizontal semicircular canal. It offers the advantage that each side can be tested separately. The head is tilted back by about 60° if the subject is seated, or raised by 30° if he is supine, so that the horizontal semicircular canal is exactly vertical. Then the **external meatus** of the ear is rinsed with cold or warm water. The outer edge of the semicircular canal is very close to the meatus, and there is sufficient heat transfer to cool or warm it. In accordance with the theory of BÁRÁNY, when the endolymph is warmed its specific gravity is lower; therefore the warmed part of the endolymph rises, creating a pressure difference between the two sides of the cupula which deflects the cupula and ultimately causes nystagmus (cf. Fig. 12-3; the situation there corresponds to warming of the left meatus). Because of its origin, this form is called **caloric nystagmus.** Rinsing with warm water causes nystagmus toward the treated side, and cold water produces nystagmus in the opposite direction. The nystagmus of people with vestibular disorders differs qualitatively and quantitatively from the norm. Details of the tests of nystagmus are given in [3]. It should be mentioned that caloric nystagmus can also be elicited in space vehicles, under zero-

gravity conditions [28], in which differences in endolymph density are irrelevant. Therefore at least one additional, still unknown mechanism must be involved in producing caloric nystagmus – for instance, a direct thermal influence on the vestibular organ.
The function of the macula organs can be tested by observing the eye-rolling response to head tilt or by moving the subject sinusoidally back and forth on a platform.

Disorders of the vestibular system. Strong excitation of the vestibular apparatus is often associated with unpleasant sensations – dizziness, vomiting, sweating, rapid pulse etc. The term **kinetosis** (motion sickness) is applied to these symptoms [23]. Kinetoses are most likely to result from the action of stimulus constellations to which the organism is unaccustomed (for example, at sea). Coriolis accelerations are particularly effective in this regard, as are any discrepancies between visual impressions and signals from the vestibular apparatus. Infants and patients without labyrinths do not exhibit kinetoses.
To understand how kinetoses are produced, one must keep in mind that the vestibular system evolved to meet the requirements of locomotion on foot, and not to deal with the forces of acceleration encountered in modern vehicles. Therefore sensory illusions can easily occur in this system. They have often caused accidents; for instance, when a pilot no longer notices an ongoing rotation and the rotation stops, the pilot can sense a rotation in the opposite direction and react inappropriately.

Acute interruption of labyrinthine function on one side causes nausea, vomiting, sweating and the like, nystagmus toward the healthy side and vertigo toward the healthy side. There is also a tendency for the patient to fall toward the affected side. But often the clinical picture is complicated by ambiguity in the directions associated with dizziness, nystagmus and falling. In some diseases, such as Menière's syndrome, in which there is excessive pressure within the endolymph space on one side, the initial result is stimulation of the receptors, which naturally causes symptoms opposite to those of receptor destruction described above. In contrast to the dramatic effects of acute vestibular disorders, the **chronic elimination of one labyrinth** is relatively well compensated. The central vestibular system can habituate so as to reduce the response to unusual states of excitation [21, 26]. This adjustment is especially successful when other sensory channels provide corrective inputs – visual or tactile, for instance. Thus the difficulties experienced in the chronic condition become more pronounced in the dark.
Bilateral acute malfunction is rare in man. In animal experiments the symptoms are far less severe than those of unilateral destruction, for when the neuronal inputs to the vestibular nuclei are interrupted on both sides, symmetry still prevails. Weightlessness (in space travel) does not affect the semicircular canals. The gravitational forces acting on the otoliths, however, are eliminated; therefore in all the maculae the otolith membrane takes a position determined by its own elastic properties. The resulting constellation of excitation never occurs on earth and may be involved in producing space sickness. As a person habituates to the weightless condition, visual stimuli gain in significance and inputs from the otolith apparatus become less significant [16].

12.2 Physiology of Hearing

The customary distinction between the physical and biological aspects of hearing is reflected in the terminology of this field. The term "acoustic" and its derivatives are used with reference to the physical properties of sound and to the mechanical devices or anatomical structures that affect these properties, whereas "auditory" refers to the physiological processes in hearing and their anatomical correlates.

The Physical Properties of the Sound Stimulus (Acoustics)

Sound is an oscillation of the molecules[1] of an elastic medium, propagated through the medium as a longitudinal pressure wave. Air is one such medium. The oscillations in general are set up by oscillating bodies – for example, a tuning fork or loudspeaker cone – that impart enery to the surrounding medium by accelerating the adjacent molecules.
These pass the oscillation energy on to molecules a little further away, and so on. The process expands as a wave with the sound source at its center, with a velocity of ca. 335 m/s in air. Oscillation of the molecules creates zones in

[1] The molecules are also of course constantly in Brownian motion of considerable amplitude, upon which the oscillations that concern us here are superimposed.

which molecules are densely packed and other zones containing fewer molecules. Accordingly, the pressure in these zones is higher or lower than average. The amplitude of this pressure variation is called **sound pressure.** Sound pressure can be measured with suitably designed microphones, and either its effective value (cf. a textbook of physics) or its time course can be recorded and used to characterize the sound. Like other pressures, sound pressure is given in N/m^2 (= Pa). In acoustics, however, it is customary to use a relative measure, the so-called **sound pressure level** (SPL). It is expressed in decibels (dB), as follows. The sound pressure of interest p_x is compared with the arbitrarily chosen (because it is near the human threshold) reference sound pressure $p_0 = 2 \cdot 10^{-5}\ N/m^2$, by taking the ratio p_x/p_0. The logarithm (to the base 10) of this ratio is multiplied by 20. The complete definition is thus

$$\text{sound pressure level} = 20 \cdot \log_{10} \frac{p_x}{p_0}\ [\text{dB}]$$

The logarithmic scale was chosen because it makes the wide range of audible sound pressures considerably more manageable. The "20" has a simple explanation: the log of a ratio of sound power (I) was originally defined as a "bel" (in honor of ALEXANDER GRAHAM BELL), in which there are 10 decibels. The sound pressure p, however, can be more easily measured than power. Because power is proportional to the pressure amplitude squared ($I \propto p^2$) and $\log p^2 = 2 \cdot \log p$, one ends up with the above equation. Corresponding definitions are generally applied in communications technology. As an example of the use of the above equation, the sound pressure level of a tone with sound pressure $p_x = 2 \cdot 10^{-1}\ N/m^2$ is found as follows:

$$\frac{p_x}{p_0} = \frac{2 \cdot 10^{-1}}{2 \cdot 10^{-5}} = 10^4$$

$$\text{sound pressure level} = 20 \cdot \log_{10} 10^4 = 20 \cdot 4 = 80.$$

Thus the sound pressure $2 \cdot 10^{-1}\ N/m^2$ corresponds to a sound pressure level of 80 dB. Similar calculations show that doubling the sound pressure increases the sound pressure level by 6 dB, and increasing sound pressure by a factor of 10 adds 20 dB. The ordinates on the left in Fig. 12-8 illustrate the relationship between sound pressure and sound pressure level.

In acoustics it is customary to specify that one is using "dB SPL" because dB scales are widely used for other phenomena (voltages, for example) and with other arbitrary reference values. The appended "SPL" emphasizes that the numbers were obtained as described by the above equation, with the reference pressure $p_0 = 2 \cdot 10^{-5}\ N/m^2$.

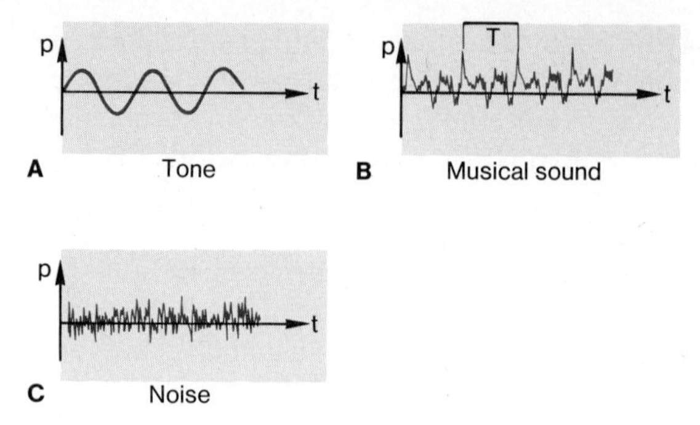

Fig. 12-5 A–C. Time course of the sound pressure of a tone (**A**), a musical sound (**B**) and a noise (**C**). T is the period of the fundamental frequency in the musical sound; there is no period in the noise

Sound intensity is the amount of energy passing through a unit area per unit time. It is given in W/m^2. $10^{-12}\ W/m^2$ in a planar sound field corresponds to $2 \cdot 10^{-5}\ N/m^2$.

The frequency of a sound is expressed in hertz (Hz); one hertz is equal to one cycle per second. A sound has the same frequency as its source as long as the source is not moving in space.

When a sound is composed of only a single frequency it is called a **tone.** Fig. 12-5 A shows the time course of the sound pressure in this case. Pure tones, however, practically never occur in everyday life; most sounds are made up of several simultaneous frequencies (Fig. 12-5 B). Usually this mixture consists of a fundamental frequency plus several harmonics, integral multiples of the fundamental frequency. Such sounds have a **musical** quality. The fundamental is reflected in the period of the complex sound-pressure wave (T in Fig. 12-5 B). Because different sound sources produce harmonics to differing extents, the quality of sounds at a given fundamental frequency can vary; the abundance of subtle shadings produced by an orchestra arises in this way [25]. A sound comprising very many unrelated frequencies is called **noise** (Fig. 12-5 C), or "white noise" if essentially all frequencies in the audible range are equally represented. No periodicity is detectable in the sound-pressure record of a noisy sound.

Anatomical Bases of the Process of Hearing; the Peripheral Ear

The sound waves are channeled into the auditory system by way of the **external ear,** traveling along the external auditory meatus to the

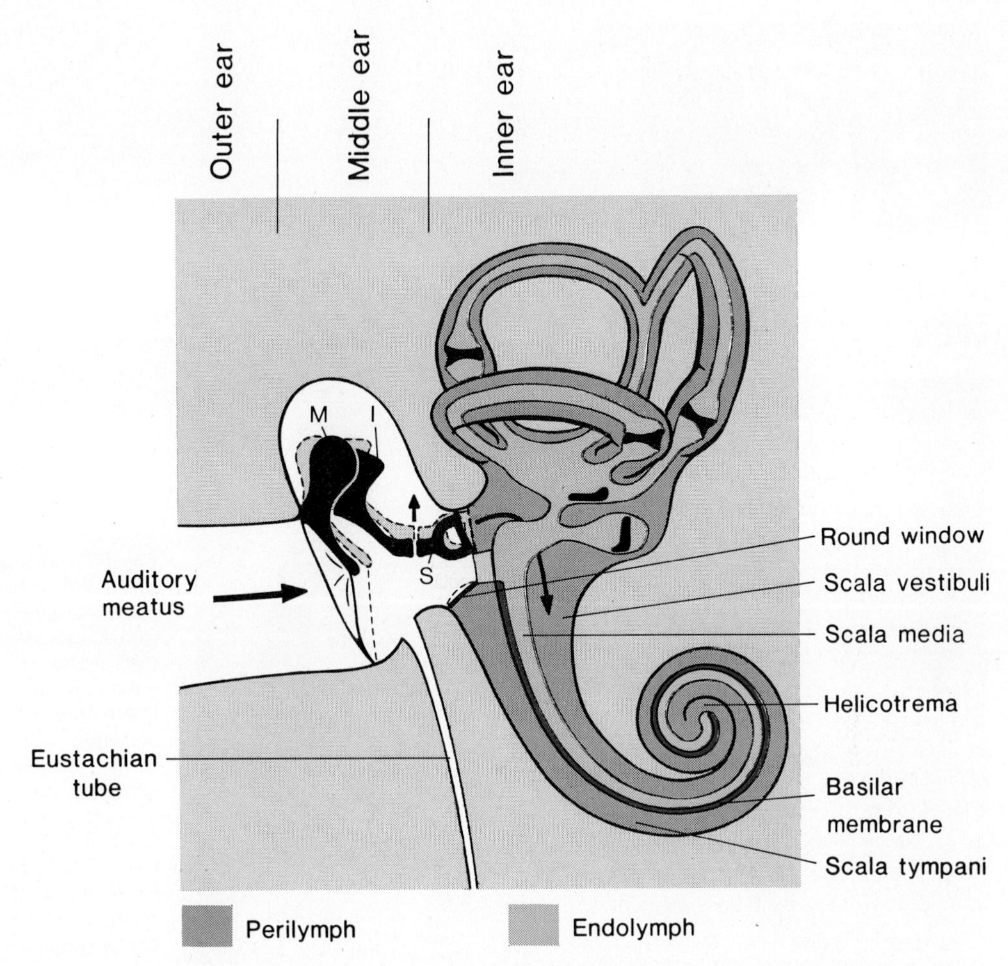

Fig. 12-6. Schematic drawing of the outer, middle and inner ear. M, malleus; I, incus; S, stapes. The arrows indicate the direction of movement of the tympanic membrane and incostapedial joint and the fluid shift when the tympanic membrane bulges inward

eardrum or **tympanic membrane** (cf. Fig. 12-6). This delicate membrane, with a mother-of-pearl sheen, closes off the meatus and forms a partition between it and the **middle ear,** which is also filled with air. Within the cavity of the middle ear is a chain of three flexibly linked **ossicles,** the *hammer (malleus), anvil (incus)* and *stirrup (stapes).* The "handle" of the hammer is firmly fused to the eardrum, and the foot-plate of the stapes (which really does look like a stirrup) fits into an opening in the petrous bone, the oval window. There the stapes borders the **inner ear.** The sound energy is transmitted from the eardrum to the inner ear by way of the malleus, incus and stapes, as these structures oscillate in synchrony with the eardrum. The cavity of the middle ear communicates with the pharynx by way of the eustachian tube. Whenever one swallows, the tube opens, ventilating the middle ear and equalizing its air pressure with that of the atmosphere. When inflammation causes the mucous membranes in this region to swell, opening of the tube is impeded. Then if the external air pressure should change (as in an airplane) or if the air is reabsorbed from the middle-ear cavity, the resulting pressure differences are felt as "pressure on the ears." The pressure in this air space is also an important factor in diving; the diver must try, by pressing or swallowing, to match it to the increased external air pressure. If the attempt fails, the eardrum is in danger of rupturing.

The inner ear is embedded in the petrous part of the temporal bone. It comprises the organs of equilibrium and of hearing. Because of its shape the auditory organ is called the **cochlea** (Latin for "snail shell"). The cochlea consists of three parallel canals coiled together. These are the **scala tympani, scala media** and **scala vestibuli.** *Scala tympani* and *scala vestibuli* communicate with one another at the **helicotrema** (Fig. 12-6). They are filled with **perilymph,** a fluid resem-

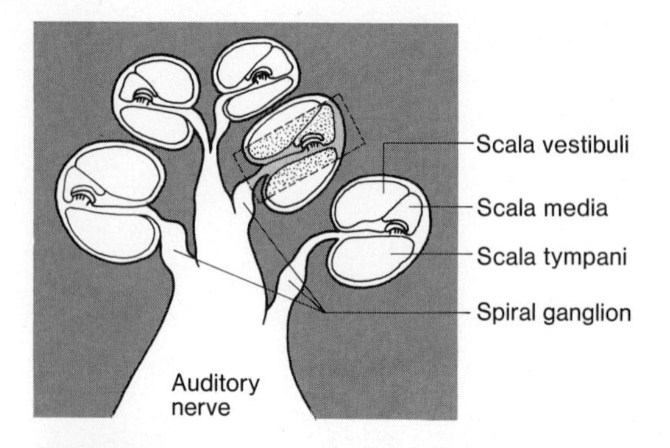

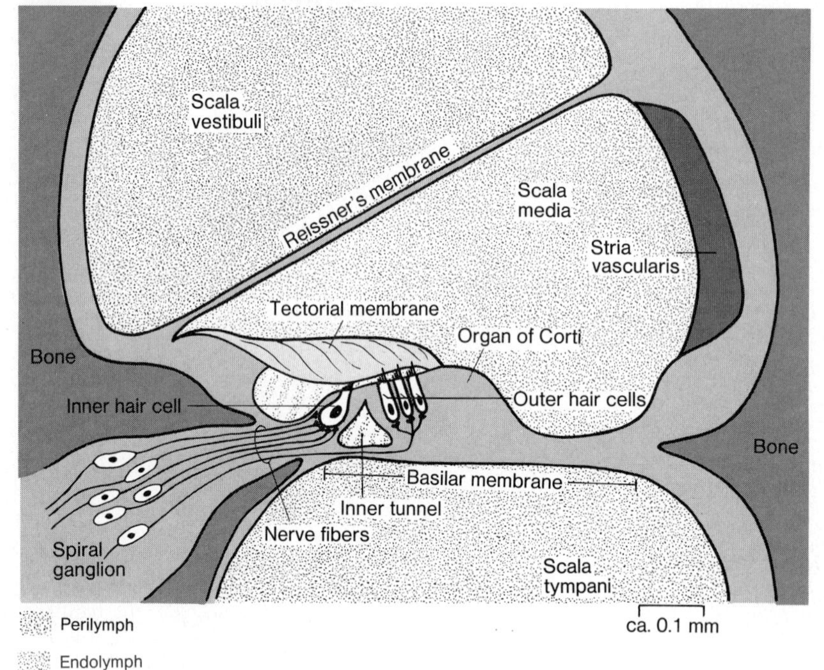

Fig. 12-7. Schematic section through the inner ear. The upper drawing gives an impression of the relative positions of the cochlear coil, the spiral ganglion and the auditory nerve. The lower drawing shows the most important elements in one turn of the spiral and the different lymph spaces, further enlarged. The composition of the subtectorial lymph has not been definitively determined. The lower drawing also shows the spatial relations of the tectorial membrane and the receptor cells in the organ of Corti

bling extracellular fluid in its composition and thus containing much Na^+ (ca. 140 mmol/l[2]). It is probably an ultrafiltrate of plasma. There are sites of communication between the perilymph and the cerebrospinal-fluid spaces, but their functional significance, if any, is unknown. In any case, the CSF and the perilymph are very similar in chemical composition.

The *scala media* is filled with **endolymph.** This fluid is rich in K^+ (ca. 155 mmol/l) and thus resembles an intracellular fluid [2]. The peri- and endolymphatic spaces of the cochlea communicate with the respective spaces of the vestibular organ (cf. Fig. 12-6). At the oval window the foot-plate of the stapes adjoins the perilymph of the scala vestibuli; the opening is sealed off by an **annular ligament,** so that no perilymph can leak out. At the base of the scala tympani is another opening to the middle ear, the **round window.** This window is sealed by a fine membrane to prevent leakage of perilymph.

Fig. 12-7 shows a cross section through the cochlea. The scala vestibuli is separated from the scala media by **Reissner's membrane,** and the **basilar membrane** separates the scala media from the scala tympani. A thickened ridge running along the basilar membrane, the **organ of Corti,** contains the *receptors* surrounded by supporting cells. The former again are hair cells, but they have only stereocilia; in the receptors of the organ of Corti the kinocilium is regressed [39]. A distinction is made between **inner** and **outer hair cells.** The latter are arranged in three rows, whereas the inner hair cells form a single row. In man there are about 3,500 inner and 12,000 outer hair cells [12].

Here, as in the vestibules, the hair cells are secondary sense cells. The afferent nerve fibers innervating the hair cells come from the bipolar cells of the **spiral ganglion,** which lies at the center of the cochlea; the central processes of these cells run to the CNS. About 90% of the nerve fibers in the spiral ganglion terminate on inner hair cells, each of which thus makes contact with many nerve fibers [39]. Only the remaining 10% of fibers innervate the far more numerous outer hair cells. These fibers must branch extensively in order to supply all the outer hair cells, though the many receptors supplied by one such fiber are all fairly close to one another. Altogether, the auditory nerve contains ca. 30,000 to 40,000 afferent fibers [12]. The organ of Corti also receives efferent fibers. Their functional significance is uncertain [37], though it is known that they can inhibit the activity of afferent fibers.

Over the organ of Corti lies the **tectorial membrane,** a gelatinous mass attached to the inner wall of the cochlea in the region of the central bone, and to the organ of Corti. The tectorial membrane separates a narrow, fluid-filled space below it from the actual endolymph space above. The stereocilia of the outer hair cells adhere at their ends to the underside of the tectorial membrane. Probably the cilia of the inner hair cells also contact the tectorial membrane, though considerably less rigidly, but this question is not yet definitely settled [39].

On the outer side of the scala media is the **stria vascularis** – a region well supplied with blood, as its name implies, and highly active metabolically. It plays an important role in *providing energy* to the cochlea and determining the composition of the endolymph. Various ion pumps here, including one for K^+, maintain the ionic milieu and the positive potential (cf. p. 291) in the endolymph [2, 20]. Some diuretics (drugs that increase the output of urine) have ototoxic side effects that can lead to deafness; they act on ion pumps in the stria. In the kidney they poison certain ion carriers in the tubule epithelia (cf. p. 742), which are responsible for the reabsorption of salts. Evidently some of the ion pumps in the stria operate on principles similar to those of some ion-transport mechanisms in the kidney and are thus also poisoned by these drugs.

Psychophysics of Auditory Sensations

Auditory thresholds. A sound must exceed a certain sound pressure level in order to be heard. This **auditory threshold** (Fig. 12-8) is frequency-dependent, the human ear being most sensitive in the range 2,000–5,000 Hz. In the higher and lower frequency ranges considerably higher sound pressure levels are required to exceed the threshold.

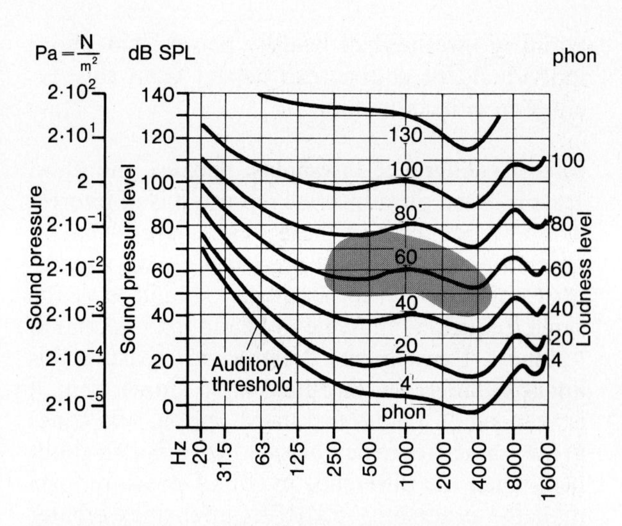

Fig. 12-8. Curves of equal loudness (isophones) according to the standard DIN 45630. The ordinates on the left give the equivalent values of sound pressure and sound pressure level. The *red shading* indicates the speech region (see text)

Loudness. A tone at any frequency, once the threshold has been passed, is sensed as becoming louder as the sound pressure increases. The relationship between the (physically defined) sound pressure level and the subjectively experienced **loudness level** can be described quantitatively. That is, a subject can be asked not only if a tone is audible (above threshold) but also whether two sequentially presented tones of the same or different frequency sound **equally loud** or not. For example, a test tone and a reference tone at 1,000 Hz are presented one after the other, and the subject is told to adjust a potentiometer so as to change the loudness of the reference tone until it seems the same as that of the test tone. When this is achieved, the two tones are said to have the same loudness level. The loudness level of a sound is expressed in **phon** – the sound pressure level of a 1,000-Hz tone that sounds equally loud. Thus if the 1,000-Hz tone has been set at 70 dB SPL when the subjective sensation of loudness equals that produced by a test tone, the test tone has the loudness level 70 phon. Because it is used as the standard, a 1,000-Hz tone necessarily has *identical* dB and phon values, as can be seen in Fig. 12-8. This figure also shows **equal-loudness contours** above the threshold curve, plotted from the average responses of a large, international sample of healthy young subjects. All the tones on one of these curves are regarded as equally loud, regardless of their frequency. Such curves are also called **isophones.** The threshold curve is also an isophone, for all the tones on it seem equally loud – just above threshold. The mean auditory threshold of healthy people is 4 phon; individuals, of course, can depart from this average in either direction.

Intensity-difference thresholds. Because the phon scale is based on subjective reports it is of interest to know how precise these reports are – that is, how different the sound pressures of two consecutive tones (which for simplicity should have the same frequency) must be to be judged unequal in loudness. Experiments designed to measure this **intensity-difference threshold** have shown that it is very small. In the threshold region, two tones at the same frequency are said to differ in loudness when the difference in sound pressure level is of the order of 3–5 dB. At intensities greater than ca. 40 dB above threshold the difference threshold falls to 1 dB [49].

The phon scale in itself tells nothing about the *increase* in subjective loudness as sound pressure level rises. The phon scale was constructed by asking subjects only to say when a test and a reference tone seem equally loud; the way the loudness of a given tone changes is not examined at all. But the relationship between loudness and sound pressure is of interest, for to evaluate disturbing noises one must know something about the increase in the sensation of loudness. To reveal such relationships, subjects were required to adjust a test tone at 1,000 Hz so that it was n times as loud (e.g., 2 times or 4 times) as a reference tone set by definition at 1,000 Hz and 40 dB SPL. From the sound pressure levels so obtained one can describe quantitatively the strength of the sensation; this unit of loudness is the **sone.** A tone that seems four times as loud as the standard (1,000 Hz, 40 dB) has a loudness of 4 sones, a tone half as loud has a loudness of 0.5 sone, and so on.
It turns out that above 30 dB SPL the loudness sensation is related to sound pressure by a power function with exponent 0.6 for 1,000 Hz (Stevens' power function; cf. p. 191 and [17, 49]).
This is equivalent to saying that at 1,000 Hz and above 30 dB the sensation of loudness doubles when the sound pressure increases by 10 dB. Note that doubling the sound pressure amounts to an increase of only 6 dB, and thus does not double the loudness; to do that, the sound pressure must be roughly tripled. This in turn, because $I \propto p^2$, means that the sound intensity must be raised by a factor of ten to double the loudness sensation. Ten musical instruments, all playing the same tone at the same level, sound only twice as loud as one playing alone.
Because the loudness level (in phon) of a given tone is by definition determined by comparison with a 1,000-Hz tone, the loudness in sones of a tone can be calculated from its loudness level and the loudness function of a 1,000-Hz tone [49]. In this indirect way the loudness level provides information about loudness sensations. To this extent, for the technical measurement of disturbing noise, it is justified to use a simplified procedure which provides an approximation of the loudness level.

Devices to measure sound pressure level and loudness level. As was stated at the outset, isophones are derived from psychophysical experiments. It follows directly that the phon values of a sound cannot simply be measured by a physical method like those used for sound pressure – a physically defined entity measurable by suitable microphones and amplifiers (sound-level meters). To obtain at least approximate measurements of loudness level one can use sound-level meters incorporating frequency filters, with filter characteristics described roughly by the hearing threshold or other isophones. The device is thus made differentially sensitive to different frequencies, in nearly the same way as the human ear, being less sensitive in the low-frequency and high-frequency ranges. There are three internationally accepted filter curves, designated A, B and C. When results obtained with such a device are reported one must indicate which of these curves was used, by adding the letter to the dB reading. For example, a measurement might be given as 30 dB (A), a value approximately equal to 30 phon. The filter curve A is designed to match the auditory threshold curve and should actually be used only in the low-intensity region. However, to simplify the measurement procedure practically all data are now given in dB (A), even if additional error is introduced. Similarly, for simplification, measurements of disturbing noise are done with the dB (A) filter although strictly speaking the sone scale should be used. For example, the noise of an idling car is about 75 dB (A).

Sound trauma. If the sound pressure level of a sound is greatly increased, the eventual result is a sensation of *pain* in the ear. Experiments have shown that pain coincides with a loudness level of about 130 phon. Moreover, such intense sounds cause not only pain but also reversible loss of hearing (TTS, temporary threshold shift) or – if exposure is prolonged – even irreversible damage to the sensory cells and the microcirculation in the cochlea (permanent threshold shift, sound trauma). In fact, sound trauma can be caused even by sounds at considerably lower intensities if the exposure is long enough. Long-term exposure can be expected to cause injury if the intensity is 90 dB (A) or more [14].
The hearing of a worker regularly exposed to sound exceeding this level is therefore endangered, and must be protected by sound-damping devices (earplugs or ear muffs). Without this protection the person will become hard of hearing in a matter of years (see also p. 297).

Subjective reactions to noise. Apart from sound trauma – objectively demonstrable damage to the inner ear by loud sounds – sound can have distinct harmful subjective effects (though these too may be accompanied by objective symptoms such as elevated blood pressure or insomnia). The "annoyance" caused by a sound depends a great deal on a person's psychological attitude toward the sound source. For example, a tenant in an apartment block may feel seriously disturbed by the piano playing of another tenant, even though they live two floors apart, other tenants have no complaints, and the loudness level of the music in the apartment of the aggrieved person is low. It is difficult to find general rules to prevent annoying noise, and the guidelines offered in civil regulations are often an unsatisfactory compromise [14].

Audible range and speech region. The audibility of a tone, as Fig. 12-8 shows, depends on its frequency as well as its sound pressure. A healthy young adult can hear frequencies from 20 Hz to 16,000 Hz (16 kHz). Frequencies above 16 kHz are called **ultrasound,** and those lower than 20 Hz **infrasound.** The audible range of man thus extends from 20 Hz to 16 kHz and from 4 phon to 130 phon. This is the **audible area** enclosed by the top and bottom curves in Fig. 12-8. In the middle of this area are the frequencies and intensities produced in speaking. This smaller area, shaded red in Fig. 12-8, is called the **speech area.** For speech to be adequately understandable, transmission systems (e.g., the telephone) must transmit frequencies at least in the range 300 Hz to 3.5 kHz. In older people sensitivity to high frequencies regularly declines, a phenomenon known as **presbycusis.**

Frequency-difference threshold. As we know from everyday experience, we can evaluate a tone not only by its loudness but also by its **pitch,** which is correlated with the frequency of the tone. We call a tone "high" when its frequency is high, and conversely. The ability to discriminate the pitches of tones heard in succession is astonishingly good. In the optimal range, around 1,000 Hz, the **frequency-difference threshold** is 0.3%, or about 3 Hz [14, 49].
Musical sounds composed of several frequencies can also be assigned a particular pitch; in general they are regarded as having the same pitch as a pure tone at a frequency equal to the fundamental frequency of the sound [25].

The ordinary musical scale is based on the octave, a doubling of frequency. In equal-tempered tuning the octave is divided into 12 equal steps, each differing from the next by the factor $\sqrt[12]{2} = 1.0595$. This difference is considerably greater than the threshold difference given above. Nevertheless it is interesting to find that when two pure tones are presented simultaneously their frequencies must be much further apart than the sequentially discriminable difference for two components to be detectable [17, 25, 49]. Evidently the two simultaneously stimulated regions of the inner ear (cf. p. 292) must be separated by a certain minimal distance if they are to be resolved.
This finding corresponds to the formation of "critical bandwidths". For example, the auditory system has been found to be incapable of resolving pure tones within a range of about a third of an octave (the critical bandwidth); such tones fuse to give the sensation of a single sound. The loudness of this sensation increases regularly with the number of subcomponents, but the pitch sensed by the subject remains the same. The sound energy within a critical bandwidth is thus integrated, resulting in a unitary sensation.
The critical bandwidth – about a third on the scale – is astonishingly large, for it means that two *pure* tones separated by almost a third cannot be resolved. (In the case of mixed tones the situation is of course different; for example, it is easy to tell that two adjacent keys on a piano have been struck simultaneously, for the harmonics accompanying the fundamentals of each are not all within a single critical bandwidth.)
The human audible range comprises about 24 critical bandwidths. For further information see [17, 49].
When two tones sound at the same time the thresholds to the two are reciprocally affected. For example, during presentation of a steady tone at 500 Hz and 80 dB SPL, tones at other frequencies are not heard at the intensities on the auditory threshold curve of Fig. 12-8. Far higher sound pressures are required – in this example, about 40 dB SPL for a 1,000-Hz tone [17, 49]. This phenomenon is called masking. It is of considerable practical significance, because in daily life important acoustic information, such as a conversation, may be masked by background noises so that it cannot be understood. Further details about psychoacoustic phenomena can be found in [17, 25, 49].

The Role of the Middle Ear

As described above, the eardrum is set into oscillation by sound and passes the energy of oscillation along the chain of ossicles to the perilymph in the scala vestibuli. Sound transmitted by this route is said to be **airborne.**
Airborne sound must be transmitted form the air to the fluids in the inner ear. When sound passes from air to liquid most of the arriving sound energy is ordinarily *reflected,* because the two media differ in their characteristic acoustic impedances. In the middle ear, however, the **tympanum-ossicle apparatus** effectively matches the acoustic impedances of air and inner ear to one another, considerably reducing the losses by reflection. The mechanism corresponds roughly to treating the objective lens of a camera so as to reduce reflection of light at the air-glass interface. The *impedance matching* is achieved by two mechanisms in particular: 1. The area of the eardrum is considerably larger than that of the stapes foot-plate. Because pressure = force/area, the pressure at the oval window is higher than at the eardrum. 2. An additional pressure increase is brought about by the differing lengths of the lever arms in the chain of ossicles. Thus the system operates like an electrical transformer, though still other factors are also involved – the masses and elasticities in the transmission chain,

and the curvature and oscillatory properties of the eardrum. The net effect of the impedance-matching mechanism is an improvement of hearing by 10–20 dB, depending on the frequency range, which is the equivalent of doubling to quadrupling the loudness sensation. The transmission properties of the tympanum-ossicle apparatus are frequency-dependent. Transmission is best in the intermediate frequency range, which accounts in part for the shape of the threshold curve.

But a sensation of sound also occurs when an oscillating body such as a tuning fork is placed directly on the skull, so that the primary energy transmission is to the skull bones. This process is called **bone conduction.** As will be shown in the next section, excitation of the inner ear requires fluid motion like that produced by the stapes movement induced by airborne sound. Bone-conducted sound produces such fluid motion in two ways. First, zones of compression and rarefaction traveling through the oscillating skull bones displace fluid from the voluminous vestibular labyrinth into the cochlea and back again (compression theory [12]). Second, the tympanum-ossicle apparatus has a certain mass, and because of its inertia oscillation of the ossicles lags behind that of the skull bones. The stapes therefore moves relative to the petrous bone, exciting the inner ear (mass-inertia theory [12]).

Bone conduction does not contribute appreciably to hearing in everyday life. Because some of the sound energy during speech production is conducted through bone to the ear of the speaker, particularly in the low-frequency range, a tape-recording of one's own voice sounds quite strange. As a disgnostic aid to the physician, however, bone conduction is very useful (see p. 297).

The **middle-ear muscles,** the tensor tympani and the stapedius, insert on the malleus and stapes. The reflex contractions of these muscles that accompany exposure to sound impair transmission, because they change the impedance of the middle ear. This mechanism cannot provide effective protection against excessively loud sounds, although such a possibility has been discussed. The functional significance of the middle-ear reflexes remains obscure [12].

Auditory Processes in the Inner Ear

Mechanical events. When the stapes is set into oscillation by sound entering the ear, it transmits sound energy to the perilymph in the scala vestibuli (cf. Fig. 12-6). Because the fluids of the inner ear are incompressible, there must be some structure permitting pressure equilibration. This structure is the round window; the membrane of the round window moves out as the stapes moves in, and vice versa. At the same time, the movements of the stapes displace the adjacent, basal part of the scala media, with the Reissner's and basilar membranes enclosing it, from the resting position; it swings up and down, toward the scala vestibuli and scala tympani in alternation. For simplicity, in the following discussion we shall refer to the scala media with its bounding membranes simply as the *endolymphatic duct*. This displacement of the endolymphatic duct at its base generates a wave, which passes along the duct from stapes to helicotrema like a wave along a taut horizontal rope. In Fig. 12-9 A two states of such a wave are shown, with the endolymphatic duct represented by a single line. Because the stapes is continually in oscillation during a sound, there is a steady succession of waves along the endolymphatic duct to the helicotrema. These are called **traveling waves** (cf. [45]). The stiffness of the basilar membrane decreases from the stapes to the helicotrema. Therefore the velocity of wave propagation becomes progressively lower as the helicotrema is approached, and the wavelength decreases. For the same reason, the amplitude of the waves traveling toward the helicotrema at first increases (Fig. 12-9), becoming very much larger than in the stapes region where the waves originated. However, because of the damping properties of the liquid-filled inner-ear channels the waves are soon attenuated; they rapidly decrease in am-

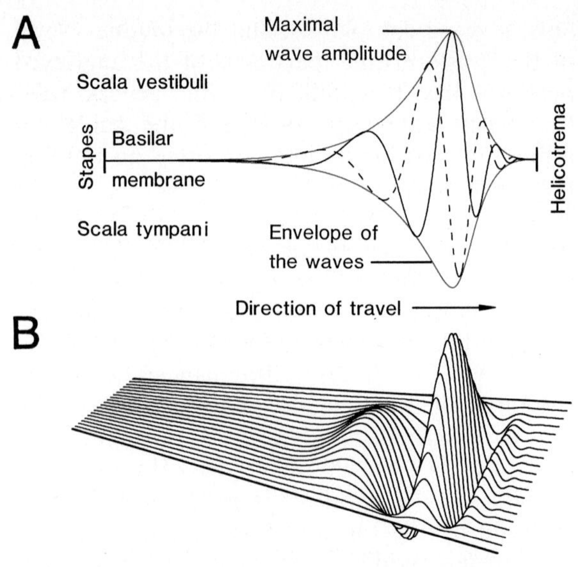

Fig. 12-9. A Diagram of a traveling wave, showing the wave contour at two different times. The envelope shows the maximal amplitude of the wave generated by a fixed frequency, at the different sites on the cochlea. **B** Three-dimensional representation of the wave

plitude and ultimately disappear, usually before they have reached the helicotrema. Somewhere between the sites of origin and extinction of the waves, then, there must be a place where the amplitude is maximal (Fig. 12-9). This *amplitude maximum* is found at a **different position for each frequency** – the higher the frequency, the closer to the stapes, and the lower the frequency, the closer to the helicotrema. The existence of this maximum results in a mapping of each frequency in the audible range onto **one** particular **place** in the endolymphatic duct (or on the basilar membrane). This situation is described by the term **frequency dispersion.** The sensory cells are most excited at the site of the oscillation maximum, so that different frequencies excite different sense cells **(place theory).**

The wave movements described above, and in particular the position of the oscillation maximum, can be demonstrated by means of the MÖSSBAUER technique, the capacitive probe, or interferometric methods [45]. One remarkable finding is that the amplitudes of the waves are extremely small, even at the site of the maximum. For sound at the auditory threshold, the deflection would be only about 10^{-10} m (close to the average diameter of a hydrogen atom!). Another is that the oscillation maximum is very sharply localized, so that the various places on the basilar membrane are very sharply tuned to particular frequencies – but only if the cochlea is completely intact. If it is damaged (for example, by only slight hypoxia), the oscillation amplitudes decrease and the sharp tuning is lost. That is, the basilar membrane does not just oscillate passively; active processes create a frequency-specific amplifier mechanism (see p. 293).

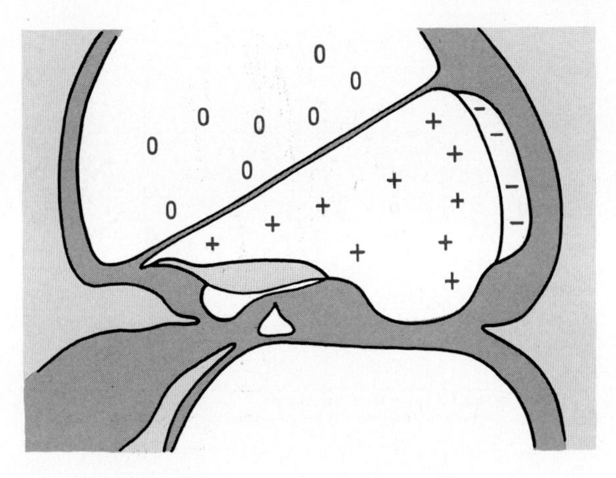

Fig. 12-10. Standing potentials in the cochlea

The transduction process at the hair cells. As was shown in the preceding section, because of the mechanical properties of the cochlea exposure of the ear to a particular sound frequency causes the basilar membrane to oscillate with appreciable amplitude only at a single, narrowly delimited place, in the region of the amplitude maximum. Among the events then occurring at this place are **relative movements** of the basilar and tectorial membranes. These movements exert a shear force on the cilia, either by way of a direct contact between the cilia and the tectorial membrane or by displacement of the subtectorial lymph; in either case, as in the vestibular receptors, the bending of the cilia is the adequate stimulus.

Bending of the cilia triggers the *transduction process,* in which minuscule mechanical deformations of the cilia bring about the opening of ion channels and hence depolarization of the hair cell. An initial prerequisite for this process is the **endocochlear potential.** Measurements with microelectrodes show that the endolymph space is positively charged (ca. +80 mV) with respect to the scala vestibuli and to the other extracellular spaces in the body. The stria vascularis and the organ of Corti are negatively charged (ca. −70 mV; Fig. 12-10). The potential measurable in the organ of Corti is probably the intracellular potential of the hair and supporting cells. The positive endocochlear potential is maintained by energy-supplying processes in the stria vascularis. Shearing of the cilia changes the membrane resistance of the hair cells in synchrony with the stimulus, by opening the ion channels. Because of the standing (i.e., steady) potentials there is a large potential difference between the endolymph space and the interior of the hair cells, at least 150 mV; therefore these stimulus-synchronized changes in membrane resistance must produce local ionic currents that change the membrane potential of the hair cell – they build up "receptor potentials" (the so-called **battery hypothesis** [7, 29, 48]). To record these receptor potentials in the hair cells is difficult, but possible [7, 29, 48]. It is simpler to place macroelectrodes near the receptors, in the scala tympani or at the round window; these record a potential called the **cochlear microphonic** (Fig. 12-11).

This potential behaves like the output voltage of a microphone, reflecting the changes in sound pressure quite accurately. A tape recording of speech made not with a microphone but by picking up the microphonic potentials of an experimental animal is entirely understandable. The origin of the microphonic potential is not understood; the earlier assumption that it consists

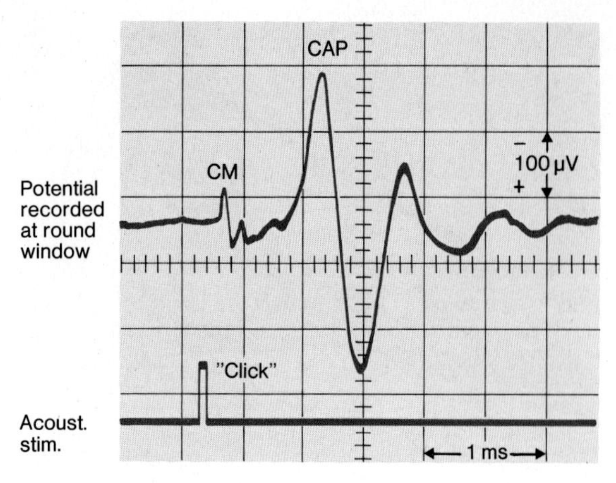

Fig. 12-11. Cochlear microphonic potential (CM) and compound action potential in the auditory nerve (CAP) recorded at the round window when a click is presented to the ear

of extracellularly recordable components of the hair-cell receptor potentials is no longer fully tenable. Intracellular recordings from inner and outer hair cells [7, 33, 34] have shown that although these cells do generate receptor potentials, at high stimulus frequencies only a steady voltage is recorded. That is, the membrane potential of the hair cells cannot follow high sound frequencies. The microphonic potential

(i) follows the sound stimulus with practically no latency,
(ii) has no refractory period or
(iii) measurable threshold, and
(iv) is not subject to fatigue; in all these respects, it does not behave like a neuronal action potential.

The depolarization of the hair cells caused by the sound stimulus causes the release of a transmitter at the bases of the hair cells. This transmitter, which is possibly glutamate [38], excites the afferent nerve fibers. When a click (a brief pressure pulse) is presented to the ear, the fibers in the auditory nerve are activated synchronously, and a compound action potential can be recorded at the round window in addition to the microphonic potential. More prolonged sounds elicit asynchronous discharge, which does not sum to form a discrete action potential. Fig. 12-11 shows the cochlear microphonic (CM) and compound action potential (CAP) elicited by a click. This record was obtained from a cat, but similar potentials can also be recorded in humans when – as is sometimes necessary for diagnostic purposes – an electrode is inserted through the tympanic membrane and positioned near the round window.

The coding of sound in auditory nerve fibers. 90% of the afferent fibers in the cochlear nerve are myelinated and come from the inner hair cells. Each of them contacts a single inner hair cell, and thus represents a very small place in the cochlea. These fibers are thick enough that their action potentials can be recorded with microelectrodes and the responses to sound observed. (The fibers coming from the outer hair cells are too thin for such recording.) Because certain places in the cochlea are associated with certain frequencies, it follows that each nerve fiber coming from an inner hair cell is maximally excited by a specific frequency – the **characteristic frequency** of the fiber. That is, a single fiber in the cochlear nerve is most readily excited by presentation of sound at this characteristic frequency. If the ear is stimulated with other frequencies, this fiber cannot be activated, or is activated only by appropriately increasing the sound pressure level. This situation is illustrated in Fig. 12-12, a plot of threshold vs. stimulus frequency for two different fibers. The criterion for threshold is an increase above spontaneous activity by a certain amount. Each fiber can be activated by the frequencies and intensities within the shaded region. The **tuning curves** outlining these regions have a narrow, sharply tuned part where the threshold is low and another part covering a broad high-threshold range of frequencies. The tuning curve reflects the spatial mapping of frequency on the basilar membrane. The response of the single fiber to a sound stimulus, expressed as a tuning curve, represents a spectral analysis of the sound. If a sound stimulus comprises several frequencies, all the associated groups of nerve fibers are stimulated. The *duration* of a sound stimulus is

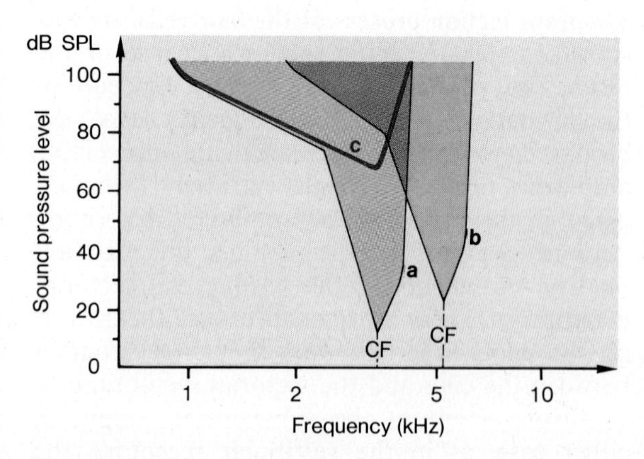

Fig. 12-12. Schematized graph, showing tuning curves of two afferent fibers in the auditory nerve (a, b) with different characteristic frequencies (CF). Curve c is typical of a pathological fiber, such as are found in cases of inner-ear damage

encoded in the duration of neural activity, and its *intensity* by the level of activity. As sound pressure increases, so does the discharge rate of the neurons. Each fiber can be activated only up to a certain discharge rate, beyond which it saturates. However, high sound pressure levels not only increase the discharge rate of the fibers already firing, but also bring adjacent, previously unexcited fibers into action. This recruitment is also apparent in Fig. 12-12; both fibers are activated when the sound is in the area where the curves overlap. In summary, then, we can say that at the level of the primary afferent fibers the sound stimulus is broken down into its frequency components. The individual components excite the associated afferent fibers. At higher stations in the auditory pathway the neurons behave differently.

When the cochlea is damaged, the afferent fibers become less sensitive and less frequency-selective (Fig. 12-12). The receptor potentials of the inner hair cells are similarly altered and, as mentioned above, the same is true of the mechanical oscillation properties of the basilar membrane. Therefore the properties of the inner hair cells and of the afferent nerve fibers coming from them are currently thought to be determined by the oscillation properties of the basilar membrane. However, the latter depend on an active mechanical amplification process, for which the outer hair cells may be responsible. The assumption is that outer hair cells are first stimulated by the sound and thus triggered to produce more oscillatory energy of that same frequency. This energy is then fed into the inner hair cells. If so, these cells would be a kind of hybrid between sense cell and generator of mechanical energy [7, 44]. Many questions remain unanswered here, but it is certain that the cochlea can produce as well as analyze sound energy. The sound produced in the cochlea can be measured just outside the tympanum [7, 36], and demonstrates the presence of active processes in the inner ear. These processes are very easily disrupted by damage (see p. 296).

The outer hair cells are considered candidates for the active amplifier elements because they contain contractile proteins and have an extremely prominent efferent innervation, and because their afferent fibers evidently play no appreciable role in transferring information to the brain [7, 13].

That sound frequencies can be coded by the place principle has been discussed above; a second kind of coding is also realized in the auditory nerve, as follows. Up to frequencies of about 5 kHz, the neuronal discharges in the auditory nerve tend to occur at certain phases of the sound cycle. As a result, temporal structure in the stimulus (e.g., the period T in Fig. 12-5B) is represented by groups of action potentials at the appropriate times and thus is conveyed to the CNS in the auditory nerve. The brain is evidently capable of evaluating the temporal structure in the discharge pattern and calculating the underlying sound frequencies (so-called **periodicity analysis.**) Especially clear evidence is obtained by direct electrical stimulation of the auditory nerve of deaf patients; such periodic stimuli are processed so as to produce a sensation of pitch, indicating that periodicity analysis is in fact an important element in hearing [30, 46].

The Central Auditory System

Anatomy of the auditory pathway. Fig. 12-13 is a much simplified diagram of the auditory pathway. For clarity, only pathways from the left ear are included. Each arrowhead indicates a synapse with a higher-order neuron. To avoid overcrowding of the picture, recurrent collaterals and interneurons are not shown, although connectivity of this sort is common throughout the auditory system.

The primary afferent fibers bifurcate, sending one end into the **ventral cochlear nucleus** and the other into the **dorsal cochlear nucleus.** The fine

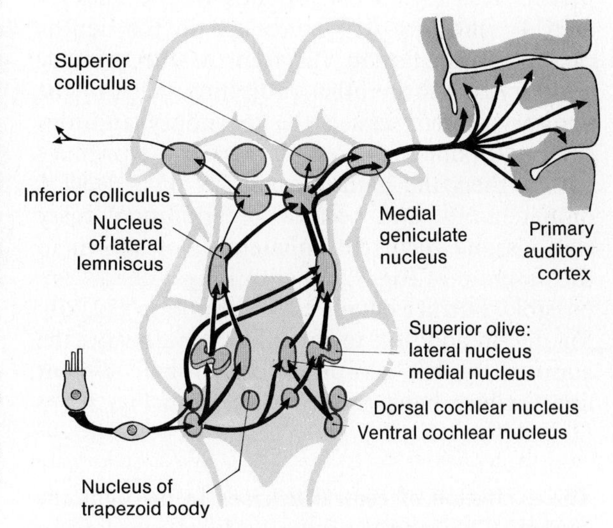

Fig. 12-13. Greatly simplified diagram of the auditory pathway, showing only the tracts originating on the left side. To indicate the binaural connectivity in the superior olive, inputs from the ventral cochlear nucleus on the *right* are also indicated. The centrifugal tracts are omitted

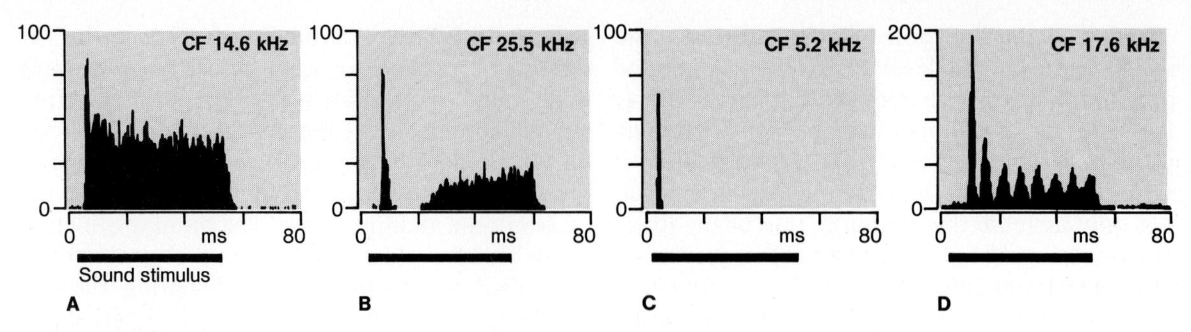

Fig. 12-14. Discharge patterns of 4 neurons in the dorsal cochlear nucleus, in response to a 50-ms tone at the CF (modified from [27]). *Abscissa:* time; *ordinate:* number of action potentials

structure of these nuclei, the dorsal one in particular, is very complicated [11, 12, 40]. From the ventral nucleus a ventral tract runs (in part by way of the nucleus of the trapezoid body) to the olivary complexes of the same and the opposite side. The nerve cells of the olivary complex thus receive inputs from both ears. It is at this neuronal level that the opportunity to compare acoustic signals acting on the two ears with one another first arises. We shall return later to these comparisons. From the dorsal cochlear nucleus a dorsal tract crosses to the opposite side and there terminates in the **nucleus of the lateral lemniscus.** The ascending projections of the cells of the olivary complex are both ipsilateral and contralateral. After synaptic relay the auditory pathway proceeds through the **inferior colliculus** and the **medial geniculate body** to the **primary auditory cortex,** in the transverse temporal gyri in the upper part of the temporal lobes (Heschl's gyrus). This region corresponds to Brodmann's area 41; most of it is concealed in the depths of the sylvian fissure. Adjacent to the primary auditory cortex are other projection fields of the auditory system, called the secondary auditory cortex (Brodmann's area 42). Up to the primary cortex, then, the pathway consists of at least 5 or 6 neurons, and because of additional relay stations and recurrent collaterals not shown in the diagram of Fig. 12-13 even longer chains are possible. Further details can be found in [12, 20]. Finally, in addition to the afferent pathways the auditory system comprises centrifugal, efferent fibers, which have been omitted from Fig. 12-13 [37].

The excitation of central neurons in the auditory system. Whereas the primary afferent neurons in the auditory nerve are excitable by pure tones, very simple acoustic stimuli, neurons at higher levels in general are not. The neurons in the **ventral cochlear nucleus** still behave like those in the auditory nerve; here pure tones at suprathreshold intensities always excite the neurons, which have sharp tuning curves and short latencies. Therefore these are called "primary-like" cells. But in the **dorsal cochlear nucleus** the picture is fundamentally altered [11, 12, 47]. Although most of the neurons here can also be excited by pure tones, their response patterns vary widely. As an example, Fig. 12-14 shows responses of fibers leaving the dorsal cochlear nucleus, in each case to a 50-ms tone at the characteristic frequency of the neuron. The neuron in Fig. 12-14A behaves like a primary fiber, but the others are quite different. Some neurons in the dorsal cochlear nucleus can be inhibited by sound, and others are excited by certain frequencies and inhibited by slightly different frequencies. Still others are particularly responsive to tones of changing frequency (so-called frequency-modulated tones), although they also respond to pure tones. The anatomical bases of these complex responses are collateral connections, some excitatory and some inhibitory.

The *functional implication* is evidently that the neurons respond particularly well to certain features of the sound stimulus, contributing to pattern recognition even at this early station in the pathway. At higher levels such specificity becomes progressively better developed.

The further away from the cochlea in the auditory pathway, the more complex the sound patterns required to activate the neurons [20]. Many cells do not respond at all to pure tones. In the *inferior colliculus,* for example, there are cells excitable only by frequency-modulated tones with particular directions and degrees of modulation. Other cells in the inferior colliculus respond to a tone only if it is amplitude-modulated – that is, if its intensity changes. In this case, too, the modulation must often have certain properties in order to excite the neuron.

In general, we can say that the information con-

tained in a sound stimulus is multiply recoded as the neuronal excitation passes the various stations in the auditory pathway. In the process, different types of neuron extract particular properties of the sound stimulus, so that the higher neurons each activates respond more or less specifically to this property alone.
In everyday life we are hardly ever confronted with pure tones. The sounds we hear are made up of various frequency components, which can change continually and independently. The amplitude of such sounds can change as well as the frequency, their duration varies, they begin and end abruptly or gradually, they can be repeated or not, their source can be nearby, far away or moving, and so on. People can evaluate all these properties of sound, at least if their hearing has been suitably trained. Neuronal processes underlying such evaluation have been found especially in the **auditory cortex** [47]. For example, in the primary auditory cortex some neurons respond only to the onset of a sound stimulus and others, only to its end. Still others fire only when the sound has lasted for a certain time, and others are excited only by repeated sounds. Some neurons are activated only if the stimulus is frequency- or amplitude-modulated in a particular way. Many can be activated by a broad frequency band – that is, by noises – and others have tuning curves with one or several sharp minima. Most of the cortical neurons are activated by the contralateral ear, but some respond to ipsilateral stimulation and others only when both ears are stimulated simultaneously. A considerable percentage of the neurons in the primary auditory cortex cannot be excited at all under laboratory conditions; presumably these neurons are highly specific, responding only to stimuli too complicated to be reproduced by the experimental equipment [47].
On the whole, the responses of cells in the *primary auditory cortex* resemble those of the complex or hypercomplex neurons in the visual cortex (cf. p. 261). They are evidently involved in auditory pattern recognition – a process of fundamental importance, for example, in understanding speech. Indeed, cells have been found in the auditory cortex of monkeys that respond predominantly to certain conspecific communication sounds. But the properties of these neurons often depend on other, unknown parameters as well, so that their responses are subject to unpredictable variability [42].
Because the auditory cortex is located there, brain lesions involving the temporal lobes cause difficulty in understanding speech, in spatial localization of a sound source (see below) and in the identification of temporal patterns of sound. However, such injuries do not affect the ability to discriminate frequencies and intensities. Details about the central information processing involved in hearing can be found in [11, 12, 20, 47].

Recent studies have shown that the tonotopic organization found in the cochlea is preserved at all higher stations in the auditory system, including the cortex. The tonotopic organization of the primary auditory cortex – that is, a systematic arrrangement by sound frequency – had previously been denied.
Another result contradicting earlier assumptions is that in the higher-level auditory neurons there is evidently no appreciable sharpening of tuning. The tuning curves of the primary neurons in the auditory nerve are already extraordinarily sharp, if the experimental animals are in optimal physical condition.

Auditory orientation in space. The central auditory system also makes an important contribution to *spatial orientation*. We know from ordinary experience that the direction of a sound source can be specified quite closely. This capability requires both ears (**binaural** hearing). The physical basis of **directional hearing** is the circumstance that one ear is usually further away from a sound source than the other. Because sound is propagated with finite velocity it arrives **later** at the more distant ear; moreover, its **intensity** there is lower, and in comparing intensities at the two ears the auditory system is able to detect intensity differences as small as 1 dB [5, 11, 13, 43]. Fig. 12-15 illustrates the method of calculating differences in conduction time. The difference in distance is $\Delta s = d \cdot \sin\alpha$, where d is the distance between the two ears and α is the angle of the sound source with respect to the receiver. The time delay Δt is then $\Delta t = \Delta s/c$, where c is the speed of sound. Delays of as little as $3 \cdot 10^{-5}$ s can be reliably detected; this corresponds to a divergence of the sound source from the midline by

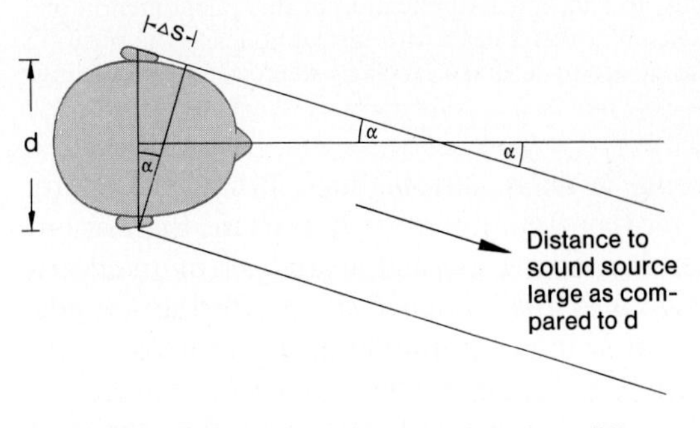

Fig. 12-15. Calculation of conduction-time differences in directional hearing (see text)

ca. 3°. Under optimal conditions angles only half as large can be identified.
In both psychophysical and neurophysiological experiments it can be shown that directional hearing is in fact based on **differences in conduction time and intensity.** When earphones are used for independent stimulation of the two ears, delay or intensity reduction of the signal to one ear produces a spatial sensation – the sound is localized in the other ear. But a delay can be compensated by simultaneously increasing the intensity at the same ear; in this case the sound still seems to be in the middle of the head [5]. Similar results are obtained in neurophysiological experiments. In the superior olive complex, the first station at which inputs from the two sides come together, there are neurons that behave similarly with regard to the timing and intensity of a stimulus [11, 13, 42, 43]. They are maximally excited when the sound presented to one ear is louder than **and** precedes that at the other ear. Another type of cell here is maximally active when the sound stimulus is presented to the two ears with certain differences in timing or intensity. That is, the first type responds maximally to sounds on the axis of one ear, whereas the other gives a maximal response to sounds incident at particular angles [11, 13, 42]. In the superior colliculus auditory and visual inputs are combined to construct a three-dimensional map. In the **auditory cortex** there are also cells that can be activated only if the sound source is at a particular location. If the auditory cortex is destroyed, spatial orientation is impaired. However, there is as yet no good explanation of the way the central nervous system manages to detect minimal time differences of less than of 10^{-4} s.

Conduction-time and intensity differences do not suffice to determine whether the sound source is in front of the head or behind it, above or below. To make this decision we require an accessory device, the pinna of the ear. The pinna has a directional characteristic, "distorting" a sound signal in a particular way depending on the position of the sound source. This property is turned to advantage in localizing sounds. In a technical application of this phenomenon one can use an artificial head with microphones in the position of the eardrums to make excellent stereophonic recordings [5].

Hearing in noisy surroundings. Binaural hearing has another function more important than orientation in space; it assists the analysis of an acoustic signal in the presence of interfering sounds. In this case interaural differences in intensity and direction are used by the CNS to suppress the background sound and bring out the signal of interest (e.g., when one pays attention to a particular conversation at a party). This selective filter process improves the audibility of a signal about 10 dB [13]. In someone who is deaf in one ear this process cannot occur (as is easily demonstrated by holding a hand over one ear). Therefore it is important for people with impaired hearing to have the binaural function restored, by supplying both ears, if necessary, with a hearing aid.

Adaptation in the auditory system. The auditory system, like other sensory systems, exhibits the phenomenon of **adaptation.** Both the peripheral ear and central neurons are involved in this process. Adaptation is manifest in an increased auditory threshold (temporary threshold shift, TTS). It is not a useless or undesirable mechanism, for it results in a reduction of the difference threshold and thus assists differentiation of our auditory experiences. The reason for this improvement is that in the adapted state the isophones are shifted upward and at the same time move closer together. For further information see [14, 49].

Pathophysiology of Auditory Defects

Hearing difficulties and deafness greatly change the life of the affected person, and are therefore of great clinical significance. The causes of hearing impairment can be grouped into three categories.

1. Disturbance of sound conduction. Here the damage affects the middle ear, the sound-conducting apparatus. In cases of inflammation, for example, the tympanum-ossicle apparatus does not transmit the usual amount of sound energy to the inner ear. As a result, hearing deteriorates even though the inner ear may be intact. There are microsurgical procedures by which hearing defects due to middle-ear damage can be effectively treated.

2. Disturbances of sound sensation. In this case the hair cells of the organ of Corti are damaged, so that either the process of transduction or the release of transmitter is disturbed. The net result is interference with the transmission of information from the cochlea to the CNS.

3. Retrocochlear damage. This group includes conditions in which both middle and inner ear are intact. Either the central parts of the primary afferent nerve fibers or other parts of the auditory pathway are damaged (e.g., by a brain tumor).
The process of testing a patient's hearing ability is called **audiometry.** A variety of tests are avail-

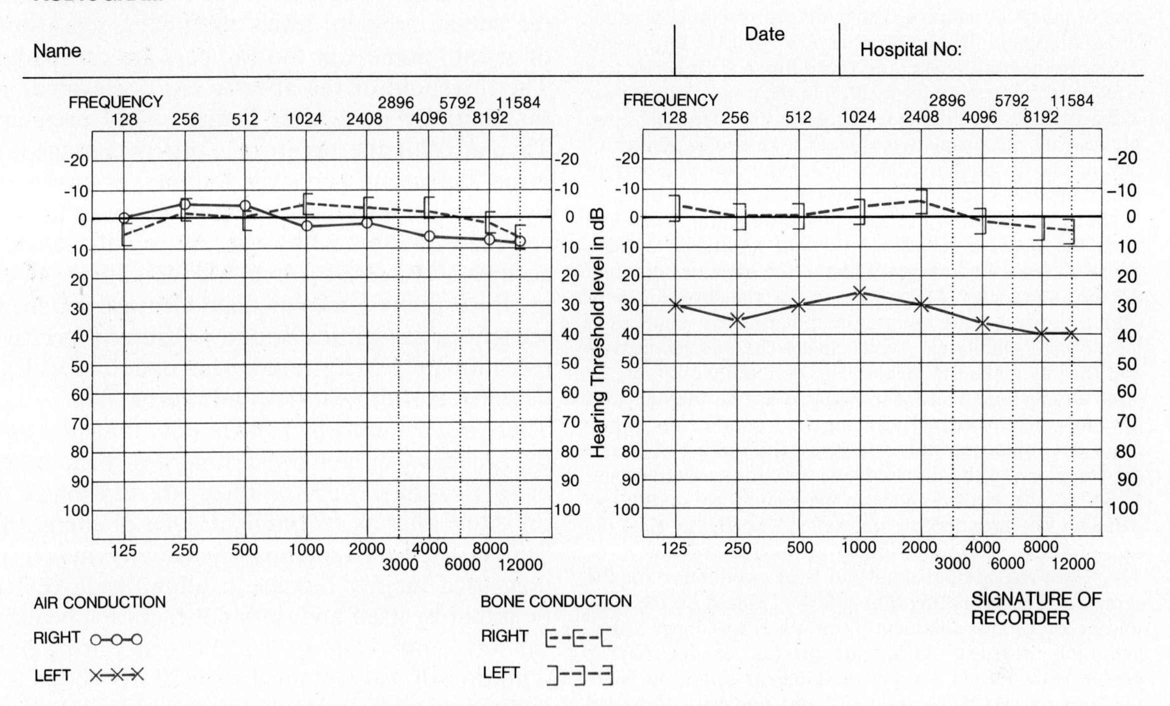

Fig. 12-16. Audiogram of a patient with impaired sound conduction on the left side

able to demonstrate damage and indicate its site (for details see [24]).

The most important clinical test is **threshold audiometry.** Various tones are presented to the patient by a single earphone. The physician begins with an intensity certain to be subthreshold and gradually raises the sound pressure until the patient reports hearing a sound. This sound pressure is then recorded in a graph (Fig. 12-16) called an *audiogram.* In the preprinted form the normal auditory threshold is represented by a straight line labelled "0 dB". In contrast to the graph of Fig. 12-8, higher thresholds (which amount to hearing loss) are plotted below the zero line, to indicate by how many dB the threshold of the patient differs from normal. Note that these are not sound pressure levels, which would be given in dB SPL. When the threshold of a patient is a certain number of dB above normal, he is said to have a hearing loss of that many dB. As a practical demonstration, try closing both ears with your fingers. The hearing loss produced in this way is about 20 dB (in doing this experiment, of course, care must be taken not to produce too much noise with the fingers themselves). The clinical procedure employing earphones tests the reception of *airborne sound. Bone conduction* can be tested similarly by using, instead of the earphones, an oscillating object placed on the mastoid process on the side to be tested, so that the oscillation is transmitted directly to the skull bones. By comparing the threshold curves for air and bone conduction one can distinguish between middle-ear deafness and inner-ear deafness.

Middle-ear deafness is a **disturbance of sound conduction.** The inner ear is not damaged. In this condition, therefore, a hearing loss is measured with airborne sound (cf. Fig. 12-16) while the threshold to bone-conducted sound is normal, for the sound energy transmitted by the bones arrives at the hair cells without the assistance of the middle ear.

Inner-ear deafness arises from damage to the hair cells, the middle ear remaining intact. In this case the thresholds to both airborne and bone-conducted sound are raised, as both are transduced by the same receptor process. Retrocochlear damage also raises the threshold for both types of conduction.

With the aid of a tuning fork (customarily 256 Hz) impaired conduction can very simply be distinguished from inner-ear or retrocochlear damage, as long as one knows which ear is affected **(Weber's test).** The stem of the oscillating tuning fork is set on the middle of the skull. A patient with inner-ear damage reports hearing the tone on the healthy side, whereas with middle-ear damage it is lateralized to the affected side.

There is a simple explanation of this phenomenon in the case of inner-ear damage. The damaged receptors produce less excitation in the auditory nerve, so that the tone seems louder in the healthy ear, and this difference gives rise to a directional impression (cf. p. 295). In the case of middle-ear damage three simultaneous processes are involved. First, because the impairment is due to a restricted ability of the ossicles to oscillate, there is a reduction not only in the transport of sound from the outside inward, but also in sound propagation in the opposite direction. Therefore when the inner ear is excited by sound conducted through the skull, less sound energy is lost to the exterior here than on the intact side (MACH's theory of the dissipation of sound). Second, there are usually inflammatory changes in the affected middle ear, which make the ossicles heavier and thereby make the inner ear more readily excitable by bone conduction. Third, the diseased ear is adapted to a low noise level, because the impaired conduction allows fewer environmental noises to reach the inner ear. Hence the receptors on the diseased side are more sensitive than those on the healthy side. In patients with middle-ear damage, all three factors act synergistically to give the sensation that the tone is louder at the affected ear.

The **Rinne test** compares air and bone conduction for the same ear. The oscillating tuning fork is placed on the mastoid process (bone conduction) until it is no longer heard, and then held just outside the ear (air conduction). A person with normal hearing or impaired sensation hears the tone again (Rinne positive), and one with impaired conduction does not, or hears it very briefly (Rinne negative).

Hearing loss in older people is a routine occurrence in developed countries. This condition, called *presbycusis,* first becomes apparent in the high-frequency range. A 60-year-old, on the average, can expect to have a hearing loss of ca. 40 dB at 8 kHz and ca. 30 dB at 4 kHz. The damage is of the cochlear-retrocochlear type, and because it often extends to frequencies important for understanding speech, it is a severe handicap. Although the prefix "presby" denotes a relationship to old age, much of this hearing loss is due not to processes of aging but rather to damage resulting from the noises of civilization, which could easily be avoided.

In contrast to threshold audiometry, other test procedures examine the ability of the auditory system to differentiate among suprathreshold sounds. In **speech audiometry** a tape recording of spoken numbers or standardized syllables is played to the patient, to test his **understanding of speech.** With inner-ear damage complete understanding cannot be achieved even with high sound pressures, because in this condition the tuning curves of the auditory-nerve fibers are altered (see below).

If hearing is impaired on one side, measurement of so-called **recruitment** enables one to decide whether the organ of Corti is affected. Sounds are presented through earphones, and the sound pressure levels producing sensations of equal loudness in the two ears are compared. The threshold of the affected ear is elevated, so that initially it requires higher sound pressure. Thereafter, if the organ of Corti is damaged, a given increase in perceived loudness is produced by a smaller increase in sound pressure at this ear than at the healthy ear. As sound intensity is further increased a level is eventually reached at which the two ears mediate identical loudness sensations at identical sound pressures ("positive recruitment"). With middle-ear or retrocochlear damage, recruitment does not occur [24].

There are a number of other tests that measure the increase in perceived loudness with other methods; the results of these are explained in the same way as recruitment. One of them, the **SISI test** (**S**hort **I**ncrement **S**ensitivity **I**ndex), is now used mainly because it allows each ear to be tested by itself and does not require a healthy ear for comparison. In the SISI test, during presentation of a maintained tone 20 dB above the auditory threshold the intensity is briefly raised by 1–5 dB. Patients with inner-ear damage can detect an increment as small as 1 dB, whereas healthy people require as much as 5 dB.

Finally, hearing can also be tested by recording the brainstem and cortical potentials evoked by acoustic stimuli. The EEG deflections produced by several single stimuli are added by a computer, so that the background activity that otherwise obscures the potential fluctuations elicited by a single stimulus are averaged out and the responses are revealed (see p. 134). The average curves so obtained comprise several potentials varying in latency, the number of which depends on the technique selected to suit the purpose of the study (**E**voked **R**esponse **A**udiometry, **ERA**). The early potentials have latencies below 10 ms [19]. They are thought to originate in the various auditory nuclei or fiber tracts of the brainstem below the inferior colliculus. In any case, there can be no doubt that the potentials reflect the specific processing that occurs in the basal parts of the auditory pathway. Although these potentials can also be used to determine auditory threshold, the method is considerably better suited for fine neurological diagnosis. It enables the examiner to infer the extent to which the neuronal processes following an acoustic stimulus are intact. Disorders in the brainstem region alter these potentials.

The later potentials (latencies around 150 ms) are less specific, and in recent times have not been regarded as of practical significance.

Mechanism of inner-ear damage. Although the causes of inner-ear damage may be very diverse, animal experiments have shown that in all cases the result is that the thresholds of individual fibers in the auditory nerve are raised and their tuning is less sharp [31]. The tuning curve of one such pathological fiber is shown in Fig. 12-12. This change affects very many or even all fibers, at least in a particular frequency range. It explains the increase in auditory threshold and also the deterioration of frequency discrimination, which ultimately makes it difficult to understand speech. The relatively flat tuning curves also offer an explanation of recruitment, as follows. The fibers are not excited at all when the sound pressure level is low. But once the threshold has been passed, further increase in sound pressure rapidly activates many fibers, for a flat tuning curve implies low frequency selectivity. Soon just as many fibers are activated as in the healthy ear, and at sound pressures above this level the test tone seems equally loud in both ears.

A person who is hard of hearing or completely deaf faces a severe difficulty. Cut off from verbal communication, the deaf lose the most important contacts with other people and their surroundings, and change their behavior considerably. The tasks for which the sense of hearing is responsible are very unsatisfactorily performed by other sensory channels. Indeed, hearing is the most important human sense, and its loss cannot be taken seriously enough. It is required not only to detect and analyze the speech of others, but also to learn how to speak and to control one's own speech. Children born deaf do not learn to talk, because they lack the auditory stimulus. For this reason prelingual deafness (existing before speech is acquired) is an especially serious problem. A speech deficiency causes a further handicap because it considerably reduces general learning ability. Therefore children who are hard of hearing at birth should be fitted with a hearing aid before the age of 18 months.
Congenital hearing difficulty is to be suspected when a child at the end of its first year does not progress from babbling to syllables or simple word structures, but rather vocalizes more rarely or stops entirely. Furthermore, a normal child will turn toward sound stimuli by the middle of its second year, at the latest.

12.3 Physiology of the Speech Apparatus

In this section we consider the physiology of the peripheral speech apparatus. The interesting central nervous processes that constitute the real foundation of language, failure of which disturbs the communication system far more than damage to the peripheral apparatus, will not be discussed here; mention is made of them on p. 150.

Basic Properties of the Acoustic Signal Produced in Speaking

Everyday experience tells us that the voices of different people can vary in "pitch." For example, the voice of a man is about an octave deeper than that of a woman. Moreover, a speaker is capable of changing his own pitch, and a singer still more so. Now, if someone sings the syllables "la la la ..." (to the tune, perhaps, of "Row, row, row your boat") the vowel sound /a/ is clearly identifiable in each syllable, even though the "pitch" of the sung tone changes. Conversely, we can keep the pitch constant and change the vowel sound in successive syllables (e.g., /a, e, i, o, u/). A listener will be quite aware that the pitch is maintained while the syllables vary. Thus the acoustic signal produced during speaking or singing and analyzed by the auditory system must contain at least two independently variable parameters, of which one provides information about pitch and the other, information about the phonemic content – for example, by transmitting certain characteristics of the vowel sound /a/. This is indeed the case. The two parameters are produced by two fundamentally different mechanisms. The mechanism controlling pitch is called **phonation** and is located in the larynx; its physical basis is oscillation of the vocal cords. The mechanism that determines phonemic structure is called **articulation.** Its physical basis is the resonance of the hollow spaces in the oral cavity (in some cases also the naso-pharyngeal region). That the two mechanisms are in fact distinct is evident in whispering (p. 304). The whispering voice cannot be assigned any pitch, for the processes of phonation are eliminated and only articulation is done.

Phonation

Functional anatomy of the larynx. The larynx is the upper end of the trachea (Fig. 12-17). It consists of the annular **cricoid cartilage,** the **thyroid cartilage** and the paired **arytenoid cartilages.** The thyroid cartilage can move with respect to the cricoid cartilage in two ways – by sliding forward, and by tilting forward and down. The arytenoid cartilages are seated on the upper rear edge of the cricoid cartilage, where they can (i) be rotated about their long axes, (ii) be moved toward or away from one another by sliding over the cricoid cartilage (cf. Fig. 12-18), and (iii) be tilted forward. Between the thyroid cartilage and the vocal processes of the arytenoids are the two **vocal cords,** folds of membranous tissue enclosing ligaments; the gap between them is the **glottis.** Air must pass through this opening both in breathing and in speaking. The laryngeal muscles are of special functional significance. The **cricothyroid mus-**

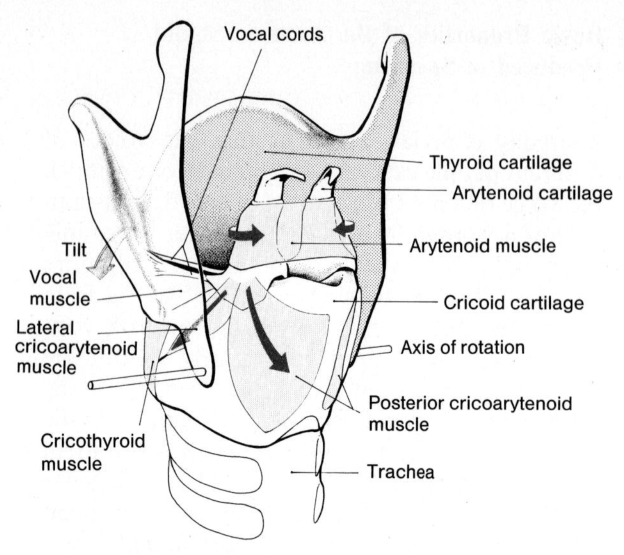

Fig. 12-17. Schematic drawing of the larynx and its musculature. The *gray arrow* shows the direction in which the thyroid cartilage can tilt

cle is ventrally situated, between the cricoid and thyroid cartilages. The **cricoarytenoid muscle** consists of two parts on each side, the lateral part passing from the arytenoid cartilage to the lateral surface of the cricoid cartilage, and the posterior part passing to its posterior surface. The **arytenoid muscles** join the two arytenoid cartilages at their dorsal surfaces. The **vocal muscles** are within the vocal folds, passing from the thyroid cartilage to the arytenoids. Lateral to each is another muscle, the thyroarytenoid.

The larynx is supplied by two branches of the vagus nerve. The superior laryngeal nerve contains sensory fibers from the mucosa and motor fibers to the cricothyroid muscle. The inferior laryngeal nerve is the terminal branch of the recurrent nerve, with the motor supply to the remaining laryngeal muscles and sensory fibers from the subglottal region.

The role of the laryngeal muscles is to adjust the *width of the glottis* and the *tension of the vocal cords* as required for phonation. Their action is assisted by that of other muscles that can exert, directly or indirectly, force on the larynx – for example, the sternohyoid muscle. The glottis is expanded by the posterior cricoarytenoid muscle, which pulls the arytenoid cartilages apart and turns their vocal processes to the sides (cf. Fig. 12-18). The gap is narrowed by the arytenoid muscles, the lateral cricoarytenoids and the thyroarytenoids. The **tension** of the vocal cords, finally, is regulated by the cricothyroid and vocal muscles. The cricothyroid muscles tip the thyroid cartilage forward (cf. Fig. 12-17), moving it further away from the vocal processes of the arytenoid cartilages, so that the vocal cords are stretched. The vocal muscles, on the other hand, increase the tension of the vocal cords by the change in the modulus of elasticity associated with their contraction. During normal respiration the posterior cricoarytenoid muscles keep the glottis wide open (cf. Fig. 12-18).

Mechanism of phonation (voice production). The first step in speaking or singing is to prepare to exhale. Unlike the situation in normal breathing, however, the glottis is closed or only slightly open. As a result a higher pressure builds up in the thorax than would be the case in normal expiration (subglottal pressure). It is always in the range above 400–600 Pa (4–6 cm H_2O) and can easily reach 2,000 Pa (20 cm H_2O) or more. If the glottis is closed, the vocal cords are pushed apart by this pressure. At that moment air flows through the glottis into the oropharyngeal cavity. The glottis amounts to a *bottleneck* in the expiratory tract, at which the flow velocity of the expired air is far higher than in the trachea. It follows from Bernoulli's law that the air pressure here will be very low; therefore the glottis closes again, and the process begins anew. The vocal cords thus perform **Bernoulli oscillations.**

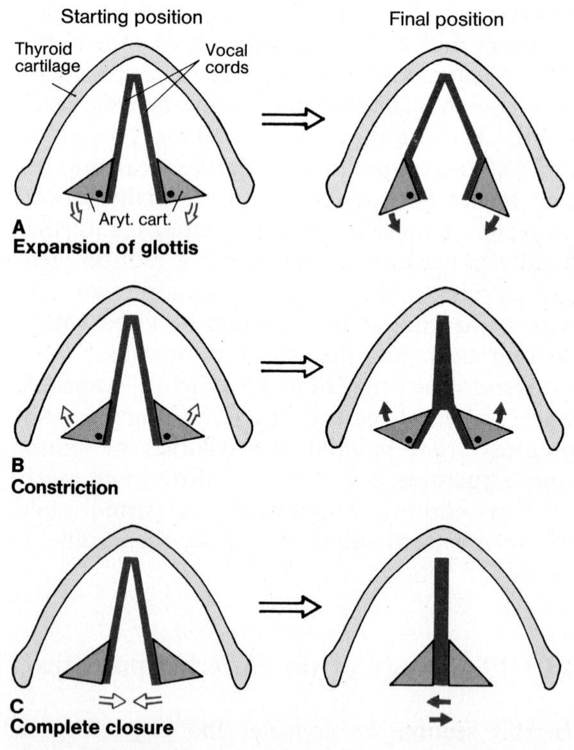

Fig. 12-18 A–C. Schematic illustration of the operation of the laryngeal muscles. The larynx is drawn about as it appears when examined with an inserted mirror; the thyroid and arytenoid cartilages and the vocal cords are shown. **A** Expansion of the glottis by the posterior cricoarytenoid muscle. **B** Constriction by the lateral cricoarytenoid, leaving only a small triangular gap. **C** Complete closure by the arytenoid muscles

The airstream is continually interrupted in the rhythm of these oscillations, producing an audible sound – the voice – with a fundamental frequency ("pitch" in common parlance) corresponding to the rate of airstream interruption. Because the airstream cannot be sinusoidally modulated by the opening and closing of the vocal cords, the sound produced is not a pure tone, but a mixture rich in harmonics [6]. The number of glottal openings or closings per unit time, and thus the fundamental frequency of the sound, depends primarily on the tension of the vocal cords, and only secondarily on the subglottal pressure. Both parameters, however, can be changed by the laryngeal and thoracic musculature. The higher the tension in the vocal cords (or the higher the subglottal pressure), the higher the fundamental frequency of the sound produced. In this way the fundamental frequency of the sound produced in speaking or singing can be changed at will. This is the procedure underlying our first introductory example, in which the vowel sound /a/ is to be sung at different "pitches." On the basis of the anatomical differences in the larynx – the length of the vocal cords in particular – that cause variation in this oscillatory behavior, voices are classified as **bass, tenor, alto** and **soprano.** Within each of these ranges various **registers** can be distinguished.

For a singer to produce and hold a "tone" the contractions of the muscles involved must be extremely finely coordinated. Among the mechanisms participating in this control are proprioceptors in the laryngeal muscles and the mucosa, and auditory feedback. The results are astonishingly good; practiced singers can repeat a test tone with a frequency error less than 1%. The situation becomes especially difficult when it is necessary to change the intensity of a tone while maintaining the pitch. Because the increasing subglottal pressure required to raise the intensity also slightly raises the frequency, the cricothyroid muscle must be relaxed to compensate, by reducing the tension of the vocal cords. That this actually occurs can be demonstrated by electromyographic recording of the activity of the muscles concerned.
In singing, sounds of considerable intensity can be produced; a soprano voice (measured at a distance of 1 m) can easily exceed a sound pressure of 100 dB SPL.
Auditory feedback is extraordinarily important. When a person becomes deaf, speech deteriorates appreciably. Children born deaf do not learn to speak.

In **whispering,** the vocal cords do not oscillate. They lie close together, leaving only a small triangular opening in the region of the arytenoid cartilages (cf. Fig. 12-18). The air passing through this opening makes a noise that can be used for articulation and thus produce the whispering "voice."

Articulation

Functional anatomy of the "vocal tract." Emerging from the glottis, air first enters the oropharyngeal cavity, which in this context is called the **vocal tract.** Comprising the pharyngeal, nasal and oral cavities, its form is very variable. The nasopharynx and adjacent part of the throat can be separated from the oropharynx by the soft palate (velum). The *configuration* of the oral cavity can be changed considerably by altering the positions of tongue and jaws. Moreover, the tongue can form a hump to divide the oral cavity into two spaces (Fig. 12-19). The palatal musculature, the chewing musculature, and especially the tongue musculature are responsible for these changes. The tongue can occupy practically every conceivable position within the mouth, with the help of both its internal muscles and those that radiate into it from various sites of origin on bones, or are so arranged as to shift the position of the tongue bone.

Mechanism of articulation. The periodic interruption of the airstream at the glottis is not the only acoustic event in phonation. At other places where the respiratory tract narrows, if the velocity of expiration is high enough, turbulence produces a relatively weak noise, comprising a broad range of frequencies. The spaces in the vocal tract have particular **natural frequencies** of their own, depending on their momentary configuration. These are the frequencies produced when the air in these spaces is set into oscillation. For example, by tapping your cheek with a finger while the mouth is in different positions, you can make the different natural frequencies of the oral cavity audible (try this in a quiet room!). The noise produced at constrictions in the tract and the overtone-rich sound of the voice produced at the vocal cords also contain these frequencies. When the natural frequencies are present

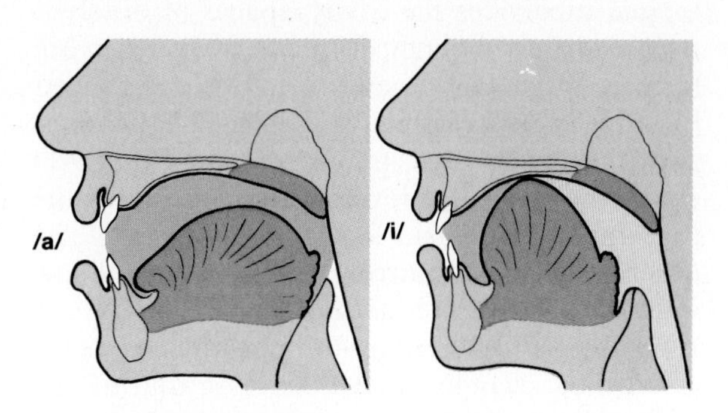

Fig. 12-19. Oropharyngeal space during pronunciation of /a/ (as in "father") and /i/ (as in "seat")

the vocal tract **resonates** [1, 7], amplifying these frequencies to above-threshold intensities so that they are distinctly audible. Each of the spaces formed in the many different configurations of the vocal tract has a different natural frequency. At each articulation position – that is, each particular position of jaw, tongue, and velum – quite specific frequencies or frequency bands are heard as soon as the cavities begin to resonate [6, 15]. The frequency bands characteristic of the different positions are called **formants.** They depend **only** on the configuration of the vocal tract, and not on the voice produced in the larynx. It is very easy to demonstrate experimentally that resonance phenomena are the essential factors in articulation, by breathing not air but another gas with a sound-conducting velocity different from air (e.g., helium). Under these conditions the resonance properties of the vocal tract are altered; speech becomes almost incomprehensible, even though the vocal-cord oscillations are unchanged.

Vowels. In normal speaking the vowels are produced by voiced resonance of the vocal tract; the configuration of the vocal tract is relatively stable, and the mouth is open to emit the sound [6]. When the vowels in the English language are spoken, the velum is normally closed and the nasopharyngeal space does not oscillate with the oral cavity. The **formants** associated with this resonance are responsible for the facts that the vowel sound /a/ in our introductory example is recognized as such regardless of pitch or of the speaker, and that it and the other vowel sounds can be distinguished from one another. The formant – in some cases, a combination of formants – is thus the acoustical equivalent of a particular vowel (or some consonants). Fig. 12-19 gives an example of the configuration of the oral cavity when the vowel sounds /a/ and /i/ are spoken. Depending on whether and where the tongue subdivides the cavity, spaces of different sizes and thus different formant frequencies are formed. In general a vowel sound is determined by at least two formants. Table 12-1 summarizes the vowels used in English, and Fig. 12-20 shows the associated formant frequencies for the first and second main formants (from [1]). The other frequently occurring formants are of low intensity and are not considered here.
By trying out different mouth positions it is easy to see how changes in the configuration of the oral cavity produce the transition from one vowel to another.

Table 12-1. Vowels in the English language (adapted from [1])

Front vowels (tongue forward)		Middle vowels (tongue in the middle)		Back vowels (tongue back)	
/i/	seat	/ɜ/	dirt	/ɑ/	cart
/I/	bit	/ʌ/	hut	/o/	rod
/ɛ/	head	/ə/	the	/ɔ/	cord
/æ/	hat			/ʊ/	would
				/u/	rude

Diphthongs and semivowels. These phonemes resemble the true vowels except that the position of the vocal tract is not stable; it changes during articulation. Examples of diphthongs are the /ɛi/ in *pay* or the /ɑi/ in *high*. The transition is more rapid in the semivowels (or glides) – for example, /j/ in *y*ou or /w/ in *w*all. These two phonemes start out like an /i/ or /u/. The consonants /r/ and /l/ are also in this phonetic group.

Consonants. This group includes a large number of phonemes, in the formation of which the vocal tract is not stable and the sound is not necessarily emitted through the mouth. They can be either voiced (i.e., accompanied by vocal-cord oscillation) or voiceless (without oscillation of the vocal cords). In general the vocal tract is more constricted than during vowel production, and the particular kind of constriction – by means of teeth, lips and tongue – determines which consonant is pronounced. A distinction is made between **fricatives** and **plosives** (or **stop consonants**).
The **fricatives** are accompanied by turbulent airflow at the constriction, which produces an audible sound. If the constriction is formed between the upper teeth and the lower lip (labio-dental),

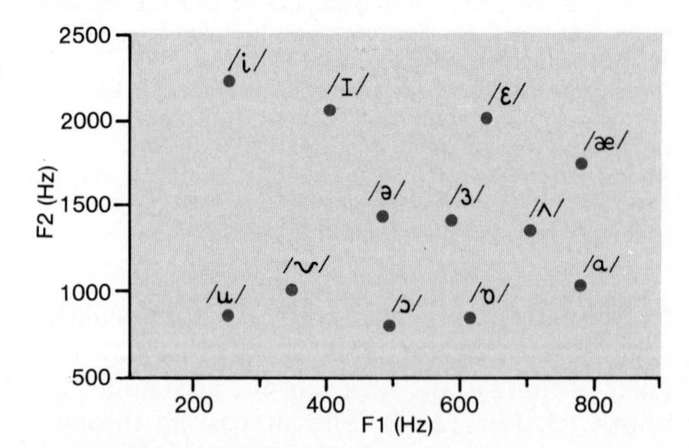

Fig. 12-20. Frequency of the second formant versus frequency of first formant for the vowels of English spoken by a typical male speaker. (From [1])

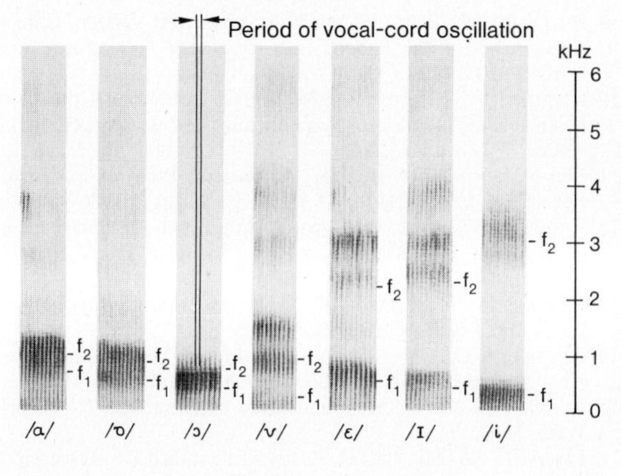

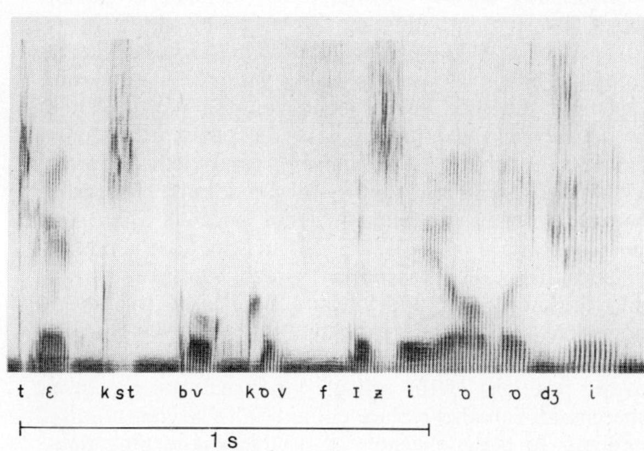

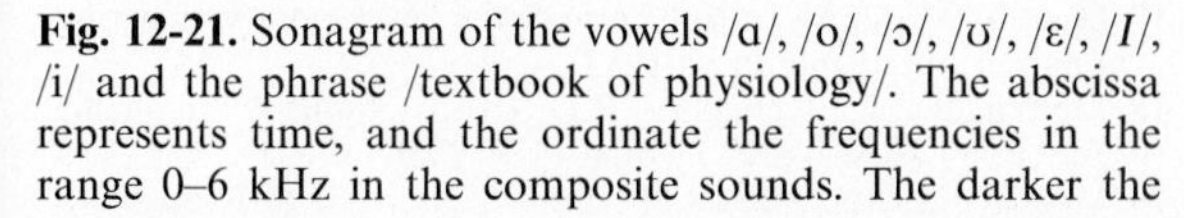

Fig. 12-21. Sonagram of the vowels /ɑ/, /o/, /ɔ/, /ʊ/, /ε/, /I/, /i/ and the phrase /textbook of physiology/. The abscissa represents time, and the ordinate the frequencies in the range 0–6 kHz in the composite sounds. The darker the shading, the more sound energy in a particular frequency band. f = formant (Recordings by courtesy of Dr. W.A. AINSWORTH)

the consonants /v/ or /f/ are produced. Pressing the tip of the tongue against the upper teeth (dental) produces /ð/ and /θ/. /z/ and /s/ are produced by putting the upper and lower teeth close together and placing the tip of the tongue against the upper row (alveolar). If the tongue is shifted toward the hard palate (palatal) /ʒ/ and /ʃ/ are produced. Finally, /h/ is produced by a half-open position of the glottis (glottal). The various consonants are listed in Table 12-2.
The **plosives** are produced by the abrupt opening of the completely closed vocal tract, which suddenly releases the pressure in the lungs. Again, the site of the closure determines which stop consonant results (Table 12-2). If the tract is closed by the velum, /g/ and /k/ are produced. The individual plosives often differ hardly at all in frequency spectrum. Here the time course of the sound is the crucial factor in identifying the phoneme (cf. Fig. 12-21).

Table 12-2. Consonants in the English language (adapted from [1])

Voiced			Unvoiced	
Fricatives				
Labio-dental	/v/	**v**an	/f/	**f**ix
Dental	/ð/	**th**is	/θ/	**th**ick
Alveolar	/z/	**z**oo	/s/	**s**at
Palatal	/ʒ/	a**z**ure	/ʃ/	**sh**ip
Glottal			/h/	**h**at
Stop consonants				
Labial	/b/	**b**at	/p/	**p**ig
Alveolar	/d/	**d**og	/t/	**t**ell
Velar	/g/	**g**et	/k/	**k**ick
Nasals				
Labial	/m/	**m**an		
Alveolar	/n/	**n**ull		
Palatal-velar	/ŋ/	si**ng**		

Nasals. In pronouncing the nasal consonants the nasopharyngeal cavity is wide open and the sound is emitted through the nose (as is easily demonstrated by closing the nose with the fingers: /m/ and /n/ cannot be produced for very long under these circumstances).

Sound Spectrography

Speech can be picked up by a microphone and broken down into its frequency components by a set of band-pass filters. The record of the frequency composition of sound as a function of time, the **sound spectrogram** (Fig. 12-21), is a representation of the acoustic characteristics just discussed, especially the formants. Time is on the abscissa, and frequency on the ordinate: the darkening indicates the time at which certain frequencies appear in the spoken sound. The darker the mark, the greater the sound energy in the designated frequency range. The formants are clearly distinguishable in the diagram. It is also evident that plosives (/t/) and fricatives (/s/, /z/) have a broad frequency spectrum with high-frequency components.

Speech Impediments

The complicated mechanism of speaking can be disturbed at many sites. A major distinction is that between *peripheral* and *central* disturbances. **Peripheral disturbance** is frequently caused by unilateral or bilateral paralysis of the laryngeal muscles, due to paralysis of the recurrent nerve. Slight damage causes hoarseness, whereas complete bilateral paralysis makes phonation impossible **(aphonia).** Because in this condition the glottis cannot be actively widened (paralysis of the posterior cricoarytenoids), breathing is considerably hampered. Nevertheless, verbal communication is still possible by **whispering,** because formant articulation is not affected. Even after surgical removal of the larynx patients can learn a method of speaking, called **esophageal speech.** Air is swallowed into the esophagus, and when it is released it makes a noise that sets the cavities of mouth and throat into resonant oscillation, producing the formant corresponding to the positions of the articulation structures. Electronic speech aids can also replace phonation in laryngectomized patients. In these, a generator produces a rasping noise, and when the device is pressed against the floor of the mouth resonant oscillations are induced. Because the vocal tract can still be put into the configurations required for articulation, formants can be produced, giving tolerably understandable speech.

But if the musculature of tongue and throat fail to function properly speech is often severely impaired, because the formants can no longer be produced. An example is the "doughy" speech in bulbar paralysis, a neurological disease affecting the motor nuclei of the cranial nerves so as to damage the innervation of the tongue musculature.

A congenital cleft palate also prevents the production of normal formants, because the mouth and throat cavities communicate through the gap. The remedy is surgical closure of the opening.

A major cause of **central speech disturbances** is destruction of Broca's speech center. In this case the ability to speak is lost even though the primary motor cortex for the speech musculature, the corresponding cranial nerves and their nuclei, and the peripheral apparatus are all completely intact. This condition is called **motor aphasia** (cf. p. 151). Further discusssion of speech impediments can be found in [15].

12.4 References

Textbooks and Handbooks

1. AINSWORTH, W.A.: Mechanisms of Speech Recognition. Oxford: Pergamon 1976
2. ALTSCHULER, R.A., BOBBIN, R.P., HOFFMANN, D.W.: Neurobiology of Hearing: The Cochlea. New York: Raven Press 1986
3. BALOH, R.W., HONRUBIA,V.: Clinical Neurophysiology of the Vestibular System. Philadelphia: F.A. Davis Company 1979
4. BERLIN, CH.J. (ed.): Hearing Science. London and Philadelphia: Taylor and Francis 1985
5. BLAUERT, J.: Spatial Hearing. MIT Press, Cambridge Mass 1983
6. FLANAGAN, J.L.: Speech Analysis, Synthesis and Perception. 2nd Edition. Berlin-Heidelberg-New York: Springer 1972
7. FLOCK, A., WERSÄLL, J. (eds.): Cellular Mechanisms in Hearing. Hear. Res. *22,* 1–323 (1986)
8. GUALTIEROTTI, T. (ed.): The Vestibular System: Function and Morphology. New York-Heidelberg-Berlin: Springer-Verlag 1981
9. HONRUBIA, V., BRAZIER, M.: Nystagmus and Vertigo. Clinical Approaches to the Patient with Dizziness. New Yord: Academic Press 1982
10. IGARISHI, M., BLACK, F.O.: Vestibular and Visual Control on Posture and Locomotor Equilibrium. Basel: Karger Verlag 1985
11. IRVINE, D.R.F.: The Auditory Brainstem; Progress in Sensory Physiology Vol. 7. Berlin, Heidelberg: Springer 1986
12. KEIDEL, W.D., NEFF, W.D. (eds.): Handbook of Sensory Physiology. Berlin-Heidelberg-New York: Springer, Vol. V, 1 (1974), Vol. V, 2 (1975), Vol V, 3 (1976)
13. KLINKE, R., HARTMANN, R. (eds.): Hearing – Physiological Bases and Psychophysics. Berlin: Springer 1983
14. KRYTER, K.D.: The Effects of Noise on Man. 2nd Edition. New York-San Francisco-London: Academic Press 1985
15. LENNEBERG, Biological Foundations of Language. New York: Wiley 1967
16. LONDON, N., MELITA, O. (eds.): Life Sciences Research in Space. Paris: European Space Agency 1984
17. MOORE, B.C.J.: An Introduction to the Psychology of Hearing. London: Academic Press 1982
18. MOORE, B.C.J., PATTERSON, R.D. (eds.): Auditory Frequency Selectivity. New York: Plenum Press 1986
19. MOORE, E.J. (ed.): Bases of Auditory Brain-Stem Evoked Responses. New York: Grune & Stratton Inc. 1983
20. PICKLES, J.O.: An Introduction to the Physiology of Hearing. 2nd edition. London: Academic Press 1988
21. PRECHT, W.: Neuronal Operations in the Vestibular System. Berlin-Heidelberg-New York: Springer-Verlag 1978
22. PROCTOR, D.F.: Breathing, Speech and Song. Wien: Springer 1980
23. REASON, J.T., BRAND, J.J.: Motion Sickness. New York: Academic Press 1975
24. RINTELMANN, W.F.: Hearing Assessment. Baltimore: University Park Press 1979
25. ROEDERER, J.G.: Introduction to the Physics and Psychophysics of Music. New York: Springer 1975
26. WILSON, V., JONES, G.M.: Mammalian Vestibular Physiology. New York: Plenum Press 1979

Research Reports and Reviews

27. ADAMS, J.C.: Single unit studies on the dorsal and intermediate acoustic striae. J. comp. Neurol. *170,* 97–106 (1976)
28. BAUMGARTEN, R.V. et al.: Effects of rectilinear acceleration and optokinetic and caloric imulations in space. Science *225,* 208–212 (1984)
29. DALLOS, P.: Cochlear physiology. Ann. Rev. Psychol. *32,* 153–190 (1981)
30. EVANS, E.F.: Place and time coding of frequency in the peripheral auditory system: some physiological pros and cons. Audiology *17,* 369–420 (1978)
31. EVANS, E.F., KLINKE, R.: The effects of intracochlear and systemic furosemide on the properties of single cochlear nerve fibres in the cat. J. Physiol. *331,* 409–427 (1982)
32. HARTMANN, R., KLINKE, R.: Discharge properties of afferent fibres of the goldfish semicircular canal with high frequency stimulation. Pflügers Arch. *388,* 111–121 (1980)
33. HUDSPETH, A.J.: Mechanoelectrical transduction by hair cells in the acousticolateralis sensory system. Ann Rev. Neurosci. *6,* 187–215 (1983)
34. HUDSPETH, A.J.: The cellular basis of hearing: The biophysics of hair cells. Science *230,* 745–752 (1985)
35. JOHNSTONE, B.M., PATUZZI, R., YATES, G.K.: Basilar membrane measurements and the travelling wave. Hear. Res. *22,* 147–153 (1986)
36. KEMP, D.T.: Stimulated acoustic emissions from within the human auditory system. J. Acoust. Soc. Am. *64,* 1386–1391 (1978)
37. KLINKE, R., GALLEY, N.: Efferent innervation of vestibular and auditory receptors. Physiol. Rev. *54,* 316–357 (1974)
38. KLINKE, R.: Neurotransmission in the inner ear. Hear. Res. *22,* 235–243 (1986)
39. LIM, D.J.: Functional structure of the organ of Corti: A review. Hear. Res. *22,* 117–146 (1986)

40. Moore, J.K., Osen, K.K.: The cochlear nuclei in man. Am. J. Anat. *154*, 393–418 (1979)
41. Oman, C.M., Young, L.R.: The physiological range of pressure difference and cupula deflections in the human semicircular canal. Acta Oto-Laryng. *74*, 324–331 (1972)
42. Pettigrew, J.D.: Mobile maps in the brain. Nature *309*, 307–308 (1984)
43. Philipps, D.P., Brugge, J.F.: Progress in neurophysiology of sound localization. Ann. Rev. Psychol. *36*, 245–274 (1985)
44. Pickles, J.O.: Recent advances in cochlear physiology. Progress in Neurobiol. *24*, 1–42 (1985)
45. Rhode, W.S.: Cochlear mechanics. Ann. Rev. Physiol. *46*, 231–246 (1984)
46. Sachs, M.B.: Neural coding of complex sounds: Speech. Ann. Rev. Physiol. *4*, 261–273 (1984)
47. Webster, W.R., Aitkin, L.M.: Central auditory processing. In: Handbook of Psychobiology, Gazzaniga, M.S., Blakemore Colin (eds.) p. 325. New York: Academic Press 1975
48. Weiss, T.F.: Relation of receptor potentials of cochlear hair-cells to spike discharges of cochlear neurons. Ann. Rev. Physiol. *46*, 247–259 (1984)
49. Zwicker, E.: Psychoakustik. Berlin: Springer 1982

13 Taste and Smell

H. ALTNER and J. BOECKH

13.1 Characterization of the Chemical Senses

The sensations of taste and smell are derived from a selective and highly sensitive reaction of specialized sense cells to the presence of the molecules of certain compounds. In a broader sense, specific reactions to molecules – a hormone (p. 371), for instance, or a neurotransmitter (p. 43) – are characteristic of many cells and tissues. But gustatory and olfactory sense cells act as exteroceptors; their reactions to molecules provide important information about external stimuli, which is processed in areas of the brain reserved for these senses and which gives rise to sensations. Other chemoreceptive cells serve as interoceptors – for example, to measure CO_2 (p. 573).

Taste and smell can be characterized and distinguished by morphological and physiological criteria. The most clear-cut difference between the two senses lies in the classification of their respective stimulus qualities (Table 13-1). Other characteristics, such as sensitivity or the physical properties of the adequate stimulus, differ in certain respects but with some overlap.

In comparison to other senses, taste and smell exhibit a high degree of **adaptation** (cf. Fig. 8-5, p. 181). The excitation in the afferent pathways declines markedly during a maintained stimulus, and perception is correspondingly diminished; for example, after only a short time in a scented environment we stop perceiving the smell. An equally characteristic property of the chemical senses is the high sensitivity to certain stimuli. The range of stimulus intensities which are discriminated is relatively low (1:500), and the differential threshold is high. The exponent in Stevens' power function $\psi = k \cdot (\Phi - \Phi_0)^a$ is 0.4–0.6 for odors and about 1 for taste stimuli (cf. Fig. 8-14, p. 192).

Table 13-1. Subdivision and characterization of the chemical senses

	Taste	Smell
Sensors (Receptors)	Secondary sense cells	Primary sense cells; endings of cranial nerves V (IX and X)
Position of sensors	On the tongue	Nose and throat
Afferent cranial nerves	VII, IX	I, V, (IX, X)
Stations in central nervous system	1. Medulla oblongata 2. Ventral thalamus 3. Cortex (postcentral gyrus) Connections to hypothalamus	1. Olfactory bulb 2. Cerebrum (prepiriform area) Connections to limbic system and hypothalamus
Adequate stimulus	Molecules of organic and inorganic substances, mostly nonvolatile. Stimulus source near or in direct contact with sense organ.	Molecules of almost exclusively organic, volatile compounds in gas form, becoming dissolved only near sensor. Stimulus source usually at a distance.
Number of qualitatively distinguishable stimuli	Small 4 basic quantities	Very large (thousands), in many poorly-defined quality classes
Absolute sensitivity	Relatively low At least 10^{16} or more molecules/ml solution	Very high to some substances (10^7 molecules per ml air, as little as 10^2 or 10^3 in animals)
Biological characterization	Contact sense Used for testing food and control of food intake and processing (salivary reflexes)	Long-distance sense Used to test environment (hygiene) and food, and by animals in foraging, communication, reproduction. Strong emotional weighting

Primary processes and chemical specificity. The first event in stimulation of a chemoreceptor is now generally thought to be an interaction based on weak binding forces between the stimulus molecule and a *receptor protein.* Proteins with the character of enzymes have been isolated from taste organs; their substance-specificity and turnover dynamics are the same as those of the sense cells themselves. The subsequent events leading to the electrical response of the cell membrane are unknown. Each receptor cell responds very selectively to a particular group of substances. Slight changes in the structure of a substance can alter its sensory quality or render it ineffective. It is likely that the effectiveness of a molecule is crucially affected by its size (e.g., chain length) and the distribution of electrical charge within it (e.g., the positions of functional groups). But the fact that in many cases molecules that are quite different chemically elicit the same olfactory sensations remains unexplained. For example, the three following compounds all smell musky despite their structural differences (cf. BEETS in [1]).

$CH-(CH_2)_7$
$\|$ $\quad C=O$
$CH-(CH_2)_7$

Civetone

O_2N NO_2 O

5,7-Dinitro-indan 1,3,4,6,7,8-Hexahydro-cyclopenta[f]-2-benzopyran

It has been proposed that chemoreceptors bear **reception sites** specific to particular groups of substances. This view is supported by cases of partial anosmia, the selective failure to perceive a limited number of odors, quite closely related chemically (cf. p. 311). The selective action of certain drugs on taste organs can be interpreted similarly. When potassium gymnemate, a substance from the Indian plant *Gymnema silvestre,* is placed on the tongue the perception of sweetness alone is eliminated – sugar "tastes like sand." A protein contained in the fruit of the western African plant *Synsepalium dulcificum* changes acid flavors to sweet, so that lemon tastes like orange (cf. KURIHARA in [1]). Placing cocaine on the tongue causes the loss of all four taste qualities at different times, in the following order: bitter, sweet, salty, sour.

13.2 The Sense of Taste

Sensors and Neurons

The **gustatory sense cells** (*taste cells*) in adults are on the surface of the tongue. Together with supporting cells, in groups of 40–60 elements, they form **taste buds** in the epithelium of the lingual papillae (Fig. 13-1). Large vallate papillae at the base of the tongue contain as many as 200 taste buds each, whereas the smaller fungiform and foliate papillae on the anterior and lateral parts of the tongue each contain only a few. Altogether, an adult has a few thousand taste buds. **Glands** between the papillae secrete a fluid that rinses the buds. The distal parts of the receptor cells (sensor cells), which are sensitive to stimuli, are convoluted to form *microvilli.* These project into a common chamber that communicates with the exterior by a pore on the surface of the papilla (Fig. 13-1). The stimulus molecules reach the taste cells (sensors) by diffusing through this pore.

Like other secondary sense cells, the taste cells produce a receptor potential when stimulated. This excitation is transmitted synaptically to **afferent fibers** in **cranial nerves,** which conduct it to the brain in the form of nerve impulses. The nerves involved are the **chorda tympani,** a branch of the **facial nerve** (VII) that innervates the anterior and lateral parts of the tongue, and the **glossopharyngeal nerve** (IX) to the posterior part (Fig. 13-2). By branching, a single afferent fiber receives excitation from the sensors in various taste buds.

There is a remarkably high taste-cell **turnover rate;** the life span of a cell is about 10 days, after

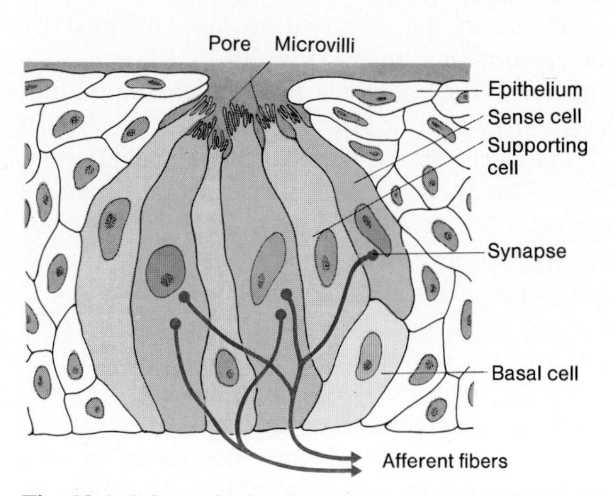

Fig. 13-1. Schematic drawing of a taste bud embedded in a lingual papilla, showing basal cell, sense cells, supporting cell and afferent fibers of the associated cranial nerve

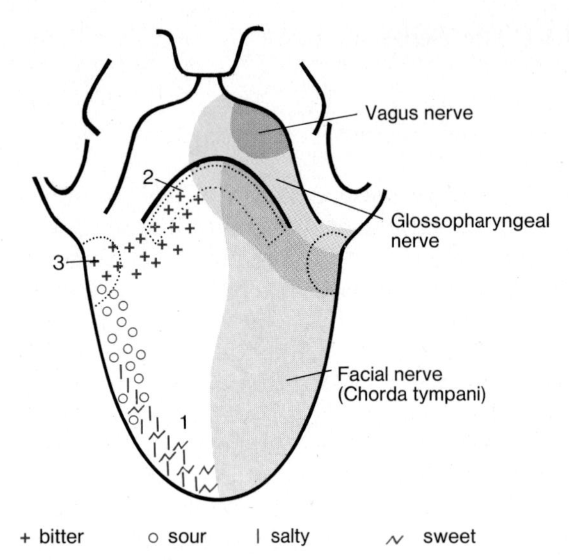

Fig. 13-2. Schematic drawing of the human tongue, showing the afferent innervation by different cranial nerves (*shading*) and the distribution of the papillae (1 fungiform, 2 vallate, 3 foliate). The inhomogeneous distribution of taste qualities is indicated by symbols

which it is replaced by a new sensor derived from a basal cell. The new taste cells become associated with the afferent fibers in such a way that the specificity of the fibers is unchanged. The mechanisms that ensure this match between receptor and fiber are not yet known (cf. OAKLEY in [12]).

Reactions of the cells and fibers. A single **taste cell** in most cases responds to substances representative of several taste qualities, and may be either depolarized or hyperpolarized (Fig. 13-3). The amplitude of the receptor potential (sensor potential) increases with the concentration of the stimulating substance. However, the nature and amplitude of the response are also affected by the surrounding milieu (Fig. 13-4).

The generator potentials produce corresponding levels of excitation in the afferent fibers, to give a response pattern called the "taste profile" (Fig. 13-5). The discharge in the fibers is governed by the response of the sensor in such a way that depolarization of the sensor has an excitatory and hyperpolarization an inhibitory effect.

Among the fibers in Nerve IX, many give particularly strong responses to bitter substances; those in Nerve VII are more excited by salt, sugar or sour stimuli, one class of fibers responding more strongly to sugar than to salt, another more strongly to salt than to sugar, etc. This taste-specific difference in level of excitation in different fiber groups contains the information

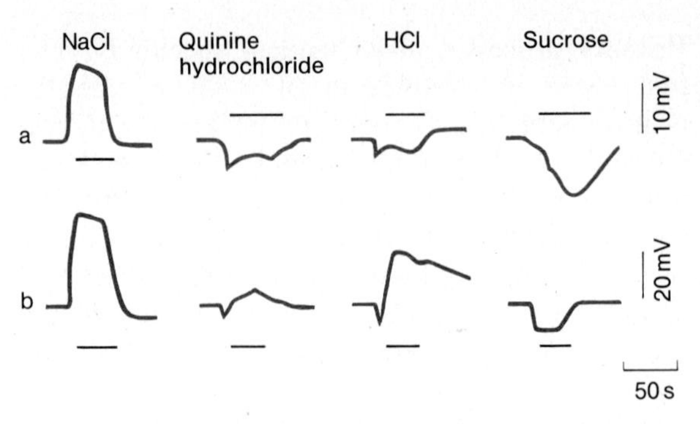

Fig. 13-3. Receptor potentials measured intracellularly in two taste cells **(a, b)** in the tongue of a rat. Stimuli: 0.5 mol/l NaCl, 0.02 mol/l quinine hydrochloride, 0.01 mol/l HCL and 0.5 mol/l sucrose. The duration of each stimulus is indicated by a *horizontal bar*. (Modified from SATO and BEIDLER, in [11])

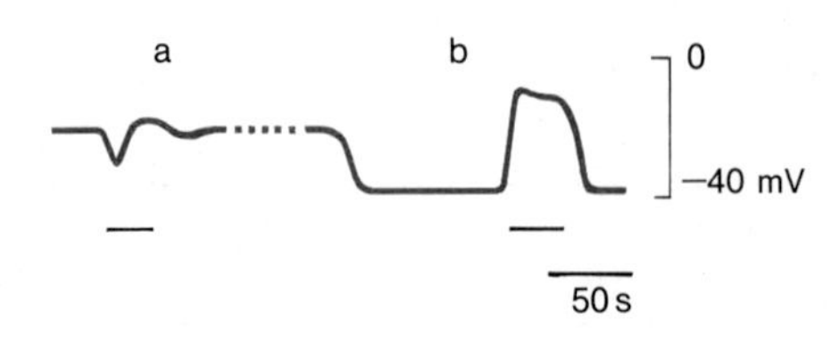

Fig. 13-4. Effect of the surrounding medium on the shape and amplitude of intracellularly measured receptor potentials of single taste cells in the tongue of a rat, stimulated with 0.02 mol/l quinine hydrochloride. The surrounding media are 41.4 mmol/l NaCl **(a)** and distilled water **(b).** (Modified from SATO and BEIDLER, in [11])

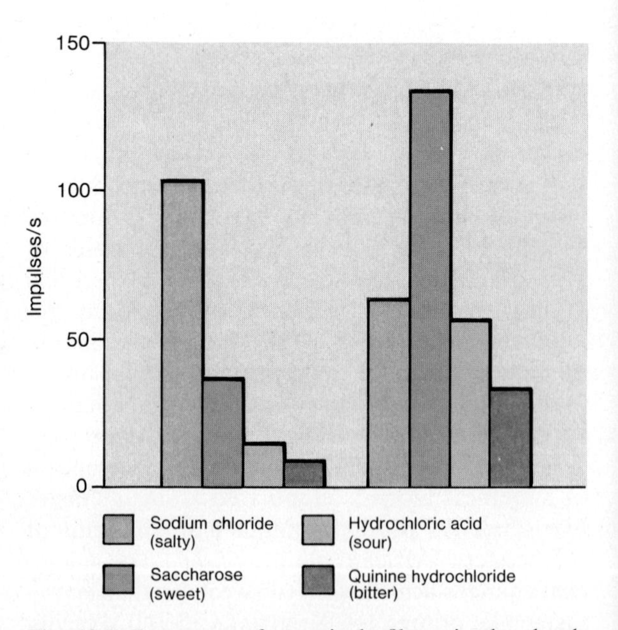

Fig. 13-5. Responses of two single fibers, in the chorda tympani of a rat, to various substances: 0.1 mol/l NaCl, 0.5 mol/l sucrose, 0.01 N HCl, 0.02 mol/l quinine hydrochloride. (Modified from SATO, in [12])

about **taste quality** – that is, the kind of molecule. The overall level of excitation in the population of fibers contains the information about **stimulus intensity** – that is, the number of the molecules.

Central neurons. The **taste fibers** of Nerves VII and IX terminate in, or in the vicinity of, the **solitary nucleus** of the *medulla oblongata.* This nucleus is connected, by way of the medial lemniscus, with the **thalamus** in the region of the *ventral posteromedial nucleus.* The third-order neurons pass through the internal capsule and terminate in the region of the *postcentral gyrus* of the **cerebral cortex.** As a result of processing in these stations, the number of highly taste-specific neurons increases. Some of the cells in the cortex respond only to substances of a single taste quality. The positions of these neurons indicate a degree of spatial organization on the basis of effective taste quality. Other neurons in these centers respond not only to taste, but to thermal or mechanical stimulation of the tongue as well.

Gustatory Ability in Man

The qualities. Humans basically discriminate 4 taste qualities: **sweet, sour, bitter, salty.** These are quite well characterized by representative compounds (Table 13-2). A sweet taste is associated chiefly with naturally occurring sugars such as sucrose or glucose, and NaCl tastes salty; other salts, such as KCl, taste salty and bitter at the same time. Such **mixed sensations** are also characteristic of many natural taste stimuli, and correspond to the nature of their components. For example, orange tastes sweet and sour, grapefruit sour, sweet and bitter. Substances with a sour taste are acids; many plant alkaloids have a bitter taste.

Table 13-2. Characteristic taste substances and their effectiveness in eliciting taste sensations in man. (From PFAFFMANN, in [1])

Quality	Substance	Threshold (mol/l)
Bitter	Quinine sulfate	0.000008
	Nicotine	0.000016
Sour	Hydrochloric acid	0.0009
	Citric acid	0.0023
Sweet	Sucrose	0.01
	Glucose	0.08
	Saccharin	0.000023
Salty	NaCl	0.01
	$CaCl_2$	0.01

Zones of specific sensitivity can be spatially demarcated on the tongue. Bitter stimuli act primarily on the *base* of the tongue, and the other qualities act at the *side* and *tip* in overlapping regions (Fig. 13-2).
There is no unequivocal correlation between the **chemical properties** of a substance and its **gustatory action.** For example, not only sugars but also lead salts taste sweet, and the most effective sweet stimuli are artificial sweeteners such as saccharin. The *perceived quality* of a substance, moreover, depends on its *concentration.* Table salt in low concentrations tastes sweet, and is purely salty only when more concentrated. Sensitivity to bitter substances is remarkably high. Because such substances are often poisonous, it makes sense that one should be warned of even small concentrations in water or food. Fairly strong bitter stimuli readily elicit *vomiting* or *retching reflexes.* The **emotional components** of taste perceptions vary widely, depending on the condition of the body. A person with a salt deficiency finds food acceptable even though its salt concentration is so high that a normal person would reject it.

The sense of taste is evidently quite uniform in **mammals in general.** Behavioral experiments have shown that other mammals discriminate the same taste qualities as man does. However, single-fiber recordings have revealed certain abilities beyond the scope of the human taste sense. For example, in cats *"water fibers"* have been found, which either respond only to water or have a taste profile that includes water along with other qualities as an effective stimulus (cf. SATO in [1]).

Biological significance. The biological role of the sense of taste is not only to *test the edibility of food* (see above); tastes also affect the process of digestion. Connections with autonomic efferents form reflexes that enable taste inputs to control the secretion of digestive glands. Not only is the amount of secretion influenced, but also its composition – depending, for example, on whether a sweet or salty taste predominates in the food.
As one **grows older** gustatory ability declines. Consumption of drugs such as caffeine and heavy smoking also reduce taste sensations.

13.3 The Sense of Smell

The surface area of the nasal mucosa is increased by conchae, ridges that project from the side into the nasal cavity. The **olfactory region** containing most of the sense cells is restricted to the upper concha, although the middle concha bears small islands of olfactory epithelium (Fig. 13-6).

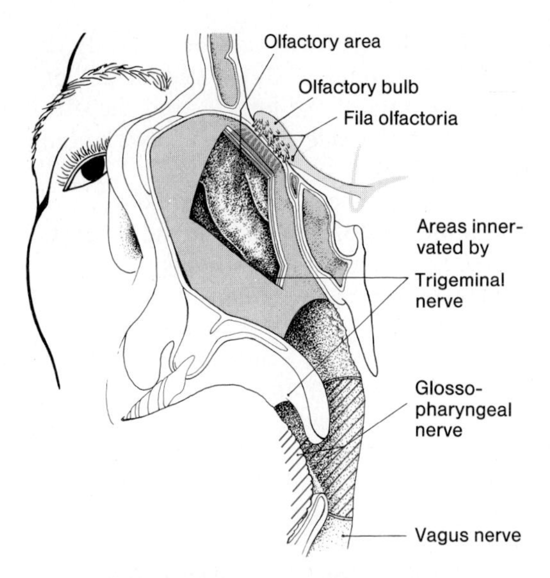

Fig. 13-6. Schematic drawing of the human nose and throat cavities (sagittal section). The olfactory region is restricted to the upper and middle conchae. The regions innvervated by the trigeminal (V), glossopharyngeal (IX) and vagus (X) nerves are indicated

Sensors

The **olfactory cells** are primary, bipolar sense cells, sending out two processes – at the apex a dendrite bearing **cilia,** and at the base an axon. The internal structure of the cilia differs from that of normal kinocilia; incapable of active movement, they are embedded in the layer of mucus that covers the olfactory epithelium. Odor substances carried in by the respired air can come into contact with the membranes of the cilia, the most likely site of the interaction between stimulus molecule and receptor. The axons run to the olfactory bulb in bundles, the *fila olfactoria.* In addition, the entire nasal mucosa contains free endings of the *trigeminal nerve,* some of which also respond to odor stimuli. In the throat region, olfactory stimuli can excite fibers in the glossopharyngeal and vagus nerves (Fig. 13-6). The mucus layer over the olfactory epithelium protects it from drying out; it is continually replenished by secretion and distributed by the movement of the kinocilia in the surrounding epithelial regions.

Odor molecules are conveyed to the receptor cells (sensor cells) periodically, during inspiration through the nostrils. To a lesser extent, odors can move to the olfactory epithelium from the oral cavity, by diffusion through the choanae. While eating, therefore, one experiences mixed sensations in which gustatory and olfactory sensations are combined. Sniffing, a conspicuous behavior

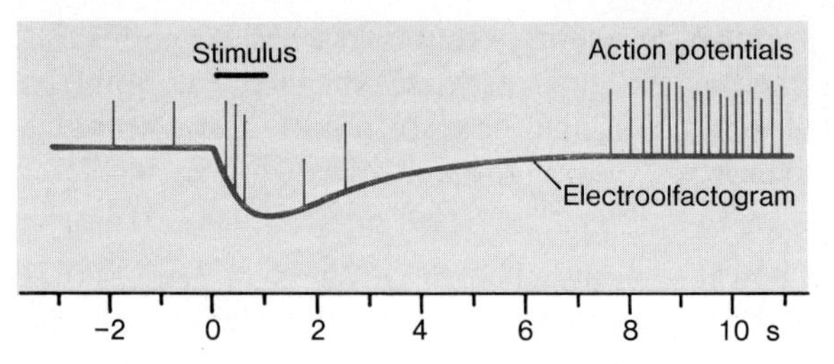

Fig. 13-7. Simultaneous recording of electroolfactogram *(red)* and action potentials of a single receptor in the olfactory epithelium of the frog during stimulation with nitrobenzene. Duration of stimulus *(black)* 1 s. (From GESTELAND, in [1])

of many mammals, can considerably increase the intake of air and thus the concentration of stimulus molecules in the mucosa.

Altogether the human olfactory region, ca. 10 cm^2 in area, contains about 10^7 sensors (olfactory cells). The number in other vertebrates is greater (e.g., $2.2 \cdot 10^8$ in a German shepherd dog). Olfactory cells, like taste cells, are regularly replaced; presumably, then, not all the cells are functional at the same time.

Electrodes in contact with the vertebrate olfactory epithelium record slow potentials of complex form and a few millivolts amplitude during odor stimulation. These **electroolfactograms** (EOG; Fig. 13-7; cf. OTTOSON in [1]), like electroretinograms (ERG), represent the summed activity of many units, so that they give no information about the properties of the individual sense cells. Recording from *single sense cells* in the olfactory mucosa of vertebrates has been accomplished only occasionally (Fig. 13-7). Such records show that the spontaneous discharge rate of these cells is very low, only a few impulses per second, and that each sensor responds to a large number of substances. As in the recording of taste profiles (cf. p. 308), it is possible to construct *response spectra* of single sense cells (cf. GESTELAND in [1]).

Odor Qualities

Humans can distinguish the smell of thousands of different substances. The olfactory sensations can be arranged in groups on the basis of certain similarities, so that **odor** or **quality classes** can be defined. However, this classification is by no means as clear-cut as that of taste qualities. The uncertainty in such categorization is evident in the widely varying number of classes proposed by the different authors. Quality is even less well correlated with chemically definable properties than in the case of taste stimuli (cf. p. 309). As

Table 13-3. Distinguishing characteristics of odor classes. (From AMOORE and SKRAMLIK)

Odor class	Known representative compounds	Smells like	"Standard"
Floral	Geraniol	Roses	d-1-β-phenyl-ethylmetyl-carbinol
Ethereal	Benzyl acetate	Pears	1,2-dichlor-ethane
Musky	Muscone	Musk	3-methyl-cyclopentade-can-1-one
Camphor	Cineole, camphor	Eucalyptus	1,8-cineole
Putrid	Hydrogen sulfide	Rotten eggs	Dimethylsulfide
Pungent	Formic acid, acetic acid	Vinegar	Formic acid

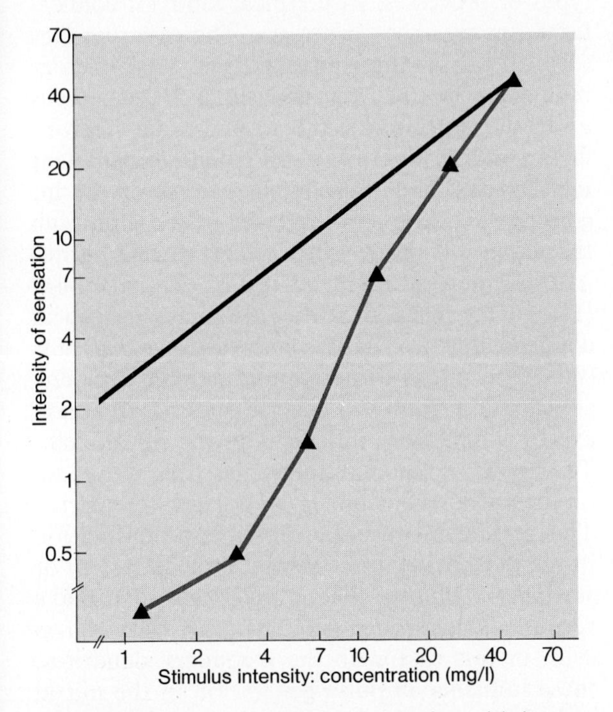

Fig. 13-8. Increase in intensity of sensation with increasing stimulus intensity (stimulus: propanol), unadapted *(straight black line)* and after adaptation to pentanol *(black triangles, red curve)*. (Modified from CAIN and ENGEN, in [10])

Table 13-3 shows, the odor classes as a rule are named for the natural sources of the odor substances, or for typical representatives; the classes can be characterized by "standard odors."

So far no neurophysiological basis for assigning odor substances to quality classes has been found. The view that groups of closely related odor substances can be distinguished from one another is supported by cases in which a person's ability to smell is partially impaired (**partial anosmia;** cf. p. 307). In this disorder the thresholds to certain odor substances are elevated; at least some such cases are genetic in origin. Often the thresholds to several substances are affected, and as a rule these prove to belong to the same odor class. Experimental data relevant to odor classification can also be obtained by analysis of *cross-adaptation.* These experiments are based on the observation that when prolonged exposure to an odor results in decreased sensitivity to that substance, the thresholds to certain other substances are raised as well (Fig. 13-8). By testing the degree to which the threshold to any arbitrary odor substance is affected by previous presentation of other substances, as well as the reciprocal interaction, one can construct a diagram of cross-adaptational relationships (Fig. 13-9). This procedure, however, does not provide an unequivocal, detailed organization of the great variety of odor substances [7].

When interpreting human olfactory sensations, it must be kept in mind that the fibers of the *trigeminal nerve* that terminate in the nasal mucosa also respond to odor substances and contribute to these sensations, as do the endings of *glossopharyngeal-* and *vagal-nerve fibers* in the throat (Fig 13-6). These sensations, not medi-

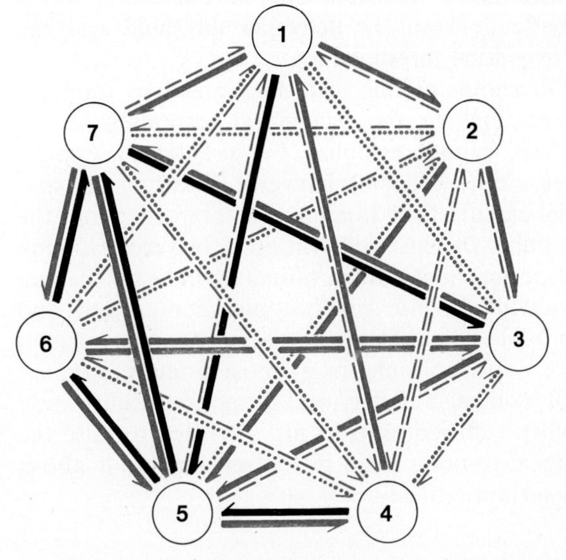

Fig. 13-9. Cross-adaptational relationships among 7 odor substances (1 citral, 2 cyclopentanone, 3 benzyl acetate, 4 safrole, 5 m-xylene, 6 methyl salicylate, 7 butyl acetate). As a rule the reciprocal interactions are not equally strong. The degree to which the detection threshold is raised is indicated by the connecting lines as follows: *black lines,* very large increase; *red continuous lines,* large increase; *red dashed lines,* moderate increase; *red dotted lines,* slight increase in threshold. (Modified from KÖSTER [7])

ated by the olfactory nerve, persist when the olfactory epithelium becomes nonfunctional – for example, as a result of infection (flu), tumors (craniotomy), or skull traumata. In such cases, together termed **hyposmia,** thresholds are considerably higher than normal, but the ability to discriminate among the odors that are detected is only slightly diminished. In hypogonadotropic hypogonadism (Kallmann's syndrome) olfaction is mediated entirely by these cranial nerves, for in this congenital disorder the olfactory bulbs are aplastic. Noxious thermal and chemical stimuli, depending on their nature and mode of action, can cause reversible or irreversible acute or chronic hyposmias or anosmias. Finally, sensitivity is also reduced as one grows old.

Sensitivity, Coding

The human sense of smell is very sensitive, even though some animal olfactory organs are known to perform still better. Table 13-4 gives the concentrations of two odor substances that just suffice to elicit a sensation in man. With very low concentrations the sensation is unspecific; only at somewhat higher concentrations can an odor be not only detected but identified. For example, the smell of skatole at low concentrations is regarded as not at all unpleasant, whereas above a certain limit the typical repulsive smell of this substance is manifest. Therefore a distinction is made between the **detection threshold** and the **recognition threshold.**

Thresholds of this sort, determined by reported sensations or the behavioral responses of animals, cannot establish the *sensitivity of single sense cells* (sensors). However, knowing the spatial extent of the human olfactory organ and the number of sense cells within it, one can estimate their sensitivity. Such estimates indicate that an individual sense cell becomes depolarized and produces an action potential in response to a single odor molecule, or at most a few molecules. Of course, a behavioral response results only when sufficient sensors are activated to raise the signal-to-noise ratio in the sensory input above a certain critical level.

Table 13-4. Detection threshold to butyric acid and butyl mercaptan. (From NEUHAUS and STUIVER)

Substance	Molecules per ml air	Concentration at stimulus source
Butyric acid	$2.4 \cdot 10^9$	10^{-10}
Butyl mercaptan	10^7	$2.7 \cdot 10^{-12}$

Coding. The coding of odor stimuli by the sensors can as yet be described only to a first approximation. The first consideration is that the individual sense cells respond to a fairly large number of different odor substances. Accordingly, the sensors (like gustatory sensors) have overlapping response profiles. Thus each odor substance would be associated with a specific pattern of excitation in the population of sense cells. For a given pattern, the concentration of the odor substance would be reflected in the overall level of excitation.

Central Processing

Olfactory bulb. Histologically, the olfactory bulb is subdivided into several layers characterized by cells of particular shapes that send out certain types of processes, with typical kinds of connections among these processes. The essential features of information processing in the olfactory bulb are (i) marked **convergence** of the sense cells upon the mitral cells, the second-order neurons in the auditory pathway, (ii) extensive **inhibitory mechanisms,** and (iii) **efferent control** of the incoming excitation. In the layer of the glomeruli the axons of about 1,000 olfactory cells terminate on the primary dendrites of one *mitral cell* (Fig. 13-10). These dendrites also make reciprocal dendrodendritic synapses with the *periglomerular cells.* The mitral-to-periglomerular-cell contacts are excitatory, and those in the opposite direction exert an inhibitory influence on the mitral cells. The axons of the periglomerular cells terminate on the mitral-cell dendrites of adjacent glomeruli. This arrangement makes possible a modulation of the local dendritic response; it mediates *self* or *surround inhibition.* The *granule cells* also make reciprocal dendrodendritic synapses with mitral cells, in this case with the secondary dendrites; these influence impulse generation in the mitral cells. Here, too, the synapses directed toward the mitral cell are inhibitory, so that the reciprocal contacts subserve self inhibition. Finally, the granule cells make contact with mitral-cell collaterals as well as with *efferent (bulbopetal) axons* of various origins. Some of the centrifugal fibers come from the contralateral bulb, by way of the anterior commissure.

The special feature of inhibition by the granule cells, which lack axons, is that in contrast to the typical Renshaw inhibition these cells can be partially activated – that is, with a spatial gradation. This pattern of highly complex interactions is entirely comparable to the situation in the retina, although the retinal processing is based on a different kind of cellular organization [13]. The foregoing is only a rough

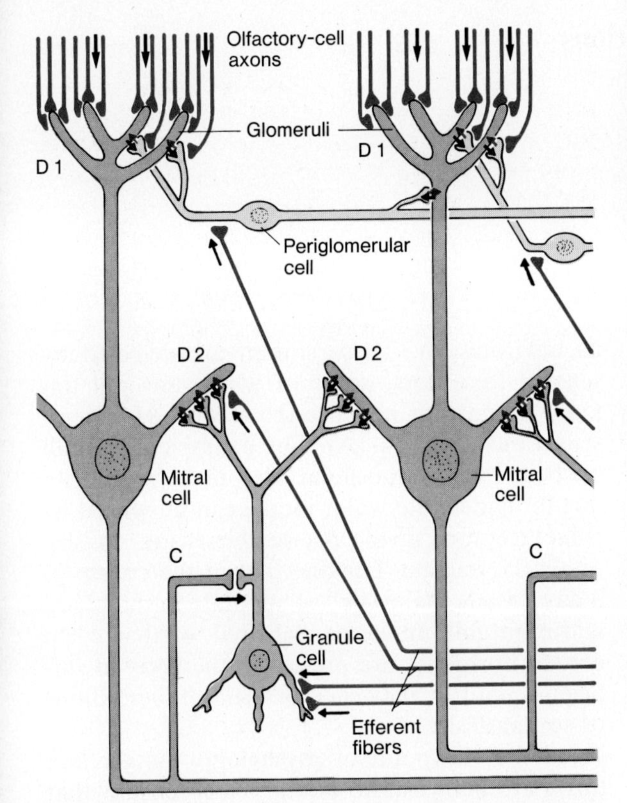

Fig. 13-10. Survey of the neuronal connections in the olfactory bulb. In the glomeruli the olfactory-cell axons terminate on the primary dendrites (D1) of the mitral cells. Periglomerular cells and granule cells make reciprocal synapses on the primary and secondary (D2) dendrites of the mitral cells. C, collaterals. The direction of synaptic transmission is indicated by arrows (excitation, *black;* inhibition, *red*). (Combined and modified from SHEPHERD, in [13])

outline of events in the olfactory bulb. In addition to the mitral cells, various forms of tufted cells also serve as secondary neurons; these differ from the mitral cells in their projections and transmitters.

Central connections. The axons of the *mitral cells* form the *lateral olfactory tract,* among the destinations of which are the *prepiriform area* and the *piriform lobe.* Synapses with higher-order neurons provide connections to the *hippocampal formation* and, by way of the amygdaloid complex, to the autonomic nuclei in the *hypothalamus.* Neurons responding to olfactory stimuli have also been found in the *reticular formation* of the mesencephalon and in the *orbitofrontal cortex.*

The influence of olfaction on other functional systems. The direct connection to the limbic system (cf. p. 365) explains the marked **emotional component** of olfactory sensations. Odors readily give rise to feelings of enjoyment or aversion (hedonic components of sensation), and the affective state of the organism is altered correspondingly. Moreover, the significance of olfactory stimuli in *control of reproductive behavior* should not be underestimated, although the results of animal experiments – especially the olfaction-blocking experiments on rodents – cannot be applied directly to humans. Animal experiments have also shown that the responses of neurons in the olfactory pathway can be altered by testosterone injection. Thus the flow of excitation is also under the influence of the sex hormones.

Functional disorders. In addition to the states of impaired olfaction called hyposmia and anosmia (cf. p. 312), odors may be incorrectly perceived **(parosmia)** or olfactory sensations may occur in the absence of odor substances **(olfactory hallucinations).** Such disturbances can have various causes. For instance, they can result from allergic rhinitis or head traumata. Olfactory hallucinations of unpleasant character (cacosmia) are experienced primarily by schizophrenic patients.

13.4 References

Textbooks and Handbooks

1. BEIDLER, L.M. (Ed.): Chemical Senses, Part 1: Olfaction, Part 2: Taste, Handbook of Sensory Physiology, Vol. IV. Berlin-Heidelberg-New York: Springer 1971
2. PFAFF, D. (Ed.): Taste, Olfaction and the Central Nervous System. New York: Rockefeller University Press 1985

Original Papers and Reviews

3. BREIPOHL, W. (Ed.): Olfaction and Endocrine Regulation. London: IRL Press 1982
4. DENTON, D.A., COGHLAN, J.P. (Eds.): Olfaction and Taste, Vol. V. New York: Academic Press 1975
5. HAYASHI, T. (Ed.): Olfaction and Taste, Vol. II. Oxford-London-New York-Paris: Pergamon Press 1967
6. KARE, M.R., MALLER, O. (Eds.): The Chemical Senses and Nutrition. New York-San Francisco-London: Academic Press 1977
7. KÖSTER, E.: Adaptation and Cross-Adaptation in Olfaction. Rotterdam: Bronder 1971
8. LE MAGNEN, J., MAC LEOD, P. (Eds.): Olfaction and Taste, Vol. VI. London-Washington DC: IRL Press 1977
9. NORRIS, D.M. (Ed.): Perception of Behavioral Chemicals. Amsterdam-New York-Oxford: Elsevier/North Holland 1981
10. PFAFFMANN, C. (Ed.): Olfaction and Taste, Vol. III. New York: Rockefeller University Press 1969
11. SATO, T.: Receptor potential in rat taste cells. In: AUTRUM, H., OTTOSON, D., PERL, E.R., SCHMIDT, R.F., SHIMAZU, H., WILLIS, W.D. (Eds.): Progress in Sensory Physiology, Vol. 6, p. 1–37, Berlin-Heidelberg-New York-Tokyo: Springer 1986
12. SCHNEIDER, D. (Ed.): Olfaction and Taste, Vol. IV. Stuttgart: Wiss. Verlagsges. 1972
13. SHEPHERD, G.M.: Synaptic organization of the mammalian olfactory bulb. Physiol. Rev. **52,** 864 (1972)
14. VAN DER STARRE, H. (Ed.): Olfaction and Taste, Vol. VII. London-Washington DC: IRL Press 1980
15. ZOTTERMAN, Y. (Ed.): Olfaction and Taste, Vol. I. Oxford-London-New York-Paris: Pergamon Press 1963
16. Chemical Senses. London: IRL Press (published in regular installments)

14 Thirst and Hunger: General Sensations

R.F. Schmidt

From the viewpoint of **sensory physiology,** the feeling of thirst we experience when we have not drunk enough liquids, and the feeling of hunger when we have not eaten recently, cannot be ascribed to a particular sense organ or part of the body. For this reason they are called **general sensations.** Other examples of general sensations are tiredness, shortness of breath, and sexual appetite. A characteristic they all share is that they can be elicited by one or more *adequate stimuli originating within the body itself* rather than in its environment. These stimuli are detected by sensors (receptors) some of which are still unknown, and thus produce the associated general sensations (Fig. 14-1A). For example, we shall see below that intracellular osmotic hypertonicity due to inadequate water intake can be sensed by osmoreceptors, giving rise to thirst (Fig. 14-1B). Similarly, one can imagine that in the course of a day "waste materials" accumulate in the blood and eventually make us feel tired, or that when certain hormones are present in the body in sufficient quantity, they elicit or facilitate sensations of sexual desire.

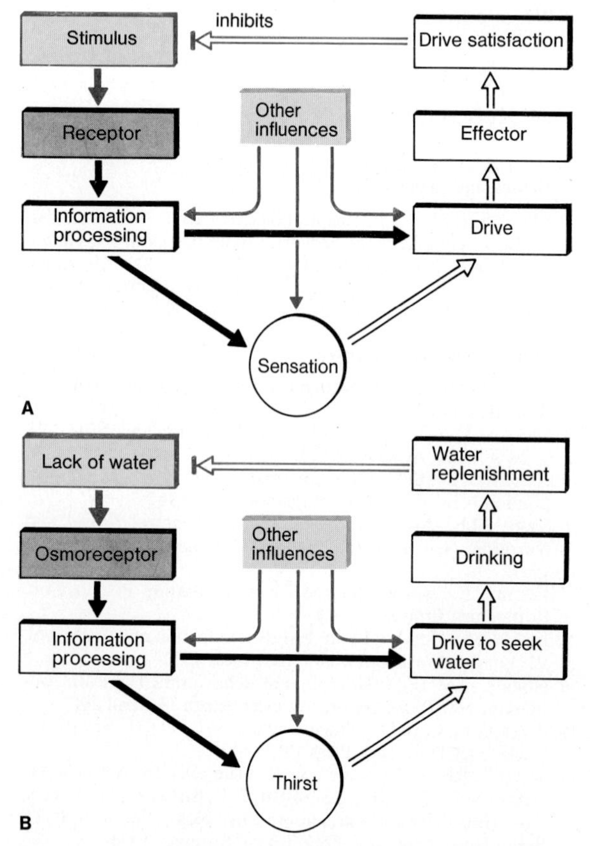

Fig. 14-1 A, B. Diagram of the relationship between general sensations and drives. **A** General representation of the origin of general sensations and drives. **B** Production, by water deficiency, of the feeling of thirst and of the drive to find water. Other receptors, in addition to the osmoreceptors, contribute to the sensation of thirst (cf. Fig. 14-2). The *vertical red bars* at the tips of the top arrows indicate that satisfaction of the drive (the provision of water in B) leads to elimination of the stimulus (water deficiency in B)

From the viewpoint of **psychology,** hunger and thirst are **homeostatic drives,** which ensure that the body takes in enough food and liquid. Seen in this light, activation of a drive is controlled directly by the drive-related stimuli (horizontal black arrow in Fig. 14-1A), although we have the subjective impression that these stimuli first produce the general sensation (e.g., thirst in Fig. 14-1B) and that this in turn triggers the drive to search for water and drink it.

Hunger and thirst must be satisfied in order to maintain homeostasis of the body and thus to **ensure survival** (the concept of homeostasis is discussed on p. 333). These drives are innate and need not be learned. But during a lifetime they are modified by numerous influences, especially at the more advanced phylogenetic levels. These influences act at various points in the overall process (see Fig. 14-1A, B). No description of drives and their modification can be given here (see [2, 9, 10, 21]); only those aspects of thirst and hunger related to sensory physiology will be discussed, as examples of the category of general sensations.

14.1 Thirst

The Origin of Thirst

Conditions under which a sensation of thirst appears. The adult human body consists of about 70%–75% water by weight (without taking account of the fat deposits). This water content is maintained within very narrow limits. Normally it fluctuates by only about ±0.22% of the body weight, or ca. ±150 ml. If the body loses water amounting to more than 0.5% of its weight (ca. 350 ml for a person weighing 70 kg) thirst results [3, 7, 11, 16]. (Usually people drink without being thirsty; see p. 317).

The physiological forms of water loss (urine, sweat, water vapor in the exhaled air) together cause water to be **lost from the extra- and the intracellular compartments,** with a concomitant, though normally slight, *osmotic hypertonicity.* Moreover, the *secretion of saliva* is reduced, causing the **feeling of dryness** in mouth and throat so characteristic of thirst. Assuming the presence of suitable receptors (sensors), then, water deficiency in the body could be measured (i) intracellularly, by the volume or osmotic pressure of the *cells,* (ii) by the volume or osmotic pressure of the *extracellular fluid,* and (iii) indirectly by the reduction of *saliva secretion* and the resulting dryness of the oral and pharyngeal mucosa.

Adequate stimuli for the sensation of thirst. To decide which of the above changes is or are responsible for generating the thirst sensation, experiments must be designed in which *only one* of them is altered; the intra- or extracellular water or salt content is changed, or the secretion of saliva is modified. Most of these experiments have been done on animals, the amount of water drunk by the animals being taken as an indicator of the degree of experimentally produced thirst [3, 7, 11, 13, 14]. The most important results so obtained are as follows.

Following intravenous infusion of a hypertonic NaCl solution, a dog drinks twice as much water as it does after i.v. infusion of an osmotically equivalent solution of urea. In the former case, because the cell membranes are impermeable to Na^+ ions, the resulting Na^+ concentration gradient between the interior of the cells and the extracellular space causes water to leave the cells. But the cell membranes are readily permeable to urea, so that when it is injected, the concentrations in the intra- and extracellular spaces equilibrate, with a distinctly smaller change in volume and tonicity of the cells. This finding has been confirmed by repetition of the experiment, with many modifications, on a wide variety of mammals. The inference to be drawn is that **reduction of cell volume** (by water loss, the *salt content* of the cells remaining constant) elicits thirst [3, 14]. This thirst is called **osmotic thirst.**

If the amount of Na^+ in the extracellular space is experimentally reduced (for example, by a change in diet or by peritoneal dialysis), the extracellular compartment loses water; part is released from the body and part diffuses into the cells. Under these conditions thirst is experienced despite the increase in cell volume. A hunger for table salt also appears. If the total volume of the extracellular fluid is reduced without changing the NaCl concentration, thirst is also induced. We can conclude that **decrease in volume of the extracellular fluid** also elicits thirst.

This thirst is called **hypovolemic thirst.** Experiments have shown that the effects of the above two factors are **additive,** so that *simultaneous decrease in cell volume and in extracellular fluid* gives rise to particularly **intense thirst** [3]. On the whole, however, osmotic thirst is more significant than hypovolemic thirst.

The **dryness of the mouth** accompanying essentially all forms of thirst is caused, as mentioned above, by the *reduced secretion of saliva.* It reflects the water deficit and, contrary to previous opinion, appears to be a **symptom** rather than a cause of the general feeling of thirst. This is demonstrated by the following findings. Moistening of the mouth and throat surfaces does not eliminate the sensation of thirst, though it can relieve it somewhat. Nor can thirst be relieved or prevented by local anesthesia of the oral mucosa, or even by complete denervation of the mouth and throat region. Finally, congenital absence of the salivary glands (in humans) or their surgical removal (from animals) has no appreciable effect on water consumption.

All the conditions giving rise to *thirst* simultaneously lead to the **release of ADH** (antidiuretic hormone or vasopressin; cf. p. 377). Conversely, excessive drinking causes inhibition of ADH release and hence water diuresis [14].

Sensors and Central Mechanisms

Intracellular sensors. The neural structures chiefly responsible for regulating salt/water balance are located in the diencephalon, especially in the **hypothalamus and its vicinity.** There are numerous **osmoreceptors,** particularly in areas in *front* of the hypothalamus, which are activated by the increased **intracellular** salt concentration when the cell loses water. The injection of very small amounts (less than 0.2 ml) of hypertonic solutions of NaCl into certain parts of this region, for example, causes goats to begin drinking 30–60 s later, and to continue for 2–5 min, consuming 2–8 liters of water. Electrical stimulation of the same neural structures also elicits prolonged drinking. In many experiments the ablation or

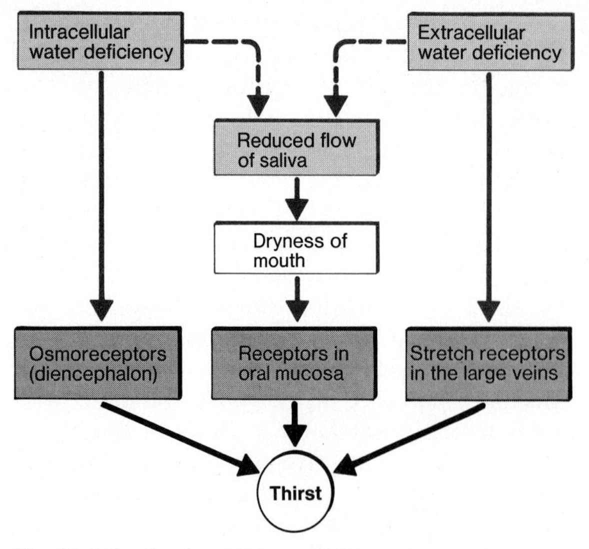

Fig. 14-2. Production of the sensation of thirst. The receptors (sensors) involved are marked by the *gray* shading. Above them their adequate stimuli are indicated. Dryness of the mouth is an indirect consequence of intracellular and extracellular lack of water

coagulation of certain constellations of hypothalamic structures has resulted in reduction or cessation of drinking even though body water is depleted **(adipsia).** All these results indicate that **osmoreceptors in the diencephalon,** especially in the areas anterior to the hypothalamus, serve as *sensors* for the thirst induced by **cellular water deficiency** (Fig. 14-2). Neuronal structures in the hypothalamus evidently play a crucial role in processing the information from these osmoreceptors (osmosensors) [5, 7, 14, 17, 18, 19, 22].

Extracellular sensors. As far as the sensors underlying the *thirst elicited by lack of water in the extracellular space* are concerned, we have only suggestions and indirect evidence. At present it appears most likely that **stretch receptors** in the walls of the large veins near the heart, in addition to their influence on the circulation, also participate in the regulation of water balance and the induction of thirst (Fig. 14-2). The hypothalamus is an important processing center for signals carried in vagal afferents from the stretch receptors to the CNS. Moreover, there is evidence that the neuronal mechanisms giving rise to thirst are supplemented by **hormonal factors.** Extracellular dehydration causes the release of **renin** and thus the formation of **angiotensin II** (cf. p. 517). Intravenous administration of angiotensin II or its direct application to various parts of the hypothalamus, including the subfornical organ, elicits intense thirst. It seems certain, therefore, that angiotensin II plays a role in hypovolemic thirst, but at the moment its precise position and significance in the complex of mechanisms underlying thirst are unclear [3, 18, 22].

The same applies to the role of other hormones, such as **ADH,** mentioned above, and the recently discovered **atrial natriuretic factor, ANF.** The latter is a polypeptide, also called **atriopeptin,** that was first discovered in muscle cells of the atrium of the heart. It is released by stretching of the atria, especially the right atrium. In the kidneys it induces massive sodium and water diuresis; it also has inhibitory actions there, one of which is to suppress the release of renin. ANF may also serve as a transmitter substance in the hypothalamic-hypophyseal system, affecting *(as a thirst inhibitor?)* the thirst process at that level.

Sensors in mouth and throat. The *dryness of the mouth caused by reduced flow of saliva is signaled by sensors in the oropharyngeal mucosa* (Fig. 14-2). Experiments on animals have shown that various kinds of sensors are present there (mechanoreceptors, cold and warm receptors, and perhaps water receptors), but the extent to which each participates in eliciting this **peripheral component** of thirst is not known. If these sensors are stimulated when there is no general water deficiency in the body, as may happen as a result of speaking, smoking, breathing through the mouth or eating very dry food, the **false thirst** they elicit can be satisfied by moistening the oral mucosa; in the case of genuine thirst, as mentioned above, this procedure may lessen the feeling of thirst, but cannot eliminate it.

Central integration. Thirst is thus a general sensation based on the **combined action of many sensor types,** some in the periphery and others in the central nervous system itself. The **diencephalon,** the hypothalamus in particular, appears to play a dominant role in integrating this multitude of afferent inputs. We do not know how accurately the results of experiments on animals can be applied to humans, nor do we know which central structures give rise to the sensation of thirst. One may assume, however, that the relationships diagrammed in Fig. 14-2 are indicative of those operating in humans [3, 5, 14, 17].

The sensation of thirst does not adapt. Again, animal experiments have corroborated this subjective experience. The amount of water consumed after i.v. injection of hypertonic saline solution has been shown to be independent of the rate of infusion. In other words, the thirst elicited by the injection of a specific amount of solution was the same whether the NaCl concentration rose very slowly or very rapidly. As a rule, because thirst does not adapt, the only way to alleviate the sensation is to consume water (Fig. 14-1B).

The Quenching of Thirst

Preabsorptive and postabsorptive satiety. There is a considerable delay between the moment drinking is begun and the time the water deficiency in the intracellular space is abolished, for the water must first be absorbed in the gastrointestinal tract and transferred to the bloodstream. But it is a common observation, and one repeatedly confirmed in animal experiments, that the feeling of thirst ceases (i.e., drinking is stopped) long before compensation of the water deficiency in the extracellular and intracellular compartments is possible. **Postabsorptive satiety** is preceded by **preabsorptive satiety,** a mechanism to prevent the intake of excessive water until the absorbed water becomes effective (Fig. 14-3). Experiments on animals have shown that this *preabsorptive mechanism* operates with *great precision,* for the amount of water drunk corresponds quite closely to that actually required [1, 3, 7].

The **sensors and underlying mechanisms of preabsorptive satiety** are not known. A dog with an esophageal fistula drinks about twice as much water as a normal dog with the same water deficit, and then stops drinking for 20–60 min. Therefore drinking itself, or the associated motor and sensory processes, causes a certain transient relief of thirst. Sensors in the stomach and duodenum also seem to play a role. Monkeys have been prepared with a gastric tube so that when the animal has stopped drinking, the liquid can be siphoned out of the stomach; in this case, the monkey soon begins to drink again.

On the other hand, drinking ceases immediately when a small amount of water is introduced directly into the duodenum, by a catheter. If isotonic NaCl solution is introduced instead of water, drinking is not interrupted. Hence it appears that the duodenum contains osmoreceptors that detect the water intake. But most questions in this regard remain open [3, 16].

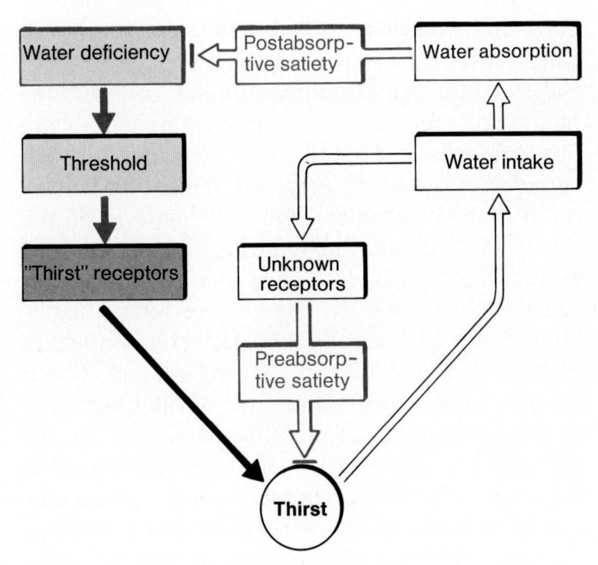

Fig. 14-3. Diagram of preabsorptive and postabsorptive satiety resulting from water intake. The sensors shown in Fig. 14-2 are indicated here by the single box labelled "thirst" receptors

Thirst threshold. Once the thirst has finally been quenched **(postabsorptive satiety),** by elimination of the relative (following excessive salt intake) or absolute water deficit, a certain time elapses before the sensation of thirst recurs, even though there is a steady, slow physiological loss of water. There is thus a *threshold* for thirst, which in humans is equivalent – as mentioned at the outset – to the loss of an amount of water corresponding to ca. 0.5% of the body's weight. This **thirst threshold** prevents slight water losses from inducing a thirst sensation. Physiologically, then, the water content of the human body fluctuates at least between a maximum following postabsorptive satiety and a minimum that in the ideal case is just below the thirst threshold. But the normal fluctuations in water content of the human body are often greater than this, for we frequently consume more liquid than necessary and we cannot always satisfy our thirst as soon as it becomes noticeable.

The amount of liquid that is drunk also depends on its **flavor.** Sugar-containing liquids are drunk in distinctly larger amounts than plain water by humans, monkeys and rats (but not by cats). When various drinks are available more is consumed than if only one kind is provided. Conversely, a drink (even water) is considered to **taste better, the greater one's thirst.** Such an evaluation of flavor is least positive just after thirst has been quenched [15].

Primary and secondary drinking. Drinking that results from an absolute or relative lack of water in one of the fluid spaces of the body is called **primary drinking,** while drinking with no apparent necessity for water replenishment is called **secondary drinking.** The latter is normally the usual way that water is supplied! In general we (and other mammals) tend to consume the physiologically required water in advance. For example, liquid is drunk during and after eating, and we seem to have learned to adjust the amount drunk to the kind of food eaten; if it is salty we drink more, even though no sensation of thirst has yet occurred. Habits also appear to play a role, but our information about the mechanisms by which we estimate our water requirements in advance is very sparse. In any case, *primary drinking* is basically an *emergency response* seldom experienced by people leading well-regulated lives.

Clinical Thirst

An increase in thirst during illness can be the consequence of abnormally large water loss, with the thirst mechanisms functioning normally. On the other hand, it can indicate disturbances of the thirst mechanisms or, more commonly, of control of salt/water balance. Outstanding examples of the first case are the **water losses due to continual vomiting or to severe diarrhea,** as occurs in cholera (the English physician THOMAS LATTA was the first, in 1832, to quench the thirst of cholera victims by intravenous administration of fluid – a procedure which alleviated all the symptoms of the disease at once). Another example of the first case is **diabetes insipidus,** in which the lack of antidiuretic hormone (ADH) causes the body to excrete many liters of hypotonic urine per day. These patients, if untreated, suffer from unquenchable thirst, and their entire daily routine revolves about the constant need to drink.

14.2 Hunger

Origin of the Sensation of Hunger

Short-term and long-term regulation of food intake. Energy balance is maintained in the human and animal body as long as the energy content of the food corresponds to the energy expenditure involved in muscular work, chemical processes (growth, reconstruction) and the loss of heat from the body. When food intake is excessive, the surplus is stored as fat and the body weight increases. When it is insufficient, the fat deposits are used up and weight is lost; an energy deficiency leads to a deterioration of performance and ultimately to death.

Normally, both humans and animals rapidly adjust their food intake to their current requirements (nature and amount of work, climatic conditions) and to the nutritional value (energy content) of their food. This **short-term regulation** of food intake is superimposed on a **long-term regulation** that makes up for temporary inadequacies in the diet and ensures a return to the normal body weight. For example, when animals are fattened by *force-feeding* and then returned to normal conditions, they eat distinctly less than control animals. As the animals return to their original control weights, their food consumption slowly increases. Conversely, *after a period of fasting* the original body weight is regained by temporarily increased food consumption [5, 6, 12].

A lack of food causes **hunger,** and the feeding drive associated with hunger leads to food intake and eventually to **satiety** (cf. Fig. 14-1A). The mechanisms by which the feelings of hunger and satiety are brought about are of interest here, as is the question whether the short-term regulation of food intake is based on the same mechanisms as the long-term regulation. Despite considerable scientific effort, these mechanisms have not yet been entirely clarified, so that the following description must remain incomplete. The analyses carried out so far have shown clearly that several factors are involved in generating the feeling of hunger, but the relative importance of each is not known in detail and it may be that some factors have not yet been identified. The same applies to the factors that produce the feeling of satiety (see below).

Factors eliciting hunger. Subjective experience indicates that hunger is a **general sensation** localized in (or projected to) the stomach region; it appears when the stomach is empty, and vanishes or gives way to a **feeling of satiety** once the stomach is filled with food. Some early students of the problem postulated that hunger is elicited by **contractions of the empty stomach.** This view is supported by the observation that the stomach, in addition to the ordinary contractions by which food is processed and transported, contracts still more powerfully when it is empty, and these contractions are closely correlated with the occurrence of hunger. The contractions may be detected by **mechanoreceptors in the stomach wall** (Fig. 14-4).

But the influence of empty-stomach contractions on hunger should not be overestimated; when the stomachs of animals are experimentally *denervated* or *surgically removed,* the eating behavior is hardly affected. The contractions of the empty stomach are one factor in the sensation of hunger but an entirely **dispensable** one [4, 6, 13].

Glucostatic hypothesis. The glucose (grape sugar, "blood sugar") dissolved in the blood appears to play a crucial role in eliciting hunger. (With regard to the hormonal control of the blood glucose level and the availability of glucose to the cells see p. 391). Experiments have shown that reduced **availability of glucose** (not the blood glucose level itself) is closely correlated with feelings of hunger and powerful contractions of the stomach. It was concluded that this factor is a critical parameter in the development of hunger [5, 6, 13, 18, 20].

Fig. 14-4. Production of the sensation of hunger. The receptors (sensors) involved are shown below their adequate stimuli. The factors and receptors involved in short-term and long-term regulation of food intake, respectively, are grouped by *gray-shaded* areas

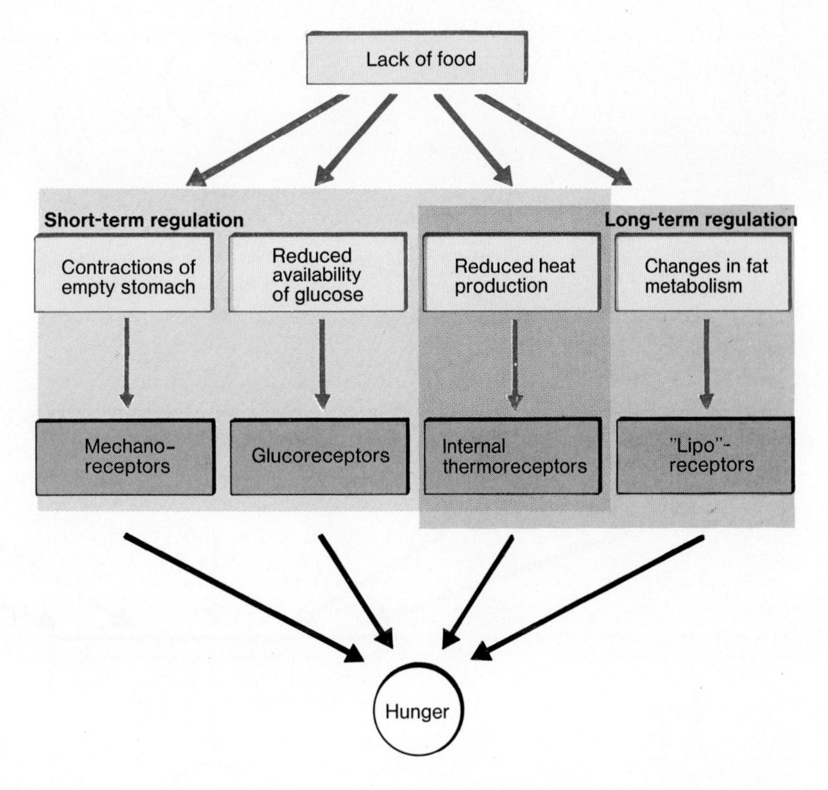

This **glucostatic hypothesis of hunger** is further supported by various experimental findings indicating that **glucoreceptors** probably exist in the diencephalon, liver, stomach and small intestine. For example, when mice are injected with gold thioglucose (gold is a cell poison), many cells in the diencephalon are destroyed; evidently these cells take up particularly large amounts of glucose. Their destruction causes severe disturbances of feeding. That is, these central glucoreceptors detect reduced availability of glucose and thereby contribute to the production of feelings of hunger (Fig. 14-4).

Thermostatic hypothesis. The **thermostatic hypothesis** of the generation of hunger is less well supported than the glucostatic hypothesis. It is based on the observation that warm-blooded animals consume food in amounts inversely proportional to the temperature of the environment. The thermoreceptors within the body (see p. 634) could act as sensors for integration of the overall energy balance. A **decline in total heat production** would then cause the **internal** thermoreceptors to trigger the sensation of hunger (Fig. 14-4). It can be shown experimentally that local cooling and warming in the diencephalon, the seat of the central thermoreceptors, can bring about changes in feeding behavior as predicted by this hypothesis; but other, less specific interpretations cannot be ruled out [6].

Lipostatic hypothesis. Excessive food intake leads to the deposition of fat in the body, and if food is insufficient the fat deposits are used up. Assuming the existence of *liporeceptors,* such departures from the ideal weight of the body could be monitored by way of the intermediate products of the associated fat metabolism and interpreted as hunger or satiety signals (Fig. 14-4, right). There is some good experimental evidence for the **lipostatic hypothesis,** in particular the above-mentioned observation that force-fed animals subsequently eat less than under control conditions, until their fat deposits are gone [6, 18, 20].

The elicitation of hunger and short/long-term regulation. The lipostatic hunger mechanism, as shown by the experiment just described, serves chiefly in the long-term regulation of food intake, whereas the contractions of the empty stomach and the glucostatic mechanism are primarily involved in short-term regulation. The thermostatic mechanism possibly participates in both (cf. the gray shading in Fig. 14-4). With such a variety of physiological mechanisms subserving the feeling of hunger, even under the most complex conditions the sensation of hunger and the feeding drive ensure the consumption of food in appropriate amounts.

Food intake without hunger. Humans are not the only animals that eat when not hungry; other warm-blooded animals also eat amounts of food that depend not only on the amount actually re-

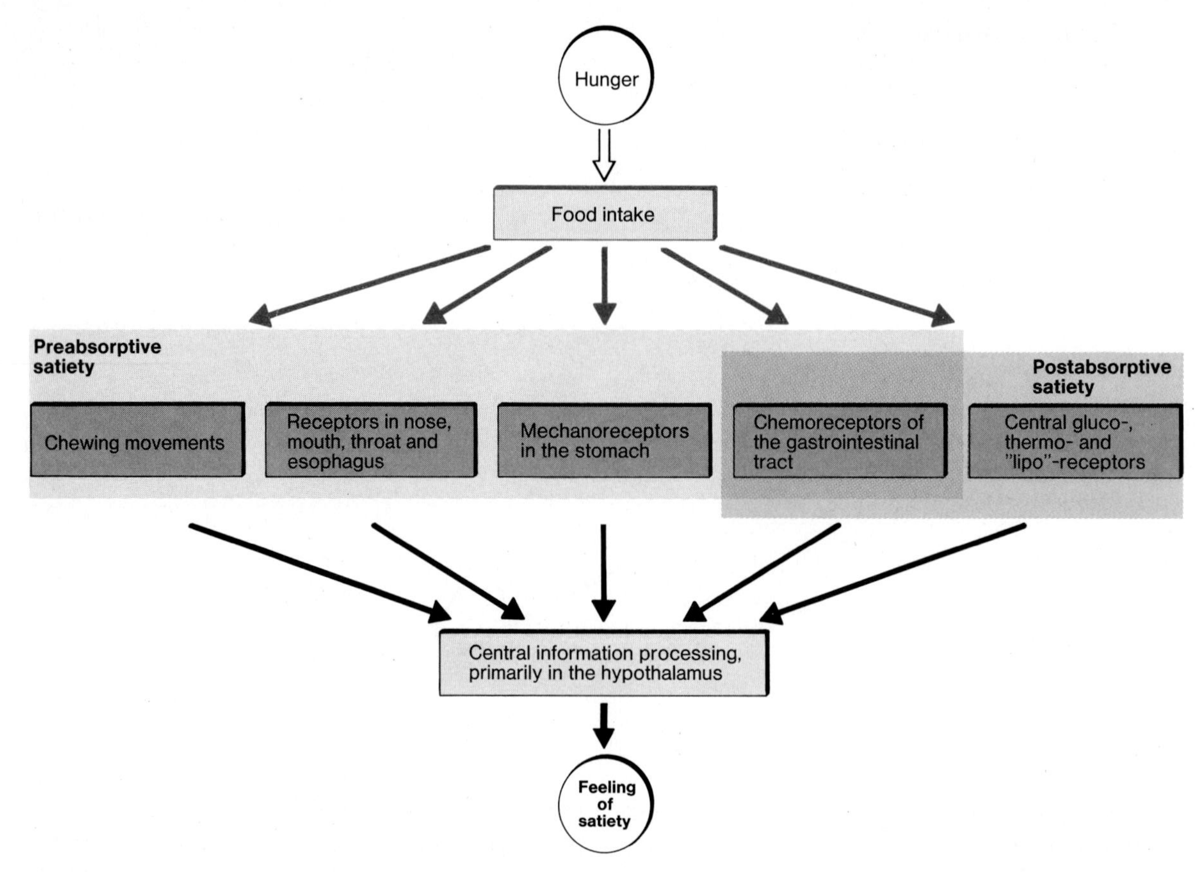

Fig. 14-5. Production of the feeling of satiation by food intake. The factors and receptors (sensors) involved in preabsorptive and postabsorptive satiety are grouped within the *gray-shaded* areas. Chewing movements can contribute to preabsorptive satiety by way of a direct central efference copy of the motor patterns, by way of the activation of sensors during chewing (e.g., muscle spindles, tendon organs), or both together

quired or on psychological factors (p. 321), but also on when the next mealtime is expected and on the amount of energy likely to be consumed in the meanwhile. This sort of **predictive food intake** does not compensate an existing deficit (as discussed above), but rather **covers in advance the expected energy expenditure.** Such behavior corresponds to predictive water intake (secondary drinking, p. 317), which is the normal way in which water is supplied to the body.

Satiety

Preabsorptive and postabsorptive satiety. As in the case of drinking, food consumption by humans and animals is usually stopped long before absorption of the food from the digestive tract has eliminated the energy deficit that originally led to hunger and feeding. All the processes that cause an organism to end its meal are together termed **satiety.** The **feeling of satiation,** as everyone knows, is something more than just the disappearance of hunger; among its unique aspects (some of which are associated with pleasure) is the distinct feeling of **fullness** if too much food has been eaten. The *feeling of satiation* gradually recedes as time passes after a meal and eventually, after a neutral period, gives way to renewed hunger. Thus we can infer that satiation is initially **preabsorptive** (i.e., results from processes associated with food intake itself), whereas the subsequent **postabsorptive satiety** prevents the immediate recurrence of hunger.

Factors in preabsorptive satiety. Animals with an esophageal fistula feed for considerably longer periods than before the operation, and repeat their meals at shorter intervals, but they do spontaneously stop eating. Since no food has entered the stomach, this apparent satiation is presumably mediated by non-gastric influences – **stimulation of olfactory receptors, gustatory receptors and mechanoreceptors** in the nose, mouth, throat and esophagus during feeding, and possibly the act of chewing itself (Fig. 14-5, left). However, the data available at present suggest that their

contribution to the initiation and maintenance of satiety is slight.
Another factor seems to be the **stretching of the stomach** and perhaps also the adjacent parts of the intestine by the food (Fig. 14-5, middle). If the stomach of an experimental animal is filled through a fistula or tube before its mealtime, there is a reduction in the oral food intake that partially compensates the filling. The *degree of compensation* depends not on the nutritional value of the food, but rather on the volume of the initial stomach content and the time it was introduced. In the extreme case, if large amounts of high-energy food are put directly into the stomach shortly before the scheduled mealtimes, oral food consumption can be inhibited completely for weeks.
The above factors are supplemented by the **effects of chemoreceptors** in the stomach and upper small intestine (Fig. 14-5, right), which are apparently sensitive to the **glucose and amino-acid content** of the food. While food is still being eaten, for example, the glucose level in the blood rises by an amount related to the carbohydrate content of the food. This response could also have a humoral basis, of course, but the presence of *glucoreceptors* and *amino-acid receptors* in the intestinal wall has been demonstrated electrophysiologically [1, 5, 6, 13].

Of the gastrointestinal hormones (see p. 694) the one most likely to play a **role in satiety** is thought to be **cholecystokinin, CCK.** When injected intraperitoneally into hungry rats, cats and dogs, it causes them to stop eating; moreover, CCK is released by the duodenal mucosa as soon as food enters the duodenum. The satiating action of intraperitoneal CCK injection is lost after the vagal nerve fibers to the stomach are cut. Therefore CCK seems to excite peripheral sensors, either directly or by eliciting contraction of the smooth musculature [23].

Factors in postabsorptive satiety. The **chemoreceptors in the digestive tract** mentioned above may also be involved in postabsorptive satiety, because they can signal the concentrations of utilizable nutrients still remaining in the intestine. But all the enteroceptive sensory events introduced during the discussion of hunger contribute to the process. The **increased availability of glucose, increased heat production** as the food is processed, and the **changes in fat metabolism** affect the corresponding central receptors (on the right in Fig. 14-5); the effects are the reverse of those giving rise to hunger (red shading in Fig. 14-4).
Hunger and **satiety** are thus to a certain extent two sides of the same coin. The (short-term) sensation of hunger triggers eating ("go" signal) and the feeling of (preabsorptive) satiety brings it to an end ("stop"signal). But the amount of food eaten and the duration of the pauses between meals are also determined by the processes we have called "long-term regulation of food intake" and "postabsorptive satiety" – processes, as we now realize (cf. Figs. 14-4 and 14-5), that overlap more or less extensively.

Psychological Factors in Hunger; Appetite

In addition to the above *physiological factors,* a number of **psychological factors** are involved in the control of feeding behavior, which we can mention only briefly here. For example, the time at which food is eaten and the amount consumed are determined not only by one's hunger but also by many other things, including the habit of eating at "mealtimes" and the amount and palatability of the food offered.
Our desire for certain food is called **appetite.** It can be part of the feeling of hunger, but it can also appear independently (e.g., at the sight or presentation of particularly delicious food). Appetite often has a somatic basis, as in the case of the craving for salty food when the body has lost salt, but it can also be independent of physical needs; in the latter case it reflects innate or acquired individual preferences for certain foods. Such preferences in turn, as well as the (often highly consistent) *rejection* of other foods, are formed by the regional availability of certain kinds of food and modified by the standards of the individual's particular culture; these are usually rooted in religion, although they may be rationalized subsequently. Viewed in this light, the **"palatability"** of a dish – the predominant elements of which are its smell, taste, consistency, temperature and the way it is prepared and served – depends very much on our **affective attitude** toward it. Examples can easily be found at regional, national and supranational levels [1, 2, 4].
Under the influence of strong external stimuli, such as a particularly tempting and abundant selection of food, practically everyone occasionally eats more than is required to supply energy. The **biological mechanisms for short-term regulation are overruled.** The overeating is, or should be, compensated subsequently by a corresponding reduction in food consumption, but not everyone in today's affluent societies behaves in this way. The reasons for this **failure of biological long-term regulation** in the face of external inducements are, unfortunately, barely understood. Therefore it is difficult to find ways of prevent-

ing and treating **obesity,** a condition presenting great risks to health that has reached epidemic proportions in many western countries [2, 8, 9, 10, 21].
Mention should also be made of the major role played by food consumption in **behavioral disturbances.** Both excessive eating and the refusal of food are often observed in this context. The best-known example is *anorexia nervosa,* a form of abstinence from eating most common in girls at puberty; this disturbance in development of the psyche can be so severe as to result in death by starvation.

Central Mechanisms of Hunger and Satiety

The **hypothalamus** is apparently the most important central *relay and integration structure* for hunger and satiety, as it is for other regulatory functions. Bilateral destruction of small amounts of tissue in certain ventromedial regions of the hypothalamus (VMH) causes extreme obesity in experimental animals as a result of overeating **(hyperphagia);** destruction of more lateral areas (LH) can result in refusal to eat **(aphagia)** and eventually death by starvation. Conversely, electrical stimulation (with chronically implanted electrodes) of the VMH region produces aphagia and stimulation of the LH region produces hyperphagia [17, 18].
These striking findings have long attracted the attention of researchers so strongly to the hypothalamus that very little is yet known about the significance of other brain structures in the regulation of food intake. On the basis of the experiments just mentioned, it might be proposed that the entire central processing of the relevant information occurs in two hypothalamic "centers", the VMH serving as a **"satiety center",** the destruction of which results in disinhibition of a lateral **"hunger center"** and hence in compulsive eating; conversely, destruction of the "hunger center" would give rise to a permanent feeling of satiation, causing all food to be rejected henceforth [6, 13, 17, 18]. This, however, is certainly an oversimplification. That higher centers of the brain must also be involved is indicated, for instance, by the anticipatory eating and drinking mentioned above; among the structures implicated are the **limbic system** and the cortical areas associated with it (cf. p. 362).
Finally, it should not be overlooked that eating and drinking are complex motor acts, demanding correspondingly extensive participation of the **motor system.** The limbic (especially hypothalamic) motivation areas probably have access to the motor centers by way of the central **catecholaminergic systems,** which project from the brainstem to cerebellum, basal nuclei and cortex (p. 366). These projections may thus be an important link between the drives and their expression in motor patterns [6].

14.3 References

Textbooks and Handbooks

1. CODE, C.F. (Ed.): Handbook of Physiology. Section 6: Alimentary Canal. Vol. I: Control of Food and Water Intake. Washington: American Physiological Society 1967
2. FERSTL, R.: Determinanten und Therapie des Eßverhaltens. Berlin: Springer 1980
3. FITZSIMONS, J.T.: The Physiology of Thirst and Sodium Appetite (Monographs of the Physiological Society NO 35) Cambridge, England: Cambridge University Press 1979
4. GLATZEL, H.: Verhaltensphysiologie der Ernährung. München, Berlin, Wien: Urban & Schwarzenberg 1973
5. MORGANE, P.J. (Ed.): Neural Regulation of Food and Water Intake. Ann. N.Y. Acad. Sci. *157,* 531 (1969)
6. NOVIN, D., WYRWICKA, W., BRAY, G.A. (Ed.): Hunger. Basic Mechanism and Clinical Implications. New York: Raven Press 1976
7. PETERS, G., FITZSIMONS, J.T., PETERS-HAEFELI, L. (Ed.): Control Mechanisms of Drinking. Berlin, Heidelberg, New York: Springer 1975
8. PUDEL, V.: Zur Psychogenese und Therapie der Adipositas. 2. Aufl. Berlin: Springer 1982
9. STUNKARD, A.J. (Ed.): Obesity. Philadelphia: Saunders 1980
10. THOMPSON, C.I.: Controls of Eating. Jamaica, New York: Spectrum 1980
11. WOLF, A.V.: Thirst: Physiology of the Urge to Drink and Problems of Water Lack. Springfield/III: Ch. C. Thomas 1958

Original Papers and Reviews

12. ANAND, B.K.: Nervous regulation of food intake. Physiol. Rev. *41,* 677 (1961)
13. ANDERSSON, B.: Receptors subserving hunger and thirst. In: Handbook of Sensory Physiology, Vol. III/1 (Ed. E. NEIL), Belin, Heidelberg, New York: Springer 1972
14. ANDERSSON. B.: Regulation of water intake. Physiol. Rev. *58,* 582 (1978)
15. CABANAC. M.: Physiological role of pleasure. Science *173,* 1103–1107 (1971)
16. EPSTEIN. A.N.: The physiology of thirst. In: D.W. PFAFF (Ed.): The Physiological Mechanisms of Motivation, pp. 165–214, New York: Springer 1982
17. HAYWARD, J.N.: Functional and morphological aspects of hypothalamic neurons. Physiol. Rev. *57,* 574 (1977)
18. LEIBOWITZ, S.F.: Neurochemical systems of the hypothalamus. Control of feeding and drinking behavior and water-electrolyte excretion. In: P.J. MORGANE, J. PANKSEPP (Eds.): Handbook of the Hypothalamus, Vol. 3, Part A, Behavioral Studies of the Hypothalamus. New York, Basel: Marcel Dekker 1980
19. MALMO, R.B., MALMO, H.P.: Experiments on the neuropsychology of thirst. Int. J. Psychophysiol. *1,* 25–48 (1983)
20. MAYER, J.: Regulation of energy intake and body weight: Glucostatic theory and lipostatic hypothesis. Ann N.Y. Acad. Sci. *63,* 15 (1955)
21. RODIN, J.: Current status of the internal-external hypothesis for obesity. American Psychologist *36,* 361–372 (1981)
22. ROLLS, B.J., WOOD, R.J., ROLLS, E.T.: The initiation, maintenance, and termination of drinking. In: J.M. SPRAGUE, A.N. EPSTEIN (Eds.): Progress in Psychobiology and Physiological Psychology, Vol. 9. New York: Academic Press 1980
23. SMITH, G.P., JEROME, C., CUSLIEN, B.J., ETERNO, R., SIMANSKY, K.J.: Abdominal vagotomy blocks the satiety effect of cholecystokinin in the rat. Science *231,* 1036–1037 (1981)

IV
Neuronal and Hormonal Regulatory Processes

15 General Principles of Regulation

M. ZIMMERMANN

Many processes within the body have regulatory functions; that is, they serve to keep constant a particular, quantifiable state [1, 4, 5, 8, 14]. Examples include the regulation of body temperature, of blood pressure, and of the position of the body in the field of gravity. A related term used in medicine, **homeostasis**, denotes the regulatory processes that keep the operating conditions within the body constant. It is chiefly by way of the nervous system and/or the hormonal system that all these kinds of regulation are accomplished.

Many biological regulatory processes can usefully be described in terms of the **control theory** originally developed in a technological context [7, 10, 11]. In a similar approach, the presentation of communication in biology was made more systematic by reference to information theory (see Chapter 7). The sciences of control systems and communication together constitute the field of **cybernetics,** a discipline that subsumes technology, physiology, psychology and social sciences [5, 13].

As a general introduction to the basic concepts of control theory, in the following sections certain spinal motor functions will be described in the language used for technical control systems.

15.1 Basic Elements of Biological and Technical Control Circuits

Reflexes versus Control Systems

Many biological functions characterized as **reflexes** in classical physiology can also be considered as **regulatory processes.** For instance, the stretch reflex of skeletal muscles (see Chapter 5), in this interpretation, is a system for regulating the length of a muscle [3, 6, 9, 22]: whenever there is stretching of the muscle, disturbing its length, the reflex tends to counteract this disturbance by a contraction of the muscle. Similarly, the baroreceptor reflex is a component of the regulation of arterial blood pressure. The HENRY-GAUER reflex is a manifestation of the regulation of the volume of water in the body. Cutaneous vasomotor reflexes in response to changes in skin temperature are components of temperature regulation.

However, the classical description of a reflex does not make clear its regulatory function: a "stimulus" acts by way of a "reflex center" to produce a (usually stereotyped) "response" (Fig. 15-1A). This description is incomplete because it ignores two things:

- that the reflex response in turn acts on the stimulus; that is, the reflex is a **closed-loop** operation (red in Fig. 15-1A), and
- that the **information flow** in the closed loop is **continuous** and is not only initiated by sudden experimental stimuli (e.g., tapping with a reflex hammer).

In the stretch reflex of skeletal musculature, for example, the loop is closed by the mechanical coupling (parallel arrangement) of extrafusal muscle fibers and muscle spindles within the muscle (Fig. 15-1B). Information is continuously flowing through this closed loop because both the muscle spindles and the α-motoneurons are

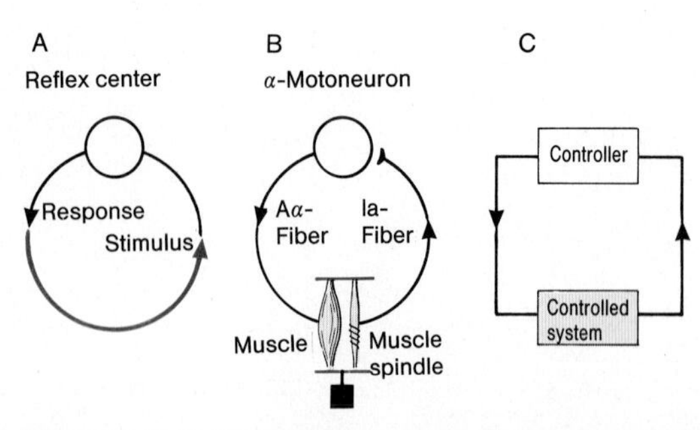

Fig. 15-1 A-C. Closed-loop functional situations. **A** Schematic diagram of a generalized reflex, showing inherent feedback *(red)* of reflex response to the stimulus. **B** Stretch reflex (monosynaptic component only), in which feedback is brought about by parallel arrangement *(red)* of extrafusal musculature and muscle spindle. **C** Simplest block diagram of a control circuit to keep a state variable constant

continuously discharging, at a rate dependent on the force exerted by gravity on the muscle.
When the situation is viewed in this light it becomes clear that many reflexes act to keep a **physiological variable constant** or regulate it. When some disturbance has altered this quantity, the reflex (or regulatory action) returns it to the normal value. Therefore the schematic anatomical picture of the stretch reflex is supplemented by the block diagram of a **control circuit** (Fig. 15-1C). Here the controller and the controlled system are linked so that each affects the other (the controlled system comprises all the devices that are involved in the regulation). Of course, there are also biological control circuits that do not appear as reflexes.

The Structure of a Control Circuit

The block diagram introduced in Fig. 15-1C is shown in a more extended version in Fig. 15-2A; it illustrates the basic concepts in control theory [5, 7, 8, 10, 11]. A system for controlling room temperature, for example, can be constructed in this way.
The **controlled variable** represents a state that is to be kept constant (room temperature, in our example). The physical devices within which regulation occurs are the **controlled system** (room with heater). A **sensor** (thermometer) measures the current value of the controlled variable and sends an appropriate **feedback signal** to the **controller** (thermostat). The controller compares the feedback signal with a **reference signal** (from the temperature selector) that represents the **set point** of the circuit (desired temperature). If the feedback signal differs from the reference signal, the **error** causes the controller to initiate corrective measures. It does so by sending a **control signal** to a device capable of appropriately altering the situation, the controlling element or **effector** (heater with variable fuel feed). Control signals are sent out continuously until the feedback and reference signals match. There may also be various sources of **disturbance,** factors that cause the controlled variable to depart from the set point (e.g., loss of heat from the room).
The essential feature of a control circuit is thus the closed-loop arrangement, operating so that any disturbance of the controlled variable is automatically corrected. Because the function of the loop in principle is to minimize the deviation of the controlled variable from the set point, the term *negative feedback* is used.

Open-loop systems. The standard elements of a control system can also be arranged in an open circuit, without feedback (e.g., no signal representing current temperature). Such a system can compensate for a disturbance that is known in advance (e.g., an estimated amount of cooling at night) but not for a variable, unpredictable disturbance (e.g., loss of heat due to changing outdoor temperature and the opening of doors and windows at irregular intervals).

Regulators and servomechanisms. So far we have been concerned with the ability of a control sys-

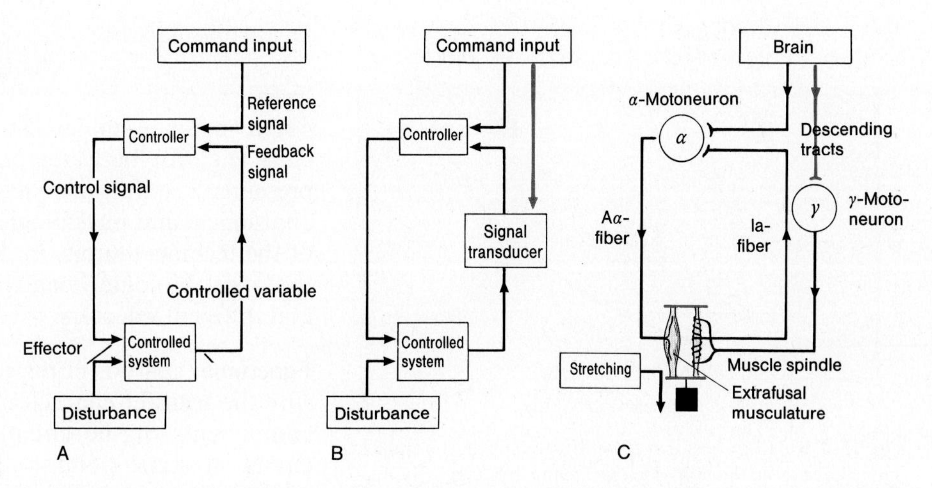

Fig. 15-2 A-C. Control-system diagrams, in principle and as applied to the stretch reflex. **A** Block diagram of a simple control circuit. The *lines* with *arrows* show the directions in which the elements of the circuit (controller, controlled system) interact via information flow. The feedback signal informs the controller of the current state of the controlled variable, which is to be kept constant. **B** Block diagram of an elaborated control circuit (new parts, as compared to A, shown in *red*). Here, in contrast to (A), the reference signal affects both the controller and the transducer of the feedback signal. **C** Diagram of the spinal stretch reflex, including the input descending from the brain, arranged to show the points of correspondence with the circuit in (B)

tem to keep a controlled variable at a constant preset level. A system functioning in this way is usually called a regulator. Now we turn to the mode of operation in which the **set point is changed** arbitrarily. We change the set point, for example, when we turn the temperature selector on the thermostat for room heating. The controller's response to a change in the reference signal is in principle the same as to a change in the feedback signal; the difference between the two is measured and the effector acts on the controlled variable until it has reached the new set point. Closed-loop systems designed so that the controlled variable will follow changes of the reference signal are called **servomechanisms.**

The Stretch Reflex – a Control Circuit for Muscle Length

An isolated muscle preparation is elastic, in that it stretches when placed under tension (Fig. 15-3). The relation between muscle tension T and length L is known as the resting length-tension curve (see Chapter 4).

The same experiment can be done with a muscle in situ. For present purposes an extensor muscle of a decerebrate animal is particularly suitable. In this situation, with the brainstem transected at the midbrain level so that there is no connection to the cerebrum (see Chapter 5), the muscle resists externally imposed tension more strongly; it has become less yielding, or stiffer. Now an increase in tension, ΔT, produces a considerably smaller increase in length, ΔL_1, than in the isolated muscle (Fig. 15-3). When the dorsal or ventral roots are transected in the spinal segment from which the muscle is innervated, the increased resistance disappears and the resting length-tension curve is like that of an isolated muscle.

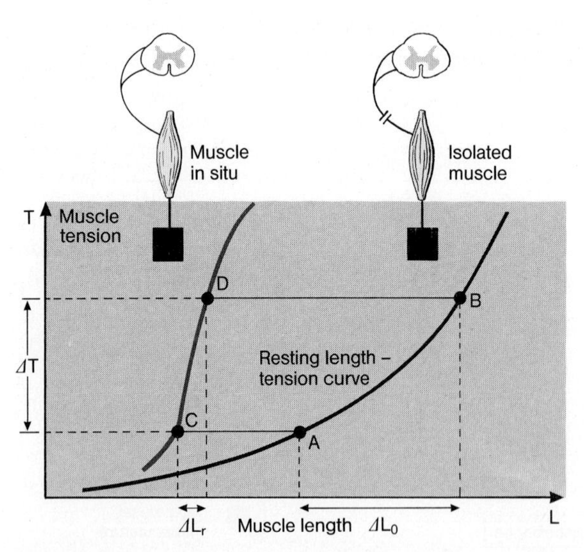

Fig. 15-3. Relation between tension and length of a muscle. The increase in tension ΔT *(ordinate)* by a gravity load (weight) causes a large change in length ΔL_0 *(abscissa)* in the isolated muscle preparation corresponding to the curve segment *AB*. When the muscle is *in situ*, with intact nervous connection to the spinal cord *(red curve)*, the reflex contraction induced by the increase in tension ΔT (due to the weight load) results in only a small change in muscle length ΔL_r, corresponding to curve segment *CD*

When the spinal nerves are intact, the system "spinal cord plus muscle" evidently behaves in such a way as to **counteract** lengthening of the muscle, by reflex muscle contraction (reflex tone). One could also say that the muscle length is kept approximately **constant,** so that the stretch reflex amounts to a **control system for muscle length.** The elements of this control circuit are as follows (Fig. 15-2):

Controlled system	Muscle with tendons and joint
Controlled variable	Muscle length L
Controller	α-motoneuron
Effector	Extrafusal musculature
Control signal	Frequency F_α in the α-motoneuron
Sensor with transducer	Muscle spindle
Feedback signal (coded)	Frequency F_{Ia} in the Ia fiber
Reference signal	Frequency F_D in neurons descending from the brain
Disturbing factors	Gravity, muscle fatigue, changing loads

Try to make a similar list for other control circuits (e.g., for body temperature, arterial blood pressure, respiration); that is, find the specific anatomical and physiological equivalents of each of the technical terms. In doing so, bear in mind that most biological control systems include several different effectors.

Functional analysis of the control circuit. To measure the transfer characteristics of the individual components of the circuit, one must **open** the circuit at some point to prevent feedback. To analyze the stretch reflex in this open-loop condition, one can either cut the dorsal or ventral roots or temporarily block conduction in the nerves by cooling them.

With the circuit open the transfer characteristics of sensor, controller and effector are measured.

The **dynamic properties** of the control circuit and its elements – that is, the behavior while and immediately after the controlled variable is altered by a disturbing influence – are characterized by the **step response** of the system; this procedure is discussed in the next section. The steady-state characteristics of the circuit and its components are described by **characteristic curves** or functions, each of which represents the relation between an input and an output variable. In the stretch reflex the characteristic curve for sensor function relates muscle length L to the discharge frequency in the Ia afferent fibers from the muscle spindle, F_{Ia}. The characteristic curve for the effector is the graded increase in contractile force of the extrafusal musculature with increasing discharge frequency in the Aα motor axon, F_{α}. Serial combination of the characteristic curves for the individual elements in the circuit gives the overall **control characteristic**, i.e., the relationship between muscle length and force of muscle contraction (see, for example, the red curve in Fig. 15-3). The steeper the slope of this control characteristic, the more nearly constant is the length of the muscle and hence the more accurate is the regulation.

Before proceeding, one qualitative comment on the **polarity of the control circuit:** In transmission at the sensor (muscle spindle) changes occur in the same direction; that is, an increase in length L causes an increase in discharge frequency F_{Ia}. The same is true for transmission at the controller (α-motoneuron), the transformation of frequency F_{Ia} into the frequency F_{α} of the α-motoneurons. In transmission at the effector (extrafusal musculature), however, the changes are **opposed:** an increase in F_{α} produces a decrease in L. It is here that we find the **reversal of sign** required for negative feedback in a control system.

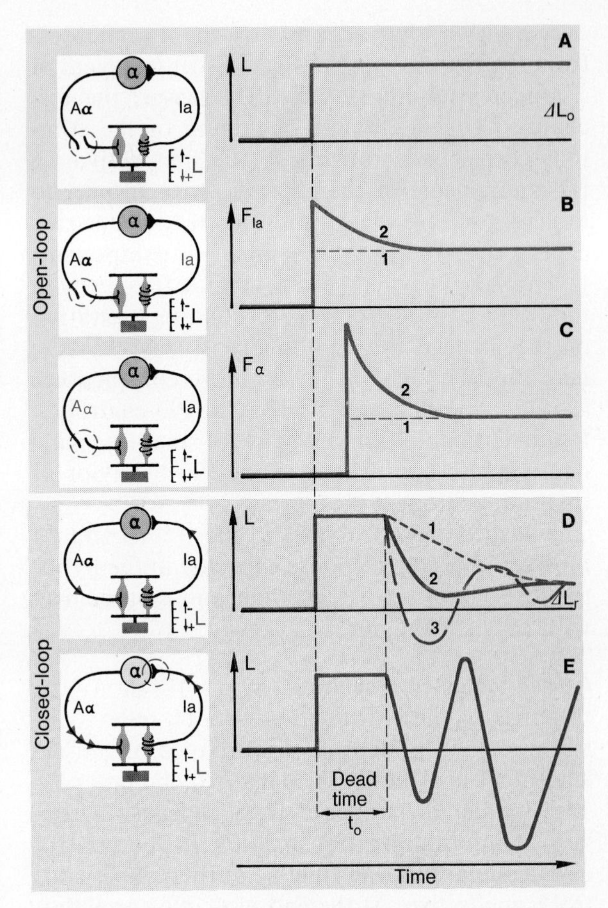

Fig. 15-4 A-E. Step responses in the control system for muscle length. The elements of the stretch reflex corresponding to each response are emphasized *(red)* in the diagrams at the left. **A** Stepwise change ΔL_0 in muscle length L by sudden increase in the load on the muscle (disturbance). **B** Discharge frequency F_{Ia} of the muscle spindle (sensor plus transducer) in response to the disturbance. **C** Discharge frequency F_{α} of the α-motoneuron (control signal, response of the controller) resulting from the disturbance. The functions in A, B and C are measured in open-loop conditions. In each case Curve 1 shows the behavior of a sensor and controller with response proportional to length (P elements), whereas Curve 2 contains an additional component corresponding to the time derivative of muscle length (rate of length change): proportional-differential sensor and controller (PD elements). **D** Step response of the controlled variable L under closed-loop conditions, with P elements (Curve 1) or PD elements (2, 3) and either low (2) or high (3) gain. When the regulatory process is completed, the controlled variable deviates from the set point by a small amount, ΔL_r. **E** Undamped oscillation of an unstable system – e.g., one with excessively high gain

15.2 Dynamic and Static Behavior of Control Circuits

The Step Response

The step response, the time course of the response of the entire control circuit or of its components to a disturbance with stepwise onset, can be measured in either closed-loop or open-loop conditions. Fig. 15-4 shows step responses of the stretch reflex. The disturbance here is an abrupt increase in muscle length L (step function, Fig. 15-4A) caused by sudden application of an external force to the tendons of the muscle.

Open-loop step responses. Here we consider the behavior of individual components of the circuit following a step-function disturbance. The

overshoot in the response of the Ia afferents from the muscle spindle (Fig. 15-4B) is typical of a **proportional-differential (PD) sensor:** the discharge frequency at the beginning of the stimulus corresponds roughly to the first derivative (D component) of the stimulus with respect to time, dL/dt, and the subsequent steady-state discharge frequency is proportional (P component) to length L. The change in discharge frequency in the Ia fibers produces a corresponding excitation of the associated α-motoneurons (Fig. 15-4C); here the PD behavior is still more conspicuous, as the α-motoneuron itself is a **PD-controller.** Recurrent inhibition by way of the Renshaw neurons also contributes to the PD behavior of the motoneurons.
The dashed lines (Curves 1 in Fig. 15-4B and C) represent the step response expected in the hypothetical case of a muscle spindle and motoneuron with only P behavior.

Closed-loop step responses. Fig. 15-4D shows the response of the entire closed stretch-reflex control circuit to a stepwise disturbance of muscle length. At first the muscle length L changes passively under the imposed force; because of delays in information transmission in the control circuit there is a **dead time** t_0, during which control is ineffective. At the end of t_0 effector action – contraction of the muscle – begins. The imposed length change ΔL_0 is largely compensated by the contraction, as the controlled variable L returns nearly to its set point, the length before the disturbance occurred. The dead time t_0 of the circuit for the stretch reflex is the reflex latency, the sum of the times required for conduction and synaptic transmission; it is ca. 30 ms in the stretch reflex of the human triceps surae muscle (the Achilles tendon reflex).
The time course of the step-response function varies, depending on whether we assume pure proportional (P) regulation (Curve 1 in Fig. 15-4D) or proportional-differential (PD) regulation (Curve 2). When the D component is large, there can be an **undershoot** of the controlled variable followed by damped oscillations (Curve 3). Under certain conditions, the regulation can even become unstable and produce **undamped oscillations** (Fig. 15-4E).
The dead time t_0 limits the speed of regulation. In the stretch reflex it is minimized, to some tens of milliseconds, inasmuch as the nerve fibers involved (Ia, Aα) have the highest conduction velocities found in peripheral nerves. The dead time in the neural control of arterial blood pressure is several seconds, so that regulation proceeds considerably more slowly than in the stretch reflex. When a recumbent person stands up, it takes 10–20 s for the gravity-induced drop in arterial blood pressure to be compensated. Temperature regulation is even slower, with time courses on the order of hours.

Accuracy and stability of regulation. If there were no regulation in the muscle system of Fig. 15-2, the application of an external force ΔT would change the muscle length by ΔL_0 (as in Fig. 15-4A). With regulation, once the initial transients have died out, there remains a residual length change ΔL_r (Fig. 15-4D). The accuracy or quality of regulation can be described by the **regulation factor** R:

$$R = \frac{\Delta L \text{ with regulation}}{\Delta L \text{ without regulation}} = \frac{\Delta L_r}{\Delta L_0}$$

That is, a low regulation factor signifies good regulation. The quality of regulation can be improved by raising the **gain** of the controller; the gain is the factor relating the magnitude of the control signal to the difference between set point and current value of the controlled variable. However, the increase in accuracy of steady-state regulation by raising the gain is limited by the occurrence of undesirable transients in the step response. These may amount to a temporary overshoot followed by damped oscillations (Fig. 15-4D, Curve 3) or actual **instability** of the system (Fig. 15-4E), in which the controlled variable oscillates between two extremes and never reaches a steady state.
How do such **undamped oscillations** come about? The disturbance causes the controller to initiate a response in the opposite direction, which can overshoot the target level considerably if the gain is high. The sensor signals this excessive change in the controlled variable to the controller, which now produces a response in the opposite direction, again with considerable overshoot. This sequence of events may be repeated indefinitely; the frequency of the oscillation depends on the speed of operation of the control system. It is easy to see that the occurrence of undamped oscillation is facilitated by high gain of the controller and a long dead time t_0 of the control circuit.
Certain pathological changes of the motor system can enhance the **facilitation of the spinal stretch reflexes** by the brain [2, 19]. Among the resulting neurological symptoms are clonus (rhythmic reflex twitches following a hammer tap to trigger a stretch reflex) and the tremor of a

limb in Parkinson's disease. In both cases the oscillations of muscle length can be interpreted as malfunction of the control system because of excessive gain of the controller.
Damped and undamped oscillations can also occur in the systems controlling other biological variables, such as blood pressure.
In summary, gain can be increased to improve the effectiveness of regulation, but only up to the point beyond which the system becomes unstable.

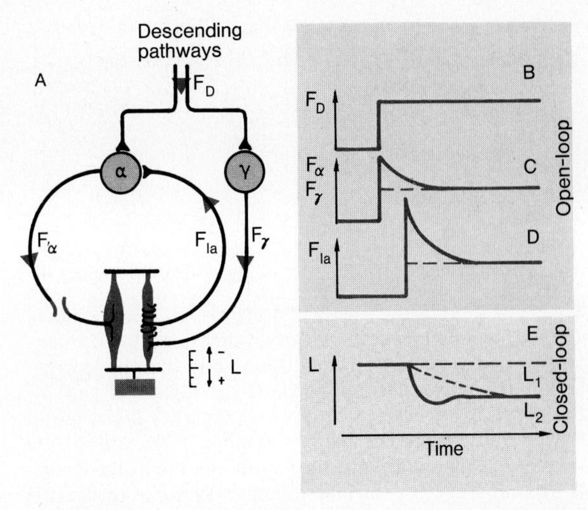

Fig. 15-5 A-E. Supraspinal control of the stretch reflex, in which the control system for muscle length operates as a servomechanism. **A** Simplified diagram of the stretch reflex, including an influence of the brain exerted by way of descending pathways to α- and γ-motoneurons. **B** Time course of discharge frequency F_D in descending pathways at the beginning of a movement commanded by the brain (step change of reference signal). **C** Response of α- and γ-motoneurons (discharge frequencies F_α, F_γ) to the change in descending activity (reference signal acts on controller). **D** Response of the muscle spindle (discharge frequency F_{Ia}) to the descending activity relayed by γ-motoneurons (reference signal acts on transducer); the functions in C and D are measured in open-loop conditions. **E** Response of the controlled variable (muscle length L) to a stepwise change in the reference signal F_D, closed-loop system. In C-E the dashed curves are based on P elements and the solid curves, on PD elements.

Operation of a Servomechanism

So far the only aspect of a control circuit we have considered is its ability to keep a controlled variable constant. Now we turn to the use of such circuitry in a **servomechanism**. As mentioned above, in this case it is a change in the reference signal that creates an initial discrepancy between the input signals to the controller (Fig. 15-2B); the controlled variable must be shifted to a new set point. For example, to change the angle at a joint the length L of a muscle must be suitably altered. The reference signal, which may be a program for a time-varying set point, is represented by the flow of excitation in descending pathways from the brain to the motoneurons in the spinal cord [13, 17, 18]. In temperature regulation, the elevation of body temperature during **fever** and its reduction at night or in hibernation can be regarded as readjustments of the set point.
The time course (step response) of the **stretch reflex as a servomechanism** is illustrated in Fig. 15-5. To understand the following discussion, you should be able to see the qualitative correspondence between this diagram (Fig. 15-5A) and the block diagrams of the control circuit (Fig. 15-2). The **reference signal** is provided by the motor pathways descending from the brain to the spinal cord (Fig. 15-5A), and can be represented by a change in frequency F_D in the **descending axons** (Fig. 15-5B). An increase or decrease in the descending activity causes the discharge frequency in the α- and γ-motoneurons to change in the same direction (Fig. 15-5C), with a corresponding change in the discharge of the Ia afferents from the muscle spindles (Fig. 15-5D). The end result is the same as that produced by a disturbing influence (see Fig. 15-4), a shortening or lengthening of the muscle (Fig. 15-5E).

As we have seen in Chapter 5, excitation of the descending motor pathways usually leads to simultaneous synaptic activation of α- and γ-motoneurons, **α-γ coactivation** [3, 8]. From the viewpoint of control theory, both these ways of entering supraspinal commands into the stretch-reflex system are equivalent to resetting the reference signal. However, the arrangement of α–γ coactivation seems to have advantages over a system in which the reference signal is reset only at the controller (α-motoneurons). For one thing, intrafusal contraction via descending activation of γ-motoneurons adjusts the sensitive range or **working range of the muscle spindle** to different muscle lengths. For another, because the proportional and differential behaviors of the muscle spindle are influenced differentially through the complex γ-innervation, the circuit can be better adjusted for optimal stability than if the reference signal were altered only at the controller.
Amphibians have no separate γ-system; here the intrafusal fibers of the muscle spindles and the extrafusal fibers share a common efferent innervation. The presence of a separate, highly differentiated γ-motor system must be regarded as a phylogenetic advance in the mammals.

Steady-State Operation of a Control System

In stable regulation, the step response (whether to disturbance or to a change in the set point) eventually settles down to a **steady state** (Figs. 15-4D, 15-5E); the controlled variable and the

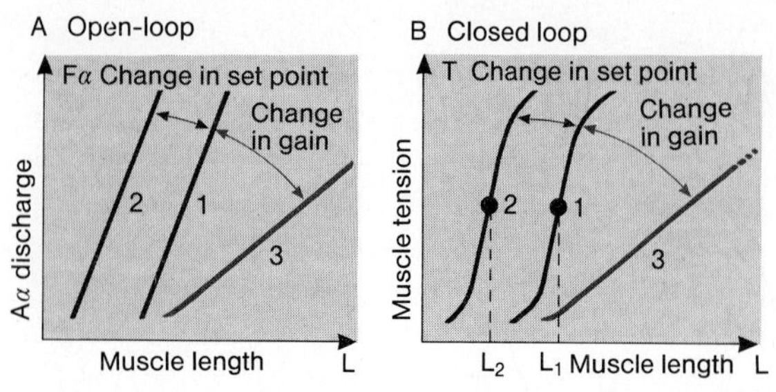

Fig. 15-6 A, B. Steady-state characteristics of the control system for muscle length. **A** Curves measured for the controller under open-loop conditions, relating the current length (L) to the control signal (F_α). A parallel shift of the curve *(from curve 1 to curve 2)* signifies a change in the reference signal; a change in slope *(from curve 1 to curve 3)* implies a change in gain of the controller *(red)*. **B** Characteristics of the closed control circuit, represented by length(L)-tension(T) curves of the muscle under spinal control. When the set point is altered *(1→2)*, the muscle length changes from L_1 to L_2. A gain reduction *(1→3)* increases the compliance of the muscle

feedback and control signals are no longer time-dependent but have constant values. In this state the elements of the control circuit can be described by **static characteristic curves**. In general, the characteristic curves of a system give the relation between input and output magnitudes. The static **characteristic of the sensor** (muscle spindle) – the relation between the frequency of the Ia fiber and the length of the muscle, $F_{Ia} = f(L)$ – was treated previously (see Fig. 5-8). The characteristic of the controller (a population of homonymous α-motoneurons) can also be represented in this way, with the frequency of impulses in the Ia fibers, F_{Ia}, as the input and the frequency of impulses in the associated α-motoneurons, F_α, as the output. The curves in Fig. 15-6A give the overall relation between the experimentally altered muscle length L and the discharge frequency of the associated α-motoneurons F_α when the motor fibers had been transected in the ventral roots (open loop); that is, these characteristics combine the transfer properties at the muscle spindle and at the α-motoneurons.

First we return to the **open-loop** operation of the circuit (Fig. 15-6A), to examine two effects on the curves that reflect important properties of the control system in the steady-state situation. When the excitability of the α- and γ-motoneurons is changed (by descending pathways from supraspinal centers, see Fig. 15-5), the **curves are shifted in parallel** along the abscissa (transition from Line 1 to Line 2 in Fig. 15-6A). In principle a change in excitability of either the α- or the γ-neurons alone could cause such a shift, but from the available experimental results we must conclude that usually both mechanisms are operating (α-γ coactivation; see above). The parallel shifting of the characteristics means a new **working range of the control circuit;** the controlled variable is adjusted to a new set point.

To characterize the **closed-loop function in the steady state** of the control circuit (Fig. 15-6B) we can use the relationship between muscle tension T and length L (as introduced in Fig. 15-3). The effect of the reference signal, the descending excitation F_D, is again manifest as a shift of the curve along the L coordinate – e.g., from Curve 1 to Curve 2 when the descending excitation increases F_D (Fig. 15-6B). The controlled variable (muscle length) follows the reference signal to the new set point L_2; the system is operating as a **servomechanism**. At the new set point the controlled variable is again kept constant despite disturbances, with the system operating as a **regulator**.

15.3 Special Features of Control Systems

Variable gain. It is evident in Fig. 15-6B that the controlled variable is kept at the set point more precisely, the steeper the characteristic curve of the system. In technical devices the slope of such a curve in general is called the amplification factor or **gain**. The higher the gain, then, the more accurate the regulation (cf. the section on regulation factor, p. 328). To account for this property in the control circuit, the block diagram

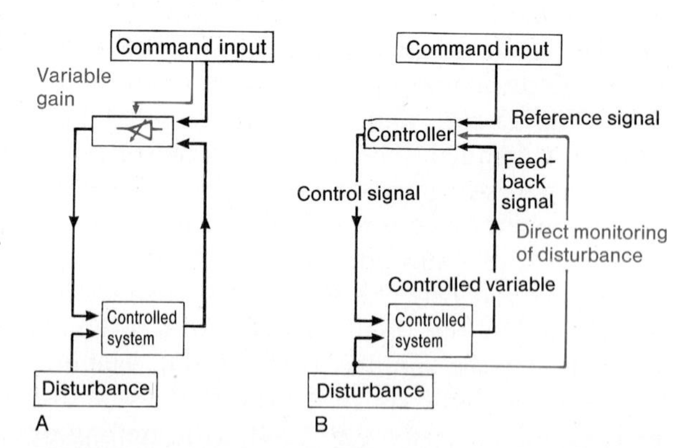

Fig. 15-7 A, B. Control-system variants. **A** Block diagram differing from Fig. 15-2A in that it includes a symbol representing variable gain of the controller. **B** Circuit in which disturbances are signalled directly to the controller, so that compensatory action can be taken before the disturbance affects the controlled variable

shown in Fig. 15-2A has to be modified to the block diagram of Fig. 15-7A.

It was noted above (Fig. 15-4) that high gain increases the risk of oscillations, especially if there are delays in information flow to and from the controller (resulting, e.g., in a dead time in the step response: t_0 in Fig. 15-4E). To guarantee **stable regulation**, therefore, there must be an upper limit on the gain such that no undamped oscillations of the controlled variable may occur. On the other hand, when the controlled variable is to be changed – and especially in the early stages of this change (e.g., beginning of a step response, see Fig. 15-4 and 15-5) – it is useful to have high gain in order to compensate for delays and ballistic inertia in the controlled system (e.g., the muscle to be shortened). It would make sense for the gain to be adjustable, to suit the variable requirements of different situations in the operation of the control system.

It can be shown that our spinal control system does in fact have variable gain. The amplification factor is reduced primarily by **inhibition at the α-motoneuron**, resulting in decreasing slopes in the characteristic functions of the control system (Lines 3 in Fig. 15-6). That is, Renshaw inhibition, autogenic inhibition (initiated by the Ib afferents) and antagonist inhibition can be interpreted as gain-reducing mechanisms. Supraspinal influences also continually change the gain of the stretch-reflex control system.

Anticipatory control function. It can be an advantage in a control circuit if disturbing influences that are frequently present and have predictable actions are signaled directly to the controller (Fig. 15-7B). The function of a slowly-responding system, in particular, is improved by such **direct monitoring**, because a disturbance can be compensated before it causes an appreciable change in the controlled variable.

A familiar technical example is the use of an **outdoor temperature sensor** in a central-heating system. This sensor continually signals the outdoor temperature to the furnace controller. Because the heat loss from a house is known to increase in proportion to the difference between inside and outside temperature, the information from the outdoor sensor can be taken into account in the electronic setting of the control signal to be sent out by the controller. The regulation can be initiated before the temperature inside the house has actually changed, so that the room temperature is kept closer to a constant level.

This principle of anticipatory control is also followed in biological control systems. A familiar example is **thermoregulation** (see Chapter 25). Here the equivalent of an outdoor sensor is the **set of cutaneous thermoreceptors.** When the organism is exposed to colder surroundings, the cutaneous cold sensors signal this event to the control center for body temperature in the hypothalamus. Thermoregulatory responses to the cold stimulus soon follow; for instance, muscle tone is increased and shivering may occur, and thermal insulation is improved by a reduction in blood flow through the skin. These anticipatory control processes begin while there is no change in core temperature and hence no excitation of the temperature sensors in the hypothalamus.

In analyzing motor control, one can interpret influences of the vestibular organs and the visual system on spinal motoneurons as a form of direct access of disturbing factors. The enhancement (facilitation) of the stretch reflex of leg extensors by Jendrassik's maneuver can also be interpreted in this way, as follows. When the arms of a standing person suddenly exert force (e.g., by lifting a weight or pushing the hand against an opponent), the load stretching the leg extensors always increases. The length control of these muscles, which enables the two-legged stance to be maintained, is improved by providing the length controller directly with information about the movement command to the forelimbs.

Coupling of Control Circuits

Various biological control circuits can often be seen to be functionally **coupled** to one another. For instance, when regulation of breathing is initiated by excitation of the chemoreceptors in the carotid body, the regulation of blood pressure is also affected; in case of oxygen deficiency the increased respiration is accompanied by an increase in blood flow through the organs. Osmoregulation and the regulation of fluid volume, which in principle can be described as independent control systems, are coupled by the use of the same two hormones for the control signals (ADH and aldosterone) and by having a common effector organ, the kidney.

Certain motor control circuits are also coupled; an example is the interaction of the **stretch reflexes of antagonistic muscles.** These are coupled mechanically by the opposed actions of the two muscles at a given joint, and they also interact by way of their reciprocal inhibitory circuits, producing antagonist inhibition in the spinal cord (Fig. 5-7, p. 90). When a supraspinal command is issued for a muscle to shorten during movement about a joint, there is always a gain reduction in the control circuit (i.e., the stretch reflex) for the antagonist, so that the latter becomes more compliant.

The **reference signals in the spinal control circuits** for muscle length sent out by the supraspinal motor centers [2, 12, 21] can be regarded as innate and learned **movement programs**, each of which coordinates many stretch reflexes. This coordination in turn involves feedback from the muscle receptors and also from joint and skin afferents; primarily in the cerebellum and the motor cortex, these inputs cause immediate and continuous regulatory modification of such a movement program while it is running. The ascending and descending connections between spinal cord and motor centers in the brain can be regarded as components of **superordinate control circuits** that mesh with the spinal length regulators. However, as yet we know too little about the neurophysiological details of supraspinal control of movements to describe completely, in terms of control theory, the execution of a movement.

15.4 References

Textbooks and Handbooks

1. BAYLISS, L.E.: Living Control Systems. New York: Plenum Press 1966
2. DESMEDT, M.E. (ed.): Cerebral Motor Control in Man: Long Loop Mechanisms. Progr. Clin. Neurophysiol. *4*, Karger 1978
3. GRANIT, R.: The Basis of Motor Control. London-New York: Academic Press 1970
4. GRODINS, F.S.: Control Theory and Biological Systems. New York: Columbia Univertiy Press 1963
5. HASSENSTEIN, B.: Biologische Kybernetik. Heidelberg: Quelle & Meyer 1967
6. HOMMA, S. (ed.): Understanding the Stretch Reflex. Progr. Brain Res. *44*, 1976
7. LUENBERGER, D.G.: Introduction to Dynamic Systems, Theory, Models, and Applications. New York: John Wiley 1979
8. MILSUM, J.H.: Biological Control Systems Analysis. New York-San Francisco-Toronto-London: McGraw-Hill 1966
9. MOUNTCASTLE, V.B. (ed.): Medical Physiology, Vol. 1. Saint Louis: Mosby 1984
10. NALECZ, M. (ed.): Control Aspects of Biomedical Engineering. Oxford: Pergamon Press 1986
11. SINGH, M.G. (ed.): Systems and Control Encyclopedia. 8 Vols. Oxford: Pergamon Press 1987
12. TALBOTT, R.E., HUMPHREY, D.R. (eds.): Posture and Movement. New York: Raven Press 1979
13. VARJU, D.: Systemtheorie für Biologen und Mediziner. Berlin-Heidelberg-New York: Springer 1977
14. WAGNER, R.: Probleme und Beispiele biologischer Regelung. Stuttgart: Thieme 1954

Original Papers and Reviews

15. HOUK, J.C.: On the significance of various command signals during voluntary control. Brain Res. *40*, 49 (1972)
16. HOUK, J.C., SINGER, J.J., GOLDMAN, M.R.: An evaluation of length and force feedback to soleus muscles of decerebrate cats. J. Neurophysiol. *33*, 784 (1970)
17. MARSDEN, C.D., MERTON, P.A., MORTON, H.B.: Servoaction in the human thumb. J. Physiol. *257*, 1 (1976)
18. MERTON, P.A.: How we control the contraction of our muscles. Sci. Amer. *226*, 30 (1972)
19. NELSON, P.: Interaction between voluntary contraction and tonic stretch reflex transmission in normal and spastic patients. J. Neurol. Neurosurg. Psychiat. *6*, 853 (1972)
20. NICHOLS, T.R., HOUK, J.C.: Improvement in linearity and regulation of stiffness that results from actions of stretch reflex. J. Neurophysiol. *39*, 119 (1976)
21. PHILLIPS, C.G.: Motor apparatus of the baboon's hand. Proc. Roy. Soc B *173*, 141 (1969)
22. ZIMMERMANN, M., HANDWERKER, H.O., PAAL, G.: Dehnungsreflex. Farbtonfilm (16 mm) zum Physiologieunterricht für Medizinstudenten. Inst. f. d. Wiss. Film, Göttingen 1975

16 Autonomic Nervous System

W. JÄNIG

The autonomic nervous system, which innervates primarily the smooth musculature of all organs, the heart and the glands, mediates the neuronal regulation of the internal milieu. The actions of this system, as its name implies, are in general not under direct voluntary control. These characteristics distinguish the autonomic nervous system from the somatic nervous system, which mediates afferent and efferent communication with the environment and, for the most part, is subject to voluntary control and accessible to consciousness.

The autonomic and somatic systems operate hand in hand. At the central level – particularly in the upper brainstem, the hypothalamus and the cerebrum – their neuronal morphological substrates are indistinguishable. In the periphery, however, the two are quite distinct.

The functions of the autonomic nervous system are to keep the internal milieu of the body constant (homeostasis; see CANNON [3]) or adjust it as required by changing circumstances (e.g., mechanical work, food intake, water deprivation, heat or cold). The autonomic nervous system also controls organs and organ systems that are only indirectly related to the homeostatic functions (e.g., neuronal control of the reproductive organs and the intraocular muscles).

16.1 Peripheral Autonomic Nervous System

Subdivisions

The peripheral autonomic nervous system consists of **three different parts:** the **sympathetic,** the **parasympathetic** and the **enteric nervous systems.** The terminal *sympathetic* and *parasympathetic neurons* are entirely outside the CNS, with their cell bodies grouped in autonomic ganglia. Because their axons project from the ganglia to the target organs, these neurons are called postganglionic neurons. The neurons that send axons into the ganglia to synapse on the dendrites and somata of the postganglionic neurons are called preganglionic neurons; their somata are located in the spinal cord and brainstem. That is, the basic peripheral element in both the sympathetic and the parasympathetic system is a set of two neuron populations in series (see Figs. 16-2 and 16-10). These two autonomic systems originate in different parts of the neuraxis. The sympathetic preganglionic neurons emerge from the thoracic cord and the upper 2–3 segments of the lumbar cord *(thoracolumbar system),* while those of the parasympathetic system emerge from the brainstem and the sacral cord *(craniosacral system).*

The *enteric nervous system* is a special system confined to the gastrointestinal tract; it functions independently, even with no extrinsic input from spinal cord and brainstem (see pp. 343ff.).

The term "sympathetic" originally embraced the entire peripheral autonomic nervous system. Around the turn of the century, the English physiologist LANGLEY [1, 36] introduced the idea of a tripartite subdivision; this subdivision, along with LANGLEY's names for the three parts, is now becoming established. The primary criteria are *anatomical;* furthermore, LANGLEY restricted the terms "sympathetic" and "parasympathetic" to the *efferent* pre- and postganglionic neurons. Afferents from the visceral organs are described with the neutral term "visceral afferents". LANGLEY's classification and terminology have remained appropriate and useful, although, astonishingly, the existence of the enteric nervous system as an independent entity was almost entirely ignored until about 1970. Unfortunately, the terms sympathetic and parasympathetic are often generalized in a functional sense and also applied to the visceral afferents.

Sympathetic system. The cell bodies of the preganglionic sympathetic neurons are in the intermediate zone of the thoracic and lumbar spinal cord. The axons of these neurons are thin, but many are myelinated; their conduction velocities range from 1 to 20 m/s. They leave the spinal cord in the ventral roots and the white rami communicantes (Fig. 16-12, p. 346), and terminate in the paired paravertebral ganglia or the unpaired prevertebral abdominal ganglia. The paraverte-

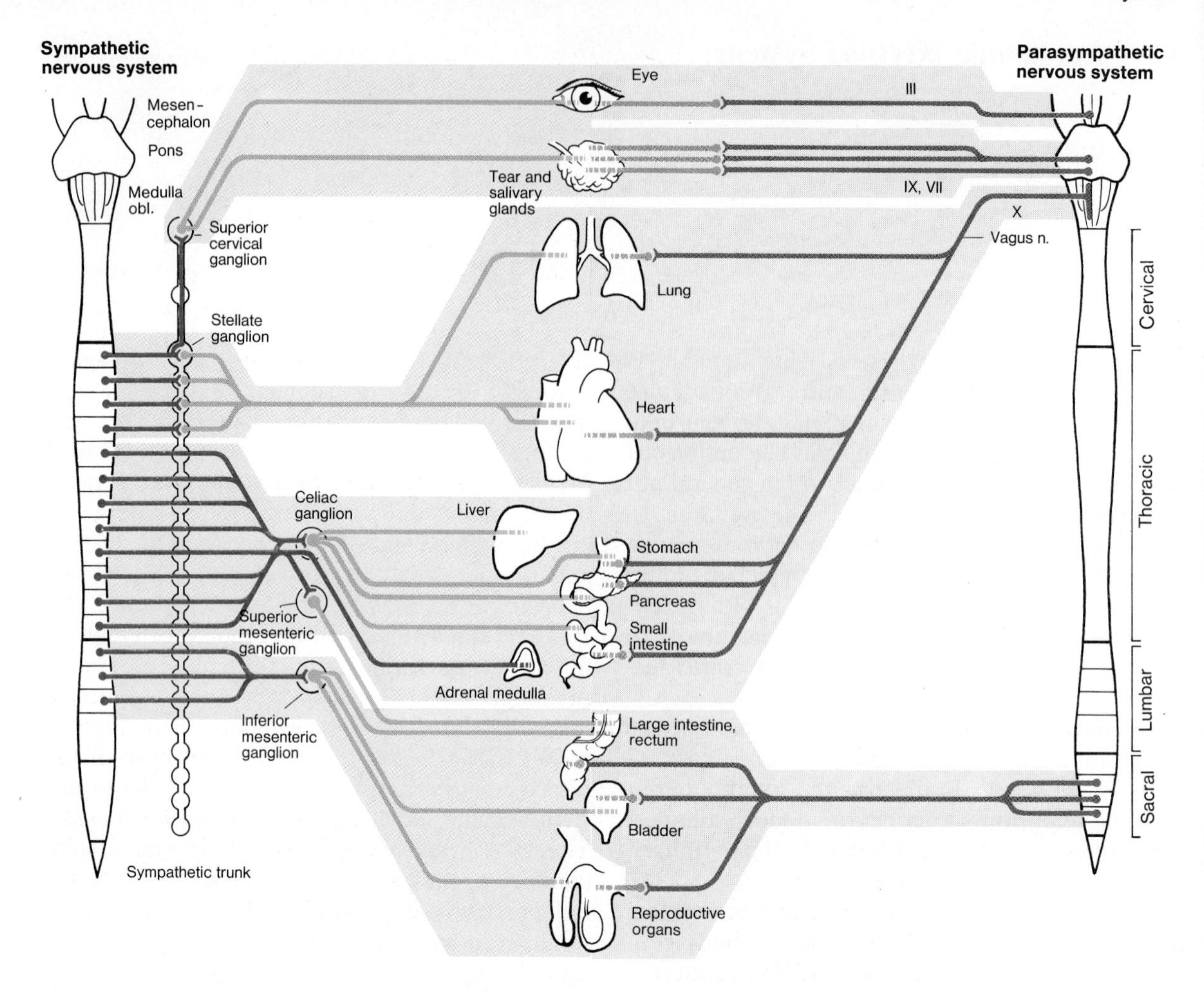

Fig. 16-1. Arrangement of the peripheral autonomic nervous system. *Continuous lines:* preganglionic axons. *Lines dotted at the end:* postganglionic axons. The sympathetic innervation of vessels, sweat glands and piloerector muscles is not shown

bral ganglia are connected by nerve strands to form a chain on either side of the vertebral column, extending from the base of the brain to the sacrum. From these **sympathetic trunks** the even thinner, unmyelinated postganglionic axons either pass in the gray rami (Fig. 16-12) to the effectors in the periphery of the body, or form special nerves that supply organs in the head region or in the thorax, abdomen and pelvis (Fig. 16-1). From the prevertebral ganglia (celiac, superior mesenteric and inferior mesenteric) the postganglionic fibers pass through plexuses or special nerves to the organs in the abdomen and pelvis.

Most sympathetic ganglia are *remote* from the organ supplied; correspondingly, their postganglionic axons are long. Only a few, relatively small sympathetic ganglia are situated near the pelvic organs, and send out short postganglionic axons. The effectors supplied by the sympathetic system are the smooth muscles in all organs (vessels, viscera, excretory organs, lungs, hairs, pupils), the heart and some of the glands (sweat, salivary and digestive glands). In addition, sympathetic postganglionic fibers innervate adipose cells, liver cells and perhaps the renal tubules and lymphatic tissue (e.g., thymus, spleen, Peyer's patches and lymph nodes).

Parasympathetic system. The cell bodies of the preganglionic parasympathetic neurons are in the sacral cord and the brainstem (Fig. 16-1). Some of the axons are myelinated and others unmyelinated; all are very long as compared with those of the sympathetic preganglionic neurons. They form special nerves to the parasympathetic postganglionic neurons, which are **near or in** the effector organs. The preganglionic parasympa-

thetic fibers for the muscles within the eye and for the glands in the head leave the brainstem in cranial nerves III (oculomotor), VII (facial) and IX (glossopharyngeal). The preganglionic parasympathetic fibers to the organs in the thorax and abdomen run in the *vagus nerve* (cranial nerve X). The sacral parasympathetic fibers to the pelvic organs run in the pelvic nerve.
Parasympathetic ganglia are found only in the head region and near the effector organs in the pelvis; the other postganglionic cells are scattered in or on the walls of the gastrointestinal tract **(intramural ganglia),** the heart and the lungs. The parasympathetic system innervates the **smooth musculature** and glands of the gastrointestinal tract, the excretory organs, the genitalia and the lungs; it also innervates the atria of the heart, the tear and salivary glands, and the intraocular muscles. Except for the arteries of the genitalia (especially the penis, the clitoris and the labia minora) and possibly those in the brain and the coronaries, it does *not* innervate the smooth muscles in blood vessels.

Visceral afferents. About 80% of the axons in the vagus nerves and about 50% of those in the splanchnic nerves (greater, lesser, lumbar and pelvic) are afferent. They are called **visceral** afferents because they come from sensors in the internal organs. Their cell bodies are in the superior and inferior vagal ganglia (vagus nerve) and in the spinal ganglia (spinal afferents). Afferents from the arterial presso- and chemosensors in the carotid bifurcation run in the glossopharyngeal nerve (cell bodies in the superior and inferior glossopharyngeal ganglia). The visceral afferents to the brainstem and the sacral cord are involved in the neuronal regulation of internal organs (lungs, heart, circulatory system, gastrointestinal tract, excretory and genital organs). Most of these afferents are from mechanosensors stimulated by stretching the walls of the hollow organs; they measure either the intraluminal pressure (e.g., the arterial pressoreceptors and the sacral afferents from the urinary bladder) or the volume within the organ (e.g., the afferents from the muscles of the gastrointestinal tract, from the right atrium and from the lung). For other mechanosensitive afferents from the intestinal mucosa, shearing force is the adequate stimulus. Some afferents are chemosensitive (e.g., arterial chemoreceptors in the walls of aorta and carotids, osmoreceptors in the liver, glucoreceptors in the intestinal mucosa). Stimuli that can elicit visceral pain sensations (e.g., strong stretching and contraction of the gastrointestinal tract and the urinary bladder, mesenterial tension, ischemic stimuli) are encoded in the discharge of spinal visceral afferents but not of vagal afferents. The sensors of these spinal afferents are situated in the serosa, at the attachment sites of mesenteries and perhaps also in the organ walls [4]. The functions of visceral afferents are treated in the chapters dealing with the associated organs.

The Action of Sympathetic and Parasympathetic Fibers on Effector Organs

The actions of the peripheral autonomic nervous system on the various organs it innervates can be studied by the electrical stimulation of autonomic nerves. The study of these actions is necessary (i) to understand the operation of the organs in the body during autonomic regulation under physiological conditions, and the interplay of the sympathetic and parasympathetic systems in vivo, (ii) to evaluate the responses of autonomically innervated organs under pathological conditions and (iii) to judge the effect of therapeutic drugs that simulate or block the sympathetic and parasympathetic actions.
Many internal organs receive both sympathetic and parasympathetic innervation (cf. Table 16-1). The influences exerted by the two are largely **antagonistic.** For example, stimulation of the associated sympathetic nerves causes increase in beat frequency and stroke volume of the heart, decrease in intestinal motility, relaxation of the gallbladder and bronchi and contraction of the sphincters of the gastrointestinal tract. Excitation of parasympathetic fibers to these organs (electrical stimulation of the vagus nerve; cf. Fig. 16-1) has the opposite effects: decrease in heart rate and the contractile force of the atria, increase in intestinal motility, contraction of gallbladder and bronchi and relaxation of the sphincters of the gastrointestinal tract. Under physiological conditions it is always the sum of these opposed effects that regulates the activity of these organs.
In most situations the two systems act "synergistically". This **functional synergy** is particularly evident in the reflex effects exerted on the heart by the baroreceptors (cf. Fig. 20-27). Excitation of the baroreceptors when the arterial blood pressure rises decreases the beat frequency and contractility of the heart. This decrease is brought about by an *increase* in the activity of parasympathetic fibers to the heart, accompanied by a *decrease* in sympathetic activity (compare the data in Table 16-1 with Fig. 20-28).

Table 16-1. Effects of sympathetic and parasympathetic activation on various organs

Organ or organ system	Parasympathetic stimulation	Sympathetic stimulation	Adrenergic receptors
Cardiac muscle	Decreased heart rate	Increased heart rate	β
	Decreased contractile force (atria only)	Increased contractile force	β
Blood vessels:			
Arteries in skin and mucosa	–	Vasoconstriction	α
Arteries in abdomen	–	Vasoconstriction	α
Arteries in skeletal muscle	–	Vasoconstriction	α
		Vasodilation (by circulating adrenalin only)	β
		Vasodilation (cholinergic)	
Arteries in heart (coronaries)	Vasodilation (?)	Vasoconstriction	α
		Vasodilation (by adrenalin only)	β
Arteries in penis (clitoris and labia minora?)	Vasodilation	?	
Veins	–	Vasoconstriction	α
Brain	Vasodilation (?)	Vasoconstriction	α
Gastrointestinal tract:			
Longitudinal and circular muscle	Increased motility	Decreased motility	α and β
Sphincters	Relaxation	Contraction	α
Capsule of spleen	–	Contraction	α
Urinary bladder:			
Detrusor muscle	Contraction	Relaxation	β
Trigone (internal sphincter)	–	Contraction	α
Genital organs:			
Seminal vesicle	–	Contraction	α
Vas deferens	–	Contraction	α
Uterus	–	Contraction	α
		Relaxation (depends on species and hormonal status)	β
Eye:			
Dilator muscle of pupil	–	Contraction (mydriasis)	α
Sphincter muscle of pupil	Contraction (miosis)	–	
Ciliary muscle	Contraction (accommodation)	Slight relaxation (insignificant)	β
Tracheal-bronchial musculature	Contraction	Relaxation (mainly by adrenalin)	β
Piloerector muscles	–	Contraction	α
Exocrine glands:			
Salivary glands	Copious serous secretion	Slight mucous secretion (submaxillary gland)	α
Tear glands	Secretion	–	
Digestive glands	Secretion	Decreased secretion or –	α
Nasopharyngeal glands	Secretion	–	
Bronchial glands	Secretion	?	
Sweat glands	–	Secretion (cholinergic)	
Metabolism:			
Liver	–	Glycogenolysis Gluconeogenesis	β
Adipose cells	–	Lipolysis (free fatty acids in blood increased)	β
Insulin secretion (from β-cells in islets of Langerhans)	–	Reduction	α

In many organs receiving both sympathetic and parasympathetic innervation the parasympathetic regulation predominates under physiological conditions; these organs include the urinary bladder and some exocrine glands (cf. Table 16-1). There are also organs with only sympathetic or only parasympathetic innervation – almost all blood vessels, the spleen, the smooth eye muscles, some exocrine glands and the smooth musculature of the hair follicles (cf. Table 16-1).
Glycogenolysis in the liver and lipolysis in fat cells, which cause an increase in the blood concentrations of glucose and free fatty acids, respectively, can be elicited by sympathetic stimulation but are unaffected by parasympathetic activity. This influence of the sympathetic system on *metabolism* is discussed on pp. 396, 397. The actions of the autonomic nervous system on the individual organs are described in detail in the relevant chapters.

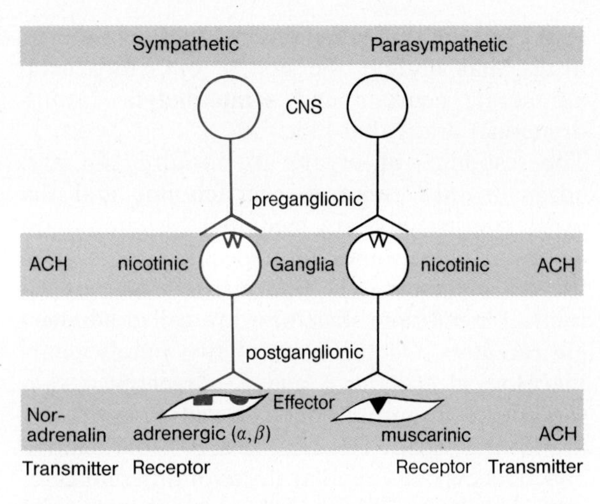

Fig. 16-2. Transmitter substances in the peripheral autonomic nervous system

Neurohumoral Transmission in the Peripheral Autonomic Nervous System

Excitation is transmitted chemically from the preganglionic to the postganglionic neuron and from the postganglionic neuron to the effector. As far as is known, neurohumoral transmission in the peripheral autonomic nervous system in principle occurs by the same mechanisms as that at the neuromuscular end plate (see pp. 43ff.) and at central synapses (see pp. 49ff.). In contrast to the end plate, however, the pre- and postsynaptic structures in the autonomic nervous system are extremely variable (myocardial cells, smooth muscle cells, gland cells, neurons). Moreover, the density and pattern of innervation varies greatly among the different smooth muscles (see p. 78).

Acetylcholine. Acetylcholine is probably released at all preganglionic autonomic nerve endings and by most postganglionic parasympathetic neurons (Fig. 16-2). Some sympathetic postganglionic neurons are also cholinergic – those to the sweat glands and perhaps the vasodilator neurons to the resistance vessels in the skeletal musculature.
The actions of acetylcholine on the postsynaptic membranes of the postganglionic neurons can be simulated by *nicotine*, and its action on the effector cells, by *muscarine* (a toxin from the mushroom *Amanita muscaria)*. This finding led to the hypothesis that there are two kinds of macromolecular (pharmacological) receptors with which acetylcholine reacts; the actions produced at the two are called nicotinic and muscarinic (Fig. 16-2).
There are drugs that *selectively* block one or the other action. These compete with acetylcholine to react with the postsynaptic cholinergic receptors without having any agonistic (cholinergic) effects of their own, and thereby prevent acetylcholine from acting. The nicotinic action of acetylcholine on the postganglionic neurons can be blocked by quaternary ammonium bases, which are thus called ganglion-blocking agents. The muscarinic action of acetylcholine can be selectively blocked by *atropine* (the poison in the deadly nightshade).
In pharmacology drugs that have the same action on effector cells as (cholinergic) postganglionic parasympathetic neurons are called **parasympathomimetics.** Drugs that block or weaken the action of acetylcholine on autonomic effector cells are called **parasympatholytics.** The latter substances are "antimuscarinic" drugs; a typical example is atropine.

Noradrenalin, adrenalin: α/β receptor concept. Because the transmitter substance in sympathetic postganglionic nerve endings is **noradrenalin,** these neurons are called **adrenergic neurons** (Fig. 16-2). The cells in the adrenal medulla release mainly adrenalin into the bloodstream (see p. 339). Noradrenalin and adrenalin are catecholamines (see p. 46). Isoproterenol is an artificial catecholamine, not naturally present in the body.
As in the case of the parasympathetic sys-

tem, there are **sympathomimetic** (adrenomimetic) drugs that imitate the action of sympathetic adrenergic neurons and **sympatholytic** (antiadrenergic) drugs that block it.

The responses of organs to noradrenalin and adrenalin, like those to acetylcholine and the other transmitters, are mediated by interaction of the catecholamines with specific structures in the cell membranes of the organs. These hypothetical membrane structures are called **adrenergic receptors.** On the basis of two purely pharmacological criteria, α **and** β **adrenergic receptors** (usually simply called α **and** β **receptors)** are distinguished. The criteria are (i) the relative effectiveness of equimolar doses of different catecholamines (usually adrenalin, noradrenalin and isoproterenol; cf. Fig. 16-3A) in eliciting α and β adrenergic actions, and (ii) the effectiveness of sympatholytic drugs in blocking these α and β actions. The molecular structures of the α and β receptors are still essentially unknown.

An α *adrenergic* action is defined by (i) a progressive decrease in effectiveness in the sequence noradrenalin, adrenalin, isoproterenol (NA $\geqq$ A $\gg$ I), and (ii) selective blocking of these effects by specific drugs **(α blockers;** Fig. 16-3B) in low concentrations.

The β adrenergic actions are characterized pharmacologically as follows. (i) Equimolar doses of isoproterenol, adrenalin and noradrenalin are of decreasing potency in that order (I > A $\geqq$ NA); the artificially synthesized catecholamine isoproterenol is therefore more effective than the natural ones. (ii) The β adrenergic actions can be eliminated by specific β **blockers** (Fig. 16-3B), such as *dichlorisoproterenol,* a derivative of isoproterenol (cf. Fig. 16-3A).

In Fig. 16-4 the α/β receptor concept is illustrated by the action of adrenalin on the arteries in the vascular bed of a skeletal muscle. The smooth musculature of these vessels contains both α and β receptors (Table 16-1). Excitation of the α receptors causes vasoconstriction, and excitation of the β receptors causes vasodilation (cf. Fig. 16-3B). When the adrenalin level in the blood is high the vessels in the muscle constrict, because the α action predominates (Fig. 16-4A). After blockade of the α receptors by a specific blocking agent the administration of adrenalin is followed by vasodilation (decrease in the peripheral resistance to flow) in the muscle (Fig. 16-4B), because now only the β receptors are excited *(adrenalin reversal).* After additional blockade of the β receptors by a β blocker adrenalin has practically no more effect on the vascular bed in the muscle (Fig. 16-4B). Under physiological

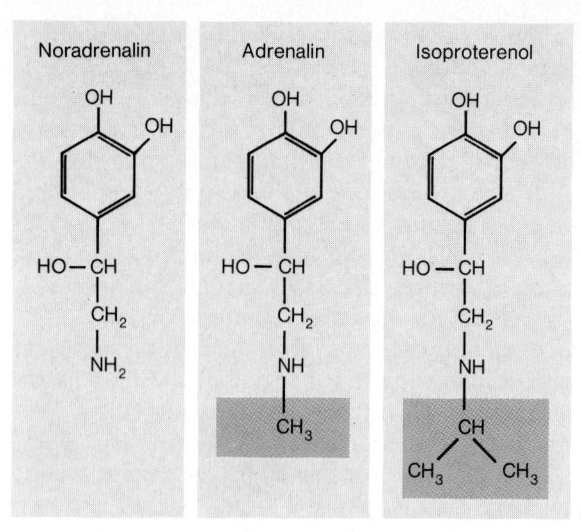

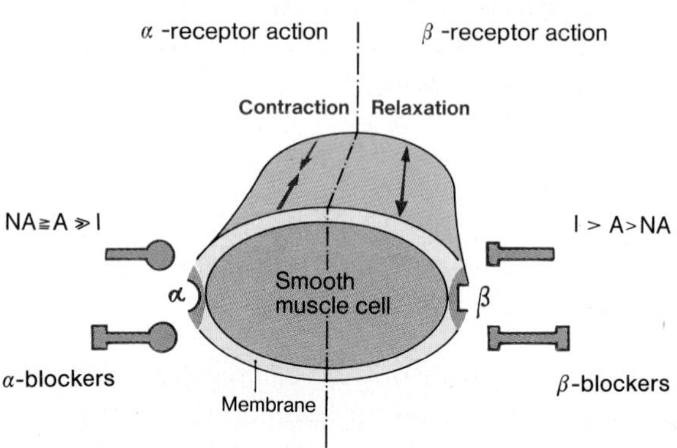

Fig. 16-3 A, B. The catecholamines noradrenalin (NA), adrenalin (A) and isoproterenol (I) and their actions on adrenergic receptors. ">"and "=" signify stronger and equally strong action, respectively

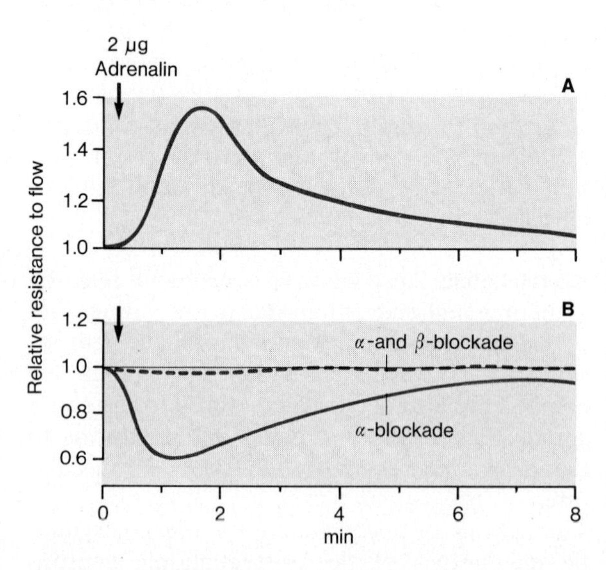

Fig. 16-4 A, B. Action of α and β blockers on the change in resistance to flow *(ordinates)* through an isolated, perfused skeletal muscle after intraarterial injection of adrenalin. [From SCHMIDT-VANDERHEYEN and KOEPCHEN: Pflügers Arch. *298,* 1–11 (1967)]

conditions low adrenalin levels in the blood are thought to have a dilating influence on the arteries of the muscle vessels, because the β receptor action predominates (see Fig. 16-5).
Most of the organs and tissues affected by catecholamines contain both α and β receptors in their cell membranes, and in most organs the two mediate opposite (antagonistic) effects. Under physiological conditions the response of an organ to the adrenalin and noradrenalin in the bloodstream or to excitation of its sympathetic innervation depends on whether the α or the β adrenergic action predominates.
Table 16-1 shows which receptors mediate these **physiological actions** of the two catecholamines at the most important organs. Because noradrenalin very strongly activates the β receptors of the myocardium but reacts only weakly with the β receptors of the smooth musculature of the vessels and of the bronchi and trachea, the β receptors of the heart are designated β_1 and those of the vessels and bronchi, β_2. It is not yet possible reliably to separate the entire population of β receptors into the categories β_1 and β_2 [10, 35, 46].

Other transmitters in the peripheral sympathetic and parasympathetic systems. Noradrenalin and acetylcholine are probably not the only transmitter substances in the peripheral autonomic nervous system. Experimental studies have shown that the effects elicited in many organs by stimulation of the autonomic nerves cannot be eliminated by blockade of either adrenergic or cholinergic transmission. For example, the cutaneous vessels of mammals are innervated by postganglionic vasodilator neurons, the transmitter of which is neither noradrenalin nor acetylcholine. Neuronal activation of the exocrine glands (sweat and salivary glands) is accompanied by vasodilation (increased blood flow) in the vicinity of the glands. These glands are activated by acetylcholine; the vasodilation is thought to be produced by the neuropeptide "vasoactive intestinal polypeptide" (VIP). Acetylcholine and VIP have been found together (colocalized) in the varicosities of the postganglionic neurons that innervate the glands, and both are released when the neurons are excited. Many preganglionic spinal neurons contain a neuropeptide (e.g., metenkephalin, neurotensin, VIP, cholecystokinin, substance P) in addition to acetylcholine. However, none of these substances has yet been shown beyond all doubt to function as a neurotransmitter or neuromodulator in the peripheral nervous system [26, 32].

The Adrenal Medulla. The Systemic Actions of Adrenalin and Noradrenalin

The adrenal medulla (AM) is a modified sympathetic ganglion. Its cells are ontogenetically *homologous* to the postganglionic neurons. These cells are activated by way of cholinergic synapses with preganglionic axons (cf. Fig. 16-1). The release of the catecholamines from the AM cells is entirely under neuronal control. Excitation of the preganglionic axons in man normally causes the release into the bloodstream of a mixture of a little over **80% adrenalin** and just under **20% noradrenalin.** The ratio of adrenalin to noradrenalin in the AM varies considerably among different species. For example, the whale's AM contains 70–80% noradrenalin, and that of the rabbit contains almost exclusively adrenalin. Adrenalin and noradrenalin are produced by different AM cells.
The catecholamines released by the AM act on the same effector organs as the postganglionic sympathetic neurons. Normally, however, it is likely that this action is important only in the case of organs or parts of organs with little or no postganglionic innervation (e.g., the media of arteries; cf. Fig. 16-6 A, C). Organs with extensive innervation (e.g., the vas deferens; cf. Fig. 16-6B, C) are probably not appreciably affected by the blood-borne catecholamines. The catecholamines from the AM appear to serve chiefly in the regulation of **metabolic processes.** They act as catalysts to mobilize *free fatty acids* from adipose tissue, and *glucose* and *lactate* from glycogen (cf. Table 16-1). Adrenalin and noradrenalin from the AM should thus be regarded primarily as **metabolic hormones** (see pp. 396, 397). These metabolic actions of the catecholamines are mediated predominantly by β *receptors* (cf. Table 16-1).
In a person **at rest** the adrenal medulla releases ca. 8–10 ng of catecholamines per kg body weight per minute. This rate of release depends on the resting activity in the preganglionic fibers – that is, it is determined by the CNS. In **emergency situations** such as loss of blood, hypothermia, hypoglycemia, hypoxia, burning or extreme physical loads the rate of release increases. During hard physical work, for example, the sympathetic nervous system brings about an increased transport of oxygen and oxidizable substrates to the skeletal musculature, the heart and the brain, by way of the catecholamines from the adrenal medulla as well as by postganglionic neurons. The AM catecholamines increase, by β adrenergic action, the levels of free fatty acids, glucose

and lactate in the blood. Moreover, adrenalin acts on β receptors to produce vasodilation of the arteries of the skeletal muscles and myocardium (Fig. 16-5). Simultaneously, chiefly by the excitation of postganglionic neurons, the cardiac output increases, there is general venoconstriction and constriction of the arteries in skin and viscera, and the bronchi dilate. These actions are mediated either by α or by β receptors (Fig. 16-5) [13].

Apart from emergency situations, the chief factor influencing the adrenal medulla is the **emotional state** of the organism. Under emotional stress the rate of catecholamine release can rise transiently to more than 10 times the resting rate. This release of AM hormones is controlled by the hypothalamus and the limbic system. The central-nervous mechanisms underlying this activation are largely unknown. It is conceivable that when stress situations are repeated indefinitely – a common feature of modern urban life and many types of work – the elevated blood catecholamine concentration can promote the occurrence of various illnesses.

The reactions of the effector organs in emergencies and severe emotional stress, brought about by the activation of the postganglionic sympathetic neurons and the adrenal medulla, can be called **emergency reactions.** They involve *uniform* responses of almost all outputs of the sympathetic nervous system, so that in this connection one can speak of a **sympathico-adrenal system** [4]. This uniform reaction of the sympathetic nervous system under internal and external extreme conditions is elicited chiefly by the hypothalamus.

Surgical removal of the peripheral sympathetic nervous system in an animal (e.g., cat or dog) causes no serious deficits that interfere with the normal vital functions at rest and in constant environmental conditions. But in extreme situations – e.g., thermal stress or physical effort – the animals can no longer adapt, because the brain, heart and skeletal musculature can no longer be supplied rapidly enough with adequate oxygen, glucose and free fatty acids (see Fig. 16-5) [3].

Synaptic Organization of the Peripheral Autonomic Nervous System

The adrenergic neuron. Neuroeffector transmission. Most adrenergic neurons have long, thin axons (Fig. 16-1) that branch repeatedly in the effector organs to form a so-called adrenergic

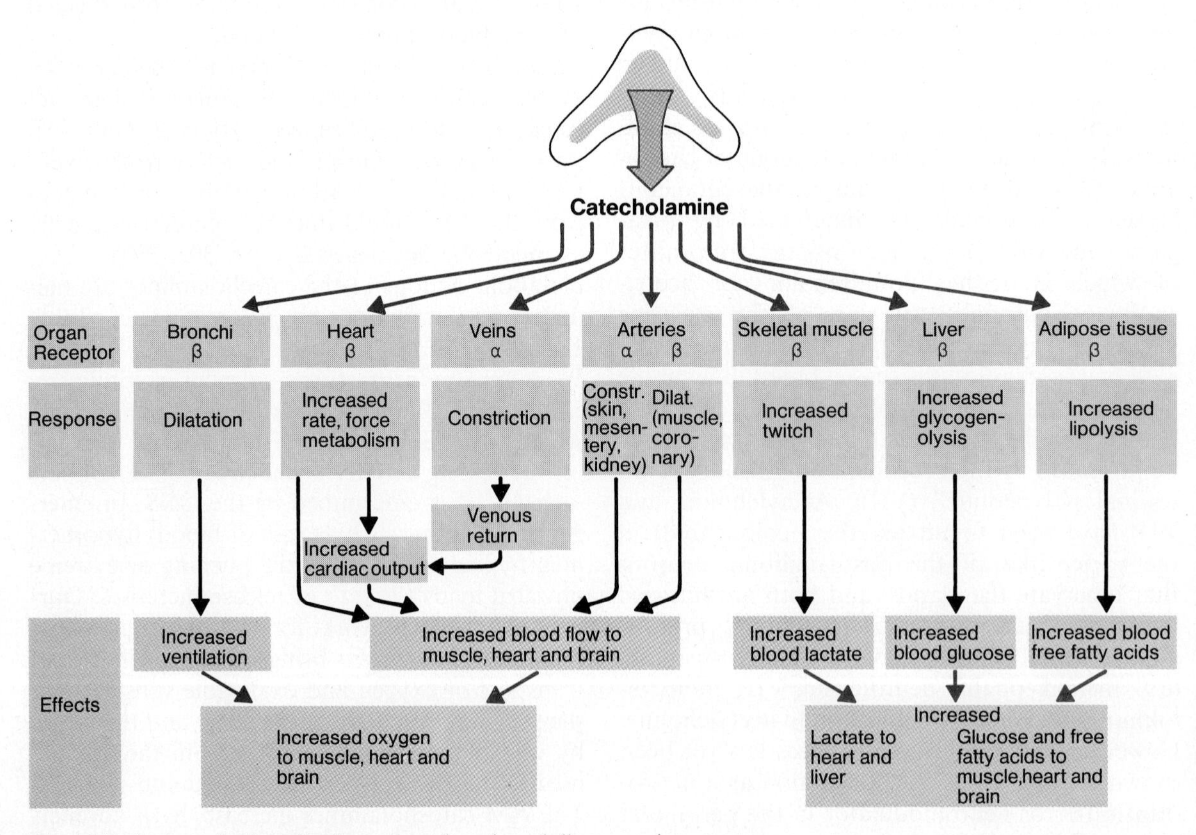

Fig. 16-5. Action of adrenalin from the adrenal medulla on various organs

plexus. The total length of the terminal branches of a neuron has been estimated to be as great as 10–30 cm. These branches exhibit **varicosities** (250–300 per mm) within which noradrenalin is synthesized, stored and inactivated. Excitation of the adrenergic neurons causes the release of noradrenalin from the varicosities into the extracellular space. The process occurs simultaneously in a large number of varicosities, and thus tends to affect the **smooth muscle tissue** as a whole rather than single smooth muscle cells. The individual muscle cells are joined by contacts having low electrical resistance (Fig. 16-6). By way of these "tight junctions" or *nexus* postsynaptic potentials and action potentials are transmitted *electrotonically* to neighboring cells (coupled muscle cells in Fig. 16-6C, D). More distant muscle cells are reached only by action potentials, which are generated in the directly innervated muscle cells when the postsynaptic potentials exceed threshold, and spread as a conducted wave of excitation through the entire mass of muscle (indirectly coupled muscle cells in Fig. 16-6C, D). In this way there is a *synchronized contraction* of all the smooth muscle cells in a muscle following direct depolarization of only a few cells by the transmitter.

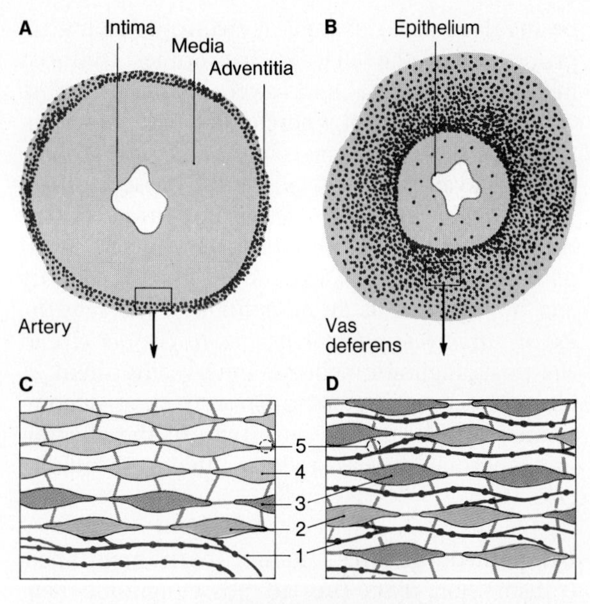

Fig. 16-6 A–D. Neuroeffector transmission in the peripheral autonomic nervous system. Distribution of the adrenergic innervation *(red)* in the smooth muscle of an artery in the rabbit ear (**A, C**; resistance vessel) and in the vas deferens (**B, D**). From [2]

The **density of innervation** of smooth muscles varies greatly from organ to organ. Smooth muscles with very dense innervation contain many cells having direct neuromuscular contacts. The distance between the varicosities and the membranes of these smooth muscle cells is ca. 20 nm (Fig. 16-6B, D; e.g., spermatic duct and ciliary muscle). This smooth musculature is entirely under neuronal control; circulating catecholamines have essentially no influence on it. Most blood vessels, by contrast, are innervated almost entirely by way of the adventitia; only the outer cells of the media are directly innervated (the neuromuscular separation, between the varicosities and the smooth muscle cells, is ca. 80 nm or more). Most of the smooth musculature of the media is influenced indirectly, by electrotonic transmission (Fig. 16-6A, C). As a result of this nonuniform neuronal action, this musculature is exposed to the influence of catecholamines diffusing from the blood in the lumen of the vessel, for here they are not inactivated by being taken up into the varicosities.

Smooth musculature with little or no direct innervation by postganglionic axons, because the neuromuscular separation is too large, is more strongly affected by the circulating catecholamines. Examples of such smooth muscles are the large (elastic) arteries, the circular and longitudinal musculature of the intestine, and the uterine musculature [2].

Supersensitivity of autonomic effectors after denervation. Autonomic effector organs may exhibit atrophy to a certain degree due to inactivity, but do not degenerate when their innervation is destroyed. Within 2 to 30 days (varying from one organ to another) following denervation or decentralization (by transection of preganglionic axons) they become **supersensitive** to the transmitter substances of the peripheral autonomic nervous system and to chemically similar drugs. For example, if the pupil of an animal is deprived of sympathetic innervation by removal of the superior cervical ganglion, the first result is constriction of the pupil owing to predominance of the parasympathetic action (Table 16-1). After several weeks the pupil dilates again. The dilation increases when the animal is exposed to emotional stimuli. This expansion of the pupil is ascribable to *sensitization* of the denervated dilator muscle to the adrenalin and noradrenalin released into the blood by the adrenal medulla (see p. 339). Emotional stimuli and frightening situations cause the concentrations of these substances in the blood to increase. Supersensitivity is usually more pronounced after denervation than after decentralization.

The mechanisms that can produce supersensitivity are not well understood. Some factors likely to be involved are a change in electrophysiological properties of the effector membranes (reduced membrane potential and lower threshold) and in calcium distribution (increased calcium permeability of the effector membrane; increased intracellular availability of calcium). These changes are brought about by the elimination of the transmitters ordinarily produced by the postganglionic neurons. Denervation supersensitivity can be regarded as an *adaptation of the sensitivity of autonomic effector organs to the activity* of the postganglionic neurons innervating them. A chronic decrease in neuronal activity is accompanied by an elevated sensitivity of the effector, and a chronic increase reduces effector sensitivity [1, 33].

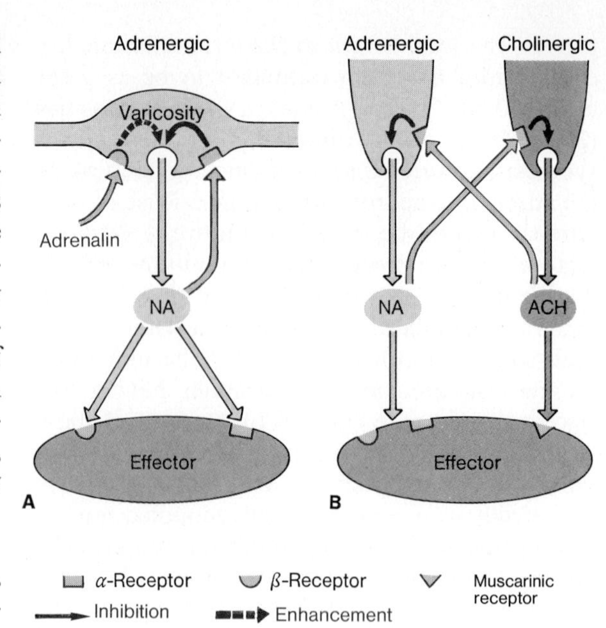

Fig. 16-7. Presynaptic control of transmitter release by the transmitters. NA noradrenalin, ACH acetylcholine

Sympathetic ganglia. As has been mentioned, transmission from pre- to postganglionic neurons in the autonomic sympathetic ganglia is *cholinergic* (Fig. 16-2). Many preganglionic axons converge on each postganglionic neuron; on the other hand, the collaterals of each preganglionic axon diverge onto many postganglionic neurons. There is an extraordinary variability among species and among ganglia in the quantitative degree of **convergence** and **divergence** for a given effector organ. The number of postganglionic neurons in a ganglion is usually considerably higher than the number of preganglionic axons innervating them. In humans, for example, a million postganglionic neurons in the superior cervical ganglion are innervated by ten thousand preganglionic axons; that is, one preganglionic axon diverges to at least 100 postganglionic neurons. The divergent and convergent synaptic connections guarantee a high safety factor for the transmission of excitation in the ganglia. Here spatial and temporal summation of postsynaptic potentials plays a crucial role, for single impulses in preganglionic axons usually cannot elicit suprathreshold postsynaptic potentials.

In addition to the *nicotinic* synaptic transmission in the sympathetic ganglia, acetylcholine and other substances released presynaptically elicit slowly rising, prolonged postsynaptic depolarizations or hyperpolarizations. These *slow cholinergic synaptic potentials* are brought about largely by the *muscarinic action* of acetylcholine (see p. 337). The functional significance of these slow postsynaptic potentials is still unclear. They are thought to control the excitability of the postganglionic neurons and thus the threshold for the generation of conducted action potentials. In this case the sympathetic ganglia would be simple *integrative centers* [9, 32].

Presynaptic control of transmitter release. The transmitter substances in the peripheral autonomic nervous system do not only act postsynaptically on the effector membranes and – in the autonomic ganglia – on the postganglionic neurons; they also influence the release of transmitter from the presynaptic structures themselves. These *presynaptic actions* of transmitter substances are mediated by **adrenergic** and **cholinergic receptors** in the presynaptic membranes.

The reaction between noradrenalin and presynaptic α adrenergic receptors decreases the rate of transmitter release, whereas the reaction with presynaptic β adrenergic receptors increases it (Fig. 16-7). Under physiological conditions a high concentration of noradrenalin in the synaptic cleft, during intense excitation of the postganglionic neurons, may limit the release of noradrenalin by way of the presynaptic α receptors *(negative-feedback mechanism)*.

Circulating adrenalin from the adrenal medulla may react with the presynaptic β receptors and thereby enhance the release of noradrenalin *(positive-feedback mechanism)*.

In organs with both sympathetic and parasympathetic innervation (e.g., the heart, bronchial musculature, gastrointestinal tract) the adrenergic and cholinergic presynaptic endings may interact with one another, producing reciprocal inhibition of transmitter release (Fig. 16-7B). It can be demonstrated that in the heart less acetylcholine is released from excited parasympathetic neurons when the sympathetic neurons to the heart are stimulated at the same time. This action is mediated by α adrenergic receptors in the presynaptic cholinergic endings (Fig. 16-7B). Conversely, excitation of parasympathetic neurons to the heart lowers the rate of noradrenalin release from postganglionic sympathetic neurons to the heart. This inhibitory action is mediated by muscarinic cholinergic receptors (see p. 337; Fig. 16-7). The inhibitory interaction between cholinergic and adrenergic presynaptic endings shows that the *antagonism* between the sympathetic and parasympathetic systems may also exist at the presynaptic level [45, 52].

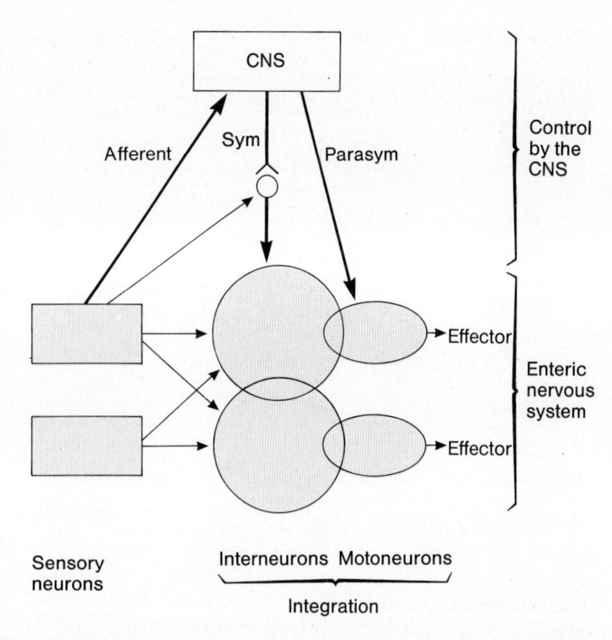

Fig. 16-8. Heuristic model of the organization of the enteric nervous system. (From WOOD: Am. J. Physiol. *247,* G 585-G 598, 1984)

Pharmacologists have demonstrated the existence of pre- and postsynaptic receptor types other than the cholinergic and adrenergic receptors, in the peripheral autonomic nervous system; these include dopamine, opiate, angiotensin, and other peptide and prostaglandin-E receptors. These pharmacological receptors probably have no physiological significance, although they are of potential use in *therapeutic medicine.* All the pharmacological receptors identified in the peripheral autonomic nervous system have also been found in the central nervous system, at pre- and postsynaptic sites. These central receptors may be involved in the regulation of central nervous processes under physiological conditions (see p. 368), and they are the sites of action of many centrally effective drugs.

The Enteric Nervous System

The gastrointestinal tract consists of a great variety of effector systems – non-vascular smooth musculature, epithelia, blood vessels and endocrine cells (see pp. 693ff.). Responsibility for control and coordination of these effector systems lies with the enteric nervous system, the extrinsic parasympathetic and sympathetic autonomic systems and the visceral spinal and vagal afferents. Most of the elementary functions of the gastrointestinal tract are not impaired by interrupting its extrinsic (parasympathetic and sympathetic) innervation. The cell bodies of most neurons in the enteric nervous system are in the **myenteric plexus** (AUERBACH's plexus) and the **submucosal plexus** (MEISSNER's plexus). The system comprises afferent neurons (the neurites of which have receptive properties), interneurons and motoneurons. The human enteric nervous system consists of about 10^8 neurons, about the same as the total number of neurons in the spinal cord and far more than the ca. 2,000 preganglionic parasympathetic axons in the vagus nerve that project to the enteric system.

The general functions of the enteric nervous system can be described in terms of the basic concepts diagrammed in Fig. 16-8. The enteric system contains **sensorimotor programs** for the regulation and coordination of the effector systems. These programs reside in the afferent neurons, interneurons and motoneurons and the excitatory and inhibitory connections among them; such a program (represented in the figure by a combination of box, circle and ellipse) is an expression of the integrative functions of the enteric nervous system. The CNS can influence the local neuronal activity by way of the extrinsic autonomic efferent innervation, but its influence is mainly confined to modulation of ongoing events. Some motoneurons in the enteric system (especially in the stomach and lower colon) serve simultaneously as postganglionic parasympathetic neurons (see Fig. 16-9). Postganglionic sympathetic neurons that do not innervate blood vessels have no direct influence on effector cells apart from the smooth musculature of the sphincters (see Fig. 16-9). The CNS is informed about events in the gastrointestinal tract by the visceral afferents to the spinal cord and medulla oblongata. There is also afferent feedback to the postganglionic sympathetic neurons in the prevertebral ganglia (*3* in Fig. 16-9). In its overall organization, the enteric nervous system operates like an **intelligent computer terminal.** Near the effector organs there are reflex circuits that continually

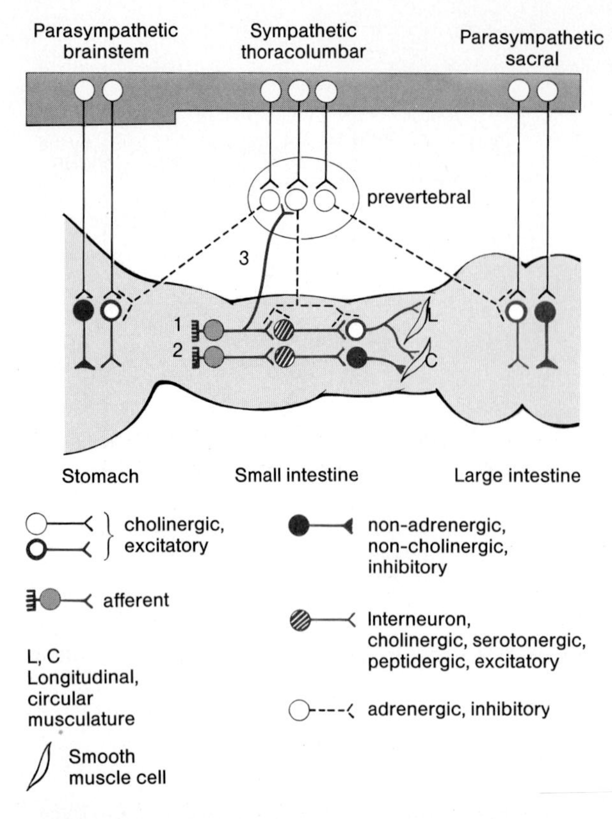

Fig. 16-9. Organization of the enteric nervous system and its extrinsic parasympathetic and sympathetic control. *1, 2* Excitatory and inhibitory pathways involved in the peristaltic reflex. *3* Collaterals of an afferent neuron to postganglionic sympathetic neurons in the prevertebral ganglion. (Modified from BURNSTOCK: Pharmacol. Rev. *24,* 509–581, 1972, and HOLMAN in [1])

adjust the behavior of the effector systems to the conditions in the lumen. The CNS (as the main computer) keeps a record of the activity of the gastrointestinal tract by monitoring the discharge of the visceral afferents, and shifts its functional state in accordance with the behavior of the organism. That is, the CNS tends to play a strategic role, being less involved with driving individual motoneurons than with modulating neuronal programs and their execution in the enteric nervous system. It is at the beginning and end of the gastrointestinal tract that the CNS is most likely to exert direct neuronal control (of food intake or evacuation).

On the basis of electrophysiological, pharmacological, biochemical, histochemical and ultrastructural criteria, more than 10 different types of neurons can be distinguished in the enteric nervous system. Interneurons and motoneurons have both excitatory and inhibitory actions on other neurons or effector cells. In addition to acetylcholine, the neurons contain about 10 substances (e.g., serotonin, ATP, neuropeptides) that could serve as neurotransmitters or neuromodulators or have paracrine functions. Little is known about the structures of the reflex arcs for individual functions of the gastrointestinal tract (e.g., peristalsis, segmentation, oscillatory movements, local control of blood flow). The neuronal substrate of the **propulsive mechanics** probably consists of two reflex pathways with an oral-aboral orientation in the intestinal wall, one of them inhibitory *(2* in Fig. 16-9) and the other excitatory *(1* in Fig. 16-9). The first effect of stretching the intestinal wall is reflex inhibition of the circular musculature (by pathway *2*), which causes relaxation of the wall musculature. This inhibitory reflex is followed by reflex excitation of the circular and longitudinal musculature by pathway *1,* which takes the form of a descending contraction of the intestinal wall. The inhibitory motoneurons are neither cholinergic nor adrenergic; they may use ATP or a neuropeptide (e.g., VIP, see p. 47) as a transmitter. The afferent neurons are probably peptidergic. Some of the excitatory neurons are cholinergic, but other transmitters such as serotonin and somatostatin also play a role.

Sympathetic postganglionic (adrenergic) neurons to the intestine directly affect the resistance and capacitance vessels and the smooth muscles of the sphincters (e.g., the internal sphincter muscle of the anus), but have only weak direct actions on the smooth non-sphincter musculature. They inhibit the release of transmitters from the presynaptic endings of preganglionic parasympathetic axons (see p. 342) and probably other axons as well. In the prevertebral sympathetic ganglia, the postganglionic sympathetic neurons receive synaptic input not only from preganglionic neurons but also, by cholinergic synapses, from afferent neurons with cell bodies in the intestinal wall (see *3* in Fig. 16-9); they may also make peptidergic synapses with collaterals of primary afferent neurons, the cell bodies of which are in the spinal ganglia.

Parasympathetic preganglionic axons synapse in the enteric nervous system not only on motoneurons that activate the intestinal musculature but also on motoneurons with an inhibitory action (Fig. 16-9). This centrally initiated inhibition is most pronounced at the oral and anal ends of the gastrointestinal tract; it probably has an important function in producing the reflex relaxation of the stomach when food is eaten and in regulating continence at the rectum [1, 26, 36, 53].

16.2 Central Organization of the Autonomic Nervous System in Spinal Cord and Brainstem

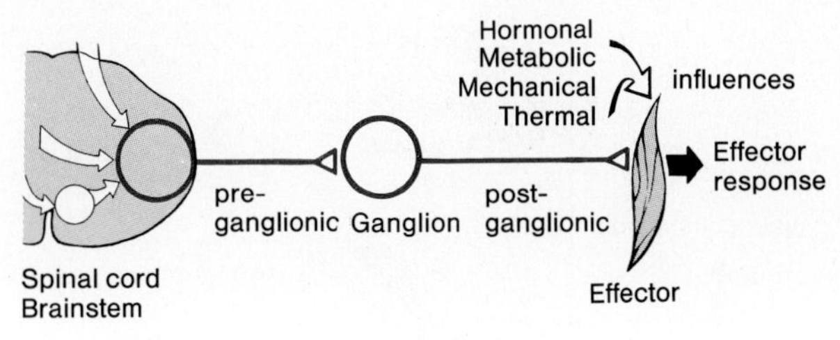

Fig. 16-10. Autonomic neuronal final common path

The Final Common Autonomic Pre-/Postganglionic Path; Positions of the Preganglionic Neurons

The preganglionic sympathetic and parasympathetic neurons in the spinal cord and brainstem are activated as a result of integrative processes in the CNS. Their activity is transmitted synaptically to the postganglionic neurons and from those neurons to the effector organs. There is sufficient direct and indirect experimental evidence that many autonomic effector organs are innervated by functionally – and probably also anatomically – separate pre- and postganglionic "neuron channels". For instance, the pre- and postganglionic neurons that regulate the secretion of sweat are different from the neurons that regulate blood flow through the skin; the sympathetic neurons that inhibit motility in the gastrointestinal tract (see Fig. 16-9) are different from the sympathetic neurons that adjust the diameters of resistance and capacitance vessels in the viscera. Recent experimental results indicate that the pre- and postganglionic neuron chains leading to the effector organs can, in analogy with the motoneurons to the skeletal musculature, be regarded as the final common paths of the autonomic system (Fig. 16-10). This idea does not rule out integrative processes in the sympathetic ganglia (see Fig. 16-9) and in some parasympathetic ganglia (see p. 342). It also does not exclude the possibility that the behavior of many effector organs is governed not only by the activity in the postganglionic neurons but also by hormonal and metabolic changes near the effector cells and by mechanical processes and influences (e.g., thermal) from the surroundings (see Fig. 16-10). For instance, the resistance to blood flow in the vascular bed of a muscle depends on the activity in the postganglionic vasoconstrictor neurons to that muscle, on the myogenic activity of the smooth musculature of the vessels, on the metabolic state of the skeletal muscle and on the concentration of circulating catecholamines in the blood.

The preganglionic sympathetic and sacral preganglionic parasympathetic neurons have their cell bodies in the intermediate zone of the thoracolumbar and sacral spinal cord. The intermediate zone in the thoracolumbar cord consists of the **intermediolateral nucleus** (IL), the nucleus intercalatus (IC) and the central autonomic nucleus (CA in Fig. 16-12). Most of the preganglionic sympathetic somata are in the funicular (white matter) and principal parts of the IL (IL_f, IL_p in Fig. 16-12). It is likely that functionally different preganglionic neurons are located at different places in the spinal intermediate zone; for example, preganglionic sympathetic neurons that regulate effector organs in the skeletal musculature and skin tend to occupy lateral positions in the IL, whereas preganglionic sympathetic neurons to the visceral region are more medial to the IL. Preganglionic parasympathetic neurons to the urinary bladder are in the lateral part of the sacral cord, at the edge of the white matter, and neurons to the colon are more medial in the sacral cord.

Preganglionic parasympathetic neurons to the heart, to the tracheal and bronchial musculature, and to the gastrointestinal tract lie in the dorsal nucleus of the vagus nerve and the nucleus ambiguus of the medulla oblongata. Preganglionic parasympathetic neurons to the salivary glands and lacrimal glands originate in the salivatory nuclei of the medulla, and preganglionic neurons to the smooth eye musculature, in the Edinger-Westphal nucleus of the mesencephalon [4, 39, 42].

Resting Activity in the Autonomic Nervous System

The significance of resting activity in the regulation of autonomic organs. Many pre- and postganglionic neurons – especially to the blood vessels and the heart – are spontaneously active. This **neurogenic resting activity** is a fundamental factor in the autonomic control of organ function. For example, in vasoconstrictor fibers it keeps the smooth musculature of the vessels in a state of relative contraction. The degree of contraction determines the cross-sectional area of the blood vessels and thus the peripheral resistance to flow. With a resting state of interme-

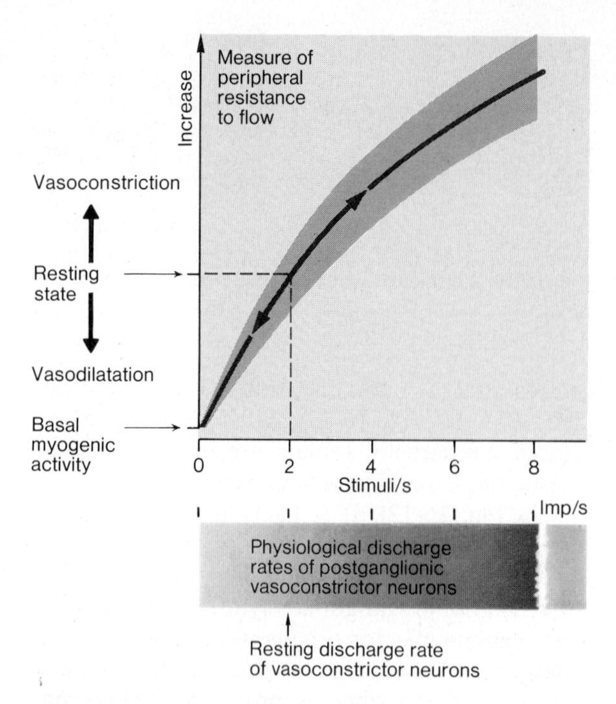

Fig. 16-11. Relation between resistance to blood flow in the skeletal muscle of a cat hindlimb *(ordinate)* and the frequency of suprathreshold electrical stimulation of the preganglionic axons in the lumbar sympathetic trunk. The *red area* indicates the range of measured data. [Modified from MELLANDER: Acta physiol. scand. *50*, Suppl. *176*, 1–86 (1960)]

diate contraction, blood flow through an organ can be either increased or decreased by changes in vasoconstrictor-fiber activity. Thus a single set of postganglionic neurons can produce both vasoconstriction and vasodilation.

The situation is illustrated in Fig. 16-11. The diagram shows the increase in resistance to flow in the arterial bed of a cat leg, when the lumbar sympathetic trunk is stimulated at increasing frequencies. The peripheral resistance prevailing at rest in vivo can be produced by ca. *two stimuli per second.* Decrease in stimulus frequency results in vasodilation and thus reduction of the peripheral resistance, whereas an increase causes vasoconstriction and greater peripheral resistance. When the resting activity of the vasoconstrictor fibers is abolished surgically or pharmacologically, the peripheral resistance is determined only by the spontaneous activity of the smooth musculature of the vessels **(basal myogenic activity)** and by the catecholamines adrenalin and noradrenalin circulating in the blood (see pp. 339 ff.). The range within which blood flow can be regulated *physiologically* by change in vasoconstrictor activity is shaded red in Fig. 16-11 (cf. Fig. 20-24, p. 507).

The activity of many autonomically innervated organs is regulated as shown in Fig. 16-11. The **level of resting activity** in peripheral autonomic neurons can be estimated by indirect methods (e.g., measuring the response of an effector organ during electrical stimulation of autonomic nerves) and by direct recording from pre- and postganglionic neurons. It varies from ca. 0.1 Hz to 4 Hz, and is likely to average about 1–2 Hz in vasoconstrictor neurons to the vessels in skin and muscle under resting conditions in a neutral ambient temperature [39, 41].

Evidently the level of tonic activity in the autonomic neurons is adjusted to the properties of the smooth musculature. Because of the prolonged, relatively slowly rising and falling contractions of this musculature, low-frequency neurogenic resting activity produces a smooth contraction **(tonus)** [8].

Autonomic Reflexes of the Spinal Cord

Segmental organization of autonomic reflexes. The synaptic connection between afferents and autonomic efferents at the spinal segmental level is called the **autonomic reflex arc.** Unlike the monosynaptic stretch reflex, even the simplest autonomic spinal reflex arcs probably have no direct connections between the (visceral and somatic) afferents and the preganglionic neurons; the shortest pathway is disynaptic. The autonomic reflex arc thus has a total of at least **three synapses** between the afferent and postganglionic

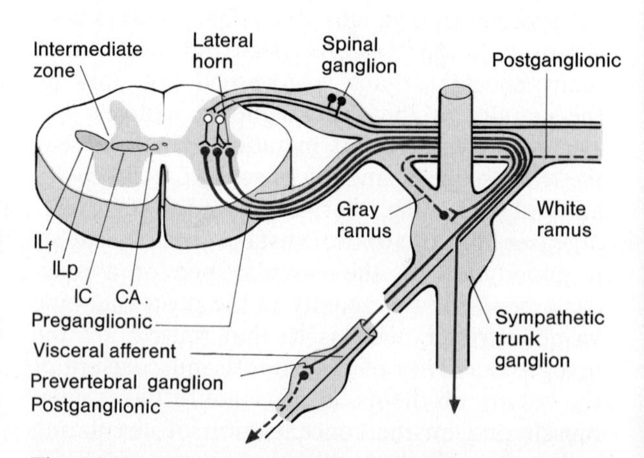

Fig. 16-12. Arrangement of the autonomic spinal reflex arc. *Left:* Nuclei containing the preganglionic sympathetic neurons in the intermediate zone; Il_f, Il_p, funicular and principal parts of the intermediolateral (IL) nucleus; IC nucleus intercalatus; CA central autonomic nucleus. (From RANSON and CLARK: The Anatomy of the Nervous System, 1959; Petras and Cummings, J. Comp. Neurol. *146*, 189–218, 1972)

neurons (Fig. 6-12) – two in the spinal gray matter and one in the autonomic ganglion.

A very specific segmental organization characterizes the afferent and autonomic innervation of certain organs. Afferents from the heart and from the excretory organs make synaptic contacts, at a segmental level, with preganglionic sympathetic and parasympathetic neurons innervating the same organs (intestino-intestinal reflexes; cardio-cardiac reflexes; evacuation reflexes, see pp. 350ff.). It is likely that similar specific spinal-segmental reflexes are also associated with other organs.

The segmental organization of the autonomic innervation of organs can also be observed in the **clinic.** In pathological conditions of the viscera (e.g., gallbladder or appendix inflammation) the musculature over the site of the disorder is taut and the area of skin *(dermatome)* innervated by afferents and efferents of the same spinal-cord segment that serves the affected organ is reddened. This situation is explained by an inhibitory action of the visceral afferents from the affected viscus on the sympathetic cutaneous vasoconstrictor efferents from the same segment (skin reddening) and an excitatory action on motoneurons (protective tension of the abdominal musculature. Conversely, stimulation of thermoreceptors in the skin causes reflex inhibition of the viscera innervated by the same spinal segment, by way of sympathetic neurons.

An important clue to the physician is the enhanced sensitivity to touch **(hyperesthesia)** and excessive pain sensitivity **(hyperalgesia)** in circumscribed skin areas that accompany internal disorders. It is likely that cutaneous nociceptive and non-nociceptive afferents and visceral afferents of a given spinal segment converge onto the same neurons of the spinothalamic tract (p. 209). Thus some of the information about the origin of the excitation from the internal organs is lost, and the cortex ascribes the excitation to the corresponding skin areas as well. Visceral pain ascribed to the skin is called **referred pain** (see p. 232), and the areas to which it is referred are called **Head's zones** (cf. Fig. 9-18).

Many patients with disorders of these organs (e.g., angina pectoris resulting from inadequate perfusion of the coronary vessels, gallbladder inflammation, gastric ulcers) report pains in the corresponding skin regions. This information assists the clinician in diagnosis (see Chapter 10).

Hyperpathia and the sympathetic system. Some conditions of chronic pain are distinguished by the peculiar unpleasant, burning or stinging sensations elicited by a number of normally painless skin stimuli. These painful sensations appear only after a considerable latency, require some time to disappear, and spread into adjacent regions (frequently over an entire limb). Such pain conditions are called **hyperpathia.** They are often accompanied by hyperesthesia, disturbances of vasomotion and sweat secretion, and in particular trophic disturbances of the affected tissue. For example, one observes cold or warm damp thin skin with trophic changes in the subcutaneous adipose tissue and demineralization of the bones. Such symptoms can appear posttraumatically in the distal parts of the extremities when the median nerve, cervicobrachial plexus, sciatic or tibial nerve has been damaged. Clinical neurologists call the various combinations of these symptoms *causalgia, Sudeck's syndrome, posttraumatic pain syndrome, reflex sympathetic dystrophy* etc. Blockade of the sympathetic innervation of the affected limbs (by interrupting conduction in the sympathetic trunk, by administering drugs that empty the peripheral noradrenalin stores in the sympathetic nerve fibers, or by surgical sympathectomy) often relieves the chronic intolerable pain and improves the abnormal regulation of blood flow and sweating and trophic condition of the tissue. Therefore the efferent adrenergic sympathetic neurons are thought to be involved in producing the chronic pains (hyperpathia). But we can only guess at the process leading to hyperpathia, with its accompanying abnormal regulation of blood flow and sweating and trophic disturbances. It may be that when injury alters the afferent input, sympathetic activity excites or changes the excitability of the receptors of thick and thin afferent fibers, producing abnormal patterns of excitation in response to normally painless stimuli. These pathological excitation patterns may give rise to abnormal information processing in the spinal cord, resulting in pathological pain perception and impaired autonomic regulation [15, 40].

Autonomic reflexes following spinal cord transection. Transection of the spinal cord causes **paralysis** in the parts of the body below the cut (see p. 95). The autonomic reflexes involving segments below the interruption are extinguished for 1–6 months in humans. During the first one to two months the skin is dry and rosy, because the resting activity in the sympathetic fibers to sweat glands and vessels is very low. The somatosympathetic reflex activity of sudomotor and vasoconstrictor fibers elicited by painful or painless skin stimuli increases slowly in the course of months, eventually reaching a stage of **hyperreflexia.**

The bladder and colonic evacuation reflexes and genital reflexes (see pp. 351 and 354) require similarly long times for recovery following spinal transection [11, 44]. The spinal cord isolated from the brain by transection is capable of a number of regulatory functions after recovery from spinal shock. For example, when the body is moved from the horizontal to the erect position, or when blood is lost, there is a general reflex constriction of arteries and veins, which prevents the arterial blood pressure from falling to a very dangerous level. On the other hand, a general reflex activation of the vasoconstrictor neurons can also be caused by the excitation

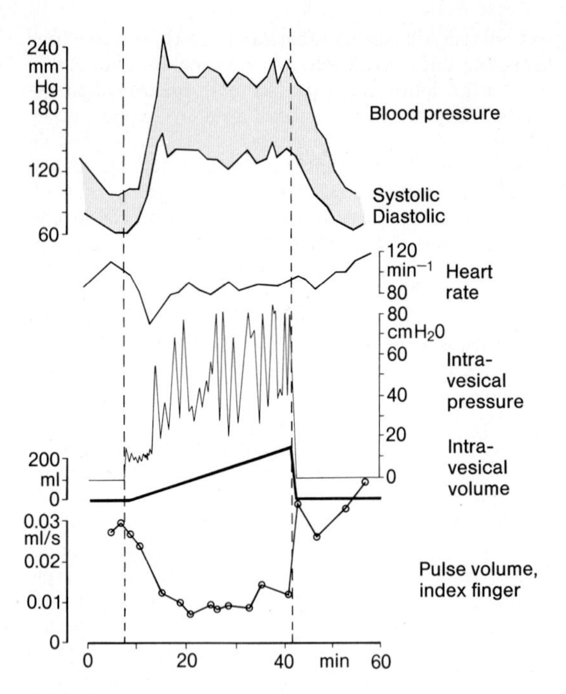

Fig. 16-13. Chronic paraplegic patient (spinal cord transected at level T 2/3). Responses of cardiovascular parameters (arterial blood pressure; heart rate; blood flow through the skin, pulse volume of an index finger) during slow filling of the urinary bladder. Note that the bladder contracts. Modified from [11]

of deep somatic and visceral afferents (e.g., during flexor spasm or contraction of a full bladder), in which case there can be a dangerous rise in blood pressure, piloerection and sweat secretion. Figure 16-13 shows a typical example in a paraplegic patient (cord sectioned at the level T 2/3). Slow filling leads to isovolumetric contractions of the urinary bladder, with an increase in the intravesical pressure. The excitation of visceral lumbar and sacral afferents from the bladder initiates a spinal reflex that results in vasoconstriction in the skeletal musculature, in the visceral region and in the skin (reduced pulse volume in the index finger) and the release of catecholamines from the adrenal medulla. These processes cause an increase in systolic and diastolic blood pressure. The heart rate decreases, because the arterial pressoreceptor reflex arc by way of the medulla oblongata and the parasympathetic (vagal) cardiac innervation is still intact (see Fig. 16-14, right).

The disappearance of the spinal autonomic reflexes after spinal transection is one aspect of **spinal shock** (p. 96). It is probably due to interruption of the descending pathways from the brainstem (see Fig. 16-14, left) that control the spinal autonomic reflex motor output. This descending control is much more pronounced in primates than in the lower vertebrates (e.g., frog). Therefore the duration and extent of the suppression of spinal reflexes after spinal transection are much greater in primates than in the lower vertebrates.

Two factors that may contribute to recovery from spinal shock are the amplification of postsynaptic events at existing synapses and the development of new synapses on interneurons, preganglionic neurons and motoneurons.

Autonomic Capabilities of the Brainstem

The sites of the neuronal **autonomic "centers"** in the brainstem (medulla oblongata, pons, mesencephalon; cf. Fig. 5-13), which affect the operation of the internal organs and organ systems (cardiovascular system, digestive tract, evacuation mechanisms; cf. the relevant chapters) by way of the peripheral autonomic nervous system, have been only approximately established. Such information has been obtained from experiments in which the performance of the organ systems was studied before and after transection of the brainstem, after the ablation of certain nuclear regions or tracts, and during the electrical stimulation of groups of neurons. At the cellular level, essentially nothing is known about the organization of the autonomic nervous system in the brainstem.

This lack of knowledge on one hand is due to technical difficulties, for the neurons and groups of neurons in the brainstem that are responsible for autonomic regulation are usually very small and thus hard to identify either neurophysiologically or neuroanatomically. On the other hand, there are conceptual difficulties; the notion that autonomic neuronal regulation of certain organs is based on discrete functional groups of neurons that can be readily located histologically ("centers") is only partially correct. Rather, single neurons and small groups of neurons appear to participate in the autonomic control of various organs that are functionally related to one another (e.g., reflex regulation of swallowing and vomiting, control of the salivary glands and the gastrointestinal tract, control of respiration and circulation). This implies that one cannot expect to find all the neurons that influence a particular organ in direct proximity to one another. Therefore the term "center" should be used only with reservations.

Control of autonomic spinal systems by brainstem and hypothalamus. The spinal parasympathetic and sympathetic systems are subject to descending inhibitory and excitatory influences from the brainstem and hypothalamus. It is in these parts of the brain that spinal systems with different functions [4, 15, 39, 42] are organized into **higher-order functional complexes.** Examples of systems that must be coordinated to serve more general functions include (i) the cutaneous vasoconstrictor system and the sudomotor system, for thermoregulation, (ii) the vasoconstriction systems of the resistance vessels (in skeletal muscle and vis-

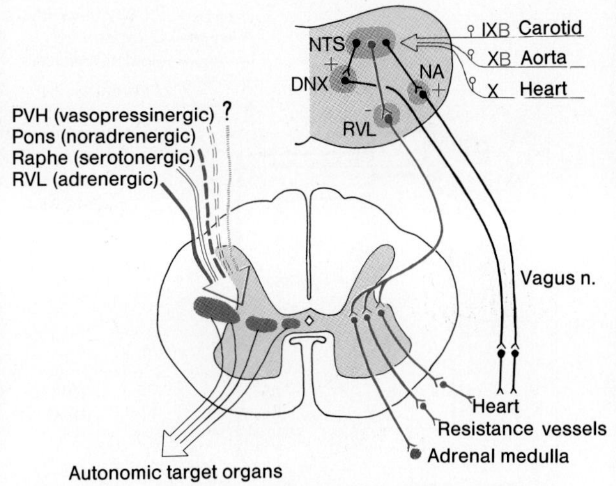

Fig. 16-14. *Left:* Descending systems from brainstem and hypothalamus that converge on preganglionic neurons in the intermediate zone of the thoracolumbar spinal cord. *Right:* Diagram of the neuronal regulation of arterial systemic blood pressure. +,– Excitation and inhibition resulting from stimulation of the arterial baroreceptors *(B)*. NTS Nucleus of the solitary tract, *DNX* dorsal nucleus of the vagus nerve, *NA* nucleus ambiguus, PVH paraventricular nucleus of the hypothalamus, *RVL* rostral ventrolateral nucleus of the medulla. X Vagus nerve, IX glossopharyngeal nerve. From [31]

cera) and the sympathetic innervation to heart and adrenal medulla, for regulation of arterial systemic blood pressure, (iii) the parasympathetic and sympathetic systems to urinary bladder and lower colon, for control of evacuation, and (iv) the parasympathetic and sympathetic systems to the reproductive organs, for regulation of sexual functions. The diversity of these functions and of the spinal autonomic systems is matched by the diversity of descending spinal systems from the brainstem and hypothalamus, which project into the intermediate zone, to preganglionic neurons (Fig. 16-14, left). Although the functions of these systems are not understood in detail, the systems can be described in terms of their origin and biochemical characteristics. For instance, serotonergic neurons project from the raphe nuclei, adrenergic neurons from the rostral ventrolateral medulla oblongata, noradrenergic neurons from the pons, and peptidergic neurons (vasopressinergic, oxytocinergic) from the paraventricular nucleus of the hypothalamus – each to preganglionic neurons or the corresponding interneurons. It is not known whether these substances function as neurotransmitters and/or neuromodulators.

The medulla oblongata and the circulation. The role of the medulla in the regulation of arterial systemic blood pressure is impressively revealed by comparing high-spinal animals (transection of the cord in the upper cervical region) with decerebrate (see p. 97) animals, in which the medulla oblongata remains intact. In acutely spinalized animals the blood pressure falls sharply, because the resting activity in the sympathetic neurons to the blood vessels, heart and adrenal medulla disappears. Only cardiac function can still be regulated neuronally by the medulla oblongata, by way of the vagus nerves (see Fig. 16-14). The blood pressure of decerebrate animals is normal; here the vascular beds (resistance and capacitance vessels in the visceral region) give coordinated reactions to changes in the position of the body in space, so that the perfusion pressure in the tissues they supply remains the same. In decerebrate animals, with intact medulla oblongata, a stable level of arterial blood pressure is maintained even after transection of all the afferents in the vagus and glossopharyngeal nerves that are important for cardiovascular regulation. These results imply that the neuronal reflex circuits for regulation of arterial systemic blood pressure run through the medulla, and that the resting activity in the sympathetic neurons to the cardiovascular effectors mentioned above originates in the medulla. The part of the medulla that contains the neurons involved in maintenance and control of arterial blood pressure is called the **"cardiovascular center"**.

A rostro-ventrolateral area in the medulla oblongata (RVL in Fig. 16-14, right) is important in this respect; topical stimulation of the neurons here increases the blood pressure, the heart rate and the release of catecholamines from the adrenal medulla. Destruction of this area causes a drop in blood pressure like that following high spinalization. The axons of the neurons in the **rostral ventrolateral medulla oblongata** project directly, in the dorsolateral column of the spinal cord, to the sympathetic preganglionic neurons in the intermediate zone (Fig. 16-14). Afferents important for neuronal regulation of the cardiovascular system (from the arterial baro- and chemoreceptors and from the heart) run in the vagus and glossopharyngeal nerves to the **nucleus of the tractus solitarius** (NTS); the neurons of the NTS project to various nuclei in the brainstem and hypothalamus, including the rostral ventrolateral area of the medulla, which in turn send axons to the sympathetic preganglionic neurons in the intermediate zone (Fig. 16-14, right). Neurons in the medial part of the NTS are excited by natural stimulation of the **arterial baroreceptor afferents;** these neurons project to neurons in the rostral ventrolateral medulla, some of which they inhibit. That is, the inhibition of activity in the sympathetic neurons to the heart and to the resistance vessels that follows stimulation of the arterial baroreceptors (see p. 512) occurs at least partially in the medulla oblongata. On the right in Fig. 16-14 are shown the basic neuronal elements, between the cardiovascular afferents to the NTS and the effectors, in the system for the regulation of arterial systemic blood pressure. The preganglionic parasympathetic neurons to the heart are situated in the dorsal nucleus of the vagus nerve (DNX) and in the nucleus ambiguus (NA). The nuclei in the medulla oblongata (NTS, NA, DNX and RVL in Fig. 16-14) are of course under the control of other neuron populations in the brainstem, hypothalamus and limbic system [4, 24, 31].

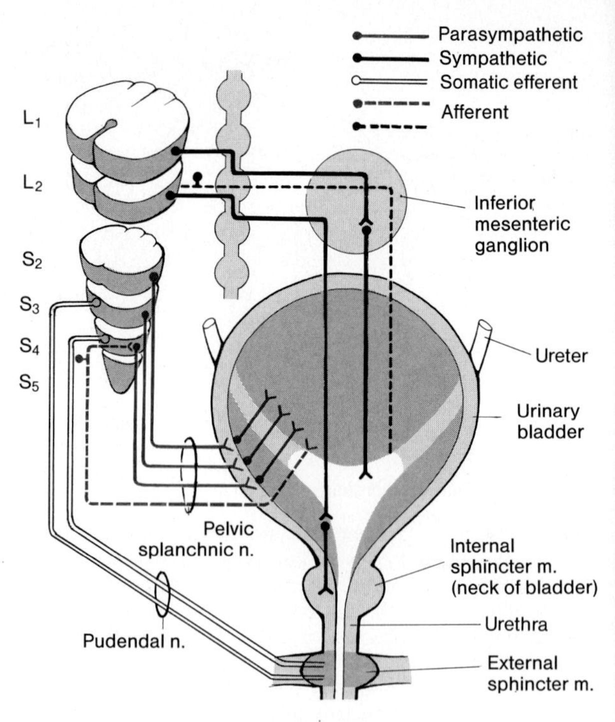

Fig. 16-16. Innervation of the urinary bladder

16.3 Micturition and Defecation

Neuronal Control of Bladder Evacuation

The urinary bladder stores and periodically evacuates completely the urine being continually produced by the kidneys. This function, so important for our social life, is based on myogenic mechanisms in the smooth muscle of the bladder and neuronal (autonomic and somatic) mechanisms. In the neural control of the bladder long collecting phases alternate with brief emptying phases. During the **collecting phases** emptying is prevented or made difficult by neural activity. The bladder fills at a rate of ca. 50 ml urine per hour. The plasticity of its smooth musculature (cf. p. 79) ensures that the pressure inside the bladder increases only slightly during the filling phase (Fig. 16-15). When the bladder has collected ca. 150–250 ml urine, the first signs of a brief *urge to urinate* appear. This urge is triggered by brief increases in the intravesical pressure. When the bladder contains ca. 250–500 ml, the **evacuation phase** normally begins. The ability of the bladder to retain the urine is called **continence,** and the act of emptying is called **micturition** (Fig. 16-15).

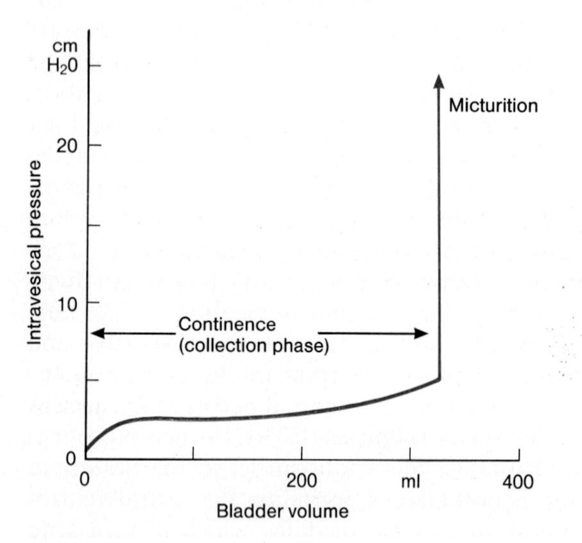

Fig. 16-15. Pressure-volume diagram (cystometrogram) of the human urinary bladder during slow (physiological) filling. The phase of urinary continence is defined by the flat part of the diagram. The sudden rise in intravesical pressure coincides with micturition. From SIMEONE and LAMPSON: Ann. Surg. *106*, 413, 1937

Structure and innervation of the urinary bladder (Fig. 16-16). The urinary bladder is a hollow muscle *(detrusor vesicae)*. Its wall consists of a network of long **smooth muscle cells.** At the base of the bladder is a triangular area of fine smooth muscle fibers (the *trigonum vesicae*), at the upper corners of which are the openings of the ureters. These ducts enter *obliquely,* so that when the intravesical pressure rises no urine can be forced back into the ureters. At the lower tip of the trigone the bladder opens into the urethra. A special arrangement of the muscle cells in this region provides a functional sphincter (the *internal sphincter*). The internal sphincter cannot be relaxed for micturition without the assistance of the detrusor muscle; when the bladder musculature contracts, the fibers radiating into the urethra shorten it, producing an automatic

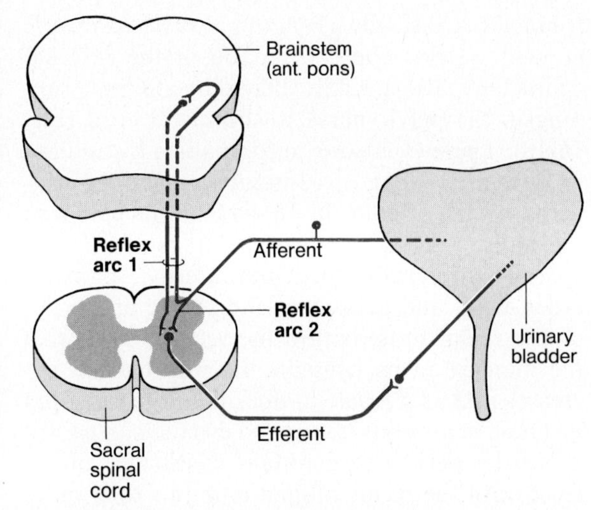

Fig. 16-17. Bladder-emptying reflex arc in a cat with brain intact *(1)* and a chronic spinal cat *(2)*. Reflex path 2 does not function in the intact animal. Interneurons in spinal cord and brainstem are not shown. From [38]

passive opening of the internal sphincter. The urethra is also closed by an *external sphincter* formed by the striated musculature of the pelvic floor. This outer sphincter muscle is poorly developed in women.
The innervation of the bladder and the sphincters is illustrated in Fig. 16-16. The bladder musculature is excited by **parasympathetic fibers** in the pelvic splanchnic nerve that arise in the 2nd to 4th sacral segments. This innervation is required for the normal control of bladder emptying. The sympathetic innervation, originating in the upper lumbar cord, inhibits the detrusor muscle and excites the musculature of the trigone; it may function to improve bladder continence. The external sphincter receives somatic innervation by way of motor axons in the pudendal nerve, the somata of which are in the middle segments of the sacral region. Information about the degree of bladder filling is sent to the central nervous system from stretch receptors in the wall of the bladder, by way of afferent axons in the pelvic nerve. Events in bladder and urethra that produce painful and non-painful sensations are probably signaled by both sacral and lumbar visceral afferents.

The voiding reflex. Urine is propelled from the renal pelvis into the bladder by peristaltic waves in the ureters. The more the bladder wall is stretched, the stronger is the stimulus to the stretch receptors within it. The activation of these receptors excites the parasympathetic neurons to the detrusor muscle, by way of reflex arc 1 in Fig. 16-17. The end result is evacuation of the bladder. As Fig. 16-17 shows, the reflex arc is complete only if the **anterior pontine region** of the brainstem is intact. Electrical stimulation of this brainstem region can also elicit bladder emptying.
Once the bladder has begun to empty the process accelerates explosively until emptying is completed. This self-intensifying – that is, *positive-feedback* – process is probably based chiefly on the following reflexes: (i) increased activation of the bladder afferents by contraction of the detrusor, (ii) reflex activation of parasympathetic bladder efferents by afferents from the urethra excited by *urine flow,* and (iii) reflex blocking of central inhibitory processes at spinal and supraspinal levels. There is additionally a reflex **relaxation of the external sphincter** owing to inhibition of the motoneurons in the sacral cord.
After transection of the spinal cord above the sacral level, neither animals nor humans at first exhibit reflex emptying of the filled bladder. Not until the chronic stage has been reached, 1 to 5 weeks after the transection, does the voiding reflex again begin to operate **(automatic bladder).** This reflex arc is entirely spinal (pathway 2 in Fig. 16-17). It is very likely that micturition in infants is controlled by the same spinal reflex arc, which later is probably suppressed by inhibitory influences exerted at the spinal level by bladder afferents or elicited supraspinally.

During the first stages of **paraplegia** and quadriplegia the bladder is *flaccid* and *atonic* for days to weeks. If the patient is properly cared for and urinary-tract infections are avoided, there is a gradual transition to the automatic-bladder phase, in which slight bladder filling causes reflex contractions of the detrusor and frequent urination. With adequate training paraplegics can learn to control their bladder evacuation. They can initiate reflex detrusor contractions themselves by tapping the lower abdomen (cf. segmental reflexes, pp. 346), choosing a suitable time by observing their own autonomic rhythms and aiding the evacuation process by pressing on the abdomen.

Suprapontine control of bladder function. The regulation of micturition and continence is a largely automatic, reflex process, but it is subject to modulation by the upper *brainstem,* the *hypothalamus* and the *cerebrum.* Neuronal control chiefly takes the form of *inhibition,* though some outputs are excitatory. The ascending and descending spinal pathways that conduct signals from and to the bladder and urethra, and the positions of the associated neuron populations in brainstem, hypothalamus and cortex, are largely unknown. The tasks of the "higher centers" are (i) to maintain continence even when the bladder is very full (to prevent emptying at unsuitable times) and (ii) to trigger and enhance evacuation at will, whenever it is desirable and possible [7, 11, 38].

Disturbances of micturition are very common and diverse. Involuntary **urine retention** follows paralysis or damage of the detrusor muscle (e.g., by inflammation or traumatic nerve injury), displacement of the urethra (e.g., by prostate tumor) or sphincter-muscle cramp. Urinary **incontinence** is the inability to retain urine voluntarily. It is especially common in women after giving birth (e.g., due to prolapse of the uterus because of pelvic-floor weakness) and in cases of organic brain disease (e.g., multiple sclerosis or arteriosclerosis of the cerebral vessels in the aged), and can also be purely psychogenic [16].

Neuronal Control of Bowel Evacuation

Evacuation of the bowel **(defecation)** and maintenance of **fecal continence** are the most important tasks of the rectum and anus. These two functions are controlled by the enteric nervous system, by the parasympathetic sacral innervation and by somatomotor mechanisms. Though the internal anal sphincter has a very dense sympathetic innervation, sympathetic influence on the lower intestine has been little studied.

Continence. The distal end of the rectum is closed by two sphincters. The *internal anal sphincter* consists of smooth muscle and is not under voluntary control. The *external anal sphincter* is a striated muscle, innervated by motoneurons from the sacral cord (S_2–S_4) with axons running in the pudendal nerve. Normally both sphincters are closed. *Tonic contraction* of the external sphincter is maintained by a spinal reflex involving afferent impulses from the muscle and the surrounding tissue, especially the anal skin.
When the rectum is filled with intestinal contents, by peristaltic contractions of the descending colon, its wall is stretched and as a result there is simultaneous relaxation of the internal anal sphincter and enhanced contraction of the external sphincter. The relaxation of the internal sphincter is basically a *reflex by way of the enteric nervous system*. The contraction of the external sphincter is also a reflex, elicited by afferents running in the pelvic nerve to the sacral cord (Fig. 16-18). These events are accompanied by an urge to defecate – that is, conscious sensations triggered by the afferent impulses from receptors in the walls of colon and rectum. After some tens of seconds the relaxation of the internal sphincter fades away, and because of the plastic properties of the rectal musculature the rectum adjusts to the increase in its contents. Its wall tension decreases and as a result so does the urge to empty it. These neuronally controlled events may permit a healthy person to maintain continence of the feces until the rectal content amounts to about 2 liters. Supraspinal, especially *cortical mechanisms* make a large contribution to continence by exciting the motoneurons to the external sphincter and probably by inhibition of the parasympathetic spinal reflexes.

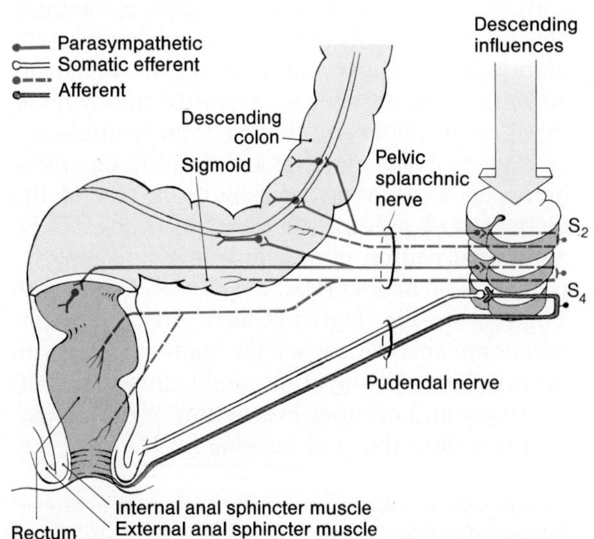

Fig. 16-18. Afferent and efferent pathways in the spinal defecation reflex. Interneurons between afferents and efferent neurons in the spinal cord are not shown

Defecation. Evacuation of the lower intestine is normally initiated by a *voluntary effort*. Supraspinal facilitation of the spinal parasympathetic reflex pathways to the lower intestine causes reflex contraction of the descending and sigmoid colon and the rectum (the longitudinal musculature in particular). At the same time both sphincters relax. A prerequisite for defecation is a *rise in intraabdominal pressure* owing to increased tension in the muscles of the abdominal wall and to lowering of the diaphragm by contraction of the thoracic musculature, in the expanded position with glottis closed. By interaction of these mechanisms the floor of the pelvis is depressed and the entire column of feces in descending colon, sigmoid and rectum is expelled.
Destruction of the sacral cord completely eliminates the defecation reflexes. After *transection of the spinal cord* above the sacral level the spinally organized defecation reflexes persist, but the voluntary motor patterns that assist defecation are abolished. They can be replaced by other actions (e.g., manual expansion of the external anal sphincter), so that paraplegics can achieve a *regular* daily control of fecal evacuation [7, 50].

16.4 Genital Reflexes

The genital reflexes in mammals – humans in particular – are very complex temporal and spatial sequences of reflex elements, involving *parasympathetic*, *sympathetic* and *motor efferents* as well as *visceral* and *somatic afferents*. Our knowledge of these reflexes in men is still very incomplete, and those of women are even less well understood. What we do know has been learned from experiments on animals, from studies of healthy people, and from clinical examination of patients with damaged spinal cord, sacral parasympathetic system or thoracolumbar sympathetic system [21, 29, 30].

Genital Reflexes in the Man

The sexual response cycle of the man consists of several successive phases – **erection** of the penis, **emission** of semen (sperm and glandular secretion) into the posterior urethra, and the actual **ejaculation** of semen from the anterior urethra. **Orgasm** begins with or before emission, and ends with the end of ejaculation.

Erection. *Dilation of the arteries* in the two corpora cavernosa of the penis and the corpus cavernosum of the urethra causes erection of the penis. The venous sinuses in the erectile tissue fill and expand maximally as the pressure rises. There is still some debate as to whether restriction of the venous outflow from the erectile tissue is passive, by compression of the veins as they pass through the tunica albuginea. Dilation of the arteries is probably brought about by activation of *postganglionic parasympathetic neurons* with cell bodies in the pelvic ganglia (see Fig. 16-19). The transmitter substances of these neurons may be acetylcholine colocalized with a neuropeptide (vasoactive intestinal polypeptide, VIP). The neurons are activated both *reflexly*, by afferents from the external genitalia and surrounding tissues, and *psychogenically* by supraspinal, probably cortical, structures. At the same time the afferent impulses from the genital organs give rise to sexual sensations. The **glans penis** bears the greatest concentration of mechanoreceptors; their afferents run in the dorsal nerve of the penis. The adequate stimulus to these receptors is provided by the sliding and massaging shear motion that accompanies copulation. An important factor in maintaining a state of excitation of the receptors in the glans penis during copulation is slipperiness of the surfaces of vagina and penis, which is produced reflexly by vaginal transudation (see p. 355) and the activation of the bulbourethral glands in the man.
The erection reflex involves only the sacral cord (S_2–S_4), so that it functions in men with spinal

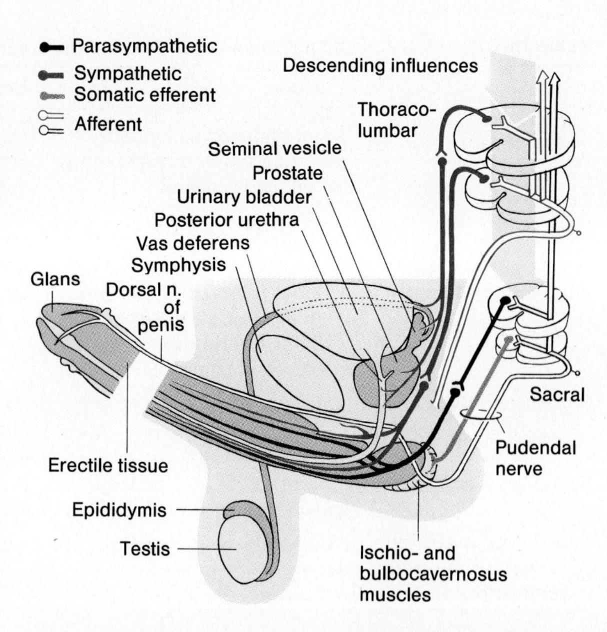

Fig. 16-19. Innervation of the male genitalia. Interneurons between afferents and efferent neurons in the spinal cord are not shown

transection as long as the cut is above this level. About a quarter of men with destroyed sacral cords can accomplish psychogenic penis erection. This erection is elicited by *sympathetic neurons in the lower thoracic and upper lumbar regions* (cf. Fig. 16-19). Their axons synapse with the postganglionic sympathetic neurons in the inferior mesenteric ganglion or in the vicinity of the genitalia. It is not known whether these postganglionic neurons to the arteries in the erectile tissue are also cholinergic, nor whether (or to what extent) the sympathetic system contributes to the erection of a healthy man (Table 16-2).

Emission and ejaculation. Emission and ejaculation are the high point of the male sexual act. As the afferents become highly excited during copulation, sympathetic efferents in the lower thoracic and upper lumbar segments become activated. The afferents that trigger emission run in the pudendal and pelvic nerves to the sacral cord, and with the sympathetic fibers to the thoracolumbar cord (Fig. 16-19). Excitation of the sympathetic neurons causes contraction of the epididymis, vas deferens, seminal vesicle and prostate, which propel the semen into the posterior urethra. At the same time a reflex involving excitation of sympathetic fibers closes the internal sphincter of the bladder (cf. Fig. 16-16) to prevent reflux of the secretions into the bladder.
After emission **ejaculation** begins. It is triggered by excitation of the afferents from the prostate

Table 16-2. Summary of the neuronal control of the male genital reflexes. From [30]

	Erection	Emission and ejaculation	Orgasm
Afferents	From glans penis and surrounding tissue to sacral cord (in pudendal nerve)	From external and internal genitalia to sacral cord (pudendal and pelvic nerves) and to thoracolumbar cord (hypogastric plexus), afferents from skeletal musculature	Present if at least one afferent input intact (from genitalia to sacral or thoracolumbar cord, from skeletal muscle to sacral cord)
Autonomic efferents	1. Parasympathetic sacral (reflex and psychogenic) 2. Sympathetic thoracolumbar (psychogenic)	Sympathetic thoracolumbar	
Somatic efferents	–	To bulbo- and ischiocavernous muscles and muscles of pelvic floor	
Sacral cord destroyed	Present in 25% of patients (psychogenic), thoracolumbar	Present if erection can be elicited	Present
Spinal cord destroyed in upper thoracic or cervical region	Almost always present (reflex)	Almost never present	Always absent

and from the posterior urethra, which run in the pelvic nerves, and possibly by afferents to the thoracolumbar cord from the epididymis, vas deferens and seminal vesicle. Stimulation of these afferents during emission initiates a reflex, through the sacral cord, that produces *tonic-clonic contractions* of the bulbocavernous and ischiocavernous muscles, which enclose the proximal erectile tissue (Fig. 16-19), and of the musculature of the pelvic floor. These rhythmic contractions expel the secretions, from the posterior through the anterior urethra, with simultaneous *rhythmic contractions* of the muscles of trunk and pelvic girdle. The latter contractions cause jerky movements of the pelvis, and serve chiefly to transport the semen into the proximal vagina and the cervix of the uterus. During the ejaculation phase the excitation of the parasympathetic and sympathetic innervation of the genitalia becomes maximal. This maximal excitation is partly due to the continuous afferent feedback from the skeletal musculature during the rhythmic contractions. After ejaculation the activity in the parasympathetic vasodilator neurons declines and the blood flows out of the erectile tissue through the veins, so that the erection gradually subsides.

Men with **sacral-cord disorders** often remain capable of emission and ejaculation, if these have been preceded by an erection, and they may experience orgasm. Efferent and afferent information to and from the genitalia in this case is conveyed by sympathetic fibers and afferents to the thoracolumbar cord (Fig. 16-19, Table 16-2). Paraplegics or quadriplegics with *transection above the mid-thoracic region* have lost essentially all capacity for emission, ejaculation and orgasm (Table 16-2). It is thought that in this case the sympathetic neurons in the lower thoracic and upper lumbar segments are permanently inhibited by sacral elements [16, 30].

Genital Reflexes in the Woman

The responses of female genitalia during the sexual response cycle have been studied quite thoroughly in recent years [21]. But the roles of the parasympathetic and sympathetic innervation are in part still a matter for speculation.

External genitalia. *Sexual stimulation* causes reflex and/or psychogenic changes in the external reproductive organs of the woman. The **labia majora,** which normally touch one another in the midline to protect the labia minora and the openings of vagina and urethra, spread apart, become thinner, and move in an anterolateral direction. If the excitation is continued they become congested with venous blood. The **labia minora** become so filled with blood that they double or triple in thickness, pushing out between the labia majora and lengthening the vaginal channel. The swollen labia minora change color from pink to bright red. The color changes are so typical of a sexually excited woman that the labia minora have been called the "sex skin". **Glans** and **clitoris** also swell, increasing in both length and thickness. As excitation increases, the clitoris is drawn against the margin of the symphysis.

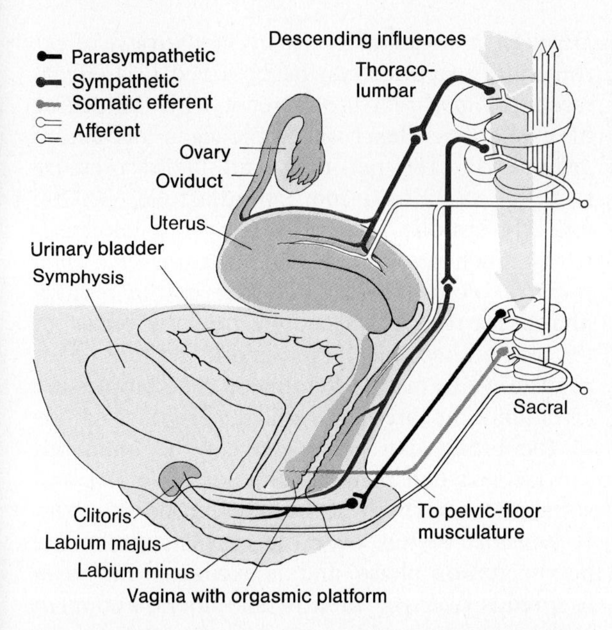

Fig. 16-20. Innervation of the female genitalia. Interneurons between afferents and efferent neurons in the spinal cord are not shown

Two mechanisms bring about these changes of the external genitalia during sexual excitation. The receptors in the genital organs, with axons running in the pudendal nerve to the sacral cord (S_2–S_4), initiate **reflexes** (Fig. 16-20); on the other hand, the responses can be entirely **psychogenic,** produced by the brain. Because of its dense afferent innervation, the *clitoris* plays a special role. Its mechanoreceptors are excited both by direct touch and indirectly – especially after retraction of the clitoris to the edge of the symphysis – by pull on the prepuce, by manipulation of the other external genitalia or by the thrusting of the penis. Stimulation of the afferents from the mons pubis, the vestibule of the vagina, the perineal region and especially the labia minora can have just as marked effects during sexual excitation as stimulation of the clitoral afferents. Excitation is enhanced by the swelling of the organs. It is not known whether afferents running with the sympathetic fibers also participate in these reflex events, but it appears likely.

The enlargement of the external genitalia results from a general **vasocongestion,** probably produced by preganglionic parasympathetic vasodilator neurons in the sacral cord that send out axons in the pelvic nerves (Fig. 16-20). The erection of the clitoris, like that of the male penis, is produced by the engorgement of erectile tissue by blood. It is plausible that in analogy with the findings in the man (cf. Table 16-2), sympathetic innervation from the thoracolumbar cord also participates in the production of vasocongestion.

Internal genitalia. The internal reproductive organs of the woman undergo remarkable changes in the sexual response cycle. Within 10 to 30 s after afferent or psychogenic stimulation the *transudation* of a mucoid fluid through the squamous epithelium of the **vagina** begins. This transudate lubricates the vagina and is a prerequisite for the adequate stimulation of the penis during intercourse. The large vestibular glands (Bartholini's glands) play hardly any role in lubrication. Transudation results from a general venous congestion in the vaginal wall, probably under the influence of parasympathetic neurons from the sacral cord and sympathetic neurons from the thoracolumbar cord. The details of the transudation mechanism are as yet unknown.

Transudation is accompanied by a reflex expansion and elongation of the vagina. As excitation builds up, local vasocongestion in the outer third of the vagina forms the **orgasmic platform** (Fig. 16-20). This thickening, together with the swollen labia minora, provides a long channel with the optimal anatomical characteristics for production of an orgasm in man and woman. During the orgasm the orgasmic platform contracts 3 to 15 times, depending on the intensity of the orgasm. These contractions are probably neuronally mediated, by the sympathetic system, and are comparable to the emission and ejaculation of the man.

The **uterus** changes its position during sexual excitation, rising in the pelvis from its anteverted and anteflexed position so that at the height of excitation the cervix has moved away from the posterior wall of the vagina, leaving room in the inner third of the vagina for the reception of semen *(seminal receptacle).* At the same time the uterus enlarges by as much as 50%. The *erection, elevation* and *enlargement* of the uterus are brought about by vasocongestion in the true pelvis, probably assisted by the neuronally produced contractions of the smooth musculature in the ligaments supporting the uterus. During orgasm the uterus contracts regularly. These contractions begin at the fundus and pass over the body of the uterus to its lower segment. The contractions of the uterus are probably mediated neuronally, by the sympathetic system.

After orgasm the changes in the external and internal genitalia usually disappear. The outer cervix remains open for ca. 20–30 min, extending into the seminal receptacle. Should *orgasm fail* to occur after intense excitation, the resolution phase proceeds more slowly (Fig. 16-21B).

Extragenital Reactions during the Sexual Response Cycle

MASTERS and JOHNSON [21], on practical grounds, subdivided the **sexual response cycle** into four phases (Fig. 16-21) – the *excitation, plateau, orgasm* and *resolution phases.* The time course of this cycle varies widely among individuals. The excitation and resolution phases are the longest, with the plateau phase shorter and orgasm usually the shortest of all. In the **man** the overall cycle tends to be *stereotyped,* with little interindividual variation (Fig. 16-21A). A *refractory period* follows the peak of orgasm and extends into the resolution phase; during this time a second orgasm cannot be produced by sexual stimulation. In the **woman** the sexual response cycle is considerably *more variable* in both duration and intensity (Fig. 16-21B). Women are capable of multiple orgasms. If orgasm is not reached, the resolution phase lasts longer.

Orgasm is a response of the entire body. It consists of the reactions of the genitalia produced by the autonomic nervous system (particularly ejaculation in the man and the contraction of orgasmic platform and uterus in the woman), general autonomic reactions and excitation of the CNS, usually intense, which enhances sexual sensations and – in women, especially – tends to exclude other sensory perceptions.

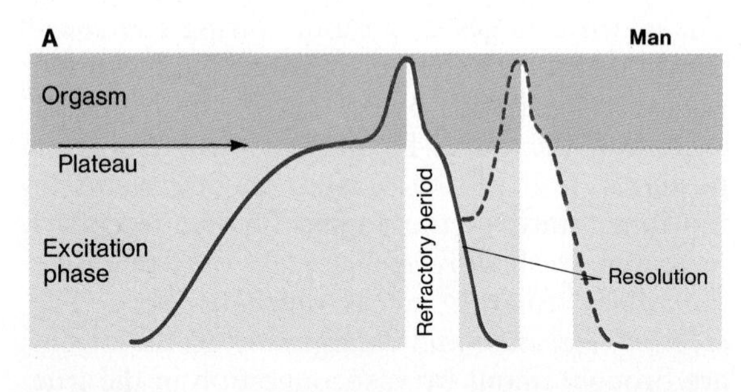

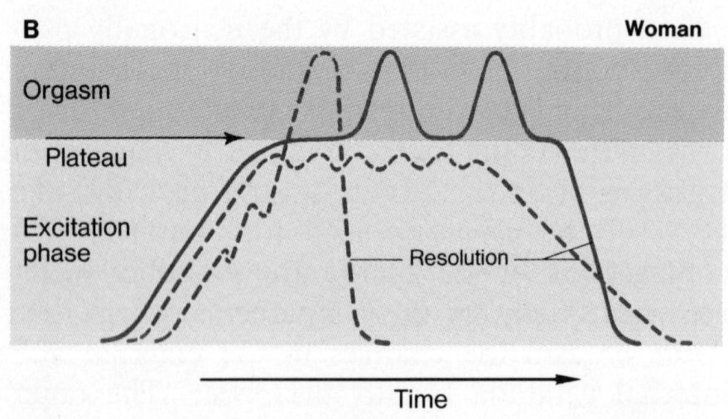

Fig. 16-21 A, B. Sexual response cycles of man and woman. Duration *(abscissa)* and intensity *(ordinate)* of the various phases vary widely among individuals. Modified from [21]

During the sexual response cycle a variety of extragenital reactions can be observed [21]. *Heart rate* and *blood pressure* increase with the degree of excitation. Heart rate reaches a maximum around 100–180 per min, and blood pressure rises by ca. 20–40 mm Hg diastolic, 30–100 mm Hg systolic. The *respiratory rate* increases to as much as 40 per min. The *external anal sphincter* contracts rhythmically in the orgasm phase. Because of vasocongestion the **breast** of the woman becomes larger, and its pattern of superficial veins more pronounced. The nipples are erect and the areolae swollen. These reactions of the breast can also occur in the man, but are far less conspicuous. In many women and some men a **sexflush** of the skin can be observed. It typically begins over the epigastrium in the late excitation phase, and as excitation increases it spreads over the breasts, shoulders, abdomen and under some circumstances the entire body. The *skeletal musculature* contracts both voluntarily and involuntarily. Eventually there are nearly spastic contractions of the facial, abdominal and intercostal musculature. A common feature of orgasm is extensive loss of voluntary control of the skeletal musculature.

16.5 Functions of the Hypothalamus

In the vertebrates the **hypothalamus** is the part of the brain most important in regulating the internal milieu. It is a *phylogenetically old part of the brain,* and among the terrestrial vertebrates its *structure* has remained relatively constant, in contrast to that of the more recent parts of the brain such as neocortex and limbic system [22]. It is the center governing all the essential homeostatic processes in the body. A decorticate animal can be kept alive with no particular difficulty, whereas an animal without the hypothalamus requires extreme care if it is to survive, for many of the homeostatic regulatory mechanisms have been eliminated. The *integrative functions* of the hypothalamus include *autonomic, somatic and hormonal* pathways. They are treated in the parts of the book related to the specific functions – for example, thermoregulation (p. 634), regulation of electrolyte balance (p. 763), endocrine regulating mechanisms (p. 375), regulation of sexual maturation (p. 782) and regulation of the sleeping/waking rhythm (p. 144).

Functional Anatomy of the Hypothalamus

Topographic position and subdivisions. The hypothalamus is a small part of the brain, weighing only ca. 5 g, with rather diffuse boundaries. It is more a part of a *neuronal continuum* extending from the midbrain through the hypothalamus to the basal regions of the telencephalon, which are closely associated with the phylogenetically old olfactory system. As the ventral part of the *diencephalon,* the hypothalamus bounds the ventral half of the third ventricle, lying below (ventral to) the thalamus. It is bounded caudally by the mesencephalon and rostrally by the lamina terminalis, the anterior commissure and the optic chiasm (Fig. 16-22). Lateral to it lie the optic tract, the internal capsule and subthalamic structures.

Within the hypothalamus are three mediolaterally arranged zones [25], a periventricular, a medial and a lateral zone. The periventricular zone is a thin sheet adjacent to the third ventricle. Passing from front to back through the **medial hypothalamus** one can distinguish several nuclear regions (cf. red shading in Fig. 16-22). The preoptic region is phylogenetically part of the telencephalon, but is usually considered a hypothalamic structure. The ventromedial part of the hypothalamus gives rise to the hypophyseal stalk (infundibulum), with the adeno- and neurohypophyses. The anterior part of the hypophyseal stalk is called the **median eminence.** Many neurons in the preoptic and anterior hypothalamic regions and in the ventromedial and infundibular nuclei (nuclei 1, 4, 5 and 6 in Fig. 16-22) project into the median eminence and there release hormones from their axons into the portal circulation to the adenohypophysis (anterior pituitary gland). The nuclear regions containing hormone-producing neurons are together called the *hypophysiotropic zone* (dashed outline in Fig. 16-22). Neurons in the supraoptic and paraventricular nuclei (nuclei 2 and 3 in Fig. 16-22) project into the neurohypophysis (posterior pituitary gland) and control the production and release of oxytocin and ADH (vasopressin; see p. 376). With few exceptions (the supraoptic and paraventricular nuclei; see p. 376), it is impossible to assign particular functions to the individual nuclei.

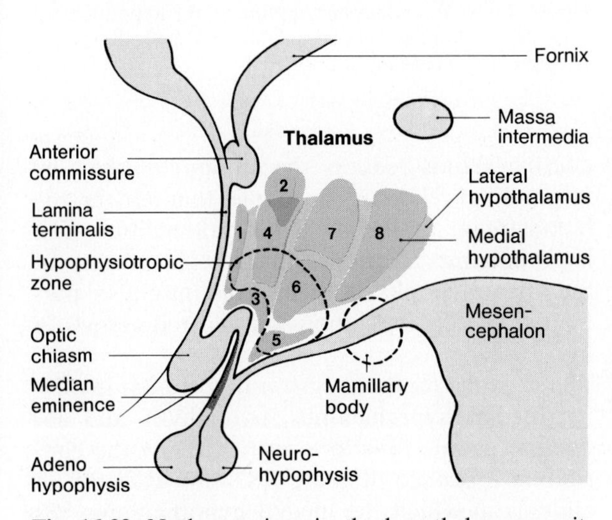

Fig. 16-22. Nuclear regions in the hypothalamus; sagittal section through the third ventricle, diagrammatic. 1. preoptic nucleus (preoptic area), 2. paraventricular nucleus, 3. supraoptic nucleus, 4. anterior nucleus (anterior area), 5. infundibular nucleus, 6. ventromedial nucleus, 7. dorsomedial nucleus, 8. posterior nucleus (posterior area). [From Benninghoff-Goertler, Lehrbuch der Anatomie des Menschen, Vol. III, Urban und Schwarzenberg (1977)]

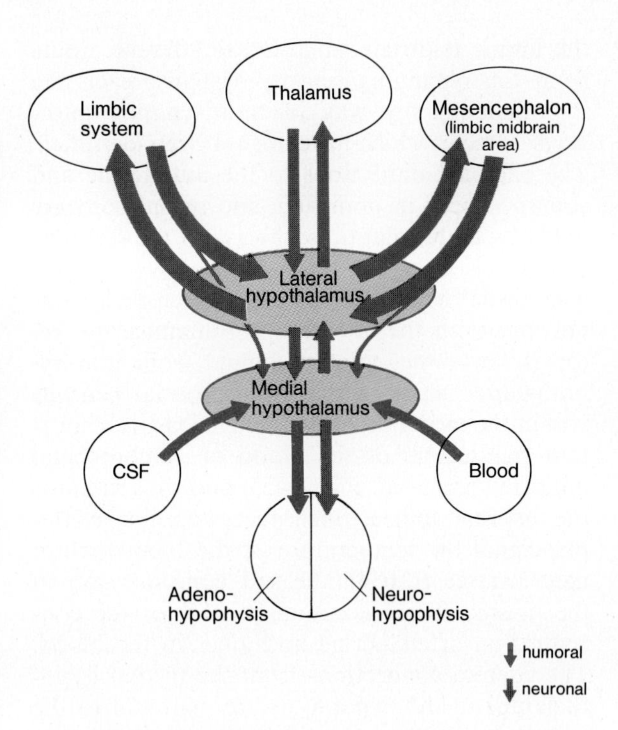

Fig. 16-23. Afferent and efferent connections of the hypothalamus. Simplified schematic drawing

In the **lateral hypothalamus** (Fig. 16-22) no nuclear regions can be distinguished. The neurons dispersed through the lateral hypothalamus surround the *medial forebrain bundle,* which rostrally continues into the basolateral structures of the limbic system and caudally passes to rostral structures of the midbrain. It consists of long and short ascending and descending axons (cf. Fig. 16-29B).

Afferent and efferent connections of the hypothalamus [25]. The afferent and efferent connections of the hypothalamus indicate that this part of the brain is an important integration center for somatic, autonomic and endocrine functions (Fig. 16-23). The **lateral hypothalamus** is reciprocally connected with the upper brainstem, the paramedian mesencephalic region (limbic midbrain area [24, 25]), and the limbic system. It receives afferent inputs from the surface and interior of the body by way of ascending spinobulboreticular pathways. These pathways project into the hypothalamus by way of either the thalamus or the limbic midbrain area. Other afferent inputs from the remaining sensory systems reach the hypothalamus by way of multisynaptic pathways, some of which have not yet been identified. The efferent connections to the autonomic and somatic nuclei in brainstem and spinal cord are made by multisynaptic pathways in the reticular formation.

The **medial hypothalamus** makes reciprocal connections with the lateral hypothalamus and receives few direct afferent inputs from non-hypothalamic parts of the brain. Special neurons within the medial hypothalamus measure important parameters of the blood or cerebrospinal fluid (red arrows in Fig. 16-23) and thus monitor the **internal milieu.** Such receptors, for example, signal the temperature of the blood (warm neurons; see p. 634), the salt concentration in the plasma (osmoreceptors, p. 316) or the concentration of endocrine hormones in the blood. The efferent connections from the medial hypothalamus to the hypophysis are neuronal to the neurohypophysis and hormonal to the adenohypophysis. Thus the medial hypothalamus constitutes a boundary region between the endocrine and neuronal systems; it serves as a **neuroendocrine interface.**

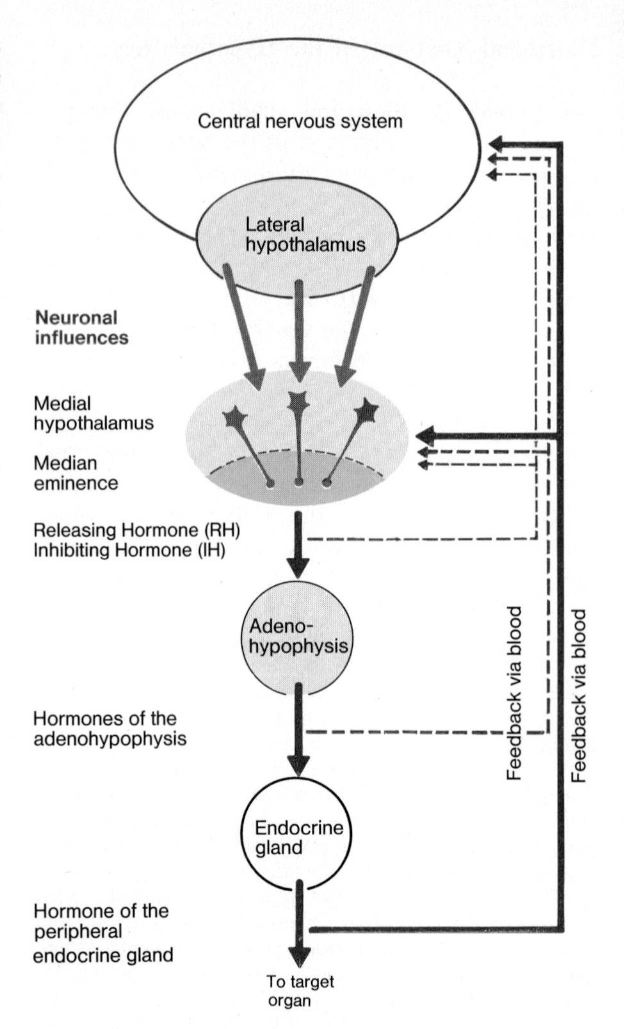

Fig. 16-24. Neuroendocrine coupling by the hypothalamo-hypophyseal system. RH stimulatory releasing hormone; IH inhibitory releasing hormone

The Hypothalamo-Hypophyseal System

The activity of most endocrine glands is regulated by hormones from the adenohypophysis (anterior pituitary gland). These hormones in turn are released under the control of hormones produced by neurons in the hypophysiotropic zone of the medial hypothalamus (cf. Fig. 16-22). We call these hypothalamic hormones *stimulating* and *inhibitory* **releasing hormones** (RH, IH in Fig. 16-24; see p. 379). The releasing hormones are liberated from the axons of neurons in the median eminence and are carried to the adenohypophysis by the blood in the hypothalamo-hypophyseal portal system.

Secretion of the hypothalamic hormones into the portal system by the neurons in the hypophysiotropic zone is controlled by the plasma concentrations of the hormones of the peripheral endocrine glands (long red arrows in Fig. 16-24). For example, when the cortisol level in the plasma rises, less CRH (corticotropin releasing hormone) is released in the median eminence, and thus the amount of ACTH released from the adenohypophysis is reduced (cf. Fig. 17-10, p. 380). In general, an increase in the plasma concentration of the hormones of peripheral endocrine glands reduces the amount of the corresponding releasing hormone that enters the bloodstream in the medial hypothalamus. The hypothalamic hormones and the hormones of the adenohypophysis themselves may also participate in this regulation (dashed red arrows in Fig. 16-24).

The *negative-feedback system* (Fig. 16-24) involving medial hypothalamus, hypophysis and endocrine glands functions even without the controlling influence of the CNS – for example, in animals in which the medial hypothalamus has been surgically isolated from the rest of the CNS in situ. The CNS serves to adjust the system to the internal and external needs of the organism. Cortisol secretion by the adrenal cortex, for instance, increases when severe demands are made on the organism (*stress;* see p. 388). The elevated cortisol secretion is brought about by an increase

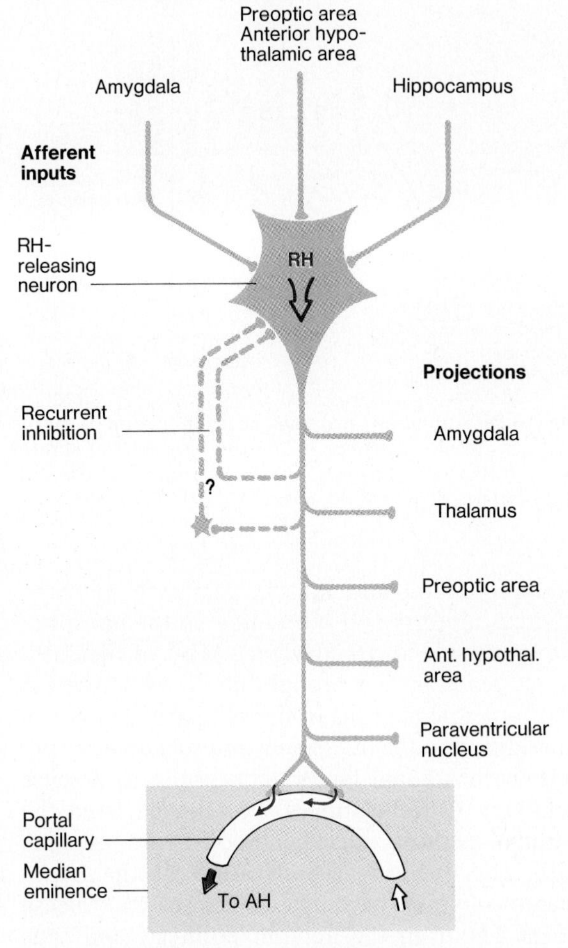

Fig. 16-25. Releasing-hormone-producing neuron in the hypophysiotropic zone, the basic element of neuroendocrine coupling in the hypothalamus. RH releasing hormone; AH adenohypophysis. From RENAUD [28]

in activity of the CRH-producing neurons in the medial hypothalamus and thus an increase in the release of CRH in the median eminence. This central nervous control of the endocrine hypothalamo-hypophyseal system is mediated chiefly by the lateral hypothalamus and is initiated primarily by the preoptic region, structures of the limbic system (e.g., hippocampus and amygdala) and structures of the mesencephalon.

It is likely that these parts of the CNS also receive feedback information about the concentrations of the endocrine hormones in the plasma (Fig. 16-24). The neurons involved can be shown to respond very specifically to endocrine hormones and to store these hormones intracellularly. As examples of the biological significance of CNS modulation of endocrine activity consider the circadian rhythmicity of ACTH release, the control of ovarian-hormone release during the menstrual cycle (p. 782), control of cortisol release under stress (p. 388) and the increase in metabolic rate due to increased thyroxine release during prolonged exposure to cold (p. 385).

The extensive intermeshing of neuronal and endocrine structures in the hypothalamus can be illustrated by the connectivity of the neurons in the *hypophysiotropic zone.* A neuron that produces releasing hormone can be influenced by afferent neurons from structures in the limbic system (amygdala and hippocampus; see p. 363) and from the preoptic area and anterior hypothalamus (Fig. 16-25, upper part). The axon collaterals of this neuron project into a wide variety of brain structures (Fig. 16-25, right). It is also subject to autoregulation by recurrent inhibition (Fig. 16-25, left). The transmitter elaborated by the various axon collaterals is probably the releasing hormone. These cells of the hypophysiotropic zone are thus **terminal integrating neurons** on one hand, and on the other, hormone-producing *endocrine cells* [28].

Hypothalamus and Cardiovascular System

The *simple servocontrol* of the cardiovascular system (arterial systemic blood pressure, cardiac output, distribution of blood) resides in the lower brainstem (see Fig. 16-14; circulatory center, see p. 521). The efferents are sympathetic and parasympathetic axons to the various cardiovascular effectors, and the afferents come from arterial baro- and chemoreceptors and mechanoreceptors in the atria and ventricles of the heart (pp. 512). This *medullary regulation* of the cardiovascular system in turn is under the control of the upper brainstem, and especially of the hypothalamus. This control involves neuronal connections between hypothalamus and medullary circulatory center, as well as direct neuronal connections from the hypothalamus to the preganglionic neurons. The cardiovascular system is under *higher-level neuronal control* by the hypothalamus during all of the more complex autonomic functions that go beyond simple servocontrol – for example, thermoregulation, the regulation of food intake, defensive behavior, physical work (see below), and so on.

Adjustment of the cardiovascular system during work. A mechanism of very special practical and theoretical significance is the matching of cardiovascular performance to the demands of physical work. During muscular effort the cardiac output rises (mainly by increase in heart rate) and at the same time more blood flows through the musculature, while less is channelled through skin and viscera (cf. Fig. 16-26). This circulatory adjustment occurs practically as soon as work begins. It is initiated by the *central nervous system, by way of the hypothalamus.* Electrical stimulation of the lateral hypothalamus of dogs, at the level of the mammillary bodies, produces autonomic responses that resemble in detail those of animals working on a treadmill. If the animal is anesthetized, locomotor movements and accelerated breathing can be observed during electrical stimulation of the hypothalamus. By changing the position of the stimulating electrode slightly one can also elicit autonomic and somatic reactions independent of one another. The responses are abolished by bilateral **lesions** of the neuronal regions that produce them when stimulated; a dog with such a lesion cannot adjust its cardiovascular system to working conditions (it tires rapidly on the treadmill). This finding indicates the existence in the lateral hypothalamus of neuronal structures controlling the modification of the circulation during muscular work. These hypothalamic regions are subject to **neocortical control.** We do not know whether the hypothalamus alone can accomplish this central-nervous adjustment; to do so, it would require a relatively specific afferent input from the skeletal musculature [49].

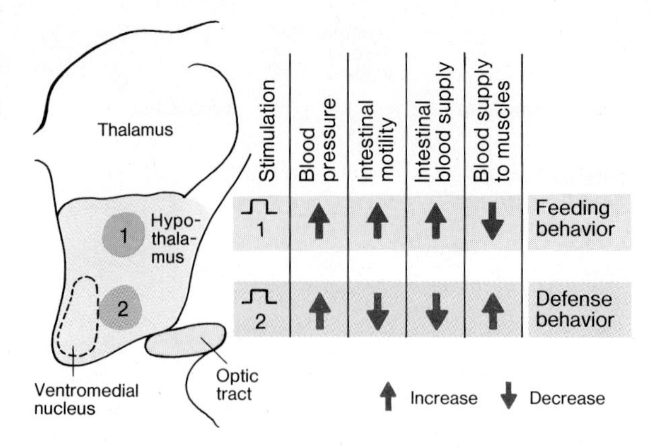

Fig. 16-26. Autonomic reactions in the induction of nutritive and defense behavior in the cat by electrical stimulation of the hypothalamus. [Modified from FOLKOW and RUBINSTEIN: Acta physiol. scand. *65*, 292–299 (1966)]

Hypothalamus and Behavior

Electrical stimulation of small areas in the hypothalamus, with microelectrodes, causes animals to exhibit characteristic behavior patterns. The diversity of such behavior resembles the range of natural species-specific behavior patterns of the animal concerned. Chief among them are *defense and flight behavior, eating and drinking* (nutritive behavior), *reproductive (sexual) behavior* and *thermoregulatory behavior.* These behavior patterns subserve **survival of the individual** and the **species.** Thus in a broad sense they can be considered as homeostatic processes. Each of them consists of somatomotor, autonomic and hormonal components.

Local electrical stimulation in the caudal hypothalamus (stimulus site 2 in Fig. 16-26), for example, elicits **defense behavior** in a waking cat. This behavior comprises typical somatomotor reactions such as arched back, hissing, spreading of the toes and extension of claws, as well as autonomic reactions such as increased respiration, pupil dilation and piloerection on back and tail. Blood pressure and muscle perfusion increase, whereas motility and blood flow in the intestines are reduced (Fig. 16-26, right). Most of the autonomic reactions are brought about by activation of adrenergic neurons in the sympathetic system. In addition to the *autonomic* and *somatomotor* reactions, hormonal factors contribute to defense behavior. **Catecholamines** are released from the adrenal medulla into the bloodstream (see pp. 339f. and Fig. 16-5). Activation of the hypothalamo-hypophyseal system causes the release of **ACTH** from the adenohypophysis and thus the release of **corticosteroids** from the adrenal cortex.

Similar behavior patterns can be produced in *diencephalic* cats with hypothalamus intact, by natural (painful and non-painful) stimulation of the skin. Because these animals lack the whole forebrain, the behavior they exhibit has no reference to their surroundings. When the caudal hypothalamus is destroyed only fragments of such behavior can be elicited, by painful stimuli. These studies have shown that the neuronal substrate integrating this behavior is situated in the posterior hypothalamus.

The **nutritive behavior** produced by the hypothalamus is nearly complementary to the defense behavior. Nutritive behavior is elicited by local electrical stimulation of a hypothalamic area 2–3 mm dorsal to the "defense area"(stimulus site 1 in Fig. 16-26). An animal in which this behavior is induced exhibits all the characteristics of an animal in search of food; when it comes to a full dish it begins to eat even though it is satiated, and it chews on inedible objects. Examination of the autonomic parameters shows that the behavior is accompanied by increased salivation, intestinal motility and intestinal blood flow, and decreased muscle blood flow (Fig. 16-26). The characteristic changes in autonomic parameters during nutritive behavior bring about a certain autonomic adjustment to the event **food intake.** This behavior pattern is characterized by excitation of the parasympathetic innervation of the digestive tract.

Principle of hypothalamic organization. Systematic study of the hypothalamus with *local electrical stimulation* indicates that this structure contains neuronal substrates for regulation of a wide range of behavior patterns. Studies employing other methods, such a *lesions* or *chemical stimulation,* have supported and extended this conclusion.

For example, lesion of the area in the lateral hypothalamus in which electrical stimulation can induce eating behavior (the so-called feeding or hunger center; see p. 322) causes aphagia (refusal of food), whereas lesion of the area in the medial hypothalamus that when stimulated inhibits eating behavior (the satiety center) elicits hyperphagia (excessive eating). *Chemical stimulation* of neuron populations can be achieved with substances that are candidate synaptic transmitters in the hypothalamus – for example, noradrenalin, acetylcholine, glycine, gamma-aminobutyric acid, neuropeptides. Microinjection of noradrenalin into the hypothalamus, for instance, dramatically increases food intake, whereas microinjection of acetylcholine can selectively elicit the intake of liquid [27].

The regions in the hypothalamus in which stimulation elicits behavior patterns overlap extensively. For this reason no one has yet succeeded in describing, neurophysiologically and neuroanatomically, the neuron populations responsible for the regulation of behavior patterns. For example, the hypothalamic nuclei revealed by neurohistological methods (cf. Fig. 16-22) correspond only vaguely or not at all to the regions associated with particular behavior patterns by stimulation techniques. Thus the neuronal structures that integrate the subunits to form behavior patterns must *not* be conceived as *anatomically well-defined* structures, as the term "satiety center" and "hunger center" might suggest.

The neuronal organization in the hypothalamus that enables this small area of the brain to control the multitude of vital behavior patterns and neurohumoral regulatory processes remains a great puzzle. Presumably functionally different groups of neurons in the hypothalamus are characterized by the specificity of their afferent and efferent connections, their synaptic transmitters, the spatial organization of their dendrites and other parameters. It must be assumed that the hypothalamic neural networks as yet inaccessible to us contain a large number of **programs.**

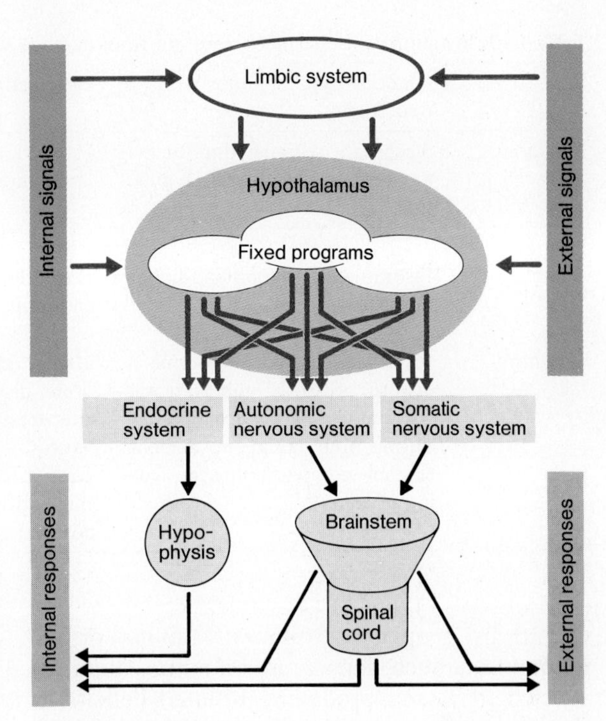

Fig. 16-27. Diagram of the functional organization of hypothalamic behavior patterns

Activation of these programs, by neuronal commands from superordinate brain structures (e.g., structures in the limbic system) and/or by signals from the sensory systems and from the interior of the body, would then produce the observed broad spectrum of behavior patterns and neurohumoral regulation (Fig. 16-27.).

For a long time it was assumed that the cranial parts of the hypothalamus integrate somatic, autonomic and endocrine reactions to promote recuperation of the body and conservation of its energy, as well as digestion and excretion. This function was thought to be associated with excitation of the parasympathetic system, and the entire process was termed the **trophotropic reaction.** It was further assumed that activation of the caudal parts of the hypothalamus causes excitation of the noradrenergic sympathetic system, mobilization of bodily energy and enhancement of performance capacity. This process was termed the **ergotropic reaction.** These concepts, introduced by Hess [14], imply that the hypothalamus consists of two *functionally and anatomically different systems,* the antagonism between sympathetic and parasympathetic found in the peripheral autonomic system being carried over into the hypothalamus. Many experiments performed in order to confirm or refute this hypothesis have contributed a great deal to our understanding of the functional significance of the hypothalamus. The hypothesis itself, however, appears too general to be able to explain the various functions of the hypothalamus.

Functional disturbances resulting from damage to the hypothalamus in man. Disturbances of hypothalamic function in man are most often

Table 16-3. Functional disturbances resulting from damage to hypothalamus in humans. From [28]

	Anterior hypothalamus with preoptic region	Intermediate hypothalamus	Posterior hypothalamus
Function	Sleeping/waking rhythm, thermoregulation, endocrine regulation	Perception, caloric and fluid balance, endocrine regulation	Perception, consciousness, thermoregulation, complex endocrine regulation
Lesions:			
Acute	Insomnia, hyperthermia, diabetes insipidus	Hyperthermia, diabetes insipidus, endocrine disorders	Hypersomnia, emotional and autonomic disturbances, poikilothermia
Chronic	Insomnia, complex endocrine disturbances (e.g., pubertas praecox), endocrine disturbances resulting from damage to median eminence, hypothermia, no feeling of thirst	*Medial:* impaired memory, emotional disturbances, hyperphagia and obesity, endocrine disturbances *Lateral:* emotional disturbances, emaciation and loss of appetite, no feeling of thirst	Amnesia, emotional disturbances, poikilothermia, autonomic disturbances, complex endocrine disturbances (e.g. pubertas praecox)

caused by neoplasms (tumors), trauma or inflammation. Such damage is sometimes quite restricted in extent, producing isolated deficits in the anterior, intermediate or posterior hypothalamus. The functional disturbances the clinician observes in patients (with the exception of diabetes insipidus; see p. 378) are complex phenomena. They also depend on whether the damage is acute (e.g., due to trauma) or chronic (e.g., due to a slowly growing tumor). Small acute injuries can cause notable functional disturbances even though the disturbance caused by slowly growing tumors does not become apparent until the damage has become extensive. The complex functions of the hypothalamus and the associated disorders are listed in Table 16-3. Disturbances of perception, memory and the sleeping/waking rhythm are in part brought about by damage to the ascending and descending systems from and to structures in the limbic system (cf. Figs. 16-23 and 16-29B) [28].

16.6 Limbic System and Behavior

In a simplified view, the cerebrum consists of the neocortex and the limbic system. By its integral activity it generates goal-directed human behavior. In this process, the *neocortex* tends to regulate the precise spatiotemporal communication with the environment and the formal-intellectual and stereognostic capabilities, whereas the *limbic system* is more concerned with moods and incentives to action – that is, a person's motivational interactions and emotions – and the processes of learning and memory. The limbic system endows the information derived from the internal and external worlds with its particular significance to humans, and thus determines their characteristic purposeful behavior.

The limbic system comprises phylogenetically old parts of the telencephalon and the subcortical structures derived from them. Originally the term "la grande lobe limbique" was introduced by Broca [47]. This term at first denoted only cortical areas of the central nervous system, arranged in a bilateral *ring-shaped* belt bordering the neocortex (*limbus* is Latin for "border") and separating it from the brainstem and hypothalamus. It included the cingulate and hippocam-

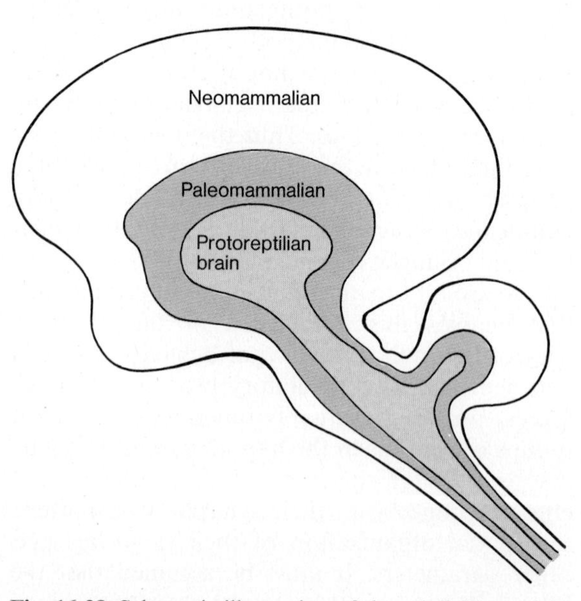

Fig. 16-28. Schematic illustration of the subdivision of the brain into three brain types. From McLean [48]

pal gyri as well as others close to the fibers from the olfactory bulb (Fig. 16-29 A). Because these structures were assumed to have an olfactory function, they were called the *rhinencephalon.* Recently MacLean [47, 48] has given the cortical and subcortical telencephalic structures described by Broca the purely descriptive name "limbic system". He proposed that these cerebral structures are a functional unit containing the neuronal substrate of the mechanisms of expression and generation of emotional behavior in mammals [48].

MacLean [48] proposed that the mammalian brain be subdivided into three systems on functional, neuroanatomical, ethological and phylogenetic grounds; these subdivisions are the *protoreptilian, paleomammalian* and *neomammalian* brains (Fig. 16-28). The **protoreptilian** brain consists of the brainstem, diencephalon and basal ganglia. It integrates stereotyped, largely innate behavioral patterns (instincts) that are important for survival. It is distinguished by a lack of flexibility and thus requires stability of the environment. The **paleomammalian brain** comprises the structures of the limbic system. According to MacLean, it is the first step in nature toward the development of consciousness. He also calls this brain *"visceral brain"* because of the large amount of information it receives from the interior of the body - information important in forming the content of memory and its affective shading. This brain is capable of overriding and modifying the genetically fixed phylogenetic behavioral repertoire; it contains the structures for species-specific behavior of mammals. The **neomammalian brain** consists of the neocortex. This brain can process signals from within the body at a largely unconscious level. It analyzes the signals from the environment in a spatiotemporal coordinate system and develops concepts and strategies for action. It is a brain that plans the future and modifies the "conservative", "traditional" strategies laid down in the paleomammalian brain.
This subdivision is speculative. There is no evidence that a reptile ever existed with a brain corresponding to the protoreptilian brain. As far as is known, all the living reptiles also have brain elements homologous to the structures of the limbic system and the neocortex. The argument in favor of subdividing the brain into three prototypes is that this subdivision reflects the association found between general behavioral functions of organisms and gross anatomical structures. Thus this brain model is a graphic expression of the hierarchical organization of brain and behavior.

Elements of the Limbic System

The **cortical components** of the limbic system are three-layered (allocortex) and five-layered (transitional cortex, mesocortex) at the transition to the six-layered neocortex (isocortex; see p. 127). They consist of the *hippocampus* (Ammon's horn, dentate gyrus and subiculum), *parahippocampal gyrus* (entorhinal area and presubiculum), *cingulate gyrus* (with subcallosal cortex) and old elements of the olfactory brain (ol-

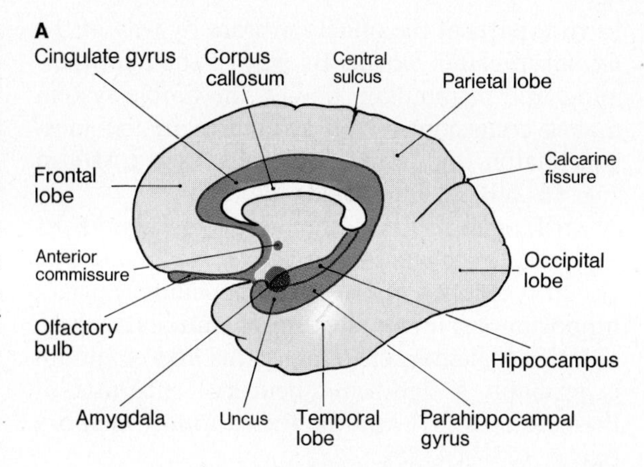

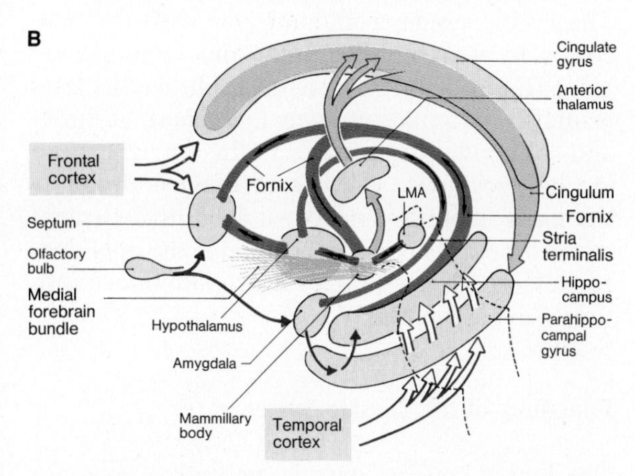

Fig. 16-29 A, B. Structures of the limbic system. **A** Curved arrangement of the limbic system around the border of the neocortex. **B** Afferent and efferent connections of the limbic system. LMA limbic midbrain area

factory bulb, olfactory tubercle, cortical areas above the amygdala). Many authors also include the orbitofrontal cortex, the insular cortex and parts of the temporal cortex in the limbic system. The *subcortical components* include the *amygdala,* the *septal nuclei* (with nucleus accumbens and Broca's diagonal band) and the *anterior thalamic nucleus.* Many authors also count the preoptic region, hypothalamus and mammillary bodies as part of the limbic system (Fig. 16-29).

The afferent and efferent connections of the structures in the limbic system, with neighboring structures and with one another, are extremely diverse, and not all of them are known (Fig. 16-29B). Most conspicuous are the massive **reciprocal connections with the hypothalamus.** The hypothalamus and the mammillary bodies communicate with the hippocampus and the septum by way of the *fornix,* with the amygdala by way of the *stria terminalis* and *amygdalafugal bundle* (not shown in Fig. 16-29 B) and with the frontobasal parts of the olfactory brain by way of the *medial forebrain bundle*. By way of the hypothalamus and mammillary bodies, the limbic system makes connections with structures in the mesencephalon (the limbic midbrain area, LMA in Fig. 16-29B; cf. Fig. 16-23) [24, 25].

A striking feature of the limbic system is its organization in *multiple circuits of excitation*. The circuit consisting of the parahippocampal gyrus, hippocampus, fornix, septum, mammillary body, anterior thalamus, cingulate gyrus and cingulum is probably a significant neuronal substrate of the emotions [47] and the formation of memory (see p. 153) [24, 25].

The limbic system communicates with the neocortex by way of the frontal and temporal regions (Fig. 16-29 B). The **temporal brain** mediates primarily information from the visual, auditory and somatosensory cortices to the amygdala and the hippocampus. The **frontal brain** is probably the most important neocortical control element of the limbic system. Moreover, it is the only neocortical region with direct neuronal connections to the hypothalamus.

Functions of the Limbic System

The limbic system controls emotional behavior and thus the complex of internal factors motivating animal and human actions. It brings about an *overall* improvement in **adaptation** to constantly changing surroundings. If this adaptation is disturbed, by pathological changes in or experimental interference with the limbic system, inappropriate behavior patterns result; that is, there are disturbances in the functional complexes controlled by the limbic system, which have their neuronal substrate in the hypothalamus and upper mesencephalon – nutritive behavior, behavior to protect the individual and the species, and sociosexual behavior. The regulation of these functional complexes in a particular animal is manifest in its **species-specific behavior patterns.** In man, changes in the limbic system disrupt **emotional behavior patterns,** which are probably homologous to species-specific behavior. In the following paragraphs the functions of some limbic-system structures are discussed with reference to clinical and experimental examples.

Amygdala. In man the amygdala (or amygdaloid body) is a large, highly differentiated subcortical nuclear region deep within the temporal lobe (Fig. 16-29). Electrical stimulation of the various parts of the amygdala of the cat or monkey elicits in principle the same response patterns as are elicited by electrical stimulation of the hypothalamus (see pp. 360f.), or inhibits these patterns. Such patterns include both elementary, homeostatic responses and behavior comprising autonomic, endocrine and somatic reactions.

Bilateral destruction of the amygdala of an animal produces no serious disturbance of the homeostatic functions integrated in the hypothalamus. By contrast, the *behavior* of a bilaterally **amygdalectomized animal** is severely disrupted. Monkeys are no longer capable of functioning as members of social groups. They cannot recognize the social significance of the exteroceptive (especially visual, auditory and olfactory) signals that regulate social behavior, or relate them to their own affective states (moods), which regulate approach to or avoidance of other members of the group and are thus the building blocks of social interactions. Amygdalectomized monkeys avoid the other members of the group and seem anxious and insecure.

When kept alone in a cage the same monkeys develop symptoms of the classical **Klüver-Bucy syndrome.** This syndrome was first described by KLÜVER and BUCY [43] from their observations of rhesus monkeys with both temporal lobes removed, including the uncus, amygdala and hippocampal elements (Fig. 16-29). The monkeys exhibited severe disturbance of affective behavior, consisting of the following symptoms: psychic blindness (inability to distinguish edible from nonedible objects); extreme oral tendencies (the monkeys grasp all objects with the lips and take them into the mouth) and abnormal feeding habits; hypersexuality; turning towards any object that comes into view; severe deficiency in fear and affective responses. The behavioral disturbances exhibited in the Klüver-Bucy syndrome of monkeys in a cage and by amygdalectomized monkeys in a social group are only apparently contradictory. From both sets of observations one can conclude that the animals are incapable of recognizing the significance to their own behavior of sensory stimuli from the environment (especially visual and acoustic signals, in the case of primates) and cannot relate them to their own affective states. This failure disrupts the normal interaction between own behavior and the surroundings, particularly in the *social context* with members of the own group and with strangers [19].

The behavioral disturbances of the monkeys are thought to be caused by the bilateral interruption of information transfer between the **temporal lobes** and hypothalamic neuronal mechanisms, which eliminates the opportunity for evaluating sensory information in the context of affective states. In this view, the amygdala would be the brain structure responsible for such evaluation. Among the findings corroborating this view are the following:

1. In electrophysiological experiments the neurons in the amygdala can be activated by way

of the temporal lobes, by stimulation of the primary neocortical sensory areas.
2. Temporal-lobe epilepsy in man is characterized by complex sensorimotor and autonomic disturbances. In such cases of (focal) epilepsy the (pathological) excitation originates in the temporal lobes and causes excitation of the amygdala. At the onset of an attack the patients frequently experience complex differentiated hallucinations about past events, before the amygdala becomes excited; the same hallucinations can also be elicited in these patients by topical electrical stimulation of the temporal lobe [19, 23, 37].

The clinical and experimental observations in humans and animals indicate that the temporoamygdalar system contains important neuronal substrates for learned motivated behavior and emotions. In this system complex sensory information is presumably compared with corresponding information (the contents of memory) acquired in the past. The sensory information thus becomes significant to the organism, and by way of the amygdala brings about the activation of those affective behavior patterns that have proved appropriate in previous occurrences of equivalent environmental constellations. In this process the amygdala activates and/or inhibits the relevant hypothalamic mechanisms [19, 37].

We do not know how the neocortex is informed about affective states, or how the consciousness of emotions arises. The information may travel from the hypothalamus, mammillary bodies and limbic midbrain area through the anterior thalamus to the cingulate gyrus (Fig. 16-29) and through the mediodorsal thalamus to the frontal brain, or directly from the amygdala to the neocortex [23]. Moreover, we do not know how the organism learns to relate the exteroceptive signals important to it (especially in the social context) to its affective states. It has been proposed that information about the *environment* from the temporal cortex and information about the homeostatic state of the *internal milieu* from the hypothalamus converge on the neurons of the amygdala, changing the synaptic connectivity there. These items of memory must be very stable and enduring, so that permanent associations between environmental stimuli and motivated behavior patterns can be created [19, 37].

Emotions and the Limbic System

Although the term "emotion" is understandable to everyone, it cannot be given a precise scientific definition [18]. Emotions are understood to comprise our *feelings* and *moods* and their *expression* in our motor behavior and in the responses of the autonomic nervous system and the endocrine system. For example, when a person is watching an exciting film there are increases in blood pressure, heart rate, sweat secretion and the concentration of the catecholamines in the blood. The emotions comprise all the negative and positive affective states, from anxiety and fear to love and happiness. Feelings and moods can only be experienced introspectively. We become conscious of them and able to communicate them through our capacity for speech. On the other hand, the expression of these experiences in motor behavior and in the autonomic and endocrine reactions is accessible to *objective scientific observation,* and can be measured in various emotional states.

So far the attempt to describe objectively, and thus to classify, the different emotions by the accompanying pattern of motor, autonomic and endocrine reactions has failed. Only at a very gross level can emotions be treated in this way. This failure made futile two approaches that would have had important theoretical and practical consequences, as follows. 1. It became impossible to make an operational definition of emotions on the basis of autonomic parameters, excluding introspection and inference by analogy. 2. It proved impracticable to make an objective diagnosis of the affective disturbances in so-called psychosomatic conditions, from the pattern of peripherally observable autonomic and humoral disturbances.

The expression of the emotions is probably based largely on **inherited, inborn reactions** [6]. These reactions serve as *signals* to conspecifics and the members of other species, and have certainly conveyed biological advantages during evolution. For example, an enraged monkey with bristling hair is a more obvious signal to its conspecifics and other animals than one without bristling hair. Therefore the emotions can most probably be considered biologically as a category of *"species-specific behavior"*. Emotions also act as inward-directed signals, in that they cause the individual to adjust itself to changes in the environment by developing new reactions.

The production of emotions is associated with the cognitive abilities of mammals and thus with *perception* and *evaluation* of sensory stimuli and with *memory*. The motor, autonomic and endocrine disturbances observed in various emotional states are on one hand the expression of such cognitive processes; on the other, these reactions can affect the emotions by afferent feedback. As yet there is neither a unified scientific theory of the emotions that is generally accepted nor a sufficiently precise idea of where and how the emotions arise and what their neuronal substrate is. Probably *all* structures of the limbic system, the hypothalamus, the limbic midbrain area and the frontal lobe participate in the development and differentiation of the emotions. For example, *organic brain disorders* (tumors, inflammations, systemic diseases) that affect these structures and injury to these structures by external forces frequently change the patient's emotional behavior. Conversely, when people are suffering from otherwise intractable and intolerable *behavioral disturbances* – compulsive neuroses, insatiable sexual drive, severe anxiety states, depression and so on – these conditions have been and still are ameliorated or cured by stereotaxic destruction of small areas in these brain structures. Structures removed or isolated in such treatment include the anterior cingulate gyrus, the cingulum, the fornix, the frontal-lobe tracts and nuclei in the thalamus, hypothalamus or amygdala. Such surgical intervention must of course not be undertaken lightly, in view of its irreversibility and the undesirable and in part unpredictable postoperative personality changes (cf. psychosurgery, p. 164).

A very common emotional disturbance with which the practicing physician is confronted is **anxiety.** It is characterized by unrest and agitation because the patient feels himself threatened by a real or imagined danger with which he cannot cope. Anxiety states are expressed in *motor disturbances* such as gesticulation and facial expressions, and in *autonomic disturbances* such as sweating, tachycardia, extrasystoles, hypertension, disturbances of the digestive tract (upset stomach, diarrhea), insomnia, dry mouth and dilated pupils. Anxiety can also be very discretely expressed, in a single autonomic disorder; in this case it is usually diagnosed as autonomic dystonia or as a psychosomatic disorder [18, 23].

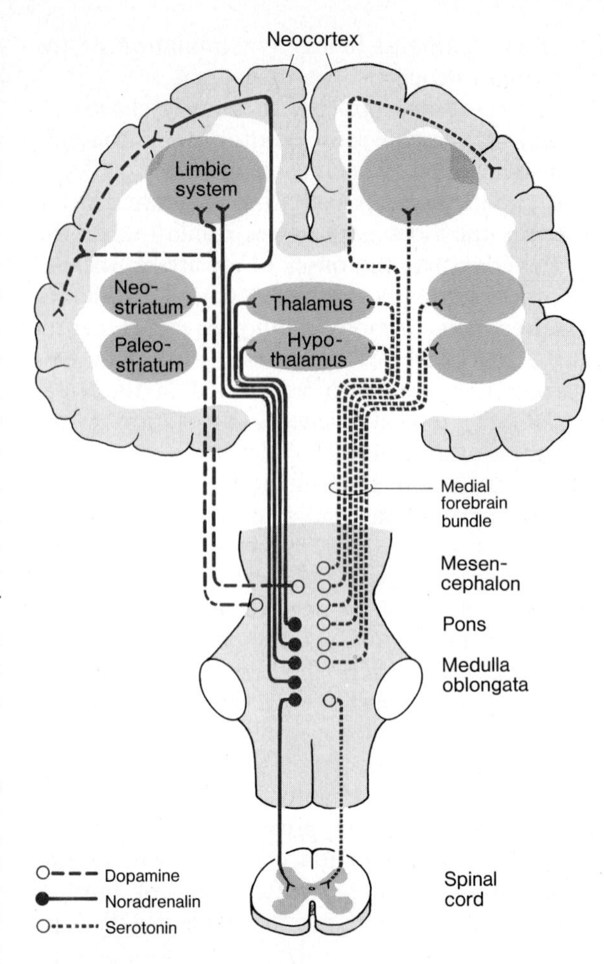

Fig. 16-30. Schematic diagram of the central monoaminergic systems. [Modified from ANDEN et al.: Acta physiol. scand. 67, 313 (1966)]

Monoaminergic Systems and Behavior

Central organization of monoaminergic systems. The neuronal monoaminergic systems appear to be of great importance in the *global regulation* of animal and human behavior. The group includes *dopaminergic, noradrenergic* and *serotonergic* systems, which originate in the brainstem and innervate practically all regions of the brain.

When tissue is treated with aldehydes or glyoxylic acid the monoamines in it form complexes, which fluoresce at characteristic wavelengths (depending on the amine) under illumination with UV light. This property is exploited in *histofluorescence microscopy* to reveal selectively the somata, axons and nerve endings of the monoaminergic neurons in the CNS.

Noradrenergic neurons (Fig. 16-30, left) have cell bodies in distinct groups within the medulla oblongata and pons, especially in the *locus coeruleus.* Most of the ascending axons run in the *medial forebrain bundle.* The axons in the dorsal parts of the brainstem come chiefly from the *locus coeruleus.* They innervate various structures in the mesencephalon, thalamus and telencephalon, primarily the amygdala, hippocampus, cingulate gyrus, entorhinal cortex and neocortex. The innervation of the neocortex is very diffuse and uniform as compared with the dopaminergic innervation (see below). The more ventrally located axons in the brainstem innervate predominantly mesencephalic structures, the hypothalamus, preoptic area and olfactory bulb. Some of the noradenergic neurons send their axons into the ventral, lateral and dorsal horns of the spinal cord (the substantia gelatinosa in particular), and into the cerebellum. Occasional noradrenergic neurons in the locus coeruleus, with their collaterals, can project simultaneously to the neocortex, hippocampus, cerebellum and spinal cord.

Recently adrenergic neurons have also been discovered in the lower region of the brain. It is likely that the adrenergic neurons of the rostral ventrolateral medulla play a special role in cardiovascular regulation (Fig. 16-14).

The dopaminergic neurons (Fig. 16-30, left) originate in the ventral mesencephalon (mesotelencephalic dopaminergic system). The laterally situated neurons from the zona compacta of the *substantia nigra* innervate the neostriatum (putamen and caudate nucleus) and the nucleus accumbens. Destruction of these dopaminergic neurons causes *Parkinson's* disease (see p. 111). The neurons lying more medially in the ventral mesencephalon innervate primarily nuclei of the limbic system (amygdala, septum, olfactory tubercle) and allo- and neocortical areas (chiefly the *frontal cortex, cingulate gyrus* and entorhinal cortex). Most of the axons of dopaminergic neurons, like those of the noradrenergic neurons, pass through the *medial forebrain bundle*. Other dopaminergic systems with short axons, which project into the median eminence and probably participate in the liberation of releasing hormone, are located in the hypothalamus. In addition, there is a periventricular dopaminergic system in the medulla oblongata, which projects chiefly to medial structures of the brainstem and to the diencephalon.

Serotonergic neurons (Fig. 16-30, right) have their somata in the median and paramedian midline nuclei (*raphe nuclei*) of the medulla oblongata, the pons and the lower mesencephalon. Their axons pass in part through the medial forebrain bundle, like the noradrenergic neurons innervating practically all of the diencephalic and telencephalic regions of the brain. Some of the serotonergic neurons project to the spinal cord and to the cerebellum [5, 20, 24].

Monoaminergic systems and intracranial self-stimulation. By implanting a stimulating electrode in the *medial forebrain bundle* in the lateral hypothalamus of a rat and allowing the animal to stimulate itself by pressing a bar in the Skinner box (cf. Fig. 6-25, p. 155), one can use this intracranial stimulus as a reward to establish behavior by operant conditioning; the *intracranial stimulus reinforces* the desired behavior. The reinforcing action of the electrical stimulation is so great that the animals normally prefer it to any other kind of reinforcement, including food. Rats and monkeys are commonly observed to stimulate themselves by electrodes in the medial forebrain bundle until they are in danger of death from exhaustion. The bar-pressing rates can reach 7,000 per hour.

Systematic study of the whole brain by means of intracranial self-stimulation shows that stimulation is rewarding in practically the entire limbic system, the frontal lobe, the lateral hypothalamus and tracts of the mesencephalon, pons and upper medulla oblongata. The strongest effects, however, are obtained from the **medial forebrain bundle,** which links the upper mesencephalon, hypothalamus and limbic system (Fig. 16-31 A). In addition to the brain regions in which electrical stimulation provides positive reinforcement, there are others, electrical stimulation of which is avoided. These regions are smaller in extent and are arranged **periventricularly in the di- and mesencephalon** (Fig. 16-31 A). There is some overlap between the regions for positive and for negative reinforcement.

Various experimental findings and theoretical arguments support the inference that the neuronal substrates, stimulation of which provides positive or negative reinforcement of behavior, are

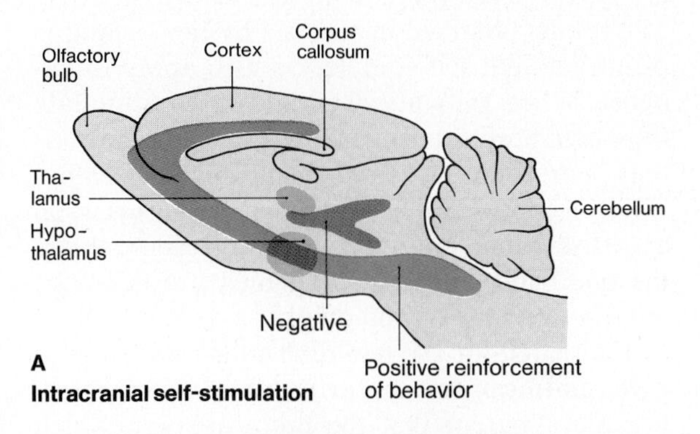

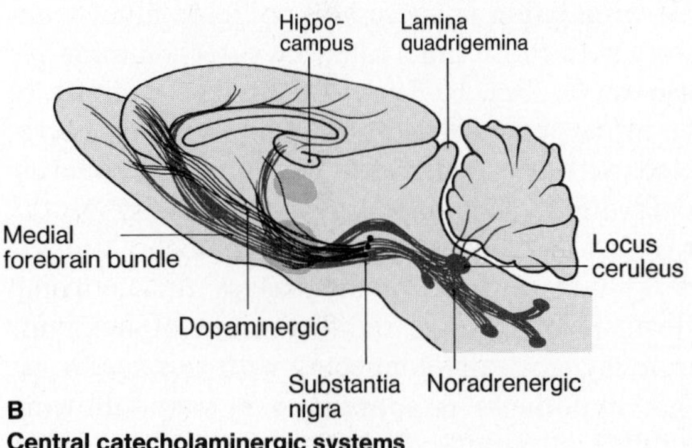

Fig. 16-31 A, B. Comparison of the brain areas, intracranial self-stimulation of which results in positive and negative reinforcement of behavior, with the course of the central catecholaminergic systems. **A** Intracranial self-stimulation. Positive reinforcement of behavior: *light red.* Negative reinforcement: *dark red.* **B** *Red:* noradrenergic system; *black:* dopaminergic system. Rat brain. Modified from OLDS [27]

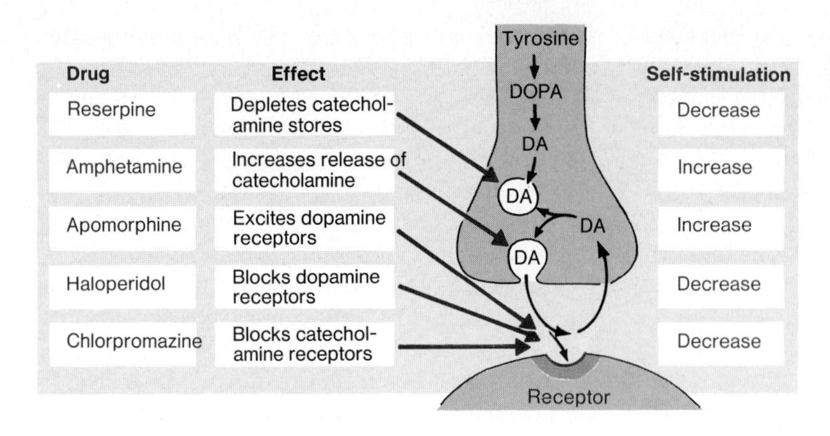

Fig. 16-32. Actions of drugs on the central dopaminergic synapse and their effects on intracranial self-stimulation (see also Fig. 16-31)

not identical to those in which specific homeostatic response patterns (pp. 360f.) can be elicited [12, 28]. Therefore the two sets of structures providing positive and negative reinforcement have been given different names: the *pleasure and unpleasantness, approach and avoidance,* or *reward and punishment* systems. The existence of these systems supports the notion that pleasure and aversion are actively produced by excitation of the corresponding brain structures.

The results obtained in animals by the technique of intracranial self-stimulation also apply to **humans.** When patients are allowed to stimulate their own brains during neurosurgical operations they can elicit *pleasant or unpleasant feelings.* These feelings can be described by terms such as satisfaction, joy, relaxation and comfort on the one hand, and discouragement, restlessness, anxiety and fear on the other.

In the search for the neuronal substrates of positive reinforcement, in particular, it immediately became apparent that the brain areas in which **self-stimulation** is successful coincide almost entirely with those innervated by **catecholaminergic neurons** (cf. Fig. 16-31 A and B). The strength of the intracranial self-stimulation is roughly correlated with the density of the catecholaminergic innervation. This topographic similarity of the two regions suggested that the catecholaminergic systems either are themselves the neuronal substrate of positive reinforcement of behavior or are synaptically connected with this substrate. This hypothesis is supported by the following findings. 1. *Transection* of the medial forebrain bundle reduces or abolishes intracranial self-stimulation by electrodes cranial to the lesion. 2. When 6-hydroxydopamine, a substance that selectively *destroys* catecholaminergic neurons, is injected into the ventricles or into central catecholaminergic structures, intracranial self-stimulation is abolished. 3. *Drugs* that interfere with catecholamine metabolism or affect storage, release or uptake of catecholamines, and those that interact with the postsynaptic catecholamine receptors, influence intracranial self-stimulation (Fig. 16-32) [12, 27].

It is not yet clear whether the dopaminergic or the noradrenergic system contributes more to intracranial self-stimulation and thus to positive reinforcement of behavior. Many arguments suggest that both systems are activated simultaneously. The neuronal mechanisms that bring about the behavioral changes when the catecholaminergic systems are activated are essentially unknown. It has not been ruled out that the central catecholamines in many parts of the brain do not act as transmitters at all, but rather serve as neuromodulators (see p. 46) [20].

Electrophysiological studies have shown that the noradrenergic neurons of the **locus coeruleus** (Figs. 16-30 and 16-31 B) have an *inhibitory* action in almost all the CNS regions they innervate. Because these neurons are activated during **stress** of all kinds, it is thought that their action is twofold: (i) to depress the activity of CNS structures during stress, so that the CNS is protected from overexcitation, and (ii) to keep the excitability of the neurons at an intermediate level, in order to ensure optimal signal transmission. In this regard it is interesting that the afferents to the locus coeruleus come from parts of the brain that regulate affective behavior – particularly from structures in the limbic system, from the hypothalamus and from the mesencephalon. The morphological, biochemical and electrophysiological characteristics of the noradrenergic neurons of the locus coeruleus closely resemble those of peripheral noradrenergic neurons. In the cortex, many noradrenergic fibers from the lower brainstem appear to innervate the arterioles and capillaries. These noradrenergic neurons may participate in regulating blood flow through the cortex. One might thus be tempted to regard them as a central sympathetic system [24, 25, 34].

Monoaminergic systems and psychotropic drugs. Humans are very vulnerable to psychiatric disorders. About 1% of the population suffer from schizophrenia, and about 15–30% exhibit one of the various forms of depression at some time in their lives [23]. The genesis of these and other mental illnesses, and the central-nervous disturbances underlying them, are largely unknown. The disturbances are probably associated with higher-order CNS structures, predominantly those of the *limbic system.* In the last three decades a great number of *drugs* have been used to treat these diseases. Studies of the effects of these compounds on human and animal behavior **(psychopharmacology)** and on their neuronal structures **(neuropharmacology)** have shown that most psychotropic drugs influence, directly or indirectly, the central monoaminergic systems. Therefore the monoaminergic systems are thought to be involved in many or most mental diseases; either they themselves are disturbed, or they play some as yet unknown role in originating and determining the nature of such diseases, or mediate the effects of drug therapy.

Anxiety states, mental tension and extreme irascibility – accompaniments of both neuroses and organic diseases – are often treated with **tranquilizers** of the *benzodiazepine type* (Valium, Librium). These drugs lower the metabolic rate of the monoaminergic systems. Their suppressant action is thought to reside particularly in a reduction of serotonin metabolism and thus, under some circumstances, in a damping of the central negative-reinforcement system (Fig. 16-31A).

Depressions of the most diverse origin may have in common an inadequate activatability of central noradrenergic systems. *Antidepressive* drugs of the tricyclic type (e.g., imipramine) potentiate the action of noradrenalin and serotonin at synapses, by inhibiting presynaptic uptake. Drugs that empty the central catecholamine stores often cause depression (e.g., reserpine; Fig. 16-32).

One of the most puzzling mental diseases, and one of the most severe and variable in its symptoms, is **schizophrenia.** This disorder is classified as an endogenous psychosis, and is roughly characterized by the following primary symptoms: impaired associative thinking, inappropriate affect (mood), withdrawal from the outside world, deficient communication and autistic behavior. Additional (secondary) symptoms important for the differential diagnosis of schizophrenia are auditory hallucinations, delusions of grandeur and other kinds of delusion. The central-nervous disturbances underlying this disease are unknown, but presumably they are in the area of the complex mutual adjustments of *perception, memory* and the *inner world* and thus amount to a disturbance of communication between the neocortex and the limbic system. A special role is played by the central dopaminergic mesolimbic/mesocortical system (Figs. 16-30 and 16-31 B). *Neuroleptic drugs* in the phenothiazine (e.g., chlorpromazine) and butyrophenone (e.g., haloperidol) series, used throughout the world in the treatment of schizophrenia, block the central dopamine receptors (Fig. 16-32). Drugs that increase the rate of dopamine release – for example, those in the amphetamine group (Fig. 16-32) – can produce a psychosis with symptoms practically indistinguishable from those of schizophrenia, or they exacerbate existing or latent schizophrenia [5, 23, 51].

16.7 References

Textbooks and Handbooks

1. Bülbring, E., Brading, A.F., Jones, A.W., Tomita, T.: Smooth muscle: an assessment of current knowledge. London: Edward Arnold 1981
2. Burnstock, G., Costa, M.: Adrenergic Neurons. London: Chapman and Hall 1975
3. Cannon, W.B.: The wisdom of the body. 2nd Edition. New York: W.W. Norton & Co., Inc. 1939
4. Cervero, F., Morrison, J.F.B. (Eds.): Visceral Sensation. Progress in Brain Res. 67, Amsterdam, New York, Oxford: Elsevier Biomedical Press 1986
5. Cooper, J.R., Bloom, F.E., Roth, R.H.: The biochemical basis of neuropharmacology. 4th Edition. New York, Oxford: Oxford University Press 1982
6. Darwin, C.: The expression of the emotions in man and animals. London: John Murray 1872
7. Davson, H., Segal, M.B.: Introduction to Physiology, Vol. 3, Chapter 4. "Control Mechanisms in the Alimentary Process" pp. 276–403. London: Academic Press. New York: Grune & Stratton 1976
8. Folkow, B., Neil, E.: Circulation. New York, London, Toronto: Oxford University Press 1971
9. Gabella, G.: Structure of the autonomic nervous system. London: Chapman and Hall 1976
10. Gilman, A.G., Goodman, L.S., Gilman, A.: Pharmacological Basis of Therapeutics. 6th Edition, New York: Macmillan Publ. Co., Inc. 1980
11. Guttmann, L.: Spinal cord injuries. 2nd Edition. Oxford, London, Edinburgh, Melbourne: Blackwell Scientific Publications 1976
12. Hall, R.D., Bloom, F.E., Olds, J.: Neuronal and neurochemical substrates of reinforcement. Neuroscience Research Program Bulletin, Cambridge, Mass.: MIT Press 1977
13. Handbook of Physiology. Section 7: Endocrinology, Volume VI: Adrenal Gland. Americal Physiological Society, Washington, D.C. 1975
14. Hess, W.R.: Die funktionelle Organisation des vegetativen Nervensystems. Basel: Benno Schwabe 1948
15. Jänig, W., Brooks, C.McC.: The autonomic nervous system in health and disease: neurobiology and pathophysiology. J. auton. Nerv. Syst. 7, 193–415, 1983
16. Johnson, R.H., Spalding, J.M.K.: Disorders of the autonomic nervous system. Oxford, London, Edinburgh, Melbourne: Blackwell Scientific Publications 1974
17. Kandel, E.R., Schwartz, J.J.: Principles of neural science. 2nd Edition. Amsterdam, New York, Oxford: Elsevier Biomedical Press 1985

18. LEVI, L. (Ed.): Emotions. Their parameters and measurement. New York: Raven Press 1975
19. LIVINGSTONE, K.W., HORNYKIEWICZ (Eds.): Limbic mechanisms. New York, London: Plenum Press 1978
20. MASON, S.T.: Catecholamines and behaviour. Cambridge: Cambridge University Press 1984
21. MASTERS, W.H., JOHNSON, V.E.: Human Sexual Response. Boston: Little Brown and Co. 1966
22. MORGANE, P., PANKSEPP, J. (Eds.): Handbook of Hypothalamus. Vol. 1–3 New York: Marcel Dekker 1980/81
23. NICHOLI, A.M., JR. (Ed.): The Harvard guide to modern psychiatry. Cambridge (Massachusetts), London: The Belknap Press of Harvard University Press 1978
24. NIEUWENHUYS, R.: Chemoarchitecture of the brain. Berlin-Heidelberg-New York-Tokyo: Springer Verlag 1985
25. NIEUWENHUYS, R., VOOGD, J., VAN HUJZEN, CHR.: The human central nervous system. 2nd Edition Berlin, Heidelberg, New York: Springer Verlag 1981
26. NILSSON, S.: Autonomic nerve function in the vertebrates. Berlin, Heidelberg, New York: Springer Verlag 1983
27. OLDS, J.: Drives and reinforcements. Behavioral studies of hypothalamic functions. New York: Raven Press 1977
28. REICHLIN, S., BALDESSARINI, R.J., MARTIN, J.B.: The hypothalamus. Research publication: Association for research in nervous and mental disease. Vol. 56. New York: Raven Press 1978

Original Papers and Reviews

29. BELL, C.: Autonomic nervous control of reproduction: circulatory and other factors. Pharmacol. Rev. *24*, 657–736 (1972)
30. BORS, E., COMARR, A.E.: Neurological disturbances of sexual function with special reference to 529 patients with spinal cord injury. Urol. Survey *10*, 191–222 (1960)
31. CHALMERS, J.P. (Eds.): Control of blood pressure. Clinical and Exper. Hyper.- Theory and Practice A6, 1 & 2 (1984)
32. ELFVIN, L.-G. (Ed.): Autonomic ganglia. Chichester, New York, Brisbane, Toronto, Singapore: John Wiley & Sons. (1983)
33. FLEMIG, W.W., MCPHILLIPS, J.J., WESTFALL, D.P.: Postjunctional supersensitivity and subsensitivity of excitable tissues to drugs. Ergeb. Physiol. *68*, 55–119 (1973)
34. FOOTE, S.L., BLOOM, F.E., ASTON-JONES, G.: Nucleus locus ceruleus: new evidence of anatomical and physiological specificity. Physiol. Rev. *63*, 844–914 (1983)
35. FURCHTGOTT, R.F.: The classification of adrenoceptors (adrenergic receptors). An evaluation from the standpoint of receptor theory. In Handbook of Experimental Pharmacology Volume XXXIII "Catecholamines", BLASCHKO, H., MUSCHOLL, E. (Eds.) pp. 282–335, Berlin-Heidelberg-New York: Springer Verlag 1972
36. GERSHON, M.D.: The enteric nervous system. Ann. Rev. Neurosci: *4*, 227–272 (1981)
37. GLOOR, P.: Temporal lobe epilepsy: its possible contribution to the understanding of the functional significance of the amygdala and of its interaction with neocortical-temporal mechanisms. In: ELEFTHERIOU, B.E. (Ed.): "The Neurobiology of the Amygdala". pp. 423–457. New York: Plenum Press 1972
38. GROAT, W.C. DE: Nervous control of the urinary bladder of the cat. Brain Res. *87*, 201–211 (1975)
39. JÄNIG, W.: Organization of the lumbar sympathetic outflow to skeletal muscle and skin of the cat hindlimb and tail. Rev. Physiol. Biochem. Pharmacol. *102*, 119–213 (1985)
40. JÄNIG, W.: Causalgia and reflex sympathetic dystrophy: in which way is the sympathetic nervous system involved? Trends in Neurosciences, *8*, 471–477 (1985)
41. JÄNIG, W.: Pre- and postganglionic vasoconstrictor neurons: differentiation, types, and discharge properties. Ann. Rev. Physiol. *50*, 525–539 (1988)
42. JÄNIG, W., MCLACHLAN, E.M.: Organization of lumbar spinal outflow to distal colon and pelvic organs. Physiol. Rev. *67*, 1332–1409 (1987)
43. KLÜVER, H., BUCY, P.C.: Preliminary analysis of function of the temporal lobe in monkeys. Arch. Neurol. Psychiat. *42*, 979–1000 (1939)
44. KUHN, R.A.: Functional capacity of the isolated human spinal cord. Brain *73*, 1–51 (1950)
45. LANGER, S.Z.: Presynaptic regulation of the release of catecholamines. Pharmacol. Rev. *32*, 337–362 (1981)
46. LEVITZKI, A.: Catecholamine Receptors. Rev. Physiol. Biochem. Pharmacol. 82, 1–26 (1978)
47. MACLEAN, P.D.: Psychosomatic disease and the "visceral brain". Recent developments bearing on the Papez theory of emotion. Psychosom. Med. *11*, 338–353 (1949)
48. MACLEAN, P.D.: The triune brain, emotion and scientific bias. In: Intensive Study Program in the Neurosciences. Neurosciences Research Program. Chapter 23, pp. 336–349, New York: Rockefeller University Press 1970
49. RUSHMER, R.F.: Structure and function of the cardiovascular system. Philadelphia, London, Toronto: Saunders 1972
50. SCHUSTER, M.M., MENDELOFF, A.I.: Motor action of rectum and anal sphincters in continence and defecation. In: Handbook of Physiology Section 6: Alimentary Canal. Volume IV: Motility. American Physiological Society Washington. D.C. pp. 2121–2145 (1968)
51. SNYNDER, S. H.: Neurotransmitters and CNS disease: schizophrenia. Lancet *2*, 970–974 (1982)
52. STARKE, K.: Regulation of noradrenaline release by presynaptic receptor systems. Rev. Physiol. Biochem. Pharmacol. *77*, 1–124 (1977)
53. SZURSZEWSKI, J.H.: Physiology of mammalian prevertebral ganglia. Ann. Rev. Physiol. *43*, 53–68 (1981)

17 Endocrinology

W. Wuttke

17.1 General Aspects of Endocrinology

Hormones as Information Carriers

Functions of hormones. In the classical definition hormones are *internal secretions,* chemicals produced by specialized gland cells and released into the bloodstream to be distributed within the body. **Endocrinology** is the field of physiology concerned with these secretions. The hormones serve as chemical carriers of information; when a hormone reaches its particular target organ it acts to produce specific effects. This specificity is achieved by *receptor* molecules in the cells; only the cells of the target organ have receptors for the corresponding hormone and are thus able to "read" the chemically coded information.
Hormones influence bodily functions that are initiated or regulated in a matter of minutes or hours. That is, *hormonal information transfer* is slower by orders of magnitude than neural information flow, which allows the organism to respond immediately to environmental factors and to endogenous functional changes.

Hormone production. Hormones are produced in secretory cells. These cells can constitute an organ in themselves (a gland) or be scattered, singly or in groups, within organs not devoted to hormone production. Hormones are stored as *granules,* intracellular organelles separated from the cytoplasm by a membrane. A granule contains many hormone molecules in a protein matrix. In response to the specific stimulus for hormone release, the granule membrane fuses with the cell membrane, and at the site of fusion an opening forms through which the hormone molecules are expelled into the interstitial space. This process is called **exocytosis** (p. 10) The granules and the process of exocytosis have been thoroughly documented morphologically. The exocytosis of hormones from secretory cells is analogous to the release of neurotransmitters from nerve terminals.

Classification of hormones. Because the information to be transferred is encoded in the molecular structure of a hormone, a basic knowledge of hormone chemistry is necessary for an understanding of endocrine function. Additional details can be found in textbooks of physiological chemistry.
All hormones are either *proteins* (including *amino-acid derivatives*) or *lipids.* They can be classified in three groups on the basis of the location of the receptors in the target cells, as follows [27, 32].
The hormones of the **lipid group,** being fat-soluble, can diffuse through the cell membrane

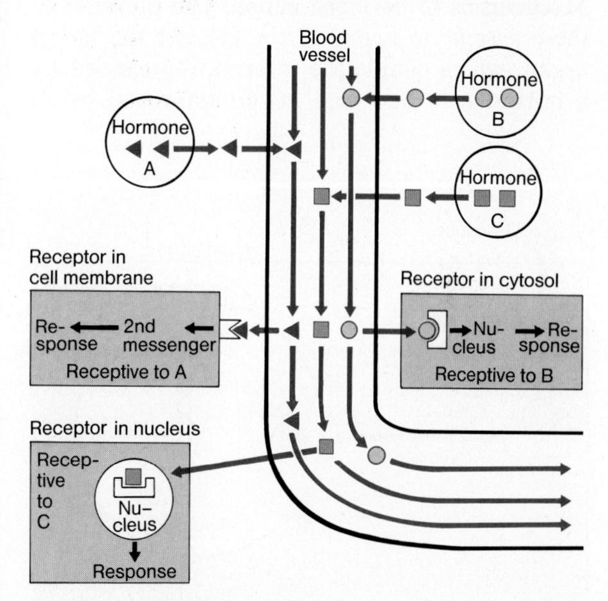

Fig. 17-1. Mechanisms of hormone action. Three hormone-producing cells release the hormones A, B and C, respectively, into the interstitial tissue immediately adjacent to capillaries. The hormone molecules diffuse into the blood vessel and are carried to their target cells, which have receptors for the hormone. Hormone A binds to a receptor in the plasma membrane, which induces the response of the cell by way of a second messenger. Hormone B forms a cytoplasmic hormone-receptor complex which, after translocation into the nucleus, has a genomic action (i.e., by altering nuclear DNA synthesis). The result is a change in the cell's protein synthesis. Hormone C binds to a receptor in the nucleus, and then has an action analogous to that of Hormone B. The only difference between B and C is the location of the receptor.

and bind to receptors located within the cell, usually in the cytoplasm (Fig. 17-1).

Protein and peptide hormones consist of amino acids; as a rule they have a higher molecular weight than the lipid hormones and are less lipophilic. Therefore they have great difficulty crossing the cell membrane, and for this reason their receptors are situated at the surface of the cell membrane (Fig. 17-1). That is, the protein and peptide hormones do not enter the interior of the cell.

The low-molecular-weight **thyroid hormones** are the third chemical group of hormones. They are formed from two amino acids joined by an ether bridge. All the cells in the body are readily penetrated by these hormones, which bind to receptors in the nucleus (Fig. 17-1). A given cell can have receptors of all three types – in the nucleus, in the cytosol and in the cell membrane. A cell can also have various receptors of a single type; for instance, the membrane can contain several receptors for different protein/peptide hormones.

Mechanisms of hormone action. The presence of these *specific receptors* in the cells of the target organ, which enable the information carried by a hormone to be "read", is fundamental to all

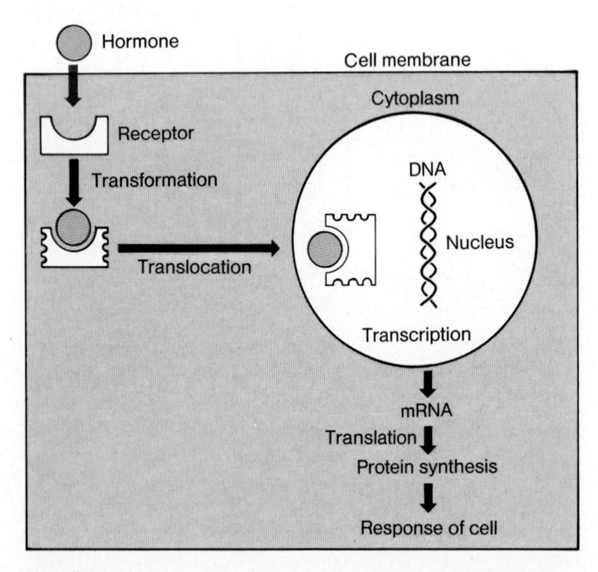

Fig. 17-2. Action of a hormone with an intracellular receptor. The hormone diffuses through the cell membrane and binds to the receptor. The hormone-receptor complex is then translocated into the nucleus, where it influences DNA synthesis, changing the rate of transcription of genetic information to messenger RNA (mRNA). The resulting increase or decrease of mRNA alters protein synthesis by way of the process of translation. The consequence is a modification of cell function

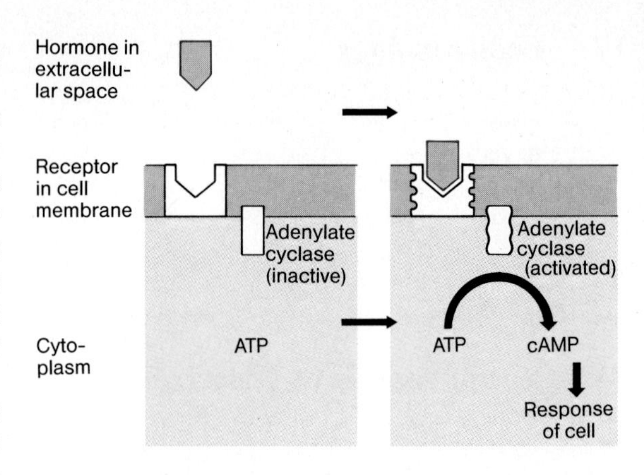

Fig. 17-3. Action of a hormone by way of a receptor in the cell membrane. The hormone diffuses to the receptor and transforms the receptor molecule by binding to it. The transformation activates an adenylate cyclase also situated in the cell membrane. This enzyme brings about the dephosphorylation of adenosine triphosphate (ATP) to cyclic adenosine monophosphate (cAMP). the cAMP can have diverse intracellular actions, culminating in the response of the cell

endocrine function. When a hormone comes into contact with a cytoplasmic or nuclear receptor, or a receptor in the cell membrane, a hormone-receptor complex is formed (Fig. 17-1) [27]. There are two completely different mechanisms of action, depending on whether the complex is produced within the cell or in the cell membrane. the **intracellular hormone-receptor complex** can influence directly the expression of genetic information; that is, a *genomic action* is exerted by the complex itself. These genomic effects in turn affect synthesis within the cell (Fig.17-2). That is, protein synthesis can be turned on and off by hormone-receptor complexes [27].

The **membrane-bound hormone-receptor complex** acts differently. When the hormone becomes associated with a receptor in the membrane, the activity of the cell is influenced by complicated biochemical events that ordinarily involve a *second messenger* within the cell. The best-known example of activation of a second messenger is the formation of *cyclic adenosine monophosphate (cAMP)* from adenosine triphosphate (ATP). The hormone-receptor complex activates an *adenylate cyclase,* which dephosphorylates ATP and converts it to cyclic AMP (Fig. 17-3). In subsequent steps cAMP alters cell function [8]. For instance, it can modify the ionic conductance of the cell membrane so that the response to the hormonal message is a change in the rate of secretion by the cell.

Other substances that seem to act as second messengers are *cyclic guanosine monophosphate (cGMP), calmodulin* and *phosphoinositol.* In all these cases, the highly specific process by which a particular hormone and receptor combine to produce a particular cellular response is mediated by a nonspecific intracellular mechanism – the production of one or several second messengers.

Synthesis and Breakdown of Hormones

Hormone synthesis. The synthesis of the lipid hormones and the amino-acid derivatives (thyroid hormones) will be described later in the context of their function (p. 384, p. 390). The **protein and peptide hormones** are produced in the *Golgi apparatus* of the cell by *translation* of the information contained in RNA into a protein sequence. Synthesis of these hormones is no different from that of other proteins in the body. However, the hormone first appears not in the biologically effective form but as a larger precursor molecule, the so-called *prepro form* of the hormone [4]. This molecule contains the amino-acid sequence of the definitive hormone plus some extra residues, which ultimately are split off enzymatically; this step is called "posttranslational processing". In its final form the hormone is packed in granules, where it is kept ready for release. In summary, hormone synthesis produces not only the protein and peptide hormones themselves but also the pieces that are split off from the prepro form. Little is known about the biological function of the latter sequences. It has become evident, however, that in some systems these "remnants" also have some biological significance. As an example of this, the proopiomelanocortin cell will be discussed below (pp. 386f.) [4, 7, 12].

Hormone breakdown. The *protein and peptide hormones* are rapidly broken down in the body by mechanisms based on two different principles:

1. Many hormone molecules in the blood never bind to a receptor, but it is important that they should not continue to circulate too long. There are a number of **enzyme systems** in various organs (liver, lungs, brain, kidneys) that are responsible for the enzymatic breakdown of protein/peptide hormones [12]. Because binding of a hormone to the receptor is *reversible,* some of the bound hormone molecules are eventually released, and these too are inactivated by enzymatic degradation.
2. Some of the hormones that bind to a receptor are thereafter degraded intracellularly, either while still in the hormone-receptor complex or as free hormones. This breakdown occurs in the **lysosomes.**

New Aspects of Endocrinology

Paracrine actions of hormones. Before proceeding to the individual hormone systems, we should consider a recent development that is currently calling many traditional concepts into question and making it necessary to formulate new definitions. It had been established that hormones are chemical information carriers, produced by secretory cells that release them into the bloodstream for transport to a target organ. The target organ is characterized by its ability to read the hormonal information. In some circumstances this information can also be read by cells in the immediate vicinity of the hormone-producing cell. In that case the hormone simply diffuses through the interstitial spaces to the target cells; therefore it is not actually a hormone by the classical definition, for it is not transported by the blood. When such information carriers act on neighboring cells, they are said to be hormones with a *paracrine action* [2]. Hormones that are not released into the blood but act on nearby cells

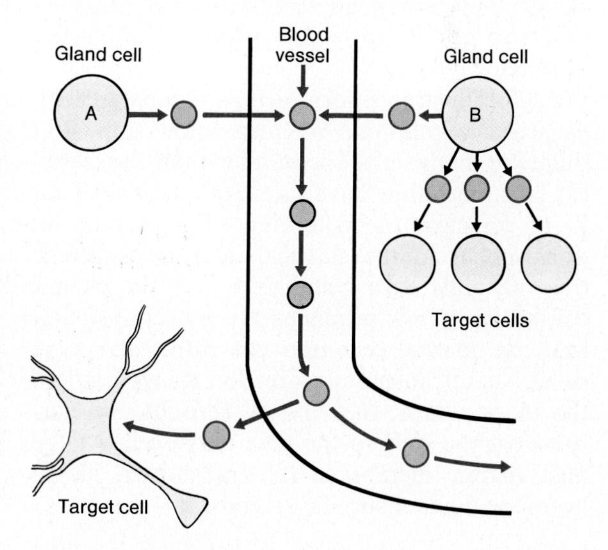

Fig. 17-4. Difference between hormonal and paracrine regulation. The gland cell A produces a hormone that fits the classical definition; i.e., it is carried to the target cell by the blood. Gland cell B produces a hormone with a paracrine action; i.e., it influences the neighboring cells. However, the hormone of the cell B can also travel in the blood to target organs

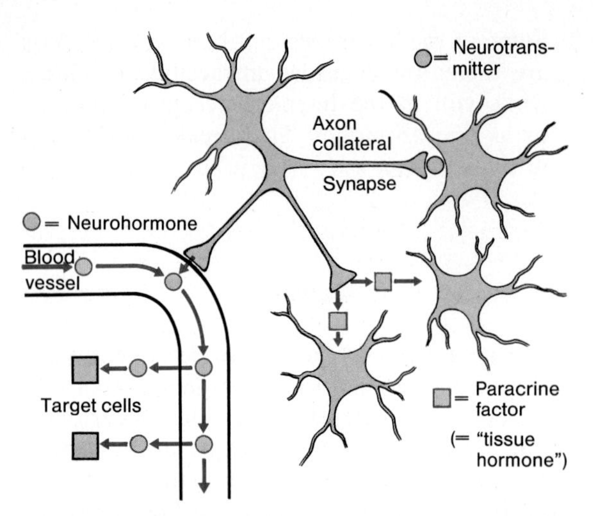

Fig. 17-5. Difference between neurotransmitter, neurohormone and paracrine neurohormone. The neuron (schematic drawing) produces a substance. If this substance is released at a synapse, it corresponds to the definition of a neurotransmitter. The same cell can have axon collaterals that terminate on blood vessels and release the same substance into the bloodstream. In that case, it is behaving as a neurohormone. From another axon collateral, the same substance can diffuse into the surrounding tissue and influence groups of cells there; in this case it has a paracrine action

have occasionally been called "tissue hormones", but this name has previously been reserved for the prostaglandins, which have been known to act in this way for some time. Now we know that classical hormones can also have a paracrine action and hence satisfy the definition of "tissue hormones".
Fig. 17-4 illustrates hormonal as compared with paracrine regulation. We also know now that there are many substances other than the classical hormones that have paracrine actions. That is, in principle the definition of paracrine action applies to the classical neurotransmitters, the only difference being that here the chemical information is produced not by cells specialized for internal secretion but rather by nerve cells. Neurotransmitters are not transported in the bloodstream; they diffuse through the narrow synaptic cleft to the next nerve cell. At the postsynaptic membrane the transmitter, like a hormone, finds a specific receptor.

Neurohormones. It has very recently been shown that nerve cells can also produce peptide and protein hormones [7, 12]. These cells often also release their secretions into the blood; that is, they produce neurohormones. Indeed, large parts of the CNS must be regarded as hormone-producing. What, then, is the fundamental difference between a hormone and a neurotransmitter? The neurotransmitter diffuses through the synaptic cleft, whereas the neurohormone reaches its target organ by way of the bloodstream. There are even situations in which axon terminals of a nerve cell release their product as a neurotransmitter while axon collaterals of the same neuron, terminating on blood vessels, release the product as a neurohormone (Fig. 17-5).
Because peptides influence the activity of neighboring nerve cells, they too must be regarded as neurotransmitters. Neurophysiological experiments have in fact shown that neurons with a given classical transmitter can be assigned to subpopulations with different neuropeptides. Little is known about the functions of such subpopulations. At present it seems likely that many neurons may be able to produce one or several peptides in addition to a classical transmitter substance.

Methods of Study

In 1848 A.A. BERTHOLD published experiments that mark the beginning of modern research on hormones. It was known that after castration cocks lose the swollen comb and behave less aggressively; at that time it was assumed that the testes and CNS communicate by way of neurons. BERTHOLD castrated cocks and reimplanted the testes in the abdominal cavity. The combs of these cocks remained swollen, and the animals continued to exhibit aggressive dominance behavior. This experiment demonstrated that one or more humoral signals reach the CNS from the testes. Similar methods are still used today to test the actions of hormones; that is, hormone-producing organs are removed and the resulting deficits are analyzed. Hormonal effects can also be studied by **bioassays,** in which hormones are administered to a suitable animal in vivo and the biological effects are examined [3].
Because such biological methods are very insensitive, they have been almost entirely superseded by highly sensitive **immunological assay techniques.** It has become possible to produce, for each hormone, a specific antibody which binds only that hormone and not its precursors, its breakdown products or other similar molecules. The hormone-antibody complex can be precipitated and measured quantitatively. Some semiquantitative tests (e.g., pregnancy tests) are carried out by this procedure.
Test sensitivity is further increased in **radioimmunoassays** (RIA). These also employ specific antibodies, which are incubated with a mixture of radioactively labelled hormone and the nonradioactive hormone molecules in a biological sample; the amount of hormone exceeds the binding capacity of the antibodies, so that there is competition for binding sites. After the antibody-bound hormone has been separated from the remaining free hormone the radioactivity is measured and the amount of hormone in the biological sample is found from standard curves (for details see textbooks of clinical chemistry). Exceedingly

small amounts of hormone – in concentrations down to the femtomolar level – can be detected by these modern analytical techniques.

Endocrine Control Circuits

Feedback systems. Endocrine regulation can be described in terms of a *control circuit* (pp. 324f.) in which the result produced by action of a hormone is directly or indirectly communicated to the element that determines the amount of hormone available. Normally this communication takes the form of *negative feedback;* that is, when a hormone has been released and has acted on the cells of the target organ, their response is signaled back to the hormone-producing centers with the effect of diminishing the release of that hormone. Such a system is diagrammed in Fig. 17-6. The feedback signal can be either humoral or neural. There are very rare cases of *positive feedback,* in which the response of the target cell to a hormone serves to increase the rate of hormone release.

In either case, the feedback signal is mediated chemically at some stage. If a neural route is used, the mediators are neurotransmitters. When the feedback is mediated by hormones, the controlling element must contain cells with receptors for those hormones, and the *hormone concentration* itself provides the feedback signal. In the most direct feedback route, a hormone regulates its own rate of release often by way of so-called *autoreceptors.* This mechanism can be seen as analogous to the presynaptic inhibition (autoinhibition) of neurotransmitters (pp. 342f.). Another important endocrine control circuit operates as follows: Hormone A stimulates the release of Hormone B, and Hormone B inhibits the secretion of Hormone A. But usually such systems are much more complicated, with a chain of humoral and neuronal signals involving more than one messenger (neurotransmitter or hormone).

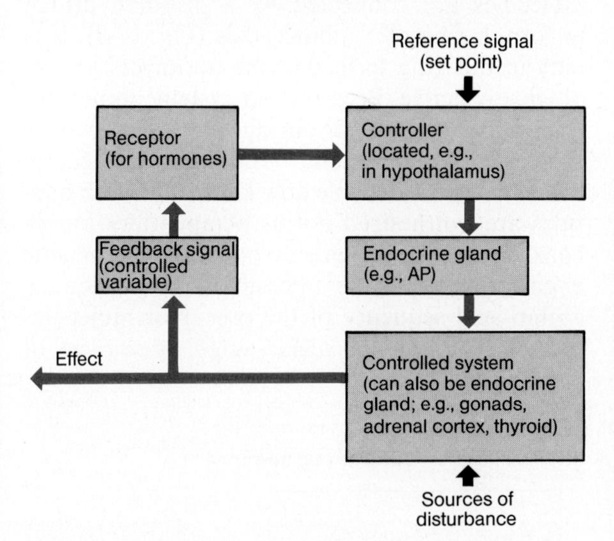

Fig. 17-6. Diagram of a control circuit for endocrine regulation. The set point is the desired value of the controlled variable; it is compared with the actual value by a controller, which sends out a signal to alter the function of an endocrine gland accordingly. The endocrine gland secretes hormones at a rate that can be changed by disturbing factors. The hormones regulate a system that responds to the hormonal information, producing a physiological effect. At the same time, the new value of the controlled variable is signaled to the controller, closing the loop

Neuroendocrine control circuit. *Neuroendocrinology* is the study of the *interaction of hormones* in the bloodstream with the *CNS* and its response to them. The response is a complex alteration of the production and release of neurotransmitters and/or neurohormones, as a result of which the production of other hormones can be enhanced or suppressed. The neuroendocrinologist is concerned not only with the regulation of hormone levels by such CNS control circuits but also with the modulation of corresponding forms of *behavior* (e.g., gonadal activity and sexual behavior, glucose regulation and hunger, osmoregulation and thirst).

In neuroendocrine control circuits the feedback to the CNS is mediated by hormones stimulated by secretions from the anterior pituitary (adenohypophysis). Therefore neurons receptive to these hormones must exist. It has in fact been found that thyroid hormones, as well as gonadal and adrenal steroids, can influence *neuronal activity* in various regions of the brain. The steroid-"reading" neurons have been particularly thoroughly studied. The *steroid receptors* of these neurons, like the receptors of all lipid hormones, are located in the cytoplasm. The hormone-receptor complex acts on the genome to stimulate or inhibit activity in the nucleus, with profound effects on the metabolism of the steroid-receptive neurons. The electrical activity of the neuron can also be affected, so that changes in the concentration of a steroid hormone circulating in the blood can be communicated to neurons that are not themselves receptive to steroids. Still other neurons in the CNS regulate the steroid-producing cells indirectly, often by way of the *pituitary.* Information about the concentration of steroid in the bloodstream is also transmitted to behavior-modifying centers in the brain. In this way a given hormonal state can be coordinated with appropriate behavior.

17.2 The Posterior Pituitary System

Functional Organization

Relations between hypothalamus and pituitary. In the sense of the "classical" definition of endocrinology, parts of the CNS have the character of endocrine glands; they produce neurohormones and release them into the blood, which carries them to the target organ. One such structure is the pituitary, or hypophysis. It lies within the skull in the *sella turcica*, a bony enclosure that offers good protection from trauma. It is a composite organ, with three entirely different parts (Fig. 17-7). The **posterior** pituitary or *neurohypophysis* is a lobe containing the axon terminals of neurons with somata (perikarya) in the hypothalamus. The **anterior pituitary** or *adenohypophysis* is not a neural structure, but rather a conglomerate of hormone-producing cells. Adeno- and neurohypophysis are separated by a thin layer of cells; these few cells constitute the *intermediate lobe* of the pituitary. They are innervated by nerve fibers from the hypothalamus. The intermediate lobe is of considerable importance in the lower vertebrates but much less so in mammals. Because there is no known pathological condition involving the intermediate lobe, the hormone it produces will not be discussed here (but see proopiomelanocortin system, pp. 386f.).

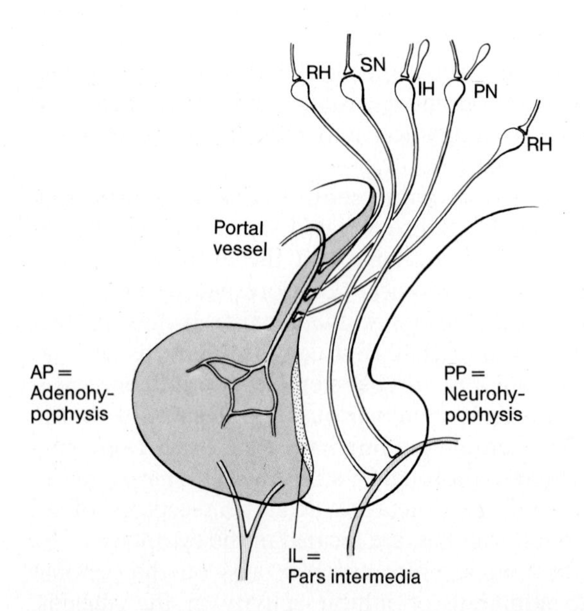

Fig. 17-7. Positions of the anterior lobe of the pituitary (AP), the intermediate lobe (IL) and the posterior lobe (PP) with respect to the hypothalamus and the portal vessels. The posterior pituitary consists of the terminals of axons that come from the large cells in the supraoptic nucleus (SN) and the paraventricular nucleus of the hypothalamus (PN). The IL comprises only 1–2 layers of cells and probably no longer has any significance in humans. The anterior pituitary has an epithelial structure. Cells in the AP are controlled by neurohormones released by hypothalamic cells in the PP and the hypothalamic neurons that produce releasing or inhibiting hormones (RH and IH) are innervated by limbic and mesencephalic as well as intrahypothalamic neurons. The hypothalamic cells thus receive information about internal and environmental influences

Hormones of the posterior pituitary. Within the hypothalamus there are two groups of very large nerve cells forming the magnocellular nuclei: the *supraoptic* and *paraventricular nuclei.* The axons of neurons in these nuclei run through the *pituitary stalk* into the sella turcica, to form the neurohypophysis (Fig. 17-7). In the dilated terminals of the axons two hormones are stored, *oxytocin* and *antidiuretic hormone (ADH,* or vasopressin). Because the name "antidiuretic hormone" best describes the function of the hormone, it should be preferred; in humans the hormone probably has a vasopressor action only at extremely high concentrations (p. 520) such as are found exclusively in pathological situations.

Oxytocin and ADH are released from the posterior pituitary into the systemic blood. The molecule in each case consists of 9 *amino acids,* two of which are cysteine. The two cysteine molecules are connected by a disulfide bridge to form a ring of 5 amino acids (Fig. 17-8). It is only in this ring form that the hormones are biologically active. Because two cysteine molecules joined by a disulfide bridge make a cystine molecule, oxytocin and ADH are in general called octapeptides. We now know that both peptides are synthesized not as octapeptides but as considerably larger precursors. Modern genetic engineering has made it possible to determine the amino-acid sequence of the precursor molecules [4, 14]. The *high-molecular-weight precursors* of

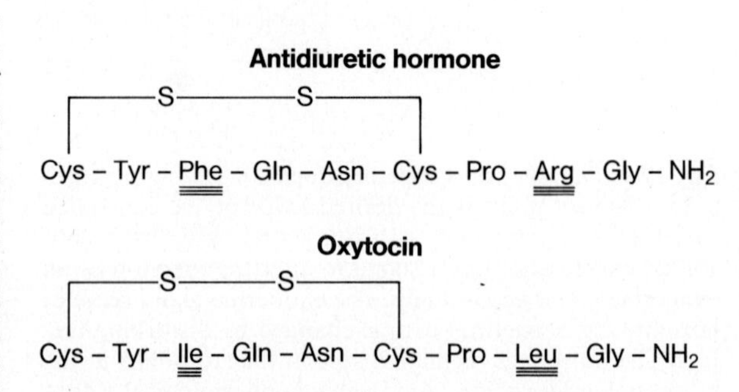

Fig. 17-8. Amino acid sequences of antidiuretic hormone (ADH, also called vasopressin) and oxytocin

oxytocin and ADH are synthesized in the *Golgi apparatus* of cells in the magnocellular nuclei. It was previously thought that oxytocin was synthesized only in the paraventricular nucleus and ADH only in the supraoptic, but now we know that both are produced in both nuclei. A given cell, however, can synthesized only one or the other.

Axonal transport and hormonal release. The precursor molecules are sent to the posterior pituitary by axonal transport. In the soma, the axon and the axon terminal, the oxytocin or ADH is split off by enzymes in the *transport granules*. Not long ago large peptides called *neurophysins* were extracted from the granules and analyzed. The neurophysins were thought to be synthesized separately from oxytocin or ADH and to serve as carrier proteins for those hormones. We know that the neurophysins are components of the large precursors from which oxytocin or ADH are split off. In addition to the two neurophysins (one from the oxytocin precursor and one from the ADH precursor) the granules contain other peptide fragments, the biological function of which is unknown.
Oxytocin and ADH are stored in granules in the axon-terminal structures of the neurohypophysis. Whenever an action potential is generated in a supraoptic or paraventricular cell, it is conducted along the axon into the terminal structure. By way of *electro-secretion coupling,* depolarization of the terminal causes the *exocytotic release* of hormone from the neurosecretory granule into the systemic blood.

Antidiuretic Hormone

ADH actions. Under physiological conditions the target organ of the ADH is the *kidney*. The *osmoregulatory effect* of this hormone was revealed by the pioneering neurophysiological experiments of VERNEY [42]. He recorded summated potentials from the supraoptic nucleus of cats while injecting hyper- or hypotonic NaCl solutions into the carotid artery. The hypertonic saline increased the activity of neurons in the supraoptic nucleus, whereas the hypotonic saline distinctly reduced it. That is, a hyperosmotic stimulus raises the discharge rate of the ADH-producing neurons, which causes more antidiuretic hormone to be released into the circulation and carried to the target structures, the *collecting tubules* and *ducts* of the kidney. Without the action of ADH the epithelium of the collecting tubules is impermeable to water. ADH makes it permeable, so that water can be passively reabsorbed (pp. 757f.). That is, ADH ensures that under *hyperosmolar* conditions the body produces a concentrated, hyperosmolar urine and loses as little water as possible. As a result, the osmotic load is reduced. Correspondingly, under *hyposmolar* conditions the release of antidiuretic hormone is inhibited. It is still further inhibited by alcohol consumption, which explains the marked diuresis that follows the intake of hypotonic liquid together with alcohol. Because ADH secretion is reduced or halted, the epithelium of the collecting tubule becomes impermeable to water, and the tubule urine becomes only moderately concentrated. Injection of ADH would promptly raise the water-permeability of the collecting tubule and thus cause concentration of the urine.
If large amounts of ADH are injected, there is a distinct constriction of the arteries and hence an increased blood pressure (vasopressor property of the hormone), and it is for this reason that the name vasopressin (AVP = arginine vasopressin) has been commonly used in the Anglo-American literature. A pronouced *drop in blood pressure* such as can be caused by bleeding or shock does indeed trigger an increase in the rate of ADH release and thereby raise the blood pressure. In the *portal system* of the liver, however, ADH acts to lower blood pressure.

Osmoreceptors and volume regulation. It follows from the above that the body must contain *osmoreceptive sensors,* capable of detecting the current osmotic pressure, as well as volume detectors to monitor the degree of filling of the blood vessels and hence the blood pressure in the high- and low-pressure systems, for information of both kinds must be signaled to the ADH-producing cells in the hypothalamus. The osmotic pressure of the blood is probably recorded mainly in the *hypothalamus*. It may be that the ADH-producing cells are themselves osmoreceptive. There are indications that osmosensors are also present in the portal vessels between the gastrointestinal tract and the liver, which signal the local osmotic pressure to the hypothalamus. *Barosensors* that report to the ADH-producing neurons are located in the carotid and aortic sinuses – that is, in the arterial high-pressure region (pp. 512f.). There are *volume sensors* with the same function in the intrathoracic low-pressure region and in the atria (p. 515). The secretion of ADH is fine-tuned by these volume sensors so as to increase or decrease the circulating ADH when one stands up or lies down (Gauer-Henry reflex, p. 520).

Pathophysiological aspects. When ADH production ceases (e.g., due to tumors or hypophysectomy) the condition called *diabetes insipidus* results (p. 748). As the name implies, a large volume of insipid (tasteless) urine is produced. The physicians in earlier generations actually did taste the urine of patients as an aid to differential diagnosis; if it was sweet, the disease diabetes mellitus was indicated (the Latin *mel* means "honey"). If the urine was extremely dilute it had no taste and was so named; at that time it was not known that the cause was a deficient production of ADH.
Antidiuretic hormone can now be produced synthetically, so that the very rare condition of diabetes insipidus no longer presents a major therapeutic problem.

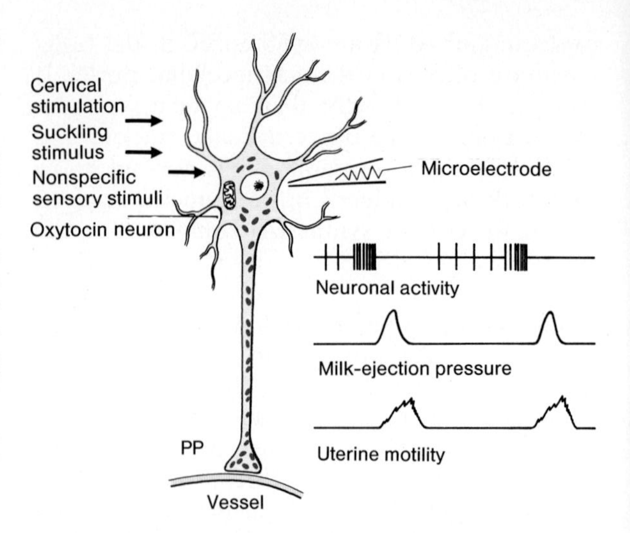

Fig. 17-9. Basis of the milk-ejection reflex. By mechanical stimulation of the uterine cervix or the nipples, and sometimes by nonspecific sensory stimuli, oxytocin-producing neurons in the supraoptic and paraventricular nuclei are phasically and synchronously activated. As a result, oxytocin is released in boluses into the systemic blood. Upon reaching the mammary glands, it raises the milk-ejection pressure. The uterine musculature is also activated by the oxytocin bolus.

Oxytocin

Like ADH, *oxytocin* is synthesized in the hypothalamus by large cells of the supraoptic and paraventricular nuclei, and transported through their axons into the posterior pituitary, where it is stored. The target organ of oxytocin is the *myometrium* (the musculature of the uterus) and the *myoepithelium* of the *mammary gland.*

Milk-ejection reflex. Under physiological conditions the mammary glands produce milk within 24 h after delivery, so that the baby can suckle. The act of sucking provides an intense stimulus to the nipple, which is extremely well innervated. The stimulus is communicated neurally to the oxytocin-producing neurons in the hypothalamus, which respond by releasing more oxytocin. The latter causes a *contraction of the myoepithelium* lining the gland; this contractile structure, unlike others in the body (the muscles), is of epithelial origin. The myoepithelium is arranged around the alveoli of the gland in such a way that milk is ejected when it contracts. That is, the infant need not depend on active sucking to draw out the contents of the gland, for it is assisted by the milk-ejection reflex.

Experiments on animals have shown that the oxytocin-producing neurons are all activated simultaneously by the suckling stimulus [43], so that the hormone is released from the neurohypophysis as a bolus (Fig. 17-9). Therefore all the myoepithelia in the mammary gland contract at the same time, producing a stepwise increase in the intramammary pressure. This milk-ejection reflex has been portrayed by artists; there are paintings of mothers ejecting milk at the sight of the infant. Indeed, it is a familiar clinical finding that after weaning lactation stops more slowly in the presence of the child than in its absence.

Action on the sensitized myometrium. Mechanical stimulation of the vagina and cervix excites neural afferents to the hypothalamus that increase the release of oxytocin *(Ferguson's reflex).* Toward the end of pregnancy, estrogens cause the myometrium in the uterus to be particularly sensitive to oxytocin. After about 280 days of pregnancy the posterior pituitary releases oxytocin at a higher rate, producing slight *contractions of the estrogen-sensitized myometrium* that press the fetus toward cervix and vagina. The stretching of these tissues is detected by their abundant mechanoreceptors and signaled to the oxytocin-producing cells in the hypothalamus, which respond by releasing still more oxytocin, so that the pressure on the mechanoreceptors increases further. This process builds up into **labor,** which ultimately expels the fetus and placenta. The mechanical stimulus to the cervix and vagina is thus removed, and the release of oxytocin is temporarily interrupted.

Other actions of oxytocin. FERGUSON'S reflex is of no great practical significance in a woman who is not pregnant, though oxytocin released during coitus may cause uterine microcontractions that facilitate the ascension of sperm. No functions of oxytocin in the male body have yet been discovered. It might possibly increase peristalsis of the cremaster musculature during the ejaculation of semen.

17.3 The Anterior Pituitary System

During embryogenesis the anterior lobe of the pituitary originates as an evagination from the roof of the mouth called *Rathke's pouch.* During embryonic developement this pouch migrates to the interior of the skull. This situation has pathophysiological significance in that often bits of the embryonic tissue are left behind on the way from the mouth to the final site in the sella turcica, and in later life these can develop into tumors. Having arisen as an ectodermal structure rather than from the neuroectoderm, the anterior lobe has the character of a glandular epithelium – hence the term *adenohypophysis.* The anterior pituitary is not innervated by the CNS; its function is regulated entirely by neurohormones (p. 380). By simple histological procedures, three types of adenohypophyseal cell can be distinguished. The *acidophilic (eosinophilic) cells* take up acidic stains, and *basophilic cells* take up basic stains; the *neurophilic, chromophobic cells* are difficult to stain at all.

Hormones of the Adenohypophysis

The anterior pituitary produces six hormones (according to the traditional definition). The nomenclature of these hormones can be rather confusing; it is summarized in Table. 17-1.

Glandotropic hormones. Four of the adenohypophyseal hormones each have a gland as the target organ and therefore are called glandotropic hormones. In general they stimulate the function of these glands. One of the target organs is the *thyroid gland.* It is stimulated by the *thyroid-stimulating hormone (TSH),* also called thyrotropin. Similarly, the pituitary hormone that stimulates activity of another peripheral gland, the adrenal cortex, is called *adrenocorticotropic hormone (ACTH);* this name also has a short form, corticotropin. The two remaining glandotropic hormones stimulate gonadal activity and are therefore both called *gonadotropic hormones* or gonadotropins. One stimulates maturation of the ovarian follicles and is called *follicle-stimulating hormone (FSH).* The other causes rupture of the follicle, ovulation, and formation of the corpus luteum; it is called *luteinizing hormone (LH).* Both of these were named for their function in the woman, but they are also present in the man. Here FSH serves an important function in sperm maturation, and LH stimulates the interstitial cells of Leydig to increase testosterone production. The hormone that produces the latter effect was once thought to be different from LH and was thus called *interstitial-cell-stimulating hormone (ICSH),* but it is now clear that ICSH and LH are identical. TSH, LH and FSH are glycoproteins (i.e., they contain sugar residues).

Table 17-1. Hormones of the anterior pituitary

Abbreviation	Name	Acts on
Glandotropic hormones		
ACTH	Adrenocorticotropic hormone (synonym: corticotropin)	Adrenal cortex
TSH	Thyroid-stimulating hormone (synonym: thyrotropin)	Thyroid gland
FSH	Follicle-stimulating hormone	Gonads
LH	Luteinising hormone	Gonads
(FSH and LH are the two gonadotropins)		
Non-glandotropic hormones		
GH	Growth hormone (synonym: somatotropic hormone, STH)	All body cells
	Prolactin	Many body cells (breast, gonads)

Non-glandotropic hormones. In addition to these four glandotropic hormones, the anterior pituitary produces two hormones that act on organ systems or the entire organism rather than on glands. One is the *human growth hormone (HGH, GH),* also called *somatotropic hormone (STH, somatotropin).* The second non-glandotropic pituitary hormone is *prolactin.* As the name implies, it is involved in lactation, but there are also specific binding sites for prolactin in many other organs besides the mammary glands. The actions of the hormone at these other organs are largely unknown. In the rat prolactin has a luteotropic function, and for this reason it was formerly called luteotropic hormone (LTH). Because it does not affect the human ovary in this way, the latter name should be discarded.

Regulation of Adenohypophyseal Secretion

Releasing and inhibiting hormones. Although the cells in the adenohypophysis are not innervated by the CNS, their activity is regulated by a central nervous structure, the hypothalamus. Hy-

Table 17-2. Releasing and inhibiting hormones

Abbreviation[a]	Name	Acts on
Releasing hormones		
TRH	Thyrotropin-releasing hormone	TSH
LHRH	Luteinising-hormone-releasing hormone (syn.: GnRH)	LH and FSH
CRH	Corticotropin-releasing hormone	ACTH
GHRH	Growth-hormone-releasing hormone	GH
PRH	Prolactin-releasing hormone	PRL
Inhibiting hormones		
GHIH	Growth-hormone-inhibiting hormone (syn.: somatostatin, SS)	GH
PIH	Prolactin-inhibiting hormone	PRL

[a] There is as yet no universally accepted nomenclature. The original, optional use of the term "factor" rather than "hormone" is still reflected in certain alternative abbreviations, such as CRF (instead of CRH) and PIF (instead of PIH).

pothalamic nerve cells synthesize chemical information carriers, which are released from the axon terminals in the median eminence when the neurons are activated. These terminals are in close proximity to a specialized vascular system, the **portal system** that links hypothalamus and hypophysis. In these blood vessels, the chemical messenger sent out by a hypothalamic neuron is transported to the anterior pituitary. There it either causes a pituitary hormone to be released, in which case it is called a *releasing factor (RF)* or *releasing hormone (RH)*, or it inhibits the secretion of a pituitary hormone, and is called an *inhibiting factor or hormone (IF, IH)*. The terms currently most widely used for these hypothalamic neurohormones are listed in Table 17-2 (see also Fig. 17-10). Until recently it was thought that each glandotropic hormone was stimulated by a specific releasing hormone, and the name given to the latter reflected this belief: *thyrotropin-releasing hormone (TRH), corticotropin-releasing hormone (CRH), luteinising-hormone-releasing hormone (LHRH)* and *follicle-stimulating-hormone-releasing hormone (FSHRH)*. The regulation of the glandotropic hormones has since proved to be more complicated. In particular, it has been shown that a decapeptide isolated from the hypothalamus stimulates the secretion of both LH and FSH. Therefore this hypothalamic hormone, first known as LHRH, is now called *gonadotropin-releasing hormone (GnRH)*.

The two non-glandotropic hormones of the adenohypophysis, growth hormone and prolactin, are subject to multifactorial regulation. GH secretion is controlled by a *growth-hormone-releasing hormone (GHRH)* and by a *growth-hormone-inhibiting hormone (GHIH)*. When the structure of GHIH was first published, the author preferred the name *somatostatin* [20]. It had long been known that prolactin secretion is controlled by a hypothalamic inhibiting factor *(PIF)*. PIF is unusual in that it is not a peptide but rather the biogenic amine *dopamine*. It strongly suppresses the secretion of prolactin. In addition to dopamine, peptides probably also play a crucial role in the regulation of prolactin secretion (pp. 382f.).

Factors influencing hypothalamic hormone production. The hypothalamic neurons that produce the releasing and inhibiting hormones are innervated by many intra- and extrahypothalamic neurons. The most massive inputs come from the *midbrain*, by way of noradrenergic, adrenergic and serotonergic neurons, and from *limbic structures*, especially the amygdala and hippocampus. This innervation allows the integration of environmental and internal influences (mainly by way of the mesencephalon) and emotional urges (mainly by way of the limbic structures) with the

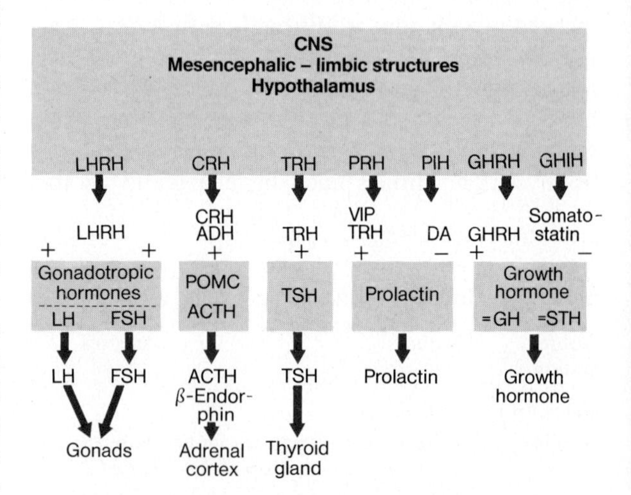

Fig. 17-10. Basic principles of regulation of anterior pituitary hormones *(lower boxes)* by the hypothalamus it (upper boxes). For nomenclature see Tables 17-1 and 17-2. Each of the four glandotropic hormones LH, FSH, ACTH and TSH has only one target organ in the body, a gland in each case. The two other hormones (prolactin and growth hormone) act on the cells of many organs. The significance of the *proopiomelanocortin cell POMC* in connection with the ACTH-producing cell is described on pp. 386f.. All hormones of the anterior pituitary are regulated by hypothalamic neurohormones. VIP, vasoactive intestinal polypeptide; DA, dopamine

neuroendocrine regulation. Mesencephalic and limbic structures receive afferents from the hypothalamus, so that there is a reciprocal exchange of information. Production of the releasing and inhibiting hormones is also influenced by feedback regarding the concentrations of the pituitary hormones or the results of their actions.

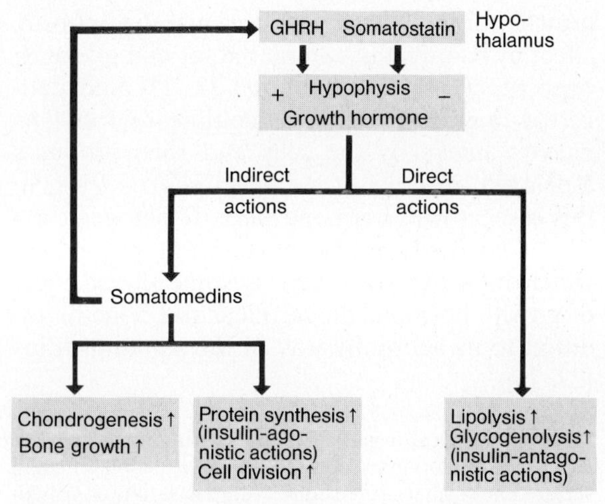

Fig. 17-11. Regulation of growth hormone by GHRH and somatostatin, and its actions. Growth hormone directly promotes lipolysis and glycogenolysis, and in the liver it stimulates the formation of somatomedins. The somatomedins feed back to the hypothalamus, closing the loop of the control system. In the body they stimulate chondrogenesis and bone growth as well as protein synthesis and cell division.

Growth Hormone

Release of growth hormone. Production and release of growth hormone are regulated by a hypothalamic releasing hormone (GHRH) and an inhibiting hormone (GHIH, somatostatin). Many physiological stimuli promote the release of growth hormone. It is not yet clear whether they are mediated chiefly by increased secretion of GHRH or decreased secretion of somatostatin. Conditions that increase the secretion of GH include *fasting hypoglycemia,* certain kinds of *stress* and, in particular, vigorous *physical activity.* The hormone is also released during *deep sleep.* But the hypophysis also secretes large amounts of GH *episodically,* with no discernible inducing factor. It is important to know the conditions under which growth hormone is released in order to evaluate its concentration in the blood. As is the case with many other hormones, because secretion can be episodic, the GH level found in a single measurement may not be representative of the actual situation.

Effects on growth. Although much is unclear about the actions of growth hormone, it is certainly *necessary for normal physical development* of children. Under physiological conditions the release of growth hormone, like that of many other hormones, is pulsatile. The 3–4 pulses per day are distinctly larger in children than in adults, as is the amount of GH released nightly during deep sleep, and these quantities decrease further in old age.

The functions of GH in the body are many and varied. For a long time researchers were puzzled by a discrepancy between results obtained in vitro and in vivo. Growth hormone in vivo stimulates both *chondrogenesis* and *myogenesis* and thus accelerates somatic growth. But when GH was incubated in vitro with cartilage or muscle tissue, no such effect was ever observed. It turned out that this action of GH is not a direct one but is exerted by the stimulation of *hepatic factors;* under the influence of GH the liver produces **somatomedins** (Fig. 17-11), substances that mediate the action of somatotropic hormone. The effect of the hepatic somatomedins on the chondrocytes is to promote the uptake of inorganic sulfate ions into the growing cartilage and bone cells. For this reason, the factor produced by the liver was at first called *sulfation factor.* Soon afterward came the report that the blood contains a substance that resembles insulin in reducing blood sugar but continues to be secreted even when the blood sugar level is extremely low. It was referred to as "nonsuppressible insulin-like activity" (NILA). Later, when NILA was found to be stimulated by growth hormone, the name was changed to *insulin-like growth factor (IGF).* It has now become clear that the most important IGFs (there are several) are the same substances that had been called somatomedins, and that they mediate the crucial growth-promoting actions of the growth hormone [19, 25, 36]. Chief among the somatomedins is *somatomedin C.* It increases the rate of protein synthesis in all cells of the body, which in turn stimulates cell division.

Metabolic actions. Growth hormone itself can also act directly on various cells. It *mobilizes fatty acids* from adipose tissue, decreasing fat deposits to obtain an additional reserve of energy. With respect to carbohydrate metabolism, GH has two seemingly contradictory actions. After acute administration there is a *reduced blood glucose level* for about 1 hour, reflecting the insulin-like action of somatomedin C [19]. Thereafter, however, the growth hormone itself produces just the opposite effect by its direct action on the fat and glycogen deposits. These are mobilized [3, 11] and converted to glucose. At the same time, GH *inhibits glucose uptake* by the cells and thus produces a delayed *elevation of the blood glucose level;* in this case, growth hormone has a diabetogenic action. Chondrocytes also have receptors for GH, which indicates that there is some direct effect of growth hormone on cartilage and bone in addition to its action by way of the somatomedins [23, 25].

Pathophysiological aspects. Children with *growth-hormone deficiency* develop into "normal" dwarves, people of small stature but normal proportions. Administration of growth hormone or of GH-releasing hormone (GHRH), which has recently been made available, produces distinct stimulation of somatic growth. Reduced GH secretion is often coupled with generally impaired pituitary function *(panhypopituitarism),* in which case other processes under hypophyseal control are also subnormal. Deficient secretion of growth hormone is not known to produce symptoms in adults.
The important role of somatomedin C as a mediator of the action of GH is illustrated by the pygmies. These people have an entirely normal GH level, but because of a genetic mutation they are unable to produce somatomedin C. It is probably for this reason that they remain small.
It is not altogether uncommon for the pituitary cells that produce growth hormone to be modified into benign tumors, with *hypersecretion of GH.* If the adenoma develops during childhood the child grows larger than normal, until the increased secretion of sex hormones at puberty (pp. 782f.) terminates bone growth by epiphyseal closure, the ossification of the cartilage at the ends of the bones. This condition is called **gigantism.**
A growth-hormone-producing tumor in an adult cannot cause the bones to grow longer because the epiphyses have already fused under the influence of gonadal steroids (p. 783). However, the acral parts of the body – primarily the ears, nose, chin, fingers and feet – can continue to grow, producing the condition known as **acromegaly** [33]. Appositional bone growth continues to be stimulated, resulting in bony outgrowths (exostoses) and an overall appearance of coarse bone structure. The organs of the alimentary tract (tongue, stomach, intestine) are also enlarged. Because GH acts as an insulin antagonist, as discussed above, these patients are inclined to develop hyperglycemia and are in a latent *diabetic metabolic state.* As a result, the cells in the islets of Langerhans are compelled to hypersecrete insulin continually, in some cases to the point of exhaustion. Blood-sugar level then remains elevated; diabetes mellitus has developed. This diabetic condition can be alleviated by removal of the tumor or, in some patients, by medication. But the somatic changes that have occurred are irreversible.

Prolactin

In the course of phylogenesis prolactin has served a number of functions, all related to reproduction. Almost all the actions of this hormone are somehow directed toward creating the biochemical prerequisites for nurturing the young, and hence for preservation of the species. The main target organ for prolactin in mammals is the mammary gland. In humans prolactin initiates and maintains lactation *(galactopoiesis).* However, prolactin receptors are found in almost all the other organs of the body; the biological actions of the hormone in these organs are unknown.

Influences on prolactin secretion. Prolactin is produced by the lactotropic cells of the pituitary and released by a very complex mechanism. Synthesis and secretion of prolactin are regulated chiefly by an inhibitory principle, *prolactin-inhibiting hormone (PIH),* produced in hypothalamic neurons. Today it is known as the biogenic amine **dopamine** [31, 34, 44]. In the basal part of the hypothalamus of all mammals there are dopaminergic cells that project to the median eminence, where they terminate on portal vessels. They continually release dopamine into the blood, so that the pituitary secretion of prolactin is tonically inhibited. When the secretion of dopamine in the hypothalamus is turned off, the result is disinhibition of prolactin secretion and increased prolactin in the blood.
It has recently been suggested that disinhibition of the lactotropic cells by cutting off the hypothalamic dopamine supply is not the main mechanism responsible for raising the rate of hypophyseal prolactin secretion. The hypothalamus has also been found to release into the portal system many peptides that are capable of stimulating hypophyseal prolactin secretion. That is, all of these would be prolactin-releasing factors or *prolactin-releasing hormones (PRH).* Substances with this action include the *thyrotropin-releasing hormone (TRH), vasoactive intestinal polypeptide (VIP)* (pp. 694f.), *angiotensin II* (pp. 517f.) and perhaps the endogeneous opioid peptide *beta-endorphin* [44]. The physiological role of these prolactin-stimulating peptides is still uncertain. Finally, prolactin synthesis and release are also stimulated directly by circulating *estrogens.* Because of this mechanism, a maintained increase in estrogen level produces hyperprolactinemia.

Prolactin actions. Under optimal homeostatic conditions (normal levels of cortisol, insulin and thyroid hormones), an increase in the blood prolactin level *initiates and maintains milk synthesis* in the female mammary gland. The gland does not produce any hormones that could provide feedback to close the control circuit. Therefore

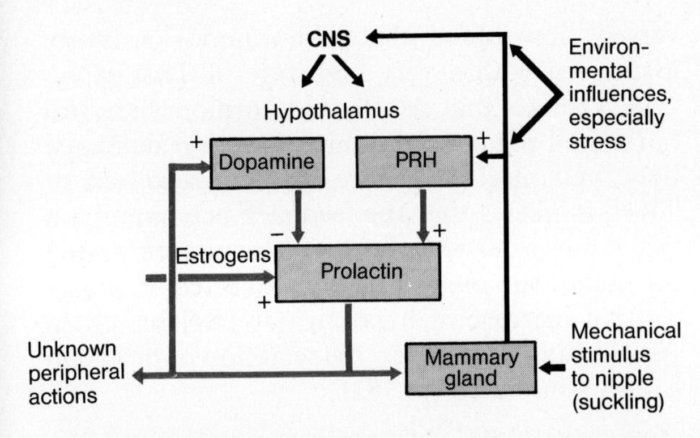

Fig. 17-12. Regulation of prolactin. The hypothalamus contains tuberoinfundibular dopaminergic (TIDA) cells, which continually release dopamine as a prolactin-inhibiting hormone. Prolactin provides autoregulatory feedback to the TIDA neurons. This control circuit can be influenced by many environmental and internal factors that cause the release of one or several prolactin-releasing hormones (PRH). A high estrogen level is an internal factor with a prolactin-stimulating action. The remainder of the CNS also participates in the regulation of prolactin secretion by way of limbic and mesencephalic influences on PRH neurons and dopaminergic cells

prolactin itself acts as a negative-feedback signal to the hypothalamus. *An elevated prolactin level increases the hypothalamic output of dopamine,* so that the rate of prolactin secretion is reduced. Fig. 17-12 is a highly simplified diagram of the hypothalamo-pituitary-peripheral control system. Stimulation of the numerous mechanoreceptors in the nipples activates a chain of neural afferents leading to the hypothalamus, resulting in the release of PRH of one or several kinds, which stimulates the secretion of prolactin in the pituitary. It is not yet clear whether the same mechanical stimulus to the nipples also reduces the release of dopamine from the hypothalamus and thereby antagonizes the *autoregulatory* action of prolactin. Normally this mechanism plays a subordinate role, but it becomes important when the infant is weaned (p. 788).

Pathophysiological aspects. The results of animal experiments suggest that hypothalamic dopamine also inhibits the cells that produce LHRH; when the dopaminergic cells in the hypothalamus become more active, hypothalamic LHRH secretion is reduced. Therefore hypophyseal LH and FSH secretion becomes subnormal, probably by inhibition of the pulsatile mode of secretion (pp. 781f.), and the menstrual cycle is interrupted. This condition is called **lactation amenorrhea** (in animals, lactation anestrus). Only in frequently nursing mothers does this mechanism operate fairly reliably; if the baby is not exclusively breast fed it provides no contraceptive protection.

Hyperprolactinemic amenorrhea is a significant pathological condition. It is not uncommon for a woman to develop spontaneously a *benign pituitary tumor* in which the cells produce large amounts of prolactin. As a rule these tumor cells are still dopamine-receptive, but they are evidently no longer under hypothalamic control by way of the blood in the portal veins. Their nutritive supply is entirely by way of the hypophyseal arteries. The high blood prolactin level often triggers lactation; in a woman who is not nursing this conditions is called *galactorrhea.* The prolactin stimulates the hypothalamic dopaminergic neurons in the autoregulatory feedback mechanism that normally would counteract the excess prolactin secretion. But although the hypothalamic dopamine is carried to the pituitary, it does not reach the tumor cells, so that their secretory activity is not inhibited. The extra dopamine does, however, inhibit the hypothalamic LHRH neurons and hence the pulsatile secretion of LHRH. Cyclic activity ceases and the woman becomes *amenorrheic.* The situation can easily be resolved by administration of dopamine agonists; carried in the systemic blood, they are able to reach the hypophyseal prolactin-producing tumor cells and inhibit their secretory activity. After normalization of prolactin secretion, the cyclic activity almost always resumes.

The tonic inhibition of prolactin secretion by dopamine is also of pharmacological importance for other reasons. Many *drugs* (very often psychotropic drugs) *block dopamine receptors;* that is, they form an inactive complex with the dopamine receptor. This complex is incapable of triggering the intracellular mechanisms that are activated by the complex formed by the receptor with dopamine itself. Such substances are called *dopamine antagonists,* because they oppose the action of dopamine by competing with it for the receptors. This is the desired effect of such drugs, but it also results in a marked increase in prolactin secretion, with the possible consequences of galactorrhea and amenorrhea.

17.4 The Thyroid System

Production and Release of the Thyroid Hormones

Regulation of hormone production. In 1969 the groups headed by SCHALLY and GUILLEMIN succeeded in simultaneously but independently analyzing a tripeptide, obtained from hypothalamic extracts of sheep and pigs, that stimulates the secretion of TSH in the pituitary [20, 38]. This was the first analyzed and synthetically available *releasing hormone (TRH).* The peptide is produced by hypothalamic neurons and released into the portal system (Fig. 17-13). When it reaches the TSH-producing cells in the pituitary it stimulates the release of *thyroid stimulating hormone (TSH).* The TSH stimulates the thyroid gland to increase its synthesis and release of the hormones **thyroxine** and **triiodothyronine.** The thyroid hormones provide *negative feedback* to the hypothalamus and pituitary, so that when the concentration of thyroid hormones in the blood is high the secretion of TSH is minimal. Con-

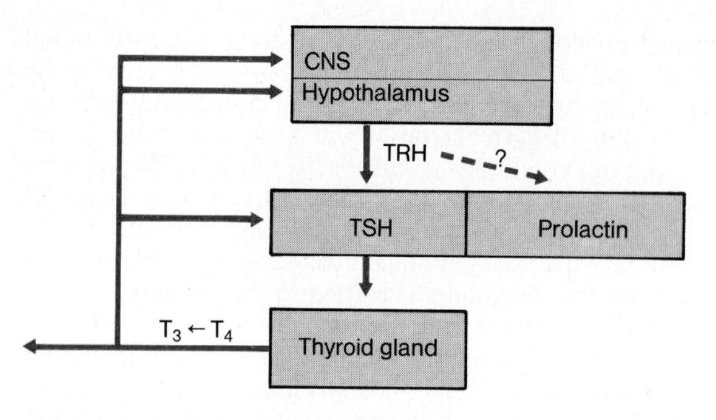

Fig. 17-13. Hypothalamic-pituitary-thyroid control system. Hypothalamic neurons produce thyrotropin-releasing hormone (TRH). This passes through the portal vessels to the pituitary, where it stimulates the secretion of thyroid-stimulating hormone (TSH). In the thyroid gland, TSH induces the production of thyroxine and triiodothyronine. T3 feeds back to the pituitary and probably, to a lesser extent, to the hypothalamus, so as to modulate TSH secretion. It is not clear whether the TRH released by the hypothalamus also stimulates prolactin secretion under physiological conditions (see p. 382)

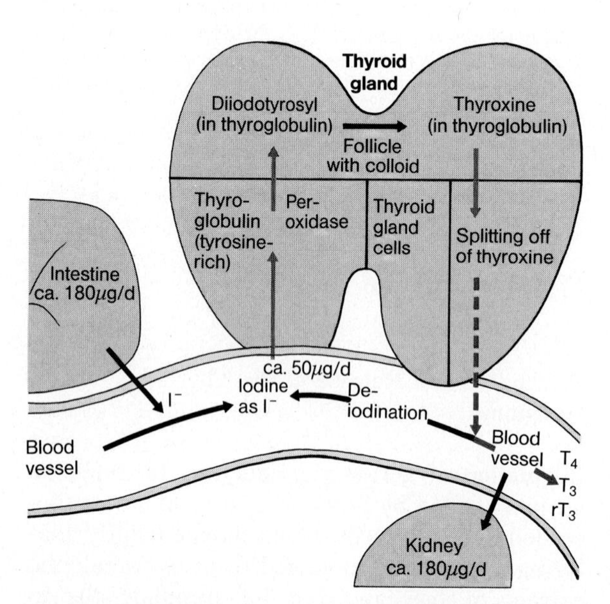

Fig. 17-14. Formation, storage and release of the thyroid hormones. Most of the iodine required daily is absorbed in the intestine in the form of iodine. This iodine is taken up by the cells of the thyroid gland and oxidized to atomic iodine by peroxidases. Thyroglobulin, also produced in the thyroid gland, is rich in tyrosine; the iodine becomes embedded in these tyrosine molecules. Thyroxine is formed by condensation of two molecules of diiodotyrosine in the thyroglobulin molecule, to which it remains bound. The thyroglobulin-bound thyroxine is later retrieved from the colloid by the thyroid cells, and thyroxine is split off enzymatically and released into the bloodstream. In the blood it is deiodinated to produce the active thyroid hormone, triiodothyronine. Only a small amount of triiodothyronine is formed directly in the thyroid gland. Some of the iodine freed by this deiodination circulates back to the thyroid gland, but most is excreted by the kidneys

versely, low blood thyroid-hormone levels are associated with a very high rate of TSH secretion. The fact that the thyroid hormones are still fairly well regulated in animals with a damaged hypothalamus, and hence with no secretion of TRH, indicates that the feedback acts mainly in the pituitary. Synthetic TRH can be employed for diagnostic purposes; when injected, it causes a rapid increase in hypophyseal TSH secretion. Astonishingly, however, the secretion of prolactin is also stimulated (p. 382).

Synthesis and secretion of the thyroid hormones. Synthesis of thyroid hormones requires a certain iodine intake, ca. 150 μg/day. Iodine is consumed as a constituent of food, absorbed in the intestine and taken up by the thyroid cells (Fig. 17-14). All the events now to be described are stimulated by TSH. First, because the intracellular iodine concentration is higher than the blood concentration, iodine cannot enter by diffusion but must be actively transported into the cell, with the expenditure of energy. The thyroid cell synthesizes a high-molecular-weight protein, **thyroglobulin,** which contains many *tyrosine molecules.* Having entered the cell, iodine is incorporated into thyroglobulin at position 3 and/or 5 of the benzene ring of the tyrosine, producing mono- or diiodotyrosyl (Fig. 17-14). Iodination can occur spontaneously in vitro, but in the thyroid gland a *peroxidase oxidizes* iodide to atomic iodine, which then combines with the tyrosine radicals of thyroglobulin. The iodinated tyrosyl radicals condense to *thyroxine* (tetraiiodothyronine, T4). A small amount of *triiodothyronine (T3)* is also formed. T3 and T4 eventually leave the cell as part of the thyroglobulin molecule and enter the follicles of the thyroid gland, spaces surrounded by the secretory cells. Here *the thyroid hormones are stored as thyroglobulin,* forming a gelatinous substance called *colloid.*

For the thyroid hormones to be released, the colloid must be taken back into the gland cells; this is done by pinocytosis. Within the cells the thyroglobulin is broken down to set free molecules of thyroxine and triiodothyronine, which diffuse into the blood. There they are bound to plasma proteins, in non-covalent form; only a small fraction is free in the blood. The most important plasma proteins to which the thyroid hormones are bound are *thyroxine-binding globulin (TBG), thyroxine-binding prealbumin (TBPA)* and certain other albumins.

All the thyroxine found in the blood is secreted by the thyroid gland, but only 10–20 % of the triiodothyronine circulating in the bloodstream

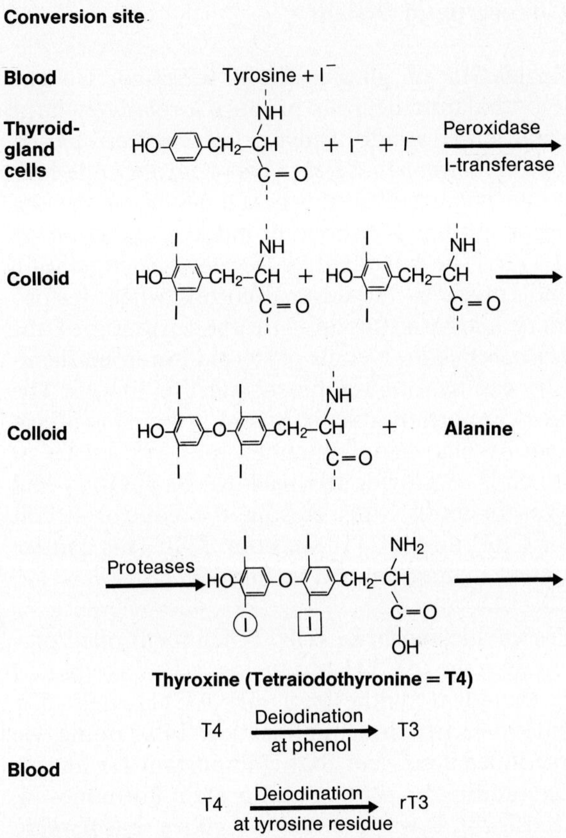

Conversion site

Blood Tyrosine + I^-

Thyroid-gland cells HO–C₆H₄–CH₂–CH(NH)(C=O) + I^- + I^- Peroxidase, I-transferase →

Colloid (two iodinated tyrosine residues) →

Colloid (thyronine residue) + **Alanine**

Proteases → HO–C₆H₂I₂–O–C₆H₂I₂–CH₂–CH(NH₂)–C(=O)OH →

Thyroxine (Tetraiodothyronine = T4)

Blood

T4 —Deiodination at phenol→ T3

T4 —Deiodination at tyrosine residue→ rT3

Fig. 17-15. Structural formulas of thyroxine (T_4), triiodothyronine (T_3) and reverse triiodothyronine (rT_3). Only T_3 is biologically active in the body. However, the thyroid gland releases considerably larger amounts of T_4; this is converted to T_3 by deiodination at the phenol ring. Deiodination at the tyrosine ring produces the biologically inactive rT_3

originates in this way. It follows that about 80–90% of the *triiodothyronine* is formed outside the gland by *deiodination of thyroxine.* About 35% of the thyroxine is converted to triiodothyronine (Fig. 17-15). *The biologically active thyroid hormone is T3;* T4 is practically ineffective. In addition to the normal T3, the blood contains a so-called *reversed T3 (rT3),* which is also biologically inactive. It is produced by deiodination at the "wrong" position, at the tyrosine ring rather than the phenol ring. Like the biologically active triiodothyronine, rT3 is mainly formed outside the thyroid gland.
Small amounts of thyroxine and triiodothyronine can be deiodinated in the liver and kidney, so that a small part (ca. 50 μg) of the body's iodine requirement can be supplied from this source (see Fig. 17-14). Sufficient thyroid hormone is stored in the colloid of the thyroid gland that the body can manage without iodine intake for some months, but thereafter it is no longer possible for the thyroid hormones to be formed in amounts adequate to support normal function.

Functions of the Thyroid Hormones

The functions of the thyroid hormones are crucial, for they *stimulate metabolism throughout the body.* The mechanisms underlaying all the individual effects have not been completely clarified [10. 11].
Triiodothyronine probably binds to a receptor molecule in the nucleus of the cell, causing *genomic effects* that stimulate both *transcription* and *translation.* As a result, **protein synthesis** is promoted in all the cells of the body. Furthermore, *sodium outflow* and the *potassium transport* between the extracellular fluid and the cytosol seem to be influenced by thyroid hormones. Finally, they also increase the activity of many enzymes, especially those that degrade carbohydrate, so that the **utilization of carbohydrates** is particularly enhanced by a high thyroid-hormone level.
Because most of the processes described above take place in the *mitochondria,* these organelles are also particularly active when the thyroid-hormone level is high, and they become enlarged. The increase in enzymatic activity caused by the thyroid hormones is accompanied by an increase in the rate of energy turnover in the body. Therefore the *basal metabolic rate* is directly correlated with the quantity of circulating thyroid hormone.
In children, thyroid hormones also promote *physical growth.* This effect is particularly important for normal *postnatal development of the brain.* A fetus in utero with a thyroid gland that produces too little hormone is still adequately supplied by the mother, but after birth thyroid deficiency becomes fatal for cerebral development (see below).

Pathophysiological Aspects

There are many pathophysiological situations in which too little or too much thyroid hormone is produced. The resulting conditions are called *hypo- and hyperthyroidism,* respectively.

Hypothyroidism. Thyroid deficiency in adults is characterized by a slowing of all metabolic processes. Conspicuous symptoms include delayed reactions to stimuli in the surroundings and the typical "tired" appearance of these patients, caused in part by the doughy consistency of the skin. This syndrome is called **myxedema.** The symptoms in adults are completely reversible by oral administration of thyroid hormone. When thyroid hormones are lacking in early childhood, however, the result is severe *bodily and mental retardation* **(cretinism).** Cretins are small in stature because stimulation of the epiphyseal increase in bone length by growth hormone is impaired in the absence of the thyroid hormones. Because appositional bone growth is less disturbed, cretins have a bulky, coarse appearance. Extreme hypothyroidism in the newborn requires rapid replacement of the hormone to prevent irreversible brain damage; thyroid-hormone deficiency, depending on its severity, can cause complete idiocy. Therefore in almost all civilized countries the blood of the newborn is routinely analyzed for thyroid hormone ("hypothyroidism screening"). Thyroid hormone can be produced in adequate quantities only if the food contains sufficient iodine. There are great regional differences in the iodine content of food; in general, it is low in mountainous regions and high in coastal areas. In some regions with an endemic iodine scarcity cretinism and myxedema were, until recently, frequently encountered. Now these conditions can be cured by appropriate *iodine prophylaxis,* such as the addition of iodine to table salt in the form of small amounts of NaI.

Hyperthyroidism. Pathological overproduction of thyroid hormone is a common condition. Basal metabolism is elevated, synthesis and breakdown of protein, carbohydrates and fat are accelerated, and the patients appear overexcited. Hyperthyroidism can be accompanied by a croplike swelling of the neck *(goiter* or struma), but often the enlargement is diffuse or takes the form of autonomous "hot nodules". Many hyperthyroid patients are characterized by protruding eyeballs *(exophthalmos);* the pathogenesis of this condition is unclear, although the blood has been shown to contain a substance called *exophthalmos-producing factor,* which may be derived from the pituitary [26]. Hormone production by the thyroid gland can be normalized by administration of antithyroid drugs.
In either condition – an excess or a deficiency of thyroid hormone – practically all cells of the body are fundamentally affected. It is not surprising, therefore, that many functions not immediately related to the action of the thyroid hormones are also disturbed. This is a particularly important consideration with respect to the therapy of reproductive disorders in man and woman. The cause of such disorders often lies not in the hypothalamo-pituitary-gonadal control system but rather in deficient or excessive activity of the thyroid gland.

17.5 The Adrenal Cortex Systems

The cortex of the adrenal gland is made up of three morphologically distinct layers; from the interior outward these are the *zona reticularis, zona fasciculata* and *zona glomerulosa.* The three zones produce different kinds of hormones. In the zona reticularis these are mainly androgens but also glucocorticoids; the cells of the zona fasciculata synthesize mainly glucocorticoids, and those of the zona glomerulosa, mineralocorticoids [1, 28].

Glucocorticoid System

Regulation of glucocorticoid secretion. Certain hypothalamic neurons produce a relatively large peptide (41 amino acids) called *corticotropin-releasing hormone (CRH).* This neuropeptide hormone is carried in the portal blood to the anterior pituitary, where it induces secretion of *ACTH.* The latter enters the general circulation and travels to the adrenal cortex, where its primary action is to stimulate the secretion of the *glucocorticoids.* Details of steroid hormone chemistry can be found in biochemical textbooks. The most important glucocorticoid in humans is **cortisol.** It has many functions (pp. 388f.), one of which is to provide feedback to the pituitary and hypothalamus, thus closing the control circuit for CRH and ACTH secretion [28]. This control system is diagrammed in Fig. 17-16.

Proopiomelanocortin cells. When mentioned previously, the ACTH-producing cell was treated as though it synthesized only ACTH; it is now time to rectify this simplification. In so doing, we introduce a concept that is important for an understanding of peptide and protein hormones [4, 18, 22, 24]. It was pointed out above that peptide hormones are not synthesized in their biologi-

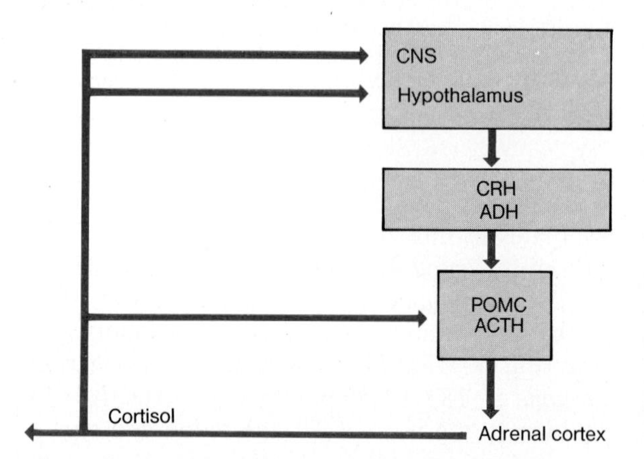

Fig. 17-16. Hypothalamic-pituitary-adrenal control system. Hypothalamic neurons produce corticotropin-releasing hormone (CRH), which passes through the portal vessels to the pituitary; here it stimulates ACTH secretion. ACTH causes the adrenal glands to synthesize and release larger amounts of cortisol. Cortisol feeds back to both the pituitary and the hypothalamus. The equilibrium of this system can easily be upset by environmental influences (especially various stressors). It is not yet clear whether antidiuretic hormone (ADH) should be regarded as an additional CRH under physiological conditions. By way of suprahypothalamic influences, in particular those from the mesencephalon and limbic structures, information about emotions, pain etc. can be transmitted to the hypothalamic ACTH-producing cells

cally active form but are split off enzymatically from larger precursor molecules. The amino acid sequence in the ACTH precursor has recently been established [18]. In addition to the 39-amino-acid sequence of ACTH the molecule contains the sequence of an endogenous opioid peptide, *β–endorphin,* as well as the sequence of the α–melanocyte-stimulating hormone *(α–MSH).* Therefore cells, the genetic information of which enables them to synthesize this precursor, are no longer called ACTH cells but rather *proopiomelanocortin cells (POMC cells).* That is, these are cells that can produce three substances – β–endorphin, melanocyte-stimulating hormone and ACTH – from a single high-molecular-weight precursor. The classical ACTH cells in the anterior pituitary are POMC cells. As far as is known at present, their most important secretory product is ACTH. Although β–endorphin and α–MSH are also produced and released along with ACTH [4, 12, 18], these two substances probably play no important hormonal role. However, there is a disorder in which the adrenal glands produce too little cortisol and aldosterone. The pituitary is thereby stimulated to secrete larger amounts of ACTH; because equimolar amounts of MSH are also released, the MSH level in the blood becomes too high, which causes darker skin pigmentation. The main symptoms of this disorder, called *Addison's disease,* are ultimately explained by the deficient mineralocorticoid production.

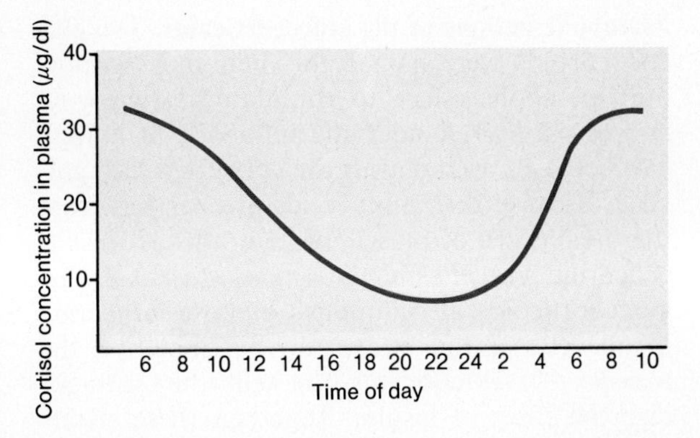

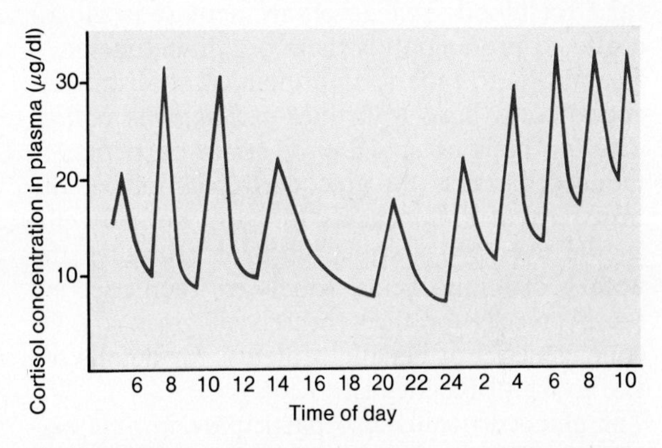

Fig. 17-17. *Below:* Episodic cortisol secretion from the cells of the adrenal cortex. In the early hours of the morning the number of cortisol secretion episodes and their intensity are distinctly increased. *Above:* Change in plasma cortisol concentration in the course of the day (average for a large population), with a peak in the early morning and a minimum in the late evening. The episodic pattern of cortisol secretion results from an episodic secretion of ACTH.

It has very recently been shown that proopiomelanocortin cells are present not only in the anterior lobe of the pituitary but also in the intermediate lobe and in the hypothalamus, the autonomic nervous system, adrenal medulla and the gonads [7]. Here the ACTH fraction of the molecule is probably not physiologically effective. The hypothalamican POMC cells are also called *β–endorphinergic cells* because their main secretory product, the information carrier, is β–endorphin. The β–endorphinergic cells in the hypothalamus project to extensive regions of the brain by way of long axons with branching collaterals. They may have something to do with the processing of stress and pain; they are certainly involved in regulation of the pituitary hormones and possibly also in stress amenorrhea. However, the exact functions of these β–endorphinergic neurons are still largely unknown. Nor is anything yet known about the role of the peptide molecules derived from the POMC in the intermediate pituitary lobe, the autonomic nervous system, the adrenal medulla and the gonads.

Fluctuation of the cortisol level. ACTH is the regulatory hormone that stimulates the cells in the adrenal cortex to increase their rate of synthesis and release of cortisol. The blood cortisol level fluctuates widely over 24 hours, in an endogenous *circadian rhythm.* The level is distinctly higher in the morning than in the evening (Fig. 17-17). These fluctuations depend on the time of day and not on sleeping habits. Assays after a person's sleep phase has been changed (e.g., in shift workers) have shown that the entraining signal for the circadian rhythm adjusts only slowly to such a change. That is, high cortisol levels in the morning are physiological, but the same level in the afternoon or evening can be pathological.

The adrenal glands in all humans release cortisol *episodically* as a result of the episodic release of ACTH. The lower graph in Fig. 17-17 demonstrates that the main cause of the circadian fluctuation is a higher frequency of episodes at night and in the early morning, which causes the blood cortisol to build up [11]. The occasional bursts in the afternoon and early evening can temporarily raise the blood cortisol level. In the clinic, an understanding of this episodic release is important for the differential diagnosis of hypercortisolism (Cushing's syndrome, p. 389).

Metabolic actions of the glucocorticoids. The glucocorticoids were named for their most important metabolic effect, to stimulate *gluconeogenesis in the liver.* Under the influence of a high cortisol level, amino acids are converted into glucose. Because the amino acids are derived from the breakdown of muscle protein, this process is called the *protein catabolic action of cortisol.* The glucocorticoids also diminish glucose *utilization* in all cells of the body, and by impeding the *transport* of glucose into the cells they antagonize the effect of insulin. Together, these effects raise the blood sugar level; an increase in glucocorticoid production is therefore diabetogenic.
In addition to enhancing protein catabolism, glucocorticoids have a distinct *antianabolic action.* The synthesis of *muscle proteins* in particular is reduced, because the glucocorticoids inhibit the transport of amino acids into the muscle cells. In the liver, by contrast, cortisol promotes the uptake of amino acids, which are then used by the liver cells for the synthesis of glucose (gluconeogenesis) or hepatic proteins (for details see textbooks of biochemistry) [6].
The glucocorticoids also participate in *lipid metabolism.* Triglycerides are split, so that the level of fatty acids in the blood rises. Because the uptake of glucose into adipose cells is impeded, fewer triglycerides are formed, which reduces the body's fat stores.

Stress reaction. Under physiological conditions these metabolic actions of the glucocorticoids are delicately balanced; they serve to make energy available quickly when required. This function is crucial, because the hypothalamus-pituitary-adrenal axis is activated primarily in acute *stress situations.* Under the acute action of stressors, there is rapid **elevation of the cortisol level** in the blood. When the same stressor is repeated or prolonged, the response of the hypothalamus-pituitary-adrenal axis becomes progressively weaker *(habituation).*
Another important function of cortisol during stress is the *permissive effect on the action of catecholamines on the smooth musculature of the vessels.* Stress stimulates the release of adrenalin and noradrenalin from the adrenal medulla. These catecholamines cause contraction of the smooth musculature of the cutaneous and intestinal vessels, while the muscle fibers in the vessels of the skeletal musculature relax. The result is a redistribution of oxygen- and nutrient-containing blood to the muscles, in case effort is required for fighting or flight. The catecholamines elicit this response only if cortisol is also present. That is, cortisol does not itself act on the smooth muscle fibers, but its presence enables the catecholamines to act – hence the term **permissive effect.**
The glucocorticoids from the adrenals resemble the mineralocorticoids structurally, and hence also always exert a slight secondary influence of the mineralocorticoid type (pp. 389f.).

Pharmacological aspects. Because substances with a glucocorticoid action are among the major drugs in current use, a knowledge of the physiology and pharmacology of glucocorticoids is particularly important. When the body produces them in excessive amounts, or when large doses of such a hormone are administered, the effects described above are intensified. The protein breakdown can lead to *muscular atrophy.* The *protein matrix of the bone* can degenerate, causing the condition called *osteoporosis.* Because of the associated increase in glucose production, the blood glucose concentration becomes too high; as a result, the liver converts the glucose to glycogen. But this conversion proceeds optimally only in the presence of sufficient insulin (pp. 391), and insulin secretion is easily inhibited by glucocorticoids. Hence a high glucocorticoid level puts the organism into a *prediabetic metabolic state.*

Antiinflammatory action. At higher concentration, the glucocorticoids have notable effects in addition to the possible metabolic maladjustments. All glucocorticoids *inhibit the symptoms of inflammation* in several ways. Any inflammation is characterized by three symptoms (summarized as "color, tumor, dolor"), as follows:
1. Reddening, owing to the increased blood flow through the inflamed area,
2. Swelling, because the permeability of capillaries in the inflamed region rises and more edema fluid leaks out,
3. Pain, resulting from irritation of the tissues by symptoms 1 and 2.

All three symptoms are inhibited by glucocorticoids.
Glucocorticoids also *inhibit the production of antibodies,* thereby impairing the body's defense against infection. This effect is negligible during short-term stress reactions, but becomes noticeable when a high cortisol level is maintained. This action is exploited therapeutically to reduce allergic reactions of the body and counteract immunological rejection of organ transplants.
Given the diversity of these actions, it is understandable that drugs with a glucocorticoid action are often used in medicine. It is important for the physician to be aware that such drugs can simultaneously suppress inflammatory symptoms and weaken immunological defenses. Because the glucocorticoids affect only the symptoms of inflammation and have no antibacterial action, bacterial infections can be masked with-

out becoming less dangerous. Therefore a patient to whom glucocorticoids are given should be kept under continuous observation. Another undesirable side effect of glucocorticoids is the inhibition of scar formation; it is particularly serious when it interferes with the healing of gastric ulcers or other internal wounds. Furthermore, glucocorticoids stimulate the secretion of hydrochloric acid. For these reasons, they are contraindicated for patients with gastric ulcers.

Pathophysiological aspects. It should be clear from the above that either too much or too little glucocorticoid has a deleterious effect on homeostasis of the body. An excess of corticol can be due to elevated CRH production and the resulting constant stimulation of pituitary ACTH secretion. On the other hand, the ACTH-producing cells in the pituitary can develop into benign tumors that produce too much ACTH autonomously. The pathological overstimulation of adrenal cortisol production gives rise to **Cushing's disease,** in which both adrenal glands are enlarged. The same symptoms are seen when an adrenal cortex itself becomes tumorous (benign or malignant) and produces too much cortisol; in this case the term **Cushing's syndrome** is used. Differential diagnosis here is assisted by a knowledge of the underlying control system (see Fig. 17-16). When a cortisol-producing adrenal cortical tumor is present, CRH and ACTH secretion is maximally inhibited and the blood ACTH level is especially low. But if the cause of the disorder is excessive secretion of CRH or ACTH, the blood ACTH level will obviously be high. On the basis of a measurement of the serum ACTH one can decide whether one is dealing with a CNS-pituitary or an adrenal defect. On rare occasions, however, ACTH can be produced ectopically (outside the pituitary) by a malignant tumor such as a pulmonary carcinoma.

Adrenal Androgens

Physiological androgen production. Lifelong production of fairly large quantities of *androgens* occurs in the *zona reticularis* of the adrenal cortex [1, 9, 11, 39] (for synthesis pathway see Fig. 17-18). There are several of these 19-carbon steroids. The most effective physiological androgen in humans is testosterone, but only very small amounts of it are produced in the adrenal cortex. On the other hand, the reticular zone synthesizes larger amounts of 19-carbon steroids with less androgenic effect. The most important adrenal androgen is *dehydroepiandrosterone (DEHA)*. In the woman, under physiological conditions this androgen is derived from the adrenal, but under certain pathological conditions the ovary also secretes considerable quantities of androgen. In the man 2/3 of all androgens are of testicular origin and about 1/3 derives from the adrenals. A high ACTH level not only increases the synthesis and secretion of glucocorticoids and (to a lesser extent) of mineralocorticoids, but also of the adrenal androgens.

Pathophysiological aspects. The above action of ACTH is a central feature in the **adrenogenital syndrome (AGS, also called congenital adrenal hyperplasia).** In this case the *formation of cortisol is reduced* or completely blocked because of enzyme defects. In the hypothalamic-pituitary-adrenal control system of the fetus this reduction has the same effect as adrenalectomy; that is, the *negative feedback normally provided by cortisol is absent.* As a consequence, the hypothalamus releases more CRH and thereby stimulates the pituitary to secrete more ACTH. Because of the enzyme defect, the adrenal cannot produce enough cortisol, but it secretes larger quantities of the other steroids. The *excessive androgens* can cause virilization of genetically female fetuses, so that phenotypically they are boys. The adrenogenital syndrome can be more or less severe. Some variants exhibit not only virilization but also salt loss, because of reduced aldosterone production. In some cases enzyme defects are manifest later, so that the symptoms may not appear until puberty or shortly thereafter *(late-onset AGS)*.
For unexplained reasons, the adrenal cortex sometimes produces abnormally abundant androgens (often DHEA sulfate) in the absence of an enzyme defect for cortisol formation. The affected women frequently complain of increasing hairiness of the male type (hirsutism) and other symptoms of virilization (enlarged clitoris, loss of head hair, seborrhea, etc.).

Mineralocorticoid System

The adrenal mineralocorticoids are synthesized predominantly in the zona glomerulosa. The most important representative of this group is *aldosterone* (synthesis pathway in Fig. 17-18).

Actions of aldosterone. The mineralocorticoids, in particular aldosterone, are involved in the *regulation of electrolyte and water balance* (p. 747). Aldosterone increases *sodium reabsorption* in the tubules of the kidney, which is associated with the reabsorption of water by osmosis. It also promotes the *excretion of potassium and protons.* Similar influences are exerted on ion and water transport in the intestine as well as in the salivary and sweat glands.

Regulatory mechanisms. The production and release of aldosterone are regulated in several ways. First, *sodium deficiency* and *elevated potassium* in the blood directly stimulate the cells of the zona glomerulosa, causing them to release greater amounts of aldosterone. Second, when *decreased sodium concentration* is accompanied by restricted renal blood flow, as can happen following severe loss of blood, *renin* is released from the epithelioid cells of the afferent vessels in the kidney (pp. 517, 747). Renin is a protease that acts on angiotensinogen, an α_2-globulin, formed in the liver, to split off angiotensin I. The decapeptide *angiotensin I* is converted into the effective octapeptide *angiotensin II* by a peptidase present in the blood and in the lungs, called converting enzyme. Removal of an additional amino acid produces angiotensin III. Angiotensin II has two effects; it acts as a vascoconstrictor (p. 518) and stimulates the release of aldosterone, which promotes sodium reabsorption in the distal tubule and collecting tubule system and thereby increases renal water retention (p. 747). That is, the *renin-angiotensin system* is involved in the control of sodium balance, of extracellular fluid volume and of blood pressure.

The renal-adrenal control system receives inputs from many *extrarenal and extraadrenal mechanisms.* For instance, adrenal aldosterone secretion can be stimulated by the release of pituitary ACTH. However, this mechanism produces only a single acute activation of the cells of the zona glomerulosa; with multiple exposure to ACTH, the secretory response is progressively attenuated. Such decreasing cellular responses to chemicals are relatively common in biology; the phenomenon in general is called *tachyphylaxis.* It can be explained by desensitization of receptors, by the unavailability of occupied receptors or by a reduction in number of receptors.

It has long been known that electrical stimulation of the renal nerves also increases the rate of renin release. β-receptor blockers can diminish this effect. It may be inferred that the sympathetic noradrenergic innervation of the kidney serves for the *fine adjustment* of renin secretion by the juxtaglomerular apparatus. Many direct or indirect effects on renin secretion can be exerted by way of direct innervation and possibly also by the release of adrenomedullary catecholamines (and peptides) [29]. For example, the influences of other baroreceptive structures (e.g., in the carotid sinus) or other sympathetic-activating internal or external factors can modulate renin secretion. For additional details of the renin-angiotensin-aldosterone system see pp. 520f. and p. 747.

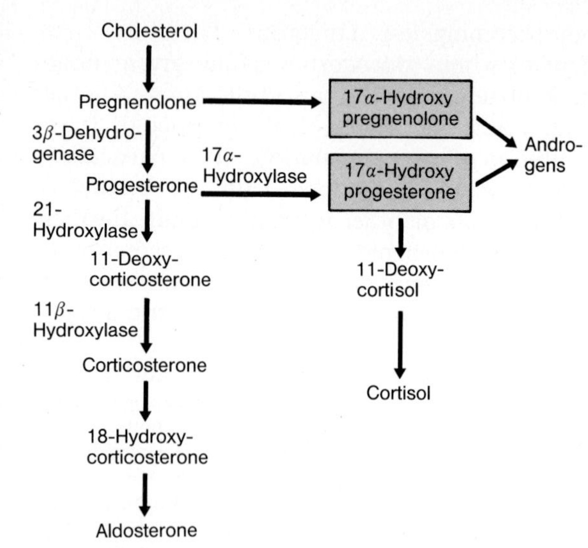

Fig. 17-18. Formation of adrenal steroids from cholesterol. Pregnenolone is a common precursor of all adrenocortical steroids. ACTH drives the reactions in the direction of cortisol synthesis, whereas angiotensin II drives them in the direction of aldosterone synthesis. It is important for the clinician to be familiar with the main steroid-forming enzymes, because of the characteristic syndromes produced by enzyme defects

Survey of the Steroid Hormones

Structure and synthesis. The steroid hormones are in the category of *lipids.* They are synthesized in a series of reactions involving progressive enlargement of the original precursor, acetyl-coenzyme A; the basic substance common to all steroids is *cholesterol.* The side chain of the cholesterol is split off by an enzyme system (side-chain-cleaving enzyme) between C-21 and C-22 to produce the 21-carbon steroids (Fig. 17-18; structural formulas can be found in textbooks of biochemistry). The next step forms a precursor common to all steroid hormones, *pregnenolone.* This is a mildly effective *gestagen* and hence has an action like that of progesterone (pp. 779f.); but because it appears only as an intermediate during steroid synthesis, it is hardly ever encountered in the circulation. In the ovary pregnenolone is converted to progesterone. Cells of the corpus luteum release considerable amounts of progesterone into the bloodstream, as does the placenta (p. 787). However, the hormone can also be present in other cells as an intermediary product in *androgen and estrogen synthesis.* Estrogen production always involves androgens as intermediates. In the adrenal cortex pregnenolone is converted to still other steroids – *glucocorticoids, mineralocorticoids* and androgens, whereas the androgens are always 19-carbon steroids, regardless of whether they are formed in the adrenals, the testes or the ovary. The androgens are produced by splitting off the 2-carbon side chain at C-17 of the 21-carbon steroids. The ovary and, to a lesser extent, the testes can produce estrogens from certain 19-carbon steroids, by *aromatization of the A ring* and removal of an additional CH_3 group. In Figs. 17-18 and 23-1 the enzymes involved in steroid synthesis are also noted. Some of them play a certain role in the diseases mentioned on p. 389.

Release, transport and inactivation. The *release of the steroid hormones* is influenced by other hormones. At the adrenal cortex *ACTH* increases the synthesis and release of *cortisol;* it also makes some contribution to the production and release of the androgens. *Angiotensin II* stimulates the synthesis and release of *aldosterone* in the adrenal cortex. At the ovary, *FSH* and *LH* enhance the synthesis of *estrogen* and *progesterone* and their release from granulosa or luteal cells (pp. 778f.). In the testes *Leydig's interstitial cells* are stimulated to produce more testosterone by *LH* (pp. 776f.). It is not entirely clear whether FSH influences the aromatization of testosterone to estrogen, with an effect on spermatogenesis.
As lipids, steroid hormones are poorly soluble in water; for this reason, in the blood they are joined by non-covalent bonds to *plasma proteins* [40]. Although the amount of steroids circulating in free form is small, it is only this fraction that is active. Some steroid hormones are not converted to their active form until they have entered the target cell; for instance, testosterone itself is ineffective in skin structures such as the sebaceous glands and hair follicles, but becomes effective after reduction to *5-α–dihydrotestosterone* (5-α–DHT). The feedback signal to the CNS is provided by testosterone itself; here it binds primarily to testosterone receptors, although some of its effects evidently occur only after it has been aromatized to estrogens. Indeed, the male as well as the female CNS contains enzymes (aromatases) that can aromatize testosterone [32]. The greater fraction of the steroid hormones never interacts with a target cell and is eventually inactivated by conversion to the glucuronide. In this form the hormones are readily water soluble and can be excreted by way of the kidneys.

17.6 The Pancreatic Hormones

The hormones by which homeostasis of the blood sugar is preserved – *insulin, glucagon* and *somatostatin* – are secreted by the *islets of Langerhans* in the pancreas. These structures are conglomerates of so-called A, B and D cells, endocrine cells scattered in groups of a few thousand through the exocrine tissue that makes up most of the pancreas. About 60 % of the islet cells are B cells, which produce insulin, 25 % are

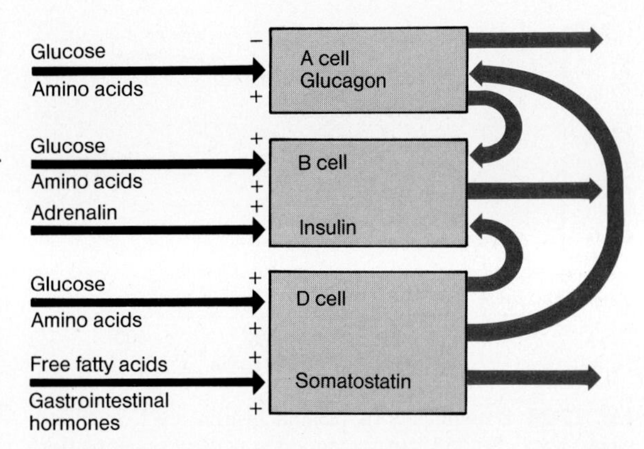

Fig. 17-19. Regulation of the islet cells. The secretory products of the cells in the islets of Langerhans are glucagon from the A cells, insulin from the B cells and somatostatin from the D cells. Secretion of insulin is stimulated by high blood concentrations of glucose and amino acids, and inhibited by adrenalin. The secretory activity of the glucagon-producing A cell is inhibited by high blood glucose levels and stimulated by low glucose levels; amino acids have the opposite effect. Glucagon from the A cell inhibits secretion of insulin by the B cell, in a paracrine action. The D cells are stimulated to produce more somatostatin by high levels of glucose and amino acids as well as fatty acids and gastrointestinal hormones. Somatostatin also has a paracrine action, inhibiting insulin secretion by the B cell

glucagon-producing A cells, and the remaining 15 % are D cells, producing somatostatin. The principles of regulation of these cells, by nutritive and paracrine effects, are diagrammed in Fig. 17-19. For the islet cells to function normally, they also require normal levels of thyroid hormone as well as of gonadal and adrenal steroid hormones [30].

Insulin

Structure and action on blood sugar. Insulin, synthesized in the B cells of the pancreas, is a polypeptide comprising two peptide chains. The *A chain,* with 21 amino acids, is joined by disulfide bridges to the *B chain* of 30 amino acids. The insulins of different animals differ only slightly in their amino acid sequence and have identical biological actions.
The overall effect of the *diverse metabolic actions* of insulin is to *lower the blood sugar level,* the normal range of which is 0.8–1.0 g/l. When the glucose concentration in the plasma rises, immediately after consumption of carbohydrates, the result is a stimulation of insulin secretion. Under the influence of the insulin the uptake of glucose into almost all cells of the body is increased, so

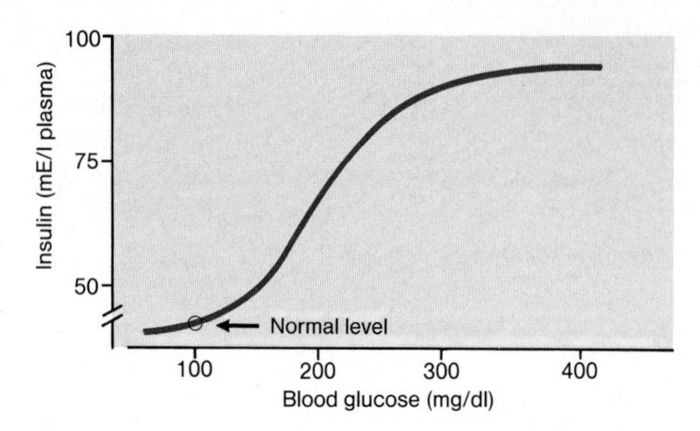

Fig. 17-20. Dependence of plasma insulin level on blood sugar level. With a normal blood glucose concentration (about 100 mg/dl), insulin is almost undetectable, but under physiological conditions the insulin level rises sharply when the blood sugar level rises

that the plasma glucose concentration falls again (Fig. 17-20).

Actions on glucose metabolism in the liver. The liver is one of the most important *glucose-storing organs.* Glucose can diffuse freely into its cells and leave them again when the blood glucose level is low. Under the influence of the carbohydrate-induced release of insulin, the cells in the liver convert glucose to glycogen, thereby lowering the blood glucose concentration. One of the foremost biochemical actions of insulin is activation of the enzyme *glucokinase,* which is responsible for phosphorylation of the glucose that diffuses into the hepatic cells. Insulin also stimulates other enzymes, especially phosphofructokinase and glycogen synthetase, which polymerize the phosphorylated glucose to glycogen. Finally, insulin *inhibits the glycogen-degrading enzymes* (phosphorylases), so that when the insulin level is high, glycogen is conserved. By the combination of rapid glycogen synthesis and inhibition of glycogenolysis, the postprandially (i.e., after eating) elevated glucose concentration is quickly returned to the normal level. The most important factor inducing insulin secretion is thus eliminated, and the insulin level in the blood also returns to normal.

When the body requires energy without eating during the hours that follow, the glycogen is converted back to glucose. Because of the low insulin level phosphorylases are activated that convert glycogen to glucose phosphate, which is dephosphorylated by a glucose phosphatase. The glucose so formed can leave the cell by diffusion, so that the blood glucose level is kept constant between meals. In people on a normal diet, about 60 % of the glucose consumed in food is temporarily stored on the liver and later made available by this rapid buildup and breakdown of glycogen [3, 5, 6, 11].

Actions on glucose metabolism in muscle cells. When the insulin level is low, muscle cells are normally impermeable to glucose, and obtain all the energy they need by fatty-acid metabolism. The *high insulin level* that prevails postprandially, as a consequence of the high glucose level, makes the muscle cell *permeable to glucose,* which can then be used as an energy source. However, when muscles are very active, their cell membranes can become permeable to glucose by an insulin-independent mechanism. In this case the working muscle meets its energy requirement with glucose even at a basal insulin level. The details of this mechanism are unknown. Musculature that is not active can also form and store a slight amount of *glycogen* postprandially (i.e., under the influence of high insulin and glucose levels). In emergencies, this glycogen is reconverted to glucose molecules and metabolized by the muscle cell (p. 77, p. 654). As a rule, it does not diffuse back into the blood and therefore plays no role in postprandial blood-sugar regulation.

Insulin initiates a transmembrane *glucose-transport mechanism* when it becomes bound to an insulin receptor in the muscle-cell membrane. It is not yet known whether the insulin-receptor complex is itself the carrier protein or whether it activates another transport system.

Glucose metabolism in nerve cells. The cells of the CNS meet their not inconsiderable energy requirements *almost exclusively by way of glucose,* by a process *independent of insulin.* Neither the membrane permeability to glucose nor intracellular enzyme systems are appreciably stimulated or activated by insulin. The fact that the CNS obtains its energy entirely from glucose explains why decrease of the blood glucose below a critical level (0.5–0.2 g/l) can lead to *hypoglycemic shock,* with clouded consciousness or even coma.

Most of the other cells in the body respond like muscle cells to high insulin levels.

Action on lipid metabolism. The liver can store up only a certain amount of glycogen under the influence of insulin. The surplus glucose that diffuses into the liver cells is phosphorylated, and thus retained in the cell, but it is then converted to fat rather than glycogen. This *fat formation* is also a direct action of insulin. The fatty acids so produced travel in the bloodstream to adipose cells, where they are taken up and stored. In the blood these fats are transported as *lipoproteins.* These lipoproteins are significant elements in the development of arteriosclerosis, with its associated risks of embolism and infarcts.

In principle, the action of insulin on *adipose cells* resembles that on liver cells. However, fatty acid production in the liver considerably exceeds that in the adipose tissue, so that the fatty acids are transferred from the former to the latter as described above. Fatty acids are *stored in the form of triglycerides.* An additional crucial action of insulin on adipose cells is to make available glycerine for the conversion to triglycerides. Each glycerine molecule can be esterified with three molecules of fatty acid.

The above effects of insulin on lipid metabolism are reversed when little insulin is secreted; that is, triglycerides are split to form glycerine and free fatty acids. A particularly important feature of this process is the *inhibition of a hormone-sensitive lipase by insulin.* The result is an acceleration of lipolysis when the insulin level is low. The free fatty acids formed by breakdown of triglycerides enter the blood, along with the glycerine, and are then available to the rest of the body as an energy source. All the cells except nerve cells can utilize these *free fatty acids.* A large proportion of the fatty acids removed from storage during insulin deficiency is taken up again by the liver. The liver cells can synthesize triglycerides even without insulin, so that during insulin deficiency the fatty acids released from storage accumulate as triglycerides in the liver. It is for this reason that patients with insulin deficiency (i.e., with diabetes mellitus) become thin but nevertheless develop a fatty liver.

The abundance of fatty acids in the liver causes the formation of activated acetic acid *(acetyl-CoA).* Being unable to use up all of this acetyl-CoA as an energy source, the liver converts it to *acetoacetic acid,* which passes into the blood. When the insulin level is high enough, peripheral cells can retrieve acetyl-CoA from acetoacetic acid, which thus offers a supply of energy. But *in the absence of insulin* this conversion does not occur; instead, some of the acetoacetic acid is converted to *β–hydroxybutyric acid* and acetone. These three metabolites are called ketone bodies, and the resulting metabolic state is *ketosis.* Because of it, a patient in a diabetic coma has an acetone-scented breath and metabolic acidosis of the blood.

Actions on protein metabolism. The protein consumed in food is broken down to amino acids, which are then used for the synthesis of the body's own proteins. This synthesis proceeds optimally only under the influence of insulin. *Insulin enables the active transport* of many, but not all, amino acids into the cell. *Growth hormone* has a similar action, but insulin and growth hormone promote the uptake of different groups of amino acids. The postprandial elevation of the intracellular amino acid levels rapidly increases ribosomal protein synthesis. In addition, insulin brings about a *medium-term increase in protein synthesis* by raising the rate of DNA transcription in the nucleus, so that more RNA is available. In summary, then, *insulin promotes the production of protein.* Accordingly, the absence of insulin has opposite effects. The body cannot maintain its protein reserves. Amino acids are either used directly as a source of energy or redirected into the process of gluconeogenesis. Because insulin is almost equal in importance to growth hormone for protein synthesis, a child's body can grow only with optimal secretion of both hormones [41].

Glucagon

Like insulin, the glucagon produced in the *A cells* of the islets of Langerhans is a polypeptide comprising a chain of 29 amino acids. It has various *insulin-antagonistic* actions. Glucagon *stimulates the breakdown of liver glycogen* (glycogenolysis), so that when the blood sugar level becomes too low (hypoglycemia) glucose is rapidly made available to the body (Fig. 17-21).

Having formed a complex with its receptor in the cell membrane, glucagon stimulates *adenylate cyclase,* with the result that more ATP is

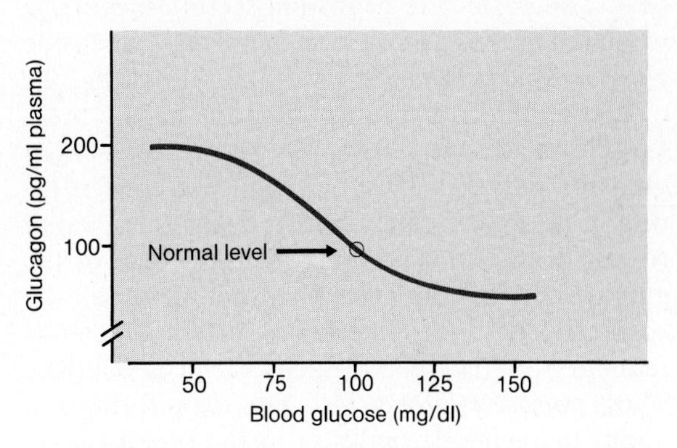

Fig. 17-21. Dependence of blood glucagon on the blood sugar level. Under normal conditions and in hyperglycemia, the glucagon concentration in the blood is low, but it rises distinctly in hypoglycemic states

converted to cAMP. The cAMP is the intracellular second messenger for the action of glucagon; it stimulates a cascade of biochemical processes that ends with the breakdown of glycogen. Because the liver is the main glycogen depot, it is the crucial target organ for glucagon. In cases of *chronic hypoglycemia,* the prolonged action of glucagon can deplete the stores of glycogen in the liver, but hepatic gluconeogenesis continues nevertheless. The reason is that glucagon enables the liver cells to take up more of the amino acids circulating in the blood; these amino acids can then be used in the synthesis of glucose.

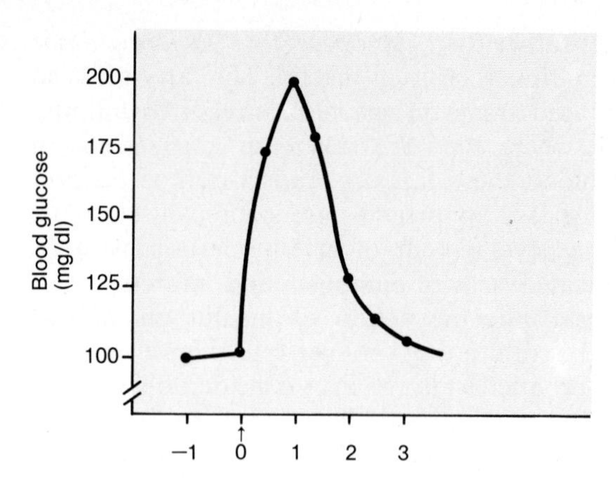

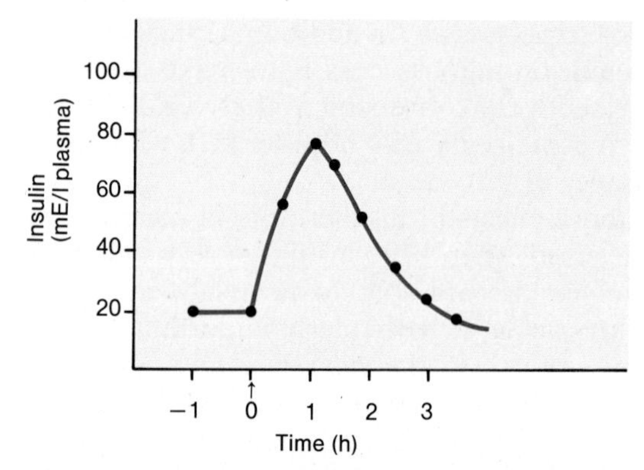

Fig. 17-22. Glucose tolerance test. Normally the blood glucose concentration is about 100 mg per dl of plasma. Under these conditions basal plasma insulin levels are observed. When a healthy subject drinks a solution containing 100 g glucose, the blood glucose level rises sharply *(above)*. As a reaction to this glucose load the insulin level also rises, with a slight delay *(below)*.

Somatostatin

Somatostatin is a peptide consisting of 14 amino acids, which was originally identified in the hypothalamus. There this peptide acts to inhibit the production of hypophyseal growth hormone (somatotropin; p. 381), and it is for this action that it was named. Somatostatin has since been found in many other cells of the body, where its actions are again predominantly *inhibitory.* In the islets of Langerhans it is produced by the *D cells.* Here it has a paracrine action, inhibiting the secretion of *insulin* and *glucagon.* This peptide also has extrapancreatic effects; it inhibits the motility of the gastrointestinal tract and of the gallbladder, and reduces the secretion of digestive juices. As a result, the absorption of food is slowed. Altogether, then, the actions of somatostatin serve to diminish digestive activity and hence to prevent excessive fluctuation of the blood sugar level.

Regulation of Glucose Balance

An elevated blood glucose level is the strongest stimulus for the **secretion of insulin** from the B cells. The basal rate of insulin secretion prevails when the blood glucose level is normal; when the glucose concentration is lower than 0.9 g per liter of blood, the insulin in the blood is hardly measurable at all. After a healthy subject has taken glucose orally (ca. 100 g), the glucose concentration in the blood rises rapidly, causing the rapid release of insulin. The subsequent declines of the glucose and insulin levels have well-defined time courses (Fig. 17-22). In cases of insulin deficiency reduction of the blood glucose level is delayed. These *glucose-tolerance tests* provide information about the general condition of the blood-sugar-regulating B cells in the pancreatic islets. It has recently been shown that amino acids and free fatty acids stimulate insulin secretion in the same way, though considerably less effectively. But B cells can be activated not only by these food constituents, but also by certain *gastrointestinal peptide hormones* and by their *parasympathetic innervation.* Such effects are counteracted by *sympathetic* activity, which inhibits insulin secretion by way of a β–adrenergic receptor. These opposed influences of the sympathetic and parasympathetic systems make sense, inasmuch as under resting conditions the parasympathetic predominates and food can be digested. In stress situations energy must be made available, so that glucose should not be converted to glucogen. It also makes sense that catecholamines inhibit insulin secretion, enabling the glucose to be used directly as an energy source.

The **secretion of glucagon** from the A cells is regulated in almost exactly the opposite way. Hypoglycemia strongly stimulates glucagon secretion, which is sensible because glycogen is a source of glucose and therefore counteracts hypoglycemia.

The **secretion of somatostatin** from the D cells in the islets is stimulated by a high glucose level and by an increase in the amino-acid and fatty-acid content of the blood. That is, somatostatin acts as a brake on the secretion of insulin, preventing an overshoot that might be caused by hyperglycemia if this regulation were not available.

Pathophysiological Aspects

A detailed discussion of the pathophysiology of insulin regulation is outside the scope of this section, but the major disorders will be summarized. If too little insulin is produced, or if insulin is unable to act at the target cells, the blood sugar level rises and **diabetes mellitus** is produced. The name of this condition comes from the fact that the urine becomes sweet ("mel" means honey), because some of the excess blood glucose is excreted in the urine. In severe insulin deficiency it becomes impossible to remove all of the unutilized glucose by way of the urine. Furthermore, insulin deficiency stimulates lipolysis, so that *ketone bodies* (p. 393) are formed. When the disease is advanced, the patient can fall into a *diabetic coma.* If the body produces too much insulin (e.g., because of islet-cell tumors) or too much is injected by the physician, the body's glucose levels fall, the CNS is no longer adequately nourished, and the result is *hypoglycemic shock.* Both conditions can be lethal if not treated, by administering either glucose (for hypoglycemic shock) or insulin (for diabetic coma).

17.7 Homeostasis of Calcium and Phosphate Balance

Calcium-ion homeostasis is subject to extremely fine regulation [13, 15, 35], primarily by way of three hormones:
- *parathyroid hormone (PTH),* which consists of 84 amino acids and is produced in the four parathyroid glands (epithelial bodies),
- *calcitonin* (thyrocalcitonin), formed by the C-cells scattered throughout the thyroid gland and consisting of 32 amino acids,
- the *vitamin D hormone,* formed in the kidney from vitamin D.

The actions of these three hormones are diagrammed in Fig. 17-23 and described separately below.

Actions of the Regulatory Hormones

Parathyroid hormone (PTH). The physiological stimulus for the release of PTH is a *reduced calcium-ion concentration* in the blood [21, 35].

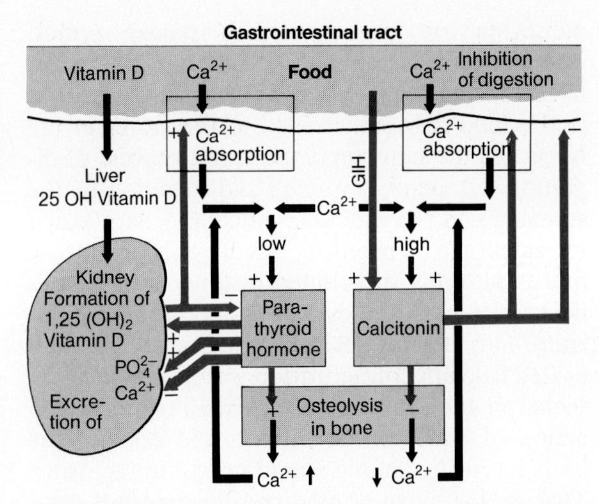

Fig. 17-23. Regulation of calcium homeostasis by parathyroid hormone, calcitonin and vitamin D hormone. Low blood calcium ion concentrations stimulate the secretion of parathyroid hormone, and hence osteolysis; simultaneously, they promote the formation of vitamin D hormone in the kidney, thereby increasing calcium absorption in the intestine. High calcium concentrations cause the release of calcitonin, which retards osteolysis and intestinal calcium absorption. Gastrointestinal hormones (GIH) stimulate calcitonin secretion.

PTH acts at the bones, where it *activates osteoclasts* to increase the rate of bone resorption, so that calcium and phosphate ions are released into the blood. Binding of the calcium to phosphate ions is prevented by the simultaneous action of PTH to promote the excretion of phosphate in the kidneys. Parathyroid hormone has an additional important influence on the kidney; it stimulates an enzyme that hydroxylates 25(OH)-vitamin D in position C-1. As a result, more of the biologically active *1,25 $(OH)_2$ vitamin D hormone* is produced [17]. This vitamin D hormone is also important for the regulation of calcium homeostasis (see below). Calcium retention in the body is also assisted by a direct action of PTH on the kidney, which reduces the excretion of calcium ions. When the calcium-ion concentration in the blood is high, the secretion of PTH is inhibited.

Calcitonin. The C cells of the thyroid gland always release calcitonin at a higher rate when the blood calcium level is elevated [15, 35]. The consequence is *diminished osteolysis* and the *increased incorporation of calcium* into the bones. That is, calcitonin functions as an antagonist to PTH. Another physiological stimulus for calcitonin secretion is food intake; the C cells are stimulated by the postprandial rise in the amounts of circulating gastrointestinal hormones, gastrin, cholecystokinin (pancreozymin) and glucagon (see also [7]). Because of the enhanced calcitonin release, the calcium consumed in the food is rapidly added to the stores in the bones. At the same time, the entire process of digestion – stomach emptying and secretion by the stomach and the exocrine pancreas – is retarded by calcitonin. Therefore calcium absorption is more uniformly distributed in time, and there is no sudden postprandial peak in the blood calcium. This effect is desirable because a greatly elevated calcium concentration would inhibit PTH secretion and thus negate the calcium-conserving action of PTH on the kidney; the calcium the body has just acquired would be lost in the urine. That is, the slowing of digestion amounts to a useful *calcium-conserving action* of calcitonin in combination with PTH.

Vitamin D hormone. A third crucial factor in blood calcium constancy is the hormone derived from vitamin D [13]. By definition, a vitamin is a substance not synthesized by the body itself; in the case of vitamin D, the precursors of the provitamin must be obtained from food either as ergosterol (preprovitamin D_3), of animal origin, or as dehydroxycholesterol (preprovitamin D_2), of plant origin. Under irradiation of the skin by sunlight, a bond between two C atoms of these precursors is split to produce the provitamins D_2 and D_3. In the liver, these D vitamins are hydroxylated at position C-25 to form 25-hydroxycholecalciferol. When this compound reaches the kidney, it is again hydroxylated, now at position C-1; as mentioned above, the enzyme in the kidney that catalyzes this reaction is activated by PTH. The 1,25-dihydroxycholecalciferol is the effective vitamin D hormone, which contributes to homeostasis of calcium ions in the blood. That is, the vitamin D consumed in food is a prohormone. When the blood calcium-ion concentration is too low, the release of PTH is enhanced, which increases the synthesis of vitamin D hormone, and the latter *assists absorption of calcium ions at the intestinal epithelium.* The vitamin D hormone provides negative feedback to the parathyroid glands; that is, the secretion of PTH is inhibited by vitamin D hormone. The two hormones thus constitute a closed-loop control system.

Pathophysiology of Calcium Homeostasis

Primary hyperparathyroidism. There is a rare condition in which adenomas of the parathyroid glands develop; these produce too much PTH, and the resulting increase in osteolysis causes *hypercalcemia.* Renal symptoms are the most prominent: polyuria and polydipsia. But these patients often also exhibit neurological symptoms: asthenia, weakened reflexes and uncharacteristic EEG changes.

Secondary hyperparathyroidism. In chronic renal disease the production of vitamin D hormone is disturbed, and there is inadequate calcium absorption. Because of the chronic hypocalcemia, PTH is continually released. In this state of secondary hyperparathyroidism *decalcification of the bones* occurs, with effects ranging from slight osteopathic changes to severe skeletal damage.

Hypoparathyroidism. Cases of hypoparathyroidism are considerably less common. The most frequent cause used to be removal of the parathyroid glands during thyroidectomy, but today autoimmune diseases are the major factor in the development of hypoparathyroidism. The characteristic clinical symptoms are *hypocalcemia* and *hyperphosphatemia.* Muscular hyperexcitability is a common result. A typical feature of hypocalcemic spasms *(tetany)* is strong flexion of the wrists. Sometimes children experience laryngospasm, in which the contraction of the vocal cords can cause death by suffocation.

Disturbances of calcitonin production. It is also possible for the C cells in the thyroid gland to produce too much or too little hormone. Excessive calcitonin production can be due to malignancy of the C cells; osteolysis is inhibited but the calcium-ion concentration in the blood is not lowered. However, the resulting hypercalcemia causes hardly any clinical symptoms. Diagnosis of this condition is difficult and can be reliably performed only by the radioimmunological determination of calcitonin. Ectopic tumors that produce calcitonin are extremely rare.

Vitamin-D-hormone deficiency. When the production of vitamin D hormone is impaired, the symptoms of *rickets* appear. Because insufficient calcium is absorbed from the intestinal tract, the bones are not adequately calcified and the concentration of calcium ions in the blood is too low. The low blood calcium enhances PTH secretion, which would ordinarily stimulate the production of vitamin D hormone in the kidneys. Because the precursors of vitamin D must be obtained from food, one reason for a deficiency in vitamin D hormone is a diet deficient in these precursors; however, rickets can also be caused by renal disease and genetic defects.

17.8 Hormones of the Adrenal Medulla

Catecholamines

Distribution. The catecholamines are synthesized from the amino acid tyrosine. One of them, noradrenalin (norepinephrine), is produced as a neurotransmitter by postsynaptic neurons in the sympathetic nervous system; the presynaptic transmitter in this system is acetylcholine (p. 397). The adrenal medulla contains cells that have migrated from the neural folds during embryogenesis. Despite their origin, they differentiate not into neurons but rather into cells lacking dendrites and axons. These cells produce **noradrenalin** or **adrenalin** (epinephrine) and, like the sympathetic neurons, are innervated by cholinergic fibers. In the CNS there are both noradrenergic and adrenergic neurons. These three adrenergic/noradrenergic systems often function synergistically.

Actions in stressful situations. Under resting conditions the adrenomedullary cells continually secrete small amounts of adrenalin and probably also of noradrenalin. However, most of the noradrenalin circulating in the blood originates in the terminals of sympathetic neurons. Under the influence of *environmental or internal stress* – for instance, situations requiring great physical or mental effort, infections, injury, or hypoglycemia – both the adrenomedullary and the sympathetic secretion of noradrenalin and adrenalin are *strongly stimulated.* The two hormones act as important regulatory factors in stressful situations. Both catecholamines increase cardiac activity (p. 340), contract vessels in the splanchnic region, and dilate the vessels that supply muscles. They also inhibit gastrointestinal motility and dilate the bronchi. The vascular effects cause an appropriate change in the physiological state of the organism, as follows. When an animal or person is in danger, digestive processes should not be continued; therefore gastrointestinal activity can be reduced. Because oxygen and glucose must be made available to the musculature if the need to fight or flee should arise, the bronchi and the vessels in the muscle are expanded.

Metabolic actions. The catecholamines have metabolic actions [6] that provide energy for impending fight or flight. The primary source of energy is glucose; therefore *catecholamines induce glycogen breakdown* in the liver and musculature, and also promote gluconeogenesis in the liver. These actions are chiefly due to adrenalin. Both catecholamines stimulate *lipolysis in adipose tissue* and *proteolysis in hepatic tissue,* ensuring that the energy sources will be replenished in the medium term. These metabolic actions of catecholamines are also important in regulating hypoglycemia. When the blood sugar level drops too rapidly, adrenomedullary catecholamine secretion is strongly stimulated and the hypoglycemia is counteracted. Under these conditions the catecholamines act synergistically with glucagon. Furthermore, both catecholamines inhibit the secretion of insulin by the islet cells, so that all insulin-dependent mechanisms are restricted. This action also serves to maintain an elevated blood glucose level as an adjustment to emergencies.

Receptor systems. There are at least two different receptor systems for adrenalin and noradrenalin: the *α– and β–receptor systems* [6]. Each can be subdivided according to their affinity for pharmacological substances, so that there are α_1, α_2, β_1 and β_2 receptors. This diversity of receptor types can explain the high specificity of catecholamines at certain organs. For instance, vasoconstriction in the splanchnic region is mediated by α receptors, whereas β receptors mediate the metabolic actions and the vasodilation in the skeletal musculature. The inhibition of insulin secretion is mediated by α receptors, and lipolysis and the cardiac actions by β receptors. The β–receptor-mediated catecholamine actions involve activation of an adenyl cyclase to produce cAMP, as an intracellular second messenger. The existence of different receptor types is clinically important, because of the many receptor-blocking substances that are used to treat cardiovascular diseases and disturbances of organ perfusion.

Peptides of the Adrenal Medulla

It has recently been shown that, in addition to noradrenalin and adrenalin, the adrenomedullary cells produce *peptides* known to have regulatory functions in the CNS and gastrointestinal tract. Those so far identified are Substance P, VIP, somatostatin, met-enkephalin and substances resembling cholecystokinin (CCK). The two types of catecholamine-producing cells can be assigned to various subclasses according to their peptide content. It is not yet known whether cells of different subtypes are regulated differently [4].

17.9 Additional Hormonal Systems

Pineal body. The pineal body or gland is an evagination of the roof of the third ventricle, which has many functions in the animal kingdom. In phylogenetically older species it is *light-sensitive* and mediates the influence of light signals on reproduction and circadian rhythms. In mammals a direct influence of light on pineal function is probably of subordinate importance but cannot be discounted, because photons can presumably reach the organ even through the skin and skull. The mammalian pineal body is also involved in the *control of circadian rhythms* [37]. Light is detected by way of the retina, and the information is conducted by nerve fibers directly to the hypothalamus *(retinohypothalamic tract)*. From there it is transmitted through a chain of neurons to the cervical sympathetic trunk and relayed by ascending sympathetic fibers that pass through the superior cervical ganglion to the interior of the skull and finally innervate the pineal body. The transmitter here, as in almost all structures with sympathetic innervation, is *noradrenalin*. It is by this complicated route that the pinealocytes are informed about the light/dark rhythm. Their most important secretory product is thought to be the biogenic amine *melatonin*. The synthesis and release of melatonin are inhibited by light and stimulated in the dark. This diurnal oscillation is very clear in measurements of melatonin in the blood of healthy people. The many functions of melatonin in animals are all related to reproduction; the relevance of such mechanisms to humans remains to be determined.

Thymus. This organ, situated behind the sternum, produces a number of *peptides*. These peptides are thought to play a role in immunological defense mechanisms, but no details are known.

Kidneys. The kidney has been mentioned above as an *endocrine organ* for the production of *renin and vitamin D hormone* (p. 737, p. 395). Reference is made to the renal production of the hormone *erythropoietin* and its significance in erythropoiesis in the chapter on functions of the blood (p. 411).

"Tissue hormones". At the beginning of this chapter mention was made of the historical difficulty in distinguishing between the hormones of endocrine glands and the substances produced in various tissues that have a hormone-like action on neighboring cells in the same tissue (pp. 373f.). The latter group of *paracrine* substances is now thought to comprise chiefly the *prostaglandins, prostacyclins* and *thromboxanes*. These play an important role in various bodily functions and enhance or inhibit the action of other hormones. Details can be found in textbooks of biochemistry.

There are sure to be a number of as yet undiscovered hormones, in addition to the hormones and sites of production discussed here. In the light of present knowledge, it is likely that many organs have hormone-producing elements. For instance, the *heart* has recently been recognized as an endocrine organ, because it produces a peptide that increases sodium excretion in the kidney [16]. This hormone is called *atrial natriuretic factor (ANF)*.

17.10 References

Textbooks and Handbooks

1. Besser, G.M., Rees, L.H.: Clinics in Endocrinology and Metabolism. Vol. 14, No. 4. The Pituitary-Adrenocortical Axis. W.B. Saunders Company 1985
2. Franchimont, P.: Clinics in Endocrinology and Metabolism. Vol.15, No. 1. Paracrine Contr. W.B. Saunders Company 1986
3. Guyton, A.C.: Textbook of Medical Physiology. W.B. Saunders Co. 7th Edition 1986
4. Hakanson, R., Thorell, J.: Biogenetics of Neurohormonal Peptides. Academic Press, New York, 1985
5. Johnston, D.G., Alberti, K.G.M.M.: Clinics in Endocrinology and Metabolism. Vol. 11, No. 2. New Aspects of Diabetes. W.B. Saunders Company Ltd. 1982
6. Jungermann, K., Möhler, H.: Biochemie. Springer Berlin Heidelberg New York 1980
7. Krieger, D.T., Brownstein, M.J., Martin, J.B.: Brain Peptides. Wiley and Sons, New York 1971
8. Robinson, G.A., Butcher, R.W., Sutherland, E.W.: Cyclic AMP. Academic Press, New York 1971
9. Shearman, R:P.: Clinical Reproductive Endocrinology. Churchill Livingstone Edinburgh London Melbourne and New York 1985
10. Toft, A.D.: Clinics in Endocrinology and Metabolism. Vol. 14, No. 2. Hyperthyroidism. W.B. Saunders Company 1985
11. Wilson, J.D., Foster, D.W.: William's Textbook of Endocrinology. W.B. Saunders Co. 7th Edition 1985
12. Wuttke, W., Weindl, A., Voigt, K.H., Dries, R.-R.: Brain and Pituitary Peptides. S. Karger 1980

Original Papers and Reviews

13. Brommage, R., DeLuca, H.F.: Evidence that 1,25-Dihydroxyvitamin D3 is the Physiologically Active Metabolite of Vitamin D3. Endocr. Rev. *6/4*, 491–511 (1985)
14. Brownstein, M.J., Russell, J.T., Gainer, H.: Biosynthesis of Posterior Pituitary Hormones. (Eds.: Ganong, Martini). In: Frontiers in Neuroendocrinology, Vol. 7, pp. 31–43, Raven Press NY 1982
15. Canalis, E.: The Hormonal and Local Regulation of Bone Formation. Endocr. Rev. *4/1*, 62–77 (1983)
16. Cantin, M., Genest, J.: The Heart and the Atrial Natriuretic Factor. Endocr. Rev. *6/2*, 107–127 (1985)
17. DeLuca, H.F.: Recent Advances in the Metabolism of Vitamin D. Ann. Rev. Physiol. *44*, 141–162 (1981)
18. Eipper, B.A., Mains, R.E.: Structure and Biosynthesis of Pro-Adrenocorticotropin/Endorphin and Related Peptides. Endocr. Rev. *1/1*, 1–27 (1980)
19. Froesch, E.R., Schmid, Chr., Schwander, J., Zapf, J.: Actions of Insulin-like Growth Factors. Ann. Rev. Physiol. *47*, 443–467 (1985)
20. Guillemin, R.: Peptides in the Brain: the New Endocrinology of the Neuron (Nobel Lecture). Science *202*, 390–402 (1978)
21. Habener, J.F.: Regulation of Parathyroid Hormone Secretion and Biosynthesis. Ann. Rev. Physiol. *43*, 211–223 (1981)
22. Herbert, E., Roberts, J., Phillips, M., Allen, R., Hinman, M., Budarf, M., Policastro, P., Rosa, P.: Biosynthesis, Processing, and Release of Corticotropin, β-Endorphin, and Melanocyte-Stimulating Hormone in Pituitary Cell Culture Systems. In: Frontiers in Neuroendocrinology, Vol. 6. pp. 67–101. Raven Press NY 1980
23. Hughes, J.P., Friesen, H.G.: The Nature and Regulation of the Receptors for Pituitary Growth Hormone. Ann. Rev. Physiol. *47*, 469–482 (1985)
24. Imura, H., Nakai, Y.: "Endorphins" in Pituitary and Other Tissues. Ann. Rev. Physiol. *43*, 265–278 (1981)
25. Isaksson, O.G.P., Eden, S., Jansson, J.-O.: Mode of Action of Pituitary Growth Hormone on Target Cells. Ann. Rev. Physiol. *47*, 483–499 (1985)
26. Jacobson, D.H., Gorman, C.A.: Endocrine Ophthalmopathy: Current Ideas Concerning Etiology, Pathogenesis, and Treatment. Endocr. Rev. *5/2*, 200–220 (1984)
27. Jensen, E.V., Greene, G.L., Closs, L.E., DeSombre, E.R., Nadji, M.: Receptors Reconsidered: A 20-Year Perspective. Recent Progress in Hormone Research, Vol. *38*, 1–40. Academic Press (1982)
28. Keller-Wood, M.E., Dallman, M.F.: Corticosteroid Inhibition of ACTH Secretion. Endocr. Rev. *5/1*, 1–24 (1984)
29. Kotchen, T.A., Guthrie, G.P.: Renin-Angiotensin-Aldosterone and Hypertension. Endocr. Rev. *1/1*, 78–99 (1980)
30. Lenzen, S., Bailey, C.J.: Thyroid Hormones, Gonadal and Adrenocortical Steroids and the Function of the Islets of Langerhans. Endocr. Rev. *5/3*, 411–434 (1984)
31. Leong, D.A., Frawley, L.S., Neill, J.D.: Neuroendocrine Control of Prolactin Secretion. Ann. Rev. Physiol. *45*, 109–127 (1983)

32. McEwen, B.S., Biegon, A., Davis, P.G., Krey, L.C., Luine, V.N., McGinnis, M.Y., Paden, C.M., Parsons, B., Rainbow, T.C.: Steroid Hormones: Humoral Signals Which Alter Brain Cell Properties and Functions. Rec. Progr. Horm. Res. *38,* 41–92 (1982)
33. Melmed, S., Braunstein, G.D., Horvath, E., Ezrin, C., Kovacs, K.: Pathophysiology of Acromegaly. Endocr. Rev. *4/3,* 271-290 (1983)
34. Neill, J.D.: Neuroendocrine Regulation of Prolactin Secretion. Frontiers in Neuroendocrinology, Vol. 6, pp. 129–155. Raven Press NY 1980
35. Raue, F., Ziegler, R.: Pathophysiologie der Nebenschilddrüsen und der Calciumhomöostase. Endokrinologie der Kindheit und Adoleszenz. Georg Thieme Verlag Stuttgart 1986
36. Rechler, M.M., Missley, S.P.: The Nature and Regulation of the Receptors for Insulin-like Growth Factors. Ann. Rev. Physiol. *47,* 425–442 (1985)
37. Reiter, R.J.: Neuroendocrine Effects of the Pineal Gland and of Melatonin. Frontiers in Neuroendocrinology, *7,* 287–316 NY (1982)
38. Schally, A.V.: Aspects of hypothalamic regulation of the pituitary gland (Nobel Lecture) Science *202,* 18–28 (1978)
39. Ser"n-Ferrù, M., Jaffe, R.B.: The Fetal Adrenal Gland. Ann. Rev. Physiol. *43,* 141–162 (1981)
40. Siiteri, P.K., Murai, J.T., Hammond, G.L., Nisker, J.A., Raymoure, W.J., Kuhn, R.W.: The Serum Transport of Steroid Hormones. Rec. Progr. Horm. Res. *38,* 457–510 (1982)
41. Straus, D.S.: Growth-Stimulatory Actions of Insulin in Vitro and in Vivo. Endocr. Rev. *5/2,* 356–369 (1984)
42. Verney, E.B.: The antidiuretic hormone and the factor which affect its release. Proc. R. Soc. Lond. *135,* 25–106 (1947)
43. Wakerley, J.B., Lincoln, D.W.: The milk-ejection reflex in the rat. A 20 to 40-fold-acceleration in the firing of paraventricular neurons during oxytocin release. J. Endocr. *57,* 477-493 (1973)
44. Wuttke, W., Horowski, R.: Gonadal Steroids and Brain Function. Exp. Brain Res. Suppl. *3,* 182-199 (1981)

V
Blood and the Circulatory System

18 Functions of the Blood

CH. WEISS and W. JELKMANN

18.1 Basic Concepts

Blood is an opaque red fluid consisting of the pale yellow *plasma* (called serum when the fibrinogen is removed) and the cells suspended in it – the red corpuscles *(erythrocytes)*, the white corpuscles *(leukocytes)* and the platelets *(thrombocytes)*. Blood has an important role in clinical diagnosis, because it is easy to collect and there are many diseases in which the blood composition and properties of the components are characteristically altered.

Functions of the Blood

Transport. Blood is primarily a medium by which substances are conveyed within the body. It transports the respiratory gases oxygen and carbon dioxide both in physical solution and in chemically bound form – O_2 from the lungs to the respiring tissues and CO_2 from the tissues to the lungs. It moves nutrients from the places where they are absorbed or stored to the sites of consumption. The metabolites produced there are transferred to the excretory organs or the places where they can be further utilized. Blood serves as a vehicle for the hormones, vitamins and enzymes produced by the body itself, taking them up at the sites of production or storage and carrying them – distributed throughout the intravascular space – to their target organs. Thanks to the high heat capacity of water, its chief component, blood distributes the heat produced by metabolism and disperses it into the environment by way of the lungs and respiratory passages and the exposed body surface.

Homeostasis. As the blood circulates through the body its composition and physical properties are continually monitored by certain organs and, if necessary, corrected so as to ensure constancy of the *internal milieu.* This condition of homeostasis – approximate constancy in the concentration of dissolved substances, in temperature and in pH – is a basic requirement for the normal functions of all cells.

Prevention of hemorrhage. Another important function of the blood lies in its capacity to counteract bleeding by the closing of small injured vessels and by coagulation (see pp. 419ff.).

Defense against foreign agents. The body is capable of making foreign bodies and pathogenic organisms harmless; this ability is associated primarily with phagocytic and antibody-forming blood cells (see pp. 425ff.).

Blood Volume

Blood accounts for about 6–8% of the weight of the body in adults, and in young children (because of their higher water content in general) 8–9%. In an adult this corresponds to a blood volume of 4–6 liters (**normovolemia**). An above-normal blood volume is called **hypervolemia,** and a subnormal volume is **hypovolemia.** The way this volume is measured is explained on p. 541, and its distribution among the different parts of the vascular system is described on p. 490.

Hematocrit

Definition and normal levels. *The fraction of the blood volume made up of erythrocytes is called the hematocrit.* In a healthy adult man it is 0.44–0.46, and in a woman 0.41–0.43. In the clinic hematocrit is still sometimes given in vol. % (ml cells/dl blood). A healthy person exhibits appreciable and maintained departures from this value only when adapted to high altitudes. The newborn hematocrit is about 20% higher, and that of small children is about 10% lower than that of women [6, 25].

To **determine hematocrit** (by Wintrobe's method) the blood, having been prevented from clotting, is centrifuged for 10 minutes at about 1,000 g (g = relative acceleration due to gravity) in standard hematocrit-tubes of small diameter. The blood cells, having higher specific gravity than the plasma, sink to the bottom; because the leukocytes are lighter than the erythrocytes, they form a thin whitish layer between the sedimented erythrocytes, and the plasma. Because of the special flow properties of the erythrocytes, the hematocrit values of the various organs differ, and there are differences among the venous, arterial and capillary values. The average whole-body hematocrit can be derived by multiplying by 0.9 the hematocrit obtained for cubital-vein blood with the Wintrobe method.

Hematocrit and viscosity of blood. Taking the viscosity of water as 1, the mean **relative blood viscosity** of healthy adults is 4.5 (3.5–5.4), and that of the blood plasma is 2.2 (1.9–2.6). The internal friction of the blood, its viscosity, increases more than proportionally as the hematocrit increases (cf. Fig. 20-3, p. 482).
Because resistance to flow rises linearly with viscosity, any pathological increase in hematocrit puts a greater load on the heart and can result in inadequate circulation through certain organs.

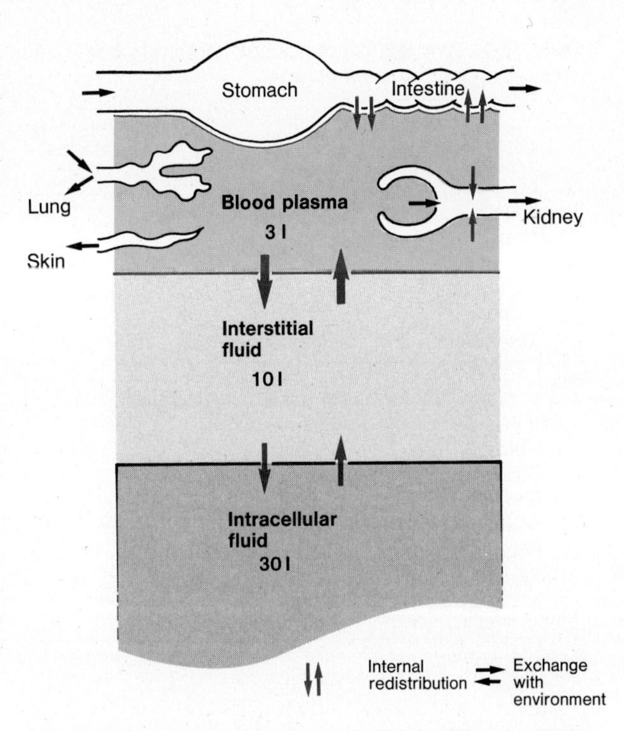

Fig. 18-1. Diagram of the fluid compartments in the body. The volumes are indicated in round figures, for a person weighing 70 kg. Modified from [8]

18.2 Blood Plasma

A liter of human **plasma** contains 900–910 g of water, 65–80 g of protein, and 20 g of substances of low molecular weight. The specific gravity of plasma is 1.025–1.029; its pH varies slightly (7.37–7.43) about a mean of 7.40 (arterial blood).
Fig. 18-1 is a diagram of the three great fluid compartments in the body, the **blood-vascular system,** the **interstitial space** (the spaces between cells) and the **intracellular space.** The interstitial fluid constitutes the environment of the mass of cells in the body. By way of the large surface of the capillary walls (highly permeable to water and electrolytes) it exchanges substances with the plasma. Because the exchange of water and small molecules between plasma and interstitial space is very rapid, the range within which the composition of the interstitial fluid can vary is small despite the considerable variations in uptake and release of substances by the cells. For example, experiments with heavy water (deuterium-labelled, D_2O) have shown that over 70% of the plasma fluid is exchanged with the interstitial fluid in one minute.
There are appreciable *concentration differences between plasma and interstitial space* only with respect to the proteins, for these molecules are so large that they cannot pass readily through the capillary membrane.

Plasma Electrolytes

Electrolyte concentrations. Table 18-1 and Fig. 18-2 summarize the ionic composition of plasma. Among the substances in the group called simply "organic acids" are lactic acid, the amino acids, citric acid and pyruvic acid.

It is preferable no longer to give concentration as w/v ratio (g/dl or mg/dl) but rather in terms of **molarity** (mol/liter) and **normality** or equivalent concentration (eq/liter = mol/valence · liter). When it is necessary to allow for the reduced volume of solvent in a solution in which the dissolved particles require a great deal of space, **molality** (mol/kg solvent) is often used as a measure of concentration (see Table 18-1).

Osmotic pressure. The concentration of dissolved substances in the plasma can be expressed by the *osmotic pressure.* That of normal plasma is about 7.3 atm (5,600 mm Hg = 745 kPa), which corresponds to a freezing-point depression of −0.54 °C. Solutions with the same osmotic pressure as plasma are called *isotonic,* and by the same convention *hypertonic* solutions have higher, and *hypotonic* solutions lower osmotic pressure. Plasma is isotonic with a barely 1/3 molal solution of a nonelectrolyte. 96% of the osmotic pressure of blood is due to the presence of inorganic electrolytes, mainly sodium chlo-

Table 18-1. Average concentrations of electrolytes and nonelectrolytes in human plasma

	g/l	meq/l	mmol/kg plasma water
Electrolytes			
Cations:			
Sodium	3.28	143	153
Potassium	0.18	5	5
Calcium	0.10	5	3
Magnesium	0.02	2	1
Total		155	
Anions:			
Chloride	3.65	103	110
Bicarbonate	0.61	27	28
Phosphate	0.04	2	1
Sulfate	0.02	1	1
Organic acids		6	
Protein	65 to 80	16	~1
Total		155	
Non-electrolytes			
Glucose	0.9–1.0		5
Urea	0.40		7

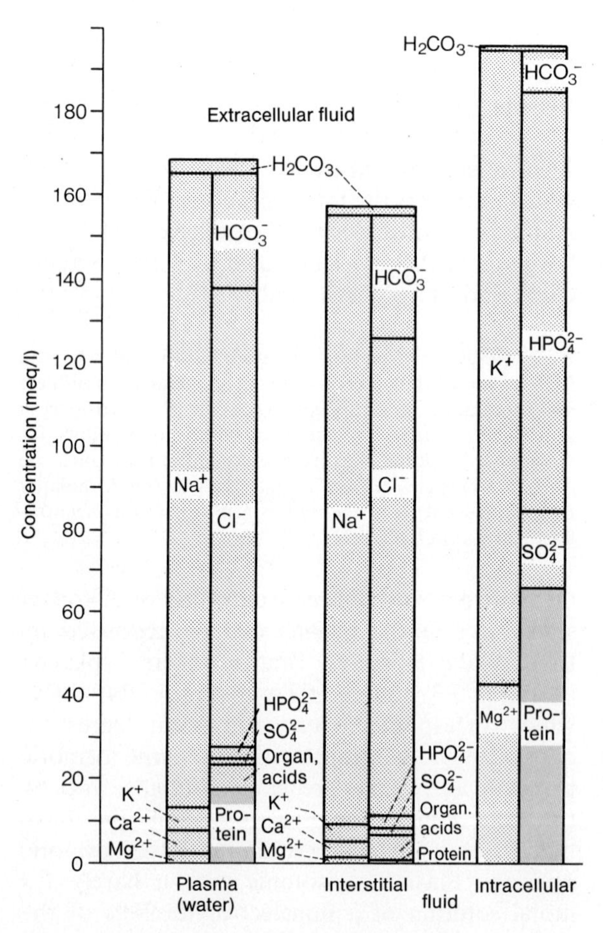

Fig. 18-2. Electrolyte composition of plasma, interstitial fluid, and intracellular fluid. Modified from [8]

ride (crystalloid osmotic pressure). The molecular weight of NaCl is low, so that there are many molecules per unit weight.

Constancy of the internal milieu, or **homeostasis,** depends critically on regulation of the osmotic pressure of the plasma. Any departure from the normal extracellular osmotic pressure (plasma and interstitial fluid) causes a redistribution of water between the cells and their surroundings. *Hypotonicity* of the extracellular fluid causes influx of water into the cells and hence swelling *(cellular edema).* Great increases in volume can destroy the cell membrane (cf. osmotic hemolysis of erythrocytes, p. 413).

Hypertonicity, on the other hand, causes the cells to lose water and shrink, so that the normal tissue turgor is lost. In both cases the ability of the cells to function is more or less severely impaired.

Functions of the plasma electrolytes. Isotonicity of the suspension medium is one of the fundamental requirements for the maintenance of function in isolated, surviving tissue. In itself, however, it does not suffice to preserve cell function; the various ions must be present in suitable proportions. Table 18-2 gives the composition of some "balanced" saline solutions which have proved useful as *suspension media* for living tissue in vitro. Although the different actions of the various ionic species have long been known, the mechanisms underlying these effects are not understood in all details.

Plasma Proteins

General properties and functions. The high relative viscosity of plasma, 1.9–2.6 (water = 1), is almost entirely due to its protein content, 65-80

Table 18-2. Composition of some commonly used suspension media. The numbers indicate the concentration (meq/l) of each ion.

Ringer				Tyrode	
Amphibians		Mammals		Mammals	
Na^+	115	Na^+	146	Na^+	149.4
K^+	1	K^+	4	K^+	2.7
Ca^{2+}	2	Ca^{2+}	5.4	Ca^{2+}	3.6
Cl^-	106	Cl^-	155.4	Mg^{2+}	2.1
HCO_3^-	12			Cl^-	145.1
				HCO_3^-	12.0
				HPO_4^{2-}	0.7
				Glucose	5.5 (mmol/l)

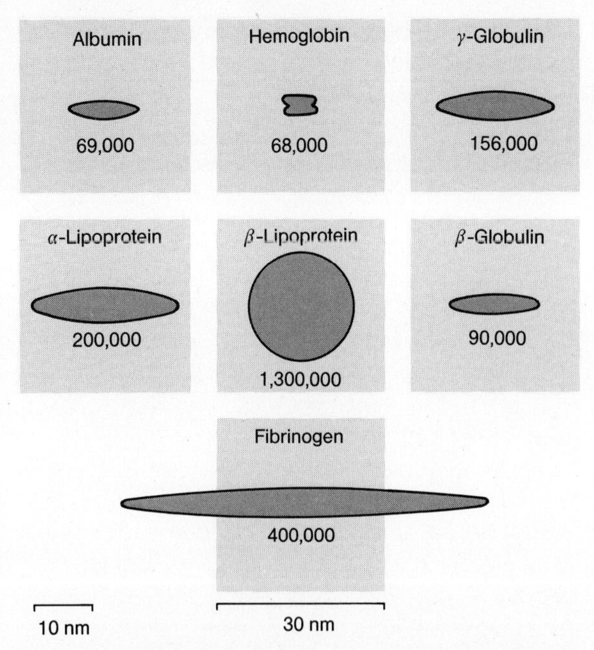

Fig- 18-3. Molecular weights and shapes (schematic) of some plasma proteins and of hemoglobin. Modified from [28]

$g \cdot l^{-1}$. Because of the high molecular weight of proteins, the molal concentration, as Table 18-1 shows, is considerably less impressive – only about 1 mmol $\cdot$ kg^{-1}. The protein fraction of plasma is a mixture of many individually identifiable proteins. Their **molecular weights** range from 44,000 to 1,300,000. Particles of this order of magnitude are classified as colloids (Fig. 18-3). The plasma proteins function in a number of different ways.

1. Nutrition. The approximately 3 liters of plasma in an adult's body carry about 200 g of protein in solution, a convenient reserve supply. In general the cells of the body take up not proteins but rather their components, the amino acids; however, certain cells – especially those of the *reticuloendothelial system* (RES) – can take in whole plasma proteins and break them down by means of intracellular enzymes. The amino acids thus produced diffuse into the blood and are immediately available to other cells for the synthesis of new protein.

2. Transport. Many small molecules (see pp. 408f.) are bound to specific plasma proteins during transport from the intestine or storage organs to the places where they are needed. The large surface area of these proteins, with numerous hydrophilic and lipophilic attachment sites, makes them especially suitable to serve as vehicles. By binding of their lipophilic groups to water-insoluble fat-like substances they can hold these substances in solution. Their ability to bind a large number of low-molecular-weight substances during their transport in the bloodstream also assists in maintaining a constant osmotic pressure.

3. Unspecific carrier function. All the plasma proteins bind blood cations in a non-diffusible form. For example, about 2/3 of the calcium present in plasma is unspecifically bound to proteins. This bound calcium is in equilibrium with the physiologically effective, ionized calcium freely dissolved in the blood. The binding of calcium is pH-dependent, being enhanced at high pH (alkalosis, p. 593).

4. Production of colloid osmotic pressure. The contribution of the proteins to the total osmotic pressure of the plasma is very small, because of their low molecular concentration. Nevertheless, the colloid osmotic (oncotic) pressure plays an important role in *regulating the distribution of water between plasma and interstitial fluid.* Because the capillary membranes are essentially freely permeable to small molecules, the concentration of these molecules – and thus the osmotic pressure associated with them – is approximately the same in the two fluids. But the plasma-protein molecules are so large that they encounter a relatively large resistance in passing through the capillary wall (for example, isotope-labelled albumin leaves the bloodstream with a half-time of about 14 hours). This effect, combined with the removal of protein by uptake into cells and transport through the lymph, brings about a protein concentration gradient between plasma and interstitial fluid; the colloid osmotic pressure in the plasma is ca. 25 mm Hg (3.3 kPa) and that in the interstitial fluid is ca. 5 mm Hg (0.7 kPa), giving a difference of ca. 20 mm Hg (2.7 kPa).
Any change in the osmotically effective concentration of plasma protein disturbs the exchange of substances and the distribution of water between blood and interstitial fluid. Because albumin (see p. 407) represents the largest fraction of the plasma protein (a relatively small molecule, its molal concentration is about 6 times higher than that of all the other plasma proteins), changes in albumin concentration have an especially pronounced effect on colloid osmotic pressure. Reduction of the plasma albumin concentration often leads to retention of water in the interstitial space *(interstitial edema).* Therefore

artificial plasma solutions in general should have the same colloid (and crystalloid) osmotic pressure as the plasma. Polysaccharides (hydroxyethyl starch, dextran) and polypeptides (gelatine) are usually used as the colloids, because it is very expensive to extract human blood proteins in pure form.

5. Buffer function. Because proteins are *amphoteric* – able to bind H^+ or OH^- ions, depending on the pH – the plasma proteins act as buffers, helping to keep the blood pH constant (see pp. 591f.).

6. Protection against loss of blood. The coagulability of blood, which interferes with bleeding, is based in part on the fibrinogen content of the plasma (see p. 408). The process involves a chain of reactions in which a number of blood proteins that act as enzymes cooperate, terminated by the conversion of dissolved fibrinogen into the fibrin meshwork of which the clot is composed (see pp. 419f.).

Fractionation of plasma proteins. Qualitative and quantitative analyses of the plasma proteins are carried out routinely (Fig. 18-4). Protein electrophoresis is an important diagnostic aid, for many diseases involve characteristic changes in the plasma-protein spectrum.

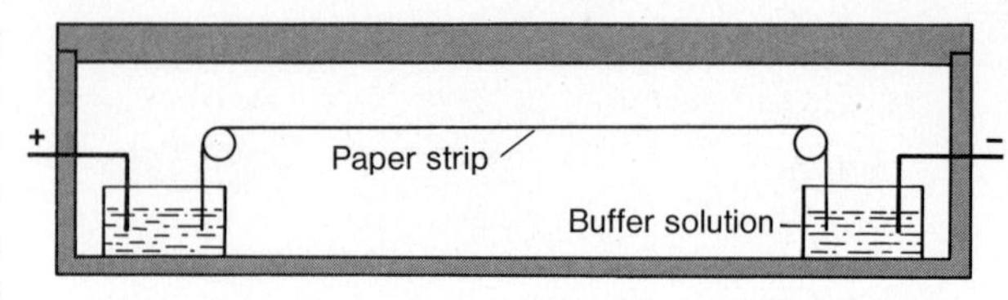

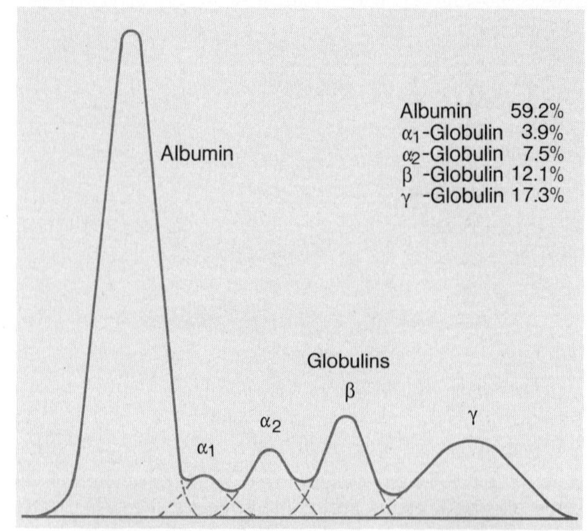

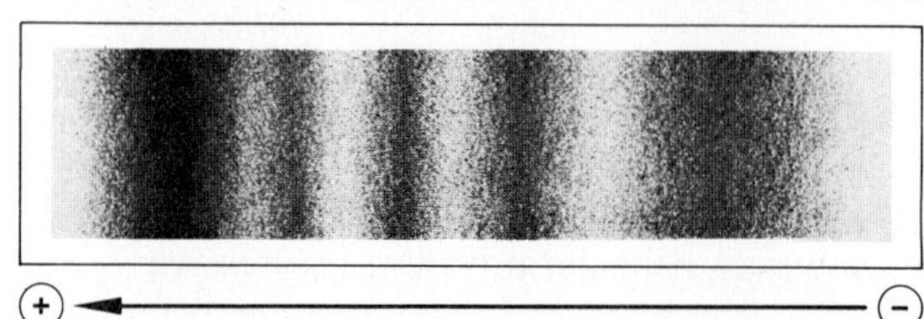

Fig 18-4. Electropherogram of human serum. The stained bands on the paper strip *(bottom)* correspond to peaks in the photometric curve, which represent the indicated percentages of the various protein fractions. *Top:* diagram of the apparatus for paper electrophoresis

Electrophoresis is the migration of electrically charged particles, dissolved or suspended in a fluid, along a voltage gradient. Protein molecules are built up of single amino acids joined together by peptide bonds. The electrolytic nature of these molecules is derived in part from the ionization of amino ($-NH_2$) and carboxyl ($-COOH$) groups; especially when these are present in side chains, they are electrically charged in accordance with the pH of the solvent ($-NH_3^+$ or $-COO^-$). As far as the buffering action is concerned, the pH-dependent *imidazole groups* of the amino acid histidine (a major component of the hemoglobin molecule) are even more significant.
The **electrophoretic mobility** of a protein is basically a function of the applied voltage, the size and shape of the molecule, and its electric charge, which depends on the difference between its isoelectric point (IP) and the pH of the solution. As can be seen in Table 18-3, the IPs of the different plasma proteins are below pH 7 by varying amounts. In neutral or alkaline solutions, then, the proteins will migrate in the same direction, toward the anode, but with different velocities (Fig. 18-4).
In another method of fractionation, which allows simultaneous determination of molecular weight, the **ultracentrifuge** (Svedberg) is used to generate accelerational forces from 100,000 to 750,000 times the earth's gravity. For a given centrifugal force, the rate of sedimentation depends on the specific weight and the shape of the molecule (Fig. 18-3) and on the density of the suspension medium. In **density-gradient centrifugation** the protein components of a mixture can be especially well separated, for each becomes concentrated at a particular level in the tube.
A still more refined separation of plasma proteins can be achieved with a combination of electrophoresis and immunoprecipitation. In this procedure, **immunoelectrophoresis,** electrophoretically separated protein fractions are allowed to diffuse within a gel into a drop of antibody-containing serum. When the protein antigen encounters the serum, antibody precipitation occurs, and is evident as a whitish zone of turbidity in the gel. In this way it has been shown that electrophoretically uniform protein fractions can consist of several immunologically distinguishable proteins (cf. Table 18-3).

Properties and functions of individual fractions. Because electrophoresis is the analytical procedure most commonly used, discussion will be restricted to the components distinguishable by this method. Fig. 18-3 shows diagrammatically the size relationships and the shapes of the most important plasma proteins.

Plasma albumin. About 60% of the total plasma protein is albumin (35–45 $g \cdot l^{-1}$). With a molecular weight of 69,000, it is one of the smallest proteins in the plasma. Because of its relatively high concentration and the small size of the molecule, it is responsible for almost 80% of the colloid osmotic pressure of the plasma. The many small molecules have a very large total surface area, so that they are especially well suited to act as carriers, binding a number of substances for transport in the bloodstream. Among the substances bound by albumin are bilirubin, urobilin, fatty acids, bile-acid salts and a few extraneous substances such as penicillin, sulfonamides and mercury. A single albumin molecule, for example, can bind 25–50 molecules of bilirubin (MW 500) at a time. In many pathological states – in particular, inflammatory diseases and cases of *liver* and *kidney damage* – the amount of albumin is reduced.

Plasma globulins. The term "globulin" designates a group of electrophoretically separable components. In order of diminishing mobility in the electric field, these are called α_1-, α_2-, β- and γ-globulins (Fig. 18-4). Even these subfractions, however, do not represent individual proteins. With other procedures, such as immunoelectrophoresis, each can be further separated (Table 18-3).

The subgroup of **α_1-globulins** consists of a number of conjugated proteins, with carbohydrate prosthetic groups predominantly in the form of hexoses and hexosamines; these are called *glycoproteins.* About 2/3 of the glucose in the plasma is bound as glycoprotein. This bound glucose is not detected by clinical tests for blood sugar in deproteinated plasma. It can be measured only after it is released from the protein by acid hydrolysis, when its concentration is found to be 0.8–1.65 $g \cdot l^{-1}$. This subfraction also includes another group of carbohydrate-containing proteins, the *proteoglycans* (mucoproteins); these contain glucosaminoglycans (mucopolysaccharides).

Other proteins that migrate with the α_1 group are *thyroxine-binding globulin,* vitamin-B_{12}-binding globulin *(transcobalamin), bilirubin-binding globulin,* and cortisol-binding globulin *(transcortin).*

In the **α_2-globulin** fraction there are haptoglobin, which chemically is classified as a proteoglycan, and the copper-containing *ceruloplasmin.* The latter has 8 atoms of copper per molecule, which are responsible for the oxidase activity of the protein. About 90% of the total plasma copper is bound to ceruloplasmin. However, the copper

Table 18-3. Protein fractions in human plasma. MW, molecular weight; IP, isoelectric point. From [15, 25, 27]

Protein fraction		Mean concentration		MW	IP	Physiological significance
Electrophoretic	Immunoelectrophoretic	g/l	μmol/l	($\cdot 10^{-3}$)		
Albumin	Prealbumin	0.3	4.9	61	4.7	Binding of thyroxine; colloid
	Albumin	40.0	579.0	69	4.9	osmotic pressure, vehicle function; reserve protein
α_1-globulins	Acid α_1-glycoprotein	0.8	18.2	44	2.7	Product of tissue degeneration?
	α_1-lipoprotein ("high-density lipoproteins")	3.5	17.5	200	5.1	Lipid transport (esp. phospholipids)
α_2-globulins	Ceruloplasmin	0.3	1.9	160	4.4	Oxidase activity, binds copper
	α_2-macroglobulin	2.5	3.1	820	5.4	Plasmin and proteinase inhibition
	α_2-haptoglobin	1.0	11.8	8.5	4.1	Binds hemoglobin to prevent loss in urine
β-globulins	Transferrin	3.0	33.3	90	5.8	Iron transport
	β-lipoprotein ("low-density lipoproteins")	5.5	0.3 to 1.8	3,000 to 20,000	–	Lipid transport (esp. cholesterol)
	Fibrinogen	3.0	8.8	340	5.8	Blood clotting
γ-globulins	IgG	12.0	76.9	156	5.8	Immunoglobulins: Antibodies against bacterial antigens and
	IgA	2.4	16.0	150	7.3	foreign protein
	IgM	1.25	1.3	960		Isohemagglutinins
	IgE	0.0003	0.002	190	–	Antibodies (reagins)

transported in the bloodstream to the cells of the body is bound to albumin rather than to ceruloplasmin.

The **β-globulins** include the most important carrier proteins for lipids and polysaccharides. The lipoproteins are of great functional significance in that they can hold non-water-soluble fats and lipoids in solution and act as a vehicle for their transport in the blood. About 75% of all fats and lipoids in the plasma are bound as lipoproteins. Small amounts of lipoproteins are also found in the α_1-fraction, but the majority migrate with the β-globulins. Of these, the most important is β_1-lipoprotein, a molecule of which can comprise as much as 77% lipid. Analysis of the lipoprotein mixture in the plasma by means of ultracentrifugation and electrophoresis (the electrophoretic mobility of the lipoproteins is due to their protein component) has become a useful tool in diagnosis of the various forms of *hyperlipoproteinemia* (cf. textbooks of biochemistry). Apart from the lipoproteins, the fraction comprises a group of metal-binding proteins; one of these, *transferrin,* serves as a carrrier of copper and, most importantly, of iron. This metalloprotein binds 2 (ferric) iron atoms per molecule, and is the vehicle for iron transport in the blood. The serum transferrin is normally only about 30% saturated with iron (1 mg Fe^{3+}/l serum).

The heterogeneous group of **γ-globulins** includes the proteins with the lowest electrophoretic mobility; their isoelectric points, accordingly, are nearer the neutral point than those of the other plasma proteins (cf. Table 18-3). Among the γ-globulins are most of the *protective and defensive* substances of the blood (immunoglobulins; see p. 429). Because the demand for proteins with such special functions varies, there are wide fluctuations in the quantity and composition of the γ-globulin fraction; in almost all diseases, particularly the inflammatory ones, the amount of γ-globulins increases. The total amount of plasma protein in general remains approximately the same, however, because the increase in γ-globulins is accompanied by a roughly equal decrease in albumin; the so-called *albumin-globulin ratio* is reduced. The erythrocyte-agglutinating substances anti-A and anti-B are also γ-globulins.

Fibrinogen appears as a narrow separate band, between the β- and γ-globulin fractions. Fibrinogen is the dissolved precursor of fibrin, which precipitates out of solution to form a blood clot (see pp. 419ff.). Fibrinogen is an elongated molecule with an axial ratio (length: width) of 17 : 1. The high viscosity of fibrinogen solutions results from the tendency of these molecules to aggregate in a string-of-beads formation.

Characteristic changes in the fibrinogen fraction appear only in a few rare diseases, so that there is little diagnostic value in electrophoretic demonstrations of altered fibrinogen concentration. Moreover, the mobility of this elongated molecule in paper electrophoresis is more dependent on the kind of paper used than is that of the other plasma proteins. For these reasons, serum rather than plasma is usually used in clinical paper electrophoresis of blood proteins; the typical electropherogram shown in Fig. 18-4 thus has no fibrinogen band.

Synthesis and turnover of plasma proteins. A human on a normal diet synthesizes about 17 g albumin and 5 g globulin in 24 hours. The half-life of albumin in the human is 10–15 days, and that of globulin is about 5 days. That is, when these times have elapsed 50% of the protein present on the first day has been replaced by newly synthesized protein.

Transported Plasma Components

As has been shown in the preceding sections, the inorganic electrolytes and the proteins transported by the plasma critically affect, by their very presence, its most important functional properties. In this sense the *inorganic electrolytes and the proteins are functional elements of the plasma.*

There is another group of plasma components which are simply transported and have little effect – within the physiological range of concentrations – on the characteristic physicochemical properties of the plasma. For this heterogeneous group of substances the plasma is first and foremost a means of transport. Among them are (a) *nutrients, vitamins and trace elements,* (b) *products of intermediary metabolism,* (c) *hormones and enzymes,* and (d) *substances to be excreted.*

Transported nutrients, vitamins and trace elements. The largest fraction, by weight, of the nutrients transported in the plasma is made up of **lipids** (all ether-soluble substances: fats, lipoids and steroids). The concentration of these substances, however, fluctuates widely (Table 18-4). After a very fatty meal the lipid content can rise to such an extent (up to 20 $g \cdot l^{-1}$) that the plasma looks milky white *(lipemia).* About 80% of the fatty acids are bound to globulin as glycerides, phospholipids and cholesterol esters (lipoproteins); most of the non-esterified fatty acids form albumin complexes. In contrast to the plasma lipids, the concentration of which depends on the momentary metabolic state, the concentration of **glucose,** the most important carbohydrate, stays relatively constant at 0.8–1.2 $g \cdot l^{-1}$ (4–7 $mmol \cdot l^{-1}$) despite differences in uptake and widely varying rates of utilization. Another group of transported nutrients, the **amino acids,** are present in the

Table 18-4. Nonprotein nitrogen and lipids (g/l) in human plasma. Data from [27].

Substance	Mean	Range
Urea N	0.14	0.1–0.2
Amino-acid N	0.05	0.03–0.07
Uric-acid N	0.017	0.01–0.023
Creatinine	0.005	0.004–0.005
Ammonia N	0.002	0.001–0.002
Total N.P.N.	0.25	0.22–0.30
Fats, neutral fat		0–4.5
Fatty acids		2–4.5
Steroids, cholesterol		1.2–3.5
Free cholesterol		0.4–0.7
Bile acids		0.002–0.03
Bile salts		0.05–0.12
Phospholipids, total		1.5–2.5
Lecithin		1.0–2.0
Cephalin		0–0.3
Sphingomyelin		0.1–0.3
Total ether-soluble material		3.8–6.8

plasma in an intermediate concentration of about 0.04 $g \cdot l^{-1}$. These are derived primarily from the proteins in food.

All the **vitamins** (see pp. 684f.) and the essential nutrients with the character of vitamins (e.g., choline) are continually present in the plasma. But their concentration varies, not only because of differences in the amounts present in food or synthesized by the intestinal flora. The concentration of some vitamins depends on the presence of specific factors that facilitate absorption; for example, absorption of vitamin B_{12} is affected by CASTLE's "intrinsic factor." Whereas many vitamins are transported in free solution in the plasma, others – especially the fat-soluble vitamins and a few water-soluble ones such as vitamin B_{12} – are bound to proteins.

One of the more important **trace elements** (elements indispensable as components of structural molecules as well as of hormones and the like) is *iron.* It is absorbed from the intestine at a rate that depends not on supply but on the body's demands. Iron is absorbed as a protein complex *(mucosal transferrin)* [33].

Most of the other metals among the trace elements are found in the serum as metalloproteins; 90% of the copper, for example, is bound to the protein *ceruloplasmin* (see p. 407). Cobalt is an essential component of vitamin B_{12} *(cobalamin).* Practically all the iodine takes the form of a complex with the so-called *thyroxine-binding protein* (see p. 407).

Transported products of intermediary metabolism. Among the intermediary products of metabolism, **lactic acid** is present in the greatest quantities. Its concentration rises in oxygen deficiency and during hard muscular work. Another organic acid that is always present is **pyruvic acid,** a key substance in energy metabolism because of its involvement in the metabolism of both amino acids and carbohydrates.

Transported hormones and enzymes. The substances in this third group include proteins, polypeptides, amines, amides and steroids.

Transported substances to be excreted. The substances in this group are not utilized further, but are end products of metabolism which must be eliminated from the body. The most important of these are *carbon dioxide, urea, uric acid, creatinine, bilirubin* and *ammonia.* All of these except carbon dioxide contain nitrogen and are excreted by the kidneys. When kidney function is impaired, their plasma concentration rises. They are measured as an aid to the diagnosis of kidney diseases, by Kjeldahl's method for determining nitrogen content of plasma after precipitation of the proteins. The value for **nonprotein nitrogen** (N.P.N.) thus obtained corresponds, for practical purposes, to the nitrogen in the above-mentioned waste products. But about 1/5 of the N.P.N. is incorporated in the plasma amino acids, which are not waste products. In Table 18-4 the most important components of the N.P.N. of normal plasma are summarized.

18.3 Erythrocytes

Number, Shape and Size

Of the cellular components, which make up about 44 vol. % of the blood, the red corpuscles are the most numerous; *men average 5.1 million, and women 4.6 million, per μl blood.*[1] Apart from their water content, the mass of the erythrocytes is chiefly composed of hemoglobin. 34% of their wet weight, and 90% of the dry weight, is attributable to this protein (see pp. 578ff.).

During *childhood* the erythrocyte count changes. In the newborn it is high (5.5 million per μl blood) because of the transfer of blood from the fetal placenta into the child's circulation at birth and the subsequent marked water loss. In the following months the production of erythrocytes does not keep pace with general body growth, so that the "trimester reduction" develops (a decrease in erythrocyte count to about 3.5 million per *μl* blood in the third month of life). Preschool and school children have somewhat lower erythrocyte counts than adult women [6].

Shape and size of the erythrocytes. Human erythrocytes are flat, round disks without nuclei, indented in the middle on both sides. Their greatest thickness (at the edge) is only 2 μm; their diameters, in healthy people, form a normal distribution, the **Price-Jones curve** (Fig. 18-6), about a mean of 7.5 μm *(normocyte).* The biconcave shape of the normocyte results in an increase in surface area, as compared with a sphere. The total surface area of the erythrocytes of an adult man is about 3,800 m^2. The main function of

[1] Values for Central Europe; for North America (according to WINTROBE), 5.4 and 4.8 million/μl respectively

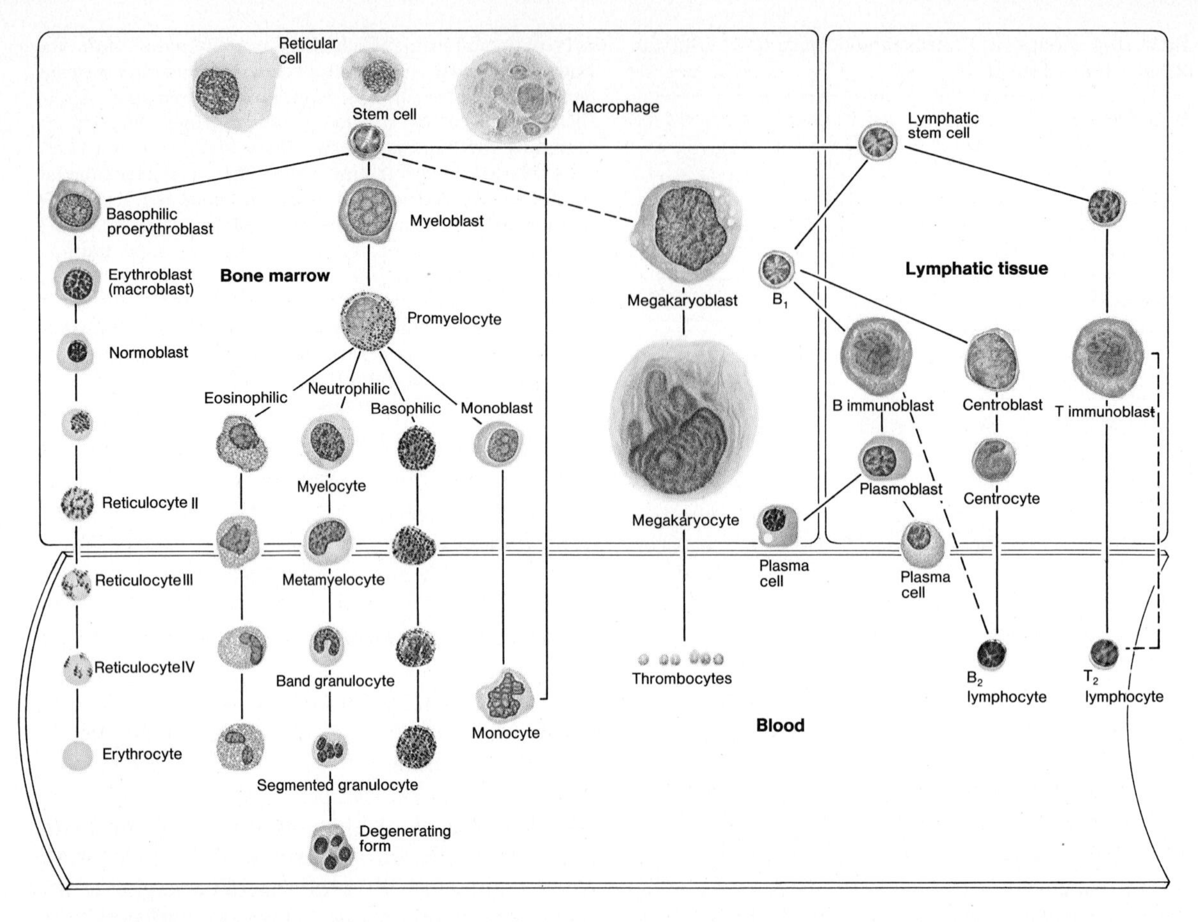

Fig. 18-5. The cells found in peripheral blood and their precursors in the germinal centers, the bone marrow and lymphatic system. From [2]

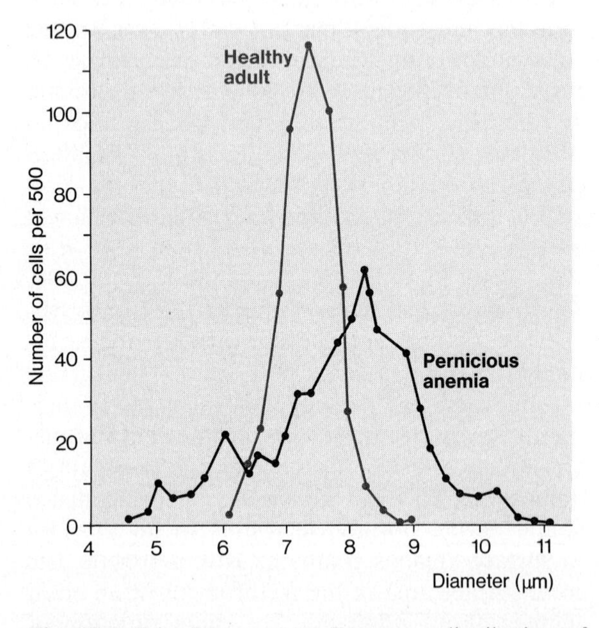

Fig. 18-6. Price-Jones curves. Frequency distribution of erythrocyte diameter in a healthy person (*red* line) and in a patient with pernicious anemia (*black* line). Modified from [38]

the erythrocyte, gas transport (see pp. 582ff.), is facilitated by this characteristic shape, for the diffusion area is large and the diffusion distance small. Moreover, it is easier for cells so shaped to be reversibly deformed in order to pass through narrow, curved capillaries. The *plasticity of the erythrocyte* is less in older cells. It is also reduced in pathological forms of erythrocytes, such as *spherocytes* and *sickle cells;* the loss of plasticity is one reason why such cells are retained in the meshwork of the spleen and subsequently destroyed there.

Principle of erythrocyte counting. A measured quantity of capillary blood is diluted 100- or 200-fold with isotonic saline solution. The cells in a specified volume of this mixture are counted by microscopic examination, and the dilution factor is applied to determine the cell count in the original blood.
In recent years it has become increasingly common to use more precise, non-microscopic procedures. The erythrocyte concentration in a diluted suspension is determined from the degree of scatter of transmitted light, or from the changes in electrical conductance observed during passage of the cells through a thin tube.

When **impairment of the erythropoietic system** causes a shift of the Price-Jones curve to the right – i.e., a significant increase in the number of erythrocytes over 8 μm in diameter – the condition is termed *macrocytosis.* In pernicious anemia some of the erythrocytes *(megalocytes)* can have diameters of over 12 μm. A leftward shift of the Price-Jones curve (a significant increase in the number of erythrocytes with diameters < 6 μm) is called *microcytosis.* The diameter of these short-lived dwarf forms can be as little as 2.2 μm. When the Price-Jones curve is flattened, as a result of the simultaneous increase in both macro- and microcytes, a state of *anisocytosis* exists. *Poikilocytosis,* in which there is abnormal variation in erythrocyte shape, can accompany pernicious anemia and thalassemia. Among the characteristically altered cells are rounded spherocytes (spherocytic anemia) and sickle cells (sickle-cell anemia).

Production, Life Span and Destruction

Erythropoiesis. Erythrocytes are produced in the hemopoietic tissues – the yolk sac of the embryo, the liver and spleen of the fetus, and the red marrow of the flat bones in adults. These structures contain the *pluripotent stem cells,* the common progenitors of all kinds of blood cells. At the next level of differentiation are the *committed progenitors,* capable of forming only one kind of blood cell (erythrocyte, monocyte, granulocyte, thrombocyte or lymphocyte). Several stages of differentiation and maturation are distinguished, until finally the young, anuclear erythrocyte leaves the bone marrow as a *reticulocyte* (Fig. 18-5). Erythrocytes circulate in the blood for 100–120 days. Then they are phagocytized by cells of the reticuloendothelial system in the bone marrow, and under pathological conditions also in the liver and spleen. In fact, as is evident in the gradual disappearance of the "black and blue" marks caused by intracutaneous bleeding, any tissue is capable of degrading blood corpuscles. About 0.8% of the $25 \cdot 10^{12}$ erythrocytes of an adult are renewed in 24 hours. This implies an *erythropoiesis rate of* $160 \cdot 10^6$ *erythrocytes/min.*
After loss of blood, and when the erythrocyte life span is pathologically shortened, the erythropoiesis rate can increase severalfold. The effective stimulus that triggers erythropoiesis is a fall in the O_2 partial pressure in respiring tissue (an imbalance between O_2 supply and demand). Under such conditions there is an increased plasma concentration of a hormone called **erythropoietin,** which accelerates erythropoiesis. Human erythropoietin is a heat-stable glycoprotein (MW ca. 34,000; 30% sugar), the amino acid sequence of which has recently been established (165 amino acids). The kidneys play a central role in the synthesis of erythropoietin [34]; the blood erythropoietin concentration falls sharply after bilateral nephrectomy, and the synthesis of erythropoietin is also reduced in various kidney diseases. The kidneys were once thought not to synthesize erythropoietin themselves but rather to release an enzyme that cleaves the hormone from a plasma globulin. But recently the kidney has been found to contain both the active hormone and the messenger ribonucleic acid (mRNA) that initiates the synthesis of erythropoietin. Small amounts are also synthesized extrarenally, primarily in the liver.
Erythropoietin stimulates the differentiation and accelerates the proliferation of the erythrocytic progenitors in the bone marrow (Fig. 18-5, p. 410), thus increasing the number of hemoglobin-forming erythroblasts. Various other hormones, including *androgens, thyroxine* and *growth hormone,* enhance the action of erythropoietin. The differences in erythrocyte count and hemoglobin concentration in the blood of men and women (see above) result from the fact that erythropoiesis is promoted by androgens and inhibited by estrogens.

Reticulocytes. Counts of the reticulocytes in the blood (Fig. 18-5) can give information about erythropoiesis that is useful in diagnosis and therapy. Reticulocytes are the stage immediately preceding the mature erythrocyte. Whereas the latter has no intracellular structures visible by light microscopy, vital staining of the reticulocytes (staining of the living cells with, e.g., brilliant cresyl blue) reveals granular or filamentous structures. These young blood cells can be found in bone marrow and in the circulating blood. Under normal conditions they account for 0.5–1% of the erythrocytes in healthy blood. Any acceleration of erythropoiesis increases this percentage, and any retardation decreases it. When the rate of erythrocyte degradation rises, the proportion of reticulocytes can increase to over 50%. In cases of excessively rapid erythropoiesis, even normoblasts can occasionally appear in the blood.

Anemia means, literally, bloodlessness. In clinical usage, the term refers primarily to the diminished ability of the blood to transport oxygen, because of the lack of hemoglobin. In this state, there can be a reduction in the number of erythrocytes as compared with the norm and/or in the hemoglobin content of the individual erythrocytes. The term "anemia" implies nothing about the causes of the hemoglobin deficiency.
The most common form of anemia is *iron-deficiency anemia.* This can be produced by a diet with inadequate iron content (especially common among infants), by diminished iron absorption from the digestive tract (for ex-

ample, in the so-called malabsorption syndrome), or by chronic loss of blood due, for example, to ulcers, carcinomas and polyps and diverticuli in the gastrointestinal tract, esophageal varicosities, hookworm infestation (common in the tropics), and heavy menstrual bleeding. In iron-deficiency anemia the blood contains small erythrocytes with a subnormal hemoglobin content *(hypochromic microcytic anemia).*

Another group of anemias is termed *megaloblastic anemia;* the most important common characteristic of these anemias is the presence of abnormally large erythrocytes (megalocytes) and their immature precursors (megaloblasts) in the blood and bone marrow. Production of these giant cells is caused by a deficiency of the erythrocyte-maturation substances vitamin B_{12} (pernicious anemia) and/or folic acid, due to inadequacies in either diet or absorption. When these substances are lacking, cell division is delayed although the rate of growth hardly changes, so that the cells develop to an abnormally large size. Megalocytes have a shorter life span than normal erythrocytes and this, together with the delayed maturation of erythrocytes, leads to anemia.

Pathological states in which the rate of hemolysis increases, because the erythrocytes have become more vulnerable to degradation, can give rise to *hemolytic anemia* if the production of erythrocytes cannot keep pace with the accelerated destruction. Examples of this condition include the heriditary form of spherocytosis and the (also hereditary) diseases sickle-cell anemia and thalassemia. The anemia that accompanies malaria, accelerated hemolysis due to autoimmune responses (see p. 432) and erythroblastosis fetalis (anemia caused by incompatibility of rhesus factors; see below) are also in this category.

Cases of *aplastic anemia* and *pancytopenia* are characterized by diminished cytogenesis in the bone marrow, even though all the materials necessary for the production of blood cells are present. In the aplastic anemia only the erythrocytes are affected, whereas in the pancytopenias all the blood cells produced in the bone marrow are reduced in number. Among the aplastic anemias are both hereditary (Diamond-Blackfan, Fanconi) and acquired, idiopathic forms. The inhibition of cell production in the pancytopenias can be caused by bone-marrow damage due to ionizing radiation (X rays or exposure to radioactive elements), cell toxins (cytostatics, benzene etc.), or tumor metastases, which take the place of normal tissue.

Metabolism and Membrane Properties

The metabolic activity of the mature, anuclear erythrocyte is specialized for its oxygen-transporting function and its intermediary role in the transport of carbon dioxide. Erythrocyte metabolism is thus unlike that in the other cells of the body. One of its prime tasks is to maintain the cell's ability to bind oxygen reversibly, not least by providing a means for reduction of the heme ion. The ferrous iron it contains is continually changed to the ferric state by spontaneous oxidation, and must be returned to the ferrous form before it can again combine with oxygen.

Whereas the nucleated precursors of the erythrocytes contain the familiar enzymes for the oxidative release of energy and protein synthesis, the mature erythrocyte must rely on glycolysis, with glucose as the chief substrate. The main energy source, as in other cells, is ATP; it is required in particular for the active transport of ions through the erythrocyte membrane and thus serves to maintain the intracellular ion-concentration gradient. When ATP is derived from glycolysis, reducing substances such as NADH (reduced nicotinamide-adenine dinucleotide) and NADPH (reduced nicotinamide-adenine dinucleotide phosphate, derived from the pentose-phosphate cycle) are produced as well. NADH is required for the above-mentioned reduction of **methemoglobin** to hemoglobin, which can bind oxygen; NADPH is involved in the reduction of the glutathione in the erythrocyte. Glutathione, which is readily oxidizable, protects a number of important enzymes with SH groups in the cell (especially those associated with the hemoglobin molecule and the cell membrane) from inactivation by oxidation.

The **erythrocyte membrane** is a flexible molecular mosaic composed of protein, lipo- and glycoproteins and, probably, regions of pure lipoid. The membrane is about 10 nm thick; it is about a million times more permeable to anions than to cations. Substances that can pass through the membrane do so in several ways, depending on their chemical properties: by diffusion or hydrodynamically, moving as a solution through water-filled membrane pores, or – if they are lipid-soluble – by penetrating the lipoid areas. Certain substances can be bound in readily reversible form to carrier molecules in the membrane, and are thus channelled through the membrane either passively or by way of so-called active transport (see pp. 7ff.).

Special Physicochemical Properties

Deformability. The shape of a normal erythrocyte can easily be changed by external forces. As a result, the cells can pass through capillaries with inside diameter smaller than the mean diameter of a free erythrocyte (7.5 μm). Because of this deformability, the relative viscosity of the blood in small-bore vessels is effectively lower than in vessels of diameter well above 7.5 μm. The plasticity of the erythrocyte is associated with the presence of Type A hemoglobin (see p. 579); in certain hereditary hemoglobinopathies the cells are much more rigid and circulation is impeded.

Osmotic properties. The concentration of protein in the erythrocyte is higher than in plasma, and that of small molecules is lower. The osmotic effect of the higher internal protein concentration is to a great extent compensated by the lower concentration of small molecules, so that the intracellular osmotic pressure is only slightly higher than that of the plasma, and just suffices for the normal turgor of the erythrocyte. (Na^+ and K^+ are actively transported through the membrane, Na^+ out of the cell and K^+ into it; cf. Fig. 18-2). In principle, the erythrocyte membrane is permeable to small molecules, to different degrees depending on the ion concerned. Because of this permeability, inhibition of the active transport of ions results in a reduction of their transmembrane concentration gradient, so that the continued high intracellular protein concentration is no longer compensated, and the osmotic pressure increases.

Therefore water flows into the erythrocyte, until the membrane bursts and hemoglobin emerges into the plasma – a process called (colloid) **osmotic hemolysis.** When the extracellular fluid is only slightly hypotonic, the erythrocytes swell and approach a spherical shape (spherocytes). In a hypertonic medium the cells lose water and become *crenated* (Fig. 18-7).

Systematic study of the **osmotic resistance** of erythrocytes suspended in media of progressively reduced osmotic pressure has demonstrated that in some diseases, certain forms of anemia in particular, osmotic resistance is changed. The curve in Fig. 18-8 shows that 50% of the erythrocytes of a healthy person are hemolyzed when the tonicity of the medium reaches $4.3 \, g \cdot l^{-1}$ NaCl.

Osmotic hemolysis also occurs when erythrocytes are suspended in an isosmotic solution of substances, such as urea, to which the membrane is highly permeable. **Urea** becomes uniformly distributed within the erythrocyte and in the suspension medium. Because the erythrocyte membrane prevents the larger molecules from leaving the cell, the intracellular osmotic pressure rises above that of the medium, in proportion to the influx of urea. Water enters the cell and causes mechanical disruption of the membrane. Finally, **lipid solvents** such as chloroform, ether and the like can make leaks in the membrane by dissolving out its lipid components, which also leads to hemolysis. The hemolytic effect of soaps, saponins and synthetic detergents results from reduction of the surface tension between the aqueous and lipid phases of the membrane. The lipids are emulsified and drawn out of the membrane, leaving holes through which the cell contents emerge.

Sedimentation rate of blood corpuscles. The specific weight of erythrocytes (1.096) is higher than that of plasma (1.027), so that in an anticoagulated blood sample they slowly sink toward the bottom. The *erythrocyte sedimentation rate* (ESR) of a healthy man is 3–6 mm in the first hour; the value for women is 8–10 mm. Sedimentation is more rapid in certain pathological states (particularly inflammation and increased tissue breakdown due to tumors), chiefly because of the greater tendency for the red cells to gather into clumps. The frictional resistance of such an *aggregate* is less than the total resistance of its individual elements because of the smaller surface-to-volume ratio, so that the aggregates sink more rapidly.

ESR is influenced primarily by the composition of the plasma proteins. Erythrocytes from a patient with accelerated ESR as a rule sink at the normal rate when introduced into plasma of the same blood type from a healthy person. Conversely, erythrocytes from the healthy subject sink more rapidly in the patient's plasma. ESR is retarded by increase in the plasma albumin concentration, and accelerated by increase in the concentration of fibrinogen, haptoglobin,

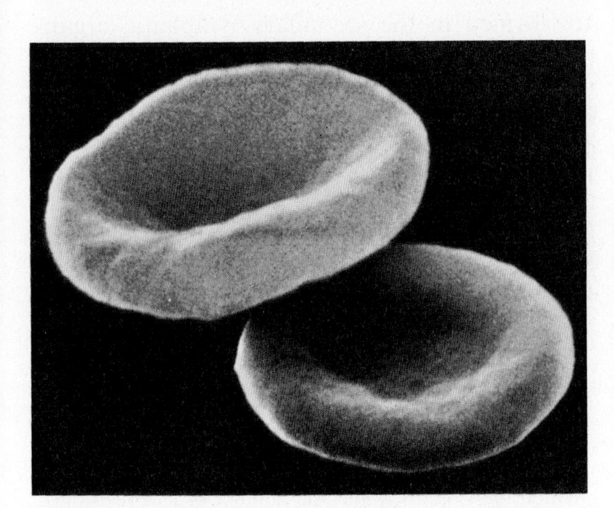

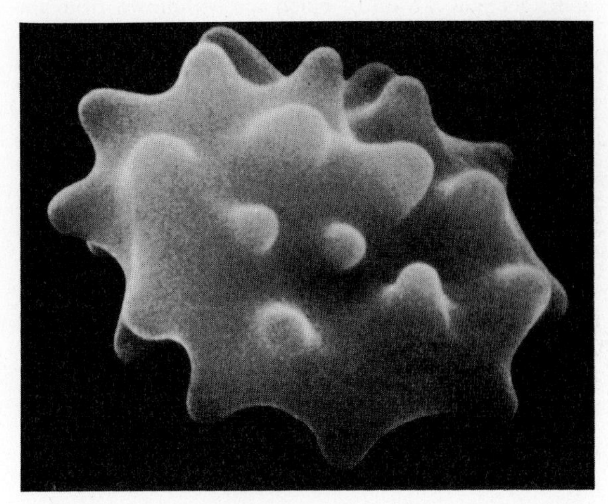

Fig. 18-7. *Left:* biconcave discoid shape of normal erythrocytes. *Right:* crenated erythrocyte, the result of exposure to hypertonic saline solution. From [5]

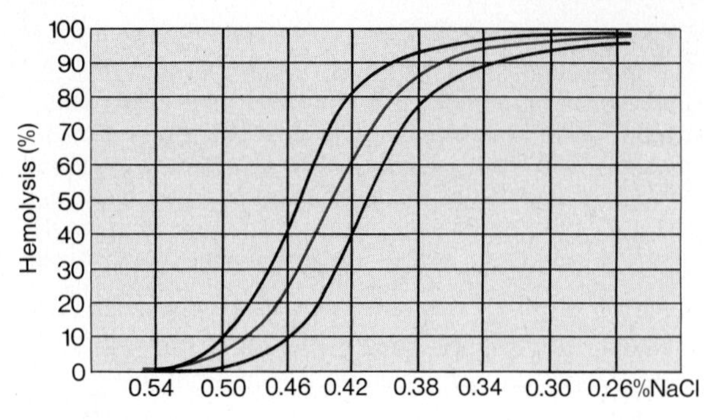

Fig. 18-8. Osmotic resistance of erythrocytes in a blood sample diluted 1:40 with solutions of the indicated salinity. Normal curve with range of deviation. *Ordinate:* photometrically determined degree of hemolysis as % of total hemolysis. *Abscissa:* salinity of NaCl solution in % (g/dl). From [16]

ceruloplasmin, α and β lipoproteins and *paraproteins* (immunoglobulins produced in abnormally large numbers in certain illnesses; cf. textbooks of biochemistry and immunology). The effects of each of these plasma components are additive. Plasma proteins that accelerate sedimentation are called *agglomerins.* The observation that albumin and globulin have opposite effects on ESR explains the earlier finding that shift of the albumin-globulin ratio in favor of globulin is associated with an increased sedimentation rate.

A marked reduction of cell concentration (lowered hematocrit) reduces the viscosity of the blood and thus accelerates sedimentation; increase in the hematocrit has the reverse effect. Change of erythrocyte shape, as occurs in sickle-cell anemia, and extreme nonuniformity of shape (*poikilocytosis,* as in pernicious anemia) interfere with aggregation and thus reduce the ESR. Various steroid hormones (estrogens, glucocorticoids) and medicines (e.g., salicylate) raise the ESR.

Measurement of ESR is most commonly done by Westergren's method. 1.6 ml of blood are withdrawn from the cubital vein with a 2-ml syringe containing 0.4 ml 3.8% sodium citrate solution to prevent clotting. A Westergren tube (2.5 mm i.d., with 200-mm graduation) is filled with this mixture to the zero mark and fixed in a vertical position. After some time, the height of the erythrocyte-free supernatant is read off (readings at one hour and two hours are customary).

18.4 Leukocytes

Properties Common to All Leukocytes; Formation

Leukocyte number. Leukocytes, or white (colorless) corpuscles, are nucleated cells lacking hemoglobin. The blood of a healthy person contains *4,000–10,000 per μl.* Whereas the number of erythrocytes in healthy blood is relatively constant, that of leukocytes varies widely with the time of day and the functional state of the organism. When there are more than 10,000 leukocytes per μl the condition is called **leukocytosis;** in **leukopenia** there are less than 4,000 per μl. Leukocytosis is most commonly associated with inflammatory diseases and – in its severest form – with leukemia.

Table 18-5. Leukocyte counts (cells/μl) in healthy blood. From [27]

	Mean	%	Range
Granulocytes			
Neutrophils	4,150	(59)	712– 7,588
Eosinophils	165	(2)	0– 397
Basophils	44	(<1)	0– 112
Monocytes	456	(7)	66– 846
Lymphocytes	2,185	(31)	1,029– 3,341
Leukocytes	7,000		2,800–11,200

The leukocytes are not a homogeneous population of cells. Three major groups, the **granulocytes, monocytes and lymphocytes,** are distinguished on the basis of morphology, function and site of origin (Table 18-5 and Fig. 18-5). All of them, like the erythrocytes and thrombocytes, are descended from the *pluripotent hemopoietic stem cells.* Granulocytes and monocytes are formed in the bone marrow under the influence of certain hormone-like glycoproteins derived from the mesenchyme ("colony stimulating factors", CSF), the structure of which has only partially been worked out. The precursors of the lymphocytes are the first to branch off from the common stem-cell line (Fig. 18-5). Lymphocytes are formed in the secondary lymphatic organs (p. 427). The specific growth factor for the lymphocytes is *interleukin-2,* which itself is produced by antigen-stimulated lymphocytes.

Infants and small children normally have higher leukocyte counts (about 10,000 per μl blood) than adults. The proportions are also different, with relatively more lymphocytes and monocytes in early childhood.

Leukocyte counts are made by microscopic examination, on the same principle as used for erythrocytes. Because there are considerably fewer white than red corpuscles, the sample is diluted only 1 : 10 in the calibrated pipette, with 0.3% acetic acid to which methylene blue has been added. The acetic acid destroys the erythrocytes, and the leukocyte nuclei, which are not destroyed, are stained blue. 0.1 μl of the resulting suspension is placed in a standard chamber for counting, and the number of leukocytes in 1 μl blood is computed from the chamber volume and the dilution factor.

Emigration. All leukocytes are capable of ameboid movement, which permits them to emigrate through the walls of blood vessels (this process is also called *diapedesis*). They are attracted *(chemotaxis)* by bacterial toxins, the products of decomposition of bacteria or body cells, and antigen-antibody complexes; they can surround foreign bodies and take them into the cytoplasm *(phagocytosis)*. Each type of leukocyte contains certain enzymes; among them are proteases, peptidases, diastases, lipases and deoxyribonucleases. Most of the leukocytes (> 50%) are to be found in the extravascular, interstitial space; more than 30% are in the bone marrow. Evidently the blood is primarily a transport medium for these cells (with the exception of the basophilic granulocytes; see p. 416), carrying them from the sites of production in bone marrow and lymphatic tissue to the places where their action is required.

Granulocytes

Granulocytes are so called because of the granules revealed in their cytoplasm by the customary fixation and staining procedures. The various types are produced in the bone marrow (and hence may be called the *myelocytic series*). The diameters of cells observed in a dry-smear preparation range from 10 to 17 μm. *About 60% (50–70%) of the leukocytes in the blood are granulocytes.* The time a granulocyte spends in the bloodstream can be very brief and amounts at most to two days (the life span of these cells). According to the staining properties of the granules, the granulocytes are classified as *neutrophils*, *eosinophils* and *basophils*. The proportions of these three types can be seen in Table 18-5.

Neutrophilic granulocytes. About 50–70% of all leukocytes (and the majority of granulocytes) are neutrophils (ca. 4,500 cells per μl). These cells are also called polymorphonuclear leukocytes. Because of their high rate of emigration into the mucosa, they circulate in the blood only briefly, 6–8 hours on average. About 50% of the neutrophilic granulocytes in the intravascular space do not circulate but cling to the endothelial wall, particularly in the vessels of the lungs and spleen [30]. These *resting cells* can be rapidly *mobilized* in stress situations (under the action of cortisol and adrenalin). With the onset of acute infections the number of neutrophilic granulocytes in the blood rapidly increases.

The neutrophilic granulocytes are the most important functional elements in the unspecific defense system of the blood (see also p. 433). They are able to obtain energy by glycolysis, and therefore can live in oxygen-deficient conditions, in tissue that is inflamed, edematous, and poorly perfused. There they form *cytotoxic* substances with free oxygen radicals, which destroy cell walls. They phagocytize bacteria and tissue debris, and decompose them with their *lysosomal enzymes* (e.g., proteases, peptidases, oxidases, deoxyribonucleases and lipases). **Pus** is largely composed of neutrophils or remnants of these cells. The lysosomal enzymes released during neutrophil degradation cause softening of the surrounding tissue *(abscess formation)*.

The cell membranes of activated neutrophilic granulocytes release the unsaturated fatty acid

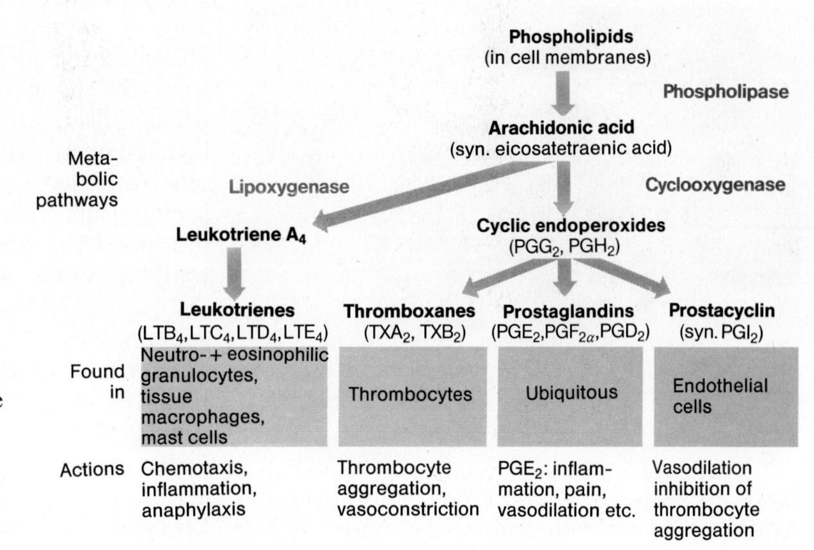

Fig. 18-9. Formation and action of arachidonic acid derivatives *(eicosanoids)*, substances with a paracrine influence on the functions of the blood. The metabolic pathways shown here are also found in other cells of the body, though their quantitative contribution varies

arachidonic acid, the precursor for synthesis of *leukotrienes, thromboxanes* and *prostaglandins* [29]. This group of paracrine substances (see p. 398) plays an important role in regulating the diameter and permeability of the blood vessels, in the initiation of inflammatory responses and pain, and in blood clotting (see below). The formation of the eicosanoids most important for the blood functions is diagrammed in Fig. 18-9.

The neutrophils can be employed for sex determination in humans, for in a genetically female person at least 7 out of 500 neutrophil nuclei exhibit sex-specific lobules, so-called **drumsticks** ("heads" 1.5–2 μm in diameter, attached to a segment of the nucleus by fine chromatin bridges; cf. Fig. 18-10). Such clues to the sex of a patient are useful, for example, in deciding on therapy for malformation of the primary reproductive organs, as in hermaphroditism.

Eosinophilic granulocytes. 2–4% of the leukocytes in the blood are eosinophils (100–350 cells per μl). The blood eosinophil count follows a marked 24-hour periodicity; their numbers are about 20% lower than the 24-h average in the late afternoon and early morning, and about 30% higher at midnight. These fluctuations are associated with the secretion of glucocorticoids by the adrenal cortex. The number of blood eosinophils is decreased when the blood corticoid level rises, and increased when it falls. The cells are capable of phagocytosis. They contain large, oval, acidophilic granules made up of amino acids, proteins and lipids. Increase in eosinophil number beyond the range of the daily fluctuation is called *eosinophilia.* This is especially likely to accompany *allergic responses,* worm infestations and the so-called autoimmune diseases, in which the body elaborates antibodies against its own cells.

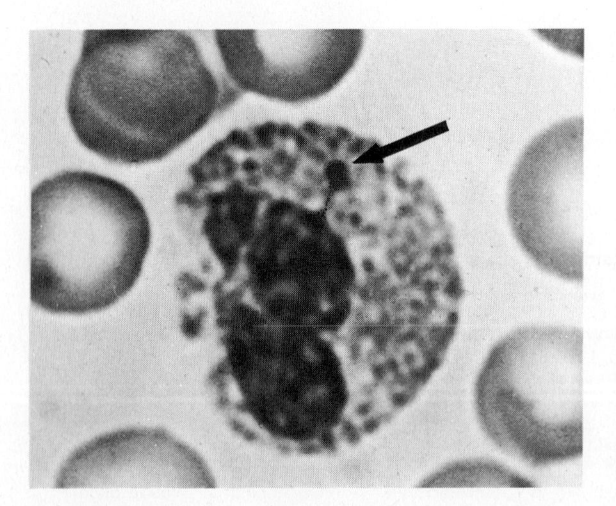

Fig. 18-10. Sex-specific nuclear lobule ("drumstick") in a granulocyte of a genetically female person

Basophilic granulocytes. 0.5–1% (about 50 cells per μl) of the leukocytes in the blood are basophils. Their mean circulation time is 12 h. Their diameter in a dry smear is 7–11 μm. The granules in the cytoplasm of these cells are relatively large, stain deeply with basic dyes, and contain heparin and histamine in salt-like compounds. Recent studies have shown that after absorption of food fats the number of basophils in the peripheral blood is increased. By *releasing heparin* they activate **serum lipolysis** via the so-called *clearing factor;* heparin may be the prosthetic group of the serum lipase. This enzyme (or enzyme complex) cleaves the ester bonds of the triglycerides bound to polypeptides in the chylomicrons of the blood. As a result, the plasma opalescence due to its fat content is diminished and the content of free fatty acid is increased.
In the surface of the blood basophils are IgE-specific receptors to which IgE antibodies (see p. 430) are attached; these in turn can bind antigen – for example, in cases of *hay fever,* when exposed to pollen. The formation of this immunocomplex at the surface of the basophils causes release of *histamine* from the granules, which gives rise to **allergic symptoms** such as vascular dilation, reddening of the skin, an itchy rash and in some cases bronchial spasm.

Monocytes

A second group of leukocytes with agranular cytoplasm comprises the monocytes, cells with diameters of 12–20 μm as seen in a dry smear. *These make up 4–8%* (on average, 450 cells per μl) *of the blood leukocytes.* Monocytes emerge from the bone marrow into the bloodstream while still relatively immature. They have a higher content of unspecific esterase than any other leukocyte, and *exceed the phagocytic capacity of all other blood cells.* After 2–3 days in the blood the monocytes migrate into the surrounding tissue, where they grow in size and in the number of lysosomes and mitochondria they contain. Now, as mature cells, they become stationary and are called *histiocytes* or **tissue macrophages.** Activated monocytes and tissue macrophages form *cytotoxins, leukotrienes* (see Fig. 18-9), *interleukin-1* (p. 427), *interferons* (p. 432) and factors that promote the growth of endothelial cells and smooth muscle cells. In the vicinity of inflammation monocytes can multiply by cell division. Histiocytes form isolating walls around foreign bodies that are invulnerable or highly resistant to enzymatic destruction. These cells are always present in large numbers in the lymph nodes, the alveolar walls, and the sinuses of liver, spleen and bone marrow.

Lymphocytes

25–40% of the blood leukocytes (1,000–3,600 cells per μl) in adults are lymphocytes, and as many as 50% in small children. An increase beyond this range (to over 4,000 cells/μl in adults and a proportional increase in children) is called *lymphocytosis;* a decrease to less than the mean number is called *lymphopenia.* Lymphocytes are produced by a number of organs: the lymph nodes, tonsils, Peyer's patches, appendix, adenoids, spleen, thymus gland and bone marrow. Lymphocytes are functional elements in the *specific immune system* (see pp. 426ff.).

By addition of certain plant proteins *(phytohemagglutinins)* to cultures of blood lymphocytes it can be demonstrated that these cells, previously thought to be relatively highly differentiated and inactive, are capable of considerable enlargement, mitotic division, development of more organelles, and increased synthesis of RNA, DNA, proteins and enzymes. Evidently these changes, triggered in situ by antigens, have a specific defensive function in making available more immunoglobulins.

Leukocyte Counts: Method and Pathophysiology

To determine the *numbers of leukocytes of the different types,* a capillary-blood smear on a microscope slide is left to dry in air and stained with standard mixtures of acidic and basic dyes (e.g., that of Giemsa). When examined microscopically at high magnification, the individual types can be distinguished on the basis of stain affinity and structure. At least 100 leukocytes are included in the sample, and the proportion of each type is given as a percentage.

During **infectious diseases** the proportions of the various types of leukocytes change in characteristic ways. Acute bacterial infections induce a neutrophilic leukocytosis accompanied by a decline in the numbers of lymphocytes and eosinophils. As the battle against the infection proceeds it enters a phase of monocytosis – a sign that the bacteria are being overcome. The final phase is a clean-up operation, in which lymphocytes and eosinophils participate. Chronic infections are accompanied by lymphocytosis.

In the tables used clinically to survey the various forms of leukocytes in the blood, those with less segmented nuclei are customarily shown on the left side. Therefore when these forms become relatively more numerous one can speak of a *"leftward shift".* It was once thought that the greater the number of lobules in the granulocyte nucleus, the older the cell; recent autoradiographic studies have shown that there is no such correlation. Evidently the degree of segmentation is predetermined. In a number of diseases (e.g., pernicious anemia), however, granulocyte nuclei with an unusually large number of lobes are produced.

A pathological leukocyte deficiency, *leukopenia* or – in the most severe form – *agranulocytosis,* results in collapse of the body's defense against bacterial infection. In leukopenia the neutrophils are most markedly affected. The deficiency can be caused by a lowered rate of cell production or a more rapid disappearance of the cells from the blood. As in the case of erythrocyte production, physical (ionizing radiation) or chemical (benzene, cytostatics, etc.) agents can retard multiplication of the leukocyte stem cells and the maturation of the committed progenitors in the bone marrow. The most severe acute infections (e.g., sepsis and miliary tuberculosis) and diseases involving enlargement of the spleen (splenomegaly) induce leukopenia.

In *leukemia,* on the other hand, there is an uncontrolled (cancer-like) proliferation of leukocytes. The cells produced in excessive numbers are usually not completely differentiated and are incapable of performing their physiological functions – especially in defense against bacterial infections. The causes of human leukemia are still unknown. On the basis of the origin of the leukemic cells, a distinction is made between *lymphogenous* and *myelogenous* leukemia. In the former the overabundant cells are lymphocytes, and in the latter they belong to the myelocytic series (Fig. 18-5, p. 410).

18.5 Thrombocytes

By the method (of Fonio) ordinarily used in the clinical determination of the blood thrombocyte count, healthy adults are found to have 150,000 –350,000 platelets per μl blood. These anuclear cells, flat and irregularly circular in outline, have longest diameters of 1–4 μm and are 0.5–0.75 μm thick. They are produced in the bone marrow (cf. Fig. 18-5) by the shedding of cytoplasmic buds of *megakaryocytes.* One thousand thrombocytes can be formed from one of these giant cells. Thrombocyte formation, like erythropoiesis, is regulated by a glycoprotein hormone produced in the kidney, **thrombopoietin.** Thrombocytes *circulate in the blood* for 5–11 days, and finally are destroyed in the liver, lungs and spleen.

While in circulation, thrombocytes are in a *"resting" state.* They can be converted to an *activated state* by surface contact and by certain blood-clotting factors. Activated thrombocytes release substances required for *hemostasis.*

In the electron microscope one can see, just inside the outer membrane of the platelet, a zone of apparently unstructured protoplasm, the *hyalomer.* Not until the platelet has been activated does it become possible to detect microfilaments in this

Table 18-6. Substances contained in the thrombocyte granules. From [32]

Electron-dense granules	α-granules	Lysosomes
Anions	*Plasma-type proteins*	*Acidic hydrolases*
ATP, ADP, GTP, GDP, inorganic phosphate	Fibrinogen, clotting factors V and VIII, fibronectin, albumin, kallikrein, α_2-antiplasmin, thrombospondin	β-hexosaminidase β-galactosidase β-glucuronidase β-arabinosidase β-glycerophosphatase, arylsulfatase
Cations		
Calcium, serotonin	*Platelet-specific proteins* Platelet factor 4 (antiheparin), β-thromboglobulin, growth factor ("platelet-derived growth factor")	

protoplasm; these are composed of actin, myosin and tropomyosin. In the central part of the cell is the organelle zone, the *granulomer,* within which are mitochondria, glycogen vesicles and granules. Thrombocytes contain glycolytic enzymes and those of the pentose phosphate cycle, the citric acid cycle, and the respiratory chain. ATPase is also present, along with large amounts of ATP.

The granules differ morphologically and in chemical composition; there are *"electron-dense" granules, α-granules* and *lysosomes* (Table 18-6). The substances contained in the electron-dense granules and α-granules are released when the platelets aggregate and play an important role in coagulation (see below). The significance of the lysosomal enzymes of the thrombocytes is not well understood. **Platelet factor 3,** which is particularly important for coagulation, is not part of the thrombocyte contents in the strict sense [32, 35]. As a *phospholipoprotein complex,* it is a component of the outer thrombocyte membrane. Thrombocytes are also able to release arachidonic acid from cell membranes and convert it to *thromboxanes* (Fig. 18-9), which in turn enhance the tendency of the platelets to aggregate.

Some findings suggest that thrombocytes can take up dissolved plasma constituents and possibly are even capable of the phagocytosis of non-living foreign materials, viruses and antibodies. However, the thrombocytes seem to be of relatively little significance in the unspecific defense system of the body (see p. 433).

Thrombocytopenia is a condition in which there are fewer than 60,000 platelets per μl blood. It is associated with a greater tendency to bleed *(hemorrhagic diathesis);* in some cases, small punctate hemorrhages *(petechiae)* can occur from the capillaries of all the organs *(thrombocytopenic purpura).* Thrombocytopenia can be caused by inadequate thrombocyte formation *(amegakaryocytosis)* due to bone-marrow damage (e.g., by ionizing radiation, mitosis poisons, neoplastic diseases or chronic inflammatory processes) or by increased destruction of thrombocytes (e.g., in immune responses, virus infections, consumption coagulopathy).

There are also congenital hemorrhagic diatheses in which the thrombocyte count is normal but the storage capacity of the α-granules *(grey-platelet syndrome)* or of the electron-dense granules *(storage pool disease)* is reduced.

18.6 Hemostasis and Coagulation

The Process of Hemostasis

Thrombocyte adhesion. When a healthy person is injured in such a way that some small blood vessels are opened, bleeding stops of its own accord after 1–3 minutes (the *bleeding time*). This initial **primary hemostasis** is brought about chiefly by vasoconstriction and the mechanical blockage of small vessels by a plug of thrombocytes. Adhesion of the platelets to connective-tissue fibers at the edges of the wound is mediated by **von Willebrand factor** (vWF), an oligomeric glycoprotein in subendothelial tissue and blood platelets [40].

vWF is also found in the plasma, and here the clotting factor VIII is bound to it (hence the earlier name Factor VIII-associated antigen). vWF forms bridges between the subendothelial structures and a specific receptor (glycoprotein Ib) in the thrombocyte membrane. In patients with a hereditary deficiency of glycoprotein Ib, platelet adhesion is impaired *(Bernhard-Soulier syndrome).*

As a part of the process of adhesion, the *platelets change shape,* becoming rounded with spiny projections. Under the influence of ADP (some of which comes from injured cells) and adrenalin, the tendency of the thrombocytes to *aggregate – reversibly,* at first – is enhanced. The contents of the electron-dense and α-granules (Table 18-6) are now released and can go into action; among them are serotonin, which serves as a vasoconstrictor, stored catecholamines and ADP (partially derived from ATP). By the action of the vasoconstrictors the lumen of the injured vessel becomes smaller (a functional ischemia is induced), and it is obstructed by the mass of platelets adhering to the collagen fibers.

Irreversible thrombocyte aggregation. At practically the same time **thrombin,** produced from prothrombin in small amounts in this phase of clotting, under the influence of tissue thromboplastin (see below), initiates irreversible thrombocyte aggregation. By reacting with specific receptors in the thrombocyte membrane, thrombin induces the *phosphorylation of intracellular proteins* and the *release of Ca^{2+}* in the thrombocytes (Fig. 18-11); the effect is enhanced by the presence of ADP and collagen. It results in activation of the Ca^{2+}-dependent phospholipase A_2, which catalyzes the release of arachidonic acid. The latter is converted by the enzyme *cyclooxygenase* into the cyclic endoperoxides PGG_2 and PGH_2, from which the thromboxanes A_2 and B_2 (relatively ineffective) are formed (Figs. 18-9 and 18-11). The **endoperoxides** and **thromboxane A_2** initiate the irreversible aggregation and structural breakdown of still more platelets, which thereupon release their active contents. Thromboxane A_2 also enhances vasoconstriction. As the thrombocytes disintegrate, phospholipoproteins of the cell membrane become accessible from outside [35]. The important role of these lipoproteins (called **platelet factor 3**) in blood clotting is discussed below.

The exact *sequence* of the events in thrombocyte activation presented above is not yet known for certain. One reason is that in some reaction steps there is *positive feedback;* that is, activated platelets produce substances that in turn activate new platelets. ADP is such a substance, and another example is the loop involving activation of platelet factor 3 and the effect of thrombin (Fig. 18-11). These interactions create an avalanche, in which thrombocytes are drawn into the reaction at an ever increasing rate.

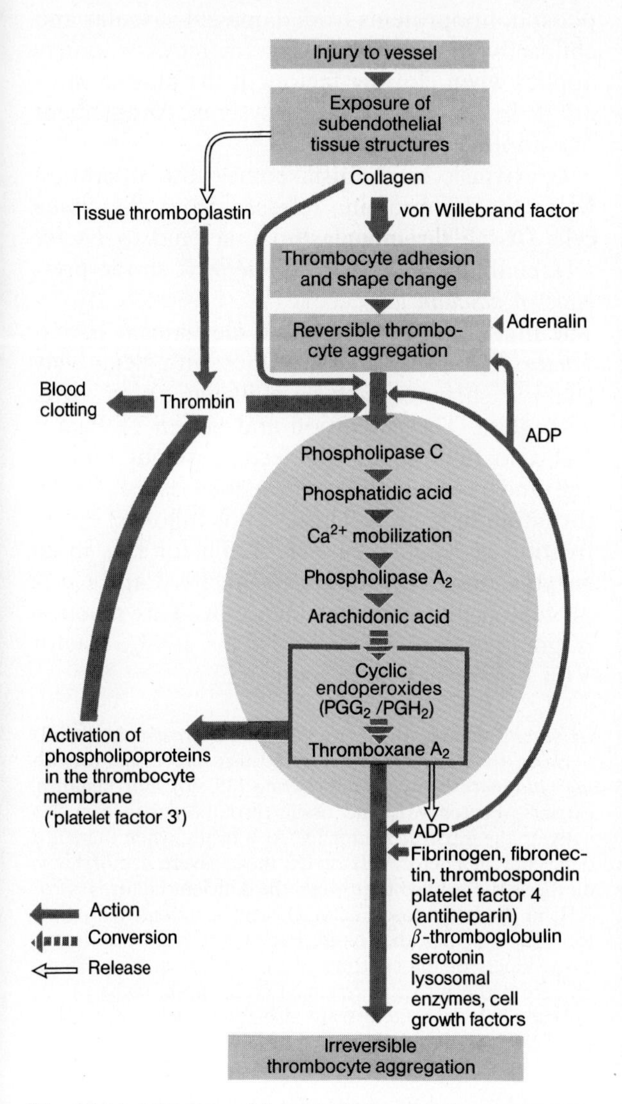

Fig. 18-11. Diagram of thrombocyte activation and aggregation

The irreversible thrombocyte aggregation also requires **fibrinogen.** This substance not only encloses thrombocytes during clot formation (see secondary hemostasis, below) but also reacts specifically with receptors (glycoproteins IIb and IIIa) in the activated platelet membrane. Patients who lack these receptors tend to hemorrhage even though their thrombocyte count is normal *(Glanzmann-Naegeli thrombasthenia).* Effects like those of fibrinogen are also thought to be exerted by the glycoproteins fibronectin and thrombospondin, which are stored in the α-granules of the thrombocytes (Table 18-6).

Endothelial defects can also initiate thrombocyte aggregation when there has been no externally imposed injury. In an effort to prevent *thromboses* drugs (e.g., acetylsalicylic acid) are prescribed that reduce the enzymatic activity of cyclooxygenase and thus inhibit thromboxane synthesis (Fig. 18-9). The antiaggregatory action of cyclooxygenase inhibitors should also be kept in mind when they are used to treat inflammatory rheumatic diseases.

Coagulation. Once the white *platelet plug* has been formed, the vessels in the injured region are no longer so strongly constricted and might allow the plug to be washed out and bleeding to resume. However, by this time the *fibrin coagulation* in the course of **secondary hemostasis** has advanced sufficiently to obstruct the vessel completely with a clot (red *blood clot,* containing other blood cells such as erythrocytes).

The main steps in the clotting of blood have been known for some time. As early as 1905 MORAWITZ described the basic sequence, and his description is still valid (Fig. 18-12). Outside the body blood clots in a few minutes. Disintegration of the thrombocytes produces the *"prothrombin activator"* (also known as thrombokinase) that converts the plasma protein **prothrombin** into thrombin. Thrombin splits the **fibrinogen** dis-

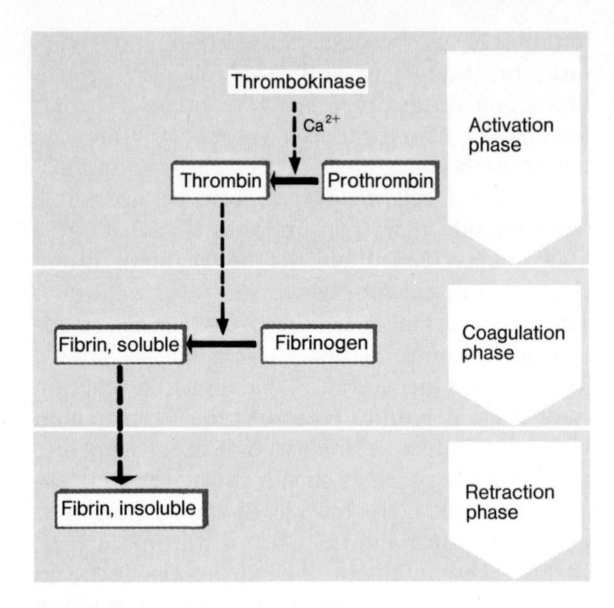

Fig. 18-12. Classical scheme of blood coagulation, from MORAWITZ

solved in the plasma to form fibrin, which constitutes the filamentous skeleton of the fibrin clot. The conversion of fibrinogen to fibrin transforms the blood from a fluid to a gelatinous mass.

Subsequent events. Within a few hours the fibrin filaments *retract,* squeezing out a clear yellowish fluid, the serum (fibrinogen-free plasma). The firm, compact red clot that remains is composed of a fibrillar mesh with blood cells in its interstices. The thrombocytes are also involved in this process. They contain **thrombosthenin,** a protein resembling actomyosin that can contract by splitting ATP. Retraction stabilizes the clot mechanically and pulls the edges of the wound together, creating favorable conditions for the growth of connective tissue cells into the area.
The clotting process can be followed, after some time, by a phase of **fibrinolysis,** in which the clot dissolves and the vessel eventually becomes passable again.

Clotting Factors and the Process of Coagulation

The basic sequence illustrated in Fig. 18-12 has been expanded to include a number of additional factors that are necessary for clotting to proceed normally. Absence of any one of these factors can impair thrombin formation and interfere with clotting (Table 18-7). The various factors are identified by names or, more clearly, by Roman numerals. In general they are *proteolytic enzymes* (the factors XII, XI, X, IX, VII, II and kallikrein are serine proteases) present in the plasma in *inactive form,* as proenzymes. When clotting begins they activate one another, in a *cascade-like* chain of reactions. The active form of the factors is indicated by a subscript "a" (e.g., II_a).

Initial steps in clotting. The destruction of tissue cells and activation of thrombocytes releases **phospholipoproteins** and these, together with the clotting factors X_a and V_a in the plasma plus ionized calcium, constitute an *enzyme complex* that serves as the *prothrombin activator.* According to the origin of the lipoproteins, a distinction is made between a *tissue* and a *blood* prothrombin activator. The term *extrinsic system* of clotting is used when the process is initiated by phospholipoproteins from damaged vascular and connective-tissue cells; the term *intrinsic system* applies when clotting factors in the plasma initiate it. In the body the two systems complement one another (Fig. 18-13).
The extrinsic mechanism comes into operation when the lipoproteins released from the tissue cells **(tissue thromboplastin)** first bind to *Factor VII,* enabling it to activate *Factor X* in the presence of *calcium ions.*
The first step in the intrinsic mechanism is that *Factor XII* comes into contact with negatively charged surfaces such as collagen or, in vitro, with glass. The activation and action of Factor XII also involve high-molecular-weight kininogen and proteolytic enzymes such as kallikrein, thrombin or trypsin. This event is followed by activation of *Factors XI and IX.* Factor IX_a, in an enzyme complex with *platelet factor 3* and Ca^{2+}, proteolytically activates Factor X. This reaction is greatly accelerated by *Factor* VIII_a. Factor VIII itself is activated by thrombin.

In several phases there are functional cross-connections between the extrinsic and the intrinsic processes, providing *"alternative routes" for clotting* [35, 36]. For instance, extrinsic Factor VII_a and tissue thromboplastin can also activate the intrinsic Factor IX. As a result, when there is a deficiency of Factor VIII or IX, more severe hemorrhagic diathesis is observed than when the deficient factor is XI or XII; in the latter case Factor IX can be activated by Factor VII_a. On the other hand, Factor VII can be activated by products of the splitting of Factor XII and by Factor IX_a from the intrinsic system. Furthermore, some of the "plasma" clotting factors are also found in thrombocytes (cf. Tables 18-6 and 18-7).

Thrombin production. Prothrombin activator splits the inactive precursor **prothrombin** (MW

Table 18-7. Blood-clotting factors; a, activated forms. From [19, 25, 40]

Factor	Name, synonym	Most important site of production	MW ($\cdot 10^{-3}$)	Concentration in plasma, mean (μmol/l)	Properties, function	Deficiency syndrome	
						Name	Cause
I	Fibrinogen	Liver	340	8.8	Soluble protein, precursor of fibrin	Afibrinogenemia, fibrinogen deficiency	Hereditary (autosomal recessive); consumption coagulopathy, damage to hepatic parenchyma
II	Prothrombin	Liver (vitamin-K-dependent)	72	1.4	α_1-globulin, proenzyme of thrombin (protease)	Hypoprothrombinemia	Hereditary (autosomal recessive); liver damage, vitamin K deficiency, consumption coagulopathy
III	Tissue thromboplastin	Tissue cells			Phospholipoprotein; active in extrinsic clotting system		
IV	Ca^{2+}			2,500	Necessary for activation of most clotting factors		
V	Proaccelerin, accelerator globulin	Liver	330	0.03	Soluble β-globulin, binds to thrombocyte membrane; activated by Factor II_a and Ca^{2+}; V_a is a component of the prothrombin activator	Parahemophilia, hypoproaccelerinemia	Hereditary (autosomal recessive); liver diseases
VI	Deleted (activated Factor V)						
VII	Proconvertin	Liver (vitamin-K-dependent)	63	0.03	α-globulin, proenzyme (protease); Factor VII_a, with Factor III and Ca^{2+} activates the Factor X in extrinsic system	Hypoproconvertinemia	Hereditary (autosomal recessive); vitamin K deficiency
VIII	Antihemophilic globulin, AHG	? (vWF: endothelium, megakaryocytes)	260 to 10,000 (polymeric complexes with vWF)	<0.0004	β_2-globulin, forms complex with *von Willebrand* factor; activated by Factor II_a and Ca^{2+}; Factor VIII_a is cofactor in conversion of Factor X to Factor X_a	Hemophilia A (classical hemophilia); *von Willebrand* syndrome	Hereditary (X-chromosomal recessive); Hereditary (usually autosomal dominant)
IX	Christmas factor	Liver (vitamin-K-dependent)	57	0.09	α_1-globulin, contact-sensitive proenzyme (protease); Factor IX_a, with platelet factor 3, Factor VIII_a and Ca^{2+}, activates the Factor X in intrinsic system	Hemophilia B	Hereditary (X-chromosomal recessive)
X	Stuart-Prower factor	Liver (vitamin-K-dependent)	60	0.2	α_1-globulin, proenzyme (protease); Factor X_a is a component of the prothrombin activator	Factor X deficiency	Hereditary (autosomal recessive)

Table 18-7 (continued)

Factor	Name, synonym	Most important site of production	MW ($\cdot 10^{-3}$)	Concentration in plasma, mean (μmol/l)	Properties, function	Deficiency syndrome Name	Cause
XI	Plasma thromboplastin antecedent, PTA	?	160	0.034	γ-globulin, contact-sensitive proenzyme (protease); Factor XI_a, with Ca^{2+}, activates Factor IX	PTA deficiency	Hereditary (autosomal recessive); consumption coagulopathy
XII	Hageman factor	?	80	0.45	β-globulin, contact-sensitive proenzyme (protease) (i.e., changes shape on contact with surfaces); activated by kallikrein	Hageman syndrome (usually not apparent clinically)	Hereditary (usually autosomal recessive); consumption coagulopathy
XIII	Fibrin-stabilizing factor	Megakaryocytes	320	0.1	β-globulin, proenzyme (transamidase); Factor XIII_a causes intermeshing of fibrin	Factor XIII deficiency	Hereditary (autosomal recessive); consumption coagulopathy
	Prekallikrein, Fletcher factor	?	90	0.34	β-globulin, proenzyme (protease); activated by Factor XII_a; kallikrein assists activation of Factor XII and Factor XI	Deficiency usually not apparent clinically	Hereditary
	High-MW kininogen, Fitzgerald factor	?	160	0.5	α-globulin; assists contact-activation of Factor XII and Factor XI	Deficiency usually not apparent clinically	Hereditary

72,000) proteolytically to produce the enzymatically active **thrombin** (MW 35,000). The plasma of a healthy person contains 0.10–0.15 g of prothrombin per liter. *Vitamin K* is required for its production in the liver; thus vitamin K deficiency (due, e.g., to defective enteral fat absorption) interferes with blood clotting. The half life of prothrombin in the plasma is 1.5–3 days. Thrombin is a peptidase particularly effective in splitting arginyl bonds; it causes partial proteolysis of the fibrinogen molecule.

Fibrin production. The first step is that the two subunits of the dimer **fibrinogen** (MW 340,000) are split apart; each subunit consists of three polypeptide chains (α, β, γ). **Thrombin** then breaks four arginyl-glycine bonds, one in each of the two α and the two β chains, to release the fibrinopeptides A and B. Both of these act as vasoconstrictors. The fibrin monomers that remain after the fibrinopeptides have been removed are initially brought into parallel alignment with one another by electrostatic forces, forming so-called fibrin polymers. This **polymerization** requires the presence of fibrinopeptide A, a plasma factor and calcium. The gel that results can be liquefied again by the addition of reagents (such as *urea*) that break hydrogen bridges. The **fibrin-stabilizing Factor XIII_a**, a transglutaminase activated by thrombin in the presence of Ca^{2+}, is required for the establishment of covalent bonds between the fibrin monomers that give them a firm structure. Factor XIII is found in the cytosol of the thrombocytes and in the plasma (Table 18-7). The three-dimensional network of fibrin, within which blood cells and platelets are trapped in large numbers, is still relatively open at this stage and does not take its final form until retraction occurs (see above).

Fibrinolysis

Significance of fibrinolysis. The dissolution of a clot is a process similar in complexity to clot formation (Fig. 18-14). Even in the intact organism some of the fibrinogen is continuously being converted to fibrin. In a state of functional equi-

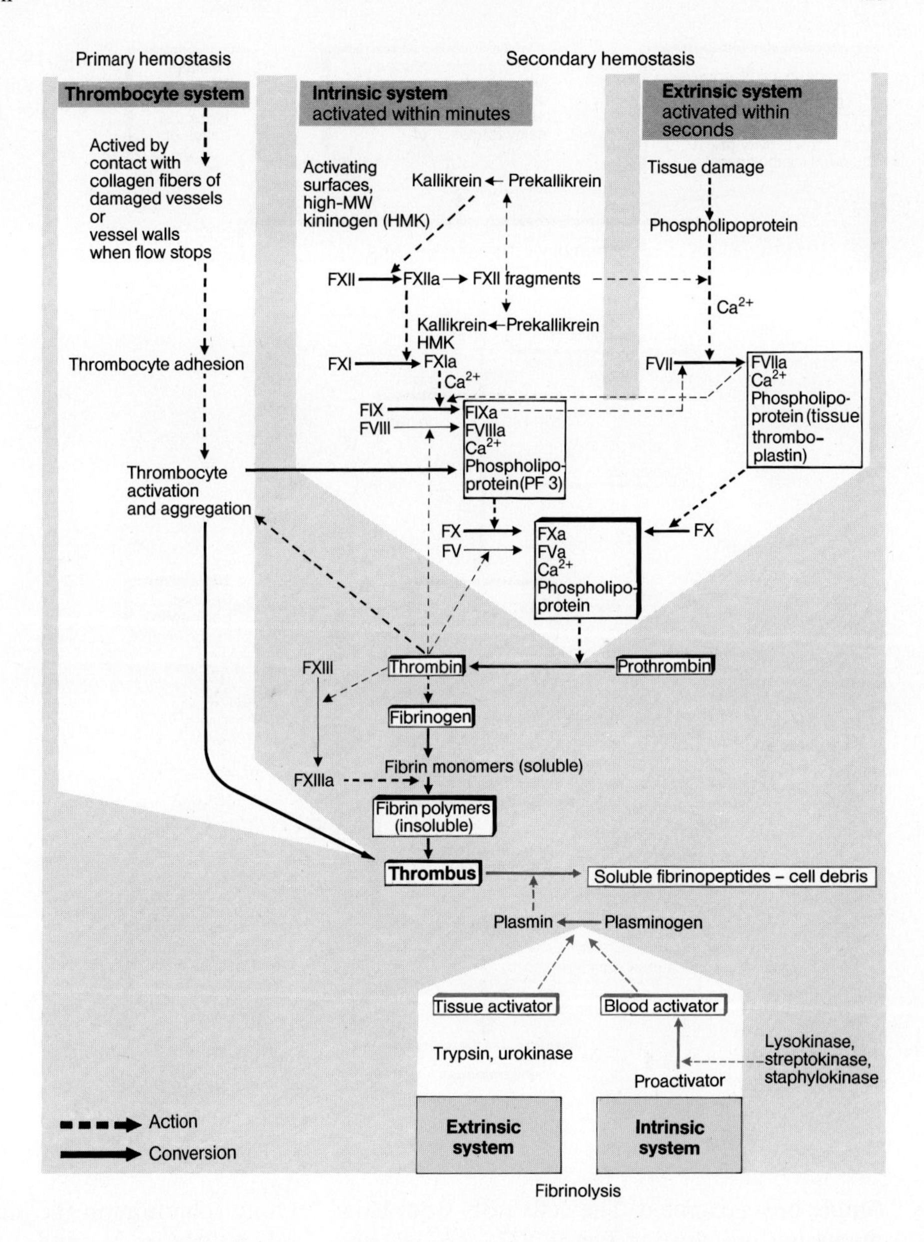

Fig. 18-13. Diagram of blood clotting and fibrinolysis. For data on clotting factors see Table 18-7 (PF3 = platelet factor 3). Modified from [14, 26, 35, 36]

librium, this fibrin is continuously removed by the process of fibrinolysis. Only when the clotting system is additionally stimulated by injury does fibrin production temporarily dominate at the site of the injury, so that localized coagulation becomes apparent.

Activation of fibrinolysis. One of the globulins among the plasma proteins is **plasminogen** (profibrinolysin, MW 81,000). Like prothrombin, this substance can be converted to an active form, **plasmin** (fibrinolysin) by tissue or blood factors (fibrinolysokinases) in ways analogous to the extrinsic and intrinsic systems of coagulation. Plasmin, a serine protease, disintegrates the clot by virtue of its special affinity to fibrin. It splits soluble peptides off from the fibrin by hydrolysis; furthermore, these peptides inhibit the action of thrombin and hence counteract the formation of additional fibrin. Plasmin also splits fibrinogen, prothrombin and the clotting factors V, VII, IX, XI and XII. Therefore plasmin not only dissolves clots but also reduces the ability of the blood to coagulate.

The **plasminogen activators** derived from **tissue,** the most active of which is found in the myometrium of the uterus, convert plasminogen directly to plasmin (Fig. 18-13 and 18-14). An especially effective tissue activator, *urokinase,* is found in the urine. It is not known whether it serves to prevent the formation of or to dissolve fibrin clots in the urinary tract, or whether it is

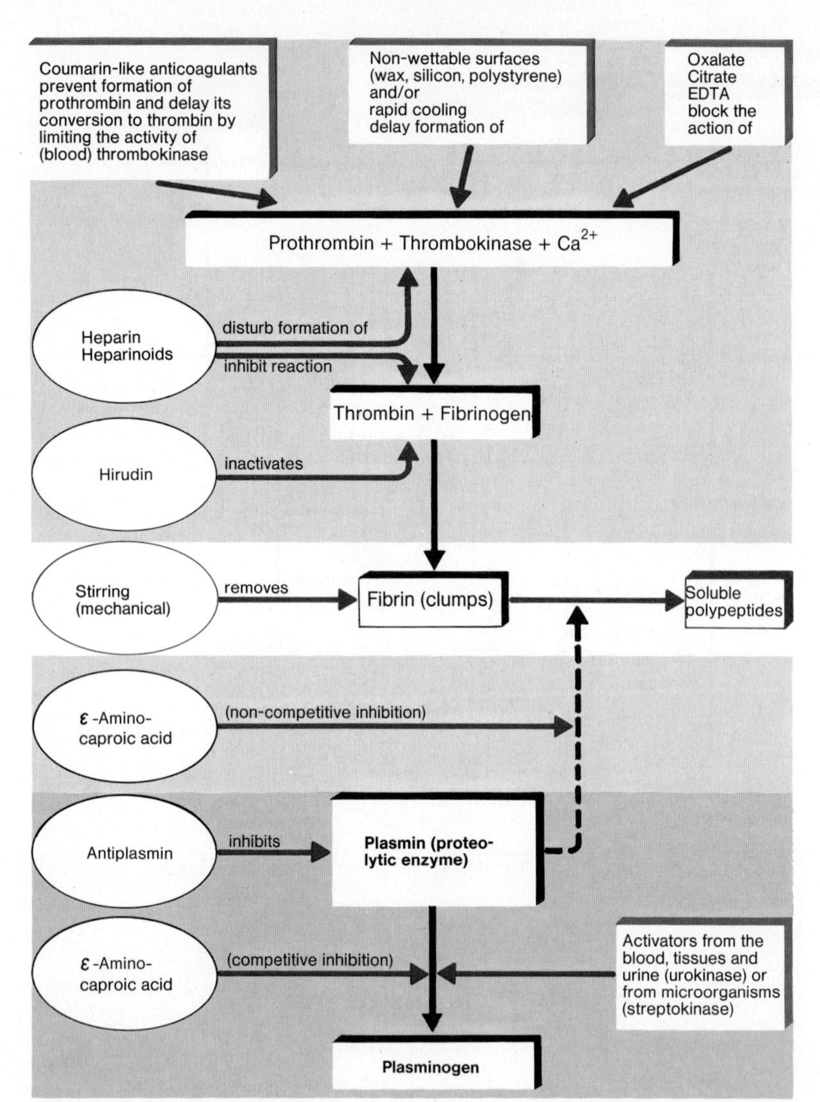

Fig. 18-14. Mode of action of some anticoagulants and fibrinolytics. Modified from [3]

simply being excreted. The activators from **blood** (including the clotting factor VII_a) are effective only under the influence of so-called *proactivators.* The most important proactivators (one of which is prekallikrein) are *lysokinases* released from blood cells by traumatic or inflammatory damage to tissue. A therapeutically important lysokinase produced by hemolytic streptococci, streptokinase, is used in the treatment of thromboses [14].

Factors produced in the body that inhibit clotting and fibrinolysis. Plasma contains several *serine protease inhibitors,* which restrict the activity of the fibrin-forming and the fibrinolytic enzymes [19]. *Antithrombin III* is a particularly important inhibitor of clotting; it acts on Factors II_a, X_a, IX_a, XI_a, XII_a and kallikrein – that is, it inhibits the formation and action of thrombin. Other inhibitors in the plasma are *protein C* (inhibits Factors V_a and VIII_a), *α_2-macroglobulin* (inhibits Factor II_a, kallikrein and plasmin) and *C1 inactivator* (inhibits Factors XI_a and XII_a and kallikrein).

The main factor responsible for *inhibiting the fibrinolytic activity of plasmin is α_2-antiplasmin.* Because of its presence in the plasma, plasmin can exert its fibrinolytic influence without restraint only in the interior of a clot. There, because plasminogen is adsorbed to fibrin, the plasmin concentration is high; the concentration of *α_2-antiplasmin,* which can enter the clot only by slow diffusion from the blood flowing past, is low. To retard fibrinolysis for therapeutic purposes synthetic protease inhibitors are used; an example is *ε-aminocaproic acid,* the actions of which are diagrammed in Fig. 18-14.

Disturbance and Inhibition of Coagulation; Tests of Clotting Activity

Equilibrium between the factors in plasma, thrombocytes and vessel wall that promote clotting and those that inhibit it is a fundamental requirement for undisturbed blood flow and – when needed – successful clotting. If the balance is upset the result can be either a *greater tendency to bleed* or *excessive clotting activity*. The latter is clinically more common.

The symptoms of **defective clotting** are *hematomas and serious bleeding tendencies, especially in the joints*. That is, individual relatively large vessels are affected, and the bleeding is usually induced by trauma. This situation differs from the thrombocytic disorders, which are characterized by spontaneous punctate bleeding from capillaries (see above).

A **hereditary deficiency** of – *usually several* – plasma clotting factors can become manifest after severe bleeding (**consumption coagulopathy**) or in infectious diseases. Severe forms of inflammatory and degenerative **liver disease** can restrict the synthesis of factors II, VII, IX and X so greatly that clotting defects appear. Clotting is also impaired when there is **vitamin K deficiency** without liver damage. An "internal" deficiency of this fat-soluble vitamin, which is present in vegetables and can be synthesized by intestinal bacteria, occurs when enteral fat absorption is inadequate (particularly due to insufficient bile secretion) and when the intestinal flora has been destroyed by antibiotics. Vitamin K is necessary for synthesis of Factors II, VII, IX and X in the liver.

In the **congenital deficiency states** usually only a *single* clotting factor is subnormally active (Table 18-7). The sex-linked (overt in males, carried by females), recessive hereditary disease *hemophilia* is associated in the great majority of cases with a *lack of Factor VIII* (**hemophilia A**). In a few bleeders, however, it is *Factor IX* that is lacking (**hemophilia B**). The two forms are indistinguishable in symptomatology, mode of inheritance, and pathology as revealed by global coagulation tests.

Prevention of coagulation (Fig. 18-14). **Cooling** retards extravascular coagulation, though it does not prevent it. Coagulation of blood samples can also be retarded by the use of cannulas and storage containers coated with silicon or paraffin. These **unwettable surfaces** do not induce aggregation and the subsequent degradation of thrombocytes as rough, wettable surfaces do. Therefore the formation of thrombin is considerably delayed under these conditions. Extravascular clotting can also be prevented by adding substances that remove from solution the ionic calcium required at many stages in the coagulation process, by *binding calcium in relatively insoluble or weakly dissociated compounds*. Suitable additives include **sodium, potassium or ammonium oxalate, sodium citrate,** and the chelating agent **EDTA** (ethylenediamine-tetraacetic acid). Sodium citrate is most commonly used, because it is nontoxic in small amounts, so that inadvertent injection while a sample is being drawn is not dangerous.

Heparin inhibits coagulation both in vivo and in vitro. This anti-coagulant is a mixture of polysulfonated esters of a glucosamine glycan. It is particularly abundant in the tissues of liver, lung, heart and muscle, as well as in mast cells and basophilic granulocytes. Heparin forms a complex (known as antithrombin II) with antithrombin III, thereby increasing its effectiveness in inhibiting the formation and action of thrombin. Heparin also serves as a fibrinolysis activator, promoting the dissolution of blood clots. In cases of heparin overdose (basic) protamine chloride can be given as an antidote; it binds to heparin to form an inactive compound.

Because heparin must be administered parenterally, and is broken down and excreted so rapidly that it acts for only 4–6 hours, **coumarin derivatives** are preferred for long-term anticoagulant therapy. These drugs can be given orally; they act as *vitamin K antagonists,* preventing the vitamin from binding with its apoenzyme (γ-glutamyl carboxylase) in the liver. This effect can be overcome by increasing the concentration of vitamin K (competitive inhibition).

Other anticoagulants. In addition to the clotting inhibitors with a systemic action there are certain substances of animal origin that can be used to inhibit clotting locally. One is **hirudin,** an antithrombin in the saliva of the medicinal leech. Some snake toxins inhibit clotting by preventing the formation of fibrin. The saliva of blood-sucking insects also acts as an anticoagulant; the antithrombin **tabanin** has been isolated from the salivary gland of a biting fly (*Tabanus*).

Tests of clotting activity. For measurement of **recalcification time,** blood anticoagulated with sodium citrate is put into a test tube with a glass bead, and the tube is left to rotate slowly, in a slanted position, in a water-bath at 37 °C. After the temperature has equilibrated, an excess of calcium chloride is added and the time until clot formation (indicated when the bead rotates with the tube) is measured. *Normal range: 80–130 s.*

The **thromboplastin time (Quick test)** is the most common method of estimating the effectiveness of coumarin therapy. Tissue thromboplastin and calcium chloride are added in excess to oxalated or citrated plasma, and the time until clotting begins is measured. Departures from the normal clotting time *(ca. 14 s)* in general result from a deficiency in the factors of the extrinsic clotting system, prothrombin or fibrinogen.

To determine the **partial thromboplastin time** (PTT) platelet factor 3 and calcium chloride are added in excess to citrated plasma and the clotting time is measured. This test demonstrates the activity of the intrinsic clotting system (e.g., Factor VIII and Factor IX) as well as that of prothrombin and fibrinogen. *Normal time: 40–50 s.*

The **thrombin time** (TT) is found by measuring the clotting time after a test thrombin solution has been added to citrated plasma. The thrombin time can be used to evaluate fibrinogen deficiency or fibrinolysis therapy with streptokinase. *Normal time: 17–24 s.*

18.7 The Role of the Blood in Defense

Classification of the Defense Mechanisms

The body has three complementary systems with which to defend itself against pathogens:

1. The specific immune system (Latin *immunis,* free or exempt). It is capable of responding to cellular, particulate and molecular foreign agents *(antigens)* by forming specific defensive substances in or on cells **(specific cellular defense)** or dissolved in the plasma (*antibodies,* **specific**

humoral defense) that attack the foreign bodies and bind to them (antigen-antibody reaction).

2. The unspecific humoral systems. The factors of the *complement system* and other plasma proteins are able to break apart antigen-antibody complexes, to kill foreign cells and to activate the body's own cells that are involved in the inflammatory reaction.

3. The unspecific cellular systems. *Phagocytizing leukocytes* and *macrophages* destroy pathogens and antigen-antibody complexes. Tissue macrophages also play an important role in the identification of foreign substances by the specific immune system.

The *unspecific defense systems* can make foreign bodies harmless even though they have not been previously encountered. By contrast, the *specific defense systems* become effective (immunity is acquired) only after the initial interactions with the foreign body.

Specific Defense Mechanisms

Structure and function of the specific immune system. The specific immune system serves the organism in two ways, to *protect it from pathogens* that have invaded from outside, and to attack *transformed cells of the body itself*, such as tumor cells. The *immunocompetent* cells, those able to produce an immune reaction, recognize foreign bodies by their surface structure *(antigenic determinants)* and form **antibodies** of an appropriate shape to bind with these particular elements. The immune system can also remember the antigenic structure, so that the next time the same antigen is encountered the response is more rapid and more antibody is produced than at the primary contact (**immunological memory**). The ability of the body to defend itself can change in such a way that when infection with a given pathogen is repeated, symptoms of the illness no longer appear. It is for this reason that some infectious diseases are found mainly in children (the "childhood diseases" such as measles, chicken pox, mumps, scarlet fever); when infected again in later life, the organism is *immune*. That is, immunity is *acquired* and not inherited.

The **lymphatic system** plays a central role in both antibody production and the immunological memory. Although the only morphological difference among the **lymphocytes** in the blood is their size, *several types of lymphocytic cells* can be distinguished on the basis of their chemical surface characteristics and their function. There are three main groups, the *B lymphocytes, T lymphocytes* and *null cells.* Lymphocytes develop from **lymphatic stem cells,** which are derived from the

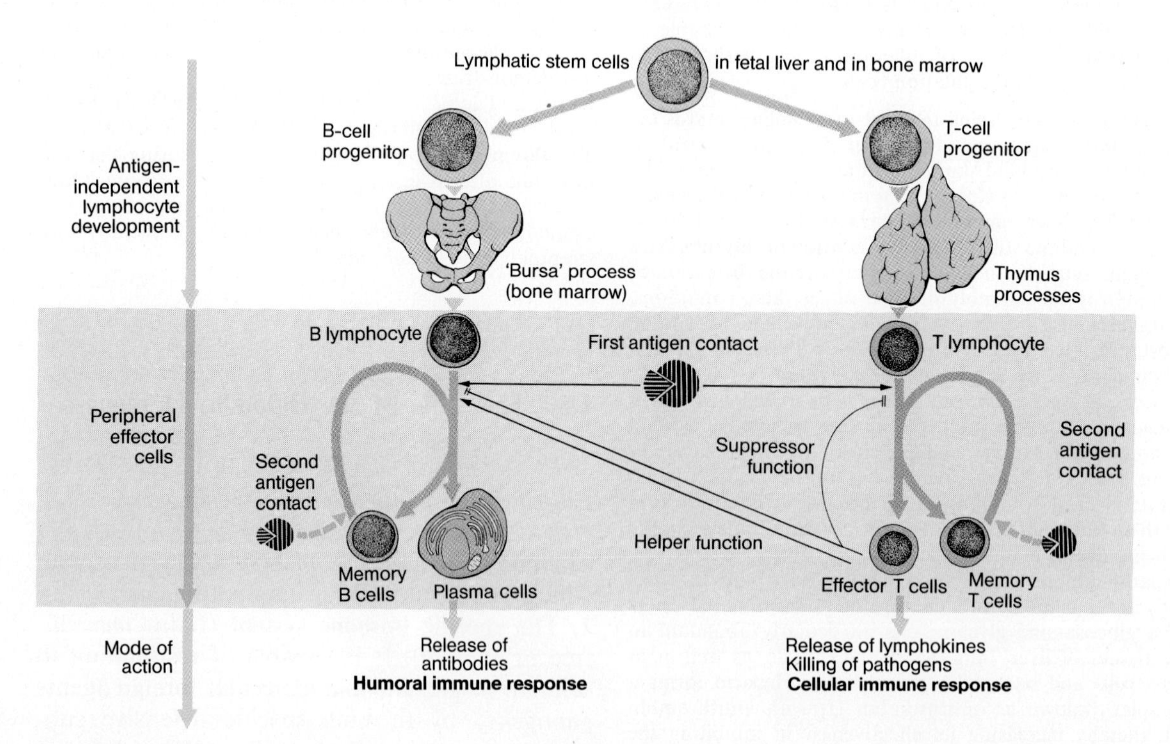

Fig. 18-15. Diagram of the production of T and B lymphocytes and their involvment in the cellular and humoral defense of the blood

Table 18-8. Specific hemopoietic growth factors

Name	Origin	Target cells
Thymosin, Thymopoietin, Splenin	Thymus Thymus Spleen	T-lymphocyte progenitors (+) B-lymphocyte progenitors (–)
Interleukin-1	Macrophages	Lymphocytes and their progenitors
Interleukin-2	T inductor cells	T lymphocytes
Interleukin-3	T lymphokine cells (monocytes?)	Hemopoietic stem cells
B-cell growth factors	T helper cells	B lymphocytes
CSF (colony stimulating factors)	Lymphocytes, macrophages etc.	Monocyte and granulocyte progenitors
Erythropoietin	Kidney, liver (macrophages?)	Erythrocyte progenitors
Thrombopoietin	Kidney	Megakaryocyte progenitors

pluripotent hemopoietic stem cells (Fig. 18-5). Lymphatic stem cells are found in the liver during the fetal period, and in the bone marrow later on. During ontogenesis **lymphocytic progenitors** migrate out of the hemopoietic organs and are carried in the blood to the *primary lymphatic organs,* the **bone marrow** and **thymus** (Fig. 18-15). Here they proliferate, at the same time developing the morphological and functional features that characterize the different kinds of cell; that is, they become *committed* lymphocytes. Lymphocytes that undergo this process in the bone marrow are called **B lymphocytes** (the "B" originally stood for *bursa-dependent,* with reference to a lymphatic organ at the end of the gut in birds, the bursa fabricii, which does not exist in humans; conveniently, it can also stand for "bone marrow", which is assumed to be the equivalent human organ). Lymphocytes that become committed in the thymus, under the influence of certain growth factors (Table 18-8), are called *thymus-dependent* or **T lymphocytes.** B and T lymphocytes are carried in the bloodstream from the primary to the *secondary lymphatic organs,* the **lymph nodes** and **spleen.** At the first contact with an antigen they proliferate and differentiate into the actual immunocompetent cells (plasma cells, T effector cells).

B-cell system. About 15% of the lymphocytes in the blood are B lymphocytes. They are responsible for the **humoral immune response.** Immunoglobulins (mainly IgM monomers and IgD) anchored in the surface of their cell membranes are the specific receptors for the antigens. When they first make contact with an antigen *(sensitization)* some of the B lymphocytes transform themselves into **plasma cells** and begin to form immunoglobulins specific to the antigen, which are then released into the surrounding medium *(humoral antibodies).* Antigenic stimulation of the B lymphocytes occurs only in the presence of certain regulatory tissue hormones; some of these are secreted by T lymphocytes (*lymphokines* from T helper cells; see below) and others by macrophages (*monokines* such as interleukin-1) (Table 18-8). Plasma cells do not circulate in the blood; they are *incorporated into tissue* throughout their 2- to 3-day life span.

Other antigen-stimulated B lymphocytes develop into long-lived **B memory cells.** Unlike the plasma cells, the memory cells (which can proliferate) retain the immunoglobulins in their membranes. All the descendants of an antigen-stimulated lymphocyte, including those of the B memory cells, synthesize antibody with the same antigen specificity *(monoclonal antibodies).* The ability of the B-cell system to "remember" is thus based on an increase in the numbers of antigen-specific memory cells.

T-cell system. The T lymphocytes comprise about 70–80% of the lymphocytes in the blood. These bring about the **cellular immune response.** T lymphocytes do not circulate continually in the blood and lymph; occasionally they spend some time in the secondary lymphatic organs. After antigenic stimulation they proliferate and differentiate into either **T effector cells** or the longer-lived **T memory cells.**

Two subpopulations of T effectors, the T4 and T8 cells, can be distinguished on the basis of certain surface properties. These groups are further subdivided according to functional criteria [37]. T cells assigned mainly to the T4 type include the *T lymphokine cells* (which release lymphokines, hormone-like substances that activate other body cells such as macrophages and hemopoietic stem cells), the *T helper/inductor cells* (which secrete interleukin-2, a lymphokine that promotes the differentiation of additional T cells) and the *T helper cells* (these produce the so-called B-cell growth factors, which promote the differentiation of B lymphocytes into antibody-producing plasma cells). Those belonging predominantly to the T8 type are the *T killer cells* (which destroy antigen-bearing cells) and the *T suppressor cells* (which inhibit the activities of B and T lymphocytes and thus prevent overshooting immune responses). Hence the T cell system also regulates the function of other kinds of cells with responsibilities for defense, the B lymphocytes in particular (Fig. 18-15, Table 18-8).

The long-lived *T memory cells* circulate in the blood and in some cases can "recognize" an antigen when they meet it again even years after the first exposure. At the second contact with the antigen, the memory cells trigger a secondary reaction in which they proliferate still more vigorously than in the primary reaction, rapidly forming a large number of T effector cells.

Unlike B lymphocytes, T lymphocytes do not bear the usual set of membrane-bound immunoglobulins. Instead, their *antigen receptor* (T3/T-cell receptor) consists of an antigen-specific dimeric glycoprotein (T4 or T8 glycoprotein) and three antigen-unspecific – i.e., identical in all T cells – proteins (T3 proteins) [39].

T cells can bind antigens only when the latter are associated with certain antigenic structures on the surface of all the nucleated cells native to the body [11, 17]. These antigenic structures are called **major histocompatibility complex,** MHC (synonyms: transplantation antigens, human leukocyte antigens = HLA). For example, when a macrophage delivers a pathogen to a T lymphocyte, the T lymphocyte recognizes both the foreign object (the pathogen) and the body's own histocompatibility antigen (on the macrophage). The specific pattern of the histocompatibility antigen is genetically fixed and differs from one individual to another. Histocompatibility antigens play an important role in the development of immunological tolerance, and are also involved in the rejection of transplanted organs from other individuals.

Before transplantation of an organ is attempted, the antigenic similarity between donor and receiver is evaluated by examination of the histocompatibility antigen pattern. The leukocytes are used for this purpose, as they are easily obtained.

Null cells are the 10% of the lymphocyte-like cells in the blood that cannot be definitely assigned to either the B or the T categories on the basis of their surface characteristics. Part of the null-cell fraction consists of *hemopoietic progenitor cells* (see p. 410) that have "strayed" into the blood from the bone marrow. It also includes the K (killer) cells. *K cells* have receptors for the Fc component of IgG (see below) and destroy cells that bear IgG. Hence attack by the K cells is *antigen-dependent* but *antigen-unspecific,* so that these cells cannot be considered part of the specific immune system in the strict sense. The action of K cells, unlike that of the T killer cells, does not involve the major histocompatibility complex. Another group of cytotoxic null cells comprises the "natural killer cells" or *NK cells* [7]. The operation of activated NK cells is independent of antigens and antibodies; they are particularly effective in killing *tumor cells.*

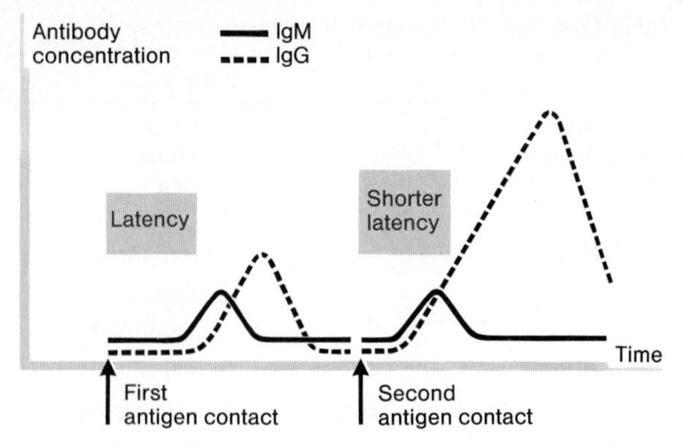

Fig. 18-16. Serum immunoglobulin concentration during the primary and secondary immune responses. Modified from [11]

Humoral and cellular immune responses. Immunological defense in general employs both the humoral and the cellular mechanisms, but to different degrees. In measles, for instance, the humoral response predominates; in other cases, such as contact allergies and transplant rejections, the main actions are cellular.

The **secondary reaction** elicited by a second or subsequent contact with a particular antigen is more rapid and intense than the primary reaction in both the humoral and the cellular system. The blood concentration of the immunoglobulin against the inducing antigen rises sharply (Fig. 18-16). Because the humoral immune response is more rapid than the cell-bound response, the former is also called the *immediate immune response.* This category includes many hypersensitivity reactions – reactions to medicines and pollen (hay fever), for example, as well as the allergic form of bronchial asthma and the transfusion reactions when donor and recipient blood groups do not match.

Although the cell-bound immune response also begins relatively rapidly, reaching a peak after about 48 h, it is called a *delayed immune response* by comparison with the still more rapid development of the humoral secondary response. The delayed responses include many of the so-called contact allergies (e.g., reactions occurring in some people when the skin is exposed to certain synthetic products, to leather tanned with chromium salts, and to jewelry containing nickel), the symptoms of which are reddened skin, blistering and discharge.

Young children are protected from infection by the cellular mechanism, which is present from birth. The humoral immune mechanisms, however, do not become effective until weeks or months after birth. The IgG present in the newborn has been acquired transplacentally from the mother. Not until the beginning of the second month of life, when the plasma cells appear, is there an appreciable increase in immunoglobulin formation.

Antigens are potentially harmful substances (pathogens, protein from another species, inert substances) which, when they invade the body, trigger the formation of specific antibodies to neutralize them. An antigen is composed of an unspecific, large **carrier molecule** (polysaccharide, protein, lipid; MW > 10,000) and the structural components (**determinants**) exposed on the surface of the molecule that are responsible for its serological specificity. Pure lipoids have essentially no immunogenic action and nucleic acids are only weakly effective. A macromolecular antigen can have several determinants. Determinants separated from the macromolecular carrier are called *haptens*. A hapten is capable of reacting with the appropriate (homologous) antibody, but cannot trigger the synthesis of new antibodies.

Antigens can enter the organism by way of mucous and other membranes, the respiratory system and the alimentary canal. The primary contact with the lymphocytes takes place in the lymphatic organs (lymph nodes, tonsils, spleen, bone marrow), where the antigen-stimulated cells proliferate. All the descendants of a sensitized immunocompetent cell react to the same antigenic determinant, and hence form a **cell clone.** It has been estimated that the adult body contains cell clones against at least 10^6 different antigenic determinants.

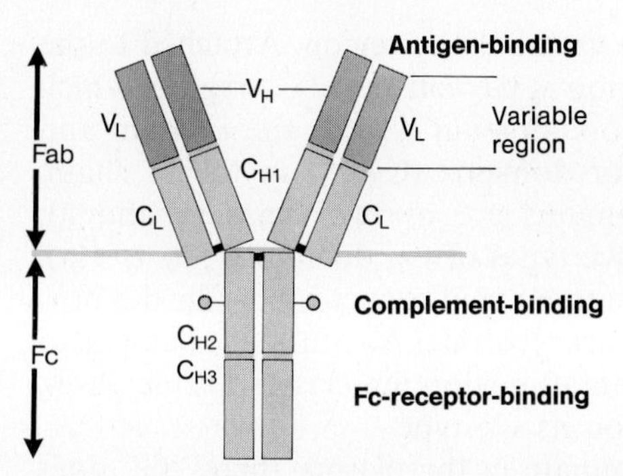

Fig. 18-17. Basic structure of an immunoglobulin molecule (IgG). Modified from [7, 11]

Antibodies are specific products of the response of the organism to invasion by antigens. Antibody molecules have antigen-binding sites shaped so that the three-dimensional antigen determinant can fit into them (like a key into a lock).

Antibodies are also called **immunoglobulins (Ig).** They are glycoproteins with molecular weights from 150,000 to 1,000,000. In their simplest form (Fig. 18-17) they consist of four chains: two identical heavy chains (*H:* MW 50,000) and two identical light chains (*L:* MW 25,000). Each chain is made up of *domains* (MW 12,500) joined by disulfide bridges. The four chains are symmetrically arranged in a **Y shape.** The N-terminal arms of the H and L chains form the antigen-binding fragments (**Fab**). These are connected by a flexible "hinge" to the crystallizable fragment (**Fc**). The Fc fragment is not involved in antigen binding but can react with macrophages, lymphocytes and complement factors (see below). The amino acid frequency of the N-terminal domain of the Fab fragment is antigen-specific; this

Table 18-9. Classification and structure of human immunoglobulins. From [7, 11, 17]

Ig class	Configuration	MW ($\cdot 10^{-3}$)	Heavy chain type	Antibody function	Complement activation: classical route	Complement activation: alternative route	Passage through placenta
IgG	Monomer	150	γ	Opsonization	+	+	+
IgM	Pentamer	800	μ	Neutralization, agglutination	+	+	–
IgA	Monomer in plasma Dimer in secretions	160 320	α	Neutralization	–	+	–
IgE	Monomer	170	ϵ	Binding to mast cells and basophilic granulocytes	–	–	–
IgD	Monomer	160	δ	Component of the B-lymphocyte membrane	–	–	–

is called the variable *(V)* region. Attached to the variable region is the constant *(C)* region, which consists of one domain (C_L) in the L chain and three or four domains (C_{H1-4}) in the H chain. The C_L domains are of two types (κ and λ). There are five types of C_H domain (γ, μ, α, ε, δ), differing in amino acid sequence and in the proportion of carbohydrate. An antibody belongs to one of five immunoglobulin classes (Table 18-9), depending on its C_H type.

IgG predominate in the plasma (here "G" does not stand for a single immunoglobulin but rather for a large number of polyclonal antibodies similar to one another in structure). IgG activate the complement system (see below) and bind to cellular surface antigens, making the affected cells easier to phagocytize *(opsonization)*. Because the monomeric IgG are relatively small molecules, they can cross the placental barrier from the maternal to the fetal blood. There is no appreciable antibody production before birth (contact with foreign substances is required), so that the IgG obtained from the mother provide important protection against infection in the newborn.

IgM are the largest antibody molecules. They consist of five identical subunits joined to one another by disulfide bridges. IgM can *neutralize* foreign bodies and, because of their many binding sites, *agglutinate* cells. The IgM class includes the antibodies in the ABO blood-group system, cold agglutinins and rheumatic factors.

IgA can be either monomeric or polymeric. IgA is contained in the saliva and in gastrointestinal secretions. It is responsible for *local defense* against foreign bodies that contact mucous membranes.

The (monomeric) **IgD** and **IgE** are present in plasma in very low concentrations. They probably act as cell-bound antigen receptors. IgE are bound by their Fc fragment to special receptors on the surfaces of basophilic granulocytes and mast cells. When IgE encounter a matching antigen, the carrier cell secretes histamine and other vasoactive substances that produce an *allergic response*. IgD are formed by *B lymphocytes* and remain on the surface of the lymphocyte. Relatively little is known about the physiological significance of IgD.

Recently the question of the **genetic control** of immunoglobulin synthesis has been partially answered [31]. As mentioned above, each plasma cell produces antibodies with a single specificity. Nevertheless, the organism is capable of forming antibodies against hundreds of thousands of different antigens. In addition monoclonal antibodies of different classes may be produced against a single antigen. Our understanding of this situation was crucially improved

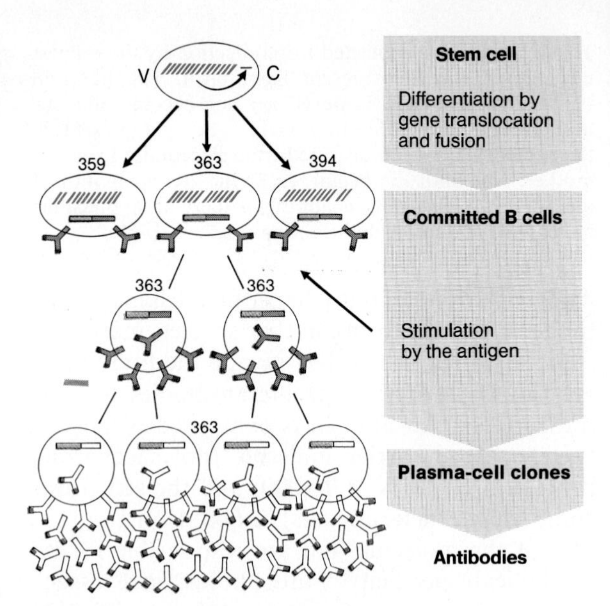

Fig. 18-18. Diagram of the differentiation of a lymphocyte stem cell (which has the capacity to produce a variety of antibodies) to form plasma cells (each of which makes only one specific kind of antibody). As the stem cell differentiates into a B cell one of the many variable (V) gene segments is transferred to the constant (C) gene segment. The antibody is incorporated into the cell membrane of the *committed* B cell as a receptor. The antigen stimulates the B cells bearing the matching receptor (here No. *363*) to proliferate, forming B memory cells and plasma cells. If the V gene segment is later transferred to another C gene segment, antibodies of a different class are produced. Modified from [31]

by the finding that the *gene segments for the H and L chains in the lymphocyte progenitors are initially scattered along the chromosome and thus spatially separated from one another.* At first, there are a great number (at least 10^3) of different gene segments for each V region; the stem cell is prepared for *multiple antibody production.* During differentiation to a *unipotent B cell,* one of the variable gene segments at random (i.e., selection from the set is not determined by an antigen) joins to the constant gene segment for the C region. Not until the *V and C gene components have fused* does the cell become capable of forming antibodies. Because the H and the L chains of the antibody each have their own V regions, which participate in antigen binding, the various combinations give at least 10^6 different antibody specificities. An antigen encountering this great assortment causes the B-lymphocytes that fit it to proliferate (Fig. 18-18).

Because creation of the pattern of antibody specificities is antigen-independent, some of the antibodies are originally directed against substances that form part of the body itself. Normally, however, these cause neither a humoral nor a cellular autoimmune response *(immunological tolerance)*. The ability to distinguish "foreign" from "own" is developed before birth. The activity of the autoimmune cell clones is thought to be suppressed under the influence of T suppressor cells.

The fact that a B cell can synthesize *antibodies of different immunoglobulin classes with identical specificity* is explained by double combinations of the gene segments. That is, the V gene segment responsible for synthesis of the variable region of the H chains is first paired with a C_μ gene segment (synthesis of IgM) and later with a C_γ gene segment (synthesis of IgG) or a C_α gene segment (synthesis of IgA).

Antigen-antibody reaction. The reaction between an antigen and an antibody, which in principle is reversible, results in the formation of an **antigen-antibody complex.** In some circumstances the binding of antigen to antibody in itself makes the antigen harmless (**neutralization;** e.g., of tetanus toxin). The **affinity** of antibodies for matching antigens varies; antiserum against a particular antigen always contains a mixture of many antibody molecules with different affinities for the antigen. Antigens with similar but not identical determinants in some cases can react with the same antibody molecules, but with different affinities (**cross reaction**).

If an antigen molecule has more than one determinant group with the same antigen specificity, the molecular aggregates that form in the presence of the specific antibody can grow so large that the antigen-antibody complex can no longer remain in solution and **precipitation** occurs. For diagnostic purposes, precipitability is used to determine the nature of the antigens and the specificity of the antibodies (e.g., in the agar-diffusion and radial diffusion methods or immunoelectrophoresis).

The reaction of particulate or cellular antigens (blood corpuscles, bacteria) with antibodies can also form large aggregates, sometimes visible to the naked eye. This **agglutination** or *clumping* is useful in blood-group determination and in the identification of such things as bacterial species, antibodies against bacterial proteins (e.g., tuberculosis protein) and hormones in blood and urine (e.g., growth hormone). **Complete** and **incomplete antibodies** are distinguished on the basis of their serological properties. For example, appropriate complete antibodies (usually of the IgM type) cause erythrocytes to agglutinate directly, whereas incomplete antibodies (usually of the IgG type) react with the erythrocyte-bound antigen but are too small to form the bridges between cells that lead to clumping. The antigen attached to the specific binding sites of incomplete antibodies is no longer accessible to complete antibodies that arrive later; therefore the incomplete antibodies are also called *blocking antibodies.*

But agglutination of erythrocytes, the antigenic determinants of which are occupied by incomplete antibodies, can be brought about by adding a second, *heterologous antibody* against human immunoglobulin to the suspension. The heterologous antibody can react with the incomplete antibodies bound to the erythrocytes so as to form a bridge between the cells, causing them to agglutinate (Fig. 18-19). This reaction is used in blood-group serology – for example, in the *Coombs test,* to demonstrate *isoantibodies* that are not otherwise identifiable (isoantibodies react with an antigen found on cells and in body fluids of other individuals of the same species but not in the individual itself).

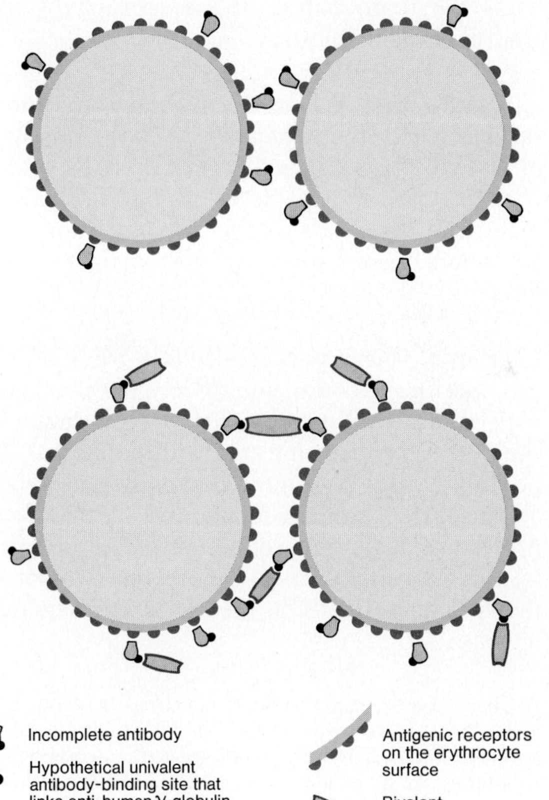

Fig. 18-19. Demonstration of incomplete or non-agglutinating antibodies, by addition of anti-human γ-globulin. From [13]

Unspecific Humoral Defense Mechanisms

Complement. Many of the biological effects that accompany an antigen-antibody reaction require the participation of a group of **nine plasma factors** together called complement (C1–C9). Like the clotting factors, the complement factors are present in the blood as inactive proenzymes or *zymogens,* which activate one another (mainly enzymatically) in a particular sequence (Fig. 18-20). There are also at least eleven **regular proteins** that influence the activity of the *complement system.* The complement factors are synthesized in part by hepatocytes, intestinal epithelial cells and macrophages. In case of infection their rate of formation rises distinctly within a few days. The initial activation of the complement system is brought about primarily by *antigen-antibody complexes* and *bacterial agents.*

A distinction is made between the *classical complement activation* and the *alternative route* that was subsequently discovered (Fig. 18-20). The first component in the classical route, *C1,* is a complex structure involving three proteins (C1q, C1r, C1s). The other complement factors are also identified with a "C" and Arabic numerals *(C1,*

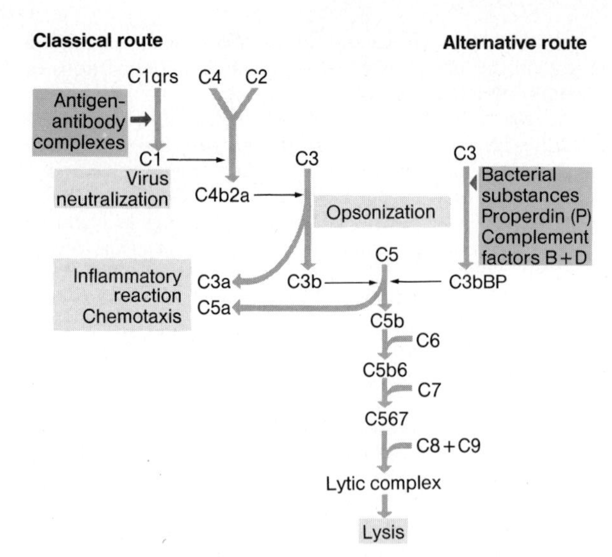

Fig. 18-20. Diagram of complement activation by the classical and alternative routes. Modified from [7, 11]

C4, C2, C3, C5, C6, C7, C8, C9, in the order in which they are activated). The state of activation is indicated by a horizontal bar over the numeral in the name (e.g., $C\bar{1}$). Complement activation by the alternative route requires, among other things, the plasma protein **properdin.** When the complement factors are activated they are split into smaller and larger fragments. The larger fragments, in general identified by *"b"*, have two main abilities: they bind to cell membranes, and they activate the next component in the complement reaction cascade. The small peptide fragments, in general identified by *"a"*, have *chemotactic* and *permeability-enhancing* actions, activate granulocytes and macrophages, and cause *inflammatory responses.* When the intermediary complement factors are split, the products cause *immune adherence* (aggregation of foreign cells) and *opsonization* (a change in the surface properties of foreign cells that makes them more readily phagocytizable) as well as *virolysis* (the destruction of viruses). Finally the *cytolytic complex C5b–9* is formed; it damages and destroys foreign cells bearing antibodies (immunohemolysis, bacteriolysis). The hemolyzing, bacteriolyzing and cytotoxic actions of antibodies, in particular, occur only in the presence of complement.

In vitro activation of the complement factors in plasma can be prevented by adding reagents that form complexes with Ca^{2+} or Mg^{2+} (e.g., citrate or EDTA) or by heating. This step is important in studies of cell cultures to which serum must be added to enable cell growth.
Because antigen-antibody complexes bind firmly to certain complement factors, in some kinds of tests the observation that the concentration of soluble complement factors in the serum is decreasing can indicate that an antigen-antibody reaction is occurring. This so-called **complement-binding reaction** is used to demonstrate particular antibodies in the serum of patients (for example, the Wassermann reaction to demonstrate syphilis) or to identify unknown antigens by means of known test sera.
Various **diseases** result from an inherited deficiency of individual complement factors. The patients are susceptible to *bacterial infections* and have a greater tendency to *autoimmune diseases,* in which damage is caused by antibodies against the body's own cells. In hereditary *angioneurotic edema* too little is produced of the $C\bar{1}$ inhibitor that is normally present. In patients with *paroxysmal nocturnal hemoglobinuria* the component $C\overline{3b}$ is bound too strongly to the erythrocyte membrane. Excessive activity of the complement system can, in some circumstances, cause *hypersensitivity reactions* such as bronchial asthma.

Lysozyme. In many tissues and body fluids the growth and reproduction of bacteria and viruses are inhibited by *lysozyme,* a basic enzyme with a mucolytic action. It is found in high concentrations in the granules of the polymorphonuclear leukocytes and in the macrophages of the pulmonary tissue. When these cells disintegrate lysozyme is released into the extracellular fluid. The mucous membranes of the intestine and the nasopharyngeal cavity also contain lysozyme, as does the conjunctival secretion. Presumably it limits the reproduction of the saprophytic microorganisms living there.

C-reactive protein. During bacterial infections the plasma contains abnormally large amounts of the so-called C-reactive protein (*CRP:* MW 21,000). CRP is capable of activating complement, and it also assists the conglutination, precipitation, opsonization and phagocytosis of bacteria.

Interferon. This term is applied to a group of species-specific glycoproteins (MW 20,000–30,000) with an **antiviral** action. They are produced by the body when it is infected with pathogens, especially viruses. Interferon is rapidly synthesized and released (within a few hours), so that some protection against reproduction of the invading viruses is available even before the content of the specific antibody in the blood has begun to increase.

A distinction is made between *α-interferons,* formed by leukocytes, *β-interferon,* formed by fibroblasts, and *γ-interferon,* formed by antigen-stimulated T lymphocytes. Interferons act by reducing viral protein synthesis and thus inhibiting reproduction. They do not attack the viruses directly, but rather react with their host cells. Unlike the immunoglobulins, interferons are not directed against specific pathogens. Interferons also reduce the ability of the body's own cells to divide; they inhibit the proliferation

of lymphocytes (the reason for the immune suppression during viral infections). On the other hand, they enhance the cytotoxic activity of macrophages.
It has recently become possible to obtain interferons in pure form by genetic engineering. Preliminary clinical results have shown that interferons may be effective in the treatment of viral infections and neoplastic diseases.

"Natural antibodies". The plasma contains antibodies against foreign materials to which the body has presumably never been exposed (for example, blood-group agglutinins). These have been called "natural antibodies". But because no such antibodies have been found in animals raised in a strictly germ-free environment, it is doubtful whether they are really "natural". Their existence can probably be explained by a previous unrecognized exposure to the corresponding antigen or by cross reactions due to low specificity of the antibodies.

Unspecific Cellular Defense

The unspecific cellular defense system is based on the capacity of the white corpuscles for **phagocytosis,** which is most pronounced in the **monocytes** and the **neutrophilic granulocytes.** These cells are well equipped with lysosomal enzymes, which they use to break down the phagocytized material (microorganisms, cell debris, antigen-antibody complexes). Neutrophilic granulocytes are attracted to the inflamed sites by **chemotactic substances,** including the *complement factors C3a and C5a, kallikrein, lymphokines* and *secretions from mast cells.* The attracted phagocytes extend pseudopodia that enclose the foreign bodies in a sort of vesicle *(phagosome formation).* Breakdown of the foreign bodies begins when the phagosome fuses with intracellular lysosomes, forming a *phagolysosome.*
Blood monocytes and tissue macrophages also play an important role in the initial *recognition and presentation of antigens.* In the cell membranes of macrophages there are Fc receptors to which immunoglobulins become attached, enabling the macrophages to bind antigens that they then break into small fragments by means of lysosomal enzymes *(antigen processing).* This fragmentation can expose additional antigenic structures so that they are accessible to lymphocytes. Furthermore, macrophages produce substances *(monokines)* that stimulate the growth of lymphocytes – for example, interleukin-1. Hence there are important *functional links between the specific and the unspecific defense mechanisms.*

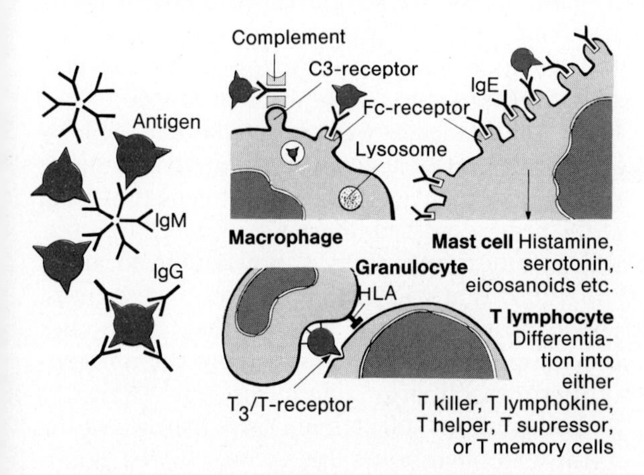

Fig. 18-21. Schematic drawing to show certain defense mechanisms and the cells that cooperate in them. *Left:* neutralization and agglutination of antigens by soluble antibodies. *Upper right:* opsonization and phagocytosis by macrophages that bind antigen-antibody complexes with their Fc and C3 receptors; also, an anaphylactic reaction triggered by the binding of antigens to mast-cell reagins (IgE). *Lower right:* sensitization of T lymphocytes, which recognize the antigenic determinants and the histocompatibility antigen (HLA) of the antigen-processing granulocyte

Major Events in Immune Reactions

Summary of the physiological defense functions (Fig. 18-21).

a. Disease-producing foreign substances in some conditions are neutralized, agglutinated or precipitated by soluble immunoglobulins. Phagocytes, primarily macrophages, remove the antigen-antibody complexes.
b. Opsonization of foreign cells, mediated by antibodies and complement factors, makes them easier to phagocytize. Neutrophilic granulocytes and macrophages have Fc receptors to bind pathogens by way of IgG, as well as C3 receptors to bind pathogens by way of complement factor $\overline{C3b}$.
c. Cytotoxic cells destroy the pathogens either antigen-specifically (T killer cells) or antigen-unspecifically (K and NK cells). Some pathogens are killed directly by antibody- and complement-specific mechanisms.
d. Interferons inhibit the growth of viruses.
e. Permeability-increasing substances and vasodilators (histamine, eicosanoids, complement factors) and chemotactic substances (lymphokines, complement factors, kallikrein) facilitate the movement of cytotoxic and phagocytizing cells into the infected region, producing the typical signs of inflammation (reddening, swelling, pain).

Immunity and allergy. When the defense system of an organism is able to render a foreign sub-

stance harmless without any pathological reaction, the organism is immune to that substance. Repeated exposure to a given foreign substance often changes the response of the organism, so that it becomes "allergic". In principle the altered response can be enhanced *(hyperergic)*, weakened *(hypergic)* or abolished *(anergic)*, but in normal usage the term *allergy* usually denotes a hyperergic (overly sensitive) reaction.
Immediate hypersensitivity reactions, which result from overshooting antigen-antibody reactions, are of two types. The *anaphylactic forms* are typically associated with a greater capillary permeability, increased blood flow through skin and mucous membranes, a rash, enhanced secretion from exocrine glands and bronchiospasms. The *cytotoxic forms* include, for example, the hemolysis following transfusion of blood in an incompatible group and the damage caused by the *deposition of immune complexes* in capillary walls (e.g., the "serum sickness" induced by the foreign protein in a vaccination serum). One of the *delayed hypersensitivity reactions* of considerable clinical importance is the *rejection of a transplant;* this category also includes the *contact allergies.*

Immunological tolerance. An individual who fails to form antibodies after exposure to a foreign substance that has an antigenic action in other people is said to be in a state of *immunological tolerance* or immunological paralysis. The situation is dangerous because there is no protection against damage by the foreign agent. Nevertheless, immunological tolerance can be therapeutically useful. For instance, to prevent or delay the rejection of the foreign protein in a transplant, specific defensive responses can be suppressed artificially (by selective inhibition or removal of lymphocytes, by administering antimetabolites, or by the use of ionizing radiation). Immunological tolerance can also result from prior exposure to excessively high doses of an antigen, because very large amounts of antigen can prevent the development of a normal immune response.

Immunization. *"Active immunization"* is brought about by **vaccination,** a method of increasing the defensive potential of the body before a natural encounter with an antigen occurs. The primary reaction is induced intentionally, by exposing the body to harmless quantities of an antigen or antigen producer (living but attenuated or dead bacteria or viruses). If there is a subsequent exposure to the same antigen (often years after the vaccination), specific memory cells are already present, so that the cellular and humoral defensive responses develop much more rapidly than at the time of the first exposure. In *"passive immunization"* the patient is injected with an antiserum against a particular antigen.

18.8 Human Blood Groups

Agglutination. When blood samples from two people are mixed on a microscope slide, in about 70% of the cases the erythrocytes clump together, a phenomenon known as agglutination. This process is occasionally combined with *hemolysis.* The same thing would occur in the circulatory system following blood transfusion, when two such *incompatible* types of blood came into contact. The consequences of such a mixture would be blockage of the capillaries by agglutinated erythrocytes, damage to the tubules in the kidney by hemolysis, and other difficulties such as anaphylaxis – which in some cases could be lethal.
The **cause of agglutination** is an antigen-antibody reaction. The erythrocyte cell membrane includes specific glycolipids that function as antigens. These are called **agglutinogens** (synonyms: *hemagglutinogens, agglutinable substances*). The specific antibodies that react with these agglutinogens on the erythrocyte membrane are dissolved in the plasma. They are part of the γ-globulin fraction, and are called **agglutinins** (or *isohemagglutinins*). In the antigen-antibody reaction the antibodies form bridges between several erythrocytes, so that a clump is produced.
The blood of each person is characterized by a particular set of specific erythrocyte agglutinogens. Of the many erythrocyte antigens that have so far been identified, there are about 30 reasonably common ones (that is, not limited to just a few tribes) that trigger fairly vigorous responses. The 9 most important systems, their antibodies and the phenomena accompanying the antigen-antibody reaction are summarized in Table 18-10. Today about 400 characteristic features of the erythrocyte membrane are known. In the classified groups alone, there are almost 300 million possible combinations. If one takes into account the unclassified groups as well, the possible combinations number more than 500 billion. Fortunately, the antigen properties of most of the group characteristics are so weak that they can be neglected for purposes of blood transfusion. The **ABO and Rh systems** are of the greatest significance in clinical practice.

Table 18-10. Some important blood-group-specific antibodies. From [27]

Blood group system	Antibody	Hemolytic transfusion reaction	Erythroblastosis fetalis caused by incompatibility
ABO	Anti-A	yes	yes
	Anti-B	yes	rare
	Anti-A_1	very rare	no
	Anti-H	no	no
Rh	Anti-C	yes	probably
	Anti-c	yes	probably
	Anti-C^W	yes	rare
	Anti-D	yes	yes
	Anti-E	yes	probably
	Anti-e	yes	probably
MNSs	Anti-M, -N, -S, -s	very rare	very rare
P	Anti-P_1	no	no
Lutheran	Anti-Lu^b	yes	rare
Kell	Anti-K	yes	yes
Lewis	Anti-Le^a, – Le^b	yes	no
Duffy	Anti-Fy^a	yes	probably
Kidd	Anti-Jk^a	yes	rare

ABO System

Blood groups in the ABO system. Landsteiner's discovery, in 1901, of the ABO groups marked the beginning of systematic study of blood-group properties. In the **ABO system** human erythrocytes are described in terms of three different antigenic properties: *property A, property B,* and *property AB (A plus B).* There is no antigenic property "O"; at most one can refer to a *characteristic H,* but antibodies with the specificity anti-H are of very little clinical importance. The blood group of an individual is thus determined by the antigenic properties of his erythrocytes. It depends entirely on the nature of the terminal sugar of certain glycolipids in the erythrocyte membrane (Fig. 18-22).

The blood of a newborn, as a rule, contains no antibodies of the ABO system; during the first year of life antibodies (isoagglutinins, anti-A and anti-B) are produced against those antigens *not* carried by the child's own erythrocytes. The serum of blood group O, for example, contains anti-AB (anti-A and anti-B), whereas that of group AB contains neither of these. It has been suggested that the production of antibodies for which there is no antigen in the individual's own blood is triggered by substances that enter the body in food or are released by the intestinal bacteria. It is clear that there are intestinal bacteria with the same antigenic determinants as erythrocytes (so-called *heterophilic antigens*). Most of the antibodies in the ABO system are of the IgM type, with 10 binding sites for the antigen. Therefore they can cause erythrocytes to agglutinate (complete antibodies).

Inheritance of blood-group properties. Two of the three **alleles A, B, O (H)** (blood-corpuscle properties located in the genes) are found in the diploid chromosome complement of each individual; together they determine the **blood-group phenotype** (the antigenic properties of the erythrocytes). Table 18-11 lists the phenotype for each of the possible combinations of genes. It is evident that the blood-group properties A and

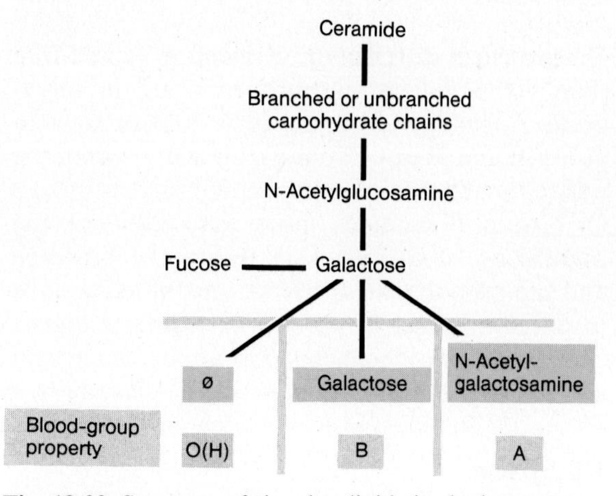

Fig. 18-22. Structure of the glycolipids in the human erythrocyte membrane that determine blood group. Simplified from [12, 13]

Table 18-11. Antigens and antibodies of the blood groups in the ABO system

Group name (phenotype)	Genotype	Agglutinogens (on the erythrocytes)	Agglutinins (in serum)
O	OO	H (practically ineffective)	Anti-A Anti-B
A	OA or AA	A	Anti-B
B	OB or BB	B	Anti-A
AB	AB	A and B	–

B are *dominant,* so that O is expressed as a phenotype only when homozygotic. Because the genotype AO or BO can be hidden behind the phenotype A or B, respectively, it is entirely possible for parents in blood groups A or B to bear children in blood group O. The principle of *codominance* applies to A and B; each is expressed if present, with no interaction between the two.

Knowing the way blood groups are inherited, one can draw conclusions about the parents from the blood-group phenotype of a child. For legal purposes it has been accepted that a man with blood group AB cannot be the father of a child with blood group O. Paternity can be excluded with greater certainty, the greater the number of blood-group factors considered. Today about 99% certainty is achievable.

Blood group A can be subdivided into the *subgroups A_1 and A_2*. The chief difference between the two is that A_1 erythrocytes in contact with anti-A serum agglutinate considerably more extensively and rapidly than do A_2 corpuscles. A_2 erythrocytes possess more H-structures than A_1 erythrocytes. About 80% of the people in group A have Type A_1 erythrocytes, while the remaining 20% have A_2. This distinction is of no practical significance to transfusion, because antigen-antibody reactions between A_1 and A_2 blood are rare and not very strong.

Geographical distribution of blood groups. More than 40% of Central Europeans are in blood group A, barely 40% in group O, 10% or more in group B and about 6% in group AB. Among the native inhabitants of America, 90% are of group O. Group B includes more than 20% of the population of central Asia. From the presence and the proportions of the various blood groups in different parts of the world, anthropologists can draw certain conclusions about the origin and mixing of populations.

Rh System

Serum taken from rabbits previously immunized to the erythrocytes of rhesus monkeys (by injection of rhesus erythrocytes) agglutinates the blood of most Europeans; it is **Rh-positive.** Red blood cells that do not agglutinate are, accordingly, called **Rh-negative.** After receiving a transfusion of Rh-positive blood, an Rh-negative recipient gradually, over a period of months, produces antibodies against the Rh-positive erythrocytes.

Rh properties of the erythrocytes. The response of an erythrocyte to the Rh test is determined by several antigens *(partial antigens)* located in different regions of the red-cell surface. The most important of these are called **C, D, E, c and e.** Of these, *D has the strongest antigenic effect.* Blood containing D erythrocytes is therefore, for the sake of simplicity, called **Rh-positive** (Rh+ or Rh), and those lacking the D property ("d") are called **Rh-negative** (Rh– or rh). In Europe 85% of the population are in the Rh+ group, and 15% are Rh–. The phenotype Rh+ can have either DD or Dd as the genotype; in phenotype Rh– the genotype is always dd.

One **difference between the Rh and the ABO systems** that is of practical significance is that the agglutinins of the ABO system are always present after the first few months of life, whereas anti-D antibodies do not appear unless the carrier has been exposed to Rh antigens *(sensitization).* It follows that the first transfusion of unmatched blood does not usually result in an overt reaction; antigen-antibody reactions appear only when Rh-incompatible blood is given repeatedly.

Another difference between the two systems lies in the fact that most of the antibodies of the Rh system are *incomplete IgG antibodies* which, in contrast to the complete ABO agglutinins, are small enough to pass the placental barrier.

Rh incompatibility and pregnancy. During pregnancy, small quantities of erythrocytes can move from the blood of an Rh+ fetus to that of an Rh– mother, and there trigger the production of antibodies against Rh corpuscles. In general

it is not until birth that larger volumes (10–15 ml) of fetal erythrocytes enter the maternal circulation. Because the antibody concentration in the mother's blood rises relatively slowly, over a period of months, the first pregnancy is usually completed without serious difficulties. But if the mother should again become pregnant with an Rh+ child, her antibody level can become so high that the diaplacental movement of antibodies destroys the child's red cells so extensively as to cause severe injury or intrauterine death *(erythroblastosis fetalis)*. Antibody formation in the Rh-negative mother can be reduced or eliminated by so-called **anti-D prophylaxis.** When an anti-D γ-globulin is administered immediately after a woman gives birth (or after miscarriage), the Rh+ erythrocytes that have invaded her circulatory system are destroyed and her immunological apparatus is not stimulated to produce antibodies. Differences between mother and fetus with respect to other blood-group characteristics, especially those of the ABO system, can also result in antigen-antibody reactions, but the symptoms of these are usually very mild.
Remarkably, an incompatibility in the ABO system can prevent sensitization resulting from a simultaneous Rh incompatibility; in this case, the fetal erythrocytes are removed from the bloodstream by the anti-A or anti-B agglutinins that are already present, before the Rh property of the erythrocytes can activate the maternal immune system.

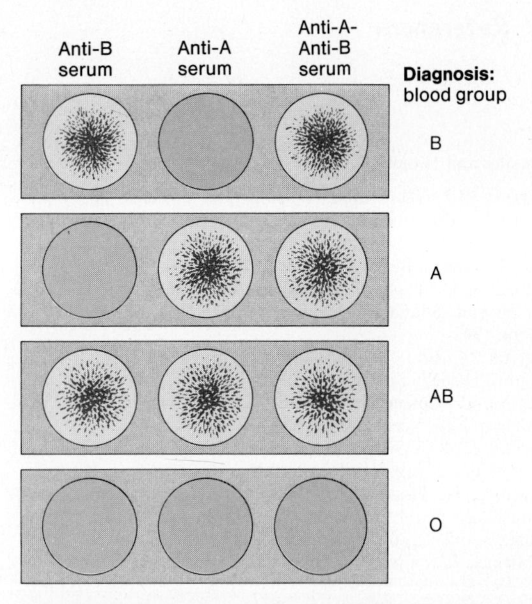

Fig. 18-23. Tests for blood-group in the ABO system. A droplet of blood is mixed with anti-B serum, another with anti-A serum and a third with anti-A-anti-B serum. The agglutination reactions *(dark red* clumping of the erythrocytes) show the group to which the blood belongs. From [24]

Blood Transfusion

Blood-group tests. Only blood compatible in the ABO characteristics is considered acceptable for transfusion. As far as the Rh system is concerned, a match with respect to the D antigen is ordinarily considered sufficient; that is, the blood is identified as Rh-positive (D) or Rh-negative (no D). However, all blood given to women of childbearing age and patients requiring repeated transfusions should also be matched in the Rh subgroups, to avoid sensitization in the Rh system.
To determine blood group in the ABO system, erythrocytes from the person to be tested are mixed on a microscope slide with commercially available antiserums against the agglutinogens A and B, and the slide is examined for agglutination (Fig. 18-23). As a reverse test, serum from the test subject is mixed with erythrocytes of a known blood group. To minimize the possibility of error due to the wrong choice of serum, misinterpretation of the result, or the rare occurrence of incompatibility due to other group characteristics, the blood is **cross-matched** prior to transfusion; erythrocytes from the donor are combined with fresh serum from the receiver at 37 °C. This procedure, to determine whether the receiver serum contains antibodies against antigens on the donor erythrocytes, is called the *major test*. Transfusion is permissible only if this test is indisputably negative – that is, there is no agglutination or hemolysis. In the reverse test, erythrocytes from the receiver are suspended in donor serum at 37 °C *(minor test)* to check whether the donor serum contains antibodies against antigens on the receiver erythrocytes.

The question of the "universal donor". Although persons of *group O* were formerly called "universal donors" and their blood was given to recipients of other groups, such transfusions are no longer considered acceptable. It is true that the A and B antigenic activity of group-O erythrocytes is absent or negligible, so that practically any desired quantity of O erythrocytes can be transferred to recipients of other groups without causing a reaction. But because group-O plasma contains agglutinins against A and B erythrocytes, only a limited amount of plasma can be transfused without reaction. When larger volumes are transfused the donor agglutinins are not sufficiently diluted by the recipient's plasma, and the recipient's erythrocytes are extensively agglutinated.

18.9 References

Textbooks and Handbooks

1. ATASSI, M.Z. (Ed.): Immunochemistry of Proteins. Vol. 3. New York, London: Plenum Press 1979
2. BEGEMANN, H., RASTETTER, J.: Atlas der klinischen Hämatologie. 3. Auflage. Berlin, Heidelberg, New York: Springer 1978
3. BELL, G., DAVIDSON, J.N., SCARBOROUGH, H. (Eds.): Textbook of Physiology and Biochemistry. Edinburgh, London: Livingstone 1965
4. BESSIS, M. (Ed.): Living Blood Cells and their Ultrastructure. Berlin, Heidelberg, New York: Springer 1973
5. BESSIS, M.: Corpuscles. Atlas of Red Blood Cells. Berlin, Heidelberg, New York: Springer 1974
6. BETKE, K., KÜNZER, W. (Eds.): Lehrbuch der Kinderheilkunde. 5. Auflage. Stuttgart: Thieme 1984
7. CHAPEL, H., HAENEY, M. (Eds.): Essentials of Clinical Immunology. Oxford, London, Edinburgh, Boston, Melbourne: Blackwell Scientific Publications 1984
8. GAMBLE, J.L.: Chemical Anatomy, Physiology and Pathology of Extracellular Fluid, 6th ed. Cambridge Mass.: Harvard University Press 1954
9. GUYTON, A.C. (Ed.): Textbook of Medical Physiology. 6th ed. Philadelphia, London: Saunders 1981
10. Hämatologische Tafeln Sandoz. 2. Aufl. (1972)
11. HARBOE, M., NATVIG, J.B. (Eds.): Medisinsk immunologi. Oslo: Stiftelsen Medisinsk Immunologi 1977
12. HUGHES, R.C.: Glycoproteins. London, New York: Chapman and Hall 1983
13. HUMPHREY, J.H., WHITE, R.G.: Immunology for Students of Medicine. Blackwell Scientific Publications (latest edition)
14. JAENECKE, J. (Ed.): Antikoagulantien- und Fibrinolysetherapie. 3. Auflage. Stuttgart, New York: Thieme 1982
15. KABOTH, W., BEGEMANN, H.: Blut. In: Physiologie des Menschen (Eds. GAUER, KRAMER, JUNG), Band 5. München, Berlin, Wien: Urban & Schwarzenberg 1971
16. KEIDEL, W.D. (Ed.): Kurzgefaßtes Lehrbuch der Physiologie. 6. Auflage. Stuttgart, New York: Thieme 1985
17. KELLER, R. (Ed.): Immunologie und Immunpathologie. Stuttgart, New York: Thieme 1981
18. KLEIHAUER, E. (Ed.): Hämatologie. Berlin, Heidelberg, New York: Springer 1978
19. PARVEZ, Z.: Immunoassays in Coagulation Testing. New York, Berlin, Heidelberg, Tokyo: Springer 1984
20. PUTNAM, F.W. (Ed.): The Plasma Proteins. New York: Academic Press 1975 (Vol. 1, 2), 1977 (Vol. 3)
21. RIECK, W.: Klinische Chemie und Mikroskopie, 5. Auflage. Berlin, Heidelberg, New York: Springer 1977
22. ROITT, J.M. (Ed.): Essential Immunology. 5. Printing. Oxford: Blackwell Scientific Publications 1971
23. SPIELMANN, W., KÜHNL, P.: Blutgruppenkunde. Stuttgart, New York: Thieme 1982
24. THEWS, G., VAUPEL, P.: Grundriß der vegetativen Physiologie. Berlin, Heidelberg, New York: Springer 1981
25. WINTROBE, M.M. (Ed.): Clinical Hematology, 8th ed. Philadelphia: Lea & Febiger 1981
26. WINTROBE, M.M. (Ed.): Blood, Pure and Eloquent. New York: McGraw-Hill 1980
27. Wissenschaftliche Tabellen Geigy. Teilband Hämatologie und Humangenetik. 8. Aufl. Basel: 1979

Original Papers and Reviews

28. COHN, E.J.: Chemical, physiological and immunological properties and clinical uses of blood derivatives. Experientia (Basel) *3*, 125 (1947)
29. HAMMARSTRÖM, S.: Leukotrienes. Annu. Rev. Biochem. *52*, 355 (1983)
30. HARLAN, J.M.: Leukocyte-endothelial interactions. Blood *65*, 513 (1985)
31. HILSCHMANN, N.: Die Immunität – eine vorprogrammierte Reaktion auf das Unerwartete. In: H. v. DITFURTH (Ed.): Mannheimer Forum, Studienreihe Boehringer Mannheim, pp. 101 (1982/83)
32. HOLMSEN, H.: Platelet metabolism and activation. Semin. Hematol. *22*, 219 (1985)
33. HUEBERS, H.A., FINCH, C.A.: Transferrin: physiologic behavior and clinical implications. Blood *64*, 763 (1984)
34. JELKMANN, W.: Renal erythropoietin: properties and production. Rev. Physiol. Biochem. Pharmacol. *104*, 139 (1986)
35. MARCUS, A.J.: The role of lipids in platelet function: with particular reference to the arachidonic acid pathway. J. Lipid Res. *19*, 793 (1978)
36. MARLAR, R.A., KLEISS, A.J., GRIFFIN, J.H.: An alternative extrinsic pathway of human blood coagulation. Blood *60*, 1353 (1982)
37. MORETTA, A., PANTALEO, G., MAGGI, E., MINGARI, M.C.: Recent advances in the phenotypic and functional analysis of human T lymphocytes. Semin. Hematol. *21*, 257 (1984)
38. PRICE-JONES, C.: The variation in the size of red blood cells. Brit. med. J. II, 1418 (1910)
39. VAN DEN ELSEN, P., SHEPLEY, B.-A., BORST, J., COLIGAN, J.E., MARKHAM, A.F., ORKIN, S., TERHORST, C.: Isolation of cDNA clones encoding the 20K T3 glycoprotein of human T-cell receptor complex. Nature *312*, 413 (1984)
40. WALSH, P.N.: Platelet-mediated coagulant protein interactions in hemostasis. Semin. Hematol. *22*, 178 (1985)

19 Function of the Heart

H. Antoni

19.1 General Structural and Functional Aspects

The blood can perform its many-faceted role only if it circulates continually through the body. The pump that drives the blood through the vessels is the heart. It can be considered as two hollow organs – the right half and the left half (Fig. 19-1) – with muscular walls. Each half comprises an atrium and a ventricle. The right half receives oxygen-depleted blood from the entire body and sends it to the lungs, where it is charged with oxygen. The oxygenated blood is returned to the left half of the heart and thence distributed to the organs of the body. The right heart, then, pumps out only deoxygenated blood, and the left half only oxygenated blood.

Subdivisions of the circulatory system. The movement of the blood from the right to the left heart, by way of the lungs, is called the **pulmonary circulation.** Its distribution to, and return from, all the rest of the body is the **systemic circulation.** Strictly speaking, of course, the two constitute a single pathway of blood movement, with the propulsive force provided at two points by the two halves of the heart (cf. Fig. 19-1).

The discovery of the closed circulation of blood is attributed to the English physician William Harvey (1578–1657), who refuted the established doctrine of his time with reasoning of exemplary clarity in his famous treatise, published in 1628, "De motu cordis et sanguinis in animalibus." Until that time the prevailing view was that of Galen (120–201 A.D.), who held that the blood was formed in the liver from food components, sent to the heart by way of the vena cava, and from there passed through the veins to the organs where it was used up.

Systole and diastole. The pumping action of the heart is based on a rhythmic sequence of relaxation *(diastole)* and contraction *(systole)* of the ventricles. During diastole the ventricles fill with blood, and during systole they expel it into the large arteries (aorta and pulmonary artery). Backflow out of the arteries is prevented by the valves at their openings. Before entering the ventricle, the blood passes from the large veins (venae cavae and pulmonary veins) into the associated atrium. The systole of each atrium precedes that of its ventricle, so that the atria act as booster pumps to help fill the ventricles.

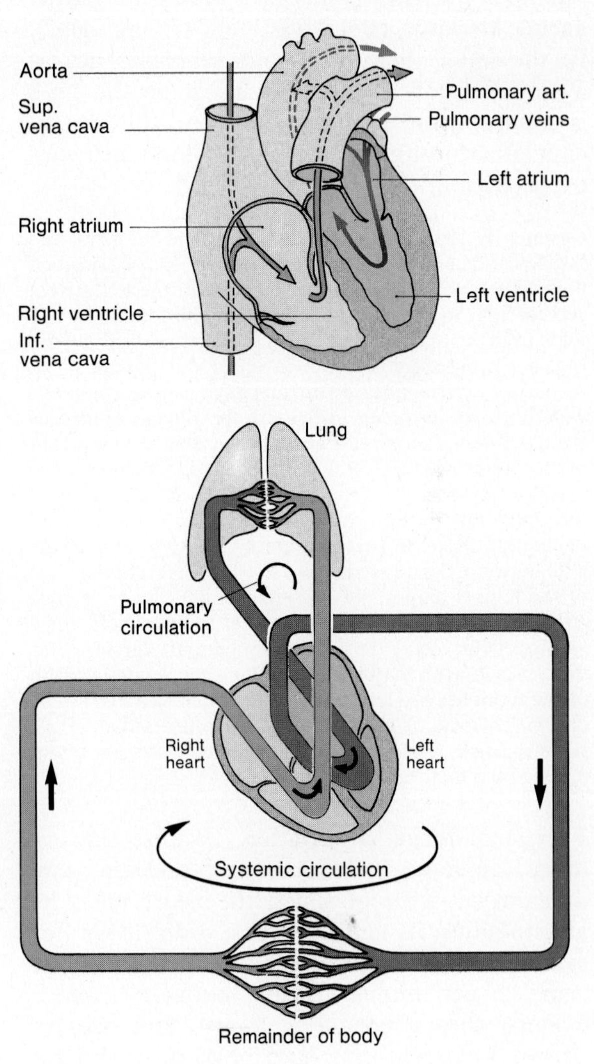

Fig. 19-1. *Top:* Frontal view of the opened heart and the large vessels. The direction of blood flow is indicated by the *arrows. Bottom:* Schematic diagram of the connections of the two halves of the heart with the pulmonary and systemic circulations

Arteries and veins. The distinction between these two kinds of vessels is based on the direction of blood flow within them, rather than on the state of the blood itself. Veins carry the blood to the heart, and arteries carry it away. In the systemic circulation the arteries carry oxygenated blood, and in the pulmonary circulation the oxygenated blood is carried by the veins. When the term "arterial blood" is used to denote oxygenation, the reference is thus to the systemic circulation.

Fetal heart. The functional subdivision of the heart into a right, pulmonary half and a left, systemic half develops during birth. In the heart of the fetus the two atria communicate with one another by way of the foramen ovale, and there is a short-circuit between the aorta and pulmonary artery, by way of a wide passage, the **ductus ateriosus** (Botallo's duct: cf. Fig. 19-2). In the fetus, then, atria and ventricles act as a single hollow organ. At this stage the lung is collapsed and nonfunctional, and little blood circulates through it. The fetal blood becomes oxygenated in the placenta.

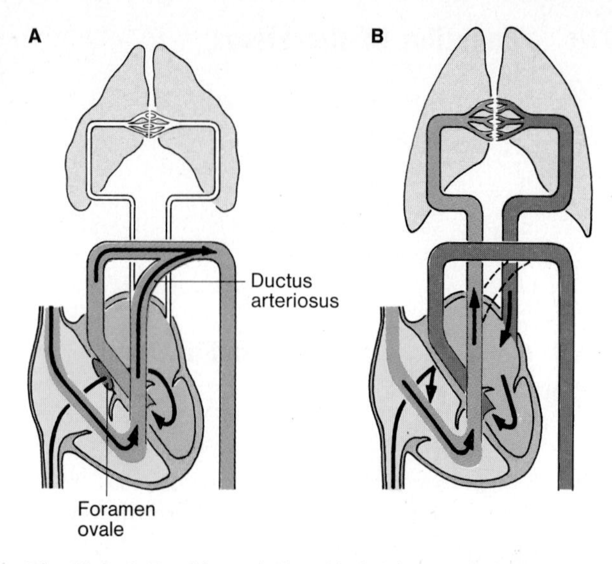

Fig. 19-2. A Fetal heart before birth. The two halves are in parallel, with the lung on a side circuit. **B** After birth the two halves are in series. This conversion involves expansion of the circuit through the lungs and closure of two shunt passages – the foramen ovale between right and left atrium, and the ductus arteriosus between aorta and pulmonary artery

Changes at birth. When the lungs expand at birth and begin to function in respiration, their resistance to blood flow decreases. As a result, the pressure in the left atrium exceeds that in the right. The valve at the foramen ovale folds over the opening and closes it off temporarily; there is also a progressive constriction of the ductus arteriosus. About two weeks after birth the conversion is complete, with both the foramen ovale and the ductus arteriosus tightly closed. The **parallel** arrangement of the two halves of the heart in the fetus has been converted to a **serial** arrangement (Fig. 19-2A and B). This reorganization of the circulatory pattern during birth causes the work load of the right heart to be considerably less than that of the left. Because the resistance to flow in the vascular bed of the lung is only about one-eighth that in the systemic circulation, the right ventricle needs to exert less force to propel the blood through the pulmonary circuit. This difference in work load brings about an accelerated growth of the more heavily loaded left ventricle, which eventually develops a mass of muscle almost three times that of the right ventricle. The heart of an adult accounts for about 0.5% of the total body weight.

Functional range of variation. Because the demands made on the circulating blood are quite different at different times, the heart must be able to adjust its activity over a wide range. For example, the volume of blood expelled by one ventricle per minute *(cardiac output)* is about 5 liters when a person is at rest, and rises to almost 30 liters during hard physical work. Optimal adaptation is achieved only when all the partial functions of the heart – time course of excitation, contractility, valve action, its own blood supply, and so on – change together in an orderly way. Even slight departures from the norm can severely impair cardiac activity.

19.2 Basic Processes of Excitation and Excitation-Contraction Coupling

The functional elements of the heart are the cardiac muscle fibers. The term *myocardial fiber* is applied to a chain of myocardial cells arranged end-to-end and enclosed in a common sarcolemmal envelope (the basement membrane). There are two types of myocardial fibers, identifiable by morphological and functional criteria:

1. the fibers of the **working myocardium** of atria and ventricles, which make up the main mass of the heart and do the mechanical work of pumping.
2. the fibers of the **pacemaker and conducting system,** which are specialized to generate excitatory impulses and send them to the working cells.

Origin and Spread of Excitation

Myocardial fibers, like nerve or skeletal muscle fibers, are excitable structures – that is, they have a *resting potential,* respond to suprathreshold stimuli by generating *action potentials*, and are capable of propagating action potentials without decrement. The cell boundaries, which can be seen in the microscope as the *intercalated discs*, offer no obstacle to the conduction of excitation [24]. The musculature of the atria and ventricle behaves functionally as a *syncytium*. Excitation arising anywhere in the atria or ventricles thus spreads out over all the unexcited fibers, until the very last cell is brought into play. This property provides the explanation of the **all-or-none response of the heart;** that is, when stimulated the heart either responds with excitation of all its fibers or gives no response, if the stimulus does not reach the suprathreshold level in any cell. In a nerve or skeletal muscle, by contrast, each cell responds individually, so that only those fibers exposed to suprathreshold excitation discharge conducted impulses.

Autorhythmicity. The rhythmic pulsation of the heart is maintained by excitatory signals generated within the heart itself. Under suitable conditions, therefore, a heart removed from the body will continue to beat at a constant frequency. This property is called *automaticity* or *autorhythmicity*. Ordinarily, the spontaneous rhythmic triggering of excitation is performed exclusively by the specialized cells of the pacemaker and conducting system. The various elements in this system are diagrammed in Fig. 19-3.

Geometry of propagation. Normally the heartbeat is initiated in the **sinoatrial (SA) node**, in the wall of the right atrium at the opening of the superior vena cava. When the body is at rest, the SA node drives the heart at a rate of about 70 impulses/min. From the SA node the excitation first spreads over the **working myocardium of both atria.** The only pathway available for conduction to the ventricles is shown in red in Fig. 19-3. All the rest of the atrioventricular boundary consists of inexcitable connective tissue. As the excitation propagates through the conducting system it is briefly delayed in the **atrioventricular (AV) node.** Propagation velocity is high (ca. 2 m/s) through the remainder of the system – the **bundle of His,** the left and right **bundle branches** and their terminal network, the **Purkinje fibers** – so that the different ventricular regions are excited in rapid succession. From the subendocardial endings of the Purkinje fibers, excitation spreads at a speed of ca. 1m/s over the **ventricular musculature.**

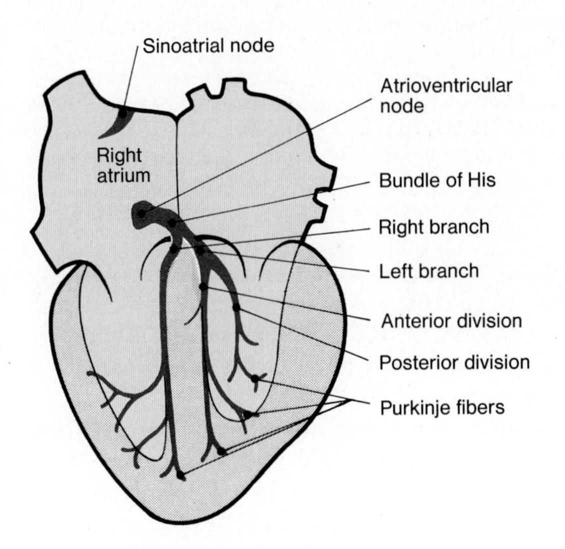

Fig. 19-3. Diagram of the arrangement of the pacemaker and conducting system as seen in frontal section

Hierarchy of pacemaker activity. The autorhythmicity of the heart is not entirely dependent on the operation of the SA node; as mentioned above, the other parts of the pacemaker/conduction system are also spontaneously excitable. But the intrinsic rhythm of these cells becomes considerably slower, the further away from the SA node. Under normal conditions, therefore, these cells are always triggered into action by the more rapid build-up of excitation in the higher centers, before they have a chance to trigger themselves. The SA node is the leading **primary pacemaker** of the heart, because it has the highest discharge rate.

Escape rhythms. If for any reason the SA node should fail to initiate the heartbeat, or if the excitation is not conducted to the atria (sinoatrial block), the AV node can substitute as a **secondary** pacemaker (the *AV rhythm* has a frequency of 40–60/min). If there should be a complete interruption of conduction from the atria to the ventricles **(complete heart block),** a **tertiary** center in the ventricular conducting system can take over as pacemaker for ventricular contraction. With respect to pacemaker activity, the SA node can be termed the **nomotopic** (in the normal place) center and the remainder of the system, the **heterotopic** (in an abnormal place) centers.
In the case of complete heart block, atria and ventricles beat entirely independently of one another, the atria at the frequency of the SA node and the ventricles at the considerably lower frequency of a tertiary center (30–40/min). When there is a sudden onset of total heart block several seconds can elapse before the ventricular automaticity "wakes up". In this pre-automatic pause an insufficient supply of blood to the brain may cause unconsciousness and convulsions **(Adams-Stokes syncope).** If the ventricular pacemakers fail altogether, the ventricular arrest leads to irreversible brain damage and eventually to death.
Artificial pacemakers. Even in the absence of autorhythmicity, the working myocardium remains excitable for a

time. It is therefore possible to keep the blood in circulation by artificial **electrical stimulation** of the ventricles. If necessary, the electrical impulses can be applied through the intact wall of the chest. When attacks of Adams-Stokes disease are frequent, and in cases of complete heart block with very low-frequency ventricular automaticity, electrical stimulation can sometimes be continued for years. The stimuli are generated by subcutaneously implanted battery-driven miniature pacemakers and conducted to the heart by wire electrodes.

Bundle-branch block. When conduction along the bundle branches is interrupted the result is an incomplete heart block, as long as at least one branch or subdivision of a branch remains functional. In this case the excitation spreads out from the terminals of the intact conduction system and eventually covers the whole ventricular myocardium; the time required for complete excitation, of course, is considerably longer than normal.

Characteristics of the Elementary Process of Excitation

The **action potential** of the cardiac muscle cells, like that of neurons or skeletal muscle fibers, begins with a rapid reversal of the membrane potential, from the resting potential (ca. –90 mV) to the *initial peak* (ca. +30 mV; see Fig. 19-4). This rapid phase of depolarization, lasting only 1–2 ms, is followed by a special feature of the myocardium, a prolonged *plateau.* This is terminated by *repolarization* to the resting potential. The action potential of the cardiac musculature lasts ca. 200–400ms – more than 100 times as long as that of a skeletal-muscle or nerve fiber. The functional consequences, as we shall see, are considerable.

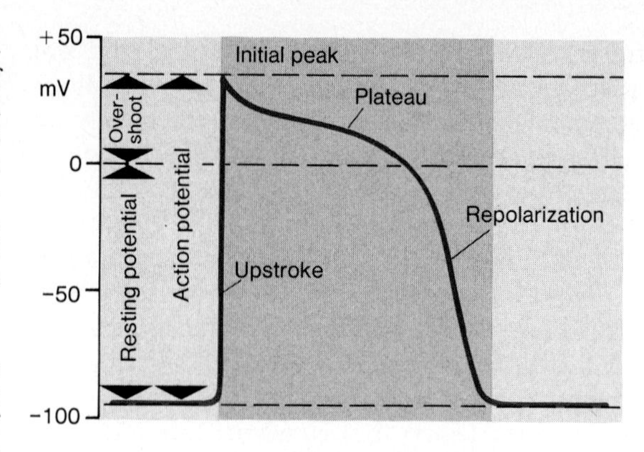

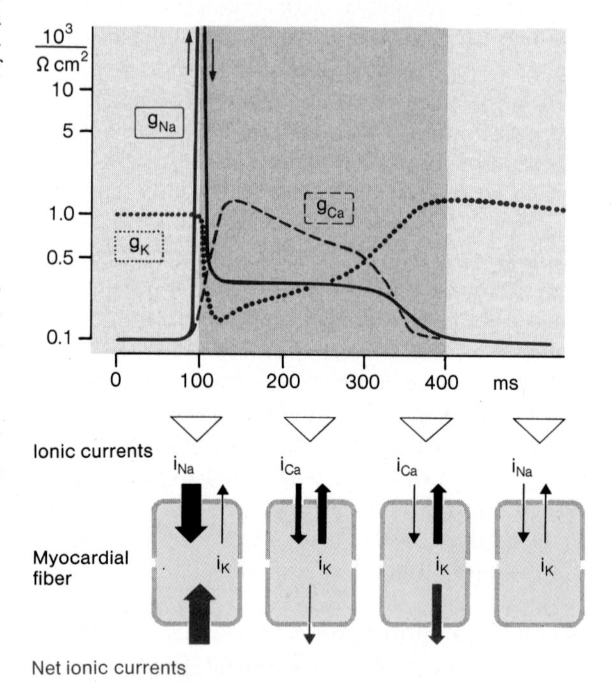

Fig. 19-4. *Top:* general form of the action potential of a muscle cell in the heart. *Middle:* diagram of the changes in Na^+, Ca^{2+} and K^+ conductance that underlie the action potential. *Bottom:* direction and magnitude of the ionic currents and the net current during the action potential. The magnitude (indicated by the thickness of the arrows) of an ionic current depends on the conductance and on the distance between the membrane potential E_m and the equilibrium potential of the ion (e.g., $i_{Na} = g_{Na} \cdot (E_m - E_{Na})$; cf. p. 23)

Ionic mechanisms. The action potential is generated by a complicated interplay of membrane-potential changes, changes in ionic conductivity, and ion currents. The fundamentals of the ionic theory of excitation have been discussed in detail elsewhere (see pp. 19ff.); here we shall give only a short recapitulation, with reference to the specific peculiarities of cardiac muscle [2, 9, 20, 23]. The *resting potential* of the myocardium is primarily a *K^+ potential,* maintained by an electrogenic Na^+ pump. As in the neuron, the rapid upstroke phase of the action potential is brought about by a brief pronounced increase in Na^+ conductance g_{Na}, which results in a massive Na^+ influx (cf. Fig. 19-4). This initial Na^+ influx, however, as in the neuron, is very rapidly inactivated. Hence, further mechanisms are required for the considerable delay in repolarization of the cardiac muscle tissue. These are (i) an *increase in Ca^{2+} conductance (g_{Ca}),* with delayed onset and slow decline, which causes a depolarizing influx of calcium *(slow inward current)* [21], and (ii) a *decrease in K^+ conductance (g_K)* with depolarization, which reduces the repolarizing K^+ outward current [2, 23].

Repolarization of the myocardium results from a *gradual decrease* in g_{Ca} and an increase in g_K due to the more *negative membrane potential.* The decrease in g_{Ca} diminishes the slow inward current, and the increase in g_K enhances the K^+ outward current. When the membrane is at its resting potential, the depolarizing and repolarizing currents are in balance.

The mechanism underlying the slow Ca^{2+} inward current and that of the fast Na^+ inward current differ in several ways, among them the time course, potential-dependence and susceptibility to blocking agents. The so-called fast Na^+ channel is blocked by tetrodotoxin, while the slow Ca^{2+} channel is blocked by Cd^{2+} and organic Ca^{2+} antagonists (e.g., verapamil, nifedipine, diltiazem) [5]. The threshold for activation of the Na^+ channel is ca. −60 mV, and that of the Ca^{2+} channel is ca. −30 mV. Depolarization of the membrane to about −40 mV inactivates the Na^+ system. Under these conditions, more intense stimuli can elicit so-called Ca^{2+} *action potentials*, which have a slower upstroke phase, because in this case both the upstroke and the plateau are generated by the slow inward current. These action potentials are propagated at low speed (slow response [3]).

Refractory period. Cardiac musculature shares with other excitable tissues the property of reduced responsiveness to stimuli during particular phases of the excitatory process. The terms **absolute** and **relative refractory period** are used for phases of abolished and diminished responsiveness, respectively. Fig. 19-5 shows how these are related to the action potential. During the absolute refractory period the cell is inexcitable, and during the subsequent relative refractory period excitability gradually recovers. Thus a new action potential can be elicited sooner, the stronger the stimulus. Action potentials generated very early in the relative refractory period do not rise as sharply as normal action potentials, and have a lower amplitude and a shorter duration (Fig. 19-5).

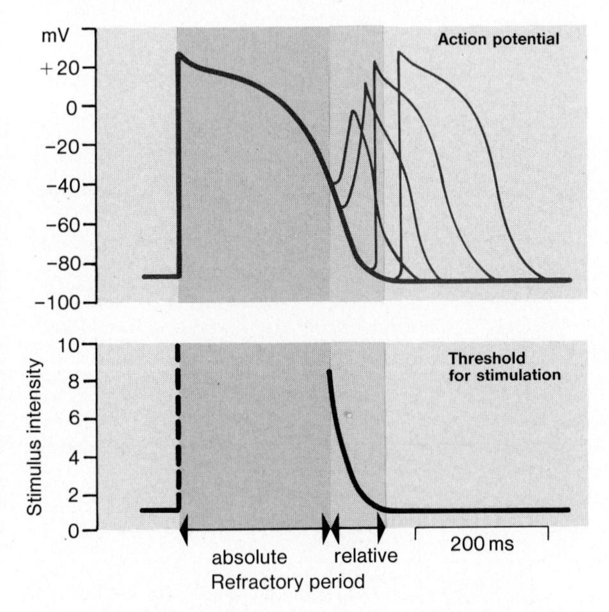

Fig. 19-5. The absolute and relative refractory periods of the myocardial action potential. Threshold during the latter is indicated in multiples of the minimal threshold intensity. During the absolute refractory period – from the action-potential upstroke to about the end of the plateau – the threshold is infinitely high

The chief **cause of refractory behavior** is the inactivation of the fast Na^+ channels during prolonged depolarization (see pp. 25f.). Not until the membrane has repolarized to ca. −40 mV do these channels begin to recover. The duration of the refractory period is therefore, as a rule, closely related to the duration of the action potential. When the action potential is shortened or lengthened, the refractory period changes accordingly. But drugs that act as local anesthetics, inhibiting the initial Na^+ influx or retarding its recovery after inactivation, can prolong the refractory period without affecting action-potential duration.

Functional significance of the refractory period. The prolonged refractory period protects the musculature of the heart from too-rapid reexcitation, which could impair its function as a pump. At the same time, it prevents recycling of excitation in the muscular network of the heart, which would interfere with the rhythmic alternation of contraction and relaxation. Because the refractory period of the excited myocardial cells is normally longer than the time taken for spread of excitation over the atria or ventricles, a wave of excitation originating at the SA node or a heterotopic center can cover the heart only once and must then die out, for it encounters refractory tissue everywhere. *Reentry* thus does not normally occur.

Frequency-dependence of action-potential duration. An action potential triggered immediately following the relative refractory period of the preceding impulse is normal, as Fig. 19-5 shows, in upstroke rate and amplitude. Its duration, however, is distinctly less than that of the preceding action potential. In fact there is a close relationship between the duration of an action potential and the interval that preceded it, and thus between duration and repetition rate. This effect is illustrated in Fig. 19-6 by an original recording from a fiber in human ventricular myocardium.

The main cause of this phenomenon is an increase in g_K, which outlasts the repolarization phase of the action potential and returns only gradually to the basal level (Fig. 19-4). When the interval between action potentials is short, the increased K^+ conductance accelerates repolarization of the next action potential.

The elementary events in impulse formation. The working myocardium of atria and ventricles is not automatically active; action potentials are

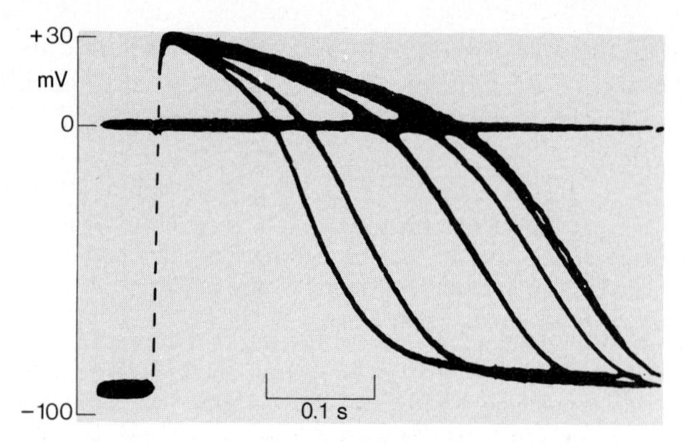

Fig. 19-6. Superimposed action potentials of a single fiber in an isolated ventricular trabecula obtained during an operation on a human heart. The record shows shortening of the action potential duration as stimulus frequency is raised in steps from 24/min to 162/min. From TRAUTWEIN et al.: Circul. Res. *10*, 306 (1962)

generated by spread of excitation. The response is triggered by current loops, whereby current flowing from excited parts of the fiber cable passes through unexcited parts and there lowers the membrane potential from the resting level. When this depolarization has reached a critical threshold level the action potential begins (see p. 23). In all cardiac muscle cells capable of autorhythmicity, by contrast, depolarization toward the threshold occurs spontaneously. This elementary process of excitation can be observed directly by intracellular recording from a pacemaker cell. As shown in Fig. 19-7, the repolarization phase of such an action potential is followed – beginning at the *maximal diastolic potential* – by a *slow depolarization* which triggers a new action potential when the threshold is reached. The **slow diastolic depolarization** *(pacemaker potential, prepotential)* is a local excitatory event, not propagated as the action potential is.

Actual and potential pacemakers. Normally only a few cells in the SA node are in fact responsible for timing the contraction of the heart (*actual* pacemakers). All the other fibers in the specialized tissue are excited in the same way as the working musculature, by conducted activity. That is, these *potential* pacemakers are rapidly depolarized by currents from activated sites before their intrinsic slow diastolic depolarization reaches threshold. Comparison of the two processes, as illustrated in Fig. 19-7, shows how a potential pacemaker can take over the leading role when the actual pacemaker ceases to function. Because the slow diastolic depolarization of the potential pacemaker, by definition, takes longer to reach threshold, its discharge rate is lower. In the working myocardium there is no automatic depolarization; the upstroke of the action potential triggered by the imposed current rises sharply from the resting-potential baseline (Fig. 19-7, bottom).

Mechanism of the pacemaker potential. According to current opinion, the slow diastolic depolarizations of the SA node are produced by mechanisms different from those in the ventricular conducting system [17]. First, there is a higher constant background Na^+ conductance in the SA node, which opposes a shift of the membrane potential toward the K^+ equilibrium potential E_K. Therefore the membrane potential is kept relatively low, and the rapid Na^+ system (insofar as it is present) is largely inactivated. During the repolarizing phase of the action potential the K^+ conductance g_K of the membrane rises above the resting value, so that the membrane potential shifts in the direction of E_K and reaches the maximal diastolic potential (Fig. 19-7). As g_K slowly returns to the resting level, the membrane potential departs from E_K and approaches the threshold for activation of the slow inward current, which is responsible for the action-potential upstroke. The

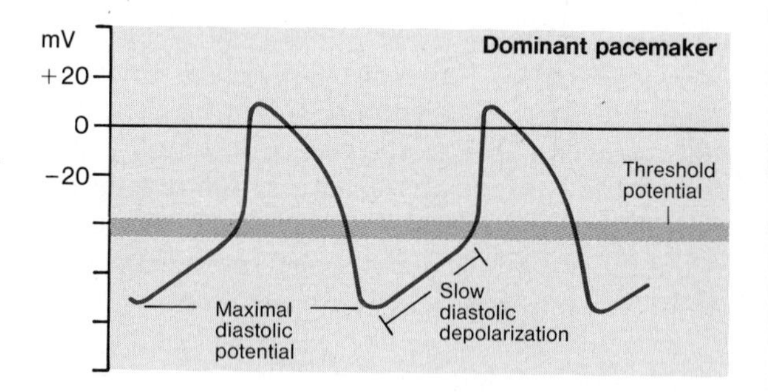

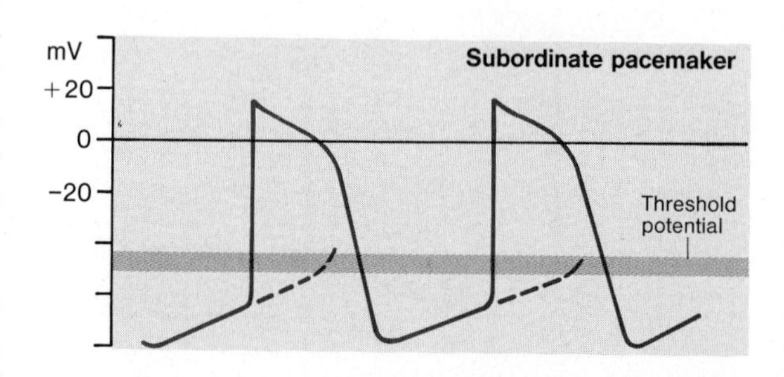

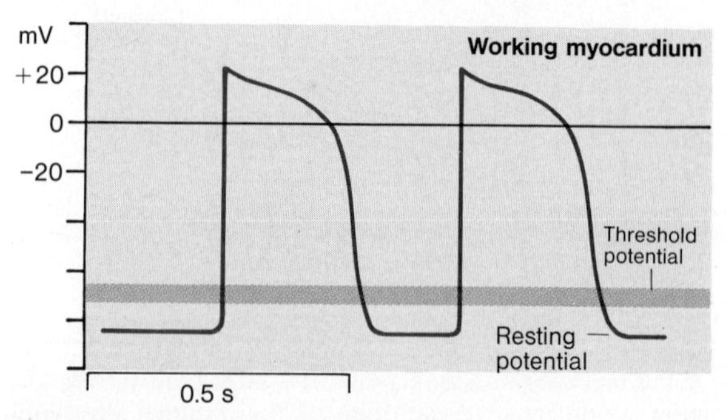

Fig. 19-7. General form of the process of excitation in autorhythmic tissue, compared with that in the non-autorhythmic working myocardium

action potentials of the SA node, then, correspond approximately to the Ca^{2+} action potentials of the depolarized working myocardium, described above. The situation in the AV node is similar.

In the ventricular conducting system the background Na^+ conductance is normally low. Therefore the membrane potential reaches relatively high levels just after the action potential, which permits extensive recovery of the rapid Na^+ system. The subsequent diastolic depolarizations involve a special ionic channel that does not operate in the SA node; it is activated only during the polarization to high membrane potentials and allows the passage of both Na^+ and K^+ [16]. The action potentials are triggered by activation of the rapid inward Na^+ current, as is manifest in the high rate of rise of the action potential.

Ectopic pacemakers. The capacity for spontaneous excitation is primitive rather than a highly specialized function of myocardial tissue. In the early embryonic stage all the cells in the heart primordium are spontaneously active. As differentiation proceeds, the fibers of the prospective atrial and ventricular myocardium lose their autorhythmicity and develop a stable, high resting potential. But the stability of the resting potential can be lost under various conditions associated with partial depolarization of the membrane (catelectrotonus, stretching, hypokalemia, Ba^{2+} ions). Then the affected fibers can develop diastolic depolarizations like those of natural pacemaker cells, and in some circumstances can interfere with the rhythm of the heartbeat. On the other hand, depolarization due to elevated K^+ does not produce autorhythmicity, because a concomitant rise in K^+ conductance inhibits spontaneous activity. A center of autorhythmicity apart from the regular pacemaker tissue is called an *ectopic center* or *ectopic focus*.

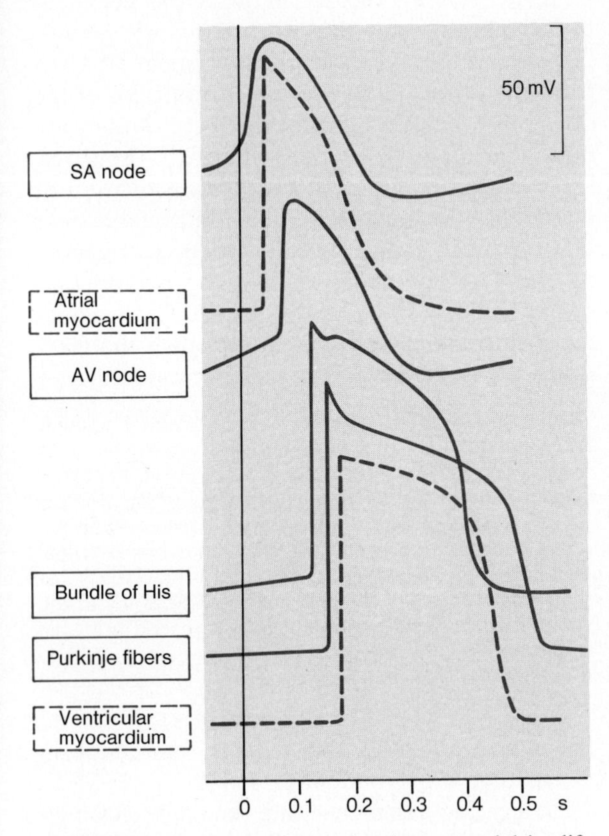

Fig. 19-8. Characteristic forms of action potential in different regions of the heart. The *continuous lines* represent potentials in the pacemaker and conducting system. The shift along the time scale corresponds to the arrival time in each region, as the excitatory wave spreads through the heart

Types of action potential. The action potentials in different parts of an individual heart differ in characteristic ways. A few typical forms are shown in Fig. 19-8, where the sequence (top to bottom) and time shift (left to right) correspond to their position in the excitatory cycle of the heart. In the various parts of the pacemaker and conduction system the slope of the slow diastolic depolarization becomes distinctly less steep with increasing distance from the SA node. Moreover, both upstroke rate and amplitude of the potentials in the SA and AV nodes are conspicuously less than the remainder of the system. The duration of the plateau in the atrial myocardium is less than in the musculature of the ventricle, and the refractory periods are correspondingly related. Because of the greatly prolonged action potential in their terminals, the Purkinje fibers act as a "frequency filter" between the atria and the ventricular muscles, protecting the ventricles from abnormally high atrial discharge rates.

Relationships between Excitation and Contraction: Excitation-Contraction Coupling

As in the case of skeletal muscle (pp. 66f.), it is the action potential that gives rise to contraction of the myocardial cell. However, there is a characteristic difference between the two types of muscle with respect to the temporal relation between action potential and contraction [11]. Whereas the action potential of skeletal muscle lasts only a few milliseconds, and contraction does not begin until the excitatory process is nearly over, in the myocardium the two events overlap considerably in time (Fig. 19-9, top). The myocardial action potential ends only when the musculature has begun to relax again. Because a new contraction must be initiated by new excitation, which can occur only after the absolute refractory period of the preceding excitation has elapsed, cardiac muscle – unlike skeletal muscle – is incapable of responding to a rapid sequence of action potentials with superposition of single contractions or with a tetanus (cf. p. 72).

The "**non-tetanizability**" of the myocardium is a property that seems entirely appropriate to the pump function of the heart; a tetanic con-

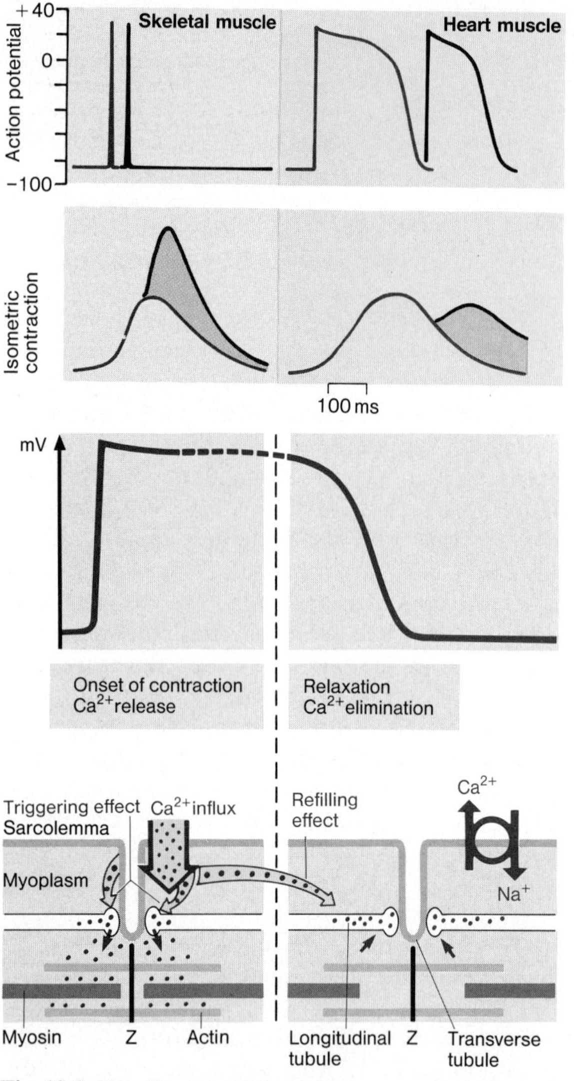

Fig. 19-9. *Top:* Temporal relation between action potential and contraction in skeletal and cardiac muscle. *Bottom:* Diagram of the interplay of excitation, Ca^{2+} movement and activation of the contractile apparatus. Events at the onset of contraction shown on the *left*, those during relaxation on the *right*

traction of the heart that outlasted the blood-ejection phase would interfere with refilling. On the other hand, the superposition property of skeletal muscle enables the force of contraction to be varied with action-potential frequency; myocardial contractions cannot be graded in this way. Moreover, because the myocardium is a functional syncytium the force of contraction cannot be graded by recruitment of a variable number of motor units (see p. 71), as is possible with skeletal muscle. Myocardial contraction is an all-or-none event, in which all fibers participate at each occurrence. In compensation for these physiological disadvantages, the opportunity for influencing contraction by way of the excitatory processes or by direct interference with the excitation-contraction coupling is considerably greater in cardiac muscle.

The mechanism of excitation-contraction coupling in the myocardium. The myocardial fibers of man and other mammals in principle comprise the same structural elements as are involved in the electromechanical coupling processes in skeletal muscle (pp. 62f. and Fig. 19-9, bottom). The **transverse tubular system (T system)** is clearly a feature of the myocardium, particularly in the ventricles, where it also has connections in the longitudinal direction. By contrast, the **longitudinal system** of tubules, which functions as an intracellular Ca^{2+} reservoir, is less well developed than in skeletal muscle. Both the structural peculiarities of the myocardium and its functional behavior offer evidence of a close interaction between the intracellular Ca^{2+} stores and the medium external to the fibers. A key event in contraction is the **influx of calcium** during the action potential. This Ca^{2+} current does not only serve to prolong the action potential (as mentioned above), and thus the refractory period; because of the associated displacement of Ca^{2+} from the extracellular space to the interior of the cell, it also helps to control the force of contraction. The quantity of inflowing Ca^{2+}, however, is evidently not sufficient for direct activation of the contractile apparatus. The additional release of Ca^{2+} from the intracellular depots triggered by the Ca^{2+} influx appears to be a more important effect [24]. The influx of Ca^{2+} across the membrane also serves to replenish the Ca^{2+} stores for the following contractions.

If one experimentally shortens the duration of a single action potential by applying an anodal current pulse, so that the Ca^{2+} influx is prematurely interrupted, the corresponding contraction is attenuated only slightly, whereas the following contraction, elicited by a normal action potential, is considerably reduced. When an action potential is artificially prolonged the reverse effect is observed – that is, an enhancement of the next contractions. If the action potential is shortened or lengthened for several beats, an equilibrium is attained after 5 to 7 beats, with a level of contraction that may be considerably decreased or increased, respectively [14].

The action potential, then affects contraction in at least two important ways. It has

- a **triggering action**, eliciting the contraction by (Ca^{2+}-triggered) liberation of Ca^{2+}, primarily from intracellular depots, and
- a **replenishing action**, renewing the intracellular stores of Ca^{2+} during relaxation in preparation for subsequent contractions.

Mechanisms by which contraction is influenced. A number of influences on the force of myocardial contraction are exerted indirectly, by way of a change in **duration of the action potential** accompanied by corresponding modifications of the inward Ca^{2+} current. Examples include shortening of the action potential by elevated K^+ or by acetylcholine, which weakens the contraction, and lengthening of the action potential by cooling, which increases the contractile force (cf. Table 19-1). An increase in the number of action potentials per unit time acts in the same direction as an increase in action-potential duration (*frequency inotropism*, increased contractile force due to *paired pulse stimulation, postextrasystolic potentiation*). The so-called **staircase phenomenon**, a stepwise increase in the amplitude of contraction following temporary arrest, is also associated with the replenishment of intracellular Ca^{2+} [14].
In view of all these effects it comes as no surprise that **changes in the extracellular Ca^{2+}** concentration rapidly affect the force of cardiac contraction. Complete **excitation-contraction uncoupling** can be achieved by the experimental withdrawal of extracellular Ca^{2+}; the action potential of the myocardium remains almost unchanged, but it is no longer accompanied by a mechanical response.

From all that has been said one would expect Ca^{2+} withdrawal to **shorten** the action potential, since the inward Ca^{2+} current (which acts to lengthen the action potential) has been eliminated. There are several reasons for the absence of such an effect. One is that the slow channel allows Na^+ to pass as well as Ca^{2+}; with a normal extracellular Ca^{2+} concentration the proportion of Na^+ in the slow inward current is small, but in low-Ca^{2+} conditions a slow inward current is provided by Na^+. Second, the intracellular Ca^{2+} concentration affects K^+ conductance. Lowered Ca^{2+} (e.g., as a consequence of extracellular Ca^{2+} withdrawal) reduces the K^+ conductance and thereby delays repolarization of the action potential [20, 21].

An effect similar to that of removing the extracellular Ca^{2+} can be achieved by means of *Ca^{2+} antagonists* (verapamil, nifedipine, diltiazem etc.), which block Ca^{2+} influx during the action potential [5].
On the other hand, the amplitude of contraction can be increased both by raising the extracellular Ca^{2+} concentration and by agents that enhance Ca^{2+} influx during the action potential (adrenalin, noradrenalin; see p. 450). In clinical practice the heart action is made more forceful by administering **cardiac glycosides** (digitalis, strophanthin).
In the current view, the cardiac glycosides increase the myocardial force primarily by inhibiting the Na^+-K^+ ATPase (sodium pump), so that the intracellular Na^+ concentration rises. The result is a reduced exchange of intracellular Ca^{2+} for extracellular Na^+, which depends on the Na^+ gradient across the membrane, and hence an accumulation of Ca^{2+} within the cell. This extra Ca^{2+} can be stored and thereby made available for activation of the contractile system [11].

Autonomic Innervation; the Basic Actions of Autonomic Transmitters

The cardiac centers in medulla and pons (see pp. 521f.) exert a direct influence on the activity of the heart, by way of **sympathetic and parasympathetic nerves.** This influence governs the rate of beat (**chronotropic** action), the systolic contractile force (**inotropic** action), and the velocity of atrioventricular conduction (**dromotropic** action). These actions of the autonomic nerves are mediated in the heart, as in all other organs, by chemical transmitters – **acetylcholine** in the parasympathetic system, and **noradrenalin** in the sympathetic.

Parasympathetic innervation. The parasympathetic nerves supplying the heart branch off from the **vagus nerves** on both sides in the cervical region. These *preganglionic cardiac fibers* on the right side pass primarily to the right atrium and are concentrated at the SA node. The AV node is reached chiefly by cardiac fibers from the left vagus nerve. Accordingly, the predominant effect of stimulation of the **right** vagus is on *heart rate*, and that of **left**-vagus stimulation is on *atrioventricular conduction*. The parasympathetic innervation of the ventricles is sparse; its influence is indirect, by inhibition of the sympathetic action.

Sympathetic innervation. The sympathetic nerve supply, unlike the parasympathetic, is nearly uniformly distributed to all parts of the heart. The preganglionic elements of the sympathetic cardiac nerves come from the lateral horns of the upper thoracic segments of the spinal cord, and make synaptic connections in the cervical and upper thoracic ganglia of the sympathetic trunk, in particular the stellate ganglion. The postganglionic fibers pass to the heart in several *cardiac nerves*. Sympathetic influences on the heart can also be exerted by catecholamines released from the adrenal medulla into the blood [4].

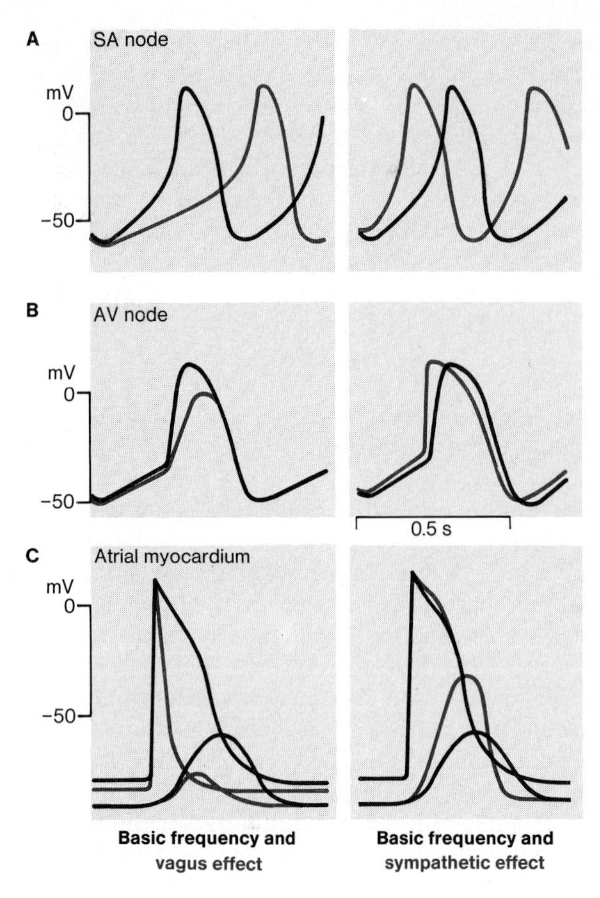

Fig. 19-10 A–C. Characteristic effects of the efferent autonomic cardiac nerves or their transmitter substances on the action potentials of SA node (**A**), AV node (**B**) and atrial myocardium (**C**). The isometric contraction of the atrial myocardium is also shown. The action of the sympathetic system on the ventricular myocardium is like that on the atrium. By contrast, the vagus has little or no direct effect on the musculature of the ventricle

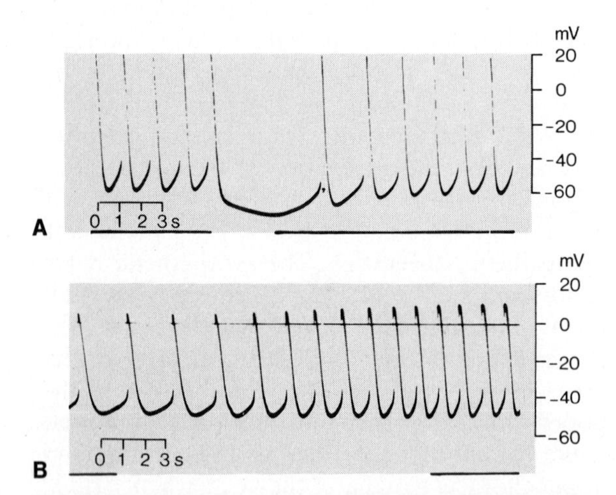

Fig. 19-11 A, B. Influence of vagus (**A**) and sympathetic (**B**) fibers on pacemaker activity in the primary center of the frog heart. The duration of nerve stimulation (20 Hz) is shown by the break in the line below the time scale. From HUTTER, O.F. and W.TRAUTWEIN: J. gen. Physiol. *39,* 715 (1956)

Chronotropy. Stimulation of the right vagus or direct application of acetylcholine to the SA node causes a *decrease in heart rate* **(negative chronotropy)**; in the extreme case cardiac arrest can result. Sympathetic stimulation or application of noradrenalin increases the heart rate **(positive chronotropy)**. When vagus and sympathetic nerves are stimulated at the same time, the vagus action usually prevails. Modification of the autorhythmic activity of the SA node by these autonomic inputs occurs primarily by way of a change in the time course of the slow diastolic depolarization (Fig. 19-10A). Under the influence of the *vagus* diastolic depolarization is retarded, so that it takes longer to reach threshold. In the extreme case, diastolic depolarization is eliminated and the membrane actually becomes hyperpolarized (Fig. 19-11A). The *sympathetic* fibers act to increase the rate of diastolic depolarization and thus shorten the time to threshold. Fig. 19-11 shows both effects, in original intracellular recordings from the sinus venosus of the frog heart.

Because the positive chronotropic action of the sympathetic nerves extends to the entire conducting system of the heart, when a leading pacemaker center fails the sympathetic input can determine when and to what extent a subordinate center takes over as pacemaker. Moreover, the sympathetic system also has a positive chronotropic action on pacemaker cells when their spontaneous activity has been suppressed by external influences such as increased K^+ or an overdose of drugs that interfere with automaticity. In the same way, however, an ectopic focus of rhythmicity can be stimulated to greater activity, so that the danger of arrhythmia increases.

Vagal and sympathetic tone. The ventricles of most mammals, including humans, are influenced predominantly by the sympathetic system. By contrast, the atria can be shown to be subject to the continual antagonistic influence of both vagus and sympathetic nerves; this effect is most clearly evident in the activity of the SA node. It can be observed, for example, by transecting or pharmacologically blocking one of the two sets of nerves; the action of the opponent then dominates. When the vagus input to the dog heart is removed the rate of beating increases, from ca. 100/min at rest to 150/min or higher; when the sympathetic input is removed it falls to 60/min or less. This maintained activity of the autonomic nerves is called *vagal and sympathetic tone.* Because the rate of the completely denervated heart (the *autonomic rate*) is distinctly higher than the normal resting rate, it can be assumed that under resting conditions vagal tone predominates over sympathetic tone.

Inotropy. Change in heart rate in itself has a considerable effect on the strength of myocardial contraction (see p. 447). In addition, the autonomic nerves to the heart act directly on mechanical force generation (cf. Fig. 9-10). The *vagus* acts to reduce the strength of contraction of the atrial myocardium; at the same time, the rise time of the mechanogram – the time from the initial deflection of the contraction curve to the peak – decreases. This **negative inotropic action** results from a primary shortening of the action potential (Fig. 19-10C). *Sympathetic* activity increases the strength of contraction in both atrial and ventricular myocardium **(positive inotropic action)**. The contraction curve rises more steeply, the peak is reached sooner, and relaxation is accelerated. By contrast, the shape of the action potential is hardly changed (Fig. 19-10C).

Dromotropy. An influence of the autonomic nerves on the conduction of excitation can normally be demonstrated only in the region of the *AV node* (Fig. 19-12). The *sympathetic* fibers accelerate atrioventricular conduction and thus shorten the interval between the atrial and ventricular contractions **(positive dromotropic action)**. The *vagus* – especially on the left side – retards atrioventricular conduction and in the extreme case can produce a transient complete AV block **(negative dromotropic action)**. These effects of the autonomic transmitter substances are associated with a particular feature of the cells in the AV node. As discussed above, the fibers of the AV node closely resemble those of the SA node. Because there is no rapid inward Na^+ current, the upstroke is relatively slow and hence the conduction velocity is low. It is evident in Fig. 19-10B that the vagus acts to decrease the rate of rise still further, whereas sympathetic activity increases it, with the corresponding effects on the velocity of atrioventricular conduction (cf. Fig. 19-12).

Bathmotropic action. The term "bathmotropy" denotes an influence on *excitability* in the sense of a *lowered or raised threshold*. However, experimental observations of bathmotropic effects of the autonomic transmitters on the heart are not consistent. All that is fairly certain is that sympathetic activity increases excitability when it has been reduced (low resting potential). The notion of a bathmotropic action has introduced more confusion than clarity, and it should be discarded.

Mechanism of autonomic transmitter action. The effects of *vagal stimulation* and of application of the parasympathetic transmitter, **acetylcholine**, are attributed to one fundamental action – an

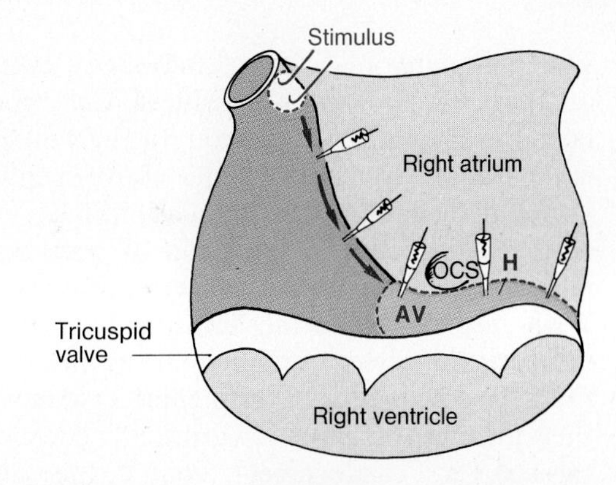

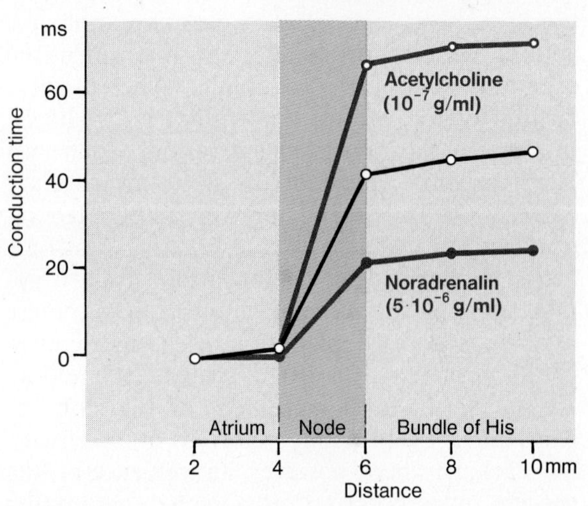

Fig. 19-12. Measurement of conduction times (from stimulus onset to arrival of excitation at the recording electrode) in an isolated preparation from rabbit atrium. AV, atrioventricular node; H, bundle of His, OCS, ostium of coronary sinus. *Below:* Dependence of conduction time on the distance between stimulus site and recording electrode, under control conditions and in the presence of acetylcholine and noradrenalin. The autonomic transmitters affect conduction time only in the region of the AV node; prolongation of conduction time is equivalent to reduction of conduction velocity and vice versa. Modified from B.F.Hoffman et al.: Circul. Res. 7, 11 (1959) and our own results

increase in the K^+ conductance of the excitable membrane. In general, such an influence is expressed in the tendency of the membrane potential to approach the K^+ equilibrium potential, which is opposed to depolarization. This tendency is evident in both the retardation of the slow diastolic depolarization in the SA node, described above, and in the shortening of the action potential of the atrial myocardium, which in turn weakens the contraction. The reduction of the rate of rise of the action potential in the AV node can also be explained on this basis, in that a stronger outward K^+ current counteracts the slow inward Ca^{2+} current.

The possibility of a direct inhibitory influence on the slow Ca^{2+} influx **(reduced Ca^{2+} conductance)** is also under discussion. In the ventricular myocardium, by contrast, the above-mentioned **sympathetic-antagonistic action** dominates – that is, the main action is inhibiton of noradrenalin release from the sympathetic nerve endings [30]. With respect to the mechanisms by which the **sympathetic** fibers (or their transmitters) act, there is convincing experimental evidence that they increase the slow inward Ca^{2+} current **(increased Ca^{2+} conductance)**. That is, the contractile force becomes greater (positive inotropic action) because this effect has intensified the excitation-contraction coupling. The positive dromotropic action on the AV node is also likely, in view of the above considerations, to be related to enhancement of the slow inward Ca^{2+} current. On the other hand, the accelerated relaxation associated with the positive inotropic action is ascribed to a **stimulation of Ca^{2+} uptake into the intracellular depots**. As yet there is no satisfactory explanation of the mechanism of the positive chronotropic sympathetic action. At the SA node enhancement of the slow inward current is probably involved. In the case of the Purkinje fibers, however, an influence on the specific, hyperpolarization-activated pacemaker current is regarded as more likely [16, 20].

Pharmacological effects. The actions of autonomic transmitter substances are thought to involve binding of the transmitters to certain molecular configurations on the effector cell (the word "receptor" is used both for these subcellular structures and for sensory cells). The effects of noradrenalin and adrenalin on the heart, described above, are mediated by so-called β receptors (see pp. 337f.). Sympathetic effects can be prevented by β-receptor blockers such as dichloroisoproterenol (DCI) and pronethalol (cf. p. 338). In the heart, as in other organs, the deadly-nightshade poison *atropine* acts as an antagonist to the parasympathetic effects of acetylcholine.

Afferent innervation. In addition to the efferent autonomic supply, the innervation of the heart comprises a large number of afferent fibers, divided among the vagus and sympathetic nerves. Most of the *vagus afferents* are myelinated fibers originating in receptors in the atria or the left ventricle. Recordings from single fibers in the atria have revealed two types of mechanoreceptors; the **B receptors** signal passive stretching and the **A receptors**, active tension.
Apart from the myelinated afferent fibers from specialized sensory receptors, the main group of fibers leaving the heart comes from dense subendocardial plexuses of non-myelinated fibers with free endings; these fibers run in the *sympathetic nerves*. It is probably these fibers that mediate the severe, segmentally radiating pains experienced

Table 19-1 The action of various physical and chemical influences on the electrical and mechanical activity of the heart. + increase; – decrease; 0 no effect, ( ) weak effect, → change as influence is intensified

	Resting potential	Action potential			Conduction velocity	Pacemaker potential (slope)	Strength of contraction
		Amplitude	Duration	Rate of rise			
Heart-rate increase	0	0	–	0	0	+	Staircase +
Heart-rate decrease	0	0	+	0	0	–	–
Temperature increase	0	0	–	0	0(+)	+	–
Temperature decrease	0 → –	0 → –	+	0 → –	–	–	+
Acidosis	0	0	+	–	–	–	–
Alkalosis	0	0	(–)	(+)	(+)	+	+
O_2 deficiency	–	–	–	–	–	+ → –	–
K_o^+ increase	–	–	–	–	(+) → –	–	–
K_o^+ decrease	0 → –	0 → –	+ → –	0	0	0(+)	+
Ca_o^{2+} increase	0 → +	0	0 → –	0 → +	0	+	+
Ca_o^{2+} decrease	0 → –	0	0 → +	0 → –	0	(+)	–
(Nor)adrenalin	0	0 → +	(+)	in AV node +	in AV node +	+	+
Acetylcholine (in region of atria)	(+)	0	–	in AV node –	in AV node –	–	–

when circulation within the heart itself is impaired (angina pectoris, myocardial infarction).

Effects of the ionic environment. Of all the features of the extracellular solution that can affect the activity of the heart, the K^+ *concentration* is of the greatest practical importance. An *increase* in extracellular K^+ (K_o^+) has two effects on the myocardium: (i) the resting potential is lowered because the gradient K_i^+/K_o^+ is less steep, and (ii) the K^+ conductance of the excitable membrane is increased – as it is by acetylcholine in the atrial myocardium. Doubling of the K^+ concentration, from the normal 4 mmol/l to about 8 mmol/l, results in a slight depolarization accompanied by increased excitability and conduction velocity, and in the suppression of heterotopic centers of rhythmicity. A large increase in K^+ (over 8 mmol/l) reduces excitability and conduction velocity, as well as the duration of the action potential, so that the strength of contraction is diminished and the SA node eventually ceases to function as pacemaker. When the extracellular K^+ concentration is *lowered* to less than 4 mmol/l the stimulating influence on pacemaker activity in the ventricular conducting system dominates. The enhanced activity of heterotopic centers can lead to cardiac arrhythmias.

The excitability-reducing action of large extracellular K^+ concentrations is turned to advantage during heart operations, to immobilize the heart briefly for the surgical procedures **(cardioplegic solutions)**. While the heart is inactive, circulation is maintained by an extracorporeal pump (heart-lung machine). Impairment of cardiac function due to increased blood K^+ during extreme muscular effort or in pathological conditions can be largely compensated by sympathetic activity.

Table 19-1 summarizes the most important physical and chemical influences on excitation and contraction of the heart; only the dominant effects are considered.

19.3 Electrocardiogram

As excitation spreads over the heart and dies out, an electrical field is produced that can be sensed on the surface of the body. The changes in magnitude and direction of this field in time are reflected in alterations of potential differences measurable between various sites on the body surface. The **electrocardiogram (ECG)** is a representation of such potential differences as a function of time. It is thus an indicator of cardiac *excitation – not contraction!*

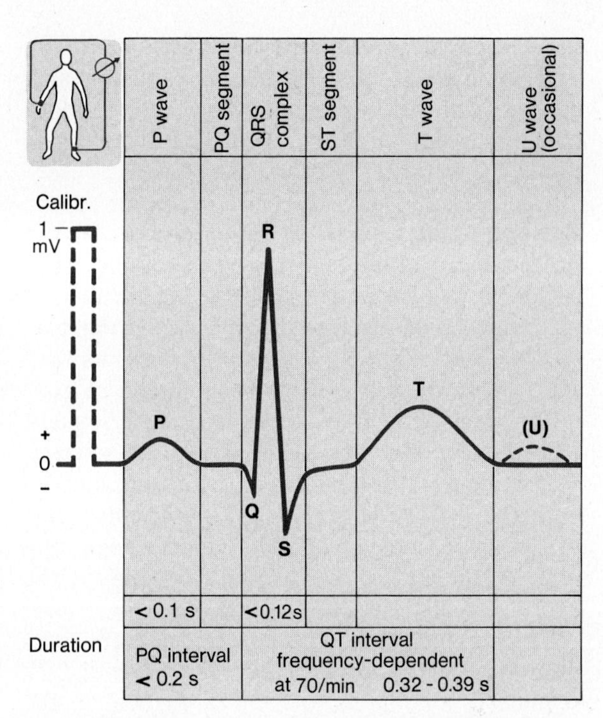

Fig. 19-13. Normal form of the ECG with bipolar recording from the body surface in the direction of the long axis of the heart. The times below the ECG curve are important limiting values for the duration of distinct parts of the curve

Because the directly measured potentials amount in some cases to less than 1 mV, the commercially available ECG recorders incorporate electronic amplifiers. The amplifier inputs include capacitive coupling – high-pass filters with a cutoff frequency near 0.1 Hz (a time constant of 2 s). Therefore d.c. components and very slow changes of the potentials at the metal recording electrodes, which would be distracting, do not appear at the output. All electrocardiographs have a built-in means of monitoring amplitude, in the form of a 1-mV calibration pulse set to cause a deflection of 1 cm.

ECG form and nomenclature. With electrodes attached to the right arm and left leg, the normal ECG looks like the curve shown in Fig. 19-13. There are both positive and negative deflections *(waves)*, to which are assigned the letters P to T. By convention, within the QRS group **positive** deflections are always designated as **R** and **negative** deflections as **Q** when they precede the R wave or as **S** when they follow it. By contrast, the P and T waves can be either positive or negative. The distance between two waves is called a *segment* (e.g., the PQ segment extends from the end of the P wave to the beginning of the QRS complex). An *interval* comprises both waves and segments (e.g., the PQ interval, from the beginning of P to the beginning of QRS). The RR interval, between the peaks of two successive R waves, corresponds to the period of the beat cycle and is the reciprocal of beat rate (60/RR interval (s) = beats/min).

Relation to the cardiac excitation process. Before proceeding to analyze the sources of the ECG curve, let us consider the general significance of its elements. An **atrial part** and a **ventricular part** can be distinguished. The atrial part begins with the **P wave**, the expression of the spread of excitation over the two atria. During the subsequent **PQ segment** the atria as a whole are excited. The dying out of excitation in the atria coincides with the first deflection in the ventricular part of the curve, which extends from the beginning of Q to the end of T. The **QRS complex** is the expression of the spread of excitation over both ventricles, and the **T wave** reflects recovery from excitation in the ventricles. The intervening **ST segment** is analogous to the PQ segment in the atrial part, indicating total excitation of the ventricular myocardium. Occasionally the T wave is followed by a so-called *U wave*; this probably corresponds to the dying out of excitation in the terminal branches of the conducting system.

The normal ECG. The **PQ interval** is the time elapsed from the onset of atrial excitation to the onset of ventricular excitation, and is normally less than 0.2 s. A longer PQ interval indicates a disturbance in conduction in the region of the AV node or the bundle of His. When the QRS complex extends over more than 0.12 s, a disturbance of the spread of excitation over the ventricles is indicated. The **overall duration of the QT interval** depends on heart rate. When the heart rate increases from 40 to 180/min, for example, the QT duration falls from about 0.5 to 0.2 s. The amplitudes of the individual waves are about as follows: P < 0.25 mV; Q < $^1/_4$ of R; R + S > 0.6 mV; T = $^1/_6$ to $^2/_3$ of R.

Origin of ECG

The following explanation of the origin of the ECG is based on a number of facts which will first be summarized and then, where necessary, explained in more detail.

- The complex electrical field of the excited heart results from the **superposition** of many **elementary field components** arising in individual fibers (for definition of the cardiac muscle fiber see p. 440).
- Each excited cardiac muscle fiber acts as a **dipole**, and determines the direction and amplitude of an **elementary dipole vector**.
- Many single vectors summate at each moment during the excitation process to give an **integral vector**.
- The amplitude of a **voltage measured far from the source** is determined chiefly by the **magnitude** of the integral vector and by the relationship between the **recording and vector directions**.

Excitation wave and length of free way. The ventricular conducting system distributes excitation rapidly to many parts of the ventricles. As a result, each section of the ventricular myocardium supplied by a single Purkinje-fiber ending – so that a wave of excitation continually advances along it – is relatively short (about 1 cm long). This distance is called the **length of free way**. The length of the excitation wave can be computed from the product of conduction velocity (ca. 1 m/s) and duration of excitation (ca. 0.3 s),

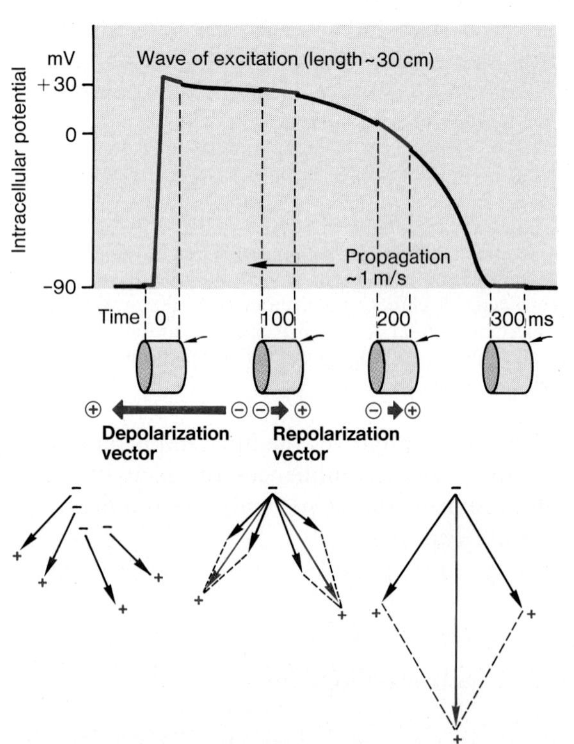

Fig. 19-14. Wave of excitation in the myocardium; intracellular potential plotted as a function of position. The cylinders below the curve symbolize a myocardial segment over which the wave passes (length of free way), in four successive phases of excitation. The front of the wave generates a depolarization vector; during the recovery phase repolarization vectors in the opposite direction are produced. *Below:* The principle of vector addition. 4 single vectors are replaced by 2 resultants and these in turn by one resultant, the so-called integral vector

and amounts to 0.3 m = 30 cm. It follows that at each moment of the excitation cycle only small sections of the excitation wave are actually in existence, as diagrammed in Fig. 19-14.

The myocardial fiber as a dipole. As a wave of excitation passes over a cardiac muscle fiber a *potential gradient* dV/dx is generated along the length of free way, the magnitude of which depends on the momentary phase of excitation (Fig. 19-14). At the front of the wave there is a steep gradient of 120 mV (corresponding to the amplitude of the action potential) over a distance of only ca. 2 mm (= 600 mV/cm). During the repolarization phase, by contrast, there appear much smaller gradients in the opposite direction. To a first approximation the excited myocardial fiber behaves in the physical sense as a *variable dipole*, the magnitude and direction of which are symbolized by an arrow *(vector)*. By definition, the **dipole vector points from minus to plus** – that is, from the excited to the unexcited region; an excited site, as seen from the outside, is effectively electronegative as compared with an unexcited site. We can call the dipole vector at the front of the excitatory wave a **depolarization vector**, and the vector in the opposite direction at the end of the wave, a **repolarization vector**.

Integral vector. At every moment during the excitatory process, all the individual vectors in the heart summate to an integral vector. The formation of the integral vector can be compared to the construction of the resultant in a force parallelogram, in which two vectors are replaced by a third (cf. Fig. 19-14, bottom). A large fraction of the vectors will neutralize one another, as observed from outside the system, because they exert equal effects in opposite directions. It has been estimated that in the excitation of the heart at times 90% of the individual vectors balance each other out in this way.

Relationship of the integral vector to the excitatory cycle of the heart. In Fig. 19-15, the instantaneous integral vectors for successive phases of

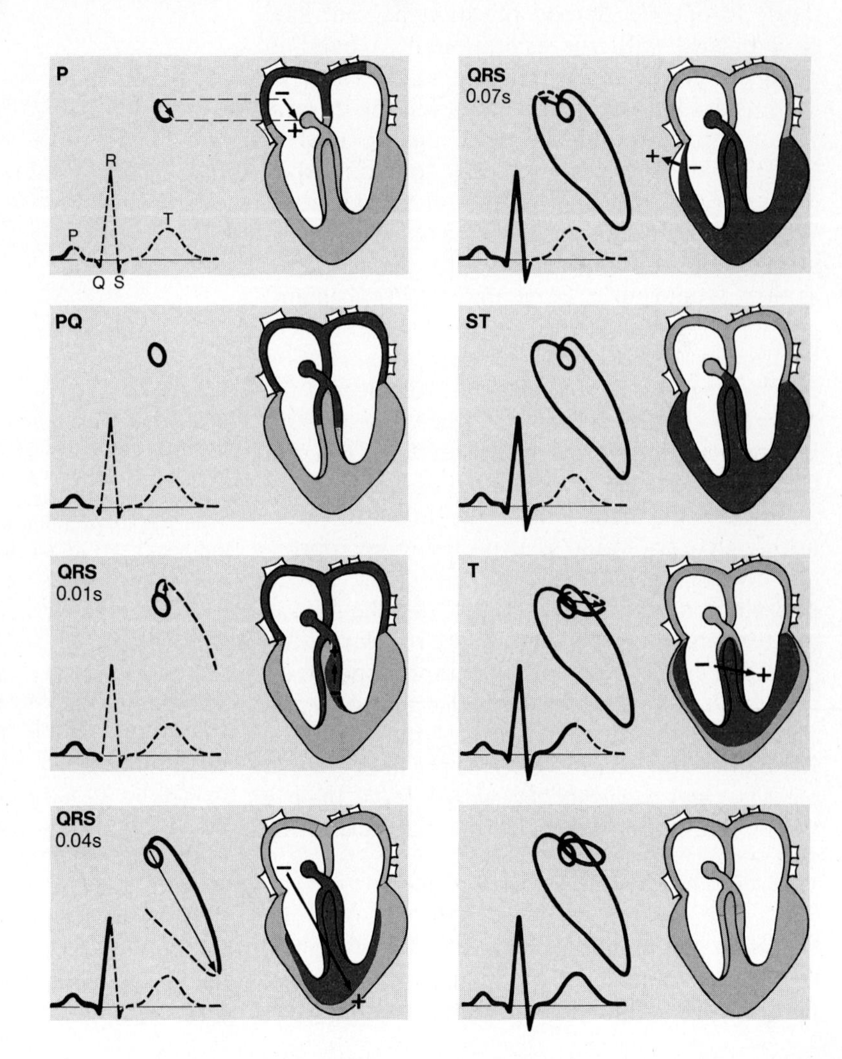

Fig. 19-15. The phases of cardiac excitation associated with particular parts of the ECG. The excited regions are shown in red. The *light red shading* shows where excitation is dying out. The *black arrows* indicate the momentary direction and relative magnitude of the integral vector. The curve between ECG and heart is the envelope of the vector-tip movement in frontal projection (the frontal vectorcardiogram), from the onset of excitation to the time represented by each diagram

cardiac excitation are repesented. As excitation spreads over the atria **(P wave)** the predominant direction of spread is from top to bottom; that is, most of the individual depolarization vectors point toward the tip of the heart and thus generate an *integral vector pointing toward the apex.* When the atria are excited as a whole, the potential differences disappear transiently, for all the atrial fibers are in the plateau phase of the action potential (cf. Fig. 19-14). The simultaneous onset of the spread of excitation through the ventricular conducting system, because of the small mass of excited cells, produces no appreciable potential difference **(PQ segment)**. Only when the excitation moves into the ventricular myocardium do demonstrable potential gradients reappear. Spread of excitation over the ventricles begins on the left side of the ventricular septum and generates an integral vector pointing *toward the base* of the heart **(beginning of QRS)**. Shortly thereafter, spread *toward the apex* predominates **(largest QRS vector)**. During this phase excitation moves through the ventricular wall from inside to outside. Spread through the ventricles is completed with the excitation of a band in a region of the right ventricle at the base of the pulmonary artery, at which time the integral vector points toward the right and up **(end of QRS)**. While the excitation was spreading over the ventricles (QRS), it died out in the atria. When the ventricles are totally excited **(ST segment)** the potential differences disappear briefly, as they did during atrial excitation (PQ segment) and for the same reasons. During the subsequent ventricular recovery phase **(T wave)** the direction of the integral vector hardly changes; during the entire process of recovery it points *to the left.* If repolarization of the ventricles took place in the same sequence as depolarization and at the same rate, the behavior of the integral vector during recovery would be expected to be approximately the opposite of that during the spread of excitation. This is not the case, for the following reasons. First, the process of repolarization is fundamentally slower than that of depolarization. Moreover, the *rates of repolarization are not the same* in the different parts of the ventricles. Repolarization occurs *sooner at the apex than at the base,* and *sooner in the subepicardial than in the subendocardial* layers of the ventricles (Fig. 19-15).

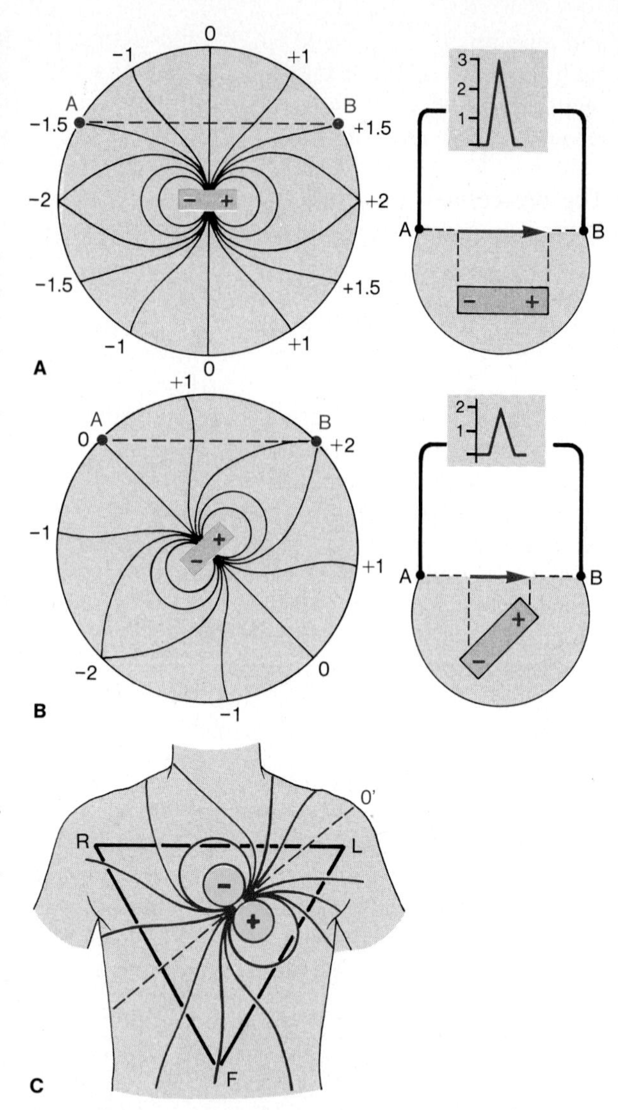

Fig. 19-16 A, B. Bipolar recording in the electrical field of a dipole within a homogeneous medium with a circular boundary. Relative potential of isopotential lines indicated at the edge. Rotation of the dipole (**B**), with the electrodes at the same sites, causes the recorded voltage to fall from 3 to 2 relative units. **C** The electrical field generated by a dipole heart at a particular moment, projected onto the anterior wall of the thorax. RLF, Einthoven's triangle (cf. p. 456)

Direction and amplitude of the ECG deflections. In order to understand the relationship between the behavior of the integral vector and the ECG waves, let us consider the electrical field surrounding a dipole in a homogeneous conducting medium (Fig. 19-16). All points at the same potential lie on the so-called **isopotential lines**. Parts A and B of the figure show that the potential difference (voltage) measurable between points A and B depends fundamentally on the relation of the **lead axis** (the line joining A and B) to the dipole direction. The voltage behaves as the *projection of the integral vector onto the lead axis*; that is, the voltage is greatest when the

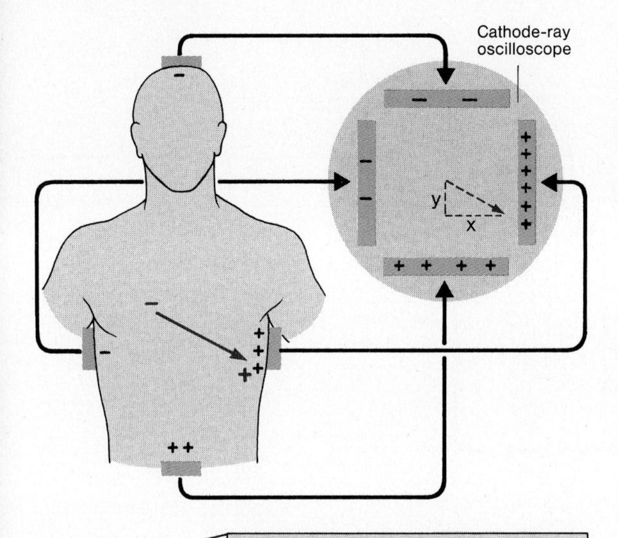

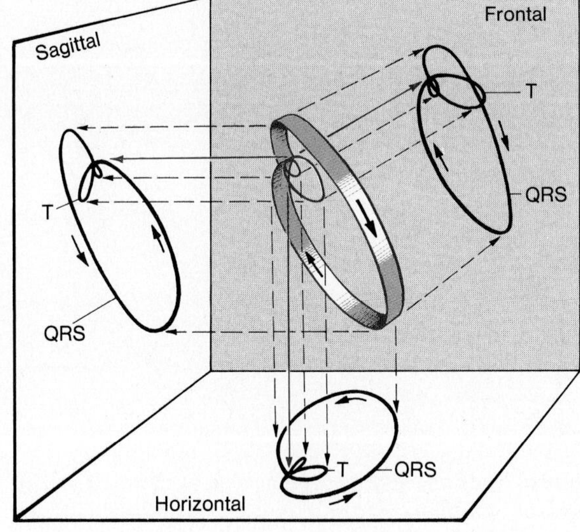

Fig. 19-17. *Upper diagram:* Principle of vector cardiography. Pairs of recording electrodes are connected to the paired deflector plates of an oscilloscope by way of preamplifiers. The potential field of the integral vector is projected onto the plates and deflects the cathode ray away from the center of the screen, to a degree and in a direction corresponding to the integral vector at that moment *(red arrow). Lower diagram:* Three-dimensional vector loop and its projection onto three planes of the body

two directions are the same, and is zero when they are perpendicular to one another. This idea can in principle be applied to the human heart (Fig. 19-16C), though in this case the situation is considerably more complicated. One reason is that the body is not an electrically homogeneous medium; another is that the heart does not, as in the ideal case, lie at the exact center of a spherical conductor. Because of these factors, the electrical field of the heart is distorted at the surface of the body.

Vector loops and vector cardiography. If one thinks of the integral vectors during one cycle of cardiac excitation as having a common starting point, with their tips connected by a continuous line, the result is a three-dimensional figure, the **vector loop**. Fig. 19-15 illustrates the development of the vector loop in projection onto the frontal plane, during a single cycle. By using the recording technique shown in Fig. 19-17 it is possible to display the vector loop directly on an oscilloscope screen. This recording method is called **vector cardiography**. The principle is illustrated in Fig. 19-17, with an integral vector projected onto the frontal plane taken as an example. One pair of electrodes, arranged horizontally, is connected by way of amplifiers to the vertical plates of the oscilloscope, so as to produce a deflection x of the cathode ray. Another pair, arranged vertically, is connected to the horizontal plates and causes deflection y. The cathode ray is displaced from the middle of the screen as the resultant of these two inputs, so that its position corresponds to the direction and magnitude of the integral vector under study (red arrow). Because the principle is the same for all the other integral vectors, during a cycle of excitation the beam traces out the enveloping curve for all the vector tips – that is, the vector loop. By shifting the electrode pairs into the sagittal and horizontal planes, the projections of the vector loop onto these planes can be drawn. From any two of these projections one can obtain the three-dimensional vector loop (Fig. 19-17, bottom).

Types of ECG Recording

The different curve forms obtained with the arrangement of leads ordinarily used, on extremities and chest wall, are basically projections of the three-dimensional vector loop onto certain lead axes. That is, the vector loop contains just as much information as all these recordings together. For practical purposes, however, the preferred ECG representation is the familiar curve of voltage as a function of time; apart from the less extensive apparatus required for direct recording with paired leads, the changes in excitation that are of practical significance – particularly alterations in the rhythm – are more easily detectable in such records than by the analysis of vector loops. The disadvantage is that several recordings must be compared for an exhaustive evaluation.

A distinction is made betweem **bipolar** recordings and so-called **"unipolar"** recordings. In the latter,

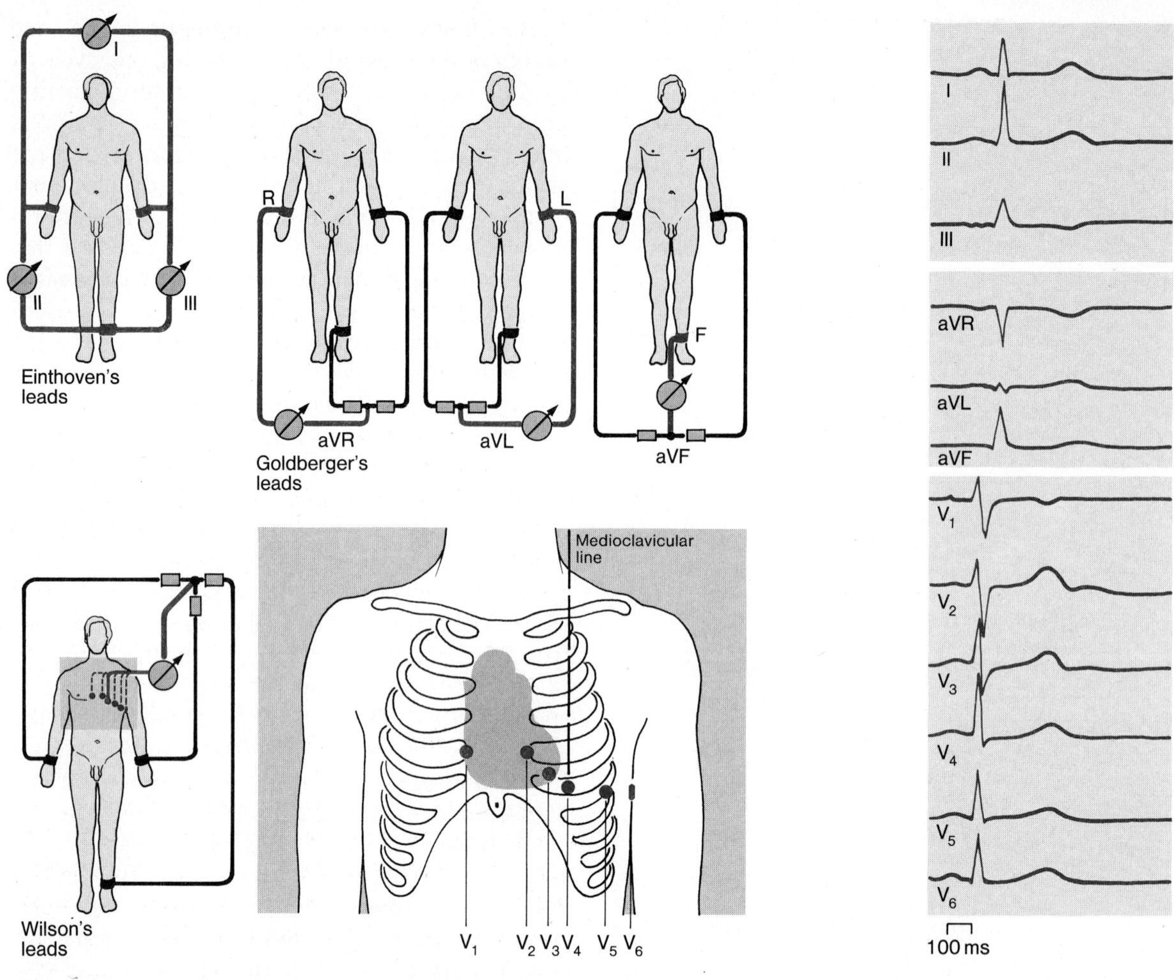

Fig. 19-18. Arrangements of ECG leads in common use. For the so-called unipolar leads (GOLDBERGER, WILSON) the recording electrode is shown in red. For Wilson's precordial leads, the general arrangement is shown at the left and the recording-electrode position at the right. *Right:* Typical curves recorded from a healthy subject

a recording electrode is placed at a defined site on the body surface and the potential with respect to a *reference electrode* is monitored (cf. Fig. 19-18). This electrode can be thought of as positioned at the null point of the dipole, between positive and negative charge. In clinical practice, the following recording arrangements are the most commonly used today.

Limb Leads

Bipolar: Standard Einthoven triangle (leads I, II, III)
Unipolar: Goldberger's augmented limb leads (aVR, aVL, aVF).

Chest Leads

Bipolar: So-called small chest triangle of Nehb (D, A, I); not shown in Fig. 19-18
Unipolar: Wilson's precordial leads (V1–V6).

Einthoven's triangle. Because in bipolar recording from the limbs by the method of EINTHOVEN the arms and legs act as extended electrodes, the actual recording sites are at the junction between limbs and trunk. These three points lie approximately on the corners of an equilateral triangle, and the sides of the triangle represent the lead axes. Fig. 19-19 illustrates the way in which the relative amplitudes of the various ECG deflections in the three recordings are derived from the projection of the frontal vector loop onto the associated lead axes. The temporal relationships here are assumed to be those of a normal ECG.

Types of QRS-axis orientation. As Figs. 19-15 and 19-19 show, the frontal vector loop has an elongated shape. The direction of the largest integral vector (the **chief vector**) during the spread of excitation is rather inappropriately called the

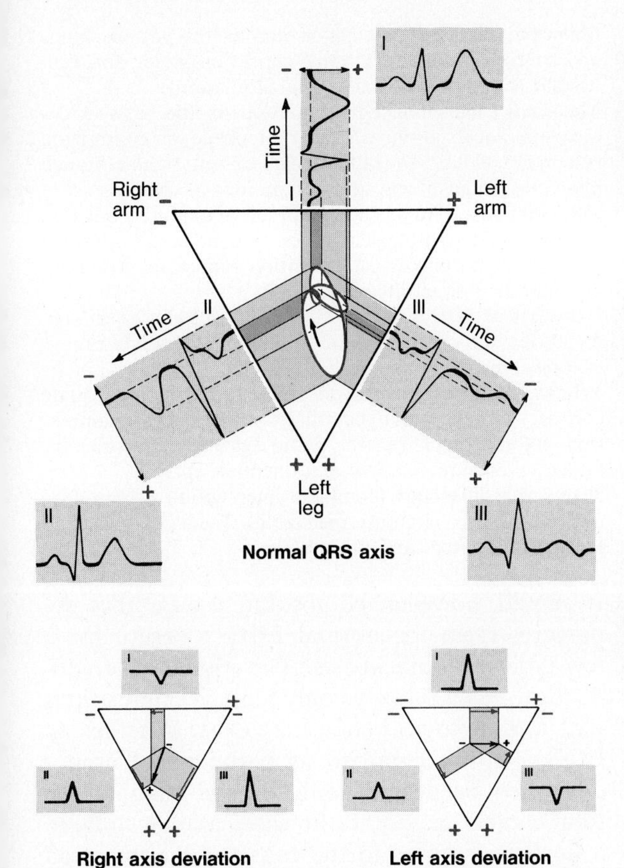

Fig. 19-19. *Top:* The triangle diagram of Einthoven. The recording sites at the extremities are represented as the corners of an equilateral triangle, and the sides of the triangle correspond to the lead axes. The projection of the frontal vector loop on the three axes is shown, and in the *gray areas* the relative magnitude of the various deflections in each axis is indicated by the customary curves. The curves should include a time calibration for precise analysis of the vector loop. *Bottom:* Direction and relative magnitudes of the maximal deflection in the QRS complex with right and left axis deviation. The deflection is positive when the polarity of the projected vector is as indicated for the leads.

electrical axis of the heart. When the spread of excitation is normal its direction in frontal projection agrees well with the anatomical long axis of the heart. Therefore limb recordings can be used to infer the **orientation of the heart**. The various categories are based on the **angle α** between the electrical axis and the horizontal. In the **normal range** (shown at the top in Fig. 19-19) the angle to the horizontal varies from 0° to +90°. Angles above the horizontal are given a negative sign. The general categories of QRS-axis orientation are: **normal range** ($0° < \alpha < +90°$); **right axis deviation** ($+90° < \alpha < +180°$); **left axis deviation** ($-120° < \alpha < 0°$).

For the construction of the electrical axis from the ECG by means of Einthoven's triangle (Fig. 19-19, bottom) two lead pairs suffice, for the third can be derived from the other two. At each instant during the excitatory cycle it holds that: deflection in II = deflection in I + deflection in III (downward deflections having negative sign). The electrical axis of the heart coincides approximately with the anatomical axis only when the spread of excitation is normal; under abnormal conditions the two axes can be quite different. The main direction of the QRS loop then contains no information about the orientation of the heart, but it is still a useful diagnostic characteristic in combination with other signs that indicate alterations in the process of excitation.

Unipolar limb leads. In GOLDBERGER's method, the voltage measured is that between one extremity – for example, the right arm (lead aVR) – and a reference electrode formed by voltage division between the two other limbs (cf. Fig. 19-18). With aVR recording, the lead axis on which the vector loop is projected is represented by the line bisecting the angle between I and II in the Einthoven triangle (Fig. 19-20A). The axes for aVL and aVF are found in the analogous way. The terminology derives from a system no longer in widespread use, in which V stands for voltage with respect to a reference electrode and L, R, and F stand for recording electrodes on left arm, right arm and left leg; the "a" in aVr stands for "augmented" (the recorded voltage is greater in this method). In the diagram of Fig. 19-20B the directions of the bipolar and unipolar limb leads have been shifted, without change in orientation, so that they all intersect the origin of the vector loop. It is evident that each lead line forms an angle of 30° with those on either side. This hexaxial reference system provides all the essential information contained in the frontal vector loop.

Unipolar precordial leads. Whereas the limb leads just described are fundamentally related to the frontal projection of the vector loop, the unipolar precordial leads of WILSON provide information chiefly about the *horizontal* vector projection. A reference electrode is produced by joining the three limb leads, and an exploring electrode records from specific points on the chest at the level of the heart (cf. Fig. 19-18). Fig. 19-20C illustrates the lead axes onto which the vector loop is projected with the recording elecrode in different positions. A positive deflection is seen when the instantaneous vector, projected onto the appropriate axis, points toward the recording site. If it points in the opposite direction, the deflection is negative. The *onset of a shift in the negative direction* thus indicates the moment

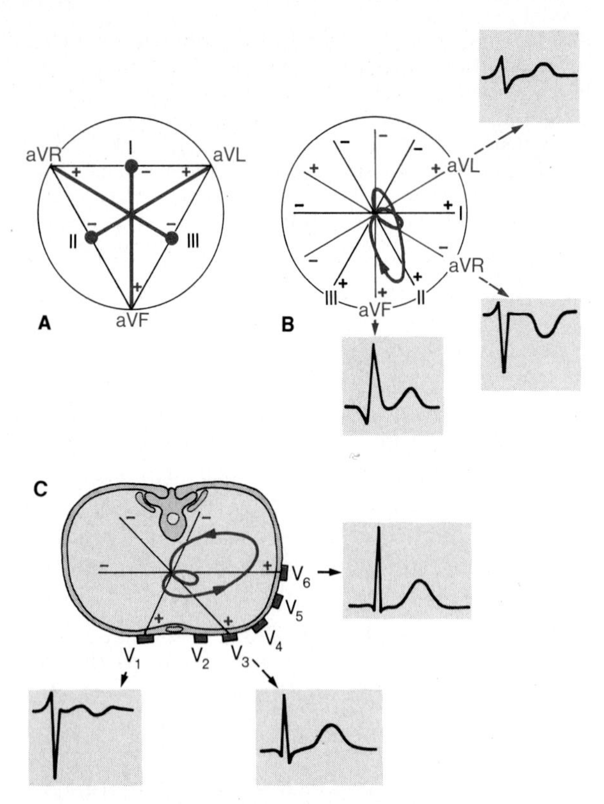

Fig. 19-20. A Lead axes onto which the frontal vector loop is projected with Goldberger's unipolar limb leads. **B** Summary of axis orientations with the unipolar (Goldberger) and bipolar (Einthoven) limb leads. Lead aVR is an exception to the usual polarity rule. **C** Cross section through the thorax at the level of the heart, indicating the lead axes onto which the horizontal vector loop is projected with Wilson's precordial leads. Three sample records are shown (V1, V3, V6)

when the vector loop switches from movement toward the recording site to movement in the opposite direction. This moment is of special diagnostic significance (delayed excitation due to a disturbed spread of excitation in certain regions).

Use of the ECG in Diagnosis

The ECG is an extremely useful tool in cardiological practice, for it reveals changes in the excitatory process that cause or result from impairment of the heart's activity. From routine ECG recordings the physician can obtain information of the following basic kinds:

Heart rate. Differentiation between the normal rate (60–90/min at rest), tachycardia (over 90/min) and bradycardia (below 60/min).
Origin of excitation. Decision whether the effective pacemaker is in the SA node or in the atria, in the AV node or in the right or left ventricle.
Abnormal rhythms. Distinction among the various kinds and sources (sinus arrhythmia, supraventricular and ventricular ectopic beats, flutter and fibrillation).
Abnormal conduction. Differentiation on the basis of degree and localization, delay or blockage of conduction (sinoatrial block, AV block, right or left bundle-branch block, fascicular block, or combinations of these.)
QRS-axis orientation. Indication of anatomical position of the heart; pathological types can indicate additional changes in the process of excitation (unilateral hypertrophy, bundle-branch block, etc.).
Extracardial influences. Evidence of autonomic effects, metabolic and endocrine abnormalities, electrolyte changes, poisoning, drug action (digitalis) etc.
Primary cardiac impairment. Indication of inadequate coronary circulation, myocardial O_2 deficiency, inflammation, influences of general pathological states, traumas, innate or acquired cardiac malfunctions, etc.
Myocardial infarction (complete interruption of coronary circulation in a circumscribed area). Evidence regarding localization, extent and progress.

It should, however, be absolutely clear that departures from the normal ECG – except for a few typical modifications of rhythmicity or conduction – as a rule give only tentative indications that a pathological state may exist. Whether an ECG is to be regarded as pathological or not can often be decided only on the basis of the total clinical picture. In no case can one come to a final decision as to the cause of the observed deviations by examination of the ECG alone.

Examples of ECG Abnormality

A few characteristic examples follow, to indicate how disturbances of rhythmicity or conduction can be reflected in the ECG. The recordings, where not otherwise indicated, are from Einthoven's limb lead II (cf. Fig. 19-13).

SA rhythm. As a basis for comparison, we first consider the normal ECG (Fig. 19-21A), with the pacemaker in the SA node and the QRS complex preceded by a P wave of normal shape. Above the ECG trace in Fig. 19-21A, the process of excitation is diagrammed in a way that has proved useful in characterizing impairments of rhythmicity or conduction. The successive stages in the spread of excitation are shown from top to bottom, and the duration of the absolute refractory period in atria and ventricles is represented along the abscissa.

Rhythms originating in the AV junction (Fig. 19-21B). A source of rhythmicity in the AV junctional region (the AV node itself and the immediately adjacent conductile tissue) sends excitation back into the atria (including the SA node) as well as into the ventricles. Because excitation

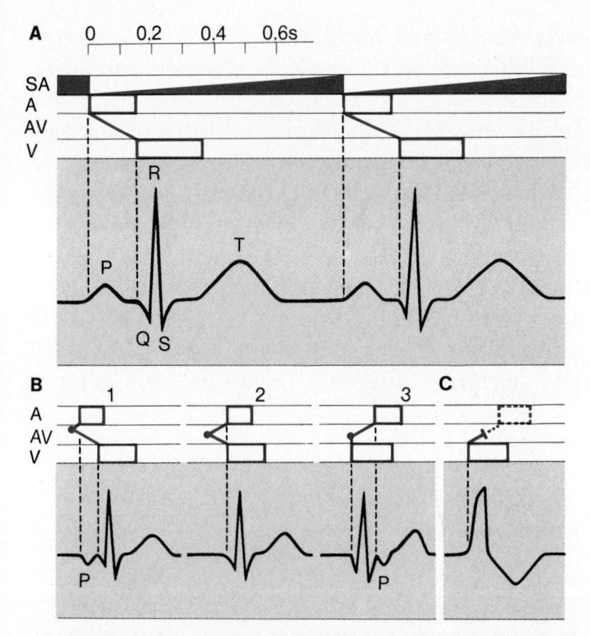

Fig. 19-21. A diagram of the normal time course of cardiac excitation. The successive stages in the spread of excitation are shown from top to bottom, with the absolute refractory periods of atria (A) and ventricles (V) indicated along the abscissa. In the bar SA the rhythmic discharge of the SA node is symbolized; AV summarizes the total atrioventricular conduction. **B** (1–3) Excitation generated at various parts of the AV junctional region, with retrograde excitation of the atria (negative P wave). In (2) atrial excitation coincides with QRS. **C** Excitation originating in the ventricles spreads more slowly and the QRS complex is severely deformed. Conduction back into the atria is possible

spreads through the atria in a direction opposite to normal, the *P wave is negative*. The QRS complex is unchanged, conduction occurring normally. Depending on the degree to which the retrograde atrial excitation is delayed with respect to the onset of ventricular excitation, the negative P wave can precede the QRS complex (Fig. 19-21B(1)), disappear in it (2) or follow it (3). These variations are designated, not very precisely, as upper, middle and lower AV junctional rhythms.

Rhythms originating in the ventricles (Fig. 19-21C). Excitation arising at an ectopic focus in the ventricles spreads over various paths, depending on the source of the excitation and when/where the excitation enters the conducting system. Because myocardial conduction is slower than conduction through the specialized system, the duration of spread through the myocardium is usually considerably extended. The differences in conduction path can cause pronounced deformation of the entire QRS complex.

Extrasystoles. Beats that fall outside the basic rhythm and temporarily change it are called *extrasystoles.* These may be **supraventricular** (SA node, atria, AV node) or **ventricular** in origin. In the simplest case an extrasystole can be *interpolated* halfway between two normal beats, and does not disturb the basic rhythm (Fig. 19-22A). Interpolated extrasystoles are rare, since the basic rhythm must be so slow that the interval between excited phases is longer than an entire beat. Interpolated extrasystoles always arise from a ventricular focus, for such excitation cannot propagate over the conducting system (which is still refractory from the previous beat) to the atria and thus cannot interfere with the SA rhythm. When the basic heart rate is higher, a ventricular extrasystole is ordinarily followed by a so-called **compensatory pause**. As shown in Fig. 19-22B, the next regular excitation of the ventricles is prevented because they are still in the absolute refractory period of the extrasystole when the excitatory impulse from the SA node arrives. By the time the next impulse arrives the ventricles have recovered, so that the first post-extrasystolic beat occurs in the normal rhythm; the interval between the last normal beat before the extrasystole and the first one after it corresponds exactly to two regular RR intervals. But with supraventricular extrasystoles or ventricular extrasystoles that penetrate back to the SA node, the basic rhythm is shifted (Fig. 19-22C). The excitation conducted backward to the SA node interrupts the diastolic depolarization that has begun there, and a new cycle is initiated. These events result in an abrupt phase shift of the basic rhythm.

Atrioventricular disturbances of conduction. The ECG observed in cases of *complete AV block* is shown in Fig. 19-22D. As described on p. 442, the atria and ventricles beat independently of one another – the atria at the rate of the SA node, and the ventricles at the lower rate of a tertiary pacemaker. The QRS complex has the normal configuration if the ectopic pacemaker is in the bundle of His, so that excitation spreads over the ventricles in the normal way. *Incomplete AV block* is characterized by interruption of conduction at intervals, so that (for example) every second or third beat initiated by the SA node is conducted to the ventricles (2:1 or 3:1 block, respectively). In some cases the PR interval increases from beat to beat, until eventually a QRS complex is eliminated and the process begins again *(Wenckebach phenomenon)*. Such disturbances of atrioventricular conduction can readily be produced under experimental conditions (increased K^+, oxygen deficiency etc.) in which the resting potential is lowered.

Changes in ST segment and T wave. Myocardial damage due to oxygen deficiency and other influences in general causes a depression of the single-fiber action-potential plateau, before there is a noticeable decrease in the resting potential. In the ECG such effects are evident during the recovery phase, as a flattened or negative-going T wave or as an elevated or lowered (with respect to the baseline) ST segment. When circulation through a coronary blood vessel is prevented *(infarction)*, an area of dead tissue develops; its location can usually be determined only by analysis of several recordings, precordial recordings in particular. It must be kept in mind that ECG alterations due to infarction can change considerably in time (cf. Fig. 19-22E). The monophasic form of the QRS complex which results from ST elevation, a characteristic of the early stage of infarction, disappears when the infarct has become demarcated from the excitable surrounding tissue by the formation of a boundary zone.

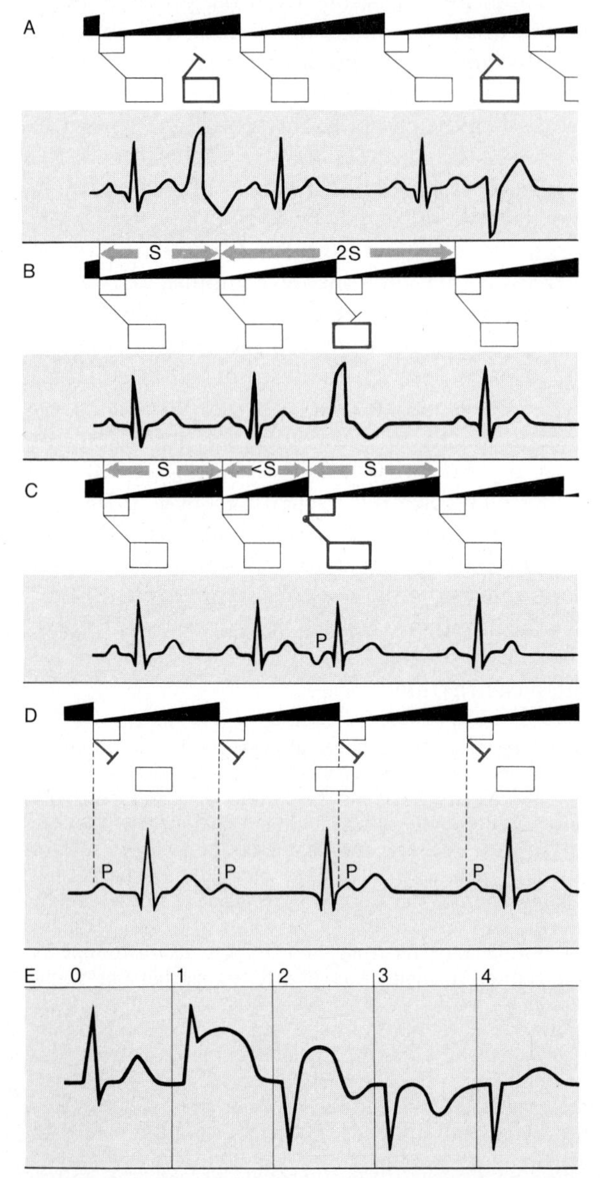

Fig. 19-22 A–E. Examples of typical alterations in the ECG. **A** Interpolated ventricular extrasystoles. The differences in form indicate different ectopic foci within the ventricles. No conduction back to SA node. **B** Ventricular extrasystole with fully compensating pause. S, normal SA interval. **C** Supraventricular extrasystole from the region of the AV node, with incompletely compensating pause. **D** Complete (third-degree) AV block. **E** Progressive ECG deformation during myocardial infarction: in this example, Wilson's lead V3 with infarction of the anterior wall of the heart. (0) Normal picture before infarction. (1) Early stage, a few hours after onset. (2) Intermediate stage, after hours to days. (3) After several days to weeks. (4) Final stage, months to years after infarct formation

Atrial flutter and fibrillation. These are arrhythmias resulting from an uncoordinated spread of excitation over the atria, so that some atrial regions contract at the same time as others are relaxing *(functional fragmentation)*. **Atrial flutter** is reflected in the ECG by so-called flutter waves with a regular sawtooth shape and a frequency of 220–350/min, which take the place of the P wave (Fig. 19-23A). Because of incomplete AV block due to the refractory period of the ventricular conducting system, normal QRS complexes appear at regular intervals. In the ECG associated

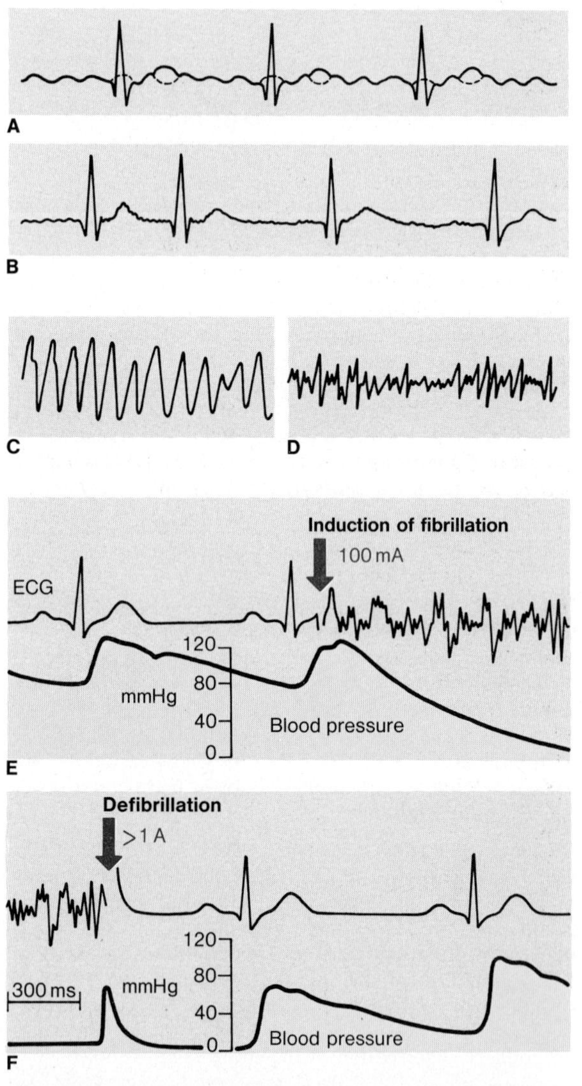

Fig. 19-23 A–F. ECG changes during flutter and fibrillation. **A** Atrial flutter; the flutter waves during the ventricle complexes are shown by the *dashed* lines. Here conduction to the ventricles occurs after every 4th flutter wave. **B** Complete ventricular arrhythmia due to atrial fibrillation. **C** Ventricular flutter. **D** Ventricular fibrillation. **E** Triggering of ventricular fibrillation by an electrical shock (100 mA) during the vulnerable period. **F** Interruption of ventricular fibrillation by a strong counter shock (> 1A)

with **atrial fibrillation** (Fig. 19-23B) atrial activity appears only as high-frequency (350–600/min) irregular fluctuations of the baseline. The QRS complexes appear at irregular intervals **(absolute arrhythmia)**, but their configuration is normal as long as there is no additional disturbance. There is a continuum of intermediate states between atrial flutter and fibrillation. In general the hemodynamic effects are slight; the patient is frequently quite unaware of the arrhythmia.

Ventricular flutter and fibrillation. When the ventricles are affected by the same sort of disturbance, the consequences are much more severe. Because the electrical activity is uncoordinated, the ventricles do not fill and expel the blood effectively. Circulation is arrested and unconsciousness ensues; unless circulation is restored within minutes death results. The ECG during **ventricular flutter** exhibits high-frequency, large-amplitude waves (Fig. 19-23C), whereas the fluctuations associated with **ventricular fibrillation** are very irregular, changing rapidly in frequency, shape and amplitude (Fig. 19-23D). Flutter and fibrillation can be set off by many kinds of heart damage – oxygen deficiency, coronary occlusion (infarction), overstretching, excessive cooling, and overdoses of drugs, anesthetics etc. Ventricular fibrillation is the most common acute cause of death in electrical accidents.

Causes of flutter and fibrillation. The basic problem in cases of flutter and fibrillation is disruption of electrical activity. Two main mechanisms are currently under consideration as causes of this disorganization, (i) abnormalities in the **generation** of excitation, and (ii) abnormalities in its **spread**. In the first case, fibrillation would result when one or more ectopic foci come into action, driving the associated part of the heart at a high rate and thus overcoming the regular pacemaker and conductile activity. In the second case, **reentry** would be responsible for fibrillation [13]. In this situation the excitation circles through the myocardium, a process for which there are two prerequisites. First, the **length of the excitatory wave** (product of conduction velocity and refractory time) must be **shortened** sufficiently to enable reentry within the myocardial network. This can occur by shortening of the refractory time, reduction of conduction velocity, or both. Second, the **conduction of excitation** must be temporarily **blocked in one direction,** so that the excitation fronts do not collide and extinguish one another (Fig. 19-24).

At present it is generally accepted that both mechanisms are probably involved in fibrillation, ectopic foci being primarily responsible for triggering fibrillation, and reentry of excitation for its persistence. Between flutter and fibrillation there are gradations in the degree of functional fragmentation – i.e., in the sizes of the independently activated areas.

Vulnerable period. Flutter and fibrillation can be induced by a single suprathreshold electrical shock – either experimentally or accidentally – if it occurs in a particular phase of the *recovery of excitability*. This so-called *vulnerable period* coincides approximately with the rising flank of the T wave in the ECG (cf. Figs. 19-23E and 19-24). At this time parts of the heart are still absolutely refractory and others, relatively so. As described on p. 443, when the heart is excited during the relative refractory period, the following refractory period is shorter. Furthermore, as shown in Fig. 19-24, the conduction of excitation can be blocked in one direction. In this situation, then, the prerequisites for reentry are met. Spontaneous extrasystoles can give rise to fibrillation in the same way as does stimulation, if they occur during the vulnerable period following previous excitation.

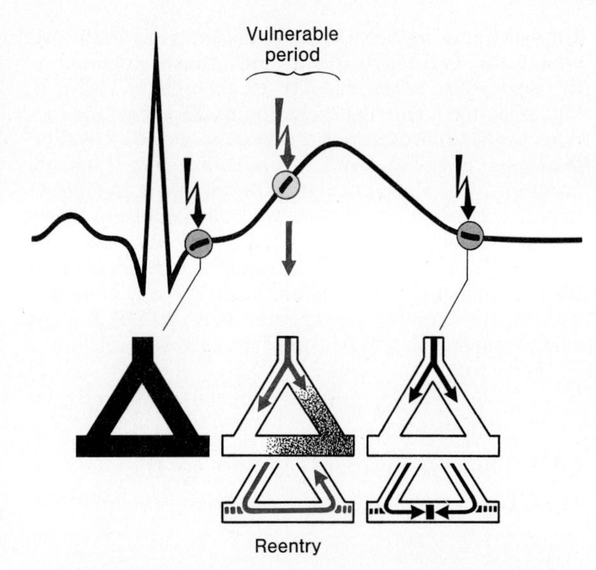

Fig. 19-24. Diagram to explain the vulnerable period of the ventricles. The triangles below the ECG curve symbolize the branched network of the myocardium. In the vulnerable period the conduction pathway is still partially refractory, so that the wave of excitation generated by stimulation can propagate in only one direction. When this region has emerged from the refractory state, reentry in the opposite direction becomes possible, on the condition that the length of the wave of excitation is no greater than that of the conducting pathway. If stimulated earlier the ventricles would still be inexcitable (absolute refractory period), and at a later time reentry is no longer possible

Electrical defibrillation. Electrical current can trigger flutter and fibrillation of the heart. But if suitably applied, it can also stop ongoing ventricular flutter or fibrillation. A single brief shock is required, a few amperes in magnitude; when applied through the intact chest wall with large superficial electrodes such a shock usually stops the disorganized contraction instantly (Fig. 19-23F). Electrical *defibrillation* is the most effective method of abolishing life-threatening ventricular flutter or fibrillation.

The synchronizing effect of this application of current over a large area is probably due to simultaneous excitation of the myocardial zones that are in an excitable state, so that when the reentering excitation reaches them they are refractory and further spread is blocked. For electrical defibrillation to be successful, it is of course crucial that the interruption of blood circulation during the preceding period of fibrillation not cause irreversible damage to organs (the brain can be revived if circulation resumes in 8–10 minutes). This danger can be averted if a minimal circulation is maintained by external heart massage combined with mouth-to-mouth resuscitation (see pp. 552f.). Every medical student should be competent in this procedure.

19.4 The Mechanical Action of the Heart

The excitatory events just described are of importance in that they govern the mechanical activity of the heart; excitation causes the myocardial cells to contract. For the alteration between contraction and relaxation of the myocardium to propel blood in the appropriate directions, from the venous to the arterial systems, an arrangement of precisely operating valves is required to prevent backward flow. There are two sets of such valves in the heart.

Action of the Heart Valves

There are valves covering the inlets and the outlets of both ventricles. The *atrioventricular valves* (mitral valve on the left, tricuspid on the right) prevent regurgitation of blood into the atria during ventricular systole. The *aortic and pulmonary valves,* at the bases of the large arteries, prevent regurgitation into the ventricles during diastole (Fig. 19-25).

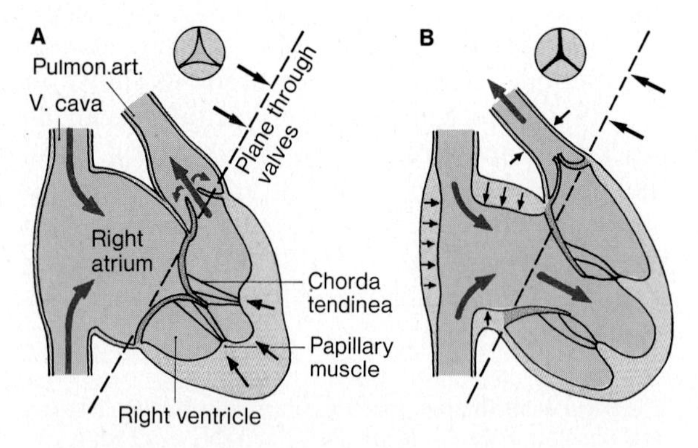

Fig. 19-25 A, B. Semidiagrammatic longitudinal section through the right half of the heart, to show valve operation and the valve-plane mechanism. **A** Atrial diastole and ventricular systole; tricuspid valve closed, pulmonary valve open. **B** Atrial systole and ventricular diastole; tricuspid valve open, pulmonary valve closed. The *insets* above show the pulmonary valves as seen from inside the ventricle

The AV valves are composed of membranous leaflets or cusps that hang into the ventricles to form a sort of funnel. Their free edges are attached to the papillary muscles by fine tendons, which prevent the cusps from being pushed back into the atria during systole. The total surface area of the cusps is considerably greater than that of the opening they cover, so that their margins are pressed together. This arrangement guarantees reliable closure even if the ventricle changes size. The aortic and pulmonary valves are somewhat different in structure; they form three crescent-shaped pockets around the opening of the vessel (hence the term *semilunar valves*). When the valves are closed the cusps touch one another to form a "Mercedes star" (Fig. 19-25). In diastole, the valves close rapidly, keeping regurgitation to a minimum, owing to the currents of blood flowing past and eddying behind them (Bernoulli effect). The edges of the cusps draw closer together, the higher the velocity of flow.

Sequence of Activity Phases

Opening and closing of the valves of the heart is brought about basically by pressure changes in the adjacent heart cavities or vessels. The motion of the valves in turn affects the mode of contraction of the myocardium.

Accordingly, in both systole and diastole periods of action can be distinguished, in which the dominant feature is either pressure change with constant volume, or volume change with relatively little change in pressure. During systole there are an **isovolumetric contraction period** and an **ejection period,** and in diastole an **isovolumetric relaxation period** and a **filling period.** In Fig. 19-26 the temporal relations between these phases and certain variables in the cycle are diagrammed, for the left heart.

Isovolumetric contraction period. At the onset of ventricular systole, the rise in intraventricular pressure causes immediate closure of the AV valves. Because the arterial valves also remain closed at first, the ventricular musculature continues to contract about the incompressible contents, so that there is a further sharp increase in pressure (cf. Fig. 19-26). Although the ventricular volume in this phase does not change, the con-

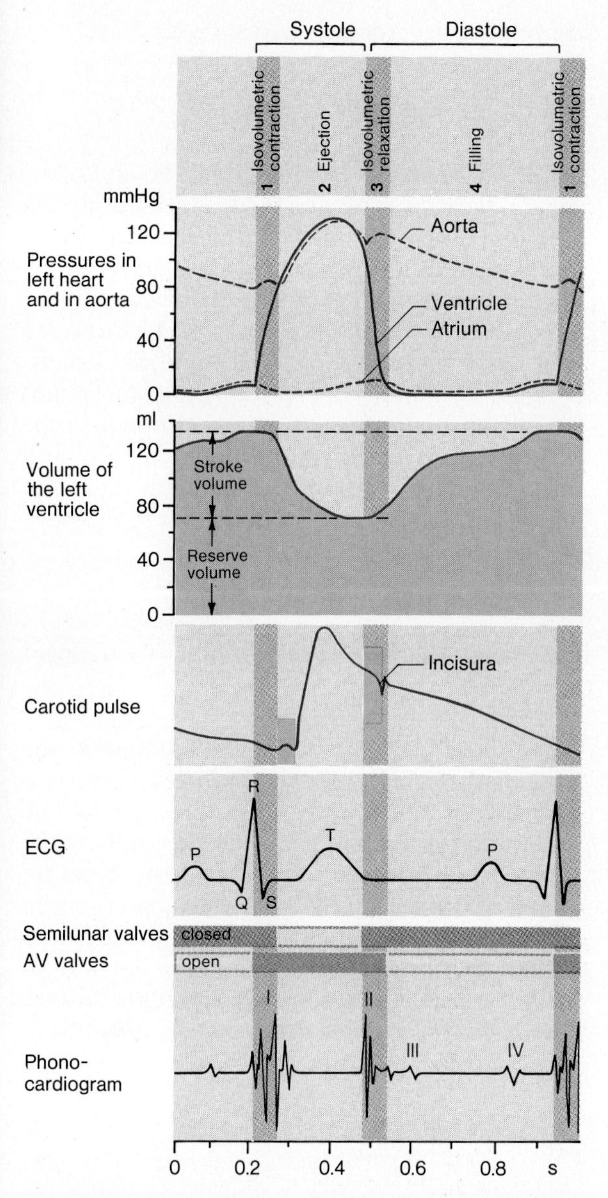

Fig. 19-26. The changes in certain processes and variables during the course of a heartbeat; the four periods are marked at the top. The *red* Roman numerals designate the first to fourth heart sounds

traction is not entirely isometric because there is a change in shape of the ventricle; it approaches a spherical conformation, and practically all the fibers of the ventricular myocardium – some actively and some passively – change in length. With the heart rate at the normal resting level, the duration of the isovolumetric contraction period in the left ventricle is about 60 ms.

In clincal practice the isovolumetric contraction period is ordinarily understood to span the time from the beginning of the QRS complex in the ECG to the beginning of ejection. Within it, a **deformation phase** (QRS onset to onset of first heart sound) is distinguished from a **pressure-increase phase** (onset of first heart sound to ejection).

Ejection period. When the left intraventricular pressure exceeds the diastolic aortic pressure of ca. 80 mm Hg, the semilunar valves open and blood begins to be expelled. Initially the intraventricular pressure continues to rise, until it reaches a maximum of ca. 130 mm Hg; toward the end of systole it falls again. As the volume curve in Fig. 19-26 shows, under resting conditions the ventricle ejects only about half of the ca. 130 ml blood it contains; this is the **stroke volume** (SV). At the end of systole, therefore, a **reserve volume** (RV) of ca. 70 ml remains in the ventricle. The ratio between the stroke volume and the end-diastolic volume is called the **ejection fraction**; in the present case it is about 0.46 (46%). Closure of the aortic valve, which marks the end of systole, occurs somewhat later than would be expected from the observed pressure change (cf. Fig. 19-26). This discrepancy can be explained by the inertia of the systolically accelerated blood volume; because of the kinetic energy imparted to it, it continues to flow for a short time, even against the existing pressure gradient.

Isovolumetric relaxation period. Diastole, like systole, begins with a brief period (ca. 50 ms) during which all the valves remain closed. Relaxation during this time is thus isovolumetric. The intraventricular pressure falls rapidly almost to zero. When it is lower than the atrial pressure the AV valves open, and the ventricle begins to fill in preparation for the next systole.

Filling period. During this phase the intraventricular pressure rises only slightly. Volume increases rapidly at first *(rapid filling period)* and then more slowly *(diastasis)*. When the heart is beating at the normal rate, the ventricle is almost completely filled by the time the atrium contracts, so that atrial systole has but a slight additional effect (the volume is increased by about 8%). But when the heart rate is high, diastole is shortened more than systole. Under these conditions contraction of the atrium can make a considerable contribution to ventricular filling.

Comparison with the right heart. The periods just described for the left heart can be shown to be in principle the same in the right heart. But because the vascular resistance is lower in the pulmonary circulation, the pressure the right heart must develop in systole is considerably lower (cf. pp. 475, 478). The stroke volumes of the two ventricles are about the same. The periods are not exactly synchronous in the two halves of the heart. Isovolumetric contraction of the right ventricle begins after that of the left and lasts for a shorter time, because the rise in pressure is less. Accordingly, the ejection period begins earlier in the right ventricle than in the left. The end of systole, however, occurs somewhat later in the right ventricle than in the left. These time differences are relatively small (of the order of 10–30 ms) and have practically no effect on the hemodynamics.

Valve malfunction. Anyone who has the opportunity to observe the opening and closing of the valves through a window in an animal heart is surprised at the rapidity and precision of their movement. It follows that when anything interferes with this movement – for example, when inflammation of the valves causes them to open too little **(stenosis)** or not close firmly enough **(insufficiency)** – the activity of the heart is seriously impaired. The parts of the heart affected are burdened with the need to develop greater pressure or move a larger volume, a burden to which the myocardium responds with hypertrophy or dilation. By adjustments of this sort the heart can in some cases compensate for disturbances in valve function over a period of years.

General relationships between wall tension and pressure. The rise in intraventricular pressure in the ejection phase (Fig. 19-26) is not, as one might easily suppose, brought about by the exertion of additional force by the ventricle musculature. Rather, it is a physical effect associated with change in size of the heart, which can be explained as follows. The muscular tension in the heart wall F (force per unit cross-sectional area of wall) and the internal pressure P of a hollow sphere of radius r and wall thickness h are related, according to LAPLACE, as

$$F = P \cdot \frac{r}{2h} \quad \text{or} \quad P = F \cdot \frac{2h}{r} \quad \text{(Fig. 19-27).}$$

If the ventricle is considered to be a hollow sphere, the radius of which decreases during the ejection phase while the wall thickness increases, it is evident in the above equation that when the force is constant (or even already decreasing) an increase in internal pressure is to be expected (Fig. 19-27 bottom). Conversely, under constant-pressure conditions the force acting on a unit area of wall cross section is proportional to the radius and inversely proportional to the wall thickness. This relationship (Laplace's law) has important consequences, to which we shall return in various contexts.

Functional Anatomy and Pattern of Ventricular Movement

When the heart is viewed in cross section at the level of the middle of the ventricles, there is a conspicuous difference in the thickness of the wall on the two sides. This difference reflects the adaptation of the heart to the different forces required of the ventricles. This adjustment is not in muscle mass alone; the substructure of each ventricle is characteristic of its function. The wall of the left ventricle is made up primarily of a very powerful *circular musculature:* these fibers form

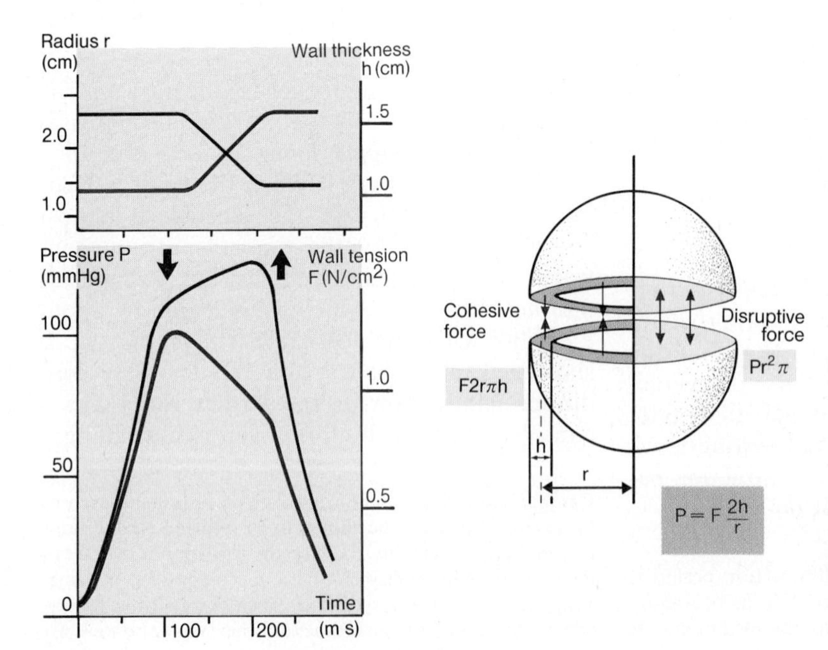

Fig. 19-27. *Right:* Relation between internal pressure and tension in the wall of a hypothetical spherical ventricle. The two influences are shown separately for clarity. The internal pressure P (force per unit area) tends to push the two hemispheres apart with the total force $Pr^2\pi$. The wall tension opposes this force. When the thickness of the wall (h) is small as compared with r, the force holding the sphere together is $F2r\pi h$, where F is the force per unit area of the wall cross section. By setting the two expressions equal to one another one obtains the Laplace relation. *Left:* Change in the radius, wall thickness, internal pressure and wall tension of a left ventricle during the ejection period (between the *arrows*)

a hollow cylinder on the inside and outside of which are layers of so-called spiral muscles running from base to apex. The wall of the right ventricle consists almost exclusively of such spiral muscles; the circular musculature is relatively poorly developed.

Contraction of the right ventricle. The arrangement of the musculature of the right ventricle in itself indicates its mode of operation. The right ventricle is apposed to the left like a thin-walled, crescent-shaped shell. The wall area of this cavity is therefore large with respect to its volume, so that a slight movement of the wall toward the septum must cause a relatively large change in volume. Because the resistance to flow in the pulmonary circulation is low, no great expenditure of force is necessary to produce the pressure required to eject the stroke volume. Moreover, the systolic decrease in right ventricular volume is aided by contraction of the left ventricle, which increases the curvature of the septum.

Contraction of the left ventricle. The powerful circular musculature of the left ventricle is an effective generator of the high pressure required to eject the stroke volume into the systemic circulation. With normal diastolic filling, ejection is brought about primarily by the shortening of these fibers. But if ventricular filling should decrease for any reason, the radius of the ventricle is necessarily reduced and the amount by which the circular fibers can shorten is therefore smaller. The more longitudinally oriented spiral muscles are similarly affected, but to a relatively lesser degree, so that as filling diminishes they take over a growing proportion of the work of ejecting blood. Whereas with normal filling the dominant effect of contraction is reduction of ventricle cross-section, when the end-diastolic volume is small the ventricle tends more to shorten in the longitudinal direction. This effect is of crucial importance in the so-called valve-plane mechanism now to be discussed.

Valve-plane mechanism. Ventricular systole has so far been discussed only from the viewpoint of the ejection of blood from the heart. In considering the valve-plane mechanism, we turn to an effect of systole that is closely related to diastolic filling. During the ejection period the ventricles, in a *single* operation, push blood out into the great arteries and simultaneously suck blood into the atria from the great veins. The suction is produced by a shift of the valve plane (the plane through the boundary between atria and ventricles, in which the valves lie) toward the apex of the heart; the atria, which have already relaxed, are thus stretched. This effect is most pronounced in the right ventricle because of its predominance of spiral muscles, which shorten the ventricle in the longitudinal direction. In the left ventricle the effect is enhanced as end-diastolic volume decreases, for the reasons discussed above. At the end of the ejection period, therefore, the atria are filled to capacity with blood (Fig. 19-25A). Now, as soon as the ventricle musculature relaxes, the valve plane returns to the starting position; as this movement begins the valves open, so that the plane shifts, so to speak, over the blood that fills the atria (Fig. 19-25B). In this way a rapid initial filling of the ventricles is guaranteed – a factor of special importance when the heart is beating rapidly, with correspondingly shortened diastole.

One might wonder at this point why shortening of the ventricles in the longitudinal direction pulls the valve plane down rather than the heart apex up, as would happen in an isolated heart mounted on an aortic cannula. There are at least two explanations. In situ the apex cannot be pulled up because there is an incompressible (and thus unstretchable) layer of fluid between the heart and the pericardium, which in turn is anchored to the diaphragm. Moreover, during ventricular systole there is a repulsive force on the ventricles in the direction of the apex.

It is not by this valve-plane mechanism alone that blood is made available for diastolic filling of the ventricles. The diastolic relaxation of the ventricle in itself exerts a certain suction, owing to the reversal by passive elastic effects of the deformation imposed during systole. This action is comparable to that of the rubber bulb of an eye-dropper, which snaps back into shape after being pressed. Other forces driving the venous return to the heart will be considered in the discussion of circulation.

External Signals of Heart Activity

For information about how the human heart is functioning, one must usually rely on related phenomena that are externally observable. There are a number of useful signals that can be monitored at the body surface by means of suitably designed equipment, without appreciable inconvenience to the subject. Such methods of study are called **noninvasive procedures.** One example is the ECG, a manifestation of the electrical activity of the heart that has been discussed. Of the mechanical correlates of heart action, the following are particularly accessible to noninvasive monitoring: the *apex impulse, heart sounds,* and the *arterial and venous pulses.*

Apex impulse. The movement of the heart apex in a thin person can easily be felt with the fingers and sometimes even seen, as a rapid outward (occasionally also inward) bulging in the medioclavicular part of the left fifth intercostal space. This precordial pulsation is not, however, simply due to displacement by the apex. Changes in shape, volume and orientation of the entire heart interact in a complicated way to produce the movement. A recording of the apex impulse **(apex cardiogram)** can give supplementary evidence as to the timing of the periods in the contraction cycle of the left ventricle.

Heart sounds. As the heart beats it transmits to the chest wall oscillations in the audible range (15–400 Hz); these heart sounds can be heard by placing an ear on the chest, or by means of a *stethoscope.*

While listening by either means *(auscultation)*, one can usually hear two sounds with no difficulty, the first at the onset of systole and the second at the onset of diastole. The **first heart sound** is the longer of the two, a dull noise of complicated structure. It is primarily associated with the sudden contraction of the ventricular myocardium about its incompressible contents when the AV valves close; the resulting vibration of the ventricles and valves is transmitted to the wall of the chest. The shorter, sharper **second heart sound** is caused when the cusps of the semilunar valves strike one another *(valve sound)* and set the columns of blood in the great vessels into vibration. The most favourable sites for auscultation of the second sound are therefore not directly over the heart but somewhat away from it, in the direction of blood flow (i.e., in the second intercostal space, on the right for the aortic valve and on the left for the pulmonary valve). The best auscultation sites for the first sound are directly over the ventricles – in the medioclavicular region of the left fifth intercostal space (left heart) or on the right edge of the sternum (right heart).

Phonocardiography. With suitable microphones and recording apparatus the waves composing the heart sounds can be displayed (Fig. 19-26). The so-called *phonocardiogram* not only provides a permanent record, but offers an opportunity to analyze the temporal relationships of the heart sounds to other events during the cycle. By inserting frequency filters one can distinguish the components of the sounds more clearly and classify pathological sounds.

First sound. There are three main components of this sound. The first is a low-amplitude slow wave associated with deformation of the left ventricle at the beginning of isovolumetric contraction. The following larger wave accompanies the steep rise in intraventricular pressure. The third component consists of two waves, one coinciding with the onset of ejection and the other occurring early in the ejection period.

Second sound. The beginning of the second sound usually coincides with the end of the T wave of the ECG; it signals the *end of the ejection period.* Occasionally the second sound is split into a first component associated with closure of the aortic valve and a second, synchronous with closure of the pulmonary valve.

Third and fourth sounds. The rush of blood into the ventricle early in the filling period causes a third sound, which usually is audible only in children, where sound is conducted more readily to the body surface. At the end of the P wave and before the onset of the Q wave of the ECG a sound can be recorded which is caused by contraction of the atria. This fourth sound is not detectable by ordinary auscultation.

Murmurs. The abnormal heart sounds called murmurs are produced chiefly by turbulence in the bloodstream. Murmurs have a higher frequency than normal heart sounds (800 Hz), last longer and build up and die away more gradually. Inborn or acquired stenosis or insufficiency of the heart valves frequently cause murmurs; other causes include defects in the atrial or ventricular septa. Murmurs are diagnosed on the basis of the nature of the sound, the time of occurrence (systolic, diastolic) and the site at which the sound is heard most clearly. In cases of *aortic stenosis*, for example, blood is pushed through the narrowed opening of the aorta during the ejection period. The resulting turbulence causes the first sound to be followed by a loud *systolic* murmur of gradually rising and falling intensity that is heard best in the second intercostal space to the right of the sternum. If the murmur were most distinct over the apex of the heart, one would infer *mitral insufficiency.* In this condition the murmur is caused by systolic regurgitation of the blood from the left ventricle into the left atrium, through the defective mitral valve. Systolic murmurs, however, are by no means always a sign of anatomical abnormalities. For example, they can arise from changes in the composition of the blood. *Diastolic* murmurs occur when, for example, arterial valves are insufficient or AV valves are stenosed. Again, the site of best auscultation indicates the location of the defect.

Carotid pulse. The pulsation of blood in the vessels will be discussed here only to the extent that it provides indications of the functional state of the heart. When the stroke volume is ejected from the left ventricle, a pressure wave spreads through the arterial system. Measurement near the heart (common carotid artery) reveals a typical time course of pressure change (Fig. 19-26). The first result of ejection is a sharp rise in pressure, to a distinct peak. During the subsequent falling phase the aortic valves snap shut, causing a sharply delimited deflection, the incisura, in the pressure curve. The time from the base of the rising flank to the incisura corresponds to the **duration of the ejection period** of the left ventricle. In determining the onset of the ejection period, however, it should be kept in mind that the carotid pulse is somewhat delayed with respect to the practically instantaneously transmitted electrical and acoustical phenomena, because it takes some time for the pressure wave to pass from the aorta to the carotid artery. This **central pulse-wave transmission time** can be derived from the interval between the beginning of the second heart sound and the incisura (red-shaded region in Fig. 19-26).

Venous pulse. The veins near the heart are filled with blood to different degrees during the course of a cardiac cycle; these changes can be monitored as externally visible *volume* fluctuations in, for example, the external jugular vein. The recording of this movement (the jugular phlebogram) indicates events in the right heart, the right atrium in particular (cf. Chapter 20).

X-ray examination and echocardiography. One can obtain clues as to the size and shape of the heart simply by tapping on the chest **(percussion)** and noting the distribution of dull-sounding areas. For more precise measurements, and for the sake of documentation, **roentgenograms** are useful. By placing the patient at a distance of 2 meters from the x-ray source, one can avoid the projection errors that arise at smaller distances due to divergence of the rays. Recently, the principle of echosounding has come into widespread use as a method of studying the heart. In **echocardiography** the reflection of ultrasonic waves at the heart's various surfaces (inner and outer sides of walls, valves, etc.) is recorded (Fig. 19-28). This method provides useful information about the distance between structures within the beam and about changes in these distances – for example, changes in size of the heart, valve movements, and so on. Because experience so far indicates that these controlled doses of ultrasonic waves, unlike x-rays, are harmless to humans, such examinations can be repeated as often as desired.

Invasive Techniques: Intracardial Measurement

The extracardial recordings just described, such as ECG, heart sounds and the like, are clearly of great practical importance. However, they can give only indirect evidence of heart function, and for certain questions this is not enough. In recent years diagnostic techniques have been developed in which *cardiac catheters* are used for intravascular and intracardial measurements. These are flexible tubes of various designs, lengths and diameters, which are introduced into a peripheral blood vessel and passed into the heart, usually under X-ray control. A transvenous catheter can usually reach the right atrium, the right ventricle and the pulmonary artery with no difficulty. The left heart is reached by retrograde catheterization, through a peripheral artery, or by way of the right atrium after careful perforation of the atrial septum.

Application of the cardiac catheter. The primary purpose of heart catheterization is to **measure pressure** in the various chambers of the heart and the associated vessels. Pressure curves like those of Fig. 19-26 can be obtained in this way. In Table 19-2, at the end of the chapter, the pressures of greatest practical importance are summarized. A catheter can also be used to obtain *blood samples* from regions of interest, for analysis of – for example – oxygen content. Following injection of a test substance, so-called **indicator-dilution curves** can be constructed; from these the cardiac output can be calculated (cf. p. 540). When contrast material is injected, roentgenograms can be made in rapid sequence to show the heart chambers and vessels in various phases of the beat **(angiocardiography)**. Finally, certain special questions can be answered by using the catheter for intracardial recording of electrical activity **(His-bundle electrocardiography)** or heart sounds **(intracardial phonography)**. But the apparatus required for these procedures is so elaborate that they can only be employed by clinical specialists.

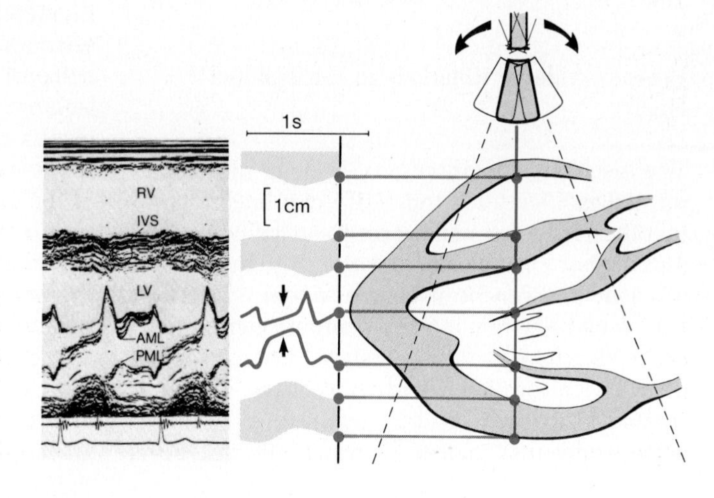

Fig. 19-28. Principle of echocardiography. The transducer acts as both sender and receiver in rapid alternation. The distances and movements of the echo-reflecting surfaces are recorded as a function of time. The closing of the mitral valve at the beginning of systole, for example, is a distinct feature *(arrows)*. In the reproduction of an echocardiogram on the *left*, RV is the right ventricle, IVS the interventricular septum, LV the left ventricle, and AML and PML the anterior and posterior mitral valves

19.5 Dynamics of Adjustment to Changing Work Loads

First we shall examine the work the heart must do to maintain adequate circulation under normal conditions. Then we shall turn to the mechanisms that permit the necessary modification of this activity. A healthy heart is capable of changing its output of blood over a wide range. The **cardiac output** – the amount of blood the right or left ventricle ejects per unit time – can if necessary be increased to more than 5 times the resting level. Because the two ventricles are arranged in series (Fig 19-1), their outputs must be nearly the same at each beat. For example, if the right ventricle were to discharge only 2% more than the left, within a few minutes pulmonary edema would be imminent as a result of accumulation of blood in the lung. The fact that such complications do not normally arise implies that there is a mechanism for precise adjustment of output. Even when the resistance to flow in the systemic circulation increases – for example, because of extensive vasoconstriction – there is normally no serious congestion; the left ventricle quickly adapts to the changed conditions by contracting more strongly and raising the pressure sufficiently to propel the same volume of blood. Changes in venous return and diastolic filling are also compensated by adjustment of the heart's output.

This astonishing adaptability of the heart arises from two basic kinds of mechanism. 1. **Intracardial regulation** is brought about by intrinsic properties of the myocardium, and therefore can be demonstrated in an isolated heart. 2. **Extracardially initiated regulation** operates under the control of the endocrine and autonomic nervous systems.

Pressure-Volume Relations in the Isolated Heart

The mechanical properties of skeletal muscle described in Chapter 4 (pp. 72ff.) can be shown to take basically the same form in strips of cardiac muscle. For example, an isolated papillary muscle is elastic and can be stretched; under a constant load it can shorten actively **(isotonic contraction)** or, if its length is kept constant, it can actively develop tension **(isometric contraction).** The contractile properties can be visualized in terms of a **two-component model**, in which the muscle is

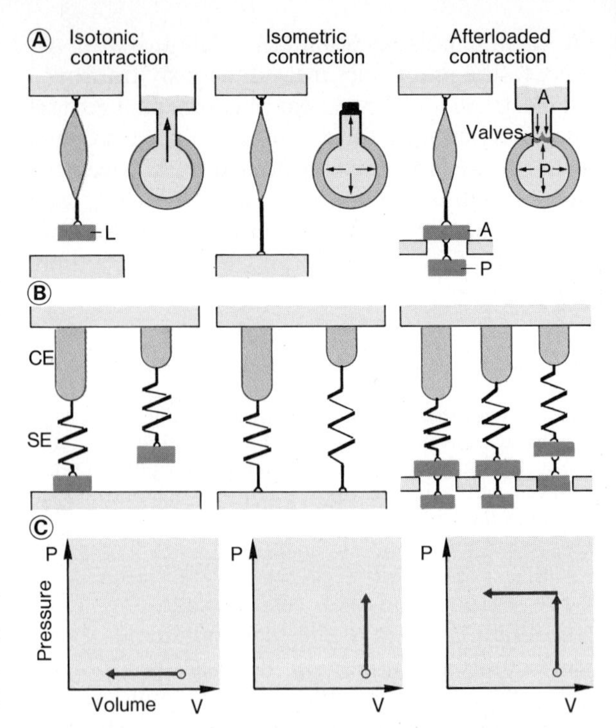

Fig. 19-29 A–C. Elementary forms of myocardial contraction (**A**). Mechanical conditions of contraction of an elongated myocardial preparation (papillary muscle) and a hollow mass of myocardium (cannulated ventricle). **B** Behavior of the two-component model during the various kinds of contraction (CE, contractile element; SE, series elastic element; L, load; P, pre-load; A, afterload). **C** Pressure-volume diagrams for the three forms of contraction

represented as consisting of two elements in series, one contractile and the other elastic (Fig. 19-29B). (A third component, in parallel with these, is required to account for certain resting properties, but can be neglected here.) Isometric contraction in the model appears as a shortening of the contractile element, with equivalent stretching of the elastic element [10].

Elementary forms of contraction. It can safely be assumed that the myocardium in an intact heart behaves in fundamentally the same way as the isolated papillary muscle. But when applying the results of experiments on linear muscles to hollow muscular structures, one must take account of the fact that volume varies as the cube of fiber length. Furthermore, for a given tension in the wall the cavity pressure is inversely proportional to the radius of the (approximately spherical) structure, according to Laplace's law discussed above (p. 464). In Fig. 19-29A the same mechanical conditions applying to the three main forms of contraction with which we shall be concerned are compared for linear muscles and hollow mus-

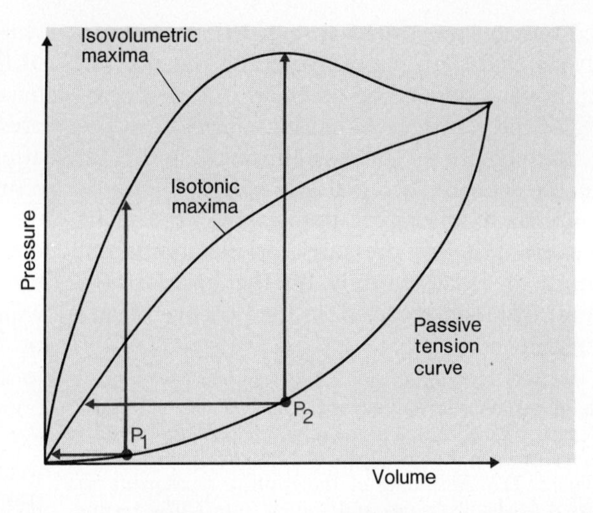

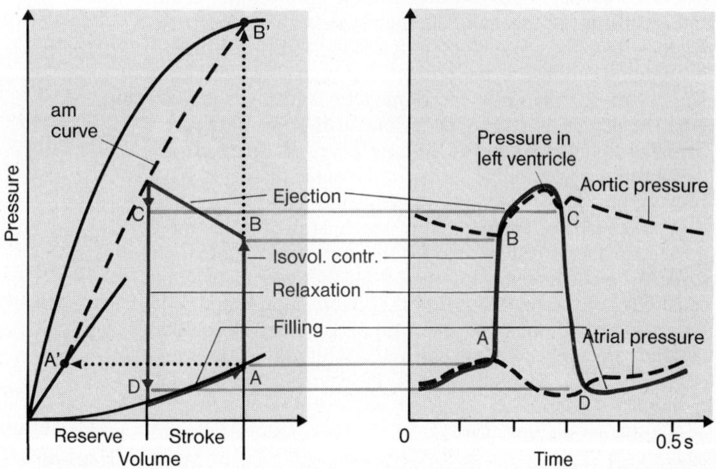

Fig. 19-30. Equilibrium curves and work diagram of the isolated heart. *Top:* In a coordinate system with intraventricular pressure on the ordinate and ventricular volume on the abscissa, three equilibrium curves are plotted – the passive tension curve, and the isovolumetric and isotonic maxima. Each point on the passive tension curve (two points are shown as examples) is associated with a particular isovolumetric and isotonic maximum *(arrows)*. *Bottom:* Diagram of a cardiac cycle (work diagram) in the above coordinate system. The continuous curve ABCDA represents the different periods of the heartbeat (cf. the curve for left-ventricular pressure in the diagram on the right). All afterloaded contractions beginning at point A must end on the dashed curve am, which indicates the afterloaded maxima from B′ (the isovolumetric maximum for point A) to A′ (the isotonic maximum for point A)

cular spheres. Fig. 19-29B shows the corresponding behavior of the elastic and contractile elements of the two-component model. By analogy with the length-tension diagrams of skeletal muscle, **pressure-volume diagrams** are constructed for hollow organs (Fig. 19-29C). An **afterloaded contraction**, the type that corresponds most closely to the natural activity of the heart, begins with an isovolumetric phase, in which the internal pressure rises while the volume remains constant. At the moment when the internal pressure equals the hydrostatic pressure of the column of fluid bearing on the valve, the valve opens and there follows an isotonic decrease in volume.

Equilibrium curves. The pressure-volume diagrams shown in Fig 19-29C refer to a single specific initial condition – a certain volume at a certain end-diastolic pressure. Variation of this pressure can bring about changes in volume which in turn affect the amplitude of the isovolumetric or isotonic contraction. These relationships are summarized in so-called *equilibrium curves* (Fig.19-30, top). Equilibrium curves represent the boundary conditions within which, *for a particular contractile state* of the hollow muscle concerned, all pressure and volume changes occur.

Equilibrium curves are obtained experimentally with an isolated heart in the following way. First the **passive tension curve** is obtained by filling the ventricle under different pressures and measuring the resulting volume (e.g., with apparatus like that shown in Fig. 19-31). The increasing slope of this curve indicates that the passive extensibility of the heart decreases as its volume increases; that is, progressively greater pressure increments are necessary for a given volume increment. Starting at any point in the passive tension curve, both isovolumetric and isotonic contractions can be elicited, as shown in Fig. 19-30. The maximal pressures and volumes so obtained are plotted and curves – of the **isovolumetric** and **isotonic maxima** – are drawn through these points. As an example, two points on the passive tension curve (P_1 and P_2) and their associated maxima are shown in Fig. 19-30. One can easily see that both the pressure and the ejection maxima vary, depending on the initial degree of filling of the ventricle. As initial volume rises the maxima increase up to a certain point, and from there on decrease (or rise less steeply). This is an important finding. It implies that the heart can exert different pressures or eject different volumes of blood entirely on the basis of the amount of blood received, in the absence of any other influence.

Cause of variation in the maxima. One reason for the dependence of the contraction maxima on the initial volume of the ventricle is the arrangement of myofilaments in the sarcomere. The shortening of the contractile element, as discussed in detail for skeletal muscle (pp. 62ff.), results from shifting of the actin filaments past the myosin filaments, like the closing of a telescope. This shifting is brought about by cross bridges between the filaments, which can operate only where the actin and myosin overlap. The degree of overlap is optimal at intermediate levels of prestretching. When the volume is very large, contraction becomes impossible, because the actin filaments have been pulled away from the myosin filaments so far that they are mostly or entirely out of reach. However, the most important factor responsible for the increase in contractile force by stretching appears to be an increase in calcium sensitivity of the myofilaments [11]. Here, again, it should be remembered that the amount of pressure developed depends not only on the contractile strength of the musculature but on the geometry of the ventricle as well (cf. p. 464).

Work diagram. The lower diagram of Fig. 19-30 shows a normal contraction cycle of the left ventricle as a red curve superimposed on the equilibrium curves of the above pressure-volume diagram. This closed pressure-volume loop is called the *work diagram.* The areas in the pressure-volume diagram (the product of P and V) do in fact have the dimensions of work (pressure-volume work; cf. p. 475). Points A to D stand for the sequential periods of the heartbeat. At Point A, on the passive tension curve, systole begins with an *isovolumetric pressure increase.* The segment AB thus corresponds to the isovolumetric contraction period. When the diastolic aortic pressure (B) is reached, the aortic valves open and ejection begins. During this **auxotonic contraction,** volume and pressure change simultaneously. At Point C the ejection of the stroke volume has been completed, and *isovolumetric relaxation* (CD) begins. Finally, when the mitral valve opens, the ventricles begin to fill (DA) in preparation for the next beat.

The normal ventricular systole, by the definition given above, is an **afterloaded contraction.** The **preload** (Fig. 19-29A) is given by the end-diastolic tension in the wall, which depends on the degree of filling. A measure of the **afterload** is the wall tension required to overcome the end-diastolic pressure in the aorta or pulmonary artery. The afterload can thus be diminished either by lowering the end-diastolic pressures or (according to the Laplace relation) by reducing the diameter of the ventricle. With a high diastolic aortic pressure the afterloaded contraction of the left ventricle would ultimately become a purely isovolumetric contraction; that is, the pressure would rise to Point B' in Fig. 19-30 before it sufficed to open the valves and allow ejection. At the other extreme, if there were no afterload, contraction would be entirely isotonic, with volume reduction until Point A' was reached. Under normal conditions neither occurs. The maxima of all the afterloaded contractions that originate at Point A lie on the line joining the extremes A' and B'; this is the curve of the **afterloaded maxima** – the **am curve** for Point A (Fig. 19-30). For each cardiac pressure-volume diagram, then, there is one passive tension curve and one curve for each of the two maxima, isotonic and isovolumetric, but a large number of am curves – one for each of the possible starting points A along the passive tension curve.

Autoregulatory Responses to Acute Volume and Pressure Loads

Heart-lung preparation. The English physiologist E.H. Starling developed a mammalian-heart preparation (Fig. 19-31) that enables variation of aortic pressure and venous return independently over a wide range, so that these factors can be correlated with the end-diastolic size of the ventricles. The heart retains its natural connections to the artificially ventilated lung, but the systemic circulation is replaced by a system of blood-filled tubes incorporating a variable resistance, with provision for pressure measurement at a number of points. The rate of venous return is determined by adjusting the outflow from a reservoir. Because the temperature of the blood is kept constant and the cardiac nerves are transected, the heart beats at a constant rate. Let us consider the extent to which a "reduced" heart of this sort can react to imposed loads.

Adaptation to acute volume loads. In the Starling preparation venous return is increased by raising the input reservoir. Fig 19-32A shows how the left ventricle responds to such volume loading. Under the initial conditions, with an

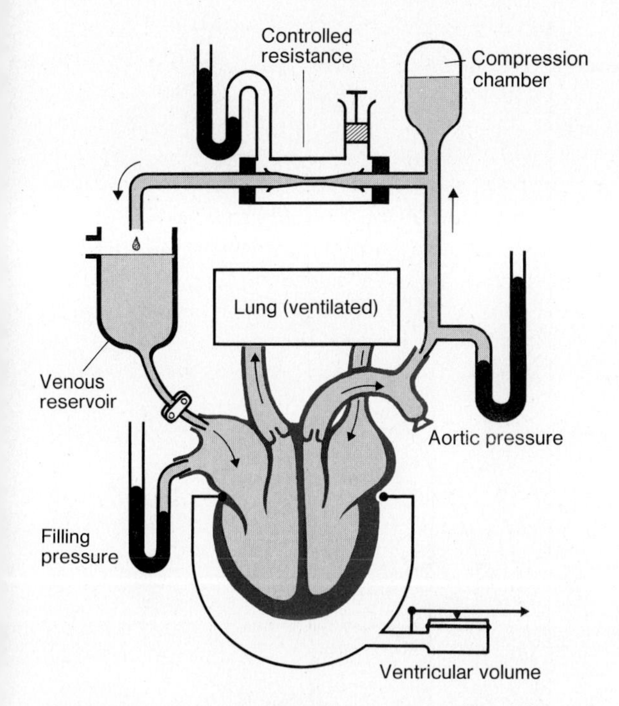

Fig. 19-31. Starling's heart-lung preparation. The pulmonary circulation is kept intact, while a blood-filled measuring system replaces the systemic circulation. The blood is oxygenated in the artificially ventilated lung. A venous reservoir catches the blood expelled from the left ventricle, and can be raised and lowered to change the filling pressure in the right ventricle (and in the left ventricle, because of the low resistance to flow in the lung) by controlled amounts. The resistance to flow can be adjusted by the variable compression of a thin-walled rubber tube when the pressure in the surrounding glass tube is altered

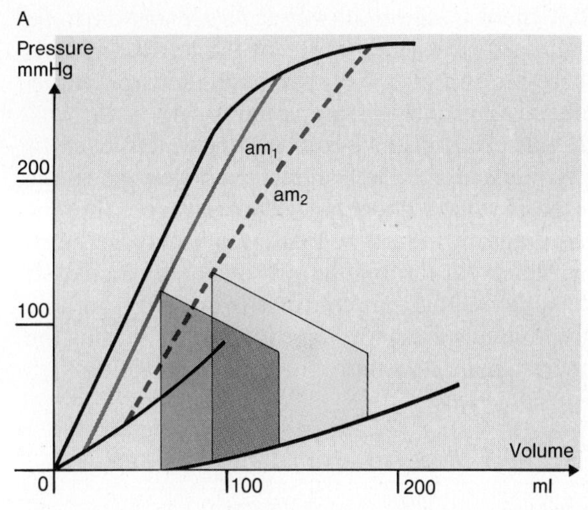

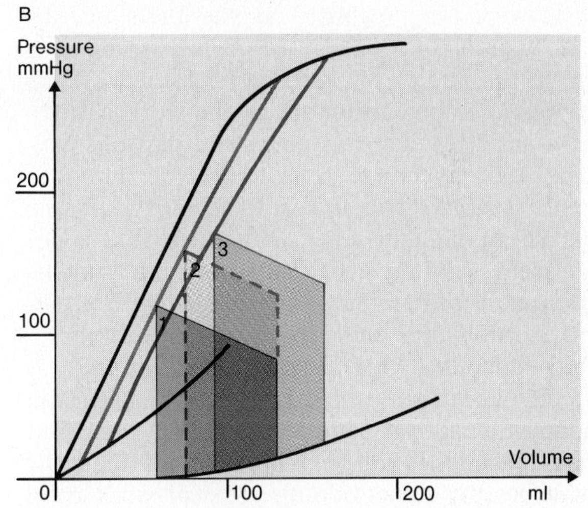

Fig. 19-32 A, B. Pressure-volume diagrams for the left ventricle, to show how the Frank-Starling mechanism provides adaptation to acute volume or pressure loads. **A** Adaptation to an acute volume load due to increased diastolic filling. **B** Stepwise adaptation to acute pressure load due to increase in the peripheral resistance to flow. Further explanation in text

end-diastolic volume of 130 ml, the gray-shaded work diagram applies and the stroke volume is 70 ml. Thus the *end-systolic volume* is about 60 ml. When venous return is increased the end-diastolic volume rises to 180 ml. Now the red-shaded work diagram applies. It is evident that an increase in stroke volume, to around 90 ml, is achieved with no change in the isovolumetric or isotonic maxima. The diastolic aortic pressure remains nearly the same; the systolic pressure rises, because the aorta is under greater tension due to the larger stroke volume. The end-systolic volume has also increased. Because the starting point of the diagram is different, it has to be constructed with reference to another am curve (am_2). The essential point of this result is that the isolated heart, beating at a constant rate, can of its own accord – by *autoregulation* – compensate for increased diastolic filling by ejecting a greater stroke volume. This kind of adaptation is called the **Frank-Starling mechanism** in honor of its discoverers. In principle it also underlies adaptation to increased pressure loads.

Adaptation to acute pressure loads. If the resistance to flow in the artificial part of the heart-lung preparation is increased, the activity of the heart adjusts in a *stepwise* manner, represented in the work diagram of the heart as follows (Fig. 19-32B). Because of the higher resistance to outflow of blood, the aortic pressure in diastole does not return to the original level, so that the left ventricle must exert greater pressure (here 126 rather than 90 mm Hg) in the following systole before ejection can begin (dashed red diagram). This necessarily results in *diminution of the stroke volume.* At the end of systole, therefore, the **reserve volume is greater.** In this arrangement the venous return is held constant, so that there is automatically a *larger end-diastolic volume*. The working range of the left ventricle is therefore shifted along the passive tension curve, to a progressively larger volume with each beat. By this process a new equilibrium state is eventually reached, in which the left ventricle ejects **the original volume under higher pressure** (continuous red diagram). Pressure loading is thus also compensated by autoregulation, owing to increased diastolic volume. In contrast to primary volume loading, however, the increased stretching of the fibers results in a more forceful contraction.

Dynamics of the Innervated Heart in situ

The mechanisms by which the *isolated* heart adjusts were long regarded as the basis of cardiac dynamics in general. According to what was called *Starling's Law*, the heart in situ was also supposed to perform more stroke work entirely as a result of increase in its end-diastolic volume, with no change in its contractile state (i.e., in its isovolumetric and isotonic maxima). The current opinion, however, is that this view is not generally valid; at least, it does not apply to the changes in cardiac output correlated with physical exertion. Starling's Law would predict that a fully functional heart is small when the body is at rest, and when a load is imposed enlarges in adaptation to the increased venous return. But just the opposite happens! For example, the heart of a healthy subject doing physical work on a bicycle ergometer can be monitored on an x-ray screen; such experiments show a clear *reduction* in the end-diastolic and end-systolic size of the heart shadow during exercise. This adaptation occurs under the influence of the *sympathetic nervous system*, and results from an increase in the contractile force of the myocardium that is independent of the degree of prestretching. We have encountered this *positive inotropic action* of the sympathetic system in an earlier discussion (p. 449).

Enhanced contractility (positive inotropic action) reflected in the work diagram. The adaptation of the heart to physical exertion just described appears in the work diagram of the left ventricle (Fig. 19-33) as an upward shift of the curve of isovolumetric maxima, with a corresponding increase in slope of the afterloaded-contraction line. Study of Fig. 19-33 reveals that this rearrangement enables the ventricle *either to overcome a* **higher pressure** *or to eject a* **larger stroke volume, without increase in the end-diastolic volume.** The increase in stroke volume leaves a *smaller systolic reserve volume,* so that if venous return does not increase, the end-diastolic volume must be less – which explains the observed reduction in size of the heart. But even when venous return increases simultaneously, the rise in heart rate caused by sympathetic activity (positive *chronotropic* action) increases the amount of blood propelled through the system and thus prevents excessive filling.

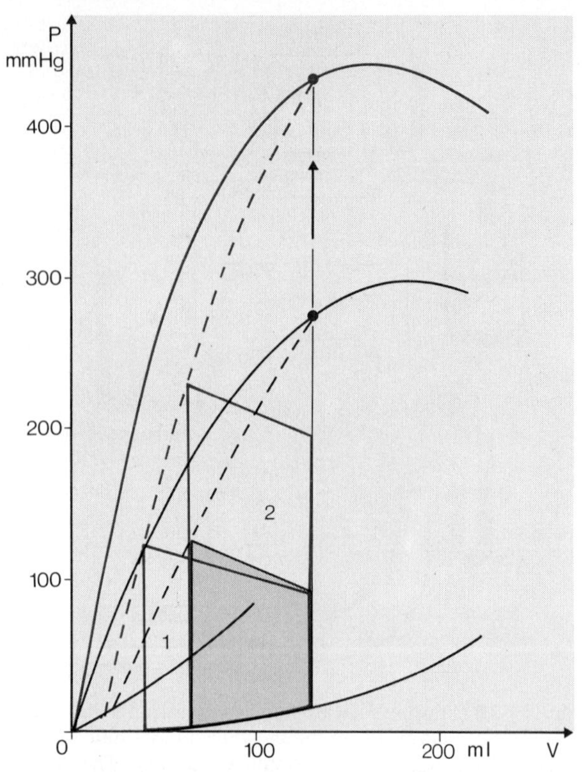

Fig. 19-33. Effect of increased contractility (positive inotropic action) on the work done by the left ventricle. Under sympathetic influence the curve of isovolumetric maxima is shifted to greater pressure (arrow). The slope of the associated am curve is thus increased. Now, although its end-diastolic volume remains the same, the ventricle is able either to eject a larger stroke volume (1) or to eject the same stroke volume against a higher pressure (2). When the stroke volume increases, the end-diastolic volume decreases – that is, the heart becomes smaller during systole

Cardiac reserve. Under the influence of the sympathetic system, then, the heart can increase its output even before the venous return begins to increase. The further possibility, as yet untapped, of increasing output by enlarging end-diastolic volume remains available. The *cardiac reserve* – the ability of the heart to meet unusual demands – thus appears in a new light. In the earlier view the reserve was thought to depend on the extent to which the heart can increase its end-diastolic volume in conditions of exertion compared with that at rest. By contrast, under the positive inotropic influence of the sympathetic system the reserve is limited by the size of the *end-diastolic volume at rest.* The hearts of trained athletes, for example, are conspicuously large at rest, and in some cases can hold 3 to 4 times the normal stroke volume – as opposed to 2 stroke volumes in an untrained person. The athletic heart (cf. Fig. 19-34), accordingly, has a large reserve. In the old view its reserve would have had to be considered very small.

Influence of heart rate on cardiac dynamics. One of the most conspicuous differences between the isolated heart and the heart in situ is that the rate of beating of the latter varies. The *increase in heart rate* caused by sympathetic activity in fact is the most important mechanism for *increasing the cardiac output* under load. An increase in heart rate not only raises the number of beats per unit time but also changes the temporal relations between systole and diastole in a characteristic way. An example is given by the following table:

Beats per min.	Duration of systole(s)	Duration of diastole(s)	Net working time(s/min)
70	0.28	0.58	19.6
150	0.25	0.15	37.5

As can be seen in this example, **shortening of the period** of the cardiac cycle primarily affects the **diastolic phase.** This means that the **net working time** of the ventricles (the sum of all the systole durations in a minute) increases considerably at higher heart rates, and the recovery pauses decrease correspondingly. Adequate *filling of the ventricles* despite even very brief diastole is guaranteed by the facts that most of the inflow occurs at the beginning of diastole, and that sympathetic activity causes a distinct increase in the rate of relaxation (cf. p. 449 and Fig. 19-10C). The sympathetic system also causes the atria to contract more strongly, which accelerates filling of the ventricles. Therefore when the heart rate rises under sympathetic influence, up to a frequency of ca. 150/min there is usually no critical diminution of ventricular filling.

Role of the Frank-Starling mechanism in the intact heart. The dominant influence of the sympathetic system in adjusting cardiac output does not exclude the possibility that under some conditions the heart is governed by other factors. For example, the capacity of the heart to regulate its activity by end-diastolic volume in the sense of the *Frank-Starling mechanism* is brought into play when *changes in filling* occur *without a general increase in activity*. This applies in particular to the *coordination of the output of the two ventricles.* Because the ventricles beat at the same rate, the outputs of the two can be matched only by adjustment of stroke volume. Other examples include changes in the position of the body which affect venous return (greater stroke volume when reclining than when standing), acute increase in the volume of the circulating blood (transfusion), and increase in the resistance to outflow. Moreover, when the sympathetic system is pharmacologically inactivated by β-sympatholytics the autoregulatory mechanisms continue to operate and their effect becomes more important.

Measures of contractility (maximal rate of pressure increase, ejection fraction). The positive inotropic action of the sympathetic system enables the heart, without increased diastolic filling, to eject a larger stroke volume or to eject the stroke volume against a higher pressure. A similar effect on cardiac dynamics can be obtained by raising the extracellular *Ca^{2+} concentration,* by administering *cardiac glycosides,* and as a direct consequence of *increasing heart rate.* A common feature of all these effects is that they enhance cardiac performance independently of the degree of stretching of the myocardium – in other words, they increase its **contractility.** There is no increase in contractility *(positive inotropy)* when the stroke volume or the peak systolic pressure rise entirely as a result of greater diastolic filling, as in the Frank-Starling mechanism.
Changes in myocardial contractility can be detected by examination of the maxima curves in the pressure-volume diagram (Fig. 19-33), as discussed above. But the shape of these curves can be determined only under experimental conditions involving surgery. To obtain data for an analysis of contractility of the heart in situ, especially the human heart, one must draw on other criteria – for example, the **maximal rate of pressure increase (dP/dt max)** in the *isovolumetric contraction period,* which can be measured with cardiac catheters (norms for the human are 1,500–2,000 mm Hg/s, or 200–333kPa/s).

The **theoretical justification** for the use of this parameter as a measure of contractility is ultimately based on the finding that influences which increase contractility for a given degree of prestretch of the myocardium enhance not only the maximal isometric force, but also the **maximal possible rate of shortening** (V_{max}) of the contractile element under isotonic conditions. Here V_{max}, by definition, refers to the limiting case of afterloaded contraction, in which the load approaches 0 (cf. p. 469). An increased rate of shortening of the contractile elements would naturally stretch the series elastic elements more rapidly and thus increase the rate of the isovolumetric rise in pressure – hence the choice of this parameter to measure contractility [8, 10]. The measure of contractility of the heart during the *ejection period* is the ratio of stroke volume to end-diastolic volume, the **ejection**

fraction (p. 463). It gives the proportion of the blood in the heart that is expelled during systole: norms for a person at rest range from 0.5 to 0.7 (i.e., 50–70%). The ejection fraction is usually measured by echocardiography (p. 467).

Adaptation of the Heart to Prolonged Exertion

Hypertrophy. All the adaptive processes considered so far have enabled rapid adjustment of the heart's activity to acute changes in the demands upon it. If the demand for increased effort is repeated or continuous, structural changes occur [18]; the heart enlarges. An example of such *hypertrophy* is the large heart of the trained athlete, mentioned above (p. 473). Typically, enlargement of the heart is greatest (a mass of up to 500 g, the mass of a normal heart being 300 g) in athletes who specialize in endurance sports (long-distance runners, bicycle racers and the like; Fig. 19-34). As hypertrophy develops in a chronically loaded heart, the number of myocardial cells at first remains constant, while their length and thickness uniformly increase (Fig. 19-34, bottom). During this process the cavities within the heart must necessarily increase in volume. According to Laplace's law (p. 464), the result is that a greater wall tension is required to produce a given pressure. But because the muscle mass has grown, the force per cross-sectional unit area of muscle is still essentially the same. That is, the athletic heart contains a large volume of blood but does not pay for this advantage, as the acutely stretched heart does, with an unfavorable ratio for the conversion of muscle tension to pressure. When an athlete's training is terminated, the hypertrophy disappears within a few weeks.
Once the mass of the hypertrophied heart reaches the critical level, ca. 500 g, both size and number of the fibers increase. This condition is called **hyperplasia.**

Pathological states. When only parts of the heart are subjected to an increased chronic load, the hypertrophy is limited to the affected region. In general, this occurs only in pathological conditions. Here two forms of adaptation can be distinguished. When increased **pressure** alone is required, the initial hypertrophy is not accompanied by appreciable increase in cavity volume (for example, in hypertrophy of the left ventricle due to aortic stenosis). But if the extra work is required to propel an increased **volume**, hypertrophy and cavity enlargement occur together (for example, hypertrophy and dilation of the left ventricle due to aortic valve insufficiency). The degree to which the heart can compensate for such defects by changes in myocardial structure, however, is limited. As myocardial fiber radius increases, so do the diffusion paths between the capillaries and the interior of the fibers (Fig. 19-34), which threatens an inadequate O_2 supply. Hence when severe pathological states persist for some time they may eventually result in heart failure (myocardial insufficiency).

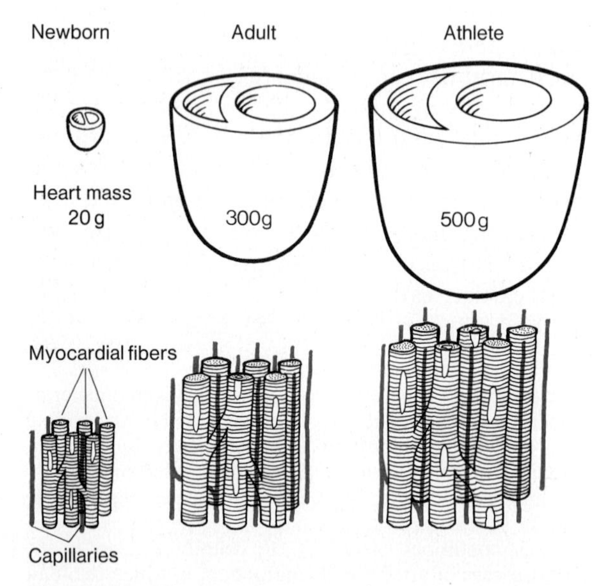

Fig. 19-34. Diagram for comparison of natural heart growth and the further development of an athletic heart. The heart enlarges because the individual myocardial cells increase in thickness and length. In the adult there is about one capillary per muscle cell; in the newborn the relative capillary density is lower. From LINZBACH, J.: Klin. Wschr. 1951, 621

19.6 Energetics of the Heartbeat

In the preceding sections the *work* performed by the heart has been treated in various contexts. Now we turn to certain quantitative aspects of the subject, and consider more closely those processes that serve to provide energy to the heart [19]. First let us look at the debit side of the energy balance sheet.

Cardiac Work and Power

Physical forms of work during the heartbeat. Work is defined as the product of force and distance; the unit of work is the N·m (Newton-meter = joule). This formula applies, for example, to the work done by a skeletal muscle when it shortens and lifts a weight for a certain distance (work = weight·distance). Cardiac muscle also, in the last analysis, does its work by shortening of the fibers and development of force. But in this case no weight is lifted; rather, a certain volume of blood (V) is displaced against a resistance by the development of pressure (P). The **pressure-volume work** thus performed is computed as the product P·V. To the pressure-volume work is added the so-called **acceleration work** expended to bring the inert mass (m) of the blood to a relatively high velocity (v). This is computed from the formula for kinetic energy ($\frac{1}{2}m \cdot v^2$).

Calculation of cardiac work. Because the individual factors that determine cardiac work change continually during the work phase of the cardiac cycle, the time-dependent products P·V and $\frac{1}{2}m \cdot v^2$ ought to be integrated over the duration of the ejection period. Here, however, we shall be content with a simplification that permits satisfactory approximation, taking:
for **P**, the *systolic mean pressure* at the outlet from the ventricle (here 1 mm Hg corresponds to 133 N/m^2 (= 133Pa));
for **V**, the *stroke volume* (in m^3)
for **m**, the *mass of the accelerated blood* (stroke volume, in kg);
for **v**, the *mean ejection velocity* (in m/s).
The values of these for a single systole are as follows.

Pressure-volume work: P·V

Left ventricle		
P = 100 mm Hg	$\hat{=}$ 100 · 133 N/m^2	P · V = 0.931 N · m
V = 70 ml	$\hat{=}$ 70 · 10^{-6} m^3	
Right ventricle		
P = 15 mm Hg	$\hat{=}$ 15 · 133 N/m^2	P · V = 0.140 N · m
V = 70 ml	$\hat{=}$ 70 · 10^{-6} m^3	

Acceleration work: $\frac{1}{2}m \cdot v^2$

Left ventricle	m = 70 g $\hat{=}$ 70 · 10^{-3} kg v = 0.5 m/s	$\frac{1}{2}m \cdot v^2 = 0.009$ N · m
Right ventricle		$\frac{1}{2}m \cdot v^2 = 0.009$ N · m

Total work W = 1.089 N·m

The dimension N·m for acceleration work results naturally from kg·$m^2 \cdot s^{-2}$ (see Appendix). In the older literature cardiac work is usually expressed in kilogram-force-meter (kgf·m) rather than N · m = 0.102kgf · m.
The acceleration work performed by the left ventricle is much less than its pressure-volume work, only about 1%. The work performed by the whole heart per systole is determined chiefly by the size of the stroke volume and the level of aortic pressure. It is of the *order of magnitude of 1 N · m (= 0.1 kgf · m).*

The **proportion of acceleration work** in the total cardiac work can increase considerably when greater volumes are ejected, so that the velocity of blood flow increases. A decrease in the elastic extensibility of the aorta in old age has the effect of increasing the acceleration work of the heart, for the greater rigidity of the "compression chamber" (cf. Fig. 19–31) severely reduces the rate of blood flow in the aorta during diastole. Then the left ventricle during systole must accelerate not just the stroke volume, but a considerably greater amount of blood. Under such conditions the acceleration work can almost equal the pressure-volume work.

Cardiac power and power-to-weight ratio. Power is work per unit time. If we assume about one systole per second, *cardiac power* is of the order of 1 W (= N · m/s) or 0.1 kgf·m/s. A useful figure of merit for engines in general is the *power-to-weight ratio;* for the heart, given a weight of ca. 3 N, this works out to 0.3 W/N. This is a far poorer performance than is achieved by most engines (the motor of a car, for example, puts out 15–25 W/N). During muscular work, however, cardiac power can be considerably greater, so that the power-to-weight ratio approaches that of mechanical pumps. In any case, this calculation shows that it must be possible to construct artificial pumps that could, under appropriate conditions, replace a living heart and weigh less.

Oxygen and Nutrient Consumption

The energy the heart requires for its mechanical work comes primarily from the oxidative decomposition of nutrients. In this regard cardiac and skeletal muscle differ fundamentally, for the latter can obtain a large part of the energy needed to meet short-term demands by anaerobic processes: the "oxygen debt" that is built up can be repaid later. The dependence of the heart on oxidative processes is manifest in the large numbers of mitochondria in the myocardial cells; these organelles are the site of the enzymes that catalyze oxidation in the cell.

O_2 consumption and efficiency. The oxygen consumption of a heart in situ is ordinarily found by measuring the difference in O_2 content of the arterial and coronary venous blood (avD_{O_2}) and multiplying this by the rate of blood flow through the coronary vessels. When the body is at rest the cardiac oxygen consumption so determined is of the order of 0.08–0.1 ml·$g^{-1} \cdot min^{-1}$. A heart with a mass of 300 g thus consumes 24–30 ml O_2/min. This is about 10% of the total resting O_2 consumption of an adult – though the

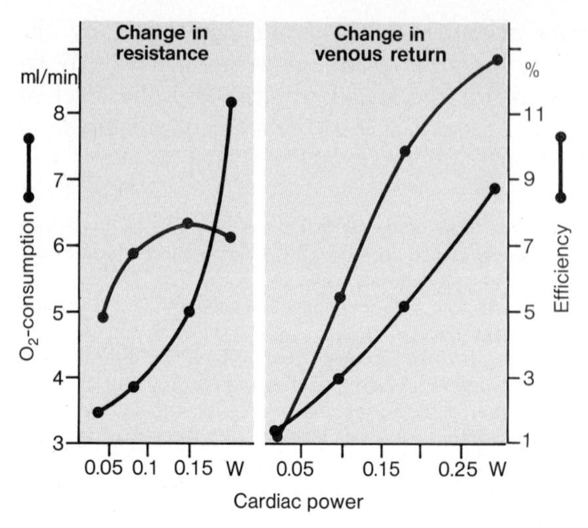

Fig 19-35. Dependence of oxygen consumption and efficiency of the dog heart on cardiac power, as resistance and venous return are varied. From results obtained with heart-lung preparations by GOLLWITZER-MEIER and KROETZ: Klin. Wschr. *18*, 869 (1939)

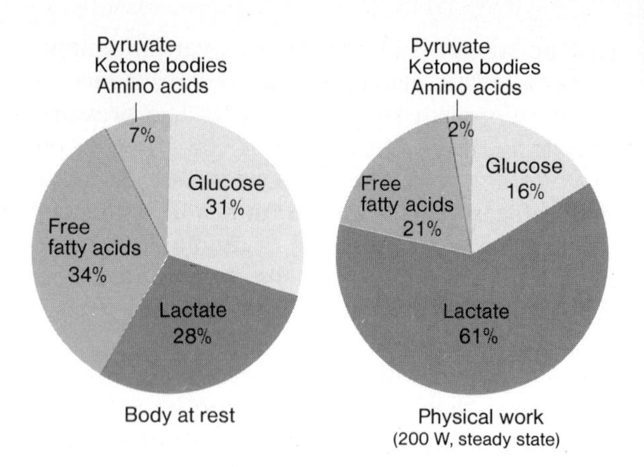

Fig. 19-36. Relative amounts of various substrates in oxidative metabolism of the human heart, with the body at rest and doing hard work. Substrate uptake is expressed as the percentage of total cardiac oxygen consumption that involves the substrate concerned (O_2-extraction quotient). From KEUL et al.: Pflügers Arch. ges. Physiol. *282*, 1 (1965)

weight of the heart is barely 0.5% of the total body weight. When the body is performing hard work the O_2 consumption of the heart can rise to 4 times the resting level. One would expect the O_2 consumption of the heart to be determined basically by its per-systole contribution to the work of the body as a whole. But this is not the case; for a given amount of cardiac work the heart consumes considerably more oxygen when it is working against high pressure than when it is ejecting a large volume against a correspondingly low pressure. The **efficiency** of the heart – that is, the fraction of the total energy expenditure that is converted to mechanical work – is therefore less when **pressure loading** predominates than when **volume loading** predominates (Fig. 19–35). The efficiency of a fully sufficient heart depends on the prevailing conditions, and lies in the range 15–40%.

In cases of *coronary insufficiency,* when the O_2 consumption of the heart tends to exceed the O_2 supplied by the blood, an attempt is made to reduce the resistance to flow in the systemic circulation so as to lower arterial pressure and thus lessen cardiac oxygen consumption. The beneficial action of nitroglycerine in attacks of angina pectoris is an example of such an effect.

Factors that determine O_2 consumption. Recent studies indicate that the per-systole O_2 consumption of the heart depends primarily on the myocardial *fiber tension,* and increases with the duration of contraction. The customary reference is the **tension-time index,** the product of mean myocardial fiber tension and systole duration. When the size of the ventricles is constant (Laplace's law, p. 464), the mean systolic aortic pressure can be used instead of fiber tension. Changes in **heart rate** affect O_2 consumption to about the same extent as they change the **net working time** (the product of systole duration and heart rate). As a result, O_2 consumption rises and falls about in proportion to the square root of heart rate. Furthermore, a small fraction (ca. $0.015\,ml\,g^{-1}\cdot min^{-1}$ of the O_2 consumption of the active heart must be maintained when the heart is quiescent to prevent irreversible changes in the structure of the organ (the **basal consumption**).

Nutrient consumption. The kinds and quantities of substances used by the heart to obtain energy can be determined by the same principle as was applied to the measurement of O_2 consumption. That is, the concentration difference between arterial and coronary venous blood is multiplied by the coronary flow rate. Such experiments have shown that the heart – as compared, for example, with skeletal muscle – is a sort of "omnivore" (Fig. 19-36).

An especially noteworthy feature is the large proportion of **free fatty acids** in the substrate, as is the fact that cardiac muscle, unlike skeletal muscle, can metabolize **lactic acid** (lactate). Because during hard muscular work the anaerobic glycolysis within the muscles releases lactic acid into the bloodstream, the heart is automatically provided with a certain amount of supplementary fuel to support the additional work demanded. In breaking down lactic acid the heart does not

only obtain energy; at the same time, it contributes toward stabilization of the pH of the blood.
The properties of the different substrates consumed are primarily determined by supply – that is, by their **arterial concentration.** Because the heart is so remarkably adaptable, using whatever happens to be available, the chief danger of coronary insufficiency lies not in a substrate shortage but in oxygen deficiency.

Energy-rich phosphates. Breakdown of the various substrates results in the formation of **ATP,** the direct source of energy for the contraction process. The ATP content of cardiac muscle is 4–6 μmol/g. This is a small amount in comparison with that required for the work of contraction; the active myocardium *recycles it several times within seconds* – that is, splits it to form ADP and inorganic phosphate and then resynthesizes ATP. Another phosphate found in the myocardium in about the same amount as ATP is **phosphocreatine** (7–8 μmol/g). This is a particularly sensitive indicator of the adequacy of the substrate and of the oxygen supply to the heart, for the metabolic resynthesis of split ATP initially relies on the breakdown of phosphocreatine.

The Myocardial Blood Supply

The coronary vessels, which supply the heart, are part of the systemic circulation (cf. Fig. 19-1), but they exhibit special features closely related to the way the heart operates. Therefore it seems appropriate to treat this part of the circulatory system here. In the human heart there are as a rule two coronary arteries, both arising from the base of the aorta. The right coronary artery supplies most of the right ventricle and various parts of the septum and of the posterior wall of the left ventricle; the rest of the heart is supplied by the left coronary artery. Venous drainage is mainly through the coronary sinus; only a few percent returns by way of the anterior cardiac veins and the Thebesian veins.

Flow rate through the myocardium. In experiments on animals, blood flow through the heart can be determined directly by electromagnetic flow-meters. With humans one must fall back on indirect methods; some of these involve determination of the uptake or dilution in the heart of nonphysiological gases (NO_2, argon, xenon), the tissue solubility of which is known. Such measurements have shown that flow through the heart of a resting human amounts to ca. 0.8–0.9 ml $g^{-1} \cdot min^{-1}$. The coronary circulation accounts for about 5% of the cardiac output. During muscular work circulation through the heart can rise to 4 times the resting level (cf. Table 19-2). The increase in the heart's O_2 consumption during hard work is of the same order of magnitude (cf. p. 476).

Variation in blood flow during the cardiac cycle. The coronary circulation, in contrast to that through other organs, exhibits marked fluctuations of flow rate in the rhythm of systole and diastole. The rhythmic pulsations in *aortic pressure* are partially responsible for these phasic fluctuations; the other main contributing factor is changes in the *interstitial myocardial pressure.* The latter acts to compress the blood vessels in the middle and inner parts of the heart wall. As Fig. 19-37 shows, the result is complete interruption of flow into the *left* coronary artery at the beginning of systole. Not until diastole, when the intramural pressure falls, is there a high rate of influx. In the branching region of the *right*

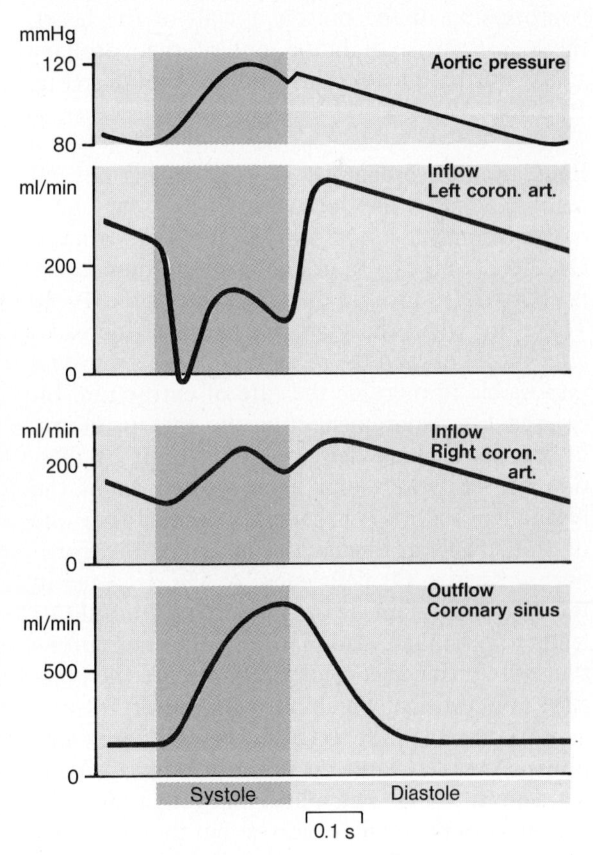

Fig. 19-37. Variations in coronary blood flow in relation to systole, diastole and aortic pressure

Table 19-2

(A) Physiological pressures (mm Hg) in the heart and the large arteries of a resting adult human

	Highest systolic pressure	End-diastolic pressure	Mean pressure
Right atrium	–	–	5
Right ventricle	25	5	
Pulmonary artery	25	10	
Left atrium	–	–	10
Left ventricle	120	10	
Aorta	120	70	

(B) Coronary blood flow and artery-coronary vein O_2 difference (avD_{O_2}) of the human heart at rest and under work load

	Rest	Work
Coronary blood flow ($ml \cdot g^{-1} \cdot min^{-1}$)	0.8	3.2
avD_{O_2} (ml/dl blood)	14	16
Coronary venous O_2 content (ml/dl blood)	6	4

coronary artery the intramural pressure is lower, so that influx basically follows the fluctuations in aortic pressure. During systole, because of the compression of the muscular wall of the heart, there is a surge of blood out of the coronary sinus; during diastole this outflow subsides (Fig. 19-37).

Regulation of coronary flow. Even during normal resting activity the heart withdraws far more oxygen from the blood than do the other organs. Of the 20 ml/dl O_2 in the arterial blood, the heart extracts around 14 ml/dl (cf. Table 19-2). Therefore when the load on the heart increases and more oxygen is required, it is essentially impossible to increase the rate of extraction. **Increased O_2 requirement** must be met primarily by **increased blood flow,** brought about by dilation of the vessels and hence reduction of the resistance to flow. It is generally agreed that one of the *strongest stimuli to dilation* of the coronary vessels is **O_2 deficiency.** A 5% decrease in the oxygen content of the blood (ca. 1 ml/dl O_2) leads to coronary vasodilation. Other conditions that may produce coronary dilation are the presence of **adenosine,** which plays an important role as a product of the breakdown of energy-rich phosphates [22], and an increased extracellular **K^+ concentration.** The additional direct effect of the **autonomic cardiac nerves** on the coronary vessels is difficult to evaluate because of their other simultaneous influences on cardiac activity. Recent studies, however, indicate that the sympathetic fibers act directly to constrict the vessels, and the parasympathetic fibers to dilate them.

Factors of endothelial origin such as nitric oxide (NO) also tend to cause dilation of the coronary vessels. Their release from the endothelium is stimulated by an increased rate of blood flow (shear forces) and by various substances (acetylcholine, histamine, serotonin, noradrenalin, and others), the direct effects of which are thereby modified [15].
The combination of all these influences provides a regulatory system with a large safety factor. When one or another individual component fails, the regulation is hardly affected.

Adequacy of coronary supply; coronary reserve. The heart is adequately supplied with blood when the amount of oxygen available corresponds to the amount consumed. The ratio of the two is taken as a criterion for the adequacy of coronary flow. A ratio of less than 1.2 indicates a critical restriction of the oxygen supply to the heart *(coronary insufficiency)*. The degree to which the supply can be adjusted as conditions change is also of interest; this is the **coronary reserve,** expressed as the difference between the maximal available O_2 and the actual O_2 consumption, divided by the actual consumption. The reserve of a fully adaptable coronary system is 4 to 5 times as great as the amount required by the heart under resting conditions.

Anoxia and resuscitation. Because cardiac metabolism relies so heavily on oxidative reactions to provide energy, it is understandable that a sudden interruption of circulation *(ischemia)* results in extensive loss of function within a few minutes. In an experiment in which the heart is deprived of oxygen while coronary perfusion is maintained *(anoxia)*, the changes produced are practically identical; as the contractions grow progressively weaker a marked dilation develops, and after about 6–10 minutes the heart stops beating. The severe impairment of the energy-providing system under these conditions is reflected in the dramatic reduction in the amount of *energy-rich phosphates* (phosphocreatine, ATP). The heart is capable of anaerobic glycolysis to a small degree, producing lactic acid. But lactic-acid breakdown in the myocardium comes to a halt during O_2 deficiency, so that the concentration of this substance in the coronary veins builds up to exceed that in the arteries. If anoxia lasts longer than 30 min, the myocardium undergoes irreversible structural changes in addition to the functional impairment, so that resuscitation is impossible. At normal body temperature, then, a 30-min duration of cardiac anoxia is a critical limit called the **resuscitation limit.** The resuscitation limit of the heart can be extended considerably if the metabolic rate is lowered by cooling. Advantage is taken of this possibility in modern heart surgery. When anoxia affects the entire organism, as in cases of suffocation, the possibility of successful resuscitation is limited by the brain, which is more sensitive than the heart and suffers irreversible damage after anoxia lasting only 8–10 minutes.

Cardiac Insufficiency

Cardiac insufficiency *(heart failure)* denotes the situation in which the heart cannot supply the body as a whole with the blood it requires, even though sufficient blood is being delivered to the heart from the veins and the compensatory mechanisms are in operation. This can happen even when the body is at rest **(resting insufficiency),** but it may become noticeable only during physical exertion **(active insufficiency).** The symptoms of **left** ventricular malfunction are pulmonary congestion, with shortness of breath and cyanosis; insufficiency of the **right** heart causes systemic venous congestion with edema and ascites. An inadequate pumping action can result from several conditions not primarily associated with the heart's contractile function (valve defects, pericardial induration, extreme bradycardia etc.).

In a narrower sense, cardiac insufficiency denotes *diminished contractility* **(myocardial insufficiency).** This can result when the heart is chronically overworked due to an increase in either pressure or volume (cf. p. 474). Myocardial insufficiency can also be induced by oxygen deficit (coronary sclerosis, myocardial infarction), inflammation (myocarditis) and certain poisons or overdoses of certain drugs.

The sites at which such influences interfere with the fundamental cellular processes of excitation, excitation-contraction coupling and contraction are extremely varied. It is particularly useful in practice to distinguish two types of myocardial insufficiency, on the basis of metabolism of the energy-rich phosphates, especially phosphocreatine [15]. In the first case, the resynthesis of phosphocreatine is hampered by an inadequate energy supply (oxygen deficiency, metabolic poisons, etc.). The diminished contractility results because *insufficient energy is provided* to the contractile proteins, and is associated with a *reduction in phosphocreatine content*. In the second, enough energy-rich phosphates are available but they are not properly utilized because of *inadequate activation* of the excitation-contraction coupling (overdose of Ca^{2+} antagonists, poisoning with local anesthetics, barbiturates, etc.). This form of insufficiency is characterized by *high tissue content of phosphocreatine*. Agents that stimulate excitation-contraction coupling (catecholamines, cardiac glycosides) can restore nearly normal contractility in cases of utilization difficulty. When the energy supply is inadequate, by contrast, such treatment tends to make matters worse; here treatment must be designed to save energy by lightening the work load of the heart.

19.7 References

Textbooks and Handbooks

1. BERNE, R.M., SPERELAKIS, N., GEIGER, S.R. (Eds.): Handbook of Physiology. Section 2: The Cardiovascular System. Vol. I The Heart. Bethesda: Amer. Physiol. Soc. (1979)
2. CARMELIET, E., VEREECKE, J.: Electrogenesis of the action potential and automaticity. In: BERNE et al. (1)
3. CRANEFIELD, P.F.: The Conduction of the Cardiac Impulse. Mount Kisco-New York: Futura Publishing Company (1979)
4. DELIUS, W., GERLACH, E., GROBECKER, H., KÜBLER, W. (Eds.): Catecholamines and the Heart. Berlin Heidelberg New York: Springer (1981)
5. FLECKENSTEIN, A.: Calcium Antagonism in Heart and Smooth Muscle – Experimental Facts and Therapeutic Prospects. New York-Chichester-Brisbane-Toronto-Singapure: Wiley-Interscience Publ. (1983)
6. FOZZARD, H.A., HABER, E., JENNINGS, R.B., KATZ, A.M., MORGAN, H.E. (Eds.): The Heart and Cardiovascular System. New York: Raven Press (1986)
7. HILLE, B.: Ionic Channels of Excitable Membranes: Sunderland Mass.: Sinauer (1984)
8. LANGER, G.A., BRADY, A.J. (Eds.): The Mammalian Myocardium. New York: Wiley (1974)
9. NOBLE, D.: The Initiation of the Heartbeat. Oxford: Clarendon Press (1979)
10. PORTER, R., FITZSIMONS, D.W. (Eds.): The Phhysiological Basis of Starling's Law of the Heart. Ciba Foundation Symposium. Amsterdam-New York: Associated Scientific Publishers (1974)
11. RÜEGG, J.C.: Calcium in Muscle Activation. Berlin-Heidelberg-New York: Springer 1986
12. RUPP, H. (Ed.): Regulation of Heart Function – Basic Concepts and Clinical Applications. New York: Thieme Inc. (1986)

Original Papers and Reviews

13. ALLESSIE, M.A., BONKE, F., SCHOPMAN, F.J.G.: Circus movement in rabbit atrial muscle as a mechanism of tachycardia. Circ. Res. *33*, 54 (1973)
14. ANTONI, H., JACOB, R., KAUFMANN, R.: Mechanical response of the frog's and mammalian myocardium to modifications of the action potential duration by constant pulses. Pflügers Arch. *306*, 33 (1969)
15. BASSENGE, E., BUSSE, R.: Endothelial modulation of coronary tone. Progress in Cardiovasc. Diseases, *30*, 349 (1981)
16. DI FRANCESCO, D.: A new interpretation of the pacemaker current in calf Purkinje fibres. J. Physiol. *374*, 359 (1981)
17. IRISAWA, H., NAKAYAMA, T., NOMA, A.: Membrane currents of single pacemaker cells from rabbit S-A and A-V nodes. In: D. NOBLE and D. Powell (Edit.): Electrophysiology of Single Cardiac Cells. London: Academic Press (1987)
18. JACOB, R., KISSLING, G., EBRECHT, G., HOLUBARSCH, C., MEDUGORAC, I., RUPP, H.: Adaptive and pathological alterations in experimental cardiac hypertrophy. Advan. Myocardiol. *4*, 55 (1983)
19. JACOB, R., JUST, H.J., HOLUBARSCH, C. (Eds.): Cardiac Energetics – Basic Mechanisms and Clinical Implications. Basic Res. Cardiol. 82 (Suppl. 2) (1987)
20. NOBLE, D.: The surprising heart: A review of recent progress in cardiac electrophysiology. J. Physiol. (Lond.) *353*, 1 (1984)
21. REUTER, H.: Exchange of calcium ions in the mammalian myocardium. Mechanisms and physiological significance. Circ. Res. *34*, 599 (1974)
22. SCHRADER, J.: Sites of action and production of adenosine in the heart. In: BURNSTOCK, G.: Purinergic Receptors. London: Chapmann & Hall, pp. 120 (1981)
23. TRAUTWEIN, W.: Membrane currents in cardiac muscle fibres. Physiol. Rev *53*, 793 (1973)
24. WEIDMANN, S.: The diffusion of radiopotassium across intercalated discs of mammalian cardiac muscle. J. Physiol. *187*, 323 (1966)

20 Functions of the Vascular System

E. WITZLEB

General structure and function of the vascular system. The **vessels** – arteries, capillaries and veins – together with the **heart** constitute the **cardiovascular system.** This is a *transport system,* within which the medium to be transported (blood) is propelled by a pump (the heart) in a closed circuit through elastic tubes (vessels).

This continual circulation of fluid throughout the body serves, most importantly, as a means of delivery and removal of substances; it provides all the living cells of the organism with the *materials required* for their normal functions (e.g., O_2 and nutrients), and it carries away the *products* of cell metabolism (CO_2 and other metabolites). These substances do not enter and leave the bloodstream directly; their passage is *indirect,* by way of the interstitial (extracellular) fluid. The many other functions of the circulatory system, discussed elsewhere in this book, are summarized on p. 402.

The human **circulatory system** consists of two main sections arranged one after the other (in series):

1. the *systemic circulation,* with the left ventricle as the pump, and
2. the *pulmonary circulation,* with the right ventricle as the pump.

Because of this serial arrangement the amounts ejected by the two ventricles must always (apart from short-term imbalance) be *exactly matched* (Fig. 20-1).

In the **systemic circulation** the blood is propelled during systole from the left ventricle into the aorta, which gives rise to numerous *arteries.* The stream of blood is thus divided among many regional vascular beds *in parallel,* each of which supplies a **particular organ** (heart, brain, liver, kidney, musculature, skin, etc.). Each artery bifurcates repeatedly, so that the total number of vessels increases while the individual vessels become progressively smaller in diameter. The smallest arteries (arterioles) branch to form the *capillary bed,* a very dense network of narrow vessels with extremely thin walls; the total surface area of the capillaries is enormous (ca. 1,000 m^2 in the entire body). The capillaries are the part of the circulatory system in which the specific functions of the blood circulation occur – the many and varied exchanges, in both directions, between the blood and the cells in the surrounding tissue. The capillaries merge to

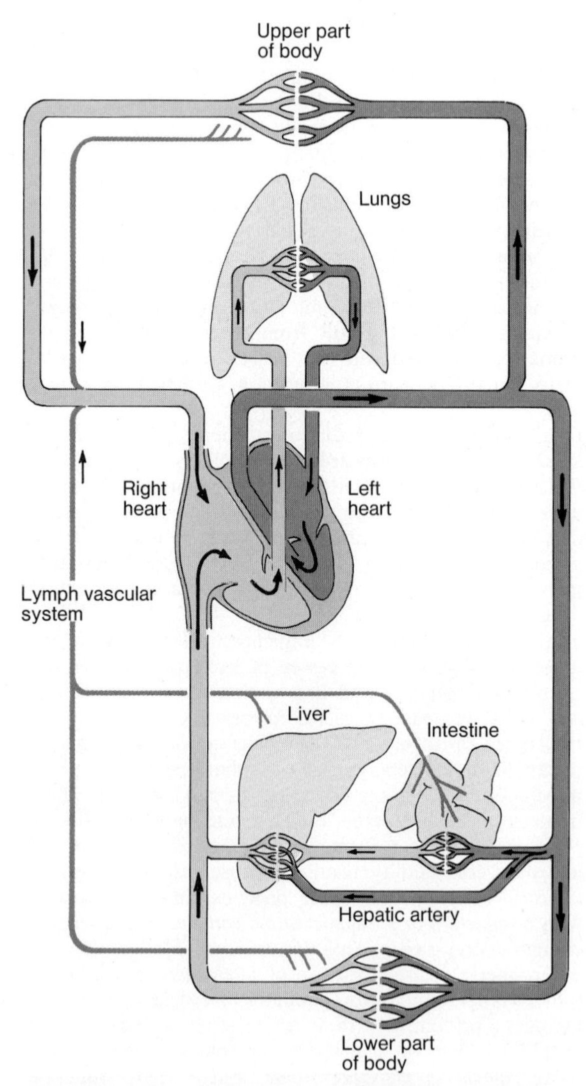

Fig. 20-1. Schematic diagram of the cardiovascular system. The vessels containing O_2-saturated blood are *dark red,* and those with partially unsaturated blood are *light red.* The systemic and pulmonary circulation together form a closed circuit. The lymphatic system *(grey)* is a supplementary transport system.

form *venules,* which in turn join to form the *veins.* As this fusion progresses, there is a steady decrease in number and increase in diameter of the vessels, so that ultimately only two, the superior and inferior vena cava, remain to pass the blood into the right atrium. One of the vascular subcircuits, the splanchnic circulation, departs somewhat from this general pattern; from the mesenteric and splenic capillary beds, in the intestine and spleen respectively, the blood passes through a second capillary bed in the liver before returning to the heart (Fig. 20-1). This type of subcircuit is called a portal circulation. In general, however, the **arteries distribute** and the **veins collect** the blood.

In the **pulmonary circulation** the blood passes from the right ventricle through the *pulmonary trunk* into the vascular system of the lungs, which has in principle the same arrangement as the systemic circulation. Four large pulmonary veins carry the blood to the left atrium; it then enters the left ventricle, completing the circuit.

There is a fundamental **functional difference** between the pulmonary and systemic circulations, in that the volume of blood propelled by the heart in a given time through the **systemic circulation** must be distributed to *all organ systems* and tissues, which differ in their basic requirements and in addition vary from time to time in the amount of blood they need, depending on their activity level. These variations are monitored and the blood supply regulated by a number of control mechanisms. The **pulmonary circulation,** through which the same total amount of blood passes, represents a relatively constant load, serving essentially only for *gas exchange and heat dissipation.* Therefore a less elaborate system is required to monitor and regulate blood flow through the lungs.

The blood vascular system is supplemented by the **lymph vascular system,** within which the fluid from the **interstitial space** is collected and transported to the blood vessels (Fig. 20-1).

20.1 Fundamentals of Hemodynamics

Blood flow is brought about by pressure differences between the individual vascular regions, so that the blood flows from regions of higher pressure to those where the pressure is lower. The *pressure gradient* provides the force that overcomes the resistance to flow. The latter varies in time and space, depending on differences in the *vascular architecture* (e.g., the number, length, diameter and degree of branching of the vessels in a particular region) and the *viscosity* of the blood [2, 4, 5, 15, 19, 20, 33].

The Physics of Blood Flow

Flow, pressure and resistance. To a rough approximation, the factors that determine flow can be summarized in an equation analogous to Ohm's law:

$$\dot{V} = \frac{\Delta P}{R} \qquad (1)$$

That is, the volume flow $\dot{V}$ is equal to the ratio of ΔP, the average pressure difference between the arterial and venous parts (or other parts) of the system, and the resistance R to flow in the region concerned.

The **volume flow** $\dot{V}$, which describes an organ's blood supply, is the amount of blood flowing through a vascular cross section per unit time ($ml \cdot s^{-1}$). It can be calculated from the linear velocity of flow ($\bar{v}$) through the cross section and the cross-sectional area ($A = \pi \cdot r^2$); that is,

$$\dot{V} = \bar{v} \cdot A \qquad (2)$$

According to the **law of continuity of flow,** the volume flow in a system composed of tubes of different diameters (such as the vascular system) is constant in each segment with a given cross-sectional area, regardless of the size of that area (cf. Fig. 20-2); that is, for two segments (a and b) in series,

$$\dot{V} = \bar{v}_a \cdot A_a = \bar{v}_b \cdot A_b \ldots \qquad (3)$$

The consequence is that with equal volume flow in the successive segments, the *linear velocity* of

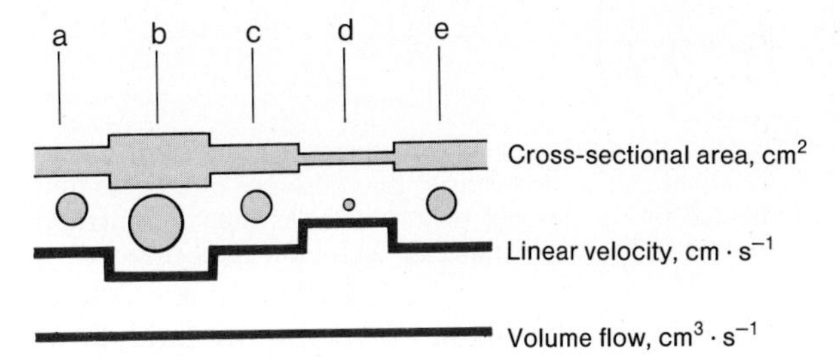

Fig. 20-2. Changes in linear velocity and volume flow in a series of vessels differing in cross-sectional area.

flow in each segment is *inversely proportional* to its cross-sectional area.
The **pressures** in the vascular system, the arterial and venous **blood pressures,** are equivalent to the forces per unit area exerted by the blood on the walls of the vessels. Because of the long history of clinical measurements with mercury manometers, blood pressure is usually expressed in mm Hg, though it is sometimes given in cm H_2O (1 mm Hg ≈ 13.6 mm H_2O ≈ 133 Pa; 10 mm H_2O ≈ 98 Pa. For further conversion factors see p. 797).
The **resistance** R cannot be measured directly, but can be calculated from the *pressure difference* between two points in the vascular system and the *volume flow* by rearrangement of Eq. (1).
Resistance to flow arises from the internal friction between the fluid layers and against the wall of the vessel, which is determined by the dimensions of the vessels, the viscosity of the fluid and the type of flow.

Resistance to flow in systems of tubes. For a system consisting of tubes in *series,* the total resistance (according to KIRCHHOFF's first law) is the sum of all the series resistances; that is,

$$R_{tot} = R_1 + R_2 + \ldots \quad (4)$$

For tubes in *parallel,* such as the vascular beds of the various organs, KIRCHHOFF's second law applies and it is the conductances that add, so that

$$C_{tot} = C_1 + C_2 + \ldots \quad (5)$$

or, because C is the reciprocal of resistance,

$$C_{tot} = \frac{1}{R_1} + \frac{1}{R_2} + \ldots \quad (6)$$

According to Equation (1), then,

$$\dot{V} = \Delta P \cdot C, \text{ or } C = \frac{\dot{V}}{\Delta P} \quad (7)$$

That is, for a given pressure difference the volume flow increases in proportion to the conductance.
Because resistance is the reciprocal of conductance, the total resistance of two tubes in parallel is

$$R_{tot} = \frac{1}{\frac{1}{R_1} + \frac{1}{R_2}} \quad (8)$$

That is, the *total resistance of several tubes of equal diameter in parallel* corresponds to the resistance of a single tube divided by the number of tubes, and is thus considerably smaller than the resistance of each individual tube.

Viscosity of the blood. Whenever a fluid flows over a stationary surface (and hence when it flows through a tube) the layers within it move at different velocities, so that a shear force arises between the layers - the faster layer tends to drag along, and to be held back by, the slower layer. This "internal resistance" is represented by the *viscosity* (η) of the fluid.
η is a temperature-dependent constant for many fluids. According to Newton's viscosity equation, it is given by the ratio of shear force τ (force per unit surface area, in Pa) to the velocity gradient between adjacent layers γ (the shear rate):

$$\eta = \frac{\tau}{\gamma} (\text{Pa} \cdot \text{s}) \quad (9)$$

As will become clear below (Hagen-Poiseuille law), not only the *driving pressure* but also the *radius and length of the vessel* affect the forces required to move layers past one another, or to develop and maintain flow.
Viscosity is often given in *relative units,* the viscosity of water at 20 °C (10^{-3} Pa · s) being taken as 1.0.
Homogeneous (newtonian) fluids (for example, water, electrolyte solutions and plasma) have *constant* viscosity. Blood, being composed of plasma plus corpuscular elements, is a heterogeneous (non-newtonian) fluid; its viscosity varies, depending mainly on the quantity of suspended cells and to a lesser extent on the protein content of the plasma. The viscosity of heterogeneous fluids is also related to the dimensions (radius vs. length) of the conducting tube.
In humans the viscosity of blood is **3–5 relative units,** and that of plasma is **1.9–2.3 relative units** (Fig. 20-3).

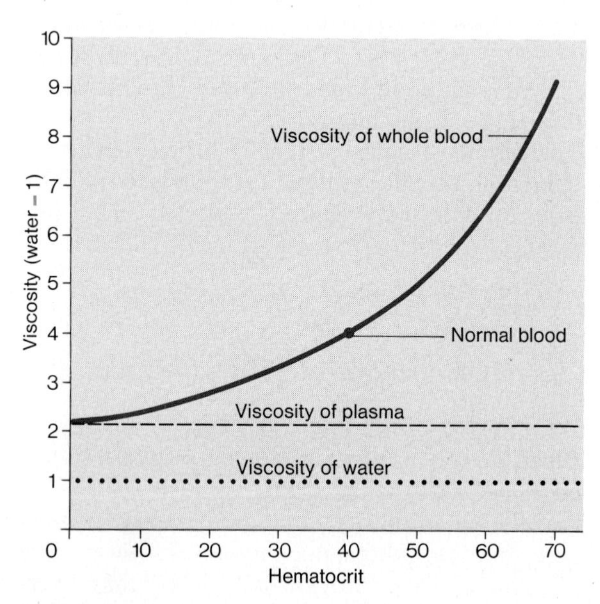

Fig. 20-3. Relative viscosity of the blood as a function of hematocrit

Viscosity in blood vessels. The above values for relative viscosity apply only to blood that is flowing relatively rapidly (with correspondingly high shear stress) and has the normal composition (e.g., a hematocrit of about 40 and a plasma protein concentration of 6.5–8.0 g/dl). Where the velocity of flow (and thus the shear stress) is *low*, viscosity *increases as flow becomes slower*, reaching more than 1,000 relative units at very low flow velocities. Under *physiological conditions* these effects play a role only in the smallest vessels, where the effective viscosity can rise by about tenfold because the shear stress is so small. But under certain *pathological conditions* even greater increase in viscosity can be brought about by a reduced rate of flow. For example, blood flows more slowly in the part of a vessel distal to a constriction (the same effect occurs in the venules, where the cross-sectional area is larger than in the capillaries); moreover, velocity is less when the driving pressure is lowered. In such cases the increased viscosity can reduce the velocity still further, until flow ceases altogether. Lowered flow velocity increases viscosity because of the **reversible agglomeration** of the erythrocytes, which form rouleaux (rows like stacks of coins) or clumps at the wall of the vessel.

This agglomeration is mediated by large protein molecules in the plasma (fibrinogen, α_2-macroglobulin, etc.). Under pathological conditions it can be considerably enhanced, to the extent that greater than normal forces are required to keep the blood flowing. Another factor is that the erythrocytes adjust to high flow velocities by becoming oriented to the current and changing their shape; the low-velocity increase in viscosity is due in part to the absence of these effects [53].

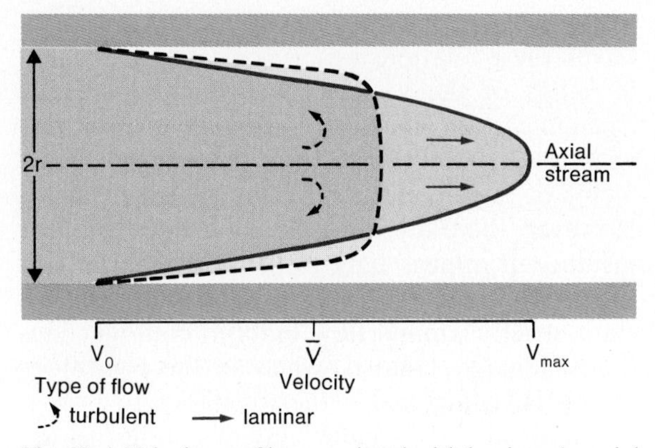

Fig. 20-4. Velocity profiles associated with laminar (coaxial cylindrical) flow *(continuous red line)*. In turbulent flow *(dashed black line)* both axial and mean velocities are lower than in laminar flow.

On the other hand, there is another mechanism which causes the effective viscosity to decrease considerably in tubes with diameters less than 500 μm **(sigma phenomenon** or **Fåhraeus-Lindqvist effect).** Because of this effect, which becomes more pronounced at smaller diameters, the effective viscosity of blood in the capillaries is only 50% of that in the large vessels – that is, it is reduced to about the viscosity of plasma. One reason for the reduction is an alignment of the erythrocytes along the axis of the vessel, so that they advance through the capillary like a "snake" sheathed in plasma. The low-viscosity, cell-free surrounding zone acts as a layer over which the cells slide smoothly, so that the conditions of flow are improved and pressure drops reduced. These effects counteract, at least partially, the tendency for low flow velocity to increase blood viscosity in small vessels as described above.

Types of Flow

Laminar flow. Under physiological conditions flow is *laminar* or layered in nearly all segments of the vascular system. The fluid moves in *coaxial cylindrical layers,* within which motion of all particles is exclusively *parallel* to the axis of the vessel. The individual fluid layers shift past one another like the parts of a telescope tube, with the layer immediately adjacent to the wall of the vessel held still by adhesion, the second layer moving over it, the third over the second, and so on. The resulting **parabolic velocity profile** has maximal velocity at the axis of the vessel (Fig. 20-4).

The smaller the vessel, the more the central "layers" are slowed by viscous interaction with the stationary wall, because they are closer to it; the mean velocity of flow is therefore low. In larger vessels the more centrally situated layers are further from the wall; as the axis of the vessel is approached, the successive fluid cylinders glide more and more rapidly, so that the mean velocity of flow is considerably increased.

A peculiarity of the laminar flow of blood is that the corpuscular elements are forced toward the axis more strongly, the larger they are. The **axial stream** is therefore composed almost entirely of erythrocytes, which move like a fairly *compact cylinder* within a largely cell-free coating of plasma. Their mean velocity of flow is thus greater than that of the plasma.

Turbulent flow. Under certain conditions, laminar flow can give way to *turbulent flow;* the latter is

characterized by eddies in which the fluid particles move not only parallel to the vascular axis but also perpendicular to it. This turbulence increases the internal friction appreciably, and the flow profile becomes flattened (Fig. 20-4). Now volume flow is no longer linearly related to the pressure gradient as in laminar flow, because additional pressure losses are introduced by the eddies. The magnitude of these losses is related to the square of the volume flow, so that as volume flow rises the pressure loss must increase disproportionately.
The presence or absence of turbulent flow depends on a number of factors, the net effects of which are summarized in the dimensionless **Reynolds' number.** Reynolds' number is directly proportional to the diameter of the vessels 2r (in m), the mean velocity of flow $\bar{v}$ (in $m \cdot s^{-1}$), and the density of the fluid ρ (for blood, 1,060 $kg \cdot m^{-3}$), and is inversely proportional to the viscosity η (in $Pa \cdot s$):

$$Re = \frac{2r \cdot \bar{v} \cdot \rho}{\eta} \tag{10}$$

Where Reynolds' number exceeds 400, local vortices can be generated near the walls of branching and constricted arteries or of vessels that are sharply bent; when it is between 2,000 and 2,400 there is a complete transition from laminar to turbulent flow. This so-called **critical value** is far exceeded in the proximal parts of the aorta and pulmonary artery during the ejection period, and there is thus transient turbulence in these places. If the velocity of flow is increased (for example, during muscular exercise) or the blood viscosity reduced (for example, in severe anemia) turbulence can occur in all the large arteries. The noise of this turbulent flow can sometimes be heard even without a stethoscope.

Relations between Volume Flow and Resistance to Flow

As discussed above, laminar flow in tubes with circular cross section can be visualized as a process in which individual layers of the fluid slide past one another like the hollow cylinders that make up a telescope. The analogy can be carried further by applying Newton's law of the internal friction of fluids, to derive relations between the flow velocity (or volume flow) and the viscosity of the fluid, the pressure difference and the dimensions of the tube (length and inside radius).

In steady-state laminar flow the forces exerted by the pressure difference on the two ends of each concentric hollow cylinder must be in equilibrium with the frictional forces acting on the side surfaces. This relation produces the parabolic velocity profile characteristic of laminar flow, in which the mean velocity depends on the square of the radius of the tube. The **volume flow** is thus given by the **Hagen-Poiseuille law (HPL):**

$$\dot{V} = \frac{\pi \cdot r^4}{8 \cdot \eta \cdot l} \Delta P \tag{11}$$

where ΔP is the *pressure difference,* r is the *radius,* η is the *viscosity* of the fluid, l is the *length* of the vessel and the factor 8 arises from *integration of the velocity profile.*
In terms of *Ohm's law,* the **resistance to flow** is then

$$R = \frac{8 \cdot l \cdot \eta}{\pi \cdot r^4} \tag{12}$$

Furthermore, since $\dot{V} = \bar{v} \cdot \pi \cdot r^2$ (Equation 2), the **mean flow velocity** is

$$\bar{v} = \frac{r^2}{8 \cdot \eta \cdot l} \Delta P \tag{13}$$

We see that *volume flow* and *resistance to flow* are directly and inversely proportional, respectively, to the 4th power of the radius. Therefore both of these variables are much more strongly affected by changes in vessel diameter than by changes in length, pressure difference or viscosity. For example, the volume flow in a vessel through which the flow is initially 1 $ml \cdot s^{-1}$ will rise to 16 $ml \cdot s^{-1}$ when the diameter of the vessel is doubled and to 256 $ml \cdot s^{-1}$ when it is quadrupled, while the resistance to flow falls to 1/16 or 1/256, respectively.
Given these relationships, it is clear that *changes in radius* of the vessels constitute the decisive mechanism for effective *regulation of flow rate and pressure,* whether local or large-scale adjustments of the circulatory system are required.
However, there are limitations on the HPL; for instance, it applies only to (i) rigid, unbranched tubes with circular cross sections, (ii) steady-state, strictly laminar flow, and (iii) homogeneous fluids. Ideally – that is, when all the conditions of the HPL are met – the resistance to flow is minimal. In the vascular system conditions are different; for example, the vessels have elastic properties and a complicated, branching architecture, flow is partially discontinuous or tur-

bulent, and blood is an inhomogeneous fluid. Each of these factors increases the resistance to flow by some amount. Therefore flow in the vessels of individual organs or in the circulatory system as a whole cannot be described directly by the HPL. Similarly, Ohm's law applies only to steady-state flow (direct current). A detailed analysis of circulatory hemodynamics requires complicated methods that allow for additional factors, some of them difficult to evaluate [5, 15, 33].

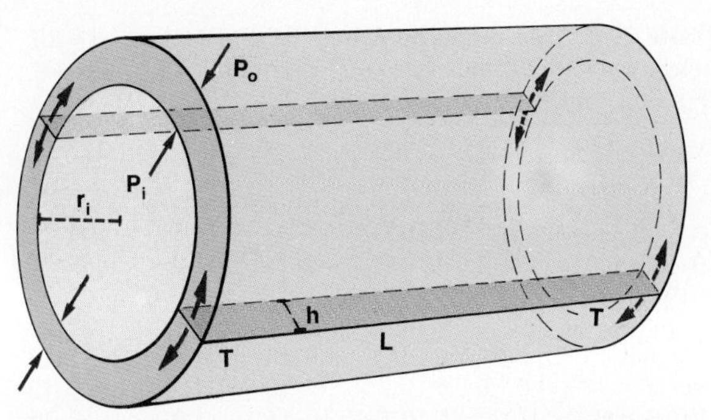

Fig. 20-5. Diagram of the effects of transmural pressure and tangential tension in a cylindrical blood vessel. P_i, intravascular pressure; P_o, pressure outside the vessel; r_i, inside radius; h, wall thickness; T, tangential tension in the vessel wall. If a longitudinal cut (L) were made in the vessel wall the edges of the cut would be driven apart with the force T.

20.2 Properties of the Vessel Walls and Variability of Vessel Diameter

Structure of the Walls

All blood vessels have an **endothelial lining,** adjacent to the lumen, which usually consists of a single layer of flat cells (near the precapillary sphincters and arteriovenous anastomoses it is a multilayered epithelium). The endothelium provides the vessel with a smooth inner surface which, as long as it is intact, *prevents blood clotting.*
In addition to the endothelium, all vessels except the true capillaries comprise varying amounts of (i) **elastic fibers,** (ii) **collagen fibers,** and (iii) **smooth muscle fibers.**
The *elastic fibers,* particularly in the *intima,* form a relatively dense network and can easily be streched to many times their original length. They exert **elastic tension,** which opposes the tendency of the blood pressure to stretch the vessel, without the expenditure of biochemical energy.
In the *media* and *adventitia* the *collagen fibers* form a network that offers a great deal more *resistance to stretch* than do the elastic fibers. They are relatively loosely embedded in the wall of the vessel and occasionally are folded, so that they begin to exert a counterpressure only after the vessel has been distended to some extent.
The spindle-shaped (ca. 4.7 μm in diameter and 20 μm long) *smooth muscle cells* are connected to one another as well as to the elastin and collagen networks. Their chief function is to provide active tension in the vessel wall (**myogenic vascular tone**), and to regulate the size of the lumen as physiological adjustments require. The smooth musculature in the blood vessels is innervated by autonomic nerve fibers.

Transmural Pressure, Vessel Diameter and Wall Tension

Transmural pressure and vessel diameter. The transmural pressure is the *pressure difference* between the *inside* and the *outside* of the vessel wall ($P_t = P_i - P_o$). Because of the elastic properties of the vessels, increases or decreases in transmural pressure cause increases or decreases in stretching and diameter of the vessel.

In most parts of the body the external pressure, that exerted by the surrounding tissue, is not very high, so that the transmural pressure is effectively the same as the intravascular pressure. But under certain conditions the transmural pressure can be considerably altered by local changes in the extramural pressure, the intravascular pressure remaining constant. In this situation, particularly when the easily deformable veins are affected, the resulting cross-sectional changes can affect flow rate and capacity.

Transmural pressure and wall tension. The stretching pressure across the walls of the vessels generates an opposed tangential tension (T) within the walls. T depends not only on the magnitude of the transmural pressure but also on the inside radius (r_i) and the thickness (h) of the vessel wall. The wall tension integrated over the wall thickness, T_h, can be calculated from a modified form of the **Laplace law:**

$$T_h = P_t \cdot \frac{r_i}{h} \, (N \cdot m^{-2}) \tag{14}$$

Figure 20-5 is a diagram of the factors involved here. The transmural pressure acts in such a way that if the vessel were halved by a longitudinal cut, it would push the two hemicylinders apart with the force $F_{pt} = 2 \cdot r_i \cdot L \cdot P_t$. Under normal conditions, this force is balanced out by the restoring force generated by the cell walls, $F_{th} = 2h \cdot L \cdot T_h$. Both the tangential wall tension and the transmural pressure have the dimensions force per unit area and are thus a measure of the tensile stress imposed on the substance of the wall. For a given pressure, this **tensile stress** is **greater,** the **larger** the radius and the **thinner** the wall of the vessel.

Table 20-1. Transmural pressures (P) and tangential wall tensions (T) in various vessels. (From data of BURTON [4], FOLKOW and NEIL [6] and others)

Vessels	r_i [m]	$\frac{r}{h}$	P [k Pa]	T_h [k Pa]
Aorta	$12 \cdot 10^{-3}$	8	13.3	106
Arteries	$0.5–3 \cdot 10^{-3}$	3–7	11.0	33–77
Arterioles	$10–100 \cdot 10^{-6}$	1–5	7.0	7–35
Capillaries	$3 \cdot 10^{-6}$	5–8	3.3	17–26
Venules	$10–250 \cdot 10^{-6}$	7–10	1.6	11–16
Veins	$0.75–7.5 \cdot 10^{-3}$	7–10	1.3	9–13
Vena cava	$17 \cdot 10^{-3}$	10–15	1.0	10–15

Table 20-1 gives the tangential wall tensions for various kinds of vessels. These values represent a simplification of the real conditions in that (i) the pressure gradients have been neglected, the pressure being taken as the mean for vessels with different radii in each category, and (ii) in some cases there is considerable variability in the ratio of inside radius to wall thickness. The table shows a marked decrease in wall tension from the aorta and large arteries to the arterioles and vessels further downstream. It is because of this *lower wall tension* in vessels of *small radius* that the capillaries, consisting of only a single cell layer, can withstand the stretching force of intravascular pressure without tearing. Another feature of small vessels is that when the radius of the vessel is reduced by contraction of the smooth musculature, the already *low wall tension is further reduced,* not only by the decrease in radius but also by the simultaneous increase in wall thickness. It is understandable, then, that changes in arteriole diameter can be achieved without difficulty by the smooth musculature of the vessels at all naturally occurring pressures.

Pressure-Volume Relationships

Elastic properties. The degree to which the vessels can be **stretched** is determined both by the number of elastic and collagen fibers and by the ratio between the two. For example, in comparable parts of the systemic vascular system the *arteries are 6–10 times less distensible* than the veins. In the pulmonary system, by contrast, the arteries are about half as distensible as the veins, which have about the same properties as the veins in the systemic system.

Volume elasticity coefficient E′. The elastic properties of a hollow structure (or of isolated parts of a vessel) can be expressed by the volume elasticity coefficient E′. The ratio of pressure change (ΔP) to volume change (ΔV):

$$E' = \frac{\Delta P}{\Delta V} (\mathrm{Pa} \cdot \mathrm{ml}^{-1}) \tag{15}$$

When the elastic elements can be *easily* stretched E′ is *small,* and conversely.
The distensibility of a vessel is also expressed as

$$\textbf{Compliance} = \frac{\Delta V}{\Delta P} \tag{16}$$

The *overall distensibility* of a system of hollow elastic elements is computed as the *sum* of the distensibilities of the elements.
The relationships between pressure and volume, in single vessels or parts of vessels as well as in the system as a whole, are represented by *pressure-volume diagrams* (cf. Fig. 20-12).

Bulk modulus of elasticity K. The elastic properties *per unit volume* – that is, the amount of pressure change required to produce a *relative* volume change – are described by the bulk modulus of elasticity K:

$$K = \frac{\Delta P}{\Delta V} \cdot V = E' \cdot V (\mathrm{Pa}) \tag{17}$$

The bulk modulus of elasticity is related to density ρ and to the propagation velocity c of the pulse wave ($\mathrm{cm} \cdot \mathrm{s}^{-1}$) as follows:

$$K = \rho \cdot c^2 \text{ or } c = \sqrt{\frac{K}{\rho}} \tag{18}$$

These relationships allow one to obtain information about the elasticity of the arterial system relatively easily, by measurement of pulse-wave velocity.

Vascular tone. In many vessels there are a limited number of smooth muscle cells that undergo repeated *spontaneous depolarization;* these cells act as "pacemakers", exciting neighboring cells (see p. 79). This activity is *independent of the innervation* of the vessel, so that it proceeds even after denervation of the vascular region. Because of it the walls of the vessels, to different degrees in different regions, have a background tension, the so-called **myogenic basal tone** (Figs. 20-25 and 20-26).
In most vessels under resting conditions this basal tone is *supplemented by contraction* of the smooth musculature of the vessel elicited by *vasoconstrictor impulses* in autonomic nerve fibers; this enhanced tension in the vessel walls is called **resting tone** (Fig. 20-25).

Stress relaxation. When an isolated piece of vessel is suddenly inflated so that its *volume in-*

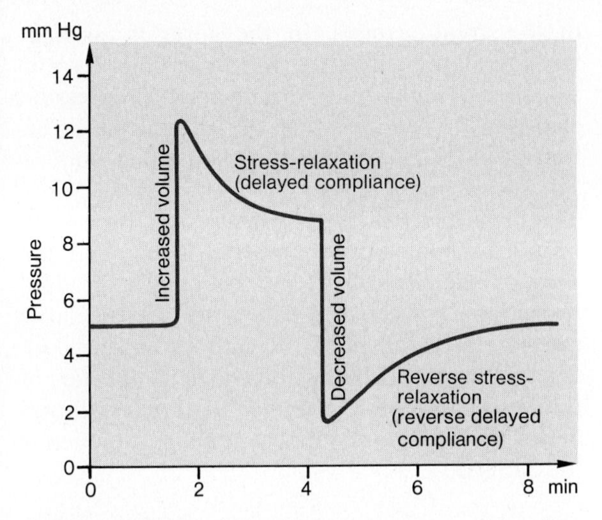

Fig. 20-6. Graph of the pressure changes resulting from stepwise changes in the volume of an isolated segment of vein. (Modified from GUYTON [8])

creases, the intravascular pressure at first rises sharply but then, while the volume remains the same, *declines steadily;* after a few minutes the pressure may be little greater than before the volume change (Fig. 20-6). The reason for this slow decline in pressure is that after the initial elastic distension the tension in the smooth muscle fibers adjusts to the greater stretch, a process called *"stress relaxation"* or *"delayed compliance"*. This **viscoelastic** behavior of the vessel wall probably results from a rearrangement of the actin-myosin bonds in the stretched muscle fibers that permits the filaments to slide slowly past one another, so that tension is reduced.

A sudden *volume reduction* has the *opposite* effect (Fig. 20-6). The tension in the smooth muscle fibers, greatly reduced at first, rises over the next few minutes by *"reverse stress relaxation"*, and the intravascular pressure rises accordingly.

These reactions are considerably more pronounced in veins than in arteries. Because of this property, together with their larger capacity, the veins can receive or give out large volumes of blood without maintained changes in intravascular pressure. Stress relaxation and reverse stress relaxation might be an important mechanism for maintenance of *filling pressure* (see pp. 490f.) *matched to the needs* of the moment under various conditions (see pp. 527ff.).

Pressure-Volume Flow Relationships in Vessels of Different Types

Passive stretch. Because the vessels are elastic, pressure changes effect volume flow not only

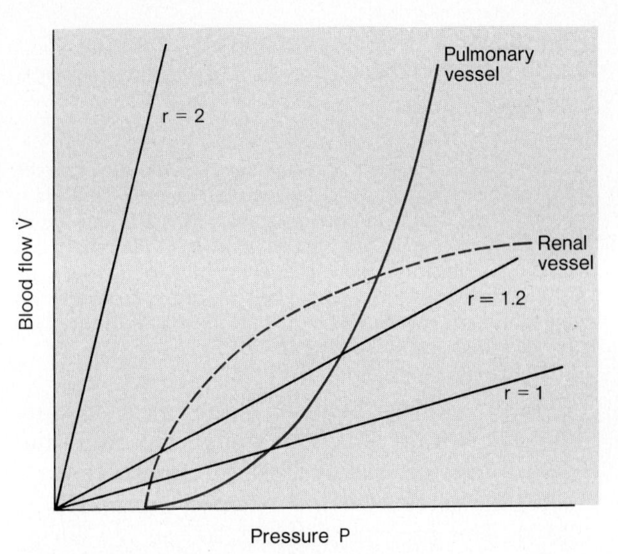

Fig. 20-7. Flow-pressure diagram for various types of vessel. As pressure increases, either passive stretch (pulmonary vessel) or autoregulatory (reactive) contraction (renal vessel) results. Therefore rising pressure produces a greater increase in volume flow in pulmonary-type vessels than in rigid tubes, and a smaller increase in those of the renal type. Below a certain pressure (critical closing pressure) flow through the vessels is arrested. By contrast, the volume flow in rigid tubes *(black lines)* rises linearly, with a slope that increases by factors of 2 and 16 as the radius increases from 1 to 1.2 and 2, respectively

directly but also *indirectly,* by way of changes in lumen diameter.

Volume flow in certain vessels is therefore much *more strongly affected* by pressure increase than would be expected according to Ohm's law for rigid tubes. The blood flow-pressure curves in these cases have continually increasing slope. The **pulmonary vessels** (Fig. 20-7) can be taken as a prototype of the kind of vessel that is distended *passively* by pressure change.

Autoregulatory contraction. In other vessels, however, pressure increases produce progressively *smaller increases in volume flow,* so that the slope of the flow-pressure curve decreases continually (Fig. 20-7). These effects are due to *autoregulatory* (mechanogenic) reactions of the smooth musculature **(Bayliss effect),** which contracts in response to stretch. The autoregulatory contractions are stronger as intravascular pressure increases, so that when pressure rises little or no increase in volume flow is possible. This mechanism *tends to stabilize* the blood supply to a tissue. In certain cases volume flow is uniform over a range of pressure from 120 to 200 mm Hg. The **renal vessels** can be taken as a prototype of this category. This myogenic autoregulation is *in-*

dependent of the autonomic innervation and thus is unimpaired by transection of the vasomotor nerves [9, 32].

The relations between pressure and volume flow can be *approximated* by a power function analogous to Ohm's law, in which the exponent of ΔP is greater than 1 for vessels of the pulmonary type, and smaller than 1 for the renal type. Shape and position of the curves are affected by the state of contraction of the vascular musculature, which depends on neural and metabolic factors, the chemical composition of the blood and so on (see pp. 506ff.).

Critical closing pressure. The flow-pressure curves often do not pass through the origin but rather intersect the abscissa at a positive pressure, the so-called *critical closing pressure* (Fig. 20-7). This pressure *averages 20 mm Hg* during perfusion with blood, but if vascular muscle tone is greatly increased it can rise to 60 mm Hg; it can fall to 1 mm Hg in the absence of tone.

The arterioles are regarded as the region in which closure occurs at the critical pressure. The cause is thought to be that as the radius of the vessel becomes smaller, owing to the lower pressure, the stretching forces decrease more than would correspond to the pressure change (see p. 485). *Increases in viscosity* at low flow velocities probably also contribute to the interruption of flow (see p. 483). In vascular regions where the ambient pressure is not negligible with respect to the intravascular pressure, flow may cease even though an arteriovenous pressure difference persists, either because the vessels collapse (lungs, veins) or because they are compressed (coronary vessels during systole). In cases of high critical closing pressure, in some circumstances flow is interrupted when an abnormally elevated blood pressure is brought down into the normal range. Therefore critical closing pressure must be taken into account when the *effective* arteriovenous pressure difference in the vascular system is being estimated.

20.3 Functional Organization of the Vascular System

The Functional Categories of Vessels

With regard to their function, vessels can be classified in 6 categories: 1. (elastic) *"Windkessel" vessels, 2. resistance vessels, 3. sphincter vessels, 4. exchange vessels, 5. capacitance vessels* and *6. shunt vessels* [10].

Windkessel vessels. These are arteries of the *elastic* type, with a relatively large proportion of elastic fibers; among them are the aorta and the pulmonary arteries plus the adjacent parts of the great arteries. In the **aorta** in particular, this large elasticity is responsible for the so-called *Windkessel* (German for "compression chamber") *effect*, by which the phasic systolic inflow of blood is converted to a smoother outflow (for details see p. 494).
The *distal arteries* are constructed of increasing proportions of smooth muscle fibers, and are thus of the *muscular type*. There is a gradual transition between the two types. In the large arteries the main effect of smooth-muscle contraction seems to be on the elastic properties of the vessel wall; the diameter of the vessel, and hence the resistance to flow, remains practically unchanged.

Resistance vessels. The *terminal arteries* and *arterioles,* and to a lesser extent the *capillaries* and *venules,* are resistance vessels. The *greatest resistance to flow* is in the *precapillary* region (terminal arteries and arterioles) – in vessels with relatively small lumens and thick walls having a large muscular component. Changes in the contractile state of the musculature of these vessels cause distinct changes in the diameter of the vessels and thus considerable changes in total *cross-sectional area,* particularly at the level of the numerous arterioles. In view of the effect of cross-sectional area on resistance to flow (see p. 481), it is understandable that the activity of the smooth muscles in these vessels is the decisive factor in *regulation of volume flow* within each vascular bed, as well as in the *distribution* of the cardiac output (volume flow through the overall circulation) among the various organs [2, 6, 10, 13, 39, 46].
The *postcapillary* resistance is determined by the venules (and veins). The ratio between precapillary and postcapillary resistance is significant with regard to the magnitude of the *hydrostatic pressure* in the capillaries and thus also to the conditions of *filtration* and *absorption* (see pp. 503ff.).

Sphincter Vessels. The constriction or dilation of the sphincter vessels, the terminal segments of the precapillary arterioles, determines the *number* of open capillaries and thus the **size of the capillary exchange surface** (cf. Fig. 20-21).

Exchange vessels. These are the *capillaries,* in which the decisive processes of **diffusion** and **filtration** occur. The capillaries are *not contractile;* capillary diameter changes passively as a result of pressure changes in the region of the pre-

and postcapillary resistance and sphincter vessels. Diffusion and filtration also occur in the *venules,* which should therefore be counted as exchange vessels.

Capacitance vessels. The main capacitance vessels are the *veins,* which because of their high distensibility can take in or pass on large volumes of blood with no marked effects on the other parameters of the circulation; they can thus act as **blood reservoirs.**
Moreover, some veins are flattened (oval) in cross section, so that a certain extra volume can be accommodated simply by the approach to a cylindrical shape, before the vessel becomes distended at all.
Certain venous regions have anatomical properties that make them particularly capacious storage areas. Chief among these are (i) the *venous vessels of the liver,* (ii) the *large veins in the splanchnic region,* and (iii) the *veins of the subpapillary plexus of the skin;* together, these vessels can hold more than 1,000 ml of blood for release when needed. The *pulmonary vessels* too, which are in series with the systemic vessels, can be used for short-term storage or mobilization of fairly large amounts of blood, by alteration of the venous return to the right heart and/or the volume ejected by the left heart (see pp. 523ff.).

In contrast to other species, *humans have no true blood depot* (such as, for example, the spleen of the dog), where blood can be stored in special structures and returned to circulation as needed.

In the closed vascular system, regional changes in capacity are necessarily associated with a **redistribution of the blood volume,** so that changes in the capacity of the veins under the control of the vascular smooth muscles affect the distribution of blood in general and thus, directly or indirectly, influence *overall cardiovascular function.*
Shunt vessels are found in certain tissues in the form of **arteriovenous anastomoses.** When these vessels are open, flow through the capillaries is reduced or entirely interrupted (cf. Fig. 20-21).

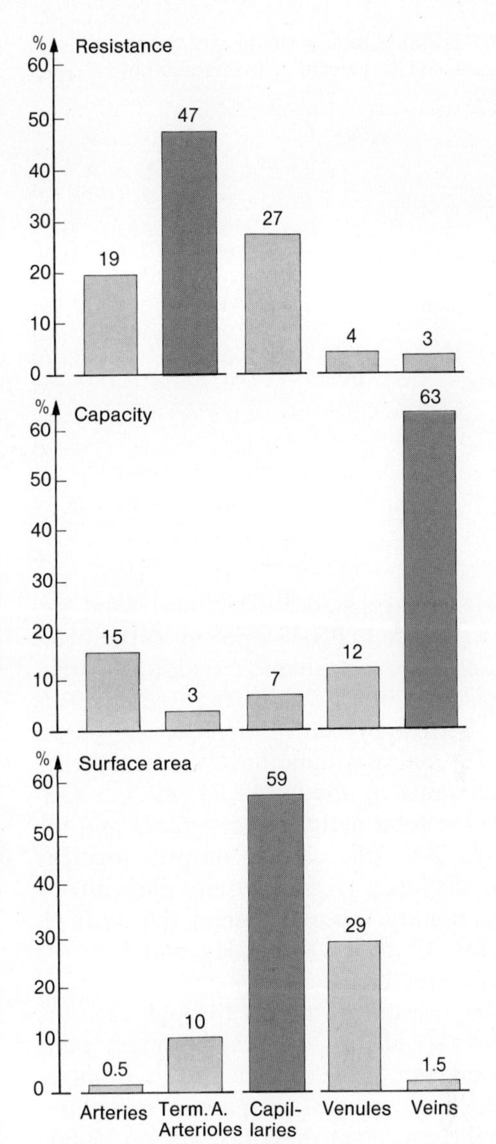

Fig. 20-8. Distribution of resistance to flow, capacity and surface area in the systemic circulation. The arterial "resistance vessels" account for ca. 50% of the total resistance; ca. 75% of the total capacity is in the venous "capacity vessels", and nearly 90% of the total surface is that of the "exchange vessels" (capillaries and venules). For further details see text. (From data of MALL, SCHLEIER and GREEN)

Resistances in the Vascular System

Variation in the different vessels. The aorta, the large arteries and the relatively long arterial branches account for about 19% of the total resistance to flow (Fig. 20-8). The contribution of the terminal arteries and arterioles amounts to just under 50%; that is, almost half of the resistance to flow lies in vessels only a few millimeters long. This enormous increase in resistance is due to the relatively small diameter of the terminal arteries and arterioles; the reduction in cross-sectional area is not fully compensated by the increase in number of parallel passages. The resistance in the capillaries is also considerable, 25% of the total. In the venous region, resistance is highest in the venules (4%), with all the remaining venous vessels contributing only 3%.

Table 20-2. Resistance to flow (R) in the vascular beds of human organs; %CO, percent of cardiac output received by the organ

	%CO	$\dot{V}$ (ml·min^{-1})	$\dot{V}$ (ml·s^{-1})	R (Pa·ml^{-1}·s)
Brain	13	750	13	1,025
Coronary vessels	4	250	4	3,330
Muscles	21	1,200	20	670
Splanchnic region	24	1,400	23	580
Kidneys	19	1,110	18	740
Skin	9	500	8	1,670
Other organs	10	600	10	1,330
Total systemic circulation	100	~5,800	~96	~140
Pulmonary circulation	100	~5,800	~96	~ 11

Total peripheral resistance. The term total peripheral resistance (TPR) is applied to the overall resistance of the systemic circulation – that is, the resistance of *all the parallel vascular beds* together. With a pressure difference ΔP of ca. 100 mm Hg and a volume flow $\dot{V}$ of ca. 95 ml · s^{-1}, it amounts to about 140 Pa · ml^{-1} · s (Table 20-2). The total peripheral resistance and the *total volume flow* (the cardiac output) together determine the *blood pressure* at any moment.
In the pulmonary vascular system the total resistance, for ΔP of ca. 8 mm Hg and $\dot{V}$ of 95 ml · s^{-1}, is about 11 Pa · ml^{-1} · s.
Because the resistances to flow through each organ system vary (Table 20-2), each receives a different proportion of the cardiac output. *Changes in the resistance* of any of the parallel organ systems, by the processes described on pp. 506ff., in combination with *changes in cardiac output* are the decisive events in *adjustment of volume flow* through the organs to meet their varying demands.

Blood Volume in the Vascular System

Total volume. The magnitude of the intravascular blood volume is an important determinant of the *filling pressure* of the heart during diastole, and thus of the *amount ejected* by the heart.

The **volume of blood** in men is 77 ml/kg body weight, and in women 65 ml/kg (±10% in both cases); the difference is due chiefly to the larger proportion of fat in the female body. The **total volume** is thus ca. 5.4 liters on the average for men, and 4.5 liters for women.
Considerable *long-term departures* from this average can occur, depending on state of *training* and *climatic and hormonal factors*. For example, the blood volume of some athletes can be greater than 7,000 ml, whereas after a long period of bed rest it can be below normal. In an advanced state of varicosis blood volume can also be increased. *Short-term changes* accompany standing upright and muscular effort.

Distribution of the blood volume. Within the vessels of an adult human (Table 20-3), about 84% of the blood is in the *systemic system*, and the remaining 16% is divided between the *pulmonary system* (barely 9%) and the *heart* (ca. 7%).
The *arteries* in the human systemic circulation contain ca. 18% of the total volume; of this about 3% is in the arterioles (Fig. 20-8). This distribution makes clear that even maximal constriction or dilation of the resistance vessels has practically no effect on the total volume of blood in other parts of the vascular system.
Despite the enormous enlargement in cross section at the level of the *capillaries* these too contain only a relatively small fraction of the total volume, ca. 6%, because they are so short.
The *storage function of the venous system* is reflected in the large proportion of blood it contains – 75% of the regional volume, or 64% of the total volume.
The *resistance vessels*, then, are characterized not only by high resistance to flow but by small capacity, and the *capacitance vessels* by low resistance to flow as well as by large capacity. Only small arteries and veins (0.5–2.0 mm diameter) occupy a special intermediate position; here changes in distension have a marked effect on both capacity and resistance.

Blood volume and mean filling pressure. The mean filling pressure or *static blood pressure* is a

Table 20-3. Distribution of blood volume within the circulatory system of a (hypothetical) human[a]

Region	Volume ml		%		%
Heart (diastole)	360		7.2		7.7
Pulmonary circulation					
Arteries	130	440	2.6		8.8
Capillaries	110		2.2		
Veins	200		4.0		
Systemic circulation					
Aorta and large arteries	300	4,200	6.0	14	84.0
Small arteries	400		8.0		
Capillaries	300		6.0		
Small veins	2,300		46.0	64	
Large veins	900		18.0		
	5,000				100.0

[a] 40 years old, weight 75 kg, body surface 1.85 m^2. (From Milnor [20])

measure of the *state of filling* of the vascular system. It corresponds to the pressure that prevails throughout the *entire* cardiovascular system in the absence of heart activity, when the different pressures in the system have equilibrated. The mean filling pressure is ca. 6 mm Hg; it can be affected both by changes in the blood volume and by changes in vascular capacity that result from changes in the state of contraction of the smooth musculature. The mean filling pressure is an important determinant of the inflow of blood from the venous system into the right atrium, and thus indirectly affects the amount ejected by the left heart.

In the "normal" circulation part of the blood volume is *transferred from the venous to the arterial side* by each beat of the heart; the resulting changes in the pressure within the vessels depend on their capacity and distensibility. The pressure in the veins is only *minimally reduced,* while that in the arteries undergoes a relatively pronounced *increase* because of the much smaller effective compliance of the arterial system (cf. Fig. 20-10). In this way a dynamic equilibrium is established, in which the regional blood volume depends on the intravascular pressure relative to the distensibility of the vessels concerned.

20.4 The Arterial Part of the Systemic Circulation

As a result of the features just described and the geometry of the vascular system, the various parts of the system exhibit the following distinctive **hemodynamic properties** [4, 5, 15, 19, 20, 24, 33].

Flow in the Arterial System

Flow pulse. Entry of blood into the ascending aorta because of heart pulsation occurs only during the *ejection period* of the left ventricle. During this so-called *flow pulse* the rate of flow rises sharply after the aortic valves open, reaches a maximum after about the first third of the ejection period, and by the end of the ejection period has returned to zero (Fig. 20-9). From the onset of the *relaxation period* to the closure of the aortic valves there is a brief backflow into the left ventricle. As diastole proceeds the blood in the ascending aorta essentially stands still, until the next ejection period begins.

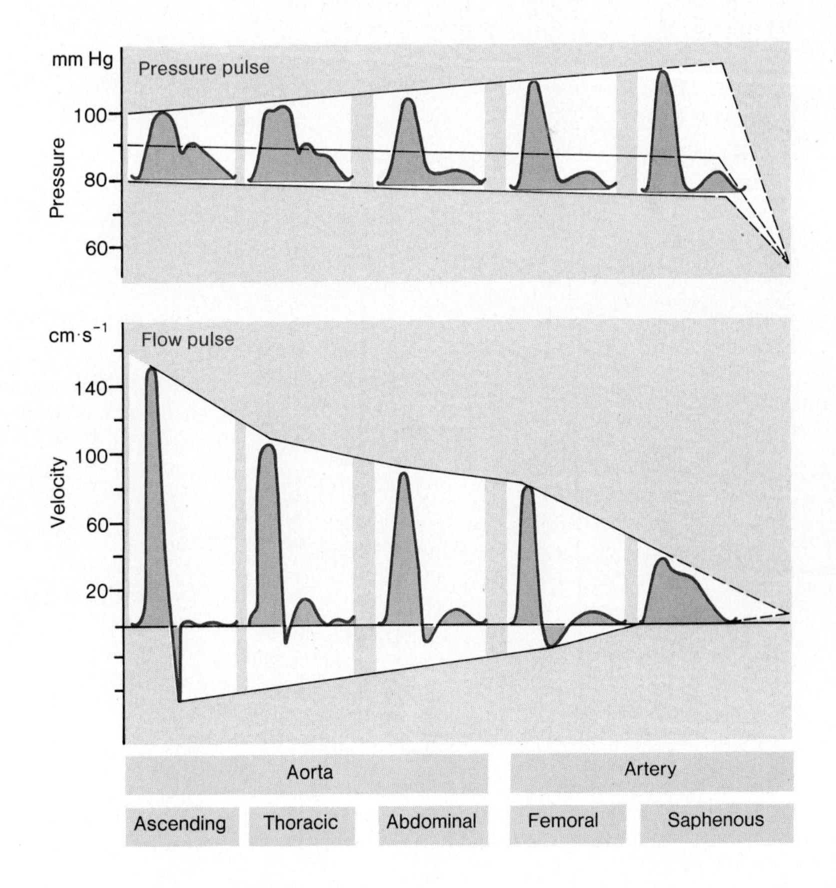

Fig. 20-9. Changes in pressure and flow pulses in the aorta and leg arteries. Note the development of an anterograde flow component during diastole and the rise in systolic pressure at increasing distances from the heart. (From McDonald [15])

In the human aorta under resting conditions, with an ejection period lasting 0.25 s and a stroke volume of 70–90 ml, the *peak velocities* far exceed 100 cm · s^{-1} and the *average velocity during the ejection period is ca. 70 cm* · s^{-1}. During fairly long parts of the ejection period Reynolds' number exceeds the critical value; during this time flow in the aorta is *turbulent*. (For measurement techniques see p. 539).

At increasing distances from the heart the *amplitude* of the flow pulse in the aorta and the large arteries (in contrast to that of the pressure pulse) *decreases continuously*. At the same time, in the thoracic aorta and in the distal arteries, an anterograde *diastolic* flow component develops (Fig. 20-9). The brief retrograde flow at the beginning of the relaxation period can be demonstrated as far away as the femoral (or brachial) artery under resting conditions. But when the cardiac output increases so does the velocity, so that eventually the pulse curve no longer crosses the zero line.

In the region of the *terminal arterial branches* and *arterioles*, there is a progressive transition from pulsatile flow to a more *continuous* flow. However, if the vessels are maximally dilated there can be small fluctuations in flow even in the capillaries and the small veins.

Velocity of flow and cross-sectional area. Because flow is discontinous, especially in the aorta and the great arteries, the *mean flow velocity* here is distinctly lower than that measured during systole. It can be calculated from $\bar{v} = \dot{V}/(\pi \cdot r^2)$. Under resting conditions, with a cardiac output of 96 ml · s^{-1}, the **mean flow velocity** in an aorta with radius 12–13 mm is 21.2 or 18.1 cm · s^{-1}, respectively – that is, about 20 cm · s^{-1} (Fig. 20-10 and Table 20-4). The mean flow velocity can rise to over 100 cm · s^{-1}, however, as a result of increased cardiac output.

Because of the inverse proportionality between mean flow velocity and cross-sectional area, the blood flows **much more slowly** in the distal arteries and especially in the region of the terminal arteries and arterioles; velocity is *lowest in the capillaries,* 0.03 cm · s^{-1} (cf. Fig. 20-10 and Table 20-4). The *transit time* through a capillary of intermediate length (750 μm) is thus ca. *2.5 s.*

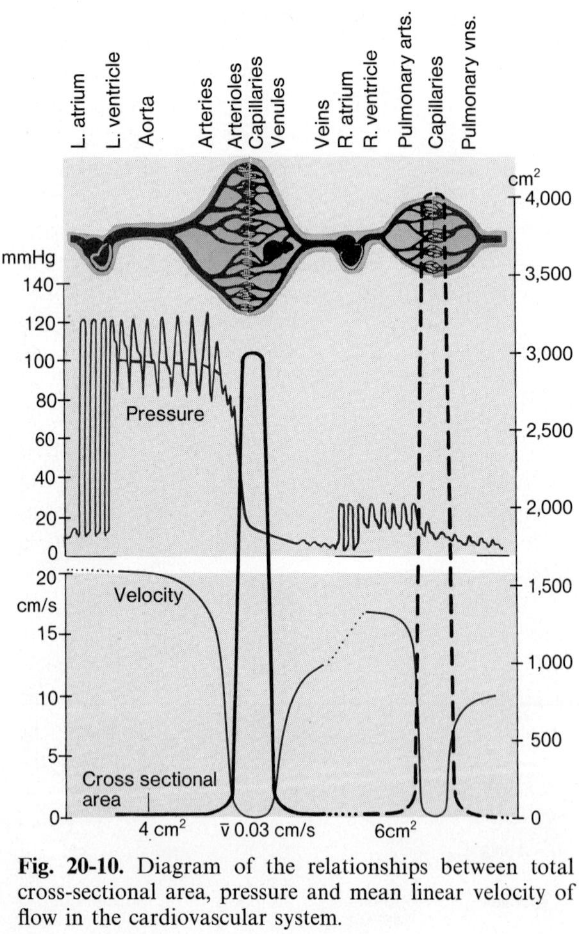

Fig. 20-10. Diagram of the relationships between total cross-sectional area, pressure and mean linear velocity of flow in the cardiovascular system.

Table 20-4. Mean flow velocities and mean pressures in the human systemic circulation

	Diameter (mm)	Mean vel. ($cm \cdot s^{-1}$)	Mean pressure (mm Hg)
Aorta	20–25	20	100
Medium-sized		10–15	95
Very small arteries		2	70–80
Arterioles	0.06–0.02	0.2–0.3	35–70
Capillaries			
arterial end			30–35
middle	0.006	0.03	20–25
venous end			15–20
Very small veins		0.5–1.0	10–15
Small to medium veins		1–5	10 or less
Large veins	5–15	5–10	
V. cavae	30–35	10–16	

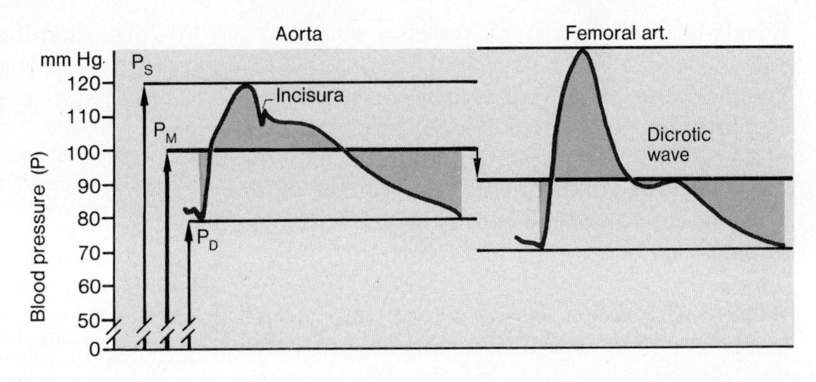

Fig. 20-11. Estimation of the mean arterial pressure in the aorta *(left)* and a peripheral artery *(right)*. P_S, systolic pressure; P_M, mean pressure; P_D, diastolic pressure. The *shaded* areas above the mean pressure are equal to the areas below the mean pressure. For further details see text

Pressures in the Arterial System

Pressure pulse. The inertia of the mass of blood prevents simultaneous acceleration of the entire column of fluid in the vessels by the volume of blood pressed into the aorta during an ejection period. Acceleration extends only to the blood in the basal segment of the ascending aorta; here there is a transient *pressure increase,* the so-called *pressure pulse* (Fig. 20-9). Pressure at first rises sharply together with the flow velocity, but then continues to rise more slowly, so that the maximum of the pressure pulse occurs later than that of the flow pulse.

The pressure then falls, but the *end-systolic pressure* reached by the time systole is completed is usually distinctly higher than that at the beginning of the ejection period. The end of systole is marked by a brief, sharp fall in pressure, the so-called **incisura,** brought about by the relaxation of the ventricle and the resulting backflow of blood until the sudden closure of the aortic valve (Fig. 20-11). During the remainder of diastole there is an essentially uniform fall in pressure. Unlike the flow pulse, however, the pressure pulse *does not fall to zero,* because of the *rectifying* effect of the aortic valves, the *elastic* properties of the arteries and the *peripheral resistance;* at the onset of the following systole the pressure is still relatively high (Figs. 20-9 and 20-11).

Systolic, diastolic and mean pressure. The maximum of the pressure-pulse curve during systole is called the systolic blood pressure (P_S), and the minimum during diastole is called the diastolic blood pressure (P_D), (Fig. 20-11). The blood-pressure amplitude ($P_S–P_D$) is called the *pulse pressure.* The "mean blood pressure" (P_M) or *arterial mean pressure,* which is the driving force for the flow of blood, is defined as the *average in time* of the pressures in a section of vessel; it is determined by integration of the pressure-pulse curve over time. In *central* arteries the mean pressure can be expressed with sufficient accuracy as the arithmetic mean of P_S and P_D, which is equivalent to the diastolic pressure plus half the blood-pressure amplitude ($P_M = P_D + (P_S - P_D)/2$); in *peripheral* arteries it is more nearly equivalent to the diastolic pressure plus one-third of the blood-pressure amplitude ($P_M = P_D + (P_S - P_D)/3$) (for measurement methods see pp. 537ff.).

In the ascending aorta of a young adult the **systolic pressure** is ca. **120 mm Hg** and the **diastolic pressure** is ca. **80 mm Hg.** The **mean arterial pressure** is thus ca. **100 mm Hg.** In the adjacent part of the aorta and in the large arteries the mean pressure decreases only slightly, so that in arteries 3 mm in diameter it is still 95 mm Hg (Table 20-4). Pulse shape and amplitude, however, change conspicuously at increasing distances from the heart. The systolic pressure in the arteries increases progressively, becoming higher than that in the ascending aorta by 20 mm Hg in the femoral artery and by as much as 40 mm Hg in the dorsal artery of the foot (Figs. 20-9 and 20-11). The diastolic pressure, by contrast, decreases slightly, so that there is a distinct increase in pressure amplitude. When pressure measurements in various parts of the arterial system are to be compared, these effects must be kept in mind to avoid misinterpretations.

In the *terminal branches* of the arteries and in the *arterioles,* the pressure falls sharply over a distance of a few mm because of the high resistance to flow, reaching 30-35 mm Hg at the end of the arterioles (Fig. 20-18 and Table 20-4). At the same time, the pulsatile pressure fluctuations are much attenuated or disappear altogether.

The changes in the pressure- and flow-pulse curves are due largely to differences in the elastic properties of the various arterial regions, which will now be discussed.

Effects of the Elasticity of Vessels

Volume pulse. The systolic rise in pressure is accompanied by a stretching of the elastic walls of the vessels. The resulting changes in cross-sectional area follow closely the course of the pressure curve, and are called the *cross-sectional* or *volume pulse.*

Windkessel function. As the vessel walls stretch, *kinetic (motion) energy* is changed into *potential (deformation) energy;* at the same time, part of the stroke volume transported into the aorta is *stored* in the stretched segments. In the falling-pressure phase the elastic forces shrink the stretched wall, *emptying* the store. In this process the potential energy is changed back into kinetic energy and blood is propelled in the direction of least resistance to flow – toward the capillaries, the "drainage channels" of the arterial system (Fig. 20-13). These effects, largely restricted to the elastic vessels (aorta and arteries of the elastic type), convert the discontinuous systolic flow in the ascending aorta into a *continuous* although not uniform flow in the peripheral arteries. The name *Windkessel* (compression chamber) has been given to these vessels and their function because of the resemblance to the air-filled chambers that similarly affect the velocity and pressure of fluids driven by pistons through systems of pipes.

In a system of *rigid tubes* there would be a much greater rise in pressure during systole, whereas during diastole negative pressures and interruption of flow would occur because of the inertia of the previously accelerated blood. In such a case, at each systole the heart would have to accelerate from zero velocity not just the stroke volume but all the blood in the system. Moreover, a given volume flow could be achieved only by higher flow velocities during systole, which would require a further increase in systolic pressure. Together, the increased mass to be accelerated and the increased flow rate would constitute a considerably greater work load on the heart.

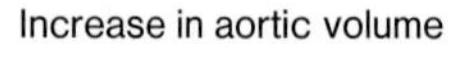

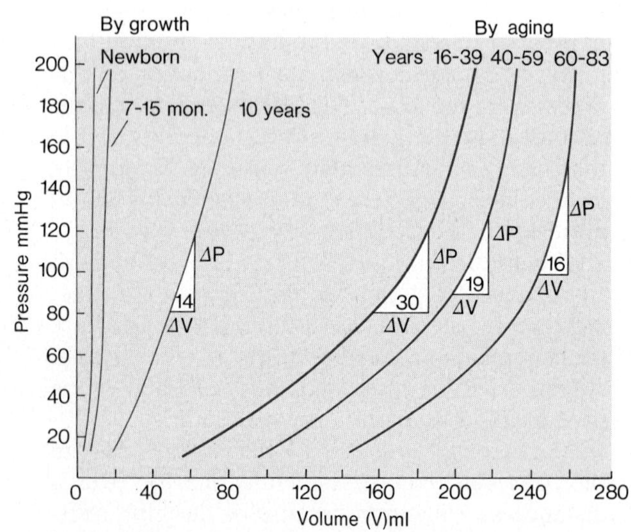

Fig. 20-12. Pressure-volume curves of the human aorta. During growth the aortic volume increases. Distensibility (compliance) is greatest in the young adult (16-39 years). Further aging is accompanied by expansion of the aorta and reduced compliance. For some of the curves the volume change (ΔV) associated with the normal pressure amplitude (ΔP) for that age is indicated. For further details see text. (From SIMON and MEYER as cited by GAUER [7])

Pressure-volume diagrams. The elastic properties of the Windkessel in humans of different ages are illustrated by the pressure-volume curves in Fig. 20-12. The upward curvature in each case reflects *decreasing distensibility at higher pressure.* On the other hand, until growth is completed distensibility increases as a result of the changes in volume (increase in length and diameter); that is, the Windkessel becomes *more compliant* because of the enlargement of the distensible surfaces and the associated (according to Laplace's law) enhanced conversion of pressure into wall tension. As a person grows older the volume contained by the aorta continues to increase, but the distensibility and thus the temporary storage space decrease for anatomical reasons – that is, the Windkessel *hardens* again. As blood pressure increases with age, these effects are enhanced by the shifting of the actual pressures into the steeper ranges of the curves.

The *age-dependent changes* in the PV diagram are probably based on a *passive* expansion under the continual pressure of the blood and on a decreased elasticity in aging tissue; in pathological conditions of high blood pressure these changes are more pronounced. Fig. 20-12 also specifies the *volume change* (of isolated human aortas) associated with the *pulse pressure* for the different age groups. In the "normal" case, the young adult, it amounts to 30 ml, which corresponds to an E′ of 177 Pa · ml^{-1}.

Under the extremely simplified assumption that the end-systolic pressure is uniform in all parts of the arterial system, 40 mm Hg above the diastolic pressure, at the end of systole a volume of 30 ml would be *stored in the aorta.* Estimates indicate that all the other arteries can be stretched only about $^1/_3$ as much as the aorta, so that by extension of the above assumption a further 10 ml would be stored, giving a total storage in the arterial system of 40 ml. With a stroke vol-

ume of 80 ml, then, 50% of the volume would *flow into the peripheral resistance vessels* during systole, and the remaining 50% would follow during diastole, as the stretched walls of the vessels returned to their original sizes and the blood pressure to its original level.
It follows for the Windkessel as a whole that

$$E' = \frac{40\,\text{mm Hg}}{(30+10)\text{ml}} = 133\,\text{Pa} \cdot \text{ml}^{-1}$$

That is, for a **volume change of 1 ml** in the entire arterial system the **pressure changes** in the same direction by **1 mm Hg.**

Propagation of the pulse wave. Flow pulse, pressure pulse and volume pulse spread out over the vascular system as a pulse wave, with a particular velocity (Fig. 20-13). In fact the various phenomena do not occur in successive steps, as in the simplified description above, but rather *continuously;* the shifts of blood into and out of storage and thus its movement through various parts of the vascular system occur simultaneously side by side.

Pulse-wave velocity. The rate of propagation of the pulse wave from one site to the next is considerably *higher than the velocity of blood flow.* The pulse wave reaches the arterioles in the feet after 0.2 s, whereas the fluid particles in the ejected blood that gave rise to the wave, with a systolic flow velocity of ca. 70 $\text{cm} \cdot \text{s}^{-1}$, by this time have only just arrived in the descending aorta.
The pulse-wave velocity (PWV) depends very much on both the distensibility of the vessels and the ratio of wall thickness to radius; it is higher, the more rigid or the thicker the vessel wall and the smaller the radius. In the *aorta* the PWV is 4–6 $\text{m} \cdot \text{s}^{-1}$, whereas in the less elastic *arteries of the muscular type* (such as the radial artery) it is 8–12 $\text{m} \cdot \text{s}^{-1}$. As vessel elasticity diminishes with increasing age, the PWV increases. It also increases in cases of high blood pressure, because the increased wall stiffness of the vessels limits the amount by which they can be stretched further. In the more elastic *veins,* by contrast, the PWV is a great deal lower – ca. 1 $\text{m} \cdot \text{s}^{-1}$ in the vena cava and ca. 2 $\text{m} \cdot \text{s}^{-1}$ in the large veins of the arm. The pulse-wave velocity is therefore a source of information about the elasticity of the vessels, which not only changes slowly over a lifetime, due to the morphological developments described above, but can also be affected in the short term by vasomotor activity or by drugs.

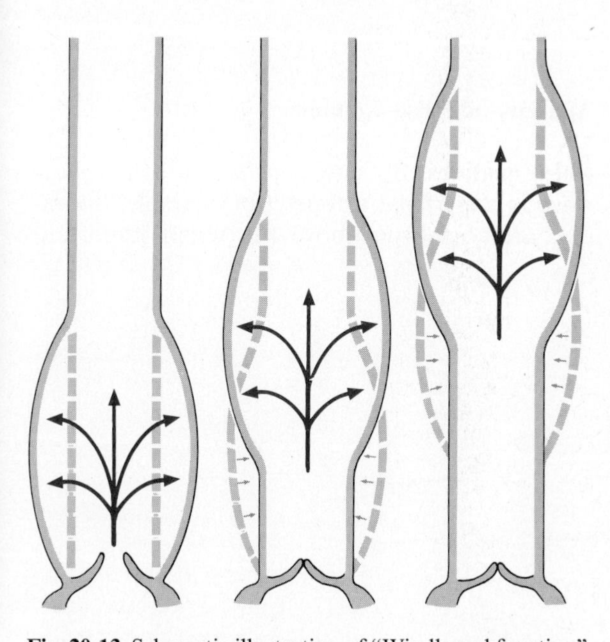

Fig. 20-13. Schematic illustration of "Windkessel function" and the mechanism of pulse-wave propagation. The initial systolic stretching of the aorta next to the heart, so that blood is stored in this region *(left),* is followed by a return to the original dimensions here and a stretching and storage of blood in the next segment *(middle);* this process is repeated in a continual progression along the elastic arteries *(right)*

Wave resistance and reflections of the pulse wave. The changes in form of the pressure waves, including the enhancement of the systolic peak in the peripheral arteries, are based on various mechanisms, the significance of which remains in debate. The most important factors are **(i) wave reflections, (ii) damping processes** and **(iii) frequency-dependent propagation velocities.**

In an elastic system the waves passing over the vessel wall are reflected at all points where the **wave resistance** (Z) increases; this resistance is the ratio of wave pressure ΔP to the wave volume flow $\dot{V}$. Wave resistance is an *impedance,* which in this case is a joint effect of the *inertia* of the fluid and the *elasticity* of the wall; friction is neglected entirely, so that Z must not be confused with frictional resistance.

In the arterial system **positive reflections** appear owing to the increase in wave resistance where vessels divide and to the decreased elasticity in the distal parts of vessels, even in the aorta and the arteries. But the strongest reflections occur in the *precapillary resistance vessels,* which affect the pulse wave like the closed end of a hose. These reflections are enhanced by vasoconstrictor reactions and attenuated by vasodilation. By *superposition* of the reflected wave on the anterograde wave the systolic pressure wave is enlarged, especially in the peripheral vessels.

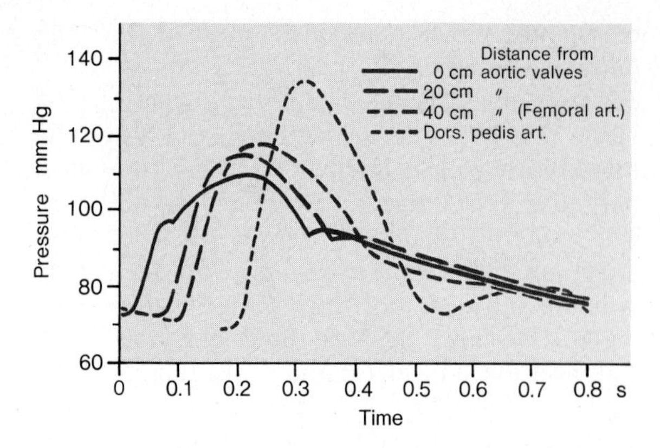

Fig. 20-14. Pulse curves in different parts of the arterial system. The increase in systolic pressure and the dicrotic wave are especially distinct in the dorsal pedis artery. The shift of the curves along the abscissa reflects the time required for spread of the pulse through the arterial system. (From REMINGTON and WOOD, modified by GUYTON [8])

At the aortic valves the reflected waves, the amplitude of which has fallen to 30–40% of that of the primary waves because of frictional energy loss, are again reflected and further attenuated. In peripheral vessels these repeated reflections produce a distinct **dicrotic wave** in the descending part of the pulse curve (Figs. 20-11 and 20-14). Because of the high degree of damping, however, it is unlikely that the reflected and re-reflected waves build up actual standing waves in the arterial system.

The **damping** depends on several factors, among them the structure of the wall and the geometry of the vascular system. It is *larger*, the more *compliant* the vessel walls. Increased damping occurs wherever the arteries *divide* or grow narrower (particularly in the region of the resistance vessels). Higher *frequencies* are more strongly damped than lower frequencies. The early disappearance of the incisura, in the lower end of the abdominal artery (Figs. 20-9 and 20-14), exemplifies this relationship.

Another factor tending to *increase the systolic peak* in peripheral arteries is the reduced compliance at higher pressures, which emphasizes the systolic component (see above). Furthermore, the pressure rises more rapidly in peripheral arteries because of the greater pulse-wave velocity at higher pressure (see Figs. 20-9 and 20-14).

Non-geometrical waves such as the flow- and pressure-pulse curves can be precisely represented by *harmonic (Fourier) analysis*. Here the curves are regarded as the sum of many sinusoidal oscillations at frequencies that are integral multiples of the fundamental frequency. The agreement between recorded and calculated curves increases as the number of computed Fourier series increases; an adequate approximation is achieved with 6–10 Fourier coefficients. In this way the ratio between pulsatile changes in pressure and flow can be used to derive the **impedance of the vascular system** (as done in describing alternating electrical currents) for the entire range of frequencies in the pressure and flow curves. The customary term *resistance to flow* (which, according to Ohm's law for direct currents, is defined as the *ratio of mean pressure differences to mean flow*) denotes only one element in the extremely complex phenomena of frequency-dependent impedance, and thus only approximates the actual situation.

Analysis of Pulse Contour

Pulse qualities. By simple *palpation of the pulse wave* in superficial arteries (for example, the radial artery a little above the wrist) important

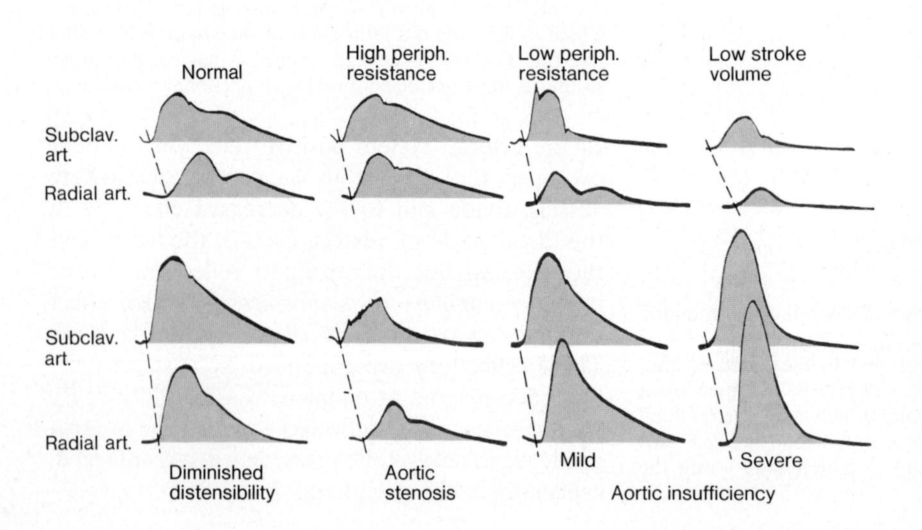

Fig. 20-15. Examples of changes in shape and amplitude of the pulse wave in the radial and subclavian arteries accompanying various cardiovascular abnormalities. For details see text. (From WIGGERS [28])

preliminary information can be obtained about the functional state of the cardiovascular system. The qualities of the pulse so identifiable are as follows:

1. *Frequency (frequent or infrequent pulse).* In evaluating the frequency of a pulse it should be remembered that the resting rates in children are higher than in adults. After athletic training, people have lower pulse rates than before. Psychological excitation and exercise increase the frequency; in a young adult under maximal load it can rise to 200/min or more.

2. *Rhythm (regular or irregular pulse).* The pulse rate can fluctuate in the respiratory rhythm, increasing during inspiration and decreasing during expiration. This "respiratory arrhythmia" is physiological and becomes more distinct when breathing is deeper; it occurs more often in younger or "autonomically labile" people. An exact analysis of other forms of arrhythmia (extrasystoles, absolute arrhythmia) can be done only with the ECG.

3. *Amplitude (strong or weak pulse).* The amplitude of the pulse depends basically on the stroke volume and the amount of blood that flows during diastole. It is also affected by the elasticity of the Windkessel; for a given stroke volume, pulse amplitude is small when elasticity is large and vice versa.

4. *Sharpness (short or long pulse).* The rate of rise of the wave front depends on the speed with which the pressure changes. For a given heart rate, a strong pulse is necessarily accompanied by sharp pressure changes, and a weak pulse by more sluggish pressure changes.

5. *Tension (hard or soft pulse).* The tension (or hardness) of the pulse is basically determined by the level of the mean arterial pressure, because the amount of pressure required to suppress the pulse wave in the distal parts of the vessel varies with mean pressure. By observation of this quality one can obtain a rough estimate of systolic pressure.

Pulse contour can be more precisely analyzed by relatively simple procedures. The most common clinical method is to place electromechanical transducers on the skin for recording either pressure changes (the **sphygmogram)** or volume changes (the **plethysmogram).**

Pathophysiology. From the shape of the pulse curve one can draw diagnostically useful conclusions about the *hemodynamics* of the arterial system as they are affected by stroke volume, vessel elasticity and peripheral resistance. Fig. 20-15 shows examples of pulse curves from the subclavian and radial arteries. Under *normal conditions* the pulse curve continues to rise during almost the whole of systole. This feature persists with increased *peripheral resistance,* but when peripheral resistance is low an initial peak appears, followed by a lower systolic peak that declines sharply into a relatively flat diastolic slope. When *stroke volume* is small (e.g., after loss of blood) the systolic rise is small, the peak rounded and the diastolic decline slow. Reduced *distensibility* of the aorta (e.g., in arteriosclerosis) produces a rapid and extensive rise; the incisura is high and diastolic decay is gradual. In analogy to the hemodynamic changes, aortic stenosis is accompanied by a sluggish, small systolic rise, whereas with aortic insufficiency the rising phase is steep and the peak high, and in severe forms the incisura is lost. The *time shift* of curves recorded synchronously at two points (cf. the slope of the dashed lines in Fig. 20-15) is an indicator of pulse-wave velocity; velocity is higher the smaller the delay – i.e., the steeper the lines – and vice versa.

20.5 Venous Parts of the Systemic Circulation

Pressures and Flow in the Venous System

Pressures in the venous system. Within the *venules* there is a relatively sharp pressure drop, from 15–20 mm Hg near the capillaries to 10–15 mm Hg in the small veins. In the *large extrathoracic veins* the pressure amounts to 5–6 mm Hg, and it is still lower at the point where the veins open into the right atrium (cf. Fig. 20-10 and Table 20-4).

Where the *inferior vena cava* passes through the diaphragm the situation is somewhat different, for here the resistance to flow is increased; caudal to the diaphragm the pressure is still fairly high, ca. 10 mm Hg, and at the point of passage through it there is a *stepwise* drop to about 4–5 mm Hg.

The pressure in the *right atrium* is identical to the **central venous pressure.** It amounts to 2–4 mm Hg, and under normal conditions exhibits fairly large fluctuations synchronous with respiration and the pulse (see pp. 500f.). But because of the subatmospheric pressure in the thorax, –4 to –7 cm H_2O, the *transmural* (effective venous) filling pressure remains positive even when the intravascular pressure is slightly negative [3, 4, 19, 36].

In some parts of the venous system there is a higher resistance to flow, and thus a somewhat *greater pressure gradient,* than in comparable parts of the arterial system. Various factors can account for this situation. For example, some veins under normal conditions are not circular in cross section but more less *elliptical,* because of "inadequate" filling, and present a correspondingly greater resistance to flow. The veins can also be *compressed* by external pressure at certain points (for example, where the

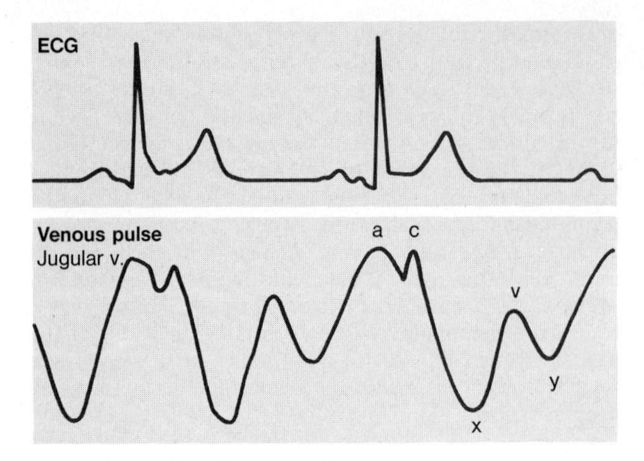

Fig. 20-16. Simultaneous recording of ECG and venous pulse in the jugular vein. For details see text

arm veins pass over the first rib) or over whole segments of varying length (for example, by abdominal organs or the intraabdominal pressure).

Venous pulse. The term "venous pulse"refers to the *pressure and volume fluctuations* that appear in veins near the heart due to *retrograde* transmission; these basically reflect the course of pressure change in the right atrium.
The venous pulse is recorded, usually noninvasively, from a recumbent subject with photoelectric devices or sensitive pressure transducers. The following features are characteristic of such measurements. The initial positive wave, the *a-wave,* is elicited by arterial contraction (Fig. 20-16). This is followed after a relatively brief interval by a second positive wave, the *c-wave,* which is caused chiefly by the bulging of the atrioventricular valve into the right atrium during the isovolumetric contraction of the ventricle. The subsequent *sharp fall (x)* is brought about by the shift of the valve plane of the heart toward the apex during the ejection period (see p. 501). As the ventricle relaxes the atrioventricular valves at first remain closed, so that there is an initial relatively rapid rise in pressure; when the valves open and blood flows into the ventricle there is a transient pressure drop. The sequence produces a third positive wave, the *v-wave,* followed by a *depression (y).* As the ventricle continues to fill, the pressure rises slowly towards the next a-wave.
Changes in the venous pulse curves can provide useful diagnostic evidence of certain forms of heart disease, such as tricuspid insufficiency.

Velocity of flow in the venous system. In the *venules* and *terminal* veins under normal conditions flow is *continuous,* for the arterial pulsations are not transmitted to the venous side unless the resistance vessels are greatly dilated. In the main branches of the veins small flow and pressure fluctuations reappear, however, owing to transmission of the pulsation of arteries lying in parallel. In the *great veins, fluctuations* in flow velocity become more pronounced as the right atrium is approached; these are associated with respiration and the heartbeat (see pp. 500f.).

The *mean flow velocity* begins to rise in the venules and vein branches as the total cross-sectional area is progressively reduced, but because the total vein area is larger than that of the arteries at the same level, the blood does not flow as rapidly in the veins as in the arteries. Under resting conditions the mean velocity of flow in the *vena cava* is between 10 and 16 $cm \cdot s^{-1}$; it can be as high as 50 $cm \cdot s^{-1}$.

Central Venous Pressure and Venous Return

The central venous pressure, together with the mean filling pressure (pp. 490f.) and the resistance to flow in the vessels, determines the *amount of venous return* to the heart, which under normal conditions critically affects the *stroke volume* [3, 36]. The pressure difference between mean filling pressure and central venous pressure is the **pressure gradient for venous return,** and under normal conditions it amounts to 2–4 mm Hg. In a normally functioning heart, then, when the mean filling pressure increases or decreases (due to a change in blood volume), the *venous return changes* in the same direction. Furthermore, venous return is impeded when the resistance to flow in the veins is high, and facilitated when it is low.
If the venous return should differ from the output of the right ventricle, adjustment of both quantities begins *automatically.* When the central venous pressure suddenly falls, the pressure gradient for venous return is increased, so that more blood is returned; at the same time, the stroke volume is reduced because the end-diastolic filling of the heart is less. As a result of the increased venous return accompanying reduced ejection into the arteries, pressure and volume in the right atrium rise. Accordingly, venous return is decreased and stroke volume increases. The effects of sudden increases in central venous pressure are just the reverse. In this way the equilibrium between venous return and cardiac output is restored within 4–6 heartbeats.

In *pathological* states, such as heart failure involving the right heart, central venous pressure can rise to 30 mm Hg, reaching the levels normally prevailing in the capillaries. In these cases the pressure gradient necessary for the blood to flow is maintained by a corresponding increase in pressure in the peripheral veins and capillaries. The central venous pressure is thus determined not only by the supply of venous blood; it is fundamentally affected by the *performance of the right heart.*

Effect of Gravity on the Pressures in the Vascular System

Because the three-dimensional vascular system is within the earth's field of gravity, **hydrostatic pressures** are superimposed on the pressures generated by the heart; the result is an increased pressure proportional to the distance of a vessel below the level of the heart, and a proportional decrease in vessels above the heart.
When a person is *recumbent* the vertical distances within the vascular system, and thus the hydrostatic effects, are negligibly *small* for practical purposes.

Pressures in the erect position. When a person is standing erect the *hydrostatic* pressure in the vessels of the foot (125 cm below the level of the heart) is about 90 mm Hg, so that with a mean *arterial* pressure of 100 mm Hg the total pressure in the arteries of the foot is about 190 mm Hg (Fig. 20-17). In the arteries overlying the brain (ca. 40 cm above the heart) the arterial pressure is reduced by ca. 30 mm Hg, to 70 mm Hg.
The pressure within the *veins* is subject to corresponding hydrostatic effects. Therefore the pressure gradient between arteries and veins, the driving force for the flow of blood, does not vary with height. However, hydrostatic effects cause considerable increases in *transmural* pressure, which are reflected primarily in the state of stretch and thus the capacity of the relatively thin-walled veins. As a result, when a person who has been lying down stands up 400–600 ml of blood accumulates in the leg veins; this amount must of course be withdrawn from other vascular beds, so that these relatively *voluminous shifts of blood* have distinct effects on the function of the circulatory system in general (see p. 527ff.).

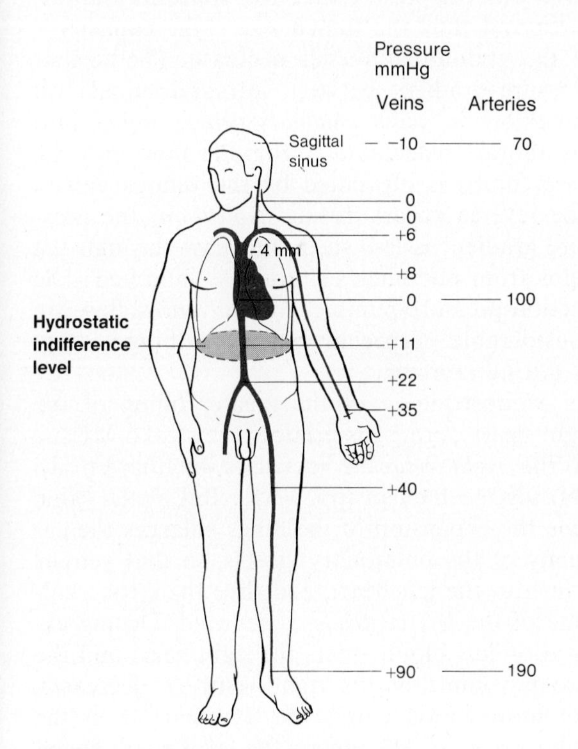

Fig. 20-17. Effect of hydrostatic pressure on the venous and arterial pressures in a quietly standing human. (Modified from Guyton [8])

Hydrostatic indifference level. Because both hydrostatic pressures and the elastic properties of the vessels differ throughout the body, it is not always entirely justified to regard the heart as the reference point for the pressure gradients in the vascular system, or to assume exclusively linear relationships between hydrostatic pressures and arterial or venous pressures.
On the contrary, pressure measurements in the main venous trunk of the human show that the hydrostatic indifference level – the *plane through the vascular system in which pressure does not change with change of position* – is about 5–10 cm below the diaphragm. In the thoracic cavity (and thus in the right atrium) and in all the other vessels above this plane, pressure is lower in the erect than in the recumbent position. At the level of the atrium the orthostatic venous pressure is about zero (i.e., equal to the atmospheric pressure), but the subatmospheric intrathoracic pressure counteracts the venous collapse that would be expected in theory, so that the superior vena cava remains open almost as far as the collar bone. In the parts of the body above this level, particularly the region of neck and face, the veins are collapsed, the pressure remaining zero in the entire region. The same is true of the pressures in the arm veins when the arm is raised.
Inside the bony skull, by contrast, the veins are prevented from collapse by their attachment to the tissue. Accordingly, there are "negative" pressures in the venous sinuses of the brain; in the sagittal sinus the pressure is ca. −10 mm Hg, because of the hydrostatic pressure difference between the top and base of the skull.

Mechanisms to Increase Venous Return

The hydrostatic effects on the vessels below the hydrostatic zero level in the erect human are not the only causes of reduced venous return. Many other factors – for example, exercise and thermal stress – can affect the capacity of the veins. Ve-

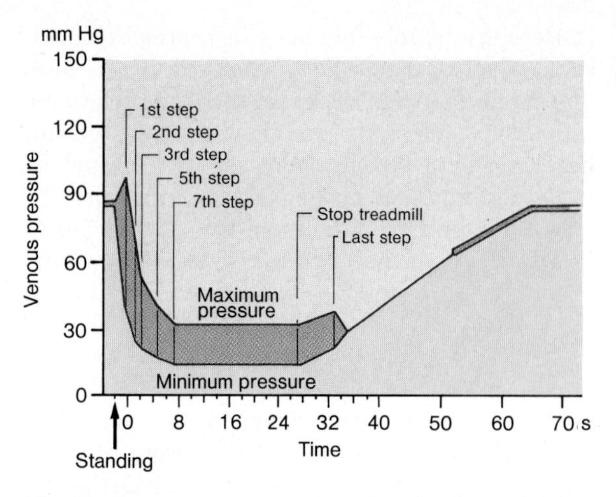

Fig. 20-18. Pressure changes in a dorsal vein of the foot during walking (on a treadmill). When the subject is standing quietly the venous pressure is increased by hydrostatic effects; the pressure drop during walking results from activation of the muscle pump. After a few steps venous pressure stabilizes at a distinctly lower level which is maintained until walking stops. During the subsequent standing period venous pressure returns to the original level. (Modified from POLLACK and WOOD [48])

nous return can be aided or improved by three main mechanisms: (i) the so-called *muscle pump,* (ii) the *respiratory pump,* and (iii) the *suction effects* of the heart (valve-plane mechanism).

The muscle pump. This "pump"acts by *compression of the veins* within the skeletal musculature when the muscles contract. The blood is squeezed out in the *anterograde* direction, toward the heart, because the venous valves prevent retrograde flow. Each muscle contraction therefore reinforces the normal flow and reduces the volume of blood in the veins of the musculature.
These effects are particularly obvious when the veins are very full, as in the legs of a standing person. At the beginning of each muscle contraction there is a distinct *acceleration* of flow, which had been slowed owing to the increase in cross-sectional area during the standing. The pressure in the veins of the foot, which during quiet standing corresponds to the full hydrostatic pressure of ca. 90 mm Hg, falls to 20–30 mm Hg in the veins emptied by muscle contraction (Fig. 20-18). The *arteriovenous pressure difference,* shifted to a higher level but otherwise unchanged during quiet standing, becomes greater along with the decrease in venous pressure, so that flow through the affected vessel segments is increased. Moreover, the decrease in venous pressure reduces the *capillary filtration pressure,* so that there is less danger of edema (see p. 505). The subsequent rise in pressure, as long as the venous valves are intact, results from anterograde filling of the veins from the capillaries rather than from backflow.

In case of venous-valve insufficiency – which can be caused, for instance, by inflammation or distension of the veins due to varicosis – the function of the muscle pump is more or less impaired, depending on the nature and degree of the disorder. Because it now has less or no pressure-reducing influence in a standing person, the veins expand progressively, fluid gradually accumulates in the leg (edema), and the blood supply is disrupted. The last effect, in severe cases, can cause tissue degeneration (leg ulcers). The slower flow is also often associated with intravascular clotting in certain parts of the vein, or thrombosis. These leg-vein diseases are considerably more common in people who stand for long times without activating the muscle pump very often (e.g., sales clerks) than in those whose jobs require it to be activated continually (e.g., postmen).

Respiratory pump. During inspiration the progressively reduced intrathoracic pressure causes an increase in the transmural pressure. The associated greater dilation of the intrathoracic vessels results in *decreased resistance to flow* and simultaneously exerts an *effective suction* on the blood in the adjacent vessels. The inspiratory enhancement of venous return is most effective in the region of the *superior vena cava* (Fig. 20-19). On the other hand, depression of the diaphragm during inspiration raises the *intraabdominal pressure,* with the result that the transmural pressures and thus the lumen size – the capacity – of the abdominal vessels decrease. The steeper pressure gradient between intraabdominal and intrathoracic veins *enhances venous influx* into the thorax, whereas a retrograde flow into the lower limbs is prevented by the venous valves. The reverse occurs during *expiration;* the pressure gradient is less steep and flow through the veins from abdomen to thorax is inhibited. The suction-pressure-pump effects on venous flow are considerable – especially when breathing is deep, as during exercise.
As a consequence of the greater filling of the right heart during inspiration, the stroke volume of the *right ventricle* increases by the Frank-Starling mechanism (pp. 471f.). But at the same time the expansion of the lungs enlarges the capacity of the pulmonary vessels, so that venous return to the left heart, and thus the stroke volume of the *left ventricle,* is reduced. During expiration less blood enters the right heart and the stroke volume of the right ventricle decreases, but more blood enters the left heart from the pulmonary vessels and so the stroke volume of the left ventricle increases. That is, the *respiratory excursions bring about phase-shifted changes*

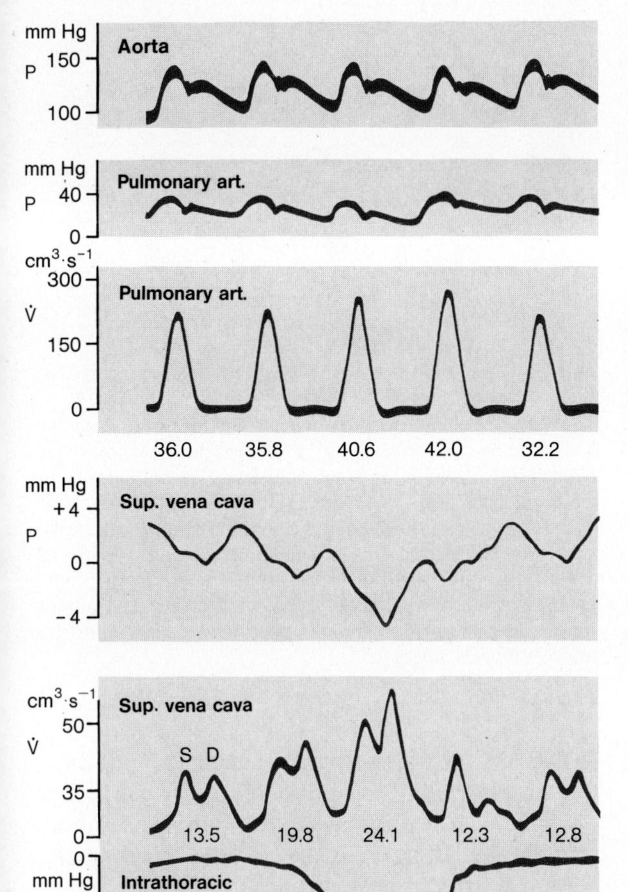

Fig. 20-19. Simultaneous recording of pressure in the aorta, pulmonary artery, and superior vena cava, the intrathoracic pressure, and the volume flow in the pulmonary artery and superior vena cava of a dog with closed thorax. A spontaneous deep inspiration produces a transient pressure drop in the vena cava and flow increase in both vein and artery. Two flow peaks are discernible in the vena cava, associated with the systolic shift of the valve plane of the heart (S) and the early diastolic filling of the ventricle (D). (From BRECHER [3])

in the stroke volumes of the right and left ventricles, by their opposed effects on ventricular filling [28].

With *above-normal pressure* in the lungs, the intrathoracic segments of vessels are compressed, which *inhibits* venous return to the heart. "Valsalva's maneuver" carries this condition to an extreme; the subject takes a deep breath and then strongly contracts the expiratory and abdominal muscles with the glottis closed. The increases in intrathoracic and intraabdominal pressures so produced essentially block venous return; the stroke volume of the right ventricle decreases and the pressure in the peripheral veins rises. On the other hand, blood is pressed out of the pulmonary vessels, so that the stroke volume of the left ventricle and the arterial blood pressure show a transient marked increase, followed by a distinct decline owing to the inadequate venous return.

Suction effects of the heart. In the veins near the heart the velocity of flow is also increased by the heart's own movement. An *initial peak flow* (S in Fig. 20-19) results from the suction exerted when downward displacement of the *valve plane* during the ejection period lowers the pressure in the right atrium and adjacent parts of the venae cavae. A *second flow peak* (D in Fig. 20-19) appears when the blood in the atrium and venae cavae enters the relaxed ventricle after opening of the *atrioventricular valve.* The two peaks S and D correspond to the x and y valleys in the venous pulse curve (cf. Fig. 20-16).

20.6 Microcirculation

The Terminal Vascular Bed

As the site of exchange between the blood and the interstitial fluid, the *capillaries* are functionally the most important part of the circulatory system. The *venules* also participate in the processes of exchange. Because the venules as well as the arterioles and metarterioles are involved in the regulation of capillary perfusion, the entire network of vessels from arterioles to venules – the so-called *terminal vascular bed (microcirculation)* – must be regarded as a functional unit. The arrangement of this system meets two crucial prerequisites for the various exchange processes, in that within the capillaries the blood makes contact with a very *large surface* for a relatively *long time* [6, 11, 17, 25, 38].

Size of the capillary exchange surface. Rough estimates of the cross-sectional and surface areas of the capillaries can be obtained as follows. The mean capillary radius is 3 μm, and the mean length is 750 μm. Thus the *cross-sectional area* ($\pi \cdot r^2$) of the average capillary is about 30 μm^2, and its surface area ($\pi \cdot 2r \cdot l$) is about 14,000 μm^2. If the part of the venule surface involved in exchange processes is included, the **effective exchange area** amounts to ca. **22,000 μm^2** per capillary.
Given a mean flow velocity of ca. 210 $mm \cdot s^{-1}$ in the aorta and ca. 0.3 $mm \cdot s^{-1}$ in the capillaries (cf. p. 492) – that is, a ratio of 700:1 – the law of continuity (Equation 2) requires that with an

aortic cross-sectional area of 4 cm^2 the *cross-sectional area of all the perfused capillaries* be 2,800 cm^2, or *about 3,000 cm^2*. Under resting conditions, however, blood is actually flowing through only about 25–35% of the capillaries in the body; thus the **cross-sectional area of all capillaries** in the systemic circulation is roughly **11,000 cm^2** [6, 11].

Number of capillaries. The above calculations imply that the *total number* of capillaries in the human body is about *40 billion,* so that the **total effective exchange surface** including the venules would have an area of about **1,000 m^2.** Assuming a uniform distribution of the capillaries within the body, this would amount to 600 capillaries per cubic millimeter of tissue, or 1.5 m^2 of capillary surface per 100 g of tissue.

Capillary density *varies* considerably, however, in the vascular beds of the different organs. For example, in the myocardium, brain, liver and kidneys there are 2,500–3,000/mm^3, in "phasic" units of the skeletal musculature 300–400/mm^3, and in "tonic" units only 100/mm^3. Bone, fat and connective tissue also have a relatively low density of capillaries. Another, independent variable is the *ratio of perfused to non-perfused capillaries* under resting conditions; again, the differences are considerable. Therefore the expansion of the exchange-surface area that can be achieved with maximal vasodilation is very different in the different organs. These relationships are summarized in Fig. 20-20; but remember that here, as in the above calculations, some of the numbers are simply rough estimates. Increase in number of "active" (i.e., perfused) capillaries is important in that it *shortens the diffusion path* to the cells and thus improves the blood supply to the tissue.

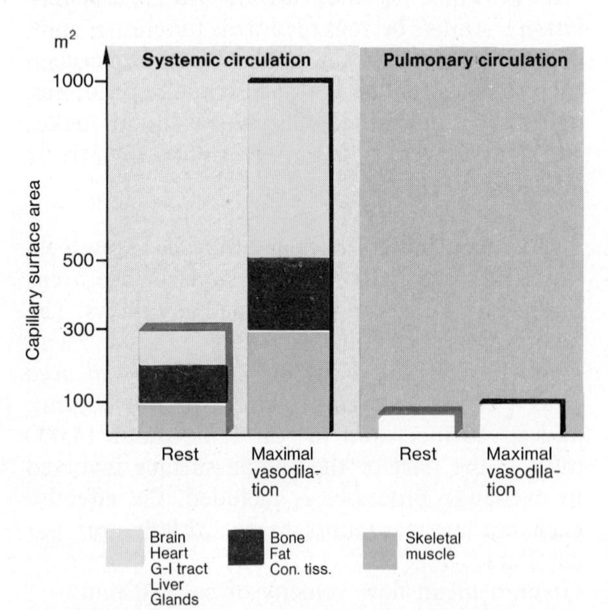

Fig. 20-20. Area of the capillary surface in various organs and in the pulmonary bed, under resting conditions and with maximal vasodilation. (From FOLKOW and NEIL [6])

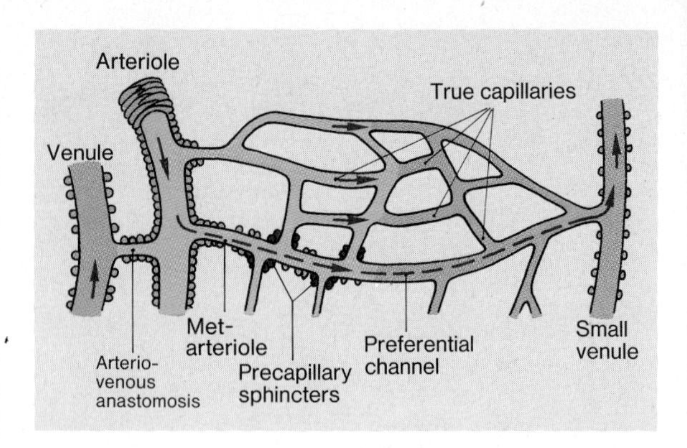

Fig. 20-21. Schematic drawing of the terminal vascular bed. The vessels branching off from the arterioles are metarterioles, which are somewhat larger in diameter than the capillaries and constitute the preferential channel for blood flow. Near their origins the metarteriole walls contain smooth muscle fibers (semicircles along the vessel walls); the smooth muscle fibers found where the capillaries branch off from the metarterioles are the precapillary sphincters. The arteriovenous anastomoses also comprise smooth muscle fibers

Structure of the terminal bed. In most cases the "true" capillaries *do not directly join* arterioles to venules (Fig. 20-21). Often they branch off at right angles from **metarterioles,** so-called "preferential channels" with walls containing smooth muscle fibers in diminishing numbers from proximal to distal; these vessels eventually merge with the non-contractile venules. Where the capillaries leave the metarterioles smooth muscle fibers are arranged to form so-called **precapillary sphincters;** other than these, there are *no contractile elements* in the capillaries. The state of contraction of the precapillary sphincters determines the fraction of blood that flows through the true capillaries, whereas the total volume flow through metarterioles and capillaries is set by the state of contraction of the smooth muscle fibers of the arterioles.

The *ratio of metarterioles to true capillaries* varies in the different organs. In skeletal muscle, with its widely fluctuating metabolic requirements, it is 1:8 to 1:10; in the mesenteric circulation, where metabolism is fairly uniform, it is about 1:2 to 1:3. In the human nail bed the capillaries are direct continuations of the metarterioles, giving a ratio of 1:1.

Another special feature is the presence of **arteriovenous anastomoses** (Fig. 20-21), which provide *direct* communication between small arteries and small veins, or arterioles and venules. Their walls are highly muscular. Arteriovenous anastomoses can be found in many tissues, and are especially common in the acral regions of the skin (fingers, toes, earlobes), where they function in thermoregulation (p. 634).

Capillary Exchanges

Ultrastructure of the capillary walls. Three types of capillary can be distinguished on the basis of fine structure: (i) capillaries with *uninterrupted* membranes, (ii) capillaries with *fenestrated* membranes, (iii) capillaries with *discontinuous* membranes.

The walls of *Type 1* capillaries consist of a continuous layer of endothelial cells having membranes with a large number of minute (4–5nm) pores. This form is widespread; it is found in both striated and smooth muscle, in adipose and connective tissue, and in the pulmonary circulation. Capillaries of *Type 2* have fenestrations within the cells, up to 0.1 μm in diameter, which are frequently closed by a very thin membrane; such capillaries are found in the glomeruli of the kidneys and in the intestinal mucosa. In *Type 3* the wall is interrupted by relatively large intercellular spaces through which fluid and blood cells can pass. This form is found in the bone marrow, in the sinusoids of the liver and in the spleen.

Exchange by diffusion. In the exchange of fluid and materials between blood and interstitial space, diffusion processes in both directions play by far the greatest role. The *rate of diffusion* here is so high that during a single capillary passage the water in the plasma exchanges 40 times with the water in the interstitial space, so that there is a continual mixing of plasma water and interstitial fluid. The numbers of molecules diffusing outward and inward are very nearly the same, so that the volume of plasma in the capillary remains practically constant. The rate of diffusion through the entire capillary surface of the body is about *60 l/min,* or ca. *85,000 l/day.*

Water-soluble substances, such as Na^+, Cl^-, glucose and so on, diffuse entirely through the *water-filled pores.* The permeability to the individual molecules depends on the relative sizes of molecule and pore; small molecules like H_2O and NaCl diffuse more readily than large molecules like glucose or albumins. The relative permeability, with water = 1, is 0.6 for glucose and < 0.0001 for albumin molecules. Because the capillary membrane is impermeable to albumin, there is a distinct and functionally important difference in the concentration of this substance in plasma and interstitial fluid (see below).

Large molecules unable to pass through the "sieve" of the pores can move through the capillary wall by *pinocytosis* – that is, invagination of the cell membrane to surround the molecule in a vacuole, with the reverse process (emiocytosis) on the other side of the cell.
Lipid-soluble substances such as alcohol, as well as O_2 and CO_2, can *diffuse freely.* Because this diffusion takes place across the entire capillary membrane, the rates of transport of lipid-soluble substances are very much greater than those of water-soluble substances [11, 17, 30].

Exchange by filtration. A second mechanism for exchange between the intravascular and interstitial spaces involves **filtration and reabsorption processes** in the terminal vascular bed. Under normal conditions, according to the classical *theory of Starling,* a **dynamic equilibrium** generally prevails between the amounts of fluid filtered out of the capillaries at their arterial ends and reabsorbed at the venous ends or carried away in the lymph vessels [11, 17, 25, 38, 40].
However, if this *equilibrium is upset* there are (relatively rapid) volume shifts between intravascular and interstitial space; these can crucially affect circulatory function in several ways, particularly in view of the necessity of maintaining an adequate volume of intravascular fluid.
Filtration and reabsorption in the capillaries are basically determined by the **hydrostatic pressure** in the **capillaries** (P_C) and in the **interstitial fluid** (P_{IF}), the **colloid osmotic pressure** in the **plasma** (π_C) and in the **interstitial fluid** (π_{IF}), and a **filtration coefficient** (K). Movement of fluid out of the capillaries into the interstitial space is brought about by P_C and π_{IF}, and that in the reverse direction by π_C and P_{IF}. The filtration coefficient K corresponds to the permeability of the capillary wall to isotonic fluids in ml fluid per mm Hg pressure in 100 g tissue per minute (at 37 °C). The volume filtered per minute ($\dot{V}$) can thus be computed as

$$\dot{V} = (P_C + \pi_{IF} - P_{IF} - \pi_C) \cdot K \qquad (20)$$

$\dot{V}$ is positive for filtration, and negative for reabsorption.

The pressure within single capillaries has been measured directly; with 30–35 mm Hg at the beginning of the capillary, and 13–17 mm Hg at the end, the **mean pressure** is about **23–24 mm Hg.** In relatively large capillary beds the *functional mean capillary pressure* is probably somewhat lower, because of the rhythmic changes in resistance to flow produced by vasomotion in the precapillary vessels (p. 508).
It is impossible to measure the *interstitial-fluid pressure* directly, because the interstitial gaps are at most 1 μm wide. The methodologically unsatisfactory indirect measurements of interstitial pressure give values between +10

mm Hg and –9 mm Hg; pressure near zero to slightly positive (ca. **3 mm Hg**) are usually regarded as normal.
A notable feature of the extracellular space is that regardless of the uncertainty as to absolute pressures, pressure changes within the normal range alter the interstitial fluid volume only slightly; that is, the *distensibility of the interstitial space* ($\Delta V/\Delta P$) *is low*. But as interstitial pressure increases, a point is rather abruptly passed beyond which distensibility becomes decidedly greater; the result is a marked increase in interstitial fluid volume and the onset of *edema* (abnormally large amounts of interstitial fluid). Edema usually does not become noticeable until the interstitial volume becomes about 30% greater than normal.
The *colloid osmotic pressure* of the plasma amounts to about **25 mm Hg;** it is produced by the plasma proteins, present in a concentration of ca. 73g/l. The capillary walls are not entirely impermeable to protein, as once was thought. Depending on their ultrastructure (see above), the capillaries release varying amounts of protein into the interstitial fluid of the different organs, which are transported away in the lymph vessels. The *average lymph protein concentration* is thus an indicator of *capillary permeability;* in the liver 1 l lymph contains 60 g protein, in the intestinal tract 30–40 g, in the skin 10 g and in the musculature 20 g.
Within a single capillary, protein permeability increases from the arterial to the venous end, for both the surface area and the number of large pores increase in the venous region. This difference is reflected, for example, in the indirectly measured protein concentration in the interstitial fluid of skeletal muscle, which rises from about 3 g/l around the arterial part of the capillaries to just under 40 g/l around the venous part. An acceptable estimate of the *mean protein concentration* of the interstitial fluid of the whole organism is 18-20 g/l; this exerts a *colloid osmotic pressure of* about **5 mm Hg** (Fig. 20-22).

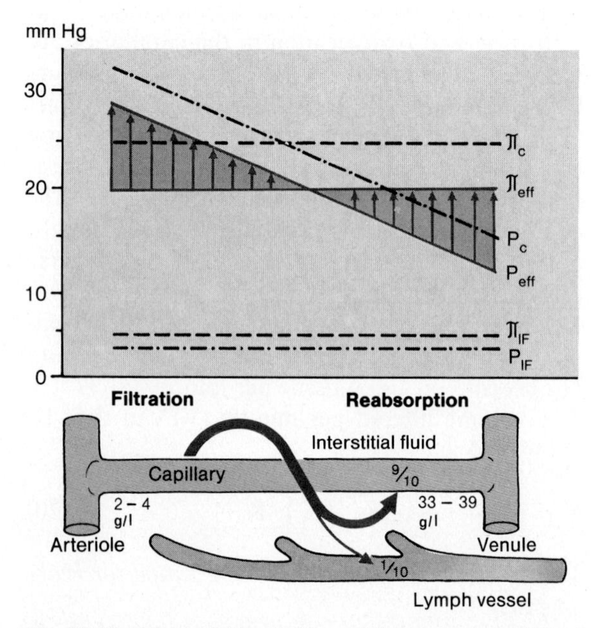

Fig. 20-22. Schematic illustration of the movement of fluid between a blood capillary and the interstitial space in the musculature. P_C, capillary pressure; P_{IF}, pressure in the interstitial space; π_C, π_{IF}, colloid osmotic pressure in the capillary and interstitial space; P_{eff}, effective transmural filtration pressure; π_{eff}, effective colloid osmotic pressure. As a simplification, π_C and π_{IF} are shown as constant over the entire length of the capillary. The whole numbers in the *lower* drawing indicate the increase in average protein concentration from the arterial to the venous end, and the fractions show the proportion of capillary reabsorption and the transport of interstitial fluid through the lymph vessels under normal conditions.

Equilibrium between intra- and extravascular fluids. From the data given above it is possible to derive a highly simplified balance for the *movement of fluid* between capillaries and interstitial space.
At the *arterial* end of the capillary there is an outward pressure of ca. 37.5 mm Hg (P_C = 32.5 mm Hg $+\pi_{IF}$ = 5 mm Hg), which is opposed by an inward pressure of 28 mm Hg (π_C = 25 mm Hg + P_{IF} = 3 mm Hg). The **effective filtration pressure** is thus **9.5 mm Hg** (Fig. 20-22).
At the *venous* end the outward pressure is 20 mm Hg (P_C = 15 mm Hg + P_{IF} = 5 mm Hg) while the inward pressure is unchanged, 28 mm Hg; thus the **effective reabsorption pressure** is **8 mm Hg.**
Under the simplifying assumption that pressure falls off linearly and the other factors are constant, the net outward pressure under normal conditions is the *mean filtration pressure* of 28.5 mm Hg (P_C = 23.5 mm Hg + π_{IF} = 5 mm Hg), and the net inward pressure is the *mean reabsorption pressure* of 28.5 mm Hg (π_C = 23.5 mm Hg +P_{IF} = 5 mm Hg). That is, filtration slightly exceeds reabsorption.
The *effective filtration pressure* causes an average of ca. 0.5% of the volume of plasma flowing through the capillaries to enter the interstitial space in the arterial segment. Because the *effective reabsorption pressure* is slightly less, only ca. 90% of this is reabsorbed in the venous segment, the remaining 10% being removed from the interstitial space in the lymph vessels (Fig. 20-22).
The average **filtration rate of all the capillaries** in the body is thus ca. **14 ml · min^{-1}** or **20 l per 24 h,** and the reabsorption rate is ca. **12.5 ml · min^{-1}** or **18 l per 24 h;** two liters per day are carried away by the lymph vessels.
This relative equlibrium between filtration and reabsorption in the capillaries must necessarily be upset if one of the factors involved should change. The *hydrostatic capillary pressure* (P_C) plays a special role in this regard. Increases in P_C shift the filtration-reabsorption conditions in the direction of enhanced filtration, whereas decreases in P_C enhance reabsorption. The level of the hydrostatic pressure in the capillaries is

greatly affected by the momentary *precapillary resistance,* which also influences the **number of perfused capillaries** and thus the **area of the exchange surface** in a vascular region. But changes in the postcapillary resistance, which under resting conditions is about $1/4$ of the precapillary resistance, also affect hydrostatic pressure and thus the filtration-reabsorption ratio in the capillaries. *Vasomotor control* of these processes, for regulation of *intravascular plasma volume* (see p. 515), is made possible by the innervation of the precapillary vessels and, to a lesser extent, the postcapillary vessels.

These relationships explain the occurrence of *enhanced filtration* in conditions so diverse as general hypertension, dilation of the resistance vessels in muscular work, erect posture, increased blood volume owing to transfusion, and isolated pressure increases on the venous side (e.g., in cardiac insufficiency), as well as the reverse effect – *enhanced reabsorption* due to general hypotension, constriction of the resistance vessels, blood loss etc. (cf. Fig. 20-23). Decreases in the *colloid osmotic pressure* of the plasma (for example, in protein deficiency) or an accumulation of *osmotically active substances in the interstitial fluid* also give rise to enhanced filtration, while increases in the colloid osmotic pressure of the plasma enhance reabsorption.

A greater displacement of fluid into the interstitial space can also be due to *increased capillary permeability;* this is induced, for example, by histamine and related substances, kinins etc. released in allergic reactions, inflammation, burns and wounds (cf. pp. 510f.). Given the many physiological conditions under which strong outward forces increase filtration over the entire length of the capillary, one would expect excessive accumulation of interstitial fluid in the form of **edema** to occur more often than it actually does. The rarity of edema is due in part to the *slight distensibility* of the interstitial space within a relatively large range of pressures, which tends to prevent the accumulation of fluid. On the other hand, as soon as the interstitial fluid begins to increase as a result of inadequate capillary reabsorption, it is *more rapidly removed* by the lymphatic system (see below). The associated increased loss of protein reduces the colloid osmotic pressure, which in turn inhibits the accumulation of fluid in the interstitial space and thus contributes to the maintenance of equilibrium between the intravascular and interstitial fluid volumes.

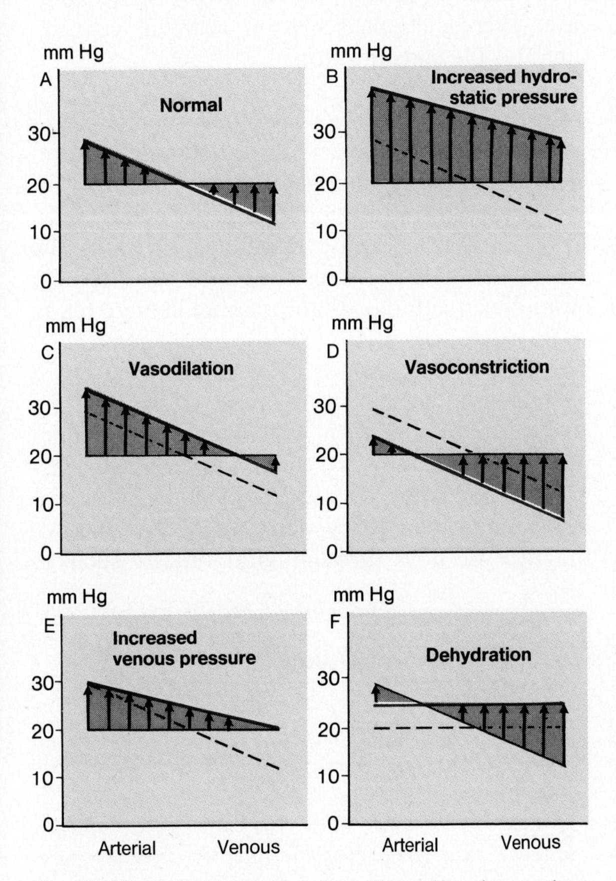

Fig. 20-23 A–F. Diagrams of capillary filtration and reabsorption under various physiological and pathological conditions. Depending on the magnitudes of P_{eff} and π_{eff}, the relative filtration-reabsorption equilibrium in the capillaries is shifted towards increased filtration **(B, C, E)** or increased reabsorption **(D, F)**

20.7 The Lymphatic System

The lymph vessels constitute a *supplementary drainage system* through which the interstitial fluid is returned to the blood vascular system.

Structure of the lymphatic system. All tissues except the superficial layers of the skin, the CNS and the bones are penetrated by an enormous number of *lymph capillaries* arranged in an extremely fine-meshed network. Unlike the blood capillaries, these are closed at one end. At their open ends the lymph capillaries join to form *larger lymph vessels* which empty into the venous system at a number of points, chiefly by way of the thoracic duct and the right lymphatic duct. The walls of the lymph capillaries are composed of a single-layered endothelium and are easily permeable to electrolyte solutions, sugar, fats and proteins. The walls of the larger lymph vessels have smooth muscle fibers and valves (like those in the veins). At various points along the larger lymph vessels are *lymph nodes,* which act as filters and retain the coarser elements in the lymph.

Amount and composition of lymph. Under normal conditions **lymph accumulates** at a rate of ca. **2 l in 24 h,** as the 10% of the capillary filtrate that is not reabsorbed. Lymph consists of interstitial fluid. *The average protein content* is 20 g/l, though there are considerable regional differences associated with the differences in permeability of the blood capillaries (60 g/l in the liver, 30–40 g/l in the intestinal tract; cf. p. 504). The lymph vessels are one of the main channels by which *absorbed substances,* particularly fats, are *transported away* from the gastrointestinal tract [59].

The *pressure* in the terminal lymph vessels is ca. 1–2 mm Hg. In the larger lymph vessels it fluctuates considerably, due to spontaneous rhythmic activity of the smooth muscle fibers, and in some cases the mean level is distinctly higher. The **mean velocity of flow** in the lymph vessels is relatively slow. In those lymph vessels with smooth muscle fibers transport occurs by *rhythmic contractions* of the smooth musculature. Backflow of lymph is prevented by the valves. In the lymph capillaries and vessels of the skeletal musculature propulsion of lymph is also assisted by the so-called *lymphatic pump,* an effect of muscle contraction analogous to that by which blood flow through the veins is facilitated; transient pressure increases in their surroundings compress the lymph vessels and expel the lymph. During muscular work the volume flow of lymph can exceed the resting level by a *factor of 15.*

The primary function of the lymphatic system is thus to *remove from the interstitial space* those proteins and other substances that cannot be reabsorbed into the blood capillaries. A second very important function is that of **drainage,** to counteract the accumulation of fluid in the interstitial space when capillary filtration increases (p. 505). When lymph vessels are tied off (during surgery) or blocked (owing to inflammation or other causes) the tissues distal to the obstruction can exhibit marked *regional edema* (so called lymphatic edema).

20.8 Regulation of Regional (Local) Blood Flow

Basic Features of Regional Regulation

The perfusion of organs under resting conditions. The distribution of the cardiac output among the vascular beds of various human organs under resting conditions is summarized in Table 20-5. Because it is technically difficult to measure organ blood flow in humans, these data are only approximate. Comparison between flow rate and O_2 uptake shows that *organs with more active metabolism are perfused more rapidly,* although – as the percentage data for the two variables indicate – there is no fixed relation between perfusion rate and O_2 consumption.

Adjustment of the regional blood supply. Local volume flow is adjusted to functional requirements chiefly by changes in *resistance to flow* accompanying alteration of the vascular cross-sectional area; because resistance varies as the 4th power of the radius, this is a considerably more effective factor than pressure change (cf. p. 484).

The theoretical amount by which flow rate can be increased varies from organ to organ (Fig. 20-24). In organs with widely *fluctuating* functional requirements (skeletal musculature, gastrointestinal tract, liver and skin) blood flow can be changed over the widest range. By contrast, the rate of flow through vital organs such as

Table 20-5. Perfusion rate and O_2 uptake in various organs of a human[a] under resting conditions

Vascular region	Blood flow		O_2 uptake		Weight	
	ml/min	% of total	ml/min	% of total	g	% of total
Splanchnic	1,400	24	58	25	2,800	4.0
Kidneys	1.100	19	16	7	300	0.4
Brain	750	13	46	20	1,500	2.0
Heart	250	4	27	11	300	0.4
Skeletal muscle	1,200	21	70	30	30,000	43.0
Skin	500	9	5	2	5,000	7.0
Other organs	600	10	12	5	30,100	43.2
	5,800	100	234	100	70,000	100.0

[a] Weight 70 kg, body surface 1.7 m^2. (From Wade and Bishop [23])

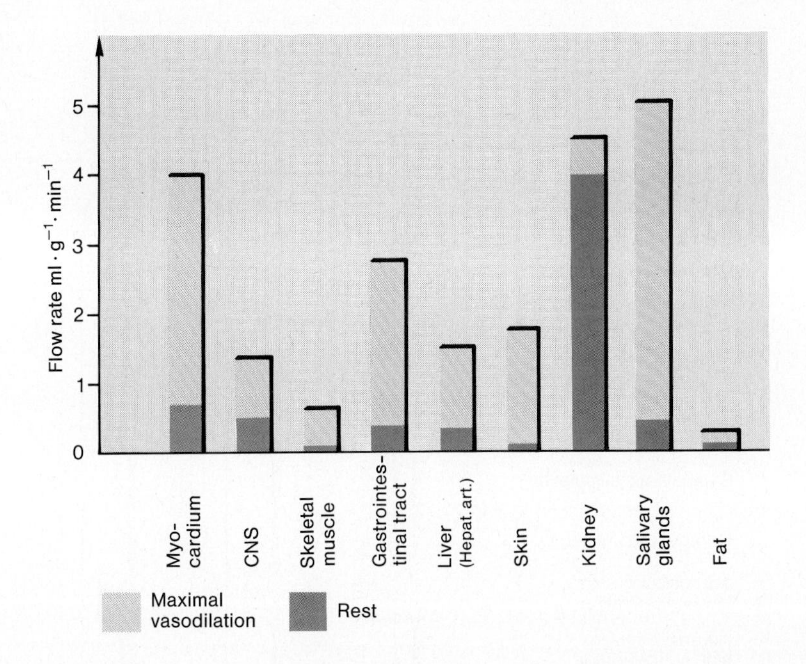

Fig. 20-24. Volume flow in the vascular beds of different organs under resting conditions *(red)* and with maximal vasodilation *(light red)*. The data were computed for a normal adult human with a body weight of 70 kg. The volume flow per g tissue also indicates the relative resistance to flow in the individual organ systems. (Modified from MELLANDER and JOHANSSON)

the brain and kidneys, with requirements that are continually high with relatively *little variation*, is kept nearly constant by special regulatory mechanisms; within limits it is very little affected by even pronounced changes in arterial pressure and cardiac output [22, 23, 35, 37, 42, 43, 54, 56, 58]. (For details of the perfusion of individual organs see pp. 533ff.).

The reactions by which the vessels adjust their output are based in part on *local mechanisms* [14, 55] and in part on *humoral and neural factors* [46, 50]. The relative effects of these different components on the smooth musculature of the vessels vary in the different organs. Often several factors are involved simultaneously, with a *synergistic* (but sometimes *antagonistic)* action on vascular tone.

In Fig. 20-25, the effect of the most important mechanisms on the vessels in skeletal muscle, skin and the splanchnic system are diagrammed; these will be discussed in the following sections.

Local Regulating Mechanisms

A number of substances which, like O_2, are required for cellular metabolism or are produced as metabolites have a *direct* effect on the state of contraction of the vascular musculature. Various processes are involved, some of which are not entirely understood; together they constitute the **metabolic autoregulation of peripheral blood flow.** The very great functional significance of these autoregulatory reactions lies in the *local adjustment of volume flow* in individual vascular beds to the momentary nutritional requirements of the tissue; here the metabolically elicited dilator responses dominate and in some cases completely overcome neurogenic constrictor effects [6, 8, 10, 14, 55].

O_2 deficiency. *Vasodilation* is elicited by decrease in the O_2 partial pressure of the blood. The changes in regional flow rate associated with altered local metabolism are thought to be based on the fact that *arteriolar O_2 partial pressure decreases when metabolism is accelerated,* and vice versa. This mechanism would require that oxygen diffuse out of the arteriole (as has been confirmed in experiments) and that the reaction be related to *changes in the O_2 gradient* along its length.

Metabolites. *Local increases in CO_2 partial pressure and/or H^+ concentration* also cause vasodilation. Of the other metabolites produced in greater amounts during exercise, *lactic acid* exerts a dilator action, not directly but by way of the pH shift it causes. *Pyruvate* is a weak vasodilator, and *ATP, ADP, AMP and adenosine* are strong vasodilators. The actions of these substances on the vessels, however, do not suffice to explain the extreme vasodilation associated with muscular work (Fig. 20-25). Other metabolic products are probably also involved. Further factors that have been proposed as vasomotor agents include changes in the extracellular concentration of osmotically effective substances, potassium in par-

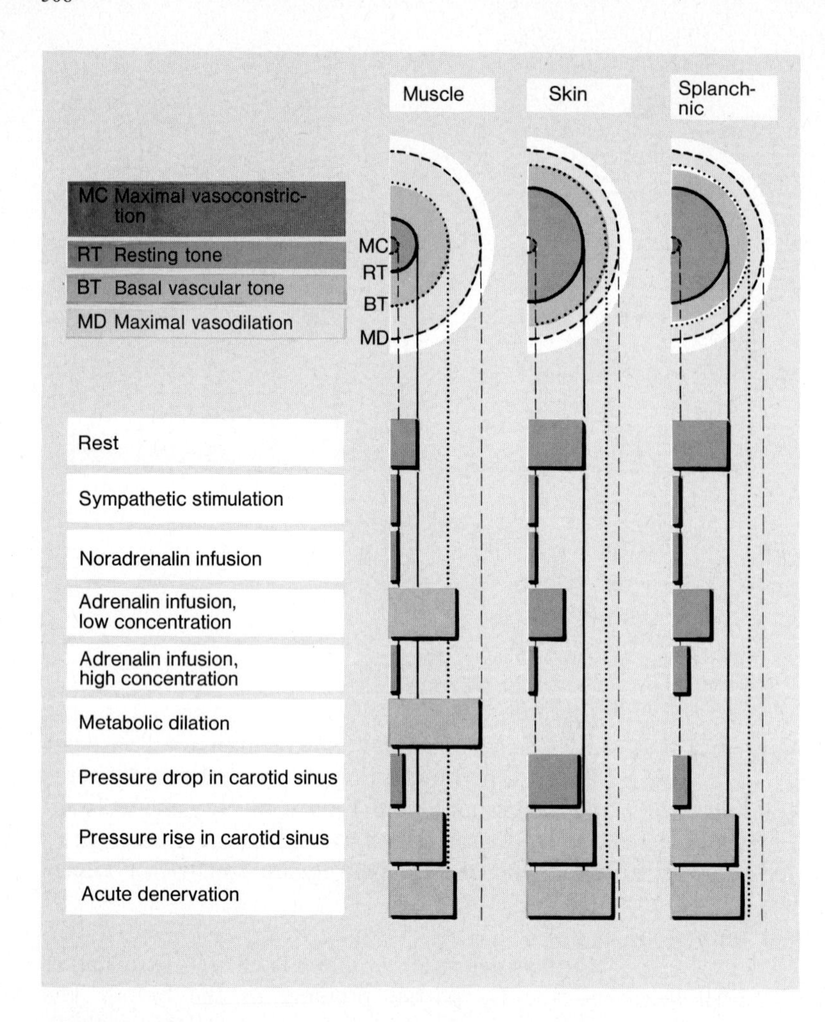

Fig. 20-25. Schematic illustration of the vascular tone in muscle, cutaneous and splanchnic vessels under various physiological and pathological conditions. The proportions of the individual components of vascular tone vary in the different organs, so that a given stimulus elicits quantitatively varying responses

ticular, owing to their more rapid release from working musculature [52] (cf. p. 535).
Changes in vascular diameter by metabolism-related processes can be elicited *directly by diffusion* of the substances, for the arterioles lie within the active tissue and thus in the immediate vicinity of the capillaries. It is not necessary to invoke "ascending" axon reflexes (see p. 510) from the capillaries, the site at which the metabolites diffuse, to the arterioles in order to explain the metabolic reactions.

Reactive hyperemia. When the blood supply to a muscle is interrupted or restricted experimentally, its restoration is accompanied by an *overshooting* response (reactive hyperemia), the extent of which depends on the *metabolic rate* and the *duration* of the interruption. Reactive hyperemia is probably caused by the same mechanisms as metabolic dilation. When venous blood is experimentally transferred from the working or ischemic musculature into vessels supplying resting musculature, dilation occurs; thus it can be regarded as proven that the eliciting agents are *humoral* in nature.

Myogenic effects. The ability of many vessels to maintain largely *constant volume flow* by smooth-muscle contraction when pressure increases and relaxation when pressure decreases (p. 487), independent of the level of pressure, is an important form of **myogenic (mechanogenic) autoregulation.** This ability is especially well developed in the renal vessels, but it is also found in those of the brain, heart, liver, mesenteries and skeletal muscle. No myogenic responses have been observed in the cutaneous circulation.

Intrinsic vasomotion. One myogenic effect that does not serve to adjust blood flow to momentary requirements is the rhythmic vasomotion [40] observable in the *arterioles, metarterioles* and *precapillary sphincters.* These contractions of the smooth muscle fibers, and the associated changes in resistance to flow, give rise to *rhythmic fluctuations in the rate of flow* through the parts of the vessels concerned. The frequency and intensity of these processes are variable. The effects are independent of the autonomic innervation, and arise from the tendency of the smooth muscle fibers to *autorhythmicity* (see p. 79).

Neural Regulation

The neural vasomotor control mechanism is mediated by the *autonomic nervous system,* predominantly by way of sympathetic fibers, though parasympathetic fibers are also involved in some responses. *All the blood vessels except the capillaries are innervated,* but the density and function of the innervation vary widely in different organs and in different parts of the vascular system.

In most *sympathetic* nerves the neuromuscular transmitter substance released by the postganglionic fibers is noradrenalin *(adrenergic fibers).* Cholinergic sympathetic fibers are discussed on p. 510.

Sympathetic adrenergic vasoconstrictor fibers. Efferent nerves in which increased impulse frequency raises the active tension of the vessel musculature are called **vasoconstrictor nerves.** These belong to the sympathetic part of the autonomic nervous system. Details of their site of origin and arrangement in the body are given in Chapter 16.

The small arteries and arterioles of the *skin, kidneys* and *splanchnic region* receive a dense innervation, whereas the innervation of those in the *skeletal muscles* and *brain* is relatively sparse. The density of innervation of the veins is much lower, on the whole, but otherwise generally corresponds to that of the arteries. Neuromuscular transmission is mediated by *noradrenalin,* which in all cases elicits constriction of the muscles.

The degree of vascular smooth-muscle contraction depends directly on the frequency of the efferent impulses. The **resting tone** of the vessels (p. 486) is maintained by the **continual (tonic) discharge** of 1–3 impulses/s. *Maximal* vasoconstrictor effects are elicited by only ca. *10 imp/s* (Fig. 20-26). Thus increases in impulse frequency produce vasoconstriction, and decreases produce vasodilation; the latter responses are limited by the *basal tone* that prevails when the vasoconstrictor fibers are silent or have been transected (see below). Because of the background discharge of these fibers *"vasomotor tone",* the neurally controlled state of contraction of the vascular muscles, can be varied in both directions to produce *both vasoconstriction and vasodilation* – and hence both decreases and increases in the resistance to flow – without the need for two sets of special fibers.

In the absence of vasoconstrictor impulses, resistance to flow is determined by the varying levels of **basal tone** in the different vascular regions. Basal tone, and thus resistance, is smaller in the

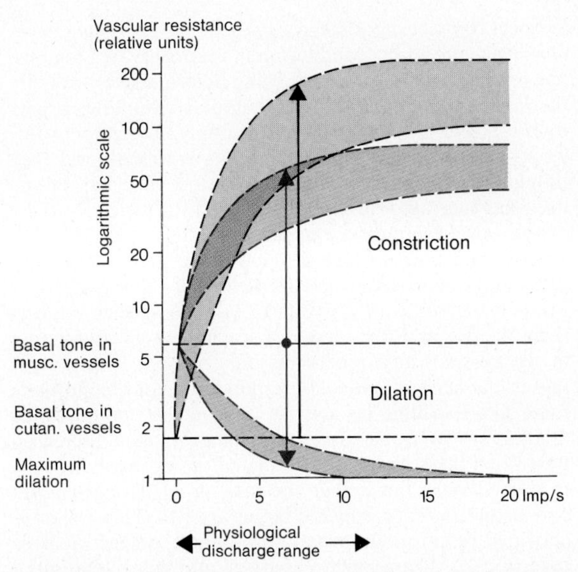

Fig. 20-26. Graph showing the vasomotor effects of efferent impulses on vessels in muscle *(red)* and skin *(black)* of the cat. After transection of the abdominal sympathetic trunk electrical stimulation distal to the cut causes weaker vasoconstriction in the muscle vessels, with their higher basal tone, than in the cutaneous vessels. Vasomotor control of the muscle vessels also involves cholinergic sympathetic dilator fibers. The vasomotor effects of the system can be distinguished by appropriate pharmacological blockade; dihydroergotamine blocks the vasoconstrictor action of the adrenergic fibers, and atropine blocks the vasodilator action of the cholinergic fibers. (Modified from CELANDER and FOLKOW)

cutaneous than in the muscle vessels (Fig. 20-25 and 20-26). When the constrictor nerve fibers are stimulated the responses of the two regions are fundamentally the same, but *for a given stimulus frequency the cutaneous vessels constrict more strongly* (Fig. 20-26). The *resistance to flow (and hence the perfusion rate)* in the vessels of the skin can thus be varied over a much wider range than that in the muscles by changes in the discharge rate of the vasoconstrictor fibers. This limitation in the muscle vessels is compensated to a great extent by *vasodilator responses* (Fig. 20-26), the mechanism of which is still in debate. The possible causes under discussion include excitation of *sympathetic cholinergic* dilator fibers (see below) and excitation of *β-receptors* in the muscle vessels by catecholamines (p. 510).

The significance of *tonic* activity in the vasoconstrictor nerves (resting tone) with regard to circulatory function is evident, for example, in the fact that when it is eliminated by *spinal anesthesia* or *ganglion-blocking drugs* the resulting vasodilation causes the mean blood pressure to fall to 40–60 mm Hg – a pressure that no longer guarantees an adequate blood supply to the organs (paralytic blood pressure; cf. spinal shock, p. 533).

Surgical transection of the sympathetic nerves *(sympathectomy)* also produces vasodilation in the denervated regions, the vessel diameter thereafter being determined entirely by the *basal tone* (Fig. 20-25). This initially low tone begins to rise a few days after sympathectomy, and after a few weeks can practically regain the pre-operational level even though the fibers have not regenerated. The basal tone itself has increased, probably because of a *hypersensitivity* of the vessel musculature to *catecholamines* and other vasoactive substances which develops after denervation and leads to an increase in the contraction of the muscles.

Sympathetic vasodilator fibers. In various species (among them the dog and cat) there is a special system originating in the cortex which innervates only the *precapillary vessels in the skeletal musculature.* Under resting conditions these fibers exhibit no activity. In contrast to metabolic dilation (p. 507), the vessels that dilate to give increased flow when these fibers are stimulated are probably not the true capillaries, but rather the *arteriovenous anastomoses* and *metarterioles* or even the larger arteries. This system is activated by emotional reactions of alarm, defense, fear or rage (p. 522). If muscular activity should ensue, the initial vasodilation in the working musculature is supplemented or replaced by dilator effects of *metabolic* origin. These sympathetic cholinergic dilator fibers have not as yet been shown to exist in humans, although dilation of the vessels in the muscles of humans anticipating activity has been observed (cf. p. 522).

Parasympathetic cholinergic vasodilator fibers. The vessels in the *external genitalia* are innervated by parasympathetic cholinergic fibers which are activated during sexual excitation and induce marked vasodilation and correspondingly increased blood flow through the organs. Cholinergic dilator fibers also innervate the *small pial arteries of the brain.* Their functional significance, however, is not yet clear.

Opinions differ as to whether other parts of the circulation are innervated by such fibers. The vasodilation of gland vessels in the *digestive tract* accompanying stimulation of the secretory nerves to the glands is thought to result primarily from the action of *kinins* formed in association with glandular activity (see below). But it cannot be definitely ruled out that specific parasympathetic cholinergic dilator fibers are involved.

Axon reflexes. Mechanical or chemical stimulation of the skin can give rise to local vasodilator responses that are ascribed to so-called *axon reflexes.* That is, it has been suggested that when thin, unmyelinated cutaneous nociceptive fibers are stimulated, the excitation not only proceeds in the afferent (orthodromic) direction, to the spinal cord, but is also carried antidromically, in efferent collateral fibers, to the arterioles in the innervated skin region. The vasodilation is *independent* of the sympathetic innervation of the cutaneous vessels; the effect disappears only after the nociceptive fibers have degenerated following a cut that disconnects them from the spinal cord. However, there is no convincing neurophysiological evidence of this atypical "axon reflex", and the vasodilation could also be elicited directly, by the release of vasodilator substances (e.g., ATP or substance P) from the receptive membranes. Such a mechanism would make it unnecessary to postulate efferent collaterals of afferent fibers.

During *prolonged exposure to cold* the initial vasoconstriction at the tips of the extremities is interrupted by *periodic dilation.* This reaction is also thought by some to be based on (nociceptive) axon reflexes. The warming due to vasodilation prevents damage to tissue in the vicinity of the vessels, which are closely packed for thermoregulatory reasons. The axon reflexes elicited by other stimuli may well also be a mechanism of *defense against local injury.* Axon reflexes are also thought to be involved in the so-called **triple response,** a sequence of reactions to progressively more intense local stimulation such as stroking the skin with a blunt instrument, as follows. 1. *Red reaction,* local reddening in the region of the mechanical stimulus (arteriolar dilation). 2. *Flare,* a brighter red flush in the surrounding area, beginning after ca. 30 s (axon reflex). 3. *Local edema* or wheal formation (damage to capillary walls).

Chemical and Hormonal Effects

Adrenalin and noradrenalin. The catecholamines adrenalin and noradrenalin are released continuously in small quantities from the adrenal medulla and circulate through the body as **hormones,** with ubiquitous effects on the vascular muscles. Whereas noradrenalin is the chief transmitter substance of the vasomotor fibers, the hormonal effects are due chiefly to adrenalin; the adrenal medulla secretes about 80% adrenalin and only 20% noradrenalin. The effects of the blood-borne catecholamines are not uniform. Adrenalin in particular elicits (i) partly constrictor, partly dilator and (ii) variously intense reactions of the vessel musculature.

Catecholamine receptors. The differential responses of the vessel musculature to circulating catecholamines can be explained by the presence of different "adrenergic receptors", the *α and β receptors,* which are particular chemical structures in the membranes of the muscle cells. Excitation of the α receptors elicits *contraction,* and excitation of the β receptors elicits *relaxation* of the smooth muscle fibers. *Noradrenalin* acts primarily on the α receptors, whereas *adrenalin* acts on both. In most (if not all) blood vessels both types of receptor are present, though their proportions and absolute numbers vary in the different parts of the circulatory system. The consequence is that *adrenalin elicits vasoconstriction where α receptors predominate, and vasodilation where β receptors predominate.*

The situation is complicated by the fact that the threshold for excitation of the β receptors is lower than that of the α receptors, whereas when both types are excited simultaneously the effects of the α receptors are dominant. Thus when adrenalin is present in *low* (physiological) concentration *vasodilation* results, whereas in high concentrations it elicits *vasoconstriction.* A largely *selective excitation of β receptors* can be achieved with the synthetic noradrenalin derivative *isopropyl noradrenalin,* but no analogous substance is known to be produced by the body itself.

A fairly large number of pharmacological substances, so-called *sympatholytics,* block the α or β receptors more less selectively. *Blocking of the α receptors* eliminates the vasoconstrictor effects of adrenalin, so that when it is injected the blood-pressure increase normally obtained owing to dominance of the α receptors is converted to a blood-pressure decrease mediated by the dilator action of the unaffected β receptors (so-called adrenalin reversal). *β-receptor blockade* has a less striking effect on the vascular responses; its chief therapeutic application is to alter the β-adrenergic effects on heart rate and the contractility of the myocardium.

Angiotensin II (see p. 518)

Vasopressin (see p. 520).

Histamine is liberated chiefly as a result of *damage to skin and muscosa,* and also in *antigen-antibody reactions;* most of it evidently comes from basophilic granulocytes and mast cells in the damaged region. It elicits local dilation of the arterioles and venules and increases capillary permeability (cf. p. 505).

Kallikrein-kinin system. *Kallikrein* is an enzyme in tissue and plasma that is ordinarily in inactive form; when activated, it splits an α_2-globulin in the plasma *(kininogen)* to produce the decapeptide *kallidin,* from which the nonapeptide *bradykinin* is formed by the removal of lysine. Bradykinin remains active for only a few minutes; then it is decomposed by *kinase I* and *II.* Kinase II is identical to the "converting enzyme" that converts angiotensin I to angiotensin II.
Kallidin and **bradykinin** have a strong *dilator* action on arterioles and enhance capillary permeability.
The marked vasodilation in glands of the gastrointestinal tract when their activity increases is brought about mainly by the action of kinins. These and similar mechanisms are also involved in providing more blood to the skin when the sweat glands are active.

Kinins appear to play a role in inflammatory and allergic circulatory responses as well (see p. 533). Moreover, the liberation of kinins when tissue is injured could be involved in the sensation of pain.

Prostaglandins, prostacyclin and *thromboxane* are produced in almost all organs and tissues. They are synthesized from the highly unsaturated C_{20} fatty acids arachidonic and linoleic acid, which are part of the phospholipid fraction of the membranes, by way of the intermediate product cycloendoperoxide.
Prostaglandins (PG) are hormone-like substances of which there are several groups and subgroups with diverse actions. For example, *PGA_1* and *PGA_2* cause the *dilation* of arteries, especially in the splanchnic region. *PGA_2* isolated from the renal medulla, known as *medullin,* lowers arterial pressure and increases renal blood flow as well as the renal excretion of water, Na^+ and K^+.
PG in the *E group* also have a dilator action when injected intraarterially and inhibit the release of noradrenalin from sympathetic nerve endings. PG in the *F group* elicit vasoconstriction and raise the arterial pressure.

Prostacyclin inhibits the aggregation of thrombocytes. **Thromboxane** promotes thrombocyte aggregation and in addition acts as a vasoconstrictor.

Renin (see p. 517).

Serotonin (5-hydroxytryptamine) is present in high concentrations in the viscera and in the thrombocytes. It acts as a *vasoconstrictor* and *raises* capillary permeability. The release of serotonin in the gastrointestinal tract increases intestinal motility and promotes secretion of the digestive juices, both by constricting the venules and by enhancing the permeability of the capillaries. Its strong constrictor action on the pial arteries in the brain might be involved in the production of vascular spasms (migraine). When serotonin is released by thrombocyte aggregation, its constrictor action contributes to obstruction of the vessel and, in the case of injury, assists hemostasis.

20.9 Regulation of the Overall Circulation

Basic Features of General Circulatory Regulation

Blood flow through the body is adjusted to the momentary situation by a combination of regional and higher-level (supraregional) mechanisms, the effects of which are closely interrelated.

The functional state of the circulation is continually monitored by **receptors** at various places in the cardiovascular system. The afferent impulses discharged by these receptors are conducted centrally to structures in the **medulla oblongata.** From these areas, the so-called **vasomotor center** (pp. 521f.), impulses are sent out both along efferent fibers to the **effectors** in heart and vessels and to other structures in the CNS, some of which participate in circulatory regulation by way of the control of neurohumoral-hormonal mechanisms [6, 10, 12, 22, 35, 42, 44, 54, 56].
The crucial mechanisms in general cardiovascular regulation are those that adjust **total peripheral resistance** and **cardiac output** in such a way as to maintain the *blood-pressure gradient* required for flow through the vascular system. Decreases in the total peripheral resistance as a result of dilation of the resistance vessels are compensated by increases in cardiac output over a wide range, and vice versa. At the same time, when the vessels in particular organs dilate to meet increased demands, the effect on the total peripheral resistance is at least partially compensated by vasoconstrictor responses in other organs.
There are other important adaptive processes that affect the relationship between **vessel capacity** and **blood volume,** which determines the *static blood pressure.* Fairly large changes in the capacity of the system are elicited by vasomotor reactions of the capacitance vessels [21, 46, 57], whereas the blood volume is affected both by the conditions of *capillary filtration and reabsorption* and by *renal fluid excretion* (in relation to fluid uptake).
The numerous adaptive processes can be classified in three groups, according to the *timing* of their action: (i) *short-term control mechanisms,* (ii) *intermediate-term control mechanisms,* and (iii) *long-term control mechanisms.*

Short-Term Control Mechanisms

The mechanisms in this category are predominantly **vasomotor adjustments** under **neural** control, which include (i) **baroreceptor (stretch-receptor) reflexes,** (ii) **chemoreceptor reflexes,** and (iii) the **ischemic reflex** of the CNS. The common characteristic of all these is a **rapid** onset of action, within a few seconds. The response is vigorous but, if activated continuously, within a few days it either dies out completely (baroreceptors) or is attenuated (chemoreceptors, CNS ischemic reflex). The neurally mediated vasomotor effects are supplemented by **hormonal** mechanisms involving **adrenalin, noradrenalin** and, with a delayed action, **vasopressin (ADH).**

Baroreceptor Reflexes

Locations of the arterial baroreceptors. In the walls of the large thoracic and cervical arteries are numerous so-called **baro- or pressoreceptors,** which are stimulated by the **stretching** of the vessel wall brought about by the transmural pressure. The baroreceptor areas of the greatest functional importance are those in the aortic arch and the carotid sinus (Fig. 20-27).

The sensory innervation of the baroreceptors in the carotid sinus is by way of the carotid-sinus nerve, a branch of the *glossopharyngeal nerve.* The baroreceptors in the aortic arch are innervated by the *left cardiac depressor nerve,* and those at the branch point of the brachiocephalic trunk by the *right cardiac depressor nerve.* Both the nerves to the carotid sinus and those to the aorta also contain fibers of *chemoreceptors* located in the carotid bodies (near the point where the common carotid artery divides) and in the aortic bodies of the aortic arch.

Pressure-discharge characteristic of the arterial baroreceptors. When the vessel wall is stretched

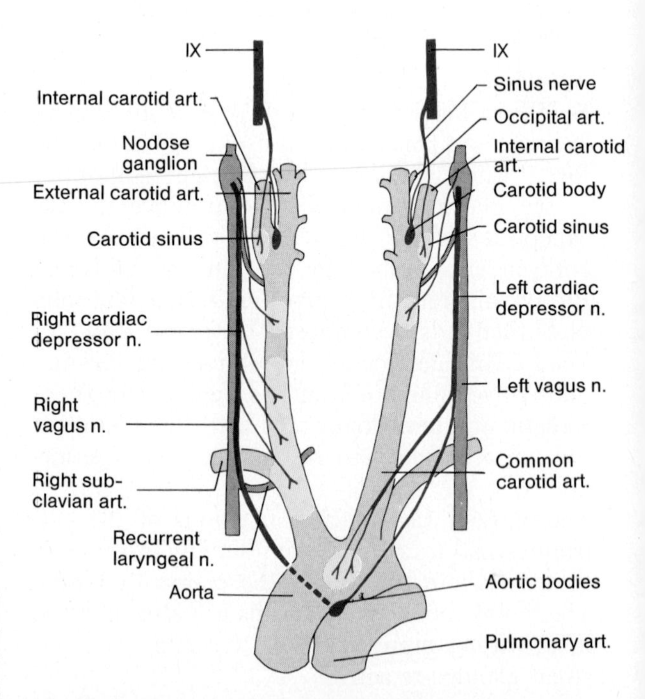

Fig. 20-27. Survey of the locations of baro- and chemoreceptors in the region of the aorta and carotid artery (from studies of dogs and cats). The baroreceptor fields are shown in *light red* and the afferent fibers in *red.* (Modified from MILNOR [18])

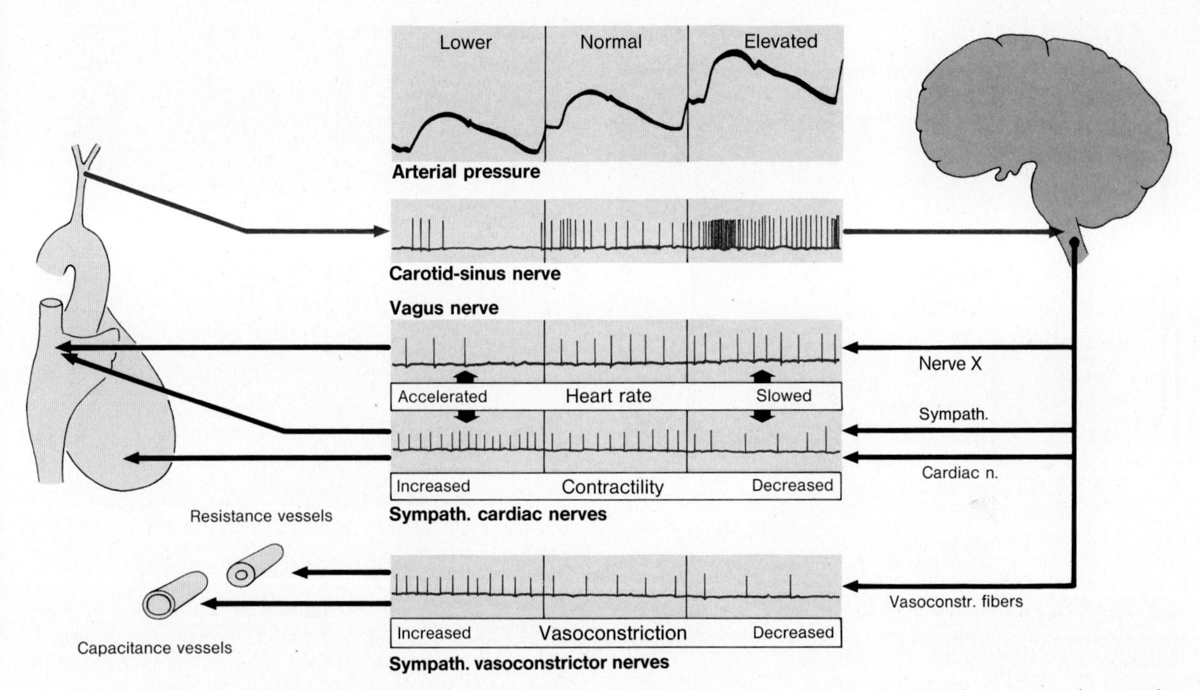

Fig. 20-28. Reflex responses to altered activity of the carotid-sinus baroreceptors. When arterial pressure falls the baroreceptors are less strongly stimulated, and the reflexly enhanced activity of the sympathetic vasoconstrictor and cardiac fibers causes increased peripheral resistance and heart rate, so that the blood pressure rises again. When arterial pressure is elevated the opposite responses occur. For further details see text. (Modified from RUSHMER)

by a *maintained* pressure, the baroreceptors discharge impulses *continuously,* at a pressure-dependent rate that follows an approximately S-shaped curve, with the steepest (nearly linear) slope at pressures between 80 and 180 mm Hg. The baroreceptors act as *proportional-differential (PD) sensors,* responding to the fluctuation of arterial pressure during the cardiac cycle with *rhythmic discharge patterns:* with increases in the amplitude and/or the rate of pressure change, the impulse frequency also increases. The frequency in the rising part of the pressure curve is therefore distinctly greater than that in the falling, less steep part (Fig. 20-28); because of this "asymmetry" (i.e., the greater excitation as pressure is increasing) the mean frequency is higher than would be associated with static pressure at the same level. It can be concluded that the baroreceptors convey information not only about the *mean arterial pressure,* but also about the *amplitude* of pressure fluctuation and the *steepness* of pressure rise (and hence the heart rate).

Effects of arterial baroreceptor activity on blood pressure and cardiac function. The afferent impulses from the baroreceptors are conducted to the *cardioinhibitory and vasomotor centers* (p. 521) in the medulla oblongata (and other parts of the CNS), where they cause an **inhibition of sympathetic structures** and an **enhanced excitation of parasympathetic structures.** As a result, the **tonic activity** of the sympathetic vasoconstrictor fibers (the so-called *vasomotor tone*) is reduced, and at the same time *heart rate* and the *contractile force of the myocardium* decrease (cf. Fig. 20-28). Because the baroreceptors are active over a wide range of pressures, these inhibitory influences are in operation even when the blood pressure is "normal". The arterial baroreceptors thus have a continual *depressor* action. When they are further excited by arterial pressure increases, the increased inhibition of the vasomotor center causes further vasodilation, to different degrees in the vascular beds of the different organs. At the level of the resistance vessels this effect results in a **decrease in the total peripheral resistance,** and at the level of the capacitance vessels in an **increased capacity.** Both processes lead to **lowered arterial pressure** either directly or indirectly, by way of reduced central venous pressure and the associated reduction in stroke volume (Fig. 20-28). This effect is further enhanced by the accompanying decreases in heart rate and in myocardial contraction. When the level of baroreceptor excitation is diminished by pressure reduction, the

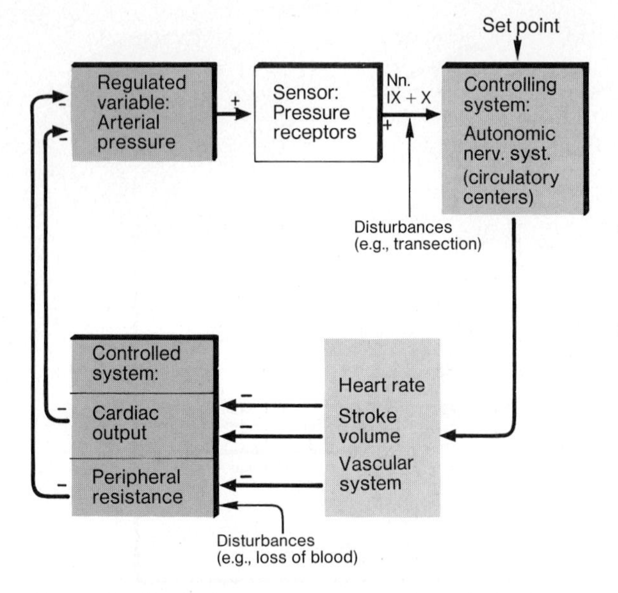

Fig. 20-29. Block diagram of the regulation of blood pressure by the arterial baroreceptors. Facilitatory effects are indicated by + and inhibitory effects by −

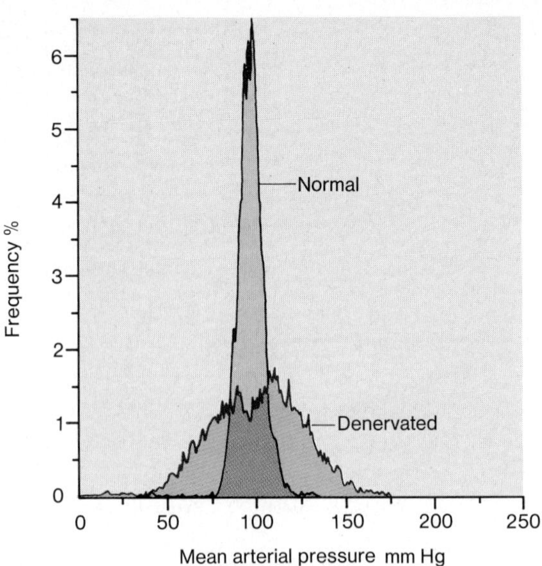

Fig. 20-30. Frequency distribution of mean blood pressure over 24 hours, in a dog with intact baroreceptors (normal) and several weeks after denervation of the baroreceptors (denervated). (From GUYTON [8])

opposite reactions ensue, with the result that arterial pressure rises again.

This **homeostatic autoregulatory mechanism** constitutes a complete *control circuit* (Fig. 20-29), whereby the reflex changes in resistance to flow and cardiac output triggered by the arterial baroreceptors in response to acute deviations of arterial pressure rapidly tend to *restore the initial conditions.*

The "stabilizing" influence of the adaptive reflexes initiated by arterial baroreceptor activity is quite evident in the distribution of blood pressures measured over 24 hours (Fig. 20-30). With the carotid sinus nerves *intact* there is a *sharp peak* in the region of the *"normal" mean pressure* of 100 mm Hg. When the homeostatic regulatory mechanisms are inactivated by denervation, there is a broad scatter in the measured pressures, both above and below the mean.

The reflex control mechanisms just described are an important element in **circulatory-system regulation,** where arterial pressure is only one of the several variables controlled.

When *chronic hypertension* (high blood pressure) is induced experimentally the arterial baroreceptors **adapt** to the increased pressure within a few days, remaining *fully functional.* Because of this resetting the pressure-stabilizing effects cause less reduction of the blood pressure, and the autoregulatory mechanism, by maintaining the high pressure, contributes to the development of further pathological changes. Recently an attempt has been made to turn the reflexly elicited effects on blood pressure to therapeutic advantage, by treating patients who have forms of hypertension not susceptible to drugs with pulse-synchronized or maintained stimulation of the sinus nerves by implanted electrodes, in order to reduce blood pressure *(baropacing).*

If the carotid sinus is *compressed* or *struck* from outside the body, the increased excitation of the baroreceptors triggers a drop in blood pressure and heart rate. In older people who have developed arteriosclerosis the blood pressure can fall drastically, with transient cardiac arrest and loss of consciousness *(carotid-sinus syndrome).* In most cases the heart resumes beating after 4–6 s, frequently with an initial AV rhythm (p. 441) until the normal sinus rhythm becomes established. But if cardiac activity is suspended for too long, death can result. On the other hand, during attacks of accelerated beating *(paroxysmal tachycardia)* it is possible under some circumstances to normalize the heart rate by applying pressure to the carotid sinus on one or both sides.

Effects of arterial baroreceptor activity on other CNS functions. Increased input from the baroreceptors to the medullary vasomotor centers results in *inhibition* of many other functions of the CNS. For example, respiration becomes more shallow, muscle tone and the activity of the efferent γ-fibers to the muscle spindles decrease, and the monosynaptic reflexes become weaker. The EEG tends to be more synchronized. Waking animals respond to marked stretching of the carotid-sinus region with motor inactivity or even with sleep.

Effects of arterial baroreceptor activity on blood volume. The reflex vasomotion of the pre- and postcapillary vessels influences the *effective hydrostatic capillary pressure* and thus the capillary *filtration-reabsorption equilibrium.* When a rise in arterial pressure causes *increased* baroreceptor activity, the ensuing vasodilation raises the effective capillary pressure and thus capillary *filtration* from the lumen into the interstitial space.
Reduced baroreceptor activity produces the opposite results. These effects probably begin even before the total peripheral resistance and the capacity of the vessels have adjusted.
Especially in skeletal muscle, where the total capillary surface is large and the interstitial volume is extremely variable, these effects can produce relatively rapid and massive shifts of fluid between the intravascular and interstitial spaces. During heavy muscular work, the plasma volume can be decreased by 10–15% in 15–20 min because of precapillary dilation. The opposite effect – increase in intravascular volume by the reabsorption of interstitial fluid – occurs, for instance, when the blood pressure falls. Here, again, the onset is rapid, though as the process continues it becomes impossible to distinguish it from other intermediate-term control mechanisms (see p. 517).

Cardiac Stretch-Receptor Reflexes

Atrial receptors. In both atria there are two functionally important types of **stretch receptors.** The **A receptors** are excited by atrial contraction and the **B receptors** during late ventricular systole, which coincides with the rise of atrial pressure toward the v-wave (Fig. 20-31). The A receptors respond to contraction of the atrial musculature and the B receptors, to passive stretch (increased atrial pressure). The afferent impulses discharged by the atrial receptors are conducted along sensory fibers of the *vagus nerve* to the *medullary circulatory centers* and other CNS structures.

Atrial-receptor influences on blood pressure and cardiac function. When the **B receptors** are excited in isolation, most of the reflex effects are similar to those of arterial baroreceptor excitation – *inhibition of sympathetic and excitation of parasympathetic* structures in the medullary circulatory centers, with corresponding cardiovascular effects (p. 513). There is a difference, however, in that the B receptors exert an especially strong vasoconstrictor influence on the *renal vessels* whereas the arterial baroreceptors

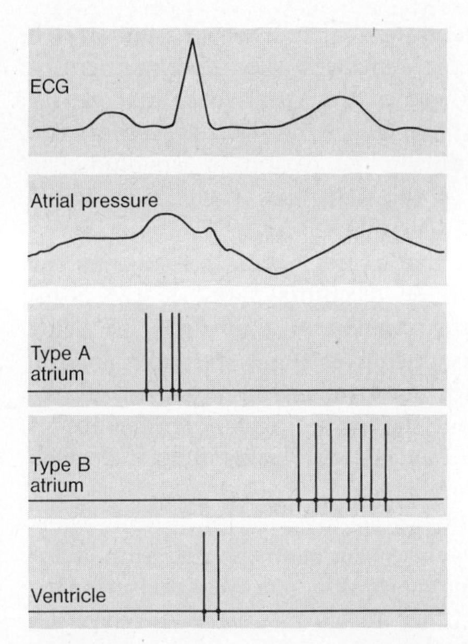

Fig. 20-31. Activity of atrial receptors of Types A and B, and of a ventricular receptor, in relation to the ECG and the pressure fluctuation in the left atrium. (From data of PAINTAL as cited in [6])

are more effective on muscle vessels (see above). When the level of B-receptor activity changes, therefore, the predominant effect is likely to be on *renal fluid excretion,* which depends in part on blood flow through the kidneys.
The receptors in the atria (together with the apparently functionally identical receptors at the entrance of the large veins into the right atrium) also occupy a special position with respect to control of *intravascular volume,* inasmuch as they are optimally situated to monitor the state of filling of the vascular system and the dynamics of ventricle filling, and are very sensitive to these variables. Accordingly, even slight changes in vascular volume affect the state of excitation of these receptors, which also send afferent impulses to *osmoregulatory structures in the hypothalamus* that control **vasopressin secretion** (see p. 520).
In contrast to the action of the B receptors, that of the **A receptors** is evidently to *increase the activity of the sympathetic system.* Tachycardia, which in experiments frequently (though not regularly) accompanies the extreme increases in atrial pressure brought about by rapid infusion of large amounts of fluid, is thought to be elicited by excitation of the A receptors **(Bainbridge reflex).** The unreliability of the response could be based on differential activation of A and B receptors depending on the conditions of the experiment. The physiological significance of the Bainbridge reflex is doubtful.

Ventricular receptors. There are also a few **stretch receptors** in the ventricles, the afferent fibers of which (like those of the atrial receptors) run in branches of the *vagus nerve.* These receptors are active only during the period of isovolumetric contraction of the ventricles (just after the R wave in the ECG; Fig. 20-31).
It is thought that under normal conditions the impulses of these receptors maintain the *negative chronotropic action* of the vagus on heart rate, whereas during extreme stretching of the ventricles they elicit reflex bradycardia and vasodilation. But the physiological significance of these effects has not yet been sufficiently well established.
After the intravenous injection of various *pharmacological* substances such as veratrum alkaloids, nicotine, serotonin etc., the excitation of stretch and other receptors causes a reflex *decrease in heart rate* and *vasodilation,* with the result that blood pressure falls **(Bezold-Jarisch reflex)** and *apnea* occurs. The cardiac and vascular effects can also be obtained by injecting the substances into the left coronary artery or applying them to the surface of the left ventricle **(coronary chemoreflex).** The apnea, however, results from the stimulation of pulmonary receptors.

Reflexes Involving Arterial Chemoreceptors

The actions of the chemoreceptors in the carotid and aortic bodies (cf. Fig. 20-27) on the cardiovascular system, unlike those of the baroreceptors, are *not true proprioceptive regulation,* for the adequate stimuli of these receptors are decreased O_2 partial pressure and increased CO_2 partial pressure (or H^+ concentration). The afferent impulses from the chemoreceptors stimulate both the "respiratory centers" (pp. 569ff.) and the "circulatory centers" in the medulla oblongata, a process which to some extent involves the superposition of antagonistic reflexes [12, 44].
The effects on circulatory function associated with breathing can be kept constant by means of artificial respiration; in such experiments *stimulation of the chemoreceptors causes* **vasoconstriction and decreased heart rate** by their direct action on the medullary circulatory centers. The increases in peripheral resistance outweigh the reduction in cardiac output, so that the *blood pressure rises.* The same effects appear when blood flow through the carotid and aortic bodies is diminished owing to lowered arterial pressure, and tend (as does reduced excitation of the baroreceptors) to oppose a further fall in pressure.
Under "normal" conditions, however, these effects are modified not only by influences related to respiration but also by possible actions on the vessels themselves. For example, when the respired air is deficient in O_2 the reflexly elicited vasoconstriction is *counteracted by local vasodilation* resulting from hypoxia (p. 507), and the *heart rate* (and output) is *increased.*

Ischemic Response of the CNS

The ischemic response involves *excitation of the medullary circulatory centers* such that *vasoconstriction* and the resulting *increased blood pressure* dominate. The response is initiated by inadequate blood supply to the brain, due to a decrease in arterial pressure, arterial hypoxia or impaired perfusion of the brain owing to vascular disorders. The structures in the medulla are evidently stimulated by way of *increased concentrations of H^+ and CO_2* (and perhaps of other metabolites). This could occur either by *direct* effects on the *reticular formation* or by the action of the extracellular [H^+] on *chemosensory areas* on the brainstem surface (as in the regulation of breathing, p. 573). In arterial hypoxia there may well be an additional reflex influence on the response associated with stimulation of the arterial chemoreceptors. The intensity of the responses depends on the degree to which blood supply is impaired. Under extreme conditions, for example, vasoconstriction in the kidneys can restrict perfusion so severely that the production of urine comes to a halt. This can cause a rise in *arterial pressure* to *250 mm Hg* or more.

Effects of Blood-Borne Adrenalin and Noradrenalin on the Circulatory System

When the sympathetic circulatory centers in the medulla are excited – and, indeed, when the sympathetic system is stimulated in any other way – the adrenal medulla, because its innervation is analogous to that of a sympathetic ganglion, releases *increased amounts of adrenalin and noradrenalin.* The rate of release, low under resting conditions, can become 50 times as high in extreme situations.

Adrenalin. Adrenalin *circulating* in the bloodstream in general produces a **decrease in total resistance** by way of its action on β receptors. Because the responses of vessels differ according to the relative numbers of α and β receptors, the **cardiac output is redistributed** (see pp. 510f.). Increased flow through the vessels in skeletal muscle is opposed by decreases in flow through the cutaneous and splanchnic vessels (Fig. 20-25). At the same time, the *cardiac output* increases because of increases in both stroke volume and heart rate. These events bring about little or no increase in mean arterial pressure. Effects of this sort are associated with *exercise or psychological agitation.* Under extreme conditions such as *hemorrhage and intense psychological stress* (anxiety, terror, rage), the adrenalin concentration in the blood can become so high that *vasoconstriction dominates* as a result of excitation of the α receptors (Fig. 20-25).

Noradrenalin. The sole effect of noradrenalin *circulating* in the blood in above-threshold concentrations is to **increase the resistance to flow** in the vessels of the systemic circulation (Fig. 20-25). Accordingly, arterial pressure rises, increasing the discharge rate of the arterial baroreceptors (p. 512), so that there is a *reflex* reduction in heart rate. Cardiac output decreases, both for this reason and because the stroke volume is less. But the relatively small proportion of noradrenalin secreted by the adrenal medulla, even when it is maximally active, is unlikely to be sufficient to enhance the similar cardiovascular responses that are elicited neurally.

Intermediate-Term Control Mechanisms

The intermediate-term mechanisms include: (i) *transcapillary volume shifts,* (ii) *stress relaxation of the vessels,* and (iii) the *renin-angiotensin mechanism.* These effects require minutes to become apparent and are fully developed only after hours have elapsed.

Transcapillary volume shifts. The filtration-reabsorption conditions in the capillaries are influenced not only by reflex vasomotor responses, which primarily affect the vessels in muscle (p. 515); the capillaries of the entire organism are affected by the pressures in the vascular system (for details see pp. 503ff.). Increases in arterial and/or venous pressure are as a rule associated with increases in the effective capillary pressure. The resulting *increased filtration* into the interstitial spaces *reduces the intravascular volume.* Because of the relationships between mean filling pressure, venous return and stroke volume (p. 498), the *arterial pressure is thereby reduced.* Primary pressure drops elicit changes just the reverse of those listed above owing to *increased capillary reabsorption,* with a resultant rise in arterial pressure.

Vascular stress relaxation. Increases in arterial pressure, which (because of the relationship to filling pressure) can also be induced by increases in intravascular volume, are attenuated by the *delayed compliance* (p. 487) of the vessels; after initial stretching by the increased pressure the distensibility of the vessels slowly becomes greater. When intravascular volume decreases, the opposite responses occur, raising the arterial pressure. These properties, called *"stress relaxation"* and *"reverse stress relaxation"*, respectively, are particularly well developed in the capacitance vessels; their effect is to return the pressures in the system to nearly the initial values within 10–60 minutes, even following quite large changes in volume.

Renin-angiotensin system (RAS). Renin is an enzyme synthesized and stored in the juxtaglomerular apparatus of the kidney. When it is released renin splits the *angiotensinogen* (an α_2-globulin) formed in the liver to produce *angiotensin I* (a decapeptide). A *"converting enzyme"* in the plasma changes the angiotensin I to *angiotensin II* (an octapeptide); this reaction occurs chiefly in the pulmonary circulation. Angiotensin II is broken down to inactive peptides by *angiotensinases* (Fig. 20-32).

Lowered renal perfusion in any form – whether due to general hypotension, local vasoconstriction or pathological changes in the renal vessels – causes **increased release of renin** (Fig. 20-32). The same effects appear to result from diminished excitation of the atrial and arterial baroreceptors when the intravascular volume is reduced. Renin

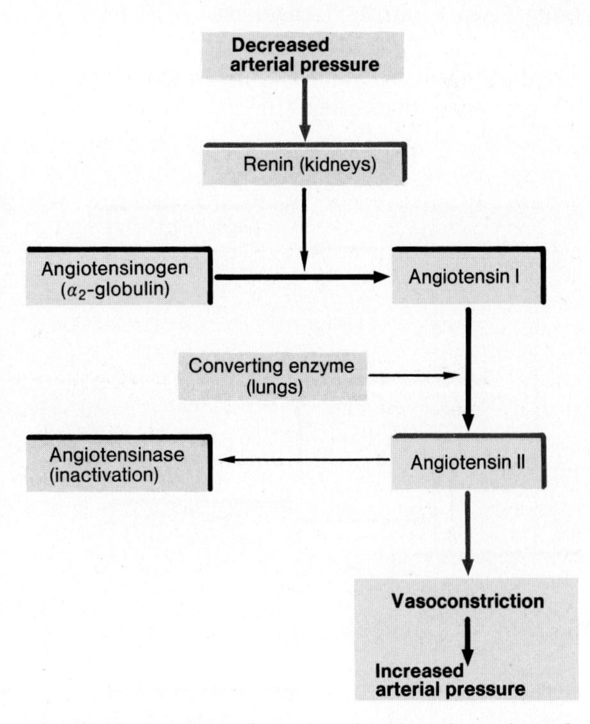

Fig. 20-32. Sequence of reactions in the renin-angiotensin system for blood-pressure regulation

release is also stimulated by changes in *electrolyte concentration,* hyponatremia in particular [27, 38].

Angiotensin II elicits very strong *direct vasoconstriction* of arteries and (less strong) of veins, as well as activation of central and peripheral structures in the *sympathetic system.* The consequence is an increase in peripheral resistance and blood pressure. Moreover, angiotensin II is the most important stimulator of the secretion *aldosterone* from the adrenal cortex (see pp. 520f.).
It takes about 20 minutes for the renin-angiotensin mechanism to become fully effective; its effects then persist, slightly attenuated, for a long time. In cases of *pathologically lowered blood pressure and/or reduced blood volume* the mechanism makes a significant contribution to the normalization of circulatory function. The renin-angiotensin concentration in the blood also appears to participate in control of the *thirst mechanism;* increases in renin-angiotensin concentration enhance the sensation of thirst, and conversely. The thirst experienced after major blood or fluid losses reflects these relationships.

On the other hand, the renin-angiotensin mechanism also seems to be involved in producing a certain form of *renal hypertension,* for in this condition the concentration of these substances in the blood is distinctly increased.

Long-Term Control Mechanisms

The long-term mechanisms are based primarily on processes that affect the *intravascular fluid volume* in relation to the *capacity* of the vessels. These can be matched in two ways. Capacity can be adjusted to blood volume by the *vasomotor responses* previously discussed (see pp. 513ff.), *stress relaxation* of the vessels (pp. 486f.), and the *renin-angiotensin* mechanism (see above) – all short- or intermediate-term mechanisms. On the other hand, *transcapillary fluid exchange* (p. 517) adjusts intravascular volume to capacity; but because the fluid is shifted only from the vessel lumen to the interstitial space (the most important compartments of the extracellular fluid volume) its effects are limited. *Quantitative changes in extracellular fluid volume* can be achieved under normal conditions only by changing the balance between **net fluid intake** (oral fluid consumption minus loss of fluid by all routes except the kidney) and **renal fluid output.** The regulation of extracellular volume is thus crucial not only for *water and electrolyte balance,* but for the *function of the circulatory system* as well. The following mechanisms are involved here: (i) the *renal volume-control system,* (ii) the *vasopressin system,* and (iii) the *aldosterone system.*

Renal volume-control system. The functions of this system with respect to blood pressure are diagrammed in Fig. 20-33. The chief effects are as follows.
An *increase in blood pressure* has several consequences. (1) Renal fluid output increases. (2) The increased renal fluid output reduces the extracellular fluid volume and hence (3) the blood volume. (4) The reduced blood volume brings about decreased mean filling pressure, as a result

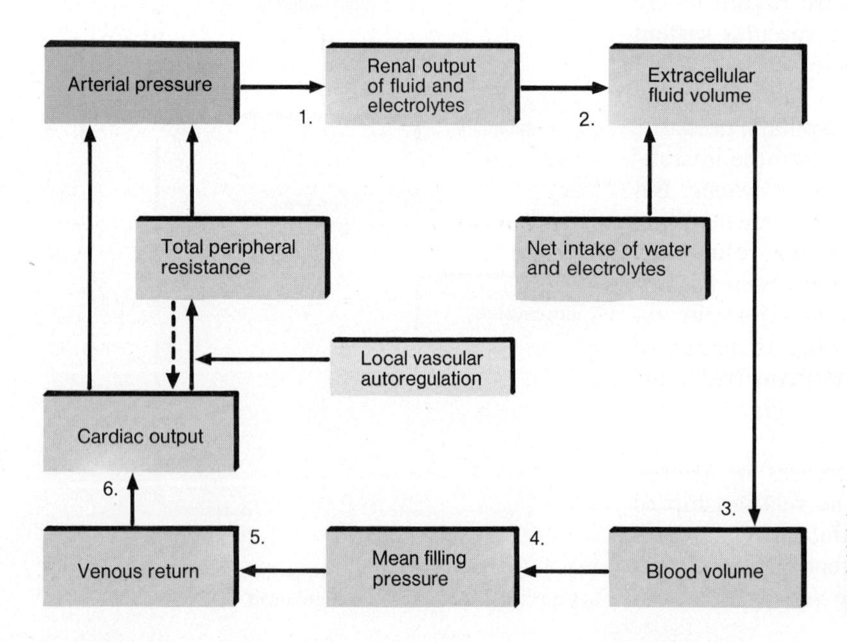

Fig. 20-33. Block diagram of the renal volume-control system for long-term regulation of blood pressure. (Modified from GUYTON [8])

of which (5) venous return and cardiac output are diminished. (6) The reduced cardiac output causes the blood pressure to return to the original level.

A *fall in blood pressure* elicits the *reverse* responses. Renal fluid output declines, blood volume enlarges, venous return and cardiac output increase and the blood pressure rises again.

Arterial pressure is affected not only by changes in cardiac output but by the *total peripheral resistance* as well (since $P = \dot{V} \cdot R$). This coupling derives from **autoregulatory responses** (pp. 487f.) which alter the resistance to flow in those resistance vessels with autoregulatory properties; the pressure changes triggering this process, which depend on volume flow, are thus *amplified* by factors of 5–10. In this way relatively small chronic increases in extracellular volume, 2–3%, can produce *blood-pressure increases of up to 50%* [8, 34, 37].

The above considerations are not inconsistent with the observation that there is *no appreciable rise* in blood pressure accompanying *acute* changes in blood volume by the rapid infusion of large amounts of fluid. In this case the predicted pressure increases are compensated by the short-term *reflex* control mechanisms; the added fluid volume is excreted by the kidneys before the neural control mechanisms can adapt to the new situation. When the reflex control systems of an animal are suppressed in an experiment, voluminous infusions elicit distinct increases in cardiac output and arterial pressure, which subsequently die away as fluid volume is normalized by a transient increase in renal output. On the other hand, human *hypertension* can in many cases be reduced by administration of diuretics to *decrease extracellular fluid volume.*

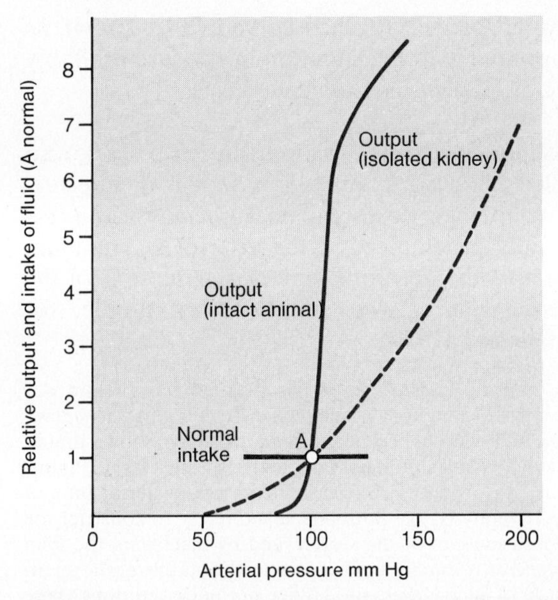

Fig. 20-34. Changes in urinary output with change in mean arterial pressure, as part of the long-term regulation of the circulatory system by the renal volume-control system. (From GUYTON [8])

Relations between blood pressure and renal fluid output. The effectiveness of blood-pressure regulation by this system depends on the degree to which the amount of fluid excreted by the kidneys changes when blood pressure changes. Fig. 20-34 illustrates the result of experiments in which water and electrolyte input are varied from the normal equilibrium condition (Point A). The sharp rise of the urinary output curve above the "normal" mean pressure of 100 mm Hg (Point A) implies that even *very small increases in arterial pressure* are associated with *considerable increases in renal fluid output.* Urine output appears to rise about by 100 % for each mm Hg, so that pressure *increases of ca. 10 mm Hg* would increase output by about sixfold. When blood pressure falls below the "normal" level, fluid output drops sharply until it stops altogether. The significance of these events in blood-pressure control is that the marked changes in renal fluid output produce corresponding changes in the extracellular fluid volume which, by the sequence of events described above, bring the arterial pressure back to the initial level.

The effect of increased fluid intake. It can also be inferred from Fig. 20-34 that even fairly large changes in net fluid intake have a *negligible effect* on mean arterial pressure. If the extra input occurs only once, the raised arterial pressure and increased fluid output soon return to the equilibrium level, whereas if the additional input is maintained a new equilibrium between net intake and output is established, with only a slight increase in mean pressure.

Sensitivity of the control system. Both position and shape of the urine excretion curve can exhibit considerable *individual differences.* Parallel shifts along the abscissa imply a shift of the equilibrium between fluid intake and output (Point A) into a higher or lower range of *arterial pressures,* which are maintained with *equal sensitivity* by alterations of renal fluid output. Such shifts can occur in the course of **vasomotor responses.** Position and shape of the urine excretion curve can also be affected by **hormones** (ADH and aldosterone) and other factors (prostaglandins, kinins, angiotensin etc.), though these extremely complex relationships are not yet understood in detail. The considerably smaller changes in fluid output when the arterial pressure in isolated kidneys is changed (dashed curve in Fig. 20-34), as compared with the situation in situ, are probably due at least in part to such effects.

Vasopressin system. Vasopressin (cf. p. 377), also called *antidiuretic hormone (ADH),* in intermediate to high doses causes *vasoconstriction,* especially pronounced in the arterioles. The main effect of the hormone, however, is to control the *reabsorption of water* in the distal tubule (for details see p. 757).

As far as its *vascular* action is concerned, vasopressin was previously thought to be ineffective in *physiological concentrations.* Recent experiments on animals have shown that at least when **blood pressure falls** severely, fairly large quantities of vasopressin are released from the posterior lobe of the hypophysis; the hormone acts directly to constrict the smooth muscles of the vessels, and by increasing the *total peripheral resistance* contributes to the stabilization or increase of blood pressure. Under normal conditions these effects are masked by the reflex control mechanisms; they can be demonstrated only after denervation of the arterial baroreceptors. In contrast to the reflex effects which dominate initially, the hormonal action on the vessels does not diminish in time. Thus the vascular action of vasopressin can be a significant regulator of the circulation in cases of *chronic malfunction* [34].

Vasopressin plays a special role in fluid-volume control, inasmuch as the *reflexly* elicited changes in vasopressin concentration are involved in the homeostasis of *intravascular volume.* When blood volume increases, the associated increase in activity of the atrial receptors inhibits vasopressin release within 10–20 minutes, so that more fluid is excreted by the kidneys. Decreases in blood volume have the opposite effect; the enhanced vasopressin release restricts renal fluid output. This **volume-control reflex,** which is triggered by *acute* changes in intravascular volume, is also called the **Gauer-Henry reflex** [7].

Aldosterone system. Aldosterone increases the *tubular reabsorption of* Na^+ (and hence, by osmotic effects, of water) and the *secretion of* K^+ *and* H^+; thus it raises the sodium and extracellular-fluid content of the body. (For further details see pp. 389f. and 747f.). At the same time, aldosterone enhances the *excitability of vascular smooth muscle by constrictor stimuli,* thereby reinforcing the pressor action of angiotensin II.
Angiotensin II, in turn, is the most effective *stimulator of aldosterone secretion.* Whenever the renin-angiotensin mechanism (p. 517) is activated, the aldosterone concentration in the blood rises. Because of this close linkage, the effects of the three substances are frequently lumped as the *renin-angiotensin-aldosterone system.*

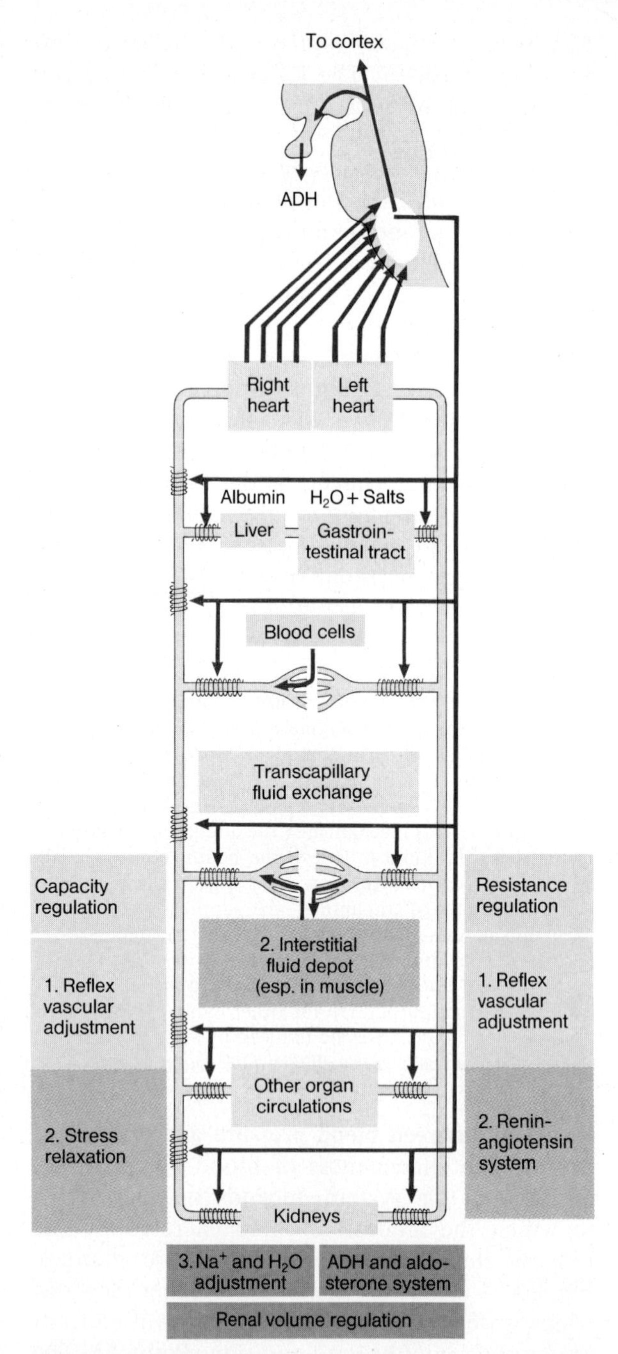

Fig. 20-35. Mechanisms for the regulation of resistance, capacity and blood volume. Mutual adjustment of vessel capacity and intravascular volume involves three "lines of defense", mechanisms activated in a specific temporal sequence as follows. 1. Adjustment of vessel capacity to the available volume of blood, mainly under neural control. 2. Alteration of the ratio between intravascular and interstitial volumes. 3. Predominantly hormonal adjustment of the renal excretion of water and electrolytes. (Modified from Folkow and Neil [6])

The *effects of aldosterone* on the circulatory system begin to appear after hours and are fully developed only after several days. Increased aldosterone production (*hyperaldosteronism* is as-

sociated with certain diseases of the adrenal cortex) causes greater retention of water and salt as well as *hypertension,* and hypotension results when aldosterone secretion is diminished.
The action of aldosterone on the *renal volume-control system* is as complex as that of vasopressin; its various mutually complementary influences together enhance the effectiveness of the control system.
It is evident in this description of the many mechanisms regulating the circulation of blood that essentially *none of them acts exclusively on a single parameter.* Nearly all the mechanisms affect, either directly or indirectly and to varying degrees, the cardiac output, the total peripheral resistance, the capacity of the vessels, and the intravascular volume. There are thus three *"lines of defense"* against disturbance of either **arterial pressure** or **blood volume,** characterized by the *timing* (onset and duration) of their actions (Fig. 20-35). Acute disturbance is counteracted by reactions of the vascular system, whereas in chronic conditions changes in blood volume dominate. Initially the latter involve modification of water and electrolyte content, followed if necessary, with varying delays, by changes in the plasma proteins and the cellular elements of the blood.

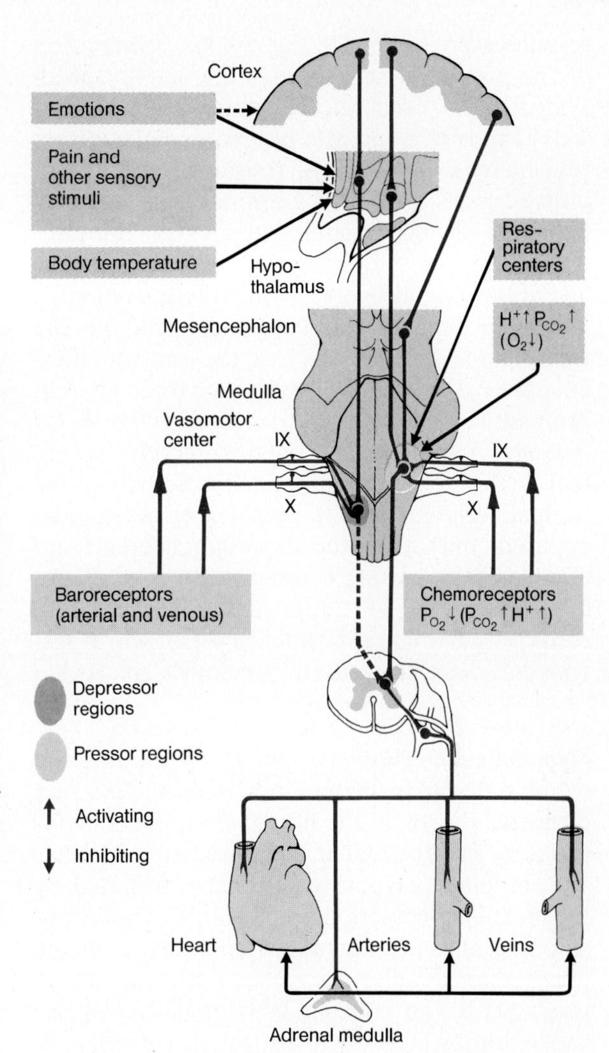

Fig. 20-36. Schematic drawing of the most important afferent and efferent connections of the medullary cardiovascular centers. The efferent fibers that activate circulation come from mostly ipsilateral "pressor regions", whereas the inhibitory fibers from "depressor regions" cross in the medulla and pass to ventrolateral areas of the spinal cord on the contralateral side.

Central Control of the Circulation

Structures at *all levels of the CNS* participate in the monitoring and regulation of circulatory-system function. Simplifying the situation greatly, we can classify the functions of the different levels in 4 groups [6, 12, 37, 42, 44, 45].

Medullary centers. In the **reticular formation** of the medulla oblongata and the *bulbar parts of the pons* there are structures, poorly defined anatomically, that together constitute the so-called **medullary** and **rhombencephalic cardiovascular control centers.** Under resting conditions homeostasis of the circulatory system can be maintained by these centers alone, as experiments on decerebrate animals have shown. Basically, this capability is due to the *tonic activity of sympathetic vasoconstrictor fibers* arising in parts of this region, the **vasomotor centers,** which is responsible for the **resting tone** of the vessels (p. 486). This tonic output is continually modulated by afferent impulses from the *cardiovascular receptors* in such a way that increased afferent input reduces tonic activity and results in vasodilation, and decreased afferent input enhances tonic activity and leads to vasoconstriction. In addition, the functional state of the vasomotor centers can be influenced by *"unspecific"* afferent impulses and by impulses from the relatively nearby *respiratory centers* and from *higher levels* of the CNS [12, 35, 44, 47, 54, 56]. The medullary control centers also give rise to facilitatory sympathetic and inhibitory parasympathetic (vagal) actions on the *heart* (Fig. 20-36).
Electrical stimulation of these structures elicits a variety of responses. In the *lateral* part of the vasomotor center mainly *pressor* responses (increased blood pressure) are elicited, whereas in the *mediocaudal* parts of the brainstem *depressor*

responses predominate (Fig. 20-36). Stimulation of the pressor areas increases the activity of all sympathetic adrenergic effectors; heart rate as well as the force and rate of myocardial contraction increase, the tone of resistance and capacitance vessels rises, and hormones are released from the adrenal medulla in greater amounts. Stimulation of the depressor areas inhibits the activity of the adrenergic sympathetic system.
When the brainstem is transected at about the level of the cuneate nucleus the pressor efferents are cut off; in the absence of tonic efferent sympathetic activity there is a *sharp fall in blood pressure*. The depressor regions, largely left intact by this operation, suppress the activity of the "spinal" centers (p. 523). Spinal control becomes apparent only after the depressor efferents are eliminated by cutting through the medulla caudal to the obex. The relationship of the medullary cardiovascular control center to other neural systems has been pointed out previously (p. 514).

Hypothalamic centers (cf. pp. 359f.). Stimulation of the **reticular formation** in mesencephalon and diencephalon, or in the hypothalamus, elicits facilitatory cardiovascular responses at some sites and inhibitory responses at others, mediated by the medullary centers (Fig. 20-36). By careful positioning and adjustment of the stimulus in the hypothalamus, selective vasoconstriction can be produced in the vascular beds of particular organs – for example, the renal, muscle or splanchnic vessels. Even under resting conditions the hypothalamus appears to exert a maintained influence on both the *tonic activity and the reflex responses of the medullary centers.*
Moreover, the hypothalamus initiates very complex autonomic **general responses,** fixed programs that are important for the survival of the individual and the species (see p. 361). Stimulation of the *caudal hypothalamus* activates the sympathetic system in such a way as to increase vasodilation in the skeletal muscles and enhances the adrenergic responses in other effectors. As a result, blood pressure, heart rate and cardiac output increase. As other parts of the CNS, including the cerebral cortex, come into play, additional autonomic responses and signs of *general excitation and greater alertness* are produced; ultimately the phenomena ordinarily accompanying aggression, rage or fear can appear. This pattern of excitation represents an **"alarm state"** in which the organs are prepared to cope, if necessary, with the demands of flight, defense or attack. Conversely, the *rostral hypothalamus* has a *suppressive* effect on cardiovascular and other functions, causing autonomic adaptations that aid recuperation of the organism and are associated with feeding and digestion.
When the rostral hypothalamus is **warmed** the cutaneous vessels dilate, and when it is **cooled** they constrict; thermoregulation is thus accomplished by modification of the organism's heat loss. Warming of the rostral hypothalamus is also associated with vasoconstriction in the viscera, and cooling with increased muscle tone or shivering.

Cortical influences. Cardiovascular responses can be elicited by stimulation of many parts of the cerebral cortex. The effective sites are concentrated in two regions: (i) in the *neocortex* at the outer convexity of the hemisphere, especially in the vicinity of the motor and premotor areas, and (ii) in the *paleocortex,* especially on the medial surfaces of the hemispheres and on the basal surface of the frontal and parietal lobes.
In the *neocortical areas* stimulation elicits predominantly *pressor* responses, usually in combination with *increased* heart rate; *depressor* responses are usually associated with *decreased* heart rate. These cortical effects can predominate over the opposite combinations of blood pressure and heart rate associated with the homeostatic reflexes.
When the *motor cortex* is stimulated, the resulting pattern of responses can closely resemble the *alarm response* apart from its affective elements. It is notable here that local increases in blood flow through the skeletal musculature can be elicited in areas where stimulation causes contraction of the corresponding muscles. These observations indicate that the motor patterns and the autonomic reactions that accompany them are initiated together in the cortex; that is, they are synchronized by central **"coinnervation".**
Taken together, these adjustments of the organism are called **anticipatory responses;** in humans, they appear prior to an intended act. They should be regarded as the expression of a *mutual adjustment of autonomically controlled circulatory function and muscle performance under somatomotor control,* which takes place independent of the subsequent actual activity and the adaptive processes it induces. The *"centrogenic"* autonomic impulses are in part mediated by the *hypothalamus,* for when the hypothalamus is selectively eliminated the blood-pressure and heart-rate responses fail to appear. The *mesencephalon* may also act as a relay station for

some of these signals. From these regions impulses are sent to the medullary cardiovascular control center and other structures in the reticular formation that are involved in activating the sympathetic system. Other vasoconstrictor fibers run directly into the spinal cord near the pyramidal tract. The sympathetic cholinergic *dilator system* that originates in the cortex of various species makes synaptic connections in the hypothalamus and mesencephalon; the vasodilator fibers leaving these regions bypass the medullary centers, so that there is no further interruption in the pathway until the lateral horns of the spinal cord are reached.
In the *paleocortical areas,* stimulation of the anterior cingulate gyrus elicits predominantly *depressor* effects, whereas the responses to nearby points on the orbito-insulo-temporal cortex are partly pressor and partly depressor in nature. The paleocortical zones that influence circulation also affect *other autonomically controlled functions* such as gastrointestinal motility and glandular activity.

Spinal influences. After *transection* of the spinal cord between C_6 and Th_1, so that the phrenic nerve and the preganglionic sympathetic fibers remain intact, the first result is a marked *fall in arterial pressure.* The animals survive, however, and after about a week the blood pressure returns to normal. At this stage moderate loss of blood (up to 25% of the total volume) can be compensated as well as in normal animals. These adjustments are mediated by the *cells of origin of the sympathetic fibers* in the lateral-horn gray matter, which develop a certain independence as *"spinal centers"* after the cord has been cut. This is probably less a matter of true reflexes than an excitation of the preganglionic neurons by hypoxia. These mechanisms are probably of no significance in the normal control of circulation, but they could become effective in anoxia.

20.10 The Pulmonary Circulation

Hemodynamics of the Pulmonary Circulation

In the **vascular bed of the lungs** the arterial and venous segments are considerably shorter and the diameter of the vessels in general larger than in the corresponding parts of the systemic circulation. The large arteries are relatively thin-walled, whereas the small arteries have thicker walls with many smooth muscle fibers. There are no typical arterioles – that is, typical resistance vessels [1].

Capillary diameter is about 8 µm; the capillaries anastomose extensively to form a dense network around the alveoli. Their length can thus be expressed only as a so-called *"functional length",* in terms of their topography with respect to the alveoli. It is *ca. 350 µm,* and the transit time of the blood is about 1 s. The capillary *surface area* under resting conditions is ca. 60 m^2; during hard work the non-perfused capillaries can be brought into play, so that the total area rises to ca. 90 m^2 (Fig. 20-20).

Pressures in the pulmonary vessels. The pressures in the pulmonary circulation of a healthy person are *relatively low.* In the pulmonary artery the **systolic pressure** is ca. **20 mm Hg,** the **diastolic pressure** is ca. **9 mm Hg,** and the **mean pressure** is ca. **13 mm Hg** (Fig. 20-10). The mean pressure in the region of the lung capillaries is ca. 7 mm Hg, and in the left atrium it is approximately 6 mm Hg. Under normal conditions pressure fluctuations of 3–5 mm Hg are present even in the capillaries of the lung, and these propagate with decreasing amplitude into the lung veins. The *pressure differences* between arteries and capillaries (6 mm Hg) and between capillaries and right atrium (1 mm Hg) are considerably smaller than in the corresponding parts of the systemic circulation.
Accordingly, the *resistance* in the pulmonary vascular bed is also *small,* barely $^1/_{10}$ of the overall resistance of the systemic system (p. 490).
Pressure-pulse and volume-pulse curves are nearly identical in shape. The *pulse-wave velocity* (p. 495) in the large pulmonary arteries is only 1–2 $m \cdot s^{-1}$, because of their relatively large mechanical compliance.

Flow in the pulmonary vessels. The hemodynamic conditions in the arteries of the lungs are basically the same as in those of the systemic circulation. The pulmonary circuit receives the *total* volume of blood ejected by the right ventricle, and to this is added, in the pulmonary veins, some of the venous blood from the bronchial circulation (at most 2% of the output of the left ventricle).
The *flow pulse* in the pulmonary artery rises and falls less steeply than in the aorta. The stroke volume ejected intermittently from the right ventricle is converted by the elastic properties of the pulmonary arteries into a forward flow even during diastole. In contrast to the attenuation in the systemic circulation, flow remains *pulsatile* with decreasing pulsation amplitude in the *capillaries and veins* of the lung, as far as the left atrium.

The **mean velocity of flow** in the pulmonary artery under resting conditions is ca. 18 cm · s^{-1}. In the capillaries of the pulmonary bed it falls to a level approximating that in the systemic system, and as the total cross-sectional area decreases in the venous segment the rate of flow rises again (Fig. 20-10).

Special Functional Features

Lung perfusion and transmural pressures. Because the intravascular pressures in the lungs are relatively low, *hydrostatic* effects have a much *stronger* influence on flow through the lungs than through the various parts of the systemic circulation. In the apical regions, which in an erect adult are ca. 15 cm above the base of the pulmonary artery, the hydrostatic and arterial pressures are about the same, so that the capillaries are barely (if at all) perfused; at the base of the lung the pressures add, and the vessels are more distended [49]. Lung perfusion thus exhibits *pronounced position-dependent inhomogeneity,* which under some conditions can be reflected in *regional differences in* O_2 *saturation of the blood.* Despite these differences and the effects of the admixture of blood from the bronchial veins, the O_2 saturation of the mixed blood in the lung veins is 96–98% (see p. 584).
Moreover, the pressures in the pulmonary vessels are affected by the *intrapleural pressure* and the respiration-dependent *fluctuation of intraalveolar (intrapulmonary) pressure* (at most +3 to −3 mm Hg). Greater positive pressures, such as can occur during artificial respiration, decrease the transmural pressure and thus cause considerable increases in resistance to flow and reduced blood volume in the lungs.

Intrathoracic vessels as blood reservoirs. Because the pulmonary vessels are so distensible, the volume of blood in the lungs can be temporarily increased or decreased by as much as 50% of the mean total volume of 440 ml (Table 20-3) with only slight change in transmural pressure or distensibility. Together with the diastolic volume of the left heart, the volume of the pulmonary circuit constitutes the so-called **central blood volume** (600–650 ml), a *rapidly mobilizable "instantaneous depot"*. When a short-term increase in output of the left ventricle is required, for example, this depot can contribute about 300 ml of blood to meet the additional demand. These effects help to compensate for imbalance between the amounts ejected by the two ventricles, until enhanced venous return can match the stroke volume of the right ventricle to that of the left.

Low-pressure system. On the basis of the distribution of pressure and volume among the various parts of the cardiovascular system, the system can be subdivided in terms of *functional organization* rather than anatomy, into a **low-pressure** and an **arterial (high-pressure) system.** The *low-pressure system* comprises the venous parts of the systemic circulation, the right heart, the entire pulmonary circulation and the left atrium; the *arterial system* consists of the arteries of the systemic circulation. The *left ventricle* joins the low-pressure system to the high-pressure system. During *diastole* it belongs to the low-pressure system, and its filling depends on the pressure in the pulmonary veins. During *systole* the left ventricle is functionally a part of the high-pressure system, in which it drives the flow of blood.
This subdivision reflects not only the distribution of pressure and volume (cf. Table 20-3 and Fig. 20-10), but in particular the largely *identical pressure-volume relationships* in the peripheral veins and the pulmonary circulation, in which regard the right ventricle does not act as a barrier. The mean pressure in the pulmonary arteries is thought to depend chiefly on the output of the right ventricle per unit time, because the changes in tone of the peripheral lung vessels are so slight; the right cardiac output depends on the central venous pressure by virtue of the *Frank-Starling mechanism* [7].
Changes in blood volume therefore, whatever the absolute pressure may be, cause pressure changes of about the same magnitude in the right atrium, the pulmonary artery and the left atrium, so that these parts of the system can be regarded as a *functional unit.* The capacity of the vascular system and the state of contraction of the vessel musculature, as well as the blood volume, are taken as (relatively) *static quantities* in this view. When the relation between vessel capacity and blood volume is disrupted, balance is thought to be restored primarily by *volume regulation* involving reflexly elicited changes in vasopressin secretion, which become effective only after a relatively long delay (see p. 520). According to this theory, changes in capacity would play only a subordinate role, although they are undoubtedly of major importance in the short-term compensation of disturbances in venous return (e.g., at the transition from lying down to standing up) [57].

Regulatory Mechanisms in the Pulmonary Circuit

Neural control of lung perfusion. The pulmonary vessels are innervated by *sympathetic vasoconstrictor fibers.* Many experiments on animals have indicated that the vessels in the lungs, like those of the systemic circulation, are under the *continual* influence of the autonomic system.

Afferent innervation and central control of pulmonary circulation. The *baroreceptors* (actually stretch receptors) in the *pulmonary arteries* are situated primarily at the bifurcation of the pulmonary trunk and near the bases of the two arteries. Their function and the reflexes they elicit correspond essentially to those of the baroreceptors in the systemic arteries; that is, increased pressure in the pulmonary arteries causes a reflex pressure drop in the systemic system, and decreased pulmonary pressure raises the systemic pressure.

On the other hand, when the baroreceptors in the carotid sinus become more active they induce vasodilation in the pulmonary circulation, whereas vasoconstriction is elicited by increased hypoxic excitation of chemoreceptors in the carotid body. The pulmonary circulation also receives *sympathetic vasodilator* and *parasympathetic cholinergic* fibers, the functional significance of which is still unclear.

Under resting conditions the vasomotor influences on the pulmonary vessels are relatively slight; accordingly, the vessels are dilated. But because of the large capacity even small degrees of vasoconstriction bring about relatively large changes in volume, with corresponding effects on the blood supply to the left heart, although the resistance to flow increases very little [6, 47].

The local control of lung perfusion. When the partial pressure of O_2 *is low* or that of CO_2 *is high* there is a *local vasoconstrictor* response that evidently involves both the small precapillary and the postcapillary vessels of the lung. Local blood flow can thus be adapted to the *regional ventilation,* the perfusion of the more poorly ventilated regions being restricted in favor of those better ventilated. In the human these effects become apparent when the arterial O_2 saturation falls below 80%.

A number of substances such as adrenalin, noradrenalin, histamine etc. also cause constriction of pulmonary vessels, though these effects are frequently masked by the changes in transmural pressure brought about *indirectly* by the action of these substances on the heart and the other vessels.

20.11 Circulatory Adjustments to Physiological and Pathological Circumstances

Human Blood Pressure

The level of an individual's blood pressure depends on *age, sex,* and *genetic and environmental influences,* as well as on other factors, some of which are unknown. When the diagnostically important **resting** or **basal blood pressure** is to be determined, these factors must be taken into account or, where appropriate, eliminated as far as possible.

Norms and age-dependence. Studies of the blood pressures of representative groups of people under approximately resting conditions reveal distinct interindividual differences, with a concentration around an intermediate value and a *Gaussian (normal) distribution* of higher and lower values. In healthy young adults the peak of the distribution of systolic pressure is 120 mm Hg, and that of diastolic pressure is 80 mm Hg. The great majority of people have systolic pressure between 100 and 150 mm Hg, and diastolic pressure between 60 and 90 mm Hg. With advancing age the systolic pressure increases to a greater extent than the diastolic pressure (Fig. 20-37).

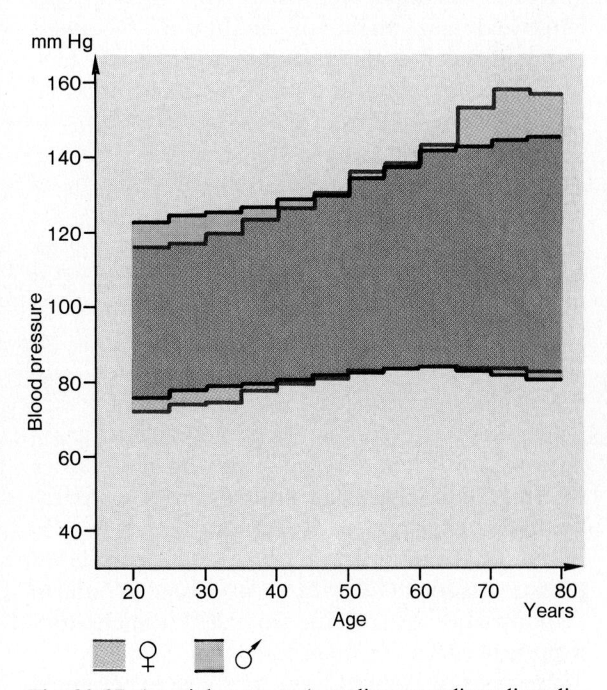

Fig. 20-37. Arterial pressure (systolic, upper line; diastolic, lower line) in men and women at different ages. (From data of MASTER et al. [16])

These effects are basically due to *loss of elasticity* in the vessels. Up to age 50 women have lower blood pressure than men, on the average, whereas above that age the blood pressure of women is slightly higher.

Rhythmic Fluctuations in Blood Pressure

A continual record of blood pressure shows not only the **pulse waves,** which are called **first-order** pressure fluctuations or waves, but also slower rhythmic fluctuations. These **second-order** fluctuations are associated with *respiration.* When a person is breathing at the normal rate (12–16/min) the inspiration coincides with the falling phase of pressure and the "wave valley", and expiration coincides with the rising phase and the "wave peak". One cause of these waves is a central coupling of respiration and circulation, but there is also a mechanical effect, in that the pressure and capacity of the pulmonary vessels, and thus the stroke volume of the left ventricle change during the respiratory cycle. Blood-pressure fluctuations of **third order,** the so-called **Mayer waves,** have a period of 6–20 s or longer, the most common mean duration being 10 s; these are probably caused by fluctuations in *peripheral vascular tone.*

Blood pressure, like heart rate and many other physiological parameters, also exhibits an **endogenous circadian periodicity** (pp. 139f.), synchronized with the 24-h rhythm of the environment by external entraining agents, in which pressure is maximal toward 3 p.m. and minimal toward 3 a.m.

Acute changes. In normal daily life the basal blood pressure is also influenced to varying degrees by environmental, physical or psychological factors; this influence may be direct (e.g., that of physical factors) or indirect, by alteration of autonomic function. The general rule that *increased activity* during arousal is associated with *raised blood pressure* and *decreased activity with lowered pressure* can be broken owing to gravitational or thermal effects on the circulatory system, so as to give an impression of a "paradoxical" blood-pressure response.

A classical example of an *acute* increase in blood pressure associated with a psychogenic alarm response (p. 522) is the so-called **anticipatory hypertension** that can accompany not only examinations or competitions, but also experiences such as a visit to the dentist. In such situations the blood pressure can reach levels corresponding to moderately hard work. Intensive *dreaming* can also be accompanied by considerably increased blood pressure, whereas in *quiet sleep* both systolic and diastolic pressure can fall to 20 mm Hg.

The changes in blood pressure associated with the effects of posture have been discussed together with the changes in other circulatory variables on p. 527; for the effects of *exercise* see pp. 529f., and for those of *thermal stress* see pp. 530f.

Food intake is followed by a moderate rise in systolic pressure, whereas diastolic pressure frequently falls slightly.

Pain also usually raises the blood pressure, though if the pain is prolonged blood pressure may fall. The blood-pressure responses to *visceral stimuli* vary; in some cases reflex decreases are observed (e.g., following mechanical stimulation of the pleura), and in some cases increases occur.

Pathophysiology of blood pressure. When the blood pressure is *above* the normal range a state of **hypertension** exists. According to the recommendations of the World Health Organization (WHO), systolic pressures above 160 mm Hg and diastolic pressures above 95 mm Hg are to be regarded as hypertensive, although in view of the changes with age there can be no rigid boundary line between normotension and hypertension. Indeed, extensive studies of large population samples make it appear better to take the upper limit of normal blood pressure as 140/90 mm Hg in juveniles, 150/100 mm Hg in adults up to 50 years of age, and 160/100 in adults over 50.

Hypertension can be produced by increase of either cardiac output *(cardiac-output hypertension)* or peripheral resistance *(resistance hypertension)* or the two together. It is customary in clinical practice to classify hypertension according to etiology, as (i) **primary or essential hypertension** and (ii) **secondary or symptomatic hypertension.**

Primary hypertension (ca 90% of all cases of hypertension) has no clear cause, and could thus be regarded as a characteristic defined by position within the Gaussian distribution. There are indications that essential hypertension may be genetic in origin and is thus inherited. On the other hand, one of the possible etiological factors that have been proposed is a disturbance of the *distribution of sodium* within the organism, such that it is concentrated in the resistance vessels. Evidence in favor of this suggestion is that blood pressure can be lowered by dietetic or diuretic measures that decrease the body's sodium content. Another proposal involves *hyperreactivity of the hypothalamic circulatory centers;* in this view the occurrence of hypertension would depend on the personality structure of the individual as well as on environmental factors. This notion is consistent with the observation that most drugs that reduce blood pressure act on the sympathetic nervous system; moreover, there is no doubt that in addition to genetic factors others – constitutional, social and environmental – can be involved in producing hypertension. On the other hand, the absence of any direct evidence of increased sympathetic activity or enhanced reactivity of the vascular system to constrictor stimuli shows clearly that these attempts at etiological interpretation of essential hypertension (and others not mentioned here) are at present only hypotheses. In this connection, finally, it should be mentioned that *frequent acute blood-pressure increases,* regardless of their cause, bring about hypertrophy of the smooth musculature of the resistance vessels; the resulting increase in peripheral resistance favors the development of chronic high blood pressure.

In the remaining 10 % of cases hypertension is **secondary** to some other clinical condition. In about 25 % of these the underlying disorder is in the parenchyma or vessels of the **kidney** *(renal hypertension),* in association with acute glomerular or renovascular disease, chronic reduction of the renal parenchyma, and other kidney diseases. **Endocrine disturbance** (pheochromocytoma, Cushing's syndrome, hyperthyroidism, etc.) is at fault in about 3%, and the remaining cases, with only a few exceptions, are associated with **cardiovascular disease** (sclerosis of the great arteries, aortic-valve insufficiency, aortic-isthmus stenosis and so on).

As a consequence of hypertension *secondary degenerative (arteriosclerotic) changes in the vessels* additionally increase the resistance to flow. The associated restriction in the blood supply can interfere with organ function, particularly in the brain, the heart and the kidneys, or when combined with high pressure can cause vessels to *rupture* (e.g., stroke). Impaired cardiac function on the one hand and increased demands on the other accelerate the development of heart failure *(cardiac insufficiency)* in all forms of hypertension.

Hypotension. Blood pressures below 100 mm Hg constitute hypotension. This condition can result from *decreases in cardiac output or in total peripheral resistance* or both. In most cases, however, reduced cardiac output predominates.

Hypotension, like its opposite, is classified etiologically as (i) **primary (essential)** or (ii) **secondary (symptomatic).** Primary hypotension is more commonly found in young people of leptosomatic physique and with signs of constitutional asthenia and enhanced activity of the sympathetic system (tachycardia, cool and moist acral regions). Secondary hypotension appears in association with **endocrine disturbances** (adrenal insufficiency, adrenogenital syndrome, hypothyroidism, hyperparathyroidism, etc.), **cardiovascular disease** (aortic stenosis, mitral stenosis, aortic-arch syndrome, cardiovascular syncope, etc.), **infectious-toxic factors** (infectious diseases, intoxications), and **hypovolemic conditions** (losses of blood or plasma fluid, endocrine disturbances, etc.).

In contrast to hypertension, the *pathological consequences* of hypotension are relatively *slight.* Hypotension is of clinical significance only when inadequate blood flow disrupts organ function, as in assumption of erect posture (see below) or shock (pp. 531ff.).

Effects of Posture

Passive effects. Chief among the effects to which the circulatory system must adjust at the transition from reclining to standing are the hydrostatic pressure changes and the associated *redistribution of the blood volume* (p. 499). There is a *transient* pooling of 400–600 ml of blood in the capacitance vessels of the legs alone, most of which comes from intrathoracic vessels. As a result there are temporary decreases in *venous return, central venous pressure, stroke volume and systolic blood pressure.*

Active processes of adaptation. The passive effects are largely *compensated* by active adaptation mediated by the baroreceptors in the arterial system and the stretch receptors in the intrathoracic vessels. The location of the baroreceptors – in the aortic arch and carotid sinus – is such that when a person stands up the decrease in hydrostatic pressure here additionally reduces their level of excitation, which in itself initiates reflex compensatory reactions. The reduced excitation in the receptors leads to (i) *vasoconstriction* in the resistance and capacitance vessels, (ii) increased *heart rate,* (iii) a higher rate of *catecholamine* secretion by the adrenal medulla (iv) activation of the *renin-angiotensin mechanism,* and (v) increased secretion of *vasopressin and aldosterone.*

Vasomotor and cardiac responses. The vasoconstrictor responses to standing involve the *resistance vessels* of the skeletal musculature, the skin, the kidneys and the splanchnic region, in such a way that blood flow through these regions decreases and the total peripheral resistance rises (Fig. 20-38).

The decrease in *brain perfusion* to be expected on physical grounds is largely *compensated* by myogenic and metabolically elicited autoregulatory vasoconstriction. Blood flow through the brain is thus only slightly diminished, reaching the critical level at which signs of *cerebral ischemia* appear only when the mean arterial pressure (in the cerebral vessels) falls below *60 mm Hg.*

Among the *capacitance vessels* it is chiefly those acting as reservoirs (i.e., the veins of the skin and the splanchnic region) that exhibit vasoconstriction.

As a result of the increase in *total peripheral resistance,* the arterial mean pressure returns to about the initial level. The compensatory decreases in *vessel capacity* contribute to maintaining the central venous pressure at a level only slightly lower than before. Because of the increased *heart rate* the decrease in cardiac output is proportionally smaller than that in stroke volume (Fig. 20-38).

The hydrostatic effects on vessels in the lower limbs can be lessened by the *pumping* action of the muscles. Even so, outward filtration predominates, so that during *prolonged* standing the *plasma volume decreases and the interstitial fluid volume in the legs increases.*

Hormonal influences. As the flow of blood through the kidneys is reduced, there is an en-

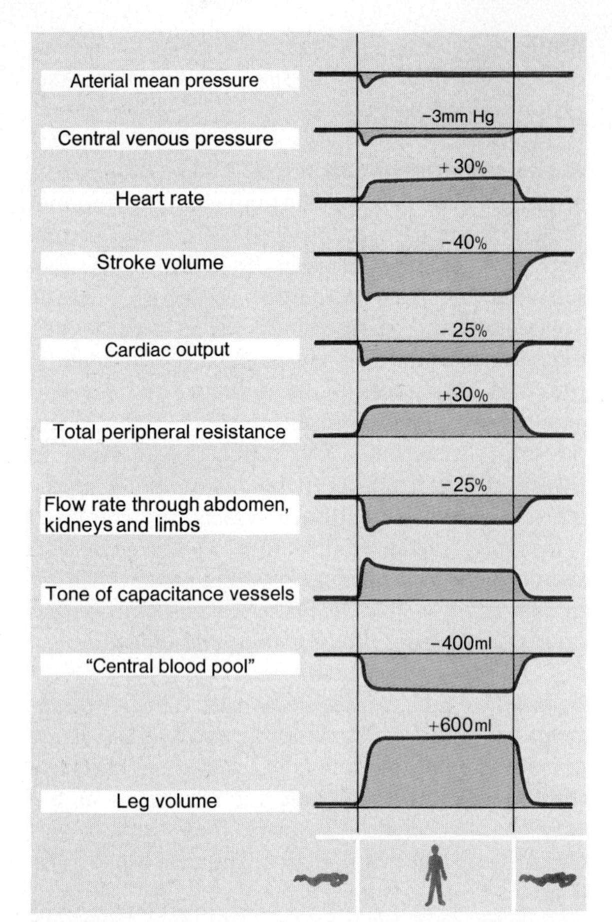

Fig. 20-38. Changes in various cardiovascular parameters at the transitions between the recumbent and erect positions. The numbers represent averages; individual variation can be considerable

hanced release of *renin* with corresponding effects on the formation of *angiotensin* and *aldosterone* secretion (p. 520). The intensified secretion of *vasopressin* additionally reduces renal fluid output, so that the plasma volume increases. These effects, unlike the vasomotor responses, become apparent only after a considerable latency.

Orthostatic syncope. In some people who frequently, but not necessarily always, have low blood-pressure levels (p. 527), the adaptive mechanisms listed above do not suffice for adequate circulatory function; their *blood pressure falls further* below normal when they are erect and the brain is inadequately perfused. Subjective symptoms such as dizziness and impaired vision appear, and the person may even lose consciousness **(orthostatic hypotension** and **orthostatic syncope** or **collapse).** Even entirely healthy people can experience the same difficulties in *warm surroundings,* where orthostatic tolerance is restricted because the vasodilation required for thermoregulation dominates over the vasoconstriction required for control of blood flow.

When the sympathetic vasoconstrictor fibers are inactivated by *sympatholytic drugs* or surgery *(sympathectomy),* and in rare diseases of the sympathetic system, orthostatic tolerance may disappear altogether. On the other hand, the cardiovascular responses to change of position fail to appear when volume shifts are avoided, as can be done by wearing so-called anti-G suits. These are double-walled pressure suits in which the abdomen and legs are compressed in proportion to the effects of gravity on them. They are used, for example, to compensate the increased gravitational effects on the circulatory system associated with acceleration or deceleration of spacecraft.

Tests of orthostatic response. The regulation of blood flow following change of position is routinely tested by measuring heart rate and blood pressure at certain intervals while the subject is recumbent and erect. It is common in clinical practice to take diastolic pressure as the criterion for evaluating the orthostatic response.

When **circulatory function is normal** the *diastolic pressure* falls by no more than *5 mm Hg* after 10 minutes of standing, and the *systolic pressure* departs from the recumbent level by *less than* $\pm 5\%$. The *heart rate,* on the average, is *increased* by as much as 30%, and the stroke volume decreases by as much as 40% (Fig. 20-39).

In cases of so-called **hyperdiastolic orthostatic hypotension** (80–85% of all cases of impairment) the diastolic pressure rises by more than 5 mm Hg, and at the same time the systolic pressure falls by an even greater amount, so that

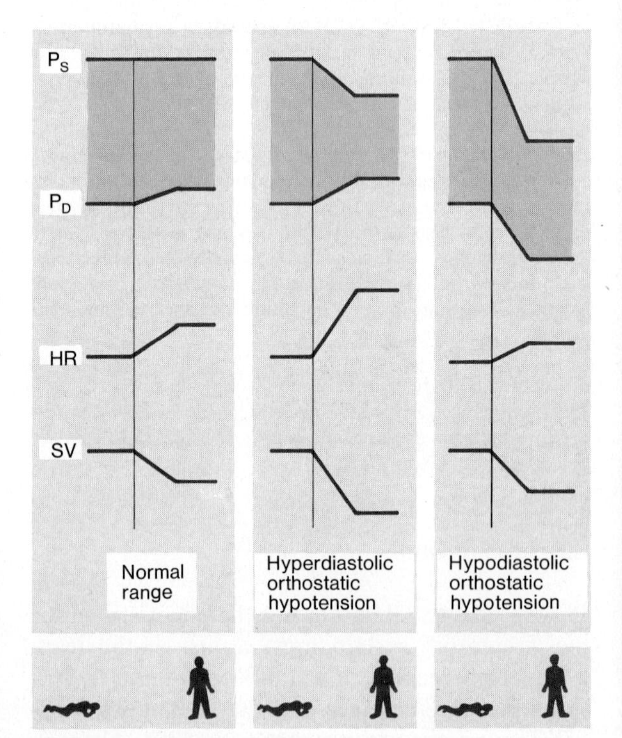

Fig. 20-39. Diagram of the changes in systolic and diastolic pressures (P_S and P_D), heart rate (HR) and stroke volume (SV) when changing from the recumbent to the standing position.

the *amplitude of the pressure oscillation becomes distinctly smaller*. There are relatively large *increases in heart rate* and decreases in stroke volume. The greater increase in diastolic pressure (which reflects a greater constriction of the resistance vessels) and the tachycardia results from a more pronounced activation of the sympathetic nervous system.

By contrast, in so-called **hypodiastolic orthostatic hypotension** both the systolic and the diastolic pressures decrease, with only slight change in pressure amplitude and little or no increase in heart rate (and moderately reduced stroke volume). In these cases the alterations in pressure and heart rate indicate a relatively low-level activation of the sympathetic system.

Exercise

In healthy young people who are not trained as high-performance athletes the *increase in cardiac output* during muscular effort, which results from increases in heart rate and stroke volume specific to the individual, rarely exceeds 25 l · min $^{-1}$. Moreover, the fraction of the cardiac output received by the skeletal musculature is *disproportionately increased,* at the cost of most of the other organs [23, 50]. In Table 20-6 the distribution of blood among the different vascular beds of a human exerting himself to different degrees is summarized.

Distribution of the cardiac output. The increased perfusion of working musculature is brought about chiefly by **local metabolic mechanisms,** which take over from those processes responsible for increased perfusion during the anticipation phase (pp. 507f.). During exercise the *sympathetic system* is activated, enhancing the peripheral vasoconstrictor influences; in *resting muscles,* and even more in the *splanchnic and renal vessels,* these influences effectively reduce blood flow (Fig. 20-40). But in the working muscles they are opposed by the local metabolic control mechanisms, which decrease the resistance to flow by an amount not fully compensated by the **collateral vasoconstriction;** the net result is that the *total peripheral resistance* is lowered. The *blood volume* in the vessels of the working musculature *does not increase* despite the far greater number of perfused capillaries; because the vessels are compressed by the contractions of the muscles, it actually tends to be reduced.

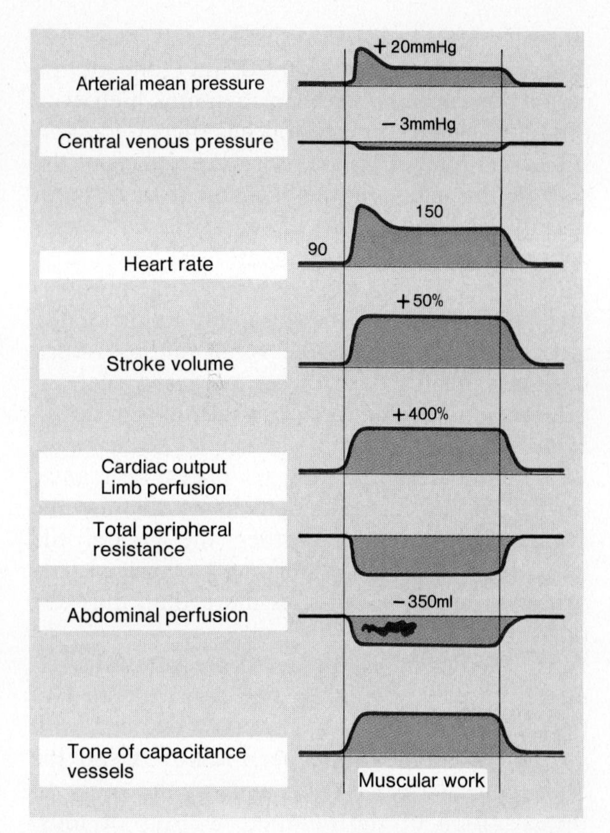

Fig. 20-40. Changes in various cardiovascular parameters when an erect person does muscular work (the curve for abdominal blood flow was obtained from measurements on recumbent subjects). The numbers represent averages; individual variation can be considerable

Table 20-6. Organ perfusion and cardiac output when the subject is at rest and when performing work at different intensities. (From WADE and BISHOP [23])

O_2 uptake (ml·min^{-1}·m^{-2})	Rest	Light work	Heavy work	Maximal work
	140	400	1,200	2,000
	Perfusion (ml·min^{-1}):			
Vascular region:				
Skeletal muscle	1,200	4,500	12,500	22,000
Heart	250	350	750	1,000
Brain	750	750	750	750
Splanchnic	1,400	1,100	600	300
Kidneys	1,100	900	600	250
Skin	500	1,500	1,900	600
Other organs	600	400	400	100
Cardiac output	5,800	9,500	17,500	25,000

During light to submaximal work *skin perfusion decreases at first* but then increases for purposes of thermoregulation. During maximal exertion, however, the thermoregulatory effect is suppressed temporarily (Table 20-6). *Coronary perfusion* increases in accordance with the work the heart must perform, while *perfusion of the brain* remains constant at all levels of exertion.

Constrictor responses in the *capacitance vessels* of the skin, together with mobilization of blood from the splanchnic and hepatic vessels, provide a *larger supply of blood* to the heart. It is notable that when work is prolonged, the tone of the cutaneous capacitance vessels remains high even though the rate of perfusion has increased. This situation implies that the resistance vessels of the skin in this phase have taken on a thermoregulatory function, while the capacitance vessels continue to function as regulators of blood flow. The venous return from the working musculature is enhanced by the pumping action of the muscles (p. 500), and the total venous return becomes greater due to the increased suction-pressure-pump effect of respiration (pp. 500f.) [31, 48].

Despite the decreased total peripheral resistance, cardiac output increases sufficiently to raise the *mean arterial pressure* further, the greater the load. Pulse pressure is distinctly enlarged, because systolic pressure rises more than diastolic pressure.

When *exercise stops,* the blood pressure falls relatively rapidly, owing on one hand to the fact that vasodilation is only gradually reduced until all the metabolites have been removed and the *O_2 debt paid* (see p. 649), and on the other to the cessation of the pumping actions of muscles (and respiration) that had been accelerating venous return. Cardiac output, heart rate, O_2 uptake and arteriovenous O_2 difference return to the initial levels the more slowly, the greater the work performed (for further details see pp. 648ff.).

The effect of training. In trained athletes the *heart rate* at rest is lower (down to 40/min) and the *stroke volume* larger than in people without training. The former thus achieve a given cardiac output with a lower heart rate then the latter. The *blood volume* is slightly increased, as are the maximal possible cardiac output and the capacity for O_2 uptake and extraction (for further details see p. 661).

Thermal Stress

Among the responses of the circulatory system to *thermally effective* ambient temperatures, changes in *cutaneous blood flow* play the leading role (cf. p. 536).

Heat stress. In a warm environment the rate of skin perfusion rises; under an extreme heat load the total blood flow rate is 3,000–4,000 ml/min, ca. 10 times as great as under thermoneutral conditions. The tone of the *capacitance vessels* in the skin is reduced, and *heart rate* and *cardiac output* increase. The changes in *systolic pressure* are slight and nonuniform, but *diastolic pressure* decreases. All these responses vary widely in degree in different individuals. In some people subjected to ambient temperatures around 44 °C and high humidity (over 85%) cardiac output can rise to 20 l/min and diastolic pressure fall by more than 40 mm Hg – a situation that regularly produces the symptoms of orthostatic hypotension (p. 528) [50].

Cold stress. In a cold environment the *opposite responses* appear; the resistance and capacitance vessels of the skin constrict, and heart rate and cardiac output decline. The blood pressure tends to rise, and intense cold stimuli can elicit overshooting blood-pressure reactions.

This phenomenon is utilized in diagnosis as a "cold pressure test" (measurement of blood pressure while one hand is dipped in ice-water) of the responsiveness of the sympathetic innervation of the vessels. People with "borderline" hypertension and patients with pheochromocytomas often respond to this treatment with very large increases in blood pressure.

When thermal stimuli are repeated frequently, the circulatory responses become weaker, an expression of **adaptation.** A similar effect, **acclimatization,** accompanies prolonged exposure to extreme climates. Both phenomena are based on extremely complex functional changes of particular organ systems or the whole body, some of which are not yet entirely understood.

Loss of Blood

Decreases in blood volume owing to hemorrhage reduce the **filling pressure** of the vascular system. The consequence is *diminished venous return and stroke volume.* The mean arterial pressure hardly changes with blood loss of up to ca. 15 ml/kg body weight, but falls considerably if more blood is lost.

Vasomotor and cardiac responses. Compensation of the above changes is initiated by several agents, among them the *baroreceptors* in the intrathoracic vessels, the atria and the arteries. Because their activity is diminished they exert a smaller inhibitory influence on the vasomotor and cardioinhibitory centers, so that reflex *vasoconstriction* and *increased heart rate* are produced. The vasoconstriction involves primarily the *resistance vessels in the skin, viscera and kidneys;* the coronary and cerebral vessels are excluded. In addition, constriction of the *capacitance vessels* in skin and viscera reduces the capacity of these regions and thus *improves the filling pressure* of the vascular system. The secretion of hormones by the adrenal medulla is accelerated and can contribute to enhancement of the vasoconstrictor responses (see p. 510). As an independent reaction, the capacity of the vascular system is also reduced by the *reverse stress relaxation* of the vessels, and thus is additionally adjusted to the reduced blood volume.

Volume-control responses. Because of the constriction of the resistance vessels and decrease in venous pressure, the *capillary pressure falls,* so that more fluid moves from the interstitial space into the capillaries (pp. 504f.). In this way the *intravascular volume* is expanded while the *interstitial* (and intracellular) *fluid volumes* shrink. When a human has lost 500 ml of blood, only 15–30 min later 80–100% of the lost plasma has been replaced by interstitial fluid. After greater loss of blood the plasma volume is normalized in 12–72 h, during which time the loss of tissue protein due to the initial influx of albumin from extracellular regions is compensated by accelerated synthesis. It takes longer (4–6 weeks, see p. 411) to replace the corpuscular elements of the blood.

Because perfusion of the kidneys is restricted, *urine production* declines, and more Na^+ and nitrogen-containing metabolites are retained in the blood. The concurrent activation of the *renin-angiotensin mechanism* stabilizes the blood pressure. The connection between the sensation of thirst following blood loss and the renin-angiotensin mechanism has been mentioned above (p. 518).

Vasopressin secretion increases as a reflex triggered by the reduced activity of the atrial receptors, and that of *aldosterone* increases owing to the greater concentration of angiotensin. The associated increased retention of salt and water encourages the rapid *restoration of volume equilibrium.*

When cardiac output and blood pressure fall severely, additional functional impairment of the cardiovascular system (and other organs) may ensue and give rise to shock (see below).

Cardiovascular Shock

The term cardiovascular shock comprises all the states in which **inadequate perfusion of tissue** and an associated O_2 deficiency or (less commonly) impairment of O_2 release or utilization cause a persistant *deterioration in the function of vital organs.*

The inadequate tissue perfusion in most cases results because *cardiac output is too small* for the prevailing conditions. There are two fundamental causes of this situation. 1. *Insufficient venous return* can result from (i) diminished blood volume, (ii) reduced vascular tone, or (iii) greatly increased resistance to flow. 2. The *function of the heart* itself may be impaired. Less frequently, inadequate perfusion results from *primary disturbance of the microcirculation.* The different forms of shock can be grouped in a highly simplified way according to their pathogenesis, as follows: 1. *hypovolemic shock,* 2. *cardiogenic shock,* 3. *neurogenic shock,* 4. *septic shock,* 5. *anaphylactic shock.*

The onset and course of shock are critically dependent on whether, and for how long, the *negative-feedback* (homeostatic) mechanisms of the circulatory system suffice to *compensate* for the disturbance, or the extent to which *positive-feedback* mechanisms resulting from the inadequate perfusion set up a *vicious circle* and progressively reduce the ability of the organism to adjust. Fig. 20-41 summarizes the most important events involved in the development of shock.

Hypovolemic shock. Hypovolemia (reduced blood volume) is brought about by loss of either *blood* or *plasma water and electrolytes.* The most common cause of hypovolemic shock is *hemorrhage,* whether external or internal, into body cavities or tissue (for example, by injury to blood vessels, gastrointestinal bleeding, rupture of liver or spleen, the cutting or crushing of tissue, fractures, and intra- or postoperative bleeding). A distinction is made between *hemorrhagic shock* (with blood loss only) and *traumatic shock* (in which damage to tissue secondarily affects the microcirculation and the clotting of the blood).

Characteristic features of hypovolemic shock are *hypotensive blood pressure* (at least with respect to the individual's initial pressure), *tachycardia, low cardiac output, cold and pale skin, severe thirst* and *oliguria* (so-called *"cold shock"*). Development of shock is reflected in the microcirculation by a transition from the reflex constriction of the *precapillary sphincters* to a dilation under metabolic control; the *venules* remain constricted, so that there is **sequestration** of blood in the capillaries. The accompanying increase in hydrostatic pressure causes more fluid to pass through the capillary walls, so that the *intravascular volume is further decreased.* As the process continues, the capillary walls are damaged so severely that there is not only a progressive increase in filtration but an actual leakage of blood into the tissue. This shift of the balance in tone of the precapillary sphincters and venules appears to be a decisive factor in the development of **irreversible shock** (see below).

The extremely slow flow in the region of the microcirculation and the resulting increased concentration of CO_2 or products of anaerobic metabolism (lactic acid) in the blood favor aggregation of the erythrocytes (so-called **sludging**). The associated *increase in viscosity* further impedes flow in

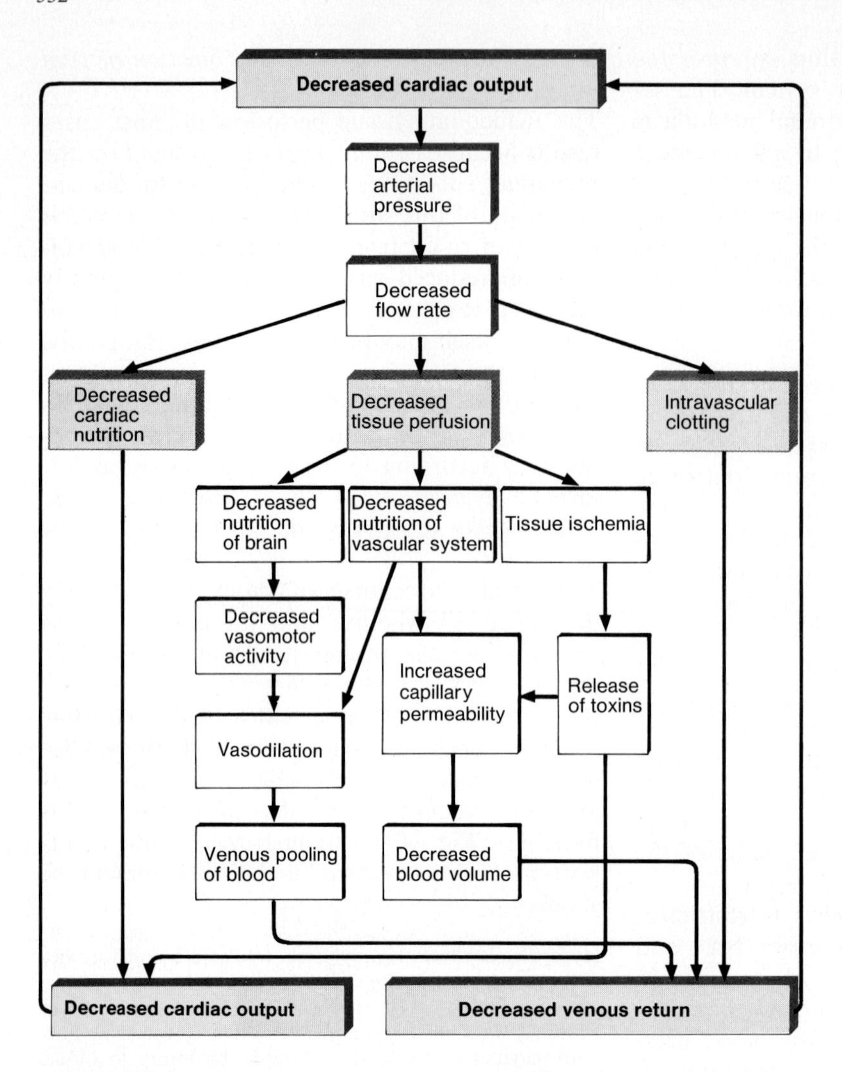

Fig. 20-41. Positive-feedback mechanisms involved in the development of shock. (From GUYTON [8])

the affected vessels. Moreover, acidosis weakens the ability of the vessels to respond to circulating catecholamines.
In the region of the *capacitance vessels* loss of tone leads to **venous pooling** and thus to further reduction of the venous return. When the *resistance vessels* lose tone, the peripheral resistance is lowered and the arterial pressure drops still further.
Myocardial function is impaired during shock both by the insufficient coronary perfusion owing to hypotension and tachycardia and by acidosis. In addition, the myocardium is likely to be damaged by toxic substances released by ischemic or necrotic cells in the body. Because the restriction of blood flow through the kidneys is disproportionately large, *renal insufficiency* can develop.
The intense stimulation of the *sympathetic system* by the *ischemic response of the CNS* can give way to paralysis in severe shock, so that decreased heart rate and elimination of the vasoconstrictor influence cause a drastic further *deterioration of cerebral perfusion.*
This incomplete list of positive-feedback mechanisms makes it clear that the disturbances that elicit the shock can also reinforce it and lead to *progressive shock.* In *irreversible shock* the damage is so severe that it cannot be repaired by any therapeutic measures; the result is *death by heart failure.*
Hypovolemic shock by *loss of plasma* can accompany extensive burns or excessive elimination of plasma water and electrolytes through the gastrointestinal tract (e.g., in peritonitis, pancreatitis or intestinal obstruction). When shock follows *burning* the plasma loss greatly increases the viscosity of the blood and thus additionally impedes the microcirculation.
Similarly, *isotonic or hypertonic dehydration* (p. 771) such as are associated with chronic vomiting, diarrhea, excessive sweating, water deprivation, vasopressin deficiency, etc. can cause hypovolemic shock.

Cardiogenic shock. Cardiogenic shock occurs when the heart is incapable of pumping enough blood. It appears in about 15% of all cases of *cardiac infarction* (necrosis of the myocardium), with a mortality of over 80%. Moreover, cardiac shock can accompany *myocardial insufficiency, ventricular tachycardia, pulmonary embolism* and other illnesses.
The symptomatology corresponds to that of hypovolemic shock, with additional signs of *venous congestion* in the pulmonary and/or systemic circulations as a result of the impaired cardiac function.

Neurogenic shock. *Loss of tone in the resistance and capacitance vessels* leads to neurogenic shock when the capacity of the vessels becomes too great for the volume of blood available. The *mean filling pressure falls,* reducing venous flow and cardiac output. At the same time the *total peripheral resistance is lowered.*

This form of shock most frequently follows high spinal anesthesia in which the efferent sympathetic fibers are blocked *(spinal shock)*. It can also appear during *deep general anesthesia* owing to inactivation of the vasomotor centers, or in persistent *cerebral ischemia* as a result of severe damage to the brain.
The category of neurogenic shock also includes the *fainting* induced by standing up in patients with various neurological disorders affecting the sympathetic nervous system or with sympathetic activity suppressed by surgical procedures or drugs (e.g., ganglion-blocking agents).
By contrast, **orthostatic collapse (syncope)** in organically healthy people (p. 528) – like the fainting associated with *intense emotions* (trauma, fright, pain) – is evidently not due to failure of vasomotor control, but rather to an *excitation of parasympathetic structures* that leads to decreased heart rate and vasodilation in the skeletal musculature. Because of the resulting fall in arterial pressure and reduced cardiac output the flow of blood through the brain becomes inadequate, hence the loss of consciousness *(vasovagal attack)*.
In overheating shock *(heat stroke)*, as in neurogenic shock, an imbalance develops between vascular capacity and blood volume, and in most cases it is augmented by *hypovolemia* due to the increased sweat production.

Septic shock. Septic shock is a complication of infection by *gram-negative bacteria* (less commonly by gram-positive bacteria), and is what is generally meant by *"blood poisoning"*. The diversity of pathogenic organisms and sources of infection explains the wide variation in onset and development of septic shock. It is probably elicited by *endotoxins* that are released by the bacteria and injure the cells.
The early stages of septic shock are characterized by *hypotension*, though cardiac output and heart rate are usually raised. There is a conspicuous general vasodilation (so-called *"warm"* or *"red"* shock), with *reduced arteriovenous O_2 difference*. Among the proposed causes of these changes are impaired O_2 transport from the capillaries to the cells owing to increased affinity of the hemoglobin for oxygen, and a primary disruption of oxidative metabolism in the cells.
In more *advanced stages*, when secondary O_2-deficiency symptoms appear, cardiac output falls and a *vicious circle* becomes established as in the other forms of shock, with the primary cell damage progressively exacerbated by increasingly inadequate perfusion of the tissue.
In *anaphylactic shock*, a rapid allergic reaction to an antigen against which the organism has developed antibodies, large amounts of *histamine* are released along with *serotonin, bradykinin* and a so-called *SRS-A* (slow-reacting substance of anaphylaxis). In the initial stages *vasodilation* predominates in the arterioles, venules and veins, and at the same time *capillary permeability* is greatly increased. The hemodynamic alterations correspond largely to those in septic shock.

Other forms of shock. *Intoxication* by medicaments (barbiturates, tranquilizers, etc.) and *endocrine malfunction* (pituitary, parathyroid, pancreas, adrenal cortex) can be accompanied by states of shock; here a number of factors may be involved, frequently including *hypovolemia* and *acidosis*.

Treatment of shock. The chief forms of therapy are steps to *eliminate the underlying causes* (by operations to stop the bleeding or remove the source of infection and by medication with antibiotics, antihistamines and so on), and *general measures* such as keeping the airways open and administering O_2. In *hypovolemic shock* the cause can be treated directly by *replacement* of the lost volume – by transfusion of blood, plasma or blood substitutes. In the other forms of shock as well (with the exception of cardiogenic shock with venous congestion) it is therapeutically effective to supplement blood volume. Additional measures to *raise blood pressure, improve cardiac force and the flow properties of the blood, eliminate acidosis* and so on may be required, depending on the kind of shock, but cannot be described here.

20.12 Circulation through Special Organs and its Control

Coronary Circulation

Cardiac perfusion. Under *resting conditions* blood flows through the myocardium at a rate of ca. 0.8–0.9 $ml \cdot g^{-1} \cdot min^{-1}$, which with a heart weight of ca. 300 g amounts to about 250 $ml \cdot min^{-1}$ or 4% of the cardiac output (Table 20-5). Under *maximal load* coronary flow can increase by a factor of 4–5, to a maximum of ca. 1,250 $ml \cdot min^{-1}$ (Table 20-6). The rate of perfusion of the heart is affected by changes in *aortic pressure*, by the *heart rate*, by *neural* activity and above all by **metabolic factors.**
The coronary vessels exhibit pronounced *autoregulation*. For details of other features of the coronary circulation see pp. 477ff.

Cerebral Circulation

Perfusion of the brain. The *average* rate of flow through the brain is 0.5 $ml \cdot g^{-1} \cdot min^{-1}$; with an adult human brain weight of about 1,500 g the total flow is ca. 750 ml/min, or 13% of the cardiac output. Circulation through the gray matter, with its densely packed cells, is considerably greater (0.8–1.1 $ml \cdot g^{-1} \cdot min^{-1}$) than through the white matter (0.15–0.25 $ml \cdot g^{-1} \cdot min^{-1}$).
In cases of extreme neuronal activity such as generalized convulsions the overall perfusion rate can rise by as much as 50%. Similar local increases have been observed in particular regions of the brain that are especially active, but the influence of these on the overall blood flow is not very great.

Regulation of cerebral blood flow. Vessel diameter is basically controlled by **metabolic factors,** especially the *CO_2 partial pressure* in the capillaries and tissues, the *H^+-ion concentration* in the perivascular space and the *O_2 partial pres-*

sure. Increase in the CO_2 partial pressure elicits marked *vasodilation,* with doubled P_{CO_2} approximately doubling blood flow. The CO_2 effects are based on the formation of H^+ by dissociation of carbonic acid. Other substances that increase H^+ concentration (lactic acid and other metabolites) also increase cerebral blood flow. The cerebral symptoms of *hyperventilation tetany* (dizziness, clouded consciousness, muscle spasms, etc.) result from the opposite effect, a restriction of cerebral blood flow due to hypocapnia. Changes in O_2 partial pressure are somewhat less effective, decrease producing vasodilation and increase slight vasoconstriction.
The well developed **myogenic autoregulation** helps to keep blood flow through the brain constant regardless of the variations in hydrostatic pressure with change of position. Cerebral perfusion is thus controlled largely by **local mechanisms,** myogenic and metabolic. The autonomic innervation of the cerebral vessels plays a subordinate and not yet entirely understood role.

Hepatic and Portal Circulation

Perfusion. The mesenteric, pancreatic, splenic and hepatic vessels are often called the *"splanchnic circulation"* because of their common innervation by the sympathetic splanchnic nerves. The blood flowing through the liver comes from the hepatic artery and the portal veins, that in the portal veins having previously passed through the capillary bed of the superior mesenteric and splenic arteries in the intestine, pancreas and spleen. The branches of the hepatic artery and portal veins, the interlobular arteries and veins, enter the peripheral parts of the liver through the portal canal; here they branch further to form a common system of large-bore capillaries that anastomose with one another, the hepatic sinusoids, which join in the middle of each lobe to form the central vein. The axial central veins fuse into collecting veins and these join as larger branches of the hepatic veins.

The mean pressure of 100 mm Hg in the hepatic artery drops in the vessels of the liver, reaching about 5 mm Hg in the central veins. The pressure in the portal veins, after the blood has passed through the capillaries in the intestines and spleen, is 10–12 mm Hg. Because resistance to flow in the sinusoids is low, the small pressure difference of 5–7 mm Hg between portal and central veins suffices to maintain blood flow here. In this large and highly elastic vascular bed even relatively small pressure changes cause considerable changes in volume. Such pressure changes can occur when flow out of the hepatic veins is impeded and when influx from the intestine is reduced. The splanchnic vessels contain ca. 20% of the total blood volume.

Under *resting conditions* blood flow through the liver amounts to ca. $1.0\ ml \cdot g^{-1} \cdot min^{-1}$, making a total of about $1{,}400 \pm 300\ ml \cdot min^{-1}$ or about 25% of the cardiac output. The hepatic artery provides about 25% of this blood, a contribution that can rise to 50% with high O_2 consumption in the liver.
About 40% of the oxygen consumed in the liver is supplied by the fully oxygenated blood from the hepatic artery and the rest by the blood from the portal veins – far greater in amount, but deoxygenated to varying degrees by its passage through the intestine, pancreas or spleen.

Regulation of blood flow. The vessels in the *splanchnic region* are innervated by **sympathetic vasoconstrictor nerves.** Constriction of these vessels can send a large fraction of the blood volume into other parts of the vascular system, and conversely – dilation greatly reduces the total peripheral resistance and augments the capacity, so that large amounts of blood can be stored.
Flow through the *mucosa and submucosa* of the intestine, which contain the glands, increases when the glands are active. The release of *bradykinin* (p. 511) is regarded as a possible cause of this increase, although it cannot be ruled out that other factors also participate in the response. In the *muscular layers* increased blood flow is associated with increased motor activity; here the vascular responses are elicited by *metabolic factors.*
The resistance vessels in intestine and liver are capable of extensive **autoregulation,** which during prolonged stimulation eventually overrides the vasoconstrictor effects. This phenomenon, called *"autoregulatory escape",* is brought about by the enhancement of local metabolic control in the ischemic conditions following vasoconstriction, so that it predominates over the neural vasoconstrictor inputs. Pressure increases in the portal veins and the veins of the liver elicit constriction of the hepatic arterioles by way of retrograde (via the capillaries) *autoregulatory constriction* of the hepatic arterioles, so that inflow is inhibited. Because the vascular structures here are so complicated, many hemodynamic questions cannot yet be definitely answered. But the mechanism of *greatest functional importance* is likely to be the *vasomotor alteration of capacity,* by which the liver alone can make available to the rest of the system, on a *short-term* basis, as much as 50% of its normal volume of ca. 700 ml blood.

Renal Circulation

Perfusion of the kidneys. Under *resting conditions* the average blood flow is ca. 4.0 $ml \cdot g^{-1} \cdot min^{-1}$, so that the kidneys, weighing about 300 g, account for ca. 1,200 $ml \cdot min^{-1}$ or about 20% of the cardiac output.

A special feature of the renal circulation is the presence of two capillary beds in series. The *afferent* arteriole feeds into the glomerular bed, which is separated from the peritubular bed by an *efferent* arteriole with high resistance to flow. Pressure in the *glomerular capillaries* is relatively high, ca. *60 mm Hg*, and that in the *peritubular capillaries* is relatively low, ca. *13 mm Hg*.

Regulation of renal blood flow. The vessels of the kidneys exhibit well-developed **myogenic autoregulation,** which allows the flow rate and capillary pressure in the nephron to be kept largely *constant* for arterial pressures between 80 and 180 mm Hg. About 90% of the renal perfusion is allocated to the cortical vessels, where the volume flow rate is 4–5 $ml \cdot g^{-1} \cdot min^{-1}$. Volume flow through the vessels of the outer and inner medulla amounts to only 1.2 and 0.2 $ml \cdot g^{-1} \cdot min^{-1}$, respectively.

The renal vessels are innervated by sympathetic *constrictor nerves* in which at rest there is little tonic activity. In *the standing human* or after *blood loss* the renal vessels participate in the vasoconstrictor responses that ensure adequate perfusion of the myocardium and brain. Flow through the kidneys also decreases during exercise and exposure to heat, a response that helps to compensate for the vasodilation in muscle and skin, with its effects on arterial pressure.

Circulation in Skeletal Muscle

Perfusion of skeletal muscle. The *resting* blood flow averages $3 \cdot 10^{-2}$ to $4 \cdot 10^{-2}$ $ml \cdot g^{-1}\ min^{-1}$. The entire mass of muscle, ca. 30 kg, thus requires a supply of about 900–1,200 $ml \cdot min^{-1}$, or 15–20% of the cardiac output. During *maximal work* the rate of perfusion in the working muscles can reach 0.5–1.3 $ml \cdot g^{-1} \cdot min^{-1}$. (cf. p. 647) [10].

Regulation of blood flow. The muscle vessels are innervated by sympathetic *vasoconstrictor* fibers. When these are maximally stimulated flow can be reduced to 25% of the resting level. On the other hand, the increased sympathetic activity in a subject expecting to perform muscular work can increase blood flow through the muscles by a factor of 4 (the complexities of this response are discussed on pp. 522f.).

During *exercise* local *metabolically controlled vasodilation* dominates. But blood flow is also affected by the *mechanical compression* of the vessels when a working muscle contracts. If contraction is prolonged and is no stronger than half of the maximum possible, the initially abated blood flow increases again until it surpasses the original level. In the *relaxation phase* there is a transient further increase *(reactive hyperemia;* p. 508). During stronger contractions blood flow falls below the starting level by an amount related to the strength of contraction, and can cease altogether. In these cases the reactive hyperemia in the relaxation phase is correspondingly more pronounced.

When the muscle contractions are *rhythmic* blood flow changes analogously, decreasing during contraction and increasing during relaxation, though the mean flow rate is always above the original level (Fig. 20-42). This difference makes it understandable that dynamic muscular work, with a continual alternation between contraction and relaxation, does not tire the muscle as rapidly as maintained static work.

Cutaneous Circulation

Perfusion of the skin. Even in the *neutral range of temperatures* blood flow through the skin under

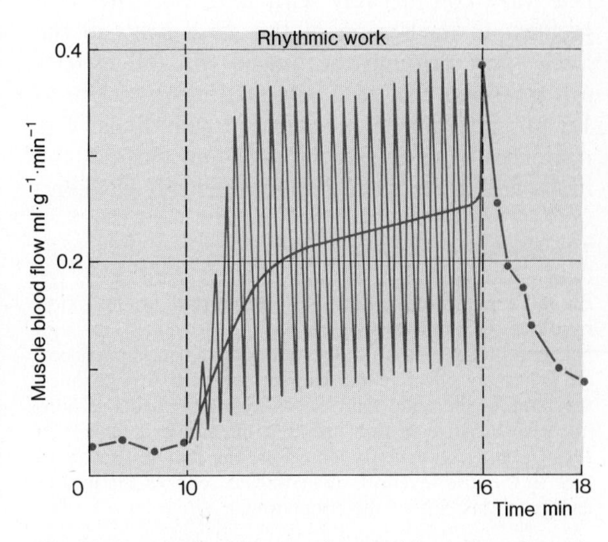

Fig. 20-42. Rhythmic fluctuations in blood flow through the calf musculature of the human leg during intermittent contraction. Flow between the contractions is considerably greater than during contraction. There is a progressive increase in mean volume flow. (From BARCROFT)

resting conditions exhibits fairly *large regional differences* depending on skin temperature. Flow rates probably range from $3 \cdot 10^{-2}$ to $0.1 \text{ ml} \cdot \text{g}^{-1} \cdot \text{min}^{-1}$, or from 150 to 500 ml/min for a total skin mass of 5,000 g.

Regulation of cutaneous blood flow. Cutaneous blood flow is controlled by two different mechanisms, the relative effectiveness of which varies in different regions. In the distal acral parts of the skin (hand, foot, ear) there are many sympathetic *adrenergic vasoconstrictor fibers* which even under thermoneutral conditions have a relatively high level of tonic activity. Dilation is thus produced by central inhibition of this activity. By contrast, vasodilation in the proximal parts of the extremities and the skin of the trunk is mainly produced indirectly, by the release of *bradykinin* associated with activation of *cholinergic sudomotor fibers* (p. 634). In all parts of the skin, vasoconstriction is based on an increase in the activity of sympathetic adrenergic fibers.
Because of the large *capacity* of the *subpapillary* venous plexus (ca. 1,500 ml), venomotor responses can shift fairly large amounts of blood into and out of the skin, so that the cutaneous vessels serve an important function as a **blood depot.**

Thermoregulatory influences. A major function of the blood flowing through the skin is thermoregulation. Under *heat stress* the total blood flow rises to 31/min, and it can be still greater under extreme conditions. But the changes in perfusion rate vary considerably with location. They are greatest in the region of the *acral parts of the limbs;* flow through the fingers can fall to $0.01 \text{ ml} \cdot \text{g}^{-1} \cdot \text{min}^{-1}$ in cold surroundings and rise to $1.5 \text{ ml} \cdot \text{g}^{-1} \cdot \text{min}^{-1}$ in warm surroundings. The responses of vessels in the proximal parts of the limbs and in the trunk are considerably weaker.

The increased blood flow induced by heat results in part from opening of the many *arteriovenous anastomoses* (cf. Fig. 20-21), through which the greater part of the blood bypasses the capillaries on its way to the veins. The high heat conductance of the tissue makes this form of perfusion an extremely effective mechanism for heat loss through the skin. At the same time the unfavorable effects of non-nutritive increase in flow through the tissue (decrease in P_{CO_2}) are circumvented. Moreover, the low resistance to flow in the arteriovenous anastomoses reduces the loss of energy in this part of the circulation.

Blood flow through the skin during exercise. As part of the general adjustment of the circulation to the conditions of exercise, increased resistance to flow due to constriction of the cutaneous vessels helps to maintain adequate arterial pressure. When thermal stress is superimposed, the thermoregulatory control mechanisms (causing dilation) dominate, so that the fraction of the cardiac output available to the working musculature becomes proportionally smaller. The greater tendency for collapse to occur when work is done in the heat is due to this interaction.

Uterine and Fetal Circulations

Perfusion of the uterus. In the non-pregnant uterus blood flow changes in parallel to the variations in metabolic activity of myo- and endometrium during the menstrual cycle.
During *pregnancy* blood flow is considerably increased. In animals 20- to 40-fold increases have been observed, and are thought to be brought about by the local action of hormones (estrogens). Because of the high O_2 consumption and roughly 100-fold increase in mass of the uterus at this time, the *O_2 saturation* of the blood in the intervillous space is *only about 80%* despite the increased blood flow. Shortly before birth perfusion of the uterus decreases, evidently because the arteries are compressed by the increasing tone of the uterine musculature or by the contractions during labor.

Placental circulation. For the **fetus,** the placenta takes over the function of *lungs, gastrointestinal tract and kidneys.* The blood of the mother flows freely through the intervillous spaces, and the fetal blood flows through the capillaries in the chorionic villi, which protrude into the sinus-like intervillous spaces. Here the fetal blood takes up O_2 and gives off CO_2. The higher O_2 capacity of the fetal hemoglobin facilitates the transport of oxygen; however, O_2 and CO_2 exchange occurs less readily through the thicker cell layer of the chorionic villi than through the alveoli of the lung. Water, electrolytes and proteins of low molecular weight can pass the placental barrier in both directions.

Fetal circulation. From the *placenta,* the fetal blood (incompletely saturated with O_2) flows through the umbilical vein in the umbilical cord. Most of it passes through the ductus venosus into the inferior vena cava, where it mixes with the deoxygenated blood from the lower part of the body (Fig. 20-43). A *smaller* amount enters the left branch of the portal vein and circulates through the liver and the hepatic veins before entering the inferior vena cava. The mixed blood in the vena cava flows into the right atrium with an O_2 content of 60–65% saturation; almost all of it passes directly from the valvula of the infe-

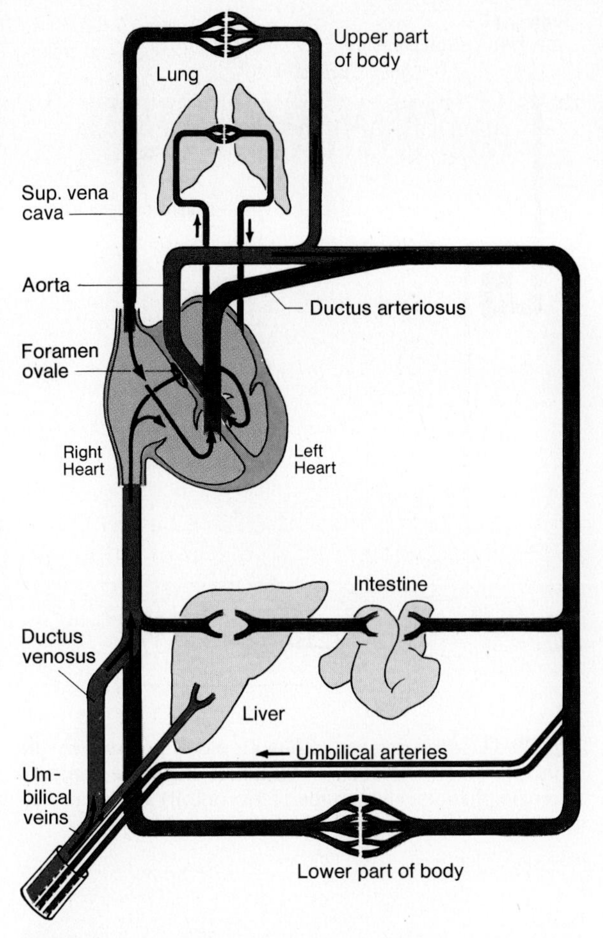

Fig. 20-43. Blood flow through the fetal circulation (from GUYTON). For details see text

rior vena cava to the foramen ovale, and through this opening into the left atrium. From the left ventricle it enters the aorta and is distributed in the systemic circulation.

The blood from the superior vena cava primarily enters the pulmonary trunk, by way of the right atrium and right ventricle. Because of the high resistance to flow in the collapsed lung, the pressure in the pulmonary trunk during systole is transiently higher than in the aorta, so that most of the blood flows through the ductus arteriosus into the aorta; only a relatively small amount flows through the capillary bed of the lungs and back to the left atrium by way of the pulmonary veins. The ductus arteriosus opens into the aorta distal to the point where the arteries to the head and upper limbs branch off, so that these parts of the body are supplied with the more highly oxygenated blood from the left ventricle. From the two umbilical arteries, which branch off from the iliac arteries, some of the blood flows through the umbilical cord to the placenta and the rest circulates through the lower part of the body. Because the two *atria* communicate by way of the *foramen ovale,* and the *ductus arteriosus* joins the *pulmonary artery and aorta,* the two ventricles are *largely in parallel.* The double ventricle can propel ca. **200–300 ml · kg^{-1} · min^{-1}**, of which about 60% flows through the placenta and 40% through the body. At the end of pregnancy the fetal arterial blood pressure is 60–70 mm Hg, and the heart rate is 140/min (120–160/min).

Changes in fetal circulation after birth. At birth the peripheral resistance is raised when the umbilical arteries are tied off, so that the pressure in the aorta rises. The CO_2 partial pressure in the fetal blood increases when contact with the placenta is lost, which stimulates the respiratory center. The infant's first gasps for breath expand the lungs; as the resistance to flow through the lungs decreases, volume flow increases. Moreover, because the intrathoracic pressure is well below atmospheric pressure more than 100 ml of blood is sucked out of the placenta into the child's circulatory system *(placenta transfusion).* The pressure drop in the pulmonary artery and the rise in the aorta cause a reversal of flow in the ductus arteriosus. When the input of blood from the placenta is cut off, the pressure in the right atrium falls, while that in the left atrium increases because of the added influx from the pulmonary veins. As a result, the pressure gradient between right and left atria reverses, so that the valvula of the foramen ovale is pressed against the atrial wall and an initial, functional closure of the foramen ovale is effected. The ductus arteriosus closes by contraction of the sphincter-like muscles. This is a slow process, not completed until several days after birth; the initial continuation of flow through the ductus arteriosus, from the aorta to the pulmonary artery, is important in ensuring adequate perfusion of the lungs. After about 1 week the pattern of circulation in the infant is like that in adults.

Of the *congenital* heart defects, persistent fetal connections in the form of a patent **ductus arteriosus** or **foramen ovale** each account for 15–20%. The associated impairment of circulatory function (when the ductus arteriosus remains open more than 50% of the increased stroke volume of the left ventricle can enter the pulmonary circulation, whereas with a patent foramen ovale the volume ejected by the right ventricle is usually increased) makes surgical correction of the defects essential.

20.13 Measurement of Pressure, Flow and Volume in the Vascular System

Pressure Measurement

Direct methods. Direct (intravascular) measurements of pressure require the introduction of cannulas or catheters into the vessels. In the past pressure was measured predominantly with simple **fluid manometers,** with mercury (for measurement of arterial pressure) or water (for measurement of venous pressure), for example, as the manometric fluids. But the inertia of such manometers severely damps out rapid pressure changes, so that they are suited only for the determination of *mean pressure.*

Membrane manometers can measure more rapid changes in pressure. In principle, these devices consist of a rigid chamber, one wall of which is an elastic membrane. The pressure in the vessel is transmitted across a rigid connection between chamber and cannula, and the displacements of the membrane, which are proportional to pressure, are recorded either *mechanically* (by a lever), *optically* (by a mirror) or *electrically* (by a pressure transducer). Modern membrane manometers, with their small mass and the minimal displacement of their very hard membranes, can monitor accurately pressure changes at 1,000 Hz or more. One kind of **transducer** is a wire or semiconductor crystal that changes its resistance (measured in a *Wheatstone bridge*) when it is stretched (by deformation of the membrane); these are called *strain-gauge manometers.* In another type the membrane is one plate of a *capacitor;* the electrical output represents the changes in capacitance as the pressure changes alter the distance between the plates. Still another possibility is to record the changes in the voltage induced in a coil by displacement of an iron core attached to the membrane.

For reproduction of rapid pressure changes to be *accurate in both amplitude and phase,* the *resonant frequency* of the manometer should be *10 times greater* than the highest frequencies to be recorded. In this case, provided that the measurement chamber and the connecting system are completely filled with suitable fluids and contain no (compressible) gas bubbles, the measurement is not affected by the inertia of the so-called effective mass and the fluid friction within the system. The original small electrical signal is amplified electronically so that the pressure curves can be displayed continuously with suitable apparatus.

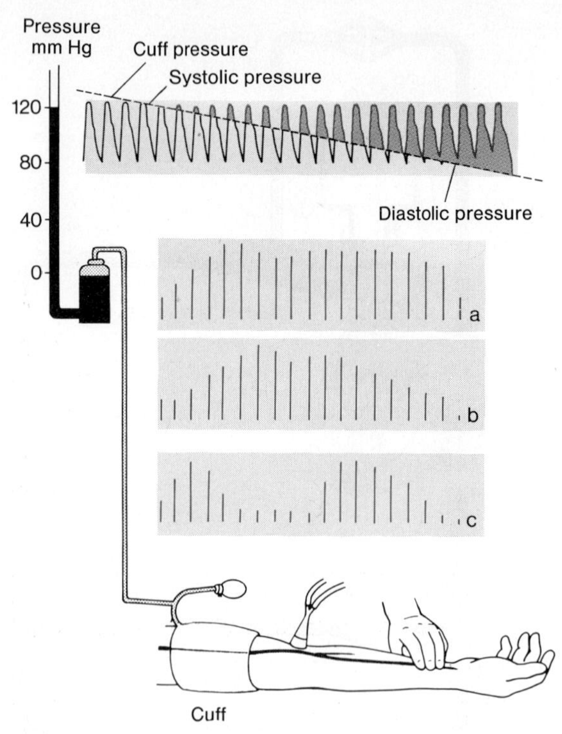

Fig. 20-44. Measurement of human blood pressure by the principle of Riva-Rocci. Diagram of the most common acoustic phenomena (sounds of Korotkoff) in the auscultatory method. For details see text

Indirect methods. The chief tool for the indirect measurement of *arterial pressure* in clinical practice is the *sphygmomanometer* designed by Riva-Rocci. In general the pressure is measured at the upper arm of a sitting or reclining patient. The device consists of an inflatable rubber cuff with a layer of non-distensible fabric on the outer surface. A hand bulb is used to pump air into the cuff and a needle valve to release it, so that the pressure in the cuff can be adjusted and read off from an attached mercury or membrane manometer.

In the **auscultatory method** (of Korotkoff), systolic and diastolic pressures are identified by characteristic sounds, which can be heard by placing a stethoscope distal to the cuff, over the brachial artery inside the elbow (Fig. 20-44). The cuff is first inflated to a pressure higher than the expected systolic pressure, so that the brachial artery is fully compressed and the flow of blood is blocked. Then the pressure is *slowly* reduced by opening of the valve. At the moment when it falls below the *systolic pressure* each pulsation is accompanied by a short, sharp sound (the *sounds of Korotkoff),* produced when the peak blood pressure transiently overcomes the cuff pressure and forces blood to flow through the compressed region. As the cuff pressure decreases further the sounds first become louder and then either remain at a constant level (Fig 20-44a) or become somewhat more faint (b). In some cases the initial increase in loudness is followed by a transient decrease, the so-called *auscultatory gap* (c), and a second increase. The *diastolic pressure* corresponds to the cuff pressure that has been reached when the sounds *suddenly become muffled and rapidly grow fainter.*

The sounds of Korotkoff probably result from *turbulent flow* owing to the increased flow velocity through the region under the cuff where the lumen of the artery is smaller. When the cuff pressure is somewhat lower than the systolic level there is brief turbulent flow only at the systolic peak, and as cuff pressure falls this period extends over the duration of systole. On the other hand, at levels somewhat below diastolic pressure the artery is still slightly compressed, so that there is continuous turbulent flow until cuff pressure is so low that the normal laminar flow is restored.

In cases of *increased cardiovascular activity* – for example, during vigorous exercise or in conditions of hyperthyroidism or aortic-valve insufficiency – the sounds frequently persist long after the transition to the quiet-muffled quality, becoming progressively fainter (sometimes until

the cuff pressure reaches zero). In these cases the pressure at which sound can no longer be heard is recorded in addition to the systolic and diastolic pressures.
The **palpation method** is useful only for determination of systolic pressure. The same device is used, and by palpation of the radial artery the pressure is determined at which the pulse *just disappears* as cuff pressure is increased and *reappears* as cuff pressure is decreased.
To obtain accurate results with the method of RIVA-ROCCI and KOROTKOFF, the cuff must be at the level of the heart, to exclude hydrostatic effects. The width of the cuff should be about half the circumference of the arm; the standard width for adults is 12 cm. For larger arms or for measurements at the thigh wider cuffs are required, and they must be smaller for children. When the cuff is too small, higher pressures are needed to compress the artery and the results are incorrectly high, and when it is too broad the measured pressure is too low.
By using *elastic manometers* one can determine the blood pressure from the pressure pulsations transmitted from the artery to the cuff *(oscillometric method)*. When the cuff pressure is suprasystolic, the pressure oscillations are small, resulting from the beating of the pulse against the compressed part of the artery. As soon as it falls below the systolic pressure and permits brief systolic opening of the artery, oscillation amplitude increases, reaching a maximum at about the diastolic pressure, when the vessel is opened throughout systole but closed during diastole. At still lower cuff pressures, when the vessels are open all the time, the pulsations rapidly fall to a small amplitude which is then maintained.
With sphygmomanometric methods the blood pressure cannot be monitored continuously. By *automating* the measurement procedure, however, and by detecting the acoustic phenomena with microphones or the flow events with ultrasound detectors, it is possible to sample the pressure repeatedly at arbitrary intervals (the shortest achievable is about 30 s). Thus even this simple procedure can be used to learn something about the changes in blood pressure over relatively long periods of time.
Measurement of venous pressure. For clinical measurements of peripheral venous pressure an *arm vein* situated precisely at the level of the right atrium of the reclining subject is usually chosen. The position of the atrium in the thorax is approximately half the sagittal thorax diameter, or 10 cm, above the level of the back. When this condition is met values between 3 and 15 cm H_2O are obtained for the *peripheral venous pressure.* By placing the patient on his side with his arm hanging down, functional separation of the measurement site from the rest of the venous system is prevented by hydrostatic expansion of the veins, so that after correction for the level-dependent pressure differences conclusions can be drawn about the *central venous pressure.* Pressures measured under these conditions are ca. 4 cm H_2O *above* the pressure in the right atrium (because of the resistance to flow between vein and heart). For exact measurement of central venous pressure a catheter with a miniature manometer at its tip must be introduced into the right atrium, or an electromanometer attached externally.
Venous pressure can be estimated roughly by observing the state of filling of the veins in the neck. The neck veins of a seated person are *not filled when venous pressure is normal.* When the pressure exceeds 15 cm H_2O, the veins in the lower part of the neck stand out clearly, and when it exceeds 20 cm H_2O they are tightly filled. Another indicator of venous pressure is the level, with respect to the heart, at which the veins in the hand or arm collapse or fill as the arm is raised or lowered.

Measurement of Flow

A number of procedures, based on quite different physical principles, can be used to measure volume flow. The most important of those in current use measure the flow through an unopened vessel.

Electromagnetic flow meters. In this method the vessel is placed with its long axis across the field between the poles of an electromagnet; the passage of the electrolyte solution (blood) induces a voltage perpendicular to the lines of force and perpendicular to the direction of blood flow, and this voltage can be picked up by electrodes appropriately arranged outside the vessel. The voltage at each moment is proportional to the *volume flow,* so that pulsatile flow can be monitored in detail. With implanted probes it is possible to make long-term measurements of flow through vessels ranging in size from 1 mm diameter to the aorta.

Ultrasonic flow meters. This procedure is based on the measurement of the transit time of ultrasonic waves. The vessel is enclosed within the two halves of a cylinder with a crystal at each end, on opposite sides. These crystals act alternately as senders and receivers of a sound burst that passes diagonally across the vessel. The transit time downstream is shorter than upstream; from the difference between these electronically determined times the *volume flow* through the vessel can be calculated.
Another ultrasonic procedure can be used to measure the *velocity of flow* in superficial vessels transcutaneously – that is, through the intact skin. The ultrasonic waves are sent diagonally into the vessel from one crystal, and the reflected waves are picked up by a second crystal. As a result of the *Doppler effect,* the frequency of the reflected waves is higher than the sender frequency when the blood corpuscles are moving toward the receiver, and vice versa; the difference between sender frequency and the reflected frequency is proportional to the rate of flow of the corpuscles.
With modified apparatus that also permits the diameter of the vessel to be measured, the *volume flow* can be determined.

Thermoelectric methods. Continuous relative measurement of **local volume flow** is possible with procedures based on perfusion-dependent changes in *heat conductivity* of tissue. The system consists of two thermoelectric elements in a bipolar recording arrangement; one of them is kept at a constant temperature slightly above that of the surroundings by an electrical current. From the difference in temperature between the heated and unheated element (at the tissue temperature) the changes in blood flow can be calculated; the difference becomes less with increased volume flow because the heat in the region of the heated element is transported away more rapidly. The recording and heating elements can be mounted in a needle-like *"thermal probe"* to permit measurement of flow through the skin and muscles of humans. In experiments on animals such probes are also used to measure flow through the myocardium, liver and brain.

Venous occlusion plethysmography. In this procedure the **increase in volume** of a limb or part of a limb when venous outflow is blocked is used to determine arterial volume flow. The part of the body concerned is enclosed in a rigid chamber with an airtight opening through which the limb enters. Proximal to this chamber a cuff is inflated to a subdiastolic pressure that arrests flow through the veins without reducing inflow through the arteries. The resulting increase in limb volume is recorded. The *arterial influx* is computed from the rate of volume increase in the initial phase. As the veins become increasingly full the venous pressure rises, eventually reaching a level above the cuff pressure and restoring venous flow. At this point a new *volume equilibrium* has been reached from which, if the venous pressure is known, conclusions can be drawn about the distensibility or **compliance** $\Delta V/\Delta P$ of the vascular bed. It is also possible to measure volume changes in a limb relatively simply, by applying to it a transducer that generates an electric current proportional to stretch as the circumference (and thus volume) of the limb increases.

Measurement of human cardiac output. In humans the output of the heart can be measured with *indirect methods* that require no major surgery. These procedures either are based directly on the *Fick principle* or employ the related technique of *indicator dilution.*

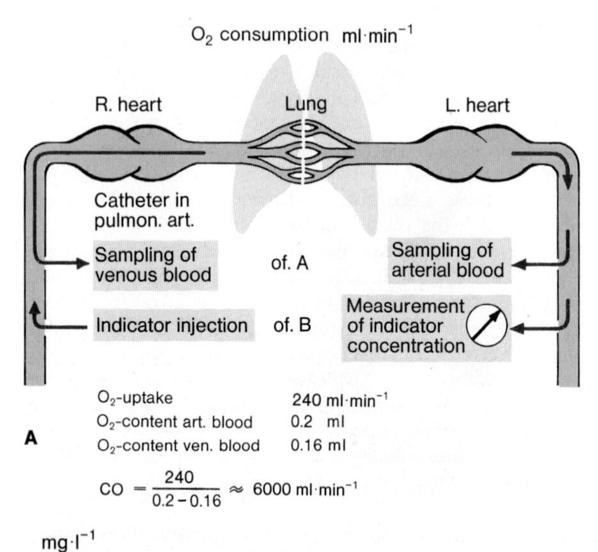

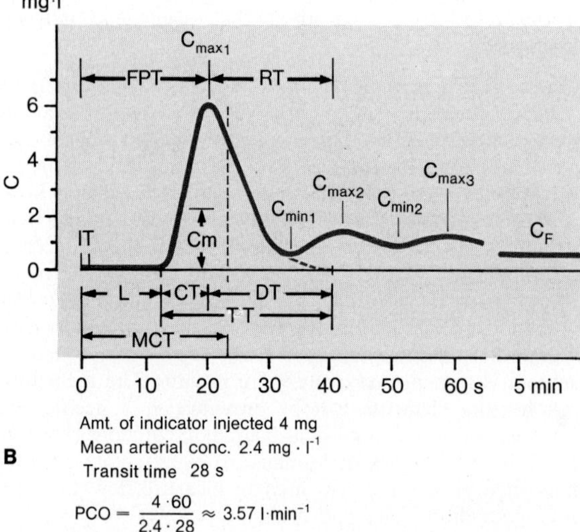

Fig. 20-45 A,B. Schematic illustrations of cardiac output (CO) measurement by Fick's principle **(A)** and by the indicator-dilution method **(B).** In **B** the plasma component of cardiac output (PCO) is computed. Assuming a hematocrit of ca. 45%, the total cardiac output is thus ca. 6,500 ml · min^{-1}

According to the **Fick principle,** O_2 uptake in the lung ($\dot{V}_{O_2}$ is related to the arteriovenous O_2 difference (avD_{O_2} and volume flow through the pulmonary circulation ($\dot{Q}_L$) as follows:

$$\dot{V}_{O_2} = \dot{Q}_L \cdot avD_{O_2} \quad \text{or} \quad \dot{Q}_L = \frac{\dot{V}_{O_2}}{avD_{O_2}} \tag{21}$$

Fig. 20-45 A shows a sample calculation, using values appropriate to resting conditions.

In humans under normal conditions the volume flow through the lung is essentially identical to that through the systemic circulation, so that data obtained in this way also apply to the *cardiac output* of the *left ventricle.* But because the O_2 content of venous blood emerging from the different organs varies, the venous blood must be sampled (by means of catheters) from the pulmonary artery, by which point it has been mixed. Similarly, cardiac output can be measured with CO_2 or foreign gases such as acetylene or nitrous oxide as the indicator.

In the so-called **indicator-dilution techniques** a certain quantity of an indicator *(dye, radioactive substance, cold fluid,* etc.) is introduced into the bloodstream as rapidly as possible, rather than continuously as is the case with O_2 uptake. The concentration of the indicator in "downstream" parts of the circulation is determined as a measure of the volume of blood that has taken up the indicator and transported it to this site. The concentration of the indicator at the measurement site can be analyzed in special cuvettes through which the blood flows or by "punctate" blood samples in rapid succession; it can also be measured without drawing blood by photoelectric recording. The dilution curves so obtained exhibit the following characteristic features (Fig. 20-45B). The injection occurs at time zero *(injection time, IT);* after a certain *latency (L)* the concentration of indicator at the measurement site begins to rise *(concentration time, CT)* to the *first peak* (C_{max_1}); the *first-peak time FPT = L+CT.* The subsequent *fall in concentration* at first follows an exponential curve, until the *recirculation* of the indicator from the various organs begins and produces further concentration peaks. The time between the first and second peaks is called the *recirculation time (RT).* For calculation of cardiac output the recirculation effects must be eliminated by extrapolation of the descending limb of the curve. In practice that is a simple graphic procedure in which the fall in concentration is represented logarithmically. Extension of the resulting straight line gives the so-called **primary curve,** the curve that would be obtained in the absence of recirculation. The distance between the first peak and the point where the straight line intersects the abscissa corresponds to the *dilution time (DT).* The sum of *CT plus DT* is the *transit time (TT).*

The *mean circulation time (MCT)* – the average time taken to transport *all* the indicator particles from the injection site to the measurement site – is obtained by taking the mean of the integrated surface under the primary curve with respect to time, and the *mean concentration* (C_m) is similarly obtained by taking the mean with respect to concentration.

Computation of the unknown volume (V_c) in which the known quantity of indicator (I) is transported from the injection site to the measurement site is done as follows:

$$V_c = \frac{I}{\int_0^{\infty} \cdot C \cdot dt} \tag{22}$$

where the denominator of the fraction is the integral of the *concentration-vs.-time curve,* which corresponds to the area under the **primary curve.** In practice this area is found by planimetry or by summation of many small rectangles with an identical baseline Δt. In this case we have

$$V_c = \frac{I}{\Sigma C \cdot \Delta t} \qquad (23)$$

The **cardiac output of plasma** (PCO in Fig. 20-45 B), for intravenous injection of the indicator and measurement of its mean concentration in the arterial blood, can be computed as follows:

$$\dot{V}(\mathrm{ml} \cdot \mathrm{min}^{-1}) = \frac{I \cdot 60}{C_m \cdot TT} \qquad (24)$$

Total cardiac output is obtained from this by taking the *hematocrit* into account. Frequently used indicators are *Evans blue* and *indocyanine green;* the latter is removed from the circulation on its first passage through the liver, so that measurements can be repeated at brief intervals. With the aid of electronic computers the cardiac output can be computed directly from the indicator-dilution curves.
In a modification of the dye dilution method, *thermodilution* is monitored; here the injected indicator is a small amount of plasma or saline at room temperature, and the "concentration change" at the measurement site is actually a change in temperature. Such measurements can be repeated rapidly, because there is no recirculation.

Measurement of circulation time. From the latency (L) and mean circulation time (MCT) on the indicator-dilution curves, the *velocity of flow* between 2 points in the vascular system can be determined fairly accurately. By means of intravascular catheters it is possible to measure **partial circulation times** in nearly all parts of the vascular system. *Norms* for a healthy adult include the following: arm-ear latency 8–12 s, lung-ear latency 3–5 s, arm-lung latency 5–7 s, and arm-ear MCT 14–26 s. The *total circulation time* is the time required for an indicator to return to the site of injection.
In central parts of the circulatory system the local circulation time gives an indication of the cardiac output, in that high velocities of flow are associated with large volumes and conversely. In peripheral parts these relationships are less clear-cut, because the vascular cross-section can change over such a wide range.
For clinical determination of *partial circulation times* it is common to inject intravenously substances that elicit sensations of *smell or taste.* For example, the time for circulation from arm vein to lung capillaries can be measured roughly by injection of ether, which is detected in the expired air by smell; similarly, the time from injection of Decholin or saccharin into an arm vein until its arrival at the tongue (10–15 s) is indicated by the bitter or sweet taste. This method of measuring circulation times is problematic, however, in that the time when ether is first noted in the lungs depends on the respiratory cycle, and in both procedures error is introduced by the imprecision of threshold-dependent subjective detection of the indicator.

Measurement of Blood Volume

Indicators can also be used to determine the volume of blood in the system. The dissolved or suspended quantity of indicator I is introduced into the vascular system in a volume V_I of fluid, and after it has become uniformly distributed throughout the blood its final concentration C_F is measured (Fig. 20-45 B). The volume V_I is usually negligible, so that the *plasma volume* is given by

$$V = \frac{I}{C_F} \quad \left(\text{or } V + V_I = \frac{I}{C_F}\right) \qquad (25)$$

A prerequisite of this method is that the indicator remain in the system long enough to become thoroughly mixed, and that its rate of elimination be taken into account. For precise measurements of *total blood volume* (cell and plasma volumes), an indicator for erythrocytes must be used as well as one for plasma. One can estimate total blood volume from plasma-volume measurements on the basis of the known hematocrit, but this method is less precise.
Among the indicators used to find plasma volume are Evans blue (= T 1824) and radioactive serum albumins; the red corpuscles injected to find erythrocyte volume may be labelled with ^{59}Fe, ^{32}P or ^{51}Cr. For blood-volume norms see p. 490.

20.14 References

Textbooks and Handbooks

1. Aviado, D.M.: The Lung Circulation. Vols. 1 and 2. New York: Pergamon Press, Inc., 1965
2. Bauereisen, E. (Ed.): Physiologie des Kreislaufs, Bd. 1 Arteriensystem, Capillarbett und Organkreisläufe, Fetal- und Placentakreislauf. Berlin-Heidelberg-New York: Springer 1971
3. Brecher, G.A.: Venous Return. London: Grune and Stratton 1965
4. Burton, A.C.: Physiologie und Biophysik des Kreislaufs. Stuttgart-New York: Schattauer 1969
5. Caro, C.G., Pedley, T.J., Schroter, R.C., Seed, W.A.: The Mechanics of the Circulation. New York-Toronto: Oxford University Press 1978
6. Folkow, B., Neil, E.: Circulation. London-Toronto: Oxford University Press 1971
7. Gauer, O.H.: Kreislauf des Blutes. In: Gauer/Kramer/Jung: Physiologie des Menschen. Bd. 3: Herz und Kreislauf. München-Berlin-Wien: Urban & Schwarzenberg 1972
8. Guyton, A.C.: Textbook of Medical Physiology. 5th Ed. Philadelphia-London: Saunders 1976
9. Handbook of Physiology, Section 2: The Cardiovascular System. Vol. II Vascular Smooth Muscle. D.F. Bohr, A.P. Somlyo, H.V. Sparks, Jr. (Eds). Bethesda, Maryland: American Physiological Society 1980
10. Handbook of Physiology, Section 2: The Cardiovascular System. Vol. III Peripheral Circulation and Organ Blood Flow. J.T. Shepherd, F.M. Abboud (Eds). Bethesda. Maryland: American Physiological Society 1983
11. Handbook of Physiology, Section 2: The Cardiovascular System. Vol. IV Microcirculation. E.M. Renkin, C.C. Michel (Eds). Bethesda, Maryland: American Physiological Society 1984
12. Heymans, E., Neil, E.: Reflexogenic Areas of the Cardiovascular System. London: Churchill 1958
13. Johnson, P.C.: Peripheral Circulation. New York-Chichester-Brisbane-Toronto: Wiley & Sons 1978
14. Keatinge, W.R., Harman, M.C.: Mechanisms Controlling Blood Vessels. London: Academic Press 1980
15. McDonald, D.A.: Blood Flow in Arteries. 2nd Ed. London: Arnold 1974
16. Master, A.M., Garfield, C.I., Walters, M.B.: Normal Blood Pressure and Hypertension. Philadelphia: Lea & Febiger 1952

17. MEESEN, H.: Mikrozirkulation. In: Handbuch der allgemeinen Pathologie III/7. Berlin: Springer 1977
18. MILNOR, W.R., in: MOUNTCASTLE, V.B.: Medical Physiology, 13th Ed. Saint Louis: Mosby 1974
19. RUCH, T.C., PATTON, H.D.: Physiology and Biophysics, Vol.II: Circulation, Respiration and Fluid Balance. Philadelphia: Saunders 1970
20. RUSHMER, R.F.: Cardiovascular Dynamics. Philadelphia: Saunders 1970
21. SHEPHERD, J.T., VANHOUTTE, P.M.: Veins and their Control. London: Saunders 1975
22. SHEPHERD, J.T., VANHOUTTE, P.M.: The Human Cardiovascular System – Facts and Concepts. New York: Raven 1979
23. WADE, O.L., BISHOP, J.M.: Cardiac Output and Regional Blood Flow. Oxford: Blackwell 1962
24. WETTERER, E., KENNER, TH.: Grundlagen der Dynamik des Arterienpulses. Berlin: Springer 1968
25. WIEDEMANN, M.P., TUMA, R.F., MAYROVITZ, H.N.: An Introduction to Microcirculation. Biophysics and Bioengineering Series Vol. 2. London: Academic Press NY 1981
26. WIGGERS, C.J.: Physiology in Health and Disease. Philadelphia: Lea and Febiger 1949

Original Papers and Reviews

27. BLAINE, E.H., DAVIS, J.O.: Evidence of a renal vascular mechanism in renin release; observations with graded stimulation by aortic constriction. Circulat. Res. *28*, suppl. 2, 118 (1971)
28. BRECHER, G.A., HUBAY, C.A.: Pulmonary blood flow and venous return during spontaneous respiration. Circulat. Res. *3*, 210 (1955)
29. COLMAN, R.W.: Formation of human plasmakinin. New Engl. J. Med *291*, 509 (1974)
30. CRONE, C., CHRISTENSEN, O.: Transcapillary Transport of Small Solutes and Water. In: GUYTON, A.C., YOUNG, D.B. (Eds): Cardiovascular Physiology III Vol. 28, p. 149. Baltimore: University Park Press 1979
31. DRAPPATZ, B., WITZLER, E.: Unterschiedliche Reaktionen von Widerstands- und Kapazitätsgefäßen der Haut an den Armen bei Beinmuskelarbeit bis zur Erschöpfung. Int. Z. Angew. Physiol. *28*, 321 (1970)
32. FOLKOW, B.: Description of the myogenic hypothesis. Circulat. Res. XIV, XV, Suppl. I, 279 (1964)
33. GREEN, J.F.: Determinants of Systemic Blood Flow. In: GUYTON, A.C., YOUNG, D.B. (Eds): Cardiovascular Physiology III, Vol. 18, p. 33. Baltimore: University Park Press 1979
34. GUYTON, A.C., COLEMAN, T.G., COWLEY, A.W., JR., MANNING, R.D., JR., NORMAN, R.A., JR., FERGUSON, J.D.: A system analysis approach to understanding long-range arterial blood pressure control and hypertension. Circulat. Res. *35*, 159 (1974)
35. GUYTON, A.C., COWLEY, A.W., JR., YOUNG, D.B., COLEMAN, T.G., HALL, J.E., DECLUE, J.W.: Integration and Control of Circulatory Function. In: GUYTON, A.C., COWLEY, A.W., JR., (Eds.): Cardiovascular Physiology II, Vol. 9, p. 341. Baltimore: University Park Press 1976
36. GUYTON, A.C., JONES, C.E.: Central venous pressure: physiological significance and clinical implications. Amer. Heart J. *86*, 432 (1973)
37. GUYTON, A.C., COLEMAN, T.G., GRANGER, H.J.: Circulation: overall regulation: Ann. Rev. Physiol. *34*, 13 (1972)
38. GUYTON, A.C., TAYLOR, A.E., GRANGER, H.J.: Circulatory Physiology II: Dynamics and Control of Body Fluids. Philadelphia: Saunders 1975
39. HADDY, F.J.: Vasomotion in systemic arteries, small vessels, and veins determined by direct resistance measurements. Minn. Med. *41*, 162 (1958)
40. HADDY, F.J., SCOTT, J.B., GREGA, G.J.: Peripheral Circulation: Fluid Transfer Across the Microvascular Membrane. In: GUYTON, A.C., COWLEY, A.W., JR. (Eds.): Cardiovascular Physiology II, Vol. 9, p. 63. Baltimore: University Park Press 1976
41. HAINSWORTH, R., LINDEN, R.J.: Reflex Control of Vascular Capacitance. In: GUYTON, A.C., YOUNG, D.B. (Eds): Cardiovascular Physiology III, Vol. 18, p. 67. Baltimore: University Park Press 1979
42. HILTON, S.M., SPYER, K.M.: Central nervous regulation of vascular resistance. Ann. Rev. Physiol. *42*, 399 (1980)
43. HUNYOR, S., LUDBROOK, J., SHAW, J., MCGRATH, M.: The Peripheral Circulation. Amsterdam: Excepta Medica 1984
44. KORNER, P.I.: Integrative neural cardiovascular control. Physiol. Rev. *51*, 312 (1971)
45. LONGHURST, J.C., MITCHELL, J.H.: Reflex Control of the Circulation by Afferents from Skeletal Muscle. In: GUYTON, A.C., YOUNG, D.B. (Eds): Cardiovascular Physiology III, Vol. 18, p. 125. Baltimore: University Park Press 1979
46. LUNDGREN, O., JODAL, M.: Regional blood flow. Ann. Rev. Physiol. *37*, 395 (1975)
47. MANCIA, G., LORENZ, R.R., SHEPHERD, J.T.: Reflex Control of Circulation by Heart and Lungs. In: GUYTON, A.C., COWLEY, A.W. JR. (Eds): Cardiovascular Physiology II, Vol. 9, p. 111. Baltimore: University Park Press 1976
48. POLLACK, A.A., WOOD, E.H.: Venous pressure in the saphenous vein at the ankle in man during exercise and changes in posture. J. appl. Physiol. *1*, 649 (1949)
49. REED, J.H., JR., WOOD, E.H.: Effect of body position on vertical distribution of pulmonary blood flow. J. appl. Physiol. *28*, 303 (1970)
50. ROWELL, L.B.: Human cardiovascular adjustments to exercise and thermal stress. Physiol. Rev. *54*, 75 (1974)
51. SCHACHTER, M.: Kallikreins and kinins. Physiol. Rev. *49*, 509 (1969)
52. SCOTT, J.B., RUDKO, M., RADAWSKI, D., HADDY, F.J.: Role of osmolarity, K^+, H^+, Mg^{++}, and O_2 in local blood flow regulation. Amer. J. Physiol. *218*, 338 (1970)
53. SCHMID-SCHÖNBEIN, H.: Microrheology of Erythocytes, Blood Viscosity, and the Distribution of Blood Flow in the Microcirculation. In: GUYTON, A.C., COWLEY, A.W., JR. (Eds): Cardiovascular Physiology II, Vol. 9, p. 1. Baltimore: University Park Press 1976
54. SMITH, O.A.: Reflex and central mechanisms involved in the control of the heart and circulation. Ann. Rev. Physiol. *36*, 93 (1974)
55. STAINSBY, W.N.: Local control of regional blood flow. Ann. Rev. Physiol. *35*, 151 (1973)
56. WESTFALL, TH.C.: Neuroeffector mechanisms. Ann. Rev. Physiol. *42*, 338 (1980)
57. WITZLER, E.: Venous Tone and Regulation of the Circulation. In: Les concepts de Claude Bernhard sur le milieu interieur. Paris: Masson 1967
58. ZELIS, R.: Peripheral Circulations. New-York: Grune and Stratton 1975
59. ZWEIFACH, B.W., SILBERBERG, A.: The Interstitial-Lymphatic Flow System. In: GUYTON, A.C., YOUNG, D.B. (Eds): Cardiovascular Physiology III, Vol. 18, p. 215. Baltimore: University Park Press 1979

VI
Respiration

21 Pulmonary Respiration

G. Thews

Subprocesses in the transport of gases. As a rule animal cells obtain energy by the oxidative breakdown of nutrients. Therefore they must continually be provided with oxygen. Moreover, if they are to function adequately it is equally important that the metabolic end product carbon dioxide continually be removed. This exchange of gases between the cells and their surroundings is known as **respiration.**

Respiratory gases are transported within the body by both convection and diffusion. The **convective processes** – ventilation of the lungs and circulation of the blood – move the gas molecules over relatively large distances. The intervening **diffusion processes** in the alveoli of the lungs and in the perfused tissues operate over short distances (<0.1 mm) only. Nevertheless, they are essential for the transfer of O_2 and CO_2 into and out of the closed circulatory system. Figure 21-1 illustrates the four sequential subprocesses of gas transport schematically. During the movement of O_2 from the ambient air to the sites where it is consumed in the cells, the order of events is as follows:

1. *convective transport to the alveoli of the lung by ventilation,*
2. *diffusion from the alveoli into the blood in the lung capillaries,*
3. *convective transport to the tissue capillaries by the circulating blood,*
4. *diffusion from the tissue capillaries into the surrounding cells.*

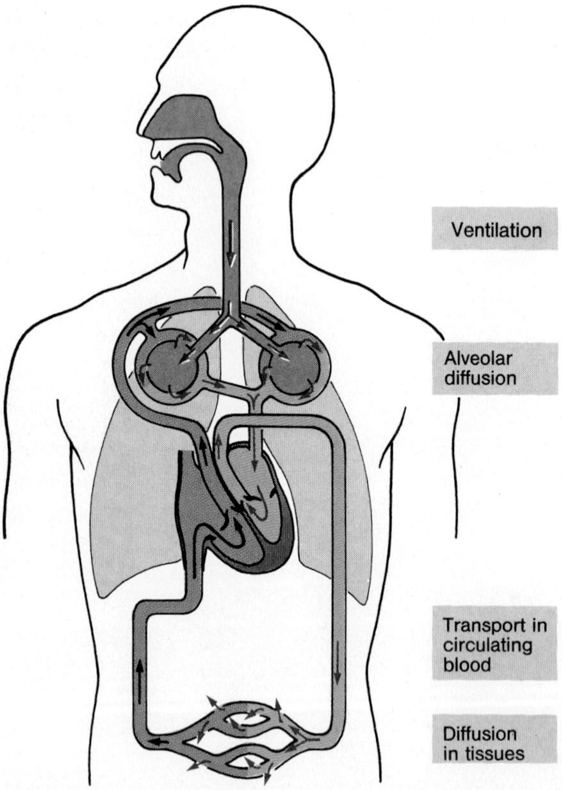

The removal of the carbon dioxide formed in the cells as a gaseous end product of oxidative metabolism is brought about by the four subprocesses in the reverse order.

Subprocesses 1 and 2 together constitute **pulmonary** *(external)* **respiration.** Subprocess 3 is called **blood gas transport,** and subprocess 4 is called **tissue** *(internal)* **respiration.**

Fig. 21-1. The route of oxygen transport in the human *(red arrows)*

21.1. Breathing Movements

Respiratory Excursion of the Thorax

The shape of the thoracic cavity is changed by movements of the ribs and diaphragm.

Rib movements. The ribs are connected to the *vertebral body* and the *transverse process* by flexible joints. The line between the two joints forms an axis about which the ribs can rotate. When the ribs are raised by contraction of the inspiratory muscles, both the lateral and the anteroposterior diameters of the thorax increase (Fig. 21-2A). Correspondingly, when the ribs are lowered, the thoracic volume decreases.

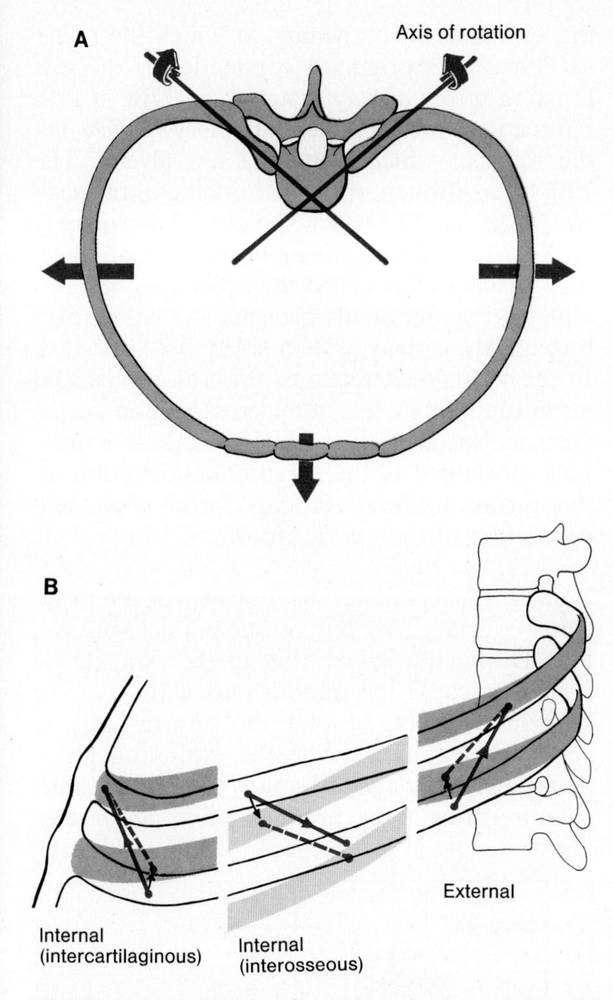

Fig. 21-2. A Expansion of the thoracic cross section (in the direction of the *arrows*) during inspiration. **B** Diagram to show the orientation of the fibers of the intercostal muscles *(red)* and the directions in which they pull during inspiration and expiration

The axis of rotation of the upper ribs lies almost *transverse*, whereas that of the lower ribs tends more toward the *sagittal* [28]. The consequence is that during inspiration the upper part of the thorax expands primarily toward the front, and the lower part toward the sides. Moreover, elevation of the lower ribs causes a greater increase in the thoracic volume.

There is a simple **test of the expansibility** of the thorax, by measurement of chest circumference in the maximal-inspiration and maximal-expiration positions. The tape measure should be placed just under the armpits, while the subject holds his arms out to the sides. The difference between the inspiratory and expiratory circumferences should be at least 7–10 cm in a young, healthy man, and about 5–8 cm in a woman.

The inspiratory elevation of the ribs is brought about mainly by the **external intercostal muscles** (Fig. 21-2B) [6, 28]. Their fibers are oriented in such a way that the insertion on the lower rib is further from the center of rotation than the point of origin on the upper rib. During contraction, therefore, the torque is greater for the lower rib, so that it is raised toward the rib above it. In this way the external intercostal muscles cooperate to elevate the thorax. Normally most of the **internal intercostal muscles** are responsible for expiration. The arrangement of their fibers is such that when they contract, the upper rib is brought closer to the rib below it, depressing the thorax. As shown in Fig. 21-2B, the intercartilaginous parts of the internal intercostals contribute to the elevation of the sternum.

When an increased amount of respiratory work must be done, particularly when one is short of breath, the regular respiratory muscles are assisted by **accessory muscles** [28]. Inspiration is assisted by all the muscles inserting on the pectoral girdle, the head or the spine that are capable of lifting the ribs. Chief among these are the *major and minor pectorals,* the *scalenes,* the *sternocleidomastoids* and parts of the *serratus* muscles (Fig. 21-3). In order for these to be used in respiration, their points of origin must be kept stable. A typical example is the behavior of a breathless person who braces his arms against a firm object to immobilize his shoulders and tilts his head back. The main accessory expiratory muscles are the *abdominal muscles* that pull the ribs down and compress the abdomen, forcing the viscera and the diaphragm upward.

Movement of the diaphragm. The most effective inspiratory muscle is the *diaphragm,* which is innervated by the phrenic nerve (from C_3–C_5). Normally it is dome-shaped, arching up into the thoracic cavity; in the expiration position it lies against the inner wall of the thorax for a distance

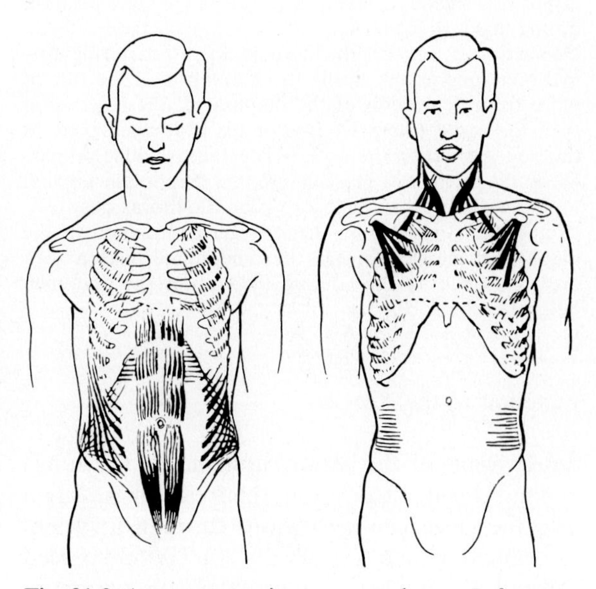

Fig. 21-3. Accessory respiratory musculature. *Left:* accessory muscles for expiration; *right:* major accessory muscles for inspiration. From [4]

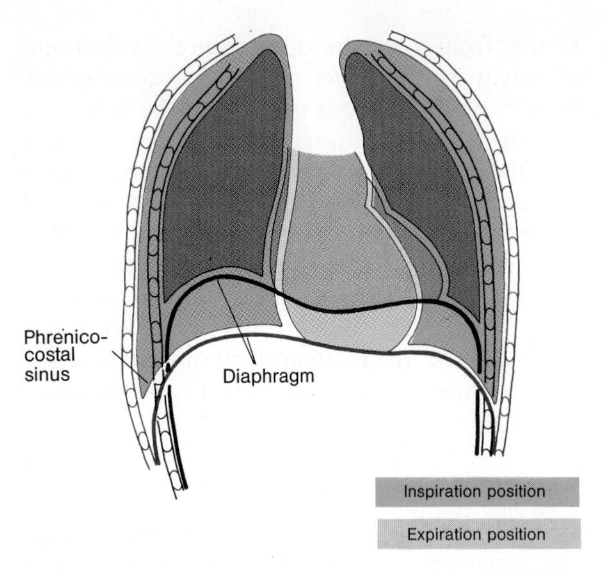

Fig. 21-4. Changes in shape of the thoracic cavity during the transition from expiratory position *(black)* to inspiratory position *(red)*

covering about three ribs (Fig. 21-4). During inspiration the bands of muscle in the diaphragm contract and flatten it, pulling it away from the inner wall of the thorax. The spaces so opened, called the *phrenicocostal sinus,* allow the nearby parts of the lungs to expand and hence to be well ventilated.

This movement of the lower boundary of the lungs can be demonstrated by **percussion** of the chest. Taps below the boundary sound dull because the sound is damped by the viscera; taps over the air-filled lung tissue are more resonant. In a young, able-bodied man the position of the lung boundaries determined in this way during maximal inspiration should be about three ribs below their position during maximal expiration.
Depending on whether the thoracic expansion during normal breathing results chiefly from elevation of the ribs or more from depression of the diaphragm, the respiration is of the **costal (thoracic) type** or the **abdominal type.** In thoracic respiration the work of breathing is done primarily by the intercostal musculature, the diaphragm tending to follow the pressure changes within the thorax passively. In abdominal respiration the stronger contraction of the diaphragm muscle displaces the abdominal viscera to a greater extent, so that during inspiration the abdomen bulges outward.

Function of the Airways

Subdivisions of the airway system. As the lungs expand during inspiration, the fresh air is drawn into the gas-exchange regions through a system of branching tubes [19, 26, 29, 30]. Having passed through the trachea, the air enters the two main bronchi and then moves on to progressively finer branches of the bronchial tree (Fig. 21-5). Until the 16th level of branching, at which the *terminal bronchioles* originate, conduction is the sole function of the airway system. The 17th to 19th bifurcations produce the *respiratory bronchioles,* the walls of which contain a few alveoli. The 20th bifurcation marks the beginning of the *alveolar ducts,* around which the alveoli are densely packed. This region, the main function of which is gas exchange, is called the *respiratory zone.*
Up to the terminal bronchioles, air moves through the airway system solely by *convection.* In the subsequent sections, the transitional and respiration zones, the total cross-sectional area becomes so large (Fig. 21-5) that there is little bulk movement in the longitudinal direction. In this region *diffusion* accounts for an increasing proportion of the gas transport.

Bronchial innervation. The diameter of the bronchi is controlled by the autonomic nervous system. During the inspiration phase, **sympathetic** influences cause the smooth musculature of the bronchi to relax, so that the bronchi expand *(bronchodilation).* Late in the expiration phase **parasympathetic** activity causes the smooth musculature to contract, producing *bronchoconstric-*

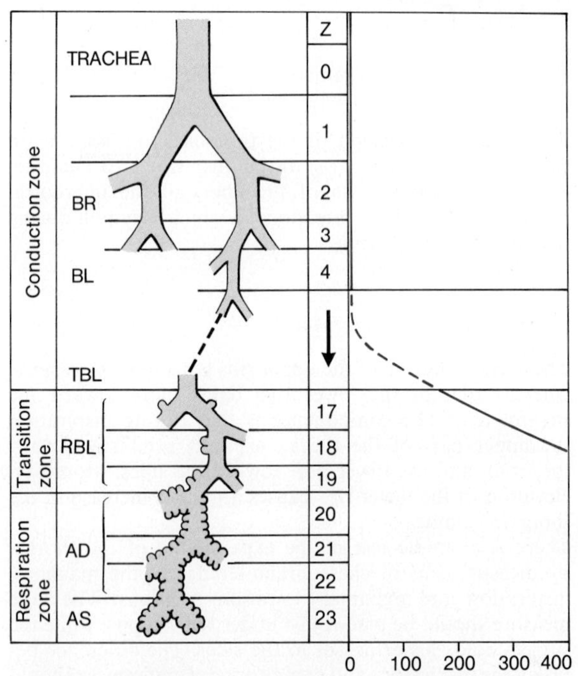

Fig. 21-5. Branching of the airway system *(left),* with a curve showing the total cross-sectional area *(right)* at each successive bifurcation (Z); modified from [29]. As the transitional zone is entered there is a marked increase in area, which continues in the respiratory zone. BR bronchi, BL bronchioles, TBL terminal bronchioles, RBL respiratory bronchioles, AD alveolar ducts, AS alveolar sacs

tion. That is, to some extent the autonomic mechanisms assist ventilation of the lungs. A failure of this autonomic regulation, such as occurs in attacks of a certain form of *bronchial asthma,* can lead to bronchospasm, which considerably increases the resistance to flow in the airways.

Functions of the airway system. The airways do not only serve as conduits for the fresh air entering the lungs and the "alveolar air" leaving them. They also have a number of accessory respiratory functions; they clean, warm and moisten the inspired air [26].
The **cleaning** of the inspired air begins in the nose, where small particles, dust and bacteria are caught up by the mucous membranes. It is for this reason that people who chronically breathe through the mouth are more susceptible to respiratory disorders. Particles that escape this filter adhere to the *layer of mucus,* secreted by goblet cells and subepithelial gland cells, that lines the walls of the airways. The mucus is continually propelled toward the epiglottis by rhythmic movements of the *cilia* in the respiratory epithelium (Fig. 21-6), and when it reaches the esophagus, it is swallowed. As a result, foreign particles and bacteria are removed from the respiratory tract. If the cilia are damaged, as occurs in *chronic bronchitis,* the mucus accumulates in the airways and increases their resistance to the passage of air.
Relatively large particles or masses of mucus in the airways irritate the mucous membranes and thereby trigger *coughing*. Coughing is a reflex in which the lungs are at first compressed with the glottis closed, and then the glottis is opened to allow an extremely rapid escape of air, to sweep out the obstructing object.

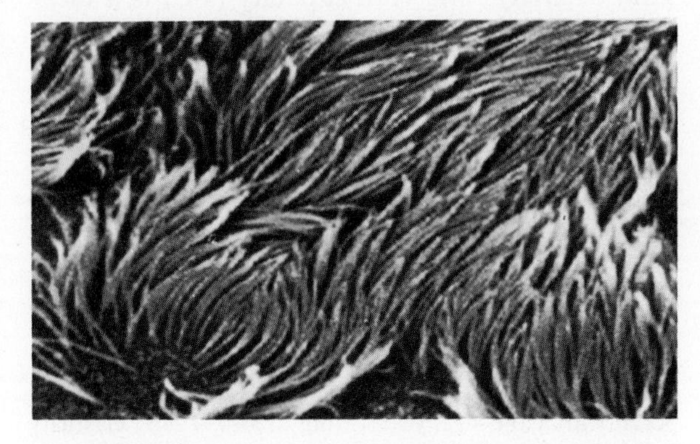

Fig. 21-6. Cilia of the respiratory epithelium in the guinea pig trachea, as seen in the scanning electron microscope. The coordinated movement of the cilia transports the mucus to the epiglottis

Warming and **moistening** of the inspired air occurs mainly in the nasopharyngeal cavity. Conditions are particularly favorable here because the conchae provide a large mucosal surface, well perfused with blood and equipped with highly active mucous glands. The air is further warmed and moistened in the lower airways, so that by the time it enters the alveoli it has reached the core temperature (37 °C) and is completely saturated with water vapor.

Function of the Alveoli

Conditions for alveolar gas exchange. In the alveoli gases are exchanged between the blood in the pulmonary capillaries and the air in the lungs. It has been estimated that there are about 300 million alveoli, with a *total surface area* of about *80 m^2* [29]. The diameter of an alveolus is 0.2–0.3 mm. Each alveolus is surrounded by a dense *capillary network,* so that the blood flowing through the capillaries contacts the alveoli over a large surface.
The exchange between the gas phase and the capillary blood occurs by *diffusion.* Effective diffusion requires not only a large surface but also the smallest possible diffusion distance (p. 564), and both requirements are met in the alveoli. The gas in the lungs is separated from the blood by only a thin layer of tissue, the so-called **alveolo-capillary membrane** (Fig. 21-7). Comprising the alveolar epithelium, a narrow interstitial space, and the capillary endothelium, its total thickness is less than 1 μm.

Surface tension of the alveoli. The inner surface of the alveoli is covered by a liquid film. Thus, the alveolar wall is subject to the forces that act at any interface between a gas and a liquid phase, which tend to reduce the surface area. A result of this *surface tension* in each of the many alveoli is the tendency of the lung to contract. Detailed calculations show that the alveoli would be extremely unstable if they were exposed to the strong surface forces associated with a film of pure water. The actual surface tension in the alveoli is about 10 times smaller than would be expected for an aqueous boundary layer, because of substances dissolved in the liquid film. Because these act to reduce surface tension, they are called **surface-active substances** or **surfactants** [17]. Reduction of surface tension results from the fact that the hydrophilic heads of these molecules are strongly attracted by the water molecules while their hydrophobic tails have only a weak attraction for one another and for other molecules in the fluid, so that the surfactant molecules form a dense hydrophobic layer at the surface. It has proved possible to

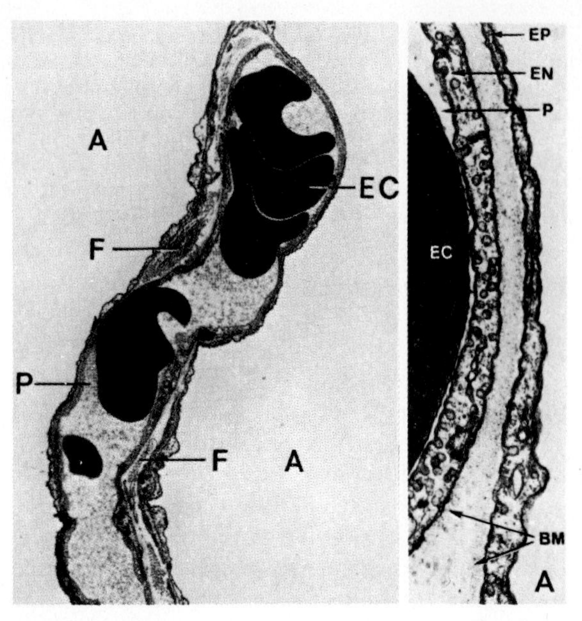

Fig. 21-7. *Left:* Alveolar septum in the lung of a dog, with a capillary; from [47]. The intracapillary erythrocytes (EC) are separated from the surrounding alveolar space (A) only by the "alveolo-capillary membrane". *Right:* Enlarged section. EP alveolar epithelium, EN capillary endothelium, BM basement membrane, F connective-tissue fibers, P plasma

wash the surfactants out of the lung tissue and identify them chemically. The film of solution lining the alveoli contains a mixture of *proteins* and *lipids,* of which the **lecithin derivatives** bear the main responsibility for the surface activity. They are formed by the alveolar epithelia.

Another function of the surfactants is to prevent the small alveoli from collapsing and discharging their contents into the larger alveoli. According to *Laplace's law* (p. 464), for a given wall tension, the internal pressure rises as the radius of the alveolus decreases, which would tend to redistribute the gas into the larger alveoli. The lung is protected from such a destabilizing effect by the fact that as the alveolar radius decreases, the surface tension is also reduced. Whereas the surface tension in expanded, highly stretched alveoli is about 0.05 N/m, it is about 1/10 as great in small, unstretched alveoli. The reason is that the surface-active substances have greater effect, the more closely packed they are; when the alveoli become smaller, they are brought closer together.

21.2 Ventilation

Lung Volumes and Capacities

The **ventilation** of the lungs depends on the depth of each breath **(tidal volume)** and the number of breaths per unit time **(respiratory frequency)**. Both of these can vary over a wide range, depending on the body's requirements.

Subdivisions of lung volume. The tidal volume at rest is small compared with the total volume of gas in the lung. That is, both at inspiration and at expiration a considerable volume of air can be moved in addition to the normal tidal volume. But even the deepest expiration cannot expel all the air from the lungs; a certain amount of air always remains in the alveoli and the airways leading to them. For quantitative evaluation of these relationships the lung volume has been subdivided into a number of components, as follows [1]; here the term *capacity* refers to sets of two or more components (Fig. 21-8):

1. *Tidal volume:* the volume exchanged in normal inspiration or expiration.
2. *Inspiratory reserve volume:* the volume that can still be inhaled at the end of a normal inspiration.
3. *Expiratory reserve volume:* the volume that can still be exhaled at the end of a normal expiration.
4. *Residual volume:* the volume remaining in the lungs after maximal expiration.
5. *Vital capacity:* the greatest volume that can be exhaled after maximal inspiration; the sum of 1, 2 and 3.
6. *Inspiratory capacity:* the greatest volume that can be inhaled after normal expiration; the sum of 1 and 2.
7. *Functional residual capacity:* the volume remaining in the lung after normal expiration; the sum of 3 and 4.
8. *Total capacity:* the volume in the lung after maximal inspiration; the sum of 4 and 5.

The only components in this list that are of much practical significance, apart from the *tidal volume,* are the *vital capacity* and the *functional residual capacity.*

Vital capacity. The vital capacity (VC) is a measure of the *expansibility of lungs and thorax.* It is not, despite the name, a "vital" quantity, because even when extreme demands are made on respiration, breathing is never as deep as is potentially achievable.

It is not practical to give a single "norm" for vital capacity, for it depends on a number of parameters such as *age, sex, height and position of the body,* and *state of training.*

As Fig. 21-9 shows, vital capacity decreases with age, especially after the 40th year, owing to loss of lung elasticity and increasing restriction of thoracic mobility. The average VC of women is about 25% smaller than that of men. That height should play a role is obvious, for the thorax is in proportion to the rest of the body. An empirical rule

Fig. 21-8. Lung volumes and capacities. The numerical values of vital capacity and residual volume *(right)* vary with age and sex

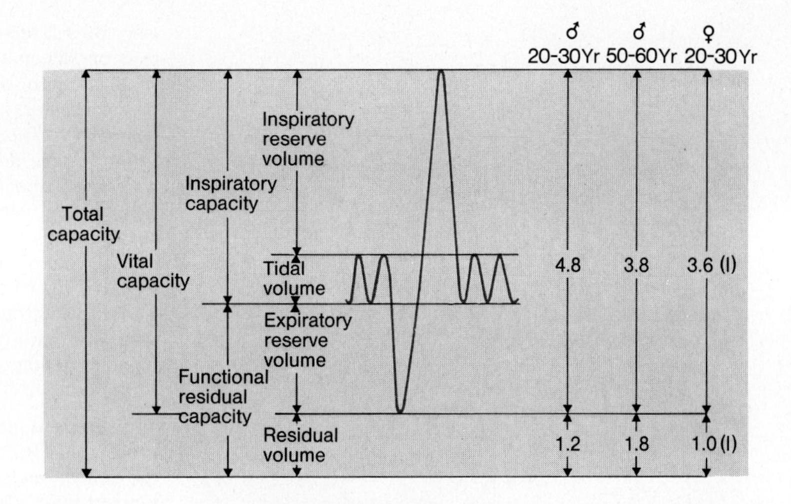

for young men is as follows [33].

$$VC(l) = 2.5 \times height(m) \quad (1)$$

A man 180 cm tall would thus have a vital capacity of 4.5 liters. Body position is significant in that the vital capacity of people standing erect is somewhat greater than that of those lying down, because in the upright position there is less blood in the lungs. Finally, vital capacity depends on the state of training. Athletes trained for endurance sports have a considerably greater vital capacity than untrained people. Especially large VCs (up to 8 liters) are found in swimmers and rowers, whose accessory respiratory muscles (major and minor pectorals) are particularly well developed. The chief significance of vital capacity lies in the area of diagnosis (p. 559).

Functional residual capacity. The physiological significance of the functional residual capacity (FRC) lies in *equalization of the inspiratory and expiratory O_2 or CO_2 concentration in the alveolar space.* If the fresh air moved directly into the alveoli, without mixing with gas already in the lungs, the alveolar concentrations of O_2 and CO_2 would increase and decrease periodically, according to the phase of respiration. Instead, it is mixed with the gas in the lungs – at rest, the FRC is several times the volume of the newly inhaled air – and therefore fluctuations in composition of the alveolar gas mixture are relatively slight.

The magnitude of the FRC, the sum of residual volume and expiratory reserve volume, depends on various parameters. On average the FRC measured in the recumbent position amounts to 2.4 liters in younger males and to 3.4 liters in older males [8]. The FRC of women is less than that of men by about 25%.

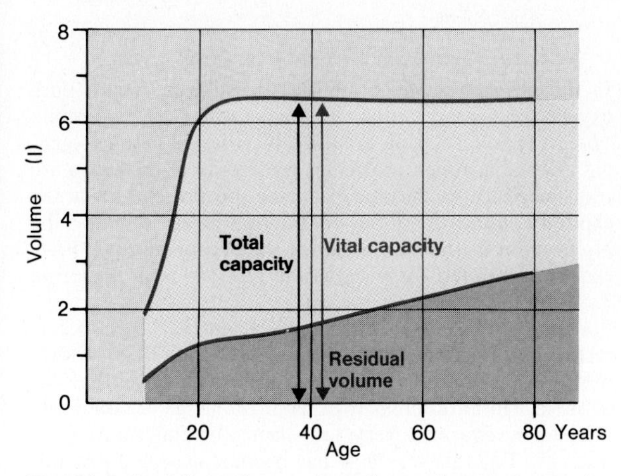

Fig. 21-9. Age-dependence of total capacity, vital capacity and residual volume in people of average height

Measurement of Lung Volumes and Volumes Respired

The volumes of air inhaled and exhaled can be recorded directly by means of a **spirometer** or a **pneumotachograph.** In contrast, residual volume and functional residual capacity can only be measured indirectly.

Spirometry. Spirometers are devices that can hold varying volumes of gas at constant pressure (Fig. 21-11). The *bell gasometer* is the most common type; this is a cylinder inverted into a tank of water so as to trap a certain volume of gas, which is thus isolated from the outside air. The weight of the bell is compensated by a counterweight. A wide tube with a mouthpiece provides communication between the enclosed space and the airways of the subject. During expiration the volume within the spirometer increases and the bell rises, and during inspiration it sinks; these volume changes can be read off from a calibrated scale or recorded with a writing lever on a kymograph drum **(spirogram).**

Pneumotachography. When respiration is to be recorded over a longer time, a so-called *open spirometric system* offers considerable advantages. Here, not the volume itself but the *flow rate* is monitored (Fig. 21-10). This is done with a *pneumotachograph,* a device consisting basi-

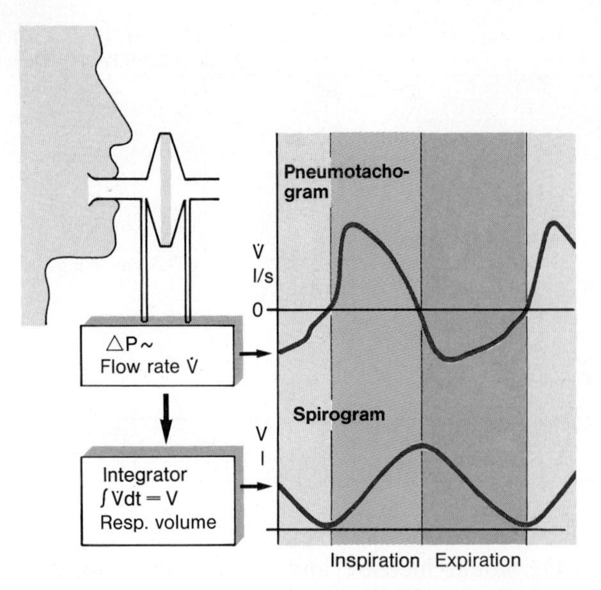

Fig. 21-10. Principle of operation of the pneumotachograph. The pressure difference across a resistor inside of the flow path near the mouthpiece is proportional to volume flow $\dot{V}$ (pneumotachogram). Integration of $\dot{V}$ over time gives the ventilated volume (spirogram)

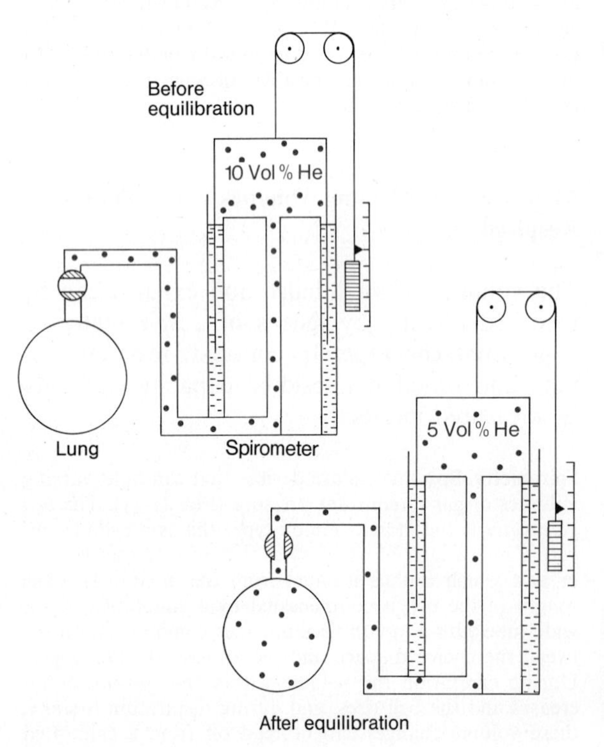

Fig. 21-11. Principle of the helium-dilution method for measuring functional residual capacity. Initial condition *above:* helium *(red dots)* is restricted to the spirometer system, at a concentration of 10 vol. %. Final situation after He dilution *(below):* helium has become uniformly distributed between lung (functional residual capacity) and spirometer, reducing its concentration to 5 vol. %

cally of a large-diameter tube incorporating a small flow resistor. When the respired air flows through the tube a small pressure difference is created between the two ends of the resistor, and this can be measured with a pressure transducer. *The pressure difference is directly proportional to the volume flow* – that is, to the amount of air passing a cross section of the tube per unit time. The record of volume flow is called the **pneumotachogram.** From such a curve of volume displaced per unit time, dV/dt, the required volume V can be derived by integration, because $V = \int \frac{dV}{dt} dt$. In most pneumotachographs this integration is done electronically, so that the curve of respired volume (spirogram) can be recorded directly along with the pneumotachogram.

Measurement of functional residual capacity (FRC). Because the FRC is the volume remaining in the lung at the end of each expiration, it can be determined only by indirect methods. In principle the technique is to introduce an insoluble gas (helium) into the lung *(dilution method)* or to wash the nitrogen already present out of the lung by breathing pure oxygen *(washout method)*. In either case, the volume can be determined from the final concentration of the gas [2].

The **helium-dilution method** is illustrated in Fig. 21-11. A closed spirometer system is filled with, say, 3 liters of a gaseous mixture containing 2.7 l O_2 and 0.3 l He. The initial He fraction thus amounts to $F_{He_1} = 0.1$ ml He/ml mixture. At the end of a normal expiration the subject is connected to the system, so that during the following breaths the He molecules become uniformly distributed throughout the lung volume FRC and the spirometer volume V_{Sp}. (Helium diffuses so slowly through tissue that for practical purposes none of it is lost from the alveoli into the blood). When the system is fully equilibrated, which requires only a few minutes, a suitable detector is used to measure the final helium fraction F_{He_2}: in our example we assume $F_{He_2} = 0.05$ ml He/ml. The FRC is computed on the basis of a mass balance; that is, the amount of helium must be the same after mixing as it was initially – in each case, the product of volume V and F:

$$V_{Sp} F_{He_1} = (V_{Sp} + FRC) F_{He_2} \tag{2}$$

Solving this equation for FRC, with the above data substituted for the variables, we have:

$$FRC = \frac{V_{Sp}(F_{He_1} - F_{He_2})}{F_{He_2}} = \frac{3(0.1 - 0.05)}{0.05} \text{liters} = 3 \text{liters} \tag{3}$$

In the **nitrogen-washout method** the subject inhales pure oxygen for several minutes following a normal expiration. The air exhaled during this time is collected in a spirometer. All the nitrogen molecules previously in the lungs are transferred to the spirometer during this process. From the expired volume, the initial N_2 fraction in the lung and the N_2 fraction in the spirometer at the end of the test, FRC can be computed by an equation analogous to Equation 3.

For the practical application of either method certain correction factors must be taken into account [2, 34]. Moreover, both methods suffer from the disadvantage that patients in whom different regions of the lungs are unevenly ventilated require a very long time for full dilution or washout. For this reason it has become accepted practice to determine FRC by means of the **body plethysmograph** (pp. 556f.).

Dead Spaces

Anatomical dead space. The volume of the conducting airways is called the anatomical "dead" space because no gas exchange occurs in this region. It comprises the cavities of the nose and mouth, pharynx, and larynx, plus the spaces of the trachea, bronchi and bronchioles. The volume of the dead space depends on the height and position of the body. As a rule of thumb, in a seated subject the *size of the dead space* (in ml) is equal to *twice the body weight* (in kg). Hence the dead-space volume of an adult is about *150 ml.* During a deep breath this value increases, because the bronchi and bronchioles are expanded as the thoracic cavity enlarges.

Measurement of the dead-space volume. The *expiratory tidal volume* (V_T) is made up of two components; one part of the expired volume comes from the *dead space* (V_{DS}) and the other from the *alveolar space* (V_{TA}):

$$V_T = V_{DS} + V_{TA} \quad (4)$$

For testing pulmonary function it is important to measure these two components separately. As in the determination of functional residual capacity, an indirect procedure is used. It is based on the fact that the fractions of the respiratory gases (O_2 and CO_2) in the two components differ. In the air from the dead space the gas fractions are still the same as in the previously inhaled fresh air (F_I). The gas mixture from the alveolar space contains gases in the fractions prevailing there (F_A). Expressing the quantity of a gas as the product of total volume V and its fraction F, for any expired gas we have

$$\begin{array}{lclcl} \textit{Amount expired} & = & \textit{Amount from dead space} & + & \textit{Amount from alveoli} \\ V_T \cdot F_E & = & V_{DS} \cdot F_I & + & V_{TA} \cdot F_A \end{array} \quad (5)$$

Substituting V_{TA} from Eq. (4) and rearranging we obtain

$$\frac{V_{DS}}{V_T} = \frac{F_E - F_A}{F_I - F_A} \quad (6)$$

This relation, called the **Bohr equation,** is valid for all respiratory gases; in the case of CO_2, however, it can be further simplified, for the fraction of this gas in the inspired air, $F_{I_{CO_2}}$, is nearly zero:

$$\frac{V_{DS}}{V_T} = \frac{F_{A_{CO_2}} - F_{E_{CO_2}}}{F_{A_{CO_2}}} \quad (7)$$

The ratio of dead space to expired volume can be calculated from Eq. (6) or Eq. (7), because all the fractions on the right side can be found by gas analysis. (With regard to the difficulties that arise in measuring alveolar fractions, see p. 562). For example, assume that measurements have shown $F_{A_{CO_2}} = 0.056$ and $F_{E_{CO_2}} = 0.04$ ml CO_2/ml mixture. It follows that $V_{DS}/V_T = 0.3$; that is, the dead space accounts for 30% of the expired volume.

Physiological dead space. The term physiological or *functional dead space* refers to all those parts of the respiratory tract in which no exchange of gas takes place. The physiological dead space differs from the anatomical in that it includes not only the conducting airways but also those alveolar spaces which, though ventilated, are not perfused by blood. Such alveoli, in which gas exchange is impossible despite ventilation, are few in healthy lungs. Therefore in a healthy person the volumes of the anatomical and the physiological dead spaces are practically identical. The situation is different in certain cases of *impaired pulmonary function,* in which both ventilation and blood flow are very unevenly distributed throughout the lung. In these cases the physiological dead space can be considerably larger than the anatomical dead space.

Measures of Ventilation

Minute volume. The minute volume, the volume of gas breathed in or out within a minute, is by definition the product of the **tidal volume** and the **respiratory frequency.** As a rule the volume exhaled is somewhat smaller than that inhaled, because less CO_2 is given off than O_2 is taken in [*respiratory quotient* (gas exchange ratio) < 1; cf. p. 619]. To be precise, one must distinguish between the inspired and the expired minute volume. It has been agreed that as a general rule calculations of ventilation should be based on the expiration phase, as indicated by the subscript E. Thus the (expiratory) minute volume $\dot{V}_E$ is

$$\dot{V}_E = V_T \cdot f \quad (8)$$

(The dot over the symbol V_E means "volume per unit time" and does not indicate a derivative; V_T is the expiratory tidal volume, and f is the respiratory frequency.)

The respiratory frequency of adults under resting conditions averages 14 breaths per minute, though there is considerable variation (10–18/min). Higher respiration rates are found in children (20–30/min), infants (30–40/min) and newborns (40–50/min) [4, 8].

By Eq. (8), therefore, an adult at rest has a *minute volume of 0.7 l/min,* if the tidal volume is taken as 0.5 l and the respiration rate as 14/min. During exercise the minute volume rises along with the increased O_2 requirement, and in conditions of extreme exertion it can reach 120 l/min. Although minute volume is of some use as a measure of ventilation, it is by no means a critical determinant of the effectiveness of breathing. The decisive factor is the fraction of the minute volume that enters the alveoli and participates in gas exchange.

Alveolar ventilation and dead-space ventilation. The part of the minute volume $\dot{V}_E$ that actually ventilates the alveoli is called the *alveolar ventilation* $\dot{V}_A$. The remaining volume constitutes the *dead-space ventilation* $\dot{V}_{DS}$:

$$\dot{V}_E = \dot{V}_A + \dot{V}_{DS} \quad (9)$$

Each of the ventilation terms is the product of the corresponding volume and the respiratory frequency ($\dot{V} = V \cdot f$). The volumes that make up the total ventilation of the resting, healthy adult are as follows. The tidal volume V_E comprises the alveolar volume V_{TA} (70%) and the dead-space volume V_{DS} (30%). Thus for $V_T = 500$ ml, $V_{TA} = 350$ ml and $V_{DS} = 150$ ml. For a respiratory frequency of 14/min, with a *total ventilation* of 7 l/min, the *alveolar ventilation is 5 l/min* and the *dead-space ventilation is 2 l/min.*

The alveolar ventilation determines the effectiveness of ventilation as a whole. Most importantly, it determines the gas fractions that can be maintained in the alveolar space. The minute volume tells us very little about the effectiveness of ventilation. For example, if a normal $\dot{V}_E$ of 7 l/min were to be achieved by shallow, rapid breathing ($V_T = 0.2$ liters and $f = 35$/min), then the dead space (which is encountered first) would be almost the only part of the lung ventilated; hardly any of the fresh air would be drawn in as far as the alveoli. This form of breathing, which sometimes occurs during *circulatory shock,* therefore represents a state of acute danger. Because the absolute magnitude of the dead-space volume is constant, the alveolar ventilation is increased whenever breathing becomes deeper.

Artificial Respiration

Respiratory failure. Interruption of breathing, for whatever reason, creates a potentially lethal situation. The moment at which arrest of respiration and circulation occurs is called the onset of **clinical death.** From this moment on, typically 5–10 min are required for the lack of O_2 and accumulation of CO_2 to damage the cells in vital organs irreversibly, so that **biological death** ensues. If during this brief time certain life-saving measures are taken, resuscitation is possible [40].

Disruption of respiratory function can have a variety of causes, among them obstruction of the airways, injury to the thorax, severe impairment of gas exchange and damage to the respiratory neurons resulting from poisoning or brain injury. After sudden respiratory arrest, the circulatory system continues to function for some time; the pulse can still be felt at the carotid artery for 3–5 min. On the other hand, if cardiac arrest is the first to occur, breathing ceases after only 30–60 s.

Maintaining the airway. An unconscious person lacks the protective reflexes that normally serve to keep the airways free. In this situation, if there should be vomiting or bleeding in the nose/throat region the conducting airways (trachea and bronchi) can become obstructed. The first step in resuscitation must therefore be rapid *clearing of the mouth and throat.* But even without these complications the airways of an unconscious person lying on his back can be plugged by the tongue if the lower jaw drops back.

This kind of blockage can be prevented by *tilting the head back* and at the same time *pulling the jaw forward.*

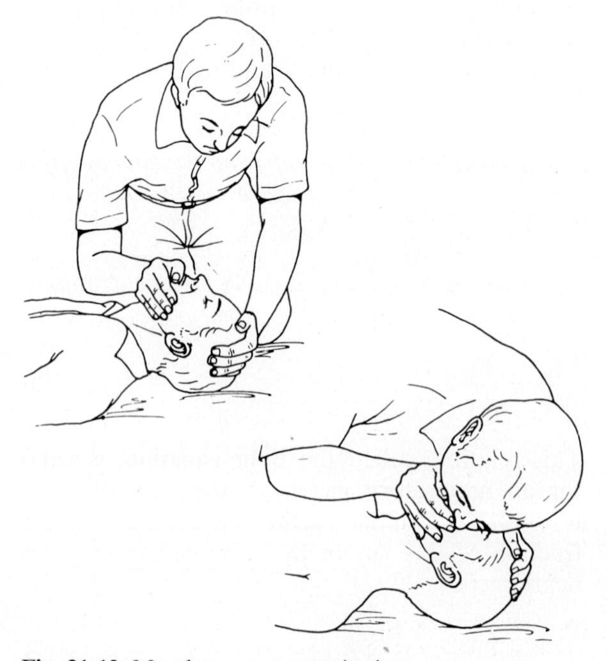

Fig. 21-12. Mouth-to-nose resuscitation

Oral ventilation techniques. For artificial respiration without mechanical devices the method of choice is one in which the rescuer breathes air directly into the patient, by way of the mouth or nose (Fig. 21-12).

In **mouth-to-nose ventilation** the head of the patient is tilted backward by placing one hand on the forehead at the hairline. The other hand is used to pull the lower jaw upward and at the same time to ensure that the mouth is closed by pressing the thumb on the lips. After a deep inspiration the rescuer places his open mouth firmly over the patient's nose. During the subsequent *insufflation* (blowing of air into the patient) the elevation of the thorax must be observed. Then the lifesaver removes his mouth from the patient's face, whereupon the air escapes passively because of the weight of the thorax and the elasticity of the lungs. The rescuer should check that the thorax has returned to its expiratory level.

In **mouth-to-mouth ventilation** the starting position is the same, with one hand at the patient's hairline and the other hand under his chin. The rescuer places his mouth over that of the patient and seals the nose with his cheek. Alternatively, he can press the nostrils together using the thumb and forefinger of the hand on the forehead. Again, the movements of the chest must be observed during insufflation and the escape of air that follows.

In both procedures respiration begins with *5–10 insufflations in rapid succession,* to eliminate the O_2 deficit and CO_2 excess in the tissues as soon as possible. From then on insufflations should be at *intervals of about 5 s.* Under these conditions the O_2 saturation (p. 583) of the patient's arterial blood is practically always over 90% [40].

Artificial respiration with mechanical assistance. There is a simple device that, if it is rapidly obtainable, can be used to assist respiration. It consists of a **mask** placed in an airtight manner over the patient's face, a *valve* and a *bag* that is rhythmically compressed and released by hand. If an O_2 cylinder is available it can be connected to the device so as to raise the proportion of O_2 in the inspired air.

In the method of gas anesthesia generally used today, a **respirator** supplies air by way of a *tracheal tube*. The machine can be controlled so that a positive pressure causes the inspiratory expansion of the lungs, the subsequent expiration occurring passively. It is also possible to control breathing by a rhythmic alternation between pressures above and below atmospheric pressure, so that the average pressure is that of the atmosphere. Because subatmospheric pressure within the thorax facilitates venous return to the heart (p. 500), respiration by alternating pressure is the preferable procedure.

The use of respiratory pumps or manually operated bags is always required during surgery in which *muscle relaxants* (see pp. 48f.) have been used to eliminate reflex muscle tension. These drugs inactivate the respiratory musculature as well, so that the lungs cannot be ventilated without assistance.

When a patient is chronically unable to breathe (as, for example, in infantile paralysis) ventilation can be maintained by means of a **tank respirator** *("iron lung")*. The body of the recumbent patient is enclosed in a chamber with head outside. In order to bring about inspiration the pressure in the tank is reduced, so that the intrathoracic pressure is greater than that outside the body.

21.3 Mechanical Factors in Breathing

The term *"respiratory mechanics"* is usually used in a very special sense, to denote the analysis and representation of the **pressure-volume** and the **pressure-flow relationships** during the breathing cycle. These relationships are determined chiefly by the **respiratory resistances** and their changes under pathological conditions. For this reason respiratory mechanics are important in the *diagnosis* of pulmonary malfunction.

Elastic Resistances

Elastic retraction of the lung. The surface of the lung is under a certain degree of **tensile stress** (Fig. 21-13) because of the *stretching of its* elastic parenchymal elements and the *surface tension of the alveoli* (p. 547). This stress tends to reduce the volume of the stretched lung. As a consequence,

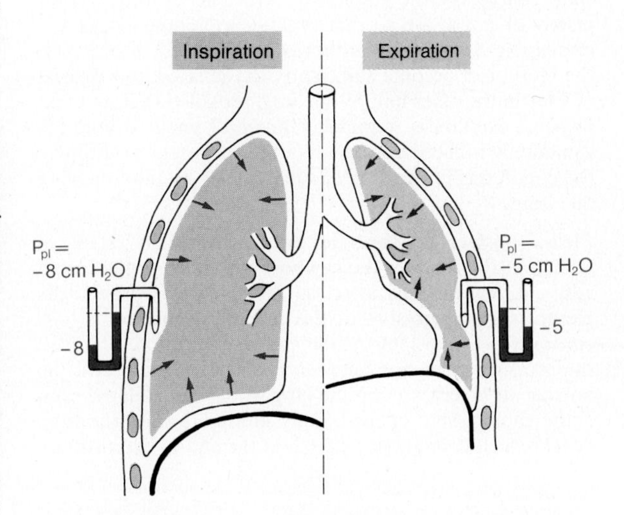

Fig. 21-13. Diagram to explain pleural surface pressure. The elastic tension of the lungs (pull in the direction of the *red arrows*) renders the pressure in the pleural space "negative" with respect to the space outside the body. This effect can be demonstrated with a manometer

the pressure in the fluid-filled space between the two pleural layers is *subatmospheric*. It can be measured by connecting a manometer to a cannula positioned with its tip in the pleural space; in a person at rest the pressure there is about 5 cm H_2O (0.5 kPa) below atmospheric pressure at the end of expiration and about 8 cm H_2O (0.8 kPa) below it at the end of inspiration. As an abbreviation, the term **pleural surface pressure** P_{pl} is applied to the *pressure difference* between the pleural space and the space outside the body. It is only because this "pressure" is actually a pressure difference that the pleural surface pressure is a negative quantity.

The measurement of pleural surface pressure changes. Because direct measurement of pleural surface pressure (Fig. 21-13) involves the risk of damaging the lung, a less hazardous, indirect method is usually employed in humans. Instead of the pressure changes in the pleural space, the changes in **esophageal pressure** are measured. The two pressures are approximately the same, because (i) the esophagus, though outside the lungs, is within the thorax and (ii) the wall of the esophagus is flexible and thus transmits the pressure changes faithfully. In practice a thin catheter with a balloon 10 cm long at its end is introduced into the esophagus. When the balloon is lying in the thoracic part of the esophagus, a manometer attached to the catheter registers with sufficient accuracy the pleural surface pressure changes associated with respiration.

Pneumothorax. The close contact between the surface of the lung and the inner surface of the chest wall is maintained only as long as there is no opening into the pleural space. If the chest wall or the lung is injured so as to let air into the space the lung *collapses* – its elastic and surface tensions contract it toward the hilus. *Filling of the space between the pleural membranes with air is called pneumothorax.* The collapsed lung, having lost contact with the chest wall, can follow the respiratory movements only incompletely or not at all, so that effective exchange of gases is impossible. If the pneumothorax is restricted to one side, the blood can become sufficiently oxygenated and cleared of CO_2 in the other half of the lung, provided that no great physical exertion is required. Unilateral pneumothorax is sometimes induced for therapeutic purposes, to improve the conditions for healing of tuberculosis by immobilizing one lung.

Pleural surface pressures in the newborn. The state of stretch of the lungs in the newborn differs from that in an adult. A few minutes after the first breath is drawn, the pleural surface pressure at the end of inspiration is −10 cm H_2O (−1 kPa) [36]. At the end of expiration, however, the pressure difference between the pleural space and the outside air is zero, so that the lung would not collapse even if the thorax were opened. Only gradually does the lung develop a state of greater stretch at the end of expiration.

Measurement of static volume-pressure relationship. The contractile force of the respiratory musculature must overcome both *elastic and viscous resistances* during ventilation. When breathing is very slow, the effect of the viscous resistance (p. 556) is slight, so that the relationship between lung volume and the associated effective pressure is determined almost entirely by the elastic properties of lung and chest wall. In order to measure this "static" volume-pressure curve one must eliminate the influence of the respiratory muscles, so that the elastic forces alone are operating. The subject must be trained to relax his respiratory musculature briefly, or muscle relaxants (pp. 48f.) must be administered to inactivate it, with the subject in a respirator.

Static pressure-volume curves.

The static pressure-volume curve of the *entire ventilatory system* – lung and chest wall together – can be constructed as follows. The subject inhales a certain volume of air from a spirometer (with nose closed). Then the connection to the spirometer is closed, and the subject relaxes his respiratory musculature as completely as possible. The pressure exerted in the alveoli by the elastic forces in lung and chest wall can now be measured by a gauge at the subject's mouth if he keeps his glottis open *(relaxation pressure method). The pressure difference between the alveoli and the ambient air* is called the **pressure of the respiratory system** P_{rs}. A typical curve of the pressures of the respiratory system corresponding to various lung volumes, measured in this way, is shown in Fig. 21-14 (red curve). The pressure-volume curve of the respiratory system is S-shaped, the nearly linear part covering most of the range of normal respiratory excursions. In this range, therefore, the ventilatory system offers an approximately *constant elastic resistance* to the inspiratory movement.
The contribution of the *elastic tension of the chest wall* is determined by measuring the pressure difference between the pleural space and the ambient air, the **pleural surface pressure** P_{pl}. If in the procedure described above the pleural surface pressures (or the esophageal pressures) are recorded simultaneously for each volume, the *pressure-volume curve for the relaxed chest wall alone* can be constructed. As shown in Fig. 21-14, the slope of this curve increases as pressure (and lung volume) increase.
The contribution of the *elastic tension of the lung* is reflected in the *difference between the pressure of the respiratory system and the pleural surface pressure.* This pressure difference is called the **transpulmonary pressure** P_L. The relationship be-

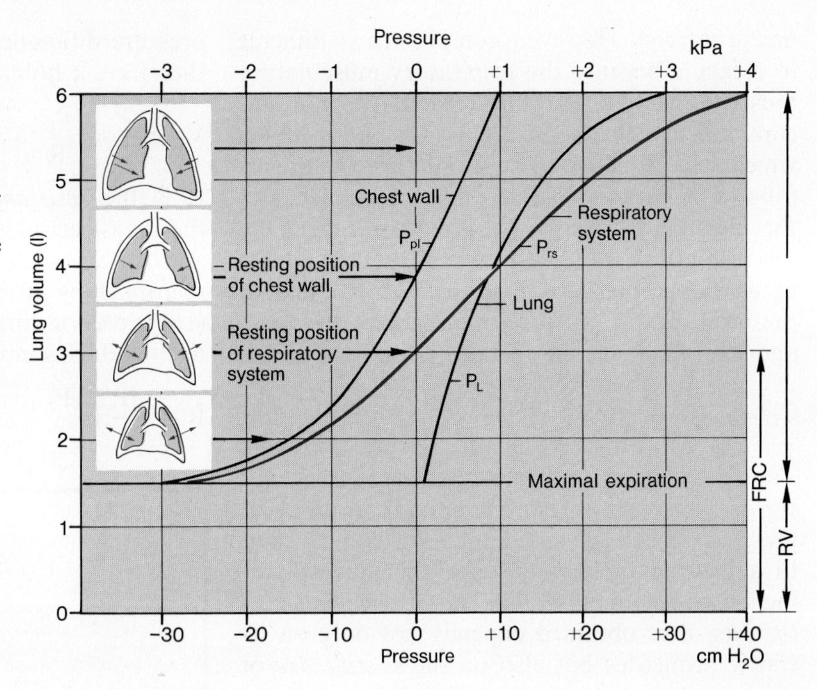

Fig. 21-14. Static volume-pressure curves of the total respiratory system *(red)*, the lung and the chest wall, modified from [24]. P_{pl}, pleural surface pressure; P_{rs}, pressure of the respiratory system; P_L, transpulmonary pressure; VC, vital capacity; RV, residual volume; FRC, functional residual capacity. Pressures are related to passive variations in lung volume with respiratory musculature relaxed. The inset drawings show the elastic forces acting at the chest wall and at the lung surface for different volumes

tween the lung volume and the transpulmonary pressure determines the *pressure-volume curve for the lung alone,* which characterizes the elastic properties of the lung. The slope of this curve decreases at higher pressures (larger lung volumes).

Comparison of the three curves in Fig. 21-14 shows the effect of the *elastic forces* when the lung is filled to different degrees. The entire ventilatory system is in an elastic *resting state* ($P_{rs} = 0$) when, at the end of a normal expiration, the lung volume corresponds to the *functional residual capacity* (FRC). In this case the tendencies of the chest wall to expand and of the lung to contract are in balance. When the volume increases owing to inspiration, the elastic inward pull of the lung is enhanced, and at the same time the outward pull generated by the forces in the chest wall decreases. At an inspired volume of about 55% of vital capacity the *chest wall* has reached its *resting position* ($P_{pl} = 0$), so that any further increase in volume reverses the direction in which the elastic forces in the chest wall act.

Compliance. A measure of the elastic properties of the breathing apparatus (or of each of its two elements) is the slope of the associated pressure-volume curve, which is called *compliance.* The *compliance of the respiratory system* is approximated by the following equation:

$$C_{rs} = \frac{\Delta V}{\Delta P_{rs}} \tag{10}$$

Similar formulae apply to the compliance of the chest wall

$$C_w = \frac{\Delta V}{\Delta P_{pl}} \tag{11}$$

and to the compliance of the lung

$$C_L = \frac{\Delta V}{\Delta P_L}. \tag{12}$$

These three equations are related as follows:

$$\frac{1}{C_{rs}} = \frac{1}{C_w} + \frac{1}{C_L} \tag{13}$$

Because compliance in each case is the *reciprocal of the elastic resistance to expansion,* it follows from Eq. 13 that the elastic resistance of the entire respiratory system is the sum of those of chest wall and lung.

As Fig. 21-14 shows, the pressure-volume curve of the ventilatory system (lung + chest wall) rises most steeply in the range of normal respiratory excursions – that is, compliance is greatest in this range. Here, the compliances found for healthy adults are as follows:

$C_{rs} = 0.1\ \text{l/cm}\ H_2O = 1\ \text{l/kPa}$
$C_w = 0.2\ \text{l/cm}\ H_2O = 2\ \text{l/kPa}$
$C_L = 0.2\ \text{l/cm}\ H_2O = 2\ \text{l/kPa}$

Any changes in these values, in particular *decreases under pathological conditions,* are of di-

nostic interest. However, compliance is difficult to measure because the respiratory musculature must be inactive. For this reason it is not uncommon to rely on determination of C_L alone, which can be done by a simpler procedure as follows. A certain volume of air is inhaled and the resulting position of the thorax is fixed by the respiratory musculature; now, with the glottis open, the pressure in the alveoli is equal to the atmospheric pressure. In this case $P_{alv} = 0$, and Eq. (12) takes the form

$$C_L = -\frac{\Delta V}{\Delta P_{pl}} \tag{14}$$

Thus it suffices to measure the *change in pleural surface pressure* (or, more simply, in esophageal pressure) for a given change in volume and to substitute these values for the corresponding terms in Eq. (14). The *static compliance of the lung* thus obtained depends not only on its elastic properties but also on the *overall size* of the lung in each case.

The smaller the initial volume, the less the volume changes, other conditions being equal. Children 9 to 12 years old have a 2 to 3 times smaller compliance than adults. For diagnostic purposes, therefore, it is necessary to express compliance with respect to the initial volume – as a rule, that is, to the *functional residual capacity* (FRC). The quantity so defined,

$$C_{L_{spec}} = -\frac{1}{FRC} \cdot \frac{\Delta V}{\Delta P_{pl}} \tag{15}$$

is called the *specific compliance of the lung.*

Nonelastic Resistances

The *nonelastic (viscous) resistances* that must be overcome during both inspiration and expiration comprise the following elements: (i) *the resistance to flow in the airways,* (ii) *the nonelastic tissue resistances,* and (iii) *the inertial resistances,* which are so small that they may be neglected.

Airway resistance. The flow of inhaled and exhaled gases through the conducting airways is brought about by the pressure difference between the ambient air and the alveoli. This pressure difference is thus the "driving force" for movement of the respired gases. Flow in the airways is predominantly *laminar.* But eddies are formed in some places, in particular the branch points of the bronchi and sites of pathological constriction, so that flow there becomes *turbulent.* Laminar air flow, like the laminar flow of liquids, is described by the **Hagen-Poiseuille law,** according to which the volume flow $\dot{V}$ is proportional to the driving pressure difference Δ**P**. For flow in the airways, therefore, it holds that

$$\dot{V} = \frac{\Delta P}{R} = \frac{P_{rs}}{R} \tag{16}$$

R is the *resistance to flow,* which depends on the cross-sectional area and length of the tube and on the viscosity of the gas. Although the relationships in turbulent flow are different, Eq. (16) is used to approximate the overall resistance to flow during respiration:

$$R = \frac{\Delta P}{\dot{V}} = \frac{P_{rs}}{\dot{V}} \tag{17}$$

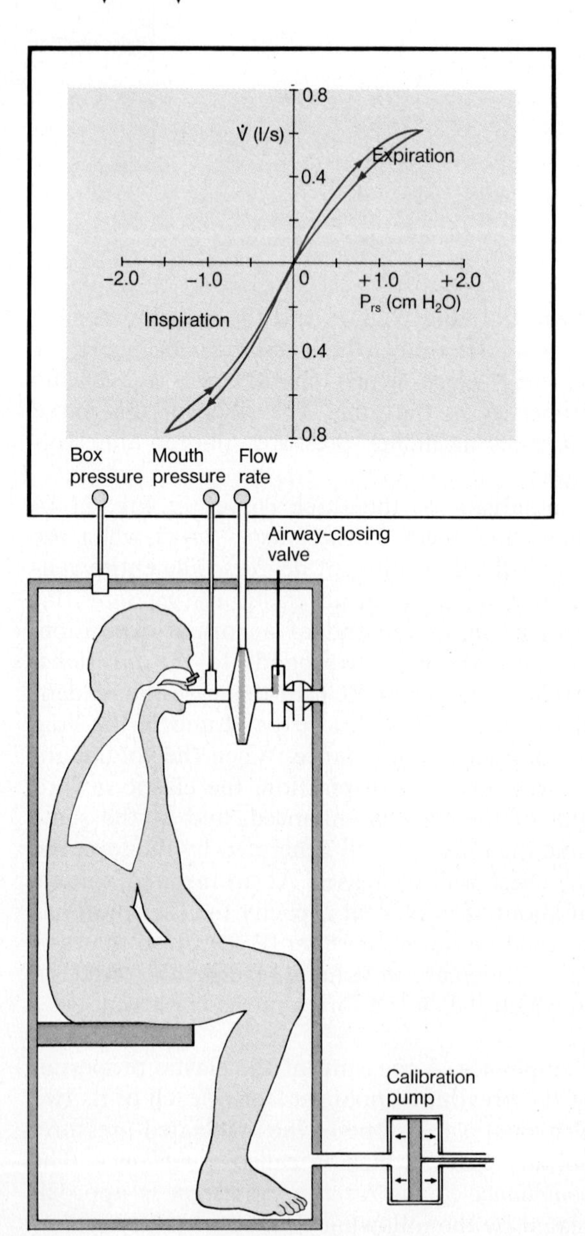

Fig. 21-15. Body plethysmograph (simplified diagram) and recording of the resistance curve *(red).* $\dot{V}$, volume flow; P_{rs}, pressure of the respiratory system

R is usually called the **airway resistance.** To find it, one must measure the pressure difference between mouth and alveoli (in cm H_2O or kPa) and, simultaneously, the flow rate (in l/s; pp. 549f.). The airway resistance normally found during calm breathing through the mouth is in the range of R =2 cm $H_2O \cdot s \cdot l^{-1}$ (0.2 kPa $\cdot s \cdot l^{-1}$) [2]. Normally the airway resistance is determined chiefly by the conditions for flow in the trachea and the large bronchi; the resistances in the small bronchi and the bronchioles make only a small contribution, because of the greatly enlarged cross-sectional area in this region (Fig. 21-5).

Tissue resistance. The second resistance that must be overcome during inspiration and expiration, in addition to the airway resistance, is the viscous resistance associated with friction in the tissues and their nonelastic deformation in the thorax and abdomen:

nonelastic resistance = airway resistance + tissue resistance

The latter, however, is relatively small. Normally 90% of the pulmonary resistance is contributed by the airways, and only 10% by tissue friction.

Measurement of resistance. *To measure resistance one must continually monitor the pressure of the respiratory system.* An indirect procedure employing the body plethysmograph is used. The **body plethysmograph** (Fig. 21-15) basically consists of an airtight chamber shaped like a telephone booth within which a person can sit comfortably. When the subject breathes, the resulting pressure changes in the lung cause the pressure in the closed chamber to change proportionally in the opposite direction. Having calibrated the system one can proceed to measure the change in the pressure of the respiratory system by way of the change in chamber pressure. The flow $\dot{V}$ can be measured at the same time with a pneumotachograph (pp. 549f.). The ratio of the two, according to Eq. (17), is the desired *resistance;* it is convenient to plot $\dot{V}$ vs. P_{rs} as a continuous curve with a two-dimensional pen-recorder.
The body plethysmograph can also be used to determine the *functional residual capacity* FRC (p. 549). In this case the mouthpiece is closed off briefly, so that the pulmonary space is separated from the outside air. As the subject makes an effort to breathe in, the changes in mouth pressure and in lung volume are measured; FRC can then be computed by the *Boyle-Mariotte law* [22].

Pressure-Volume Relations during the Breathing Cycle

During a breathing cycle the pleural surface pressure and the pressure of the respiratory system change in a coordinated way. The relationships between the two are indicated by the following considerations. When the thorax is briefly *at rest,* as it is at the transition from inspiration to expiration, the only force exerted on the pleural space is the elastic recoil force of the lung, which causes a "negative" pressure. We shall call this negative pleural surface pressure during rest $P_{pl(st)}$. The alveolar pressure $P_{rs(st)}$, however, is zero in the resting thorax because the alveoli are in communication with the mouth, so that the pressure can equilibrate. The situation is approximately the same during very slow movements of the thorax.

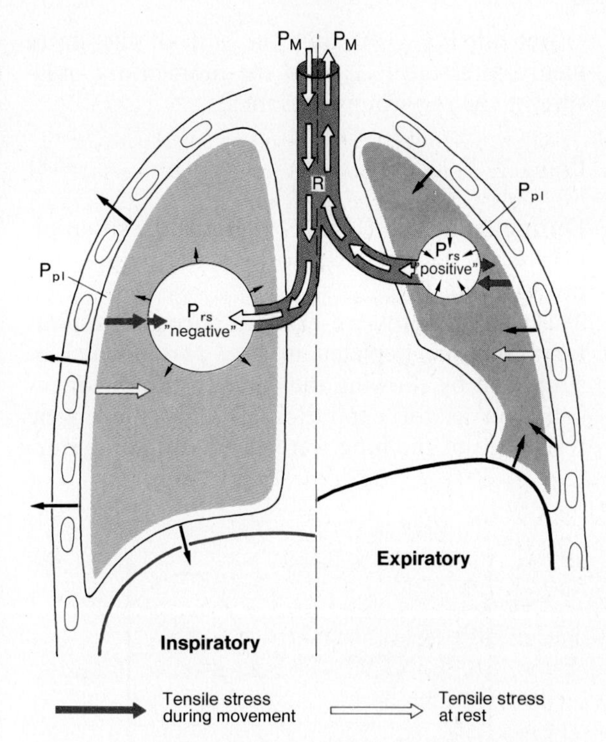

Fig. 21-16. Diagram to explain the changes in pleural surface pressure (P_{pl}) and pressure of the respiratory system (P_{rs}) during inspiration *(left)* and expiration *(right).* P_M mouth pressure; R, airway resistance

The more complex situation during *normal respiratory movements* is illustrated in Fig. 21-16. In this schematic drawing the alveolar space is represented by a large bubble. The black arrows indicate the directions of movement and the red arrows, show the directions in which the tensile stresses act. During inspiration (left) the airway resistance R prevents the air from flowing rapidly enough into the enlarged alveolar space. Therefore the pressure in the alveoli must fall, becoming negative with respect to the outside pressure. This decrease in alveolar pressure affects the pleural space in such a way as to make the pleural surface pressure still more "negative". The pleural surface pressure during respiratory movement $P_{pl(dyn)}$, is thus the sum of the static pleural pressure $P_{pl(st)}$ and the momentary pressure of the respiratory system P_{rs}:

$$P_{pl(dyn)} = P_{pl(st)} + P_{rs} \quad (18)$$

During expiration (Fig. 21-16, right) the situation is reversed. P_{rs} becomes positive and reduces the negativity of $P_{pl(st)}$.

The resulting **pressure changes during a respiratory cycle** are depicted in Fig. 21-17, which is simplified by showing the same duration for inspiration as for expiration. If only the elastic resistance of the lung were to be overcome during respiration, the pressure of the respiratory system P_{rs} would remain zero over the entire cycle and the pleural surface pressure would follow the dashed curve $P_{pl(st)}$. But because of the additional nonelastic resistances, P_{rs} becomes negative in the inspiration phase and positive in the expiration phase. By adding this curve to that for $P_{pl(st)}$ one obtains the dynamic pleural surface pressure $P_{pl(dyn)}$. It is evident here that in order to overcome the nonelastic resistances, $P_{pl(dyn)}$ must always be somewhat smaller than $P_{pl(st)}$ during inspiration and somewhat larger during expiration.

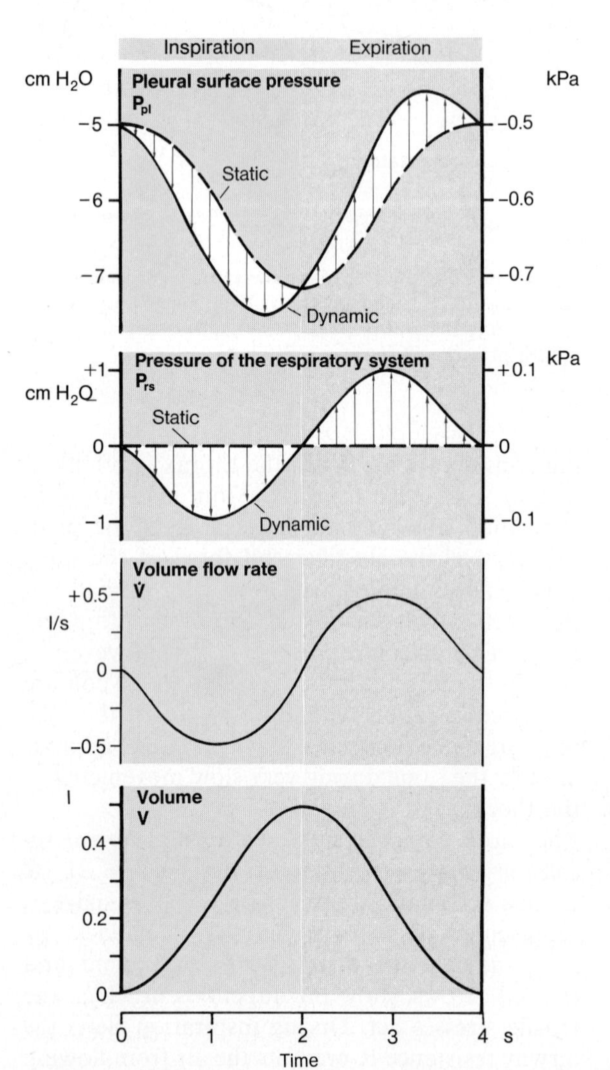

Fig. 21-17. Time course of pleural surface pressure P_{pl}, pressure of the respiratory system P_{rs}, volume flow rate $\dot{V}$ and respired volume V during a breathing cycle. The dashed lines show the pressures that would be found if respiration encountered only elastic resistances. Because viscous resistances are also present, P_{pl} and P_{rs} become more negative during inspiration and more positive during expiration *(red arrows)*

Pressure-volume diagrams. *A plot of the volume of a lung over pleural surface pressure is called, for simplicity, the pressure-volume diagram of the lung* (Fig. 21-18). All the factors determining the shape of this curve have been discussed in the preceding sections:

If inspiration encountered *elastic resistances* only, any change in the volume of the lung would have to be approximately proportional to the associated change in pleural surface pressure. In the pressure-volume diagram this relationship between the two quantities is represented by a straight line (Fig. 21-18A). During expiration the same curve would be followed in the opposite direction.

But because of the additional *nonelastic resistances* the curve for inspiration is concave (Fig. 21-18B). That is, to move a certain volume the pleural surface pressure must decrease more than the amount given by the proportionality line. Not

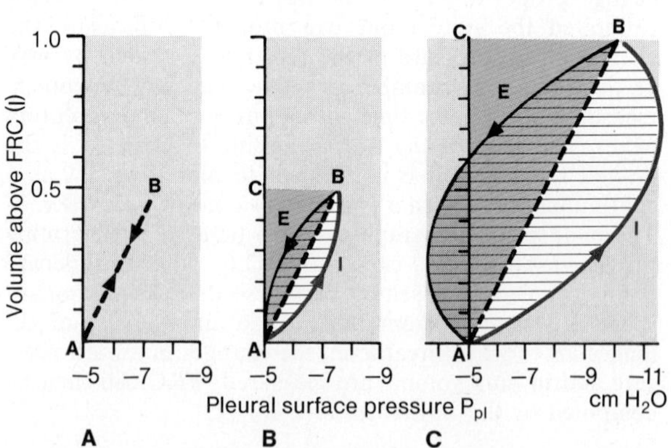

Fig. 21-18 A–C. Breathing cycle in a pressure-volume diagram. **A** Idealized breathing (as it would occur against purely elastic resistances). **B** Normal breathing at rest. **C** Deep, rapid breathing. I, inspiration; E, expiration. The respiratory work is divided as follows: *red areas,* inspiratory work against the elastic resistances; *hatched,* inspiratory and expiratory work against the nonelastic resistances; *dark gray,* the fraction of the work of expiration that must be done by the expiratory muscles

until inspiration is completed (at point B) does the inspiration curve coincide with the straight line, because at this time motion has ceased and only the elastic forces are acting. The curve for expiration is bent in the opposite direction owing to the nonelastic resistance, and returns to the starting point (A) at the end of this phase of the cycle. The dynamic pressure-volume diagram thus has the shape of a **loop.**

The loop in Fig. 21-18 B represents *resting respiration;* the shape of the loop for *deeper and more rapid breathing* is somewhat different (Fig. 21-18C). The deeper breaths are reflected in a doubling of the tidal volume, and the increase in the rate of breathing makes the curve bend more strongly. The greater curvature is explained by the fact that with more rapid changes in alveolar pressure the air flow does not adjust as quickly. *At a high respiration rate the non-elastic airway resistance has a greater effect than during resting respiration.*

The work of breathing. The physical work that must be done to overcome the elastic and nonelastic resistances is equivalent to the product **pressure × volume,** which has the same dimension as the product force × distance. If the pressure changes during the work, the product is replaced by an integral, $\int \mathbf{P\,dV}$. The value of the pressure-volume diagram lies chiefly in the fact that in it the total amount of work can be visualized as an area.

The areas that represent inspiratory work against the *elastic resistances* are shaded red in Fig. 21-18. Under dynamic conditions there is an additional component of work required during both inspiration and expiration to overcome the *nonelastic resistances.* The corresponding areas are hatched in Fig. 21-18. The nonelastic expiratory component ABEA during quiet breathing (Fig. 21-18B) is smaller than the previously elastically stored energy ABCA. Therefore expiration can occur purely *passively,* without the help of the expiratory muscles. This is not the case during accelerated breathing (Fig. 21-18C). Here the work component corresponding to the dark gray area must be supplied by the *expiratory musculature.*

During resting respiration about 2% of the oxygen uptake is required for the work of the respiratory muscles. During exercise, however, the energy requirement of the respiratory musculature rises disproportionately with respect to the increase in minute volume and oxygen uptake achieved. It is understandable, then, that during hard physical labor as much as 20% of the oxygen must be allocated to the work of breathing [7, 27].

Tests of Respiratory Mechanics

Types of ventilatory disorders. Pathological changes in the respiratory apparatus in many cases interfere with the ventilation of the lungs. For diagnostic purposes it is useful to subdivide these forms of ventilatory disorders into two groups, the *restrictive type* and the *obstructive type* [8, 9, 10, 16, 25].

Restrictive disorders include all the conditions in which the *ability of the lung to expand is limited.* This occurs, for example, as a result of pathological changes in the lung parenchyma (e.g., in *pulmonary fibrosis*), or of fusion of the pleurae. **Obstructive disorders** are characterized by *narrowing of the conducting airways* so that the flow *resistance* increases. Such obstruction can be brought about by the accumulation of mucus, swelling of the mucous membranes and spasms of bronchial muscle *(bronchial asthma, spastic bronchitis).* Because the patient must exhale against an increased resistance, in advanced stages the lung often becomes overinflated, with an enlarged residual capacity. A pathological state involving both distension and structural changes (loss of elastic fibers, disappearance of alveolar septa, reduction of the capillary bed) is called *pulmonary emphysema.*

Identification of the type of ventilatory disorder. The procedures used to distinguish between restrictive and obstructive disorders are based on their respective characteristics. That is, the limited lung expansibility in restrictive disorders can be demonstrated by the **reduced compliance** (pp. 555f.). Obstructive disorders are characterized by **increased resistance** (pp. 556f.). Fairly elaborate apparatus is required to determine either compliance or resistance, but it is also possible to differentiate roughly the types of ventilatory disorders by simpler methods, as follows.

Vital capacity. *A decrease in vital capacity can be taken as a sign of restrictive impairment.* But whereas the compliance C_L reflects only the expansibility of the lung, the vital capacity depends on the degree to which the thorax can expand as well. Thus a reduction in vital capacity can be brought about by either *pulmonary or extrapulmonary restriction.*

Forced expiratory volume (Tiffeneau test). *Obstructive impairment can easily be identified by measuring the volume expelled from the lungs by forced expiration* (Fig. 21-19) in a specified time, usually 1 second. The subject is connected to a closed or open spirometric system (pp. 549f.);

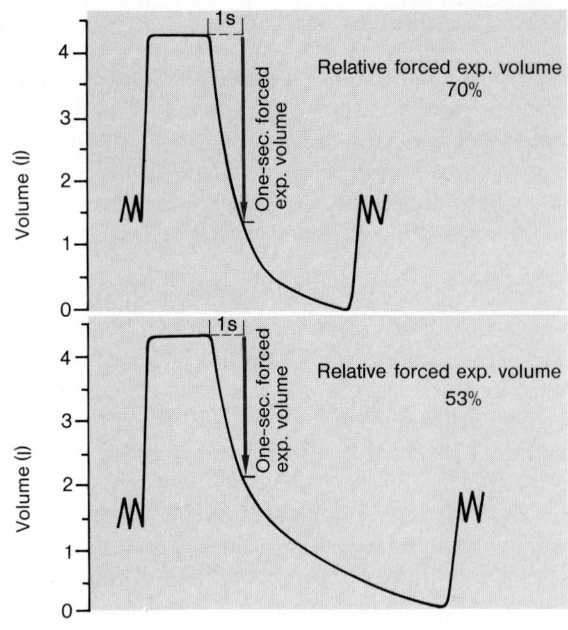

Fig. 21-19. Measurement of the relative forced expiratory volume. After inspiring deeply and holding his breath for a short time, the subject breathes out as rapidly and deeply as possible. The volume exhaled in 1 s is expressed as a percentage of the vital capacity VC. *Above:* healthy subject; *below:* patient with obstructive pulmonary malfunction

after a maximal inspiration he holds his breath briefly and then breathes out as rapidly and deeply as possible. From the recorded volume-time curve the volume exhaled in 1 s (FEV_1) can be found. The result is usually expressed as a relative quantity – i.e., as a percentage of the vital capacity. (For example, with an absolute FEV_1 of 3 liters and a vital capacity of 4 liters, the relative FEV_1 is 75%.) People up to age 50 with sound lungs have relative FEV_1 of 70–80%, and it decreases with age to 65–70%. When an obstructive disorder is present the increased resistance to flow slows down expiration, so that the relative FEV_1 is less than normal.

Maximal volume flow. *A second way of demonstrating obstruction is to measure the maximal expiratory flow.* As in the measurement of forced expiratory volume, the subject is required to inspire maximally and then perform a forced expiration. The volume flow is monitored with a pneumotachograph (p. 550). (The rate of flow also can be derived, though less precisely, from the volume-time curve of Fig. 21-19, by dividing the change in volume during a time increment by the length of this increment.) The maximal volume flow recorded in this way should be about 10 l/s for healthy lungs. When airway resistance is increased, the maximal flow becomes considerably less.

There is a limit beyond which expiratory volume flow cannot be raised, no matter how hard one tries. The reason for this limit lies in the *structure of the bronchiolar walls,* which have no cartilaginous supporting elements. Flaccid tubes are compressed when the external pressure is greater than the pressure in their lumens. *Consequently, when expiration pressure is very strong, the resistance to flow in the bronchioles increases.* This effect is especially pronounced when the recoil of the elastic fibers of the lung parenchyma that normally keep the bronchiolar lumen open is diminished. In such a situation (which can occur, for example, in *pulmonary emphysema;* see p. 559), the bronchioles can collapse when a great effort is made to exhale.

Maximum breathing capacity. *The greatest volume that can be breathed during a period of maximally forced voluntary hyperventilation is called the maximum breathing capacity.* This measure is of diagnostic interest because mobilization of the respiratory reserves can clearly reveal malfunction. The spirometric measurement is done while the subject performs forced hyperventilation at a rate of 40–60/min. The test should last for only about 10s, in order to avoid the undesirable consequences of hyperventilation (alkalosis; see p. 593). However, the value so obtained is then converted to volume per minute. Norms for the maximum breathing capacity (MBC) vary according to age, sex and dimensions of the body; that for a young man is in the range of *120 to 170 l/min.* The MBC is reduced by both *restrictive and obstructive impairment.* Therefore, when the MBC is found to be abnormal, further tests (of vital capacity and forced expiratory volume) must be carried out to distinguish the two conditions.

Table 21-1. Criteria of the differentiation of ventilatory disorders

	Ventilatory disorder	
	Restrictive	Obstructive
Compliance	Decrease	
Resistance		Increase
Vital capacity	Decrease	
Forced expiratory volume		Decrease
Maximum breathing capacity	Decrease	Decrease

21.4 Exchange of Gases

Alveolar Gas Fractions

Calculation of alveolar gas fraction. The gas mixture in the alveoli was formerly called the alveolar air. But it is now generally agreed that the term "air" should be reserved for a gas mixture with the composition of the atmosphere

($F_{O_2} = 0.209$, $F_{CO_2} \approx 0$, $F_{N_2} = 0.791$). Because the composition of the alveolar gas is different (with less O_2 and more CO_2), to be consistent we must speak of an alveolar gas mixture.
To calculate the O_2 and CO_2 fractions in the alveolar gas mixture, we begin by considering the input and output balances. The *O_2 uptake* of the blood ($\dot{V}_{O_2}$) is represented by the difference between the amount of O_2 that enters the alveoli during inspiration ($F_{I_{O_2}} \cdot \dot{V}_A$) and the amount that leaves during expiration ($F_{A_{O_2}} \cdot \dot{V}_A$). The *$CO_2$ released* from the blood ($\dot{V}_{CO_2}$) is equal to the amount removed from the alveoli during expiration ($F_{A_{CO_2}} \cdot \dot{V}_A$), because essentially no CO_2 enters the alveoli with the inspired air. These relationships are described by the equations

$$\dot{V}_{O_2} = F_{I_{O_2}} \cdot \dot{V}_A - F_{A_{O_2}} \cdot \dot{V}_A, \quad \dot{V}_{CO_2} = F_{A_{CO_2}} \cdot \dot{V}_A \tag{19}$$

which can be rearranged to give

$$F_{A_{O_2}} = F_{I_{O_2}} - \frac{\dot{V}_{O_2}}{\dot{V}_A}, \quad F_{A_{CO_2}} = \frac{\dot{V}_{CO_2}}{\dot{V}_A} \tag{20}$$

It is evident here that the alveolar gas fractions depend both on the *metabolically controlled values of O_2 uptake and CO_2 release* and on the rate of *alveolar ventilation* ($\dot{V}_A$). Note that Equation (20) applies only if the quantities in numerator and denominator are measured under identical conditions. Ordinarily, however, O_2 uptake and CO_2 release are expressed with respect to the physical standard conditions, whereas respired volumes and ventilation parameters are given for the conditions prevailing within the body. Therefore some conversion is required.

Conversion of volumes measured under different conditions. The volume V of a quantity of gas depends on the temperature T and the pressure P, and the partial pressure of water vapor P_{H_2O} must also be taken into account. For this reason, it is necessary to specify the conditions under which a particular volume was measured. In respiratory physiology the following conditions are distinguished:

1. **STPD conditions** (acronym for *s*tandard *t*emperature and *p*ressure, *d*ry). These are the physical standard conditions, in which volume data are given for T = 273 K, P = 760 mm Hg, and $P_{H_2O} = 0$ mm Hg (dryness).

2. **BTPS conditions** (*b*ody *t*emperature and *p*ressure, *s*aturated). These are the conditions within the lung – that is, T = 273K + 37K = 310K, P varies according to the current barometric pressure P_B, and $P_{H_2O} = 47$ mm Hg (water-vapor saturation at 37 °C).

Table 21-2. Characteristics of the conditions for volume measurement

Condition	T [K]	P [mm Hg]
STPD	273	760
BTPS	310	P_B–47
ATPS	T_a	P_B–P_{H_2O}

3. **ATPS conditions** (*a*mbient *t*emperature and *p*ressure, *s*aturated). These are the actual conditions outside the body at the time the measurement is made (spirometer conditions) – that is, the room temperature T_a, the current barometric pressure P_B and water-vapor saturation.
As shown in the summary of these three conditions in Table 21-2, the water-vapor partial pressure is always subtracted from the total pressure to obtain the pressure of the "dry" gas, which is the volume-determining parameter.
To convert a volume of gas from a set of conditions 1 to another set 2, the relationships given by the **general gas equation** apply:

$$\frac{V_1}{V_2} = \frac{T_1}{T_2} \cdot \frac{P_2}{P_1} \tag{21}$$

The data in Table 21-2 can be used to apply this general formula to a specific case. For example, to convert a volume measured under body conditions (V_{BTPS}) to standard conditions (V_{STPD}), we have

$$\frac{V_{STPD}}{V_{BTPS}} = \frac{273}{310} \cdot \frac{P_B - 47}{760} = \frac{P_B - 47}{863} \tag{22}$$

The effect of a change in the reference conditions on the measured volume is not negligible, as demonstrated by the following calculation. During resting respiration the alveolar ventilation under BTPS conditions is about 5 l/min. According to Eq. (22) this value decreases to 4.1 l/min under STPD conditions, the pressure being taken as the mean barometric pressure at sea level ($P_B = 760$ mm Hg).

Alveolar gas concentrations under resting conditions. To calculate the alveolar fractions of the respiratory gases from Eq. (20) we substitute numerical values all referring to standard conditions. For an adult at rest the *O_2 uptake* $\dot{V}_{O_2(STPD)}$ = 0.28 l/min and the *CO_2 output* $\dot{V}_{CO_2(STPD)}$ =

Table 21-3. Inspiratory, alveolar and expiratory fractions and partial pressures of the respiratory gases during resting respiration at sea level

	Fractions		Partial pressures	
	O_2	CO_2	O_2	CO_2
Inspired air	0.209	0.0003	150 mm Hg (20 kPa)	0.2 mm Hg (0.03 kPa)
Alveolar gas mixture	0.14	0.056	100 mm Hg (13.3 kPa)	40 mm Hg (5.3 kPa)
Expired mixture	0.16	0.04	114 mm Hg (15.2 kPa)	29 mm Hg (3.9 kPa)

0.23 l/min. The ratio of CO_2 output to O_2 intake, called the *gas exchange ratio or respiratory quotient,* therefore averages 0.23/0.28 = 0.82 (p. 619). The value used for *alveolar ventilation* is $\dot{V}_{A(STPD)}$ = 4.1 l/min (see above); the *inspiratory O_2 fraction* is $F_{I_{O_2}}$ = 0.209 (20.9 vol.%) (Table 21-3). The *composition of the* alveolar gas mixture is then found to be

$$F_{A_{O_2}} = 0.14 (14 \text{vol.\%}),$$

$$F_{A_{CO_2}} = 0.056 (5.6 \text{vol.\%}).$$

The remainder of the alveolar gas mixture consists of nitrogen plus a very small proportion of noble gases.

Analysis of the alveolar gas mixture. One of the first difficulties one encounters in measuring alveolar gas fractions is that of obtaining samples of the alveolar gas mixture. During expiration the volume of gas contained in the dead spaces is exhaled first, and only thereafter does the gas from the alveolar spaces appear. But even in this late phase of expiration the composition of the mixture undergoes continual slight change, because gas continues to be exchanged in the alveoli. For this reason devices have been developed by which the final fraction of the expired volume is collected at each breath under mechanical or electronic control [3].

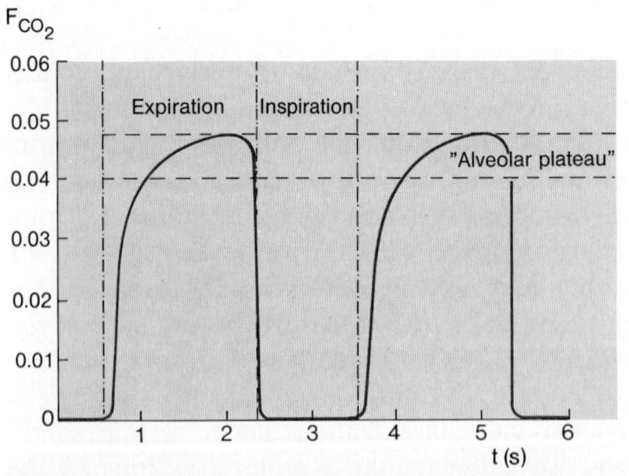

Fig. 21-20. Fraction of CO_2 during expiration and inspiration, monitored at the subject's mouth by an infrared-absorption plotter. Alveolar plateau: the part of the curve during which the alveolar component of the expired volume passes the detector

Once a sample of the alveolar gas mixture has been obtained, the fractions of the different gases can be determined with a suitable instrument. In **Scholander's procedure** O_2 and CO_2 are chemically absorbed in sequence, and the decrease in volume with each operation is measured directly; the volume that has disappeared is the volume of the gas that has been absorbed [43].
Rapid-response devices have been designed to give continuous records of the fractions of gases in the expired mixture. Devices for CO_2 measurement utilize the *specific infrared absorption* of this gas, and those for O_2 employ its *paramagnetic properties. Mass spectrometers* are also used for the analysis of both gases. The advantage of all these procedures is that with a continuous record the portion of gas originating in the alveoli can be identified directly from the curve; it is not necessary to collect a series of alveolar samples. As an example, Fig. 21-20 shows the CO_2 fraction during two breathing cycles, as recorded by an infrared plotter. The part of the curve labelled "alveolar plateau" represents the alveolar part of the expired volume.

Partial Pressures of the Respiratory Gases

Partial pressures in the atmosphere. *According to Dalton's law, each gas in a mixture exerts a partial pressure P_{gas} proportional to its share of the total volume – that is, to its fraction F_{gas}*. When this law is applied to respired gases it should be remembered that in addition to O_2, CO_2, N_2 and noble gases both the atmosphere and the alveolar gas mixture contain water vapor, at certain partial pressures P_{H_2O}. Because gas fractions are given for a "dry" gas mixture, in formulating Dalton's law the total pressure (barometric pressure P_B) must be reduced by an amount corresponding to the **water-vapor pressure** P_{H_2O}:

$$P_{gas} = F_{gas} \cdot (P_B - P_{H_2O}) \tag{23}$$

On the basis of the atmospheric O_2 and CO_2 fractions in Table 21-3 and of a P_{H_2O}=47 mmHg in the lung, the partial pressures near sea level given by Eq. (23) are about $P_{I_{O_2}}$ = 150 mm Hg (20 kPa) and $P_{I_{CO_2}}$ = 0.2 mm Hg (0.03 kPa). At higher altitudes the O_2 and CO_2 partial pressures in the inspired air decrease in proportion to the decrease in P_B (p. 666).

Partial pressures in the alveolar gas mixture. As gas exchange in the lung is governed by partial pressure gradients, it is convenient to express the proportions of O_2 and CO_2 in the alveolar gas mixture in units of partial pressure. By substituting in Eq. (20) the partial pressures given by Eq. (23) with P_{H_2O} = 47 mm Hg, and taking account of Eq. (22), we obtain

$$\begin{aligned} P_{A_{O_2}} &= P_{I_{O_2}} - \frac{\dot{V}_{O_2(STPD)}}{\dot{V}_{A(BTPS)}} \cdot 863 \text{ [mm Hg]} \\ P_{A_{CO_2}} &= \frac{\dot{V}_{CO_2(STPD)}}{\dot{V}_{A(BTPS)}} \cdot 863 \text{ [mm Hg]} \end{aligned} \tag{24}$$

With these so-called **alveolar formulas** one can calculate the alveolar partial pressures. Using the data for resting respiration at low altitudes ($P_{I_{O_2}}$ = 150 mm Hg, $\dot{V}_{O_2(STPD)}$ = 0.28 l/min, $\dot{V}_{CO_2(STPD)}$ = 0.23 l/min, $\dot{V}_{A(BTPS)}$ = 5 l/min), we have

$P_{A_{O_2}}$ = 100 mm Hg (13.3 kPa);

$P_{A_{CO_2}}$ = 40 mm Hg (5.3 kPa).

These data are norms for the healthy adult. Note, however, that they represent the means of temporally changing spatial distributions. There are slight fluctuations in the alveolar partial pressures in time, because the flow of fresh air into the alveolar space is discontinuous. Local variations arise because ventilation and blood flow are not quite the same in the different parts of the lung (p. 567).

For given exchange rates of O_2 and CO_2 ($\dot{V}_{O_2}$ and $\dot{V}_{CO_2}$), according to Eq. (24) the alveolar partial pressures depend chiefly on the *alveolar ventilation* $\dot{V}_A$. Increase in alveolar ventilation *(hyperventilation)* results in a rise in $P_{A_{O_2}}$ and a fall in $P_{A_{CO_2}}$, and decreased alveolar ventilation *(hypoventilation)* has the opposite effect. This relationship between alveolar partial pressure and alveolar ventilation is quantitatively illustrated in Fig. 21-21.

Influence of the ventilation-perfusion ratio. The respiratory gases exchanged in the alveoli must be transported to and from the alveoli in the blood. Therefore the rates of exchange are coupled with the rate of lung perfusion. To the extent that the venous and arterial gas concentrations can be regarded as constant, *pulmonary capillary perfusion* $\dot{Q}$ is proportional to $\dot{V}_{O_2}$ and $\dot{V}_{CO_2}$ (Fick's principle; see p. 540). Thus Equations (24) can also be interpreted as follows: *The alveolar O_2 and CO_2 partial pressures depend on the ratio of alveolar ventilation to lung perfusion* $\dot{V}_A/\dot{Q}$. In a person at rest with healthy lungs $\dot{V}_A/\dot{Q}$ = 0.8–1.0.

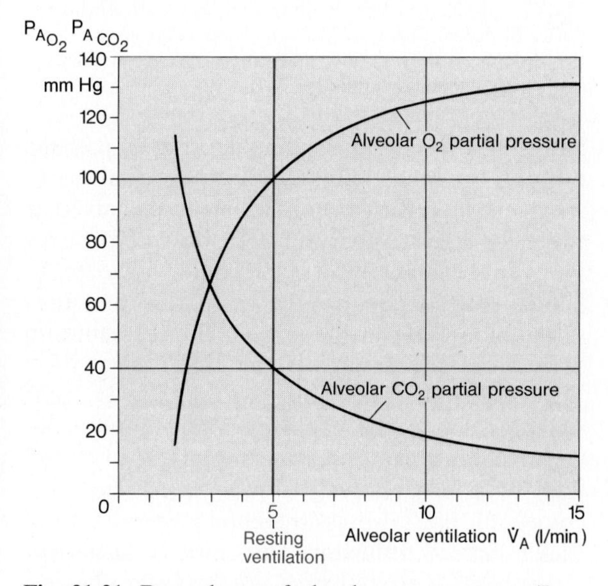

Fig. 21-21. Dependence of alveolar gas pressures ($P_{A_{O_2}}$ and $P_{A_{CO_2}}$) on alveolar ventilation ($\dot{V}_A$), at sea level under resting conditions (O_2 uptake, 280 ml/min; CO_2 output, 230 ml/min). The *straight red line* indicates the levels of $P_{A_{O_2}}$ and $P_{A_{CO_2}}$ in the case of normal ventilation

Altered states of ventilation. The temporal pattern of ventilation can change for a wide variety of reasons. Heavier breathing can be produced at will, and can also occur during work as an adaptation to the organism's metabolic requirements or in pathological conditions. Respiration can also be reduced voluntarily or by regulatory mechanisms or pathological factors. A number of terms have been coined in the past to denote such changes, but they were not systematically distinguished from one another. More recently, an attempt has been made to develop a more precise terminology, in which the alveolar partial pressures are taken as a criterion. These definitions are as follows:

1. *Normoventilation:* normal ventilation, in which an alveolar CO_2 partial pressure of about 40 mm Hg (5.3 kPa) is maintained.
2. *Hyperventilation:* increased alveolar ventilation beyond the actual metabolic needs ($P_{A_{CO_2}} < 40$ mm Hg).
3. *Hypoventilation:* alveolar ventilation decreased below the actual metabolic needs ($P_{A_{CO_2}} > 40$ mm Hg).
4. *Increased ventilation:* any increase in ventilation above the resting level (e.g., during work), regardless of the alveolar partial pressures.
5. *Eupnea:* normal comfortable respiration at rest.
6. *Hyperpnea:* increase in the depth of breathing with or without increase in respiratory frequency.
7. *Tachypnea:* increase in respiratory frequency.
8. *Bradypnea:* decrease in respiratory frequency.
9. *Apnea:* cessation of breathing, chiefly due to the absence of the physiological stimulus to respiration (decrease in arterial CO_2 partial pressure).
10. *Dyspnea:* Handicapped respiration accompanied by the unpleasant subjective feeling of shortness of breath.

11. *Orthopnea:* marked dyspnea due to congestion of the lung capillaries as a result of left-heart insufficiency, which is most severe when the patient is lying down and thus forces him to remain erect.
12. *Asphyxia:* cessation or diminution of breathing chiefly due to paralysis of the respiratory centers, with considerably restricted gas exchange (hypoxia and hypercapnia).

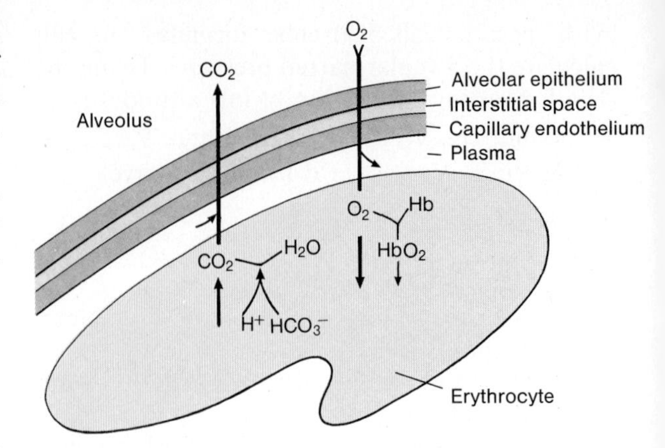

Fig. 21-22. Routes of O_2 and CO_2 transport in pulmonary gas exchange

Diffusion of Respiratory Gases

The rules governing pulmonary gas exchange. In the pulmonary alveoli the partial pressure of oxygen is kept high (100 mm Hg), whereas the O_2 partial pressure of the venous blood entering the capillaries of the lung is considerably lower (40 mm Hg). For CO_2 there is a partial-pressure drop in the opposite direction (46 mm Hg at the beginning of the lung capillaries, 40 mm Hg in the alveoli). These partial-pressure differences are the "driving forces" for the diffusion of O_2 and CO_2, and thus for pulmonary gas exchange.
According to **Fick's first law of diffusion,** the diffusive flux $\dot{M}$ (i.e., the amount of a substance that diffuses through a layer with area A and thickness h per unit time) is *directly proportional* to the effective *concentration difference* ΔC (p. 4).

$$\dot{M} = D\frac{A}{h}\Delta C \qquad (25)$$

The value of D, the **diffusion coefficient** or diffusivity, depends on the diffusion medium, the nature of the diffusing particles and the temperature. When a dissolved gas diffuses through a layer of liquid, the concentration in Eq. (25) is replaced by the partial pressure P. For a given medium, the two quantities are proportional to one another (p. 562):

$$\dot{M} = K\frac{A}{h}\Delta P \qquad (26)$$

The factor K in this equation has different dimensions and a different numerical value than D; to distinguish them, K is called **Krogh's diffusion coefficient** or the **diffusion conductivity** [45, 46]. For the diffusion media in the lung, K_{CO_2} is about 23 times larger than K_{O_2}; that is, other conditions being equal, about 23 times as much CO_2 as O_2 diffuses through a given layer per unit time. It is for this reason that sufficient CO_2 is released by diffusion in the lungs, despite the small differences in CO_2 partial pressure.

According to Eq. (26), effective diffusion requires a large exchange area A and a short diffusion distance h. Both of these prerequisites are ideally met in the lungs, where the surface area of the alveoli is about 80 m^2 and the diffusion distance is of the order of a few μm (Fig. 21-22).

As can be seen in Fig. 21-22, a considerable portion of the diffusion path and thus of the diffusion resistance is located within the erythrocyte. Here, however, the diffusion of O_2 as a gas is supplemented by other transport processes. As soon as an O_2 molecule enters the erythrocyte it binds to hemoglobin (Hb), thus converting it to oxyhemoglobin (HbO_2; p. 578). The HbO_2 molecules themselves can diffuse toward the center of the erythrocyte, accelerating the transport of O_2 (facilitated diffusion).
The CO_2 molecules diffuse along the same path in the opposite direction, from erythrocyte to alveolar space. They can do this, however, only after they have been released from their chemical bonds (p. 587).

Diffusing capacity of the lung. During its passage through the lung capillaries, an individual erythrocyte is in diffusive contact with the alveolar space for a relatively brief time, only about 0.3 s [46]. This **contact time** is sufficient, however, to almost entirely equalize the gas partial pressures in the blood and in the alveoli. (For a definition of gas partial pressures in the blood see p. 582). Fig. 21-23 illustrates this process; the O_2 partial pressure in the capillary blood approaches the alveolar partial pressure rapidly at first, and then at a progressively slower rate. This time course of partial-pressure change results from Fick's law of diffusion. The initially large difference in O_2 partial pressure between alveolus and capillary becomes progressively smaller during transit, so that the rate of diffusion must progressively decrease. The blood, which enters the capillary with an O_2 partial pressure of 40

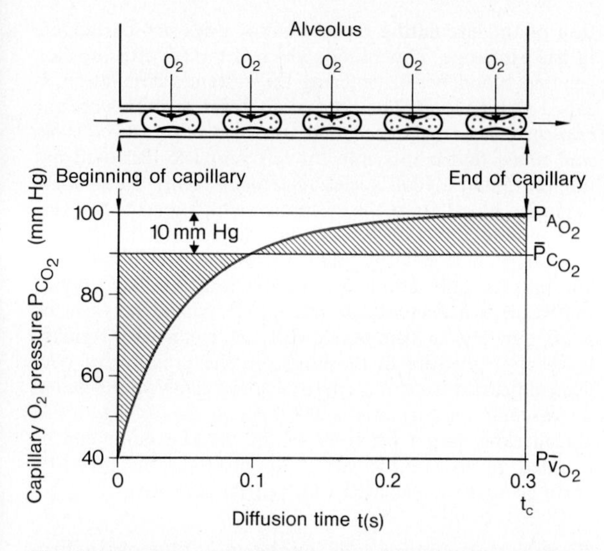

Fig. 21-23. Increase in the O_2 partial pressure in erythrocytes during passage through a lung capillary. *Above:* O_2 uptake of the erythrocytes (indicated by red dots). *Below:* corresponding capillary O_2 partial pressure $P_{C_{O_2}}$ as a function of time t. $P_{A_{O_2}}$, alveolar O_2 partial pressure; $P_{\bar{V}_{O_2}}$, mixed venous O_2 partial pressure; $\bar{P}_{C_{O_2}}$, O_2 partial pressure averaged over the duration of diffusive contact; t_c, contact time

mm Hg, leaves it with an O_2 partial pressure of 100 mm Hg. Similarly, during the contact time the blood CO_2 partial pressure approaches the alveolar pressure. The CO_2 partial pressure falls from 46 mm Hg at the beginning of the capillary to 40 mm Hg as CO_2 diffuses away. We may say, then, that *in the lung of a healthy person the partial pressures in the blood become practically identical to those in the alveoli.*

An overall measure of the "diffusive conductance" of the whole human lung is obtainable from Fick's law of diffusion (Eq. 26): the amount of oxygen that diffuses through the entire lung must be identical to the O_2 uptake $\dot{V}_{O_2}$. The factors K, A and h, which cannot be measured for each individual, are lumped in a new constant $D_L = K \cdot A/h$. Thus we have

$$\dot{V}_{O_2} = D_L \cdot \overline{\Delta P_{O_2}}; \quad D_L = \frac{\dot{V}_{O_2}}{\overline{\Delta P_{O_2}}} \tag{27}$$

The quantity D_L is called the **diffusing capacity** of the lung for oxygen. In this case $\overline{\Delta P_{O_2}}$ is the mean O_2 partial-pressure difference between the alveolar space and the blood in the lung capillaries. Because the O_2 partial pressure rises as the blood flows through the capillary, the pressure must be averaged over the entire capillary length (Fig. 21-23).

To obtain a value for the O_2 diffusing capacity, one must measure oxygen uptake $\dot{V}_{O_2}$ and the mean O_2 partial-pressure difference $\overline{\Delta P_{O_2}}$. Whereas the measurement of $\dot{V}_{O_2}$ with an open or closed spirometric system presents no difficulties, elaborate techniques are required to determine $\overline{\Delta P_{O_2}}$ [15, 46].

For a healthy adult at rest the oxygen uptake $\dot{V}_{O_2}$ is found to be ca. 300 ml/min, and the mean O_2 partial-pressure difference $\overline{\Delta P_{O_2}}$ is ca. 10 mm Hg (1.33 kPa). According to Eq. (27), then, *the normal O_2 diffusing capacity D_L is 30 ml·min^{-1}·mm Hg^{-1} (230 ml·min^{-1}·kPa^{-1}).* Under pathological conditions D_L can be considerably smaller, indicating an increased diffusion resistance in the lung; the cause can be reduction of the exchange area A or an increased length of the diffusion path h. D_L in itself is not a measure of the extent to which the O_2 partial pressure in the blood approximates that in the alveoli. As with alveolar ventilation, the diffusing capacity must be expressed with reference to pulmonary capillary perfusion $\dot{Q}$. *The ratio $D_L/\dot{Q}$ is thus the critical determinant of the effectiveness of alveolar gas exchange* [18, 46]; a decrease in $D_L/\dot{Q}$ indicates **impaired diffusion.**

21.5 Pulmonary Perfusion and Oxygenation of the Blood

Perfusion of the Lungs

Resistance to blood flow. Blood flow through the lungs, at a rate of 5–6 l/min at rest, is driven by a mean pressure difference of only 8 mm Hg (1 kPa) between the pulmonary artery and the left atrium. That is, in comparison with the systemic circulation the pulmonary vessels present a *very small resistance to flow* (p. 523). During hard physical work, when the rate of pulmonary perfusion rises to 4 times the resting level, the pulmonary arterial pressure increases by only a factor of 2. The implication is that the resistance is reduced as the perfusion rate rises.

This reduction is a passive process, brought about by *dilation of the pulmonary vessels* and by the *opening of reserve capillaries.* At rest blood flows through only about 50% of the capillaries in the lungs, and under increasing loads a progressively larger proportion of the capillaries are perfused. There is a concomitant increase in the surface area available for pulmonary gas exchange – that is, in the diffusing capacity (p. 564) – so that O_2 uptake and CO_2 release can be matched to the metabolic needs.

The pulmonary resistance to flow is influenced to some extent by the excursions of the thorax during breathing. During inspiration the arteries and veins dilate, because of the increasing tension in the elastic fibers attached to their outer walls. At the same time, however, the resistance in the capillaries rises because they are being pulled lengthwise and thereby constricted. The effect on the capillaries predominates; therefore the resistance to flow in the pulmonary vascular system as a whole becomes larger as the lungs expand [32].

Regional distribution of perfusion. Pulmonary perfusion is characterized by especially pronounced *regional inhomogeneities,* the extent of which depends mainly on the position of the body. In an upright position the basal part of the lung is considerably better perfused than the apex. The cause is the difference in hydrostatic pressure in the two regions; a 30-cm difference in level creates a pressure difference of 23 mm Hg (3 kPa) in the vessels. Therefore the arterial pressure in the upper parts of the lungs is below the alveolar pressure, so that the capillaries are nearly collapsed. In the lower parts the capillary lumen is large, because the pressure within the vessel exceeds the alveolar pressure. As a consequence of this regional distribution of resistance to flow, there is a *nearly linear decrease in perfusion per unit of lung volume from the base of the lung to its apex* [31, 32]. During exercise and in the recumbent position, pulmonary perfusion is more homogeneous.

Hypoxic vasoconstriction. Another factor affecting regional perfusion in the lungs is the composition of the gas in adjacent alveolar spaces. In particular, a *decreased alveolar O_2 partial pressure* causes *constriction of the arterioles* and hence reduced perfusion **(Euler-Liljestrand mechanism).** A result of this hypoxia-induced increase in resistance is that the amount of blood flowing through poorly ventilated regions of the lung is restricted and the blood is redirected into better ventilated regions. To a certain extent, the regional perfusion $\dot{Q}$ is adjusted to the current alveolar ventilation $\dot{V}_A$. Particularly under pathological conditions, however, this mechanism cannot prevent the development of inhomogeneities in the distribution of the ventilation-perfusion ratio $\dot{V}_A/\dot{Q}$.

Right-left shunts. Whereas most of the cardiac output comes into diffusive contact with the alveoli, a small fraction of the circulating blood volume does not participate in gas exchange. This blood, which is mixed with the oxygenated blood before entering the systemic circulation, is called shunt blood. The normal anatomical shunts are the *bronchial veins* and the small cardiac veins (the *Thebesian veins*) that empty into the left ventricle. Perfused but not ventilated alveoli act as *functional shunts*. In all these cases the blood from the systemic veins bypasses the gas-exchange regions and returns unchanged into the arteries. Although in a healthy person the shunted blood flow amounts to only about 2% of the total cardiac output, the result is a decrease in arterial O_2 partial pressure by 5–10 mm Hg as compared with the mean end-capillary O_2 partial pressure in the lungs. In the presence of congenital heart disease (e.g., *defects of the ventricular septum*) or vascular malformations (e.g., *patent ductus arteriosus*) considerably larger fractions of the blood volume can be shunted, producing *hypoxia* (lowered O_2 partial pressure) and *hypercapnia* (elevated CO_2 partial pressure).

Factors influencing gas exchange. The main factors that determine the degree to which the blood in the lungs takes up oxygen and releases CO_2 are the *alveolar ventilation* $\dot{V}_A$, the *pulmonary perfusion* $\dot{Q}$, and the *diffusing capacity* D_L (Fig. 21-24). We have seen that these quantities do not independently influence the effectiveness of respiration; it is their relations to one another – in particular, the ratios $\dot{V}_A/\dot{Q}$ and $D_L/\dot{Q}$ – that are decisive (pp. 563, 565) [31,46]. An additional factor is the *regional inhomogeneity* of ventilation, perfusion and diffusion [12, 18, 46]. Nonuniform *distribution* makes the exchange of gases less complete; that is, it causes a reduction of the O_2 partial pressure and a slight elevation of the CO_2 partial pressure in the systemic arteries.

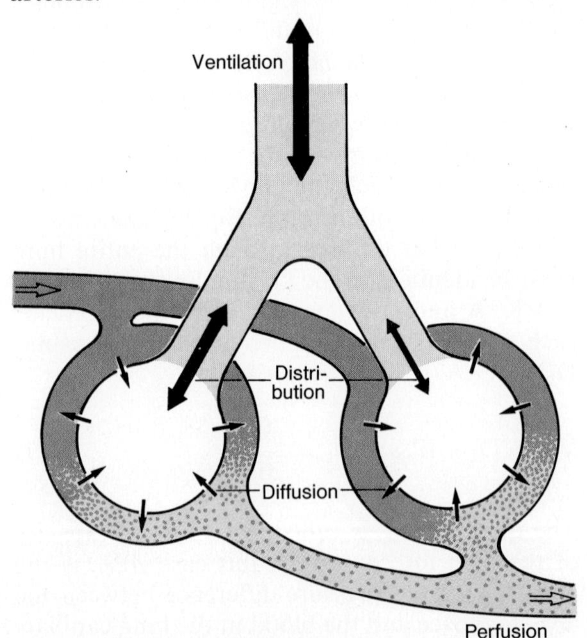

Fig. 21-24. Diagram to show the factors determining gas exchange in the lung. From [8]

Inhomogeneities in the ventilation-perfusion ratio. Nonuniform $\dot{V}_A/\dot{Q}$ distributions are of special significance in both normal and pathological physiology. Various procedures have been developed to quantify this distribution. The regional *distribution of alveolar ventilation* can be determined by adding a radioactive gas (e.g., ^{133}Xe) to the air inspired by a subject and measuring the activity at various places on the thorax. The *perfusion distribution* is found similarly. After intravenous injection of a solution containing the radioactive gas, the gas diffuses into the alveoli as the blood passes through the lungs; the magnitude of the local perfusion can be monitored by measuring the activity over various parts of the thorax. The two methods in combination provide quantitative data on the regional $\dot{V}_A/\dot{Q}$ distribution [31, 32].

Figure 21-25 illustrates the result of such a distribution analysis for a healthy subject in an upright position. The figure at the top shows the measurement sites. The curve below gives, for each value of $\dot{V}_A/\dot{Q}$, the specific values of alveolar O_2 partial pressure (on the abscissa) and CO_2 partial pressure (on the ordinate) that result from these exchange conditions in the associated alveolar spaces. In the apex of the lung $\dot{V}_A/\dot{Q} = 3.0$, and the associated alveolar partial pressures are $P_{A_{O_2}} = 131$ mm Hg and $P_{A_{CO_2}} = 29$ mm Hg. In the base of the lung, where $\dot{V}_A/\dot{Q} = 0.65$, the alveolar partial pressures are $P_{A_{O_2}} = 89$ mm Hg and $P_{A_{CO_2}} = 42$ mm Hg. There are corresponding differences in the other parts of the lung. The regional differences in the ventilation-perfusion ratio are due mainly to the inhomogeneous distribution of blood flow in the lungs. Although alveolar ventilation also increases from the upper parts of the lung to its base, this dependence is very much more pronounced for perfusion (p. 566).

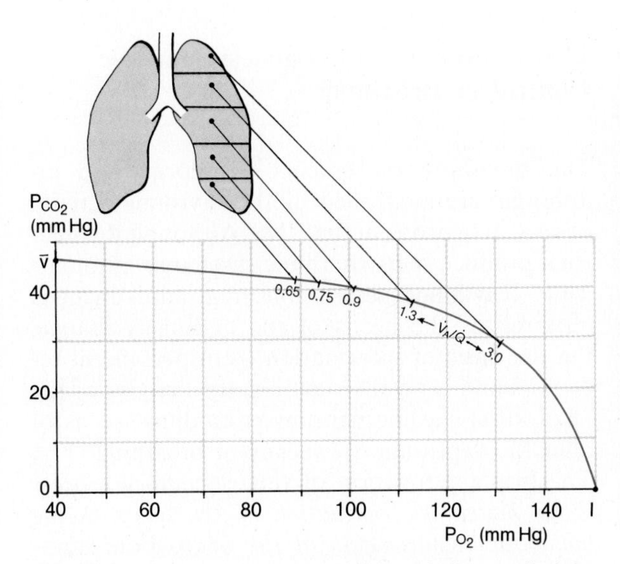

Fig. 21-25. Regional inhomogeneities of the ventilation-perfusion ratio $\dot{V}/\dot{Q}$, modified from [31]. The *red curve* gives the values of alveolar O_2 partial pressure *(abscissa)* and CO_2 partial pressure *(ordinate)* associated with the ratios $\dot{V}/\dot{Q}$ for the indicated regions of the lung. I, inspiratory partial pressure; $\bar{v}$, mixed-venous partial pressure

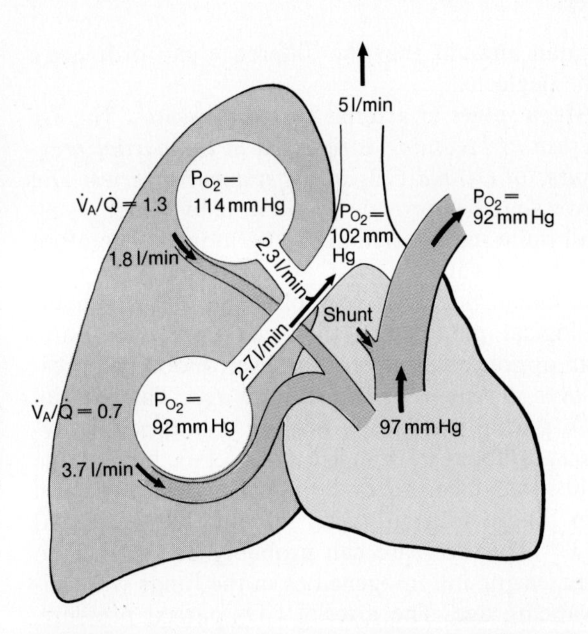

Fig. 21-26. Effects of the regional inhomogeneities in the lung on the net gas exchange with the blood. The situation is simplified by showing only two regions that differ in ventilation and perfusion; the values for these are considered to apply to both lungs. Because of the functional inhomogeneities and the right-left shunts, an alveoloarterial O_2 partial-pressure difference of 10 mm Hg is produced

Figure 21-26 illustrates the effects of the regional inhomogeneities in the lung. For simplicity, the alveolar space is divided into only two compartments, one above the other. The indicated values for alveolar ventilation and perfusion refer to both lungs. Given these values, the alveolar P_{O_2} becomes 114 mm Hg in the upper compartment and 92 mm Hg in the lower one. Taking account of the ventilation distribution, the mean alveolar P_{O_2} is 102 mm Hg. When the differentially oxygenated blood from the two compartments is mixed, its P_{O_2} is 97 mm Hg. Thus, perfusion through the basal compartment predominates. The admixture of shunt blood (p. 566) lowers the P_{O_2} by an additional 5 mm Hg, so that the arterial P_{O_2} is reduced to only 92 mm Hg. That is, although the capillary P_{O_2} has equilibrated completely with the alveolar P_{O_2} in all regions of the lung, the *arterial P_{O_2} is lower than the mean alveolar P_{O_2}* by 10 mm Hg because of the *functional inhomogeneities* and the *right-left shunts.* For the same reasons, the P_{CO_2} in the arterial blood is higher than that in the alveoli, but by such a small amount that the difference can ordinarily be neglected.

Mean values of arterial partial pressures. *The net effect of breathing is reflected in the partial pressures of O_2 and CO_2 in the systemic arteries.* The two together provide a criterion by which overall pulmonary function can be judged. Therefore "normal values" must be established for each of them, but as is very often the case with biological parameters, they can vary over quite an appreciable range. Moreover, blood gas pressures *depend systematically on age.* The arterial O_2 partial pressure in healthy young people averages about 95 mm Hg (12.6 kPa), but by age 40 it has fallen to ca. 80 mm Hg (10.6 kPa) and in 70-year-olds it is ca. 70 mm Hg (9.3 kPa) [39]. This decrease can probably be ascribed to increasing inhomogeneities in the lungs with advancing age. The arterial CO_2 partial pressure, about 40 mm Hg (5.3 kPa) in the young, changes relatively little with age.

Measurement of arterial blood gases. The method most commonly used to measure the **partial pressure of oxygen** is *polarography* (Fig. 21-27 left). A measuring electrode (platinum or gold) and a reference electrode, both submerged in an electrolyte, are polarized by a voltage source (polarization voltage 0.6 V). O_2 molecules that contact the surface of the noble metal are reduced there. The associated movement of charge in the closed electrical circuit can be measured with an ammeter; the current is directly proportional to the number of O_2 molecules that diffuse to the electrode surface and thus is proportional to the O_2 partial pressure in the solution. In the customary arrangement the electrolyte containing the electrodes is separated from the blood sample to be analyzed by a membrane permeable to oxygen. The entire measuring apparatus can be made so small that only a few drops of arterial blood are enough for the measurement of P_{O_2}. This blood is usually obtained from the earlobe, in which a maximal perfusion has been brought about; care must be taken to avoid contact with air as the blood is transferred to the measuring chamber [44].

The arterial **CO_2 partial pressure** can also be measured in very small samples of blood (Fig. 21-27 right). Here the arrangement of the electrode is that used to *measure pH* (p. 589); again, the sample is separated from the electrode by a membrane through which gas but not ions can pass. The pH of the electrolyte inside the electrode ($NaHCO_3$) can therefore be affected only by the partial pressure of CO_2 in the blood, and after calibration the electrical signal from the voltmeter is a measure of the CO_2 partial pressure. Another means of measuring the CO_2 partial pressure in small blood samples is provided by the *Astrup procedure* (pp. 595f.).

If the **concentrations of blood gases** rather than their partial pressures are required, procedures are used in which the gases are first expelled from the blood and then analyzed manometrically or volumetrically. The most common technique employs the *Van Slyke manometric apparatus* [3], which originally required fairly large blood samples (0.5–2 ml), obtainable only by puncture of an artery. The procedure has since been modified so that O_2 and CO_2 concentrations in smaller samples can be determined as well.

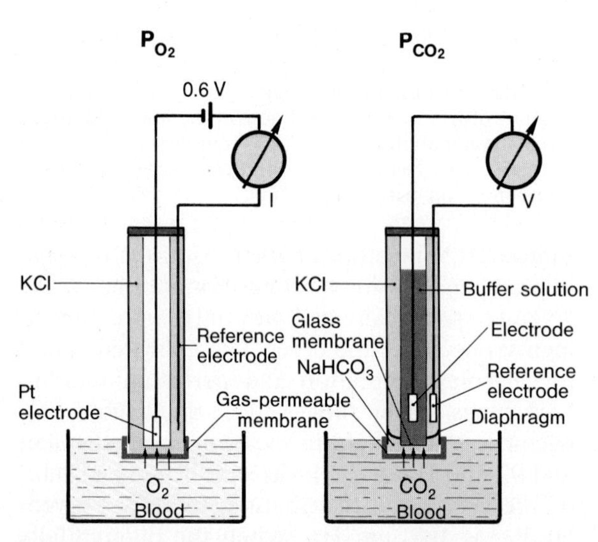

Fig. 21-27. Simplified diagram of the apparatus for measuring P_{O_2} and P_{CO_2} in the blood. **P_{O_2}** *(left):* In a closed circuit a voltage of 0.6 V is applied between a platinum electrode and a reference electrode; a gas-permeable membrane *(red)* separates this system from the blood sample. O_2 molecules that diffuse through the membrane are reduced at the surface of the platinum. The associated current I is proportional to the O_2 partial pressure in the blood. **P_{CO_2}** *(right):* Across a glass membrane permeable to H^+, a pH-dependent voltage is built up, which is displayed by the meter V. This device is separated from the blood sample by a gas-permeable membrane *(red)*. CO_2 molecules that diffuse through the latter membrane change the pH of the solution below the glass membrane. Thus the recorded voltage varies according to the P_{CO_2} in the blood

21.6 Central Rhythmogenesis and the Control of Breathing

The breathing movements of thorax and diaphragm are controlled by the rhythmic activity of special neurons in the CNS. Although the neurons produce their rhythmic discharge automatically **(rhythmogenesis)**, continual adjustment is required as the needs of the organism change. On the basis of information from peripheral receptors and central structures, the activity of the respiration-specific neurons is modified so as to alter the depth and frequency of breathing.

The primary function of this *regulatory process* is to *match the ventilation of the lungs to the metabolic requirements of the body.* For example, during exercise more oxygen is needed, and the supply of air must be increased correspondingly. Furthermore, the pattern of breathing must be altered during reflexes such as swallowing, coughing and sneezing, as well as during expressive behavior such as speaking, laughing and singing. A complex regulatory mechanism with multiple control loops is necessary if breathing is to be optimally adjusted in these diverse situations.

Central Rhythmogenesis

Locations of the respiratory neurons. Control of breathing has long been ascribed to the *medulla oblongata*, and it was originally assumed that the neuronal activity driving the breathing movements originated in a circumscribed nucleus there ("noeud vital"). But this notion of a single "respiratory center" has not been confirmed; subsequent research has shown that the rhythmic sequence of inspiration and expiration arises from the interplay of various groups of cells in the brainstem. Important information was obtained from experiments on anesthetized animals (cat, rabbit, dog) involving the transection of brain tissue and the recording of neural activity [11, 20].

The classical **transection experiments,** in which cuts were made across the brainstem and cervical spinal cord at various levels, provided the first (rough) indications of the sites of the respiration-specific structures. After transection *above the pons* spontaneous respiration persists, whereas transection of the *cervical cord* causes respiratory arrest. Between these sites, in the region of the pons and medulla oblongata, suitably placed lesions produce altered forms of breathing. One example is *apneusis,* a maintained inspiration occasionally interrupted by brief expiratory movements. With other lesions *gasping* can result; this is a maintained expiratory status interrupted from time to time by brief inspiratory movements.
More recently the main contribution toward resolving the question of central rhythmogenesis has come from **recording experiments.** Intracellular or extracellular microelectrodes are used to record the discharge of single neurons in the brainstem, and this activity is examined for evidence of correlation with the simultaneously recorded breathing movements. By systematically probing the candidate regions of the CNS in this way, one can localize those groups of cells that are active in the respiratory rhythm.

The results of the recording experiments indicate that there are two groups of *respiratory neurons* [11, 41]. The cells in one group are active mainly during the inspiration phase *(inspiratory neurons),* and those in the other discharge during the expiration phase *(expiratory neurons)* (Fig. 21-28). The inspiratory neurons (I) form a dorsal group near the *nucleus of the solitary tract* (ST) and a ventral group in the vicinity of the *nucleus ambiguus* (NA) and in *cervical segments C1-2.* The expiratory neurons (E) are situated next to the *nucleus ambiguus,* between the two

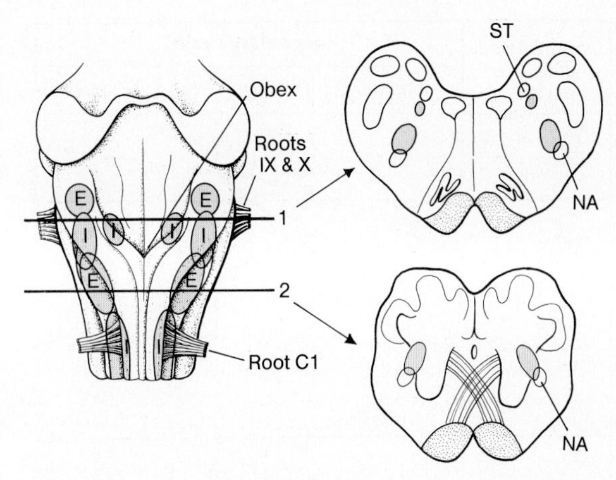

Fig. 21-28. Locations of the inspiratory neurons (I) and the expiratory neurons (E) in the medulla oblongata of the cat. *Left:* dorsal view; *right:* two cross sections, in which the positions of the solitary tract (ST) and the nucleus ambiguus (NA) are shown together with the region of the respiratory neurons *(red).* Roots IX & X, roots of the glossopharyngeal and vagus nerves; Root C1: roots of the first cervical spinal nerve

inspiration zones, and further rostral near the *retrofacial nucleus.*

Phases of the primary respiratory rhythm. In order to understand the neuronal processes involved in the control of breathing, it is important to recognize that the centrally controlled breathing cycle actually consists not of two but of *3 phases* [41]. The first phase is **inspiration.** When inspiration is completed the forces of retraction in the lung are so great that they must initially be counteracted, so that the expiratory stream of air does not flow too rapidly. Hence there is a phase called **postinspiration,** in which the inspiratory musculature remains contracted for a while and then gradually relaxes, so that the inspired volume of air is briefly retained and then exhaled passively. The final, third phase of the cycle consists of **active expiration,** assisted by contraction of the expiratory muscles.

Classes of neurons. In recording experiments *6 classes of respiratory neurons* with different discharge patterns have been found. Some discharge during inspiration, at an increasing or decreasing frequency; others are active during the postinspiration phase and still others, in the second phase of expiration. In Fig. 21-29 the patterns of *excitatory* postsynaptic potentials are shown as red areas and those of the *inhibitory* postsynaptic potentials as grey areas, for each class of neurons. For comparison, the pattern of activity

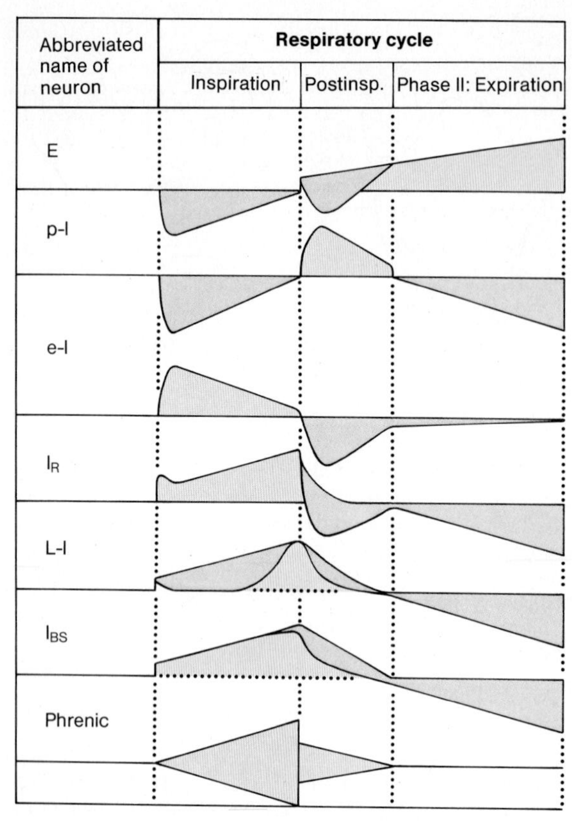

Fig. 21-29. Postsynaptic activity of the various respiratory neurons, from [41]. The patterns of excitatory postsynaptic potentials are shown as *red areas* and those of the inhibitory postsynaptic potentials, as *grey areas;* the simultaneous activity in the phrenic nerve is shown at the bottom. Postinsp.: slow relaxation of the inspiratory musculature in the first phase of expiration; Phase II: activation of the expiratory musculature

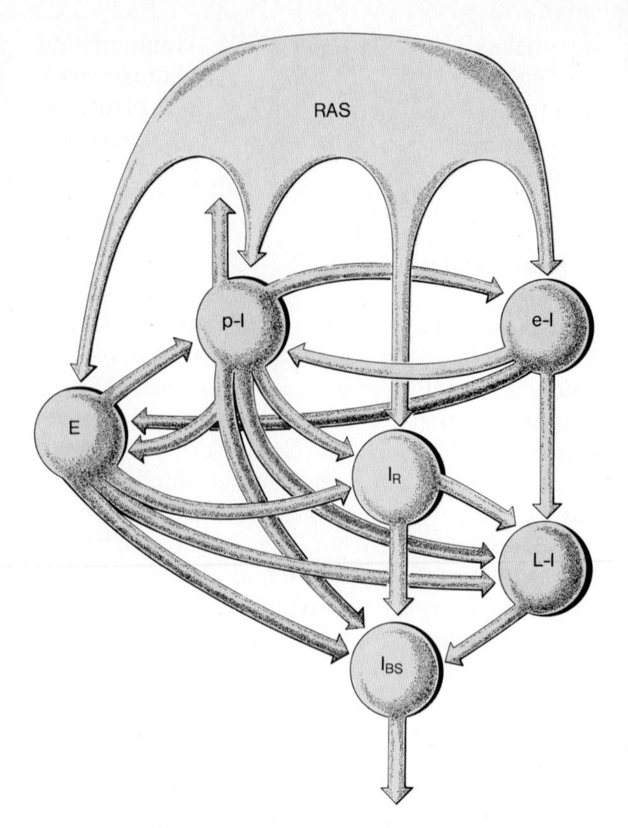

Fig. 21-30. Hypothetical diagram of the connections among respiratory neurons in the medulla oblongata, from [41]. The projections of the axons *(arrows)* of neurons in each class (abbreviations as in text) are shown. *Red arrows* indicate excitatory connections and *grey arrows,* inhibitory connections. The reticular formation (RAS) activates the neuronal network; the bulbospinal neurons (I_{BS}) activate the spinal motoneurons to the inspiratory musculature

in the phrenic nerve is also shown. The height of each of the red bands (excitatory potentials) is a measure of discharge rate.

The various classes are characterized as follows [41]:

- E: late-expiratory neurons (increasing discharge rate in the second phase of expiration),
- p-I: *postinspiratory neurons* (rapidly rising and slowy falling discharge rate in the first phase of expiration),
- e-I: *early-inspiratory neurons* (rapidly rising and slowly falling discharge rate during inspiration),
- I_R: *ramp-inspiratory neurons* (ramp increase in discharge rate during inspiration),
- L-I: *late-inspiratory neurons* (brief burst of impulses at the end of inspiration),
- I_{BS}: *bulbospinal inspiratory neurons* (discharge rate rising during inspiration and falling in the postinspiration phase).

Connections of the respiratory neurons. The rhythmic activation of the respiratory musculature is based on complex interconnections of the respiratory neurons. From the discharge patterns characteristic of the different classes of neurons one can draw certain inferences about the reciprocal relations among the classes, and these have suggested some hypothetical mechanisms for rhythmogenesis. One such hypothesis [41] is illustrated by the connectivity diagram of Fig. 21-30; here the red arrows denote excitatory connections and the gray arrows, inhibitory connections.

In this scheme, afferent inputs from the periphery of the body and from higher central nervous structures produce tonic activation of the *reticular formation* (RAS). Under the tonic influence of the RAS the *ramp-inspiratory neurons* (I_R) discharge and, by way of the *bulbospinal inspiratory neurons* (I_{BS}), the motoneurons to the inspiratory muscles are activated. Until the inspiration phase is nearly over, the *late-inspiratory neurons* (L–I) are inhibited by the *early-inspiratory neurons* (e–I). The cessation of this inhibition initiates the next phase of respiration, in which the *postinspiratory neurons* (p–I) are activated. They exert an inhibitory influence on all the other cells in the network, so that the respiratory rhythm is temporarily interrupted. Finally, the *late-expiratory neurons* (E) discharge, activating the motoneurons that innervate the expiratory muscles. When the inhibitory influence of E declines, the next breathing cycle can begin.

Mechanical Control of Respiration

Hering-Breuer reflex. The centrally controlled respiratory rhythm can be modified by peripheral influences, as shown by the following observations. When the *lungs are inflated, inspiration is reflexly inhibited,* and expiration is initiated. Conversely, fairly large *decreases in lung volume* initiate *deeper inspiration.* Evidently the state of stretch of the lung at each moment is signaled to the respiratory centers, which elicit an appropriate countermovement. This sequence of events is named after its discoverers – *the Hering-Breuer reflex.*

This reflex arc begins at **stretch receptors in the lung parenchyma.** Such receptors have been found in the *trachea,* the *bronchi* and the *bronchioles.* Some of these signal the degree of stretch by firing a train of impulses with very little adaptation, while others are excited only when the amount of stretch increases or decreases. In this way both the state of stretch of the lung and changes in that state can be monitored continually. *The afferent pathways of the lung-stretch reflex run in the vagus nerve.* Therefore bilateral transection of the vagus *(vagotomy)* eliminates the Hering-Breuer reflex. As a consequence, breathing is slowed and inspiration is deeper. With the vagus intact, information from the stretch receptors is transmitted to the medulla oblongata and processed in the system of respiratory neurons. As a result, the discharge patterns conducted to the respiratory muscles in the *efferent motor* tracts are modified to correspond to the degree of stretching of the lung.

The *physiological significance* of the Hering-Breuer reflex is that it limits the respiratory excursions. In doing so, it helps to adjust the depth of breathing to the prevailing conditions in such a way that the respiratory work is done economically. Moreover, in extreme cases the Hering-Breuer reflex serves to prevent overstretching of the lungs.

Reflexes of the respiratory musculature. The intrinsic control of breathing movements also involves spinal reflexes originating in the respiratory muscles. Like other striated muscles, the muscles used in breathing contain *muscle spindles* that function as *stretch receptors.* When either inspiration or expiration encounters difficulty the corresponding muscle spindles are stimulated, and the resulting *proprioceptive reflex* causes enhanced contraction of the muscle. This property of the musculature tends to match the mechanics of breathing to the momentary resistance and compliance in the lungs. Moreover, it is highly likely that the afferent impulses from the muscle spindles are also conducted to the respiratory centers, forming a longer reflex arc that can similarly modify the activity of the respiratory muscles.

Chemical Control of Respiration

The arterial levels of *CO_2 partial pressure, O_2 partial pressure* and *H^+ concentration* are critically determined by respiratory function, but all three can in turn affect the ventilation of the lungs. This interaction amounts to a **control circuit** that tends to maintain constancy of the three controlled variables – the partial pressures of CO_2 and O_2 and the pH of the blood. *The chemical control of respiration thus contributes to homeostasis and ensures that breathing is adjusted to the organism's metabolic state.*

The effect of CO_2 on breathing. *An increase in the arterial CO_2 partial pressure (hypercapnia) causes an increase in minute volume.* As a rule both the tidal volume and the respiration rate are increased.

The quantitative relationship between the arterial CO_2 partial pressure $P_{a_{CO_2}}$ and the associated minute volume $\dot{V}_E$ is called the **CO_2 response curve.** This curve (Fig. 21-31A) shows the extent to which ventilation depends on the CO_2 partial pressure. When $P_{a_{CO_2}}$ rises from 40 to 60 mm Hg, $\dot{V}_E$ increases from 7 to about 65 l/min. A $P_{a_{CO_2}}$ increase of this magnitude can occur, for example, when one breathes a gas mixture containing large amounts of CO_2; it is accompanied by a feeling of breathlessness *(dyspnea).* Fig. 21-31A shows further that the amount by which ventilation can be increased in this way is limited. Accumulation of CO_2 in the blood can raise the minute volume to at most 75 l/min – far less than the minute volumes achieved during extremely hard work (120 l/min). If the arterial CO_2 partial pressure exceeds 70 mm Hg ventilation declines again, because at such high concentrations CO_2 inhibits the respiratory centers.

After prolonged, intense forced respiration *(hyperventilation)* some subjects temporarily stop breathing *(apnea).* Because more CO_2 is eliminated during hyperventilation,

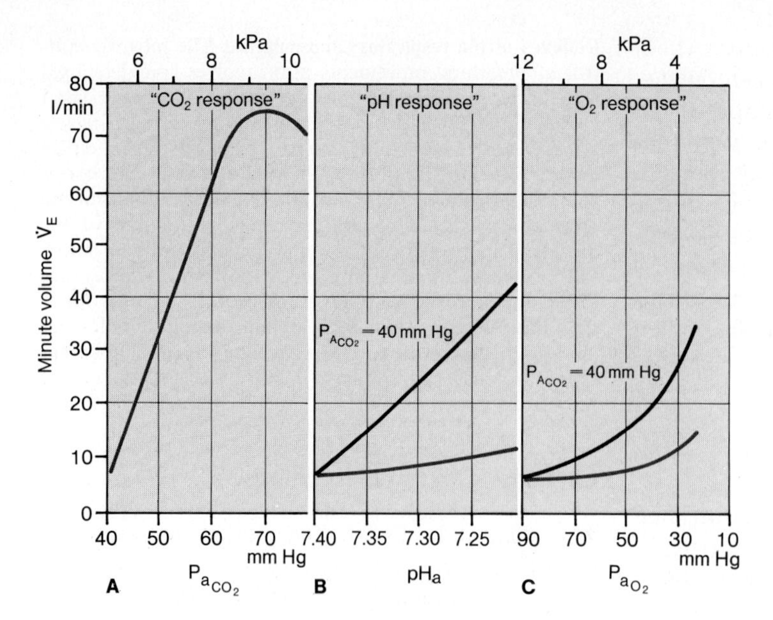

Fig. 21-31 A–C. Minute volume ($\dot{V}_E$) as a function of the arterial CO_2 and O_2 partial pressures ($P_{a_{CO_2}}$, $P_{a_{O_2}}$) and arterial pH (pH_a). *Red curves:* Ventilation response normally observed; *black curves:* response obtained when CO_2 pressure is kept constant ($P_{A_{CO_2}}$ = 40 mm Hg). Based on data in [23]

and the arterial CO_2 partial pressure falls correspondingly, this pause in breathing is generally regarded as due to the absence of the physiological "CO_2 stimulus" to respiration. But many subjects do not exhibit complete apnea following hyperventilation; their breathing is only reduced somewhat. From this observation one may conclude that there is a basic central respiratory drive that persists even without the "CO_2 stimulus" [23].

The effect of H^+ on breathing. *When the arterial pH falls below the normal value of 7.4, respiration is increased.* When pH rises above its normal value, breathing is reduced, but to a lesser extent. *The dependence of minute volume $\dot{V}_E$ on the pH of arterial blood (pH_a)* is illustrated in Fig. 21-31B. The red curve represents the **pH response** observed when pH is reduced by an increase in the blood content of nonvolatile acids (metabolic acidosis; see pp. 593f.). In this case a reduction by 0.1 pH unit causes ventilation to increase by about 2 l/min. This relatively modest increase results from the *interaction between the two "respiratory drives" pH and CO_2 partial pressure.* A change in pH alone would have a much greater effect on ventilation; the black curve, for example, was obtained by keeping the CO_2 partial pressure constant ($P_{a_{CO_2}}$ = 40 mm Hg). Normally, however, the increased ventilation induced by a decrease in pH gives off CO_2 at a greater rate, so that $P_{a_{CO_2}}$ falls. Thus when the blood pH is reduced, the CO_2 respiratory drive diminishes. The pH response curve is the resultant of the increasing (from left to right) pH drive and the simultaneously decreasing CO_2 drive.

The effect of O_2 deficiency on breathing. *When the O_2 partial pressure in the arterial blood falls (hypoxia) ventilation is increased.* Arterial hypoxia can occur in people at high altitudes, where the inspiratory O_2 partial pressure is reduced because of the lower atmospheric pressure. But it can also be the consequence of pulmonary malfunction.

Fig. 21-31C shows the relation between *minute volume $\dot{V}_E$ and the arterial O_2 partial pressure $P_{a_{O_2}}$*. The black curve applies to the case in which CO_2 partial pressure is kept constant ($P_{a_{CO_2}}$ = 40 mm Hg); that is, it represents the isolated response to the O_2 drive. In reality, however, there is an *interaction with the CO_2 drive.* Increased ventilation caused by O_2 deficiency reduces the arterial CO_2 partial pressure, so that its effectiveness in driving respiration diminishes. The **O_2 response** (red curve) under natural conditions thus exhibits a relatively slight increase in ventilation as O_2 partial pressure falls. In practice oxygen regulates breathing effectively only when its arterial partial pressure is less than 50-60 mm Hg – that is, when a state of considerable hypoxia exists.

Although the arterial O_2 partial pressure has little influence on breathing under normal conditions, it can become quite significant in **pathological states.** Its effect is especially marked when the CO_2 sensitivity of respiratory regulation is reduced by *drugs* or eliminated altogether as in *barbiturate poisoning*. Similarly, in *chronic hypercapnia* sensitivity to P_{CO_2} and $[H^+]$ stimuli is reduced.

Peripheral chemoreceptors. The effects of the blood gases and pH on breathing are mediated in part by peripheral *chemoreceptors.* Some of these are located in the bilateral **carotid bodies** [13, 14], paraganglia situated at the point where

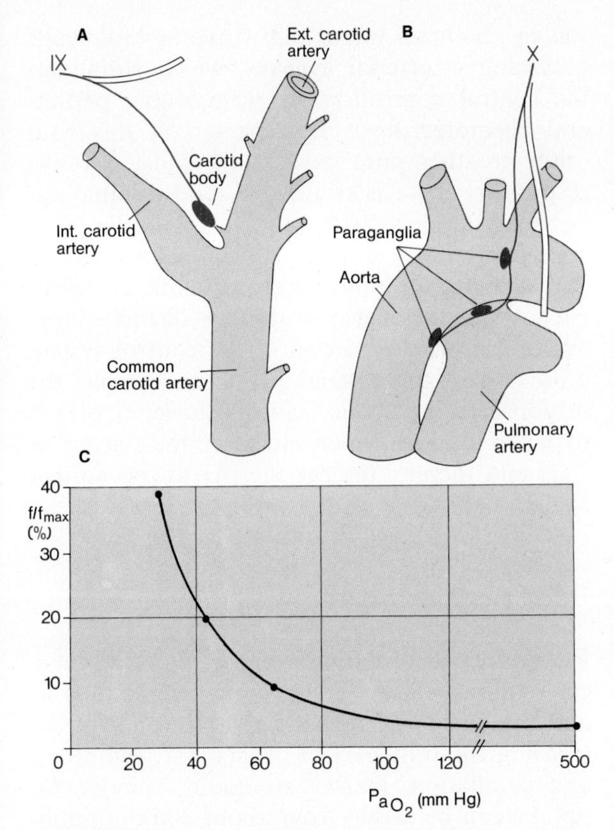

Fig. 21-32 A–C. Locations of the carotid (**A**) and aortic (**B**) bodies, and their afferent pathways. (**C**) Relations between the frequency of chemoreceptor discharge and the arterial O_2 partial pressure. As the isolated carotid sinus of the cat is perfused with blood at different O_2 partial pressures ($P_{a_{O_2}}$) and at constant $P_{a_{CO_2}}$ = 33 mm Hg and pH = 7.33, the afferent impulses in the sinus nerve are recorded. (Ordinate: aggregate activity as % of the maximal activity: f/f_{max}.) Based on data in [35]

the common carotid artery divides into the internal and external carotids (Fig. 21-32). Each carotid body is innervated by a branch of the *glossopharyngeal nerve.* Additional chemoreceptors are found in the **paraganglia of the aortic arch** (sometimes called the *aortic bodies*); their nerve impulses travel to the CNS in afferent fibers of the *vagus nerve.* The paraganglia are supplied with blood by small side arteries.

The chemoreceptors in all these paraganglia are *activated* – that is, increase their discharge rate – when the O_2 partial pressure decreases, the CO_2 partial pressure increases or the pH rises. This relation can be demonstrated by recording the afferent action potentials in animals as the blood parameters are altered (Fig. 21-32C). Such experiments are conveniently done by perfusing the arteries that supply the paraganglia with blood in which P_{O_2}, P_{CO_2} and pH have been set to the desired levels. Another approach is to denervate the chemoreceptors or block their activity by cooling, so as to establish their share in the overall chemical control of breathing.

These experiments have shown that the *O_2 effects are mediated entirely by the peripheral chemoreceptors.* The chemoreceptor activity associated with normal arterial O_2 partial pressures is enhanced when P_{O_2} falls and suppressed when P_{O_2} rises. The level of chemoreceptor activity is also affected by arterial P_{CO_2} and pH, but the influence of these signals on the central control of respiration is relatively limited.

Central chemosensitivity. CO_2 and pH affect breathing chiefly by way of their action on *chemosensitive structures in the brainstem.* The effects on ventilation produced by changes in arterial P_{CO_2} and those in arterial pH differ in degree (Fig. 21-31). This graded effectiveness does not imply that there are two different kinds of specific receptor mechanisms in the brainstem, one for CO_2 and another for H^+. It could well be that the sensors are sensitive only to H^+ ions, the effect of CO_2 being exerted by way of H^+-ion formation. The difference in degree of the influence of arterial P_{CO_2} and pH would then be interpretable as a consequence of *different resistances to the transport of CO_2 and H^+.* In fact, CO_2 diffuses very rapidly from the blood into the brain tissue, whereas biological membranes are a considerable impediment to the diffusion of H^+ ions. Many experiments support the theory that the central chemosensitivity in the respiratory control system is dependent upon H^+ exclusively [38, 42].

At present it is thought that the **H^+ concentration of the extracellular fluid** in the brainstem is the decisive factor in the central respiratory drive. This fluid probably has a composition similar to that of *cerebrospinal fluid.* Respiration could thus be affected by way of the CSF as well. When the ventricles of the brain were perfused with artificial CSF of varying composition, it could indeed be shown that breathing changes in correlation with the pH of the fluid. In addition, H^+ sensitive fields on the surface of the brainstem could be located more precisely [38, 42]. As Fig. 21-33 shows, there are *three such fields on the ventral surface of the medulla* (near the roots of the vagus and hypoglossal nerves); application of acids to these fields can elicit increased ventilation.

Control system for the chemical regulation of breathing. The entire control circuit by which the arterial blood gases and pH are kept con-

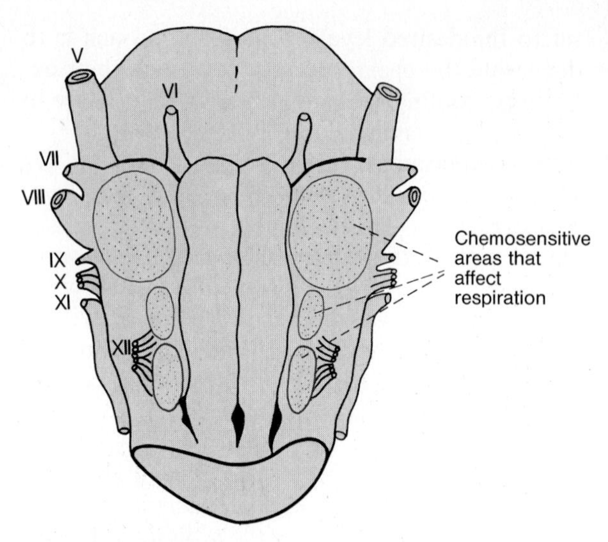

Fig. 21-33. Ventral aspect of the medulla oblongata (cat), showing the chemosensitive areas in the respiratory control system. From [38, 42]

stant is diagrammed in Fig. 21-34. The **controlled variables** P_{O_2}, P_{CO_2} and **pH** are monitored by peripheral chemoreceptors and central chemosensory structures. Whenever the sensors detect a departure of any of these variables from the set point (the endogenously prescribed value), they cause the activity of the respiratory neurons in the medulla oblongata to change. The resulting modification of the contractions of the respiratory muscles alters ventilation in such a way as to correct the error.

The three controlled variables affect the respiratory minute volume in different ways. Normally the **leading variable** is the **arterial CO_2 partial pressure.** But if the central chemosensitivity is lost, due to pulmonary malfunctions that cause *chronic hypercapnia* or to *barbiturate poisoning,* the main factor that drives spontaneous breathing is **arterial hypoxia,** which stimulates the central controllers by way of the peripheral chemoreceptors. If a person in this situation breathes pure oxygen, the most effective respiratory drive is eliminated, and a lethal *apnea* may develop. Such patients should be given pure oxygen only during artificial respiration, or with a respirator immediately available in case of need. When the acid-base status is disturbed (pp. 593f.), the primary action of the control system is to correct the **arterial pH.** For example, the response to metabolic acidosis (lowered pH) is hyperventilation, which increases the output of CO_2 and thereby returns the pH to the normal range.

Other Respiratory Drives

Respiratory drive during exercise. Working muscle requires more oxygen than resting muscle, and this increased demand must be met by increasing the transport of oxygen via respiration and circulation. During strenuous exercise, O_2 uptake can be raised from about 300 ml/min at rest to as much as 3–4 l/min – an effect achievable only by considerably increased ventilation. By what mechanisms can respiration be so well adjusted to the increased oxygen requirement? During light work the arterial P_{CO_2} rises, and during heavy work the pH of the arterial blood falls. But these changes are too slight to explain, by themselves, the increase in ventilation.

There are many indications that **central coinnervation** of the respiratory centers operates during exercise, especially in the *initial phase.* The data imply that impulses from the motor centers

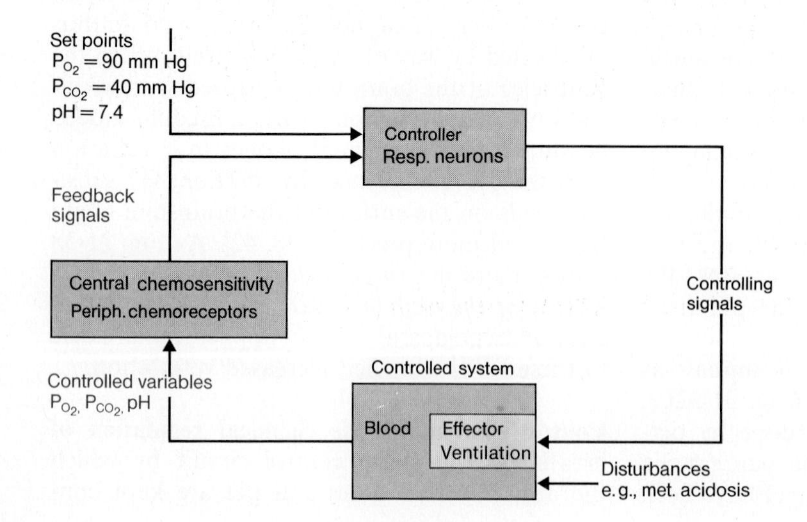

Fig. 21-34. Control circuit for the chemical regulation of breathing

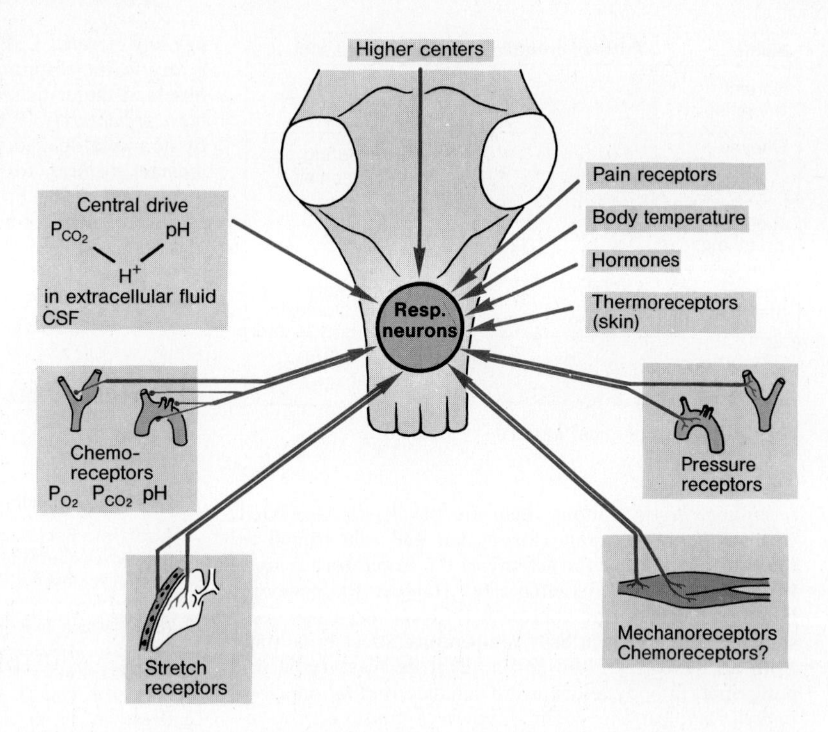

Fig. 21-35. Survey of the central respiratory drives and the peripheral receptors that can modulate breathing

are conducted not only to the working musculature but to the medulla oblongata as well, activating the respiratory neurons there. In the subsequent *steady state,* in which breathing and circulation are adjusted to the intensity of work, there are probably several factors that determine the magnitude of ventilation. In addition to the central coinnervation and the chemical respiratory drives, **neural feedback** from the mechanoreceptors and hypothetical chemoreceptors in the working musculature can affect breathing. In the *recovery phase,* finally, **parameters of blood chemistry** are the main factors determining the rate at which ventilation returns to the resting level [23].

Unspecific respiratory drives. There are factors that can alter ventilation but are not primarily involved in the control of respiration; these are usually called *unspecific*

Table 21-4. Summary of data characterizing the respiratory function of a healthy young man (body surface 1.7 m^2) at rest. Variations from these norms and modulating factors are noted in the text

Lung volumes and capacities		**Respiratory mechanics**	
Total capacity	6 l	Pleural surface pressures:	
Vital capacity	4.5 l	end of expiration	−5 cm H_2O (−0.5 kPa)
Funct. residual capacity	2.4 l	end of inspiration	−8 cm H_2O (−0.8 kPa)
Residual volume	1.2 l	Compliance of lung	0.2 l/cm H_2O (2 l/kPa)
Tidal volume	0.5 l	Compliance of thorax	0.2 l/cm H_2O (2 l/kPa)
Dead-space volume	0.15 l	Compliance of lung plus thorax	0.1 l/cm H_2O (1 l/kPa)
Ventilation		Resistance	2 cm $H_2O \cdot s \cdot l^{-1}$ (0.2 kPa $\cdot s \cdot l^{-1}$)
Respiratory frequency	14 min^{-1}		
Minute volume	7 l/min		
Alveolar ventilation	5 l/min		
Dead-space ventilation	2 l/min	**Functional tests**	
Gas exchange		Rel. forced expiratory volume	75%
		Maximal expiratory flow	10 l/s
O_2 uptake	280 ml/min	Maximum breathing capacity	150 l/min
CO_2 output	230 ml/min		
Gas exchange ratio	0.82		
O_2 diffusing capacity	30 ml·min^{-1}· mm Hg^{-1} (230 ml·min^{-1}· kPa^{-1})	**Perfusion ratios**	
		Alveolar ventilation/perfusion	0.9
Contact time	0.3 s	Shunt perfusion/total perfusion	0.02

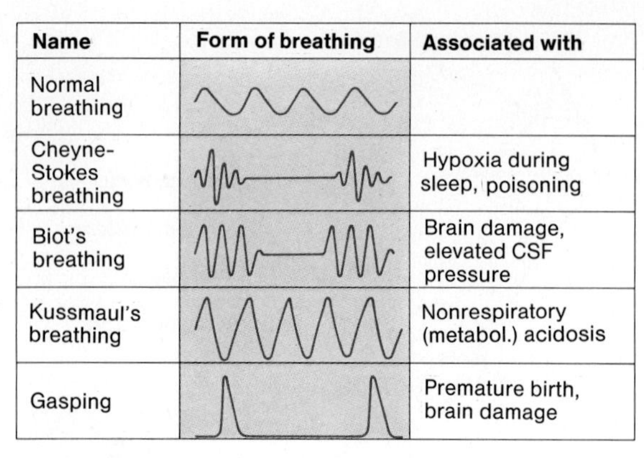

Name	Form of breathing	Associated with
Normal breathing		
Cheyne-Stokes breathing		Hypoxia during sleep, poisoning
Biot's breathing		Brain damage, elevated CSF pressure
Kussmaul's breathing		Nonrespiratory (metabol.) acidosis
Gasping		Premature birth, brain damage

Fig. 21-36. Pathological patterns of breathing

respiratory drives. Among them are the drives associated with temperature change. Strong **hot and cold stimuli** to the skin can increase the activity of the respiratory centers (e.g., it is possible to stimulate breathing in the newborn by alternating hot and cold baths). Moreover, it has been shown that changes in **body temperature** affect breathing. Both an increase *(fever)* and a slight decrease **(mild hypothermia)** in body temperature enhance ventilation. *Deep hypothermia* (extreme cooling), however, causes central inhibition of breathing. Another unspecific respiratory drive is **pain** (painful stimuli activate breathing in the newborn). The afferent signals from **baroreceptors** in the circulatory system (pp. 512f.) also affect the respiratory centers; a rise in pressure in the arterial system thus inhibits inspiratory and expiratory neurons, so that both the depth and the rate of breathing are reduced. Finally, respiration can be modulated by various **hormones**. For example, increased ventilation is observed when *adrenalin* enters the blood (during exercise or mental excitement) and when the *progesterone* level is elevated (in pregnancy).

The various specific and unspecific respiratory drives are summarized diagrammatically in Fig. 21-35.

Pathological forms of breathing. Even healthy people exhibit a type of *periodic breathing* called **Cheyne-Stokes breathing** while sleeping in the high mountains (Fig. 21-36). After a few deep breaths there is a pause *(apnea)*, followed by renewed *deep breathing*, and so on. This pattern is caused by the decreased partial pressure of oxygen in the inspired air at high altitudes in combination with an attenuation of central respiratory activity during sleep. During inspiratory O_2 deficiency the shape of the CO_2-response curve is different from that shown in Fig. 21-31A; at very low CO_2 partial pressures the curve is quite flat, but it suddenly rises sharply at somewhat higher partial pressures of CO_2. The deep breaths of Cheyne-Stokes breathing expel so much CO_2 that P_{CO_2} falls into the range where the CO_2-response curve is flat and the CO_2 drive is practically eliminated. The result is apnea. While breathing is stopped, CO_2 accumulates in the blood until P_{CO_2} is once again in the range where the CO_2 response curve rises steeply , and hyperventilation begins again. Under pathological conditions Cheyne-Stokes breathing can result from *poisoning* – for example, when toxic substances ordinarily excreted are retained due to kidney failure *(uremia)*.

Biot's breathing (Fig. 21-36) is a similar form of periodic breathing, brought about by conditions such as *brain damage and elevated CSF pressure*. It is probably the result of injury to the respiratory centers. **Gasping** (p. 569) can be observed under these conditions also, as well as in *infants born prematurely*. When the pH of the blood is lowered by non-volatile acids *(metabolic acidosis)* – a symptom of *diabetes mellitus*, for example – a special form of hyperventilation characterized by very deep breaths results. This so-called **Kussmaul breathing** (air hunger) can compensate, at least in part, for the metabolic acidosis (pp. 593f.).

21.7 References

Textbooks and Handbooks

1. Agostini, E., Hyatt, R.E.: Static behavior of the respiratory system. In:Macklem, P.T., Mead, J. (Eds.): Handbook of Physiology, Sect. 3: The Respiratory System, Vol III. Bethesda, Amer. Physiol. Soc 1986
2. Anthonisen, N.R.: Tests of mechanical function. In: Macklem, P.T., Mead, J. (Eds.): Handbook of Physiology, Sect. 3: The Respiratory System, Vol. III. Bethesda, Amer. Physiol. Soc. 1986
3. Bartels, H., Bücherl, E., Hertz, C.W., Rodewald, G., Schwab, M.: Lungenfunktionsprüfungen. Berlin-Göttingen-Heidelberg: Springer 1959
4. Bartels, H., Riegel, K., Wenner, J., Wulf, H.: Perinatale Atmung. Berlin-Heidelberg-New York: Springer 1972
5. Benninghoff, A., Goerttler, K.: Lehrbuch der Anatomie des Menschen. München-Berlin-Wien: Urban u. Schwarzenberg 1968
6. Campbell, E.J.M.: The respiraotry muscles and the mechanics of breathing. Chicago: Year Book Publishers 1959
7. Cerretelli, P., Prampero, P.E.di: Gas exchange in exercise. In: Fahri, L.E., Tenney, S.M. (Eds.): Handbook of Physiology, Sect. 3: The Respiratory System, Vol. IV: Bethesda, Amer. Physiol. Soc. 1987
8. Comroe, J.H., Forster, R.E., Dubois, A.B:, Briscoe, W.A., Carlsen, E.: The lung: Clinical physiology and pulmonary function tests. Chicago: Year Book Medical Publishers 1962
9. Cotes, J.E.: Lung function: Assessment and application to medicine. Oxford: Blackwell 1965
10. Crofton, J., Douglas, A.: Respiratory disease. Philadelphia: Lippincott Comp. 1975
11. Euler, C. von: Brain stem mechanisms for generation and control of breathing pattern. In: Cherniack, N.S., Widdicombe, J.G. (Eds.): Handbook of Physiology, Sect. 3: The Respiratory System, Vol. II. Bethesda, Amer. Physiol. Soc. 1986
12. Fahri, L.E.: Ventilation-perfusion relationships. In: Fahri, L.E., Tenney, S.M. (Eds.): Handbook of Physiology, Sect. 3: The Respiratory System, Vol. IV. Bethesda, Amer. Physiol. Soc. 1987
13. Fidone, S.J., Gonzales, C.: Initiation and control of chemoreceptor activity in the carotid body. In: Cherniack, N.S., Widdicombe, J.G. (Eds.): Handbook of Physiology, Sect. 3: The Respiratory System, Vol. II. Bethesda, Amer. Physiol. Soc. 1986
14. Fitzgerald, R.S., Lahiri, S.: Reflex responses to chemoreceptor stimulation. In: Cherniack, N.S., Widdicombe, J.G. (Eds.): Handbook of Physiology, Sect. 3: The Respiratory System, Vol. II. Bethesda, Amer. Physiol. Soc. 1986
15. Forster, R.E.: Diffusion of gases across the alveolar membrane. In: Fahri, L.E., Tenney, S.M. (Eds.): Handbook of Physiology, Sect. 3: The Respiratory System, Vol. IV. Bethesda, Amer. Physiol. Soc. 1987
16. Friend, J.A.R., Flook, V.: Clinical respiratory physiology. New York: Mac Millan Publ. Co. Inc. 1979
17. Goerke, J., Clements, J.A.: Alveolar surface tension and lung surfactant. In: Macklem, P.T., Mead, J. (Eds.): Handbook of

Physiology, Sect. 3: The Respiratory System, Vol. III. Bethesda, Amer. Physiol. Soc. 1986
18. Hlastala, M.P.: Diffusing-capacity heterogeneity. In: Fahri, L.E., Tenney, S.M. (Eds.): Handbook of Physiology, Sect. 3: The Respiratory System, Vol. IV. Bethesda, Amer. Physiol. Soc. 1987
19. Horsfield, K.: Morphometry of airways. In: Macklem, P.T., Mead, J. (Eds.): Handbook of Physiology, Sect. 3: The Respiratory System, Vol. III. Bethesda, Amer. Physiol. Soc. 1986
20. Hugelin, A.: Forebrain and midbrain influence on respiration. In: Cherniack, N.S., Widdicombe, J.G. (Eds.): Handbook of Physiology, Sect. 3: The Respiratory System, Vol. II. Bethesda, Amer. Physiol. Soc. 1986
21. Ingram, R.H., Pedley, T.J.: Pressure-flow relationships in the lungs. In: Macklem, P.T., Mead, J. (Eds.): Handbook of Physiology, Sect. 3: The Respiratory System, Vol. III. Bethesda, Amer. Physiol. Soc. 1986
22. Kellogg, R.H.: Laws of physics pertaining to gas exchange. In: Fahri, L.E., Tenney, S.M. (Eds.): Handbook of Physiology, Sect. 3.: The Respiratory System, Vol. IV. Bethesda, Amer. Physiol. Soc. 1987
23. Koepchen, H.P.: Atmungsregulation. In: Gauer, O.H., Kramer, K., Jung, R. (Eds.): Physiologie des Menschen, Bd. 6: Atmung. München-Berlin-Wien: Urban u. Schwarzenberg 1975
24. Piiper, J.: Physiologie der Atmung. In: Gauer, O.H., Kramer, K., Jung, R. (Eds.): Physiologie des Menschen, Bd. 6: Atmung. München-Berlin-Wien: Urban u. Schwarzenberg 1975
25. Pride, N.B., Macklem, P.T.: Lung mechanics in disease. In: Macklem, P.T., Mead, J. (Eds.): Handbook of Physiology, Sect. 3: The Respiratory System, Vol. III. Bethesda, Amer. Physiol. Soc. 1986
26. Proctor, D.F.: Form and function of the upper airways and larynx. In: Macklem, P.T., Mead, J. (Eds.): Handbook of Physiology, Sect. 3: The Respiratory System, Vol. III. Bethesda, Amer. Physiol. Soc. 1986
27. Roussos, C., Campbell, E.J.M.: Respiratory muscle energetics. In: Macklem, P.T., Mead, J. (Eds.): Handbook of Physiology, Sect. 3: The Respiratory System, Vol. III. Bethesda, Amer. Physiol. Soc. 1986
28. Troyer, A. de, Loring, S.H.: Action of the respiratory muscles. In: Macklem, P.T., Mead, J. (Eds.): Handbook of Physiology, Sect. 3: The Respiratory System, Vol. III. Bethesda, Amer. Physiol. Soc. 1986
29. Weibel, E.R.: Morphometry of the human lung. Berlin-Göttingen-Heidelberg: Springer 1963
30. Weibel, E.R.: The pathway for oxygen. Cambridge-Massachusetts-London: Harvard University Press 1984
31. West, J.B.: Regional differences in the lung. Academic Press 1977
32. West, J.B.: Respiratory physiology – the essentials. Baltimore: Williams and Wilkens 1979

Original Papers and Reviews

33. Baldwin, E.F. de, Cournand, A., Richards, D.W.: Pulmonary insufficiency. I. Physiological classification, clinical methods of analysis, standard values in normal subjects. Medicine (Baltimore) *27,* 243 (1948)
34. Boutellier, U., Fahri, L.E.: A fundamental problem in determining functional residual capacity or residual volume. J. Appl. Physiol. *60,* 1810 (1986)
35. Hornbein, T.F.: The relation between stimulus of chemoreceptors and their response. In: Torrance, R.W. (Ed.): Arterial Chemoreceptors. Oxford: Oxford University Press 1968
36. Karlberg, P., Adams, F.H., Geubelle, F., Wallgren, G.: Respiratory studies in newborn infants. II. Pulmonary ventilation and mechanics of breathing in the first minutes of life, including the onset of respiration. Acta paediat. scand. *51,* 121 (1962)
37. Knowles, J.H., Hong, S.K., Rahn, H.: Possible errors using esophageal ballon in determination of pressure-volume characteristics of the lung and thoracic cage. J. Appl. Physiol. *14,* 525 (1959)
38. Loeschke, H.H.: Respiratory chemosensitivity in the medulla oblongata. Acta neurobiol. exp. *33,* 97 (1973)
39. Loew, P.G., Thews, G.: Die Altersabhängigkeit des arteriellen Sauerstoffdruckes bei der berufstätigen Bevölkerung. Klin. Wschr. *40.* 1093 (1962)
40. Nolte, H.: Die Wiederbelebung der Atmung. Anaesthesiologie und Wiederbelebung. Bd. 28. Berlin-Heidelberg-New York: Springer 1968
41. Richter, d.: How is the respiratory rhythm generated? A model. NIPS *1,* 109 (1986)
42. Schlaefke, M.E.: Central chemosensitivity: a respiratory drive. Rev. Physiol. Biochem. Pharmacol. *90,* 171 (1981)
43. Scholander, P.F.: Analyzer for accurate estimation of respiratory gases in one half cubic centimeter samples. J. Biol. Chem. *167,* 235 (1947)
44. Thews, G.: Ein Mikroanalyse-Verfahren zur Bestimmung der Sauerstoffdrucke in kleinen Blutproben. Pflügers Arch. ges. Physiol. *276,* 89 (1962)
45. Thews, G.: Gaseous diffusion in the lungs and tissues. In: Reeve, E.B., Guyton, A.C. (Eds.): Physical bases of circulatory transport: Regulation and exchange. Philadelphia-London: Saunders 1967
46. Thews, G.: Der Einfluß von Ventilation, Perfusion, Diffusion und Distribution auf den pulmonalen Gasaustausch. Akadem. Wiss. Lit. Mainz; Wiesbaden: Steiner 1979
47. Weibel, E.R.: Morphological basis of alveolar-capillary gas exchange. Physiol. Rev. *53,* 419 (1973)

22 Blood Gas Transport and Acid-Base Balance

G. THEWS

22.1 The Structure and Properties of Hemoglobin

Structure of the Hemoglobin Molecule

One of the most important tasks of the blood is to transport the oxygen absorbed in the lungs to the organs and tissues, and to remove the carbon dioxide formed there and carry it to the lungs. This operation depends fundamentally on the erythrocytes. They contain the red blood pigment *hemoglobin,* which is capable of combining with oxygen in the lung capillaries and releasing it again in the tissue capillaries. In addition, hemoglobin can bind some of the carbon dioxide produced in tissue metabolism and set it free in the lungs. For these reasons hemoglobin occupies a central position in the chain of events by which respiratory gases are transported.
Hemoglobin is a chromoprotein. The molecule consists of four *polypeptide chains,* each containing a pigment component called *heme.* The **molecular weight** is about 64,500, so that each of the four subunits has a molecular weight of 16,100 [2, 17, 18].

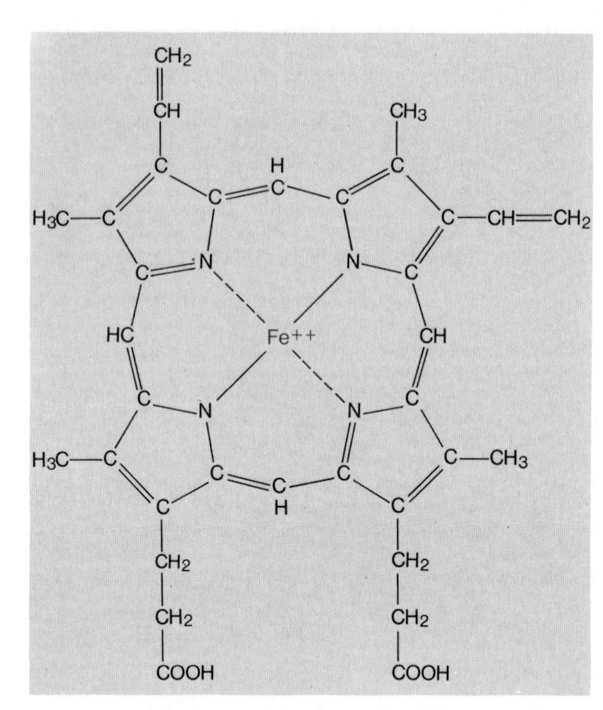

Fig. 22-1. Chemical structure of heme

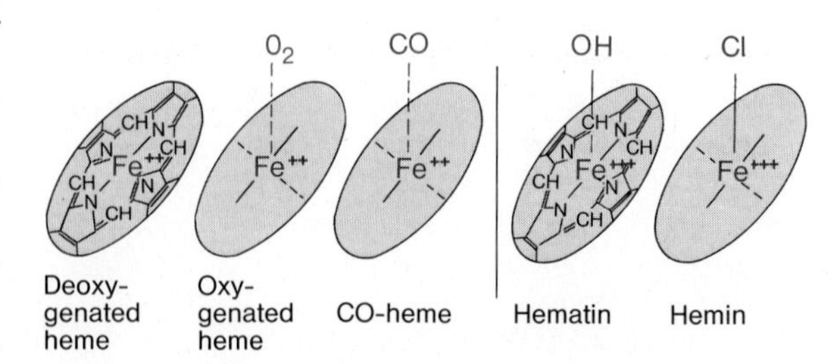

Fig. 22-2. Characteristic compounds formed by heme (with bivalent iron) and oxidized heme (with trivalent iron). The protoporphyrin rings lie in one plane (cf. red disks in Fig. 22-3)

Pigment components. The four identical heme groups in a hemoglobin molecule can be described as *protoporphyrins with central bivalent iron ions.* Each protoporphyrin structure consists of *four pyrrole rings* linked by *methene bridges* and bearing characteristic side chains (Fig. 22-1). The crucial functional component is the iron ion in the center; the incorporation of this ion by two ionic and two dative bonds converts the protoporphyrin to **heme.** The entire heme structure lies in a plane. When oxygen is transported by hemoglobin the O_2 molecule is reversibly bound to the heme without change in valence of the iron ion; the **hemoglobin** (Hb) thus becomes **oxyhemoglobin** (HbO_2). To indicate that this binding occurs without change of valence, the reaction is called *oxygenation* (instead of oxidation), and the reverse process is *deoxygenation.* Hemoglobin is called *deoxyhemoglobin* when one wishes to emphasize its oxygen-free state.
Apart from the oxygenation of the heme group, genuine oxidation can occur; the result is conversion of the bivalent iron to the trivalent state (Fig. 22-2). The oxidized pigment compo-

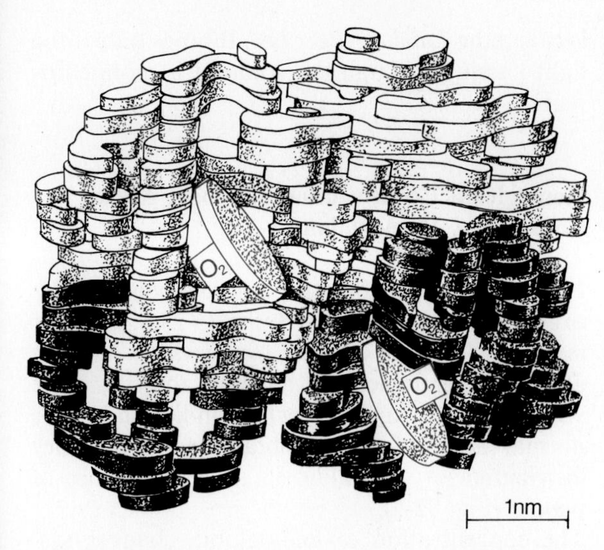

Fig. 22-3. Model of the hemoglobin molecule. From PERUTZ [26, 27]

nent is called **hematin** (metheme), and the whole molecule is **methemoglobin.** Human blood normally contains only a very small percentage of methemoglobin, but the amount can be increased by certain toxins and in some diseases. Such a condition is dangerous because oxidized hemoglobin is not available for transporting O_2 to the tissues.

Protein component. The great majority of the ca. 10,000 atoms in a hemoglobin molecule make up its protein component. This is composed of *four* individual *polypeptide chains,* each of which comprises more than 140 amino acid residues. The sequence of these amino acids has been determined by chemical analysis. The spatial arrangement of the chains within the molecule has also been elucidated to a large extent by three-dimensional X-ray diffraction analysis [26, 27]. Fig. 22-3 shows the model of a hemoglobin molecule derived from these studies. Two symmetrically arranged "white" chains interlock with two similarly symmetrical "black" chains in such a way that the whole molecule is roughly spherical. The heme groups, shown as red disks, occupy niches near the surface. In adult hemoglobin **(HbA)** the white subunits (each with 141 amino acids) are called *α chains* and the black subunits (each with 146 amino acids), *β chains.* The hemoglobin of the human fetus **(HbF)** differs from the adult form: the *β* chains are replaced by two polypeptides with a different amino-acid arrangement, the so-called *γ* chains. Soon after birth the HbF is replaced by HbA [2].

Light Absorption by Hemoglobin

Light absorption and color. The color of a dissolved substance that does not itself emit light depends on its ability to specifically absorb a fraction of the incident light. As a rule absorption occurs only in a certain range of wavelengths characteristic of the substance; light at other wavelengths is transmitted with almost no attenuation. The proportions of the different wavelengths composing the transmitted light determine the color of the dissolved substance.
The red color of a hemoglobin solution – and thus the red color of blood – results from the relatively strong absorption of short-wavelength light by this substance. A considerable amount of the light in the blue part of the spectrum is absorbed, whereas most of the red (long-wavelength) light is transmitted.
Examining the light transmitted by a solution of *oxygenated* hemoglobin with a spectroscope, one detects not only an attenuation in the blue region *(Soret's band)* but also two characteristic dark bands *(absorption bands)* in the yellow and yellow-green regions. Maximum absorption within these bands occurs at the wavelengths $\lambda = 577$ nm and $\lambda = 541$ nm (1nm $= 10^{-9}$ m) [11].
Deoxyhemoglobin absorbs light somewhat more strongly than oxyhemoglobin at long wavelengths and somewhat less strongly at short wavelengths. Therefore venous blood appears darker, with a bluish-red color. In addition, the spectroscope reveals a single, wider absorption band in the yellow-green region, with a maximum at $\lambda = 555$ nm.

Spectrophotometry. For quantitative analysis of the absorbing properties of colored solutions, a spectrophotometer is used. From a prism spectrum or a grating spectrum light of a very narrow range of wavelengths is selected, and this so-called *monochromatic* light is passed through the solution to be analyzed. In passing it is attenuated to a degree depending on the solution and the wavelength. A photocell is used to find the ratio between the intensity of the entering light (I_o) and that of the emerging light (I). The ratio I/I_o is called the **transmittance,** and the ratio $(I_o - I)/I_o$ is the **absorption.** By repeating the measurement with the different wavelengths in succession, one obtains the complete *absorption spectrum* of the solution.

Absorption spectra. Fig. 22-4 shows the absorption spectra of oxyhemoglobin and deoxyhemoglobin. Wavelength ranges in which the spectroscope reveals dark absorption bands appear as hills in the absorption spectrum. Two absorption maxima can be discerned in the spectrum of oxyhemoglobin, while that of deoxyhemoglobin has a single maximum in an intermediate po-

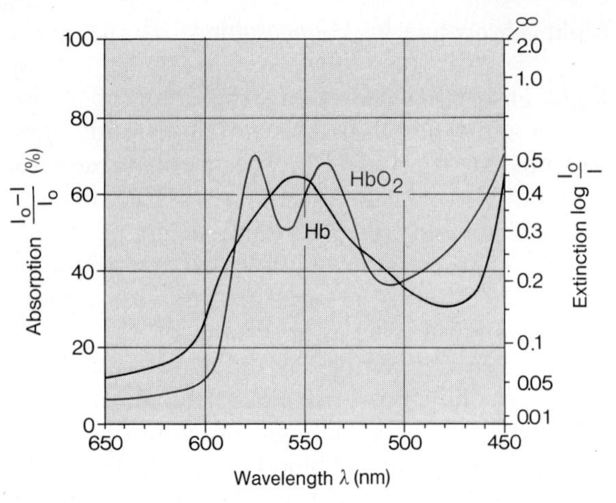

Fig. 22-4. Absorption spectra of oxyhemoglobin (HbO_2) and deoxyhemoglobin (Hb). Left ordinate: absorption; right ordinate: extinction

sition. The wavelengths associated with these maxima are those given above for the absorption bands, as can be verified in the diagram.

The points of intersection of the two absorption curves, the so-called *isosbestic points,* correspond to the wavelengths at which solutions of the two substances at equal concentrations absorb equal amounts of light. At these wavelengths, the absorption of hemoglobin is independent of its degree of oxygenation. If one wants to determine the *concentration* of hemoglobin without previously altering it chemically (see p. 581), one must use monochromatic light at the wavelength of an isosbestic point. On the other hand, if one wants to determine the O_2 saturation of hemoglobin by photometry one selects a range of wavelengths in which the difference between the absorption of oxyhemoglobin and that of deoxyhemoglobin is particularly great. According to Fig. 22-4, suitable wavelengths for this purpose would include, e.g., 600, 577 and 470 nm.

Lambert-Beer-law. Another commonly used measure of absorption is **extinction** (cf. right ordinate in Fig. 22-4), which is defined as

$$E = \log \frac{I_0}{I} \quad (1)$$

Here again I_o is the intensity of the light entering the colored solution and I is that of the emerging light. The advantage of this measure is that extinction E is directly proportional to the concentration c of a dissolved pigment

$$E = \log \frac{I_0}{I} = \varepsilon \cdot c \cdot d \quad (2)$$

where d is the thickness of the layer of solution, and ε is a substance-specific constant, called the *extinction coefficient*. This linear dependence of extinction on concentration and layer thickness is called the *Lambert-Beer law*. It holds only if the light passing through the solution is monochromatic.

Hemoglobin Concentration in Blood; Mean Corpuscular Hemoglobin

Normal values. *The average hemoglobin concentration in human blood is 158 g/l (15.8 g/dl) for men and 140 g/l (14 g/dl) for women.* As with almost all biological parameters, there is some variation even among healthy individuals. The normal range is found by obtaining the **frequency distribution** of the values in a large number of people (Fig. 22-5).
The concentration of hemoglobin changes systematically with age. The blood of the *newborn* contains an average of 200 g/l, though the interindividual variation can be considerable (Fig. 22-5). During the *first year of life* hemoglobin concentration falls to ca. 115 g/l; thereafter it rises slowly to the adult level.

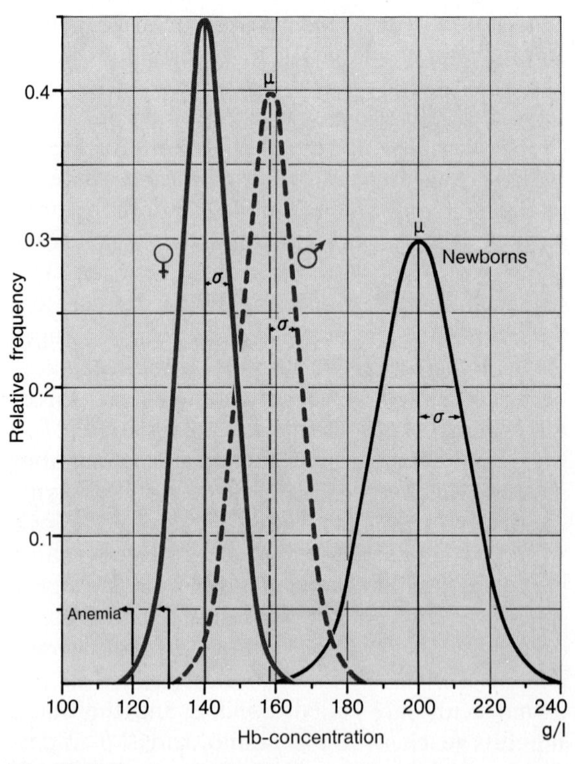

Fig. 22-5. Frequency distributions of hemoglobin concentrations in different populations: male adults (♂), female adults (♀) and newborns. Ordinate: relative frequency; abscissa: hemoglobin concentration; μ, means; σ, standard deviations (σ is the distance from the mean of a Gaussian distribution to its inflection point; it is a measure of the breadth of the distribution)

The hemoglobin concentration is relatively high not only in the *fetus* but also in the blood of people who have spent considerable time at *high altitudes* (p. 669). In both cases this increase ensures that the organs are adequately supplied with oxygen despite low O_2 partial pressures.
When the hemoglobin concentration of the blood is below normal, this condition is called **anemia.** As a rule anemia is considered to exist when the hemoglobin concentration is less than 130 g/l in a man, or less than 120 g/l in a woman.

Measurement of hemoglobin concentration. A number of different techniques can be used, as follows: 1. *Analysis of the amount of bound* O_2 (1 g Hb binds up to 1.36 ml O_2); 2. *determination of the iron content* of the blood (Hb contains 0.34% iron), 3. *colorimetry* (comparison of blood color with a standard), or 4. *extinction measurement (spectrophotometry).* The first two methods require fairly elaborate apparatus, and colorimetry is not very accurate, so that spectrophotometry is the method of choice for the routine determination of hemoglobin concentration.
Spectrophotometric analysis. The principle of this procedure is to determine Hb concentration by measuring the extinction of a blood sample with monochromatic light. But because dilute Hb is unstable, and because its extinction varies with oxygenation, it must first be *converted into a stable pigment.*

The blood is drawn into a capillary pipette and diluted with a solution containing potassium ferricyanide $K_3[Fe(CN)_6]$, potassium cyanide KCN, and sodium bicarbonate $NaHCO_3$. These chemicals cause hemolysis and convert the hemoglobin into **cyanmethemoglobin** HbCN (with trivalent iron), which is stable for weeks. In a photometer the solution is exposed to monochromatic light at the wavelength 546 nm and the *extinction E* is measured. According to the *Lambert-Beer law* (Eq. 2), the concentration c can be found directly from E if the extinction coefficient ε and the layer thickness are known. However, it is more convenient to calibrate the extinction scale with a standard solution. The cyanmethemoglobin method is considered to be the most accurate method for routine Hb-concentration measurement [23].

Mean corpuscular hemoglobin. An important diagnostic criterion for evaluating erythropoiesis and differentiating forms of anemia is the **amount of hemoglobin in the individual erythrocyte.** *The average absolute hemoglobin content of single erythrocytes is called the mean corpuscular hemoglobin (MCH).* It is found by dividing the amount of hemoglobin by the number of erythrocytes, both in the same volume of blood.

Taking the norms for healthy men as an example, for a liter of blood one would have 158 g Hb and 5.1 million $\times 10^6$ erythrocytes ($1 l = 10^6$ µl). The MCH would then be

$$\text{MCH} = \frac{158\,\text{g}}{5.1 \cdot 10^{12}} = 31 \cdot (10^{-12}\text{g}) = 31\,\text{pg}$$

When the norms for women are substituted the result is the same:

$$\text{MCH} = \frac{140\text{g}}{4.6 \cdot 10^{12}} = 31 \cdot (10^{-12}\text{g}) = 31\,\text{pg}^*$$

Eythrocytes containing the normal amount of hemoglobin (26–36 pg) are called **normochromic.** When the MCH is abnormally low they are **hypochromic,** and they are **hyperchromic** when it is high. The same terms are used to denote the different forms of anemia. For example, synthesis of hemoglobin can be reduced owing to *iron deficiency,* so that each erythrocyte contains less hemoglobin and a condition of *hypochromic anemia* exists. In other forms of anemia the production of erythrocytes by the bone marrow is inadequate. In these conditions – as, for example, in *pernicious anemia* – the misshapen erythrocytes contain a great deal of Hb; this is a case of *hyperchromic anemia.* Following massive *blood loss* the MCH is at first unchanged (normochromic anemia), but in the days that follow there is an overproduction of erythrocytes, so that the hemoglobin content of each is low (hypochromic anemia).

Relationships between the erythrocyte parameters. For the diagnostic evaluation of erythrocyte function it is usually necessary to measure three quantities: the *red cell count* RCC (μl^{-1}), the *hemoglobin concentration of the blood* [Hb] (g/l), and the *hematocrit* HCT. From these, three other characteristic parameters can be derived: the *mean corpuscular hemoglobin* MCH, the *mean corpuscular hemoglobin concentration* MCHC, and the *mean corpuscular volume* MCV. The relationships underlying these calculations are reflected directly in the definitions of the parameters and are summarized in the following diagram:

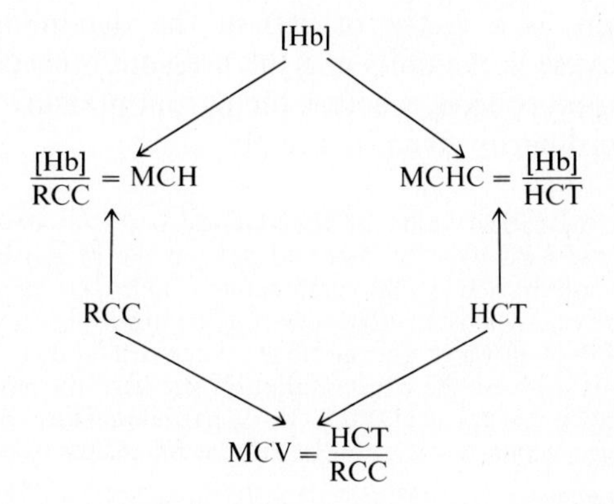

Given, for example, that RCC = $5 \cdot 10^6$µl, [Hb] = 150 g/l and HCT = 0.45, the other parameters are as follows: MCH = 30 pg, MCHC = 333 g/l, and MCV = $0.09 \cdot 10^{-6}$µl = 90 fl (femtoliters) = 90 µm³ (the conversion among units is given on pp. 796f.).

* Values for Central Europe; for North America (according to Wintrobe) MCH = 29 pg

22.2 The O_2-Transport Function of the Blood

Physical Solubility of Gases

Partial pressures of gases in liquids. Gases can be taken up by almost all liquids – that is, *physically dissolved* – in certain amounts. The amount of gas dissolved depends on its partial pressure. If the liquid is equilibrated with a gas, by bringing the two media into contact over the greatest possible area until thermodynamic equilibrium has been reached, the gas can be said to have the same partial pressure in the liquid as in the gas phase. When we refer to the "partial pressure" of a dissolved gas we are using the term in this sense.

Concentration of dissolved gases. The partial pressure of a gas, P_{gas}, is one of the factors upon which the concentration of the gas dissolved in a liquid depends. A second factor determining the amount of the gas dissolved is its particular solubility properties, which are characterized by the *Bunsen coefficient* (solubility coefficient) α. This coefficient gives the ml of a gas physically dissolved in a ml of liquid at a partial pressure of 1 atm (1 atm = 760 mm Hg = 101 kPa). These two factors are combined in the **Henry-Dalton law,** according to which the concentration of the dissolved gas is

$$[\text{gas}] = \frac{\alpha}{760} P_{gas} \tag{3}$$

There is a factor of 760 in the denominator because in the units of α the pressure is specified in atmospheres, whereas the partial pressure P_{gas} is ordinarily given in mm Hg.

The numerical value of the *Bunsen coefficient* depends on the nature of the dissolved gas, on the properties of the solvent and on the temperature. Table 22-1 presents some characteristic values of α for the atmospheric gases dissolved in water and in blood. When α is known for a particular case the concentration of the gases in physical solution can be calculated for given partial pressures by the *Henry-Dalton law* (Eq. 3). In arterial blood, for example, with P_{O_2} = 95 mm Hg and P_{CO_2} = 40 mm Hg, one finds an O_2 concentration of 0.003 ml O_2/ml blood and a CO_2 concentration of 0.026 ml CO_2/ml blood. Thus the 20-fold greater Bunsen coefficient of CO_2 more than compensates for its lower partial pressure, so that 9 times as much CO_2 as O_2 is present in physical solution.

Table 22-1. The Bunsen solubility coefficient α (ml gas · ml solvent^{-1} · atm^{-1}) for O_2, CO_2 and N_2 in water and in blood

	α_{O_2}	α_{CO_2}	α_{N_2}
Water 20 °C	0.031	0.88	0.016
Water 37 °C	0.024	0.57	0.012
Blood 37 °C	0.024	0.49	0.012

Although the volumes of O_2 and CO_2 physically dissolved in the blood are relatively small, the state of physical solution is extremely significant in biology. Before the gases can combine with any other substance, they must migrate to their partners in the reaction in dissolved form. That is, *each molecule of O_2 or CO_2 that diffuses into or out of the tissues at some time passes through the dissolved state.*

The Binding of Oxygen to Hemoglobin

Oxygen capacity of the blood. Most of the oxygen transported in the blood is *chemically bound to hemoglobin.* If we wish to know the **maximal amount of O_2 that can be bound by Hb** we must bear in mind its tetrameric molecular structure (cf. Fig. 22-3), as expressed by the following reaction formula:

$$Hb + 4O_2 \rightleftharpoons Hb(O_2)_4 \tag{4}$$

That is, 1 mol of hemoglobin is capable of binding up to 4 mol of O_2. Taking into account the volume of a mol of ideal gas (22.4 liters), this would mean that 64,500 g Hb bind 4 × 22.4 liters of O_2, or 1 g Hb binds 1.39 ml O_2. Blood-gas analysis gives a somewhat smaller value (1.34–1.36 ml O_2/g Hb); this discrepancy is ascribed to the presence of a small fraction of the hemoglobin in an inactive form [25]. A general rule of thumb is that *1 g Hb in vivo binds 1.34 ml O_2* **(Hüfner's number).**

A recent practice is to give molar quantities of hemoglobin with respect to the Hb monomer (p. 797). In this case 1 mol Hb (= 16,100 g Hb) has a maximal O_2 binding capacity of 1 mol O_2 (= 22.4 l O_2). The net result is that the same value as above is obtained for Hüfner's number.

Knowing the Hb concentration, we can use Hüfner's number to compute the *oxygen capacity* of the blood as follows: $[O_2]_{max}$ = 1.34 (ml O_2/g Hb) × 150 (g Hb/l blood) = 0.20 (l O_2/l blood). This concentration, however, is achieved only when the blood is equilibrated with an oxygen-rich gas mixture (P_{O_2} > 300 mm Hg), so that the equilibrium of the reaction in Eq. (4) is shifted far to the right. At the smaller O_2 partial pressures that determine the equilibrium in vivo, only part of the hemoglobin is converted to oxyhemoglobin.

O_2 dissociation curve. The reaction of oxygen with hemoglobin (Eq. 4) follows the law of mass action. That is, the concentration of the physically dissolved O_2, which according to the Henry-Dalton law is proportional to the O_2 partial pressure, determines the proportions of deoxyhemoglobin and oxyhemoglobin. The percentage of the total Hb concentration that is oxygenated is called the *oxygen saturation* (S_{O_2}) of the red pigment. We can express this definition, using the simplified symbol HbO_2 for oxyhemoglobin, as follows:

$$S_{O_2} = \frac{[HbO_2]}{[Hb] + [HbO_2]} \cdot 100\% \qquad (5)$$

S_{O_2} is thus 0% when all the hemoglobin is deoxygenated; if all the hemoglobin has been converted to oxyhemoglobin the oxygen saturation is 100%.

According to the law of mass action the O_2 saturation of hemoglobin depends on the prevailing O_2 partial pressure. This relationship is represented graphically by the O_2 *dissociation curve.* As Fig. 22-6 shows, the O_2 dissociation curve of hemoglobin is characteristically S-shaped. Its position, which depends on various parameters (see pp. 584f.), can most simply be characterized by the so-called **half-saturation pressure** P_{50} – the O_2 partial pressure corresponding to 50% oxygen saturation (i.e., the P_{O_2} at which 50% of the hemoglobin is oxygenated). For arterial blood under normal conditions (pH = 7.4, temperature = 37 °C), P_{50} is about 26 mm Hg (3.46 kPa) [9, 29].

Interpretation of the O_2 dissociation curve. The origin of the sigmoid shape of the curve is not yet entirely clear. If only one O_2 molecule were to react with each pigment molecule, reaction kinetics would predict a *hyperbolic dissociation curve* [11]. This condition is met, for example, in the comparable reaction of oxygen with the *red muscle pigment* **myoglobin** (Mb) [1]. The structure of myoglobin is comparable to that of one of the four subunits of hemoglobin. Its molecular weight is thus related to that of hemoglobin as 1:4. Myoglobin has only one pigment component and, accordingly, can bind with only one O_2 molecule:

$$Mb + O_2 \rightleftharpoons MbO_2 \qquad (6)$$

Fig. 22-6 shows the hyperbolic dissociation curve that describes this reaction.

The plausible notion that the sigmoid shape of the dissociation curve of hemoglobin results from the *fourfold* combination with O_2 led to the formulation of the *intermediate-compound hypothesis* (ADAIR). This theory proposes that combination with the 4 O_2 molecules occurs in steps, each stage of the reaction affecting the equilibrium of the next stage. Hence the oxygen-hemoglobin reaction is determined by **4 equilibrium constants,** which explains the sigmoid shape of the O_2 dissociation curve.

Another interpretation is based on the notion that hemoglobin can be present in two states, depending on whether it is oxygenated or deoxygenated, and that a **change in conformation** converts one state into the other. If the two postulated states have different O_2-binding equilibria, this model can also account for the characteristic sigmoid curve [11, 14].

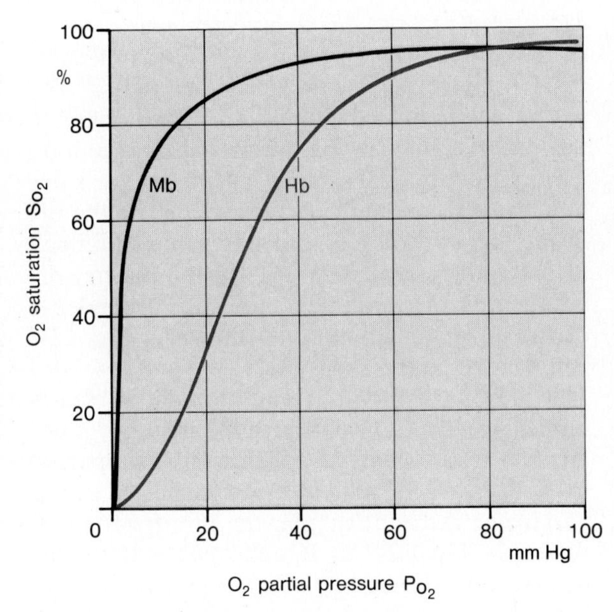

Fig. 22-6. O_2 dissociation curves of hemoglobin Hb (pH = 7.4; T = 37 °C) and myoglobin Mb

Biological significance of the O_2 dissociation curve. The special shape of the oxygen dissociation curve has important consequences for the transport of O_2 in the blood. During **oxygen uptake** in the lungs the O_2 partial pressure of the blood, P_{O_2}, closely approaches that of the alveoli (pp. 565f.). In the arterial blood of young subjects P_{O_2} averages 95 mm Hg (12.6 kPa). It is evident from Fig. 22-6 that at this partial pressure the hemoglobin is about 97% saturated with oxygen. In old age, and even more in cases of pulmonary malfunction, the arterial O_2 partial pressure can be considerably lower. Nevertheless, oxygen saturation is reduced very little, because the dissociation curve is so flat at high P_{O_2}. For example, even when P_{O_2} has fallen to 60 mm Hg (8.0 kPa) the arterial O_2 saturation is still 90%. *The flattening of the O_2 dissociation curve in the high-pressure range effectively prevents severe undersaturation of the arterial blood.*

Table 22-2. Blood-gas data and pH for arterial and venous blood of healthy young persons at rest

	P_{O_2}		S_{O_2}	$[O_2]$	P_{CO_2}		$[CO_2]$	pH
	(mm Hg)	(kPa)	%	(l O_2/l blood)	(mm Hg)	(kPa)	(l CO_2/l blood)	
Arterial blood	95	12.6	97	0.20	40	5.3	0.48	7.40
Venous blood	40	5.3	73	0.15	46	6.1	0.52	7.37
Arteriovenous difference				0.05			0.04	

On the other hand, the steep slope in the middle of the curve offers an extraordinary advantage when it comes to the **release of oxygen** to the tissues. Here it is important that enough oxygen should be released to meet local requirements without major fluctuations in the O_2 partial pressure of the blood. When the body is at rest the P_{O_2} at the venous end of the capillaries averages 40 mm Hg (5.3 kPa), which corresponds to about 73% saturation. A drop in venous O_2 partial pressure of only 5 mm Hg (0.7 kPa) owing to increased O_2 consumption reduces the O_2 saturation by no less than 7%, so that this additional amount of oxygen becomes available at almost constant P_{O_2}.

O_2 content of arterial and venous blood. The amount of chemically bound oxygen in the blood depends on the existing O_2 saturation S_{O_2}. The concentration of O_2 (l O_2/l blood) can be derived from the saturation on the basis of Hüfner's number, as follows:

$$[O_2] = 1.34 \cdot [Hb] \cdot S_{O_2} \cdot 10^{-5} \quad (7)$$

where S_{O_2} is given in % and [Hb] in g/l. Substituting the numbers found above for arterial O_2 saturation ($S_{O_2} = 97\%$) and venous O_2 saturation ($S_{O_2} = 73\%$), we find that the concentration of chemically bound oxygen is about 0.20 in arterial blood and 0.15 in venous blood. The **arteriovenous difference in O_2 concentration** avD_{O_2} is thus 0.05 (Table 22-2). That is, normally only 25% of the total oxygen capacity of the blood is utilized during passage through the tissue capillaries. Of course, the blood becomes desaturated to very different degrees in the various organs (cf. Fig. 23-2, p. 603), so that the venous entries in Table 22-2 are means of widely scattered data. During strenuous exercise the arteriovenous O_2 concentration difference can be greater than 0.1.

Factors Affecting the O_2 Dissociation Curve

Although the shape of the O_2 dissociation curve results chiefly from the reaction properties of hemoglobin, other factors can modify the O_2 affinity in the blood [2, 12, 14]. As a rule these effects amount to shifting the O_2 dissociation curve while increasing or decreasing its slope, without departure from the characteristic sigmoid shape. Factors having such an influence are temperature, pH or CO_2 partial pressure, and certain parameters that become relevant under pathological conditions.

The effect of temperature. As in most chemical processes, the equilibrium of the oxygen-hemoglobin reaction depends on the temperature. This dependence affects the dissociation curve in such a way that it rises steeply at low temperatures and progressively less steeply as the temperature increases (Fig. 22-7 A). In warm-blooded animals this effect has to be taken into consideration only in the cases of hypothermia or fever (see pp. 641f.).

The effects of pH and P_{CO_2}. The H^+ concentration in the blood has a considerable effect on the shape of the O_2 dissociation curve, as shown in Fig 22-7 B (where the pH is given as a measure of the H^+ concentration). *As pH decreases (i.e., the blood becomes more acidic), the affinity of oxygen for hemoglobin is reduced;* the O_2 dissociation curve becomes flatter. The pH values indicated in Fig. 22-7 B all refer to the plasma. In view of the causal connections, it would doubtless be more informative to show how the dissociation curve is affected by the pH inside the erythrocytes. But this value is difficult to determine, so that in general the plasma pH is taken as the parameter. The pH dependence of the O_2 dissociation curve shown in Fig. 22-7 B is known as the **Bohr effect.**

The pH of the blood at any moment is closely related to the CO_2 partial pressure (P_{CO_2}). An increase in CO_2 partial pressure is accompanied by a decrease in pH. If P_{CO_2} is chosen as the parameter rather than pH, the group of curves shown in Fig. 22-7 C results. *As the CO_2 partial pressure increases, the affinity of oxygen for hemoglobin is reduced;* the O_2 dissociation curve becomes flatter. The term *Bohr effect* is also applied to this dependence of the dissociation curve on P_{CO_2}, although precise quantitative analysis reveals that the influence of CO_2 on the dissociation curve cannot be ascribed entirely to the associated pH change. Evidently there exists an additional "specific CO_2 effect" [14].

Significance of the Bohr effect. The Bohr effect has certain physiological consequences for both *O_2 uptake in the lungs* and *O_2 release in the tissues,* though their extent should not be overestimated. First consider the situation in the lungs. Here O_2 uptake is coupled to the release of CO_2, so that the dissociation curve shifts to the left as the hemoglobin becomes more saturated with O_2. These simultaneous changes are indicated by the red curve in Fig. 22-7 C, which is sometimes called the *"effective O_2 dissociation curve"*. From the point corresponding to venous blood v (P_{O_2} = 40 mm Hg, P_{CO_2} = 46 mm Hg) oxygenation proceeds to the point of arterial saturation a (P_{O_2} = 95 mm Hg, P_{CO_2} = 40 mm Hg), accompanied by a steady increase in the O_2 affinity of the hemoglobin. The transport of O_2 occurs by diffusion (pp. 564f.), but the increased affinity results in a slight increase in the rate of diffusion. Thus the Bohr effect facilitates the uptake of oxygen in the lungs.

The importance of the Bohr effect is somewhat greater when it comes to the transfer of O_2 from the capillary blood into the tissues. Because of the simultaneous uptake of CO_2 into the blood, the O_2 dissociation curve is shifted to the right. The red "effective O_2 dissociation curve" in Fig. 22-7 C is now followed from a to v. As its O_2 affinity declines the hemoglobin becomes additionally deoxygenated, so that the O_2 diffuses away into the tissues at a higher capillary O_2 partial pressure. *Again the Bohr effect assists the exchange of oxygen.*

Pathophysiological factors. In certain pathological states the O_2-transport conditions in the blood can be altered. For example, a number

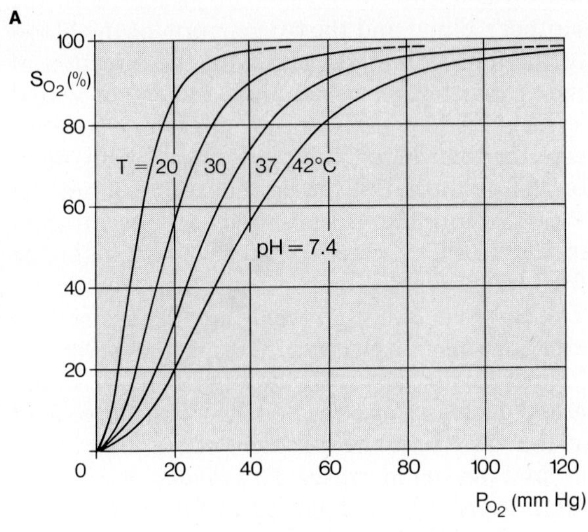

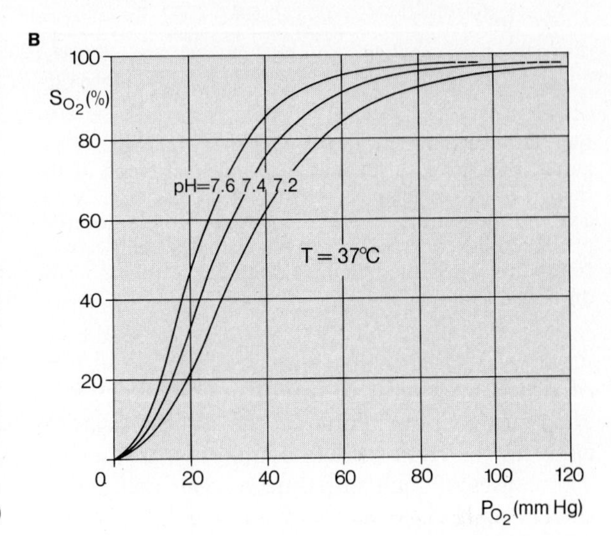

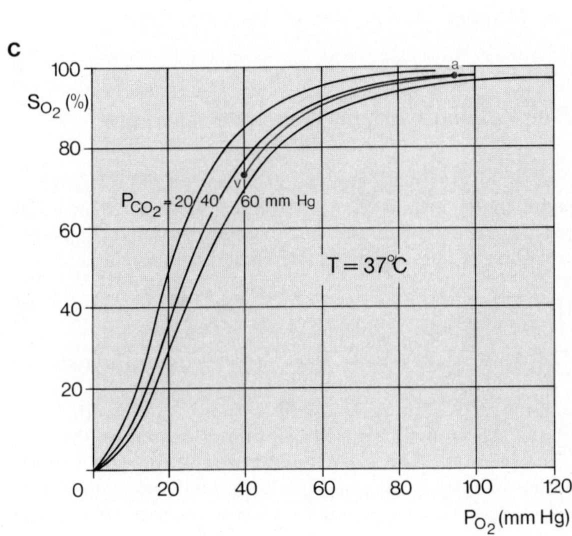

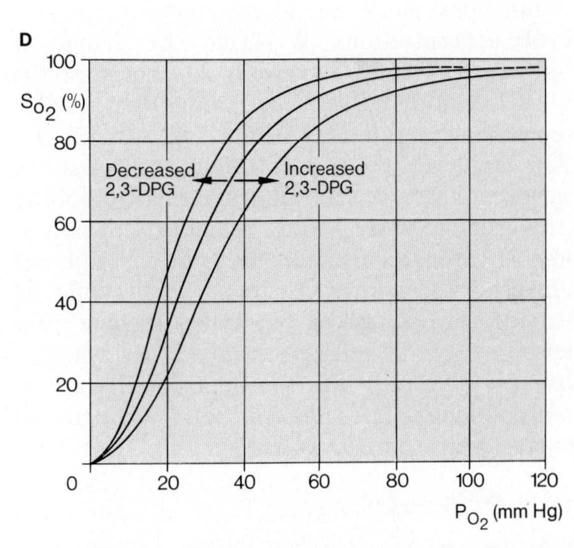

Fig. 22-7 A–D. Dependence of the O_2 dissociation curve of the blood on various parameters [9, 29]. **A** temperature-dependence; **B** pH-dependence (Bohr effect), **C** dependence on CO_2 partial pressure; **D** dependence on intra-erythrocytic concentration of 2,3-diphosphoglycerate (2,3-DPG). The *red* "effective O_2 dissociation curve" between the points a (arterial blood) and v (venous blood) applies to gas exchange under resting conditions

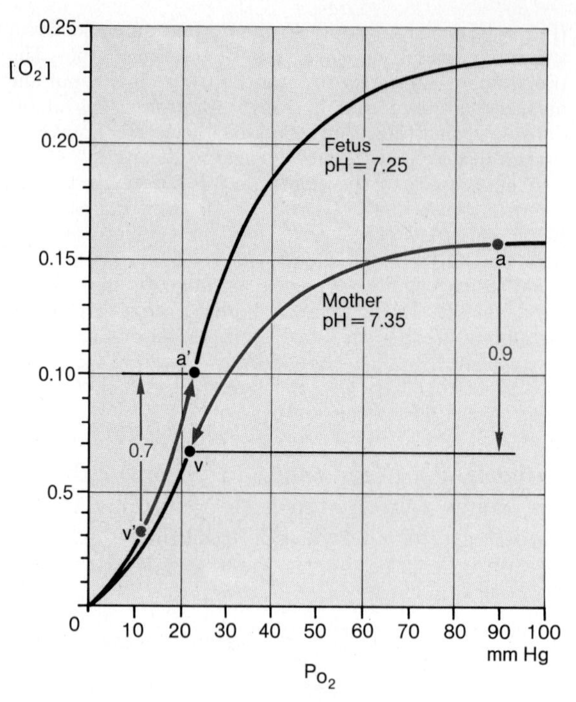

Fig. 22-8. O_2 concentrations $[O_2]$ as a function of O_2 partial pressure P_{O_2}, for maternal and fetal blood at the time of birth. During gas exchange in the placenta the O_2 concentration in the mother's blood falls from a (arterial) to v (venous), whereas in the blood of the fetus it rises from v′ (blood in the umbilical artery) to a′ (blood in the umbilical vein)

of diseases (certain forms of anemia in particular) bring about shifts of the O_2 dissociation curve to the right or, less commonly, to the left. The causes of such shifts are not yet completely understood. However, it is known that certain organic phosphate compounds, the intraerythrocytic concentrations of which can change in pathological states, have marked effects on the O_2 dissociation curve. Chief among these is **2,3-diphosphoglycerate (2,3-DPG)** (Fig. 22-7 D) [16, 22]. Moreover, the concentration of the cations in the erythrocyte can influence the O_2-binding properties of hemoglobin. The effects of pathological pH levels also deserve mention. High pH *(alkalosis)* facilitates O_2 uptake in the lung by way of the Bohr effect, but makes it more difficult for O_2 to be released in the tissues, whereas low pH *(acidosis)* has the opposite effects. Finally, extensive left shifts of the O_2 dissociation curve result from *CO poisoning.*

Fetal O_2 dissociation curve. As in all tissues, gas exchange in the placenta occurs by diffusion. Here, however, special attention must be paid to the differences in the O_2 affinity of the maternal and the fetal blood. *The O_2 dissociation curve of fetal blood* is somewhat *steeper* than that of maternal blood when the two are tested *under identical conditions.* But *in vivo* this difference is almost entirely compensated by the *lower pH* of fetal blood (Bohr effect). Thus the difference in O_2 affinity of the blood of mother and fetus has essentially no facilitatory effect on gas exchange in the placenta. However, if one takes into account the different *hemoglobin concentrations* of maternal and fetal blood, it turns out that the situation is most favorable for gas exchange [7, 21].

Fig. 22-8 shows the O_2 dissociation curves of maternal and fetal blood at the time of birth, for the average placental pH values. To allow for the difference in maternal and fetal hemoglobin concentration (120 g/l and 180 g/l, respectively), the variable on the ordinate is not O_2 saturation but O_2 concentration. The deoxygenation of the mother's blood and the oxygenation of the blood of the fetus follow the curves in the direction of the arrows between the points a and v or v′ and a′. It is evident that at a given O_2 partial pressure the fetal blood can bind considerably more oxygen than that of the mother. For example, at P_{O_2} = 25 mm Hg (3.3 kPa) the O_2 concentration in the mother's blood is 0.08 while that in the fetal blood is 0.11.

The Bohr effect has a special significance for gas exchange in the placenta. During the period of diffusive contact the O_2 affinity of the maternal blood decreases as a result of CO_2 exchange, and at the same time the tendency of the fetal blood to bind oxygen increases. This *double influence of the Bohr effect,* not reflected in Fig. 22-8, causes an increase in the rate of O_2 exchange.

Hemoglobin-Carbon Monoxide Binding

The affinity of hemoglobin for carbon monoxide (CO) is significantly greater than for oxygen. Even at exceedingly low partial pressures, CO gas is capable of converting large fractions of hemoglobin into CO-hemoglobin

$$Hb + CO \rightleftharpoons HbCO \qquad (8)$$

The equilibrium of this reaction lies well to the right, so that the CO dissociation curve rises very steeply. The high affinity of CO for hemoglobin is due to the fact that CO dissociates from Hb very much more slowly than O_2 [3]. The maximal workplace concentration for CO (MWC value, p. 674) is 30 ppm (parts per million), which corresponds to $F_{CO} = 3 \cdot 10^{-5}$ (0.003 vol.%). In the arterial blood of a person who spends considerable time in such surroundings, HbCO accounts for about 5% of the total amount of hemoglobin. The CO and O_2 partial pressures required to give 5% HbCO and 5% HbO_2, respectively, are related as 1:350. That is, in this range the relative

affinity of Hb for CO is about *350 times greater* than for O_2.
It is because of this strong affinity for hemoglobin that carbon monoxide is so *poisonous*. This colorless and odorless gas is produced by incomplete combustion of organic material; it is sometimes a component of domestic gas supplies, and is one of the waste products of combustion engines. Even in low concentrations CO can displace O_2 from hemoglobin and make it unavailable for the transport of oxygen. Normally 1% of the hemoglobin in the blood is HbCO; smokers have been found to have as much as 20% HbCO in the evening. The danger of CO exposure in street traffic is strikingly revealed by the fact that at some intersections where the traffic is heavy the concentration of CO in the air has been found to be $3 \cdot 10^{-4}$. This is the concentration at which miners underground are supposed to put on their breathing apparatus.
There is another effect, apart from the blocking of Hb, that is responsible for the toxicity of CO gas. When part of the Hb has been converted into HbCO, the hemoglobin that remains unblocked has an *O_2 dissociation curve shifted to the left* [3], which ultimately can become hyperbolic. As a result, the O_2 partial pressures in the tissue capillaries fall even further.
In cases of severe CO poisoning, detectable by the cherry-red color of the blood, immediate artificial respiration (with pure oxygen if possible) can save the victim's life. This procedure increases the O_2 partial pressure in the blood so that the O_2 can displace CO from hemoglobin. Massive blood transfusion is also helpful, for it supplies the patient with unblocked Hb that can be used for O_2 transport.

22.3 The CO_2-Transport Function of the Blood

Forms of CO_2 Transport

Carbon dioxide (CO_2), formed in the cells of the body as an end product of oxidative metabolism, is carried by the blood to the lungs and there given off to the outside air. Like oxygen, carbon dioxide can be transported in physically *dissolved* as well as in *chemically bound* form in the blood. The process of chemical binding of CO_2 is somewhat more complicated than that of O_2, for the same process that serves for *CO_2 transport* must also maintain the *acid-base balance* in the blood and thus in the organism as a whole.

CO_2 binding [15]. The arterial blood enters the tissue capillaries with a CO_2 partial pressure of 40 mm Hg (5.3 kPa). In the cells surrounding the capillaries CO_2 partial pressure is high, because CO_2 is constantly being produced; thus the physically dissolved CO_2 molecules diffuse along the partial pressure gradient into the capillary. A small fraction remains physically dissolved in the capillary blood, but most of the CO_2 undergoes further chemical conversion (Fig. 22-9). The first step in this process is **hydration** to carbonic acid, which immediately dissociates into bicarbonate and protons:

$$CO_2 + H_2O \rightleftharpoons H_2CO_3 \rightleftharpoons HCO_3^- + H^+ \tag{9}$$

This reaction proceeds slowly in the plasma, but in the erythrocyte the reaction rate is about 10,000 times as great. This acceleration is brought about by the enzyme **carbonic anhydrase** [6, 24]. Because this enzyme is restricted to the red cells, practically all of the CO_2 molecules involved in the chemical conversion must enter the erythrocytes.
The progressive increase in HCO_3^- concentration inside the erythrocyte creates a diffusion gradient toward the surrounding plasma. However, the HCO_3^- ions can move along this gradient only if their displacement does not appreciably disturb the electrical charge equilibrium. Therefore, each HCO_3^- ion that leaves the erythrocytes would have to be accompanied by a cation or an anion would have to enter in exchange. The first of these possibilities cannot be realized, for

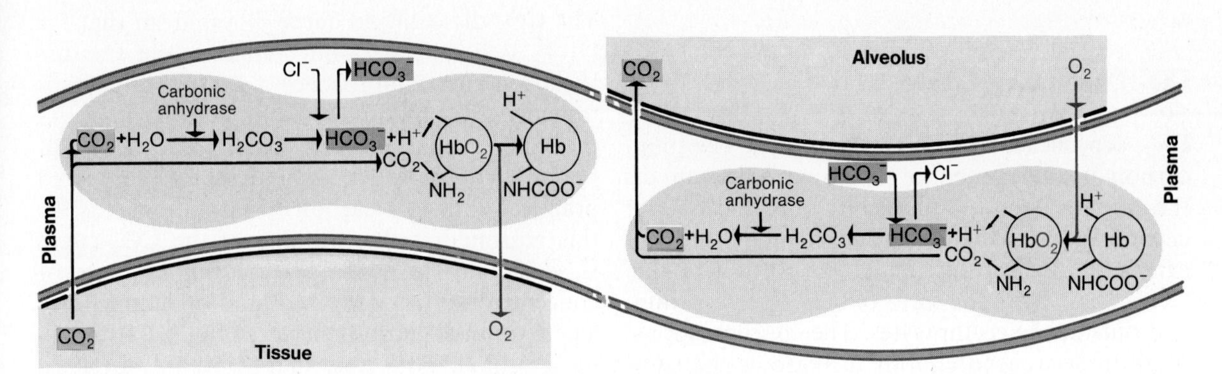

Fig. 22-9. Chemical reactions in the erythrocyte during gas exchange in tissues *(left)* and lungs *(right)*

the erythrocyte membrane is essentially impermeable to cations. Small anions, however, can pass through the membrane with relative ease. Therefore the HCO_3^- ions that leave the erythrocyte are exchanged for Cl^- ions. This exchange is called *Hamburger's shift* or the **chloride shift.**
As CO_2 enters the erythrocyte, the formation of HCO_3^- ions is accompanied by production of H^+ ions. But there is no great change in pH, owing particularly to the properties of hemoglobin. First, the red pigment has amphoteric properties and thus a large *buffer capacity*. Second, as it gives off O_2, hemoglobin becomes *"less acidic"* and can take on additional H^+ ions (p. 592).
Another way in which CO_2 can be bound is by direct combination with the protein component of the hemoglobin. The reaction takes place at the amino groups, which form a *carbamino compound* with CO_2 (carbamate):

$$Hb-NH_2+CO_2 \rightleftharpoons Hb-NHCOO^-+H^+ \quad (10)$$

The product of the reaction is called **carbaminohemoglobin,** sometimes abbreviated to *carbhemoglobin.*
These chemical reactions and their interdependence are summarized in Fig. 22-9. The left half illustrates the reactions accompanying the uptake of CO_2 in the tissue capillaries, and on the right are shown the events during CO_2 release in the lungs, in which all the reactions take place in the reverse direction.

Contributions of the forms of CO_2 binding to gas exchange. The blood enters the tissue capillaries with a CO_2 partial pressure of 40 mm Hg and, having acquired more CO_2 in transit, leaves them with an average CO_2 partial pressure of 46 mm Hg. In the process, about 1.8 mmol CO_2 are taken up per liter of blood. About 12% of this CO_2 remains in physical solution or as undissociated carbonic acid (H_2CO_3). 11% forms carbamino hemoglobin, 27% is carried in the erythrocyte as bicarbonate, and the remainder, ca. 50%, is dissolved in the plasma in the form of HCO_3^-. As the blood passes through the lungs, CO_2 is released from these four transport forms in the same proportions.

CO_2 Dissociation Curves

P_{CO_2}-dependence of CO_2 concentration. The total carbon dioxide content of the blood is the sum of the amount dissolved physically plus that bound chemically as carbonic acid, carbamate and bicarbonate. By far the greater proportion of the CO_2 is present in the form of *bicarbonate* within and outside the erythrocytes. The concentrations of all these transport forms increase as the CO_2 partial pressure P_{CO_2} rises.

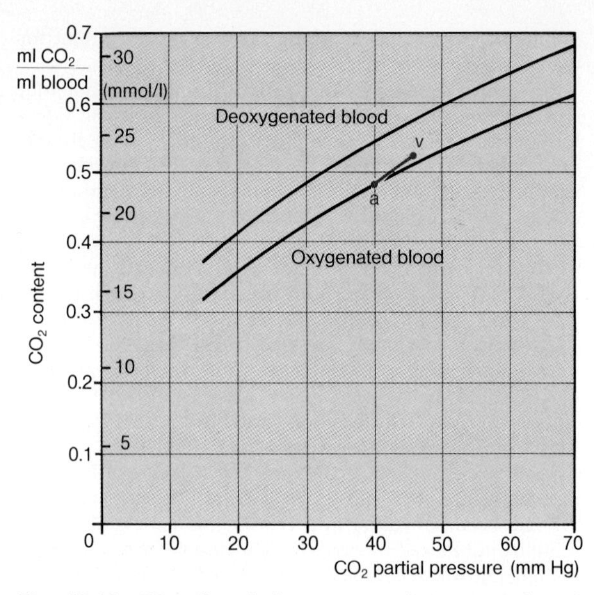

Fig. 22-10. CO_2 dissociation curves of oxygenated and deoxygenated blood. The *red* "effective CO_2 dissociation curve" connecting the points a (arterial blood) and v (venous blood) is the determinant of gas exchange

This relationship between concentration and partial pressure can be represented by a diagram analogous to the O_2 dissociation curve. Fig. 22-10 shows the **CO_2 dissociation curves** of oxygenated and deoxygenated blood. The differential binding of CO_2 in these two conditions results from the fact that oxyhemoglobin has a more acid quality than deoxyhemoglobin, and can remove fewer H^+ ions from solution. Accordingly, the dissociation of carbonic acid necessary for continued uptake of CO_2 occurs to a greater extent, the smaller the fraction of oxygenated hemoglobin. Moreover, deoxyhemoglobin binds CO_2 in the carbamino form on a larger scale than does oxyhemoglobin [6, 20]. The dependence of CO_2 binding on the degree of hemoglobin oxygenation is known as the **Christiansen-Douglas-Haldane effect** or, more briefly, as the *Haldane effect.*
The CO_2 dissociation curve differs from that for O_2 in one crucial point. Whereas the O_2 dissociation curve approaches a maximum asymptotically, CO_2 binding exhibits *no saturation.* As the CO_2 partial pressure rises, the amount of bound CO_2 continues to increase, for there is no practical limit to bicarbonate formation. It is for this reason that the ordinate of the CO_2 curve is scaled not in % saturation but in units of concentration (ml CO_2/ml blood or mmol/l).
The CO_2 dissociation curves in Fig. 22-10 apply only to blood with a normal acid-base status. In metabolic acidoses or alkaloses the curves are

shifted considerably, as can be seen in Fig. 22-16 (p. 594).

Physiological significance of the Christiansen-Douglas-Haldane effect. When considering the uptake of CO_2 in the tissues and its release in the lungs, we must keep in mind that these processes are simultaneous with O_2 exchange. The changes in the O_2 saturation of hemoglobin influence the CO_2 binding of the blood and thus affect CO_2 exchange.
When the arterial blood enters the tissue capillaries it is essentially fully oxygenated (point a in Fig. 22-10). With the loss of O_2 to the tissues during passage through the capillaries, the ability of the blood to bind CO_2 increases. The uptake of CO_2 in the tissue capillaries is thus enhanced by the Christiansen-Douglas-Haldane effect.
In the lungs the reverse exchange processes occur. Because of the O_2 uptake here, the CO_2-binding capacity of the blood is reduced and the release of CO_2 by diffusion is facilitated. During gas exchange in the lung capillaries the red curve in Fig. 22-10 is followed in the direction from v to a. This curve, which represents CO_2 exchange in both the lungs and the tissues, may be called the *effective CO_2 dissociation curve.* For both processes – the uptake of CO_2 in the tissues and its release in the lungs – it is equally true that *diffusional CO_2 exchange is assisted by the Christiansen-Douglas-Haldane effect.*

22.4 The Acid-Base Status of the Blood

The Blood pH

Acids and bases. According to the definition of Brønstedt, *acids* are substances that in solution give off hydrogen ions **(proton donors),** and *bases* are substances that bind hydrogen ions **(proton acceptors).** This definition is particularly useful in the realm of biology. From it, it follows that in the *dissociation reaction*

$$HA \rightleftharpoons H^+ + A^- \quad (11)$$

HA is an *acid* (reaction proceeding from left to right), whereas under certain conditions (with the reaction proceeding in the opposite direction) the anion A^- is by definition a *base,* as it binds hydrogen ions. Here, A^- is called the *conjugate base.* There is a balance between dissociation and association which obeys the *law of mass action.* With a strong acid such as HCl, the balance is shifted far toward the right side of Eq. (11). On the other hand, if HA is a weak acid dissociation may be incomplete, depending on the equilibrium constant (cf. Fig. 22-11).

Definition of pH. The acidity or basicity of a fluid depends on its concentration of free hydrogen ions and is characterized by the pH. *pH is defined as the negative decadic logarithm of the molar H^+ concentration:*

$$pH = -\log[H^+] \quad (12)$$

Thus a pH of 7, which identifies a neutral reaction, corresponds to a H^+ concentration $[H^+] = 10^{-7}$ mol/l. As pH decreases, the acidity of the solution increases.
The definition of pH was initially introduced as a technical convenience, but in biological systems it has a special significance. The *electrochemical potential* of ions is proportional not to their concentration but to its logarithm. For this reason the responses of the sensors or receptors in human and animal bodies that are involved in regulation of the acid-base status are likely to be proportional to pH rather than to concentration.

pH measurement. The pH of a solution can be determined with *indicators* or by *electrometry.* Most of the pH indicators are very weak acids or bases that dissociate at a characteristic pH, and in so doing change color. For continuously graded and precise measurement of pH, the most widely used procedure is electrometry with a *glass electrode.* Such an electrode ususally has a spherically expanded end made of a special glass through which H^+ ions can pass. The space inside this glass membrane is filled with a buffer solution. When the electrode is dipped into a solution a potential difference builds up according to the Nernst equation (p. 6), to a level dependent on the pH of the external solution. This potential difference is recorded by non-polarizable electrodes. Today such meters commonly take the form of an easily operable system in which measurement and reference electrodes are housed in a single jacket. After amplification of the voltage signal it is displayed by a dial or a plotter. Before the measurement is done the instrument must be calibrated with *standard buffer solutions.*

Constancy of the arterial pH. *The pH of human arterial blood (37 °C) ranges from 7.37 to 7.43 and averages 7.40.* These values, to be precise, are those of the *plasma,* for when the glass electrode is immersed in the blood sample it contacts only the plasma; the intraerythrocytic pH does not enter into the measurement. The pH within the erythrocyte is difficult to measure. It has been found to differ from that of plasma, amounting to about 7.2–7.3. As a rule, the term "blood pH" always refers to the pH of plasma.
Human blood is thus weakly alkaline. Despite the continually fluctuating release of acidic metabolic products into the blood, its pH is kept *extremely constant.* This constancy is an im-

portant prerequisite for maintenance of orderly metabolism in the cells of the body, because the activities of all the enzymes involved in metabolism are pH-dependent. Pathological changes in pH affect the various enzymes to different degrees, so that the interplay of metabolic reactions can be disrupted. Several factors participate in regulating the acid-base balance (i.e., in keeping the blood pH constant). These factors are the *buffer properties of the blood, pulmonary gas exchange, and the excretory mechanisms in the kidneys.*

The Buffer Properties of the Blood

Characteristics of buffer systems. First recall that the dissociation of a weak acid HA into hydrogen ions H^+ and the conjugate base A^- follows the **law of mass action.** Denoting the molar concentrations of the partners in the reaction by square brackets, we have

$$\frac{[H^+][A^-]}{[HA]} = K' \tag{13}$$

K′ is the equilibrium constant (dissociation constant); the "prime" signifies that the constant takes account of the special conditions in the solution, such as the ionic strength. If the concentration of H^+ ions in such a system is increased, the concentration of undissociated acid must rise simultaneously in order that the equilibrium condition of the mass-action law be fulfilled. In other words, dissociation is reduced to some extent, and some of the added free H^+ ions are eliminated. The pH change is therefore smaller than would correspond to the amount of H^+ ions added. Conversely, removal of H^+ ions from the solution produces but a small pH change. *This attenuation of the effect of added H^+ or OH^- ions is called buffering.*

For a quantitative evaluation of the buffering effect it is convenient to rearrange Eq. (13) and take the negative logarithm of all its terms:

$$-\log[H^+] = -\log K' - \log\frac{[HA]}{[A^-]} \tag{14}$$

$$pH = pK' + \log\frac{[A^-]}{[HA]} \tag{15}$$

When the law of mass action is expressed for a buffer system in this form it is known as the **Henderson-Hasselbalch equation.** Here pK′ =

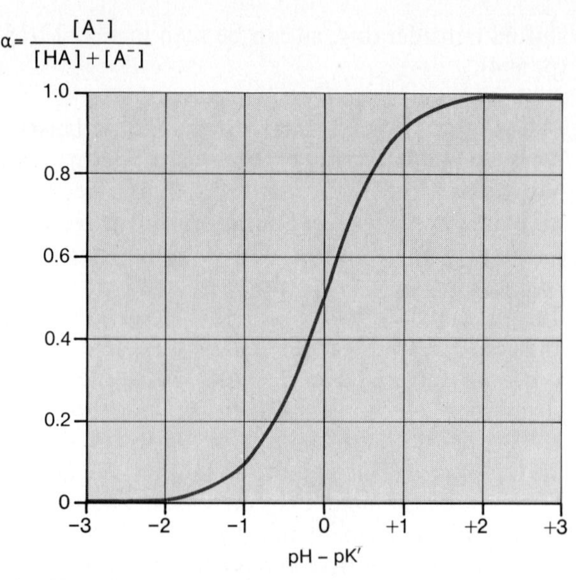

Fig. 22-11. Dependence of the degree of dissociation α of a weak acid on pH. pK′ = negative logarithm of the equilibrium constant K′. Such a buffer curve is obtained by successively adding aliquots of H^+ or OH^- to the solution and measuring the pH after each addition

$-\log K'$, like K′ itself, is a constant characteristic of the system. Eq. (15) may be rewritten

$$pH = pK' + \log\frac{\alpha}{1-\alpha}, \text{ where } \alpha = \frac{[A^-]}{[HA]+[A^-]} \tag{16}$$

The *degree of dissociation* α introduced here gives the base concentration $[A^-]$ in relation to the total concentration of acid and conjugate base $[HA] + [A^-]$. This relationship between the degree of dissociation α and the pH of the buffer solution is graphed in Fig. 22-11. The curve shows that the degree of dissociation changes only over a limited range of pH, from 2 pH units below pK′ to 2 units above it. Only in this range does the system have buffering properties.

The buffer capacity of a system consisting of a weak acid and its conjungate base is described by the **buffer value,** the ratio between the amount of H^+ or OH^- ions added and the resulting change in pH. For a given amount of H^+ or OH^- added the change in pH is smallest in the steepest part of the buffer curve (Fig. 22-11). That is, the buffer capacity of a system is greatest at pH = pK′. *The buffer value is thus determined both by the concentration of the buffer system and by the difference between the prevailing pH and the pK′ of the system.*

Bicarbonate buffer system. Of the several buffer systems in the blood, we shall first consider the bicarbonate system. Carbonic acid, formed by hydration of CO_2, is a relatively weak acid, and bicarbonate is its conjugate base.

$$CO_2 + H_2O \rightleftharpoons H_2CO_3 \rightleftharpoons H^+ + HCO_3^- \quad (17)$$

The Henderson-Hasselbalch equation for the overall reaction is

$$pH = pK' + \log \frac{[HCO_3^-]}{[CO_2]} \quad (18)$$

Here $[CO_2]$ can be replaced by the CO_2 partial pressure P_{CO_2}:

$$pH = pK' + \log \frac{[HCO_3^-]}{0.03 \cdot P_{CO_2}} \quad (19)$$

The factor 0.03 has the units $mmol \cdot l^{-1} \cdot mm\,Hg^{-1}$, so that it applies only when $[HCO_3^-]$ is given in mmol/l and P_{CO_2} in mm Hg.
pK′ (at the ionic strength of plasma) is 6.1. Therefore it at first appears that the buffer action of the system cannot be very great, pK′ being quite far from the pH of the blood (7.4). Nevertheless the bicarbonate system accounts for a great deal of the blood's buffer capacity, for its effectiveness is considerably increased by the respiratory interactions. The mechanisms maintaining an arterial CO_2 partial pressure of 40 mm Hg in themselves bring about a high concentration of HCO_3^- in the plasma, 24 mmol/l. That is, the control of CO_2 partial pressure by the respiratory system ensures *high concentrations of the buffer components.* An additional favorable circumstance is that in this "open" system ventilation can be modified so as to vary the CO_2 partial pressure and thus regulate the pH of the blood.

Phosphate buffer system. In the buffer system formed by the inorganic phosphates in the blood, *the monobasic phosphate* ($H_2PO_4^-$) *acts as the acid and the dibasic phosphate* (HPO_4^{2-}) *as the conjugate base.* The pK′ of this system is 6.8, relatively close to the blood pH. But the concentrations of phosphates in the blood are so low that their buffering effect is small.

Proteinate buffer system. The buffer properties of the blood proteins reside in the ionizable groups of the amino acids of which they are composed. The few carboxyl and amino groups at the ends of the peptide chains are essentially negligible in this respect, particularly because these groups have pK′ far from the physiological pH. *The ionizable side groups are considerably more important in buffering the blood, the most effective being the imidazole ring of histidine.*
Proteins that act as buffers include both the **plasma proteins,** *albumin* in particular, and the intraerythrocytic **hemoglobin.** Hemoglobin accounts for most of the protein buffer capacity, because it is present in high concentration and contains a relatively large amount of histidine.

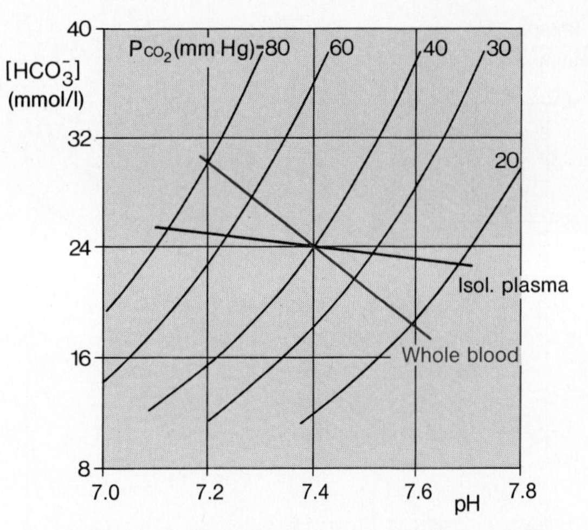

Fig. 22-12. CO_2 equilibration curves of isolated plasma and whole blood. Ordinate: bicarbonate concentration of the plasma; abscissa: pH. Reference curves for constant CO_2 partial pressure are also plotted. Because there is ion exchange between plasma and erythrocytes in whole blood the buffering function of hemoglobin is added to that of plasma, which increases the slope of the CO_2 equilibration curve

The contribution of Hb becomes especially obvious when one compares the pH change in plasma with that in whole blood, for a given CO_2 partial-pressure change. It is helpful to display the result of this comparison in a *HCO_3^--pH diagram,* which shows curves of constant CO_2 partial pressure calculated by the Henderson-Hasselbalch equation (Eq. 19). When the interdependence of the three characteristic quantities, plasma HCO_3^-, pH and P_{CO_2}, is examined by varying the CO_2 partial pressure in **separated plasma** and in **whole blood,** in which the plasma exchanges ions with the erythrocytes, the correspondingly labelled *CO_2-equilibrium lines* of Fig. 22-12 are found. The steeper slope of the whole-blood line reflects the great contribution of hemoglobin to the buffer capacity of the blood; the steeper the buffer line, the smaller the pH change resulting from a given increase or decrease in CO_2 partial pressure.

Hemoglobin is also of particular significance in buffering the blood because its acidity changes with oxygenation and deoxygenation. This dependence is illustrated in Fig. 22-13, where buffer curves (titration curves) are plotted for the nondiffusible buffer systems of the erythrocyte with

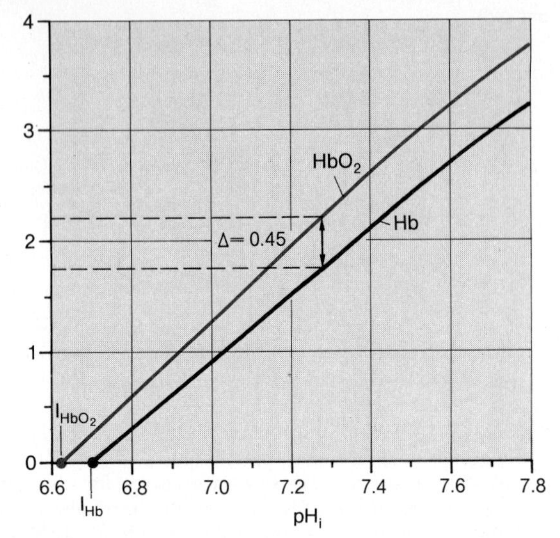

Fig. 22-13. Buffer curves of the nondiffusible systems in the erythrocyte (predominantly Hb, with small contributions from ATP and 2,3-DPG), for oxygenated (HbO_2) and deoxygenated (Hb) hemoglobin, modified from [19]. *Ordinate:* mmol nondiffusible buffer anions P_i^- per mmol hemoglobin; *abscissa:* intraerythrocytic pH; I_{HbO_2} and I_{Hb}: isoelectric points. Because of the shift of the curve by complete deoxygenation, 0.45 mmol H^+ can be tied up per mmol Hb without change in pH_i

the hemoglobin in the oxygenated and deoxygenated states. *In the physiological pH range oxyhemoglobin is evidently more strongly acidic than deoxyhemoglobin.* The cause of this difference lies in the influence of the iron-bound oxygen on the binding of H^+ to the neighboring imidazole groups of histidine. Because of this effect, when O_2 is unloaded in the tissues the hemoglobin can tie up more of the H^+ ions produced by the simultaneous uptake of CO_2. The same supplementary buffering effect operates when O_2 is taken up in the lungs. In conclusion, *O_2 exchange enhances the buffer action of hemoglobin.*

Buffer bases. The buffer properties of the blood are determined by the combined effects of all the anionic groups of weak acids, the most important of which are bicarbonate and proteinate. All of these anions with buffering effects are called *buffer bases* [10].

Fig. 22-14 summarizes the arterial ion concentrations in human plasma, erythrocytes and whole blood. The height of the columns is proportional to concentration. The anions are arranged such that the buffer bases are at the top *(dark red)*; below, there are the anions of the strong acids, which have no buffer property, with all the nonchloride anions (such as SO_4^{2-} and organic anions) lumped together as X^-. The graph shows that the buffer bases in plasma are represented mainly by HCO_3^- ions, whereas in erythrocytes the proteinate ions predominate. In whole blood more than 1/3 of all the anions are available for buffering.

The **concentration of buffer bases** in arterial blood is about *48 mmol/l*. It is of special importance that the total buffer base concentration does not change when the CO_2 partial pressure varies. This constancy is revealed by the following considerations. When the CO_2 partial pressure rises, for example, equivalent amounts of H^+ and HCO_3^- are formed. The protons so produced are almost entirely caught up by proteinate, which is thus converted into the undissociated form. Therefore the proteinate concentration is reduced to the same extent to which the bicarbonate concentration increases (Fig. 22-15).

These concentration changes in the buffer systems do not entirely counterbalance one another, because some protons remain dissolved in free form and alter the pH. For example, when the P_{CO_2} rises from 40 to 50 mm Hg, the pH in the erythrocytes falls by 0.06 pH unit and that in the plasma, by 0.1 unit. That is, the H^+ concentration increases by roughly 10^{-5} mmol/l. But this is such a small amount that it does not affect the result diagrammed in Fig. 22-15.

Because the *total buffer base concentration is independent of P_{CO_2}*, this parameter provides a

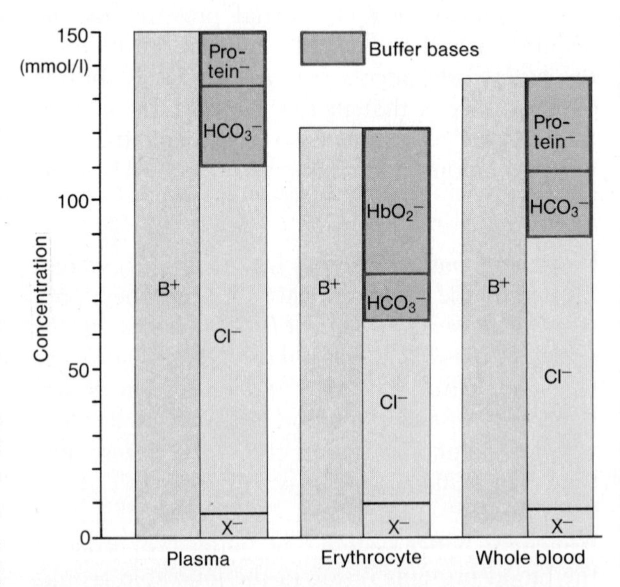

Fig. 22-14. Ion concentrations in plasma, in erythrocytes, and in whole blood. Buffer bases: anions in the buffer systems *(dark red)* (phosphate ions not shown because of their low concentration); X^-, anions of all the nonbuffering strong acids except Cl^-; B^+ sum of all cations

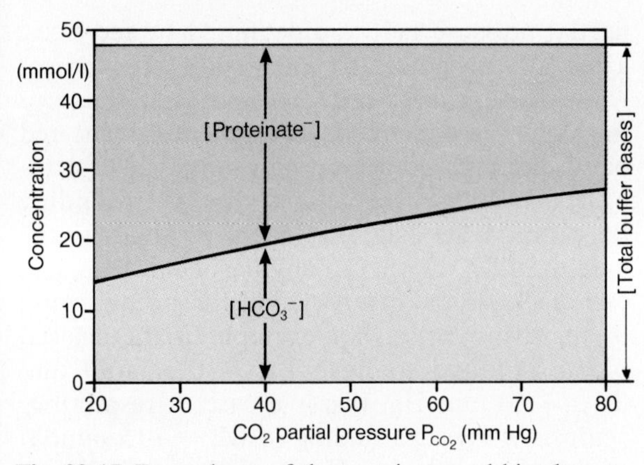

Fig. 22-15. Dependence of the proteinate and bicarbonate concentrations on the CO_2 partial pressure. The sum of the two buffer-base concentrations is constant, 48 mmol/l in the normal case

suitable measure of those changes in acid-base status that result from increase or decrease of the *nonvolatile acids* in the blood. Departures from the normal buffer-base concentration (48 mmol/l) are called **base excess BE.** By definition, the BE of blood in healthy persons is zero. A pathological rise in buffer base concentration is indicated by a positive BE, and a decrease by a negative BE. Because the term *"negative base excess"* is contradictory, **base deficit** is a preferable designation for the latter case.

pH-Regulating Mechanisms

Contribution of respiration. One of the functions of respiration is to eliminate the CO_2 produced in large quantities as an end product of metabolism. When the body is at rest 230 ml CO_2 are eliminated per minute, or about 15,000 mmol/day. At the same time, release of the "volatile" carbonic acid anhydride relieves the blood of a nearly equivalent amount of H^+. Respiration thus makes a crucial contribution to the maintenance of a stable acid-base status.
The *control of breathing* is of particular importance in compensating for disturbance of the acid-base balance. For example, when abnormal metabolic processes cause the acidity of the blood to rise, the increased H^+ concentration acts as an additional respiratory drive that leads to increased ventilation *(hyperventilation)*. CO_2 molecules derived from the reaction $HCO_3^- + H^+ \rightarrow H_2CO_3 \rightarrow H_2O + CO_2$ are breathed out in greater amounts, and the pH returns to normal. An increase in ions elicits *hypoventilation;* the CO_2 partial pressure and thus the concentration of H^+ ions rise, so that the original pH increase is at least partially compensated.

Contribution of the kidneys. Along with the lungs, the kidneys are involved in regulating the acid-base balance. Their role consists in excreting the *nonvolatile acids,* chiefly sulfuric acid. The nonvolatile acids normally provide *40–60 mmol H^+/day,* which must be eliminated by way of the kidneys. If the amount of nonvolatile acids should rise, a healthy kidney is capable of increasing considerably its rate of H^+ excretion and bringing the falling pH of the blood back to normal. Similarly, an increase in pH reduces the renal excretion of H^+ and thus compensates for the acid-base imbalance.

The excretion of H^+ ions occurs in the renal tubules, by a process in which tubular filtrate, tubule cell and capillary blood interact. Ultimately the H^+ ions are bound to HPO_4^{2-} and NH_3 in the tubular urine; only a small fraction is eliminated in the urine as free H^+ ions. On the other hand, chemical conversions and exchange processes return HCO_3^- ions to the blood (pp. 751f.).

Acidoses and alkaloses. When pathological conditions bring about an accumulation of large amounts of acids or bases in the blood, the regulatory mechanisms described above – buffering in the blood, respiration and renal function – do not suffice to keep the blood pH constant. Depending on the direction of the pH shift, these disturbances of acid-base balance are divided into two categories. An abnormally low blood pH ($pH < 7.37$) is called **acidosis,** and an abnormally high pH ($pH < 7.43$) is called **alkalosis.** Each of these categories is further subdivided according to the genesis of the pH change. Pulmonary malfunction can cause the CO_2 partial pressure in the blood to rise, and hyperventilation can lower it; in either case it is a respiratory abnormality that causes the pH change. Such a condition is called **respiratory acidosis** or **alkalosis.** Nonvolatile acids, on the other hand, can accumulate in the blood owing to metabolic disturbances (e.g., diabetis mellitus) or be removed in excess when bases are added or HCl lost (vomiting). These states are called *metabolic acidosis* or *alkalosis.* Because renal malfunction can also alter the blood pH, the terms **nonrespiratory acidosis** or **alkalosis** are used to cover both renal and metabolic disturbances.

Signs of primary acid-base disturbances. *Respiratory and nonrespiratory disturbances of the acid-base balance can be distinguished by way of CO_2 partial pressure (P_{CO_2}) and base excess (BE).*

The sign of respiratory disturbance is elevated or lowered P_{CO_2} without primary change in the buffer-base concentration (BE = 0). It is characteristic of nonrespiratory disturbance that P_{CO_2} is normal at first, whereas BE departs from the norm. When the nonvolatile acids in the blood increase (metabolic acidosis) they use up some of the buffer base (BE becomes negative), and when the amount of fixed acids is diminished (metabolic alkalosis) the buffer-base concentration rises (BE is positive).

Nonrespiratory disturbances have a marked influence on the CO_2 content of the blood, because they are associated with changes in $[HCO_3^-]$. This effect is well illustrated by a diagram of the **CO_2 dissociation curves** associated with different values of base excess (BE) (Fig. 22-16). In the case of nonrespiratory acidosis (base deficit) the curve shifts in the direction of decreasing CO_2 content, and in nonrespiratory alkalosis (base excess) it shifts in the opposite direction. By contrast, in cases of *respiratory disturbance* there is no primary alteration in the shape or position of the CO_2 dissociation curve.

The distinguishing characteristics of the 4 acid-base disturbances are diagrammed in Fig. 22-17. In a coordinate system with base excess on the ordinate and pH on the abscissa, curves of equal CO_2 partial pressure are plotted. The ranges of normal values for pH, base excess BE and CO_2 partial pressure P_{CO_2} are delimited by red lines. Thus all the points to the left of the vertical white band characterize *acidosis*, and those to the right are characteristic of *alkalosis*. The red bands are labelled according to the type of acid-base disturbance, as defined above. By finding the point in the diagram that corresponds to the measured BE and pH in any particular case, one can diagnose the category and the primal cause of the disturbance. For example, if the arterial blood is found to have BE = 0 mmol/l and P_{CO_2} = 60 mm Hg, this is a case of respiratory acidosis, whereas a finding of BE = −15 mmol/l and P_{CO_2} = 40 mm Hg implies metabolic or, more generally, nonrespiratory acidosis.

Compensation of primary acid-base disturbances. As a rule, the disturbances of acid-base balance considered so far are only primary alterations that can be compensated either immediately or with a certain delay. That is, the primary displacement of the pH toward the acidic or the alkaline side is reversed by compensatory mechanisms, so that the normal range is regained or at least approached. The mechanisms that act in this sense have been described above (p. 593):

1. A **primary nonrespiratory disturbance** of the acid-base balance can be compensated by an

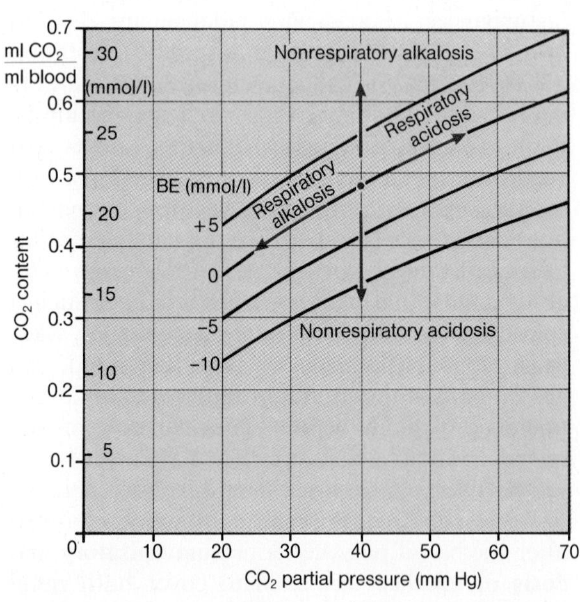

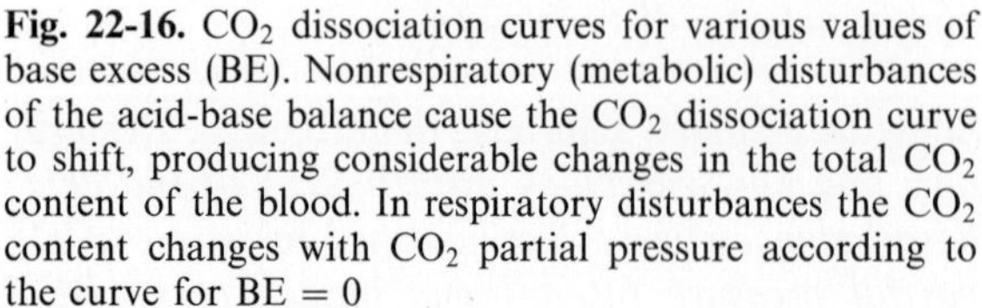
Fig. 22-16. CO_2 dissociation curves for various values of base excess (BE). Nonrespiratory (metabolic) disturbances of the acid-base balance cause the CO_2 dissociation curve to shift, producing considerable changes in the total CO_2 content of the blood. In respiratory disturbances the CO_2 content changes with CO_2 partial pressure according to the curve for BE = 0

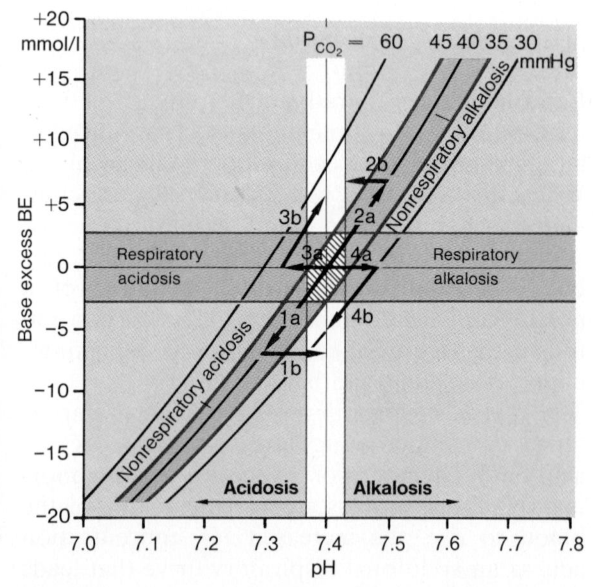

Fig. 22-17. Definitions of the primary acid-base disturbances and ways in which they can be compensated. The normal ranges of base excess BE, pH and CO_2 partial pressure P_{CO_2} are delimited by red lines. *Red cross-hatched field;* range of physiological acid-base balance. Arrow labels: a, primary acid-base disturbances; b, secondary compensations

appropriate change in ventilation of the lungs. In the special case of a metabolic disturbance, there is additional compensatory regulation by the kidneys.
2. In cases of **primary respiratory disturbance,** the kidneys can compensate by changing their HCO_3^- retention or H^+ excretion.

These possibilities, again are best illustrated by the diagram in Fig. 22-17. First let us consider **primary nonrespiratory acidosis** (arrow 1a). As the nonvolatile acids accumulate in the blood the buffer-base concentration is reduced and the pH falls. The fall in pH acts as a respiratory drive to elicit hyperventilation, as a result of which the CO_2 partial pressure drops. This compensation is represented in the graph by arrow 1b. Once the decrease in P_{CO_2} has returned the pH to the normal range, we may consider the primary nonrespiratory acidosis to be *fully compensated.* But if P_{CO_2} does not drop sufficiently to restore normal pH, the acid-base status is described as *partially or incompletely compensated* nonrespiratory acidosis. In **primary nonrespiratory alkalosis** (arrow 2a) the increase in buffer base is compensated by a P_{CO_2} increase caused by hypoventilation (arrow 2b). The degree to which ventilation can be reduced, however, is limited by the body's oxygen requirement, so that this compensation is usually incomplete. In **primary respiratory acidosis** (arrow 3a), which can be caused by pulmonary malfunction, the CO_2 partial pressure is elevated. In this case the base-retention mechanism of the kidney comes into play, with a certain latency. The buffer-base concentration in the blood rises and the pH is returned to the normal range (arrow 3b). In just the same way **primary respiratory alkalosis** (arrow 4a), which is characterized by low CO_2 partial pressure, is compensated by a decrease in the buffer-base concentration (arrow 4b) which shifts the pH back toward the normal range.

Evaluation of Acid-Base Status

Diagnostic criteria. The analysis and assessment of the acid-base status of the blood is a problem of considerable clinical significance. Such evaluation requires the measurement of those parameters that enable one to make the decisions **acidosis-vs.-alkalosis** and **respiratory-vs.-nonrespiratory,** which in turn enable decisions as to suitable therapy [4, 5, 8, 10]. To this end, the following chracteristic quantities of the *arterial blood* must be determined:

1. pH: The pH reading indicates whether the H^+ concentration of the blood is in the normal range (pH 7.37–7.43) or shifted to the acidic or alkaline side. However, normal pH does not necessarily imply that the acid-base balance is entirely undisturbed. A pathological state of primary acidosis or alkalosis could be masked by compensation.
2. P_{CO_2}*:* The presence of elevated or lowered CO_2 partial pressure indicates a primary respiratory disturbance (normal range of P_{CO_2} : 35–45 mm Hg).
3. Base excess: The BE reveals whether or not there is a primary nonrespiratory disturbance of the acid-base balance. An increase or decrease in the concentration of nonvolatile acids in the blood is directly reflected in the BE (normal range of BE: $-2,5$ to $+2.5$ mmol/l).

4. Standard bicarbonate: Another parameter sometimes used to characterize a nonrespiratory disturbance is the standard bicarbonate. This is the bicarbonate concentration of the blood plasma when a CO_2 partial pressure of 40 mm Hg has been established by equilibration at 37 °C and the hemoglobin is completely saturated with oxygen. Because this parameter (norm 24 mmol/l) does not take into consideration the buffering function of the proteins, it is less informative.

Table 22-3 summarizes the primary and secondary changes in the 3 characteristic parameters, which in combination allow the definitive identification of an acid-base disturbance.

Analytical procedures. A method of proven value for the analysis of acid-base status is that of ASTRUP, in which CO_2 partial pressure and acid-base status are determined simultaneously [10]. First the blood to be tested is *equilibrated with two gas mixtures* of known composition and different CO_2 partial pressures, and the pH of each sample is measured. The two sets of paired pH-P_{CO_2} data so obtained are entered in a diagram like that of Fig. 22-18. The straight line joining the two points (A and B) reflects the acid-base status of the blood sample. Now, if the actual pH in the arterial blood of the subject is mea-

Table 22-3. Changes in the diagnostic parameters caused by acid-base disturbances. *Thick arrows:* direction of the primary change; *thin arrows:* direction of the secondary compensation (↑ increase, ↓ decrease)

	pH	BE	P_{CO_2}
Nonrespiratory acidosis	⇓	⇓	↓
Nonrespiratory alkalosis	⇑	⇑	↑
Respiratory acidosis	⇓	↑	⇑
Respiratory alkalosis	⇑	↓	⇓

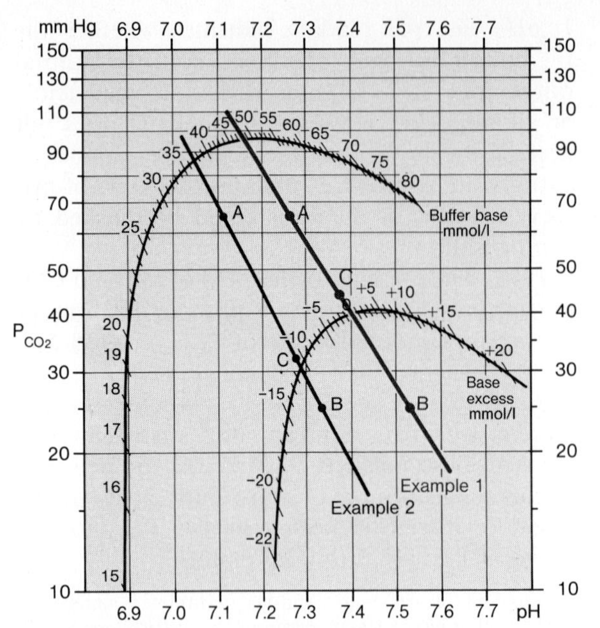

Fig. 22-18. Diagram for determination of the CO_2 partial pressure and the acid-base status of the blood by Astrup's procedure [10]. A and B, points found by measuring the pH of blood previously equilibrated with gas mixtures of known P_{CO_2}. C is the point on the straight line joining A and B that corresponds to the actual measured pH; it gives the actual P_{CO_2}. BE can be read off at the intersection between the A–B line and the base-excess scale. Example 1, *red line:* P_{CO_2} = 44 mm Hg, pH = 7.37, BE = 0 mmol/l; diagnosis: normal acid-base status. Example 2, *black line:* P_{CO_2} = 32 mm Hg, pH = 7.28, BE = −11 mmol/l; diagnosis: partially compensated nonrespiratory acidosis

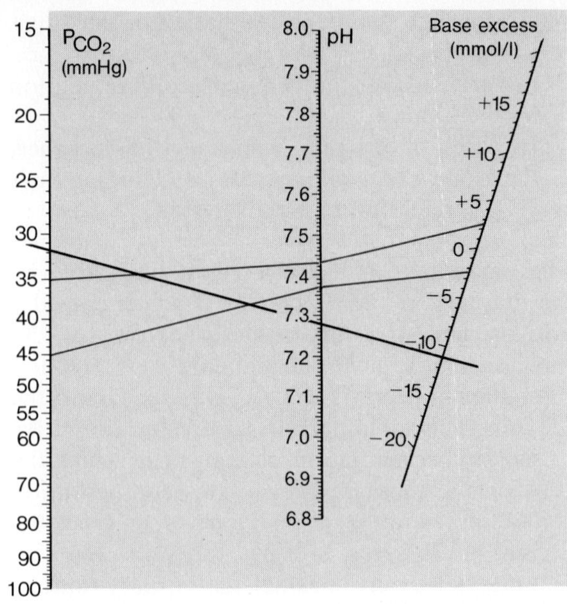

Fig. 22-19. Nomogram for finding the base excess BE from measured data for CO_2 partial pressure P_{CO_2} and pH. The straight line joining the points for P_{CO_2} and pH intersects the right-hand scale at a point corresponding to the BE of the blood. *Red lines:* limits of the normal range of acid-base status. *Black straight line:* from the measured values P_{CO_2} = 32 mm Hg, pH = 7.28 one finds BE = −11 mmol/l; the diagnosis is partially compensated nonrespiratory acidosis. From [29]

sured, the *actual CO_2 partial pressure* associated with it can be found by reference to that line (point C). At the points of intersection between the line and the appropriately labelled scales one can read off the concentration of *buffer bases* and the *base excess.* For example, the red line in Fig. 22-18 characterizes a normal acid-base balance, whereas the black line implies a nonrespiratory acidosis (BE = −11 mmol/l) that is partially compensated by lowered CO_2 partial pressure (P_{CO_2} = 32 mm Hg, black point C).

Because it has recently become possible to measure the CO_2 partial pressure in small blood samples directly with *P_{CO_2} electrodes* (p. 568), the acid-base status can now be evaluated even without previous equilibration [28]. The reason is that the measured actual values of P_{CO_2} and pH determine the base excess BE, the third quantity required for diagnosis. BE can conveniently be found from the two other parameters by means of the nomogram shown in Fig. 22-19.

When the points on the P_{CO_2} and pH scales corresponding to the measured values are joined by a straight line, the extrapolated line intersects the BE scale at a point corresponding to the required BE. For the example in Fig. 22-19, it follows directly from the measured P_{CO_2} = 32 mm Hg and pH = 7.28 that BE = −11 mmol/l. The diagnosis (as in the Example 2 of Fig. 22-18) would therefore be partially compensated nonrespiratory acidosis.

22.5 References

Textbooks and Handbooks

1. ANTONINI, E., BRUNORI, M.: Hemoglobin and myoglobin in their reactions with ligands. Amsterdam: North Holland 1971
2. BAUMANN, R., BARTELS, H., BAUER, C.: Blood oxygen transport. In: FAHRI, L.E., TENNEY, S.M. (Eds.): Handbook of Physiology, Sect. 3: The Respiratory System, Vol. IV. Bethesda, Amer. Physiol. Soc. 1987
3. COBURN, R.F., FORMAN, H.J.: Carbon monoxide toxicity. In: FAHRI, L.E., TENNEY, S.M. (Eds.): Handbook of Physiology, Sect. 3: The Respiratory System. Vol IV. Bethesda, Amer. Physiol. Soc. 1987
4. HILLS, A.G.: Acid-base balance: chemistry, physiology, pathophysiology. Baltimore: Williams and Wilkens 1973

5. Kildberg, P.: Clinical acid-base physiology. Baltimore: Williams and Wilkens 1968
6. Klocke, R.A.: Carbon dioxide transport. In: Fahri, L.E., Tenney, S.M. (Eds.): Handbook of Physiology, Sect. 3: The Respiratory System, Vol IV. Bethesda, Amer. Physiol. Soc. 1987
7. Longo, L.D.: Respiratory gas exchange in the placenta. In: Fahri, L.E., Tenney, S.M. (Eds.): Handbook of Physiology, Sect. 3: The Respiratory System, Vol. IV. Bethesda, Amer. Physiol. Soc. 1987
8. Masoro, E.J., Siegel, P.D.: Acid-base regulation. Its physiology and pathophysiology. Philadelphia-London-Toronto: Saunders 1971
9. Severinghaus, J.W.: Blood gas concentrations. In: Handbook of Physiology, Respiration II. Washington, Amer. Physiol. Soc. 1965
10. Siggaard-Andersen, O.: The acid-base status of the blood. Copenhagen: Munksgaard 1974
11. Weissbluth, M.: Hemoglobin: Cooperativity and electronic properties. Berlin-Heidelberg-New York: Springer 1974
12. Wood, S.C., Lenfant, C.: Phylogeny of the gas-exchange system: red cell function. In: Fahri, L.E., Tenney, S.M. (Eds.): Handbook of Physiology, Sect. 3: The Respiratory System, Vol. IV. Bethesda, Amer. Physiol. Soc. 1987

Original Papers and Reviews

13. Adair, G.S.: The hemoglobin system. VI. The oxygen dissociation curve of hemoglobin. J. Biol. Chem. *63,* 529 (1925)
14. Bauer, C.: On the respiratory function of haemoglobin. Rev. Physiol. Biochem. Pharmacol. *70,* 1 (1974)
15. Bauer, C., Gros, G., Bartels, H. (Eds.): Biophysics and physiology of carbon dioxide. Berlin-Heidelberg-New York: Springer 1980
16. Benesch, R.E., Benesch, R., Yu, C.I.: The oxygenation of hemoglobin in the presence of 2,3-diphosphoglycerate: Effect of temperature, pH, ionic strenght and hemoglobin concentration. Biochemistry, *8,* 2567 (1969)
17. Braunitzer, G.: The molecular weight of human haemoglobin. Bibl. heamat. (Basel) *18,* 59 (1964)
18. Braunitzer, G., Hilse, K., Rudloff, V., Hilschmann, N.: The hemoglobins. Adv. Protein. Chem. *19,* 1 (1964)
19. Brodda, K.: Zur Theorie des Säure-Basen-Haushaltes von menschlichem Blut. Akadem. Wiss. Lit. Mainz; Wiesbaden: Steiner 1975
20. Christiansen, J., Douglas, C.G., Haldane, J.S.: The absorption and dissociation of carbon dioxide by human blood. J. Physiol. XLVIII, 244 (1914)
21. Fischer, W.M., Vogel, H.R., Thews, G.: O_2 and CO_2 exchange in the human placenta. In Lübbers, D.-W., Luft, U.C., Thews, G., Witzleb, E.: Oxygen transport in blood and tissue. Stuttgart: Thieme 1968
22. Kilmartin, J.V., Rossi-Bernardi, L.: Interactions of hemoglobin with hydrogen ions, carbon dioxide, and organic phosphates. Physiol. Rev. *53,* 836 (1973)
23. King, E.J., Gilchrist, M.: Determination of haemoglobin by a cyanhaematin method. Lancet II, 201 (1947)
24. Maren, T.H.: Carbonic anhydrase: Chemestry, physiology, and inhibition. Physiol. Rev. *47,* 595 (1967)
25. Merlet-Bénichou, E., Sinet, M., Blayo, M.C., Gaudebout, C.: Oxygen-combining capacity in dog. In vitro and in vivo determination. Respir. Physiol. *21,* 87 (1974)
26. Perutz, M.F.: The hemoglobin molecule. Proc. Roy. Soc., B, *173,* 113 (1969)
27. Perutz, M.F.: Stereochemistry of cooperative effects in haemoglobin. Nature, *228,* 726 (1970)
28. Thews, G.: Ein Nomogramm für die O_2-Abhängigkeit des Säure-Basen-Status im menschlichen Blut. Pflügers Arch. ges. Physiol. *296,* 212 (1967)
29. Thews, G. (Ed.): Nomogramme zum Säure-Basen-Status des Blutes und zum Atemgastransport. Berlin-Heidelberg-New York: Springer 1971

23 Tissue Respiration

J. GROTE

23.1 Metabolism and Oxygen Requirements of the Tissues

Cellular Metabolism and Energy Conversion

The term *tissue respiration* denotes the *exchange of respiratory gases within an aggregation of cells in the course of the biological oxidation of nutrients.* The **oxygen** received by the cells from the capillary blood is consumed in oxidative metabolism, and at the same time the metabolic end product **carbon dioxide** is released into the capillary blood [8]. Here "tissue respiration" is used in a broader sense than in many biochemistry textbooks, where tissue respiration is defined as the oxidative breakdown of nutrients with the participation of molecular oxygen. Because O_2 deficiency in the tissues limits these reactions more effectively than inadequate removal of CO_2, we shall concentrate on questions related to the supply of oxygen to the tissues.

Aerobic and anaerobic mechanisms. Each living cell in the body needs a certain amount of energy in order to maintain its structure and functional capacities and to carry out its functions. This energy, under normal conditions, is acquired primarily by the **oxidative decomposition of nutrients.** For energy to be obtained by aerobic metabolism both a *substrate* – carbohydrates, proteins and fats – and *molecular oxygen* must be present in the cell in adequate concentrations.
Under anaerobic conditions the energy required by the tissues can be obtained only by **glycolysis.** This metabolic pathway is less economic than the oxidative breakdown of glucose because the end product, lactate, still has a high energy content. To make available a given amount of energy an individual cell under anaerobic conditions must metabolize ca. 15 times as much glucose as it needs when oxygen is available.
According to BURTON and KREBS [15], the *oxidative breakdown* of 1 mol glucose under conditions approximately like those within cells (T = 25 °C, pH = 7.0, P_{O_2} = ca. 150 mm Hg = ca. 20 kPa, P_{CO_2} = ca. 40 mm Hg = ca. 5.3 kPa) provides free energy amounting to ca. 689 kcal = 2883 kJ. The amount of energy obtained from the breakdown of glucose by *glycolysis* is only 50 kcal = 208 kJ. Despite its relatively low energy yield, this form of glucose breakdown plays an important role, under both anaerobic and aerobic conditions, in many tissues – for example, the renal medulla, cartilage, retinal cells, erythrocytes and the working musculature. That glycolysis can proceed at a high rate even under aerobic conditions, contrary to previous opinion, was demonstrated in studies of metabolism in working skeletal muscle and in the inner zone and papilla of the renal medulla [17, 18].

Biological Oxidation in the Mitochondria

Biological oxidation takes place in the *mitochondria.* These cell components have been found to contain not only the enzymes of the citrate cycle, the respiratory chain and oxidative phosphorylation, but also those by which fatty acids and various amino acids are broken down [5]. (The various metabolic pathways of biological oxidation in the mitochondria are illustrated schematically in Fig. 23-1).

Pyruvate, fatty acids and *amino acids* are transported from the cytoplasm through the mitochondrial membrane system into the **matrix space** of the mitochondria. There they are decomposed in specific metabolic pathways into substances that enter the *citrate cycle.* Pyruvate, which is formed chiefly as an end product of aerobic glucose metabolism in the cytoplasm, is converted by oxidative decarboxylation in the matrix space to acetyl-CoA, most of which is broken down in the citrate cycle under normal conditions. Whereas the first steps in glucose breakdown (glycolysis) take place in the cytoplasm, the oxidative decomposition of fatty acids is entirely confined to the matrix space. The fatty-acid molecules are oxidized by a series of reactions called β-oxidation; the resulting acetyl-CoA enters the citrate cycle or is used for the synthesis of fatty acids. The carbohydrate compounds produced in the matrix space by amino-acid metabolism can be fed into the citrate cycle at various points (acetyl-CoA, α-ketoglutarate, succinyl-CoA, fumarate, oxal-acetate).

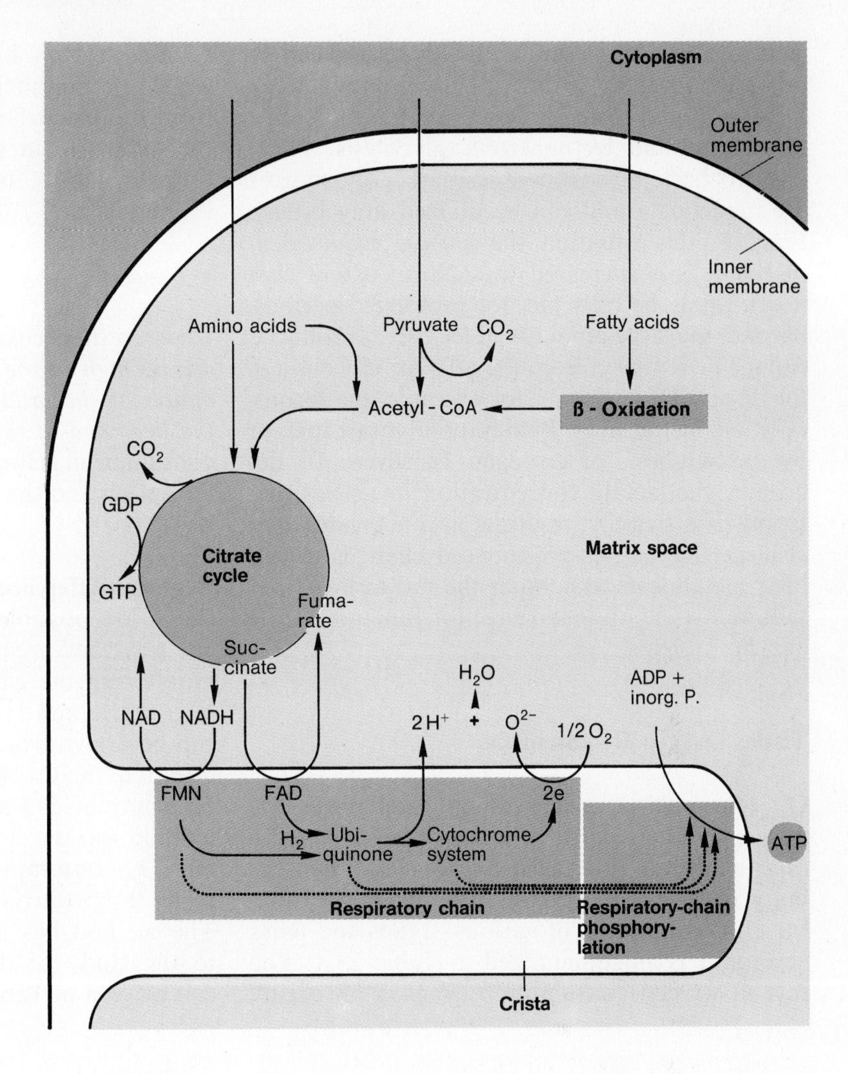

Fig. 23-1. Schematic drawing to show the most important metabolic reactions involved in biological oxidation within the mitochondrion

The *NADH* molecules formed in the citrate cycle by three dehydrogenation reactions, as well as the *succinate* produced in the citrate cycle, diffuse from the matrix space to the inner membrane of the mitochondrion, in which the enzymes of the respiratory chain and oxidative phosphorylation are embedded. There NADH is oxidized by a respiratory-chain enzyme complex that includes flavin mononucleotide (FMN) as a coenzyme, whereas the hydrogen is removed from succinate by a respiratory-chain enzyme complex with flavin adenine dinucleotide (FAD) as a coenzyme. Both of the flavoprotein complexes transfer the electrons to ubiquinone (coenzyme Q), which is then oxidized under the influence of a cytochrome complex. As a result, 2 hydrogen ions and 2 electrons are produced for each hydrogen molecule. The electrons are carried by way of specific Fe compounds (cytochrome b, FeS-protein, cytochrome c_1, cytochrome c) in the respiratory chain to cytochrome oxidase (complex of cytochrome a and cytochrome a_3), which transfers them to molecular oxygen. The reduced oxygen combines with the free hydrogen to form water. The energy released during the transport of electrons in the respiratory chain is used to pump protons from the matrix space into the space between the inner and outer mitochondrial membranes. The transport of protons results in a membrane potential at the inner mitochondrial membrane. According to MITCHELL, biosynthesis of ATP (respiratory-chain phosphorylation) is induced by the flux of protons back into the matrix space. For each oxidized NADH molecule 3 molecules of ATP are produced, and for each oxidized $FADH_2$ molecule 2 molecules of ATP are produced. In the first case the ratio of ATP production to oxygen consumption (the P/O ratio) is 3; that is, 1 gram atom of oxygen is consumed in the formation of 3 moles of ATP. In the second case the P/O ratio is 2.

The consequences of inadequate O_2 supply. When pathological conditions restrict the supply of O_2

some of the energy required by the tissues can be provided, for a short time, by the limited energy reserves stored in the form of ATP and creatine phosphate, and by anaerobic glycolysis. There are two basic reasons why these energy sources are inadequate and can be utilized only briefly. First, in this situation the *glucose requirement* of the cells is increased to such an extent that it can rarely be fully met for prolonged periods. Second, the large amounts of *lactate* so produced cannot be removed from the cells rapidly enough for disposal elsewhere – for example, by decomposition in the liver, kidney or myocardium or by the synthesis of glycogen. In severe O_2 deficiency the lactate concentration in tissues and blood rises steadily, resulting in a *nonrespiratory acidosis* that causes pronounced changes in cellular metabolism as soon as the intracellular pH falls below the optimal range for function of the enzyme systems.

Tissue Oxygen Requirements

O_2 consumption under resting conditions. *The amount of O_2 required by a tissue depends on the functional state of its component cells.* When the body is at rest and at the normal temperature, the O_2 consumption of various organs and parts of organs is as summarized in Table 23-1. The rate of oxygen consumption ($\dot{V}_{O_2}$) in an organ, normally given in ml per 1 g or 100 g fresh weight per minute, is found by the **Fick principle** from the **blood flow** ($\dot{Q}$) through the organ and the **difference in O_2 concentration** between the arterial blood entering it and the venous blood leaving it (avD_{O_2}), according to the equation

$$\dot{V}_{O_2} = avD_{O_2} \cdot \dot{Q} \tag{1}$$

Under resting conditions O_2 consumption is relatively high in the myocardial tissue, in the gray matter of the brain (e.g., the cerebral cortex), *in the liver and in the renal cortex;* the rate of O_2 consumption is lower in the skeletal musculature, the spleen and the white matter of the brain (Table 23-1).

Regional differences in O_2 consumption within an organ. It is possible to measure *blood flow through circumscribed areas of tissue* in many organs by monitoring the *clearance of inert gases* such as ^{85}Kr, ^{133}Xe and H_2. Therefore if a blood sample can be drawn from a vein draining the region in question, the O_2 consumption in that region can be determined. Furthermore, a few years ago a method was developed for measuring blood flow and O_2 consumption in parts of an organ directly, by positron emission tomography (PET). The method has been applied very successfully to the study of the human brain [21, 36]. As can be seen in Table 23-1, it had previously been

Table 23-1. Mean values of perfusion rate ($\dot{Q}$), difference in O_2 concentrations in arterial and venous blood (avD_{O_2}), and O_2 consumption ($\dot{V}_{O_2}$) in various human organs at 37 °C

Organ	Blood flow, $\dot{Q}$ $ml \cdot g \cdot min^{-1}$	Arterioven. diff., avD_{O_2}	O_2 cons., $\dot{V}_{O_2}$ $ml \cdot g^{-1} \cdot min^{-1}$	Refs.
Blood	–	–	$0.6 \cdot 10^{-4}$–$1 \cdot 10^{-4}$	[22]
Skeletal muscle				
at rest	$2 \cdot 10^{-2}$–$4 \cdot 10^{-2}$	$10 \cdot 10^{-2}$–$15 \cdot 10^{-2}$	$2.5 \cdot 10^{-3}$–$5 \cdot 10^{-3}$	[3, 32]
during hard work	0.5–1.3		0.1–0.2	
Spleen	1.0	$1 \cdot 10^{-2}$	$1 \cdot 10^{-2}$	[8, 42]
Brain	0.4–0.6	$6 \cdot 10^{-2}$–$7 \cdot 10^{-2}$	$3 \cdot 10^{-2}$–$4 \cdot 10^{-2}$	[2, 4, 19, 21, 27, 36]
cortex	0.6–1.0	$10 \cdot 10^{-2}$	$5 \cdot 10^{-2}$–$10 \cdot 10^{-2}$	
white matter	0.2–0.3	$5 \cdot 10^{-2}$–$7 \cdot 10^{-2}$	$1 \cdot 10^{-2}$–$2 \cdot 10^{-2}$	
Liver	1.0 (25% hep.art.)	$4 \cdot 10^{-2}$–$5 \cdot 10^{-2}$ (portal v.–hep.v.) $8 \cdot 10^{-2}$–$10 \cdot 10^{-2}$ (hep.art.-hep.v.)	$5 \cdot 10^{-2}$–$6 \cdot 10^{-2}$	[8, 24, 35]
Kidney	4.0	$1.5 \cdot 10^{-2}$–$2 \cdot 10^{-2}$	$5.5 \cdot 10^{-2}$–$6.5 \cdot 10^{-2}$	[10, 29]
cortex	4.0–5.0	$2 \cdot 10^{-2}$–$2.5 \cdot 10^{-2}$	$9 \cdot 10^{-2}$–$10 \cdot 10^{-2}$	
outer medulla	1.2	$5 \cdot 10^{-2}$	$6 \cdot 10^{-2}$–$6.5 \cdot 10^{-2}$	
inner medulla	0.25	$1 \cdot 10^{-2}$–$2 \cdot 10^{-2}$	$0.3 \cdot 10^{-2}$–$0.5 \cdot 10^{-2}$	
Heart				
at rest	0.8–0.9	$10 \cdot 10^{-2}$–$15 \cdot 10^{-2}$	$7 \cdot 10^{-2}$–$10 \cdot 10^{-2}$	[1, 7, 13, 20, 26, 40]
strenuous exercise	up to 4.0	up to ca. $17 \cdot 10^{-2}$	up to ca. $40 \cdot 10^{-2}$	

possible to *measure regional O_2 consumption* in only a few organs.
Studies of the oxygen supply to the brain tissue of various mammals have indicated an O_2 consumption in the *cerebral cortex* of between ca. $8 \cdot 10^{-2}$ and $0.1\,ml \cdot g^{-1} \cdot min^{-1}$. From the data on O_2 consumption measured directly for the whole brain and the cerebral cortex, the mean O_2 consumption of the *white matter of the brain* was found to be ca. $1 \cdot 10^{-2}\,ml \cdot g^{-1} \cdot min^{-1}$. Direct measurement of cerebral O_2 consumption in healthy subjects by positron emission tomography gave values between ca. 4 and $6 \cdot 10^{-2}\,ml \cdot g^{-1} \cdot min^{-1}$ for the *gray matter* in various brain areas, and $2 \cdot 10^{-2}\,ml \cdot g^{-1} \cdot min^{-1}$ for the *white matter* [21, 36]. It is to be expected that the O_2 consumption within an organ varies not only by region but also among the individual cells within a region. For example, when the *local O_2 consumption* in superficial cell layers of the cerebral cortex was studied with platinum microelectrodes, it was found that under light anesthesia the O_2 consumption within small areas varied between ca. $4 \cdot 10^{-2}$ and $0.12\,ml \cdot g^{-1} \cdot min^{-1}$. Autoradiographic studies of local blood flow (with iodo-^{14}C-antipyrine) and local glucose consumption (with ^{14}C-deoxyglucose) in the cerebral cortex indicated that these parameters also differ considerably in adjacent regions [37, 38]. In humans over 30 years old, the regional blood flow and regional O_2 uptake in the gray matter of the brain decrease with increasing age [19, 21, 36].
Comparable differences in the O_2 requirement of individual parts of organs have been found in the kidney. The mean O_2 consumption of the *renal cortex* is several times as large as that of the *inner zone and papilla* of the kidney. Because the O_2 requirement of kidney tissue is determined primarily by the extent of active Na^+ reabsorption from the tubule lumen into the tissue, the large differences in regional O_2 consumption are ascribable particularly to the differential reabsorption activity of the cortex and medulla [11].

O_2 consumption when activity is increased. Whenever higher performance of an organ is called for, its rate of energy conversion rises and its cells require more O_2. During exercise O_2 consumption of the *myocardial tissue* increases to 3 or 4 times the resting level, whereas that of working groups of *skeletal muscles* can increase by more than 20- to 50-fold. The O_2 requirement of *renal tissue* rises with the rate of Na^+ reabsorption.
In the majority of organs, when the tissue O_2 partial pressure is adequate, the *rate of O_2 uptake* into the tissue is *independent of the rate of blood flow* through it. The kidney is an exception. There is a critical perfusion rate above which the formation of ultrafiltrate begins; in this filtration range increased blood flow is accompanied by an increase in the O_2 consumption of the renal tissue. This special situation arises because the change in blood flow causes the rate of glomerular filtration (and thus of Na^+ reabsorption) to change in the same direction.

The influence of temperature on O_2 consumption. O_2 consumption in the tissues is extremely dependent on temperature. If the temperature of the body falls, energy conversion is restricted and most of the organs thus require less oxygen. As long as temperature regulation is maintained, however, those organs involved in the regulatory mechanisms are more active and consume more O_2. Among these is the skeletal musculature (enhanced muscle tone, shivering; see pp. 625f.). Elevated body temperature causes a general increase in tissue O_2 requirements. In the range between 20 °C and 40 °C, according to van't Hoff's rule, any 10 °C change in body temperature will change tissue O_2 consumption in the same direction by the factor $Q_{10} = 2$ to 3. When surgical operations require that the circulation of blood, and thus the supply of O_2 and nutrients to the organs, be interrupted for a time, *hypothermia* (lowered body temperature) is very often induced. In order to achieve a reduction in O_2 requirement of all the organs, the patient is so deeply anesthetized that the thermoregulatory mechanisms are restricted or eliminated.

23.2 Tissue Oxygen Supply

Tissue Oxygen Reserves

The amount of O_2 available to the cells for tissue respiration is determined by the magnitude of the *convective O_2 transport* with the blood and the extent of *O_2 diffusion* between the capillary blood and the tissues. Because most tissues have no O_2 stores apart from that in physical solution, a reduction in the O_2 supply leads to O_2 deficiency and diminished oxidative metabolism as soon as the momentary O_2 requirements are not completely met.

O_2-storage function of myoglobin. The *musculature* is an exception to the above rule. It contains the pigment *myoglobin (Mb)*, which can bind O_2 reversibly and thus serves to store it. However, the concentration of myoglobin in human muscle tissue is low, so that the amount of stored O_2 is not enough to carry the tissues through a long period of severe O_2 deficiency.

The limitations of the O_2 reserve bound to the myoglobin are especially well illustrated by the cardiac musculature.

The mean myoglobin content of the myocardium is 4 mg per g tissue. Because 1 g myoglobin binds at most ca. 1.34 ml oxygen, under physiological conditions about $0.5 \cdot 10^{-2}$ ml O_2 is stored in 1 g of myocardial tissue. If the supply of O_2 to the myocardium should be cut off completely, this amount of O_2 could sustain normal oxidative metabolism in the cells for only ca. 3–4 s.

The significance of myoglobin as a source of oxygen for muscle tissue. Myoglobin provides **short-term storage of O_2** and functions as an **intracellular O_2 transporter.** In binding O_2 reversibly, myoglobin acts as an *O_2 buffer*. Because of this buffering, the O_2 partial pressures at different places in muscle tissue vary much less than in tissue lacking myoglobin, and they can be kept more nearly constant under a load despite the increase in O_2 consumption. Myoglobin has a very high affinity for oxygen as compared with that of hemoglobin (see p. 583); therefore the muscle pigment can function as a buffer only at O_2 partial pressures below ca. 10–15 mm Hg (1.3–2.0 kPa). Under the conditions in muscle tissue the O_2 half-saturation pressure of myoglobin is ca. 5–6 mm Hg (0.7–0.8 kPa). The high O_2 affinity of myoglobin keeps the partial pressure of O_2 in the muscle cell low, creating a steep O_2 partial-pressure gradient between cell and capillary blood which promotes the release of O_2 into the muscle tissue [22, 25]. The transport function of myoglobin becomes operative when differences in O_2 saturation develop within a muscle cell; then oxygenated myoglobin molecules diffuse from the sites of higher to those of lower concentration (facilitated O_2 diffusion, see p. 603). In such situations large amounts of O_2 can be transported intracellularly even though the O_2 partial pressure differences are small [22, 30].
In the **myocardium** the oxygen bound to myoglobin ensures a supply of O_2 to those parts of the muscle in which blood flow is reduced or completely blocked for a brief time during systole [26].
In the **skeletal musculature** the O_2 released by the myoglobin when hard muscular work is begun can cover part of the increased demand for O_2 during the transition period until the adjustment of blood flow again delivers the amount required. The oxygen released by myoglobin accounts for part of the **O_2 debt** that can be incurred by each skeletal muscle fiber.

O_2 Availability and Utilization

O_2 availability to the organs. The amount of O_2 carried by the blood to a given organ per unit time is the product of **arterial O_2 concentration** and **the rate of blood flow:**

$$O_2 \text{ availability} = C_{a_{O_2}} \cdot \dot{Q} \tag{2}$$

This relationship implies that differences in the availability of oxygen to the various organs are entirely ascribable to differences in blood flow through the organs. Any change in blood flow, as a result of changes in vascular resistance or mean arterial pressure, results directly in a change in the amount of oxygen available to the tissue.
The average supply of O_2 to individual organs under physiological conditions can be found directly from the O_2 concentration of the arterial blood (see p. 584) and the values for blood flow given in Table 23-1. The O_2 availability is particularly large for the renal cortex, the spleen and the gray matter of the brain, and small in the cases of resting skeletal musculature, renal medulla and the white matter of the brain.

O_2 utilization coefficient in different organs. The **O_2 utilization coefficient** of an organ is the **ratio of its O_2 consumption to the O_2 availability.** It is found by combining Eq. (1) and Eq. (2) as follows:

$$O_2 \text{ utilization coefficient} = (avD_{O_2} \cdot \dot{Q})/(C_{a_{O_2}} \cdot \dot{Q}) = avD_{O_2}/C_{a_{O_2}} \tag{3}$$

Because tissues vary in their oxygen requirements, the utilization parameters must also vary. Under normal conditions the cerebral cortex, myocardium and resting skeletal musculature consume ca. 40–60% of the O_2 available in a given time. The normal O_2 utilization coefficient of the whole body is 0.3. The O_2 utilization coefficient can increase considerably in conditions of greater activity. Maximal values, as great as ca. 0.9 in the extreme case, are found when hard work is being performed, in the working skeletal musculature and in the myocardium. Under pathological conditions, reduction of the arterial O_2 concentration (arterial hypoxemia) or diminished blood flow (ischemia) can markedly increase the O_2 utilization of an organ. A particularly small fraction of the available O_2 is utilized in the kidney and the spleen. Because of the large amounts of blood that flow through these organs in support of their normal functions, both the kidney and the spleen have a very large O_2 availability although they require only moderate or slight amounts of oxygen.

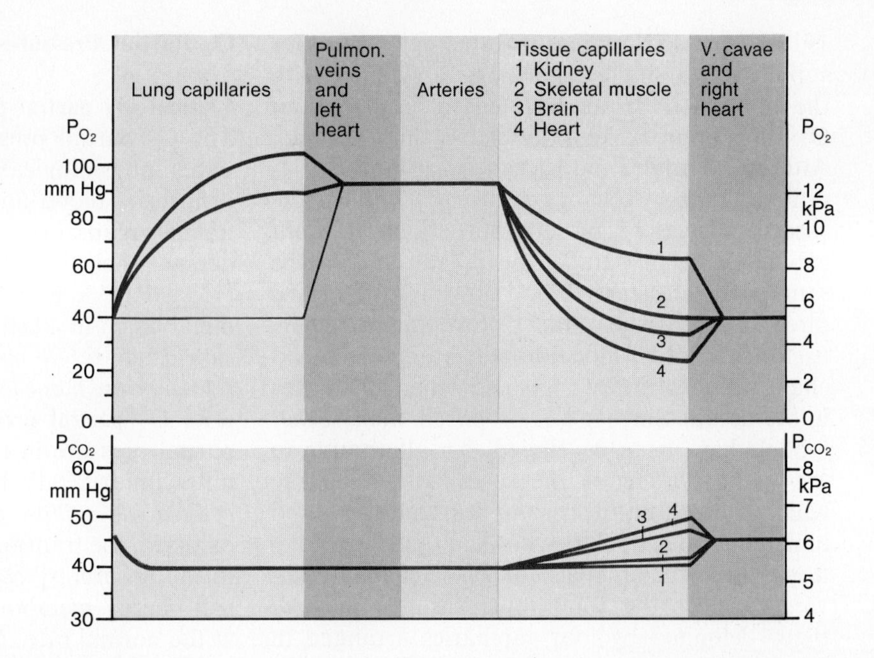

Fig. 23-2. O_2 partial pressure (P_{O_2}) and CO_2 partial pressure (P_{CO_2}) of the blood in the successive segments of the circulatory system under resting conditions. Modified from [41]

Respiratory Gas Exchange in the Tissue

Free and facilitated diffusion. The exchange of respiratory gases between the capillary blood and the cells of a tissue, like gas exchange in the lungs, occurs by **diffusion** (see pp. 4f.). The **O_2 molecules** brought to the tissues in the blood move along the O_2 partial-pressure gradient, from the erythrocytes and the plasma into the surrounding tissue. At the same time, the carbon dioxide formed during oxidative metabolism diffuses from the tissue cells with high CO_2 partial pressure into the blood, where the CO_2 partial pressure is lower. The energy driving diffusion of the respiratory gases is the kinetic energy of the individual molecules. Thus the **partial pressure of O_2 and CO_2 in the blood** is a factor of particular significance in tissue gas exchange. The mean partial pressures of both respiratory gases in the different parts of the circulatory system of a human at rest are diagrammed in Fig. 23-2. The release of O_2 from the blood to the tissues can be affected by the *diffusion of the oxygenated hemoglobin* within the erythrocytes, which accelerates the transport of the O_2 molecules to the surface of the blood cell [30]. This effect is described by the term **facilitated O_2 diffusion.** In muscle tissue the *diffusion of oxygenated myoglobin* has a comparable effect on O_2 transport. Under certain conditions – very low O_2 partial pressures accompanied by slight O_2 partial-pressure differences within the cells – facilitated O_2 diffusion makes a considerable contribution to the O_2 supply in the muscle fibers [22].

Another factor that may additionally increase the velocity of respiratory gas transport is *convection* of the cytoplasm within the erythrocytes or tissue cells as well as of the plasma and the interstitial fluid.

Both the release of O_2 from blood to tissues and the transport of CO_2 in the opposite direction are determined not only by the *partial-pressure gradient* between the capillary blood and the cells, but also by the size of the *exchange area,* the length of the *diffusion path,* and the magnitude of the *diffusion resistance* of the various structures through which the molecules pass. Under conditions of constant partial pressure or concentration gradient, the effect of these factors on the amount of gas exchanged per unit time is described by **Fick's first law of diffusion** (see pp. 4 and 564).

Models of gas exchange in the tissue. The law of diffusion can be used to analyze respiratory gas exchange in a tissue and to compute the O_2 and CO_2 partial pressures in the cells. Such theoretical analyses are based on models that incorporate the various diffusion-determining parameters in the region supplied by a single capillary or capillary network. So that the relationships can be described mathematically, such models must represent the functional and morphological conditions during tissue O_2 or CO_2 diffusion in a simplified way.

Various structural models have been proposed to assist the description of gas exchange in the tissues. The best known and most frequently used of these is **Krogh's tissue cylinder.** As early as

1918 KROGH [31] represented the region of tissue supplied by a single capillary as a cylinder with the capillary as its axis. He based his studies of O_2 diffusion in skeletal muscle on this concept. Although Krogh's model can describe the conditions for gas exchange accurately only in the case of a mass of tissue within which adjacent capillaries lie in parallel, begin and end in the same plane and carry blood flowing in the same direction, the tissue cylinder proved an extremely useful conceptual model for the study of the exchange of respiratory gases and other substances in the tissues. Since it was proposed, many other models have been developed. An alternative to the tissue cylinder is the so-called *cone-model*, which is based on the assumption that the blood in neighboring capillaries flows in opposite directions. Still other models for gas-exchange analyses consider the conditions within a *cube of tissue* delimited by four capillaries arranged in parallel, through which the blood flows in different directions; others describe the process of gas exchange in an area of tissue containing a square-meshed *network* of capillaries.

Significance of capillary density and the microcirculation. In addition to the partial-pressure gradient between the capillary blood and the cells, the *capillary density* and the *blood-flow distribution in the microcirculation* are crucial factors influencing respiratory gas exchange in a region of tissue. Both the **exchange area** for the diffusion of gases between blood and tissue and the **diffusion distance** within the tissue are directly dependent on the number of perfused capillaries, their length and the distance between them.

Capillary density varies from organ to organ, and in many cases even within a single organ. The capillary network is particularly dense, offering favorable conditions for gas exchange, in those tissues with high energy turnover.

In the *myocardium,* for example, there is one capillary for each muscle fiber; the mean distance between adjacent capillaries is ca. 25 μm. The mean intercapillary distance in the *cortex of the brain* has been found to be ca. 40 μm, and that in the *skeletal musculature* is ca. 80 μm. The capillary blood-flow distribution can be altered by increases or decreases in muscular tone of the vessels preceding the capillary bed, which change the number of capillaries that are perfused at any given time. Thus, not only the amount of oxygen available to a tissue area, but the conditions for O_2 exchange as well, can be varied by enlargement or reduction of the diffusion area and the diffusion distance.

O_2 Partial Pressures in the Tissues

Critical O_2 partial pressure in the mitochondria. The O_2 partial pressure in the cells of a tissue under physiological conditions is between that of arterial blood and a minimum, which in different organs or parts of organs with high O_2 demand has been found to be about 1 mm Hg (133.3 Pa). A prerequisite for normal oxidative metabolism in a cell is a *minimal O_2 partial pressure of ca. 0.1–1 mm Hg* (13.3–133.3 Pa) *in the region of the mitochondria* – the **critical mitochondrial O_2 partial pressure** [15, 22, 39]. If the O_2 partial pressure in the immediate vicinity of the mitochondria falls below this level, the reduced *cytochrome oxidase* can no longer be completely oxidized, the transport of hydrogen and electrons in the *respiratory chain* is curtailed, and as a result energy metabolism can no longer continue at the normal rate. *Thus the most important criterion by which to judge the O_2 supply to an organ is the cellular O_2 partial pressure.*

The development of *polarographic* techniques (p. 568) has made it possible to measure directly, with microelectrodes, the O_2 partial pressure in

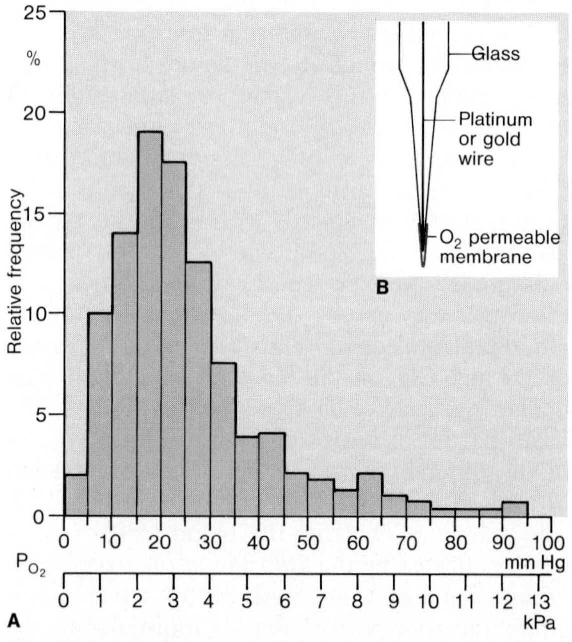

Fig. 23-3 A,B. O_2 partial pressure in the gray matter of the brain. **A** Frequency distribution of the local O_2 partial pressures in the cerebral cortex of the guinea pig during normal ventilation. The maximal levels (P_{O_2} = 90–95 mm Hg = 12.0–12.7 kPa) correspond to the O_2 partial pressure of the arterial blood. The minima, in the cells least well provided with oxygen, are 0.5–1 mm Hg (67–133 Pa), and thus are ca. 25 mm Hg (3.3 kPa) below the mean O_2 partial pressure of the venous blood in the cortex (from [34]). **B** Structure of a microelectrode for polarographic measurement of the O_2 partial pressure in tissues

single cells of a tissue. For the measurement of O_2 partial pressure in cells near the surface very small platinum electrodes are used, which can be set directly on the tissue without disrupting the microcirculation in the area under study. Measurement of the cellular O_2 partial pressure in deeper parts of the tissue can be done with needle electrodes having tip diameters of ca. 0.5–5 μm (Fig. 23-3 B).

Both of these procedures have so far been used chiefly in experiments on animals. But they have been successfully applied to human patients (to easily accessible organs in particular), and they have provided important information. For instance, there are a number of examples of muscle disease or disturbance of blood flow through skeletal muscle for which the distribution of O_2 partial pressure in the affected muscle groups has been analyzed in detail, under both resting and working conditions. Microsurface electrodes have been used during neurosurgical operations to obtain important information about the current oxygen supply in the brain area of interest. The results of such a study are shown in Fig. 23-4; the histograms show the local O_2 partial pressures in superficial cells of the cerebral cortex in arterial normoxia and arterial hypoxia [28].

In most cases, however, when one wants to know something about the O_2 supply to a human organ it is necessary to measure directly the most important determining factors – such as the rate of flow, the respiratory gas partial pressures and concentrations, and the pH of the arterial blood – and then to use the results so obtained as the basis for a theoretical analysis of gas exchange within the tissue of interest.

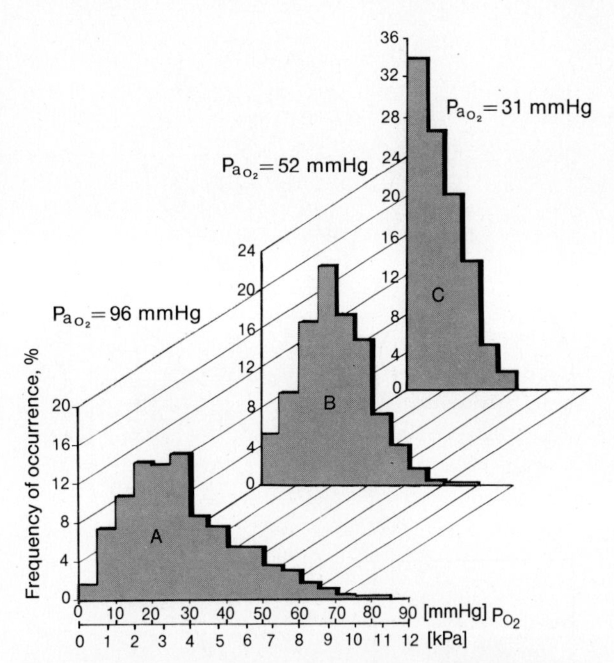

Fig. 23-4 A–C. Histograms of local O_2 partial pressure in superficial cells of the cat cerebral cortex in arterial normoxia (**A** Pa_{O_2} = 96 mm Hg = 12.8 kPa), moderate arterial hypoxia (**B** Pa_{O_2} = 52 mm Hg = 7.0 kPa) and severe arterial hypoxia (**C** Pa_{O_2} = 31 mm Hg = 4.2 kPa). As the arterial O_2 partial pressure falls, the distributions shift progressively toward lower O_2 partial pressures, with a marked increase in the number of measurements in the range from 0 to 5 mm Hg (0 and 6.7 kPa). Severe arterial hypoxia is accompanied by pronounced tissue hypoxia, with anoxia in many cells of the cerebral cortex (from [28])

Distribution of O_2 partial pressure in brain tissue. The two tissues for which it is most interesting to know the O_2 partial pressure distribution are the brain and the myocardium, for an inadequate supply of O_2 to either can be a direct cause of death. Within the cylindrical region of the *cerebral cortex* supplied by a capillary, given a tissue O_2 consumption of $9 \cdot 10^{-2}$ml $O_2 \cdot g^{-1} \cdot min^{-1}$ and a flow of 0.8 ml blood $\cdot g^{-1} \cdot min^{-1}$, one obtains the average distribution of O_2 partial pressure illustrated in Fig. 23-5. *During passage through the capillary the O_2 partial pressure of the blood falls from 90 mm Hg* (12.0 kPa) *to ca. 28 mm Hg* (3.7 kPa). The changes in O_2 partial pressure in the capillary blood conform to the shape of the *effective O_2 dissociation curve* (pp. 584f.). Perpendicular to this gradient along the capillary is a radial gradient, with an O_2 partial pressure difference of ca. 26 mm Hg (3.5 kPa) between the blood and the peripheral regions of the tissue cylinder. In those cells that are least well supplied with O_2, at the venous end of the cylinder, O_2 partial pressures between 1 and 2 mm Hg (133 and 266 Pa) are to be expected.

The calculated O_2 partial pressures – which are in close agreement with the results of direct measurements on animals [27] under comparable conditions (Figs. 23-3A, 23-4) – indicate that the brain tissue is not at all as well supplied with oxygen as had been thought. They explain why a decrease in cerebral blood flow very easily produces *O_2 deficiency* in the neurons of the most poorly supplied brain regions. The immediate consequence is an impairment of neuronal function, which in many cases results in partial or complete loss of consciousness.

Distribution of O_2 partial pressure in the myocardium. The cardiac muscle tissue differs from most organs in the **nonstationarity of its O_2 supply.** Both the *perfusion* and the *energy requirement* of the myocardium change in the course of a cardiac cycle. During systole the increased

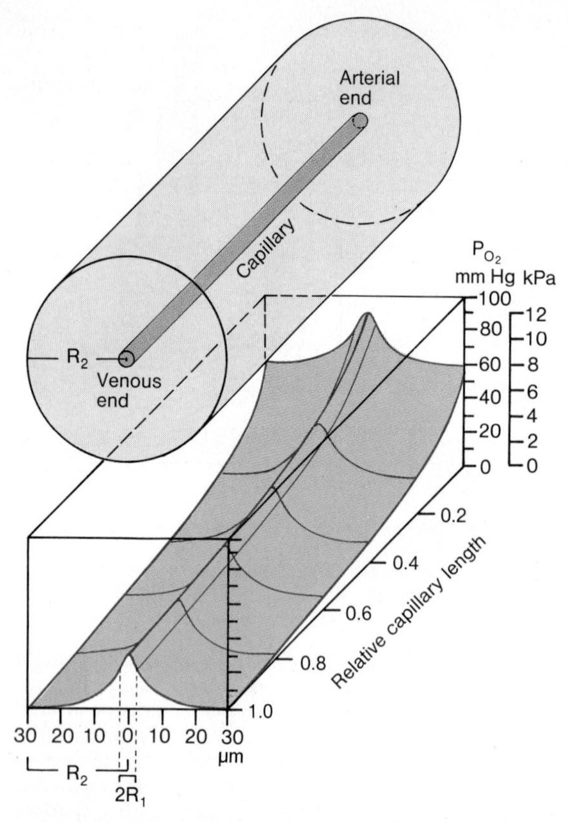

Fig. 23-5. Schematic illustration of the O_2 partial pressure distribution in Krogh's tissue-cylinder model of a capillary in the human cerebral cortex (O_2 consumption $= 9 \cdot 10^{-2}$ml $\cdot$ $g^{-1} \cdot min^{-1}$, blood flow $= 0.8$ml $\cdot g^{-1} \cdot min^{-1}$). The mean O_2 partial pressure of the blood under normal conditions falls from 90 mm Hg (12.0 kPa) at the arterial end of a cortical capillary to ca. 28 mm Hg (3.7 kPa) at the venous end. Within a cross section of the cylinder supplied by the capillary, the mean O_2 partial pressure falls by ca. 26 mm Hg (3.5 kPa) from the capillary to the edge of the cylinder

pressure in the tissue reduces the flow of blood through the region supplied by the left coronary artery; in the inner layers of the myocardium of the left ventricle blood flow can be completely interrupted for a short time (see pp. 477f.). The resulting fluctuations in the *myocardial O_2 availability,* from a *minimum in systole* to a *maximum in diastole,* are accompanied by just the opposite changes in the energy requirements of the individual myocardial cells. These need the *most energy* during the *contraction* phase, and the *least* during the *resting* phase.

Two factors ensure that the myocardium obtains all the energy needed under normal conditions in spite of the restricted O_2 supply during systole. One is that the *myoglobin functions as a short-term O_2 store* (pp. 601f.) in cells in which the O_2 partial pressure falls below ca. 10 mm Hg (1.3 kPa) during contraction, and the other is that the myocardium contains *energy reserves* (ATP, creatine phosphate) that can be called upon to meet the momentarily increased demand. During diastole the massive blood flow provides enough O_2 to resaturate the myoglobin completely with oxygen and to replenish the cellular energy stores [26].

The changes in O_2 supply during the course of systole and diastole would be expected to result in *periodic changes in the O_2 partial pressure of the myocardial cells.*

During exercise it is more difficult for an adequate supply of O_2 to the heart to be maintained. Its increased activity causes the myocardium to use up more oxygen; at the same time with rising heart rate distole is considerably shortened, so that the degree to which the available oxygen can be matched to the demand is limited. The boundary conditions for very strenuous exercise are reached at heart rates of about 200 min^{-1}. Under these conditions the ECG in many cases exhibits the typical signs of inadequate O_2 supply in the myocardial tissue (depression of ST, flattening or reversal of T; cf. pp. 459f.).

O_2 Partial Pressure Distribution in the Working Skeletal Musculature

The *function of myoglobin as an O_2 buffer and transport vehicle* most strongly affects the distribution of O_2 partial pressures in the skeletal musculature when it is working. Theoretical analyses of O_2 diffusion in myoglobin-rich muscle tissue [25] have shown that under a work load

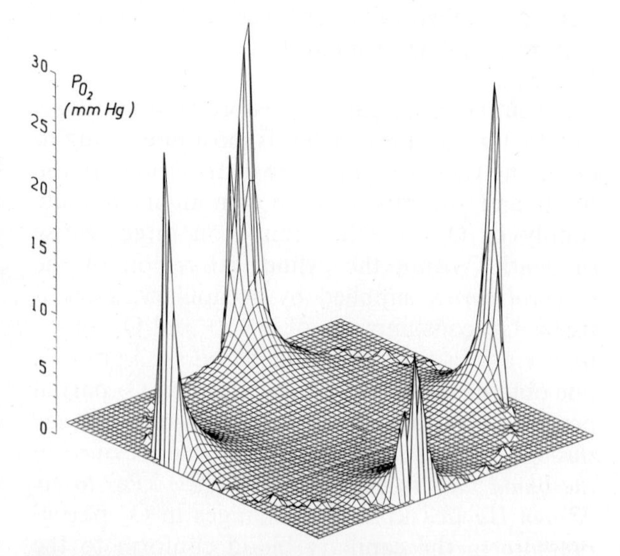

Fig. 23-6. O_2 partial-pressure distribution in a cross section through a myoglobin-rich muscle fiber and the four capillaries supplying it, under the assumption of load conditions with O_2 consumption of 0.14 ml $\cdot g^{-1} \cdot min^{-1}$ and a fiber radius of 25 μm (from [25])

particularly large O_2 partial-pressure gradients are to be expected between the capillary blood and the muscle cells to be supplied (Fig. 23-6). When the O_2 partial pressure in a muscle fiber is low, the differences in O_2 partial pressure within the fiber are small; therefore the intracellular O_2 transport in the musculature must be dominated by facilitated O_2 diffusion (see p. 603). The results of theoretical studies are in close agreement with the intracellular partial pressures calculated from the O_2 saturation of myoglobin measured directly in single muscle fibers [22].

23.2 Regulation of O_2 Supply and Effects of O_2 Deficiency

Mechanisms for Matching Supply to Demand

The increased *O_2 requirement* of an organ that is functioning more actively must be met by an increase in and more complete utilization of the amount of oxygen supplied to the tissue. As is evident in Eq. (2), in principle more O_2 can be provided to a tissue by increasing blood flow, the O_2 concentration in the arterial blood, or both. Under physiological conditions, however, the hemoglobin O_2 saturation in arterial blood is already ca. 97%, so that an increase in arterial O_2 concentration by brief hyperventilation is impracticable. Therefore adjustment of the *O_2 availability* in a tissue to a transiently raised O_2 demand must be brought about predominantly by *increased blood flow*.

Regulation of organ perfusion. The amount of blood flowing through an organ is determined primarily by the magnitude of the *cardiac output* and the level of *vascular tone in the vessels preceding the terminal vascular bed*. The neural and hormonal influences and the local chemical mechanisms that modulate organ perfusion are described in detail in Chapter 20. Here we shall consider only a few special aspects of the regulation of O_2 supply in the brain, the myocardium and the skeletal musculature.
In the **brain tissue** the O_2 supply is raised to meet an increased demand chiefly by lowering the tone of the vessel musculature; the factors that elicit this vasodilation are *lowered O_2 partial pressure (hypoxia)* and *elevated CO_2 partial pressure (hypercapnia)* in the intra- and extracellular space, as well as an *increased extracellular H^+ concentration*. Moreover, a comparable change in the tone of the smooth musculature of the cerebral vessels is brought about by the moderate increase in extracellular K^+ concentration and by an increased adenosine concentration in the perivascular space. But because calcium ions play a central role in setting vascular tone, the reactions just described are attenuated or entirely eliminated if the Ca^{2+} concentration in the perivascular space is subnormal. An increase in the extracellular Ca^{2+} concentration directly elicits vasoconstriction, and a decrease elicits vasodilation [2, 4, 13, 33]. The extent to which influences of the autonomic nervous system on vessel diameter contribute to regulation of blood flow in the brain remains unclear [2, 33].
Increased blood flow through the **myocardium** under an additional load is brought about chiefly by local chemical processes; prominent among these is the *reduced O_2 partial pressure (hypoxia)*. The concentration of adenosine, which acts as a vasodilator, rises in the myocardial tissue when the demand for oxygen exceeds the supply, and this may be a crucial factor in increasing perfusion. Furthermore, the *eicosanoids* formed mainly in the endothelium play an important role in the local adjustment of myocardial perfusion. *Prostacyclin* and the *prostaglandins* that act as vasodilators are of special significance [11]. The *increased sympathetic tone* under a work load initially reduces perfusion by the activation of α-receptors. The simultaneous activation of the β-receptors enhances metabolism and thereby eventually leads to vasodilation; the end result, if there is sufficient perfusion pressure, is an increase in blood flow through the myocardium [1, 7, 20].
The mechanisms underlying increased blood flow through the **skeletal musculature** are still largely unknown. Skeletal muscle is innervated by both adrenergic sympathetic fibers – the activity of which, as in many other organs, determines in particular the tone of the smooth musculature of the vessels – and cholinergic sympathetic fibers with a vasodilator action. The *activation of these cholinergic sympathetic fibers* is thought to cause the initial increase in perfusion when the muscles begin to work. These fibers have only a slight effect on the parts of the terminal vascular bed in which respiratory gases and other substances are exchanged. As the muscles continue to work, increased perfusion of the true (nutritive) capillaries is presumably maintained by a number of local chemical mechanisms that reduce the basal tone of the vessel musculature, which is not determined by direct neural influences. It is

thought that the *rise in K^+ concentration* and in the *osmolarity* of the extracellular fluid play a central role, to which is added the effect of *hypoxia* in the muscle tissue. On the other hand, change in the partial pressure of CO_2 and in the H^+ concentration are only subordinate factors in increasing blood flow through working skeletal muscle [3].

The consequences of prolonged or repeated increases in O_2 demand. When the heart must repeatedly perform extra work under conditions of increased O_2 demand in other organs, the myocardium undergoes *structural changes* and the *weight* of the heart increases. The physiological adaptation found, for example, in athletes trained for endurance sports can result in an increase in the mass of the heart from the normal ca. 200–300 g to a *maximum of ca. 500 g*, owing chiefly to growth of the individual myocardial fibers **(hypertrophy).** The stimulus that triggers this growth is thought to be *short-term O_2 deficiency in the myocardial tissue.* Myocardial hypertrophy is limited chiefly by the accompanying deterioration of the O_2 supply to the muscle fibers. During growth of the myocardium above a critical heart weight of about 500 g, both the mass of muscle supplied by each capillary and the number of capillaries in the tissue increase, but the precapillary part of the vascular system remains largely unaltered; as a result, the individual myocardial fibers can no longer be adequately supplied with O_2 [6]. Whereas the mean radius of a myocardial fiber under normal conditions is ca. 8 μm, at the limiting weight it is ca. 13.5 μm.
Under **pathological conditions** the critical weight can be exceeded, and the resulting O_2 deficiency in many parts of the myocardium causes the destruction of some of the myocardial fibers and a breakdown of the normal structural relationships within the myocardium *(eccentric hypertrophy,* with dilation of the heart cavity).
In addition to the changes in the heart under these conditions, there may be an **elevated O_2 capacity of the blood.** Frequently repeated increases in the O_2 requirements of the organs produce effects similar to those of the lack of oxygen at great altitudes (see p. 666) and of disturbances of pulmonary gas exchange – that is, *enhanced erythropoiesis and hemoglobin synthesis.* These processes are triggered by an increase in the production of erythropoietin, primarily in the kidney, which accelerates the formation or maturation of *proerythroblasts.* As the number of erythrocytes increases **(erythrocytosis)** and the hemoglobin concentration rises, the O_2 capacity of the blood becomes greater, so that although the partial pressure of oxygen in the arterial blood is unchanged its concentration is higher. However, the *viscosity* of the blood increases with the hematocrit, and the heart must work harder to propel the more viscous blood; thus the degree to which adaptation can be effected by erythropoiesis is severely limited.

The Causes of Inadequate O_2 Supply

Disturbances in either the exchange of respiratory gases in the lung or their transport in the blood can prevent the supply of O_2 from meeting the needs of the tissues – a condition called **tissue hypoxia** (P_{O_2} less than normal) or **tissue anoxia** ($P_{O_2} = 0$ mm Hg). Of the possible causes of inadequate O_2 supply, three predominate: (i) lowered O_2 partial pressure in the arterial blood *(arterial hypoxia),* (ii) reduced O_2 capacity of the blood *(anemia),* and (iii) restricted blood flow through the organs *(ischemia).*

Arterial hypoxia. When the ventilation-perfusion ratio in the lungs decreases *(alveolar hypoventilation;* see p. 563) there is a decrease in the O_2 partial pressure **(hypoxia)** and in the O_2 concentration **(hypoxemia)** of the arterial blood. Because of the simultaneous increase in arterial CO_2 partial pressure **(hypercapnia),** *respiratory acidosis* develops as well. Comparable reductions in arterial O_2 partial pressure and O_2 concentration are observed in people at high altitudes, but here they are accompanied by a reduction of the CO_2 partial pressure in the arterial blood **(hypocapnia)** and *respiratory alkalosis* (see pp. 595f.).
In severe arterial hypoxia the O_2 supply to the tissues is restricted and only moderate physical exertion is possible. Under these conditions, especially in organs with a high O_2 requirement, the O_2 partial pressure in the capillary blood can fall to very low levels (Figs. 23-7 and 23-8), so that **venous hypoxia** ensues. As can be seen

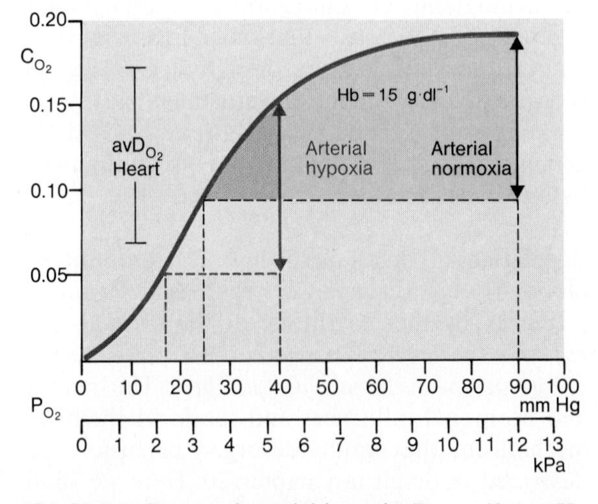

Fig. 23-7. Influence of arterial hypoxia (P_{O_2} = 40 mm Hg = 5.3 kPa) on the drop in O_2 partial pressure in the blood during passage through a capillary, for the conditions prevailing in the myocardium when the body is at rest. When the arterial O_2 partial pressure is severely decreased, the changes in O_2 partial pressure in the capillary blood are determined chiefly by the steep part of the O_2 dissociation curve. As a consequence the drop in partial pressure is less than that in normoxia, which can partially compensate for the unfavourable initial conditions for O_2 supply to the tissues *(ordinate:* O_2 concentration C_{O_2}, ml O_2 per ml blood; *abscissa:* O_2 partial pressure P_{O_2})

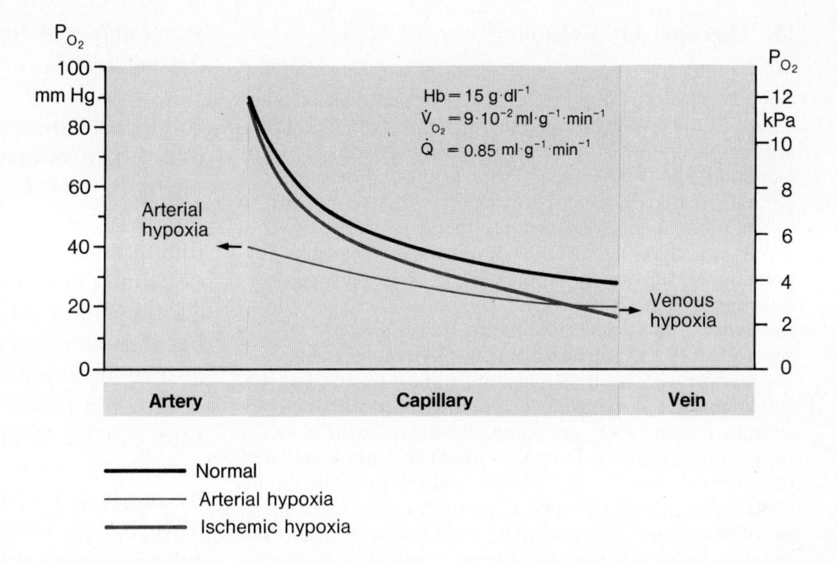

Fig. 23-8. Mean O_2 partial pressure drop in the capillaries of the human cerebral cortex under normal conditions, in ischemic hypoxia (blood flow reduced by 1/3) and in severe arterial hypoxia

in Fig. 23-7, the changes in O_2 partial pressure accompanying gas exchange in capillary blood within the organs are determined by the steepest part of the effective O_2 dissociation curve in conditions of marked arterial hypoxia. In this part of the curve a given change in O_2 concentration is associated with a smaller change in O_2 partial pressure than in the right-hand part. Therefore, although the arteriovenous O_2 concentration difference is the same as normal, the O_2 partial pressure profile in the capillaries is very flat; this effect partially compensates for the otherwise unfavorable conditions of O_2 supply to the tissues. These relationships are illustrated for the cerebral cortex in Fig. 23-8, under the assumption of an arterial O_2 partial pressure of 40 mm Hg (5.3 kPa). As soon as the O_2 partial pressure gradient between the blood and the tissue no longer suffices to enable an adequate release of oxygen, the O_2 partial pressure in the cells supplied by the venous end of the capillary falls below the critical level for the mitochondria, and energy metabolism is restricted.

Anemic hypoxia. Whenever the O_2 capacity of the blood is diminished as a result of *blood loss* or *inadequate hemoglobin synthesis* **(anemia)** or owing to *methemoglobin formation* or *CO poisoning* **(functional anemia),** the O_2 concentration in the arterial blood falls. Fig. 23-9 illustrates this situation, with myocardial tissue as an example. Under these conditions, if the amount of O_2 extracted by the tissues is unchanged the O_2 concentration in the blood becomes very low during passage through the capillary. At the venous end, in particular, levels can be reached at which it is impossible for enough O_2 to diffuse to the sites where it is needed *(venous hypoxia).*

Ischemic hypoxia. When *organ perfusion is restricted,* more than the normal amount of O_2 is extracted from the blood as it flows through the capillaries, so that there is a *greater arteriovenous difference in O_2 concentration.* The direct consequence is a more pronounced drop in O_2 partial pressure along the capillary (venous hypoxia); because the gradient in O_2 partial pressure between blood and tissue is lowered at the same time, the supply of O_2 to the cells may become inadequate (Fig. 23-8).

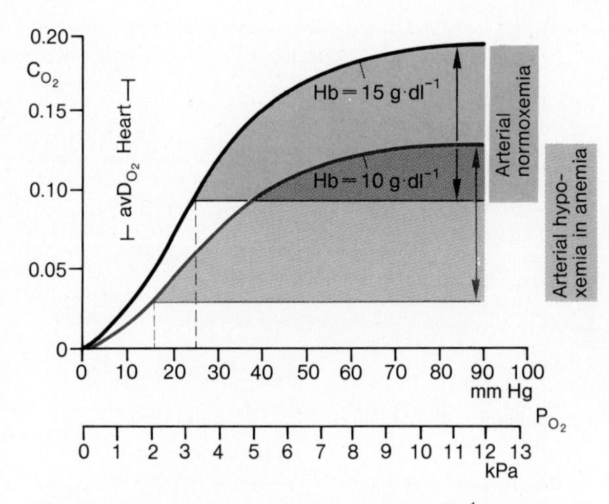

Fig. 23-9. Effect of anemia ($Hb = 10 g \cdot dl^{-1}$) on the O_2 partial pressure changes in the capillary blood, under the conditions in the myocardium when the body is at rest (ordinate: O_2 concentration C_{O_2}, ml O_2 per ml blood; abscissa: O_2 partial pressure P_{O_2})

O_2 Therapy; O_2 Poisoning

The O_2 deficiency conditions just described can in many cases be improved by oxygen therapy, directed toward raising the partial pressure of oxygen in the arterial blood by *increasing the O_2 partial pressure in the inspired air.* The patient breathes a gas mixture with a high proportion of O_2 or pure oxygen **(isobaric O_2 therapy)** or is treated in a pressure chamber at above-atmospheric pressures **(hyperbaric O_2 therapy).** O_2 therapy is of limited value in ischemic and anemic hypoxia, for under these conditions the arterial O_2 concentration can be raised only slightly by increasing the amount of O_2 in physical solution.

O_2 therapy can be used only on a short-term basis, because prolonged exposure to gas mixtures with high O_2 content results in **O_2 poisoning.** Treatment with pure O_2, for example, must be limited to about 4 hours under normal pressure conditions. The marked elevation of the O_2 partial pressure in the cells *(hyperoxia)* affects the activity of many enzymes involved in tissue metabolism. For example, the oxidation of glucose, fructose and pyruvic acid is inhibited in hyperoxia. Typical signs of O_2 poisoning are *dizziness* and *convulsions. Cardiac output decreases* owing to increased vagal tone, and *blood flow through brain and kidneys* is restricted. In the lungs changes in the alveolar membrane can give rise to diffusion impairment and the accumulation of fluid in the alveoli *(pulmonary edema).* Newborn infants treated for hours or days with pure oxygen have been found to develop *retinal damage* that impairs vision or causes complete *blindness.*

To prevent O_2 poisoning when prolonged isobaric O_2 therapy of an adult is required, gas mixtures with an O_2 concentration below 0.6 and and O_2 partial pressure less than 450 mm Hg (< 60 kPa) are used. When newborn infants are to be treated, the O_2 concentration in the gas mixture may be no greater than 0.4, and its partial pressure no greater than 300 mm Hg (40 kPa) [10].

Reversible and Irreversible Disturbance in Acute Tissue Anoxia

In all cases of acute tissue anoxia, whether produced by a sudden interruption of the O_2 supply owing to vascular obstruction or by severe arterial hypoxia, a brief **latent period** in which cell function is unimpaired is followed by curtailment of cellular metabolism and thus of cell function. As the energy stores are consumed it eventually becomes impossible for the cells to function even at a reduced level, and complete *loss of function* ensues. As can be seen in Fig. 23-10, cell structure can be maintained for minutes to hours, depending on the amount of energy required, by utilization of the energy reserves, so that the disturbances *initially are reversible* and successful resuscitation is possible. *Irreversible cellular damage* and eventually *cell death* occur when energy metabolism no longer suffices to keep the cell structure intact. In highly differentiated cells such as neurons irreparable damage occurs after about 10 min of maintained anoxia at normal body temperature. In skeletal muscle under comparable conditions and with the normal energy stores in the individual cells, irreversible damage can be detected only after anoxia has lasted for several hours.

Loss of function and resuscitation. The time from onset of tissue anoxia to complete loss of organ

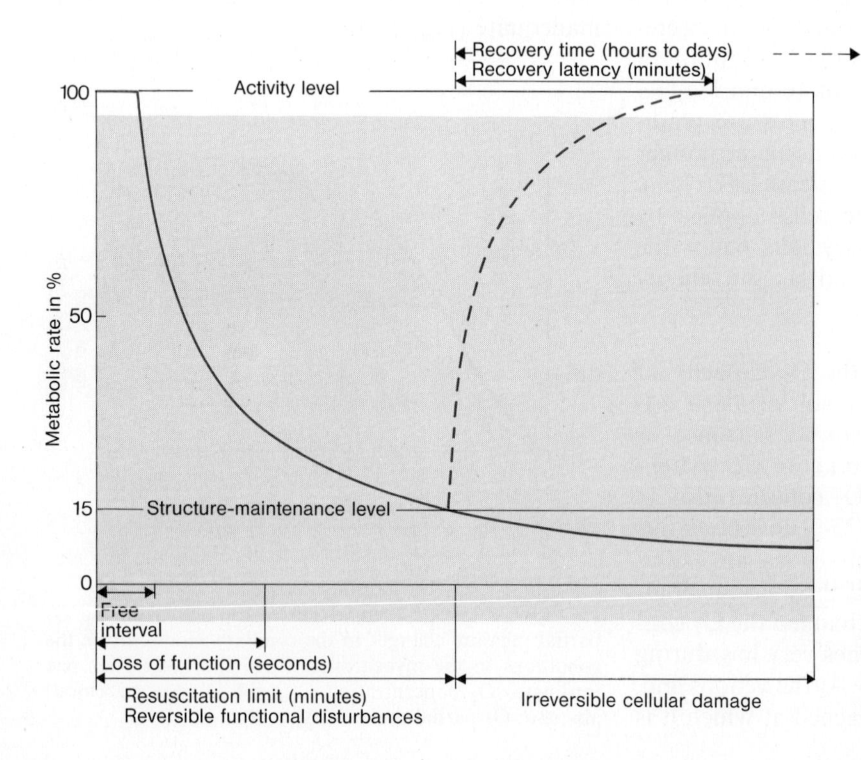

Fig. 23-10. Changes in tissue metabolism after acute ischemic anoxia, diagrammatic. *Below graph:* characteristic time intervals following anoxia within which reversible and irreversible disturbances occur. *Dashed curve:* return to normal metabolism when normoxia is restored in time. *Above graph:* characteristic time intervals for recovery

function – the **functional limit** – is shorter than the **resuscitation limit.** That is, there is a period of time following loss of function due to tissue anoxia during which *complete resuscitation of the whole organ remains possible.*

The functional and resuscitation limiting times are particularly short in the **brain.** Complete interruption of blood flow through the brain causes distinct impairment of function after a latency of only ca. 4 s, and total loss of function, with unconsciousness, after 8–12 s (the *survival time for organ function).* The first changes in the EEG appear after ca. 4–6 s, and after 20–30 s the spontaneous electrical activity of the brain tissue vanishes (flat EEG; see p. 136).

Successful resuscitation of the brain after sudden tissue anoxia at 37 °C is possible up to about the 8th to 10th minute *(resuscitation limit of the brain).* When anoxia is very brief, organ function returns after a latency of 1 minute (the **recovery latency).** After ischemia has lasted ca. 4 min, the recovery latency is ca. 10 min. Complete recovery of organ function, however, often requires hours or days **(recovery time).** Even after brain ischemia only 1 min in duration, the recovery time is 15 min. For the *kidney* and *liver,* resuscitation limits of 3–4 h and recovery times of several days have been found. The *heart* can still be resuscitated after hours at rest, but the active heart becomes incapable of resuming its normal circulatory function after only a 3-to-4-min interruption of coronary blood flow. For this reason, an acute interruption of circulation following cardiac arrest can often cause irreversible brain damage and death of the patient within a few minutes even though the heart has been successfully revived, for in the subsequent 4–5 min the damaged heart cannot develop the arterial mean pressure necessary for normal perfusion of the brain. The **resuscitation limit of the whole organism** is therefore only about 4 min – considerably shorter than the resuscitation limits of any of the vital organs.

23.4 References

Textbooks and Handbooks

1. BASSENGE, E.: Physiologie der Koronardurchblutung. In: Handbuch der inneren Medizin. Bd. 9/3, S. 1. Berlin, Heidelberg, New York, Tokyo: Springer 1984
2. BETZ, E.: Physiologie und Pathophysiologie der Gehirndurchblutung. In: Handbuch der Medizinischen Radiologie, Bd. 14, S. 194, Berlin, Heidelberg: Springer 1981
3. GOLENHOFEN, K.: Skeletmuskel. In: Lehrbuch der Physiologie in Einzeldarstellungen. Physiologie des Kreislaufs. Bd. 1, S. 385. Berlin-Heidelberg-New York: Springer 1971
4. HIRSCH, H.: Gehirn. In: Lehrbuch der Physiologie in Einzeldarstellungen. Physiologie des Kreislaufs, Bd. 1, S. 145. Berlin-Heidelberg-New York: Springer 1971
5. LEHNINGER, A.I.: Bioenergetik. Molekulare Grundlagen der biologischen Energieumwandlungen. 2. Auflage. Stuttgart: Thieme 1974
6. LINZBACH, A.J.: Pathologische Anatomie der Herzinsuffizienz. In: Handbuch der inneren Medizin., 4. Aufl., Bd. 9, S. 706. Berlin-Göttingen-Heidelberg: Springer 1960
7. LOCHNER, W.: Herz. In: Lehrbuch der Physiologie in Einzeldarstellungen. Physiologie des Kreislaufs. Bd. 1, S. 185, Berlin-Heidelberg-New York: Springer 1971
8. LUTZ, J., BAUEREISEN, E.: Abdominalorgane. In: Lehrbuch der Physiologie in Einzeldarstellungen. Physiologie des Kreislaufs, Bd. 1, S. 229. Berlin-Heidelberg-New York: Springer 1971
9. PIPER, J., KOEPCHEN, H.P.: Atmung. In: Physiologie des Menschen. Bd. 6. 2. Aufl. (Hrsg. GAUER, O.H., KRAMER, K., JUNG, R.). München: Urban u. Schwarzenberg 1975
10. POULSEN, H., JACOBSEN, E.: Die hyperbare Sauerstofftherapie. In: Anaesthesiologie. Intensivmedizin und Reanimation. 5. Aufl. S. 805. Berlin-Heidelberg-New York: Springer 1982
11. SCHRÖR, K.: Prostaglandine und verwandte Verbindungen. Bildung, Funktion und pharmakologische Beeinflussung. Stuttgart: Thieme 1984
12. THURAU, K.: Niere. In: Lehrbuch der Physiologie in Einzeldarstellungen. Physiologie des Kreislaufs. Bd. 1, S. 293. Berlin-Heidelberg-New York: Springer 1971

Original Papers and Reviews

13. BETZ, E.: Cerebral blood flow: its measurement and regulation. Physiol. Rev. *52,* 595 (1972)
14. BRETSCHNEIDER, H.J.: Sauerstoffbedarf und -versorgung des Herzmuskels. Verh. dtsch. Ges. Kreisl.-Forsch. *27,* 32 (1961)
15. BURTON, R., KREBS, H.A.: The free-energy changes associated with the individual steps of the tricarboxylic acid cycle, glycolysis and alcohol fermentation and with hydrolysis of the pyrophosphate groups of adenosintriphosphate. Biochem. J. *54,* 94 (1953)
16. CHANCE, B., OSHINO, N., SUGANO, T., MAYEVSKY: Basic principles of tissue oxygen determination from mitochondrial signals. Adv. Exp. Med. Biol. *37A,* 277 (1973)
17. COHEN, J.J.: Is the function of the renal papilla coupled exclusively to an anaerobic pattern of metabolism. Am. J. Physiol. *236,* F423 (1979)
18. CONNETT, R.J., GAYESKI, T.E.J., HONIG, C.R.: Energy sources in fully aerobic rest-work transitions: a new role for glycolysis. Am. J. Physiol. *248,* H922 (1985)
19. DEVOUS, M.D., SR., STOCKELY, E.M., CHEHABI, H.H., BONTE, F.J.: Normal distribution of regional cerebral blood flow measurement by dynamic single-photon emission tomography. J. Cereb. Blood Flow Metabol. *6,* 95 (1986)
20. FEIGL, E.O.: Coronary Physiology, Physiol. Rev. *63,* 1 (1983) Physiol *2,* 274 (1967)
21. FRACKOWIAK, S.J., LENZI, G.L., JONES, T., HEATHER, J.D.: Quantitative measurement of regional cerebral blood flow and oxygen metabolism in man using ^{15}O and positron emission tomography: theory, procedure and normal values. J. Comput. Tomogr. *4,* 272 (1980)
22. GAYESKI, T.E.J., CONNET, R.J., HONIG, C.R.: Oxygen transport in rest-work transition illustrates new functions for myoglobin. Am. J. Physiol. *248,* H914 (1985)
23. GREENBAUM, R., NUNN, J.F., PRYS-ROBERTS, C., KELMAN, G.R.: Metabolic changes in whole human blood (in vitro) at 37 °C. Respir. Physiol. *2,* 274 (1967)
24. GREENWAY, C.V., STARK, R.D.: Hepatic vascular bed. Physiol. Rev. *51,* 23 (1971)
25. GROEBE, K., THEWS, G.: Theoretical analysis of oxygen supply to contracted skeletal muscle. Adv. Exp. Med. Biol. *200,* 495 (1986)
26. GROTE, J., THEWS, G.: Die Bedingungen für die Sauerstoffversorgung des Herzmuskelgewebes. Pflügers Arch. *276,* 142 (1962)

27. GROTE, J., ZIMMER, K., SCHUBERT, R.: Effects of severe arterial hypocapnia on regional blood flow regulation, tissue PO_2 and metabolism in the brain cortex of cats. Pflügers Arch. *391*, 195 (1981)
28. GROTE, J., SCHUBERT, R.: Regulation of cerebral perfusion and PO_2 in normal and edematous brain tissue. In: Oxygen Transport to Human Tissue (Eds. LOEPPKY, J.A., RIEDESEL, M.L.), S. 169. New York, Amsterdam, Oxford: Elsevier North Holland (1982)
29. KRAMER, K., THURAU, K., DEETJEN, P.: Hämodynamie des Nierenmarks, 1. Mitteilung: Capilläre Passagezeit, Blutvolumen, Durchblutung, Gewebshämatokrit und O_2-Verbrauch des Nierenmarks in situ. Pflügers Arch. *270*, 251 (1960)
30. KREUZER, F.: Facilitated diffusion of oxygen and its possible significance: a review. Respir. Physiol. *9*, 1 (1970)
31. KROGH, A.: The number and distribution of capillaries in muscles with calculations of the oxygen pressure head necessary for supplying the tissue. J. Physiol. (Lond.) *52*, 409 (1918/19)
32. KUNZE, K.: Das Sauerstoffdruckfeld im normalen und pathologisch veränderten Muskel. In: Schriftenreihe Neurologie. Bd. 3. Berlin-Heidelberg-New York: Springer 1969
33. KUSCHINSKY, W., WAHL, M.: Local chemical and neurogenic regulation of cerebral vascular resistance. Physiol. Rev. *58*, 656 (1978)
34. LÜBBERS, D.W.: Local tissue PO_2: its measurement and meaning. In: Oxygen Supply. Theoretical and Practical Aspects of Oxygen Supply and Microcirculation of Tissue (Eds. KESSLER, M., BRULEY, D.F., CLARK, L.C., LÜBBERS, D.W., SILVER, I.A., SIRMUSS, J.). S. 151. München-Berlin-Wien: Urban u. Schwarzenberg 1973
35. LUTZ, J., HENRICH, H., BAUEREISEN, E.: Oxygen supply and uptake in the liver and the intestine: Pflügers Arch. *360*, 7 (1975)
36. PHELPS, M.E., MAZZIOTTA, J.C., HUANG, S.-C.: Study of cerebral function with positron computed tomography. J. Cereb. Blood Flow Metabol. *2*, 113 (1982)
37. SAKURADA, O., KENNEDY, C., JEHLE, J., BROWN, J.D., CARBIN, G., SOKOLOFF, L.: Measurement of local cerebral blood flow with iodo [^{14}C] antipyrine. Am. J. Physiol. *234*, H59 (1978)
38. SOKOLOFF, L., REIVICH, M., KENNEDY, C., DES ROSIERS, M.H., PATLAK, C.S., PETTRIGREW, K.D., SAKURADA, O., SHINOHARA, M.: The [^{14}C] deoxyglucose method for the measurement of local cerebral glucose utilization: theory, procedure, and normal values in the conscious and anesthetized albino rat. J Neurochem. *28*, 897 (1977)
39. STARLINGER, H., LÜBBERS, D.W.: Polarographic measurements of the oxygen pressure performed simultaneously with optical measurements of the redox state of the respiratory chain in suspensions of mitochondria under steady-state conditions at low oxygen tension. Pflügers Arch. *341*, 15 (1973)
40. STRAUER, B.E.: Dynamik, Koronardurchblutung und Sauerstoffverbrauch des normalen und kranken Herzens. Experimentell-pharmakologische Untersuchungen und Katheteruntersuchungen am Patienten: Basel, München, Paris, London, New York, Sydney: S. Karger 1975
41. THEWS, G.: Der Transport der Atemgase. Klin. Wschr. *41*, 120 (1963)
42. VAUPEL, P., WENDLING, P., THOME, H., FISCHER, J.: Atemgaswechsel und Glucoseaufnahme der menschlichen Milz in situ. Klin. Wschr. *55*, 239 (1977)

VII
Energy Balance, Work, and Environment

24 Energy Balance

H.-V. ULMER

24.1 Energy Expenditure

Energy expenditure is characteristic of every living cell; energy-rich nutrients are taken in and chemically converted, and ultimately metabolic end products with a lower energy content are eliminated from the cell (cf. pp. 598f.). The energy made available by this process is consumed in various ways. It is used, for example, to keep the cell's *structure* (and thus its *functional capacity* intact, and to fuel *specific cellular activities* (such as the contraction of muscle cells).

The term **anabolism** denotes the metabolic processes by which specific bodily materials are synthesized from the ingested foodstuffs; **catabolism** denotes those by which bodily materials or ingested foodstuffs are broken down, in the course of intermediary metabolism. The metabolism of fats and carbohydrates serves chiefly to sustain physiological functions **(functional metabolism),** whereas that of proteins primarily maintains and modifies the body's structure **(structural metabolism).**

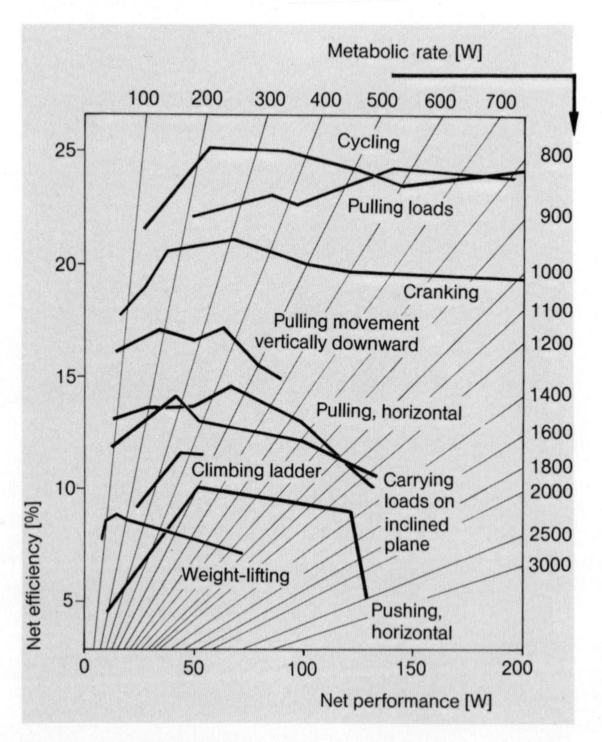

Fig. 24-1. Net efficiency for various forms of work (data from MÜLLER, see [7])

Total energy conversion. The rate of energy conversion by the body as a whole depends on the amounts of energy released (external work, heat) and stored (foodstuff depots, structural modifications) per unit time. That is, the total amount of energy converted is the *sum of external work, lost heat* and *stored energy.*

Energy units. Energy metabolism has traditionally been expressed in kilocalories (kcal) per unit time. The International System of Units, however, established the joule (J) as the basic unit of energy: $1\,\text{joule} = 1\,\text{watt}\cdot\text{second} = 2.39\cdot10^{-4}\,\text{kcal}$, $1\,\text{kcal} = 4,187\,\text{J} = 4.187\,\text{kJ} \approx 0.0042\,\text{MJ}$ (p. 797). It follows that $1\,\text{kJ/h} \approx 0.28\,\text{W}$ ($\approx 0.239\,\text{kcal/h}$), and $1\,\text{kJ/d} \approx 0.012\,\text{W}$ ($\approx 0.239\,\text{kcal/d}$).

Efficiency. If a cell does external work, the associated energy conversion necessarily produces *heat* (Second Law of Thermodynamics). The efficiency (η) of the active cell, like that of a machine, is the fraction of the energy converted that appears as work, and is always less than 100 %:

$$\eta(\%) = \frac{\text{external work}}{\text{converted energy}} \cdot 100 \qquad (1)$$

A distinction is made between *gross efficiency,* based on the total converted energy, and *net efficiency,* which is based on the amount of energy converted after subtraction of the energy for basal metabolism (p. 615). The efficiency of an isolated muscle is at best 35%; that of the whole organism during muscular work rarely exceeds 25% (see examples in Fig. 24-1).

24.2 Parameters of Metabolism

Metabolic Parameters of Cells

In view of the varied functions of metabolism in a living cell, it is useful to distinguish 3 fundamental *levels of metabolic activity:*

The **active level** is the metabolic rate of an *active cell,* which varies according to the degree of activity at any time.

The **readiness level** is the rate at which a momentarily inactive cell must metabolize in order to maintain its *capacity for immediate, unrestricted function.* This category includes, for example, the processes that maintain particular concentration differences of Na^+ and K^+ ions.

The **maintenance level** is the minimal metabolic rate that suffices to *preserve cell structure.* If this absolute requirement is not met, the cell suffers irreversible damage and dies.

It is important to keep this subdivision in mind when evaluating the *effects of disturbed energy metabolism* on a single cell or an isolated organ. Metabolism can be disturbed in a number of ways - for example, by a reduction in the oxygen supply or rate of blood flow, and by poisoning.

The **whole organism** is differently affected by metabolic level than an isolated organ. For example, if the metabolism of the respiratory musculature or the myocardium falls to the readiness level, activity of the organs is impossible. As a result, all the cells die, for the organism as a whole cannot survive unless the breathing muscles and heart are in operation.

Interruption of energy supply does not lead to immediate deterioration of cell activity, because certain energy reserves are available (p. 647). However, the time for which cells can sustain full function depends very much on the organ concerned. If the *brain* is affected, complete ischemia (pp. 136 and 610f.) results in *unconsciousness* after ca. 10 s and in *irreversible damage* after 3–8 minutes; with ischemia of resting skeletal *muscle,* however, metabolism does not fall below the maintenance level until 1–2 hours have elapsed.

Metabolic Parameters of the Whole Organism

Metabolic rate at rest. The metabolic rate of a resting organism cannot be equal to the sum of the readiness levels of all its cells, because some of the organs (for example, the brain, heart, respiratory musculature, liver and kidneys) are *always active.*

The metabolic rate of the body at mental and physical rest is not a precisely defined quantity, for various factors can affect it. To facilitate comparison, conditions have been established under which a basal metabolic rate can be measured.

Basal metabolic rate (BMR). The following four conditions are usually specified for measurement of basal metabolic rate: 1. it is done in the morning, 2. the subject is at rest (lying down), 3. the subject is fasting, and 4. the ambient temperature is neutral and the body temperature normal.

This *morning resting-fasting metabolic rate under thermoneutral conditions* was once an important clinical tool for the diagnosis of thyroid abnormalities. Now other ways of testing thyroid function are available. Thyroid function may be evaluated, for example, by examination with radioactively labelled iodine or measurement of the thyroid hormone in the blood. Therefore the basal metabolic rate is now no longer used for diagnosis.

The four standard conditions of the BMR measurement reveal the following *factors that can affect human metabolic rate:*

1. The metabolic rate is subject to **diurnal fluctuations,** with an increase in the morning and a decline during the night.
2. During *physical* and *mental* **work** the metabolic rate rises, for there is an increase in the number of cells metabolizing at rates above the readiness level. In both cases the main organ affecting metabolic rate is the musculature (cf. the section on metabolic rate during work and Fig. 24-2).
3. The **consumption of food** and the subsequent processes of digestion raise the metabolic rate, particularly after protein has been eaten. This is called *diet-induced thermogenesis* (p. 678). The increase in metabolic rate after eating is due not only to the "activity" of digestion but also to the subsequent metabolic processes. It can last for 12 hours, or for as long as 18

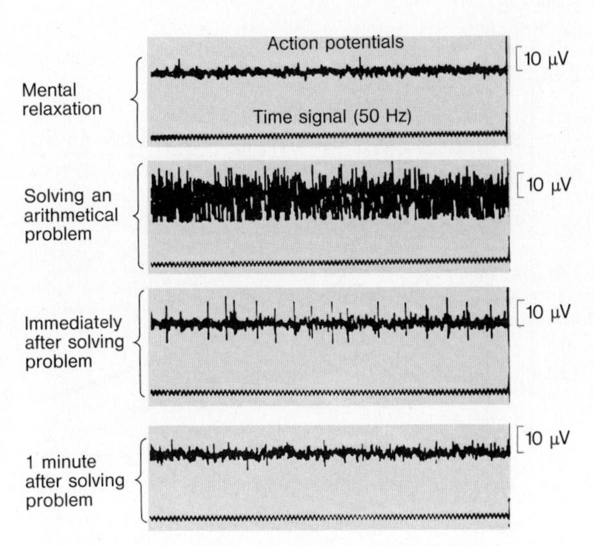

Fig. 24-2. Reflex increase in muscle tone during mental work. In this example the muscle action potentials (EMG) were recorded from the forearm. Modified from [12]

Table 24-1. The contribution of different organ systems to the basal metabolic rate of a human. From [4]

Organ:	Liver	Muscle	Brain	Heart	Kidneys	Other
Relative contrib.	26%	26%	18%	9%	7%	14%

hours after the consumption of large amounts of *protein.*

4. If the **ambient temperature** deviates from the *neutral range* (thermoneutral zone; cf. pp. 626f.), the metabolic rate increases; downward shifts in temperature effect greater increases than do upward shifts. The effects of changes in body temperature follow van't Hoff's rule (p. 624).

The liver and the resting skeletal musculature account for half of the basal metabolic rate (Table 24-1). Because muscle tone decreases during sleep, the metabolic rate of a sleeping or anesthetized person can fall below the basal rate. During starvation, the metabolic rate can be below standard because of a decrease in the metabolism of the liver.

Norms for BMR. Even with strict adherence to the standard conditions, healthy subjects can vary in basal metabolic rate. Four factors can account for this variation: *age, sex, height, and body weight* (Fig. 24-3).

These variables are taken into account in the **tables of norms** that have been derived from large samples of the population by authors such as BOOTHBY et al. [10], BOOTHBY and DUBOIS (see [9]), FLEISCH (see [9]), HARRIS and BENEDICT [13] and KESTNER and KNIPPING [2].

Small differences in the norms listed in different tables are based in part on the fact that they were obtained from different populations (North Americans, Swiss, Germans). Averages and "normal" values (p. 663) always depend on the group of subjects tested. As a rule, however, 4.2 $kJ \cdot kg^{-1} \cdot h^{-1}$ (1.2 W) can be taken as a rough estimate of the basal metabolic rate of an adult; for a person weighing 70 kg this would amount to about 7,100 kJ/d (84 W).

Metabolic rate during work. During *physical* work metabolic rate rises, by an amount dependent on the degree of exertion required. The **"leisure rate"** – the metabolic rate of a very slightly active person – is about *8,400 kJ/d (97 W)* for women and *9,600 kJ/d (110 W)* for men. This corresponds to the daily *overall metabolism of a large fraction of the population,* "desk workers" who do not exert themselves physically to any appreciable extent.

The **working metabolic rate,** as the term is used in the international literature, is the rate of energy expenditure *during* work (i.e., the rate of energy provision for basal metabolism plus the additional requirements for the work.) The

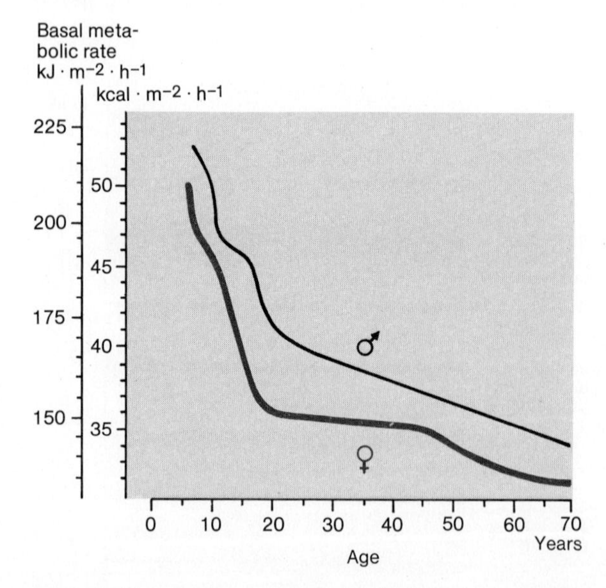

Fig. 24-3. Dependence of the relative BMR on age and sex. The surface area of the body (m^2) is a function of height and weight (p. 691). From [10]

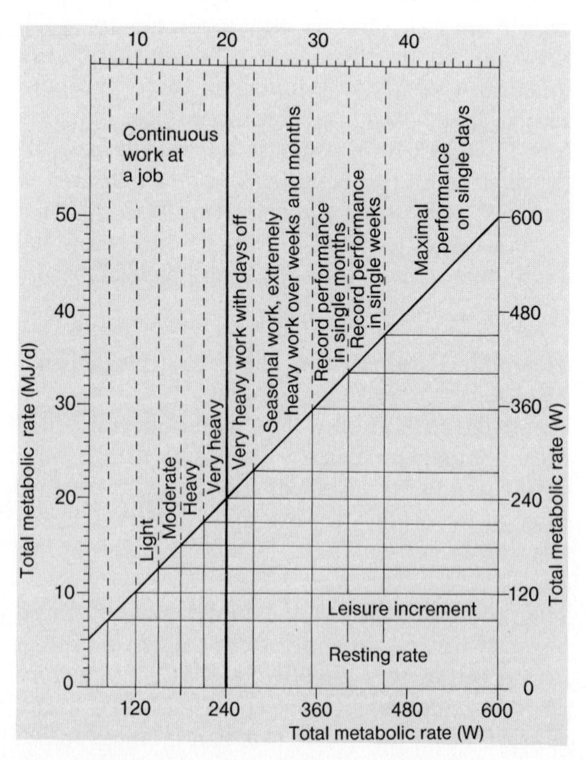

Fig. 24-4. Energy expenditure (per 24-h day) of men in jobs requiring various degrees of physical exertion, and classification of such work. Data from [4]

more strenuous the work, the higher the working metabolic rate. The *upper limits* for work continued over years have been set at 15,500 kJ/d (ca. 186 W) for women and 20,100 kJ/d (ca. 240 W) for men. But higher rates can be achieved in work done for only a short time, or if the work is interrupted occasionally for days of rest (Fig. 24-4).

During mental work the rate also rises, although the brain contributes hardly anything to this increase. As far as the brain is concerned, concentration on a particular subject amounts simply to shifting the activity from one region to another; even during sleep there are no appreciable changes in the metabolic rate of brain tissue. The reason for the increased metabolism during mental work is a reflexly produced increase in muscle tone (Fig. 24-2).

Table 24-2. Metabolic rates under typical conditions (rounded values), with the associated rates of oxygen uptake (see indirect measurement of metabolic rate). BMR = Basal Metabolic Rate

Condition		Metabolic rate		$\dot{V}_{O_2}$
		MJ/d	W	ml/min
BMR, 70 kg body weight	♀	6.3	76	215
	♂	7.1	85	245
BMR plus leisure metabolic rate	♀	8.4	100	275
	♂	9.6	115	330
Working metabolic rate (maximally hard work over periods of years)	♀	15.5	186	535
	♂	20.1	240	690
		kJ/h	W	ml/min
Total metabolic rate for endurance sport (Competitive athlete)		4,300	1,200	3,600

24.3 Metabolic Rates under Special Conditions

Some representative metabolic rates are shown in Table 24-2 and Fig. 24-4. Values for particular work and leisure activities can be estimated from Fig. 24-5 or found in the comprehensive tables published by Spitzer et al. [6]. The severity of different kinds of physical labor can be estimated by reference to Fig. 24-4.

Athletes can achieve considerably higher metabolic rates than people at work, but for much shorter periods of time. The influence of time was evident in Fig. 24-4 and can be particularly well illustrated by the metabolic rates found for the various running distances between 100 m and the marathon. The longer the distance of the race – and hence the time required – the lower is the metabolic rate (Fig. 24-6). The metabolic rate to run 100 or 200 m is 22 kW, about 13 times as great as that to run a marathon. The *work* performed during 10 s of high-speed running reaches 220 kJ, which corresponds to the caloric value of about 14 g glucose. During the more than 2 hours that it takes to run a marathon, the runner expends about 1.6 kW, far higher than the value given in Fig. 24-4 for the maximal daily metabolic rate at work for only a few days at a time. The marathon runner's metabolic rate corresponds to 2.1 "horsepower" (750 W ≈ 1 HP). Assuming that about equal amounts of carbohydrates and fats are metabolized, during a 130-minute marathon race 850 g of energy-containing foodstuffs are used up. The metabolic rates for various sporting events are shown in Table 24-3.

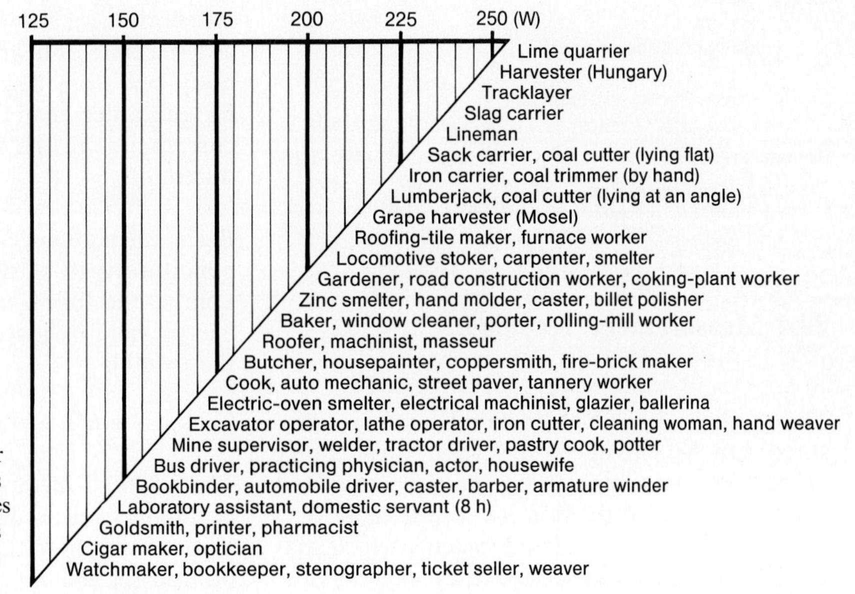

Fig. 24-5. Energy expenditure (per 24–h day) associated with various kinds of work and leisure activities (modified from [4]). Actual values may differ, depending on how the work is done

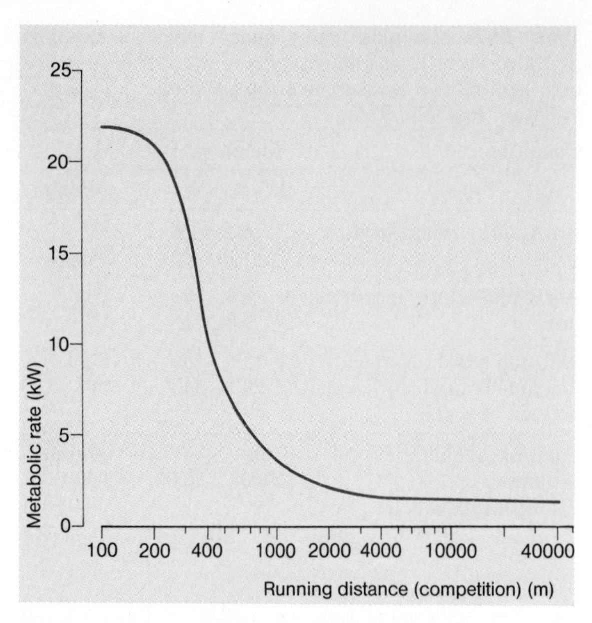

Fig. 24-6. Energy expenditure during competitive running over various distances. (Data from [6])

Table 24-3. Metabolic rates for various sports (for running see Fig. 24-6). From [6]

Kind of sport		Watts
Bicycling on level ground	20 km/h (12.5 miles/h)	545
Bicycle racing	40 km/h (25 miles/h)	1,735
Playing football		790–1,040
Playing handball		885
Playing volleyball		380–640
Swimming breaststroke	28 m/min	460
Swimming breaststroke in clothing	28 m/min	730
Rowing in a race		1,715
Skiing, schuss		610
slalom		1,605
downhill race, women		2,130
men		3,100
cross-country, women		1,285
men		1,435
Tennis, singles		490–1,100
Dancing, Viennese waltz		355

24.4 Measurement Techniques

The methods by which metabolic rate is measured can be classified in several ways. Some procedures measure heat loss *directly* and others determine heat production *indirectly,* the devices used may be *open* or *closed* systems which may or may not be *portable,* and they can provide either *continuous* or *discontinuous* monitoring of metabolic rate.

Direct Measurement of Metabolic Rate

This method is based on the direct determination of the *heat loss* of the organism ("direct calorimetry"). As early as 1780, LAVOISIER developed a means of measuring the heat released by living organisms. His "calorimeter" monitored the amount of heat released directly and continuously, though not under standard conditions. The apparatus required to measure human heat loss directly is massive and elaborate, and therefore it is used only for studying special problems. Direct measurements of metabolic rate have been particularly useful in one respect: comparison of these results with the foodstuff balance of the organism has provided proof that the *law of conservation of energy holds for living organisms.* Moreover, the results of direct calorimeter experiments can be used to check the validity of indirect procedures.

Indirect Measurement of Metabolic Rate

The indirect measurement of metabolic rate is based on observation of the **amount of oxygen** taken up by the organism. Because oxygen is consumed in every biological oxidation, and the body has only a small storage capacity for O_2, the amount of oxygen taken into the body by way of the lungs can be used to determine the amount of oxygen utilized by the tissues, from which the metabolic rate can be found.
Attempts have also been made to use CO_2 release as a measure of heat production. But because the body can store large amounts of CO_2, there is no guarantee that the amount of CO_2 released corresponds to the amount currently being produced.

Basic calculations. When the rate of energy expenditure is to be derived from data on oxygen uptake, the following considerations apply. The energy yield by **glucose oxidation** is described by the formula

$$C_6H_{12}O_6 + 6O_2 \longrightarrow 6CO_2 + 6H_2O + 2,826\ \text{kJ} \quad (2)$$

The 2,826 kJ in this reaction is the total energy *(enthalpy)* released per mol of glucose; of this amount only part (the *free enthalpy* [5]) can be utilized for cellular function.

Fuel value. Energy yield is frequently expressed with respect to the mass or volume of substrate; 1 mol of glucose has a mass of 180 g, and 6 mol of oxygen have a volume of 6 × 22.4 liters = 134.4 liters. It follows that the complete oxidation of 1 g of glucose yields 2,826/180 = 15.7 kJ. The **fuel value** of glucose is thus **15.7 kJ/g** (p. 678).
The *energy equivalent* ("caloric equivalent") expresses the yield of energy with respect to the oxygen consumed, and in the above reaction amounts to 2,826 kJ/134.4 liters = **21.0 kJ per liter O_2**. Because the mixture of carbohydrates naturally occurring in food has a somewhat higher energetic value than glucose, the energy equivalent for carbohydrate oxidation is 21.1 kJ per liter O_2 (Table 24-4).
The *Respiratory Quotient* (or Respiratory Exchange Ratio) is an indicator of the type of foodstuff metabolized; it is defined as

$$RQ = \frac{\dot{V}_{CO_2}}{\dot{V}_{O_2}} = \frac{CO_2 \text{ production}}{O_2 \text{ consumption}}. \quad (3)$$

In the oxidation of glucose just as much carbon dioxide is given off as oxygen is consumed, so that RQ = 1. *An RQ of 1* is thus an *identifying characteristic of* **carbohydrate oxidation.**

Sample calculation: Under resting conditions the oxygen uptake was found to be 280 ml/min (standard volume, STPD; p. 561) and the unusual value 1.00 was found for RQ. The metabolic rate in this situation is thus 0.280 · 21.1 = 5.91 kJ/min ≈ 8,508 kJ/d (≈ 98 W).

Similar relationships apply in the **oxidation of fats.** Because fatty acids contain less oxygen per atom of carbon than do carbohydrates, their oxidation leads to a distinctly lower RQ (0.7). When pure **food protein** is oxidized an RQ of 0.81 is obtained (Table 24-4).

End products of catabolism. These include, among other things, water (ca. 350 ml per day), carbon dioxide (ca. 230 ml per min), carbon monoxide (ca. 0.007 ml per min), urea (ca. 30 g per day) and other nitrogen-containing substances (ca. 6 g per day), and other molecules that are excreted in the urine.

Table 24-4. Respiratory quotients (RQ) and energy equivalents for the oxidation of various foodstuffs (1 kJ ≈ 0.24 Kcal)

	Carbohydrates	Fats	Proteins
RQ	1.00	0.70	0.81
kJ/l O_2	21.1	19.6	18.8

Table 24-5. Dependence of the energy equivalent on RQ, neglecting the contribution of protein (15%) to the total metabolism. The average respiratory quotient is 0.82

RQ	1.0	0.9	**0.82**	0.8	0.7
kJ/l O_2	21.1	20.6	**20.2**	20.1	19.6

Urea is the typical end product of *protein breakdown;* thus the amount of urea and other nitrogenous substances excreted can be used to determine the rate of protein catabolism. Because the proteins of a mixed diet have an average nitrogen content of 16%, the amount of nitrogen found in the urine must be multiplied by 6.25 to obtain the amount of protein involved in catabolism.

Protein metabolism, which serves chiefly for structural maintenance and growth, is nearly *constant;* protein accounts for about 15% of the total energy in a balanced Central European diet. [Structural protein metabolism is considerably increased after accidents or operations, giving rise to the term "postaggression metabolism" (cf. Table 24-6, p. 623)]. The proportions of fat and carbohydrate, by contrast, fluctuate widely in the usual diet, so that differences in RQ are basically due to these foodstuffs. For this reason the *RQ can be used to compute* the portion of the metabolism represented by *fat and carbohydrate breakdown* and to derive the amount of energy converted when 1 liter of oxygen is consumed (Table 24-5). A change in RQ of 0.1 unit corresponds to a change in the *energy equivalent* of 0.5 kJ per liter O_2. Table 24-5 can thus be used to obtain indirectly an accurate estimate of metabolic rate.

Sample calculation: Oxygen uptake, as in the preceding example, was 280 ml/min, but the RQ was 0.82 (the average value, with energy equivalent 20.2 kJ/l O_2). In this case the metabolic rate is 0.280 · 20.2 ≈ 5.66 kJ/min ≈ 8,150 kJ/d (≈ 94 W). The difference between this result and that in the previous example is 358 kJ/d, or 4%.

Factors affecting the RQ. The ratio of carbon-dioxide production to oxygen consumption depends on the following three factors:

1. *The kinds of foodstuffs metabolized.* As has been mentioned, the RQ for the oxidation of carbohydrate is 1.0, for fats 0.7 and for protein 0.81 (Table 24-4).

2. *Hyperventilation* (p. 563). The extra CO_2 blown off during hyperventilation comes from the large CO_2 stores in tissue and blood, and not from metabolism. Hyperventilation does not alter oxy-

gen uptake, because the blood and tissues cannot store additional oxygen. In the *transition phase* preceding the establishment of a new, lower CO_2 partial pressure in blood and tissue, the RQ is *distinctly increased,* in some cases to as much as 1.4. Some of the *causes* of hyperventilation are voluntary activity (e.g., blowing up an air mattress), nonrespiratory acidosis (p. 595; e.g., during and after exhausting work), psychological stress (e.g., states of extreme excitation) and artificial respiration with a minute volume above the requirement.

3. *Interconversion of foodstuffs.* When carbohydrates predominate in the diet they are converted to fats. Because fats contain less oxygen than do carbohydrates, a corresponding amount of oxygen is released. Thus with overfeeding of carbohydrates the amount of oxygen uptake through the lungs falls and the *RQ becomes larger.* In extreme cases of force-feeding, an RQ of 1.38 has been measured in geese and 1.58 in pigs. During periods of *fasting* and in *diabetics* the RQ can be *lowered* to 0.6. The latter change results from the increased conversion rate of fats and protein that accompanies diminished glucose metabolism (consumption of glycogen reserves or impaired utilization).
When obtaining an indirect estimate of metabolic rate, if one is not certain whether a measured **"respiratory RQ"** corresponds to the catabolic conditions **("metabolic RQ")** an average energy equivalent of 20.2 kJ/l O_2 should be assumed, corresponding to a metabolic RQ of 0.82. As Table 24-5 shows, the energy equivalent varies only slightly over a particularly wide range as a function of RQ, so that the error introduced by using the mean energy equivalent is at most ±4%.

Measurement of the Metabolic Rate of Single Organs

The oxygen consumption (and thus the metabolic rate) of single organs can be found by Fick's principle (p. 540), from the rate of perfusion of the organ $\dot{Q}$ and the differences between the arterial and venous fractions of O_2 and CO_2:

$$\dot{V}_{O_2}(\text{ml/min}) = \dot{Q}(\text{ml/min}) \cdot (F_{a_{O_2}} - F_{v_{O_2}}) \quad (4)$$

$$\dot{V}_{CO_2}(\text{ml/min}) = \dot{Q}(\text{ml/min}) \cdot (F_{v_{CO_2}} - F_{a_{CO_2}}) \quad (5)$$

The brain utilizes mainly carbohydrates, so that its RQ is in a range close to 1.0; the RQ of skeletal and cardiac muscle varies considerably, depending on the metabolic situation.

24.5 Measurement of the Oxygen Uptake of the Whole Body

When determining metabolic rate by indirect methods it is necessary to measure the oxygen uptake of the subject per unit time. Both "closed" and "open" respiration systems are used for this purpose.

Closed Systems

The principle of such systems is that the subject inspires gas from an *oxygen-filled* **spirometer** (pp. 549f.; Fig. 24-7). The expired gas mixture passes through a container in which *carbon dioxide is absorbed* and then returns to the spirometer, so

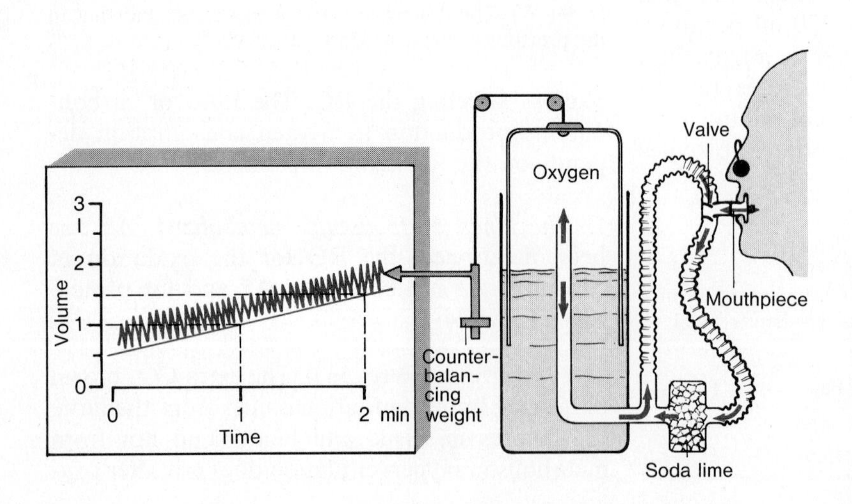

Fig. 24-7. Measurement of O_2 uptake in a closed spirometric system. The subject inspires pure oxygen from a *bell gas meter;* CO_2 is removed from the expired gas mixture by adsorption on soda lime before the mixture returns to the bell. The subject's O_2 uptake is given by the slope of the line connecting the reversal points of the *spirogram (left),* and in this example is 0.5 l/min

that the circuit is closed. The recorded *spirogram* (Fig. 24-7) has a rising slope; the steeper the slope, the more oxygen is removed from the system per unit time.

Closed systems *must be filled with oxygen,* for if air is used the oxygen is consumed so rapidly that its concentration in the inspired mixture soon falls below 8.5 ml/dl (the critical threshold, p. 667) with no increase in CO_2 concentration. Oxygen deficiency under these conditions often causes sudden unexpected loss of consciousness, because breathing is stimulated only slightly (p. 572) and other warning systems usually go unrecognized (p. 667). An advantage of closed systems is that it is unnecessary to measure O_2 concentration; a disadvantage is that the RQ cannot be determined.

Standard volume. Whatever the conditions under which oxygen uptake is measured, the results must be converted to corresponding standard conditions, so that different experiments can be compared regardless of actual temperature and air pressure. The **STPD conditions** (standard temperature and pressure, dry) are 0 °C, 760 mm Hg, and dryness of air (p. 561). The conversion factor is usually obtained from tables derived from the following equation:

$$V_0 = V \cdot \frac{P_B - P_{H_2O}}{760} \cdot \frac{273}{273 + t}, \qquad (6)$$

where V_o is the volume under standard conditions, V is the measured volume, P_B is the barometric pressure, P_{H_2O} is the water-vapor pressure in the spirometer, and t is the temperature of the measured gas volume in °C.

Open Systems

In **open respiration systems** the airways for inspiration and expiration are separate. Usually fresh air is inspired, and the expiratory airway is equipped to measure both the *volume of the expired air* and its O_2 and CO_2 *concentrations.* Since the concentrations of O_2 and CO_2 in the inspired air are known, the amount of oxygen removed from the air and the amount of CO_2 added to it can be calculated.

Basic calculations. Under the ordinary measurement procedures under normal conditions, one can obtain quite a good estimate of O_2 uptake and CO_2 release as follows (see [8]):

$$\dot{V}_{O_2} = \dot{V}_E \cdot (F_{I_{O_2}} - F_{E_{O_2}}) \qquad (7)$$

or

$$\dot{V}_{CO_2} = \dot{V}_E \cdot F_{E_{CO_2}} \qquad (8)$$

When especially high accuracy is required, it should be kept in mind that the actual gain in O_2 and loss of CO_2 are represented by the difference between the amounts of each substance in the inspired and the expired air. The CO_2 fraction in fresh air is normally so small that it can be neglected. But appreciable amounts of O_2 are exhaled, and the following formula can be used to find O_2 uptake as the difference between the inspired and expired amounts:

$$\dot{V}_{O_2} = \dot{V}_I \cdot F_{I_{O_2}} - \dot{V}_E \cdot F_{E_{O_2}} \qquad (9)$$

The amount of expired oxygen can be calculated in the same way as the expired CO_2. The O_2 fraction in the inspired air is known in the case of fresh air ($F_{I_{O_2}} = 0.2095 = 20.95$ ml/dl), but $\dot{V}_I$ is not.

Only if RQ = 1 can one assume that the expiratory and inspiratory minute volumes (adjusted to standard conditions) are identical. With an RQ below 1.0 less air is expired than is inspired. But if RQ is known, either of the minute volumes can be obtained from the other. Though we shall not describe the derivation here, these considerations allow calculation of oxygen uptake with the Douglas-bag method (see below) by the following equation:

$$\Delta\dot{V}_{O_2} = \dot{V}_E(1.265 \cdot \Delta F_{O_2} - 0.265 \cdot F_{E_{CO_2}}). \qquad (10)$$

$\dot{V}_E$ can be obtained from the amount of expired air collected in the Douglas bag during the specified time, $F_{E_{CO_2}}$, is the CO_2 fraction of the sampled, mixed expired air, and ΔF_{O_2} is the difference between the oxygen fraction in the inspired air and that in the expired gas mixture. Finally, the result must be adjusted for *STPD conditions.*

Douglas bag. The Douglas-bag procedure [11] is one of the classical methods for measuring oxygen uptake. It involves *discontinuous* measurement with a *portable* device that can be attached to a freely moving subject. In studies of work physiology the bag is worn like a backpack. The subject inspires fresh air by way of a *valve* with a *mouthpiece;* the nose is closed by a *clamp.* All the expired air is collected in the *air-tight bag* by way of a system of valves and tubes, and the collection time is measured precisely. At the end of this period the bag is kneaded to mix the various components of the expired air thoroughly, and a sample is taken for analysis of oxygen and carbon dioxide content. The total volume of air breathed is determined by emptying the bag into a gas meter.

Other procedures. Instead of a Douglas bag, the subject can carry a gas meter on his back, specially adapted so that as the flow rate is measured a sample of the expired gas mixture can be collected in a small accessory vessel. This sample must be *representative* of all the components (e.g., dead-space and alveolar air) of the mixture expired (an *aliquot portion*). Because their proportions may change during an expiration, it is

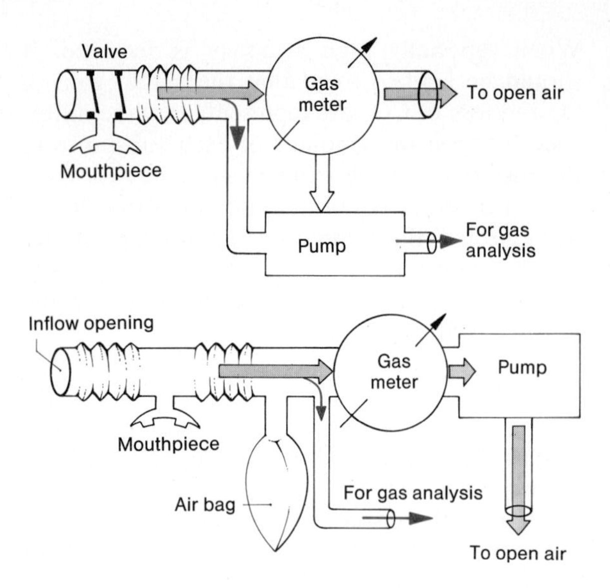

Fig. 24-8. Principles by which oxygen uptake and carbon dioxide release are measured continuously in *open* systems. *Top:* Principle of the *aliquot portion.* The subject inspires fresh air through a mouthpiece with a two-way valve; the nose is closed with a clamp. The amount of air expired is measured with a gas meter (or a pneumotachograph), which controls a suction pump in such a way that a small sample of the expired air, proportional to the rate of flow, is withdrawn and collected. This special arrangement provides a *representative* gas sample, which contains all the components of the expired air in the correct proportions (an "aliquot portion"). *Bottom:* Principle of *constant suction.* The subject breathes in and out through a valveless mouthpiece (or a breathing mask or hood), while a pump draws a constant stream of fresh air (more than required for breathing) past the mouthpiece. Before the branch to the gas analyzer the stream of mixed air is uniform, depending only on the suction of the pump and not on the respiratory minute volume. When large amounts are briefly expired, they can be stored temporarily in the air bag. As long as none of the expired air leaves the system through the inflow opening and the action of the pump is constant, the continuously recorded concentration differences of oxygen and carbon dioxide at the branch to the gas analyzer are proportional to the oxygen uptake and carbon dioxide release. For calculation see [8]

necessary that a specific fraction of the airstream be redirected continuously (Fig. 24-8); in this way a certain percentage of each component in the expired gas mixture (e.g., 1% in the portable system of MÜLLER and FRANZ [15]) is collected.
For the *continuous* measurement of oxygen uptake more elaborate procedures are required, and for a long time it was necessary to use permanently installed apparatus. Modern equipment employing telemetry (wireless transmission of the data) can also be used on a mobile basis.

Devices for the *continuous measurement* of oxygen uptake are usually based on one of the two prinicples illustrated in Fig. 24-8. In those using the principle of aliquot portion (Fig. 24-8, top) a *pneumotachograph* (pp. 549f.) is ordinarily used to monitor the discontinuous stream of expired air. The gas concentrations, however, are determined not with discontinuous, chemical absorption procedures but with continuously operating *gas analyzers* that exploit certain physical properties of oxygen and carbon dioxide (p. 562). The metabolic parameters are then calculated as in the Douglas-bag procedure.
Major advantages of apparatus based on the principle of constant suction (Fig. 24-8, bottom) are that (i) uniform airstreams can be measured simply and very accurately with gas meters, and (ii) the measured changes in the concentrations of O_2 and CO_2 in the expired air are proportional to the changes in the metabolic parameters of interest. Hence the recorded changes in gas concentrations provide a direct measure of the metabolic situation under very diverse conditions, with no need for complicated calculations and the attendant risk of mistakes.
In continuous measurement it is essential that the concentration differences and volumes to be multiplied are determined at precisely the same times. Therefore such apparatus should be checked frequently; the traditional Douglas-bag procedure has proved to be a useful reference method for such calibration. Special devices that simulate oxygen consumption by an adjustable flame [16] or by the admixture of nitrogen [17] have been designed for certain purposes.
In measuring the metabolic rate of a patient under artificial respiration, the possibility of a variable O_2 concentration in the inspired air and the addition, in some cases, of anesthetic gases should be taken into account [17].

24.6 Diagnostic Significance of Energy Expenditure

Physiological and clinical aspects of work. The physical strain imposed on a person during work or sport can in many cases be described in terms of energy expenditure. Means have been found for various kinds of work (reviewed in [4] and [6]), so that these can be *classified* according to the *exertion required* as illustrated in Fig. 24-4.

Clinical diagnosis. In **shock** (a critical drop in blood pressure caused, for example, by severe blood loss) the metabolic rate falls below the basal level due to insufficient blood flow through peripheral regions (see pp. 531f.). An *oxygen debt* is built up (p. 649); many cells begin to metabolize at a rate lower than is necessary to keep them in functional condition. When peripheral blood flow increases as the state of shock wears off, the metabolic rate rises as well, so that by monitoring the changes in metabolic rate one can evaluate the state of shock.
Metabolic rate during illness. In patients with injuries, burns or high fever considerable metabolic changes are observed (Table 24-6). The metabolic

Table 24-6. Increase in metabolic rate (with respect to resting rate) and in urinary nitrogen excretion (100% = 0.085 g· kg^{-1}· d^{-1}) in patients of various categories. From [14]

Category	% increase of	
	Metabolic rate	N_2 excretion
1. Moderately severe surgery	24	150
2. Multiple fractures with other injuries (traffic accidents)	32	275
3. Gunshot wounds	37	280
4. Like 2. plus head injuries requiring steroid therapy	61	300
5. Sepsis	79	330
6. Large-area burns	132	335

rate rises noticeably in association with *postaggression metabolism,* and as a result of the elevated protein metabolism the amount of nitrogen excreted in the urine rises by a factor of four or more. These changes should be allowed for in designing the artificial nutrient mixture for such patients.

Thyroid disorders also affect the basal metabolic rate; when the gland is overactive *(hyperthyroidism)* the BMR is elevated, and when thyroid-hormone production is diminished *(hypothyroidism)* it is lowered (the clinical picture is described on pp. 385f.). In extreme cases the metabolic rate can vary by more than +100% or −40% from the norm. However, the BMR is no longer used to diagnose diseases of the thyroid.

24.7 References

Textbooks and Handbooks

1. Consolazio, C.F., Johnson, R.E., Pecora, L.J.: Physiological measurements of metabolic functions in man. New York-Toronto-London: McGraw-Hill 1963
2. Kestner, O., Knipping, H.W.: Die Ernährung des Menschen. Berlin: Springer 1924
3. Lavoisier, A.L., de LaPlace, P.S.: Abhandlung über die Wärme (Erstveröffentlichung 1780). In: Rosenthal, J. (Ed.): Zwei Abhandlungen über Wärme. Leipzig: Wilhelm Engelmann 1892
4. Lehmann, G.: Energetik des arbeitenden Menschen. In: Lehmann, G. (Ed.): Handbuch der gesamten Arbeitsmedizin, Bd. 1: Arbeitsphysiologie. Berlin-München-Wien: Urban & Schwarzenberg 1961
5. Opitz, E., Lübbers, D.: Allgemeine Physiologie der Zell- und Gewebsatmung. In: Büchner, F., Letterer, E., Roulet, F. (Eds.): Handbuch der allgemeinen Pathologie, Bd. 4, Teil II: Der Stoffwechsel. Berlin-Göttingen-Heidelberg: Springer 1957
6. Spitzer, H., Hettinger, Th., Kaminsky, G.: Tafeln für den Energieumsatz. (6. vollst. überarb. Aufl.) Berlin-Köln: Beuth 1982
7. Stegemann, J.: Leistungsphysiologie – Physiologische Grundlagen der Arbeit und des Sports. Stuttgart: Thieme 1984
8. Ulmer, H.-V.: Zur Methodik, Standardisierung und Auswertung von Tests für die Prüfung der körperlichen Leistungsfähigkeit. Köln: Deutscher Ärtzeverlag 1975
9. Wissenschaftliche Tabellen – Documenta Geigy. (Ed. J.R. Geigy A.G., Pharma, Basel). 7. Aufl. Basel: 1969

Original Papers and Reviews

10. Boothby, W.M., Berkson, J., Dunn, H.L.: Studies of the energy of metabolism of normal individuals: A standard of basal metabolism, with a nomogram for clinical application. Amer. J. Physiol *116,* 468 (1936)
11. Douglas, C.G.: A method for determining the total respiratory exchange in man. J. Physiol. (London) *42,* 17 (1911)
12. Göpfert, H., Bernsmeier, A., Stufler, R.: Über die Steigerung des Energiestoffwechsels und der Muskelinnervation bei geistiger Arbeit. Pflügers Arch. *256,* 304 (1953)
13. Harris, J.A., Benedict, F.G.: A biometric study of basal metabolism in man. Publ. Nr. 279. Carneg. Inst., Washington 1919, cited in Stegemann, Leistungsphysiologie. Stuttgart: Thieme 1971
14. Long, C.L., Schaffel, N., Geiger, J.W., Schiller, W.R., Blakemore, W.S.: Metabolic response to injury and illness: Estimation of energy and protein needs from indirect calorimetry and nitrogen balance. J. Parent. Ent. Nutr. *3,* 452 (1979)
15. Müller, E.A., Franz, H.: Energieverbrauchsmessungen bei beruflicher Arbeit mit einer verbesserten Respirationsgasuhr. Arbeitsphysiologie *14,* 499 (1952)
16. Stegemann, J., Essfeld, D.: Advantages of the computerized breath-by-breath method for the interpretation of spiroergometric data. In: Löllgen, H., Mellerowicz, H. (Eds.): Progress in ergometry: Quality control and test criteria. p. 30, Berlin-Heidelberg-New York-Tokyo: Springer 1984
17. Semsroth, M.: Indirekte Kalorimetrie bei beatmeten Kindern. 2. Teil: Ein Meßverfahren und seine Überprüfung an einem neuentwickelten Stoffwechsel-Lungenmodell. Infusionstherapie *12,* 294 (1985)

25 Thermal Balance and the Regulation of Body Temperature

K. BRÜCK

25.1 Heat Production, Body Temperature and Body Size

Homeothermy, poikilothermy. The **metabolic** processes described in the preceding chapter are associated with the **generation of heat,** in accordance with the laws of thermodynamics. From the metabolic point of view this heat production is a side effect, but when one is concerned with the differences in body temperature and its control within the animal kingdom metabolic heat is of fundamental interest. In one group of animals – that to which humans belong – the temperature of the body is kept at a constant level considerably above that of the surroundings, owing to a **high rate of heat production** ("tachymetabolism") governed by **regulatory mechanisms.** These are the **homeothermic organisms.** In a second group (which includes, for example, fish and reptiles), far less heat is produced ("bradymetabolism"); the body temperature is only slightly above the ambient temperature, and follows the fluctuations of the latter *(poikilothermic animals).*
Inasmuch as homeotherms can maintain a uniform temperature, and thus a uniform activity level, independent of the ambient temperature, they are superior in many respects to the poikilotherms. On the other hand, poikilothermy can offer advantages when the availability of food is subject to seasonal changes. For example, when frogs are kept cool they can endure food deprivation for months with no ill effects.
Species in classes other than the mammals and birds can influence their body temperature, to a certain degree, by special forms of behavior (e.g., fish can move to warmer water, and lizards can "sunbathe"). This **"behavioral thermoregulation"** is distinquished from **autonomic thermoregulation.** True homeotherms are able to employ both behavioral and autonomic measures of thermoregulation; in particular, they can generate extra heat when necessary by activating metabolic processes, whereas the other organisms must rely on external heat sources. This distinction is expressed in the terms **endothermic** and **ectothermic** organisms [17].

Heat production and body temperature. All chemical reactions in an organism, including the processes of metabolism, are temperature-dependent. The relationship in poikilotherms is just like that pertaining to abiotic chemical processes – that is, the rate of energy conversion increases in proportion to external temperature according to **van't Hoff's rule.** Van't Hoff's rule applies to homeotherms in the same way, but it is masked by other effects. When an intact homeotherm is cooled (starting at a comfortable ambient temperature in the **thermoneutral zone**; see p. 627) its rate of energy metabolism and thus heat production rises, preventing a reduction in body temperature. But by pharmacological intervention (e.g., anesthesia) or by making lesions at specific sites in the CNS one can eliminate thermoregulation; the curve of heat production vs. temperature then resembles that of a poikilotherm (Fig. 25-1). The component of heat pro-

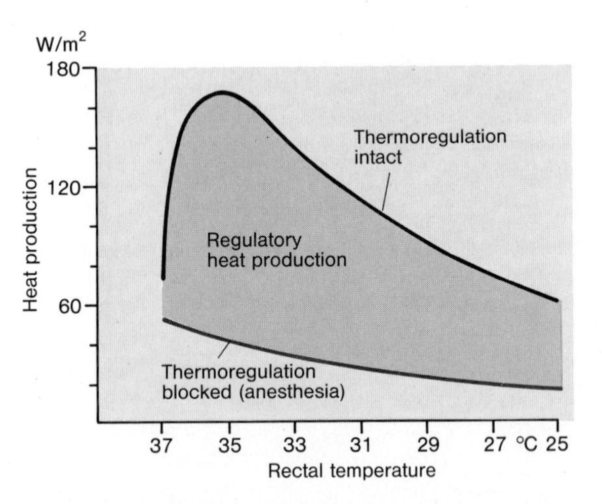

Fig. 25-1. Relationship between body temperature and metabolic rate in homeothermic organisms (from experiments on the dog). *Upper curve:* When thermoregulation is functioning the metabolic rate first rises sharply as temperature falls, passes through a maximum and then falls in accordance with van't Hoff's rule. *Lower curve:* With thermoregulation blocked by deep anesthesia the metabolic rate follows van't Hoff's rule from the onset of cooling. The difference between the two curves corresponds to regulatory thermogenesis. For further discussion see text. Modified from [21]

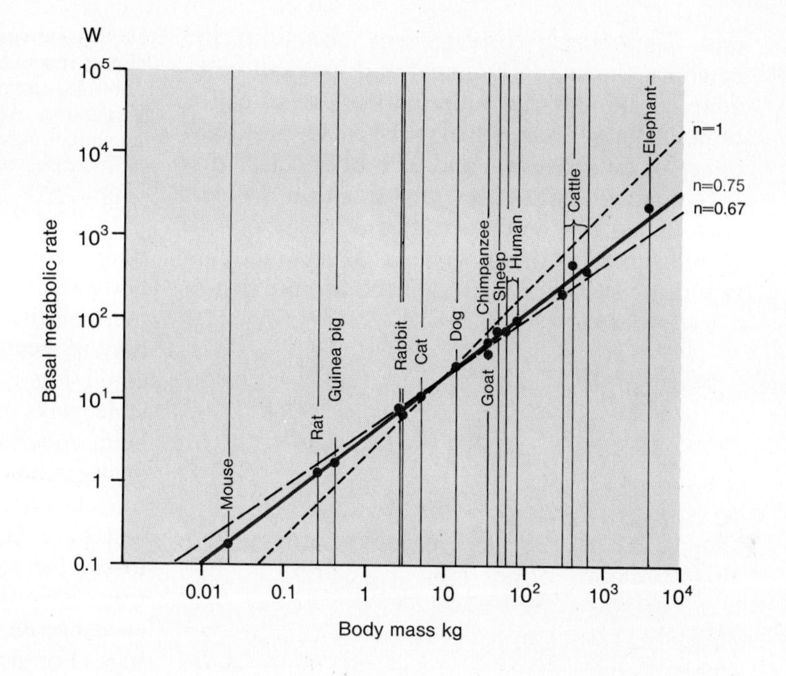

Fig. 25-2. Relationship between metabolic rate and body mass in a double-logarithmic plot. The straight line with a slope of 0.75 most closely fits the experimental data. The line with slope 1 reflects proportionality between metabolic rate and body mass, and that with slope 0.67 reflects proportionality between metabolic rate and surface area. Modified from [21]

duction that can be blocked in this way is called **regulatory thermogenesis**.

Even after blockade of the regulatory component there remains a considerable quantitative difference between the metabolic processes of poikilotherms and those of homeotherms; at a given body temperature the rate of energy conversion per unit body weight in homeotherms is at least three times that in poikilotherms.
The ratio of the reaction rates at temperatures differing by 10 °C is called the $\mathbf{Q_{10}}$. Quantitative evaluation of the falling parts of the curves in Fig. 23-1 shows that *the Q_{10} for the metabolic rate lies between 2 and 3.* Therefore anesthesia combined with lowered body temperature can bring about a quite appreciable **decrease in O_2 consumption** and hence a corresponding **postponement of structural deterioration** (see p. 610). This phenomenon is turned to advantage during cardiovascular surgery and transplant operations, when the circulation of blood must be interrupted temporarily (**induced hypothermia**; sometimes called "artificial hibernation"). Van't Hoff's rule must also be considered when organs are to be kept in storage.

Heat production and body size. The body temperature of most homeothermic mammals is in the range of 36 °C–39 °C, despite the wide differences in body size within the group – from the mouse, near one end, to the elephant and whale at the other. By contrast, metabolic rate (MR) is a power function of body mass (m):

$$MR = k \cdot m^n \quad (1)$$

This relationship gives a straight line on a double-logarithmic plot:

$$\log MR = k' + n \cdot \log m \quad (2)$$

The exponent n has been found empirically to be about 0.75 (cf. Fig. 25-2). That is, the quantity $MR/m^{0.75}$ is the same for the mouse as for the elephant, although the mouse MR per kg body mass is considerably larger than that of the elephant. This so-called **law of metabolic reduction** [8] reflects the tendency for heat production to be matched to the rate of heat loss to the surroundings. For a given temperature difference between the interior of the body and the surroundings, the loss of heat per unit mass is greater, the greater the surface-to-volume ratio, and the latter decreases with increasing body size. Moreover, the insulating shell of the body (see p. 627) is thinner in small animals.

Thermoregulatory thermogenesis. When additional heat is required to keep the body temperature constant, it can be produced in the following ways:

1. By voluntary activity of the locomotor apparatus.
2. By involuntary tonic or rhythmic muscular activity; the latter corresponds to the familiar **shivering** induced by cold. (The tonic activity can be detected by electromyography; see pp. 71f.).
3. By the acceleration of metabolic processes not associated with muscle contraction; this form of heat production is called **nonshivering thermogenesis.**

In the adult human *shivering* is the most significant involuntary mechanism of thermogenesis. *Nonshivering thermogenesis* occurs in the newborn (including humans) and in small cold-adapted animals and hibernators. The so-called **brown adipose tissue,** distinguished by an abundance of mitochondria and a "multilocular" distribution of the fat (numerous small fat droplets surrounded by mitochondria), is a major source of nonshivering thermogenesis. It is found between the shoulder blades, in the armpit and in a few other places [12, 26].

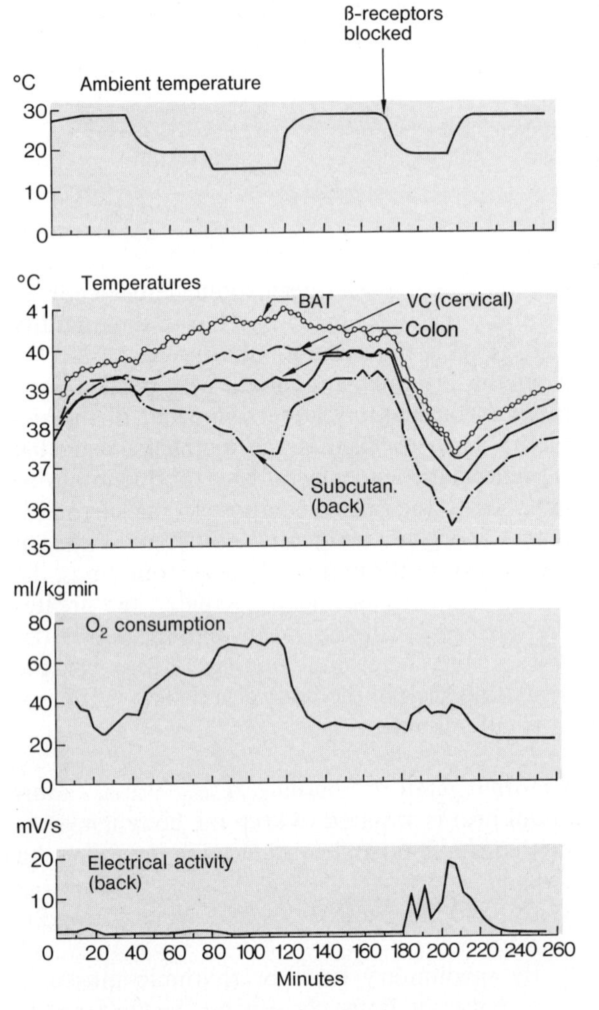

Fig. 25-3. Nonshivering thermogenesis in the newborn guinea pig can be detected by the increase in O_2 uptake while the muscles show no electrical activity. In the *second part* of the experiment nonshivering thermogenesis is inhibited by a β–receptor blocking agent; shivering resulted, as shown by the increase in electrical activity of the musculature. (The threshold for shivering is at a lower body temperature than that for nonshivering heat production.) Note the rise in temperature of the interscapular brown adipose tissue (BAT) and the vertebral canal (VC) *before* blockade and the parallel fall in all temperatures *after* it. From [21]

The **thermoregulatory function of the interscapular brown adipose tissue** can readily be demonstrated by local temperature measurement (Fig. 25-3). Whereas the subcutaneous temperature of the back falls during exposure to cold, the temperature in the brown adipose tissue rises, indicating increased metabolic activity and **thermogenesis** in the adipose tissue [29].

Body temperature and thermal balance. If the body temperature is to be kept constant, there must be thermal equilibrium in the steady state; that is, heat production and heat loss must be equal. Fig. 25-4 shows diagrammatically the possible ways in which body temperature can be held constant when the ambient temperature changes. These considerations are based on Newton's law of cooling, according to which the heat lost by a body (more precisely, the "dry" heat loss – the total loss minus the loss by evaporation) is proportional to the temperature difference between the body core and the surroundings. For a human subject, then, at an ambient temperature of 37 °C the heat loss would be equal to zero, and at lower temperatures it would increase. But heat loss also depends on the conduction and convection of heat within the body and thus on the peripheral blood flow.

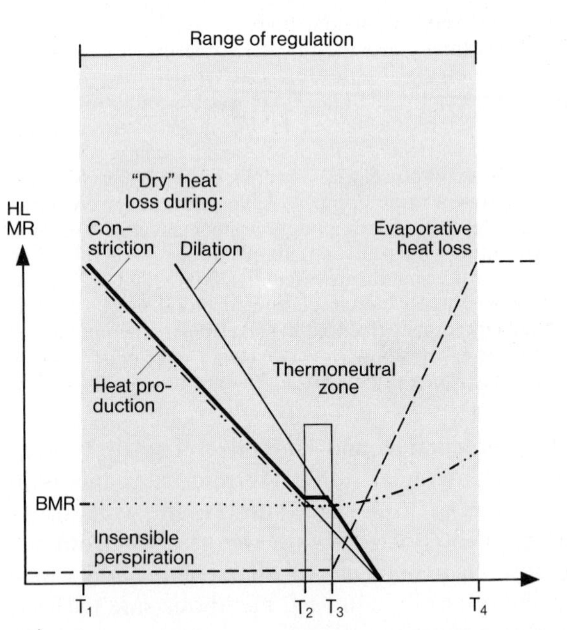

Fig. 25-4. Diagram illustrating thermal balance. In the temperature range T_1–T_4 (zone of normal thermoregulation) heat production and loss are equal. Below T_1 more heat is lost (HL) than can be produced (HL > MR; hypothermia). Above T_4 the production and influx of heat exceed the capacity for evaporative heat loss (hyperthermia). In the range T_2–T_3 (thermoneutral zone) heat loss can be matched to resting heat production by vasomotor adjustments. For further discussion see text

Accordingly, one can plot *two heat-loss curves*, one for peripheral *vasodilation* and another for *vascoconstriction*. The thermogenesis associated with resting metabolism is in equlibrium with heat loss in the range of the graph between T_2 and T_3 if blood flow through the skin is progressively reduced as the temperature falls from T_3 to T_2. Below T_2 the body temperature can be kept constant only if regulatory mechanisms increase thermogenesis in proportion to heat loss. The greatest heat production achievable by such mechanisms in humans corresponds to as much as 3–5 times the basal metabolic rate, and marks the **lower limit of the thermoregulatory range,** T_1 (for absolute values see Fig. 25-15). When this limit is passed **hypothermia** develops and ultimately can result in cold death.

At temperatures above T_3, it is conceivable that a diminished metabolic rate could maintain thermal equilibrium. In fact, however, thermal balance is achieved by an *additional heat-loss mechanism*, the evaporation of sweat. T_4 indicates the **upper limit of the regulatory range**, which is fixed by the maximal rate of sweat secretion. Above T_4 **hyperthermia** appears; this ultimately can result in heat death (for absolute values see Fig. 25-8). The range of temperatures between T_2 and T_3, within which the body temperature can be kept constant *without either supplementary heat-producing mechanisms or sweat secretion*, is called the **thermoneutral zone** (cf. Fig. 25-15). In this range metabolic rate and thermogenesis are minimal, by definition. Above T_3, because of the Q_{10} effect (see p. 625) associated with a slight rise in body temperature (the error inherent in a proportional control system) and because of the increased work of blood circulation and breathing, the metabolic rate would be expected to become somewhat higher. Measurements of this response have been inconsistent, so that no quantitative data are as yet available.

25.2 The Temperature of the Human Body

Local Temperature Differences (Temperature Gradients)

The heat produced within the body normally (i.e., under equilibrium conditions) is lost to the environment by way of the body surface. In accordance with the physical laws of heat flow, therefore, the temperature of the parts of the body near the surface must be lower than that of the central parts. In the limbs there is a **longitudinal (axial) temperature gradient,** and there is also a **radial temperature gradient** (perpendicular to the surface). The result, owing to the irregular geometry of the body, is a complicated three-dimensional temperature distribution. For example, when a lightly clothed adult is in an ambient temperature of 20 °C, the innermost part of the thigh musculature is at 35 °C, the deep layers of the calf are at 33 °C and the center of the foot is at only 27 °C–28 °C; the rectal temperature under these conditions is around 37 °C [5]. The fluctuations in body temperature produced by external temperature changes are distinctly greater near the body surface and at the ends (acral parts) of the extremities. Simplifying the situation somewhat, one can distinguish a **"poikilothermic" shell** from a **"homeothermic" core.** The isotherms in Fig. 25-5 indicate the temperature gradients within the body in cold and warm surroundings. The 37 °C isotherm, which delimits the core, is withdrawn to the interior of the body when the surroundings are cold [19].

Core temperatures of the body. On closer examination we find that the temperature of the core itself is inconstant in both space and time. Even under thermoneutral conditions the

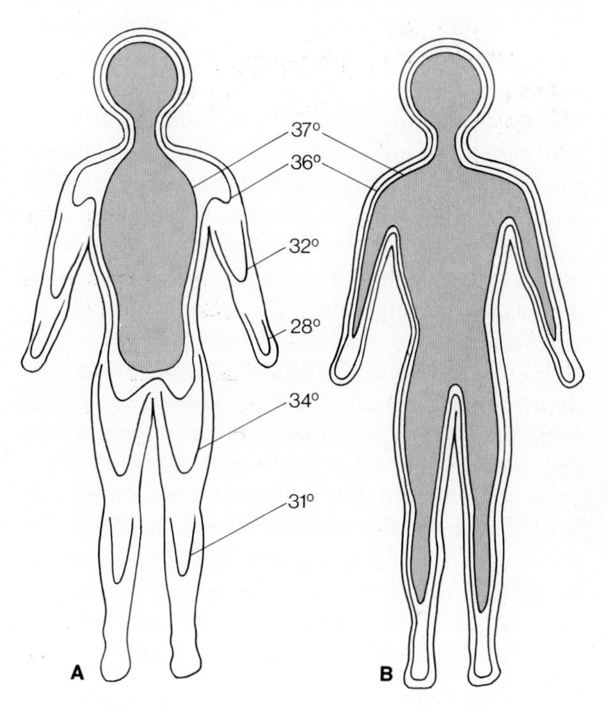

Fi.g 25-5 A, B. Isotherms within the human body in cold *(A)* and warm *(B)* surroundings. From [19]

core-temperature differences are of the order of 0.2 °C–1.2 °C, and the brain exhibits a radial temperature gradient of more than 1 °C from center to cortex. As a rule, the highest temperatures are found in the rectum and not, as was long claimed [5], in the liver. In view of this finding it is impossible to express the temperature of the body by a single number. For practical purposes, however, it suffices to find a specific site at which the temperature can be regarded as *representative of the body core,* for one is usually interested in temporal changes in temperature. For clinical measurements it is most important to select an easily accessible site with little spatial variation in temperature, so that slight changes in position of the measuring instrument do not make it difficult to establish a standard.

The preferred measure for clinical purposes is the **rectal temperature,** even though it does not entirely meet the above requirements. When a thermometer is advanced inward from the anus to a depth of 10–15 cm, temperature gradients of as much as 1 °C are observed. This spatial nonuniformity within the rectum derives in part from the communication between the venous plexuses in the rectum and those in the skin of the anal region [5]. For comparative measurements, therefore, it is important to keep to a standard depth of insertion.

The oral temperature (more precisely, the **sublingual temperature,** which has become the preferred measure for clinical purposes, is usually 0.2 °C–0.5 °C lower than the rectal temperature. Here, again, there are temperature gradients; the oral temperature is affected by the inspired air and by the temperature of food and drink.

For examinations in the area of sport medicine, the **esophageal temperature** (above the cardia) is often taken, with flexible thermosensors. This measure reflects body-temperature changes with a shorter delay than does the rectal temperature. The **axillary temperature** can also represent the core temperature, because when the upper arm is held tightly to the thorax the temperature gradients (Fig. 25-5) alter so as to displace the core boundary up to the armpit. However, the parts of the body shell pressed together for this measurement must accumulate a considerable amount of heat before the final temperature is reached. On the order of 1/2 hour must be allowed for equilibration, if the shell tissues were initially cooled by a low ambient temperature with vasoconstriction – as is especially likely to occur when a fever is building up.

Finally, the external meatus of the ear is sometimes the site chosen for core-temperature measurement, for special clinical and theoretical reasons. The **meatus temperature** is measured with a flexible probe inserted close to the tympanal membrane and insulated from external thermal influences by cotton wool.

Skin temperature. The shell temperature is usually characterized by the temperature of the skin, which is easily measurable but presents far more problems for standardization than the core temperature. Measurement at a single site is quite inadequate; the temperatures at several places must be averaged. It is common practice to obtain **mean skin temperature** from measurements at the forehead, chest, abdomen, upper arm, forearm, back of hand, thigh, calf, and dorsum of foot. In calculating the mean these values are weighted in accordance with the body-surface area they represent. The mean skin temperature found in this way for a nude person in a comfortable ambient temperature is about 33°–34 °C. The **"mean body temperature"** can be calculated from the mean skin temperature and the core temperature, with appropriate weighting factors.

Periodic Fluctuations in Core Temperature

The temperature of a human varies in the course of a day, with a minimum toward morning and a maximum (often with two peaks) during the daytime (Fig. 25-6). The amplitude of this diurnal fluctuation averages ca 1 °C. In night-active animals the temperature maximum occurs during the night. The plausible inference that the increased temperature is simply the consequence of increased physical activity has, however, proved false [18].

The 24-h fluctuation in body temperature is but one of many **diurnal rhythms**. Even when all external entraining signals are eliminated (e.g., light, temperature, feeding times), body temperature continues to oscillate rhythmically – but no longer with a period of exactly 24 hours. The "free-running" period is between 24 and 25 hours (**"circadian" periodicity;** see pp. 138f.). The diurnal oscillation of body temperature is thus based on an endogenous rhythm (the "biological clock"), which is ordinarily synchronized with external signals, the earth's rotation in particular [18]. When one travels across the earth's meridians it takes 1–2 weeks for the temperature rhythm to adjust to the living patterns set by the new local time [5].

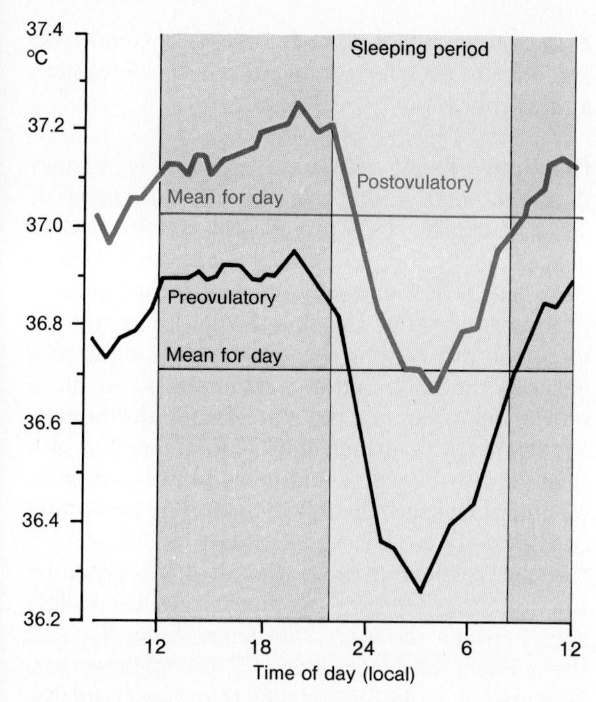

Fig. 25-6. Daily variation in body (rectal) temperature. The *lower curve* was obtained in the first (preovulatory) half of the menstrual cycle, the *upper* curve in the second (postovulatory) half (means of 8 subjects). *Red shading:* sleeping period. Modified from [49]

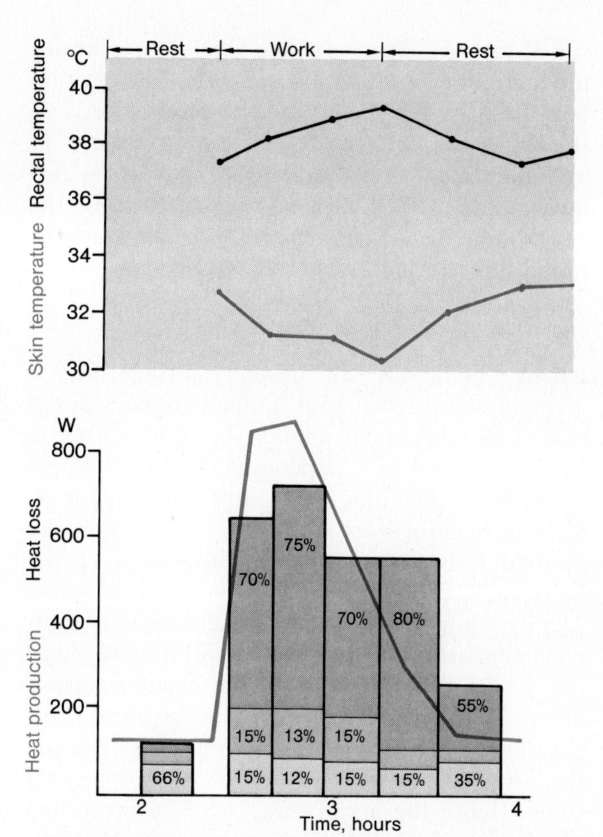

Fig. 25-7. Body temperature, heat production (curve) and heat loss (columns) at rest and during work. The columns are divided as follows: *bottom*, radiative heat loss; *middle*, convective heat loss; *top*, evaporative heat loss; conduction (see p. 630) is neglected. Modified from [33]

Superimposed on the diurnal temperature changes are rhythms with longer periods. The best known and most conspicuous of these is the temperature rhythm synchronized with the **menstrual cycle** (see Fig. 25-6 and pp. 779f.

Body Temperature during Exercise

The core temperature rises during physical activity, while the mean skin temperature falls due to the secretion and evaporation of sweat initiated by the work (Fig. 25-7). During submaximal work the core temperature increase is nearly independent of ambient temperature over a wide range (15°–35 °C), as long as the fluid lost by sweating is continually replaced [48]. *Dehydration* of the body acts to *raise its temperature* and therefore *limits performance*. The core-temperature plateau reached during submaximal work is proportional to the *relative performance* (performance as % of the individual maximum, given by $\dot{V}_{O_2max}$; see p. 663). The rectal temperatures of marathon runners have been found to reach 39°–40 °C, and in some cases almost 42 °C [41]. (The changes in temperature during exercise are discussed in terms of control theory on p. 638).

25.3 Heat Loss

Under stationary resting conditions, characterized by constant mean body temperature, the metabolic rate (MR) must be equal to the rate of heat transfer from the interior to the surface of the body *(internal heat flow H_{int})* and to the rate of heat transfer from the body surface to the surroundings *(external heat flow H_{ext}):*

$$MR = H_{int} = H_{ext} \quad (3)$$

Internal Heat Flow

Of the heat produced within the body, less than half flows to the body surface by **conduction** through the tissues; most of it is transferred by **convection,** in the bloodstream. Because of its high heat capacity the blood is particularly well suited for heat transport and thus for maintaining thermal balance within the body. The internal heat flow, as Eq. 4 indicates, is proportional to the difference between the core temperature T_c and the mean skin temperature $\bar{T}_{sk}$. It is also determined by the **thermal conductance** C, the magnitude of which depends on the rates of blood flow through skin and extremities:

$$H_{int} = C \cdot (T_c - \bar{T}_{sk}) \cdot A \quad (4)$$

where A is the area of the body surface; H_{int} is given in watts. In an adult human changes in the rate of blood flow can change the conductance C by a factor of 4 to 7, depending on the thickness of the body shell and of the subcutaneous fat [4, 5]. The reciprocal of C, $1/C = I_t$, is called the **thermal resistance** or **thermal insulation** of the body shell.

The variability in thermal conductance derives in particular from the fact that blood flow through the extremities conforms to the **counter-current principle.** The deep large vessels in the limbs lie in parallel, so that as blood flows outward through the arteries it loses heat to the accompanying veins. Hence the acral vessels receive precooled blood, and the *axial temperature gradient in the extremities becomes steeper*. In warm surroundings superficial veins open, so that more of the returning blood flows through them, diminishing the short-circuit effect. Therefore the axial temperature gradient is less steep and heat loss is promoted.

External Heat Flow

For quantitative analysis of external heat flow, and for evaluation of the effects upon it of external factors, it is necessary to consider separately its various components [5, 14]. These are heat transfer by conduction H_k, by convection H_c, by radiation H_r, and by evaporation H_e. The total heat flow is the sum of these components:

$$H_{ext} = H_k + H_c + H_r + H_e \quad (5)$$

The percentages contributed to the total by these components under resting and working conditions are summarized in Fig. 25-7.

Heat transfer by conduction occurs wherever the body is in contact (standing, sitting or lying down) with a firm substrate. The magnitude of conductive flow is determined by the temperature and the thermal conductance of the supporting material.

From the part of the body surface covered with air, heat is transferred by radiation, convection and evaporation.

Convective heat transfer. If the skin is warmer than the surrounding air, the adjacent layer of air is warmed, rises and is replaced by cooler, denser air. In this process, called **natural convection,** heat is carried away by the laminar current of air produced at the skin surface. The driving force for this flow is the temperature difference between the body and its surroundings. As more movement occurs in the external air the boundary layer within which flow is laminar, 4–8 mm thick at most, becomes thinner; air flow becomes turbulent close to the skin. This **forced convection** considerably increases the rate of heat loss. Convective heat transfer (in watts) is given by Eq. (6). The determining factors are the difference between the *mean skin temperature* $\bar{T}_{sk}$ and the *ambient air temperature* T_a, the effective surface area A (which is smaller than the geometrical surface area of the body because some surfaces touch one another), and the **convective heat transfer coefficient h_c,** the magnitude of which increases as the square root of wind velocity.

$$H_c = h_c \cdot (\bar{T}_{sk} - T_a) \cdot A \quad (6)$$

The quantity $I_c = 1/h_c$ is called the thermal resistance or **insulation of the boundary layer.**

Heat transfer by radiation. The loss of heat in the form of long-wavelength infrared radiation from the skin (which does not involve a conducting medium) is described exactly by the **Stefan-Boltzmann equation** (see physics textbooks). That is, radiation varies as the fourth power of the absolute temperature. For the small temperature range of interest in biology, radiant heat transfer H_r can be described with sufficient accuracy by the linearized Equation (7):

$$H_r = h_r \cdot (\bar{T}_{sk} - \bar{T}_r) \cdot A \quad (7)$$

where $\bar{T}_{sk}$ is the mean skin temperature, $\bar{T}_r$ is the **mean radiant temperature** (the temperature of the enclosing surfaces – e.g., walls of the room), A is the effective body-surface area and h_r is the **radiative heat transfer coefficient.** The significance of the temperature of the surrounding surfaces can be illustrated by holding one's palm a short distance away from the face. There is an immediate sensation of warmth, which results from the diminished radiant heat loss. The coefficient h_r takes account of the emissivity ϵ of the skin, which for the long-wavelength infrared radiation is nearly 1, regardless of pigmentation; that is, the skin emits almost exactly as much radiant energy as a "full radiator", or ideal black body. The emissivity of the surrounding walls must be considered only if they are very close to the body. Radiant heat is **absorbed** in rooms with radiation heaters or in the sunshine when the mean radiant temperature $\bar{T}_r$ (Eq. 7) exceeds $\bar{T}_{sk}$. In the case of *short-wavelength* infrared radiation (emitted by hot radiating bodies such as electrical radiators and the sun), both the emissivity and the absorptance of the skin are considerably smaller than 1 (0.5–0.8) and depend on the skin pigmentation.

Heat transfer by convection and that by radiation are often lumped as **"dry" heat loss.** In this case the value for ambient temperature is the *operative temperature*, a weighted average of the air and radiant temperatures. The heat transfer coefficients for convection and radiation are combined to give the coefficient h_c, the reciprocal of which is the ambient insulation I_a.

Evaporative heat transfer. About 20% of the heat lost by a human under neutral temperature conditions (see Fig. 25-7) is accounted for by the evaporation of water that has diffused to the surface of the skin or from the mucous membranes lining the respiratory tract.

Evaporative heat transfer from the skin is described by the following equation:

$$H_c = h_e \cdot (\bar{P}_{sk} - P_a) \cdot A \qquad (8)$$

where P_{sk} and P_a are the vapor pressures on the skin (the mean pressure) and in the surrounding air, and h_e is the **evaporative heat transfer coefficient.** h_e varies with the curvature of the skin surface, the atmospheric pressure and the wind velocity.

The most important conclusion to be drawn from the above equation is that evaporative heat loss takes place even when the relative humidity of the surroundings is 100%. The only critical requirement is that $\bar{P}_{sk}$ be greater than P_a; this is the case as long as the skin temperature is completely wetted by adequate secretion of sweat.

The water lost by diffusion through skin and mucosa is called **insensible** or extraglandular water loss, as distinct from the **glandular** water loss by way of the sweat glands. Only the latter, which can have a marked effect on the total amount of heat transferred, is under the control of the thermoregulatory system. When the ambient temperature exceeds that of the body, heat can be given off only by evaporation. The effectiveness of sweat secretion in thermoregulation is based on the high heat of evaporation of water, 2,400 kJ per liter. By evaporating 1 liter of water the human body can lose one-third of the resting heat production of an entire day (cf. water balance, p. 763).

The effect of clothing. Clothing, in the physiological context, is a form of thermal resistance or **insulation** I_{cl} [2] – a quantity to be added to the thermal resistances of the tissue (I_t) and of the ambient boundary layer (I_a). The effectiveness of clothing is chiefly due to the tiny air spaces trapped in the weave or nap, where no appreciable flow can occur; here heat transfer is entirely by **conduction,** and air is a poor heat conductor.

Environmental Factors and Thermal Comfort

From what has been said so far it is evident that the effect of a person's immediate environment depends on at least **four physical factors: air temperature,** the water-vapor pressure of the air **(humidity), radiation temperature** and **wind velocity.** These determine whether the person feels *"thermally comfortable"* or too warm or cold. The condition for comfort is that no thermoregulatory mechanisms must be called into play – neither shivering nor sweat secretion are activated, and blood flows through the periphery of the body at an intermediate rate. This condition corresponds to the previously mentioned **thermoneutral zone** (Fig. 25-4).

The four physical factors are to a certain extent interchangeable with regard to the sensation of comfort and the need for thermoregulation. That is, a sensation of cold produced by low air temperature can be alleviated by an appropriate increase in the radiation temperature. When the atmosphere feels sultry, the sensation can be diminished by reducing the humidity as well as by lowering the temperature. If the radiation temperature is low (cold walls) an increased air temperature is required for comfort. These interactions make it possible to express various combinations of factors by a single number – for example, the **effective temperature** [34].

According to recent extensive studies [3], the **thermal comfort point** for a lightly clothed (shirt, short underpants, long cotton trousers), seated person is about 25°–26 °C when the humidity is set at 50% and the temperatures of wall and air are the same. The corresponding value for a nude person at 50% R.H. has been found to be 28 °C. In conditions of thermal comfort the

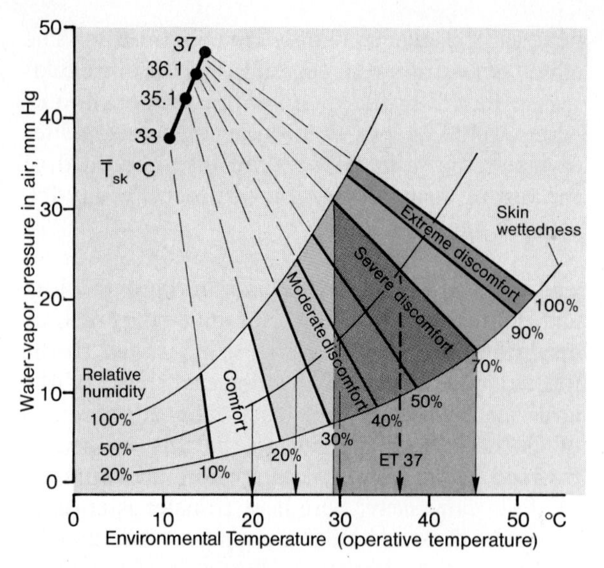

Fig. 25-8. The psychometric diagram represents the relation of ambient temperature (operative temperature: the weighted mean of radiative and air temperature) and humidity to thermal discomfort. This relation holds for conditions of moderate work ("3 met" = three times the resting metabolic rate), light sport clothing and slight relative air movement ($0.5\,m \cdot s^{-1}$). ET, effective temperature; $\bar{T}_{sk}$, mean skin temperature. Modified from [34]

mean skin temperature is about 34 °C. As more effort is exerted in physical work the comfortable temperature becomes lower. For example, a room temperature of ca. 22 °C is preferred for light office work. Curiously, however, during hard work a room temperature such that sweating remains just suppressed is felt to be too cool. Fig. 25-8 is a diagram showing how thermal comfort is related to the humidity and the ambient temperature during light work (3 met; 1 met = the resting metabolic rate). To each degree of discomfort there can be ascribed a *single* temperature, the effective temperature (ET). The numerical value of ET is found by projecting onto the x axis the point at which a discomfort line intersects the curve for 50% relative humidity [34] (an older ET scale was constructed with respect to 100% R.H.). For example, all of the combinations of temperature and humidity within the dark gray field in Fig. 25-8 (e.g., 30 °C at 100% R.H., 45 °C at 20% R.H. and so on) correspond to the ET 37 °C, and this in turn corresponds to a specific degree of discomfort. In the lower temperature ranges the influence of humidity is less (the discomfort lines slope more steeply), because here the contribution of evaporative heat transfer to the total heat loss is slight. As the diagram shows, *discomfort increases with mean skin temperature* and with the *skin wettedness* (the fraction of the total body area that is covered by sweat [34]). When the limiting conditions for maximal skin wettedness (100%) have been exceeded, thermal balance can no longer be maintained. Therefore conditions beyond this limit can be tolerated only briefly; sweat drips off the body, because more is secreted than can evaporate. The discomfort lines plotted in Fig. 25-8 shift, of course, depending on the thermal insulation provided by clothing, on the wind velocity and on the workload. When the work performed rises from 3 met to 6 met, for example, the limit for prolonged tolerance shifts from ET 40 °C to ET 33 °C.

Thermal comfort points in water. When water is the ambient medium, the boundary layer of air is replaced by water – a substance with far greater thermal conductivity and heat capacity. At a given temperature much more heat is withdrawn by convection from a resting body in water than from one in air. When the water is in motion, the resulting turbulent flow at the body surface withdraws heat so rapidly that at an ambient temperature of 10 °C even strenuous physical exertion fails to maintain thermal equilibrium, and **hypothermia** ensues. When the body is completely at rest, a water temperature of 35 °C–36 °C is required for thermal comfort. This lower limit of the thermoneutral zone depends on the thickness of the insulating adipose tissue. In a series of studies on people with different degrees of obesity the lower limit for comfort was found to lie between 31 °C and 36 °C [52].

25.4 The Regulation of Body Temperature

Biological thermoregulation can usefully be described with the terminology used in systems theory for technical control systems. **Sensors** are required for continuous monitoring of the thermal state of the controlled system. Their outputs are transmitted to a **central controller**, where the thermal information is processed and from which signals are sent out to control the operation of one or more **effectors**. The outputs from the effectors must be such as to counteract temperature changes caused by external or internal disturbances; if this is accomplished, the system is a closed loop with **negative feedback** (Fig. 25-9). Let us now consider the components of the system individually.

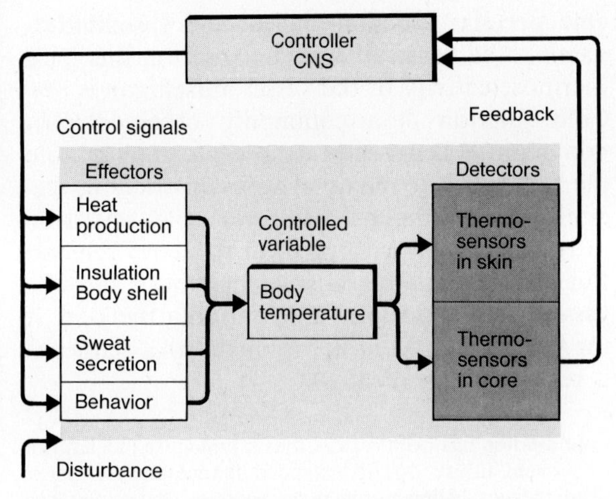

Fig. 25-9. Block diagram of thermoregulation. The system has two groups of detectors, corresponding in the organism to the cutaneous and the internal thermosensors

Effector Outputs in Thermoregulation

The effector outputs – **Heat production, tissue insulation and sweat secretion** – are predominantly under *neural control;* only in long-term adaptation do *hormonal processes* play a role. Two neural systems participate in thermoregulation: (i) the *somatomotor* system, and (ii) the *sympathetic* system (Fig. 25-10). **Thermoregulatory behavior** such as fanning oneself and adding or removing clothing can also be included in the effector category (cf. "behavioral regulation", p. 641).

Control of thermogenesis. Shivering (cf. p. 625) is induced and sustained by way of the motor system, the spinal and supraspinal elements of which (the cerebrospinal and reticulospinal tracts) are described in Chapter 5. The so-called **central shivering pathway,** which runs caudad from the posterior hypothalamus [5], links the central thermoregulatory areas with the mesencephalic and rhombencephalic nuclei of the motor system. Shivering can also be influenced pharmacologically by the action of curare and other muscle relaxants on the neuromuscular end plate (see pp. 48f.).

Nonshivering thermogenesis (see also pp. 625ff.) is controlled by way of the sympathetic nervous system. When sympathetic activity is suppressed by ganglion-blocking drugs or, more specifically, by drugs that block the adrenergic β-receptors (see Fig. 25-3), nonshivering heat production ceases. The noradrenalin released at the nerve endings stimulates the release of free fatty acids from lipid droplets surrounded by mitochondria, as well as the subsequent oxidation of the fatty acids. As for the biochemical mechanism of this form of thermogenesis, see [44].

Control of heat loss. The thermoregulatory effects on **blood flow** differ, depending on the part of the body involved. At least three functionally different regions can be distinguished: (i) the acral areas (fingers, hands, ears, lips, nose), (ii)

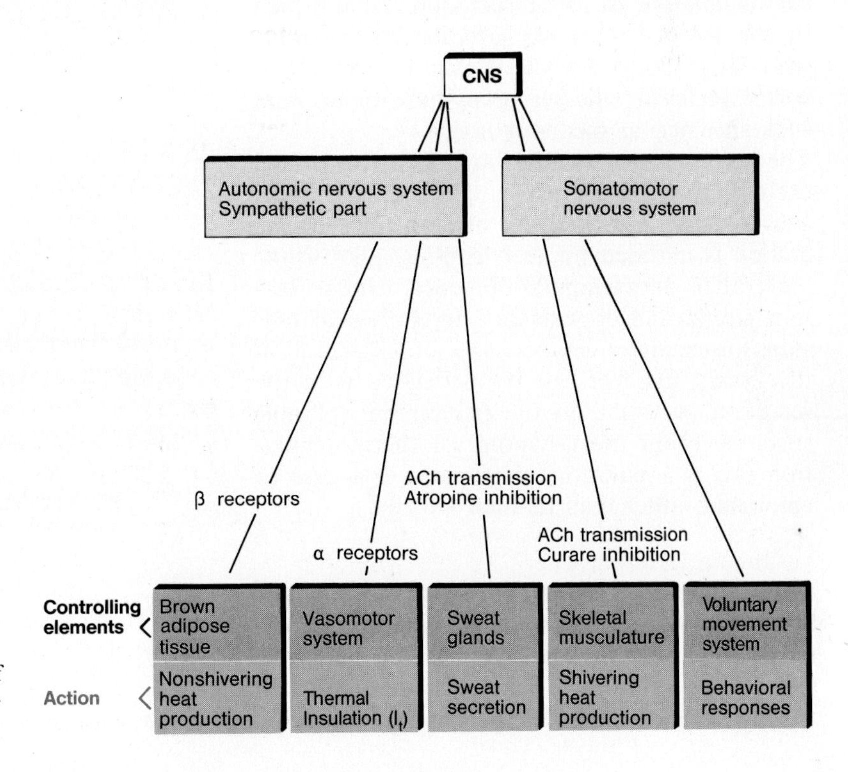

Fig. 25-10. Schematic illustration of the neural control of thermoregulatory effector elements

the trunk and proximal parts of the limbs, and (iii) the head and forehead [5].

Acral perfusion is controlled by *noradrenergic sympathetic nerves;* an increase in sympathetic tone leads to vasoconstriction and a decrease, to vasodilation. The diameter of the **arteriovenous anastomoses** in the distal parts of the limbs is affected by sympathetic activity in the same way as that of the arterioles. When the arteriovenous anastomoses open, blood flow through the extremities, and thus the **convective transfer of heat,** is markedly increased. Elimination of sympathetic activity produces nearly maximal dilation of the acral vessels. In the trunk and the proximal parts of the limbs the maximal perfusion increase induced by heat is far greater than that following blocking of the sympathetic system. This fact suggests the existence of specific vasodilator nerves, fibers that release from their endings a transmitter (presumably acetylcholine) that inhibits contraction of the muscles in the vessel walls [47]. On the other hand, vasodilation has been ascribed to an enzyme secreted in sweat, which catalyzes the formation of a vasoactive mediator (bradykinin). This view is consistent with the observation that the vasodilation initiated by external warming has two distinct phases. The second phase occurs at nearly the same time as the onset of sweating; the first phase coincides with the acral vasodilation and is therefore thought to result from the decrease in sympathetic tone. Coupling of the second phase of vasodilation to sweat secretion is confirmed by the absence of active vasodilation in people who congenitally lack sweat glands. However, it is not yet clear whether bradykinin or another substance acts as mediator [24].

The **secretion of sweat** in humans is controlled exclusively by *cholinergic* sympathetic fibers, and can thus be inhibited by atropine. Sweat secretion is initiated by acetylcholine, pilocarpine and other parasympathomimetics. Under certain circumstances (extreme psychological tension, for example) cutaneous vasoconstriction in the hands and feet can be associated with the secretion of sweat on the palmar and plantar surfaces. From the viewpoint of thermoregulation this is a paradoxical response – a case of **emotional** rather than **thermal sweating.**

Direct actions of temperature upon effector processes. Blood vessels respond directly to temperature changes; this property, which is independent of neural control, has been demonstrated by experiments on isolated segments of vessels. One peculiar reaction, called **cold vasodilation,** seems to be based to a great extent on this local thermosensitivity of the vessel musculature.

Cold dilation is a commonly observed phenomenon. When one is exposed to intense cold the first result is maximal vasoconstriction, recognizable by the paleness and cold sensation (often combined with pain) in the acral regions. But after a while blood suddenly spurts into the vessels here, reddening and warming the skin. If the exposure to cold is prolonged this sequence is repeated periodically.

Cold dilation has been regarded as a *protective* mechanism to prevent injury due to extended inadequate perfusion of the tissues, **chilblain** and **tissue necroses**. But experience shows that if the cold is sufficient to cause frostbite, severe local damage occurs despite the vasodilation; cold dilation has a protective action only in people adapted to cold (see p. 641). On the other hand, it can lethally accelerate the overall cooling of people who have fallen overboard and must float for a long time in cold water [5].

Thermoreception

The **cutaneous cold and warm receptors,** which also mediate the *sensation of temperature* (cf. thermosensors, pp. 203f.), are one of the receptor groups that act as detectors in the temperature-control circuit (Fig. 25-9). It was proposed long ago that there are also **internal thermosensors**, and considerable experimental evidence of their existence has accumulated. For example, local heating or cooling of a narrowly circumscribed part of the **anterior hypothalamus** elicits both enhanced heat loss and increased thermogenesis [1,

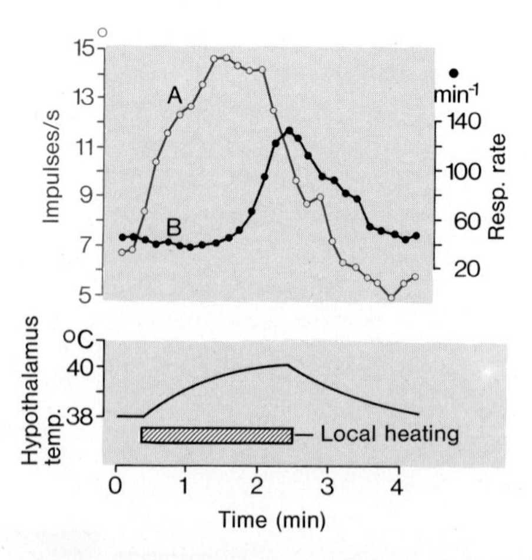

Fig. 25-11. Synchronous recording of the discharge rate of a "warm neuron" in the preoptic region of the hypothalamus (A) and of respiratory rate (B) as the temperature of the hypothalamus is varied by an implanted thermal probe. Modified from [43]

5, 43]. By electrical recording from single fibers temperature-sensitive structures have been identified – primarily **"warm neurons"**, the discharge rate of which increases during local heating. As illustrated in Fig. 25-11, the increased discharge of these neurons is associated with activation of a mechanism to counteract heating (increased respiratory rate).

In vitro studies of **hypothalamic slices** [40] and of cell cultures [20] have been informative with regard to the question whether hypothalamic thermosensitivity is tied to individual *thermosensitive ganglion cells* or is based on the temperature dependence of *synaptic transmission* between afferent and efferent neurons. After synaptic transmission had been blocked by electrolyte solutions with a low Ca^{2+} content and high Mg^{2+} content, the structures in question remained sensitive to thermal stimuli, which implies the existence of **thermosensitive cells.** In both the in vivo and the in vitro experiments, the preoptic region and anterior hypothalamus were found to contain not only warm-sensitive cells ($Q_{10} > 1$; cf. p. 625) but also thermo*in*sensitive cells ($Q_{10} = 1$) and *cold-sensitive cells* ($Q_{10} < 0.5$), the latter being less numerous than the warm-sensitive cells. No typical thermosensitive cells were found in cultures of mediobasal hypothalamic tissue. This result is consistent with the very infrequent findings of thermosensitive structures in the posterior hypothalamus in vivo.

Thermosensitive structures have also been demonstrated in the **lower brainstem** (midbrain and medulla oblongata), and thermoregulatory reactions can be initiated by local warming of these areas. However, the thermosensitivity here is distinctly less than in the preoptic region and anterior hypothalamus [39]. On the other hand, the **spinal cord is extremely thermosensitive.** When the temperature of the spinal cord is raised only a few tenths of a degree along its entire length, in dogs and other animals, the result is panting, vasodilation and inhibition of thermogenesis [51, 54]. Cooling of the spinal cord elicits shivering, but in this case a greater temperature change is required [39, 51].

In the guinea pig, a local temperature change in the region of the cervical cord suffices to trigger thermoregulatory reactions [29]. For a rigorous comparison of spinal thermosensitivity with that of the anterior hypothalamus, thermosensitive areas of equal size would have to be stimulated, but no sufficiently small-scale studies of the spinal cord are yet available. For this reason, too, nothing is known about the locations and morphology of the structures mediating spinal thermosensitivity.

Quantitative considerations suggest the existence of **thermoreceptive structures outside the CNS** and the skin [39.] There is experimental evidence of thermosensors in the region of the *dorsal wall* of the *abdominal cavity* [39, 51] and in the *musculature* [39]. Furthermore, thermosensors at still other sites cannot be ruled out; there are recent indications of subcutaneous thermosensors [38].

The distribution of thermoreceptive structures throughout the body may be regarded as a correlate of the body's complicated temperature gradients (p. 627). Such comprehensive sampling would provide the neurophysiological prerequisites for an extremely elaborate control system that takes into account the thermal state of the organism as a whole **(multiple input system)**. Primitive control systems, like those in simple domestic air conditioners, usually have only one temperature sensor, at a single position in the system. In such cases considerable spatial and temporal temperature gradients can develop.

Integrative Processes and Central Nervous Structures for Thermoregulation

The fundamental system-theoretical concepts on which our description of thermoregulation is based demand that there be some elements to "process" the thermal information originating at the receptors, and to transform these inputs from the sensors into effector outputs (cf. Figs. 25-9 and 25-10).

Information processing in the hypothalamus. There are many experimental results implicating the hypothalamus – especially the **posterior hypothalamic area**, which has no appreciable *thermosensitivity* (see above) – as an **integration center for thermoregulation.** This interpretation is supported by electrophysiological findings. For example, there are neurons in the posterior hypothalamic area, the activity (discharge rate) of which is influenced by local thermal stimulation in either the preoptic region or the cervicothoracic part of the spinal cord [57]. At the boundary between the anterior and posterior hypothalamus neurons have been found that respond to changes in the skin temperature on the limbs and trunk [28]. The posterior hypothalamus, therefore, is characterized by the presence of **thermoresponsive cells** (i.e., cells that respond to changes in the temperature of distant structures but are not sensitive to changes in their own temperature). However, there is no absolute spatial separation of *receptive* from *integrative functions.* In the preoptic region and anterior hypothalamus cells shown to be thermo*sensitive* have also been found to be affected by skin-temperature changes, and hence are simultaneously thermo*responsive* [5, 6].

Thermoafferent pathways. The signals from thermosensors in the skin of the trunk are thought to be conducted centrally by reticular branches of the **spinothalamic tract** (cf. unspecific system, p. 209). The thermal signals from the facial skin could reach the hypothalamus by corresponding projections of the *caudal trigeminal nucleus,* though such a pathway has not yet been demonstrated. The thermosensitive structures in the spinal cord are connected to the hypothalamus by ascending tracts in the region of the anterolateral funiculi [56]. According to recent investigations, some of the cutaneous afferents follow a polysynaptic route, by way of two nuclear regions in the lower brainstem (the subcoeruleus region and the raphe nuclei, Fig. 25-12), to the hypothalamus [28].

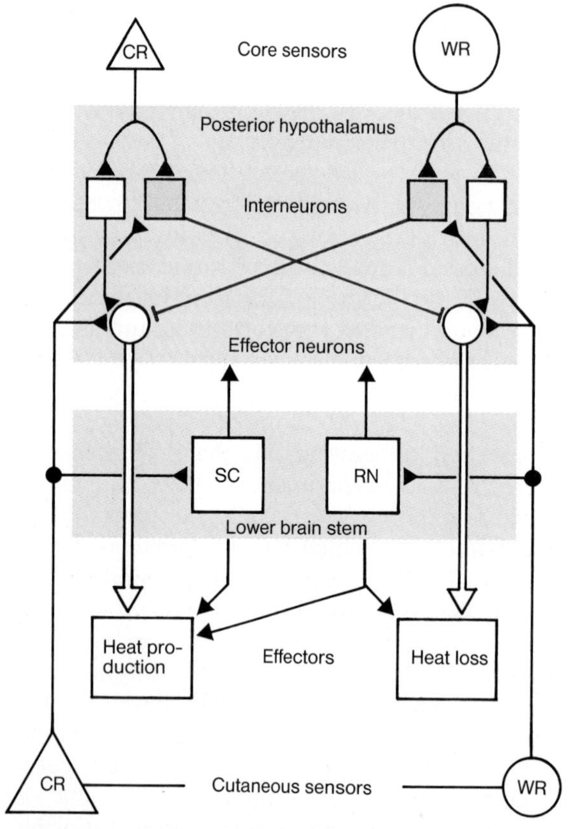

Fig. 25-12. Highly simplified model of the connections between thermal afferents and the efferent neuronal networks that control the thermoregulatory effector elements. The *shaded areas* represent the thermo-integrative regions of the hypothalamus (mainly the posterior hypothalamus) and the lower brainstem, which contains crucial structures for the processing of thermal information from the skin (the raphe nuclei: *RN;* subcoeruleus region: *SC*). The inhibitory neurons shown in *red* mediate the reciprocal inhibition of the heat-losing and heat-generating processes. *CR:* cold receptors; *WR:* warm receptors (size of the symbols indicates roughly the difference in numbers). —◂ activating, —| inhibitory synaptic connections. The symbols for neurons represent not single neurons but rather neuron pools. Some details of the connections between SC, RN and hypothalamus are known [28] but are not within the scope of this diagram. The arrows pointing down from the lower brainstem represent pathways to motoneurons and dorsal-horn neurons in the spinal cord; the latter can suppress input from the warm afferents (cf. "centrifugal control of afferent information", pp. 219f.)

Efferent pathways. One efferent connection is provided by the *central shivering pathway* [5, 6], which originates in the posterior hypothalamus and leads to the reticular motor nuclei. Connections for vasomotor control, according to studies on the rat, pass through the *medial forebrain bundle* (medial telencephalic fasciculus) [35]. A morphological substrate is therefore available for the thermointegrative functions ascribed to the posterior hypothalamus.

The most clear-cut demonstration of the involvement of the hypothalamus in thermoregulation is provided by the **classical transection experiments.** When the brainstem of a cat is cut immediately rostral to the hypothalamus, thermoregulation is unimpaired, whereas after transection rostral to the mesencephalon the animals behave like poikilotherms. If the surgery is skilfully done and the ambient temperature suitably controlled, such artificially poikilothermic animals can survive for weeks or months [5, 54].

In the rat, a certain ability to regulate body temperature and to develop fever has been shown to persist even after transection just behind the *diencephalon.* The neuronal basis for this residual function was demonstrated, though not explained in detail, by the finding of *thermoreceptive structures in the midbrain* (see above) and *synapses of thermoafferent fibers in the lower brainstem* (Fig. 25-12).

Reciprocal connectivity of cold and warm afferents. A special feature of biological thermoregulation, as compared with the familiar simple technical systems, is that *two kinds of sensors* in different locations, the cold and the warm receptors, interact antagonistically. The **cutaneous cold receptors**, more numerous and more uniformly distributed than the warm receptors, are activated when the temperature falls below the lower limit of the thermoneutral zone (below T_2 in Fig. 25-4); their activation initiates processes that *protect against cold* (see Figs. 25-9 and 25-10) – vasoconstriction and thermoregulatory enhancement of heat production. This reaction is *counteracted* by **heat-activated internal thermosensors** when the body temperature rises, as a result of overshooting cold protective mechanisms or after exercise. This circuitry enables the protective mechanisms to be set in motion very rapidly in case of external cooling, long before the core temperature has begun to fall and internal thermoreceptors can be influenced.

In conditions of **heat stress**, such as arise owing to increased thermogenesis during exercise, the **internal warm receptors** are excited and trigger **heat-elimination processes** (vasodilation, sweating). This effect is counteracted by cold-activation of the cutaneous cold receptors. The cutaneous warm receptors cannot be expected to contribute much to heat-loss initiation during exercise, because in this situation the secretion and evaporation of sweat bring the skin temperature below that corresponding to thermoneutrality (cf. Fig. 23-7). But when the body is heated externally, sweat secretion is stimulated by the combined action of cutaneous and internal warm receptors (Fig. 25-12).

A neuronal model of the central controller. Current concepts of the functional organization of the hypothalamus (pp. 356ff.) suggest the following picture of the **neuronal correlates of integrative thermoregulatory functions** (Fig. 25-12). Three kinds of neuronal elements are distinguished: (i) *efferent neurons* located in the hypothalamus, the axons of which activate the peripheral controlling elements (Fig. 25-10) either directly or, more probably, by way of a chain of interneurons, (ii) *interneurons* within the hypothalamus, and (iii) *thermal afferents*, arising in part from the cutaneous thermoreceptors and in part from internal receptors (e.g., those of the preoptic region). Cold receptors directly activate the effectors for thermogenesis; their inhibitory action on the efferents to the heat-loss effectors is exerted by way of interneurons. Activation of the warm receptors excites the efferents to the heat-loss effectors, simultaneously (again by way of interneurons) inhibiting the efferents to the effectors for heat production [1, 5].

Processing of the thermal information. Under the thermal loads ordinarily encountered, there can be a considerable difference between the *skin temperature* and the *core temperature* (cf. Fig. 25-7). Given that the thermosensitive structures are distributed over the entire body, as discussed above, the thermoregulatory effector outputs (Fig. 25-10) cannot be expected to be described as a function of any local temperature (e.g., the rectal temperature). Thus the goal of thermophysiology is to describe thermoregulatory actions *as a function of as many as possible of the temperatures associated with the various thermosensitive parts of the body*. Systems of equations with several variables are required for such a description. The data must be collected by experiments on animals in which spatially circumscribed temperature changes are produced by means of thermodes and heat exchangers [39]; in humans, there is only limited opportunity for experimental manipulation of local temperature while the temperature of the rest of the body is kept constant. Therefore one cannot be certain of the extent to which the results of animal experiments are applicable to humans. Only an approximate description is possible, in which the thermoregulatory parameters are presented as a function of two temperatures, the **temperature of the interior of the body** (measured at a representative site) and the **mean skin temperature** [23, 25, 27, 42]. For instance, shivering can be shown as sets of curves in a coordinate system with skin temperature and core temperature as the coordinates (Fig. 25-13). The curves for equivalent sweat secretion are straighter, approaching linearity. Blood flow through the skin

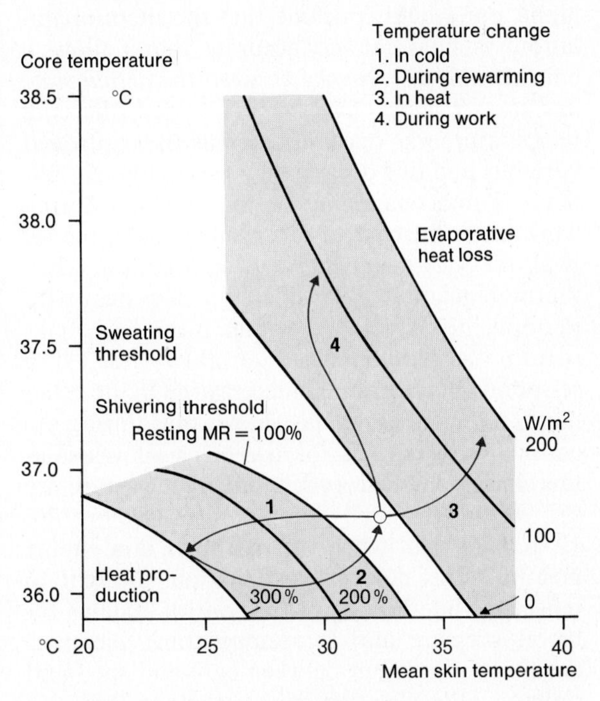

Fig. 25-13. Graph illustrating the dependence of shivering and sweating on the mean skin temperature and the core temperature. The *circle* corresponds to the temperature under thermoneutral conditions. The diagram applies quantitatively only to a particular time of day and a particular state of acclimatization. The set-point shifts described in the text would be represented by shifting the contour lines in the coordinate system. From data in [22, 42]

is described by an equation similar to that for sweating [55]. The diagram (Fig. 25-13) permits quantitative predictions of numerous thermoregulatory responses. The most important of these will now be examined.

Shivering is induced by cold when the skin temperature alone falls below the normal level (circle), as indicated by Arrow 1 in the diagram. The core temperature can actually rise slightly owing to **overshooting responses to cold**, though more pronounced increases in core temperature (for example, during exercise) would suppress the shivering triggered by cold. If the cold stress is prolonged, as during *swimming in cold water*, the core temperature eventually begins to fall. Subsequent rapid rewarming (by *sunbathing in the dunes*, perhaps) initially increases the skin temperature (Arrow 2) above the shivering threshold, so that shivering stops before the core temperature has recovered. *External heating* at first causes only the skin temperature to rise (Arrow 3); sweating begins while the core temperature is still nearly normal. During *work* (Arrow 4) sweating begins with the *initial sharp rise in internal temperature*, and evaporation then lowers the skin temperature (cf. Fig. 25-7).

For sweat secretion to become maximal **during exercise**, the core temperature must rise higher, the lower the ambient (and hence the skin) temperature. Considering the core temperature alone, one would conclude that the thermoregulation system is not very accurate, that it allows a considerable *discrepancy between the actual state and the set point (load error)*. Indeed, the core temperature was once regarded as the controlled variable, and this discrepancy was extremely difficult to understand; it was thought that during work, as in the case of fever (see p. 641), the *set point for body temperature was shifted*. But when thermoregulation is considered as a system with multiple inputs, with a weighted mean body temperature as the controlled variable [1, 5, 29], a set-point shift appears unnecessary. On the other hand, recent research has shown that during exercise the thresholds for the onset of **vasodilation during physical work** in an erect posture are shifted to higher body temperatures (see Fig. 26-12, p. 636) than when the person is in a supine position. This delayed vasodilation, thought to reflect the interlinking of the control systems for blood pressure and for temperature, increases the thermal gradient between core and shell and promotes the elevation of core temperature.
Because of the **dynamic sensitivity** of the cutaneous thermoreceptors (see p. 204), rapid temperature changes (as when one jumps into cold water) trigger marked thermoregulatory reactions [25] that soon fade away. The dynamic reactions can help to **reduce the load error.**

In the region **between the sweating and shivering thresholds** (white area in Fig. 25-13) the temperature is controlled entirely by **vasomotor and behavioral mechanisms.** Whenever possible people try to behave in such a way as to remain in the restricted region of vasomotor control, for sweating and shivering feel uncomfortable.

The Set Point and Its Adjustment

The temperature fluctuations associated with the diurnal and menstrual cycles (p. 629) and the abnormally high temperatures during fever are regarded as shifts of the set point. But when using the term *"set point"* in this connection we become aware that there is a limit to the analogy between biological and technical systems. To the technologist the term is unambiguous. It denotes precisely the value of the controlled variable that the designer intends to maintain with the smallest possible variation; it is set intentionally, and if circumstances require it can be shifted intentionally. In the case of biological systems there is no designer whose "intentions" can be specified, so that the term (if it is not to be discarded as inappropriate to such systems) must be defined indirectly. One can determine the constellation of temperatures at which the individual control processes come into operation (regulatory enhancement of thermogenesis, sweat secretion and so on). Such analysis provides the threshold curves for shivering and sweat secretion (Fig. 25-13). The "set point" of the system can be thought of as the integrated steady-state **body temperature at which neither the mechanisms for heat elimination nor those for protection against cold are active.** In other words, *the "set point" is a function of the threshold temperatures for the various control processes.*

Let us consider the possible **neurophysiological basis** for the establishment of a threshold curve at a certain level. One might propose that the particular form of a threshold curve is simply the expression of the functional characteristics of the cold and warm receptors involved. At the "normal" temperature both types would be equally active, and they would cancel each other out. With a positive or negative deviation from the set point the resulting predominance of warm or cold signals, respectively, would initiate the appropriate control processes. A "set-point shift" would then be ascribable to a change in the functional characteristics of the thermoreceptors. The functional characteristics of (internal) thermoreceptors have been found to change in experimental fever and under the action of progesterone (e.g., temperature fluctuation during the menstrual cycle, Fig. 25-6). Threshold shifts observed under other conditions, however, are not (or not completely) explicable by a change in thermosensor function. Therefore it has been

postulated that certain cells act as "reference" neurons, providing a signal independent of the temperature; when the output of a reference neuron produces postsynaptic inhibition of a neuron that receives input from thermoreceptors, the effect is to subtract a specific amount from the temperature signal. Hence the activity of the reference neuron, which can be altered by non-thermal influences, could serve to fix the threshold. However, no such reference neurons have been found, Moreover, shifting of the threshold for shivering during adaptation to cold (see p. 641) has been shown to be associated with typical changes in the **functional characteristics of non-thermosensitive interneurons** in the lower brainstem (see RN and SC, Fig. 25-12). The SC region is part of a noradrenergic system (ventral noradrenergic bundle) that raises the shivering threshold when activated by electrical stimulation [28, 30]. The current view, therefore, is that the level of the threshold and hence the **set point of the thermoregulatory system** is determined by modifiable properties of thermosensitive structures as well as by non-thermosensitive interneurons within the thermoregulatory system [1, 5, 16, 28, 30].
A change in threshold can also be produced by changing the **intercerebral Ca^{2+}/Na^{+} concentration ratio** [6]. It is not yet certain, however, whether changes in the Ca^{2+}/Na^{+} ratio as large as are required for this effect ever occur under normal physiological conditions.

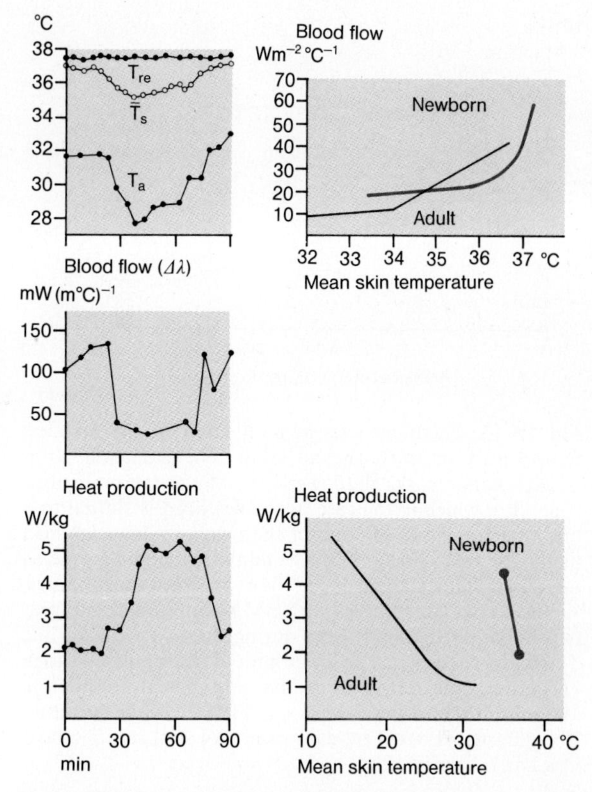

Fig. 25-14. *Left:* Thermoregulatory alterations in skin blood flow (heel: measured as thermal conductivity increment, $\Delta\lambda$) and in metabolic rate of a human newborn under cold stress (ambient temperature T_a reduced to 28 °C). It is evident that the thermoregulatory responses appear as soon as the mean skin temperature $\bar{T}_s$ begins to fall. The core temperature T_{re} is kept constant. *Right:* Total peripheral blood flow (measured as *conductance;* see p. 630) and heat production as a function of the mean skin temperature. Note that thermoregulatory heat production and vasoconstriction occur at a higher skin temperature in the newborn than in the adult. Modified from [26]

25.5 Ontogenetic and Adaptive Changes in Thermoregulation

Thermoregulation in the Newborn

The newborn of various mammalian species (ground squirrel, hamster) are incapable of thermoregulatory heat production immediately after birth; their metabolic rates change with temperature like those of poikilothermic organisms (cf. Fig. 25-1). Not until several weeks have passed do the effector mechanisms become capable of responding to a thermal stimulus. In other species (cf. Fig. 25-3), including humans (Fig. 25-14), **all thermoregulatory responses** (enhanced thermogenesis, vasomotor responses, sweat secretion, behavior patterns) **can be triggered immediately after birth,** even in premature infants weighing about 1,000 g at birth [26]. It is widely asserted that neonates and prematures are poikilothermic, certain brain structures responsible for thermoregulation not yet being fully developed. This misapprehension could arise from the fact that newborn infants as a rule rely not on shivering but on nonshivering thermogenesis (pp. 625ff.), which cannot be detected without special measuring devices. Their heat production can be raised 100–200% above the resting metabolic rate without shivering (Fig. 25-3). Only under extreme cold stress is this mechanism supplemented by shivering.
The small size of a newborn child is a disadvantage with regard to thermoregulation. The **surface-to-volume ratio** of a **mature newborn** is about three times that of an adult. Moreover, the shell of the body is not very thick and the insulating layer of fat is thin. Therefore even maximal vasoconstriction cannot restrict heat transfer to the extent possible in adults (note higher *conductance,* Fig. 25-14). These special problems must be overcome by an increased capacity for heat production – 4 to 5 times as great per unit weight in the mature newborn, and 1 to 10 times in a premature infant weighing 1,000–1,500 g. Immediately after birth the minimal metabolic rate, 1.7 W/kg, is actually below the exponential curve with n = 0.75 shown in Fig. 25-2, but during the first few days and weeks it rises to ca.

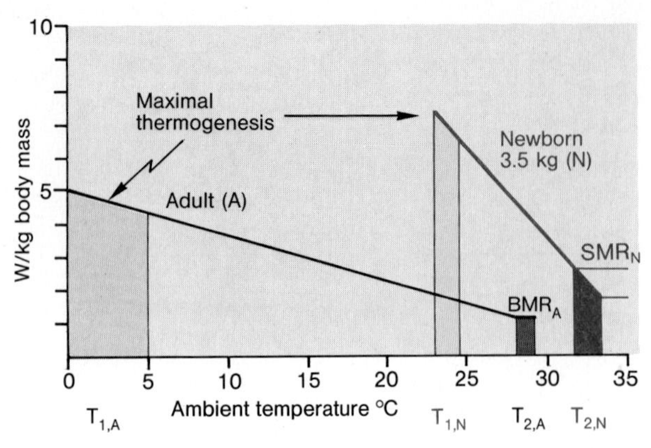

Fig. 25-15. Thermogenesis as a function of the ambient temperature in newborn and adult. The inflection point of each curve marks the lower limit of the thermoneutral zone (T_2), which in the case of the newborn is shifted to a higher temperature because of the relatively low standard metabolic rate (SMR). (SMR = minimal metabolic rate as measured under standard conditions specified for neonates, similar to but not identical with BMR conditions employed in adults). As the SMR rises during the first week of life, $T_{2,N}$ shifts to the left. The lower limit of the regulated range (T_1) is determined by the maximal rate of heat production, and is ca. 23 °C in the newborn and 0 °C–5 °C in the adult. The diagram is based on data from [26]. Evaporative heat loss has been neglected

2.7 W/kg – a value distinctly above the n = 0.75 curve.

Therefore **if thermal balance is to be maintained at the minimal metabolic rate in the newborn, the ambient temperature must be higher, 32 °C–34 °C** (Fig. 25-15). Below this temperature thermoregulatory heat production is required to maintain equilibrium, and it does in fact occur – that is, the **lower boundary of the thermoneutral zone** (T_2 in Fig. 25-15) is **shifted to a higher ambient temperature.** The *lower limit of the regulated range* (T_1 in Fig. 25-15) is also shifted to higher temperatures; in the mature newborn it is about 23 °C, and in the nude adult about 0 °C. Within this **restricted control range,** however, the newborn can regulate its body temperature just as accurately as an adult, because the threshold temperatures for vasoconstriction and thermogenesis are adjusted to body size (Fig. 25-14). In prematures T_1 and T_2 (Fig. 25-15) shift upward with decreasing body size, and the two values approach one another. In very small prematures, therefore, thermoregulation becomes ineffective; until they have grown sufficiently they must be kept in thermostatic containers (incubators).

Long-term Adaptation to the Environment

The *regulatory mechanisms*– thermogenesis, vasomotor responses, sweating – are always prepared for action, so that they can begin to operate within seconds or minutes of the onset of thermal stress. Other mechanisms are available for *long-term adaptation* to changes in the climate in which an organism lives.

These processes, also called **physiological adaptation** or **acclimation,** are based on modifications of organs and functional systems that develop only under the pressure of days, weeks or months of continuous or repeated thermal stress [5, 36].

Heat adaptation. The ability of humans to adapt to heat is crucial for life in tropical or desert climates as well as for strenuous physical work in temperate surroundings. The most important modification that occurs during heat adaptation is in the rate of sweat secretion, which can increase by a factor of 2 and in highly trained people can amount to 1–2 l/h. Furthermore, sweating begins at a lower mean skin and core temperature; that is, the threshold for activation of the regulatory mechanism is lowered, which **reduces the load error** (see p. 638). As a result of these modifications, the mean body temperature for a given heat or work load is reduced, protecting the organism from a *critical rise in heart rate and peripheral blood flow* that would lead to **heat collapse.** Adaptation is also associated with a considerable reduction in the **electrolyte content of the sweat.** This effect reduces the risk of *collapse due to loss of electrolytes* [7, 11].

Under an acute heat load the **plasma volume** and **hemoglobin concentration** are lowered, with the result that venous return diminishes and the stroke volume is smaller. In the course of heat adaptation this unfavorable development in the circulatory system is counteracted by an **increase in plasma volume and plasma protein content** [50].

If the heat load is prolonged, especially in a humid climate, after a period of profuse sweating the rate of sweat secretion declines **(hidromiosis).** This phenomenon, based on peripheral mechanisms that have not yet been fully explained, can be regarded as advantageous in that it prevents an uneconomical dripping of sweat from the body (it is only by evaporation that sweat has a cooling effect.)

One fundamental modification – contrary to popular opinion – is that as heat adaptation progresses one feels thirstier at a given level of water loss through sweating. This is due in part to the lower electrolyte content of the sweat (cf. hypertonic dehydration, p. 771). The increased thirst ensures that enough water is drunk to restore water balance. If the lost water cannot be replaced, potentially lethal hyperthermia can result.

The modifications described above are produced by short-term, intense heat loads. A different response is required by **inhabitants of the tropics,** who are exposed by night and day to high ambient temperatures but whenever possible avoid activity so strenuous as to cause sweating. In such people the sweating threshold is *shifted to higher body temperatures,* so that they sweat less intensely in the everyday heat [46]. This situation is called **tolerance adaptation** (cf. tolerance adaptation to cold).

Cold adaptation. Many animal species adapt to cold in a very conspicuous way, increasing their **thermal insulation** by growing fur. Another fundamental modification found in small animals is the development of **nonshivering thermogenesis** and brown adipose tissue (see pp. 625ff.). Nonshivering thermogenesis can be regarded as an economical mechanism of heat production, because during shivering the rhythmical movements promote air motion around the body and thus increase the rate of convective heat loss (reduction of the boundary layer; see p. 630). An adult human exposed to extreme cold for long periods cannot grow a fur coat, nor can he develop appreciable non-shivering thermogenesis. For this reason it is often claimed that adult humans are incapable of any physiological adaptation to cold – that they must rely on **"behavioral adaptation"** (clothing and heated houses). It is said that the human is a "tropical creature" who can survive the temperate or arctic climate only by virtue of his intelligence. But in recent years new light has been shed on this question. During prolonged exposure to cold humans develop **tolerance adaptation.** The shivering threshold and the curves of identical metabolic thermoregulatory reactions are shifted to lower positions in the temperature coordinate system (Fig. 25-13), and moderate **hypothermia** can result.

This sort of tolerance adaptation was first noted in Australian aborigines, who can spend the night almost naked without shivering, even though the air temperature is near freezing [36]. This ability is also well developed in the Amas – Korean and Japanese women who dive for pearls several hours a day in water at about 10 °C.

Recent studies have shown that the **shivering threshold can be shifted to lower temperatures** in the course of only a few days by repeated 30-to-60-min cold exposures [27, 30]. In this process, the threshold for the heat-dissipating mechanisms (sweating, in humans) is unchanged. That is, the white band in Fig. 25-13 becomes wider. This *expansion of the interthreshold zone* makes thermoregulation more economical – at the price, however, of precision [27, 30].

When exposure to cold is prolonged this form of adaptation seems unsuitable. In fact, the Alacaluf Indians of the western Patagonian islands have been found to employ another strategy. These people, who are continually subjected to cold air, rain and snow, have a basal metabolic rate 25–50% higher than normal [36]. A similar phenomenon (**"metabolic adaptation"**) has also been found in Eskimos.

Local adaptation. When the hands of a person who is otherwise warmly dressed are repeatedly exposed to cold, the pain felt in the hands diminishes. This effect is partly due to the fact that cold-vasodilation (cf. p. 634) occurs at higher skin temperature. But there are other events, not yet explained, which help to reduce the painful sensations due to cold [10].

25.6 Pathophysiology of Thermoregulation

Fever

Fever is thought to amount to a **shift of the "set point"** for body temperature. The fever **develops** as a result of increased heat production by shivering combined with maximal vasoconstriction of the peripheral vessels. That is, the body behaves as that of a healthy person does when external cooling has shifted the actual temperature of the body below the normal set point. During recovery from the fever just the reverse occurs; sweat secretion and vasodilation reduce the body temperature exactly as they do in a healthy person who has become too warm. While the fever persists, external thermal disturbances are compensated by the appropriate control processes – the thermoregulatory effectors remain fully functional. The temperature, however, is being regulated at an increased level.

Pathogenesis of fever [9, 37]. Certain fever-producing substances of external origin **(exogenous pyrogens),** such as the *heat-stable* lipopolysaccharides of bacterial membranes (endotoxins), stimulate granulocytes and macrophages of the reticuloendothelial system to produce a *heat-labile* peptide called **endogenous pyrogen** (EP). EP is identical to interleukin-1 (mediator of unspecific immune responses). Microinjection of EP into small regions of the hypothalamus triggers typical fever reactions, which do not appear when it is injected into other parts of the brain. EP initiates a cascade of processes: the phospholipase A_2 is activated, which converts phospholipids in cell membranes to arachidonic acid, from which (by means of cyclooxygenase) **prostaglandins** are formed.

One of the prostaglandins, *prostaglandin E* (PGE_2), has a pyrogenic action when injected into the hypothalamus in minute amounts. It produces the set-point shift described above by interacting with thermosensitive and/or integrative structures (see interneurons, Fig. 25-12) in the hypothalamus. It is notable in this regard that the standard fever-reducing medicines *(antipyretics;* the prototype is acetylsalicylic acid) inhibit cyclooxygenase activity and hence prostaglandin formation. But there is reason to believe that PGE is not the only fever mediator, because specific PGE antagonists do not prevent pyrogen fever. A search is under way for other fever mediators. It is also not known whether EP can cross the blood-brain barrier. If not, the "cascade" mentioned above must be assumed also to operate outside the CNS, in which case it would be a product of arachidonic acid that enters the brain.

It is well established that the **newborn** do not regularly give *a fever reaction* to infectious diseases [26, 37]; experimental fever can be induced in them only with extremely high doses of endotoxins or EP [53]. Recently gravid animals (sheep, guinea pigs) have been found to behave similarly for a few days before they give birth, during which time they have an elevated plasma concentration of *arginine vasopressin* (AVP; see also antidiuretic hormone, p. 377). Experiments following from this observation have shown that fever can be suppressed by flooding the septal region (a structure rostral to the hypothalamus) with AVP. It has also been discovered that in newborn guinea pigs and females in late pregnancy, *AVP activity* is elevated in neurons of the *paraventricular nucleus,* the axons of which run to the septal region [58]. Nothing conclusive can be said as yet about the physiological significance of the antipyretic action of AVP. Nevertheless, the findings are of great interest with respect to the unanswered question whether the elevated temperature is a harmful side effect of immune responses or whether it is of some benefit in the fight against infection [9].

Effects beyond the Tolerance Limits of the Control System

Hyperthermia [7, 11]. Under an extreme heat load, exceeding the capacity of the heat-loss mechanisms, the retention of heat in the body produces **hyperthermia.** The subjective sensations produced by an increase in body temperature in this situation are far more unpleasant than those accompanying the same degree of fever. In hyperthermia all the effector processes are strained to the utmost, whereas in fever they are not. The highest temperature that can be tolerated in the *short term* is the same in both fever and extreme heat, about 42 °C (cf. marathon runners, p. 629); some individuals under external heat load have survived rectal temperatures of 43 °C or more without damage [7]. But in **prolonged hyperthermia** with rectal temperatures above *39.5 °C–40 °C*, the brain suffers severe damage which usually soon leads to death; cerebral edema develops, neurons are destroyed, and the victim exhibits disorientation, delirium and convulsions. This syndrome is called **heat stroke.** The brain damage interferes with the central thermoregulatory mechanisms; in particular, sweating ceases, which exacerbates the condition. Paradoxically, the muscles can exhibit rhythmic activity resembling the shivering responses to cold [7].

These serious disorders should be distinguished from **heat syncope,** which can be caused by a relatively mild heat load. It often occurs when a person has been standing still for a long time or has stopped some prolonged activity. People with orthostatic regulatory malfunction and inadequate heat adaptation are particularly prone to heat syncope. It is characterized by extreme **vasodilation** and a sharp drop in blood pressure; the *body temperature* under resting conditions is only a little above normal, and after physical activity values between 38 °C and 39 °C (see Fig. 25-7) are measured [11].

Malignant hyperthermia. Severe hyperthermia, soon lethal if untreated, can occur under general anesthesia. It results from an excessive increase in metabolic rate and heat production in the skeletal musculature, the tone of which is greatly increased. The fever is preceded by a sudden elevation of the Ca^{2+} concentration in the cytoplasm of the musculature. Susceptibility to this syndrome is genetically determined [13].

Hypothermia. When the mechanisms for protection against cold are overloaded – that is, after long exposure to temperatures below T_1 in Fig. 25-4 – hypothermia results. The thermoregulatory processes at first operate at full capacity, but as the body temperature falls they subside. At body temperatures around 26 °C–28 °C, death can occur by myocardial **fibrillation.** Other severe effects of hypothermia are respiratory and metabolic acidosis [45]. When **"induced hypothermia"** is required for therapeutic purposes (cf. p. 625), the thermoregulatory mechanisms must be put out of action by anesthesia (cf. Fig. 25-1) or specific inhibiting agents.

Hypothermia in this sense differs from a reaction found **in the aged.** Some old people can maintain a core temperature of 35 °C or even less without the onset of shivering. The regulatory system has been reset to this low level, and it continues to function normally in other respects. To some extent, this is the counterpart of fever [31].

Paraplegia

Spinal-cord transection can affect thermoregulation because (i) descending signals for control of the peripheral autonomic nervous system and the motor system are eliminated, and (ii) ascending pathways by which thermal information is carried to the integrative structures in the brainstem are interrupted. Below the lesion that blocks the descending signals, sweat secretion, vasoconstriction and shivering are no longer elicited. In extreme temperatures vasoconstriction and sweating can be brought about by spinal reflexes, but reflex shivering due to cold has never been observed in humans below the site of a spinal lesion. Because of these failures of regulation, major departures of the core temperature from the set point occur under thermal loads [1, 5].

25.7 References

Textbooks and Handbooks

1. BligHT, J.: Temperature Regulation in Mammals and Other Vertebrates. Amsterdam-London: North Holland Publ. New York: Elsevier Publ. 1973
2. Clark, R.P., Edholm, O.G.: Man and His Thermal Environment. London: Edward Arnold Ltd. 1985
3. Fanger, P.O.: Thermal Comfort. Analysis and Applications in Environmental Engineering. New York: McGraw Hill Book Co. 1972
4. Hardy, J.D., Gagge, P.A., Stolwijk, J.A.J. (Eds.): Physiological and Behavioral Temperature Regulation. Springfield, Ill.: Ch. C. Thomas 1970
5. Hensel, H., Brück, K., Raths, P.: Homeothermic organisms. pp. 503–761. In: Temperature and Life (H. Precht, J. Christophersen, H. Hensel, W. Larcher, Eds.) Berlin-Heidelberg-New York: Springer 1973
6. Hensel, H.: Thermoreception and Temperature Regulation. London: Academic Press 1981
7. Khogali, M., Hales, J.R.S.: Heat Stroke and Temperature Regulation. Sidney-New York: Academic Press 1983
8. Kleiber, M.: The Fire of Life. New York-London: John Wiley & Sons 1961
9. Kluger, M.J.: Fever, Its Biology, Evolution and Function. New Jersey: Princeton University Press 1979
10. LeBlanc, J.: Man in the Cold. Springfield, Ill.: Ch. C. Thomas 1975
11. Leithead, C.S., Lind, A.R.: Heat Stress and Heat Disorders. London: Cassell & Company Ltd 1964
12. Lindberg, O. (Ed.): Brown Adipose Tissue. New York: Amer. Elsevier Publ. 1970
13. Milton, A.S.: Pyretics and Antipyretics. Berlin-Heidelberg-New York: Springer 1982
14. Monteith, J.L., Mount, L.E. (Eds.): Heat Loss from Animals and Man. London: Butterworths 1974
15. Sinclair, J.S. (Ed.): Temperature Regulation and Energy Metabolism in the Newborn. New York-San Francisco-London: Grune & Stratton 1978
16. Werner, J.: Regelung der menschlichen Körpertemperatur. Berlin-New York: Walter de Gruyter 1984
17. Whittow, G.C.: Comparative Physiology of Thermoregulation, Vol. I–III. New York-London: Academic Press 1971

Original Papers and Reviews

18. Aschoff, H.: Circadian rhythm of activity and of body temperature. pp. 905–919. In: see Ref. 4
19. Aschoff, J., Wever, R.: Kern und Schale im Wärmehaushalt des Menschen. Naturwissenschaften 45, 477 (1958)
20. Baldino, F., Geller, H.M.: Electrophysiological analysis of neuronal thermosensitivity in rat – preoptic and hypothalamic tissue cultures. J. Physiol (London) 327, 173 (1982)
21. Behmann, F.W., Bontke, E.: Die Regelung der Wärmebildung bei künstlicher Hypothermie. I. Experimentelle Untersuchungen über den Einfluß der Narkosetiefe. Pflügers Arch. ges. Physiol. 266, 408 (1957/58)
22. Benzinger, T.H.: Heat regulation: Homeostasis of central temperature in man. Physiol. Rev. 49, 671 (1969)
23. Bleichert, A., Behling, K., Kitzing, J., Scarperi, M., Scarperi, S.: Antriebe und effektorische Maßnahmen der Thermoregulation bei Ruhe und während körperlicher Arbeit. IV. Ein analoges Modell der Thermoregulation bei Ruhe und Arbeit. Int. Z. angew. Physiol. 30, 193 (1972)
24. Brengelmann, G.L., Freund, P.R., Rowell, L.B., Olerud, J.E., Kraning, K.K.: Absence of active cutaneous vasodilation associated with congenital absence of sweat glands in humans. Am. J. Physiol. 240, H 571 (1981)
25. Brown, A.C., Brengelmann, G.L.: The temperature regulation control system. pp. 684–702. In: see Ref. 4
26. Brück, K.: Heat production and temperature regulation. pp 455–498. In: Perinatal Physiology (U. Stave, Ed.). New York: Plenum Publ. Corp. 1978
27. Brück, K.: Basic mechanisms in long-term thermal adaptation. In: Advances in Physiological Sciences Vol 34, Contributions to Thermal Physiology, pp. 263–273, Z. Szelényi, M. Székely, eds., Oxford-New York: Pergamon Press, 1981
28. Brück, K., Hinckel, P.: Thermoafferent systems and their adaptive modifications. Pharmac. Ther. 17, 357–381 (1982)
29. Brück, K., Wünnenberg, W.: Meshed control of two effector systems: Non-shivering and shivering thermogenesis. pp. 562–580. In: see Ref. 4
30. Brück, K., Zeisberger, E.: Adaptive changes in thermoregulation and their neuropharmalogical basis. Pharmac. Ther. 35, 163–215 (1987)
31. Cooper, K.E.: Studies of the human central warm receptor. pp. 224–230. In: see Ref. 4
32. Cooper, K.E., Kasting, N.W., Lederis, K., Veale, W.L.: Evidence supporting a role for endogenous vasopressin in natural suppression of fever in the sheep. J. Physiol. (London) 295, 33 (1979)
33. DuBois, E.F.: The Mechanism of Heat Loss and Temperature Regulation. Stanford, Calif.: Stanford Univ Press 1937
34. Gagge, A.P., Nishi, Y.: Physical indices of the thermal environment. ASHRAE, J., January 1976, pp. 47–51
35. Gilbert, T.M., Blatteis, C.M.: Hypothalamic thermoregulation pathways in the rat. J. appl. Physiol. 43, 770 (1977)
36. Hammel, H.T.: Terrestrial animals on cold: recent studies of primitive man. In: Handbook of Physiology, Sect. 4: Adap-

tation to the Environment, pp. 413–434. Washington: Amer. Physiol. Soc. 1964

37. Hellon, R., Townsend, Y.: Mechanisms of fever. Pharmac. Ther. 19, 211–244 (1983)
38. Ivanov, K., Konstantinov, V., Danilova, N.: Thermoreceptor localization in the deep and surface skin layers. J. therm. Biol. 7, 75 (1982)
39. Jessen, C.: Thermal afferents in the control of body temperature. Pharmac. Ther. 28, 107–134 (1985)
40. Kelso, S.R., Boulant, J.A.: Effect of synaptic blockade on thermosensitive neurons in hypothalamic tissue slices. Am. J. Physiol. 243, R480 (1982)
41. Maron, M.B., Wagner, J.A., Horvath, S.M.: Thermoregulatory responses during competitive marathon running. J. appl. Physiol. 42, 909 (1977)
42. Nadel, E.R., Bullard, R.W., Stolwijk, J.A.J.: Importance of skin temperature in the regulation of sweating. J. appl. Physiol. 31, 80 (1971)
43. Nakayama, T., Hammel, H.T., Hardy, J.D., Eisenman, J.S.: Thermal stimulation of electrical activity of single units of the preoptic region. Am. J. Physiol. 204, 1122 (1963)
44. Nicholls, D.G., Locke, R.M.: Thermogenic mechanisms in brown fat. Physiol. Rev. 64, 1–64 (1984)
45. Paton, B.C.: Accidental Hypothermia. Pharmac. Ther. 22, 331–377 (1985)
46. Raynaud, J., Martineaud, J.P., Durand, J.: Heat adaptation in the tropics. In: Hildenbrandt, G., Hensel, H. (Eds.), Biological Adaptation. pp. 148–165. Stuttgart-New York: Georg Thieme 1982
47. Roddie, I.C.: Circulation to skin and adipose tissue. pp. 285–318. In: Handbook of Physiol., Sect. 2: The Cardiovascular System, Vol. 3: Peripheral Circulation, part 1, J.T. Shepherd, F.M. Abboud, eds., Am. Physiol. Soc. Bethesda, MD. (1983)
48. Scarperi, M., Scarperi, S., Behling, K., Bleichert, A., Kitzing, J.: Antriebe und effektorische Maßnahmen der Thermoregulation bei Ruhe und während körperlicher Arbeit. Int. Z. angew. Physiol. 30, 186 (1972)
49. Schmidt, T.H.: Thermoregulatorische Größe in Abhängigkeit von Tageszeit und Menstruationscyclus. Inaugural-Dissertation (MPI für Verhaltensforschung Erling-Andechs). München 1972
50. Senay, L.C., Mitchell, D., Wyndham, C.H.: Acclimatization on a hot humid environment: body fluid adjustments. J. appl. Physiol. 40, 786 (1976)
51. Simon, E., Pierau, F.K., Taylor, D.C.M.: Central and peripheral thermal control of effectors in homeothermic temperature regulation. Physiol. Rev. 66:235–300, 1986
52. Smith, R.M., Hanna, J.M.: Skinfolds and resting heat loss in cold air and water: Temperature equivalence. J. appl. Physiol. 39, 93 (1975)
53. Székely, M., Szelényi, Z.: The pathophysiology of fever in the neonate. pp. 479-528. In: see Ref. 13
54. Thauer, R., Simon, E.: Spinal cord and temperature regulation., pp. 22–49. In: Advances in Climatic Physiology (S. Itho, K. Ogata, H. Yoshimura, Eds.) Igaku Shoin Ltd. Tokyo. Berlin-Heidelberg-New York: Springer 1972
55. Wenger, C.B., Roberts, M.F., Nadel, E.R., Stolwijk, J.A.J.: Thermoregulatory control of finger blood flow. J. appl. Physiol. 38, 78 (1975)
56. Wünnenberg, W., Brück, K.: Studies on the ascending pathways from the thermosensitive region of the spinal cord. Pflügers Arch. ges. Physiol. 321, 233 (1970)
57. Wünnenberg, W., Hardy, J.D.: Response of single units of the posterior hypothalamus to thermal stimulation. J. appl. Physiol. 33, 547 (1972)
58. Zeisberger, E., Merker, G., Blähser, S.: Fever response in the guinea pig before and after parturition. Brain Res. 212, 379 (1981)

26 Work Physiology

H.-V. ULMER

26.1 Fundamentals of Work Physiology

The study of bodily functions during work and sport activities is an area of applied physiology closely related to environmental physiology. It is not concerned solely with the analysis of physical work loads encountered during performance of a job or sport and their effects on man.

At one time hard physical labor was a common feature of life, but most present-day workers must perform tasks requiring *pattern recognition, rapid information uptake and processing, and the ability to make plans and decisions* (e.g., on assembly lines, and at testing stations and checkpoints). The work physiologist must devote an ever greater part of his attention to such psychological aspects – even in the area of sport, although here severe to extreme physical exertion usually predominates.

If the work load is too great, whatever its nature, the body is overstrained and health deteriorates. Health is defined by the World Health Organization (WHO) as follows: *a condition of complete physical, mental and social well-being, which cannot be achieved solely by the absence of sickness and weakness.*

Human working conditions cannot be established without a knowledge of the principles of work physiology. The work physiologist is therefore concerned with the *reciprocal relations between man and his place of work* (including the sports field). Almost all areas of physiology are involved in these relations. Only by this approach can one set up guidelines to *adapt the work conditions* or machines to the worker – or, conversely, to *adapt the worker* to the work conditions (by aptitude tests or training). In this sense work physiology is a science of optimization, with special regard to human well-being. In Third World countries, of course, some of the attitudes and standards differ from those in industrialized countries.

In this chapter emphasis is intentionally placed on the physiological *phenomena* associated with work. For information about the physiological *relationships* among the many different functional systems involved, the reader is referred to the particular chapters concerned with those systems.

Load, Performance and Strain

Terminology. The **load** is the externally imposed task, the parameters of which are independent of the individual doing the work. A person's **performance** in reacting to the load, on the other hand, does depend on individual characteristics (Fig. 26-1). The **strain** the organism undergoes in producing a particular performance is reflected in the alteration of various physiological functions. All three of these quantities can be measured.

Kinds of load. A distinction is made between *psychological* and *physical* loads. The latter can usually be characterized precisely in physical dimensions, but psychological loads can often be described only verbally. Some responses to psychological loads are discussed on p. 654.

Factors determining strain. The degree to which physiological functions must be adjusted to deal with a given load depends chiefly on two fac-

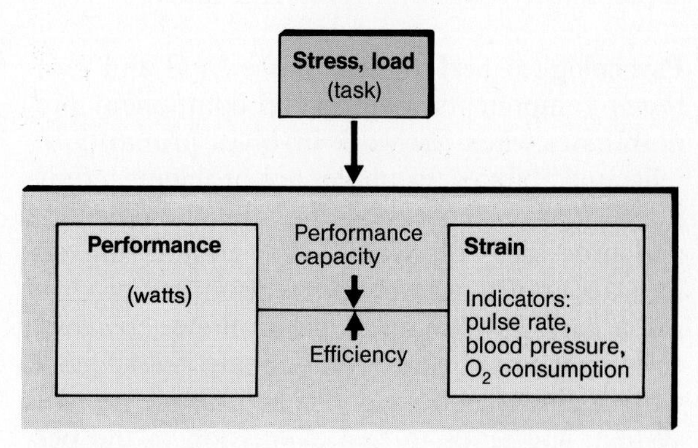

Fig. 26-1. Diagram of the load-strain concept for the case of dynamic work. The load is the assigned task; in fulfilling the task, the person produces a certain performance. The strain resulting from execution of the task depends on his performance capacity and efficiency.

tors, performance capacity and efficiency. *Performance capacity* is the ability to respond to a load so as to achieve a certain performance. It depends on one's state of *health and training*, and on *talent* (pp. 663f.). It is also affected, in any particular case, by the environment (e.g., climate, time of day, noise) and one's general mental and emotional condition. *Efficiency* is a measure of the effectiveness of the effort expended; for a given performance, the strain on an individual is greater, the lower his performance capacity and efficiency are, and conversely.

Types of Performance

Performance can also be *physical* or *psychological*, depending on the nature of the work load, though it is often difficult to distinguish the two even on the basis of strain parameters. Physical performance, like physical loads, can be expressed in physical dimensions. Mental and emotional performance – as in artistic creativity or scientific research – is often not measurable.

Physical performance. Dynamic work is done when, in a physical sense, resistances are overcome along a certain distance. In this case (e.g., bicycling and stair or mountain climbing) performance can be given in physical units (1 watt = 1 joule/s = 1 Nm/s ≈ 0.1 mkp/s). In *positive* dynamic work the muscles act as a "motor", and in *negative* dynamic work they act as a "brake" (e.g., in descending a mountain). **Static work** is done during *isometric muscle contraction.* Because no distance is traversed this is not work in the physical sense; nevertheless, the body shows *physiological strain responses* to the demand. The performance in this case is measured as the *product* of force and time.

Psychological performance has *mental* and *emotional* components. The **mental** component predominates when the work involves primarily intellectual abilities; examples are problems requiring thought or concentration, and the detection and processing of signals while monitoring objects or events (e.g., checking products or driving a car). Psychological performance in which **emotional** components predominate is associated with distinct reactions of the autonomic nervous system, and tends to find expression in the person's mood (e.g., joy, anger, sadness).

Other kinds of performance. *Sensorimotor performance* involves not strenuous muscular effort but rather a degree of dexterity, as in surgical operations or machine assembly. The tasks encountered in everyday jobs are often such as to require different kinds of performance in *combination;* in studies of these, the classification outlined above helps in distinguishing the various elements. The demand imposed by *environmental influences* are considered on pp. 666ff.

Ergometry

Ergometry is a procedure for determining physical performance capacity, especially the *ergometric performance capacity*. It is measured by imposing a specified load while performance and, in some cases, the subject's strain reactions are monitored. In the simplest case the weight of the body is lifted by *knee bends* or *stepping upward.* The associated *dynamic work* depends on the body weight and the distance it is raised. Efficiency varies greatly depending on the way the movement is done, so that it is difficult to compare the physiological strain reactions. **Ergometers** allow efficiency to be kept fairly constant during the work; they take two basic forms, as follows [16, 18].

Bicycle ergometers. The wheel of a stationary bicycle, with a specified mass, is rotated against a specified braking force (applied by a friction belt, a dynamo or an eddy-current brake). The higher the frequency of cranking (rotations/min, rpm) and the greater the braking force (f), the greater is the performance achieved. That is, performance (p) is given by: p ≈ rpm · f. Many ergometers display

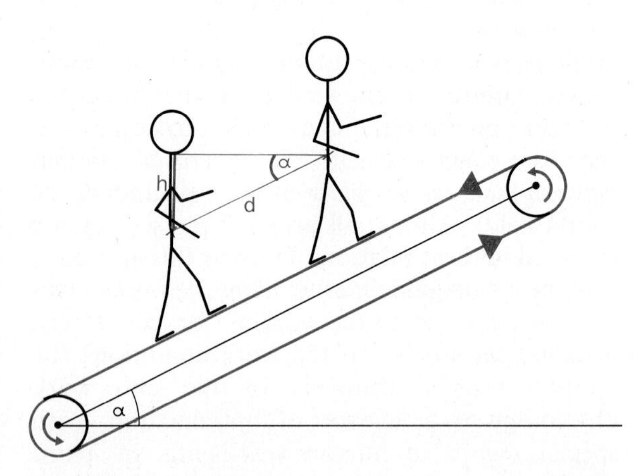

Fig. 26-2. Treadmill ergometer. Depending on the velocity of the belt, the center of gravity of the body, moving over the distance d in time t, is lowered by the amount h. To keep his height h constant, a subject must walk "in place" rapidly enough that his body weight w is raised by the amount $d \cdot \sin \alpha$. Performance P is then given by $P \doteq w \cdot d \cdot \sin\alpha \cdot t^{-1}$

performance automatically; the accuracy of this display should be calibrated every two years.

Treadmill ergometers (Fig. 26-2). When a subject maintains position by walking on an inclined treadmill the center of gravity of the body is continually raised by the same amount that the velocity and slope of the treadmill lower it. These two variables (as in mountain climbing) thus determine the performance. Like the bicycle ergometer, this apparatus permits work with an efficiency of 20–25%

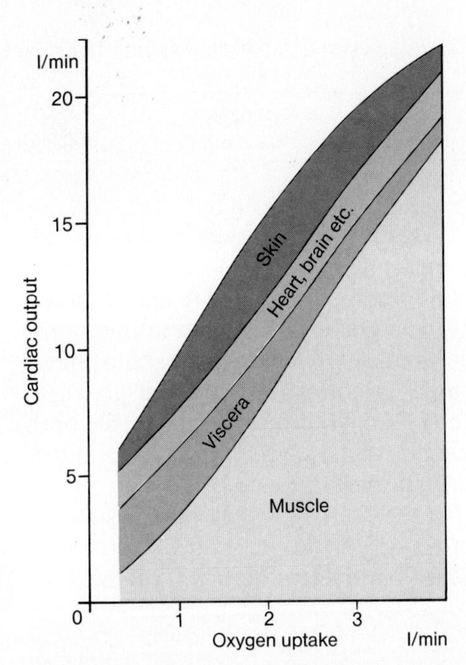

Fig. 26-3. Changes in the rate of perfusion of various organ systems with blood during dynamic work involving large groups of muscles, under normal climatic conditions. From [44]

26.2 Adjustments to Physical Work

Physical activity induces immediate reactions of various organ systems, including the muscular, the cardiovascular and the respiratory system. These *adjustments with rapid onset* are distinct from the medium- to long-term *adaptations* produced, for instance, by training (pp. 660f.). The extent of the short-term reactions is, as a rule, a direct measure of strain.

Intraindividual and interindividual differences. A given performance can require different physiological adjustments of an individual depending, for example, on the time of day or the ambient temperature; these are *intra*individual differences. There can also be considerable *inter*individual variation within a group of subjects.

Blood Flow and Metabolism in the Musculature during Dynamic Work

Blood flow through the muscles. A muscle at rest is perfused with blood at a rate of 20–40 ml · $min^{-1} \cdot kg^{-1}$. During extreme physical exertion this rate rises considerably (Fig. 26-3), reaching a maximum of 1.3 $l \cdot min^{-1} \cdot kg^{-1}$ in untrained people and as much as 1.8 $l \cdot min^{-1} \cdot kg^{-1}$ in those trained for endurance. The increased flow does not appear at the onset of work, but builds up gradually over at least 20 to 30 s; this time suffices to match perfusion to the requirements of light work. But during heavy dynamic work the demand cannot be met, and because the oxygen supply is inadequate, the proportion of energy provided by anaerobic metabolism is greater.

Muscle metabolism. During *light* work energy is obtained anaerobically only during the brief transitional period after onset of the work; thereafter metabolism is entirely *aerobic* (Fig. 26-4), utilizing glucose as well as fatty acids and glycerine [11, 12]. During *heavy* work, by contrast, part of the energy is always obtained *anaerobically.* The shift to anaerobic metabolism (with lactic-acid formation) is induced primarily by inadequate muscle perfusion or arterial hypoxia. In addition to these "bottlenecks" in the energy-providing processes, and those temporarily encountered shortly after work begins (Fig. 26-4), during extreme exertion there are enzymatic bottlenecks at various metabolic stages. When large amounts of lactic acid are formed, muscular fatigue results (pp. 77f. and 656f.).

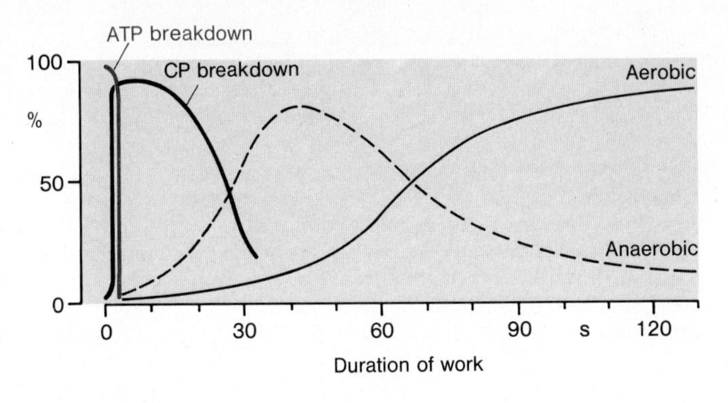

Fig. 26-4. Contribution of various substrates to the total energy yield in the muscle at the beginning of light work. Ordinate: % of the total energy contributed. In the first seconds almost all the energy is provided by adenosine triphosphate (ATP); the next source is creatine phosphate (CP). Whereas anaerobic glycolysis reaches a maximum after about 45 s, the muscle cannot obtain the major fraction of its energy by oxidative reactions until about 2 min have passed. From [11]

Table 26-1. Energy reserves of a person weighing 75 kg, in kJ. From [1]

ATP	4	Glycogen	4,600
CP	15	Fats	300,000

When work begins, a certain time is required for the aerobic energy yield of the muscle to increase; this gap is bridged by the briefly available **anaerobic energy reserves** (ATP and creatine phosphate). The amount of energy-rich phosphates stored is small as compared with the glycogen reserves (Table 26-1), but it is indispensable both for this bridging action and to support short-term extremes in performance [12].

Cardiovascular Parameters during Dynamic Work

During dynamic work there are considerable adjustments of the cardiovascular system (pp. 529f.). Cardiac output and blood flow through the working muscle are enhanced, so that supplies more nearly meet the increased demand and the heat produced is transported away from the working muscle to the point of release.

Heart rate. During light work with constant *performance* the heart rate rises during the first 5–10 min and reaches a *plateau;* this *steady state* is then maintained until the work is completed, even for several hours (Fig. 26-5). The greater the strain, the higher is the plateau. During heavy work with constant performance no such steady state is reached; heart rate *rises with fatigue* to a maximum that varies among individuals *(fatigue rise)*. This different behavior of heart rate during light and heavy work has been demonstrated in experiments lasting as long as 8 hours [19]. Thus *two* forms of work can be distinguished on basis of heart rate:

1. light, non-fatiguing work – steady state, and
2. heavy, fatiguing work – fatigue rise.

Even after the work ceases, heart rate varies according to the strain (Fig. 26-5). After light work it returns to the initial level within 3 to 5 min; after heavy work the **recovery time** (time to regain the initial level) is considerably longer, as much as several hours if the work was exhausting. Another criterion is the total number of pulse beats above the baseline (the initial pulse rate) during the recovery period **("recovery pulse sum"** in Fig. 26-5); this is a measure of muscular fatigue and hence also reflects the demands made by the preceding work.

Heart rate vs. pulse rate. When the activity of the heart is monitored directly (by measurement of ECG or pressure) the term *heart rate* should be used; *pulse rate* is used when the peripheral pulse is recorded. The two values differ only when the heart action is impaired.

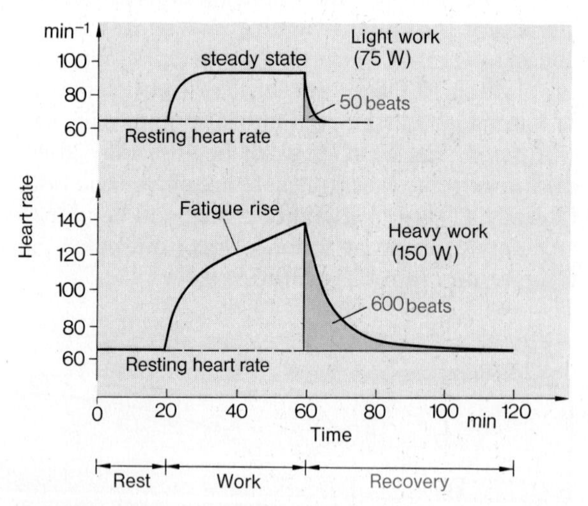

Fig. 26-5. Changes in heart rate of subjects having average performance capacity during light and heavy dynamic work with constant performance. *Red:* "recovery pulse sum", the total extra pulse beats during recovery. Modified from [19]

Stroke volume. The stroke volume of the heart rises only by 20–30% after the onset of work and then remains largely *constant.* Only when the strain is maximal does it decline slightly, because the heart rate is then so high that there is not enough time to fill the heart completely at each stroke. Both healthy athletes with their highly developed hearts (athlete's heart, p. 474)

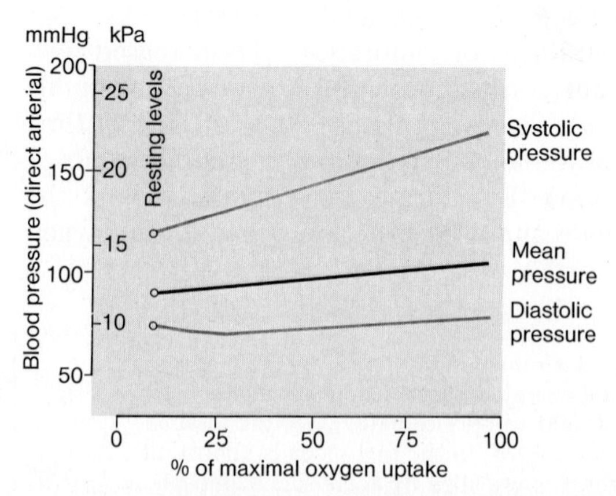

Fig. 26-6. Changes in arterial blood pressure (measured directly with a catheter in the artery) as the intensity of work (leg movement) increases. With the RR method somewhat higher systolic pressures would be measured. From [1]

and non-athletes have a nearly proportional relation between cardiac output and heart rate during work, because of this approximate constancy of the stroke volume.

Blood pressure. During dynamic work the *arterial blood pressure* changes as a function of performance (Fig. 26-6). The *systolic* blood pressure increases nearly in proportion to performance, reaching ca. 220 mm Hg (29 kPa) at 200 watts. The *diastolic* blood pressure changes only slightly, and often decreases. Therefore the *arterial mean pressure* (p. 493) rises slightly. The upper limit for a normal blood-pressure increase during bicycle ergometry (100 W) is 200/100 mm Hg seated, 210/105 mm Hg recumbent (RR method, p. 538, [3]). In the *low-pressure system* (e.g., in the right atrium) there is little increase in blood pressure during work; a distinct rise here is pathological (e.g., cardiac insufficiency).

Oxygen Uptake and Respiration during Dynamic Work

The oxygen uptake of the organism increases by an amount depending on strain, and hence on performance level and efficiency. During *light work* a steady state is reached in which oxygen uptake and consumption are in balance (Fig. 26-7) – but only after 3–5 min have elapsed, during which blood flow and muscle metabolism adjust to the new demand. Until the steady state is reached the muscle depends on the small *oxygen reserve* represented by the myoglobin-bound O_2 (pp. 601f.) and the ability to extract more O_2 from the blood. During *heavy muscular work,* even if performance is constant, there is *no steady state;* as in the case of heart rate (Fig. 26-5), oxygen uptake rises continuously until a maximum is reached [24, 28].

Oxygen debt. When work begins, the demand for energy increases immediately, but blood flow and aerobic metabolism require some time to adjust; thus an oxygen debt is incurred (Fig. 26-7). During *light work* the oxygen debt remains constant after the steady state is reached, but during *heavy work* it builds up until the work ends. Then, particularly during the first few minutes, the rate of oxygen uptake remains above the resting level – the oxygen debt is being *repaid.* But this term is problematic, for the *increased oxygen uptake following work* does not directly reflect processes of replacement in the muscle, but is affected by other factors such as increase

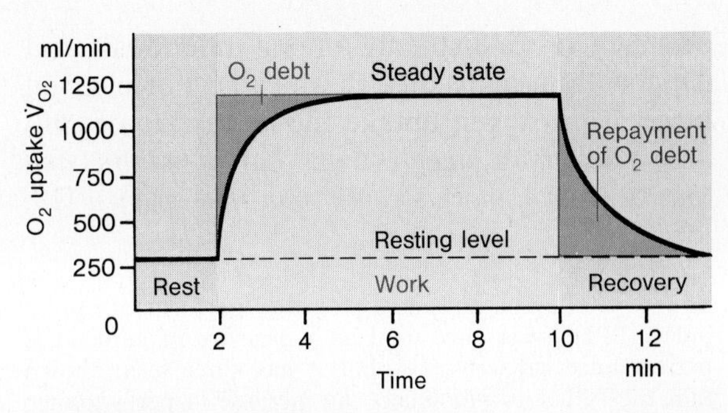

Fig. 26-7. Oxygen uptake during light dynamic work with constant performance

in body temperature and the work of breathing, changes in muscle tone and replenishment of the body's oxygen stores [11]. Thus the debt to be repaid is greater than that incurred during the work itself. After *light* work the oxygen debt amounts to as much as 4 l, and after *heavy* work as much as 20 l.

Relation between oxygen uptake and heart rate. During dynamic work with a constant efficiency heart rate is *proportional* both to oxygen uptake and to performance. When efficiency varies, the close relation between heart rate and oxygen uptake persists, but that between heart rate and performance does not. The proportionality between heart rate and oxygen uptake can be represented as a straight line (Fig. 26-8), the slope

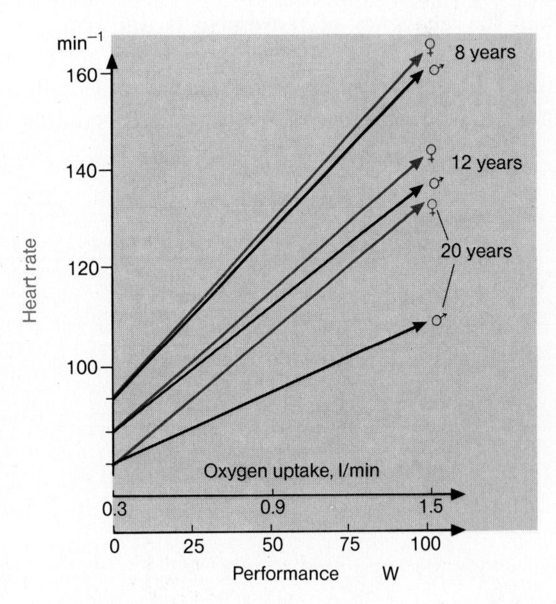

Fig. 26-8. Influence of age and sex on the relationship between heart rate and oxygen uptake (or performance) during dynamic work. The performance scale applies only to ergometer work at a constant cranking frequency of 60 rpm. From averages given in [25]

of which varies distinctly among individuals and depends especially on age and sex. For a given increase in oxygen uptake the heart rate of *children rises more steeply than that of adults, and that of women more steeply than that of men* [19, 31].

The slope of a line on such a plot, the "performance pulse index (PPI)," was once used as a measure of endurance performance capacity [19], but it has since been shown that the PPI does not reflect the increase in performance produced by endurance training.
The physiological mechanisms underlying the *close relation between heart rate and oxygen uptake* can be explained on the basis of the following hypothesis [28]. *Muscle receptors* other than the muscle spindles send information about the actual *metabolic activity* in the working musculature to the circulatory center. As a result not only local blood flow through the muscle, but the cardiac output as well, can be *adjusted to the momentary demand* over a wide range, cardiac output and heart rate changing in such a way as to maintain proportionality. The postulated muscle receptors have not yet been identified morphologically but there is much functional evidence that they exist.

Oxygen uptake and heart rate during increasing performance. As the intensity of dynamic work increases, the heart rate and the rate of oxygen uptake rise (Fig. 26-9); the greater the strain on the body, the greater is the increase above the resting level. Thus heart rate and the rate of oxygen uptake are a *measure of physical strain.* States with considerable strain are reached when one is working hard even with high efficiency (25%), as well as during light work if efficiency is low (cf. p. 646).
When the **frequency of movement** is uniform *efficiency* is about the same regardless of performance. Therefore when performance gradually increases while frequency of movement remains

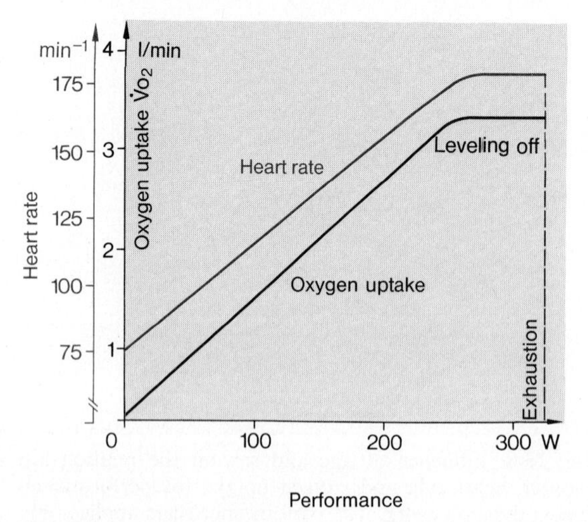

Fig. 26-9. Changes in oxygen uptake and heart rate as performance rises continuously

constant, *oxygen* uptake rises linearly to a maximum and then *levels off* (Fig. 26-9). In this plateau state the difference between oxygen demand and oxygen supply increases so rapidly that *acute exhaustion* occurs. Heart rate changes similarly with performance. Once the maximal heart rate has been reached after 10 to 30 min of heavy work, hardly any additional fatigue rise can be observed (Fig. 26-9).

Ventilation. During light dynamic work the respiratory minute volume, like the cardiac output, rises in proportion to oxygen uptake. This increase results from an increase in tidal volume and/or respiratory frequency (cf. increased ventilation, p. 563).

The *proportionality* between oxygen uptake and respiratory minute volume during light work is thought to be controlled by metabolism-dependent *muscle receptors,* like the control mechanism that adjusts heart rate. During *heavy* work the increase in respiratory minute volume is distinctly *greater than proportional* to the oxygen uptake, because the lactic acid formed in the muscle acts as a supplementary respiratory drive by causing *metabolic acidosis* of the blood.

Blood Parameters during Dynamic Work

During and after dynamic work there are many changes in the blood. Only occasionally do these permit assessment of the degree of physical strain, but they are of special importance as sources of error in laboratory diagnosis.

Blood gas levels. During *light* physical work a healthy person shows only slight changes in *arterial* CO_2 and O_2 partial pressures. *Heavy* work causes somewhat larger changes. According to Fig. 26-10, the largest deviations from the resting level are −8% for the arterial P_{O_2} and −10% for the P_{CO_2}.
The O_2 saturation of *venous mixed blood* falls distinctly as the strain increases; accordingly, the arteriovenous difference (avD_{O_2}, p. 584) rises from ca. 0.05 (resting level) to as much as 0.14 in subjects without training and as much as 0.17 in trained subjects (Fig. 26-10) [1, 29]. This increase is based on the improved extraction of oxygen from the blood in the working muscle.
Blood cells. During physical work the *hematocrit* rises, as a result both of decreased plasma volume owing to greater capillary filtration and of the release of erythrocytes from their sites of production (with an increased proportion of immature forms). An increase in number of leukocytes has also been observed (work leukocytosis).

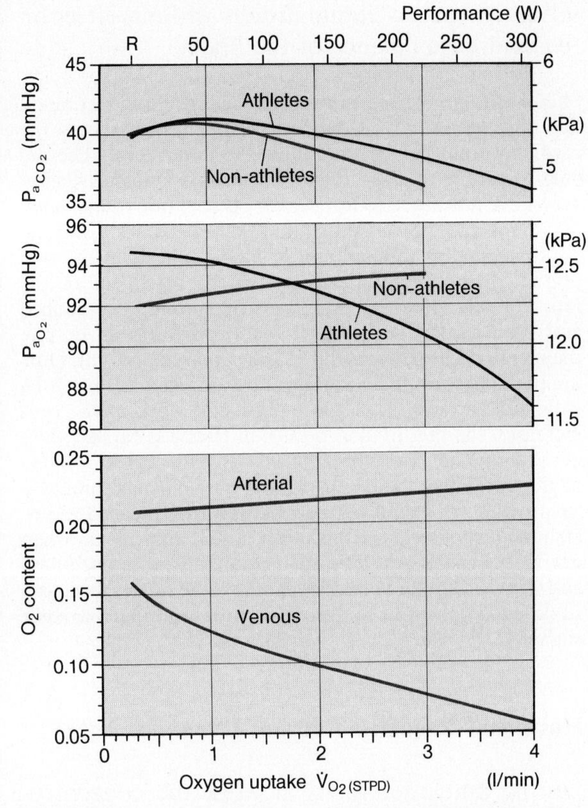

Fig. 26-10. O_2 partial pressure, CO_2 partial pressure and O_2 content of the blood during physical work at different intensities. The athletes were trained for endurance sports. R = resting level. From [29]

The *leukocyte count* in the blood of long-distance runners increases with duration of the run, by 5,000 to 15,000/µl depending on performance capacity (less in those with greater capacity) [39]. The increase is due primarily to the neutrophilic granulocytes, so that the *proportions of the different cells* change. The *thrombocyte count* also rises as a function of the intensity of work.

Acid-base status of the blood. *Light* physical work does not affect the acid-base balance, for all the additional carbonic acid produced is released from the lungs. During *heavy* work metabolic acidosis is produced in proportion to the rate of lactate production and is partially compensated by respiration (decrease in arterial P_{CO_2}).

Foodstuffs in the blood. The arterial **glucose** level of a healthy person hardly changes during work. Only when strenuous work is prolonged does the arterial glucose concentration decrease, a sign of approaching *exhaustion.* The blood **lactate** concentration, on the other hand, varies widely with the degree of strain *and* the duration of work [9, 10], depending on the rate of lactate production in the anaerobically working muscle and the rate of elimination. Lactate is broken down or converted in the non-working skeletal muscle, adipose tissue, liver, kidney and myocardium. Under resting conditions the *arterial lactate concentration* is ca. 1 mmol/l; during hard work lasting about half an hour, or short periods of exhausting work with 1-min pauses, maxima exceeding 15 mmol/l can be reached. During prolonged heavy work the lactate concentration first rises and then declines (Fig. 26-11).

When the diet is rich in carbohydrate the arterial concentrations of the *free fatty acids* and of *glycerol* are little affected by work, for the secretion of insulin brought about by carbohydrate intake inhibits lipolysis [13, 34]. But with an average diet prolonged heavy work is accompanied by fourfold or greater increases in the blood concentrations of free fatty acids and glycerol (Fig. 26-11)

Other substances in the blood. During exercise the blood concentrations of certain *electrolytes* (e.g., potassium) and *organic substances* (e.g., transaminase) rise. These changes are explained by a change in the permeability of the muscle membrane, which allows intracellular components to escape into the bloodstream. The return to the initial concentrations in some cases requires several days. Taken together, the changes in the

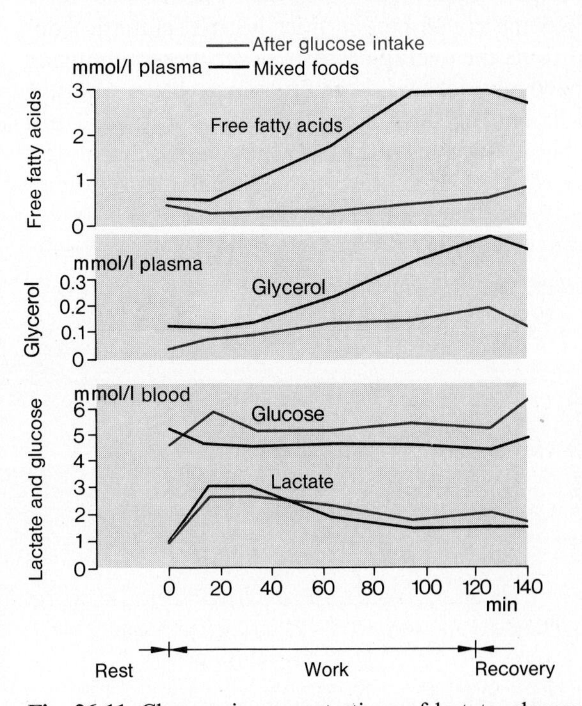

Fig. 26-11. Changes in concentrations of lactate, glucose, glycerol and free fatty acids in the arterial blood during 2 hours of ergometer work, preceded by intake of a mixed meal or of 200 g glucose; average heart rate 150 min^{-1}. There is a distinct inhibition of lipolysis after carbohydrate intake. Modified from [13]

blood produced by work can be difficult to distinguish from changes associated with diseases (e.g., in serum diagnosis).

Thermoregulation during Dynamic Work

Thermoregulation. Sweating is generally regarded as a sign of hard work. The onset of visible sweating *(sensible perspiration)*, however, depends not only on the level of work but also on the environmental conditions. Sweat secretion begins when the **neutral temperature** (cf. pp. 626f.) is exceeded, whether because of *increased heat production* during exercise or *insufficient heat loss* owing to high ambient temperature or humidity, unsuitable clothing or the absence of air movement (convection) or, finally, to heating of the body by excessive thermal radiation (e.g., in a foundry).
As performance increases, other conditions being equal, the secretion of sweat increases about in proportion to the *rectal temperature*. Because of the cooling effect of evaporation the *skin temperature* during sweating is lower than in the case of extraglandular water loss (pp. 631 and 637). After prolonged severe heat exposure the amount of sweat produced decreases, probably because the "pores" (openings of the sweat-gland ducts) have become constricted. Under normal climatic conditions the average *rate of sweat secretion* during hard physical work or sport activity is about 1 l/h. During hard work *lactic acid* (up to 2 g/l) is contained in the sweat along with electrolytes; most of it originates in the sweat glands themselves, so that its elimination is without effect on the acid-base balance of the body.

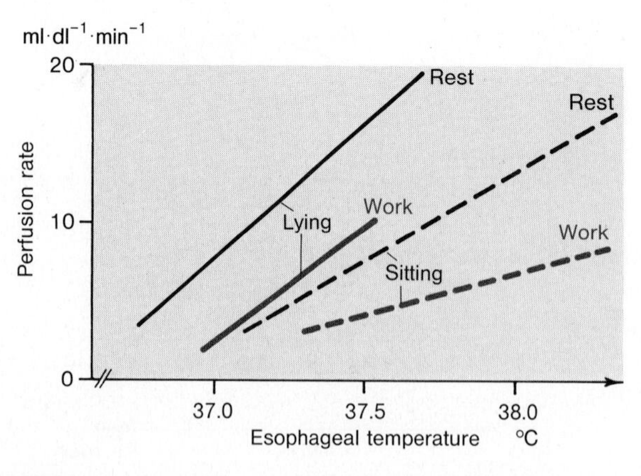

Fig. 26-12. Blood flow through the forearm ($\dot{Q}$) as a measure of skin perfusion at various core temperatures (esophageal temperature). During work (heart rate 120 to 130 min^{-1}) skin perfusion is less than under equivalent resting conditions despite the increased heat production, and it is less when sitting than when lying down. From [38]

Skin perfusion. During exposure to heat while **at rest** blood flow through the skin is increased [20]; in the process, the cardiac output can reach double the initial level. The decrease in tone of the capacitive cutaneous vessels makes very little difference to a *reclining* person, but when *standing* an increased orthostatic intolerance becomes apparent. An abnormally large amount of blood collects in the skin of the lower part of the body, to the detriment of the intrathoracic blood volume; the stroke volume is reduced and both cardiac output and blood pressure fall despite the increased heart rate, and *heat collapse* may result. During physical **work** there is a general vasoconstriction of the cutaneous arterioles; as the intensity of work in the heat increases, the rate of skin perfusion rises less rapidly than in moderate temperatures (Fig. 26-12). The degree of *filling* of the capacitive cutaneous vessels in a normal climate is less during work than during rest, but the increased vascular tone responsible for this effect largely disappears when one works in the heat [20]. As a result, intrathoracic filling and thus the stroke volume continue to be diminished, and so do maximal cardiac output and endurance performance capacity.

Hormonal Regulation during Dynamic Work

During and after physical work the concentrations of many hormones in the blood change. In most cases, however, this effect is either unspecific or not well understood. Three hormone systems are of interest here, as follows [4, 46].

1. Sympathico-adrenergic system (pp. 339ff.): During physical work more *adrenalin is released* into the blood, from the adrenal medulla in particular. *Noradrenalin* is released only in smaller amounts. Among other actions, adrenalin mobilizes the glycogen and fat depots, stimulates increased production of cyclic AMP and enhances cardiac activity and the clarity of consciousness. The secretion of adrenalin often begins before the work load is imposed **(prestart state)** and at the latest coincides with the onset of work. The increase in the rate of adrenalin release is reflected in an increased urinary excretion of *vanillylmandelic acid (VMA)*, a product of adrenalin and noradrenalin breakdown.

2. Pituitary-adrenocortical system: After work is begun, with a latency of about 2 min, there is an increase in the release of *ACTH* from the anterior pituitary, which stimulates the release of corticosteroids from the *adrenal cortex* (pp. 386ff.). The significance of the *corticosteroids* with regard to physical work is mostly unclear, though they are known to promote the mobilization of glycogen.

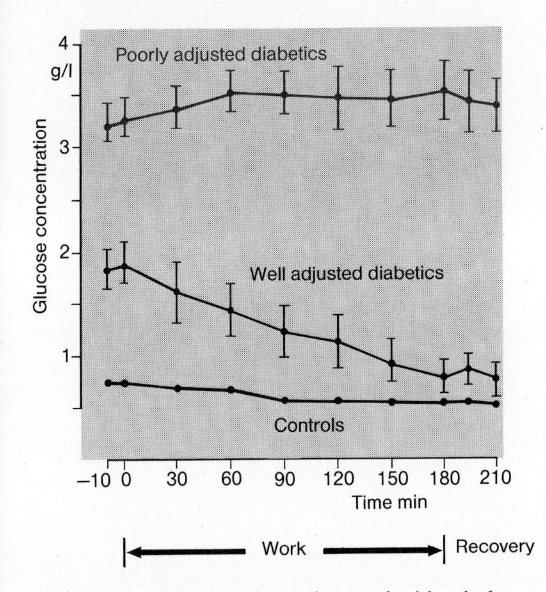

Fig. 26-13. Influence of exercise on the blood glucose concentration in control subjects and diabetics; cycle ergometer work with heart rates of about 110 min^{-1}. The standard deviation is shown by vertical bars. From [34]

3. Insulin-glucagon system. The concentration changes of insulin and glucagon are very nonuniform. Whereas the insulin concentration falls slightly during work, both increases and decreases of glucagon have been observed. This variability is related to the influence of many hormones on carbohydrate and fat metabolism, as well as to the subject's nutritional state and state of training (endurance). The interactions among insulin, the blood glucose concentration and physical work are illustrated in Fig. 26-13. Work has a clear blood-glucose-lowering effect in well-adjusted diabetics (cf. pp. 394f.).

Adjustments to Static Work

Static work is performed by means of isometric muscle contractions, and can be either *postural work* (to maintain the posture of the body) or *holding work* (by which objects are held). Like dynamic work, it requires certain adjustments of the body, characterized by the time courses of the provision of energy (Fig. 26-4, p. 647) and of the alteration of blood flow through the muscle.

Muscle perfusion and metabolism. During static work at intensities up to about 30% of the maximal force, blood flow through the muscle increases. Above 30% of the maximal force the increased intramuscular pressure opposes blood flow, and during static work at 70% of the maximal force or more perfusion of the muscle stops altogether. Experiments have shown that when blood flow through the muscles is interrupted by some external means, the maximal times for holding work at less than 50% of maximal force decrease, but those for more than 50% of maximal force do not. The reason is that when the holding work is such that the maximal time is less than 1 min (cf. Fig. 26-17, p. 656), aerobic energy production builds up too slowly (Fig. 26-4) to be a limiting factor, and therefore the rate of perfusion is irrelevant.

Respiration and circulation. Metabolic lactate acidosis produces an additional, strong *respiratory drive,* which is further increased when the work requires reflex contraction of the abdominal muscles so that breathing is hampered. During holding work with tensed abdominal musculature, blood is forced out of the thoracic and abdominal *low-pressure system* and venous flow back into the trunk region is blocked (one sign of which is swelling of the neck veins). Hence the abdominal contraction also reduces the venous return to the heart; for this reason, those who are ill or convalescing should avoid work with a large static component (e.g., lifting and carrying heavy loads).

Heart rate. During static work the heart rate rises even in the *absence of abdominal compression* (Fig. 26-14). As in the case of dynamic work, this increase is explained by the action of muscle receptors (p. 650) that strongly stimulate the circulatory center while anaerobic metabolism is in progress.

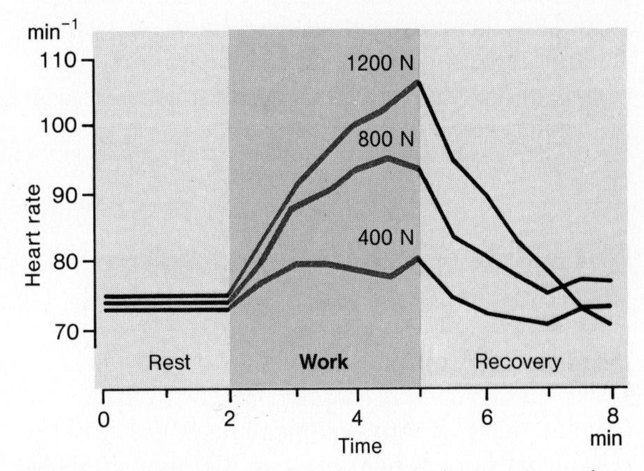

Fig. 26-14. Changes in heart rate during *static work* at different intensities (supporting a load in both arms). From [42]

26.3 Responses of the Organism to Non-Physical Loads

Responses to Psychological Loads

The rate of energy metabolism also rises during psychological performance, but the cause is an increase in muscle tone and *not* an enhanced cerebral metabolism (pp. 600f.). In many cases *autonomic responses* like those associated with physical performance appear: elevated heart rate and respiratory minute volume, increase in cutaneous blood flow and a decrease in dermal electrical resistance, increased sweating and the release of more adrenalin, with a correspondingly greater excretion of vanillylmandelic acid in the urine [40].

Although combined psychological and physical work loads are a common feature of present-day life, quantitative study of such situations is difficult. Occasional attempts have been made to evaluate the strain they induce by observation of physiological responses. But such data *by no means* provide insights into psychological and psychophysical performance as reliable as those applicable to purely physical performances.

Certain situations affect primarily the emotions; in responding to such *emotional loads* people show symptoms like those accompanying mental performance – tachycardia, hyperventilation, sweating (caused, for example, by fear or excitement), and so on. There is marked stimulation of the sympathico-adrenergic system [40], with some variation in the proportions of adrenalin and noradrenalin released. Conditions of extreme anxiety or terror do not only elicit a pronounced *ergotropic reaction* (immediate response) within a few seconds – called the *emergency reaction* by CANNON [35] – but often also stimulate the parasympathetic nervous system. The latter action can result in involuntary defecation and urination in such situations, or even in cardiac arrest.

26.4 Limits of Performance Capacity

Performance-Limiting Factors

On the basis of physiological response criteria (e.g., heart rate; p. 648) one can distinguish physically *fatiguing* work from that which is *not fatiguing*. If the body is not allowed to recover suffi-

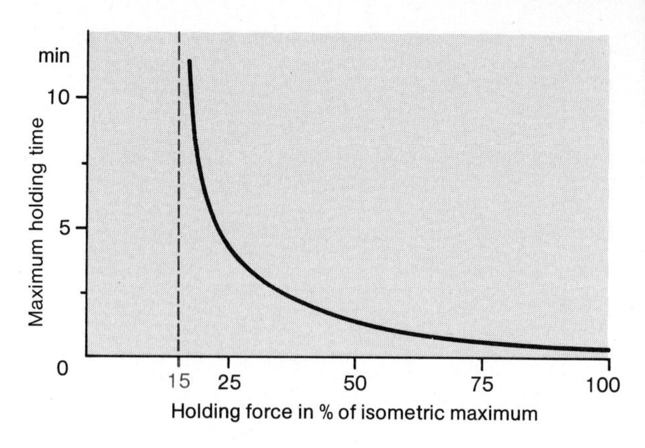

Fig. 26-15. Relation between maximal performance duration and the force exerted during *static work*. From [23]

ciently from fatiguing work, functional disorders and illness appear; these constitute an "overloading syndrome" (p. 658). The work load the body can bear – that is, a person's performance capacity – is limited by three fundamental factors: the amount of energy available in the muscle, the oxygen supply to the muscle, and the body's capacity for thermoregulation (pp. 632ff.).

The availability of energy in the muscle. During fatiguing work performance capacity is limited by the various ways the muscle can obtain energy (pp. 647f.), and these depend on the intensity and duration of the work. The basic rule is: *the shorter the duration of work, the greater the achievable performance* (Fig. 26-15) and the smaller the relative aerobic energy yield (Fig. 26-4, p. 647). This principle applies to both dynamic (cf. Fig. 24-6, p. 618) and static work.

It is useful to consider three categories of work duration, though the boundaries must be arbitrarily drawn:

Short-term performance (up to ca. 20 s duration). In this situation the intracellular stores of *ATP* and *creatine phosphate* (CP) are essential. These energy-rich phosphates can supply enough energy to support maximal performance during the first 15 to 20 s of work.

Medium-term performance. Work at the *short*-duration end of this range (up to ca. 1 min) is fueled mainly by *anaerobic glycolysis,* after the ATP and CP stores have been used up and the glycolytic process is well under way. Here the muscle's capacity for glycolytic metabolism and the resulting lactate-based acidosis are the performance-limiting factors. At the *long*-duration end (up to ca. 6 min) the *aerobic energy yield* makes an increasing contribution, so that performance is limited progressively less by the anaerobic and more by the aerobic metabolic rate.

Long-term performance (endurance tasks, ca. 6 min or more). During prolonged work *aerobic energy metabolism* predominates. Performance capacity is primarily limited by the associated factors – metabolic capacity and the glycogen stores in the muscle cells, and the supply of oxygen and substrates by the cardiovascular system. Therefore the *pumping performance of the heart* and the *capacity for aerobic metabolism* are decisive for tasks requiring endurance. Only when work is performed at moderate intensity for hours at a time is its duration limited by depletion of the glycogen reserves.

The muscular oxygen supply. The amount of oxygen available to a muscle depends fundamentally on the rate of blood flow through it. During **dynamic work** employing large groups of muscles (more than 1/7 of the total musculature) performance capacity depends less on local blood flow than on the maximal cardiac output [19]. During **static work** local muscle perfusion deteriorates progressively as the force of contraction rises above 30% of maximal, and from 70% of the maximal force on it is blocked. At high static contraction intensities, however, the maximal duration of contraction is so short that the oxygen supply is irrelevant. The oxygen supply of the musculature is also diminished if the inspired air is deficient in oxygen (at altitude, pp. 666ff.), by gas-exchange disorders and by a lowered hemoglobin concentration in the blood. In a healthy person under normal conditions (inspiratory O_2 fraction = 0.2095), however, the amount of oxygen reaching the muscles is *not limited by breathing;* the crucial factor is the maximal cardiac output. Even during exhausting work the respiratory minute volume rises only to about 80% of the maximum [9]. It is evident, therefore, that neither the popular measure "vital capacity" nor any other respiratory parameter actually determines the performance capacity of a healthy subject.

Performance capacity in the heat. The diminished performance capacity under hot conditions results from a reduction in the filling of the intrathoracic vessels and not from an increase in cutaneous blood flow, which is pronounced only at rest (p. 652). The factors that limit work in the heat are elevation of the *core temperature* and disturbances of salt and water balance. Depending on the ambient temperature, the degree of salt and water loss and the intensity of the work, various disturbances occur with rising core temperature, so that no special limit for the tolerable core temperature can be specified. The rectal temperature, however, should not exceed 38 °C during prolonged work in the heat (risk of *heat collapse*). In endurance sports such as *marathon running,* rectal temperatures as high as 41 °C can be tolerated [9], but at higher temperatures there is a risk of *heat stroke* (central nervous collapse, p. 642).

Specific Performance Limits

Endurance limit and maximal performance capacity. Not uncommonly, a distinction has been made between *light,* non-fatiguing work and *heavy* work, which causes fatigue. This distinction is based on the concept of *two ranges* of performance capacity, separated by the **endurance limit** [9, 19]. Work is considered to be below this limit when it can be performed for *at least 8 hours without muscular fatigue* (light, non-fatiguing work within the **endurance capacity);** within this range, the muscle's metabolism and blood flow are in balance. The cardiac and respiratory musculature, for example, do work of this kind.
Above the endurance limit is the region of **maximal performance capacity.** Performance in this range is *limited in duration* because metabolism and blood flow are not in balance. *The longer the working time, the lower is the performance maximum,* and vice versa (Fig. 26-15). This relation is based on the fact that in the short term more energy can be supplied anaerobically than aerobically for the muscular work (Fig. 26-4, p. 647); the greater the demand for energy, the sooner exhaustion occurs.

The endurance limit varies among individuals. Therefore the question whether work is light or heavy cannot be resolved by any absolute measure of the work load; the actual performance capacity of the *individual* is decisive. For work in the range above the endurance limit, the degree of fatigue depends on the maximal performance capacity of the individual at that moment. Both the endurance capacity and the maximal performance capacity can be altered by training (pp. 660f.).

Endurance limit for dynamic work. Work below the endurance limit is characterized as follows [19]. **Heart rate:** constant working heart rate with no increase due to fatigue (below 130 per min in untrained 20- to 30-year-olds), recovery pulse sum less than 100 beats, recovery time less than 5 min. **Other characteristics:** constant oxygen uptake (steady state), oxygen debt below ca. 4 liters, no appreciable rise in blood lactate level (limiting value: 2.2 mmol/l). In untrained men between 20 and 30 years of age the endurance limit for bicycle-ergometer work is about 100 watts, which corresponds to oxygen uptake of 1.5 l/min. Performance above this level is limited by the factors just described (p. 654).

Athletic performance limit. The blood lactate concentration provides a certain amount of information about the metabolic situation of working muscles. In sport medicine it has proved useful to refer to an *aerobic/anaerobic transi-*

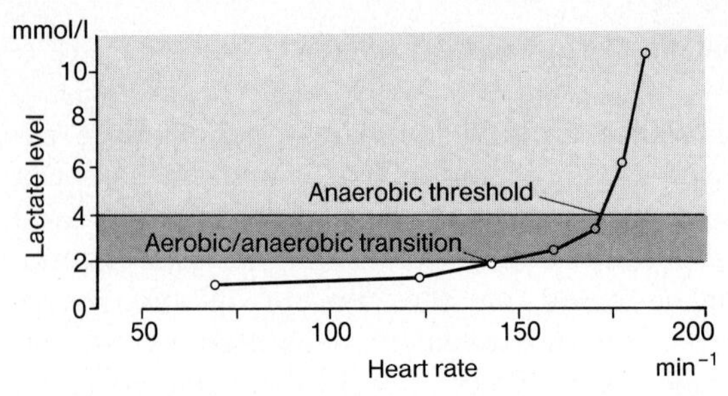

Fig. 26-16. Aerobic/anaerobic transition and anaerobic threshold as determined by blood lactate concentrations. The heart-rate values are those of an endurance athlete. Modified from [21]

tion at the point when the lactate concentration has risen to 2 mmol/l, and to an *anaerobic threshold* at 4 mmol/l (Fig. 26-16). The anaerobic threshold can be called the *athletic performance limit,* because in endurance athletes it is a useful indicator of muscular performance capacity. However, this limit is not identical to the endurance limit, which corresponds more closely to the aerobic/anaerobic transition.

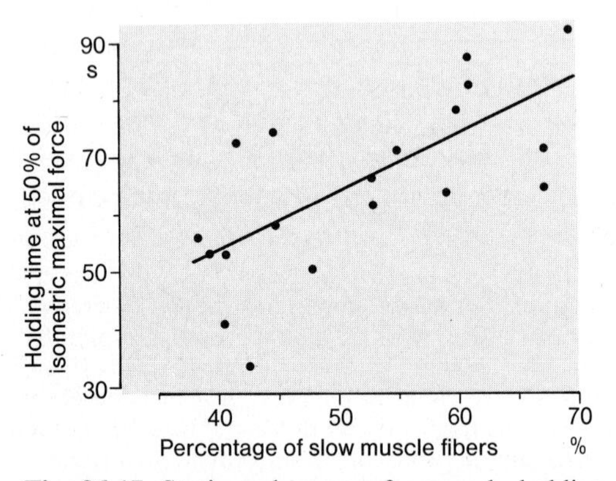

Fig. 26-17. Static endurance of a muscle holding a load with 50 % of the maximal isometric force, as a function of the percentage of slow muscle fibers in the muscle. From [37]

Endurance limit for static holding work. For a long time the limit for static holding work – that is, the contractile force beyond which metabolic balance no longer prevails (i.e., the endurance limit) – was set at 15% of the maximal force (Fig. 26-15). According to recent investigations, however, it seems very likely that the endurance limit for static holding work is lower, with distinct interindividual differences, ranging from 5% to 10% of the maximal force. The variation is probably determined by the kinds of muscle fibers of which the muscle concerned is composed, as Fig. 26-17 shows for the maximal duration of holding work at 50% of maximal force.

Performance Ranges

A supplementary descriptor of performance, in addition to the endurance and maximal performance capacities, is based on the degree to which an effort of will is required. Here four ranges of performance are distinguished [5]. The bottom range comprises **automated tasks,** ingrained motor patterns that can be voluntarily started and stopped but otherwise proceed automatically. Above these is the range of so-called **physiological readiness,** activities under continual voluntary control which never become so vigorous as to generate a sense of strain or fatigue. The **normal reserves** for exertion above this level are accessible only by application of will power; work in this range causes fatigue. The fourth, uppermost range is that of the **autonomically protected reserves,** which normally cannot be utilized even by the strongest voluntary effort and are available to the organism only in *emergencies.* (p. 658).

Performance capacity in disease states. Certain diseases are associated with reduced performance capacity or with the risk that physical activity will be additionally damaging (e.g., cardiac infarct of a jogger). Not everyone can tolerate strain corresponding to his performance capacity, even those with above-average physical performance capacity – particularly when chronic illness (e.g., certain heart disorders) makes physical activity a considerable risk to health.

In this context a distinction should be drawn between performance capacity and load tolerance. The **load-tolerance limit** corresponds to the performance that can be demanded of a person *without risk to health.* Of course, there is no reason to advise the chronically ill to avoid all physical or sporting activity. But the effects of appropriately chosen athletic activity in certain diseases such as diabetes mellitus, hypertension, and coronary heart disease are not always so clear-cut as in Fig. 26-13; often it is more the psycho-social area that is affected. Because of the risks involved, the physical activites of the ill should be under a doctor's supervision even if the person is above average in performance capacity. Similarly, in routine medical examinations of workers an above-average physical performance capacity should not automatically be taken as a sign of especially good health. *Performance capacity and state of health are correlated only to a certain extent with one another.*

26.5 Fatigue and Exhaustion

Fatigue and Recovery – Definitions

Fatigue is a state induced by *heavy* work (p. 648) and associated with a *decrease in performance capacity.* It may be **physical** (muscular) or **psychological** (central) [6, 19, 31]. The two forms are

combined in hard work, and cannot be strictly distinguished. Hard *physical* work leads primarily to *muscular* fatigue, and strenuous *mental* or *monotonous* work causes *central* fatigue. A sharp distinction should be made between fatigue and the *tiredness* associated with a need for sleep [2].
Recovery is a process initiated when performance is interrupted, reduced or changed in nature; it correlates with a reduction of fatigue and increase of performance capacity. When these parameters have returned to the initial levels, the recovery process has finished.

Recovery and the timing of pauses. When doing work above the individual endurance limit one must stop occasionally for recovery. Because the recovery processes operate most rapidly at the beginning of such a pause (as shown, for example, in the changes in heart rate; Fig. 26-5), work should be organized on the principle that *many short pauses are better than a few long ones* [19]. Recovery from heavy physical work can occur not only during pauses, but to some extent during periods of easier work (below the endurance limit).

Physical Fatigue

Physical fatigue results from *changes in skeletal muscle* – in long-term performance, the depletion of the energy stores and accumulation of lactic acid (the "fatigue substance") – which reduce performance capacity. During the recovery phase following physical work the energy stores are replenished and the lactic acid is eliminated.

Fatigue during dynamic work. *Below the endurance limit* the movements of work allow sufficient muscular relaxation time that the energy-rich phosphates used up during contraction can be regenerated and the metabolic end products transported away. The relaxation time corresponds to the required recovery time [28]. Because there is no residuum of fatigue this is called *non-fatiguing work*. During dynamic work *above* the endurance limit there is no opportunity for continual recovery, because the relaxation times amount to less than the required recovery time. Replenishment of the energy stores and removal of the lactic acid are incomplete and a *residuum of fatigue* builds up [19]. The muscle uses up its energy-rich substrates and accumulates metabolic end products, and fatigue increases. The degree of muscular fatigue during dynamic work above the endurance limit can be determined from physiological parameters (e.g., recovery time and recovery pulse sum; p. 648).
"Charley horse". This phenomenon, muscular stiffness and soreness following exertion, is not, as is commonly supposed, caused by the accumulation of lactic acid in the muscle. The muscle pain associated with pressure and movement does not appear until after the lactic acid produced during activity has been eliminated. It is also inconsistent with a lactate mechanism that the muscles most inclined to such soreness are those that have been generating large forces; this is true especially in cases of poor intramuscular coordination and in braking work (negative work). The generation of large forces causes tears in the Z bands (p. 63) and as these heal, substances are released that, with a corresponding delay, elicit the muscular pains.

Fatigue during static work. The holding work that needs to be done in everyday life is usually above the endurance limit. The fatigue it causes is based on depletion of the energy stores in the temporal sequence illustrated in Fig. 26-4. Only during holding work at intensities below 50% of the maximal force, which can be continued for more than 1 min, does blood flow become a performance-limiting factor (cf. p. 653).

Mental Fatigue

Mental (central) fatigue causes reduced performance because *central-nervous control* is disturbed [6]. Among the typical symptoms are slower information transmission, deterioration of thought and decision processes, and impaired sensory perception and sensorimotor function. Such fatigue is associated with aversion to work and diminished performance, and occasionally produces a tendency to depression, irrational anxiety or reduced drive, and irritability and emotional lability.
Situations eliciting mental fatigue include [6]: (i) prolonged work demanding close concentration, extreme mental alertness or dexterity, (ii) hard physical labor, (iii) unvaried work under monotonous conditions, (iv) noise, poor lighting and uncomfortable temperatures, (v) conflicts, worries or lack of interest, (vi) illness, pain and malnutrition.

Central fatigue, in contrast to muscular fatigue, can be *relieved instantaneously* [6] under certain conditions – for example, when (i) the fatiguing activity is replaced by another, (ii) the surroundings are changed, (iii) the organism is put into an alarm state by fear or the threat of danger, (iv) interest is reawakened by new information, or (v) a change of affective state (mood) occurs. The fact that such *sudden disappearance* of central fatigue is possible implies that neither the accumulation of "fatigue substances" nor the depletion of energy reserves is a critical factor. Rather, central fatigue is thought to involve the reticular formation (cf. ARAS, p. 146), the activity of which is affected not only by intense mental activity but also by monotony. Fatigue brought about by monotony can be reduced when the information input is changed, though it cannot prevent fatigue in the long term. For example, during long drives on the highway mental fatigue is counteracted by listening to a radio.

The occurrence of central fatigue during physical work could be caused by afferent input from the working muscles to the cerebrum, which not only generates the consciousness that the muscles are tiring (or even pain), but also suppresses cortical functions (and hence produces central fatigue) [45]. It is conceivable that these receptors are identical to the *muscle receptors* mentioned previously (p. 650).

Overloading and Exhaustion

Overloading is evident when an *overloading syndrome* appears – that is, when over long periods *fatigue is incompletely compensated* by recovery **(chronic damage)** or when maximal short-term load tolerance is exceeded **(acute damage)**, as can happen, for example, when work is performed under the influence of stimulants (cf. p. 660). The overloading syndrome is particularly conspicuous when it affects the structures involved in posture and movement (broken bones, torn muscles and tendons, slipped disks and damage to joint menisci). When certain activities place excessive mechanical strain on the musculoskeletal system for long periods of time, its function is impaired and permanent damage may be incurred – for example, *deformation of the vertebral column* in the drivers of trucks and tractors. A considerable number of joint, ligament and tendon injuries can result from overenthusiastic athletic training and competition.

Exhaustion occurs when physical or mental performance above the endurance limit is not interrupted *soon enough,* or *long enough* in the case of repeated maximal effort, to allow recovery. Exhaustion necessarily causes work to be *broken off* if the function of many regulatory systems is impaired.

The term **acute exhaustion** is applied to a sudden decline in performance capacity during fatiguing heavy work. Such states of exhaustion are accompanied by massive *metabolic acidosis* (pp. 593ff.); the pH has been found to fall to 6.8 in the blood and 6.4 in muscle. These values are almost routinely observed during athletic competitions and training, though the participants affected suffer no permanent damage. In *emergency situations* more severe exhaustion can be incurred, and in this case damage may be permanent. The time required for recovery from exhausting performance is prolonged according to the degree of exhaustion.

If strenuous work is continued for a long time or repeated too frequently, a condition of **chronic exhaustion** can develop. It is accompanied by *prolonged disorders* of regulatory systems (e.g., the adrenal cortex), in some cases so severe as to cause death.

In contrast to earlier views, it is now known that maximal physical performance does not appreciably interfere with the cardiovascular function of a healthy person. During hard physical work the skeletal musculature tires sooner than the myocardium; the "athlete's heart" (p. 661) is an adapted rather than a pathological heart. But if there is preexisting heart disease, such as hardening of the coronary vessels, extreme physical exertion can damage the heart; doping can have the same result (p. 660). Even apparently healthy people run the risk – though the probability is very small indeed – that exhaustion may lead to a lethal collapse, presumably as a result of ventricular fibrillation.

The emergency reaction and the adaptation syndrome are closely related to the autonomic nervous system and the endocrine system. Both systems respond to a wide range of loads in a stereotyped manner. First *adrenalin* and *noradrenalin* are released, and then the increased liberation of *ACTH* stimulates glucocorticoid secretion. The term **emergency reaction** is applied to this situation when it is especially pronounced (CANNON [35]); the state of the organism under these conditions is called **stress** [27], and the stress-eliciting stimuli are called **stressors** (p. 388). Among these are *all severe physical and psychological loads;* they include extremely hard work, cold and heat, inspiratory oxygen deficiency, hypoglycemia, illness, operations, wounds, noise, sudden fright, anxiety, pain and rage. When stressors act repeatedly or for a long time, an **adaptation syndrome** results (SELYE) [27]) in which the adrenal cortex is hypertrophied. The increased adrenalin release in stress (p. 388) enables *autonomically protected reserves* [5] to be mobilized (p. 656). The result is a *seeming* enhancement of performance capacity, associated with a risk to health (cf. doping, p. 660).

Psychological stressors in particular are thought to cause functional disturbance if there is inadequate opportunity for recovery; this syndrome is called "autonomic dystonia." Typical symptoms are disturbed sleep, impaired circulatory regulation, sudden outbreaks of sweat, chronic tiredness and generally diminished performance capacity.

Performance Feedback and Regulation

It is particularly clear in sporting events that people are capable of *adjusting their performance* according to their physical limits and reserves; exhaustion usually does not set in until the goal has been reached. Similar adjustments are required by seasonal work (for example harvesting) and other jobs done at specific times.

Many jobs involve alternation between heavy and light work, and these can be timed in such a way that the worker rarely becomes exhausted. In the normal case, therefore, people are able to *avoid premature fatigue or exhaustion* and thus to utilize optimally their performance reserves. Observations of this sort have led to the *hypothesis* that man has a mechanism to *control the timing and amount of physical output* [46]. If this were so, exhaustion and overloading would be signs of decompensation of this regulatory mechanism; they would be equivalent to an "emergency brake" that prevents complete collapse by enforcing a recovery period. Decompensation of this sort occurs when the balance between strain and recovery is upset by external influences – for example, by certain kinds of assembly-line work, special motivation (bonuses) or interference with the feedback signals (doping; p. 660).

26.6 Variability in Performance Capacity

Circadian Rhythm

Many of the factors that determine physical and mental performance capacity fluctuate systematically during the course of the day. Under ordinary circumstances these rhythms are often *"masked"* by external influences; therefore in most experiments to demonstrate the rhythms the subject is completely isolated from the environment. Such experiments have shown that the intrinsic "circadian" rhythm is synchronized with the 24-hour-day cycle by external *entraining agents* (Zeitgeber) of many different kinds. Systematic studies of the changes in performance in the course of a day, whether at work or in laboratory tests, reveal great variation, not only from one person to another but also depending on the demands that are made.
The curve frequently presented to show the relation between performance readiness and time

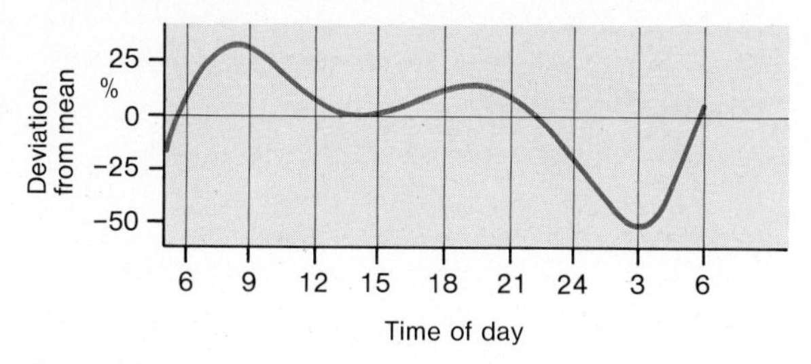

Fig. 26-18. Variation in mean "physiological performance readiness" during the course of a day. *Ordinate:* percentage deviation from the 24-h average. From [5]

of a day (Fig. 26-18) represents the mean results found for various men, over a period of 19 years, in tests of their error rates in determining and recording gas-meter readings. This curve of the mean *daily vigilance (attentiveness) rhythm* of a small group does not apply to all people or to the requirements of all kinds of jobs.

Shift Work

The most common form of shift work is the 3-shift system. The day is divided into three *8-hour* working sessions, usually beginning at 6 a.m., 2 p.m. and 10 p.m. [14, 31]. Shift workers experience *desynchronization of the external entraining signals* (pp. 138f.): the *terrestrial* timers (depending on the rotation of the earth) remain constant while some of the *social* timers vary with the different shifts. Difficulties in adjustment occur, especially on the first days after a change of shift. It has been shown that people never become accommodated to shift work at the level of their biological rhythms. But the most important problems for shift workers result from inadequate (both quantitatively and qualitatively) sleep, unsatisfactory nutrition or eating habits, and the social disconnection from family and leisure activities.
Individuals vary in the degree to which they can accomodate to permanent night or shift work. Whereas many people can tolerate permanent shift work with no great difficulty (e.g., restaurant and newspaper workers, night nurses), others cannot. Whether an individual is suited to shift work – by virtue of disposition, the current status of his private life, and the nature of the work – often becomes clear only after some months of employment. Unsuitability can be manifest, for instance, in *functional disorders.* A person who proves unsuitable should take care to change in due time to a job that does not require shift work.
There is no ideal shift schedule, as is evident in the diversity of existing shift systems. The reason lies in the great variety of contributing factors, from the viewpoint of both the worker and the demands of the job. When suggestions for improvement do not take adequate account of the complexity of an established system and the peripheral conditions, they are rarely successful.
Shift work is often unavoidable – in industry, for instance, or service areas such as hospitals. In such cases work and living conditions should be designed to allow for the shift and night worker's *increased need for recuperation.*

Menstrual Cycle

Contrary to popular assumption, there is no systematic relationship between performance capacity and the menstrual cycle [7]. Studies of athletes have shown that some individuals may vary in performance during the menstrual cycle, but when many individuals are compared the changes in performance capacity are not correlated with any particular phase of the cycle. Maximal sporting performances have been found at each phase. It is thus not advisable, except in a few special cases, to *shift the cycle* in preparation for physically demanding situations.

Maintenance and Enhancement of Performance Capacity

Maintenance of performance capacity. Several factors are influential in this regard; among them are the proper *adjustment of performance* and timing of pauses, optimal *nutrition*, and qualitatively and quantitatively adequate *sleep* [41] (pp. 138ff.). Improper diet and disturbed sleep frequently affect both performance and well-being in the highly industrialized countries. Doctors assigned to check on the health of workers and athletes can thus make an important contribution toward keeping performance levels high. The way a person spends his **leisure** and **vacations** also affects his performance capacity. As the work week of large sections of the population is shortened, leaving more time free for other activities, the choice of leisure activities will become particularly important – not least with respect to the possibility of undesirable consequences for the environment.

Improvement of performance capacity. A *genuine* increase in performance capacity can be achieved *only by training;* other influences can bring about only *seeming* increases, by mobilizing the autonomically protected reserves (p. 656). This protection can be overcome, for example, by special motivation, in emergencies or by drugs.

Doping. This term denotes the attempt to raise performance capacity by drugs. Certain substances are thought to *mobilize the autonomically protected reserves;* among them are preparations that imitate the adrenalin effect (artificial emergency reaction) or suppress the feedback controlling performance, so that information about symptoms of exhaustion is lost or its processing is disturbed (psychoactive drugs). Doping is therefore associated with large **risks to health** [9]. Stimulants have been found to produce severe functional disturbances and permanently impaired health, and even collapse resulting in death. Moreover, it is entirely controversial whether the use of such stimulants in *top-level sport* produces anything like the desired results.

The **anabolics** constitute a special case of doping; these drugs simulate the anabolic effect of male sex hormones, increasing and accelerating the formation of protein in the musculature. The risk to health lies in their side effects on hormone balance, and in the possibility of damage to tendons, ligaments and joints by overloading.

26.7 Training

Adaptive Processes in Training

Definitions. The term *training* is used here to denote the repeated performance of a specified physical or mental activity, whether it takes the form of systematic actions or occurs spontaneously in the course of daily life. It results in the activation of *adaptive processes* in the body, which preserve or enhance performance capacity [1, 10, 17, 28].

The training situation can be interpreted in the light of Fig. 26-1 (p. 645); a particular *training quota* is set as load, the act of training is a form of performance, and the state of training is expressed in the *intermediate to long term* adaptation of certain physiological systems. *State of training,* however, is not equivalent to *performance capacity.* Some people who have trained intensively and are thus in a good state of training can perform at a level only slightly above average, whereas others perform well above average with very little training. The reason, of course, is that performance is also determined by *talent.* This term comprises all the factors affecting performance capacity that are *not influenced by training.* Such characteristics are either inborn or acquired and fixed during a child's early development. The performance capacity at any time, then, depends on both training *and* talent.

The improvement in performance achievable by training depends on the *training quota* – the *intensity* and *duration* of activity. As shown diagrammatically in Fig. 26-19, the performance of a person with a constant training quota in-

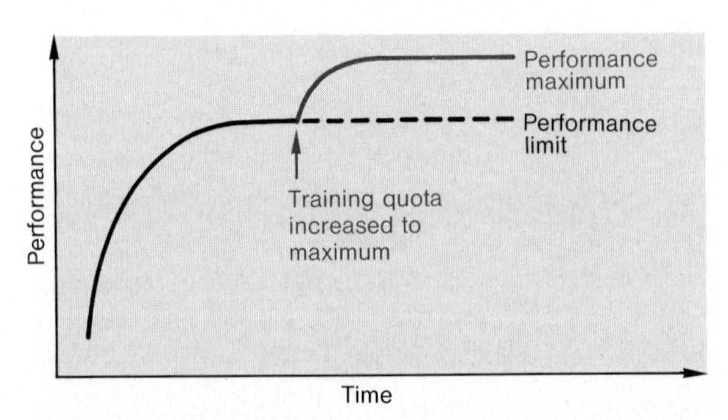

Fig. 26-19. Diagram illustrating the definition of performance limit and performance maximum

creases considerably in the first phase of training. As it proceeds the improvement is less pronounced, until a *performance plateau* is eventually reached (the **performance limit).** When this level has been attained, a further improvement is possible only if the training quota is raised. The plateau achieved when this expansion has been taken to its limit represents the **performance maximum;** continued training will have no further effect.

This time course obtains in principle for all forms of training. The physiological changes brought about by adaption during training can be reversed when training stops. In the case of cardiovascular and muscular adaptations, a *rapidly acquired state of training is also rapidly lost.* Acquired central-nervous coordination, however, is more persistent. *Movement patterns* (e.g., writing, piano playing) once learned *are lost very slowly,* even if they are not practiced for years.

Task-specific training. It is a fundamental principle that one should train that particular sequence of movements for which an increase in performance capacity is desired. Only such task-specific training ensures *optimal adaptation of all components* essential to a specific performance. To improve dexterity in surgical operations, one must operate, and to improve rowing performance one must row. Other forms of training are useful only as supplements to task-specific training.

Special forms of training. Special-purpose training programs, such as *endurance, interval* and *strength training,* improve performance only in the area for which the program was designed. The adaptive processes involved vary greatly depending on the nature of the training. There may be adaptation of skeletal muscle (metabolism or cross-sectional area), of the heart (athlete's heart), of the respiratory system (increased maximum breathing capacity) or of the nervous system (intra- and intermuscular coordination). Most of these changes are crucial for an increase in performance capacity. For example, an endurance athlete needs to improve cardiac output, but this improvement alone does not maximize overall performance; performance capacity depends on a large number of contributory elements.

Degree of adaptation. To evaluate the degree of adaptation achieved by systematic training, one must know what the *initial condition* of the trainee was. Every healthy person is exposed to *diverse training stimuli* in his daily occupations, and although these are slight they should not be underestimated. Their importance is especially well illustrated by the fact that *immobilization* (e.g., by a plaster cast or prolonged confinement to bed) results in *muscular atrophy.* It can be taken for granted that any reduction of activity will cause the state of training, and hence performance capacity, to deteriorate, and any increase will cause improvement. Thus there are not only interindividual but also intraindividual variations in state of adaptation/training, depending on the nature and extent of everyday activity.

Table 26-2. Comparison of physiological parameters of two 25-year-old, 70-kg men with and without intensive endurance training

Parameter	Untrained	Trained
Heart rate at rest, recumbent (min^{-1})	80	40
Heart rate, maximal (min^{-1})	180	180
Stroke volume at rest (ml)	70	140
Stroke volume, maximal (ml)	100	190
Cardiac output at rest (l/min)	5.6	5.6
Cardiac output, maximal (l/min)	18	35
Heart volume (ml)	700	1400
Heart weight (g)	300	500
Respiratory minute volume, maximal (l/min)	100	200
Oxygen uptake, maximal (l/min)	2.8	5.2
Blood volume (l)	5.6	5.9

Endurance training produces distinct changes in many physiological parameters (Table 26-2). The most striking are the increases in heart volume (cardiac dilation) and heart weight (hypertrophy of the wall musculature). This is a training-induced physiological adaptation of the heart *(athlete's heart)* with no pathological significance, though it was once erroneously attributed to cardiac insufficiency. There is also a clear increase in vital capacity in endurance athletes, though it is hardly relevant to performance capacity. The main factor in endurance capacity is an adequate supply of oxygen to the musculature, which is determined by the maximal cardiac output and not by respiration.

Trainability and age. As an adult grows older his physical performance capacity – muscular strength, for instance – becomes less trainable. But because trainability depends not only on age but also on individual characteristics, there are people in each age class who respond particularly well or poorly to training stimuli. In any case, regular training can clearly counteract and postpone the reduction in performance capacity associated with aging; even though training is begun at an advanced age, it can still enhance performance capacity.

Lack of Exercise; Physical Therapy

Lack of exercise effects a loss of physical performance capacity, owing to muscular atrophy, deterioration in state of endurance training, and the like. Reduced performance capacity, however, is *not equivalent* to *"illness"*, just as increased performance capacity does not mean that one is "especially healthy". Physical exercise does increase performance capacity, but at the same time it can impair health (job-related diseases, sport injuries). Medical supervision is necessary, particularly with a view toward accident prevention and other preventive measures.
Lack of exercise is frequently presented as a significant epidemiological *risk factor*. In contrast to risk factors such as smoking, high blood pressure, obesity, diabetes mellitus and disturbed fat metabolism, each of which is recognized as fundamental and *in itself* is correlated with a distinct reduction in statistical life expectancy, the *risk associated with lack of exercise* is a matter of *controversy* [26, 43]. It may be that physical activity has some slight prophylactic value in the presence of a risk factor – for instance, with regard to the typical complications seen in patients with hypertension and metabolic disorders.

Physical therapy. In addition to this *prophylactic role,* physical exercise can also have *therapeutic* value, as in the endurance training of patients with cardiovascular disease and gymnastic training for disorders of the muscular and skleletal systems. For the protection of the patient, however, movement should not be used as therapy unless prescribed by a physician and supervised by professionals. The desired therapeutic and prophylactic benefit must be weighed against the risk of accidents in sport – bearing in mind that many, but not all, people find that physical activity contributes to their general well-being.

26.8 Performance and Aptitude Tests

Tests are instruments for measuring certain traits of personality or behavior [15]. They have a role in work and sports physiology as well as in clinical examination and diagnosis. Some tests are more informative than others, and there are various **test criteria** by which the usefulness of a test can be evaluated. The *primary test criteria* include objectivity, reliability and validity; among the *secondary test criteria* are degree of standardization, comparability and economy [15].

Primary Test Criteria

Objectivity. It is characteristic of an objective test that the results are *independent of the examiner*. Many test procedures are not designed for complete objectivity; therefore they cannot be carried out and interpreted entirely by computer.

Reliability. This criterion refers to the precision with which a personality or behavioral trait is characterized. Reliability has several aspects, and depends on such factors as the nature of the test and the examiner.

Validity. The validity of a test is the degree to which it actually measures the personality or behavioral trait it is designed (or claimed) to measure. Validity, too, has several aspects.
For example, one must verify that a performance test actually measures a special performance capacity, and that a clinical test measures the particular sign of illness that is of interest. This can be done by critically comparing the result obtained with that given by another procedure *(external criterion)* – that is, a result independent of the test at issue, the significance of which is well established. In developing new test procedures, *validity usually presents the most difficult problem.* It is not sufficient to demonstrate the *plausibility* of a test, for tests that appeared plausible have repeatedly given rise to misinterpretations and thus proved unsatisfactory.
As an *example,* consider the determination of *vital capacity,* spirometer measurements of which are objective and give reproducible results when repeated – but only on condition that the subject cooperates. Because many athletes trained for endurance have an unusually high vital capacity, it may sound plausible to describe the validity of this test as follows: "The measurement of vital capacity reveals a person's capacity for endurance performance." But opera singers and the players of wind instruments also have above-normal vital capacities, without abnormally great endurance in the sense of sports physiology. Vital capacity can be increased by appropriate respiratory techniques alone – techniques that cannot be expected to improve performance in endurance trials (p. 655). If "vital capacity" were tested by the external criterion "time to run 5,000 m" (a typical endurance sport), neither the opera singer nor the trombonist would perform well. A more acceptable expression of the validity of the vital-capacity test is, "The measure 'vital capacity' reveals the maximal volume of a single breath, which depends on the respiratory mechanics of the individual." It is thus a test of respiratory mechanics and not of long-term performance capacity.
When the reliability and validity of a test are good, subjects in which a trait is developed to different degrees can be clearly distinguished from one another; that is, correct positive and correct negative decisions are possible. *But it is never the case that 100% of the decisions are correct.* The specificity and sensitivity of a test serve as criteria of the proportion of correct decisions. **Specificity** denotes the extent to which a test allows correct negative decisions (calculated as the ratio of the correct negative decisions to the total number of subjects lacking the trait). **Sensitivity** denotes the extent to which a test allows correct positive decisions (calculated as the ratio of the correct positive decisions to the total number of subjects that exhibit the trait).

The Problem of the Norm

Diagnosis is often possible only when a representative reference value is available. In practice, it turns out to be much harder than one would think to establish norms for reference (cf. [16] and *average weight*, p. 690). It does not suffice to make an arbitrary selection of *"healthy subjects"* and take the *mean* of the data obtained from them as the norm, for the following reasons. 1. The term "healthy" is not sufficiently precisely defined (p. 645). 2. The natural *interindividual variability* is considerable even among healthy people, depending (for example) on individual peculiarities, age and sex. 3. *Intraindividual variability* must also be considered; for instance, after physical activity considerable deviations from the norm may be observed, in the absence of any pathological condition. 4. Deviations from the norm need not be pathological because the conditions normal-healthy and abnormal-ill are often separated by a wide range "abnormal-healthy", with no sharp demarcation at either end.

Performance Tests

Physiological performance tests are diagnostic procedures for the determination of physical performance capacity; like many diagnostic procedures, they involve a certain *risk*. Whereas ergometric "vita maxima" tests, carried to the point of physical exhaustion, present little risk to the healthy, patients are more vulnerable and should be tested only at the indication and with the supervision of a physician. There are many kinds of performance tests [18, 30, 32], and they cannot all be described here. We shall limit ourselves to four that are commonly used to evaluate long-term performance capacity, the test criteria of which are fairly well established.

Maximal oxygen uptake ($\dot{V}_{O_2}$ max). The maximal oxygen uptake is a measure of the *aerobic performance capacity* of the organism. It is monitored during *continuous or stepwise-increasing ergometer work*. Oxygen uptake rises uniformly at first, and then levels off at the transition into the exhaustion state (maximal oxygen uptake, pp. 649f.). The average oxygen uptake in the *plateau region* for an adult male weighing 70 kg is ca. *3.0 l/min, or 43* $ml \cdot min^{-1} \cdot kg^{-1}$. Intensive endurance training can raise the maximal oxygen uptake to about twice this amount.

Physical work capacity (PWC_{170} or W_{170}). This test also requires continual or stepwise-increasing work on an ergometer; the critical measure is the performance at the time when the heart rate reaches 170 min^{-1}. Because the maximal heart rate decreases with age, the readings for older people are either extrapolated to 170 min^{-1} or expressed with respect to a lower reference rate, such as 130 min^{-1} (i.e., PWC_{130}). The result of the test has the dimension watts. The validity of this test is the same as that of maximal oxygen uptake. Although the PWC test is less reliable than the measurement of maximal oxygen uptake, it is particularly suitable for large-scale studies because it is economical with regard to both time and money. For non-athletes between 20 and 30 years of age the following average values are obtained: for women, *2.3 watts/kg;* for men *2.8 watts/kg* body weight. Intensive endurance training can double these figures.

Aerobic/anaerobic transition and anaerobic threshold. As ergometer performance increases, it is useful to measure the level of performance at which the *lactate concentration* in the blood exceeds the values 2 and 4 mmol/l (beginning of transition and threshold, respectively; cf. p. 655). This test result is more informative about *long-term endurance,* in the range of hours, than is the maximal oxygen uptake. Men 20 to 30 years old reach the aerobic/anaerobic transition with a performance of about *1.25 watts/kg* and the anaerobic threshold with about *2.5 watts/kg* body weight. The level of the anaerobic threshold, as a percentage of the performance at which oxygen uptake becomes maximal, provides information about training-dependent *adaptation processes in the musculature* (state of training). The value found for untrained people is about 50–60%, and that for people highly trained in endurance sports is ca. 80%.

Heart volume. The volume of the heart can be found from *X-rays* or by *echocardiography.* It is *not* a direct measure of performance capacity, but rather indicates the state of adaptation of the heart to endurance training (i.e., the *state of endurance training).* The heart volume of a healthy non-athlete is ca. *10 ml/kg* body weight. The heart of a highly trained endurance athlete can have a volume twice as great (see athlete's heart, p. 661).

Significance of body weight. The results of performance tests are often expressed with reference to body weight (relative values). But this generalization is not suitable for evaluating individual cases; the demands of the particular task should be taken into account, for the following reasons.

1. When the subject is moving only the weight of his own body, the physiological performance parameters of different individuals can best be compared if referred to body weight.
2. When heavy loads are to be transported, it is more useful to express the results with respect either to the absolute performance capacity or to the total weight (body weight plus load weight).
3. If the performance capacity of the musculature is to be evaluated, reference to the muscle mass (with which the "lean body mass", p. 691, is correlated) is preferable.

Interpretation of performance tests. Once the reliability and validity of a test have been established, one can draw precise and informative conclusions from the results, with two restrictions:

1. Strictly speaking, the result of the test applies only to the kind of performance being tested. Conclusions about performance capacity in other tasks are justified only if the performance-determining factors are largely identical, and the transfer should always be expected to involve a loss of validity.

2. The test result refers only to the performance capacity at the time of the test.

In many cases the *future performance capacity* is also of interest – for example, in search of talent for particular professional occupations or areas of sport. There are two objects of a search for people qualified for specific tasks:

1. To find people who have a *present aptitude,* without instruction or training, for performing particular tasks; in this case, the current performance profile should match closely the requirements of the task.
2. To find people whose *talent* (natural endowment) suggests that training or instruction will develop a *future aptitude* for performing certain tasks, so that in future a correspondence between performance profile and task profile can be expected.

Tests of aptitude. *Present aptitude* can be evaluated by practical tests in which the subject is observed while performing the task in question for a more or less long period of time, or examined by a battery of tests with subdivisions to explore each of the abilities required for the task. In neither case are prognoses regarding future increases in performance capacity possible.

When an estimate of the *future aptitude* to be expected *after* instruction or training is desired, it is necessary to use *talent tests,* the results of which are independent of training. Tests that strictly conform to this criterion are extraordinarily rare. Performance in most "talent tests" – including intelligence tests – can be improved by special test training.

A special kind of test is the medical examination of workers for the purposes of safety and health; in this case suitability for a task is evaluated in terms of general health, both at the time of hiring and at intervals during employment.

Performance prognosis. As difficult as it is to determine present aptitude by tests, the difficulty in determining future aptitude is even greater. Under certain circumstances it may be possible to predict future performance capacity for groups, but there are fundamental restrictions when it comes to the individual case. Therefore any prognostic procedure to detect the latent talent of an individual – whether for work or sport – can provide only very limited information. Estimates of a person's present or future aptitude should not be *taken too literally.* Performance levels are always based on *many factors,* and one can rarely be certain that a test result reflects all of them. Moreover, nature makes sudden jumps; many a person has proved capable of "excelling himself". It is not advisable to place any more reliance on a performance prognosis than, for example, on a weather prognosis – and the latter are based on decades of experience.

In conclusion, with regard to the widespread tendency in industry and sport to evaluate talent by elaborate test batteries and computer analysis, it should be said that the problem of prognosis lies in the *validity* of the tests and the *interpretation* of the results, and *not in the scale* of the test program.

The final test. One last cautionary word: it is the end result that ultimately matters in selecting a person suited to a particular task. The performance actually achieved determines suitability, and not the fact that the person was preselected, by whatever test or other criteria. Preselection can help to narrow the range of likely possibilities for an individual, but errors in one direction or another can never be ruled out.

26.9 References

Textbooks and Handbooks

1. ÅSTRAND, P.-O., RODAHL, K.: Textbook of work physiology. New York: McGraw-Hill 1977
2. BAUST, W. (Ed.): Ermüdung, Schlaf und Traum. Frankfurt/M: Fischer 1971
3. FRANZ, I.-W.: Ergometrie bei Hochdruck- und Koronarkranken in der täglichen Praxis. Berlin-Heidelberg-New York-Tokyo: Springer 1984
4. GALBO, H.: Hormonal and metabolic adaptation in exercise. Stuttgart-New York: Thieme 1983
5. GRAF, O.: Arbeitsablauf und Arbeitsrhythmus. In: [14]
6. GRANDJEAN, E.: Physiologische Arbeitsgestaltung. Thun-München: Ott 1979
7. HILDEBRANDT, G. (Ed.): Biologische Rhythmen und Arbeit. Wien-New York: Springer 1976
8. HOLLMANN, W.: Höchst- und Dauerleistungsfähigkeit des Sportlers. München: Barth 1963
9. HOLLMANN, W. (Ed.): Zentrale Themen der Sportmedizin. Berlin-Heidelberg-New York-Tokyo: Springer 1986
10. HOLLMANN, W., HETTINGER, T.: Sportmedizin – Arbeits- und Trainingsgrundlagen. Stuttgart-New York: Schattauer 1984
11. KEUL, J., DOLL, E., KEPPLER, D.: Muskelstoffwechsel. München: Barth 1969
12. KEUL, J., BERG, A.: Energiestoffwechsel und körperliche Leistung. In: [9]
13. KEUL, J., HARALAMBIE, G.: Energiestoffwechsel und körperliche Leistung. In: HOLLMANN, W. (Ed.): Zentrale Themen der Sportmedizin. Berlin-Heidelberg-New York: Springer 1977
14. LEHMANN, G. (Ed.): Handbuch der gesamten Arbeitsmedizin, Bd. 1: Arbeitsphysiologie. Berlin-München-Wien: Urban & Schwarzenberg 1961
15. LIENERT, G.A.: Testaufbau und Testanalyse. Weinheim-Berlin-Basel: Beltz 1969
16. LÖLLGEN, H.: Kardiopulmonale Funktionsdiagnostik. Wehr/Baden. Ciba Geigy 1983
17. MARÉES, H. DE: Sportphysiologie. Köln-Mühlheim: Tropon 1979

18. Mellerowicz, H. (Ed.): Ergometrie, München-Berlin-Wien: Urban & Schwarzenberg 1979
19. Müller, E.A.: Die physische Ermüdung. In: [14]
20. Nadel, E.R: Problems with temperature regulation during exercise. New York: Academic Press 1977
21. Nöcker, J.: Physiologie der Leibesübungen für Sportlehrer, Trainer, Sportstudenten, Sportärzte. (4. neubearb. Aufl.), Stuttgart: Enke 1980
22. Reichel, G., Bolt, H.M., Hettinger, T., Selenka, F., Ulmer, H.-V., Ulmer, W.T. (Eds.): Grundlagen der Arbeitsmedizin. Stuttgart-Berlin-Köln-Mainz: Kohlhammer 1985
23. Rohmert, W.: Untersuchung über Muskelermüdung und Arbeitsgestaltung. Berlin-Köln-Frankfurt/M.: Beuth 1962
24. Rohmert, W., Rutenfranz, J. (Eds.): Praktische Arbeitsphysiologie. Stuttgart-New York: Thieme 1983
25. Rutenfranz, J.: Entwicklung und Beurteilung der körperlichen Leistungsfähigkeit bei Kindern und Jugendlichen. Basel-New York: Karger 1964
26. Schwarz, F.W. (Red.): Herz-Kreislauf-Vorsorgeprogramme in der Bundesrepublik Deutschland. Köln-Lövenich: Deutscher Ärzteverlag 1977
27. Selye, H.: The stress of life. New York: McGraw-Hill Book Company Inc. 1957
28. Stegemann, J.: Exercise Physiology. Stuttgart-New York: Thieme 1981
29. Thews, G.: Der Atemgastransport bei körperlicher Arbeit. Wiesbaden: Steiner 1984
30. Ulmer, H.-.V.: Zur Methodik, Standardisierung und Auswertung von Tests für die Prüfung der körperlichen Leistungsfähigkeit. Köln-Lövenich: Deutscher Ärzteverlag 1975
31. Valentin, H., Lehnert, G., Petry, H., Rutenfranz, J., Stalder, K., Weber, G., Wittgens, H., Woitowitz, H.: Arbeitsmedizin, Bd. 1 und Bd. 2, Stuttgart-New York: Thieme 1985
32. Valentin, H., Holzhauser, K.P.: Funktionsprüfungen von Herz und Kreislauf. Köln-Lövenich: Deutscher Ärzteverlag 1976
33. Wenzel, H.G., Piekarski, C.: Klima und Arbeit. (2. Aufl.), München: Bayerisches Staatsministerium für Arbeit und Sozialordnung 1982

Original Papers and Reviews

34. Berger, M., Berchtold, P., Chappers, H.-J., Drost, H., Kley, H.-K., Müller, W.A., Wiegelmann, W., Zimmermann-Telschow, H., Gries, F.A., Krüskemper, L., Zimmermann, H.: Metabolic and hormonal effects of muscular exercise in juvenile type diabetics. Diabetologia *13,* 355 (1977)
35. Cannon, W.B.: Die Notfallsreaktionen des sympathico-adrenalen Systems. Erg. Physiol. *27,* 380 (1928)
36. Donald, K.W., Lind, A.R., McNicol, G.W., Humphreys, P.W., Taylor, S.H., Staunton, H.P.: Cardiovascular responses to sustained (static) contractions. Circulation Res. *20,* Suppl. 1, I-15 (1967)
37. Hultén, B., Thorstensson, A., Sjödin, B., Karlsson, J.: Relationship between isometric endurance and fibre types in human leg muscles. Acta physiol. scand. *93,* 135 (1975)
38. Johnson, J.M., Rowell, L.B., Brengelmann, G.L.: Modification of the skin blood flow-body temperature relationship by upright exercise. J. Appl. Physiol. *37,* 880 (1974)
39. Klein,G., Hilmer, W., Moser, B.: Blutbild bei Ergometrie und Langstreckenlauf. Dt. Z. Sportmed. *29,* 8 (1978)
40. Klimmer, F., Aulmann, H.M., Rutenfranz, J.: Katecholaminausscheidung im Urin bei emotional und mental belastenden Tätigkeiten im Flugverkehrskontrolldienst. Int. Arch. Arbeitsmed. *30,* 65 (1972)
41. Knauth, P., Rutenfranz, J.: Untersuchungen zum Problem des Schlafverhaltens bei experimenteller Schichtarbeit. Int. Arch. Arbeitsmed. *30,* 1 (1972)
42. Lind, A.R., McNicol, G.W.: Cardiovascular responses to holding and carrying weights by hand and by shoulder harness. J. Appl. Physiol. *25,* 261 (1968)
43. Rost, R., Hollmann, W.: Herz, Gefäßsystem und Sport. Der inf. Arzt *6,* H. 1, 46 (1978)
44. Rowell, L.B.: Human cardiovascular adjustments to exercise and thermal stress. Physiol. Rev. *54,* 75 (1974)
45. Seyfarth, H.: The behaviour of motor units in healthy and paretic muscles in man. Acta psych. neurol. (Kbh.) *16,* 261 (1941)
46. Ulmer, H.-V.: Physiologische Grundlagen menschlicher Arbeit. In: [22]

27 Environmental Physiology

H.-V. Ulmer

The environmental factors that can affect humans are many and varied. These influences activate regulatory mechanisms in the body that produce short-term *adjustments* within minutes or hours, and long-term *adaptation* of the organism within days or weeks. These modifications enable humans to live and/or work at high altitudes and under water, from the polar regions to the equator.

Such influences from our surroundings, which may be physical or chemical in nature, fit into the load/strain scheme presented on p. 645 as *environmental loads*. The organism reacts in diverse ways, corresponding to the diversity of loads; among the fields of study concerned with these reactions are toxicology, traumatology, allergology, and physiology. The physical influences first elicit a response of physiological regulatory mechanisms, but they can also produce illness and injury. The following sections present examples of basic physical environmental loads, their significance to humans at work and leisure, and their physiological – and in some cases pathological – effects.

27.1 Altitude; Low Pressures

Three main factors act as a load to people at high altitudes: (i) low O_2 partial pressure, (ii) increased solar irradiation, and (iii) the cold. The most important of these is the progressive reduction in O_2 partial pressure at higher altitudes.

Oxygen Deficiency

Acute and chronic hypoxia. As altitude increases, the atmospheric pressure decreases, whereas the O_2 concentration remains constant up to high altitude. The partial pressure of O_2 falls in proportion to the drop in atmospheric pressure; for instance, it is halved at 5,500 m above sea level

Table 27-1. Atmospheric pressure, inspiratory O_2 partial pressure (moistened inspired air) and alveolar O_2 partial pressure at different altitudes above sea level. In the last column are the O_2 fractions with which the corresponding partial pressures can be simulated at sea level (100 mm Hg $\approx$ 13.3 kPa)

Altitude (m)	Air pressure (mm Hg)	Insp. O_2 partial pressure (mm Hg)	Alveol. O_2 partial pressure (mm Hg)	Equivalent O_2 fraction
0	760	149	105	0.2095
2,000	596	115	76	0.164
3,000	526	100	61	0.145
4,000	462	87	50	0.127
5,000	405	75	42	0.112
6,000	354	64	38	0.098
7,000	308	55	35	0.085
8,000	267	46	32	0.074
10,000	199	32		0.055
14,000	106	12		0.029
19,000	49	0.4		0.014

(Table 27-1). The responses of the body to **oxygen deficiency** depend not only on the degree of deficiency but on its duration as well [10]. Depending on the times involved, three forms are distinguished: **acute hypoxia** (e.g., sudden loss of pressure in an airplane or malfunction of breathing equipment), **rapid-onset hypoxia** (e.g., ascent in a cable car) and **chronic hypoxia** (e.g., a prolonged stay at high altitudes). Altitude-tolerance also depends on the **manner of the ascent;** one can endure great heights better if one has reached them actively (on foot) than if one has been transported passively (by cable-car or airplane).

Altitude sickness. This term denotes a number of physiological disturbances induced by *oxygen deficiency*. The general symptoms are a reduction in mental and physical performance, rapid tiring and discomfort.

The *special signs* of oxygen deficiency at altitude are diminished will power, a need for sleep, loss of appetite, breathlessness, tachycardia, dizziness, vomiting, headache and apathy (though euphoria can also occur). Depending on the individual's *predisposition* and *situation*, these symptoms

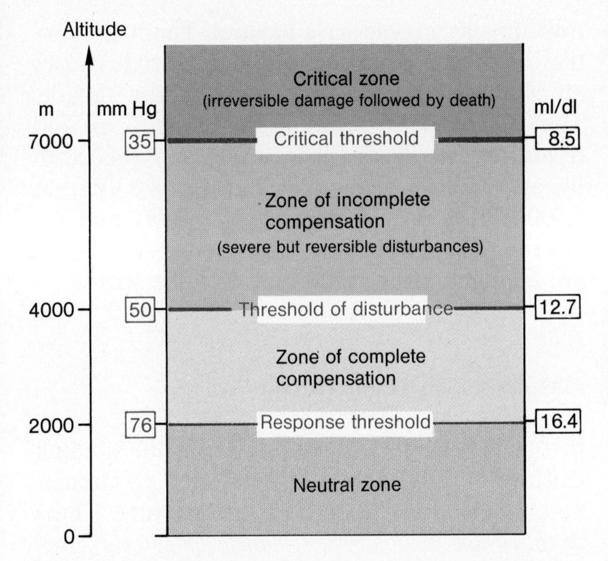

Fig. 27-1. Effects of altitude-related oxygen deficiency. The numbers in *red* give the alveolar O_2 partial pressure at the corresponding altitude, and the *black* numbers give the oxygen content of gas mixtures that would have the same effect at sea level (cf. Table 27-1). The data are rough approximations, for non-acclimatized people (100 mm Hg ≈ 13.3 kPa). From [10]

can occur separately or in various combinations. Their importance as *warning signals* is often not recognized or is underestimated. *Slowly developing oxygen deficiency is especially dangerous,* particularly for a person at rest, because it can cause unconsciousness before any warning symptoms are apparent.

Effective thresholds. The range of effects of oxygen deficiency can be subdivided into **4 zones** delimited by *effective thresholds* [10] (Fig. 27-1). This is of course not a rigid subdivision, for there are various transitional effects and the thresholds can be shifted by *acclimation* (p. 668) and *predisposition.*

Neutral zone. Up to an altitude of 2,000 m physiological functions and thus, for example, the maximal rate of dynamic work suffer little or not at all.

Zone of complete compensation. At altitudes between 2,000 and 4,000 m even at rest a response to the reduced oxygen supply becomes apparent, in the form of a slight increase in heart rate, cardiac output and respiratory minute volume. During work there is a greater increase in these variables than at sea level, so that both physical and mental performance are detectably impaired.

Zone of incomplete compensation (danger zone). At altitudes between 4,000 and 7,000 m an unacclimatized person shows various disorders. When the *threshold of disturbance* **(safety limit)** at 4,000 m is passed, physical performance is seriously affected, as are responsiveness and the ability to make decisions. Muscle twitches appear, the blood pressure drops and eventually consciousness becomes clouded. These changes are reversible.

Critical zone. From *7,000 m* on up the O_2 partial pressure in the alveolar air is below the **critical threshold,** *30–35 mm Hg* (4.0–4.7 kPa). Potentially lethal central nervous disturbances are accompanied by unconsciousness and convulsions; these can be reversed by a rapid increase in the inspiratory P_{O_2}, if they have lasted only for a short time. In the critical zone, the *duration of oxygen deficiency plays the crucial role.* If hypoxia lasts too long the central nervous control systems fail and death results.

Table 27-2. Time from oxygen cut-off to loss of function (time of useful consciousness) at altitudes above 7,000 m. From [10]

Alt. (km)	7	8	9	10	11	12	15
Time (min)	5	3	1.5	1	2/3	1/2	1/6

High-altitude intoxication. Depending on the susceptibility of the individual, this condition can appear without any other symptoms at altitudes of 3,000 m or more [7, 10]. As in alcohol intoxication, typical signs are euphoria, failure to recognize danger, and conspicuous errors of judgement.

Time of useful consciousness. When there is a *sudden onset* of oxygen deficiency at altitudes above 7,000 m (e.g., loss of pressure in an airplane) one has a brief period of grace during which normal function continues (Table 27-2). At the end of this period consciousness becomes impaired, followed by irreversible damages, leading to death.

Breathing pure oxygen at altitude. Oxygen inhalation shifts the altitude-response thresholds but does not abolish them. When pure oxygen is breathed at an altitude of 14 km the inspiratory P_{O_2} is 106 mm Hg (14.1 kPa). In the dead space at 37 °C the P_{H_2O} accounts for 47 mm Hg (6.3 kPa; p. 561), so that about 60 mm Hg (8.0 kPa) remains for the inspiratory P_{O_2}. The alveolar space still contains carbon dioxide at a partial pressure of ca. 30 mm Hg (4.0 kPa, varying according to the degree of hyperventilation; p. 563), which reduces the P_{O_2} still further: All that remains is 30 mm Hg (4.0 kPa) – less than the **critical hypoxia threshold.** A person breathing pure oxygen reaches this limit at altitudes between 13 and 14 km, so that to ascend higher *pressure suits* or *pressurized cabins* are required.

Short-Term Adjustment to High Altitude

Hypoxia at altitude (or in other situations, such as heart malfunction) elicits short-, intermediate- and long-term adaptive reactions. Short-term processes require only a few hours, whereas true acclimation (see below) to high altitudes requires several days to months.

Circulatory adjustments. At 2,000 m or higher the resting **heart rate** rises, and at 6,000 m it reaches about 120 min^{-1}. The increases brought about by a given amount of exercise are considerably greater than those at sea level. **Stroke volume** changes only slightly; both increases and decreases have been observed. Thus cardiac output is increased slightly at rest but distinctly more so during exercise. The **arterial blood pressure** during exercise does not change appreciably with altitude. But in the **pulmonary artery,** especially at rest, there can be pressure increases associated with pulmonary edema (pulmonary vasoconstriction during hypoxia is described on p. 525 and p. 566).

Respiratory adjustments. In *resting* conditions the arterial hypoxia exerts only a slight respiratory drive (p. 572); respiratory minute volume at 5,000 m is only about 10% above the comparable sea-level value, though at 6,500 m it is twice as great. During *exercise* minute volume increases markedly. **Hyperventilation** leads to a transient increase in respiratory quotient to more than 1.0 (pp. 619f.). Despite hyperventilation the amount of oxygen inhaled (expressed as $\dot{V}_{O_2STPD}$) is less, because the minute volume does not increase in proportion to the decrease in P_{O_2}.

Oxygen-transport adjustments. Because the alveolar P_{O_2} falls as altitude increases (Table 27-1), the arterial P_{O_2} also falls. At 2,000 m, under resting conditions, the alveolar P_{O_2} is 76 mm Hg (10.1 kPa) and the arterial P_{O_2} is 73 mm Hg (9.7 kPa); nevertheless, the arterial **oxygen saturation** of the hemoglobin is still **93%.** Two additional factors impede *oxygen transport.* First hyperventilation leads to *respiratory alkalosis,* which causes a leftward shift of the oxygen dissociation curve (pp. 585f.). This shift facilitates oxygen binding in the lung, but makes it more difficult for oxygen to be released in the tissues. Second, during exercise the *alveolar-arterial O_2 partial-pressure difference* AaD_{O_2} (pp. 567f.) in the lung increases as more oxygen is taken up. During exhausting work it can rise to 15 mm Hg (2.0 kPa). Taking the alveolar P_{O_2} at 2,000 m as 76 mm Hg (10.1 kPa), any increase in AaD_{O_2} causes a detectable decrease in arterial O_2 saturation because of the shift to the steeper part of the oxygen dissociation curve (p. 585). During exhausting work at 2,000 m oxygen saturation is less than 90%, which corresponds to an arterial P_{O_2} below 65 mm Hg (8.6 kPa); as a result, maximal performance at 2,000 m is reduced by almost 10% (and by ca. 20% at 3,500 m).

Adjustments in acid-base balance. The hyperventilation during adjustment to high altitude causes an increased release of stored carbon dioxide. The CO_2 partial pressure in the blood drops and **respiratory alkalosis** ensues (p. 595). At 4,000 m the arterial P_{CO_2} is about 30 mm Hg (4.0 kPa); at 6,500 m it is only 20 mm Hg (2.7 kPa), and the arterial pH rises above 7.5. *Base excess* (BE) does not change during acute high-altitude stress.

Acclimation to High Altitude

In the intermediate and long term, life at high altitudes brings about adaptations of circulation, respiration, blood and musculature. These changes are basically a *response to arterial hypoxia and respiratory alkalosis.* There are considerable individual differences in the extent and time course of these adaptations, and the adaptive response may go through an overshooting phase (e.g., in erythropoiesis). Months to years are required for complete acclimation. Expeditions have shown, however, that even after a few weeks a remarkable degree of acclimation – and thus of altitude tolerance – can be achieved. On the whole, acclimation enables people to live for short periods, without artificial aids, at altitudes that would otherwise be lethal. Acclimatized mountain climbers can spend some time at altitudes above 8,000 m without oxygen apparatus, and some individuals can go to almost 8,900 m; but the limiting altitude for a prolonged stay is considerably lower.

The *highest human settlements* are in the Andes, at about 5,300 m. This altitude is probably the highest permanently tolerable by man. But regular work at great altitudes is evidently less of a problem than permanent habitation, for mines can be operated at altitudes as high as 6,200 m. Presumably the regulation of breathing during work (by muscle receptors; p. 574) can produce tolerable physiological conditions despite the altitude, but not the regulation during rest [11]. The inhabitants of villages at great heights have undergone centuries of selection; the acclimation they show can presumably be regarded as the most that adaptation can achieve. In order to learn about the physiological changes accompanying this acclimation, the inhabitants of the city Morococha, 4,540 m high in the Andes, were studied [5]. The results are summarized in Table 27-3, in comparison with the findings in lowland dwellers (Lima).

Cardiovascular acclimation. In the initial stage of acclimation the resting heart rate rises, but then it falls again and at altitudes up to 5,000 m can stabilize below the starting level. Stroke volume does not change appreciably; accordingly, cardiac output at rest varies little and the maximal cardiac output is reduced.

Table 27-3. Various blood, respiration and circulatory parameters of residents at high altitude (Morococha) and the lowlands (Lima); all data in resting conditions. 100 mm Hg ≈ 13.3 kPa [5]

Altitude:	4,540 m	0 m
Blood:		
Erythrocytes (million/μl)	6.44	5.11
Reticulocytes (thousand/μl)	46	18
Thrombocytes (thousand/μl)	419	401
Leukocytes (thousand/μl)	7.0	6.7
Hematocrit (%)	60	47
Hemoglobin (g/l)	201	156
Blood volume (ml/kg)	101	80
Plasma volume (ml/kg)	39	42
pH of arterial blood	7.39	7.41
Buffer base (mmol/l)	45.6	49.2
Respiratory minute volume BTPS ($l \cdot min^{-1} \cdot kg^{-1}$)	0.19	0.13
P_{O_2}, alveolar (mm Hg)	51	104
P_{CO_2}, alveolar (mm Hg)	29.1	38.6
Art. O_2 saturation (%)	81	98
Heart rate (min^{-1})	72	72
Blood pressure (mm Hg)	93/63	116/79

Respiratory acclimation. As acclimation proceeds over weeks, the breathing control system becomes more and more *sensitive* to arterial oxygen deficiency and increasing P_{CO_2}. This change is evident in that the breath cannot be held as long and the CO_2-response curve changes (leftward shift and steeper slope; p. 572). However, people who live permanently at great heights have smaller respiratory responses to inspiratory oxygen deficiency than those at an intermediate stage of adaptation.

Oxygen transport during acclimation. At the beginning of a period at high altitude the number of erythrocytes in the blood sometimes decreases because of a higher rate of loss, but after a few days all the signs of *enhanced erythropoiesis* appear (p. 411). *Reticulocytes* become more abundant, the red cell count rises, and the hemoglobin concentration is increased, with a slight fall in the mean corpuscular hemoglobin (MCH; p. 581) below the normal level of *31 pg/erythrocyte.* The greater the altitude-related oxygen deficiency, the stronger the stimulus to erythropoiesis, though there is no change in the rate of production of other blood cells. Experiments have demonstrated an increase of over 10% in *red cell count* and *hemoglobin concentration* after 2 days at 4,500 m. After about 10 days the *rapid* phase of rising RCC and hemoglobin concentration is completed. The following slow increase, lasting months (*maxima:* hemoglobin, 270 g/l blood; hematocrit, 70%) is terminated by a slight decline to a stable high level (see Table 27-3). Another change in the first 2 days is an increase in the *2,3-DPG content* of the erythrocytes, from ca. 85 μg/ml blood to 140 μg/ml blood, accompanied by a shift of the O_2 dissociation curve to the *right.*

Because the hemoglobin content of the blood is increased, its *O_2-transport capacity* remains about the same up to 5,000 m despite the lowered O_2 saturation. 100 ml blood containing 15.5 g hemoglobin binds 20 ml oxygen at 97% saturation; 100 ml blood containing 20 g hemoglobin binds the same amount of oxygen at only 75% saturation (corresponding to ca. 5,000 m altitude). But because the elevated hematocrit raises the viscosity of the blood considerably, the microcirculation in the capillaries is impeded (pp. 482f.); one result is that during the middle stages of acclimation the maximal cardiac output is less. Therefore during exhausting work the maximal rate of oxygen transport is no greater, even when one returns to sea level after acclimation to high altitude. Such acclimation thus provides no appreciable improvement in long-term performance at sea level. The *leftward* shift of the O_2 dissociation curve resulting from respiratory alkalosis is at first compensated by the increase in 2,3-diphosphoglycerate; after longer adaptation overcompensation leads to a *rightward* shift, which promotes the release of oxygen in the tissues.

Acid-base balance during acclimation. In the course of acclimation increased amounts of bicarbonate are excreted by the kidney. This *renal compensation* of respiratory alkalosis brings the *blood pH* back to normal (pp. 594f.). Moreover, as the amount of hemoglobin rises, so does the buffering capacity of the blood. But the buffering capacity of the tissue decreases because of the compensatory loss of bicarbonate, so that there are *shifts of electrolytes* between the intra- and extracellular spaces.

Musculature during acclimation. As acclimation progresses the *capillary density* in the muscles increases; the diffusion paths between the capillaries and the interior of the muscles become shorter. Within the muscle cell various *enzyme systems,* especially those of the mitochondria, adapt to oxygen deficiency so that aerobic metabolism is favored despite the lowered P_{O_2}.

Aviation and Space Travel

During high-altitude flight one encounters problems of acute oxygen deficiency (pp. 666f.). In a pressurized cabin with interior pressure roughly equivalent to an altitude of 2,300 m, there are brief pressure changes during take-off and landing that affect chiefly the air-filled cavities in the skull (cf. *barotrauma,* p. 671). Moreover, as altitude increases one must take precautions against the increased radiation and lower ambient temperature. The loads imposed by the *forces of acceleration* are considered on pp. 675f..

Time-zone jumps. Flight across time zones causes discrepancies between the endogenous rhythms and external entraining signals (pp. 139f.) as well as between the phase of the traveller's daily performance cycle and that of the local residents. For example, with a time-zone jump of 6 hours to the east and a landing at 9 a.m. local time, the traveller may be at his *lowest point* on arrival (at 3 a.m. by his "internal clock"). Arriving at 9 a.m. after the same flight in the opposite direction, he may find himself at the afternoon peak of performance (3 p.m. by the "internal clock"). This is why *eastward* flights so often cause greater difficulty in adjustment than do westward flights. These are statistical statements, however, with great interindividual variability.
Biological rhythms adjust themselves at different rates (pp. 139f.). Among those that reset rapidly are the waking/sleeping and vigilance rhythms; for resynchronization of every 2 hours of time shift about one day is required.

Space flight requires pressurized cabins or suits; without them, blood at 37 °C would boil at altitudes of 19 km or more *(ebullition)*. A pressurized cabin also ensures adequate inspiratory oxygen partial pressure (pp. 666f.) and offers protection from the cold and, though not completely, from the radiation in outer space.
The absence of the pull of gravity (*weightlessness*) is discussed on p. 676. On the whole, human adaptability and technology have proved adequate to permit life in outer space for weeks and months – at the price of renewed difficulties in adapting after the *return* to earth.

27.2 Diving; High Pressures

The diver moves through an alien environment; beyond the short time of breath-hold diving, he must provide air for *breathing* and adjust to the increased *pressure* [3, 11]. Immersion in water also makes it harder to maintain *thermal equilibrium,* because heat is lost more rapidly. Conditions are thus usually outside the thermoneutral zone (p. 627). Finally, *orientation* by eyes and ears is distorted.

Diving without Equipment

The simplest form of diving, with no equipment at all, is limited to relatively slight depths. Previous **hyperventilation** is dangerous for two reasons: (i) *dizziness* or even convulsions can occur before the dive owing to respiratory alkalosis (p. 595), and (ii) the *oxygen reserve can be misestimated* at the end of the dive, because the total respiratory drive (pp. 571f.) is diminished by the lowered CO_2 partial pressure and the respiratory alkalosis. The oxygen deficiency that develops during diving in itself is only a weak stimulus, so that breathing can be suppressed longer than in a dive without previous hyperventilation – with the risk that the increasing oxygen deficiency will lead to *sudden fainting (black-out)*. Whereas the arterial O_2 saturation does not rise as a result of hyperventilation, the O_2 fraction in the lung can be increased by about 0.05 as the result of a few deep breaths.

Snorkling with face-plate or goggles gives one an opportunity to observe the underwater region without interruption; sunburn on shoulders and neck and overcooling not uncommonly result. The standard snorkel, 30 to 35 cm long, must on no account be extended. Although this enlargement of the dead space would have hardly any effect on respiration, the consequences to the *circulatory system* during a deeper dive are considerable. Because the alveolar pressure corresponds to the atmospheric pressure at the water surface, the additional external pressure of water on the rest of the body causes a *pressure gradient between the intra- and extrathoracic parts of the low-pressure system* (p. 524). The thorax would thus become increasingly filled with blood at progressively greater depths, and eventually there could be potentially lethal *overstretching of the pulmonary vessels and heart* [18]. Another danger is associated with entry into *cold-water currents;* particularly in the vagotonic phase after eating, cutaneovisceral reflexes can trigger so-called *vasovagal syncope* with a critical fall in blood pressure.

Deep breath-hold diving requires consideration of the physical gas laws, as follows: 1. *Boyle-Mariotte* law: the product of pressure and volume is constant. 2. *Dalton's* law: the sum of the partial pressures is the total pressure. 3. *Henry-Dalton* law (p. 582): the amount of a gas dissolved is proportional to its partial pressure and solubility coefficient. These laws, of course, are strictly valid only for *ideal* gases, but experience has shown that they are entirely applicable to the problems encountered in deep dives.

Depth:	0 m	10 m	40 m
P_{amb}:	1 bar	2 bar	5 bar
LV:	5.0 l	2.5 l	1.0 l
P_{AO_2}:	105 mm Hg	210 mm Hg	525 mm Hg

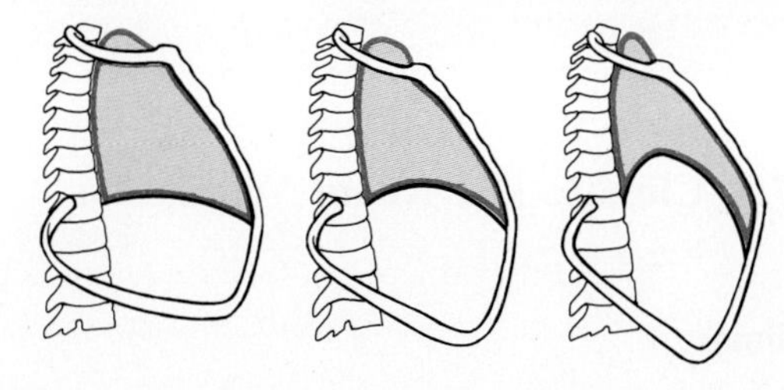

Fig. 27-2. Lung volumes (LV) and partial pressures in breath-hold deep diving. At 0 m the thorax is in the maximal-inspiration position, and at 40m it is in the maximal-expiration position (maximal diaphragm elevation). For alveolar P_{O_2} values oxygen consumption is neglected; P_{amb} = ambient pressure, the same as the intrathoracic pressure; 1 bar ≈ 100 kPa

Barotrauma *(pressure injury):* The Boyle-Mariotte law holds for all *air-filled cavities* in the body (e.g., lungs, spaces in the skull, hollow teeth or stomach). During descent the rising ambient pressure can lead to disturbances here that ultimately injure the tissues. For example, at the beginning of a dive the thorax volume and thus the lung volume decrease with no difficulty, reaching a minimum at a depth of 30–40 m (Fig. 27-2). Because the lung cannot be further compressed at greater depths, the intrathoracic pressure remains constant despite the continually increasing extrathoracic (ambient) pressure with increasing depth. The resulting *pressure difference* causes a considerable *inflow of blood into the thoracic organs* (cf. snorkling); the intrathoracic volume of air is further reduced as the pulmonary vessels and heart are stretched beyond their normal capacity. – The pressure in the air-filled parts of the skull must be equilibrated with the intrathoracic pressure by way of the nose and throat, either spontaneously or with assistance (cf. Valsalva's test with nose held closed, p. 501). It is difficult or impossible to equalize these pressures if the channels by which the middle ear and paranasal sinuses communicate with the throat are blocked (for example, when the mucous membranes are swollen by a cold). In such cases *pressure equilibration* can be achieved only by an outward bulging of the eardrum (until it bursts) and/or by further filling of the mucous membranes with blood until they swell painfully and tear.

Oxygen shortage following ascent. If a diver holding his breath stays deep underwater as long as he thinks he can resist the need to breathe, he must necessarily become unconscious when he ascends. The ambient pressure increase during the descent has elevated the alveolar P_{O_2} (Fig. 27-2), but this is an illusory advantage, for the reverse process occurs during the ascent. As the diver rises, the P_{O_2} in the lungs drops rapidly, soon reaching and passing the *critical hypoxia threshold* of 30–35 mm Hg (4.0–4.7 kPa; p. 667). The drop is especially severe near the surface, for in the last 10 m of the ascent the ambient pressure and hence the O_2 partial pressure is halved (see Fig. 27-2).

Diving with Equipment

There are three types of breathing apparatus: compressed-air, oxygen and mixed-gas devices.

Compressed-air equipment. This includes portable breathing equipment, hose-and-pump systems, or caissons. In all cases the pressure of the inspired air is matched to that of the surroundings, and the expired air is released into the water *(open system)*. The actual minute volume (BTPS, p. 561) corresponds roughly to that during equivalent exercise on land, but the minute volume converted STPD conditions rises considerably with increasing depth underwater (and hence pressure), revealing an increased air requirement. The *work of breathing* (p. 559) is increased because of the greater viscosity of compressed air.

Rapture of the deep. The greater the depth and the longer the duration of a dive, the more nitrogen becomes dissolved in the tissues. Under normal atmospheric pressures nitrogen dissolved in the body is inert, but at depths of 40 m or more the concentrations present in the tissues can, depending on the situation and the susceptibility of the diver, cause intoxication symptoms *(euphoria,* but also *anxiety),* serious mistakes and even unconsciousness. Therefore *one should never go below 50 m with compressed-air equipment.*

Decompression. As the ambient pressure falls during the ascent care must be taken to equilibrate the pressures in the body cavities filled with compressed air, if **barotrauma** is to be avoided. For example, if a diver using such a device rises from 50 m underwater to the surface with glottis closed, the lung is stretched until it tears and air enters the vascular system *(air embolism).* Moreover, *inert gases* (e.g., N_2) stored in the tissues must be gradually removed from storage and breathed out; if decompression is too rapid they form *bubbles* in the blood and tissues, in much the same way as bubbles are formed when a bottle of soda water is opened. The ascent and emergence must be done systematically and slowly, in stages (cf. decompression tables [3]). Only during the time within which the tissue concentrations critical for bubble formation have not yet been reached *(zero time)* is it advisable to emerge immediately; this is the case in almost all kinds of breath-hold diving and in all dives no deeper than 10 m. Decompression injury is also observed when a prolonged dive is followed by a rapid ascent above ground (e.g., in an airplane).

Oxygen devices. Self-contained breathing apparatus can also provide pure oxygen. In a *closed system* (the principle of recirculating devices) the oxygen-rich exhaled air can be rebreathed if the carbon dioxide it contains is removed by an absorbent material (p. 620). Such apparatus enables *prolonged diving* but is unsuitable for sport, because at depths below about 7 m pure oxygen (P_{O_2} = 172 kPa or 1,292 mm Hg) is toxic to the central nervous system; symptoms of *acute oxygen poisoning* (p. 610) include nausea, convulsions and unconsciousness, accompanied by damage to the alveolar membrane. Because they are so hazardous, oxygen-recirculation devices are used only for special purposes (by "frogmen", for instance). – When compressed air is breathed, *hyperoxia damage* can be incurred at depths of ca. 74 m or more.

Mixed-gas devices of the closed type can be used at lower depths; here pure oxygen is mixed either with compressed air or with helium. When compressed air is used dives can be deeper than 7 m, whereas the mixture with helium gives protection against nitrogen narcosis. For dives to 70 m or more, however, the mixture must contain less than the normal amount of oxygen in order to avoid hyperoxic injury.

Orientation under Water

Vision. The *light intensity* decreases rapidly with depth under water; even under favorable conditions it is permanently night at 100 m. Without diving goggles, the cornea/air interface becomes a cornea/water interface, which has different refractive properties. As a result, only objects close to the eye are in focus. *Diving goggles* eliminate this effect but narrow the field of view and, because of the refraction of rays incident at an angle, cause objects to appear smaller and further away. Furthermore, objects lateral to the visual axis appear distorted, though divers soon become accustomed to this effect.

Hearing. Sound propagates more rapidly in water than in the air (ca. 1,450 m/s instead of 330 m/s). Therefore underwater sound sources appear nearer than they actually are. Moreover, because of the shortened interaural delay (pp. 295f.) *auditory localization* becomes practically impossible.

Vestibular system. If the *eardrum* is defective water can enter the middle ear and cause caloric stimulation of the horizontal semicircular canal, which interferes with spatial orientation (p. 283). A diver who panics in this situation is in danger of his life.

Rules for diving. Under water many otherwise innocuous events and situations can present a danger. Two of the 10 most important diving rules [17], in particular, should be taken to heart by all divers, even the unambitious amateur:
1. Never dive alone!
2. Never dive when you have a cold (for fear of barotrauma)!

27.3. Climate and Room Ventilation

Climate

Climate is of interest to the physician in both a *therapeutic* context (the influences of the sun's rays, dust-poor air and lowered air pressure on humans) and with respect to the effects of *air conditioners* (devices to regulate the temperature and humidity of indoor air). Air conditioning is an example of applied physiology inasmuch as the indoor climate is designed on the basis of what is known about human thermal balance, taking into account the need for fresh air in closed rooms.

The conditions for comfort. The basic load-determining factors for the thermal balance of people in air are the *ambient temperature, relative humidity, wind velocity* and *radiation.* Depending on clothing, level of physical activity and individual predisposition, a person's subjective reactions to these factors can range over various intermediate feelings between "comfortable" and "uncomfortable" (cf. pp. 631f.). The psychologically defined *comfort zone* is in the region of the physiologically defined *neutral temperature* (cf. p. 627). There are distinct differences between the conditions for comfort, depending on whether one is in air or immersed in water, as well as on the clothes one is wearing (Table 27-4). The pro-

Table 27-4. Approximate neutral temperatures (or those felt to be comfortable) for an adult human in various conditions. (Modified from [13]; see also pp. 631f.)

Ambient medium	Other conditions	Clothing	Temperature range
Air	No wind, 40–50% humidity, physical rest, neutral radiation conditions	Normal street clothes	20–22 °C
		Nude, bathing suit	28–30 °C
Water	Rest (bathtub)	Nude, bathing suit	35.5–36 °C
	Swimming, 0.4 m/s	Nude, bathing suit	28 °C

cesses of heat and cold adaptation are described on pp. 640f..

Effects of cold. Exposure to excessively low temperatures can produce two kinds of damage, either separately or together.
Local cold injury. At temperatures below +4 °C the peripheral blood vessels become strongly constricted; as a result, parts of the body such as the nose, ears, fingers and toes are no longer adequately nourished. Tissue death *(necrosis)* under these conditions is painless, because at such low temperatures nerve conduction is impaired (cold anesthesia). The recommended therapy is rapid rewarming; massage should be avoided due to the danger of tissue destruction.
General hypothermia. As a result of the thermoregulatory peripheral vasoconstriction at low temperatures, the normal perfusion is restricted to central organs such as heart and CNS, whereas the perfusion of limbs and peripheral organs decreases more and more. Despite this progressive *circulatory centralization,* eventually the brain and heart also cool down; below a core temperature of about 30 °C one becomes unconscious, and below about 28 °C ventricular fibrillation occurs. When someone is discovered to be in a state of hypothermia, nothing should be done to cause vasodilation or muscle-pump effects (p. 500) that would set the peripheral blood into circulation too rapidly. The blood in the periphery is not only cold but also greatly altered by the diminished flow (e.g., lactate acidosis), and its rapid reentry into the central circulation would impair the function of heart and brain. Massage is contraindicated, and the hypothermic person should not run to get warm; even walking can be lethal in such cases. The simplest safe form of assistance is to wrap the patient in heat-reflecting foil and blankets, so that the body's own heat production provides slow, gentle warming.

The consequences of general hypothermia are illustrated by the survival times of people who have fallen overboard into water at different temperatures (Fig. 27-3). Water below +20 °C cools the body very rapidly, because the heat conductivity of water is about 24 times greater than that of air. Survival times like those in Fig. 27-3 also apply to people drenched in rainstorms, because evaporation from wet clothing in the wind withdraws considerable amounts of heat from the body.

Effects of heat. Extreme heat can cause circulatory collapse and heatstroke or sunstroke (see p. 642). Cutaneous vasodilation can bring about *heat collapse* – particularly when the body is at rest – if the rectal temperature rises to as little as 38.0–38.3 °C. Physical activity counteracts the tendency to collapse, in spite of the greater heat production, due to the accompanying constriction of the cutaneous vessels (cf. Fig. 26-12) and increased blood pressure (Fig. 26-6). During work in the heat, therefore, the danger of *heat stroke* is greater; this state is characterized by a breakdown of central nervous regulation when the brain temperature exceeds 40 °C. Useful countermeasures are *elevation of the legs* in case of heat collapse, and lowering the body temperature in heat stroke, by external *cooling* and prevention of further warming. Extreme cooling of the skin is of little use, however, because then the blood flow through the skin becomes so slight that the cooling effect does not extend sufficiently to the body core.
Local heat application can cause thermal skin damage. Special care should be taken with anesthetized patients and those with peripheral nerve damage (e.g., paraplegics), who can be injured by temperatures as low as 37 °C.

Climatology. *Medical climatology* is concerned with the healing action of a great variety of climatic elements, such as air purity, temperature and humidity, and the effects of precipitation, cloud, wind and solar radiation, its ultraviolet component in particular. The *high-altitude climate* is characterized by intense solar radiation, dry air and low oxygen; in the *maritime climate,*

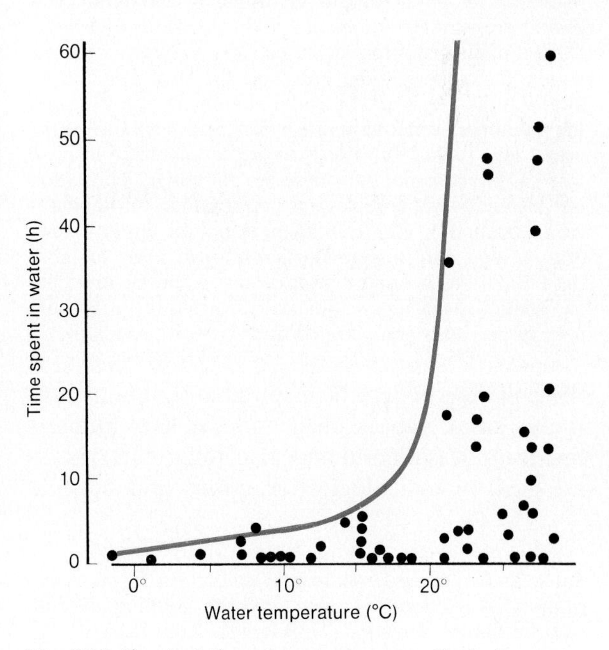

Fig. 27-3. Survival times humans in water. Each *dot* represents an individual who was rescued alive after spending the indicated amount of time in water at the indicated temperature. The *curve* marks the limiting time for survival as a function of water temperature. (Form [15])

the aerosol content of the air is one of the significant factors. The climate effects on the skin are categorized as *thermal* and *actinic;* the actinic stimuli are those related to solar radiation, especially the UV component.

The *action* of these elements of climate is twofold. On one hand, the climatic stimuli elicit specific autonomic and endocrine as well as unspecific readjustments. On the other, pure air provides an environment with few allergens. Finally, mental effects can play a role – for instance, in a stay at a health resort.

Respiratory Air and Room Ventilation

Respiratory gas fractions in closed rooms. It is commonly thought that when crowds of people occupy closed rooms, an oxygen deficiency develops that leads to inattention and tiredness. This is not the case; sufficient oxygen is provided even by the air exchange through cracks around the doors and windows, and still more if a mechanical ventilation system is operating. O_2 deficiency could occur only in hermetically sealed rooms, and then only after several hours.

Example: In an airtight room of 400 m^3 containing 100 people, the initial oxygen content is about 85 m^3, and the rate of consumption by all the people is ca. 1,800 l/h. Hence the O_2 fraction decreases by $0.45 \cdot 10^{-2}$/h, and after 9 h the O_2 fraction in the room would still be about 0.17. This reduction of 0.04 is not crucial for either respiratory regulation or physiological performance; comparable O_2 partial pressures are found at 1,700 m above sea level.
On the other hand, the increased CO_2 fraction in the air within the room would be noticeable. Given an RQ of 0.83, after 9 h the CO_2 fraction would amount to $3.3 \cdot 10^{-2}$ and the pulmonary ventilation rate would be double that at the outset (see Table 27-5). Furthermore, an increased inspiratory CO_2 fraction not only increases pulmonary ventilation but also impairs psychological performance. Although at values around $3 \cdot 10^{-2}$ CO_2 there is only a minor deterioration, and only for certain tasks, an increase to more than $5 \cdot 10^{-2}$ CO_2 in the inspired air would be expected to produce distinct psychological disturbances, especially with respect to cognitive-intellectual performance [16].

Air pollution. When the inspired air contains pollutant gases, vapors, dust and the like, humans find it unpleasant and may also suffer pathophysiological or toxicological reactions and become ill. Medical research in the field of occupational health has led to the establishment of "maximal allowable concentrations (MAC)" for a great variety of substances.

Table 27-5. Increased pulmonary ventilation $\dot{V}_E$ as inspiratory CO_2 fraction F_{ICO_2} rises, and the resulting alveolar CO_2 partial pressures P_{ACO_2}. (Averages from [14])

F_{ICO_2}	$(\cdot 10^{-2})$	0.03	2	4	6
$\dot{V}_E$	(l/min)	6.6	9.2	15.5	30.5
P_{ACO_2}	(mm Hg)	38	41	44	50

The MAC is the highest concentration of a substance that should be permitted in the air at the workplace; this is the concentration that, as far as is known at present, will neither impair the health of the workers nor cause them unacceptable annoyance even with repeated and long-term exposure (as a rule, 8 hours per day, with an average of 40 work hours per week) [1].
As examples of German MAC values, that for CO_2 is $0.5 \cdot 10^{-2}$ m^3 CO_2/m^3 air, or 5,000 ppm (parts per million, or ml/m^3); for *CO,* 30 ppm; for the solvent *tetrachloroethylene,* 50 ppm and for *nitrobenzene,* 1 ppm; and for *mercury,* 0.01 ppm [1]. An example of particulate air pollutants that can cause illness is *quartz dust;* this reaches the alveoli only if the particles are less than 5 μm in diameter, but if exposure is prolonged it can cause severe lung disease.

Room ventilation and air conditioning [8]. Many work areas and rooms for leisure activities are equipped with ventilating and air-conditioning apparatus. The purpose of these devices is to avoid giving people the unpleasant subjective sensation that the air is "bad."

"Bad air" is not equivalent to oxygen-poor air. Rather, it is air containing perceptible amounts of the volatile substances that emanate from people and their clothing and/or of cigarette smoke, machine exhaust fumes and so on. Conversely, *"good air"* is characterized not by a high oxygen fraction but by a very low content of those substances. Even the air in a forest does not have a particularly high O_2 content; the amounts of CO_2 available in the air for photosynthesis and the rate at which photosynthesis proceeds are far too low to permit a noticeable rise in the O_2 fraction.
It is uncommon for absorption filters to be used to regenerate the air. Usually it is regenerated by adding fresh air from outdoors, in sufficient amounts that the concentration of the undesirable substances is kept low. The CO_2 fraction in the indoor air has proved a useful indicator of the amount of fresh air that should be added. Values up to $0.15 \cdot 10^{-2}$ *(Pettenkofer's number)* are neither annoying nor injurious to humans under the usual conditions. If the indoor air is adjusted according to this guideline, considerable energy can be saved on air conditioning (by optimizing the amount of added fresh air).

Air-conditioning systems. Small air conditioners simply cool the air and dry it (because water vapor condenses in the refrigeration unit); both modifications make the air more cooling to people and thus create a tolerable environment in high ambient temperatures. More elaborate devices match the temperature and humidity of the air to preset values. In special areas such as operating theaters and microcomponent assembly rooms, the air can also be made germ- and dust-free; in this case care should be taken that the air filters and humidifiers do not become breeding grounds for bacteria. The *thermal comfort* of ventilated or air-conditioned rooms is fundamentally dependent on the avoidance of *drafts,* air movements at a speed of over 0.1 m/s.

27.4 Noise, Vibration and Acceleration

Noise

Noise is sound that is undesired, disturbing or damaging to the auditory system. Its effects can be categorized as *aural* (related to the ear) or *extraaural*. The aural actions cause *reversible deafening* (a temporary raising of the auditory threshold or lowering of the audiogram curve, cf. p. 297), or *permanent damage*. Among the extraaural effects of noise are interference with acoustic communication, deterioration of performance capacity and other psychological factors, and troubled sleep, which affects many physiological functions. Noise is a typical contributor to the load in many places of work. Its intensity can be measured with *sound level meters*, usually in dB (A) (see p. 288); in evaluating noise, the duration of exposure should be taken into account. The *long-term noise level* (average level) is expressed with respect to a work shift of 8 h or, in the case of environmental noises, to 16 day hours or 8 night hours. Examples of the effects of noise on humans are given in Table 27-6.

Table 27-6. Classification of noise loads and their effects on humans. (Modified from [6])

Noise level	Sound level dB (A)	Effects
I	30–65	Psychological reactions, sometimes psychological disturbances
II	65–90	Like level I plus physiological reactions, of autonomic regulatory systems in particular (elevated heart rate and blood pressure, peripheral vasoconstriction, reflex increase in muscle tone, disturbed sleep)
III	90–120	Like levels I and II plus reversible deafening, permanent hearing difficulty after years of exposure
IV	>120	Like levels I–III plus nerve-cell damage

Table 27-7. Sample values of maximal noise levels acceptable in various neighborhoods, dB (A), according to German standards authority (VDI-Norm 2058, Blatt 1)

	Day	Night
Health resorts	45	35
Purely residential areas	50	35
Mixed areas (e.g., inner cities)	60	45

The *effects of noise* are first felt in the psychological realm; depending on the situation and the nature of the noise, even low intensities can be experienced as bothersome or disturbing. People are particularly sensitive when it comes to their nighttime rest – for instance, when it is disturbed by cars, trains or airplanes. 35 dB (A) is regarded as the desirable upper limit for night noise (Table 27-7).
In addition to mental and emotional responses, noise also triggers diverse *physiological* reactions, which in the extreme can lead to manifest disorders of the auditory organ and to psychosomatic disturbances. The degree of damage is determined by individual predisposition as well as by the intensity, quality and duration of the noise. Among people exposed to noise at an intensity of 90 dB (A), with no sudden, explosive sounds, for 8 h per day, after 10 years about 5% of the individuals would be expected to begin to be hard of hearing. Those exposed to 85 dB (A) or more should wear earplugs or other sound-damping devices, and regular medical examinations should be required if the noise level is 90 dB (A) or higher.

Vibration

Oscillations (of machinery, for example) are transmitted to the trunk and head through legs, buttocks or hands and arms. The entire body and, depending on their *resonant frequencies* (f_o), the individual organs are set into oscillation. For the whole body of a seated person f_o is 4 to 7 Hz; the resonant frequencies of some organs and parts of the body are given in Table 27-8.
Vibrational loads are imposed mainly on *vehicle drivers* of all kinds. Such loads can cause *acute* deterioration of performance as well as generalized discomfort or specific pains; the control of fine movement and (due to eyeball oscillations) visual acuity can also be impaired. *Chronic* damage affects chiefly the joints, especially the elbow and the joints of the vertebral column. People who operate power saws or devices with similar frequencies typically develop circulatory disturbances in fingers and hands.

Acceleration

Modern vehicles generate both positive and negative forces of acceleration, which can act along

Table 27-8. Resonance frequencies (f_0) of various parts of the body and organs in humans; oscillation in the direction of the long axis of the body. From [2]

Part of body (lying down)	f_0 (Hz)	Part of body (seated)	f_0 (Hz)
Head	1 –4	Vertebral column	3– 5
Abdomen	1.5–6	Stomach	4– 5
Foot	1 –3	Eye	20–25

all three axes of the human body. Acceleration on a line passing through the center of the earth is called a *g load*. The accelerations encountered during vehicular transport can cause illnesses known as *kinetoses* – or, more commonly, motion (or sea, air, space etc.) sickness.

Transport by automobile can give rise to *car sickness*, especially if the velocity often changes. Because the acceleration during braking is usually greater than that while a vehicle is picking up speed, when *patients* are transported lying down the head should always be toward the front of the vehicle. In the reverse position, during braking too much blood would be driven into the lower part of the extrathoracic low-pressure system, with consequences resembling those of orthostatic collapse (p. 528).

Flying involves particularly large forces of acceleration. They act on a seated passenger in the fronto-occipital direction when the velocity of forward flight changes, in various directions during flight through turbulence, and in the direction of the long axis of the body during flight along a curve. Loads as great as 10 g (ten times the acceleration due to gravity) have been measured in jet fighters. These changes in acceleration are usually sudden and brief; they have several effects: (i) *airsickness*, (ii) *sensory illusions* with respect to visual and vestibular orientation in space, and (iii) *a critical drop in arterial blood pressure* when acceleration in the direction of the body's long axis shifts blood out of the intrathoracic part of the low-pressure system (cf. orthostatic collapse, pp. 528f.).

During **space flight** the near-absence of the pull of gravity *(microgravity)* induces diverse physiological reactions: (i) *space sickness*, with nausea and sometimes vomiting and a feeling of being seriously ill, especially in the first three days, (ii) *reduced blood volume* because the initial overfilling of the intrathoracic parts of the low-pressure system elicits compensatory regulation (reversed orthostasis), (iii) *muscular atrophy*, of the postural muscles in particular, and (iv) *calcium loss* from the bones and disturbed electrolyte balance. Locomotion and work require greatly modified *motor patterns*, which take time to learn.

27.5 References

Textbooks and Handbooks

1. Deutsche Forschungsgemeinschaft (DFG), ed.: Maximale Arbeitsplatzkonzentrationen und biologische Arbeitsstofftoleranzwerte 1985. Weinheim: VCH-Verlagsgesellschaft 1985
2. Dupuis, H., Zerlett, G.: Beanspruchung des Menschen durch mechanische Schwingungen – Forschungsbericht Ganz-Körper-Schwingungen. Schriftenreihe des Hauptverbandes der gewerblichen Berufsgenossenschaften e.V. (ed.), Bonn: im Eigenverlag 1984
3. Ehm, O.F.: Tauchen – noch sicherer! Rüschlikon-Zürich-Stuttgart-Wien: A. Müller 1984
4. Grossmann, K.: Flugmedizin –Leitfaden für die Praxis. Köln: Deutscher Ärtze-Verlag 1985
5. Hurtado, A.: Animals in high altitudes: resident man. In: Dill, D.B., ed.: Handbook of Physiology. Sect. 4: Adaptation on the environment. Washington: Amer. Physiol. Soc. 1964
6. Lehmann, G.: Praktische Arbeitsphysiologie. Stuttgart: Thieme 1962
7. Loewy, A.: Physiologie des Höhenklimas. Berlin: Springer 1932
8. Recknagel, H., Sprenger, E., Hönmann, W.: Taschenbuch für Heizung und Klimatechnik. München-Wien: Oldenbourg 1985
9. Reichel, G., Bolt, H.M., Hettinger, Th., Selenka, F., Ulmer, H.-V., Ulmer, W.T., eds.: Grundlagen der Arbeitsmedizin. Stuttgart-Berlin-Köln-Mainz: Kohlhammer 1985
10. Ruff, S., Strughold, H.: Grundriß der Luftfahrtmedizin: München: Barth 1957
11. Stegemann, J.: Leistungsphysiologie. Stuttgart-New York: Thieme 1984
12. Valentin, H., Klosterkötter, W., Lehnert, G., Petry, H., Rutenfranz, J., Weber, G., Wenzel, H.G., Wittgens, H.: Arbeitsmedizin. Bd. 1 und 2, Stuttgart: Thieme 1979
13. Wenzel, H.G., Piekarski, C.: Klima und Arbeit. Bayerisches Staatsministerium für Arbeit und Sozialordnung (ed.), München: im Eigenverlag 1982

Original Papers and Reviews

14. Lambertsen, C.J.: Carbon dioxide and respiration in acid-base homeostasis. Anesthesiology *21*, 642 (1960)
15. Molnar, G.W.: Survival of hypothermia by men immersed in the ocean. J. Amer. Med. Ass. *131*, 1046 (1946)
16. Schaad, G., Kleinhanss, G., Piekarski, C., Seebass, M., Gorges, W.: Ergonomische Aspekte zur Optimierung der Versorgung von Schutzräumen mit Atemluft in Notsituationen. Wehrmed. Mschr. *30*, 13 (1986)
17. Seemann, K.: Sporttauchen – Hinweise und Ratschläge eines Taucherarztes. Dt. Ärztebl. *75*, 1701 (1978)
18. Stigler, R.: Die Kraft unserer Inspirationsmuskulatur. Pflügers Arch. *139*, 234 (1911)

VIII
Nutrition, Digestion and Excretion

28 Nutrition

H.-V. Ulmer

The food one eats is required for both structure and function of the organism, and nutrition is also of importance in preventive medicine. At one time deficiency symptoms resulting from inadequate nutrition were the chief concern, but today more attention must be paid to the consequences of overeating. *Overeating* leads to *obesity,* which is often associated with the *"diseases of civilization"* and with a shortened statistical life expectancy. For this reason, obesity is regarded as one of the avoidable epidemiological risk factors in highly industrialized countries.

Eating habits are seldom decided rationally; since early in human history, the acquisition and consumption of food have been surrounded by tradition and ritual. The socio-cultural aspect of eating manifests itself in many ways – for example, the Holy Communion and fasting rules, the association of special foods with special occasions, the preference in many groups for rotundity as a symbol of wealth and status. It is not surprising that efforts to direct eating habits on the basis of nutritional physiology are often opposed by the "doctrines" of fanatics, sectarians and profit-seekers. However, the correctness of current nutritional concepts is documented by the fact that entirely synthetic foods, designed according to the principles of nutritional physiology, can bestow health and high performance even in the long term.

28.1 Foods: Their Composition and Functions

Foods consist of the energy-containing foodstuffs plus vitamins, salts, trace elements, spices, crude fiber and water. Food intake is regulated principally by the general sensations *hunger* and *thirst* (see pp. 314ff.).

Foodstuffs

The energy-containing components of food are the **proteins, fats** and **carbohydrates;** if the supply of these is insufficient, undernourishment results, and if it is excessive one becomes overnourished. The foodstuffs *provide energy* to the organism if they are metabolized, forming substances with a lower energy content. The amount of energy released per gram is called the **biological fuel value** (p. 619); the fuel value of fats is more than twice as great as those of proteins and carbohydrates (Table 28-1; 1 kJ ≈ 0.24 kcal; cf. p. 614).

Table 28-1. Biological fuel value (kJ/g) of foodstuffs. The values for fats, proteins and carbohydrates apply to a mixed Central European diet; 1 kJ ≈ 0.24 kcal

Foodstuff	Fats	Proteins	Carbohydrates	Glucose	Ethyl-alcohol
kJ/g	38.9	17.2	17.2	15.7	29.7

Isodynamic effect. Foodstuffs are "isodynamic" in the sense that as far as the energy they provide is concerned they are *mutually interchangeable.* However, foodstuffs are used not only for *functional metabolism* but also for *structural metabolism* (synthesis of secretions or substances of which the body is composed); for the latter purpose, certain minimal quantities of proteins, fats and carbohydrates must be made available.

Diet-induced thermogenesis. *After food has been consumed the metabolic rate increases.* This phenomenon is ascribed to a special effect of the particular foodstuff concerned and is called diet-induced thermogenesis. Consumption of a mixed meal raises the metabolic rate by *about 6%.* The increase following *protein ingestion* is much greater than that associated with carbohydrates or fats. One reason could be that the resynthesis of 1 mol ATP during breakdown of foodstuffs requires more protein energy than fat or carbohydrate energy [9].

In rats and mice a *diet-induced thermogenesis* has also been found to result from activation of the brown adipose tissue (p. 626); this mechanism is of no importance in adult humans.

Table 28-2. Energy content and composition of some foods, as of 1980. In certain cases there may be considerable deviations from these values, depending on composition (concealed fat, in particular) and preparation. 1 kJ ≈ 0.24 kcal; CH = carbohydrates. (From Polensky, as cited in [4])

Food	Energy kJ/100g	Proteins (%)	Fats (%)	CH (%)	Water (%)	Crude fiber (%)
Fruit	190	0.7	0.3	10.5	86	2.3
Vegetables	85	1.6	0.2	3.0	93	2.0
Potatoes	330	2.1	0.1	16.8	79	2.0
Nuts	2,680	16.9	57	8.2	7	10.1
Meat	860	19	13	0	68	0
Bread	1,020	7.3	1.4	47	40	4.3
Butter	3,220	0.6	82.6	0.6	16	0
Cheese	1,340	23.7	22.3	2.8	51	0
Sausage	1,500	12.9	30.4	1.1	55	0
Drinking milk	256	3.3	3.1	4.7	89	0
Fruit juices	186	0.3	0.1	10.9	89	0
Beer	200	0.5	0	4.8	95	0

Foodstuff content. There are many tables showing the *energy and foodstuff content* of various kinds of food. Because changing methods of animal feeding and agriculture can have a marked effect on the composition of food, one should use the most recent tables available (e.g., [4]; cf. Table 28-2). The *water content* of food should also be noted; in making rough estimates of energy content it is often overlooked.

Proteins consist of *amino acids* and are required for the synthesis of substances *indispensable for normal structure and function of the body.* It is absolutely necessary that the protein in food contain the **essential amino acids,** amino acids that the body *cannot,* or not adequately, *synthesize* for itself. Most of the protein consumed by humans is used in *structural metabolism* – for the synthesis and restructuring of biological materials such as musculature, enzymes and plasma proteins – and thus cannot be replaced by fats or carbohydrates.
Proteins are found in both **animal** and **plant** food. Animal protein is obtained chiefly from *meat, fish, milk* and *dairy products,* and *eggs. Bread* and *potatoes* contain appreciable amounts of plant protein, and there are small amounts in almost all kinds of vegetables and fruit (cf. Table 28-2).

Fats are composed primarily of a mixture of different *triglycerides,* triesters of glycerine and fatty acids. A distinction is made between *saturated* and *unsaturated* fatty acids. There are certain unsaturated fatty acids that the body requires and cannot synthesize for itself *(essential fatty acids).*
The fats absorbed are either oxidized to supply *functional metabolism* or deposited in the tissues as an *energy store.* Unlike fat, protein and carbohydrate can be stored in the body only in small amounts; whatever is not used in functional or structural metabolism is converted to fat and stored in that form or is excreted. Among the reactions for which the essential fatty acids are required is the synthesis of *phospholipids* – components of cell membranes and mitochondria – and prostaglandins. The essential fatty acid most important for humans is **linoleic acid.**
Fats are unavoidable components of *almost all food of animal origin* – in the important protein sources meat, fish, milk, dairy products and eggs. They are also found in plant seeds, such as nuts. Plant fats differ from most animal fats in their high content of unsaturated fatty acids, though these are no longer present in hydrogenated (artificially hardened) plant fats.
About half of the fat in food is **visible** (pure fats such as oils, lard, butter and the layers of fat in bacon and other meats), and the rest is **concealed** – distributed in droplets too small to be seen with the naked eye, particularly in meat, sausage and cheese. Modern methods of feeding animals for market encourage the deposition of *concealed fat,* and as a result the fat content of the average Central European diet is too high. Altogether, it is often difficult for the consumer to achieve an energetically balanced and qualitatively desirable diet.
Cholesterol and lipoproteins. The presence of excessive cholesterol in the blood, above the recommended maximum of 220 mg/dl serum *(hypercholesterolemia)* is under discussion as a *risk factor,* along with obesity. It has been shown statistically that hypercholesterolemia and certain forms of hyperlipoproteinemia are correlated with an increased incidence of arteriosclerosis, cardiac infarction and stroke – and thus with a decreased life expectancy.
Cholesterol is found only in animals. The average amount of cholesterol consumed in food (eggs, milk fat, fat meat) per day is 750 mg. Because the ability of the human intestine to absorb it is limited and the production of cholesterol by the liver (ca. 1 g/day) varies, depending on the amount eaten, the relationships between the intake of cholesterol and its concentration in the blood are complicated. Furthermore, the *blood cholesterol concentration* depends not only on the intake of cholesterol itself but also on other fats that are eaten; saturated fatty acids

raise the cholesterol level and unsaturated fatty acids lower it. Congenital or aquired disorders of fat metabolism can be identified by the typical protein patterns in the blood (very-low-density; low-density and high-density lipoproteins; cf. p. 407).

Carbohydrates. The basic carbohydrate molecules are the *monosaccharides* (simple sugars); compounds of 2 or more monosaccharides are called *di-, oligo- or polysaccharides.* Most of the carbohydrate in the human diet is in the form of *plant starch* (a polysaccharide). Carbohydrates are stored in the body as *glycogen* (animal starch), particularly in muscle and liver.
The monosaccharide *glucose* (grape sugar) is the element of which starches are composed and is a component of the ordinary household sugar *(sucrose),* a disaccharide with one molecule each of glucose and fructose. *Lactose,* the typical disaccharide in milk, is composed of one glucose and one galactose molecule.
Carbohydrates are the chief *sources of energy* for the cells. The energy requirements of the brain are met almost exclusively by glucose; striated skeletal muscle, however, can metabolize fatty acids if the carbohydrate supply is inadequate. Glucose serves not only as a fuel; it is also a building block for the synthesis of many important compounds.
The carbohydrates upon which humans depend are almost entirely of *vegetable origin.* In addition to the digestible carbohydrates they contain, fruit, green vegetables, potatoes, grain and legumes also include indigestible carbohydrate such as *cellulose fiber* (crude fiber).

Table 28-3. *Fat-soluble vitamins.* Classification, typical sources and biological functions ([2, 4, 6]; for requirements and deficiency symptoms see Table 28-7, p. 684)

Name and synonyms	Typical sources	Typical biological functions
Vitamin A Retinol Axerophthol	Liver and cod-liver oil, milk fat	Essential for all epithelial cells and the growth of the skeleton
Provitamins: β-carotene, Carotenoids	β-carotene in carrots and many plants	Vitamin A aldehyde (retinene) is a component of rhodopsin (visual purple)
Vitamin D group (antirachitic vitamins) Vitamin D_2 Calciferol Vitamin D_3 Cholecalciferol Vitamin D_4 Dihydrocalciferol	Liver and cod-liver oil, fish, milk fat, egg yolk	Absorption and metabolism of Ca^{2+}, interactions with parathyroid hormone, calcification of bones
Vitamin E Tocopherol	In almost all food, especially plant oils	Antioxidant (e.g., in the metabolism of the unsaturated fatty acids)
Vitamin K (antihemorrhagic vitamin) Vitamin K_1 Phylloquinone Vitamin K_2 Menaquinone β-phylloquinone	Vegetables, liver, is also formed by intestinal bacteria	Involved in synthesis of blood-clotting factors, especially prothrombin

Vitamins

The food components called **vitamins** are organic substances *necessary in small quantities for normal function of the body, which the body cannot, or not adequately, synthesize for itself;* their energy content is unimportant. **Antivitamins** are substances that act as antagonists of certain vitamins, by interfering with their absorption or metabolism.
The vitamins are extremely diverse in chemical structure (cf. biochemistry textbooks). They are classified as either **fat-soluble or water-soluble.** When vitamins were first being discovered they were named by letters of the alphabet, but the more recently discovered vitamins are known by chemical names.

Vitamins have *highly specific functions in cellular metabolism.* They are often elements in enzyme systems or have a complex effect on a system, such as that of vitamin C on connective tissue (for further details see Tables 28-3 and 28-4).
Vitamins are found in *food of both plant and animal origin.* The vitamin content of a given food can vary widely, depending on the conditions under which it was produced, stored and prepared for the table. Some vitamins – for example, vitamins A and C – are sensitive to light, heat or pH changes, especially when dissolved in infusion solutions. Certain kinds of food are especially rich in particular vitamins (Tables 28-3 and 28-4; cf. [4]). Not every vitamin must be obtained from the diet. Vitamin K, for example, is synthesized by the normal intestinal flora; other vitamins are synthesized in the body from certain amino acids or from precursors **(provitamins),** though not always in sufficient amounts. Provitamins are especially important in the vitamin-D group

Table 28-4. *Water-soluble vitamins.* Classification, typical sources and biological functions ([2, 4, 6]; for requirements and deficiency symptoms see Table 28-9, p. 685)

Name and synonyms	Typical sources	Typical biological functions
Vitamin B_1 Thiamin Aneurine	Pork, whole-grain products	Component of pyruvate cocarboxylase
Vitamin B_2 Riboflavin Lactoflavin	Milk, meat, eggs, fish, whole-grain products	Component of the flavin enzymes (yellow respiratory enzymes)
Vitamin B_6 group Pyridoxine group (pyridoxol, pyridoxal, pyridoxamine)	Meat, fish, milk, legumes, whole-grain products	Coenzyme of various enzyme systems (e.g., amino-acid decarboxylase, transaminases, dehydratases, desulfhydrases)
Vitamin B_{12} Cyanocobalamine	Liver, other *animal* foods	Component of enzymes (methylation, nucleic-acid metabolism)
Other vitamins in the B group:		
Biotin (vitamin H)	Liver, kidney, egg yolk, soybeans (also formed by intestinal bacteria)	Component of enzymes (carboxylases, carboxyl transferases, deamination)
Folic acid group Folic acid (= pteroylglutamic acid, tetrahydrofolic acid)	Vegetables, whole-grain products meat, milk, soybeans	Metabolism of one-carbon fragments, purine and methionine synthesis
Niacin Nicotinic acid Niacinamide	Meat, fish, milk	Coenzyme of many dehydrogenases (e.g., NADH)
Pantothenic acid	In almost all foods	Component of coenzyme A
Vitamin C Ascorbic acid	Fresh fruit and vegetables (esp. potatoes, citrus fruits, tomatoes, green peppers)	Important for formation of intercellular substances, involved in hydroxylation, component of ferritin
"Vitaminoids"		
Choline	In almost all foods	Fatty-acid transport
Inositol	In almost all animal and plant foods	Building blocks of inositol phosphatides, mitochondrial metabolism, cation transport

– ergosterol for D_2, 7-dehydrocholesterol for D_3, and 22-dihydroergosterol for D_4.

Fat-soluble vitamins (summarized in Table 28-3). The *vitamins A, D, E and K* are fat-soluble. Vitamin A can be formed in the body from *carotenoids* (provitamins). The effective members of the D group, vitamins D_2 and D_3, are synthesized in the skin from the provitamins ergosterol (from plants) and 7-dehydrocholesterol, in a photochemical reaction involving UV light.

Water-soluble vitamins (summarized in Table 28-4). The vitamins of the *B* group (B_1, B_2, B_6, B_{12}), biotin, the *folic acid* group, *niacin* and *niacinamide, pantothenic acid* and *vitamin C* are water-soluble. Many of the B vitamins are present in yeast, bran and liver. Foods of plant origin contain vitamin B_{12} only if they are fermented.

Antivitamins. These are found in various foods – for example, avidin (which binds biotin) in egg white and a thiaminase (which decomposes thiamin) in many kinds of raw fish. *Artificial antivitamins* are used for the therapeutic modification of certain biological processes. Coumarin derivatives (antivitamin K), for instance, lower the coagulability of the blood. Isoniazid, an antagonist of pyridoxal phosphate (the active derivative of vitamin B_6), inhibits the growth of the tuberculosis pathogen. Sulfanilamides are effective against bacterial infection because of their antagonistic action on p-aminobenzoic acid, a substance essential for bacterial growth.

Water, Salts, Trace Elements

Water. Most foods contain more than 50% water (Table 28-2). Among the common foods with less than this amount are bread, butter and cheese. To keep accurate track of the body's fluid balance, however, the water produced by metabolic processes must be taken into account as well as that consumed orally. Under resting conditions the body produces ca. 350 ml water per day.

Salts. Salts, like water, serve to maintain the internal milieu. One of the major prerequisites for unimpaired cell function is that the ionic composition and the pH of the body fluids be kept constant. The ions of greatest importance are the cations sodium, potassium, calcium and magnesium, and the anions chloride and phosphate (p. 404).

Trace elements. This category includes elements found in extremely small quantities both in the body and in food. They fall into three groups:

1. Elements with a known or suspected physiological function. Among these are **iron** (a component of heme), fluorine, iodine (component of the thyroid hormones), and such components of intracellular enzyme systems as copper, manganese, molybdenum and zinc.
2. Elements with a proved toxic effect. These include antimony, arsenic, lead, cadmium, mercury and thallium. Most of these elements are of particular importance in industrial toxicology.
3. Elements without physiological function, such as aluminum, boron, silver and tellurium.

Condiments and Crude Fiber

The category of *condiments* includes all the diverse aromatic substances that determine the taste and smell of food. These substances are not necessary for life, but their significance with regard to both *general well-being* and the *secretion of digestive juices* should not be underestimated. *Crude fiber* (dietary fiber) comprises the indigestible components of food. Chief among these substances are polysaccharides such as cellulose which reinforce the cell walls of plants and cannot be chemically decomposed in the human digestive tract. The significance of crude fiber is discussed on p. 690.

Residues

As foods are produced and stored they can acquire, whether by intent or accident, substances not directly necessary to man, which can have toxic effects if they are too abundant.

Medicines. The production of animal food today often involves treatment of the animals with medications for hygienic reasons or to accelerate growth to a marketable size. Because drugs can be stored in liver, fatty tissue and muscle, such residues may affect people who eat these products; for example, allergies, resistance to antibiotics and hormonal disturbances can result.

Metals. In addition to the toxic trace elements. metallic residues include radionuclides such as cesium^{137} and strontium^{90}.

Additives. Most of these are *flavorings, dyes* or *preservatives* introduced during the production of foods. Whatever the benefits of such substances, they should not be used without careful consideration. The carcinogenic effect of "butter yellow," for example, was demonstrated only after it had been in use for decades as a food coloring. The number of flavoring and coloring additives is vast, in the thousands. It is likely that most of them have no pharmacological effect, but they can cause allergic reactions in susceptible people.

Pesticides. These substances are used to protect plants and stored food. 4 categories are recognized: *insecticides* (against insects), *herbicides* (against weeds), *acaricides* (against mites) and *fungicides* (against fungi). Because some of them have been shown to be noxious to humans, maximal permissible levels for food have been established. Some pesticides (especially those that are fat-soluble) can be stored in the fat of animals; they are slow to leave the body and thus can have long-term effects. The plant products that offer the greatest pesticide threat to humans are fruit, vegetables and flour products; milk fat is the chief animal source.

28.2 Nutritional Requirements; Symptoms of Deficiency and Overdosage

Published figures concerning the required amounts of the individual components of food vary considerably, in part because of the difference between *requirement* and *recommended intake.* Data on nutritional requirements in the strict sense refer to metabolic equilibrium conditions, whereas recommendations as to the desirable intake often allow an extra "safety factor". The values given below are based on the recommendations of the German Society for Nutrition [6]. Recommendations of other nutritional boards occasionally differ slightly from one another. The amounts of particular nutrients required by an individual depend on a number of factors – age, sex, physical type, amount of exercise, stress, pregnancy. Because of this wide range of variability, tables of nutritional requirements always represent only *general guidelines.*
Deficiencies arise either because of inadequate *intake* or because the *requirement* has increased. In most deficiency states there is a combined lack of foodstuffs (proteins, fats, carbohydrates) and vitamins, salts or trace elements, as in *starvation* or *inadequate absorption.* But certain typical *deficiency diseases* (see Tables 28-7 and 28-9) result from the predominant lack of a single substance.
Nutritionists were once concerned primarily with the results of particular nutrient deficiencies, but they must now consider problems related to overdosage as well. The consequences of overdosage in general take the form of **obesity, hypervitaminoses** and **water and electrolyte intoxications.**

Foodstuffs

The organism's requirement for the three foodstuffs depends on its energy consumption. In addition, a *minimal amount* of each – proteins, fats and carbohydrates – is required for special purposes and cannot be replaced by either of the others (Table 28-5); the remainder can be replaced according to their isodynamic effect (p. 678). The disturbances resulting from protein deficiency are particularly severe.

Minimal requirements. Almost all the tissues in the body are continually being broken down and renewed or converted *(structural metabolism)*. This is not simply a matter of rearranging a fixed quantity of material; an additional supply is required. One reason is loss of certain substances from the body – for example, when epithelial cells are shed (from the intestinal surfaces and the skin). These losses mainly affect protein balance.

Protein balance. On a diet that supplies enough energy but contains no protein, a person loses 13–17 g protein per day. Even if this amount **(absolute protein minimum)** is added to the diet, the intake and loss of protein are still not in balance, for two reasons: 1. Protein consumption is followed by an increase in the rate of nitrogen excretion (a measure of protein loss), for reasons not yet explained. 2. Depending on the amino-acid composition of the protein in the diet, a variable fraction of it can be converted to body protein. That is, the value of proteins to man differs, according to their content of essential amino acids. The *biological value* of proteins can be expressed by the amount of human body protein that can be replaced by 100 g food protein. The biological value of animal proteins in this sense is 80–100 g – that is, from 100 g of animal protein 80–100 g of body protein can be synthesized. In the case of plant proteins the biological value averages only 60–70 g, because the amino acids essential to man are not present in the right proportions.
For protein balance to be maintained, a mixed diet must include 30–40 g protein per day **(protein-balance minimum).** Normally a state of protein balance exists when the amount of nitrogen ingested equals that excreted (the N_2 content of protein is ca. 16% by weight). It has been shown that although the balance minimum is adequate for survival, it does not suffice for normal physical performance capacity. For the body to be *optimally* supplied with protein a daily intake of *0.8 g protein per kg body weight* is recommended **(functional protein minimum),** of which about half should be of animal origin. Great care is required to design an adequate diet in which all the protein is of plant origin. When physical work is being done, during pregnancy and in severe illness the *daily* requirement is increased to as much as 2 g/kg; that of children and the aged is 1.2–1.5 g/kg body weight.

Minimal requirements of fats and carbohydrates. The minimal fat requirement is determined by the body's need for the fat-soluble vitamins fats contain (though the presence of bile acids suffices for these vitamins to be absorbed) and by the

Table 28-5. Foodstuffs. Recommended daily allowances for adult humans; symptoms of deficiency and overdosage

	Daily allowance [6]	Extra requirement	Depots and amounts stored	Deficiency symptoms	Overdosage symptoms
Proteins	0.8 g/kg body weight (must contain enough essential amino acids – e.g., at least half as animal protein)	Old people and children, 1.2–1.5 g/kg; for heavy work, muscle building, pregnancy and severe illness up to 2 g/kg body weight	Readily available pool 45 g (muscle 40 g, blood and liver 5 g)	Starvation edema, susceptibility to infection, apathy, muscular atrophy, impaired development of children	Predominance of putrefaction in intestine, predisposed individuals, gout due to excessive intake of meat and offal
Carbohydrates	At least 100 g (for the brain); alternative: 200 g protein (gluconeogenesis)	During physical work	300–400g glycogen	Underweight, reduced performance capacity, metabolic disturbances, hypoglycemia, ketosis	Predominance of fermentation in intestine, adipositas
Fats (a) saturated and monounsaturated fatty acids	(a) and (b): 25–30% of energy requirement	During physical work	Extremely variable	Underweight, reduced performance capacity, deficiency symptoms from inadequate absorption of fat-soluble vitamins	Hypertriglyceridemia and hypercholesterolemia with subsequent sclerosis, adipositas
(b) essential fatty acids	About 1/3 of total fat intake	During physical work	Extremely variable	Hematuria, changes in skin and mitochondria, metabolic disturbances	Increased tocopherol requirement (vit. E)

need for essential fatty acids. The minimal carbohydrate requirement is basically fixed by the metabolism of the brain, which depends almost entirely on glucose (ca. 100 g/day).

Foodstuff requirement (Table 28-5). The total amount of proteins, fats and carbohydrates required depends on the current rate of energy metabolism (pp. 617ff.). The requirement is higher when one is working harder, pregnant or suffering certain diseases. In case of generally increased muscle tone (e.g., shivering) or cramps it is also considerably higher. Metabolic rate can rise considerably in serious illness (cf. Table 24-6, p. 623), in cases of skull or brain injury reaching values like those for hard labor. The nutrient solutions provided to such patients should be designed with this need in mind. Children also require a more energy-containing diet than adults per unit body weight, because of their higher growth rate.

Depot reserves. Carbohydrates and proteins can be reversibly stored in the body to only a limited extent. The protein reserves available on a short-term basis amount to about 45 g, and 300–400 g glycogen are stored. Only the fat depots of the body are a relatively capacious energy reservoir (Table 28-5).

Deficiency symptoms. Among the typical deficiency symptoms are diminished physical and mental performance, susceptibility to various diseases and underweight. Protein deficiency leads, for example, to edema and in children to impaired development (Table 28-5).

Overdosage symptoms. The consequences of eating more than is needed are obesity, diminished physical performance capacity and a reduced life expectancy (Table 28-5).
In drawing up and **energy balance** one must bear in mind that nutrients are not always completely absorbed. About 6% of the energy in a mixed Central European diet escapes in this way. Moreover, the diet-induced thermogenesis (p. 678) of foodstuffs must also be taken into account (Table 28-6).

Table 28-6. Energy balance of a man doing moderately hard work (toolmaker; age: 56 years, body weight: 77 kg, height: 172 cm). From [3]

Basal metabolic rate		6,740 kJ/day
Increments for	a. Leisure activities	1,670 kJ/day
	b. Work	3,770 kJ/day
	c. Incomplete absorption (6% of total energy)	820 kJ/day
	d. diet-induced thermogenesis (6% of total energy)	820 kJ/day
Total		13,820 kJ/day

Vitamins

The daily requirements of humans for various vitamins (guidelines summarized in Tables 28-7 and 28-9) are increased during and after physical *work* and in many *illnesses.* During exercise the increase in the need for energy is greater than that for vitamins, so that if enough foods are eaten to meet the energy demand the extra vitamins are automatically supplied. In some illnesses loss of appetite is combined with a greater need for vitamins, and vitamin-deficiency symptoms appear; in these cases *prophylactic* vitamin supplements are indicated.
Given an energetically adequate diet, **vitamin deficiencies** can develop if the diet is *not sufficiently varied,* as in the case of strict vegetarians. Food can also be deficient in vitamins if it is incorrectly prepared. Some vitamins lose potency during storage, canning and cooking; it is thought that decreases in the vitamin content of various foods owing to long storage or associated with

Table 28-7. *Fat-soluble vitamins.* Deficiency symptoms, depots amounts stored, and recommended intake for adults

Vitamin	Deficiency symptoms	Depots and amounts stored	Daily allowance
A	*Night blindness,* abnormal keratinization of epithelium, impaired growth	Large amounts in the liver	0.8–1.1 mg vitamin A, ~ 1.6–2.2 mg β-carotene; max. dose: 15 mg vitamin A
D	*Rickets,* impaired bone growth and ossification	Small amounts in liver, kidneys, intestines, bones, adrenals	5.0 μg; in childhood and pregnancy 10 μg; max. dose: 25 μg
E	Disturbances in muscle metabolism and vascular permeability	Several grams in liver, adipose tissue, uterus, hypophysis, adrenals	12 mg tocopherol
K	Delayed blood clotting, spontaneous bleeding	Very small amounts in liver and spleen	None if intestinal flora intact, otherwise ca. 1 mg; as prophylaxis in prematures one dose of ca. 1 mg

Table 28-8. Supply of various vitamins provided by the body's reserves, in adults. From [15].

Vitamin B_{12}	3–5 years	Riboflavin	2–6 weeks
Vitamin A	1–2 years	Niacin	2–6 weeks
Folic acid	3–4 months	Vitamin B_6	2–6 weeks
Vitamin C	2–6 weeks	Thiamin	4–10 days

the time of year are the cause of *"spring fever"*. Fat-soluble vitamins can be absorbed only together with fats or bile acids; this is especially important in the case of β-carotene, which occurs in fat-free plants.

A few peculiarities of certain vitamins deserve mention. There are interactions between *niacin* and the essential amino acid *tryptophan*, such that lack of niacin does not produce deficiency symptoms if the diet contains enough tryptophan. More *tocopherol* (vitamin E) is required when the amount of essential fatty acids in the diet increases. Deficiencies in *vitamin K* and *biotin* can result from disturbances of the intestinal flora – for example, after treatment with antibiotics. Finally, the *thiamin* (vitamin B_1) requirement is largely supplied by grain products. Because people are now eating less of these, and tend to prefer refined flours with little thiamin content, some flour is now enriched with vitamin B_1 and other B vitamins. Those who consume large amounts of alcohol have a distinctly increased requirement for niacin, folic acid and vitamins B_2 and B_{12}.

Storage in the body. Fat-soluble vitamins can be stored in large amounts, in some cases (e.g., vitamin A; Table 28-8) a several years' supply. The same is true of the water-soluble vitamin B_{12} (Table 28-8). But many vitamins are stored only in limited quantities, so that the supply must be regularly replenished.

Deficiency symptoms. The classical **vitamin-deficiency diseases** are now rarely encountered in a fully developed form under European conditions. Deficiency states (summarized in Tables 28-7 and 28-9) can result from either *malnutrition* (unbalanced or energy-poor diet, as in strict fasting) or *malabsorption*. Rickets, a vitamin-D-deficiency disease, is still found today where infants and small children have not received sufficient *vitamin-D prophylaxis*.

Because most of the water-soluble vitamins are stored only in small amounts, *hypovitaminosis* resulting from malnutrition or malabsorption is often associated with symptoms of a *combined* deficiency of several vitamins. Hypovitaminoses nearly always cause *diminished* physical and mental *performance capacity;* an increase in performance capacity can be achieved by taking vitamin supplements. But there is *no evidence that vitamin supplements enhance the performance of properly nourished people.*

Table 28-9. *Water-soluble vitamins.* Deficiency symptoms, depots and amounts stored, and recommended intake for adults

Vitamin	Deficiency symptoms	Depots and amounts stored	Daily allowance
B_1	*Beri-beri, polyneuritis,* CNS disorders, paralysis, muscular atrophy, cardiac insufficiency	ca. 10 mg; liver, myocardium, brain	1.1–1.5 mg or 0.12 mg/MJ; more in alcoholics
B_2	Arrested growth, skin disorders	ca. 10 mg; liver, skeletal muscle	1.5–1.8 mg or 0.14 mg/MJ
B_6	Dermatitis, polyneuritis, cramps	ca. 100 mg; muscle, liver, brain	2.0–2.6 mg or 0.02 mg/g food protein
B_{12}	*Pernicious anemia, funicular myelosis*	1.5–3 mg; especially in liver	5 µg!
Biotin	Dermatitis	ca. 0.4 mg; liver, kidneys	None if intestinal flora intact, otherwise ca. 0.3 mg
Folic acid	*Pernicious anemia*	12–15 mg; liver	0.4 mg; 0.8 mg in pregnancy
Niacin	*Pellagra,* photodermatitis, paresthesia	ca. 150 mg; liver	15–20 mg; replaceable by 60 times as much tryptophan
Pantothenic acid	CNS disturbances	ca. 50 mg; adrenals, kidneys, liver, brain, heart	8 mg
C	*Scurvy,* connective-tissue disorders, bleeding gums, susceptibility to infection, psychoses	1.5 g; brain, kidneys, adrenals, pancreas, liver, heart	75 mg, +40% for smokers
Vitaminoids			
Choline	Unknown	In every cell	1.5–4.0 g
Inositol	Unknown	In every cell	ca. 1 g

Overdosage symptoms. On the assumption that vitamins can do no damage, people often take supplements in large amounts. But **hypervitaminosis** is known to occur, although for the vitamins so far recognized as potentially harmful the toxic dose is quite high. Moreover, the intravenous injection of certain vitamins can have

Table 28-10. Vitamins with known overdosage symptoms; daily allowance (as in Tables 28-7 and 28-9), toxic doses and symptoms in humans

Vitamin	Daily allowance	Toxic dose (per day)	Symptoms of overdosage
A	0.8–1.1 mg	35 mg (single dose: 600mg)	Changes in skin, mucosa and bones; headache, euphoria, anemia
D	25 μg	500 μg/kg	Ca^{2+} mobilization in bones, Ca^{2+} deposition, CNS and kidney disorders
K	0–1 mg	?	Anemia in prematures; sometimes collapse following i.v. injection
B_1	1.1–1.5 mg	?	Sometimes collapse following i.v. injection
Niacin	15–20 mg	(3–4 g?)	Gastrointestinal disorders, skin alterations, impaired vision
C	75 mg	5 g	Diarrhea, kidney stones if predisposed

undesirable results (e.g., circulatory collapse; cf. Table 28-10).
Most adults, in contrast to growing children and pregnant women, have no actual need for *vitamin D,* because their diet contains enough provitamins. Today many foods, including special diet preparations, margarine and milk, are enriched with vitamin D, so that adults often consume it in amounts far exceeding even those required by juveniles. Niacin is occasionally administered in doses of 2 g per day with the intention of lowering an excessively high blood-fat level.

Water, Salts, Trace Elements

Water. Human water requirements vary. Conditions that cause sweating (heat, hard work) and excessive salt intake markedly increase the need for water. Depending on the situation, then, the daily adult requirement is set at 20-45 ml/kg body weight. With regard to **water balance,** the following *average data* have been published [13]: A person weighing 70 kg requires at least ca. 1,750 ml water per day. Of this amount, ca. 650 ml is obtained by *drinking,* ca. 750 ml is the water contained in *solid food,* and ca. 350 ml is *oxidation water.* If more than this amount is consumed by a healthy person it is excreted by the kidneys, but in people with heart or kidney diseases it may be retained (edema; pp. 505, 771f.).

Table 28-11. Important electrolytes: recommended intake for adults, in g/day. From [6]

Na^+	K^+	Ca^{2+}	Mg^{2+}	Cl^-	P
2–3	3–4	0.8	0.30–0.35	3–5	0.8

Deficiency symptoms. Water loss amounting to 5% of the weight of the body causes a distinct *impairment of performance capacity.* A loss of 10% produces *severe dehydration,* and if 15–20% is lost *death* results. The mean water content of the body is about 60%; thus loss of about $^1/_3$ to $^1/_4$ of the total body water is lethal.

Overdosage symptoms. If large amounts of hypotonic solutions are taken within a short time into the body, or large amounts of salt are lost, there can be a transient influx of water into the *intracellular space* (pp. 771f.). The resulting syndrome, called *water intoxication,* consists of impaired performance, headache, nausea or convulsions (symptoms of *cerebral edema*).

Salts. The recommended intake of some important electrolytes is shown in Table 28-11. The causes and symptoms of salt and water imbalance are discussed on pp. 768ff. and 771ff.
More *calcium* is required during *bone growth* (as in pregnant women and children). *Calcium deficiency* is especially likely to occur when food with a high *oxalic acid* content (e.g., spinach, rhubarb) is eaten, because a considerable fraction of the calcium in the diet is bound as *insoluble calcium oxalate* and is thus not absorbed. Among the foods that are especially valuable because of their calcium content are milk and dairy products.
The minimal requirement for *sodium chloride* is less than 1 g per day; Central Europeans, on the average, consume about ten times this amount. Because it can cause high blood pressure, consumption of more than 10 g of salt per day should be avoided.

Trace elements. Of the trace elements with acknowledged physiological function we shall consider here only *iron, fluorine, iodine* and *copper.* Table 28-12 summarizes the recommended intake of these, the amount stored in the body, and the deficiency symptoms. More iron and iodine are

Table 28-12. Trace elements with known physiological functions: deficiency symptoms, amounts stored and recommended intake for adults

Trace element	Deficiency symptoms	Amounts stored	Daily allowance
Iron	Iron-deficiency anemia	4–5 g, of which 800 mg can be mobilized	Menstruating women 18 mg, otherwise 12 mg as Fe^{2+}
Fluorine		?	For caries prophylaxis 1 mg; above 5 mg toxic! (osteosclerosis)
Iodine	Goiter, hypothyroidism	10 mg	180–200 μg
Copper	Impaired iron absorption, anemia, pigmentation disorders	100–150 mg	2–4 mg

required by children and in pregnancy. Overdoses of almost all trace elements cause some disturbance of normal function, and in the case of fluorine the toxic limit is only slightly above the recommended amount (Table 28-12). The distribution of trace elements in food is described in [6].

Iodine deficiency causes an increased incidence of thyroid-gland enlargement in certain parts of the world (endemic goiter), occasionally accompanied by diminished thyroxine production. The occurrence of goiter has been much reduced by the systematic administration of small amounts of iodine (by enrichment of kitchen salt).

Chronic iron deficiency is the reason for the *only deficiency disease common under Central European conditions;* the iron content of the usual diet is barely adequate to meet normal requirements, because only about 3–8% of plant iron is absorbed, and only about 23% of animal iron (heme). The main symptoms are tiredness, headache, diminished performance capacity and impaired growth of skin and associated structures (hair, nails). Severe deficiency leads to typical *iron-deficiency anemia.* In cases of chronic *blood loss* (for example, menstruation, gastrointestinal bleeding, frequent blood donation) an average Central European diet often does not provide enough iron to replace the amount lost. Thus many menstruating women have no mobilizable iron reserves, and even slight additional blood loss (e.g., during surgery) or increased requirement during pregnancy brings on iron-deficiency anemia. In various European countries this kind of anemia has been found in 30–40% of menstruating women, though the tendency is decreasing in countries in which meat is usually eaten in abundance.

28.3 Utilization of Foodstuffs; Dietetics

Utilization

Only the foodstuffs and other food components actually *absorbed* can be metabolized by the body. Most of the substances contained in the diet must be released by digestion before they can be absorbed, and even when digestion proceeds normally not all of the substances (or the products of their decomposition) are absorbed. *Of the fuel value of a mixed Central European diet only 90–95% is utilized,* because some of its components – such as *cellulose,* a typical plant carbohydrate – cannot be broken down in the human upper digestive tract. If the cellulose walls of the plant cells are not destroyed when the food is prepared for digestion (by cooking and chewing, for example) the content of the cells cannot be absorbed. The percentage absorbed is also reduced in intestinal diseases such as dysentery or cholera and following intestinal resection; however, the transport capacity of the intestinal epithelium is rarely an absorption-limiting factor.

Biological value. The absorbed foodstuffs differ in their value to the organism, depending on their origin (cf. p. 683). This is especially true of proteins, because of their varying content of essential amino acids; *plant proteins have a lower biological value than animal proteins* (p. 683).

Balanced Diet

The planning of a balanced diet is a nutritional problem of considerable current importance, and many aspects are still the subject of vigorous debate. The following four *physiological* considerations are fundamental:

1. The **fuel value** of the diet must correspond to the person's energy requirement.
2. The diet must provide at least the **minimal required amounts** of proteins, fats and carbohydrates (Table 28-5, p. 683).

3. It must also provide at least the **minimal required amounts** of vitamins, salts and trace elements (Tables 28-7, 28-9, 28-11 and 28-12).
4. The **toxic limits** of the various vitamins, salts and trace elements must not be exceeded.

In 1875 the German physiologist v. VOIT proposed that diet be described in terms of its *Kostmaß* ("diet measure"), which gives its *energy content and relative amounts of foodstuffs* [12]. VOIT's *Kostmaß*, derived "from a large number of observations for an average worker," was 118 g proteins, 56 g fats, 500 g carbohydrates (in percentages by weight, 18:8:74), with 12,750 kJ/day. At the beginning of this century a large-scale study produced the following *Kostmaß*: 84 g protein, 65 g fats, 453 g carbohydrates (in weight percentages, 14:11:75), with 11,730 kJ/day. It is from these data that the proportions 1:1:4 by weight (15:30:55 % in terms of energy) have been derived for the relative quantities of protein, fat and carbohydrate in a desirable diet.

More recent recommendations take into account the practical need for a certain margin (Table 28-13). The recommended daily intake for a healthy adult is as follows [6]: *proteins,* 0.8 g/kg body weight (at least half of which should be of animal origin); *fats,* 25–30% of the total energy requirement ($^1/_3$ as essential fatty acids), except for those doing extremely hard labor, who can meet as much as 40% of their energy requirement with fats; *carbohydrates,* the remainder of the energy requirement (ca. 55–65%), as long as it is least 10%. Experience acquired when nutrition was generally insufficient and poorly balanced, during and after the world wars, and more recent investigations have confirmed that these proportions are appropriate to European situations; they can be regarded as optimal.
However, average *energy requirements* today are generally less than they once were because people do less hard physical work. The *actual eating habits* of the German population in 1980/81, for example, are typical of a highly industrialized society: the average diet provides *too much energy* and contains *too much fat and too little carbohydrate* (Table 28-13). In addition, the average alcohol consumption, 34–69 g/day, contributes 1,020 to 2,070 kJ/day (Table 28-13).

Table 28-13. Energy content of diet for 19- to 50-year-olds in 1980/81; average values from a survey in West-Germany [5]

	Women		Men	
	Desired	Actual	Desired	Actual
Total energy intake (kJ/day)	8,800	12,200	10,500	16,300
Protein (g/day)	45	74	55	105
Fat (g/day)	58–81	118	68–95	143
Carbohydrate (g/day)	298–352	293	354–417	380
Alcohol intake per day	34 g ≈ 1,020 kJ		69 g ≈ 2,070 kJ	
Fraction of total energy intake	8%		13%	

The striking differences between the desired and actual values in Table 28-13 should not lead one to conclude that these people were storing an average of 3,400 kJ (women) or 5,800 kJ (men) of food energy per day; that would mean accumulating 87 or 150 g of fat every day! For one thing, the amounts "consumed" are not identical to those actually eaten, because they are derived from sales statistics. Furthermore, when excess foodstuffs are taken into the body their effects on the fat depots are very complex and cannot be described by simple balance equations.

Slight **deviations from the recommended proportions** cause no serious disturbances. Fats and carbohydrates are to a great extent interchangeable with regard to their energy content (isodynamic effect; p. 678). In case of **carbohydrate deficiency** glucose can be formed from *glucoplastic amino acids (gluconeogenesis),* if these are present in excess. The first sign of a depressed blood sugar level *(hypoglycemia)* is a strong feeling of hunger and a reduction in physical and psychological performance capacity. If the situation persists until the minimal requirement of the brain for sugar is no longer met, unconsciousness and convulsions result *(hypoglycemic shock).* On the other hand, if **more carbohydrates** are consumed than are needed they are *converted to fats* and stored, leading to obesity. Excessive carbohydrate consumption can also cause digestive disturbances owing to the predominance of fermentation processes in the colon (p. 775).
A great **reduction in the fat content** of the diet interferes with the *supply of fat-soluble vitamins,* with resulting vitamin-deficiency symptoms. Other deficiency symptoms appear when the minimal requirement of essential fatty acids is not met (p. 683). An **increase** in the proportion of fat causes more fat to be stored, and an increased consumption of saturated fatty acids can produced hypercholesterolemia (p. 679), which is regarded as an epidemiological risk factor (p. 690). Conversely, increased consumption of unsaturated fatty acids is thought to lower the blood cholesterol level (p. 679f.).
When the **protein fraction is reduced**, physical and psychological performance capacity is impaired, and eventually starvation edema and muscular atrophy result. The defense mechanisms of the body deteriorate and susceptibility to infection increases. When protein is eaten in **abundance** the metabolic rate rises (diet-induced thermogenesis; p. 678), an effect that may be quite desirable in cold climates because of the associated increase in heat production. On the other hand, protein-rich food may lead to digestive disturbances because of the predominance of putrefaction in the colon. In people with a predisposition to gout consumption of increases the likelihood of an attack, because of the large quantities of purine bases such food contains.

The **origin of the food** is a significant factor in a balanced diet. Whereas the required amounts of essential amino acids are obtained chiefly from *animal products,* foods of *plant origin* are indispensable sources of the necessary water-soluble vitamins, salts and trace elements. A strictly vegetarian diet usually produces symptoms of protein deficiency because of the lack of essential amino acids. Moreover, animal and plant foods have different effects on acid-base balance (pp. 589ff.); animal products act as weak acids (H^+ donors) and plant products as weak bases (H^+ acceptors). The associated influences on the acid-base status are normally compensated by the kidneys.

Finally, the **preparation** of the food is a determining factor in a balanced diet. Improper handling can cause deterioration of vitamins (e.g., owing to heat sensitivity). The way the diet is spiced and served can exert physiological effects in that digestion is influenced by the *cephalic phase of gastric-juice secretion* (p. 713). In fact, this stimulatory action of spices and drinks (alcohol) can cause overacidity of the stomach contents in susceptible people.

In the adult German population alcohol contributes, on average, 8% (women) or 13% (men) of the daily energy intake. This corresponds to 34–69 g alcohol per day. But alcohol consumption must be evaluated not only with respect to the energy content of the diet, for it also has a *toxic effect*. Prolonged consumption of more than 80 g of alcohol (≈ 2,400 kJ) per day leads to liver damage; toxic effects are observed with consumption of about 160 g/day or more.

Special Diets

In planning a diet, attention must be paid to the subject's *age* and type of *work* as well as to the *therapeutic purpose.* With increasing age, for example, the energy requirement grows less whereas the relative requirement of essential amino acids is augmented.

Low-energy diets. Because **obesity** has attained almost epidemic proportions in Europe and North America, it is worth considering certain aspects of low-energy diets, though the multitude of vaunted slimming regimes shows that there is no one ideal solution. As in the case of strict fasting – which should be undertaken only under medical supervision – care must be taken that the low-energy diet in the long term provides the minimal required amounts of all nutrients. Diets that achieve this goal can be relatively rich in protein, fat or carbohydrate; the choice must be determined by the various advantages and disadvantages of each.

A **protein-rich, low-energy diet** has the advantage that the appetite is sufficiently satisfied and the diet-induced thermogenesis of protein (p. 678) enhances the metabolic rate. A disadvantage is that protein-rich foods are among the most expensive and ususally contain much fat (concealed fat, p. 679). A **fat-rich, low-energy diet** is effective in appeasing hunger, but because the content of saturated fatty acids is usually high hypercholesterolemia can result. Moreover, people vary in their digestive tolerance of fatty diets. A **carbohydrate-rich, low-energy diet** offers the advantage that the stomach is well filled at mealtimes, but the feeling of satiety is short-lived. Furthermore, soon after carbohydrates of low molecular weight are consumed hypoglycemic undulations often occur, with a renewed feeling of hunger.

In recent years a concerted effort has been made to produce **low-energy foods** with unchanged volume but energetic value reduced by 40–50%. The energetic reduction is achieved by removing the fat, replacing the sugar with sweeteners of lower energy content, and adding water and cellulose-containing products.

Nutrition of the aged. Diets for old people should be planned according to the following guidelines:

1. Their **energy requirement** is lower.
2. Their daily **protein requirement** is increased to 1.2–1.5 g/kg body weight.
3. At most 30% of the energy requirement should take the form of **fats** (ca. 70 g/day). Fats with *unsaturated fatty acids* are preferable.
4. The daily intake of **carbohydrates** should amount to about 300 g, mono- and disaccharides being avoided.
5. An adequate **Ca^{2+} intake** must be ensured because of the tendency to osteoporosis (softening of the bones) in the aged. Chief among the calcium-rich foods are milk and dairy products.
6. The **absolute vitamin requirement** is unchanged in old age. But because the energy requirement is less, and thus less food should be eaten, old people may suffer vitamin deficiencies. The preference of many old people for easily digestible foods like mashed potatoes and white bread can also lead to vitamin deficiency.

Formula diets are standardized foodstuff concentrates in powder form, containing all the components necessary for *balanced nutrition.* They are given to patients either as the entire diet or as a supplement.

Crude fiber. The advantages claimed for high-fiber diets are the stimulation of peristalsis and thus more rapid passage through the intestine (pp. 721f.), and the soft consistency of the feces – both factors that work against constipation and its consequences (p. 731). On the other hand, healthy life has been shown to be possible for long periods on an entirely synthetic diet without fiber. Evidently neither extreme is disadvantageous for the passage of food through the gastrointestinal canal. On the other hand, a diet containing small amounts of crude fiber may well encourage constipation.

28.4 Evaluation of Body Weight and the Surface Area of the Body

Obesity as a Risk Factor

The term **risk factor** is used in epidemiology for factors associated (though the *causal* relationship is not known) with *shortened life expectancy* and closely correlated statistically with the so-called *diseases of civilization* (e.g., cardiac infarction and stroke [1, 7, 11, 17]). One of the risk factors that can be avoided is obesity – a condition that paves the way for high blood pressure and metabolic disorders. The complex relationships between obesity and shortened life expectancy will not be treated here.

Reference weights. Various recommendations have been made for the desirable body weight, by reference to average values (so-called *normal weight)*, specific criteria (so-called *ideal weight*) and so on. Because average weights depend on the nutritional state of the population under consideration, they are very variable, with conspicuous deviations in times of famine or of overnourishment. Therefore the average weight cannot be used to estimate the weight-correlated risk to health.
The MLIC *ideal weights* are the body weights found to be correlated statistically with the longest life expectancy in studies of more than 5 million North Americans by a life-insurance company. Other reference weights (reviewed in [18]) include the *Broca index* (body height in cm − 100 = *Broca index* in kg) and the *Quetelet index*. The latter, also called the *Body Mass Index* (BMI), is found by dividing weight in kg by (height in m)^2; as a rule of thumb, the desirable body weight is associated with an index of 22 (women) or 24 (men). The German Society for Nutrition recommends (not least on grounds of practicability) the Broca index, without correction [6].

The problems associated with all these reference weights can be illustrated in terms of the MLIC ideal weight [21], as follows. Ideal weights are given for various age groups and for three categories of body frame (see [13]), small, medium or large. However, there are no generally valid criteria by which an individual can be assigned to one of these categories. Another source of difficulty is that overweight can be produced not only by increases in body fat (through overeating) but also by an increase in muscle mass (e.g., by strength training) or in the water content of the body (usually pathological). Of these possibilities, only *obesity* is relevant to preventive medicine. It is the expression of an energetic overloading of the metabolism, which is *statistically correlated* with arteriosclerosis, diabetes mellitus and gout. For the reasons given above, obesity should be diagnosed not by weighing the patient but preferable by determining the fat content of the body, which can be quantified by simple methods (Fig. 28-1).
For children, the weight-to-height relation is determined by so-called *somatograms* based on age-dependent averages [13, 20].

Composition of the Body

The weight of a person is determined principally by three factors: *water content, fat content* and *muscle mass*. The mean extracellular water content accounts for about 15% of the body's weight; the mean fat content is 20%, and the mean muscle mass is 40%. When the weight of the body changes it is due to changes in one or more of these three compartments. The relative contribution of each, especially the fat content, can deviate considerably from the average.

When the **water content** of the body increases, a state of edema or hydrops develops; the water can be distributed among different spaces. Methods for measuring changes in water content are discussed on p. 767. The **fat content** of the human body can vary between ca. 8 and 50%, women having a higher average proportion of fat than men (Table 28-14). The mean percentage of fat also rises with age. A useful method for estimating fat content is to pull up a fold of skin with a pair of *calipers*. The thickness of the fold is measured in four representative parts of the body (the biceps, triceps, subscapular and suprailiac regions; Fig. 28-1). The sum of these four values is closely related to the percentage of fat in the body [16]; cf. Table 28-14). The total body fat can also be calculated from the specific gravity of the body, the deviations from the specific gravity of water being largely due to the fat content. The **muscle mass** of the body decreases during fasting and increases as a result of special training ("body building" or isometric training). Muscle mass can be determined by

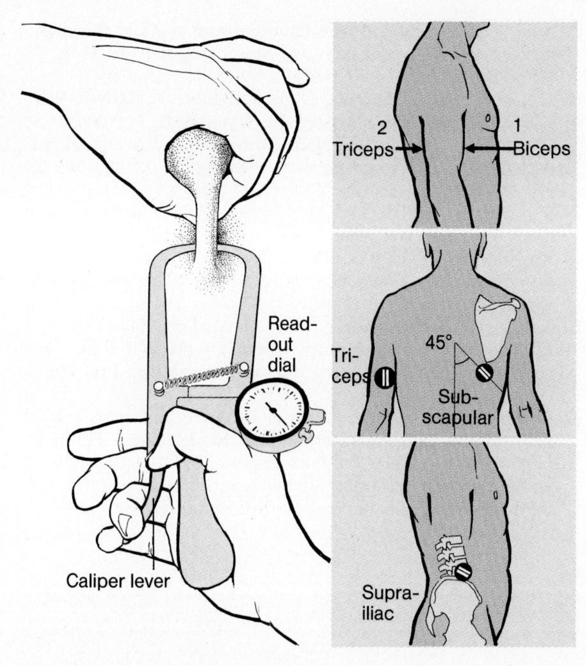

Fig. 28-1. To measure skinfold thickness with a pair of calipers: at each of the indicated sites, raise a fold of skin between two fingers, about 1 cm above the measurement point. The skinfold thickness should be read from the dial 2 s after the caliper lever has been released. (From [16] as cited in [22])

Table 28-14. Reference values for the sum of the four skinfold thicknesses (cf. Fig. 28-1) and the body fat content calculated from it, for different age groups and both sexes. Based on a sample of people at the desired weight according to the Broca index. From [19]

Age (years)	Women		Men	
	∑ (mm)	Fat (%)	∑ (mm)	Fat (%)
15–19	71.0	30.2	48.6	17.4
20–24	73.0	31.5	49.7	18.9
25–29	75.0	32.7	50.8	20.4
30–34	77.0	34.0	51.9	21.9
35–39	79.1	35.2	53.0	23.4
40–44	81.1	36.5	54.0	24.9
45–49	83.2	37.7	55.0	26.4
50–54	85.3	39.0	56.0	27.9
55–59	87.4	40.2	57.0	29.4

way of creatine excretion and also by measuring the total body content of potassium radiologically with a "body counter", because most of the body potassium is found in the musculature. A commonly used measure of *muscle mass* is the *Lean Body Mass,* defined as the total body mass minus the fat component.

Surface Area of the Body

It is very difficult to measure the area of the body's surface directly. It can be estimated, however, with the approximation formula of DUBOIS and DUBOIS: $A = 71.84 \cdot W^{0.425} \cdot H^{0.725}$ (from [13]; A is the surface area in cm^2, W is the weight of the body in kg, and H is its height in cm). Nomograms simplify the estimation of surface area, but these too give only approximate values.

WALLACE's *rule of nine* is used in cases of burn injury, to estimate roughly the area of the body surface affected. The rule divides the surface into percentages as follows: 9% for each arm, 18% for each leg, 36% for the trunk and 9% for head and neck together.

Body surface as a reference value. Many biological parameters depend on the size of the body – for example, basal metabolic rate, resting cardiac output, total blood volume or heart volume. For this reason these parameters are often expressed with respect to the surface area or weight of the body, in which case the adjective *relative* is applied (e.g., relative heart volume). Theoretical considerations indicate that it is more correct to refer to the surface area of the body than to its weight. In practice, however, the weight is most often used because it can be measured far more accurately than the surface area, with simple direct methods, and because it is one of the basic terms in the calculation of surface area.

28.5 References

Textbooks and Handbooks

1. ABHOLZ, H.-H., BORGERS, D., KARMAUS, W., KORPORAL, J. (Eds.): Risikofaktorenmedizin. Konzept und Kontroverse. Berlin-New York: de Gruyter 1982
2. BÄSSLER, K.-H., FEKL, W., LANG, K.: Grundbegriffe der Ernährungslehre. Heidelberger Taschenbuch, Nr. 119, Basistext Medizin. Berlin-Heidelberg-New York: Springer 1973
3. Deutsche Gesellschaft für Ernährung e.V. (Ed.): Die wünschenswerte Höhe der Nahrungszufuhr. 12. Ausgabe. Schriftenreihe der „Ernährungsumschau". Frankfurt: Umschau-Verlag 1966
4. Deutsche Gesellschaft für Ernährung e.V. (Ed.): Material zum Ernährungsbericht 1980. Frankfurt: Deutsche Gesellschaft für Ernährung e.V. 1980
5. Deutsche Gesellschaft für Ernährung e.V. (Ed.): Ernährungsbericht 1984. Frankfurt: Deutsche Gesellschaft für Ernährung e.V. 1984
6. Deutsche Gesellschaft für Ernährung e.V. (Ed.): Empfehlungen für die Nährstoffzufuhr. (4. erw. Überarb.) Frankfurt: Umschau-Verlag 1985
7. HEYDEN, S.: Infarkt-Prävention heute. Intervention 1970–1984. Ergebnisse – Probleme – Konsequenzen. Mannheim: Boehringer Mannheim GmbH – Galenus Mannheim GmbH 1984
8. HOLTMEIER, H.J. (Ed.): Taschenbuch der Pathophysiologie. Vol. 1 und Vol. 2. Stuttgart-New York: Fischer 1977
9. KREBS, H.A.: The metabolic rate of amino acids. In: MUNRO, H.N., ALLISON, J.B. (Eds.): Mammalian protein metabolism. Vol. I, p. 125. New York-London: Academic Press 1964

10. RUBNER, M.: Physiologische Verbrennungswerte, Ausnutzung, Isodynamie, Calorienbedarf, Kostmaße. In: BETHE, A., v. BERGMANN, G., EMBDEN, G., ELLINGER, A. (Eds.): Handbuch der normalen und pathologischen Physiologie, Vol. 5. Stoffwechsel und Energiebedarf. p. 134. Berlin: Springer 1928
11. SCHWARTZ, F.W. (Red.): Herz-Kreislauf-Vorsorgeprogramme in der Bundesrepublik Deutschland. Köln-Lövenich: Deutscher Ärzteverlag 1977
12. v. VOIT, C.: Physiologie des allgemeinen Stoffwechsels und der Ernährung. In: HERMANN, L. (Ed.): Handbuch der Physiologie, Vol. 6, Teil II. Leipzig: F.C.W. Vogel 1881
13. Wissenschaftliche Tabellen – Documenta Geigy (Ed.: J.R. Geigy AG Pharma, Basel). 7. Aufl., Basel, 1969

Original Papers and Reviews

14. BÄSSLER, K.-H.: Die Bedeutung der Brennstoffzufuhr für die Körperfunktionen. Z. Ernährungswiss. *11,* 200 (1972)
15. BITSCH, R.: Die therapeutische Anwendung von Vitaminen. Dt. Apothekerzeit. *125,* 392 (1985)
16. DURING, J.V.G.A., WOMERSLEY, J.: Body fat assessed from total body density and its estimation from skinfold thickness: measurements on 481 men and women aged from 16 to 72 years. Br. J. Nutr. *32,* 77 (1974)
17. GRUNDY, S.M., BILHEIMER, D., BLACKBURN, H., BROWN, W.V., KWITEROVICH, P.O., MATISON, F., SCHONFELD, G., WEIDMAN, W.H.: AHA Committee Report-Rationale of the Diet-Heart-Statement of the American Heart Association. Circulation *65,* (4), 839A (1982)
18. KNUSSMANN, R., TOELLER, M., HOLLER, H.D.: Zur Beurteilung des Körpergewichts. Med. Welt (Stuttg.) *23,* 529 (1972)
19. KRÄMER, H.-J., ULMER, H.-V.: Reference values for body fat content as a measure for desirable body fat content. Ernährungswiss. *23,* 1 (1984)
20. KUNZE, D.: Somatogramm. Fortschr. Med. *95,* 548 (1977)
21. Metropolitan Life Insurance Company (MLIC, Ed.): New weight standards for men and women. Statist. Bull. *40,* 1 (1959)
22. ULMER. H.-V.: Comparability of absolute and body-related performance capacity in ergometry. In: LÖLLGEN, H., MELLEROWICZ, H. (Eds.): Progress in ergometry: Quality control and test criteria. 5th International Seminar on Ergometry. 188, Berlin-Heidelberg-New York-Tokyo: Springer 1984

29 Functions of the Alimentary Canal

K. Ewe and U. Karbach

The alimentary tract serves primarily to convert food into absorbable particles and to pass them on to the other organs of the body. These events are initiated by *mechanical processes* (fragmentation, mixing, transport) and the *secretion of digestive juices* containing enzymes, which act to split proteins, fats and carbohydrates by hydrolysis into constituents small enough to be absorbed **(digestion).** These end products of digestion, together with water, minerals and vitamins, then pass through the intestinal mucosa, from the lumen of the intestine into the blood and lymph **(absorption).**

The alimentary canal is a continuous tube running from mouth to anus; it consists of the oropharynx, esophagus, stomach, and small and large intestine. Into this tract are discharged the secretions of several organs, including the salivary glands, pancreas and liver (Fig. 29-1). The structure of the wall of the tube is the same in principle throughout the gastrointestinal tract (Fig. 29-2), although the various sections of the tract differ in their primary functions.

Some parts of the alimentary canal serve chiefly to *transport food* (oral cavity, esophagus), others – stomach and large intestine – have predominantly a *storage function,* and the small intestine is the main site of *digestion* and *absorption.* These functions are controlled (i) by a large number of hormones and biologically active peptides, (ii) by the intrinsic activity of the smooth muscle cells and (iii) by the autonomic nervous system. Disturbances of normal function can produce a variety of diseases and clinical symptoms: impaired digestion (maldigestion) or absorption (malabsorption), disorders related to motility (diarrhea, constipation, vomiting, fecal incontinence) and symptoms such as heartburn, feelings of pressure and fullness, colic and nausea.

29.1 General Bases of Gastrointestinal Function

Control Mechanisms

Intrinsic and extrinsic nervous system (see also pp. 343ff.). The gastrointestinal tract has its own

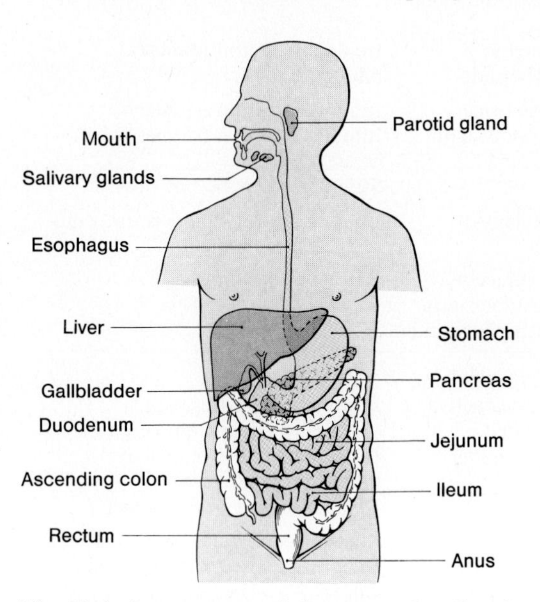

Fig. 29-1. Arrangement of the organs for digestion and absorption

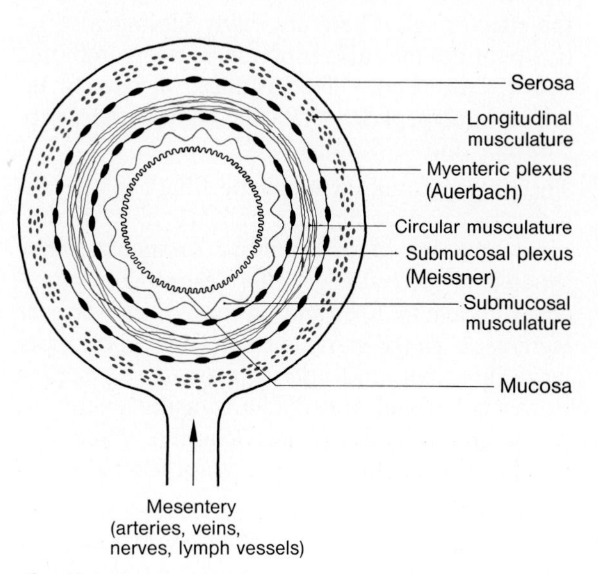

Fig. 29-2. Layers in the wall of the gastrointestinal tract, schematic

enteric or *intrinsic nervous system*, also called the "enteric brain". It can operate independently of the extrinsic autonomic nervous system to control the motor and secretory activity of stomach and bowels. This neuronal network has two compartments, the **myenteric plexus** (of Auerbach) between the longitudinal and circular musculature, and the **submucosal plexus** (of Meissner) between the circular and submucosal muscles (Fig. 29-2). The efferent fibers of the myenteric plexus terminate on the smooth muscle cells of the longitudinal and circular musculature and influence muscle tone and the rhythm of the contractions. The submucosal plexus controls primarily the secretory function of the epithelial cells. Afferent fibers from both plexuses conduct sensory signals from mechano- and nocisensors to the CNS.

The *extrinsic autonomic nervous system* has a considerable influence on the motor and secretory functions of the gastrointestinal tract, which is amply supplied by parasympathetic and sympathetic fibers. Preganglionic fibers in the **vagus nerve**, originating in the medulla oblongata, supply the esophagus, stomach, small intestine, proximal large intestine and the liver, gallbladder and pancreas; those from the sacral cord supply the sigmoid colon, rectum and anal region (p. 334). These fibers terminate on the ganglia of the intramural plexuses in the gastrointestinal canal or on the intraparenchymal ganglia of the salivary glands and liver. The transmitter of these preganglionic fibers is *acetylcholine*, which reacts with nicotinic receptors in the membrane of the ganglion cells. Acetylcholine is also the transmitter for the postganglionic nerve endings; in this case it reacts with the muscarinic receptors of the effector cell. There are many biologically active peptides that also function as postganglionic neurotransmitters – for instance, vasoactive intestinal polypeptide (VIP), the enkephalins, substance P and serotonin.

The preganglionic **sympathetic** fibers to the alimentary canal come from the 5th to 12th thoracic and 1st to 3rd lumbar segments. They synapse in the *celiac ganglion* (esophagus, stomach, duodenum, liver and pancreas), the *superior mesenteric ganglion* (small intestine and upper large intestine), and *inferior mesenteric ganglion* (lower colon and anus). The transmitter for the preganglionic fibers is acetylcholine, while that for the postganglionic fibers is noradrenalin.

Both the vagus and sympathetic nerves also contain visceral afferent fibers. The signals they carry to the CNS contribute to the production of conscious perceptions or trigger autonomic reflexes.

Gastrointestinal hormones and peptides. The gastrointestinal tract is one of the organs most affected by hormones, with respect to both their diversity and their range of actions. So far the gastrointestinal mucosa and the pancreas have been found to contain 18 different kinds of cells in which gastrointestinally effective hormones or peptides are present. The classical gastrointestinal hormones are **gastrin, secretin** and **cholecystokinin**; these substances are released into the blood in response to certain stimuli and then act on particular effector organs. In recent years the existence of a number of **biologically active peptides** has been demonstrated. These peptides do not meet all the criteria for the status of a hormone, but nevertheless affect the gastrointestinal tract in very much the same way as hormones do (Table 29-1). Some of them have paracrine actions, diffusing directly from the cell in which they are synthesized to a neighboring effector cell, with no increase in the serum concentration, and others are *neurocrine* (p. 374), being released from nerve endings at their site of action. For

Table 29-1. Hormones and biologically active peptides in the gastrointestinal tract

Hormones	*Main functions*
Gastrin	Gastric secretion, trophic effects
Secretin	Pancreatic secretion (bicarbonate)
Cholecystokinin	Pancreatic secretion (enzymes), gallbladder contraction
Biologically active peptides (hormone candidates)	
Somatostatin	Inhibits secretion (stomach, pancreas)
Pancreatic polypeptide	Inhibits secretion (pancreas, bile)
Urogastrone	Inhibits secretion (stomach)
Enteroglucagon	Inhibits secretion (stomach, pancreas) Stimulates hepatic bile flow
Neurotensin	Inhibits gastric secretion and emptying: vasoconstriction
GIP (glucose-dependent insulinotropic peptide)	Release of insulin
Neuropeptides	
VIP (vasoactive intestinal polypeptide)	Inhibits gastric secretion, Stimulates pancreatic secretion (bicarbonate) and bile-acid-independent bile flow Relaxation of smooth muscles
Substance P	Stimulates salivary glands and contraction of smooth musculature
Enkephalins, endorphins	Inhibit contraction of smooth muscles

some neuropeptides previously known to occur only in the brain, such as *enkephalins* and *endorphins*, opiate receptors have now been identified in the intestine [36].

The **stimulus for the release** of the hormones or peptides may be mediated by the vagus nerve, but the gastrointestinal endocrine cells also possess *receptors* that react with specific substances in the lumen of the intestine to cause the release of hormone granules from the basal parts of the cells into the capillaries. Here the regulation of hormone production differs from other endocrine systems, in that it is less related to the blood level of the hormones (or peptides) but rather depends on direct contact between the food components and endocrine cells in the digestive tract.

The gastrointestinal hormones and a number of peptides can be assigned to two groups, on the basis of the arrangement of their amino acid sequences. The *first group* contains *gastrin* and *cholecystokinin*, which have the same five terminal amino acids. These two substances act at the same membrane receptor with similar results, though their effectiveness can vary depending on the specificity of the receptor. For example, gastrin has a greater effect than cholecystokinin on the parietal cells of the stomach; on the other hand, cholecystokinin causes a stronger gallbladder contraction than gastrin does. The *second group* of hormones and peptides with related actions is represented by *secretin*. Other members of this group are *VIP* (vasoactive intestinal polypeptide), *glucagon* and *GIP* (glucose-dependent insulinotropic peptide), all of which are related to secretin by the presence of an identical amino acid sequence in the peptide chain. In some cases the hormones of the two groups act antagonistically to one another, but synergistic effects at a given target organ also occur. The explanation is illustrated, by the example of an acinar cell in the pancreas, in Fig. 29-3. Here enzyme secretion is stimulated by hormones of Group 1 (gastrin and cholecystokinin) and acetylcholine as well as (to a lesser extent) by some of those in Group 2 (secretin and VIP). When these *"first messengers"* have become bound to their receptors they either induce an increase in the intracellular Ca^{2+} concentration (gastrin and cholecystokinin) or activate the cAMP system (secretin and VIP). Both of these mediator substances act as *"second messengers"* to enhance secretion of enzyme by the pancreatic cell.

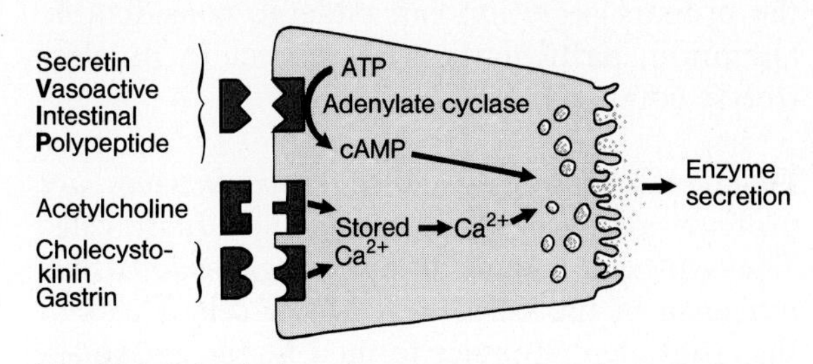

Fig. 29-3. Stimulation of enzyme secretion by various hormones and transmitter substances, and the intracellular mechanisms that mediate their action (stimulus-secretion coupling)

Gastrointestinal Motility

Motility pattern. The digestive and absorptive functions of the gastrointestinal tract depend to a great extent upon the changes in shape of the wall as its musculature contracts and relaxes. The most important motility patterns are illustrated in Fig. 29-4. *Oral-aboral transport* is brought about by **propulsive peristalsis,** a contraction of the circular musculature that progresses as a wave along the tube, usually preceded by a wave of relaxation. *Mixing* of the food mass with digestive juices occurs by **non-propulsive peristalsis,** propagated over only short distances, and by segmentation movements. **Segmentation** is the simultaneous contraction of the *circular muscles* in closely adjacent, alternating regions. Because the frequency of contraction decreases from the upper to the lower part of the intestine, the content of the lumen is also shifted slowly toward the anus by non-propulsive peristalsis. Functionally different areas are separated by **tonic contraction** with intermittent relaxation in certain specialized regions (sphincters) – for

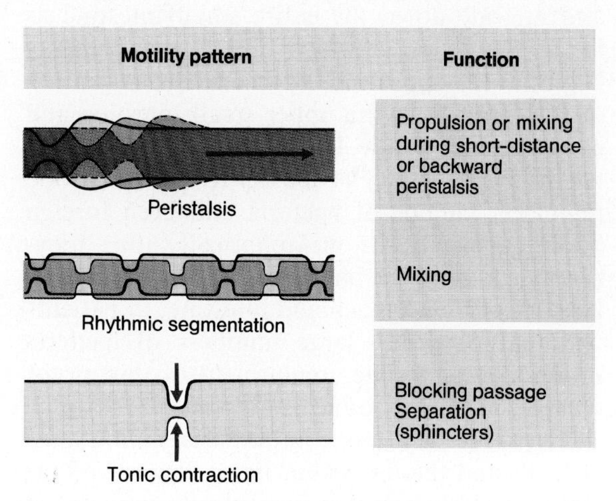

Fig. 29-4. Patterns and functions of gastrointestinal motility

instance, the *lower esophageal sphincter* between the esophagus and the stomach, and the *ileocecal valve* between ileum and cecum. These contractions ensure that transport is unidirectional, without reflux.

Control of peristalsis. The resting potential across the membrane of the smooth muscle cells in the gastrointestinal tract is characterized by *rhythmic spontaneous depolarizations* called **slow waves** (p. 79). These produce no mechanical response of the muscle. Only when brief action potentials are superimposed on the slow waves during the depolarization phase does the muscle contract, as a result of Ca^{2+} influx into the cell. The strength of contraction depends on the number of action potentials. Each muscle contraction is therefore correlated with the occurrence of a slow wave. The basic rhythm of the slow waves varies in the different sections of the tract; it is 3/min in the stomach, 12/min in the duodenum, and falls to 8/min in the ileum.

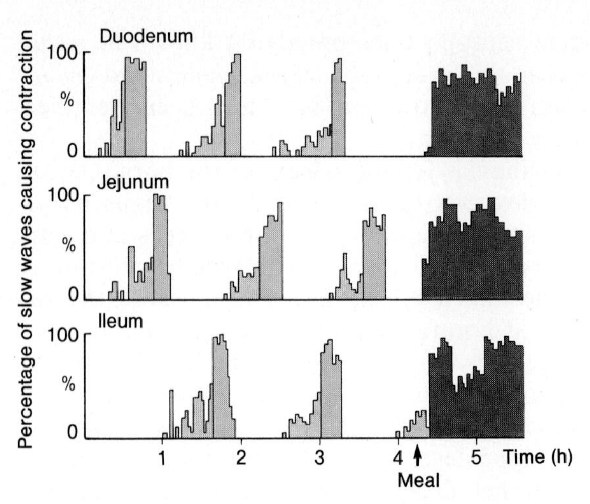

Fig. 29-5. Interdigestive myoelectric motor complex. Percentage of slow waves that are followed by muscle contraction, during the interdigestive phase. In Phase 1 the motor system is at rest; in Phase 2 *(light gray)* as many as 50% of the waves elicit contraction, and in Phase 3 *(red)* activity is practically maximal. The activity front migrates from the duodenum **(top)** to the ileum **(bottom)** in 1–1.5 h and then begins again. Eating *(arrow)* interrupts the interdigestive complex *(dark gray)*. From [1]

Interdigestive myoelectric motor complex. During the interdigestive pause, when stomach and small intestine no longer contain appreciable remnants of food, an electromechanical phenomenon peculiar to the gastrointestinal tract occurs – a repeated sequence of phasic motor activity. After relatively long periods of motor inactivity (*Phase I;* duration ca. 1 h) and of intermittent contractions (*Phase II;* duration ca. 30 min) a well-defined pattern of electrical and motor activity appears (*Phase III;* duration ca. 15 min). These phases are illustrated in Fig. 29-5. In Phase III, complexes of numerous action potentials and strongly constricting peristalsis *("interdigestive front")* with a frequency of 10–12/min begin in the antrum of the stomach or in the duodenum and migrate down the entire small intestine as far as the ileum, at which time a new complex begins at the upper end. With a rate of migration of 6–8 cm/min in the upper small intestine and ca. 2 cm/min in the lower region, a new cycle begins every 1.5 h. The activity front drives food remnants, clumps of bacteria and even foreign bodies ahead of it; metaphorically, this moving motor complex has been called the "housekeeper" of the stomach and intestine. In patients with pathologically large numbers of bacteria in the small intestine, impairment of this motor complex has been found.
The myoelectric motor complex arises in the *muscle cells* and the *intramural nerve network* of the intestine. Although it is intrinsically initiated, it can be modified by way of the autonomic nervous system or hormones. A special contribution is made by the peptide *motilin,* the main source of which is the mucosa of the upper small intestine. During Phase III of the complex its concentration in the blood plasma rises; the complex can be triggered prematurely by injecting motilin intravenously.

Basic Mechanisms of Secretion

The *digestive juices* are produced by active synthesis in secretory cells of various organs – the salivary glands in the mouth, the gastric and intestinal glands, the exocrine part of the pancreas and the liver. The *primary secretion* produced by these cells includes enzymes and other substances in an electrolyte-containing solution. On the way through the ducts leaving the organs, the primary secretion can undergo considerable alteration, particularly with respect to its electrolyte composition.

Functional anatomy. The *digestive enzymes* are proteins synthesized in special glandular cells. The synthesis begins in the *rough endoplasmic reticulum* in the basal part of the cell. Through the cisternae or tubules formed by the endoplasmic reticulum the newly formed protein reaches the apical region of the cell and enters the vacuoles of the *Golgi apparatus*, where it is concentrated in zymogen granules 3 μm in diameter. In response to a secretory stimulus the granules are expelled from the cell by exocytosis; in this process, the membrane enclosing the granule fuses with the apical cell membrane, whereupon the site of fusion opens to release the contents to the outside, into the ducts.

Control of secretion. The digestive glands can be activated by the *vagus nerve* and, correspondingly, be inhibited by atropine. In addition, specific *hormones* act to promote or suppress secretion. The second messengers in this process are Ca^{2+} and cAMP (see Fig. 29-3).

Gastrointestinal-Associated Immune System

Along with the absorbable components of food and the indigestible fibrous components, the gastrointestinal tract is exposed to many antigens such as *bacteria, viruses* and *food allergens.* Accordingly, it is well equipped with **immunocompetent lymphoid tissue.** This tissue accounts for ca. 25% of the intestinal mucosa; its total volume is about equal to that of the spleen. The *"gastrointestinal-associated lymphoid tissue"* **(GALT)** has three anatomical and functional subdivisions, as follows:

1. *Peyer's plaques.* These are aggregations of lymph follicles that collect intestinal antigens and produce antibodies in response to them.
2. *Lymphocytes and plasma cells* in the lamina propria. These enterocytes form immunoglobulins, chiefly IgA; because it has two more polypeptide chains than does serum IgA, it is called *secretory IgA (sIgA).*
3. *Intraepithelial lymphocytes,* mostly in the T-cell line. Further along the drainage system of lymph and portal blood, the *mesenterial lymph nodes* and the *reticuloendothelial system (RES) of the liver* can also be counted as part of the intestinal immune system.

The three systems of the GALT come into close contact with the intestinal antigens. The intraepithelial **lymphocytes** are separated from the lumen only by the tight junctions between the epithelial cells. Between the Peyer's plaques and the lumen are special cells, called *M cells,* which promote the transport of antigens into the lymph follicles. The lymph cells in the lamina propria, finally, are near capillaries and lymph vessels (see Fig. 29-32, p. 723). Normally this immunological barrier provides sufficient defense, but when the mucosa is infected (e.g., under the influence of especially pathogenic substances, bacteria or other noxae) it can be broken.

Gas in the Gastrointestinal Tract

Despite the clinical importance of flatulence it can produce (meteorism), little is known about gas in the gastrointestinal tract.

Volume and composition. The *volume of gas* in the body can be measured by plethysmography or by a method involving insufflation of the gas argon into the gut; the amount of gas expelled daily from the intestine can be determined with an intestinal catheter. Normally the gastrointestinal tract contains less than 200 ml of gas. The volume eliminated through the rectum averages about 600 ml/day, in about 15 40-ml portions, though there is considerable individual variation (from 200 to 2,000 ml/day). The amount of gas can be greatly increased by a diet rich in cellulose, which is broken down by bacteria in the colon. Eating beans can raise the hourly gas elimination tenfold.

A bloated feeling, however, is not always correlated with a specific increase in intestinal gas volume. When an inert gas is insufflated into the intestine of someone with the *"irritable bowel"* syndrome, or an inserted balloon is blown up, the patient experiences pressure much earlier than a control subject. In these patients the threshold to intraluminal pressure is lowered.

In the *composition of the intestinal gas mixture,* the following five gases account for 99%: N_2, O_2, CO_2, H_2 and CH_4. Their relative proportions vary widely, depending on the individual and on the origin of the gas mixture. These gases are odorless. The unpleasant odor of the flatus is due to traces of aromatic products of bacterial protein decomposition, such as indole, skatole, mercaptan and hydrogen sulfide.

Origin of the gases. The intestinal gas originates in three basic ways: as swallowed air, by intraluminal formation and by diffusion from the blood.

The gas-filled "gastric bubble" is formed by **swallowed air.** Each time something is swallowed, air enters the stomach, in an amount varying among individuals and averaging 2–3 ml. Much of this air is expelled from the stomach by burping.

CO_2, H_2 and CH_4 are **formed in the lumen** of the intestine. $\mathbf{CO_2}$ is produced by the reaction between HCO_3^-, in secretions from the pancreas, intestine and liver, and H^+ in the gastric juice and from fatty acids. Large amounts of CO_2 are generated in this way (P_{CO_2} in the duodenum is 200–500 mm Hg), but much of it is reabsorbed in the small intestine. The CO_2 in the flatus comes from the bacterial decomposition of carbohydrates in the colon. $\mathbf{H_2}$ is also released by bacterial fermentation of nonabsorbable carbohydrates in the colon. Animals raised in sterile conditions and newborn children do not excrete H_2. Similarly, because very few bacteria are present in the small intestine (see Fig. 29-40, p. 733), practically no H_2 is formed there.

Part of the H_2 formed in the colon is reabsorbed, travels in the bloodstream to the lungs and is exhaled. This sequence of events is exploited in the standard current method of determining transit time in the small intestine, the **H_2 breath test.** The subject ingests a carbohydrate that is poorly absorbed, the expired air is analyzed by gas chromatography until an increase in H_2 concentration is detected, and the time elapsed since ingestion is recorded. This test is also used to diagnose malabsorption of carbohydrates.

As in the case of H_2, $\mathbf{CH_4}$ (methane) is formed by bacterial decomposition of carbohydrates in the colon. The process is evidently genetically determined and depends on the individual's intestinal flora. About one-third of adults produce fairly large amounts of CH_4, sufficient to make the specific gravity of the feces less than 1, so that the stool floats on the water in the toilet.
Another source of gases in the intestinal lumen is **diffusion from the plasma.** The direction of diffusion is determined by the relative partial pressures of the gas in plasma and lumen. The plasma pressure is higher for N_2 ($P_{N_2} = 600$ mm Hg), for O_2 ($P_{O_2} = 50$ mm Hg) and – in fasting conditions, with low HCO_3^- and H^+ production – for CO_2; therefore these gases diffuse into the intestinal lumen. The volume of N_2 that reaches the lumen by diffusion is ca. 1–2 ml/min; the volumes of O_2 and CO_2 are very small, because of their low partial pressures in the plasma.

H_2 and CH_4 form an *explosive mixture* with O_2. Intraluminal explosions, sometimes fatal, have been reported to occur during colonoscopic removal of polyps by high-frequency diathermy after insufflation of air if the cleaning of the intestine had been incomplete or if mannitol (which is split by bacteria) had been used.

Basic Mechanisms of Intestinal Transport

The main function of the intestinal tract is the *absorption of water, electrolytes and foodstuffs.* The small and large intestines make different contributions to this task. The most important function of the *small intestine* is the transport of energy carriers, water, electrolytes, bile acids and vitamins. In addition to serving as a reservoir for the feces, the *colon* plays an important role in the final regulation of intestinal fluid absorption. Although there are functional and morphological differences, the transport mechanisms in the epithelia of the small and large intestines are similar in principle.

Terminology. The intestinal contents *(chyme)* are transported in two directions, (i) from *oral to aboral,* with the motility of the intestinal wall as the driving force (p. 695), and (ii) from *mucosal to serosal,* from the lumen across the epithelium into the subepithelial capillaries and into the lymph vessels. Here we consider the latter transport processes, in terms of the rate of transport or *flux.*
In principle, a substance can be transported across the intestinal epithelium in either direction, from the lumen to the serosa or the reverse. When the predominant unidirectional flux is from mucosal to serosal, **absorption** is occurring; if the flux is predominantly from serosal to mucosal – i.e., toward the lumen – the process is **secretion** (Fig. 29-6). The *net flux* is always the resultant of the two opposed unidirectional fluxes.

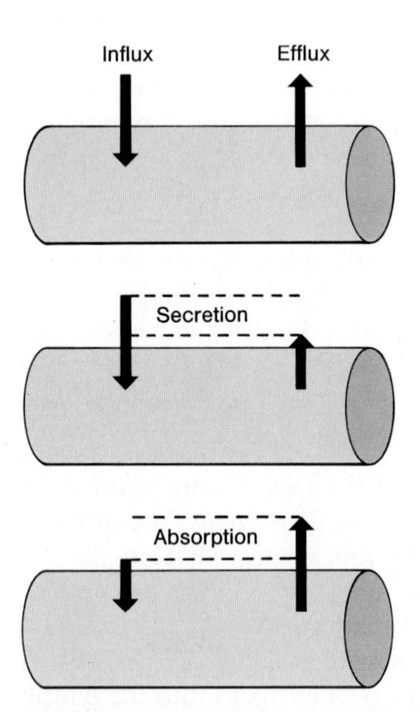

Fig. 29-6. Intestinal water and electrolyte movement. The net flux is the resultant of two unidirectional fluxes. When influx into the intestinal lumen predominates, there is net secretion. When the efflux exceeds the influx, net absorption occurs. When the two components are equal, there is zero net movement

Methods for the study of intestinal transport. Both *in vivo* and *in vitro* methods are used to examine the processes of intestinal transport. Absorption in the human bowel can be studied with the balance technique, by intestinal perfusion and by so-called tolerance tests. In **balance studies** the oral intake of a substance and its excretion in the feces and urine are measured. The difference between the two indicates whether and in what amounts the substance is taken up in the intestine.

Intestinal perfusion is carried out with multiluminal tubes introduced through the mouth into the intestine. The perfusion solution flows into the lumen of the gut from the proximal opening and is aspirated through the distal opening. Transport is analyzed by comparing difference in the amounts of substances in the aspirate with those in the initial solution.

In clinical **"tolerance tests"** a substance is administered orally and the amount of the substance or its metabolites excreted in the urine or in the expired air is measured (*d-xylose test, H_2 breath test)*. These methods give no information about the transport mechanism; for this, determination of the unidirectional fluxes is required.

Furthermore, when charged substances are being transported, the mechanism can be unequivocally characterized only if electrochemical gradients are ruled out. This can be accomplished in *in vitro* experiments with the **"Ussing chamber"** (Fig. 29-7). Here radioactive isotopes are used to determine unidirectional fluxes in both directions while electrochemical gradients are excluded, the epithelium being short-circuited by an externally applied electric current.

To analyze the individual steps in epithelial transport, the epithelium – so far considered as a black box – must be "opened". Two ways of doing this are available: (i) *intracellular electrical measurements* can be made with recording electrodes inserted in the intact tissue, and (ii) transport processes in isolated organelles can be studied by removing *vesicles* from the luminal or serosal side of the cell membrane.

Functional anatomy of the enterocytes.

The *enterocyte* (intestinal epithelial cell) and the *interstitial space* between two adjacent enterocytes constitute a functional unit (Fig. 29-8). On the *contraluminal* side the enterocytes and the interstitial space are separated by the basement membrane. This membrane is of little significance with respect to directional transport processes, because its structure is such that even large molecules can diffuse freely through it. On the *luminal side* the microvilli of the enterocytes protrude into the lumen; here neighboring enterocytes are connected to one another by *tight junctions*. They were originally called "tight" because of their dense appearance in microscopic preparations, which was thought to indicate a barrier to diffusion. It is now known that these intercellular connections are *at least partially permeable to water and the smaller dissolved molecules* and that they make a particularly great contribution to the transport processes in the upper gastrointestinal tract [24].

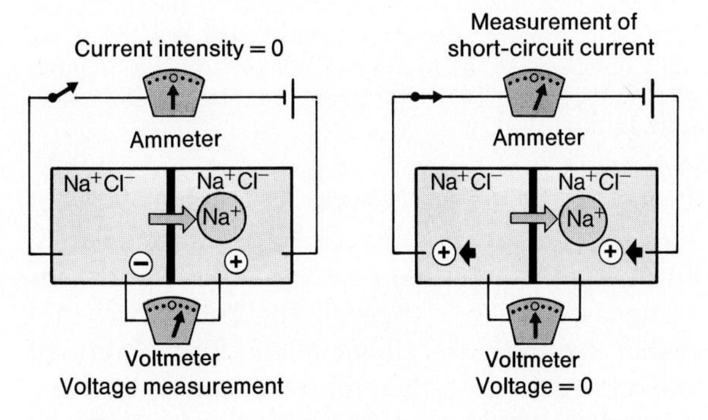

Fig. 29-7. *In vitro* measurement of unidirectional fluxes by means of the "Ussing chamber". The epithelium is suspended between two compartments filled with gassed electrolyte solution and the spontaneous transmucosal potential difference is recorded with two electrodes close to the mucosal and serosal surfaces. The potential difference is compensated by an externally applied electric current; that is, the epithelium is short-circuited. From [13]

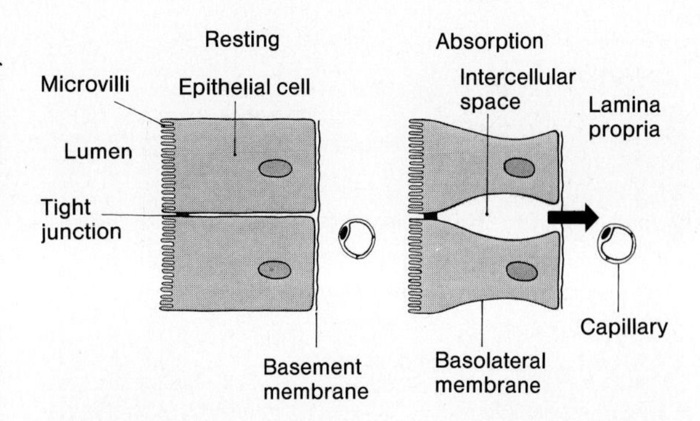

Fig. 29-8. Epithelial cells at rest and during absorption. Adjacent cells form a functional unit including the tight junction and intercellular space. The shapes of the epithelial cells and the intercellular space depend on the functional state of the epithelium

The geometry of the enterocytes and the intercellular space undergoes marked function-related changes (Fig. 29-8). In the *fasting* state the enterocytes are closely apposed, and the interstitial space is so narrow as to be barely visible. During the *absorptive phase* the volume of the enterocytes decreases; because of the transport of fluid, there is a hydrostatic pressure increase in the interstitial space, which therefore expands considerably. This *intercellular hydrostatic pressure* is the driving force for the transport of water and solute from the interstitial space into the subepithelial capillaries and lymph vessels (pp. 700f.).

The mucosal cell contains a differentiated system of organelles (Fig. 29-9). The *endoplasmic reticulum* plays an important role in protein synthesis; it synthesizes the protein components of the *chylomicrons* produced during the absorption

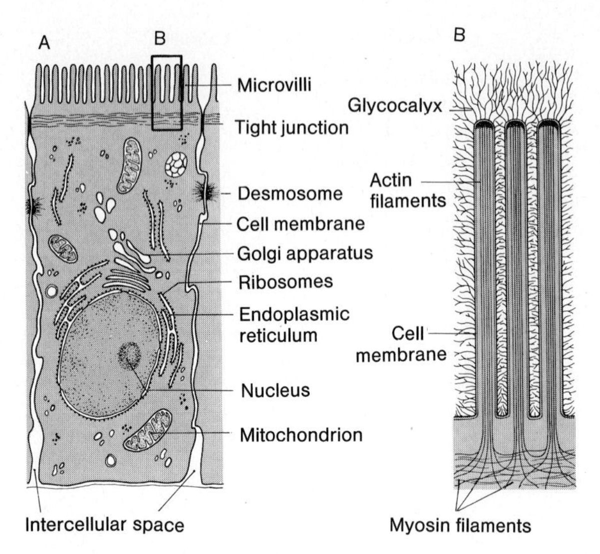

Fig. 29-9 A, B. Structure of the enterocyte **(A)** and fine structure of the brush border **(B)**

of fats. It may also be the site of synthesis of many carriers that facilitate the transport of substances into and through the cell. In the *Golgi apparatus* absorbed material and substances synthesized by the cell are stored and chemically modified. There are *lysosome-like structures* in which absorbed substances are hydrolyzed. The abundance of *mitochondria* indicates a high rate of oxidative metabolism, which is required for the transport function of the enterocytes.

The feature of enterocytes crucial to their absorptive function is the presence of **microvilli,** fingerlike projections from the luminal cell surface (Fig. 29-9). The microvilli form the 1- to 2-μm-thick *brush border* of the enterocytes. Each microvillus is a rod of cytoplasm with a contractile structure (composed of *actin filaments)* in its interior that enables the active deformation of the microvillus. In the apical region of the enterocyte the actin filaments branch to form a complex network *(terminal web).* In general the density of the microvilli decreases from oral to aboral, ranging from 650 to 3,500 microvilli per cell. In the small intestine the microvilli are covered by an additional filamentous layer *(glycocalyx, fuzzy coat)* that is synthesized within the enterocytes and secreted at the surface. The glycocalyx contains *enzymes,* either adsorbed or formed by the enterocyte itself, that assist digestive hydrolysis (p. 726); at the base of the glycocalyx these are incorporated into the microvillar membrane. The glycocalyx itself is coated with a thin layer of water, which cannot be completely removed even by powerful peristaltic contractions; it is called the *"unstirred water layer".* The passage of lipophilic substances is impeded by this layer, while the movement of hydrophilic dissolved particles is facilitated.

Trans- and paracellular transport routes. The entire enterocyte, luminal as well as basolateral surfaces, is enclosed in a three-layered **unit membrane** (see Chapter 1). Because of the chemical composition of the luminal membrane, the transport of *lipid-soluble substances* across it is a simple diffusion process. On the other hand, the transport of lipoid substances in the aqueous cytoplasm and across the basolateral membrane is energy-dependent and requires special mechanisms.

By contrast, the transport of *polar and electrically charged substances* through the lipid membrane is an extremely slow process. To provide a plausible explanation of the experimental data, it is necessary to postulate the existence of *pores* or channels in the membrane, though these have not yet been optically demonstrated. The negative charge at the surface of the enterocyte is significant with regard to the passive transport of charged particles (p. 702).

In parallel with this transcellular route, substances can be transported *paracellularly,* across the tight junctions and through the interstitial space. Because it is mainly the tight junctions that determine the permeability of the epithelium, its physical and electrical properties are also largely dependent on these intercellular structures.

When examined in the electron microscope with the freeze-fracture technique, the tight junctions appear as strands densely bridging the gap between the cells. The number of strands decreases from the proximal to the distal end of the intestinal epithelium. However, the density of the tight junctions seems to depend not only on the number of strands, as previously supposed, but also on differences in their quality [17].

Properties of the epithelium. As much as 90% of the transport of substances across the intestinal epithelium, depending on the location in the intestine, occurs not through the enterocytes but rather by the *paracellular route.* The ability of substances to pass the epithelium paracellularly, down osmotic, hydrostatic, chemical or electrical gradients, is termed **passive permeability.** The tight junctions of the small intestine are quite permeable to molecules with a diameter of up to 0.8 nm, but less so or not at all to larger molecules. Accordingly, for larger molecules the epithelium has the property of a *semipermeable*

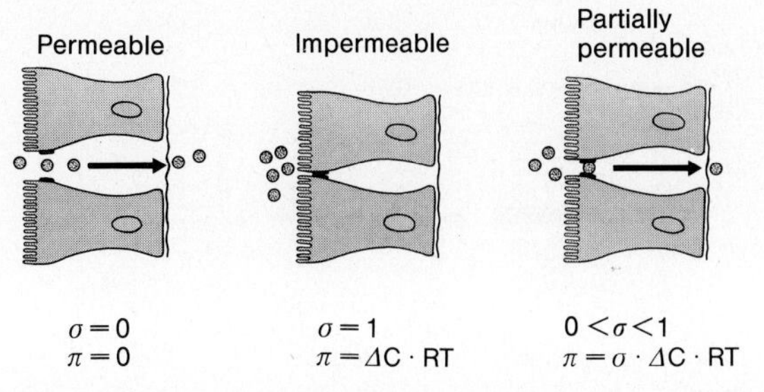

Fig. 29-10. Diagram to illustrate passive permeability of the epithelium. Transepithelial water flow is driven by the osmotic pressure produced by a dissolved substance; the permeability of the membrane to a test substance can be calculated by comparing the water flow it generates with that generated by a solute to which the membrane is completely impermeable (a marker). The measure of passive permeability given by this ratio is the reflection coefficient (σ). From [13]

membrane. It behaves like a sieve, discriminating between substances of different sizes.
If a substance to which the epithelium is impermeable is placed in hypertonic concentration on one side, the **osmotic gradient** (π) causes an influx of water from the other side of the epithelium. The magnitude of the osmotic pressure is proportional to the difference in concentration of an impermeable reference substance (a marker) on the two sides:

$$\pi = \Delta[S] \cdot R \cdot T \tag{1}$$

where $\Delta[S]$ is the concentration difference, R is the gas constant, and T is the absolute temperature.

From the osmotic gradient built up by a substance on one side of the epithelium, the permeability of the epithelium to that substance can be derived. The ratio of the flux of water caused by the osmotic pressure of an impermeable marker to that caused by a test substance is called the **reflection coefficient.** The reflection coefficient is a measure of the passive permeability of the epithelium to uncharged, water-soluble particles (Fig. 29-10). It is 0 when the epithelium is freely permeable to the substance, and 1 when it is impermeable (as with a marker). If the reflection coefficient is less than 1 but greater than 0, it follows that the substance is partially diffusible through the membrane. In this case the molecular size of the substance is comparable to the pore diameter of the tight junctions.

The *diameter of the pores* or channels in the tight junctions decreases along the intestinal tract, from proximal to distal. The human jejunum is permeable to molecules with a diameter of 0.75–0.8 nm; the corresponding values for the ileum are 0.3–0.5 nm, and for the colon, 0.22–0.25 nm. Therefore the permeability of the epithelium to water is also regionally variable. A given hypertonic solution in the intestinal lumen induces the secretion of three times as much water per unit time in the duodenum as in the colon (see also Fig. 29-34). However, the passive permeability to **charged particles** depends not only on the diameter of the epithelial channels but also on their charge. It should also be noted that the diameter of ions is determined by the configuration and the hydration coating as well as by the atomic weight.

Surface charge of the epithelial cell. As a result of the chemical composition of the unit membrane (pp. 699f.), the surface of the epithelial cell bears *fixed negative charges* with which, to preserve electroneutrality, cations become associated *(mobile cations)*. At the luminal membrane these include H^+, so that the pH at the interface between the apical enterocyte membrane and the intestinal lumen is lower than in the lumen itself *(virtual pH zone)*. Ionized bases (e.g., drugs) therefore accumulate at the luminal interface, which facilitates their absorption.

Ion selectivity of the tight junctions. Experimental data clearly show that cations move more readily than anions through the interstitial space. It follows that the *tight junctions also bear fixed negative charges* [41] (Fig. 29-11). Therefore the epithelium behaves like a cation-sensitive membrane; the paracellular permeability to substances is determined not only by the size of the molecule but also by its charge. For instance, with NaCl solutions at different concentrations on the two sides of the epithelium, the net sodium diffusion toward the side on which the concentration is lower outweighs that of chloride. Because of this *selective permeability* of the tight junctions and the resulting predominance of sodium diffusion, a transepithelial potential difference builds up **(diffusion potential)** (Fig. 29-11). The poten-

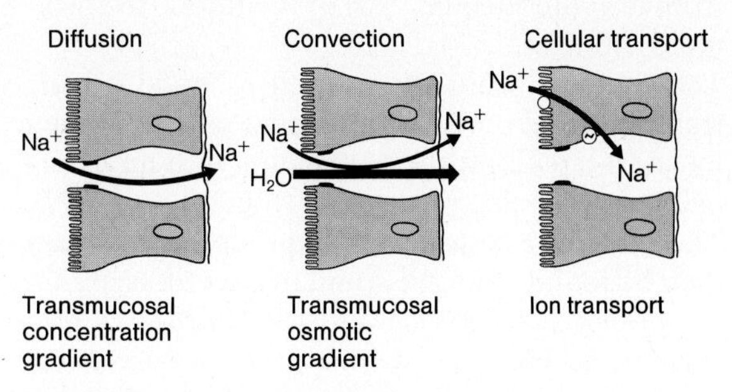

Fig. 29-11. Transport mechanisms involved in the absorption process. From [13]

tial difference created by diffusion of one ion toward the side of lower concentration is described by the Nernst equation (pp. 6f.). However, the potential actually measured is lower than the potential calculated from that equation, which implies that the tight junctions must be at least *partially permeable to chloride.* The relative values for the passive permeation of the two ions can be found from the Goldman equation (p. 7). According to this calculation, the passive permeability to sodium is 7 times as great as to chloride in the ileum and about 3 times as great in the epithelium of the gallbladder.

Another kind of transport that is affected by the selective permeability of the tight junctions is **"solvent drag"** or bulk flow. This is the tendency of water, in moving paracellularly *(convection),* to sweep dissolved substances along with it. Because more cations than anions are so transported, a **flow potential** also contributes to the transepithelial potential. The diffusion and flow potentials are produced by passive processes. The magnitude and positivity or negativity of these potentials depend on osmotic and hydrostatic gradients and on gradients in the transepithelial electrolyte concentrations. Because the direction of these gradients is variable, the potentials are also variable.

Transepithelial potential difference. By recording from both sides of the epithelium in small and large intestine one can demonstrate that a transepithelial potential difference persists even when diffusive and osmotic forces have been excluded. Because this potential requires an *active, energy-dependent transport* process in the epithelial cell, it is called a **transport potential** (Fig. 29-11). Here the epithelium is operating like a battery. The charge of this battery is maintained chiefly by **active sodium transport** from mucosa to serosa. Given this direction of sodium transport, the serosal side of the epithelium becomes positively charged relative to the mucosal side. The transepithelial potential difference increases from oral (duodenum: 3 mV) to aboral (rectosigmoid: 40 mV).

The sodium transport required to build up the transepithelial potential difference can be studied by short-circuiting the epithelium with an externally applied electric current (Fig. 29-7, p. 699). The electrical resistance of the epithelium can then be found from the spontaneous transepithelial potential difference and the short-circuiting current, according to Ohm's law. The **electrical resistance** increases from the proximal to the distal part of the bowel. It is ca. 25 $\Omega \cdot cm^2$ in the jejunum and 100–200 $\Omega \cdot cm^2$ in the colon. The epithelial cell itself has a very high resistance, and recent experiments have shown conclusively that the epithelial resistance is determined entirely by the *paracellular shunt* – that is, by the *density of the tight junctions* [41]. As a consequence, the magnitude of the epithelial resistance is indirectly proportional to the pore size of the tight junctions (Fig. 29-12). The passive permeability of the epithelium of the small intestine is relatively high, and its electrical resistance is correspondingly low; that is, the epithelium of the small intestine is relatively leaky. By contrast, the colonic epithelium is relatively tight, and its electrical resistance is correspondingly high. The tightness of the tight junctions has a considerable influence on sodium absorption (see above).

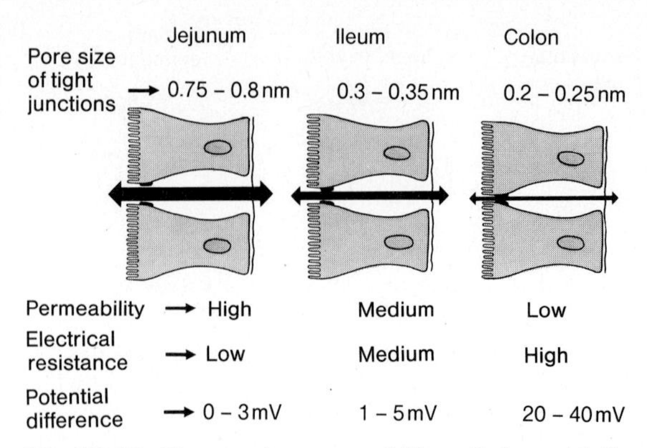

Fig. 29-12. The passive permeability of the epithelium depends on the pore size of the tight junctions, which decreases from the proximal to the distal part of the intestine. Hence the transepithelial potential difference and the electrical resistance of the epithelium increase from proximal to distal. From [13]

Routes and Mechanisms of Intestinal Transport

Two routes are available for the transport of water and dissolved particles through the epithelium: (i) transport through the *epithelial cell* and (ii) transport through the *interstitial space.* Both passive and active mechanisms are involved in the transport of substances through the epithelium.

Passive paracellular transport. The transport of substances through the interstitial space is always passive (Fig. 29-13) and is based on diffusion or convection. *Diffusion* is the movement of a substance through the epithelium down chemical or electrochemical gradients. A prerequisite for the

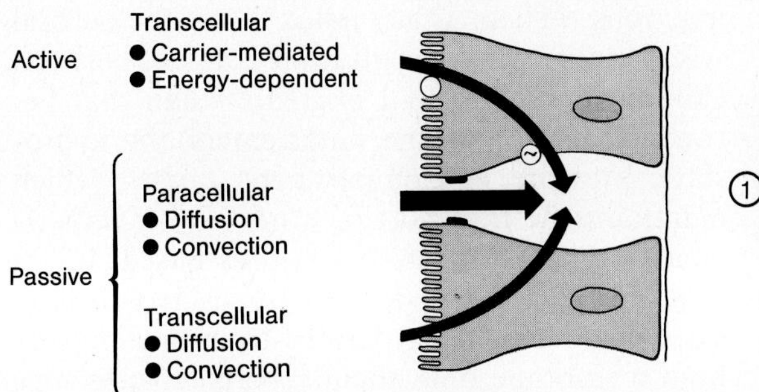

Fig. 29-13. Routes and mechanisms of the epithelial transport of solutes and water. Transcellular transport employs active and/or passive mechanisms; paracellular transport is always passive. From [13]

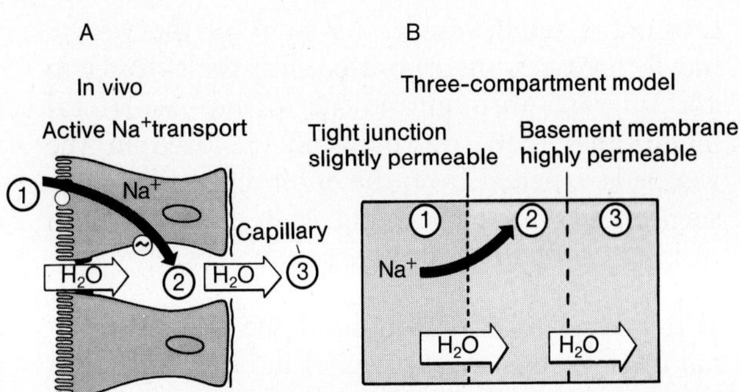

Fig. 29-15. Mechanisms of intestinal water absorption. Water absorption is a purely passive process resulting from the functional asymmetry of the epithelium. This asymmetry is produced by the osmotic gradient between intestinal lumen and interstitial space, the intercellular hydrostatic pressure and the difference in permeability of the tight junctions and the basement membrane

movement of a substance by *convection* is the transepithelial flow of water driven by osmotic or hydrostatic forces. By definition, passive transport occurs with no energy supplied by the cell. The passive flux is always proportional to the osmotic, hydrostatic or concentration gradients (Fig. 29-14) and is described by Fick's equation (pp. 4f.). Absorption of water and electrolytes by the paracellular route is of particularly great quantitative significance in the proximal parts of the intestine – that is, in "leaky" epithelia (Fig. 29-12).

Active transcellular transport. To be absorbed through the epithelial cell, a substance must be taken into the cell across the luminal membrane, transported through the cytosol, and passed across the basolateral membrane into the interstitial space (Figs. 29-13, 29-15). Clearly, this series of barriers considerably impedes passive transport through the enterocyte. For hydrophilic and negatively charged substances, in particular, the lipid cell membrane presents a major barrier.

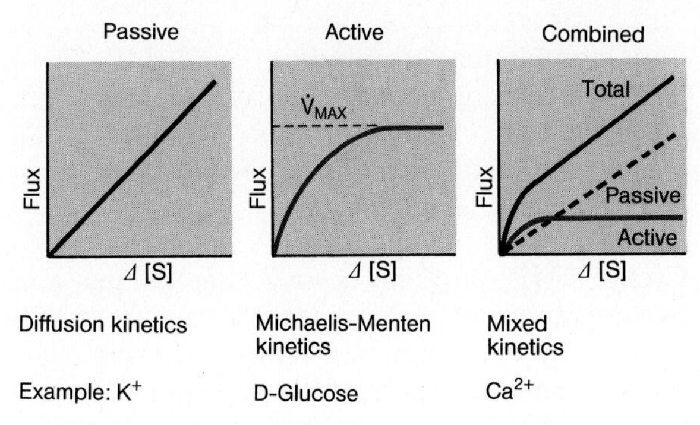

Fig. 29-14. Transport kinetics in passive diffusion and in carrier-mediated active transport

An important function of the epithelial cell is the *active transport* of substances from the intestinal lumen into the subepithelial capillaries and lymph vessels. The characteristic feature of active transport is that it moves substances "uphill" *against a concentration difference,* even when the luminal substrate concentration is low. Active transport is based on the presence of *carrier* molecules in the cell membrane, and requires *metabolic energy.* It is subjected to saturation kinetics; that is, the rate of transport cannot be increased beyond a certain saturation level (Fig. 29-14). The transport mechanisms have a high degree of substrate specificity. They are competitively inhibited by substances chemically related to the substrate, and can be blocked by certain other substances. Often the active transport system operates with maximal efficiency only when the carrier is driven by another substance (coupled transport or cotransport, p. 725).

A carrier-mediated process need not necessarily meet all the criteria for active transport. For instance, fructose is transported by a saturable, carrier-mediated mechanism with no consumption of metabolic energy. In this case transport is achieved by the difference in substrate concentration. Transport of this kind is called *facilitated diffusion.*

Many substances undergo *mixed transport*; that is, they are transported by an active and a passive process simultaneously. When the substrate concentration is low, active transport predominates. With higher substrate concentrations, when the active mechanism has been saturated, most of the transport occurs passively (Fig. 29-14).

Pinocytosis is a mode of absorption in which the cell membrane encloses extracellular material, forming a small vesicle. As soon as the vesicle has formed it is incorporated into the cytoplasm and migrates through the cell to the basolateral membrane; there the material enclosed in the vesicle is expelled from the enterocyte. Pinocytosis probably plays a certain role in the absorption of intact proteins and macromolecules.

Water absorption. Throughout the gastrointestinal tract the transport of water in both directions – mucosal to serosal (absorption) and serosal to mucosal (secretion) – is a purely *passive process.* It is not yet entirely clear whether the water transport is mainly trans- or paracellular. In any case, the volume of transepithelial water flow decreases from oral to aboral, depending on the osmotic gradient. In view of the finding that the pores of the tight junctions become progressively smaller from proximal to distal (p. 701, p. 766), it is likely that water transport by the paracellular route is of greater significance. The driving force for transepithelial water absorption comprises hydrostatic and, above all, **osmotic gradients.** A crucial role is played here by the osmotic gradient created by the *active sodium transport* between the intestinal lumen and the interstitial space (Fig. 29-15). As a result of the active expulsion of sodium from the cell through the basolateral membrane, the interstitial solution becomes hypertonic. The *standing osmotic gradient* so produced causes an influx of water from the intestinal lumen into the interstitial space, either across the tight junctions or through the epithelial cells. This influx of water induces a **hydrostatic pressure gradient** from the interstitial space toward both the mucosal and the serosal side. The basement membrane, which adjoins the epithelial cells on the serosal side, is much more permeable than the tight junctions, so that the water tends to flow out of the interstitial space in that direction, into the subepithelial capillaries. That is, *the intercellular hydrostatic pressure is the driving force for the flow of water and dissolved particles into the subepithelial capillaries.* Of course, this flow can occur only if the hydrostatic pressure in the intercellular space is greater than the capillary filtration pressure.

In Fig. 29-15B the mechanisms involved in water transport are summarized schematically in the form of a *three-compartment model.* The compartments represent the part of the intestinal lumen near the epithelium (1), the interstitial space (2) and the subepithelial space (3). First, the active transport of sodium raises the osmotic concentration in Compartment 2, causing an osmotic influx of water through the tight junctions. (There is no influx from the serosal side, because the concentration gradient between Compartments 2 and 1 is greater than that between 2 and 3.) As the water enters, the hydrostatic pressure in Compartment 2 rises, which maintains the transport of water into Compartment 3. The entire process is thus based on the *combined action of active and passive transport* in three compartments separated from one another by a membrane only slightly permeable to ions (tight junctions) and a highly permeable membrane (basement membrane). In the small intestine, where the pore diameter of the tight junctions is relatively large, the efficient water influx from the lumen counterbalances the tendency toward hypertonicity of the interstitial solution; that is, *in the small intestine sodium ions are absorbed in a solution isotonic with the plasma.* The tight junctions in the colonic epithelium have considerably smaller pores. As a result, water flows from the lumen into the interstitial space at a significantly lower rate, and dilutes the intercellular solution only slightly. Therefore, *in the colon the absorbed solution is hypertonic to the plasma,* and consequently, the fluid in the feces is hypotonic with respect to the plasma.

Secretion of electrolytes and water. Intestinal secretion occurs when more fluid is transported from the serosal to the mucosal side than in the opposite direction. Transport toward the lumen can predominate either because the movement of fluid from mucosal to serosal side is reduced *(malabsorption)* or because of an increase in movement from serosa to mucosa (Fig. 29-6, p. 698). Because the transport of water is entirely passive, there must be a change in the direction of osmotic or hydrostatic gradients to convert absorption into secretion. *Hence the secretion of electrolytes is always a prerequisite for the secretion of water.* There are several possible mechanisms for fluid secretion:

(i) active anion secretion,
(ii) reduced active absorption,
(iii) high luminal osmolarity (Fig. 29-34),
(iv) increase in serosal hydrostatic pressure, and
(v) increased permeability of the tight junctions to ions (Fig. 29-16).

Cyclic AMP plays a central role in the active secretion of electrolytes. Certain *bacterial toxins* (cholera toxin, colitoxin) and *hormones* (prostaglandins, secretin, VIP) increase the content of cAMP in the enterocyte. By changing the intracellular calcium concentration, cAMP

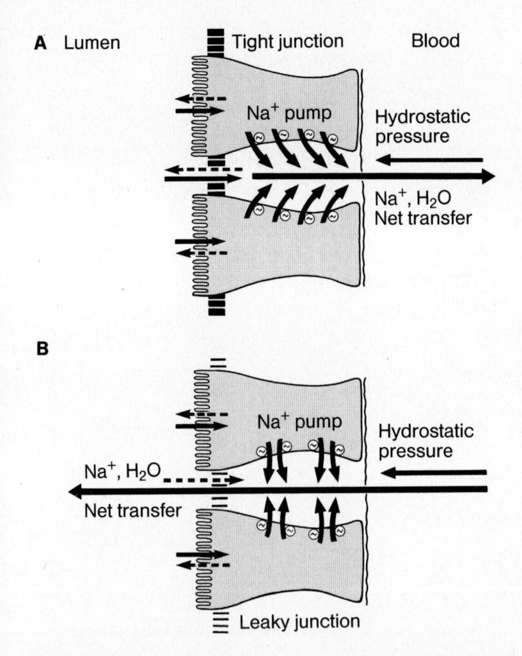

Fig. 29-16. Paracellular secretion of water and electrolytes. Dihydroxy bile acids and hydragogue cathartics increase the permeability of the tight junctions. This leak abolishes the functional asymmetry of the epithelium, and because of the hydrostatic pressure on the subepithelial side the direction of net transfer reverses. From [38]

raises the chloride permeability in the crypts of the mucosal enterocyte membrane (pp. 723, 725). Chloride passes from the cell into the intestinal lumen, and sodium and water follow – the former to preserve electroneutrality, and the latter by osmosis. In the other situations listed above, fluid secretion is produced by passive processes.

29.2 Oral Cavity, Pharynx and Esophagus

The oral cavity, pharynx and esophagus form a functional unit, in which a morsel of food is prepared for passage through the gastrointestinal tract by mastication and the incorporation of saliva, and then is transported from the mouth to the stomach.

Mastication

In this preparative step, solid food is chewed – cut, torn and ground into smaller pieces. Although such fragmentation is not an absolute prerequisite for digestion and absorption, it greatly facilitates those processes. The structures involved in chewing are the upper and lower jaws with the teeth, the striated mandibular musculature, the tongue and cheeks, floor of the mouth and palate.

The rhythmic chewing action is largely automatic, and not consciously controlled (p. 101). When food particles touch the palate and teeth, this stimulus elicits a set of reflex *chewing movements:* sideways, forward and backward, up and down. One such mastication cycle takes about 0.6–0.8 s. The *forces* so exerted amount to 100–250 N in the region of the incisors, and 300–900 N in the molar region, with a maximum as great as 1,500 N. The force is lower, the further apart the teeth are; for instance, at a distance of 1 cm 400 N was measured, and at 2 cm only 120 N [16]. For most efficient fragmentation a complete set of teeth is required; the absence of several teeth cannot be compensated by stronger or longer chewing.

The tongue and cheeks hold the mass of food between the jaws, within the chewing area. Solid food is broken down to particles a few mm in diameter. The *salivation* stimulated by chewing prepares the consistency of the food for swallowing. *Taste sensations* are enhanced by mastication and by the dissolving or suspension of solid components in the saliva. These sensations trigger a reflex that further stimulates salivation and gastric secretion (p. 713).

Secretion of Saliva

Saliva is formed in the mouth at a rate of *ca. 1 l per day.* It keeps the mouth moist and facilitates speaking, lubricates the chewed food and promotes taste. It is essential for the health of the teeth; without saliva, they become carious and fall out. Saliva has a cleaning and – because it contains *lysozymes* and *thiocyanate ions* – disinfectant action. The fluid intake is regulated by way of the feeling of thirst produced when the secretion of saliva decreases. Finally, saliva initiates the digestion of carbohydrates.

Salivary glands. The many small, mucus-secreting glands in the mucous membranes of the cheek and on the tongue do not adequately moisten the mouth. Moisture is provided by three large, paired glands, the *parotid, submandibular* and *sublingual* glands. Each is composed of acini (terminal secretory cells) and a system of intra-, inter- and extralobular ducts. On the basis of histology and the type of saliva they produce, the glands are classified as (i) *serous*, producing a saliva rich in protein as well as in water and electrolytes (parotid gland) or (ii) *mixed glands*, which produce mucopolysaccharides (mucus) in addition (submandibular and sublingual glands).

Neural control of secretion. Salivation is under both sympathetic and parasympathetic control. It is initiated by secretory centers in the *medulla oblongata*, which receive afferent signals from the mouth and palate (taste, touch) and the nose (smell) as well as from higher centers (imagination; p. 713). *Parasympathetic* activation induces the formation of large amounts of a low-protein, serous saliva. Stimulation of the glands by injection of noradrenalin into the cervical artery, which corresponds to a *sympathetic* stimulus, causes secretion of a relatively small amount of viscous saliva from the submandibular and sublingual glands, but not the parotid gland; it also produces vasoconstriction and contraction of the salivary ducts.

The transmission of neural excitation to the acinar cells and the cellular response – i.e., **stimulus-secretion coupling** – proceed according to the diagram in Fig. 29-3, p. 695. In the salivary glands the secretion of electrolytes and water is stimulated mainly by adrenergic substances and acetylcholine, whereas enzyme secretion is especially promoted by β-adrenergic stimulation.
When not stimulated, the salivary glands secrete about 0.5 ml/min. Dehydration, fear and stress reduce the volume secreted; salivation almost ceases during sleep and under anesthesia. Olfactory stimuli (e.g., amyl nitrite) can double the secretion rate, and chewing raises it by a factor of 2.3. Secretion is further increased by taking larger bites and by taste stimuli. For example, taking a 0.5 M solution of citric acid into the mouth raises the rate of salivation to 7.4 ml/min.

It is a familiar experience that *conditioned reflexes* (p. 713) triggered by the sight of food, associated sounds or even thinking about food can raise the rate of salivation. At rest the individual glands make the following contributions to the total volume of saliva: submandibular 71%, parotid 25% and sublingual 4%. After stimulation the proportions (in the same order) change to 63%, 34% and 3%.
The rate of blood flow through the salivary glands at rest varies from 0.1 to 0.6 ml · $min^{-1} \cdot g^{-1}$. During stimulation it is about 5 times higher.

Composition of the saliva. Saliva consists of 99% water, so that its specific gravity is 1. The most important dissolved **electrolytes** are Na^+, K^+, Cl^- and HCO_3^-. The primary saliva secreted in the acini is isotonic with the blood. It becomes hypotonic as it passes through the ducts, which have relatively low permeability to water, because of active Na^+ absorption accompanied by passive Cl^- absorption. Eventually its osmolarity is only about 2/3 that of plasma. The electrolyte composition of the saliva changes with the secretion rate; as a greater volume is secreted, the concentrations of Na^+ and Cl^- rise while that of K^+ falls (Fig. 29-17), because with an increased rate of flow less time is available for the absorption of Na^+ and secretion of K^+. The resting pH of saliva is in the range 5.45–6.06, and after stimulation it rises to 7.8.

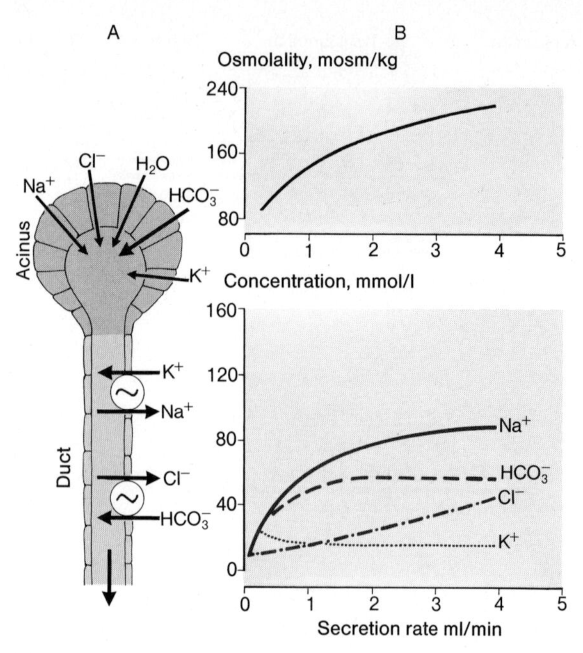

Fig. 29-17 A, B. Electrolyte transport in salivary glands **(A)** and the electrolyte composition of the saliva as a function of rate of secretion **(B)**. The isotonic primary secretion produced by the acini is altered in passing through the ducts, by the absorption or secretion of ions and water. Because the duct is relatively impermeable to water, the saliva becomes hypotonic. The greatest change in composition occurs when the secretion rate is low. When it is higher there is less time for the exchange processes, and the secretion remains closer to the primary secretion in composition. Modified from [1]

The salivary glands secrete various *macromolecules:* amylase, glycoproteins, mucopolysaccharides, lysozymes, immunoglobulins and blood-group substances. The most significant functionally are **α-amylase,** secreted primarily by the parotid gland, and the **mucoproteins** (submandibular and sublingual). α-amylase is stable at pH 4–11 and is maximally active at pH 6.9. It hydrolyzes the α-1,4 glycosidic linkage in polysaccharides, splitting the starches into maltose and maltotriose.

Disorders of the salivary glands, such as *Sjögren's syndrome* (one of the rheumatic diseases), cause *"xerostomy"* or dryness of the mouth; this condition involves a tendency to stomal ulcer formation, dental caries and difficulties in chewing and swallowing.

Deglutition

When the food has been worked into a manageable bolus, it is swallowed by propulsion through three regions: mouth, pharynx and esophagus. Hence deglutition comprises an *oral*, a *pharyngeal* and an *esophageal phase*, only the first of which is carried out voluntarily. The musculature of the oropharynx, being striated, contracts only under the influence of neuronal impulses from the CNS, and relaxes in their absence. The distal 2/3 of the esophageal wall consists of smooth muscle, and is therefore under autonomic control.

Oral and pharyngeal phases. In the first phase of deglutition, the tip of the tongue is raised to separate part of the mass of chewed food and shift it into the middle of the mouth, between the base of the tongue and the hard palate (Fig. 29-18A). Lips and jaws close, the soft palate is raised, and the anterior part of the tongue presses the bolus back into the upper part of the throat, the pharynx (Fig. 29-18B). The palate and the contracted palatopharyngeal muscles form a partition that closes the nasopharyngeal space off from the oral cavity. When this closure is selectively impaired, as can occur in poliomyelitis, the bolus is pressed into the epipharynx, and swallowed liquid runs back out of the nose.

While the tongue is pushing the bolus further back, *breathing is reflexly interrupted* for a short time. The larynx rises and blocks the airway (Fig. 29-18C). The approaching bolus bends the epiglottis over the entrance to the trachea, preventing the aspiration of food particles. When this mechanism fails, one "swallows the wrong way". Propelled by the pharyngeal musculature and tongue with a pressure of 4–10 mm Hg (Fig. 29-18D), the bolus slides over the epiglottis into the esophagus. It is allowed entry by the opening of the upper esophageal sphincter, mainly by the action of the cricopharyngeal muscle (Fig. 29-18E).

Whereas the oral phase is under voluntary control, an *involuntary reflex action* is initiated when the bolus reaches the pharynx; it is triggered by receptors in the mouth and throat. The afferent impulses are conducted in the *glossopharyngeal nerve* and the upper laryngeal branch of the *vagus*. The motor neurons supplying the pharynx are arranged in five main groups, located in the motor nuclei of the trigeminal, facial and hypoglossal nerves, in the nucleus ambiguus of the vagus nerve and in the spinal segments C1-C3.

Once the "swallowing center" in the medulla oblongata has been stimulated, the complex process of deglutition proceeds involuntarily, by a preset program. A normal adult swallows about 600 times in 24 h – 200 times while eating and an additional 350 times in the waking state and 50 times during sleep. The fine adjustment of this intricate process requires a high innervation density and correspondingly small motor units. The ratio of nerve fibers to muscle fibers is between 1:2 and 1:6 in the pharyngeal muscles, as com-

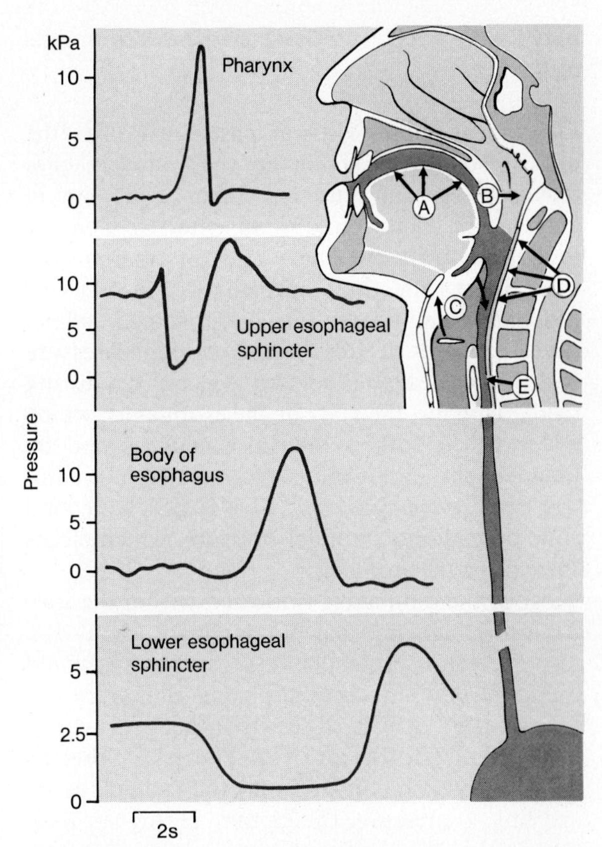

Fig. 29-18 A-E. Oropharyngeal and esophageal phases of deglutition. **A** The tongue presses up against the hard palate, **B** the nasopharynx is closed off by the soft palate, **C** the larynx rises and the epiglottis bends over the entrance to the trachea, **D** the pharyngeal muscles start peristalsis. **E** Reflex opening of the upper esophageal sphincter. The pressure changes during swallowing are represented by *curves* (left) for the pharynx, the upper esophageal sphincter, the body of the esophagus and the lower esophageal sphincter

pared with 1:2,000 in the gastrocnemius muscle in the leg.

Esophageal phase. Having passed through the upper esophageal sphincter, the bolus reaches the esophagus, a muscular tube 25–35 cm in length. The wall contains an external layer of longitudinal muscle fibers and an internal circular layer. The three specialized zones of the esophagus are (i) the *upper esophageal sphincter* (UES), a 2- to 4-cm-long tonic high-pressure zone under neuronal control that relaxes during swallowing, (ii) the *body* of the esophagus, which is controlled both by extrinsic neurons and by independent, endogenous mechanisms, and (iii) the *lower esophageal sphincter* (LES), a second zone of high intraluminal pressure, which closes the exit to the stomach.

Most of the esophagus is located within the thorax, so that its internal pressures are about 4–6 mm Hg below atmospheric pressure. Air would therefore flow into the esophagus if it were not for the UES, which closes its upper end with a pressure of 50–100 mm Hg. The LES prevents reflux of gastric contents into the esophagus by exerting a pressure 15–25 mm H higher than that in the gastric fundus.

The musculature in the upper third of the esophagus is striated, and that in the lower 2/3 is smooth. The esophagus is lined with squamous epithelium containing a few mucous glands. This is separated by a narrow, jagged line (linea dentata) from the columnar epithelium of the stomach.

The esophagus is innervated chiefly by the *vagus nerve*. The upper, striated musculature is controlled by somatic fibers, whereas the autonomic innervation of the lower, smooth musculature corresponds to the arrangement typical of the gastrointestinal tract (Fig. 29-2, p. 693).

The longitudinal and circular muscles differ in the way they are *activated*. The longitudinal muscles are controlled by cholinergic fibers and contract as long as the stimulus is effective *("on-response")*. The circular musculature produces an initial slight, brief pressure increase in response to neuronal activity but does not actually contract until the stimulus has ceased *("off-response")*. There is a latency gradient along the esophagus, such that distal regions respond later than proximal. Because the contraction is not affected by anticholinergics but is suppressed by the nerve poison tetrodotoxin, the transmitter to the circular muscles is thought to be a gastrointestinal peptide, perhaps *vasoactive intestinal polypeptide* (VIP).

The term **primary peristalsis** is used for the movement that continues the act of swallowing started in the upper esophagus (Fig. 29-18). A **secondary peristalsis** is initiated by afferent impulses from the esophagus itself – for instance, by a pressure stimulus produced by remnants of a bolus that were not moved on by the primary peristalsis.

The *peristaltic wave* in the esophagus is an area of contraction 2–4 cm in length that propagates downward at a rate of 2–4 cm/s, reaching the LES after ca. 9 s (Fig. 29-18). The *passage velocity* can vary considerably, however, depending on the consistency of the bolus and the position of the body. With the body erect, water reaches the stomach after 1 s, a viscous mass after 5 s and solid particles after 9–10 s. The pressure of the peristaltic wave rises distally, to 30–120 mm Hg in the lower esophagus. The *pressure amplitude* increases with the size of the bolus; it is smaller when one swallows "dry" (i.e., without a bolus). The LES opens before the bolus enters the stomach and closes again (i.e., returns to the resting tone after a brief phase of increased pressure) after the bolus has entered the stomach. This *relaxation* is a reflex mediated by the vagus nerve; vasoactive intestinal polypeptide (VIP) is thought to be the neurotransmitter.

The high pressure at the LES is influenced by various factors. It rises with increasing intraabdominal pressure (produced, e.g., by contraction of abdominal muscles), when the gastric pH becomes alkaline, and after consumption of protein-rich food. It is reduced by the intake of other substances: fat, chocolate, peppermint, alcohol and nicotine. Control of the UES pressure involves *neurogenic* (cholinergic), *myogenic* and *hormonal factors*. Among the latter, gastrin, motilin, substance P, pancreatic polypeptide, vasopressin and angiotensin II raise the sphincter pressure, and secretin, cholecystokinin, glucagon, glucose-dependent insulinotropic polypeptide (GIP) and vasoactive intestinal polypeptide (VIP) reduce it. It is also reduced by progesterone, which explains the heartburn that often accompanies pregnancy, with its high progesterone level.

Pathophysiological aspects. Disturbances of the normal function of the esophagus and sphincters can have relevant clinical effects. In **achalasia** peristalsis is uncoordinated and the LES fails to relax adequately in response to swallowing. Therefore food is retained in the esophagus and dilates it (megaesophagus). This disorder results from degeneration of Auerbach's (myenteric) plexus; in South America the syndrome is known as Chagas' disease and is caused by trypanosomes, but the cause in the northern hemisphere is not known. Another condition of great clinical importance is produced when the sphincter does not close properly and allows reflux of gastric contents to the esophagus; the esophageal mucosa can be so severely damaged that it becomes inflamed and ulcerated **(reflux esophagitis).** Disorderly, violent contractions of the esophagus, called tertiary contractions, can result in sharp pains behind the sternum; the character of the pain in this syndrome of **diffuse esophageal spasm** can be difficult to distinguish from that of angina pectoris. The main methods for investigating disturbances of esophageal motility are *radiocinematography*, pressure measurement *(manome-*

try) with perfused catheters, *functional scintigraphy* after a radioactively labeled bolus has been swallowed, and *long-term pH measurement*, in which a pH-sensitive probe monitors reflux in the lower third of the esophagus.

29.3 Stomach

The stomach has several functions. It stores the swallowed food and secretes the gastric juice, which mixes with the stomach contents and changes them chemically, and it also breaks up the food mechanically. The result is that the food is converted to chyme; for further digestion and absorption the chyme is released into the duodenum in appropriate portions.

Gastric Motility

Storage and transport functions. The muscular activity in the stomach serves three main functions: (i) *storage* of food, (ii) *mixing* and *grinding* and (iii) *emptying* into the duodenum. Initiation and coordination of gastric movements are basically coupled to *direct responses of the smooth musculature*, mediated by intrinsic receptors for many neurotransmitters and hormones. These regulator substances modify the myogenic excitability and modulate the basic contractile activity of the smooth muscle cells during the active phase of gastric digestion as well as in the interdigestive phase.
The stomach musculature consists of three layers: (i) the *external longitudinal layer*, (ii) the well-developed *middle circular layer*, with a sphincter-like thickening in the pyloric region, and (iii) the *oblique inner layer*, which is best developed in the anterior and posterior wall and fuses distally with the circular muscle layer. The *intrinsic nerve plexuses* (myenteric and submucosal) are situated between and below the muscle layers (Fig. 29-2, p. 693). The cholinergic and adrenergic extrinsic nerve fibers are connected with the intrinsic plexuses, and also release other stimulating or inhibitory transmitters. The proximal and distal parts of the stomach differ fundamentally in regulation and function.

Storage function of the stomach. The *proximal stomach* has no phasic rhythm of excitation and no peristalsis. It actively builds up tone that can be modified according to the intraluminal pressure. Hence the main task of the proximal stomach is to store the received food. The pressure inside the stomach falls even before the bolus has passed from the esophagus into the stomach *(receptive relaxation)*; the muscle tone is then adjusted to a larger volume under the control of stretch-sensitive receptors in the stomach wall, with no increase in pressure *(adaptive relaxation)*. This process is mediated by inhibitory vagal fibers as well as hormones; distensibility of the stomach is increased by *cholecystokinin*. As the portions of food enter the stomach, the relatively firm components become arranged in layers, while liquid and gastric juice flow around the outside into the distal stomach. Slow, tonic contractions exert a steady pressure on the ingested food, moving it gradually toward the pylorus.

Transport of solid contents. Unlike the fundus, the corpus contains *myogenic pacemakers* (p. 79), which generate cyclic triphasic potentials, the **slow waves**, beginning high up on the greater curvature and including the antrum (Fig. 29-19). These propagate to the pylorus with a frequency of 3/min, and are responsible for transport of gastric contents through the stomach. Contractions are associated with the slow waves, although not every wave elicits contraction. The slow wave brings the muscle potential close to the threshold for activation, and neuronal and hormonal influences then determine whether a contraction will occur as well as its strength and duration.
The powerful, circular **peristaltic waves** of the distal stomach propel the contents toward the pylorus and duodenum. Fluid is also rapidly emptied into the duodenum, with an exponential decrease in fluid volume. Solid components do not pass the *pylorus* until they have been broken down to particles measuring at most 2–3 mm, and 90% of the particles leaving the stomach are only 0.25 mm in diameter. When the wave of contraction approaches the distal antrum, the pylorus contracts. It forms the narrowest part (not a sphincter in the strict sense) at the junction of stomach and duodenum and closes even before the antrum has been completely traversed. The compressed contents are forcefully thrown back into the stomach; in the process, the solid elements rub against one another and are further crushed and ground.
Emptying of the stomach is controlled by extrinsic autonomic nerves, by local reflexes within the

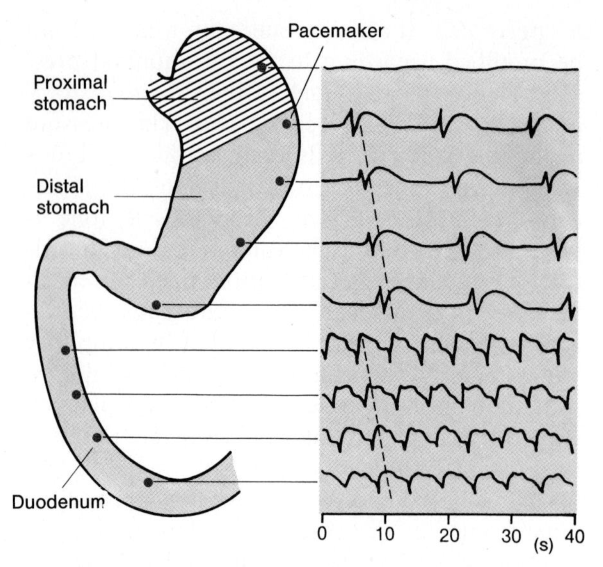

Fig. 29-19. Myoelectrical potentials (slow waves) in the stomach and duodenum. Tonic contraction of the proximal stomach is maintained without slow waves. The slow waves are initiated in a pacemaker region at a frequency of 3–4 per min; the downward migration is reflected in the phase shift of the curves. In the duodenum the frequency of the slow waves is ca. 12/min, and again there is a distal phase shift. Muscular contraction is produced when small generator potentials are superimposed to form slow waves, giving rise to action potentials. Modified from [40]

intramural plexus, and by hormones. Elimination of input from the *vagus*, as in surgical vagotomy, considerably inhibits peristalsis and interferes with emptying of the stomach, so that the contents are retained. *Hormones* such as cholecystokinin, motilin and especially gastrin enhance the contractions; secretin, glucagon, GIP, VIP and somatostatin attenuate them. The rate of stomach emptying E (the decrease in volume V per unit time, dV/dt) is a function of the pressure difference between stomach (P_s) and duodenum (P_d) and of the resistance in the pyloric region (R_p),

$$E = \frac{P_s - P_d}{R_p} \tag{2}$$

Because the pyloric resistance to liquid is low, the passage of liquid depends mostly on the pressure gradient $P_s - P_d$; the basic regulator is the pressure in the proximal stomach. On the other hand, the movement of solid components from the stomach depends mainly on pyloric resistance (R_p), and thus on their size.
An additional control on the *rate of stomach emptying*, apart from the fullness of the stomach and the particle size and viscosity of the contents, is exerted by receptors in the small intestine. *Acid contents leave the stomach more slowly than neutral, hyperosmolar more slowly than hyposmolar, and lipids (especially with long-chain fatty acids having more than 14 C atoms) more slowly than the products of protein breakdown* except for tryptophan. Both neural and hormonal mechanisms are involved, and *secretin* is probably particularly important for the inhibitory effect.
Large, solid components cannot leave the stomach during this digestive emptying phase. Such indigestible particles, with a diameter of over 3mm, can pass the pylorus only by the special mechanism of the interdigestive myoelectric complex (p. 696). In Phase III of that process the distal stomach contracts vigorously; the pylorus, closed during the digestive phase, now remains open so that the large particles can be driven into the duodenum.

Gastric Secretion

The stomach secretes into its lumen 2–3 l daily of a juice containing ions and macromolecules, and also releases the hormone *gastrin* into the blood. Gastric secretion can be subdivided into a basal (interdigestive) and a stimulated (digestive) phase. The *acid* secreted by the stomach denatures protein and activates pepsinogen by converting it to pepsin, which hydrolyzes protein; it also acts as a bactericide. *Mucus* lubricates the chyme and protects the mucosa. The *intrinsic factor* in the gastric juice is essential for absorption of vitamin B_{12}. The gastric mucosa itself absorbs very little apart from a few ions (such as Na^+) and lipid-soluble substances such as alcohol, large amounts of which can be rapidly absorbed in the stomach.

Functional anatomy of the gastric mucosa. The entire stomach is lined with a mucosa, which secretes mucus and pepsinogen II as well as bicarbonate and sodium. This columnar epithelium contains argentaffin cells, of which 9 are identified at present; these are responsible for the endocrine (into the blood), paracrine (from cell to cell) and neurocrine (at nerve-fiber endings) secretion of hormones. The *gastric glands*, which open into pits (foveolae) in the mucosa, vary topographically. Three regions can be distinguished:
- the **cardia region**, a narrow collar, 1–4 cm wide, below the esophageal opening; here the glands are tubular, with many tortuous branches.
- the **fundus-corpus region**, which constitutes about

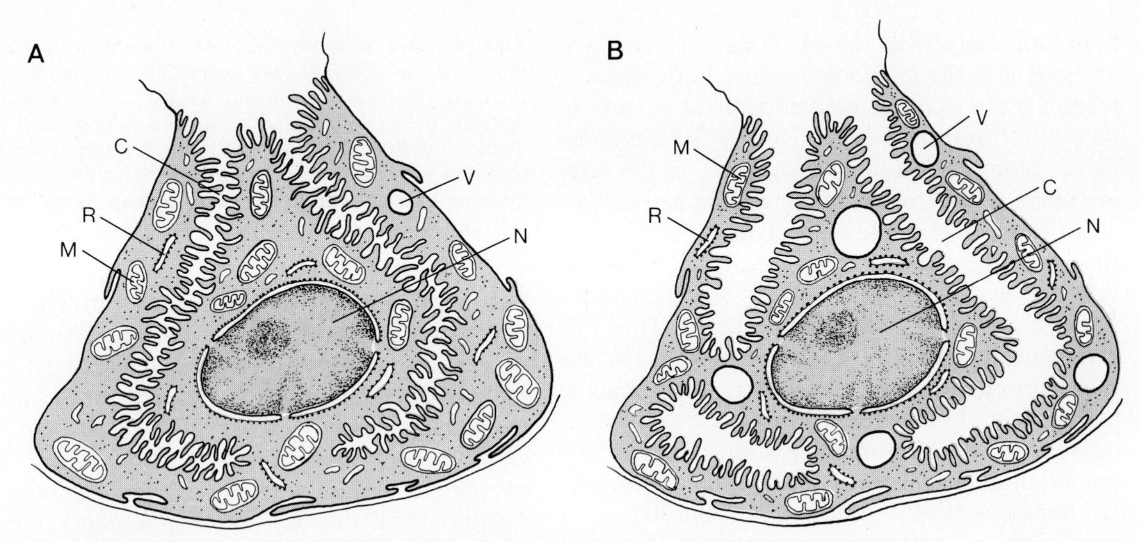

Fig. 29-20 A, B. Parietal cell in the resting state **(A)** and under stimulation **(B)**. N nucleus, R agranular endoplasmic reticulum, M mitochondria, C intracellular canaliculi that open into the lumen of the gland, V vacuole. In the stimulated state the canaliculi and vacuoles are expanded

3/4 of the stomach. The walls of its straight or slightly twisting glands contain, in addition to mucus-secreting and *argentaffin cells*, the acid-secreting *parietal cells* and *chief cells*, which produce pepsinogen I and II.

- the **pyloric region**, which includes 15–20% of the stomach and contains simply branched tubular glands that mainly secrete mucus. The special feature in this region is the *G cells*, which produce gastrin.

The mucus- and pepsinogen-producing cells resemble cells of these kinds elsewhere in the gastrointestinal tract. The **parietal cells**, on the other hand, are unique in their ability to secrete highly concentrated HCl; the H^+ concentration they achieve exceeds that in the blood by a factor of a million or more. These cells contain many large mitochondria and are characterized by intracellular *canaliculi*, which are lined with numerous microvilli and open at the apical surface of the cell, toward the lumen of the gland (Fig. 29-20). Within 10 min after the cells have been stimulated, they undergo profound morphological changes. The tubulovesicular structures in the cytoplasm, which predominate at rest, are reduced by about 90%. At the same time the microvilli in the canaliculi and the duct openings enlarge by a factor of 4-6. It is in these microvilli that the proton-transporting H^+-K^+ ATPase is located.

Formation of HCl (Fig. 29-21). *ATP* is the energy source for the *active transport of protons* out of the parietal cell and into the gastric juice. The enzyme that catalyzes this process is the H^+–K^+ ATPase in the membrane of the secretory microvilli, which exchanges H^+ for K^+ in equal amounts. The H^+ derives from the dissociation of carbonic acid, which also produces an equivalent quantity of HCO_3^-; very little H^+ is contributed by the dissociation of water. HCO_3^- moves down its concentration gradient into the blood, in exchange for Cl^-. At the peak of this process the HCO_3^- serum concentration rises appreciably, a phenomenon called the "alkaline tide".

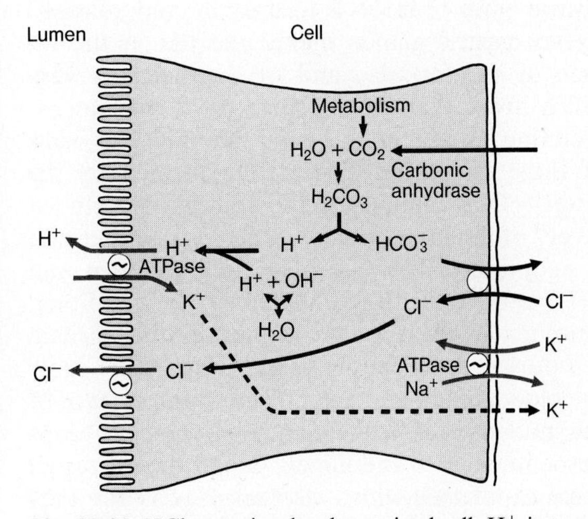

Fig. 29-21. HCl secretion by the parietal cell. H^+ is transported into the lumen by the H^+-K^+-exchange pump in the membrane of the brush border, driven by H^+-K^+ ATPase. Cl^- is also transported actively into the lumen, having entered the cell in exchange for HCO_3^-. H_2CO_3 and, to a lesser extent, H_2O are H^+ donors. From [1]

Simultaneously with the H^+ ions, *Cl^- ions* are secreted into the stomach, against both concentration and electrical gradients. That is, this is an *active transport process.* During the secretory phase, more Cl^- than H^+ is secreted. In the resting phase Cl^- secretion, together with active Na^+ absorption, is the main mechanism underlying the *electrical potential difference* (PD) of 40-60 mV between the interior of the stomach (negative) and the serosal side (positive). This PD demonstrates integrity of the membrane. When the membrane barrier is *broken* – for instance, by bile acids, lysolecithin or exogenous salicylate or alcohol – the result is back-diffusion of H^+ out of the lumen and of Na^+ and protein into the lumen, as well as a decrease in the PD.

Bicarbonate formation in the mucous cells. In addition to acid, the gastric mucosa produces an alkaline secretion, from the mucous cells on the surface and in the glands. This process involves the *active secretion of bicarbonate.* Transport is electroneutral and probably involves an exchange for Cl^-. In the secretory phase many times more H^+ is produced by the parietal cells than bicarbonate by the mucous cells, so that the latter is not apparent; the HCO_3^- is neutralized by an equimolar amount of H^+, with the formation of CO_2 and H_2O. To demonstrate secretion of HCO_3^-, H^+ secretion must be specifically blocked; because histamine stimulates H^+ secretion, histamine-receptor antagonists can serve as blocking agents *(H_2-receptor blockers).*
Together with the gastric mucus, bicarbonate offers significant *protection* against the aggressive gastric juice. The HCl formed in and released by the gastric glands makes the pH in the lumen of the foveolae and of the stomach very much lower than at the surfaces of the mucus-secreting and columnar cells that line the walls of these structures. The HCO_3^- formed by the latter cells is retained in the adjacent "unstirred layer" of liquid or mucus, so that a pH difference is maintained, between pH 2 in the lumen and pH 7 at the cell surface. Moreover, the additional amounts of bicarbonate formed in the parietal cell during the secretory phase (Fig. 29-21) enter the bloodstream and are carried to the surface of the mucous cells in the glands by capillary loops perpendicular to the lumen. Blood flow through these capillaries, which also carry away the HCl that diffuses out of the lumen, is mainly controlled by *prostaglandin E_2*; in combination with bicarbonate and the unstirred layer, then, this compound has an important role in protecting the gastric mucosa.

Recently substances have been described that completely inhibit H^+-K^+ ATPase, preventing all acid production; these are *substituted benzimidazoles* (e.g., Omeprazol) [21]. A single dose administered to humans inhibits acid production for 40 h; in vitro, cAMP- and K^+-stimulated acid secretion is inhibited even when H_2 receptor blockers and atropine have no effect. The latter finding indicates that activation of (H^+-K^+)-ATPase is a later step, perhaps even the last, in the chain of acid-producing events.

Composition of gastric juice. The **electrolyte** content of the gastric secretion depends on the rate of secretion. When stimulated, the *parietal cells* secrete H^+, K^+ and Cl^-; the *mucous cells* continually secrete Na^+, K^+, Cl^- and HCO_3^-. As the secretion rate rises, the proportion contributed by the parietal cells increases, and the concentration of Na^+ decreases correspondingly; HCO_3^- disappears altogether (Fig. 29-22).
Mucus is an important component of the gastric secretion; it covers the entire inner surface with a viscous layer ca. 0.6 mm thick. It lubricates the mucosa and protects it from mechanical and chemical damage. The mucus layer is maintained continuously; when the coating is removed mechanically or by peptic digestion, new mucus is produced. The basic constituent of mucus is a *glycoprotein* with a molecular weight of two million, a polymer consisting of a protein core with many carbohydrate side chains. There are individual genetic differences in the terminal sugar

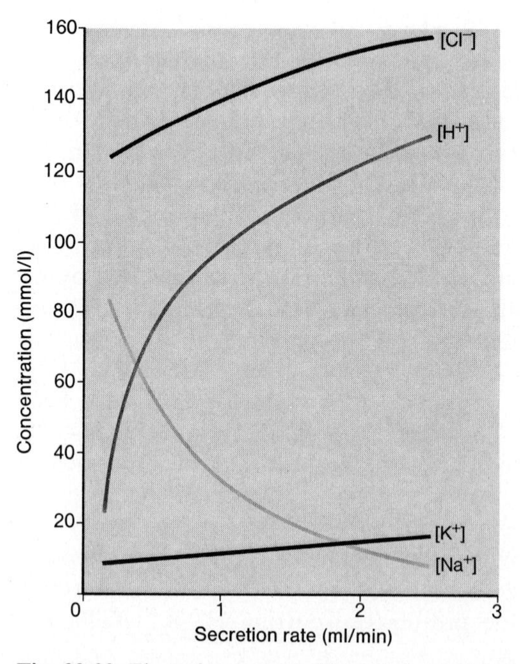

Fig. 29-22. Electrolyte composition of the gastric juice as a function of secretory state. In the resting state secretion from the superficial and foveolar mucous cells predominates. As the secretion rate rises, the H^+ concentration increases and the Na^+ concentration decreases. From [11]

sequence, which correspond immunologically to the blood groups in the ABO system.
Another important organic component is **pepsinogen**, a mixture of protease precursors. When activated by acid, it is converted to the effective protein-splitting enzyme **pepsin**; once begun, the conversion proceeds autocatalytically. At least eight different proteolytic enzymes have been demonstrated by electrophoresis. The first five rapidly migrating pepsinogens, together called *Group I*, are found only in the region of the chief and parietal cells. The remaining pepsinogens, *Group II*, are ubiquitous in the stomach and also occur in Brunner's glands of the small intestine. Pepsin originating from either group acts only in an acidic medium, with a pH optimum between 1.8 and 3.5; in an alkaline milieu it is irreversibly denatured. Pepsinogen secretion is stimulated in the same way as the secretion of HCl.
The third macromolecule in the gastric juice is **intrinsic factor**, a glycoprotein with a molecular weight of 42,000. It is secreted by the parietal cells. Intrinsic factor and another vitamin B_{12}-binding protein, called *R protein* (R for rapid, because of its high migration velocity in electrophoresis), are crucial for the *absorption of vitamin* B_{12}. In the acidic gastric juice vitamin B_{12} is bound mainly to the R protein. After this linkage has been split by the pancreatic enzymes, in the upper small intestine, the vitamin binds to intrinsic factor. This complex is resistant to proteolysis and absorption in the upper small intestine, and eventually reacts with specific receptors in the ileum. Vitamin B_{12} is then carried away in the portal blood; some of it is stored in the liver and some, bound to the transport protein *transcobalamine II*, travels further in the bloodstream.

Control of Gastric Secretion

In a fasting human, the stomach secretes only about 10% of the volume secreted after maximal stimulation. Vagotomy and removal of the antrum (site of the G cells) abolishes this basal secretion; therefore a background vagus tone is thought to be responsible for basal gastrin-dependent secretion of gastric juice. *Food intake* is the adequate stimulus for increased secretion. The influence of food begins even before the food is eaten and persists after the meal has ended. The process of secretion is subdivided into cephalic, gastric and intestinal phases, which overlap to some extent.

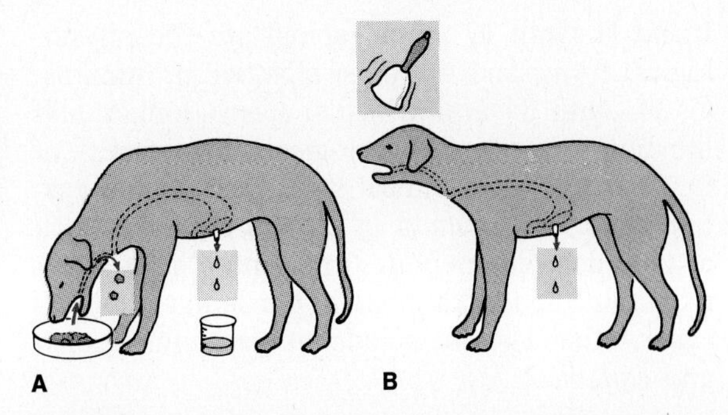

Fig. 29-23 A, B. Pavlov's experiment to demonstrate central influences on gastric secretion in a dog with esophageal and gastric fistulas. **A** Triggering of the cephalic phase of secretion by food presentation (unconditioned reflex). **B** Triggering of secretion by a bell with which the dog has learned to associate food (conditioned reflex)

Cephalic phase. This phase is initiated by the expectation of food, by imagining, seeing or smelling it, and finally by taste. The nerve impulses so generated, in various central structures, are conducted to the stomach exclusively by the **vagus nerve**. Vagotomy eliminates the cephalic phase. Secretion is thought to be brought about by a *vagus-induced release of gastrin*, since denervation of the antrum practically prevents secretion. In the cephalic phase the rate of secretion is ca. 40-50% of the maximum.

These relationships were thoroughly investigated by PAVLOV (1889) (Fig. 29-23). He prepared a dog with an esophageal fistula and, by surgery in the corpus-fundus region, created an "accessory stomach", an isolated pouch of mucosa with vagal and blood supply intact and with an opening to the exterior. A variety of experiments on such animals gave the following results.
1. A feeding during which the food swallowed falls out of the esophageal fistula (sham feeding) results in voluminous secretion of juice by the pouch (cephalic phase, *unconditioned reflex*).
2. If a bell was rung regularly each feeding time, after a few days the sound of the bell alone caused increased secretion of saliva and gastric juice, which dripped out of their respective fistulas (cephalic phase, *conditioned reflex*). The study of conditioned (learned) reflexes began with these experiments (for details see p. 155).

Gastric phase. The gastric phase is initiated by the stretching of the stomach as food enters it and by chemical influences of certain components of the food. The *distension stimulus* is mediated primarily by neuronal mechanisms in which both the afferent and the efferent signals are conducted in the **vagus nerve**, and also by short *intramural reflexes*.
The *chemical stimuli*, on the other hand, act primarily by the release of **gastrin** from the G cells of the antrum. Several gastrins are known. G 17

I and II (with 17 amino acids) are the physiological forms and are most effective in humans; G 34 (with 34 amino acids) has a longer half life but only 1/6 the biological effectiveness of G 17. The chief chemical stimulants in the gastric phase are *products of protein digestion* such as peptides, oligopeptides and amino acids (phenylalanine and tryptophan in particular) and *calcium*. Other agents include magnesium, *alcohol* and *caffeine*.

Intestinal phase. Both distension of the small intestine and the presence within it of products of protein digestion stimulate gastric secretion; the mechanism is predominantly hormonal, and the active hormone is thought to be *entero-oxyntin*. In the control system for gastric secretion, **inhibition** also plays an important role. An *acidic milieu* in the antrum, with pH below 3, inhibits the release of gastrin in the gastric phase. A considerable inhibitory influence is also exerted by the small intestine. This mechanism is triggered by *acids, fats* and *hyperosmolar solutions* in the small intestine; in their presence, secretin and bulbogastrone – hormones that reduce gastric secretion – are released from the intestinal mucosa. Fats do not inhibit secretion until they are broken down, and the effect is strongest when fatty acids with a chain length of more than 10 C atoms are split off. The mechanism probably involves neurons with *GIP* and *neurotensin* as transmitters.

Receptors of the secretory cells. Mediators that serve as first messengers in triggering secretion include acetylcholine, histamine and gastrin. The hormone or effector substance reacts with specific receptors in the cell membrane, causing the second messenger, cAMP or Ca^{2+} (calmodulin), to initiate the specific function of the cell (p. 695). The parietal cell is thought to have three such receptors (Fig. 29-24). The receptors for *acetylcholine* are muscarinic (not nicotinic as in other cells), those for *histamine* are H_2 receptors (not H_1 receptors as elsewhere in the body), and there are also *gastrin* receptors. A strong, obligate interaction has been inferred for the H_2 and gastrin receptors, with a weaker, facultative interaction of the H_2 and acetylcholine receptors. These explain why *blocking the H_2 receptor* also reduces gastrin- and acetylcholine-stimulated secretion. Competitive H_2-receptor blockers (the drugs cimetidine, ranitidine, famotidine) and specific muscarinic receptor blockers (pirenzipine) play a major role in ulcer therapy as inhibitors of acid formation.

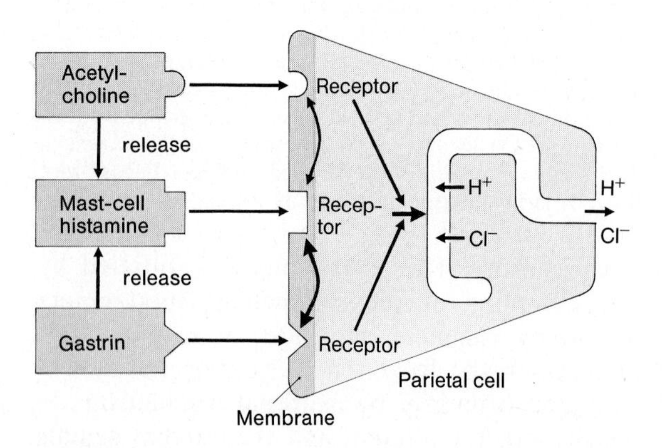

Fig. 29-24. Three-receptor model of the parietal cell. There is assumed to be a strong, obligate interaction between the histamine and gastrin receptors and a weaker, facultative interaction between the histamine and acetylcholine receptors. H_2 antagonists block the histamine receptor. From [28]

Secretory capacity of the stomach. Through a tube introduced into the lowest part of the stomach, the gastric juice can be collected by suction and analyzed quantitatively. Acid production is an easily measurable parameter of secretion. The *basal acid output* (BAO) during 1 h is 2–3 mmol H^+; in the presence of a gastrin-producing tumor this value can be increased 10- to 20-fold. Maximal gastric stimulation (e.g., by 6 µg/kg pentagastrin, a synthetic gastrin analog) elicits a *maximal acid output* (MAO) between 10 and 35 mmol H^+/h. The values for women are somewhat lower than those for men. The statistical average for patients with duodenal ulcer is above that for healthy people, but there is considerable individual variation; although acid output was formerly taken as a criterion in the diagnosis of ulcers, because of the extensive overlap with the normal range this test is now obsolete.

Pathophysiological aspects. The main disturbances of gastric function are those affecting secretion. The reduction or absence of gastric acid is a minor problem. In more than 50% of people over age 60 secretion is diminished because of *progressive mucosal atrophy*, but even in this case the secretory capacity of the pancreas is sufficient to ensure adequate protein digestion. Only with a complete *lack of intrinsic factor* can vitamin B_{12} no longer be absorbed; one result is a deficiency in erythropoiesis leading to **pernicious anemia**.
When there is *excessive secretion of gastric acid* or *deterioration of the protective mechanisms*, the gastric or duodenal mucosa can digest itself, and **peptic ulcers** result. Hypersecretion of gastrin can have several causes, including certain pancreatic tumors (non-β islet cell tumors: ZOLLINGER-ELLISON *syndrome*) and *hyperplasia of the G*

cells in the antrum; again, ulcers are produced. In the *gastric resection* method known as Billroth II the antrum is removed, the upper end of the duodenum is closed off and an anastomosis is created between stomach and jejunum. If, by mistake, the antrum is left connected to the duodenum when it is closed off, the G cells are constantly stimulated by the alkaline intestinal pH, causing hypersecretion in the remaining stomach.
Even when the cause of an ulcer cannot be determined, as in the majority of cases, healing can be accelerated by *neutralizing the gastric acid or preventing its secretion.* Maintenance of a pH above the optimum for pepsin inactivates one of the main aggressive components of the gastric juice. It is for this reason that ulcers are treated with antacids, H_2-receptor blockers and anticholinergics.

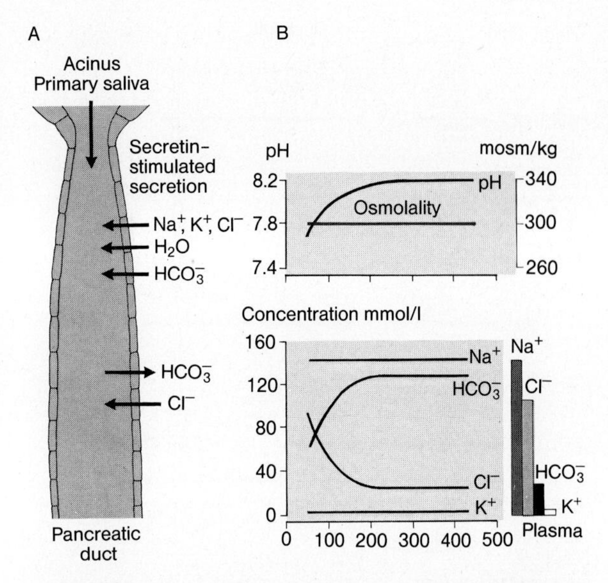

Fig. 29-25 A, B. Alteration of the primary secretion in the pancreatic duct **(A)** and composition of the pancreatic secretion as a function of rate of secretion **(B)**. After stimulation of the pancreas the concentration of Na^+ and osmolarity remain constant, while the HCO_3^- and Cl^- concentrations change in opposite directions. This change results from an increase in HCO_3^- secretion in the duct system and shortening of the time during which HCO_3^- is exchanged for Cl^-

29.4 Pancreas

When the food has been transferred from stomach to small intestine, it undergoes a period of intensive digestion prior to absorption. Crucial to this process are secretions from the pancreas, the gallbladder and the small intestine itself. The most important constituents of the pancreatic secretion are *bicarbonate* and *digestive enzymes*, which neutralize the acidic chyme and split the main food components. Pancreatic secretion is basically controlled by the hormones secretin and cholecystokinin and by the vagus nerve.
The pancreas weighs an average of ca. 110 g, but it can secrete more than 10 times its weight daily, *1–1.5 l/d* of secretion. The main pancreatic duct, the *duct of Wirsung*, passes through the entire organ and opens into the duodenum next to – or, in 30–40% of people, together with – the main duct of the liver, the choledochous or common bile duct, by way of a sphincter (the major duodenal papilla of Vater).

Pancreatic Secretion

Electrolytes in the pancreatic juice. The pancreatic juice contains a number of electrolytes and proteins. The main anions are Cl^- and HCO_3^-, and the main cations are Na^+ and K^+. Unlike saliva, the pancreatic secretion is isotonic with the blood plasma, regardless of the state of stimulation. Whereas the cation concentrations remain constant under stimulation, the concentrations of HCO_3^- and Cl^- change in opposite directions (Fig. 29-25). When secretion is at its peak, the bicarbonate concentration is 130–140 mmol/l and the pH is 8.2.

Two theories have been proposed to explain why the two anions are affected oppositely by changes in the secretory state. 1. According to the *anion-exchange hypothesis*, bicarbonate is formed in higher concentration in the acini, and during passage through the duct system it is exchanged for Cl^-. When the rate of secretion is higher, so that flow is more rapid, this exchange is diminished. 2. According to the *two-component hypothesis*, the acinar cells secrete Cl^- and HCO_3^- in concentrations isotonic with the plasma, whereas the duct cells secrete abundant HCO_3^-; in the stimulated state, the latter predominate. At present, both mechanisms are thought to operate. In addition to the above electrolytes, the pancreatic secretion contains low concentrations of Ca^{2+}, Mg^{2+}, Zn^{2+}, sulfate and phosphate.
The high HCO_3^- concentration suggests an *active secretory process.* H^+ is actively transported into the cell from the lumen in exchange for Na^+, which is secreted into the lumen (Fig. 29-26). At the basolateral cell wall, H^+ is secreted from the cell into the plasma, again in exchange for Na^+; in the plasma it reacts with HCO_3 to form CO_2 and water. CO_2 diffuses back into the cell and (together with metabolically produced CO_2) into the pancreatic ducts. Here, catalyzed by carbonic

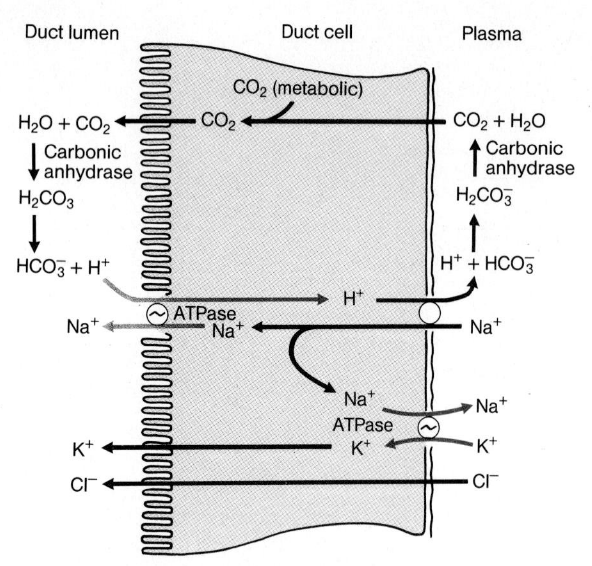

Fig. 29-26. Cellular mechanisms of pancreatic electrolyte secretion. H^+ is actively transported (in exchange for Na^+) from the duct lumen into the cell and thence into the plasma, where it reacts with HCO_3^- to produce CO_2 and H_2O. CO_2 diffuses into the lumen, where it is used to form HCO_3^-. From [1]

anhydrase, the CO_2 reacts with water to produce HCO_3^-.

Table 29-2. Enzymes secreted by the pancreas

Enzyme action	*Site of hydrolysis*
Proteolytic	
Endopeptidases	Internal peptide bonds between adjacent amino acids
Trypsin	at basic residues
Chymotrypsin	at aromatic residues
Elastase	at hydrophobic residues in elastin
Exopeptidases	Terminal peptide bonds
Carboxypeptidases A and B	at the carboxyl group (A: non-basic, B: basic residues)
Aminopeptidase	at an amino residue
Amylolytic	
α-amylase	α-1,4 glycosidic bonds in glucose polymers
Lipolytic	Ester bonds
Lipase	in triglycerides at positions 1 and 3
Phospholipase A	in phosphoglycerides at position 2
Cholesterolase	in cholesterol esters
Nucleolytic	
Ribonuclease	Phosphodiester bonds of nucleotides in ribonucleic acids

Enzymes of the pancreatic juice. 90% of the proteins in the pancreatic secretion are digestive enzymes, mostly *hydrolases*, which split various substrates (Table 29-2). The proteolytic enzymes *(peptidases)* predominate. These and *phospholipase A* are secreted as zymogens, precursors which must be activated, whereas *lipase, amylase* and the *ribonucleases* are secreted in active form. Activation is brought about enzymatically by *enterokinase*, an endopeptidase in the duodenal mucosa. It activates *trypsin* from trypsinogen, but once trypsin has been formed the process continues autocatalytically; furthermore, the trypsin also activates other proteases. A trypsin inhibitor is also present and is particularly effective in preventing the action of trypsin during passage through the pancreas, so as to counteract autodigestion of the pancreas.

Autodigestion by the organ's own enzymes can occur, however, under pathological conditions, producing the clinical syndrome *acute pancreatitis*. In the most severe cases the disease is fatal, and the pancreas is totally destroyed.

The enzyme granules within the acinar cell contain all the enzymes present in the secretion in *constant proportions*, so that their proportions in the pancreatic juice are also constant. Some adjustment is possible if the diet contains particularly large amounts of a certain component, such as fat; but this adaptation – e.g., to increase the relative concentration of lipase – requires several weeks.

Regulation of Pancreatic Secretion

Hormonal and neuronal stimulation. The hormones **secretin** and **cholecystokinin (CCK)** are the most effective stimulators of the exocrine pancreas. Secretin stimulates the cells of the duct system, which secrete mainly bicarbonate, other electrolytes and water, and CCK stimulates the acinar cells, which secrete enzymes. However, each hormone exerts a weak effect on the other system – secretin on the acini and CCK on the duct epithelia – so that the two enhance one another. *Vasoactive intestinal polypeptide* (VIP) is structurally similar to secretin, and *gastrin* is related to CCK. Both have much weaker actions than the associated main hormones, with which they compete for binding sites on the cell; that is, there is mutual competitive inhibition (p. 695), secretin vs. VIP, and CCK vs. gastrin. Other peptide hormones with a weaker *stimulating action* are substance P and

neurotensin; secretion is inhibited by pancreatic polypeptide, somatostatin and glucagon.
Neuronal activation occurs by way of the **vagus nerve.** In addition to *acetylcholine* (ACh), *VIP* has been identified as a transmitter in the nerve endings. A neuronal stimulus is followed by the release of an enzyme-rich secretion like that induced by CCK. Secretion can be suppressed by atropine.

Phases of pancreatic secretion. The **basal secretion** produced under resting conditions has 2–3% of the bicarbonate and 10–15% of the enzyme content of the secretion under maximal stimulation.
In the **cephalic phase**, initiated by thinking about food, smell, taste, chewing and swallowing, the amounts secreted rise to 10–15% of maximal in the case of bicarbonate, and 25% for enzymes. This phase is mediated by the vagus nerve and can therefore be suppressed by atropine and by vagotomy. The entry of food into the stomach initiates the **gastric phase**, in which pancreatic secretion is further increased by the same stimuli (*vagal activity* and *gastrin*) that promote gastric secretion. The most important phase of pancreatic secretion, the **intestinal phase**, begins with entry of the chyme into the duodenum. *Secretin* is released from the S cells in the mucosa of the small intestine, and *CCK* is released from the I cells. The adequate stimulus for secretin release is a pH below 4.5, which is achieved when the acidic stomach contents enter the proximal duodenum.
This acid is potentially harmful to the mucosa of the small intestine. Damage is avoided in two ways: rapid neutralization by the HCO_3^- secreted by the pancreas in response to secretin (and, to a lesser extent, CCK) as well as by the duodenal mucosa, and the absorption of H^+. The duodenal contents are brought to the *pH 6–8* necessary for action of the pancreatic enzymes; in this phase of digestion, H^+ secreted by the stimulated stomach must be eliminated at a rate of 20–40 mmol per hour.
The *release of CCK* from endocrine cells in the mucosa of the small intestine is stimulated by products of protein and lipid digestion: peptides, amino acids and fatty acids, long-chain fatty acids in particular. Carbohydrates do not have this effect. This hormonal stimulation is supplemented by vagovagal reflexes.

Despite this complex set of stimuli, the amounts secreted are only 70% of the maximum achievable by administering the hormones intravenously. The reason may lie in the release of inhibitory hormones such as somatostatin, pancreatic polypeptide and glucagon.
The pancreas functions with a large safety factor. About 10 times as much enzyme is produced as is required for adequate hydrolysis of the food. When 90% of the pancreatic tissue is removed, therefore, the residual function of the remaining 10% suffices to prevent maldigestion.

Pathophysiological aspects. Disorders of the pancreas produce clinically relevant *maldigestion* only at a relatively late stage. The symptoms are weight loss and fatty stool. Such maldigestion can be caused, for example, by *chronic pancreatitis*, which as a rule results from chronic alcoholism, and by *carcinoma of the pancreas* in its late phase. The enzyme deficiency can be partly compensated by oral administration of pancreatic enzymes.
The exocrine function of the pancreas can be checked with the rather elaborate *secretin-CCK test*. Here the secretion collected through a tube after maximal hormonal stimulation is analyzed. A simpler method is to administer orally substances that are split by the pancreatic enzymes into end products that are absorbed and excreted in the urine (e.g., *fluorescin* in the *pancreolauryl test, paraaminobenzoic acid* in the *PABA test*); pancreatic efficiency is evaluated by the urine concentration of the split-off end products.

29.5 Liver and Biliary System

The liver is the largest and most important metabolic organ in the body. It has a wide variety of functions in the metabolism of proteins, carbohydrates and fats as well as hormones and vitamins, and detoxifies a number of endogenous and exogenous substances. These relationships are treated in textbooks of physiological chemistry. Here, in the context of the gastrointestinal system, we shall concentrate on the *excretory function* of the liver, the secretion of bile. **Bile** is composed of water, electrolytes, mucus and the lipids cholesterol and lecithin, plus two kinds of specific components: bile acids and the pigment bilirubin. The bile acids are detergents, the emulsifying action of which plays an important role in the digestion of lipids. Bilirubin is the excretory end product of hemoglobin breakdown.

Bile Formation

Functional anatomy. The liver cells *(hepatocytes)* are arranged in plates one cell thick, separated by a narrow gap *(Disse's space)* from blood-filled *sinusoids*, the equivalent of capillaries. The sinusoid walls are fenestrated, permitting the passage of macromolecules such as albumin and lipoproteins. The smallest elements through which the bile is channelled, the *canaliculi*, are spaces enclosed by the plasma membranes of two adjacent hepatocytes. Beginning with the next larger elements (the *canals of Hering*, followed by the *interlobular canals* and *biliary ductules*), the duct walls are formed of a cuboid secretory epithelium. The smaller channels in and between the lobes of the liver join to form larger ones, and eventually leave the liver as the *hepatic duct*. A side branch, the *cystic duct*, connects the hepatic duct with the gallbladder. Beyond this point the *common bile duct* continues to the duodenum, into which it opens at the major duodenal papilla of Vater, next to or together with the pancreatic duct (Fig. 29-1).

Functions of the bile. The bile serves various important functions. It *eliminates end products* of metabolism such as bilirubin, drugs and toxins. *Bile acids* are essential for the emulsification and absorption of fats, and the *cholesterol content* of bile assists the regulation of cholesterol balance. Bile also contains water, electrolytes and mucus. About *600 ml* of bile is secreted daily, ca. 2/3 of which comes from the canaliculi and 1/3 from the larger ducts.
The *canalicular component* of the bile is formed, in about equal amounts, by two different mechanisms; it consists of a bile-acid-dependent and a bile-acid-independent fraction (Fig. 29-27).

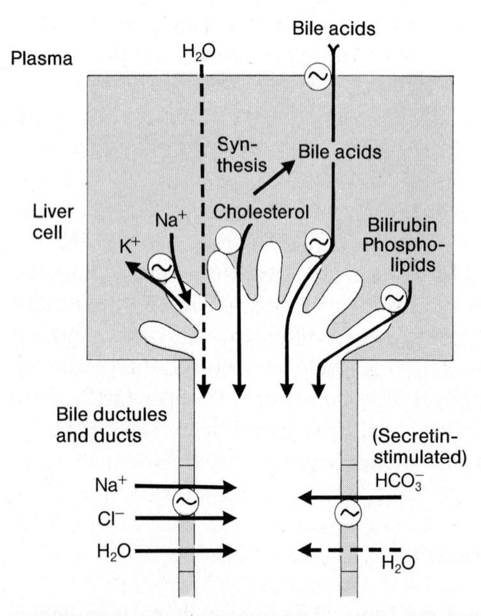

Fig. 29-27. Mechanisms of bile secretion. Bile-acid-dependent secretion *(upper right)*: Bile acids taken up from the portal blood into the liver cells or synthesized there de novo are actively transported into the canaliculi. Bile-acid-independent secretion *(upper left)*: Electrolytes are secreted with active Na^+ transport as the driving force. Modification of the primary bile *(below)*: Na^+, HCO_3^- and Cl^- are actively secreted into the bile ducts, and water follows by osmosis

Bile-acid-dependent secretion. A close correlation has been found between the *flow of bile* and the *secretion of bile acids*. The concentration of the bile acids is about 100 times greater in the canaliculi than in the portal blood; therefore a *carrier-mediated active transport* is inferred. Water follows the acids into the caniculi, down the osmotic gradient, so that the bile is isotonic with the blood. There are two sources of bile acids. First, they are formed *de novo* from cholesterol in the hepatic cells themselves, with 7-hydroxylase as the key enzyme, which controls the rate of synthesis by a feedback mechanism. Second, bile acids in the *portal blood* can also be actively taken into the hepatic cells and transferred to the canaliculi (see also Fig. 29-29). This extraction from the blood is very efficient; ca. 80% of the bile acids are eliminated from the blood in a single pass through the liver. Therefore the concentration of bile acids in the peripheral blood is much lower than in the portal system. Because extraction proceeds six times as fast as the discharge of the acids into the canaliculi, the latter is the rate-limiting step in bile-acid secretion.

Bile-acid-independent secretion. This process involves the electrolytes Na^+, Cl^- and HCO_3^- as well as water. The driving force is *active Na^+ transport,* thought to be supplemented by a bicarbonate-secretion mechanism. Bile-acid-independent secretion is particularly stimulated by *secretin.*
In addition to the bile acids, bilirubin, cholesterol and phospholipids (mainly lecithin) are actively secreted into the canaliculi (Fig. 29-27). The water-insoluble *"indirect" bilirubin*, most of which is derived from the hemoglobin of aged erythrocytes, reaches the liver cell as a colloidal aggregate, bound to albumin. Each day about 4 mg is produced per kg body weight, or 200–300 mg/day. In the hepatocytes 80% of the bilirubin is conjugated with glucuronic acid and a small amount with sulfuric acid; it is released into the bile in the conjugated form, as *"direct" bilirubin.* Most drugs and toxins are eliminated in basically the same way.

Modification of bile in the bile ducts (Fig. 29-27). In the ducts into which the canaliculi open, the primary bile is modified. The process resembles that by which the glomerulus filtrate is modified in the renal tubules (pp. 735ff.), and the *clearance* is calculated in the same way. For bile, however, rather than inulin *erythritol* or *mannitol* is used as the inert substance, which is secreted into the canaliculi but not reabsorbed. Such studies have shown that ca. 180 ml of fluid, or ca. 1/3 of the total amount of bile, is discharged into the ductules, with the active secretion of HCO_3^-. The process is stimulated by *secretin*.

Hepatic and Gallbladder Bile

Composition of hepatic bile (Table 29-3). The bile leaving the liver has a golden color because of the bilirubin; it is formed at a rate of 0.4 ml/min. Its electrolyte concentration corresponds to that of plasma except that bile has nearly twice as much bicarbonate (and slightly less Cl^-). However, the organic components of bile differ fundamentally from those of plasma, for they consist almost entirely of bile acids, cholesterol and phospholipids.

The **bile acids** are formed in the liver from cholesterol, by hydroxylation and addition of a carboxyl group. The acids synthesized in the liver are the *primary bile acids: chenodeoxycholic acid* (the dihydroxy form) and *cholic acid* (the trihydroxy form). They are not present in the liver as free acids but are conjugated with glycine and taurine. Because little taurine is available, conjugation with glycine predominates by a factor of 3. Conjugated bile acids are more water-soluble than unconjugated and have a greater tendency to dissociate and form bile salts with cations, mainly Na^+. In acid media ($pH<4$) the bile salts are insoluble and precipitate, but at the physiological pH of the small intestine they are highly soluble.

Some of the primary bile salts are dehydroxylated by anaerobic bacteria in the distal ileum and colon and converted into *secondary bile acids: lithocholic acid* (monohydroxy form) and *deoxycholic acid* (dihydroxy form). Chenodeoxycholic acid, cholic acid and deoxycholic acid are present in the proportions 2:2:1; only fractional amounts of lithocholic acid are found, because most of it is excreted.

The fat-emulsifying action of the bile acids is largely based on their ability to form **micelles**. The three-dimensional arrangement of the bile-acid molecule is such that the hydrophilic carboxyl and hydroxyl groups are on one side of the molecule and the hydrophobic part (steroid nucleus, methyl groups) is on the opposite side; hence the bile acid molecules have both *hydrophilic and lipophilic properties.*

Because of their structure, bile-acid molecules act as detergents; at the interface between an oil and a water phase, they form a nearly monomolecular film with the hydrophilic groups toward the water and the lipophilic groups toward the oil. In aqueous solution bile acids form orderly aggregates called *micelles* if their concentration is above a certain level, the *critical micellar concentration* (1–2 mmol/l). In the internal, lipophilic part of the micelle, *lipids* such as cholesterol and phospholipids can be incorporated, producing "mixed micelles" (Fig. 29-28). Although insoluble in itself, cholesterol can be carried in solution as part of a micelle. If its concentration exceeds the capacity of the micelle it forms a crystalline precipitate; this is the basic process in the formation of cholesterol gallstones (p. 721).

Composition of gallbladder bile (Table 29-3). The gallbladder has a capacity of only 50–60 ml. However, the liver secretes bile at a rate of 600 ml per day, and only about half of this flows past the gallbladder to enter the small intestine directly. The discrepancy between the volume entering the gallbladder and its capacity is compensated by the *highly efficient reabsorption* of water by the gallbladder. Within a few hours 90% of the water in the bile can be reabsorbed. The organic components remain within the gallbladder, and the concentration of the bile rises correspondingly. The driving force for reabsorption is *active Na^+ transport* by means of a "pump" in the basolateral membrane, activated by Na^+-K^+ ATPase. The Na^+ is followed by Cl^- and HCO_3^-, which either diffuse down an electrical gradient or are transported by carriers. Because of reabsorption of HCO_3^- the pH decreases, from 8.2 in the hepatic bile to 6.5 in the gallbladder bile. The high Na^+ concentration in the interstitial space of the gallbladder epithelium sets up an osmotic gradient that draws in water, which then flows out into the capillaries (p. 704).

Table 29-3. Composition of hepatic and gallbladder bile

Constituents	Hepatic bile (mmol/l)	Gallbladder bile (mmol/l)
Na^+	165	280
K^+	5	10
Ca^{2+}	2.5	12
Cl^-	90	15
HCO_3^-	45	8
Bile acids	35	310
Lecithin	1	8
Bile pigments	0.8	3.2
Cholesterol	3	25
pH	8.2	6.5

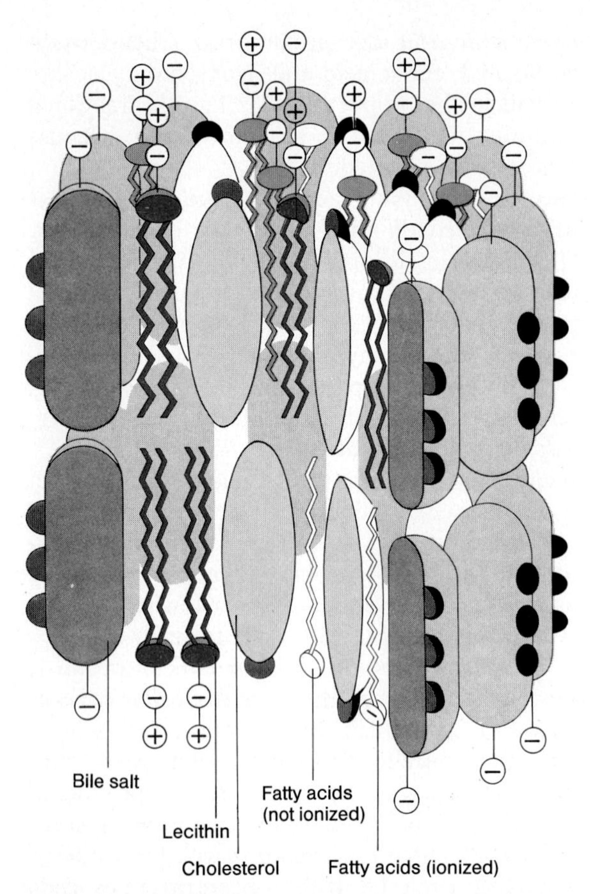

Fig. 29-28. Structure of a mixed micelle. Cholesterol, lecithin, fatty acids and monoglycerides occupy the center of the micelle, which is surrounded by bile acids with their hydrophilic groups toward the surface. From [27]

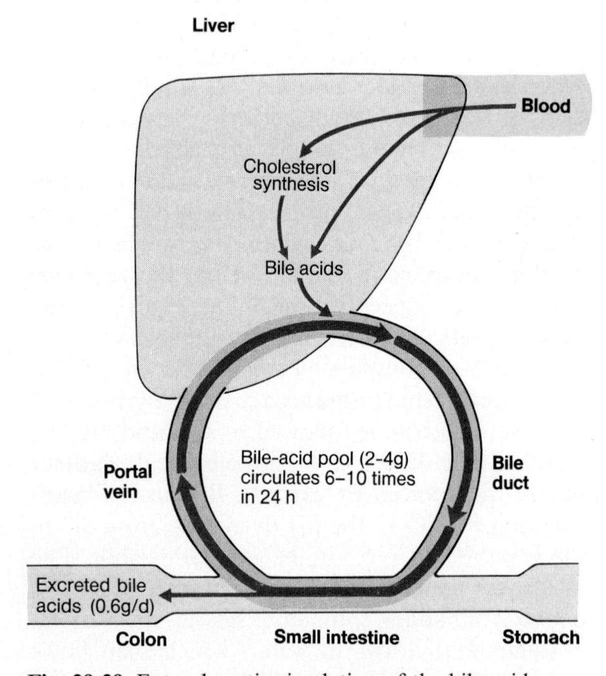

Fig. 29-29. Enterohepatic circulation of the bile acids

Gallbladder motility. The bile that flows into the gallbladder and becomes concentrated during the interdigestive phase is expelled during a meal by contraction of the gallbladder. The basic stimulus for contraction is **cholecystokinin**, released from the duodenal mucosa on the entry of lipid-containing chyme. The motor response is also stimulated to some extent by the *vagus nerve* and *parasympathomimetics*. Contraction of the gallbladder begins only 2 min after lipid products have contacted the intestinal mucosa, and emptying is complete after 15–90 min. Two motor phenomena can be distinguished: a tonic contraction reduces the diameter of the gallbladder, and superimposed on it are phasic contractions at a rate of 2–6/min. In combination, they generate pressures of 25–30 mm Hg.

Enterohepatic Circulation

Circulation of bile acids (Fig. 29-29). The bile acids enter the duodenum as mixed micelles. Despite dilution by the gastric contents to ca. 10 mmol/l, their concentration certainly remains above the critical micellar concentration. In addition to cholesterol and lecithin, products of fat digestion – *fatty acids* and *monoglycerides* – are incorporated into the micelles. When the micelles first contact the intestinal wall, the lipids diffuse through the brush-border membrane into the intestinal cell but the bile acids remain in the lumen. It is only later during passage through the intestine that they are absorbed, actively and passively.

About 50% of bile-acid absorption occurs *passively* in the small and large intestine. Deconjugation and dehydroxylation by bacterial action increase the lipid solubility of the bile acids and hence facilitate their passive diffusion. The *active absorption* of the bile acids takes place exclusively and specifically in the terminal ileum; this is a rare phenomenon, otherwise observed only for vitamin B_{12}. The bile acids best suited for active absorption are those so strongly polar that passive absorption is difficult (e.g., taurine conjugates). The process of bile-acid absorption in the terminal ileum has the typical characteristics of active transport: saturation kinetics and competitive inhibition. A small amount, 7–20%, of the total bile-acid pool escapes active and passive absorption and is excreted.

The presence of bile acids in the colon appears to play an important role in controlling stool consistency. When the colon concentration of dihydroxy bile acids is above 3 mmol/l, there is considerable secretion of electrolytes and water into the lumen, producing diarrhea. Disease or resection of the terminal ileum can cause a very severe form of this *"chologenic diarrhea"*. It can be treated by binding the bile acids to an ion-exchange resin, cholestyramine.

Having been absorbed, the bile acids are reconjugated *in the liver*, and some of the secondary bile acids are rehydroxylated. The amount lost in the stool, 0.2–0.6 g/d, is synthesized anew. The *total bile-acid pool* of the body amounts to 3 g, which is not enough to accomplish the necessary lipolysis following a meal; a fatty meal requires up to five times that much. Therefore the available bile acids circulate through the intestine and liver several times per day *(enterohepatic circulation)*. The frequency with which the ca. 3 g of bile acids makes a complete cycle depends on the food intake, ranging from 4 to 12 cycles per day.

Circulation of bilirubin. Like the bile acids and lipids, the bile pigment *bilirubin* enters the intestine as a glucuronide. Very little of this polar compound is reabsorbed in the gallbladder and small intestine. In the terminal ileum, and especially in the colon, bilirubin is deconjugated by bacterial hydrolases and converted to *urobilinogen*; this compound, together with other products of bilirubin breakdown, is responsible for the brown color of the stool. Less than 20% of it is reabsorbed. Of this amount, ca. 90% reenters the liver and is returned to the bile, and the remaining ca. 10% appears in the urine.

Pathophysiological aspects. An increased urine concentration of urobilinogen can indicate *liver disease* with impaired bilirubin excretion. When it is entirely absent from the urine and the stool is pale, and jaundice is also present, *complete obstruction of the bile ducts* is indicated; in this situation no bilirubin enters the intestine at all, so that there is no substrate for conversion to urobilinogen.
The best known and clinically most common disturbance of normal bile physiology is the precipitation of cholesterol to form **cholesterol gallstones**. These account for over 80% of gallstones. Cholesterol is held in solution together with lecithin, in mixed micelles. If the *cholesterol concentration rises* or the *proportion of bile acids or lecithin falls* below a critical level, cholesterol precipitates out of solution. Factors that predispose to an elevated proportion of cholesterol include estrogens, a high-carbohydrate diet, overweight, and processes that lower the bile-acid concentration, such as inflammation of the ileum *(Crohn's disease)* or resection. In appropriate cases the oral replacement of bile acids suffices to convert lithogenic bile back to alithogenic bile, in which cholesterol gallstones can be redissolved. Suitable acids for this purpose are chenodeoxycholic acid or, because it does not cause diarrhea, ursodeoxycholic acid.
The clinical manifestation of disturbed bilirubin metabolism is **jaundice** (icterus). The yellow skin color results from an elevated plasma bilirubin level, which can be produced in various ways:
(i) by increased bilirubin formation, as happens when the rate of erythrocyte destruction increases **(hemolytic jaundice)**,
(ii) by impaired conjugation or transport of bilirubin in the hepatocyte, as in *icterus of pregnancy* and *Gilbert's juvenile icterus* **(retention jaundice)**, and
(iii) by obstructed bile flow due to gallstones, for instance, or tumors in the region of the common bile duct **(obstructive jaundice)**.

29.6 Small Intestine

The small intestine has several important functions:
(i) *mixing* the chyme with the secretions of the pancreas, liver (bile) and intestinal mucosa,
(ii) *digesting* the components of food,
(iii) *absorbing* the equilibrated and digested contents,
(iv) *transporting* the remaining contents further down the tract,
(v) *secreting* various hormones and
(vi) *immunological protection.*
There are three subdivisions of the small intestine: the **duodenum** (20–30 cm long), the **jejunum**, which begins at the ligament of Treitz (1.5–2.5 m long), and the **ileum**, which adjoins the jejunum with no well-defined boundary (2–3 m long). The total length of the small intestine is about 4 m in the tonic state (in vivo) and 6–8 m in the atonic state (post mortem).

Motility of the Small Intestine

The motor activity of the small intestine consists of *nonpropulsive mixing movements* and *propulsive peristalsis.* It is regulated by the intrinsic activity of the smooth muscle cells and modulated by the extrinsic (autonomic) nervous system and many, chiefly gastrointestinal hormones.

Basal myogenic rhythm. Muscular contraction in the small intestine, as in the stomach, is controlled by a *basal myogenic rhythm;* these *slow waves* may or may not have action potentials superimposed on them. The pacemakers of the slow waves have a higher intrinsic frequency in the upper small intestine, ca. 12 cycles/min, than toward the ileum, where there is a stepwise decrease to 8 cycles/min. This oral-to-aboral gradient ensures that the intestinal contents are slowly shifted distally even during nonpropulsive movements. Furthermore, the excitable muscle cells are more closely coupled in the upper small intestine than further distally. The resulting phase shift down the intestine has the same effect as the pacing gradient (Fig. 29-19, p. 710).

Neuronal and hormonal control. In both the intrinsic and the extrinsic neuronal control of small-intestine motor activity, *Auerbach's myenteric plexus* is of particular significance. The transmitter substance here is **acetylcholine**; it acts to inhibit the *circular* smooth muscle layer, which makes by far the greatest contribution to the motility of the small intestine. If this inhibition is eliminated (as can be done experimentally by blocking the nerve action potentials with tetrodotoxin, without otherwise affecting the smooth muscles), the intestine contracts vigorously at the frequency of the slow waves. Temporary physiological elimination of the inhibitory effect, resulting in contraction of the circular muscles, seems to be brought about by the gastrointestinal hormone **VIP**. Acetylcholine has the opposite effect on the *longitudinal* smooth muscle layer; here it stimulates contraction. The extrinsic nerves have relatively little influence on motility of the small intestine. Activation of the *sympathetic fibers*, which leave the spinal cord in T9-10 and synapse in the celiac and mesenteric ganglia, inhibits the motor activity in the myenteric plexus, whereas *parasympathetic activation* (vagus nerve) enhances it.

Many *hormones* participate in the control of small-intestinal motility; they have endocrine, paracrine and neurocrine actions and can exert either positive or negative effects. The situation is sufficiently complicated that the various motor phenomena cannot yet be ascribed to particular hormonal actions. Both neuronal and hormonal influences are elicited by food intake and by distension of the intestine.

Movement sequences in the small intestine. The intestinal movements in the *interdigestive phase* differ from those in the *digestive phase*. In the interdigestive phase the directed, propulsive pattern of the myoelectric motor complex prevails (p. 696).

Food consumption interrupts the migrating motor complexes and the propulsive movements. In this digestive phase the dominant activity is **rhythmic segmentation** and **pendular movements**, which push the intestinal contents back and forth. This functional change is brought about by the gastrointestinal hormones *gastrin* and *cholecystokinin*. The duration and extent of digestive motor activity depend on the composition and energy content of the food. Triglycerides have a considerably longer and stronger effect than carbohydrates and proteins with the same energy content.

By infrequent **propulsive movements** and by the *phase shift of the slow waves* (pp. 709f.), the intestinal contents are slowly propelled distally. With an average velocity of 1–4 cm/min, it takes about 2–4 h for the contents to reach the cecum. The *transit time* is affected by the composition of the food and is made progressively slower in the sequence carbohydrate → protein → fat.

There are also smaller-scale movements, at the level of the *villi*, which assist mixing of the food and stir up the *unstirred layer* next to the mucosa. The villi shorten rhythmically in parallel with the contractile activity of the *muscularis mucosae*. Here, again, there is a distinct frequency gradient from proximal to distal, with the highest activity in the duodenum. The contraction of the villi also helps to empty the central lymph duct *(lacteal)*. It is induced by a hormone, *villikinin*, located in the mucosa of the small intestine.

Ileocecal junction. At the end of the small intestine is a 4-cm-long segment that controls the transfer of chyme into the large intestine. Ordinarily this *sphincter* is in a state of tonic contraction, elevating the local pressure to ca. 20 mm Hg. When the terminal ileum is dilated the sphincter relaxes, and when the pressure in the cecum rises its tone increases (Fig. 29-30). In addition, the terminal ileum projects into the cecum

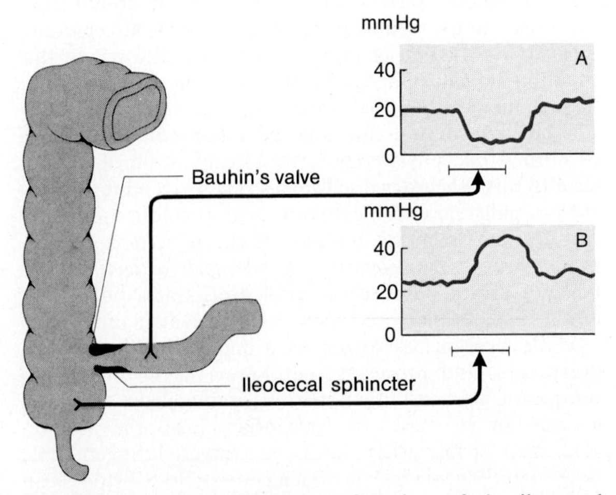

Fig. 29-30. Pressure-dependent function of the ileocecal sphincter (Bauhin's valve). An increase in the pressure within the ileum lowers the tone of the ileocecal sphincter, and a pressure increase in the cecum enhances the sphincter tone. From [1]

to form the *ileocecal valve*, which resists intracecal pressures as high as 40 mm Hg. Because of this anatomical barrier, the population of *bacteria* in the ileum is smaller by a factor of 10^5 than in the cecum (see Fig. 29-40). The method of measuring *transit time* through the small intestine is based on this difference. When a carbohydrate that is not well absorbed has passed through the small intestine and enters the cecum, bacterial action causes the formation of sufficiently large amounts of H_2 to be demonstrable with the H_2 breath test (p. 698).

Absorption in the Small Intestine

Absorbing area and blood flow. The absorbing surface of the small intestine is increased by folds and villi. Figure 29-31 shows how the circular *folds of Kerckring*, the *villi* and the *microvilli* increase the surface area of the cylindrical tube by an overall factor of 600, to a total of 200 m². The functional unit is the *villus* with its enclosed and immediately underlying structures, and the *crypt* that separates adjacent villi (Fig. 29-32). The epithelium of the small intestine is one of the tissues with the highest rates of cell division and turnover in the body. The still undifferentiated columnar cells migrate from their sites of origin within the crypt to the tip of the villus, over the course of 24–36 h. On the way they mature, developing the specific enzymes and transport systems (carriers) required for absorption, so that when they reach the tip of the villus they are fully developed **enterocytes**. The absorption of food components takes place primarily at the tip, while the equilibrating, secretory events are located in the crypts. In addition to the enterocytes, the mucosa of the small intestine contains *mucous cells* and various endocrine cells, called *argentaffin cells* because they take up silver stains. Immunologically active cells, called *M cells* because of their shape, are associated with

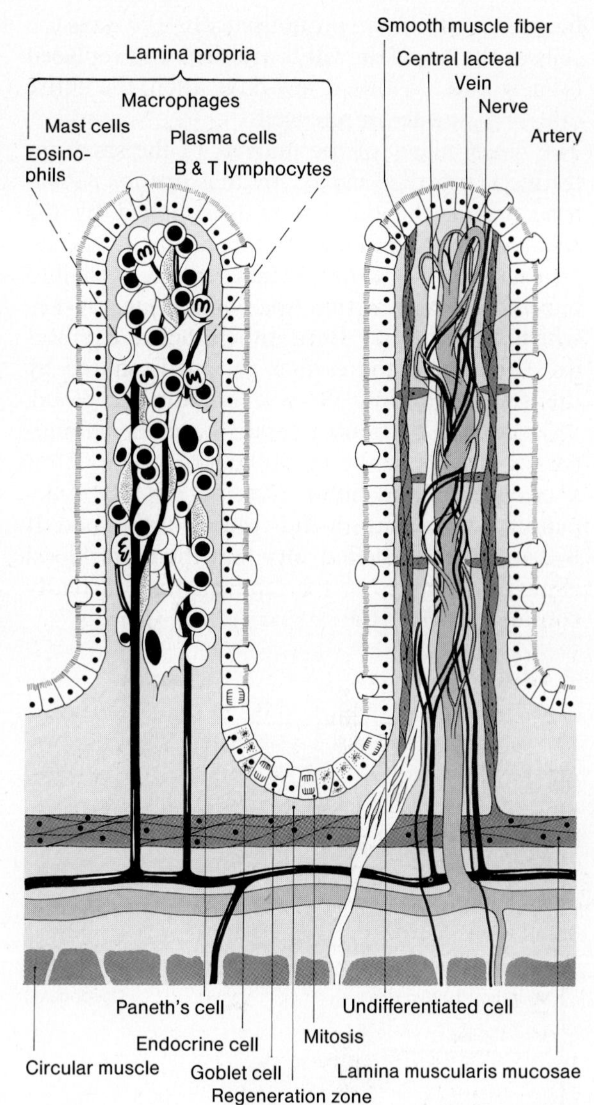

Fig. 29-32. Cross section through two villi in the small intestine and the crypt between them, showing the several forms of mucosal cells and the structures within the villi

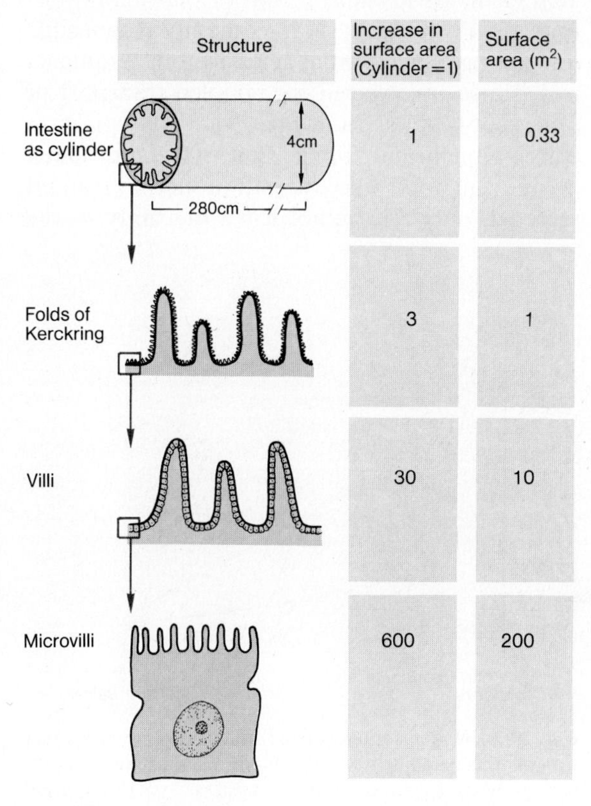

Fig. 29-31. Increase in the surface area of the mucosa by special morphological features

the gastrointestinal lymph tissue. In 3–6 days the cells at the tip of the villus are shed and replaced by new ones. Within a few days, then, the entire intestinal surface is renewed.

The *blood supply* of the mucosa of the small intestine is provided mainly by the *superior mesenteric artery*; the duodenum is supplied by the *celiac artery* and the terminal ileum, by the *inferior mesenteric artery*. These vessels feed into a central vessel within the villus (Fig. 29-32), which branches to form subepithelial capillaries. 10–15% of the cardiac output is shared by the small intestine. Of this amount of blood, 75% goes to the mucosa, ca. 5% to the submucosa and 20% to the muscularis mucosae. After a meal the blood influx rises by 30–130%, depending on the nature and volume of the food. It is distributed in such a way that the extra blood is always supplied to the segment that currently contains most of the chyme.

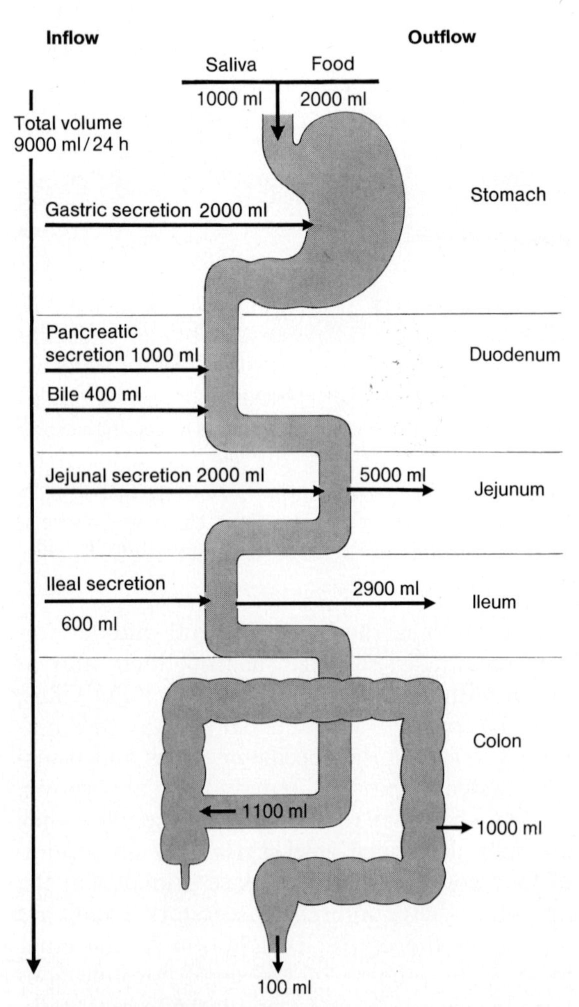

Fig. 29-33. Gastrointestinal fluid balance. Of the total amount of liquid that enters the tract, ca. 2 l from food and 7 l from endogenous secretions, only ca. 100 ml leaves the body in the feces

Water absorption. On average, *9 l of fluid* pass through the small intestine daily. About 2 l are derived from the food and ca. 7 l from the endogenous secretions of the glands and intestine (Fig. 29-33). More than 80% of this fluid is absorbed in the small intestine, about 60% in the duodenum and jejunum and 20% in the ileum. The remainder is taken up in the large intestine; only ca. 1%, or ca. 100 ml, leaves the intestine in the stool.

The *movement of water through the mucosa* is always linked to the transport of dissolved substances, electrolytes and nonelectrolytes. The mucosa is relatively highly permeable to solutes in the upper small intestine. Here the effective pore size in the mucosal cell is ca. 0.8 nm, as compared with 0.4 nm in the ileum and only 0.23 nm in the colon. Therefore when the osmolarity of the chyme differs from that of the blood, equilibration occurs within a few minutes in the duodenum (Fig. 29-34). When the chyme is hyperosmolar, water flows into the intestinal lumen, and when it is hyposmolar, water is rapidly absorbed. In its further passage down the tract, the chyme is isotonic with the plasma (see also p. 704).

Na^+ absorption (Fig. 29-35). One of the preeminent elements in the function of the small intestine is *Na^+ transport*. Na^+ is mainly responsible for setting up potential and osmotic gradients and is also involved in the coupled transport of other substances. Intestinal Na^+ absorption is extremely efficient; of the 250–300 mmol taken in daily in food and the additional 200 mmol secreted, only 3–7 mmol leave the body in the

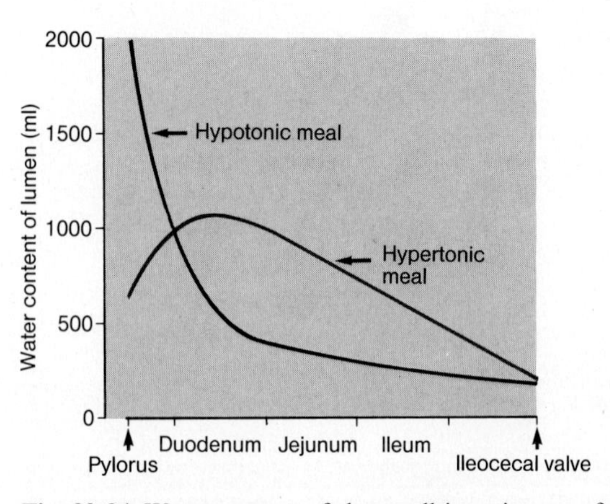

Fig. 29-34. Water content of the small intestine as a function of the osmolarity of the food. Water is rapidly absorbed from hypotonic chyme; after a hypertonic meal water enters the lumen to restore osmotic equilibrium. From [22]

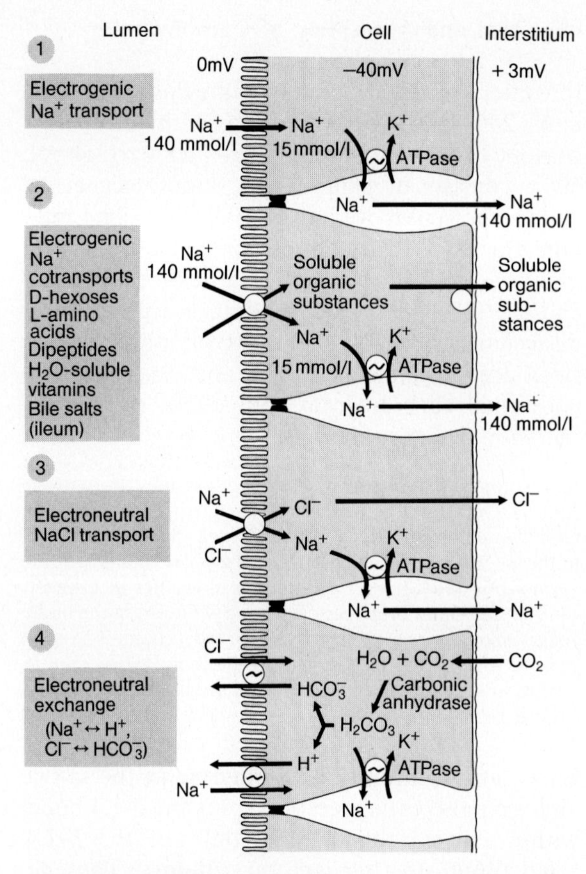

Fig. 29-35. Electrolyte absorption in the small intestine. 1. Electrogenic Na^+ absorption against an electrochemical gradient. 2. Coupled electrogenic Na^+ transport (coupled with organic substances by use of a common carrier). 3. Neutral Na^+-Cl^- cotransport. 4. Neutral Na^+-Cl^- absorption by double exchange for H^+ and HCO_3^- (particularly in the ileum). All four absorption mechanisms are driven by Na^+-K^+ ATPase in the basolateral membrane

stool. By far the greater part is absorbed in the small intestine.

Both *active and passive mechanisms* operate in the intestinal absorption of Na^+. These include electrogenic Na^+ absorption as well as absorption coupled to nonelectrolytes (e.g., glucose, amino acids), neutral NaCl absorption, Na^+-H^+ exchange and passive, convective Na^+ absorption ("solvent drag").

In **electrogenic Na^+ transport** the ions are moved through the *basolateral cell membrane* into the interstitial space by means of a *Na^+ "pump"* that obtains energy for this uphill transport from ATP hydrolysis by the enzyme Na^+-K^+ ATPase (Fig. 29-35/1). This is a central process in intestinal absorption. The gradients that must be overcome are (i) a *Na^+ concentration difference* between 15 mmol/l in the interior of the cell and 140 mmol/l in the plasma, and (ii) *potential differences* of −40 mV (intracellular) and +3 mV (interstitial) with respect to the lumen. The negative charge inside the cell arises because for every 3 Na^+ transported out, only 2 K^+ are brought into the cell. Both gradients simultaneously promote the entry of Na^+ into the cell from the lumen. The Na^+-K^+ ATPase, and hence active Na^+ transport, can be inhibited by the cardiac glycoside *ouabain.* Because of the relative permeability of the tight junctions in the upper small intestine, some of the Na^+ that has been absorbed flows back into the lumen; therefore, when the luminal Na^+ concentration is below 133 mmol/l, there is no net Na^+ absorption. The mucosa of the ileum is "tighter", so that Na^+ continues to be absorbed even with a luminal concentration of 75 mmol/l.

The situation is similar in the case of **coupled Na^+ transport** (cotransport; Fig. 29-35/2). Here nonelectrolytes (D-hexoses, L-amino acids, water-soluble vitamins, bile acids in the ileum) are pushed uphill into the cell, together with Na^+, by a *common carrier.* Hence the active transport of Na^+ through the basolateral membrane indirectly provides energy for the absorption of the nonelectrolytes.

In **neutral NaCl absorption** Na^+ and Cl^- are *cotransported* into the cell, so that the process is electroneutral (Fig. 29-35/3). An increase in the intracellular concentrations of Ca^{2+} and cAMP inhibits this neutral NaCl absorption, and if there is simultaneous active secretion of Cl^- the result is a net secretion of water, producing diarrhea (p. 733). Another model of neutral NaCl absorption postulates a **double exchange** process, in which Na^+ is exchanged for H^+ and Cl^- for HCO_3^- (Fig. 29-35/4); the H^+ and HCO_3^- are formed from H_2O and CO_2. Here, again, the driving force is active Na^+ transport through the basolateral membrane.

Passive convective Na^+ transport plays a crucial role in Na^+ absorption from the small intestine. The epithelium is sufficiently permeable that up to 85% of the Na^+ absorption occurs by *solvent drag* (p. 702). When ample glucose is available, the absorption of glucose creates a flow of water in the same direction that carries Na^+ along with it by the paracellular route.

Absorption of other electrolytes. In contrast to Na^+ absorption, **K^+ transport** is basically passive, down the concentration gradient. The K^+ concentration difference in the jejunum is 10 mmol/l (ca. 14 mmol/l in the lumen and 4 mmol/l in the plasma).

Chloride ions are in part absorbed together with Na^+ (see above), a process favored by the transepithelial potential difference (serosa positive to lumen). An interesting model that explains the origin of certain kinds of diarrhea is the *electrogenic active secretion* of Cl^-.

Bicarbonate is secreted into the lumen in the upper small intestine, by the Brunner's glands in the *duodenum* and by the above double exchange mechanism (Fig. 29-35/4) in the *ileum.* In the *jejunum,* on the other hand, HCO_3^- is absorbed. Some of the bicarbonate derived from food and secreted in the upper small intestine can be converted to CO_2 by carbonic anhydrase. This process raises the P_{CO_2} in the lumen to as much as 300 mm Hg, so that CO_2 diffuses into the cell. As a result, in the upper small intestine the direction of double exchange is opposite to that demonstrated in Fig. 29-35/4: CO_2 moves from the lumen into the cell and HCO_3^- is released into the plasma – that is, it is absorbed.
About 1 g of **calcium** is ingested daily in the form of milk and dairy products. Calcium salts dissociate and become water-soluble in the acidic pH of the stomach; about 40% is absorbed, mainly in the upper small intestine. This is achieved by *active transport* at low concentrations, with an additional passive component at high concentrations. An active process is involved in the entry and the exit of Ca^{2+}; it is taken up by a Ca^{2+}-binding protein in the brush border while entering the enterocyte, and it is transported through the basolateral membrane with the aid of a pump activated by Ca^{2+}-ATPase. *Parathormone* and the *vitamin-D hormone* (1,25-dihydroxycholecalcipherol) participate in the regulation of Ca^{2+} absorption (p. 396).

Iron balance is controlled entirely by way of intestinal absorption, since there is no mechanism for regulatory excretion. Of the 10–20 mg in the daily diet, ca. 10% is absorbed. In iron deficiency the absorption of iron is increased by a factor of 2 or more. Iron from hemoglobin is absorbed more readily than iron of vegetable origin, because the latter is often in insoluble compounds. Iron is absorbed, chiefly in the upper small intestine, in both the *divalent* and (somewhat more slowly) the *trivalent* form. Both the uptake and the release of iron by the enterocytes are *active processes,* as in the case of calcium; release from the enterocyte occurs more slowly and is the rate-limiting step in iron absorption. In the serum iron is bound to the transport protein transferrin and conveyed to its site of action. Excess iron is bound to ferritin in the enterocyte, and at the end of the cell's lifetime it is shed into the intestinal lumen and is excreted.

Digestion and Absorption of Carbohydrates

In western industrial countries the daily diet contains 250–800 g carbohydrate, with an energy content of 4.3–13.7 MJ. The greater part, about 60%, consists of *plant starch,* a polysaccharide with a molecular weight of 100,000 to one million. Ca. 30% is accounted for by *sucrose,* used as a sweetener in the form of cane or beet sugar, and ca. 10% is *lactose.* In addition to these two disaccharides, small quantities of monosaccharides are consumed (*glucose* and *fructose*). An additional carbohydrate component of food is the animal starch *glycogen.*

Starch consists of chains of glucose molecules. In *amylose* (ca. 20% of starch) these are linear chains, in which an O-bridge connects the C1 atom of each glucose molecule to the C4 atom of its neighbor (α-1,4 glycosidic linkage). In *amylopectin* (80%), after 25 glucose molecules in a linear chain a side chain branches off, with a C6 atom in the main chain linked to the C1 atom of the side chain. The side chain is also linked by α-1,4 glycosidic bonds. *Glycogen* is similar in structure except that there are branches at every twelfth glucose molecule.

Enzymatic splitting. The **α-amylase** in the saliva and the pancreatic secretion splits the α-1,4 bond within the starch molecule but not the β-1,4 bond found, for instance, in cellulose. The end products of α-amylase splitting are therefore *maltose, maltotriose* and, in the case of the branched amylopectins, α-limit *dextrins.* The optimal pH for the α-amylases is 7.1. Salivary amylase can split up to 50% of the starch in food when it is chewed long enough and layered in the fundus of the stomach in such a way as to prevent inactivation of the enzyme by gastric acid. In the duodenum starch digestion proceeds at an extremely high rate, because pancreatic amylase is formed in great abundance. A small fraction of this α-amylase acts while bound to the surface of the mucosa. This "membrane digestion" is of little physiological significance, however, in view of the tenfold surplus of amylase present in the lumen.
Because carbohydrates can be absorbed only in the form of monosaccharides, the products of amylase digestion must be broken down further. This is accomplished by **oligosaccharidases** in the *brush-border membrane,* the active hydrolytic groups of which are exposed on the luminal side. Their concentration is highest in the jejunum and less in the duodenum and ileum. The α-1,6 bonds of amylopectin and glycogen are split by **α-1,6 glycosidase**, also located in the brush border. When large amounts of an oligosaccharide are consumed, within 2–5 days the system adapts by

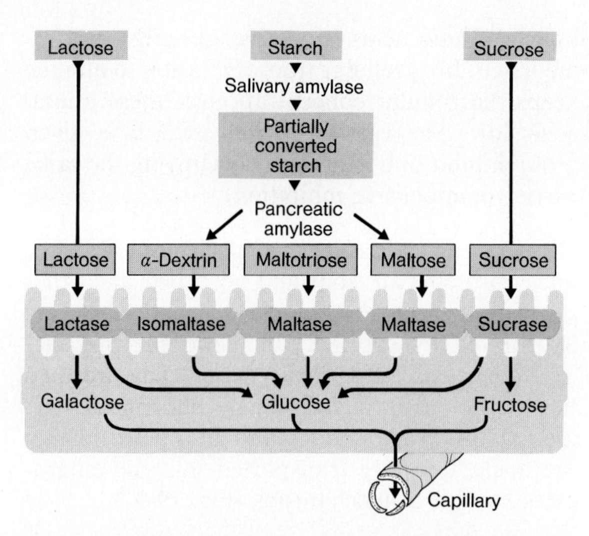

Fig. 29-36. Carbohydrate digestion and absorption. Hydrolysis of di- and oligosaccharides by enzymes in the brush border. The end products of pancreatic carbohydrate digestion and the disaccharides in food are split into their monosaccharide components at the membrane of the brush border. All components of the three carbohydrates in the middle of the picture are glucose molecules. From [12]

increasing the enzyme concentrations. The activity of the membrane-bound enzymes is so great that it is not the splitting process that limits the uptake of carbohydrate but rather the absorption of the monosaccharides. The only exception is *lactose*, which is hydrolyzed more slowly than the end product is absorbed. Furthermore, a congenital defect in lactose digestion is relatively common; the lactose intolerance is manifest as *diarrhea* due to the osmotic action of the unabsorbed lactose (see also p. 733).

Absorption of monosaccharides. The end products of hydrolytic splitting are *glucose, galactose* and *fructose* (Fig. 29-36). The aldohexoses glucose and galactose are absorbed actively, by cotransport with Na^+ (p. 725), whereas fructose absorption is passive, by facilitated diffusion. When the concentrations of glucose and galactose in the intestinal lumen are very high, as is usually the case after a carbohydrate-rich meal, these too can be absorbed passively. Absorption of the hexoses is relatively rapid, although it is slower than digestion; almost all are absorbed in the upper small intestine. Unlike starch itself, the end products are osmotically effective, but rapid absorption prevents the formation of a hypertonic solution. The sequence of events in carbohydrate digestion and absorption is summarized in Fig. 29-36.

Digestion and Absorption of Proteins

Adults consume 70–90 g protein daily, and children require 5 to 10 times as much in relation to their body weight. Almost the same amount of protein as is contained in food enters the intestinal lumen in the form of digestive secretions, desquamated cells and serum protein. In the syndrome called *protein-losing (exudative) enteropathy* so much plasma protein can be lost into the intestine that synthesis of new protein in the liver cannot compensate, and *hypoproteinemia* results.

Enzymatic splitting. Protein digestion begins in the stomach, but the gastric contribution is relatively minor; only 10-15%, at most, of the protein in food is hydrolyzed by **pepsin**. Patients with achlorhydria and no pepsin production can nevertheless digest protein normally, because digestion in the small intestine is extraordinarily efficient. Production of **pancreatic peptidases** begins 10-20 min after eating and continues as long as the intestine contains protein. Some of the enzyme is excreted in the feces; pancreatic function can be tested by measuring the fecal concentration of chymotrypsin.
The various protein-digesting enzymes formed in the pancreas attack the protein molecules at different sites (Table 29-2, p. 716). They are inactive when they enter the duodenum. There *trypsinogen* is converted to the active *trypsin* by an enterokinase, and trypsin in turn activates the other enzymes. The enzymes can be classified as **endopeptidases** (trypsin, chymotrypsin, elastase) and **exopeptidases** (carbopeptidase A and B). The endopeptidases cleave the protein molecule internally to produce oligopeptides, and the exopeptidases split off the amino acids at the ends of peptide chains. The end product consists of 30% neutral and basic *amino acids*, and 70% *oligopeptides* comprising 2–6 amino acids.
Other peptidases are located in the brush border and within the enterocytes. 90% of the di- and tripeptides are hydrolyzed in the cytosol, having been brought into the cell by special transport systems. About 10%, in particular the oligopeptides with 4–8 amino acids, are split by the superficial hydrolases in the brush border. In either case, the ultimate result is the appearance of *amino acids* in the portal blood, as the end products of protein hydrolysis.

Absorption of protein, peptides and amino acids. 50–60% of the food protein is absorbed in the *duodenum*. By the time the chyme has reached the *ileum*, 80–90% of the exogenous and endogenous protein has been absorbed. Only ca. 10% reaches the *colon*, where it is broken down by microbial action. A small amount of protein is excreted in the feces. However, this consists of desquamated cells and not of undigested remnants of food. *Intact protein molecules* are absorbed to a small extent by *pinocytosis* (pp. 703f.). This kind of absorption has no nutritive significance but can be important immunologically, causing sensitization and allergies. *Peptides* are absorbed as di- and tripeptides, either passively or actively, by carriers. The transport systems for absorption of amino acids fall into four main groups – *systems for neutral, dibasic, and dicarboxylic amino acids* and for *imino acids* – with the *glycine system* as an extra group. For the first three groups the mechanism is the coupled Na^+ transport described above (p. 725); absorption of the acidic dicarboxylic amino acids is passive, although carrier-mediated. Intracellular transamination to alanine keeps the cellular concentration of these amino acids low. The various amino acids in a given group inhibit one another by occupying the same carrier (competitive inhibition).

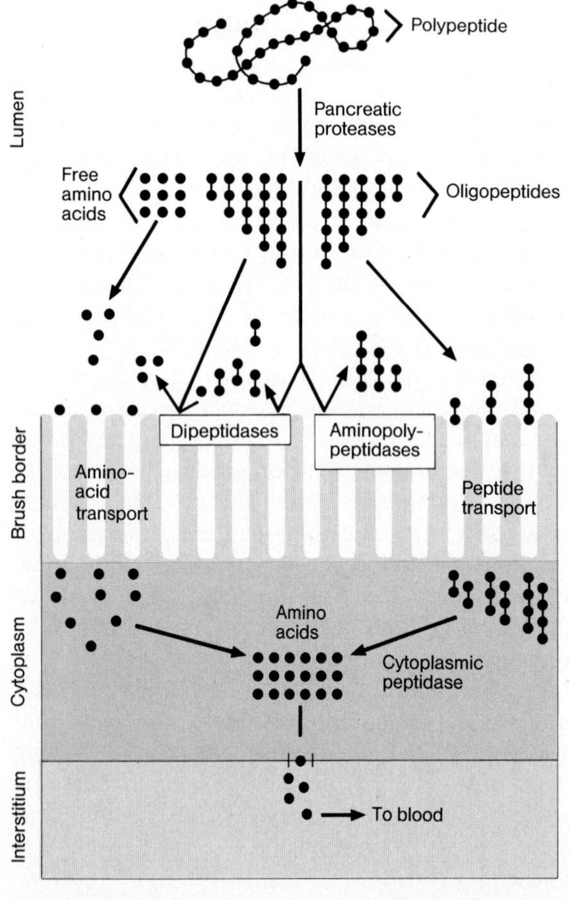

Fig. 29-37. Protein digestion and absorption. *Intestinal lumen:* Splitting of the polypeptides into oligopeptides, di- and tripeptides and amino acids. *Brush-border membrane:* Further splitting by specific peptidases and uptake of the amino acids and oligopeptides. *Cytoplasm:* Splitting of di- and oligopeptides into amino acids, by cytosol peptidases. *Contraluminal membrane:* Release of the amino acids from the cell into the blood

Digestion and absorption of nucleoproteins. The nucleoproteins are split and absorbed like other proteins. The nucleic acids, **DNA** and **RNA**, are hydrolyzed by specific pancreatic enzymes, *deoxyribonuclease* and *ribonuclease.* They are then broken down to *nucleotides* by phosphodiesterases in the brush border and by nucleotidases; the nucleotides are transported into the enterocytes by special mechanisms (Fig. 29-37).

Digestion and Absorption of Lipids

Humans consume about 60–100 g of fat per day. 90% of the lipids in food are *triglycerides,* and the overwhelming majority of these are fats with *long-chain fatty acids* having 16 (palmitic acid) or 18 (stearic, oleic and linoleic acids) carbon atoms. Only a small fraction consists of *short-chain* (2–4 C atoms) and *medium-chain* (6–10 C atoms) triglycerides. The remaining 10% of dietary fat comprises phospholipids (lecithin, in particular), cholesteryl ester and lipid-soluble vitamins (Fig. 29-38).

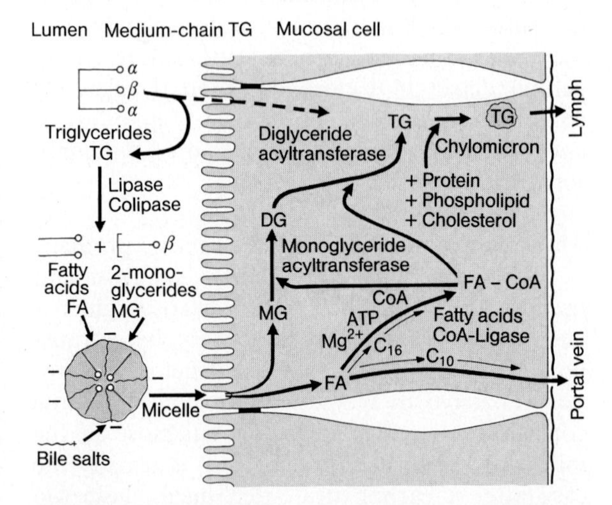

Fig. 29-38. Lipid digestion and absorption. In the lumen of the intestine, colipase and lipase split triglycerides into fatty acids and 2-monoglycerides, which enter solution in micelles and pass from the micelles into the enterocytes. In the cells triglycerides are resynthesized from long-chain fatty acids and 2-monoglycerides and enclosed in a protein envelope to form chylomicrons, which pass into the lymph. Short- and medium-chain fatty acids are absorbed and released into the blood directly. MG monoglycerides, DG diglycerides, TG triglycerides, FA fatty acids. Modified from [27]

Lipid digestion. In the stomach fats become distributed as droplets about 100 nm in diameter. In the alkaline pH of the small intestine and in the presence of proteins, products of previous lipid breakdown, lecithin and bile acids, the fat becomes an **emulsion** with a droplet size of ca. 5 nm. Fat in the small intestine is the adequate stimulus for the *release of cholecystokinin* from the mucosa, with the result that secretion of enzymes in the pancreas is stimulated and the gallbladder contracts.

The **pancreatic lipase** has two components: (i) a *colipase*, produced by the activation of procolipase by trypsin and fixed at the oil-water interface, and (ii) *lipase*, which forms a complex with colipase. In the hydrolysis it catalyzes, the outer fatty acids of the triglycerides are split at the first and third C atoms, so that a *2-monoglyceride* remains. Such a great excess of lipase is secreted from the pancreas that ca. 80% of the fat has been split by the time it has reached the middle of the duodenum. For this reason, a disturbance of fat digestion on account of lipase deficiency does not become apparent until the pancreas has almost entirely ceased to function or been extensively destroyed.

Enzymes other than lipase are also secreted by the pancreas and activated by trypsin. **Phospholipase A**, in the presence of calcium and bile acids, cleaves a fatty acid from the phospholipid *lecithin*, producing *lysolecithin*. *Cholesterol*, usually present in food as esters, is split by a **cholesterol esterase**.

The products of lipolysis are poorly soluble in water. They are brought into solution in the aqueous phase of the intestinal contents by being incorporated into *micelles* (pp. 719f.). The pure bile-acid micelles become **mixed micelles** by the inclusion of fatty acids, monoglycerides, phospholipids and cholesterol in their hydrophobic interior. Water-solubility allows a thousand-fold increase in the concentration of the products of lipid breakdown in the lumen. *Short-* and *medium-chain fatty acids* and the lipids composed of them are sufficiently water-soluble to diffuse into the mucosal cells without incorporation into micelles.

Absorption of the breakdown products. Lipids are so efficiently absorbed that over 95% of the triglycerides (but only 20–50% of the cholesterol) is removed from the lumen in the duodenum and the initial part of the jejunum. People on an average diet eliminate up to 5–7 g fat per day in the feces. With a fat-free diet, this value is reduced to about 3 g/d, derived from desquamated epithelia and bacteria.

The components of the mixed micelles must pass three barriers before reaching the interior of the enterocyte:

1. The *unstirred water layer* in contact with the cell surface. This is a major obstacle to the long-chain fatty acids and monoglycerides, and also impedes the function of the micelles.
2. The *mucus layer* covering the brush-border membrane. With a thickness of 2–4 μm, it is also an obstacle to transport.
3. The *lipid membrane of the enterocyte*. The fatty components of the micelles (which do not enter the cell as a whole) dissolve in the cell membrane and proceed by simple diffusion – rapidly, because of the concentration gradient – into the enterocyte. The remainder of the micelle is then free to return to the lumen and take up new lipid components.

Intracellular lipid synthesis. Having passed through the enterocyte membrane, the products of fat breakdown, *monoglycerides* and *fatty acids*, are transported by a small protein (MW 12,000) to the microsomes of the endoplasmic reticulum. Here they are *resynthesized to triglycerides and lipids*. First a fatty acid is activated and esterified with the monoglyceride by means of monoglyceride transferase. Binding to an additional fatty acid, a process catalyzed by diglyceride transferase, produces a complete triglyceride. Another, less important pathway for resynthesis involves glucose metabolism.

Phospholipids, like triglycerides, can also be formed by esterification in the enterocyte (e.g., formation of lecithin from lysolecithin). The re-esterification to cholesterol is catalyzed by a cholesterol esterase. Furthermore, the ileum is capable of the synthesis of cholesterol de novo, so that the small intestine plays a special role in cholesterol metabolism.

Chylomicron formation. The newly formed triglycerides and lipids cannot leave the cell until they have been enclosed in a special sheath containing cholesterol and phospholipids plus special glycoproteins synthesized in the Golgi apparatus. The completed structure, called a *chylomicron*, is composed of about 90% triglycerides, 7% phospholipids, 2% cholesterol and 1% protein. It is between 60 and 75 nm in diameter, depending on the rates of fat absorption and resynthesis.

The chylomicrons are gathered into *secretory vesicles*, which fuse with the lateral cell membrane and open, discharging their contents into the interstitial space. Then the chylomicrons proceed into the blood, by way of the *central lymph duct* and the *thoracic duct*. After a fatty meal the chylomicrons are present in the plasma in such great quantities that it appears a milky white *(digestive hyperlipemia)*. There is a congenital disease called A-β lipoproteinemia, in which release of chylomicrons from the cell is impaired. The consequence is that although fat is absorbed it cannot be transported away and remains in the cell. In addition to the chylomicrons, *very low density lipoproteins (VLDL)* also formed in the enterocytes are released into the lymph vessels.

Medium- and short-chain triglycerides. In contrast to the long-chain triglycerides, up to 30% of the medium- and short-chain triglycerides are taken *intact* into the cell; the fatty acids are split off intracellularly with the aid of esterases. Together with the medium- and short-chain fatty acids that have diffused into the cell, these diffuse out directly and reach the portal vein by way of the *capillaries*. The existence of this form of transport, much simpler than that of the long-chain triglycerides, is employed in the treatment of patients with maldigestion or malabsorption of lipids, by replacing the long-chain triglycerides in the diet with medium-chain triglycerides.

Pathophysiological aspects. Absorption in the small intestine can be impaired by defects in the mechanisms of food breakdown **(maldigestion)** or by decreased uptake of the breakdown products into the cells **(malabsorption)**. The term **malassimilation** encompasses both kinds of disorder. A common cause of maldigestion is *pancreatic insufficiency;* a typical malabsorption syndrome is *nontropical sprue (celiac disease)*, in which the tips of the villi in the small intestine are destroyed as a result of *gluten hypersensitivity*. The clinical effects are the same in both of these disorders: weight loss, vitamin deficiencies, diarrhea and steatorrhea (fatty stool). They are differentiated by tests of exocrine pancreatic function and of intestinal absorption as well as by imaging procedures (X-ray, endoscopy) and biopsy.

29.7 Colon

In the colon the chyme is mixed by nonpropulsive peristalsis, condensed by water absorption and further broken down by bacterial action, until a propulsive contraction moves the residual mass into the rectum as feces.

Functional Anatomy

The human large intestine is ca. 120–150 cm long; its diameter is 6–9 cm in the region of the cecum and decreases further distally. Different functions predominate in the various sections of the colon. In the *cecum*, where the chyme is still fluid, the emphasis is on bacterial action and electrolyte and water absorption. In the *ascending, transverse* and *descending colon* these processes continue while the contents, progressively thicker in consistency, are moved along. The *sigmoid colon* and the *rectum* serve chiefly as storage areas. The colon is delimited by two sphincters, the *ileocecal valve* (Bauhin's valve) at the proximal end and the *anal sphincters* at the distal end; the latter consist of an inner ring of smooth muscle and an outer ring of striated muscle.

In the proximal part of the colon the longitudinal musculature is limited to three bands about 0.8 cm wide, the *teniae*. The tenial tone and local contractions of the circular musculature produce a series of constrictions separated by expanded regions, the *haustra*. Beginning in the sigmoid region, the longitudinal musculature again surrounds the intestine completely; distally, it merges with the fascia of the perianal region.

The *colonic mucosa* has no villi like those in the small intestine, but it does bear *microvilli*. There are crypts in the mucosa 0.7 mm deep, lined with epithelial cells, many mucous cells and a few endocrine cells. Cells migrate from the bottom of the crypt to the opening, where they are shed; the process takes 5–7 days, somewhat longer than in the small intestine. The lamina propria contains abundant *lymphatic tissue* and *plasma cells* – particularly in the region of the appendix, where it has been called the "tonsil of the intestine". The massive development of lymphatic tissue in the colon must be seen in relation to the large bacterial population there. The immunocompetent cells secrete primarily immunoglobulin IgA (see also p. 697).

Colonic Motility

Control. The nature and velocity of motility in the colon depend on (i) the *potential changes in the smooth muscle cells*, the slow waves with their action potentials, and (ii) modulation of this activity by the *autonomic nervous system* and by *gastrointestinal polypeptides*. **Parasympathetic** inputs stimulate colonic motility, because acetylcholine depolarizes the muscle membrane, bringing the slow waves closer to the action-potential threshold. **Sympathetic** activation and noradrenalin have a hyperpolarizing and hence contraction-inhibiting effect.

By way of these autonomic actions, central nervous states can influence colonic motility. Such an influence can be demonstrated by subjecting a person to a *"stress interview"* while colonic pressure is being measured by a balloon sensor in the sigmoid. When the conversation is turned to topics that produce aggression, animosity and tension, the pressure rises. It is lowered by depression, fear and sadness.

The **gastrointestinal polypeptides** can either enhance colonic motility *(gastrin* and *cholecystokinin)* or inhibit it *(secretin* and *glucagon).*

The *frequency of the slow waves* is more variable in the colon than in the small intestine, and there is no gradient from proximal to distal. From the ascending to the descending colon the average frequency is 6/min; it is lower in the cecum and sigmoid but higher (17/min) in the rectum. The neurons in the myenteric plexus inhibit the pacemakers of the smooth muscle cells. Failure of this inhibition can have severe effects, as illustrated by *Hirschsprung's disease.* In this congenital disorder the ganglia are absent in a restricted region, usually in the distal rectum. As a result, this region is in a state of permanent tonic contraction (see p. 695); because evacuation of the bowel is impeded, fecal matter accumulates proximal to the constriction and produces a condition called *megacolon* (colonic distension).

In addition to inhibitory neurons, the myenteric plexus contains stimulatory (cholinergic and peptidergic) fibers with VIP, substance P, enkephalin and somatostatin as transmitters.

Patterns of contraction. For people on a low-fiber occidental diet, the *transit time of the chyme* from the ileocecal valve to the rectum is 2–3 days. Particles carried in the central stream can move through the colon in a shorter time. The figure of 2–3 days is obtained experimentally by feeding a subject a quantity of small markers along with a meal and noting the time required for 80% of that amount to appear in the stool. By increasing the fiber content of the food, the transit time can be shortened in parallel with an increase in weight of the feces. African villagers on a high-fiber diet had an average transit time of 36 h and a stool weight of 480 g; the comparable values for European city dwellers were 72 h and 110 g.

The long transit time in itself indicates that the main components of colonic motility are *nonpropulsive.* The contractions of the circular muscles do not follow an orderly progression and can occur at several places simultaneously; they serve to mix the contents without causing any net progression. When the circular muscles of two adjacent haustra contract in succession, the contents are shifted over a distance of ca. 10 cm, but the movement can be in the proximal as well as the distal direction. This kind of contraction occasionally involves more than two segments. The simple haustral contractions account for over 90% of the movements of the colon.

On rare occasions a true *peristaltic wave* of contraction preceded by relaxation moves the contents for about 20 cm. This peristalsis can also be directed toward the proximal or the distal end. Only a few times a day does a *mass movement* or *"peristaltic rush"* occur; this phenomenon is also called Holzknecht's movement after the radiologist who first described it. It propels the contents over a long distance, from the transverse to the sigmoid colon.

All the above forms of motility can be *enhanced by food intake.* Motility is influenced by the energy content and composition of the meal, but not by its volume or pH. Energy-rich meals with a high fat content increase motility; carbohydrates and proteins have no effect. Because the increase begins only 10 min after eating, the effect is called a *gastrocolic reflex.* This reflex is thought to involve *cholinergic stimulation* because it is suppressed by anticholinergics; the acetylcholine probably acts by causing the release of gastrin and cholecystokinin.

Pathophysiological aspects. Abnormality of the motor events in the colon can lead to **constipation** or **diarrhea.** From the above considerations one can see the error in the widely accepted idea that diarrhea is caused only by an increase in motility. The opposite can be true: that is, *intensification of the nonpropulsive contractions results in constipation.* An example is the spastic constipation that often accompanies the common functional disorder called "irritable colon". Conversely, *decreased motility can produce diarrhea,* because the resistance normally presented by the local segmental contractions is lacking. On the other hand, there are diseases of the colon (e.g., ulcerative colitis, a chronic inflammation of the colon) in which diarrhea is associated with more frequent propulsive mass contractions.

Digestion and Absorption

The motor activity of the colon converts the fluid chyme into solid feces, by microbial breakdown and the absorption of water.

Absorption of electrolytes and water. Each day 1–1.5 l of fluid chyme enters the cecum; over

90% of this volume is absorbed in the colon, so that only about 100 ml leaves the body with the feces (Fig. 29-33, p. 724). It is possible for much more to be absorbed – up to a maximum of about 5 l/d, with a steady input of fluid. Only when this capacity is exceeded (e.g., by secretory processes in the small intestine; pp. 704 and 724) does "overflow" diarrhea occur.
Electrolytes and water are absorbed in the colon with great efficiency, even against a steep osmotic gradient. The reason is that the colonic epithelium is *relatively tight*. The pore diameter in the epithelial membranes has been found to be 0.23 nm (cf. p. 701). Because of the high membrane resistance, water flows more slowly into the interstitial space. The tight junctions impede the flow of Na^+ and water back into the lumen. Therefore the colon is capable of continuing to absorb Na^+ even as the solution becomes hypotonic, down to a concentration of 30 mmol/l (cf. p. 704). The tightness of the membrane is also associated with a large transepithelial potential difference, created by the electrogenic Na^+ transport; in humans the transepithelial potential is 30–40 mV in the colon and only 2–4 mV in the jejunum.

Within the colon itself there is a gradient in "tightness" of the epithelium. The epithelium of the *cecum* is less tight and absorbs more water more rapidly from the fluid chyme; the epithelium of the *rectum* is tightest and can absorb Na^+ even from the relatively solid contents, so that the water in the feces is hypotonic with respect to plasma.

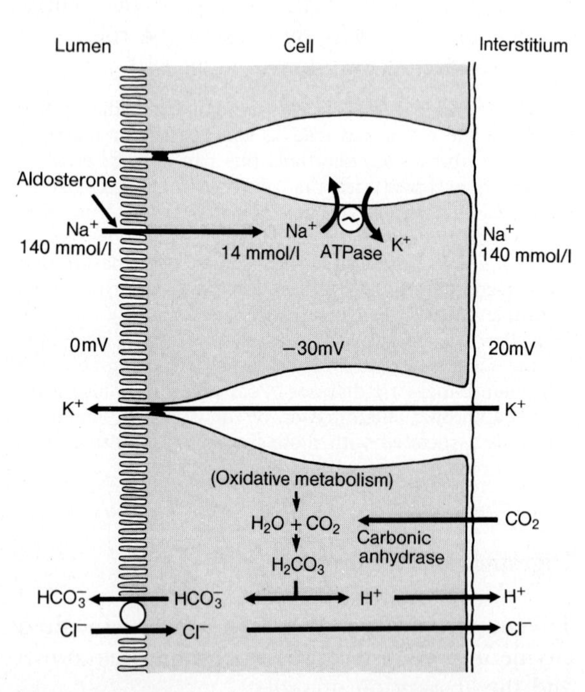

Fig. 29-39. Electrolyte transport in the colonic mucosa. *Above:* Active Na^+ absorption (promoted by aldosterone) and passive diffusion of K^+ in the opposite direction. *Below:* Exchange of HCO_3^- and Cl^-. From [1]

Na^+ enters the cell by free diffusion because of the large concentration difference, ca. 130 mmol/l, and a potential difference of −30 mV (Fig. 29-39). Removal from the cell, into the interstitial space, is accomplished by a *pump* in the basolateral cell membrane, activated by Na^+–K^+ ATPase.
K^+ is *secreted* into the lumen of the colon down the electrical gradient, passing through the tight junctions, which are relatively permeable to K^+. Only a small amount diffuses directly through the cell membrane into the lumen, despite the high intracellular concentration of 80 mmol/l.
The differences in transport of Na^+ and K^+ are reflected in their proportions in the feces. Whereas 5–10 mmol K^+ enter the colon daily in the chyme, 10–15 mmol leave the bowel in the feces, raising the K^+ concentration there to 90 mmol/l. On the other hand, 150 mmol Na^+ enter the cecum, where its concentration is ca. 130 mmol/l, and only 2–4 mmol are excreted, at a concentration of 40 mmol/l.

Na^+ absorption and K^+ secretion are increased by *mineralocorticoids* when their plasma concentration rises by physiological amounts (as happens following sodium loss), and by *glucocorticoids* in pharmacological doses such as are used in treating chronic inflammatory diseases. These hormones stimulate Na^+-K^+ ATPase, and aldosterone also increases the permeability of the apical cell membrane to Na^+.

Chloride and **bicarbonate** are also efficiently absorbed in the colon. Of the ca. 60 mmol Cl^- that reach the colon daily, at a concentration of ca. 60 mmol/l, only about 2 mmol are excreted, at a concentration of 15 mmol/l. The low final concentration suggests *active transport* against a steep chemical gradient. Cl^- absorption is coupled with HCO_3^- secretion in an exchange system (Fig. 29-39). Because of the accumulation of HCO_3^- in the lumen, the feces are slightly alkaline.

Digestion and Absorption of Organic Food Components

In addition to water and electrolytes, the colon receives organic components of food that are not absorbed in the small intestine. Only a small percentage of these are potentially absorbable substances that have somehow escaped absorption. Most were not absorbed because they could

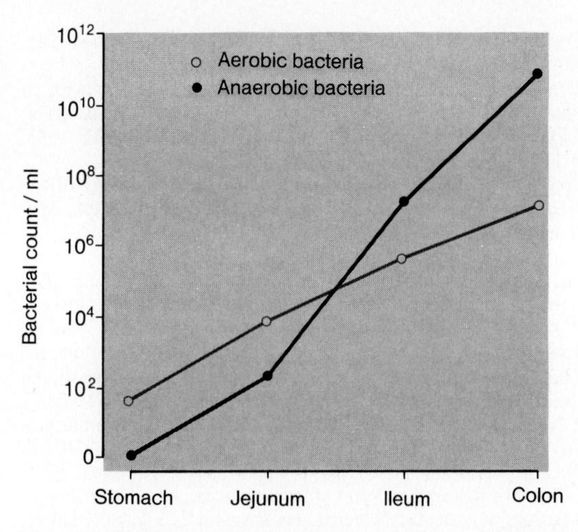

Fig. 29-40. Bacterial population of the gastrointestinal tract. In stomach and jejunum the aerobic oral flora predominates. At the transition from ileum to cecum there is a marked increase (note logarithmic ordinate) in the number of bacteria, especially anaerobes. From [12]

not be digested. These are chiefly plant fibers and other structural materials such as *celluloses, hemicelluloses, pectins* and *lignins* – carbohydrates that cannot be split by human amylases. Intestinal **bacteria** are able to split them, though not as efficiently in humans as in herbivores, which obtain most of their energy from the bacterial decomposition of carbohydrates. Even so, ca. 40–50% of this "roughage" is broken down by bacteria in the human colon and absorbed in the form of short-chain fatty acids.

Whereas the stomach and upper small intestine are essentially sterile, the bacteria count rises further along the intestine, with a steep rise by a factor of 10,000–100,000 at the ileocecal valve. The number of bacteria per ml of chyme rises from 10^6 in the ileum to $10^{11} - 10^{12}$ (Fig. 29-40). Most of the bacteria in the colon are obligate anaerobes: *Bifidus* and *Bacteroides* (gram-positive or -negative, nonsporulating bacilli). Aerobic forms such as *E. coli*, enterococci and lactobaccilli account for less than 1% of the total colonic bacteria count. There are over 400 species of bacteria in the colon; bacteria make up 30–50% of the total dry matter in the feces, or even 75% according to other calculations [42].
The anaerobic bacteria split vegetable fiber into two- to four-carbon *fatty acids:* acetic, butyric and propionic acids. These acids provide ca. 50% of the anions in the colon. Most are neutralized by secreted bicarbonate.
Whereas proteins, carbohydrates, long-chain fatty acids and glycerides cannot be absorbed in the colon, the short-chain fatty acids are taken up by passive nonionic diffusion. The long-chain fatty acids are derived from undigested or unabsorbed food lipids that reach the colon in larger amounts in cases of of malabsorption or maldigestion. These lipids can also be split by bacterial lipases, and about 25% of the resulting long-chain fatty acids are further hydroxylated by bacterial action. These hydroxy fatty acids act to produce diarrhea in the same way as ricinolic acid, the active principle in castor oil.

Defecation and Diarrhea

The entrance of feces into the rectum triggers reflexes that result in defecation (p. 352). The normal *frequency of defecation* in western industrialized countries ranges from three times a day to three times a week, and is strongly affected by events in the colon. In addition to colonic motility, the water content of the feces plays a major role. Because **diarrhea** results when the water content is increased to 200–300 ml, minor impairment of water absorption in the colon can produce it.

Pathophysiological aspects. When unsplit and unabsorbable lactose enters the colon in large amounts, owing to *lactase deficiency* in the mucosa of the small intestine (milk intolerance), it has a pronounced osmotic action. Enough water is retained in the lumen to produce diarrhea, even if some of the lactose is broken down by bacteria and absorbed. The same effect is put to therapeutic use in the *saline cathartics* containing poorly absorbable ions like magnesium and sulfate. These are examples of *osmotic diarrhea.*
Other groups of cathartics act by converting the tight junctions to *"leaky" junctions* and thus altering the absorption properties of the colonic epithelium. The mucosa then resembles that of the small intestine, in that it is no longer capable of maintaining the steep gradients required for the conservation of Na^+ and water. Among these substances are the *hydroxy fatty acids*, including ricinolic acid, *bile acids* that have escaped absorption in the small intestine and reach the colon in fairly high concentrations (chologenic diarrhea) and diphenolic laxatives such as bisacodyl. Some of these cathartics also inhibit $Na^+ + K^+$ ATPase, suppressing active Na^+ transport.

29.8 References

Textbooks and Handbooks

1. Clinical gastrointestinal physiology, Granger, D.N., Barrowman, J.A., Kvietys, P.R. eds. W.B. Saunders Philadelphia 1985
2. Colon, structure and function. L. Bustos-Fernandes ed. Plenum Medical Book Comp New York 1983
3. Digestion and the structure and function of the gut. Magee, D.F., Dalley, A.F. eds. Karger Basel 1986
4. Dünndarm A. Handbuch Innere Medizin, 5. Aufl. Bd. 3, Verdauungsorgane Teil 3 A. Caspary, W.F. ed. Springer Berlin 1983
5. Gastrointestinal disease: pathophysiology, diagnosis, management. Sleisenger, M.H., Fordtran, J.S. eds. W.B. Saunders Co Philadelphia 1983
6. Gastrointestinal pathophysiology, Brooks, F.P. ed. Oxford Univ. Press New York 1974
7. Gastrointestinale Physiologie. Konturek, S.J., Classen, M. eds. G. Witzstrock Baden-Baden 1976
8. Handbook of Physiology. Section 6: Alimentary Canal. Vol 1–5. Code C ed. Am Physiol Soc Washington 1968
9. Intestinal absorption and secretion. Scadhauge, E., Heintze, K. eds. MTP Press Lim. Lancester 1984

10. Medical physiology. MOUNTCASTLE, V.B. ed. C.V. Mosby Co St. Louis 1980
11. Physiology of the digestive tract. DAVENPORT, H.W., 5th edition. Year Book Med Publ Chicago 1982
12. Physiology of the gastrointestinal tract. JOHNSON, L.R. ed. Raven Press New York 1981
13. Undergraduate teaching project in gastroenterology and liver disease. American Gastroenterological Association Timonium: Milner-Fernwick, I.N.C., 1976
14. Taschenatlas der Physiologie. SILBERNAGL, S., DESPOPULOS, A. Thieme Stuttgart 1979
15. The large intestine. WRONG, O.M., EDMONDS, C.J., CHADWICK, V.S. eds. MTP Press Lim. Lancester 1981

Original Papers and Reviews

16. ANDERSON, D.J.: Mastication. In: Handbook of Physiology. Section 6: Alimentary canal. Vol. 4 Motility. Code C. ed. Washington: Am Physiol Soc 1968, pp 1811–1820
17. CLAUDE, P., GOODENOUGH, D.A.: Fracture faces of zonula occludentes from "tight" and "leaky" epithelia. J Cell Biol 58, 390–400, 1973
18. ECKHARDT, R., MEYER ZUM BÜSCHENFELDE, K.H.: Immunologie des Dünndarms. In: Handbuch Innere Medizin 5. Aufl. Bd. 3; Verdauungsorgane Teil 3 A. CASPARY, W.F. ed. Springer Berlin 1983, S. 73–104
19. ELSENHANS, B., CASPARY, W.F.: Resorption von Kohlenhydraten. In: Handbuch Innere Medizin 5. Aufl. Bd 3; Verdauungsorgane Teil 3 A. CASPARY, W.F. ed. Springer Berlin 1983, S. 139–156
20. ELSENHANS, B., CASPARY, W.F.: Resorption von Eiweiß. In: Handbuch Innere Medizin 5. Aufl. Bd 3; Verdauungsorgane Teil 3 A. CASPARY, W.F. ed. Springer Berlin 1983, S. 157–178
21. FELLENIUS, E., BERGHLIND, T., SACHS, G., OLBE, L., ELANDER, B. SJÖSTRAND, S.E., WALLMARK, B.: Substituted benzimidazoles inhibit acid secretion by blocking (Na^{+}-K^{+})-ATPase. Nature 290, 159–161 (1981)
22. FORDTRAN, J.S., LOCKLEAR, T.W.: Ionic constituents and osmolality of gastric and small intestinal fluids after eating. Am J Dig Dis 11, 503–521 (1966)
23. FORTH, W.: Intestinale Resorption von Eisen und chemisch verwandten Metallen. In: Handbuch Innere Medizin 5. Aufl. Bd 3; Verdauungsorgane Teil 3 A. CASPARY, W.F. ed. Springer Berlin 1983, S. 267–297
24. FRÖMTER, E., DIAMOND, J.: Route of passive ion-permeation in epithelia. Nature 235, 9–13 (1972)
25. FROMM, H., BAZZOLI, F.: Enterohepatischer Kreislauf der Gallensäure. In: Handbuch Innere Medizin 5. Aufl. Bd 3; Verdauungsorgane Teil 3 A. CASPARY, W.F. ed. Springer Berlin 1983, S. 352–372
26. GANGL, A.: Resorption von Triglyceriden und fettlöslichen Vitaminen (außer Vitamin D). In: Handbuch Innere Medizin 5. Aufl. Bd 3; Verdauungsorgane Teil 3 A. CASPARY. W.F. ed. Springer Berlin 1983, S. 179–215
27. GRAY, G.M.: Mechanisms of digestion and absorption of food. In: Gastrointestinal disease. 2nd ed. SLEISENGER, M.H.; FORTRAN, S.J. eds. Philadelphia: W.B. Saunders Co., 1983
28. HENTSCHEL, E.: Cimetidin. In: Ulcustherapie. BLUM, A.L., SIEVERT, J.R. eds. Springer Berlin 1982 S. 225–253
29. HOFMANN, A.F.: The enterohepatic circulation of bile acids in health and disease. In: Gastrointestinal disease. SLEISENGER, M.H.; FORDTRAN, J.S. eds. W.B. Saunders Philadelphia 1983, p 115–132
30. ITO, S.: Functional gastric morphology. In: Physiology of the gastrointestinal tract. JOHNSON, L.R. ed. Raven Press New York 1981, p 517–550
31. KREIJS, G.J.: Wasser- und Elektrolyttransport des Dünndarms. In: Handbuch Innere Medizin 5. Aufl. Bd 3; Verdauungsorgane Teil 3 A. CASPARY, W.F. ed. Springer Berlin 1983, S. 434–463
32. LEMBCKE, B., CASPARY, W.F.: Intestinale Gasproduktion. In: Handbuch Innere Medizin 5. Aufl. Bd 3; Verdauungsorgane Teil 3 A. CASPARY, W.F. ed. Springer Berlin 1983, S. 521–541
33. LEVITT, M.D.; BOND, J.H., LEVITT, D.G.: Gastrointestinal gas. In: Physiology of the gastrointestinal tract. JOHNSON, L.R. ed. Raven Press New York 1981, p 1301–1316
34. NELL, G.: Resorption von Gallensäuren. In: Handbuch Innere Medizin 5. Aufl. Bd 3; Verdauungsorgane Teil 3 A. CASPARY, W.F. ed. Springer Berlin 1983, S. 337–349
35. PEERENBOOM, H.: Resorption von Kalzium, Magnesium und Phosphat und ihre Regulation. In: Handbuch Innere Medizin 5. Aufl. Bd 3; Verdauungsorgane Teil 3 A. CASPARY, W.F. ed. Springer Berlin 1983, S. 233–266
36. POLAK, J.M., BLOOM, S.R., SULLIVAN, S.N., FRAZER, P., PEARSE, A.G.E.: Enkephaline-like immuno reactivity in the human gastrointestinal tract. Lancet 1, 972–974, 1977
37. RUMBERGER, E.: Physiologie des Colons. In: Handbuch Innere Medizin 5. Aufl. Bd 3; Verdauungsorgane Teil 4. MÜLLER-WIELAND, K. ed. Springer Berlin 1982
38. RUMMEL, W.: Biologische Membranfunktion. Wirkungen von Gallen-säuren und Laxantien auf den mukosalen Transfer. Cat. Med. Wiss. 32, 233–250, 1976
39. RUPPIN, H.: Motilität des Dünndarms. In: Handbuch Innere Medizin 5. Aufl. Bd 3; Verdauungsorgane Teil 3 A. CASPARY, W.F. ed. Springer Berlin 1983, S. 464–487
40. SCHILLER, L.R.: Motor function of the stomach. In: Gastrointestinal disease. SLEISENGER, M.H., FORDTRAN, J.S. eds. W.B. Saunders Philadelphia 1983, p 521–541
41. SCHULTZ, S.G.: Some properties and consequencies of low-resistance paracellular pathway across the small intestine: the advantage of being "leaky". In: Intestinal permeation. KRAMER, M., LAUTERBACH, F. eds. Amsterdam: Excerpta medica, 1977, pp 321–392
42. STEPHEN, A.M., CUMMINGS, J.H.: The microbial contribution to human faecal mass. J Med Microbiol 13, 45–66 (1980)
43. THAYSEN, J.H., THORN, N.A., SCHWARTZ, I.L.: Excretion of sodium, potassium, chloride and carbon dioxide in human parotid saliva. Am J Physiol 178, 155–159 (1954)
44. TRIER, J.S., MADARA, J.L.: Functional morphology of the mucosa of the small intestine. In: Physiology of the gastrointestinal tract. JOHNSON, L.R. ed. Raven Press New York 1981, p 925–962
45. WEISBRODT, N.W.: Pattern of intestinal motility. Annual Rev Physiol 43, 33–51 (1981)

30 The Function of the Kidneys

P. DEETJEN

30.1 Fundamentals of Renal Function

The role of the kidneys. The kidneys are responsible for controlling the fluids of the body. They ensure that the **extracellular fluid** bathing the cells has a *constant composition and volume*, guaranteeing that the conditions under which the cells operate are as uniform and as nearly optimal as possible. If either water or dissolved substances should be present in excess, the surplus is excreted by way of the kidneys. In case of a water and/or electrolyte deficiency, processes are initiated to minimize further loss without impeding the necessary excretion of metabolic end products.

Functional units in the kidney. Each kidney contains ca. 1.2 million **nephrons** (Fig. 30-1). A nephron consists of (i) the glomerulus, with Bowman's capsule, (ii) the proximal convolution, (iii) the loop of Henle, (iv) the distal convolution. The distal convolution opens into (v) the collecting duct, which is actually shared by several nephrons.
Each nephron is a functional unit capable of independently carrying out specific kinds of transport. But there are certain tasks – such as concentrating the urine – that can be accomplished only by collective action. When a considerable number of nephrons are inoperative the ability to concentrate urine is lost, even if the remaining nephrons are completely intact.

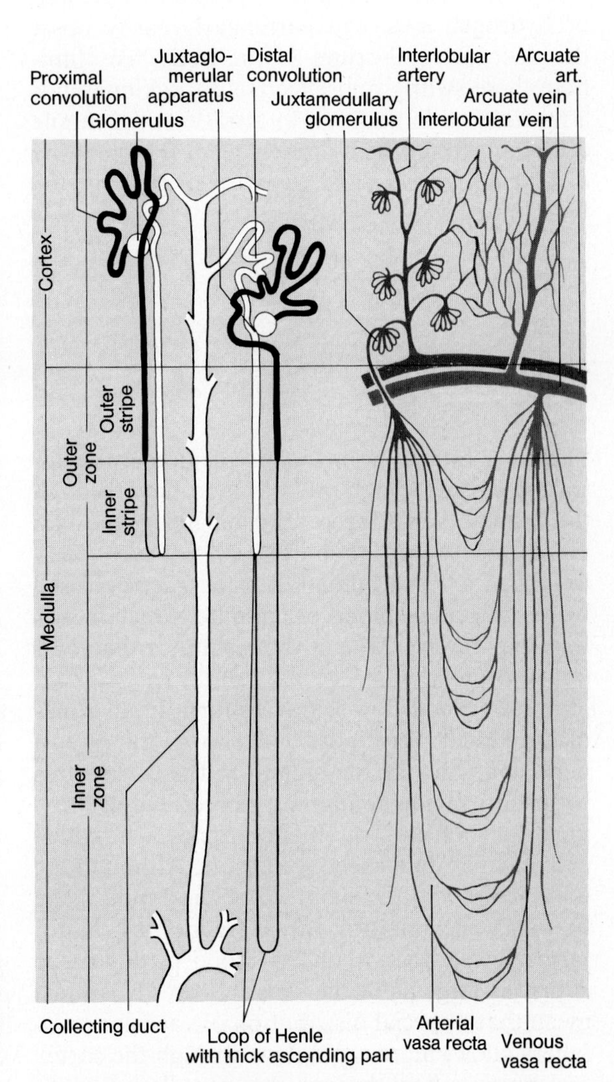

Fig. 30-1. The arrangement of the nephrons and their vascular supply, schematic. On the *left* are a cortical and a juxtamedullary nephron. (Modified from [19, 37])

Basic principles of renal function. Two main principles underlie the function of the kidneys: the separation of large amounts of extracellular fluid from the remainder by **ultrafiltration** in the glomeruli, and the **transport** of electrolytes and other solutes, together with the water in which they are dissolved, through the cells of the tubule system. In the course of evolution, the kidney has come to excel all the other structures of the body in both these functions. The glomerular capillaries can filter about 100 times more per unit area than, for instance, muscle capillaries. The transport achieved in the tubular epithelia, especially that of the proximal convolution, is also a marvel of economy and efficiency.
The entire extracellular volume, at least 17 l in a fully grown human (Fig. 31-1, p. 763), passes through the kidneys in the bloodstream about 50 times per day. One-fifth is continually separated out by *glomerular filtration* and moves on

into the tubules. Under the control of the tubule cells, everything the body still requires – water, electrolytes, vitamins, amino acids, glucose and other valuable substances – is *reabsorbed*. But metabolic end products of no further energetic use, as well as the water and electrolytes consumed in food that need not be retained, remain in the duct system and are excreted in the urine. Some substances, such as potassium or hydrogen ions, can particularly easily upset the delicate equilibrium in the body. To eliminate these swiftly and effectively the kidney has a mechanism in addition to filtration; the tubule cells can extract them directly from the blood by a *secretory process* and send them away in the final urine.

30.2 Renal Blood Flow

Perfusion rates. The high rate of glomerular filtration affords a high rate of blood flow through the kidney. Weighing a total of 300 g, the two kidneys account for only 0.4% of the body weight of a 70-kg human. But they are perfused by about 1.2 l of blood per minute, which means that they receive 25% of the resting cardiac output of 5 l/min.
However, blood flow is not uniform in all zones of the kidney. As Figure 30.2 shows, the rate of perfusion is by far the highest in the *cortex*; this is the only region containing glomeruli and proximal convolutions, the main structures in which extracellular fluid exchange occurs. Although the *renal medulla*, with its outer zone and inner zone (papilla), accounts for only a fraction of the total perfusion, the volume of blood in this tissue is just as large as in the renal cortex. This must mean that a special distribution of vascular resistances allows more rapid flow through the cortex and restricts flow through the medulla.

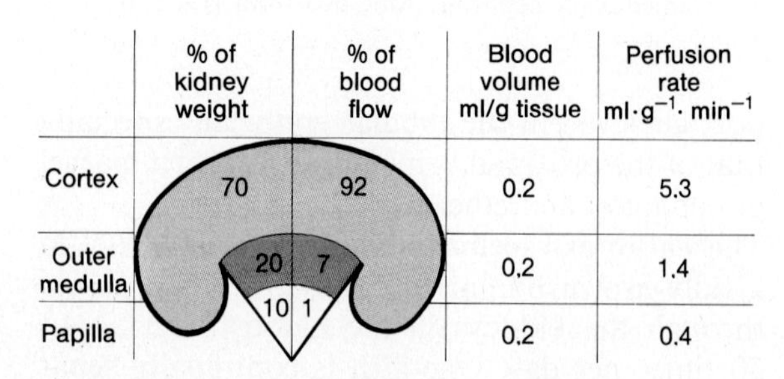

Fig. 30-2. Intrarenal distribution of blood flow

Vascular architecture. The vascular supply of the renal tissue is unique in having *two sequences of resistance vessels and capillaries in series*. After leaving the aorta the renal artery divides, in the hilus region, into two or more branches, which become the interlobar arteries. These give rise to the arcuate arteries, which run along the medulla-cortex boundary and send the interlobular arteries into the cortex (Fig. 30-1). These branch into the **afferent arterioles**, vessels capable of resistance regulation, from which the **capillary tufts of the glomeruli** arise. These drain into the resistance vessels of the second sequence, the **efferent arterioles**, which open into the **peritubular capillary networks** surrounding the convoluted tubules in the cortex.

Resistances to flow. When the arterial pressure is normal, the mean pressure drop across the afferent arterioles, from the renal artery to the glomerular capillaries, is relatively slight (Fig. 30-3). As a result, the hydrostatic pressure in these capillaries is higher than in any other capillary bed of the body, which provides the driving force for the massive filtration in the glomerulus. The *resistance* presented by the efferent arterioles is at least as great as that of the afferent arterioles, producing a pressure drop sufficient that the hydrostatic pressure in the peritubular capillary plexus is no higher than that in the proximal tubule. Therefore the tubular fluid can be reabsorbed and transported away with no difficulty.
Whereas the *afferent arteriole* has a limited role as a resistance vessel when arterial pressure is normal, its arteriolar function is clearly manifest under high-pressure conditions. As the arterial pressure rises up to about 200 mm Hg, the resistance in the afferent arterioles and the preceding interlobular arteries rises in proportion,

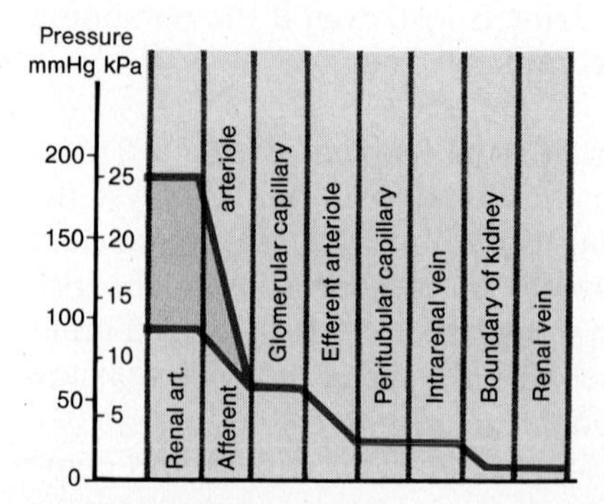

Fig. 30-3. Hydrostatic pressure drop from renal artery to renal vein. In the autoregulatory region *(red)* the glomerular capillary pressure is kept constant by preglomerular resistance changes. (Modified from [54])

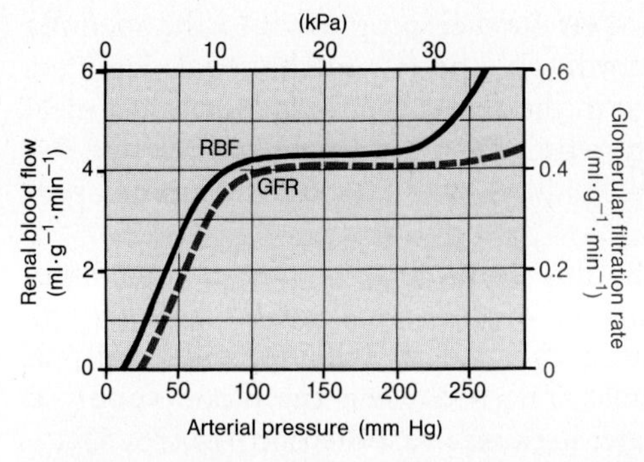

Fig. 30-4. Renal blood flow *(RBF, black line)* and glomerular filtration rate *(GFR, red line)* as a function of arterial blood pressure. In the pressure range between 80 and 200 mm Hg both RBF and GFR are kept approximately constant (autoregulation)

so that the pressure in the glomerular capillaries is practically unchanged. Because the *filtration pressure remains constant*, the output of extracellular fluid continues to be approximately the same regardless of arterial pressure fluctuations. The controlling mechanisms of the tubular fluid cannot be overloaded.

Autoregulation. The pressure-dependent adjustment of the input resistance preceding the glomeruli ensures constant renal perfusion despite pressure fluctuations, a process called autoregulation (Fig. 30-4). Autoregulation of blood flow operates just as effectively in the brain as in the kidney. The brain also requires pressure-constant perfusion in the postarteriolar bed, to avoid the risk of cerebral edema and excessive pressure on the neural tissue when the blood pressure rises. Accordingly, both organs are *effectively uncoupled from the general circulatory regulation*; normally the tone of their resistance vessels is set independently of the sympathetic tone and circulatory reflexes. Only when the level of sympathetic activation is extremely high can it cause vasoconstriction in the kidneys.

The **mechanism of autoregulation** of glomerular filtration and renal perfusion has not yet been satisfactorily explained. One factor is the *Baylis effect* (p. 487), in which the smooth musculature of a vessel responds to increased transmural pressure (p. 485) by contracting. But because the degree of constriction of the renal arterioles can be influenced by functional changes in the kidney, an additional *intrarenal feedback mechanism* is under discussion [45]. The anatomical prerequisite for an influence of the tubule on the arterioles before and after the glomerulus is provided as follows. The end of the ascending loop of Henle makes direct contact with the vessels at

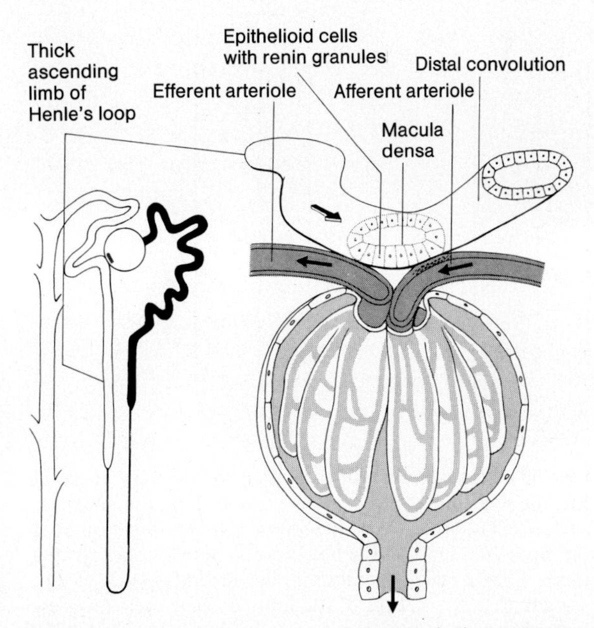

Fig. 30-5. Schematic drawing of the juxtaglomerular apparatus

the pole of the glomerulus of the same nephron (Fig. 30-5). At this contact site, the *macula densa*, its epithelial cells are conspicuously tall, and in the cells in the media of the arterioles there are abundant granules containing the enzyme renin. **Renin** is a peptidase that splits angiotensinogen, a plasma protein formed in the liver, to produce the decapeptide angiotensin I. From this another peptidase, called *converting enzyme*, produces the octapeptide **angiotensin II**. The latter is the signal substance that causes the adrenal cortex to produce and release aldosterone (p. 747), but it could also participate in regulating the tone of the renal arterioles. It has a stronger vasoconstricting action than any other substance produced by the body. That is, in addition to a mechanical, myogenic resistance-adjusting mechanism, a chemical means of reducing filtration could exist.

Perfusion of the renal medulla. Another special feature of renal vascularization is that the only vessels in the medulla are capillaries. They originate in the **juxtamedullary glomeruli**, the glomeruli in the lowest layer of the cortex, adjacent to the boundary of the medulla. The efferent arterioles here send out capillaries that do not form a peritubular network but instead run in parallel, forming characteristic *bundles*, toward the tip of the papilla (Fig. 30-1). These **arterial vasa recta** divide into fine branches that open into the ascending **venous vasa recta**, which rejoin the vascular bundles to carry the blood back to the renal cortex. The further toward the center

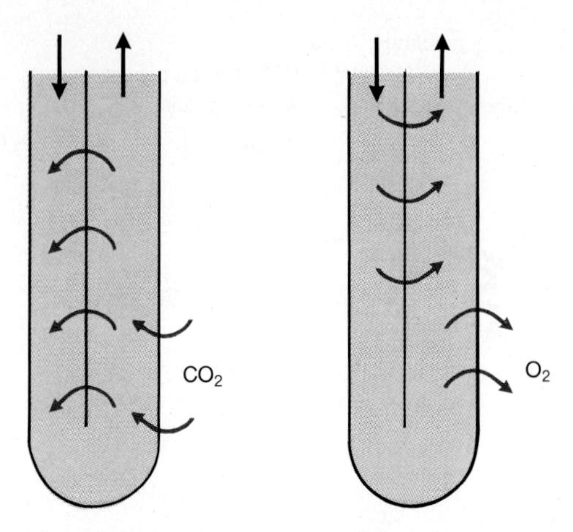

Fig. 30-6. Countercurrent exchange in the vasa recta of the renal medulla. Substances produced in the medulla, such as CO_2, are shunted by countercurrent diffusion near the tip of the loop and hence become highly concentrated there. Substances consumed in the medulla, such as O_2, are shunted at the base of the loop, so that their progress toward the tip is impeded

of a bundle these vasa recta are located, the further they extend toward the tip of the papilla.
Whereas the capillaries in the other organs of the body are about 0.5 mm long, because of the vasa-recta configuration those in the renal medulla are several centimeters long. Capillaries are the sections of the circulatory system in which exchanges between the blood and the interstitial space occur. The unusual length of the exchange region in the renal medulla has, of course, a functional significance. Because the arterial and venous vasa recta lie next to one another, and the blood within them flows in opposite directions, over the entire contact distance the blood flow itself creates a horizontal concentration gradient for all diffusible substances. These substances diffuse accordingly; those that pass from the tubule into the **vascular countercurrent system**, such as urea, are accumulated in high concentrations toward the tip of the loop (Fig. 30-6). In the case of urea, this is an important factor in maintaining a high osmotic pressure in the medullary tissue, so that the processes by which the kidney concentrates the urine are efficacious (p. 758). Substances produced in the medulla accumulate similarly; for instance, the **countercurrent diffusion** of CO_2 causes the P_{CO_2} to be higher here than anywhere else in the body. On the other hand, all the substances consumed in the renal medulla, in however small amounts (e.g., O_2 or glucose), which are therefore slightly less concentrated in the ascending than in the descending vessel, are short-circuited by countercurrent diffusion near the corticomedullary boundary, which severely impedes their further progress into the medulla [29]. Accordingly, the P_{O_2} of the renal papilla is the lowest in the body; the tissue here must meet its energy requirements – which in any case are modest – mainly by anaerobic metabolic processes.
Prostaglandins could play a role in regulating the perfusion of the renal medulla. PGE_2, in particular, is formed in the interstitial cells of the medulla; released when the blood supply is inadequate, it causes vasodilation [15, 36, 57].

30.3 Glomerular Filtration

Dynamics of Glomerular Filtration

Performance of the filtration system. The unusually high rate of blood flow through the renal cortex is the prerequisite for a high **glomerular filtration rate (GFR)**. About 1/5 of the *renal plasma flow (RPF)* is continuously filtered out. That is, the **filtration fraction**, the ratio GFR/RPF, is normally about 0.2. The total glomerular filtrate produced per day is **170 l**. Although the kidneys themselves contain less than 0.5% of the extracellular volume, an amount of fluid equivalent to about ten times the total extracellular volume is controlled each day by passage through the kidneys.
Effective filtration pressure. As is true of the capillaries of all the other organs (see STARLING's principle, p. 503), filtration through the glomerular capillaries is a *passive process* dependent on a balance of pressures. The driving force is the difference between hydrostatic and oncotic (colloid osmotic) pressures; it is called the *effective filtration pressure* (P_{eff}). The hydrostatic pressure in the glomerular capillaries (P_{cap}) is opposed by the hydrostatic pressure in the lumen of Bowman's capsule (P_{bow}) and the colloid osmotic pressure of the capillary blood (P_{onc}):

$$P_{eff} = P_{cap} - P_{bow} - P_{onc} \quad (1)$$

Direct measurements by micropuncture (p. 742) in rats have shown the pressures to be as follows: capillary pressure, 50 mm Hg (see Fig. 30-3); pressure in Bowman's capsule, 12 mm Hg; oncotic pressure at the beginning of the capillary, 20 mm Hg. The effective filtration here would be $P_{eff} = 50 - 12 - 20 = 18$ mm Hg. The hydrostatic pressure falls only slightly along the capillary (to ca. 48 mm Hg). But as a nearly protein-free ultrafiltrate is forced out, the protein concentration and hence the oncotic pressure within the glomerular capillaries rises. When P_{onc} equals the difference between P_{cap} and P_{bow} (Eq. 1), a **filtration equilibrium** has been reached and filtration stops. Given the above values, this would occur when P_{onc} is 36 mm Hg: $P_{eff} = 48 - 12 - 36 = 0$ mm Hg.

This filtration equilibrium is thought to be attained before the end of the capillary, under normal conditions. Then when the plasma flow increases, an additional section of the capillary could be drawn into the filtration process. Because of the enlarged filtration area, the GFR would rise even though the filtration fraction and effective filtration pressure are unchanged [16]. But it is not clear whether the physiological fluctuations in GFR (see below) are actually based on such a mechanism.

The amount of fluid that can be filtered per unit time by means of the effective pressure gradient depends on the *filtration area* (A) and on the *hydraulic conductance* (C) of the filter membrane:

$$GFR = A \cdot C \cdot P_{eff} \quad (2)$$

The factor C gives the volume of water that can be filtered through a membrane given unit values of time, area and pressure difference. It is sometimes lumped together with the area A (C·A) and called the *filtration coefficient* K_f.

Physiological fluctuations in GFR. Given that the amount filtered per day is 170 l, a mean GFR of **120 ml/min** results. This number is often cited as a norm. However, it should be noted that in the course of a day there is considerable physiological fluctuation. For one thing, there is a conspicuous *circadian rhythm* in which the maximum during the daytime activity phase can be 30% above the mean, with the minimum during rest at night 30% below it. *Postprandial increases* in filtration of the same order of magnitude can also occur.

A change in the amount of filtrate can be caused by each of the five factors that determine the filtration dynamics (Eqs. 1 and 2). In illness, renal failure with insufficient filtration can be brought about by pressure changes (e.g., shock or ureteral obstruction) as well as by changes in the filtration membrane (e.g., glomerulonephritis, amyloid kidney).

Measurement of filtration rate. The GFR can be measured by means of an *indicator substance*, according to *Fick's principle* (see p. 540). The indicator substance must have the following properties.

1. It must be a freely filterable nonelectrolyte. That is, it may not be bound to plasma proteins, nor may it be hindered in crossing the glomerular filtration membrane because of electrical charge (see below) or the size of the molecule.
2. Obviously, it must not be toxic.
3. It must be neither absorbed nor secreted in the tubule system.
4. It must not be broken down or synthesized in the kidney.

In sum, whatever amount of the substance enters the primary urine by filtration, exactly the same amount must appear, unaltered, in the urine that is ultimately excreted. The quantity excreted per unit time is then equal to the quantity filtered per unit time.

Because

$$\text{Quantity} = \text{Volume} \cdot \text{Concentration} \quad (3)$$

the situation can be expressed by the equation

$$\dot{V}_u \cdot U = GFR \cdot P \quad (4)$$

or

$$GFR = \frac{U}{P} \cdot \dot{V}_u \quad (5)$$

where U is the urine concentration of the indicator, P is the plasma concentration of the indicator, and $\dot{V}_u$ is the volume of urine per unit time.

One substance that meets all the requirements listed above is **inulin**. It is a polyfructoside comprising about 20 fructose molecules, obtainable from the roots of certain fruit trees. It does not naturally occur in human metabolism and must therefore be infused for measurement of GFR.

Determination of the single-nephron filtration rate. The filtration rate of a single glomerulus can be measured experimentally according to the same principle. The kidney is exposed and a micropuncture capillary (p. 742) is inserted into a superficial tubule loop; the tubule fluid is then removed quantitatively by suction for a measured period of time. From the volume flow rate of the tubule fluid ($\dot{V}_{tf}$) and the inulin concentration in the tubule fluid (TF_{In}) and in the plasma (P_{In}), the single-nephron filtration rate (SNFR) can be found:

$$SNFR = \frac{TF_{In}}{P_{In}} \cdot \dot{V}_{tf} \quad (6)$$

On average it is 50 nl · min^{-1}.

Clearance concept. The GFR found with the indicator method just described is the volume of plasma "cleared" of the test substance per unit time. Hence Eq. (5) can be generalized as the **clearance formula**,

$$C = \frac{U}{P} \cdot \dot{V}_u \tag{7}$$

For a substance that is only eliminated by glomerular filtration, such as inulin, the clearance is identical to the GFR. For substances that are freely filtered but subsequently reabsorbed (such as Na^+ or glucose), the clearance is lower; substances that are both filtered and, in addition, extracted from the blood by the activity of the tubule cells have a clearance greater than that of inulin (e.g., penicillin, PAH, see p. 756).

Creatinine clearance. One of the natural metabolic products excreted by way of the kidneys, *creatinine*, has proved to be very similar to inulin with respect to its treatment in the kidneys. But because it is secreted in small amounts, the *endogenous creatinine clearance* provides a less accurate measure than the inulin clearance. Nevertheless, it has come into widespread clinical use because it makes infusion unnecessary.
Creatinine is derived from muscle metabolism. The amount produced each day depends on the muscle mass but varies little in a given individual, so that the plasma concentration is relatively constant. On average it is 9 mg/l (80 μmol/l), though it can reach 15 mg/l (133 μmol/l) in very muscular people or 5 mg/l (44 μmol/l) in those with little muscle. Because the elimination of creatinine from the blood occurs almost entirely by glomerular filtration, an experienced physician treating a kidney disease can use the level and rate of rise of the *creatinine concentration in the plasma* to estimate the degree and progression of *renal insufficiency* (see Fig. 30-31).

Ultrafiltrate and Glomerular Filter

Composition of the glomerular filtrate. The primary urine that emerges in the glomeruli has all the characteristics of an **ultrafiltrate**: it contains none of the corpuscular elements of the blood and is nearly protein-free, but all the low-molecular-weight soluble substances are present in a concentration approximately equal to the plasma concentration.
Slight concentration differences between plasma water and filtrate result from the fact that various substances (e.g., calcium, organic acids and bases) are to some extent *bound to plasma proteins*, and this fraction escapes filtration. It should also be noted that *proteins occupy a certain volume* in the plasma, so that the space available for solutes is diminished by this volume. In whole plasma, therefore, the concentrations of certain substances are about 5% lower than the actual concentration of these solutes in the plasma water or ultrafiltrate.
Finally, a *Gibbs-Donnan equilibrium* must be established. Incidentally, this process also plays a certain role in the differential electrolyte distribution between cell interior and extracellular space (p. 768).

Gibbs-Donnan equilibrium. When *non-diffusible ions* are present on one side of a partition such as the filtration membrane or the cell membrane, the diffusible ions become distributed in such a way that their concentrations on the two sides of the partition differ, even though these ions can readily cross the membrane. This situation exists at the glomerular membrane because the non-filterable proteins in the plasma are polyanions.
For the *diffusible ions* it holds that in a state of equilibrium the electrochemical potential (see Nernst equation, pp. 6f.) associated with the cations on the two sides of the partition must equal that associated with the anions:

$$\frac{R \cdot T}{z \cdot F} \ln \frac{[C^+]_i}{[C^+]_o} = \frac{R \cdot T}{z \cdot F} \ln \frac{[A^-]_o}{[A^-]_i} \tag{8}$$

For univalent ions this reduces to

$$\frac{[C^+]_i}{[C^+]_o} = \frac{[A^-]_o}{[A^-]_i} \tag{9}$$

or

$$[C^+]_i \cdot [A^-]_i = [C^+]_o \cdot [A^-]_o \tag{10}$$

Here $[C^+]$ and $[A^-]$ are the concentrations of the diffusible cations and anions, respectively, and the subscripts *o* and *i* identify the compartments on the two sides of the partition. At equilibrium, therefore, *the product of the concentrations of diffusible anions and cations is the same on both sides of the membrane.* On the other hand, however, *electroneutrality* must be preserved on both sides. That is,

$$[C^+]_o = [A^-]_o \tag{11}$$

and on the protein-containing side,

$$[C^+]_i = [A^-]_i + [Prot^-] \tag{12}$$

Substitution in Eq. (10) according to Eqs. (11) and (12) gives

$$[A^-]_i \cdot ([A^-]_i + [Prot^-]) = ([A^-]_o)^2 \tag{13}$$

$$[C^+]_i \cdot ([C^+]_i - [Prot^-]) = ([C^+]_o)^2 \tag{14}$$

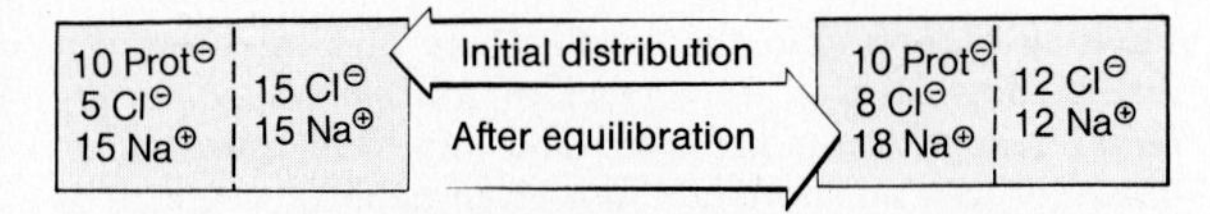

Fig. 30-7. Numerical example of the establishment of a Donnan equilibrium at a membrane through which protein anions do not diffuse but Na^+ and Cl^- can diffuse freely

Hence the diffusible ions are distributed as follows:

$$[A^-]_i < [A^-]_o \quad (15)$$

$$[C^+]_i > [C^+]_o \quad (16)$$

This relationship is illustrated in Figure 30-7 by a numerical example. The anions are initially assumed to be distributed equally across the membrane, as are the cations. When a Gibbs-Donnan equilibrium is attained, they are redistributed in such a way that the concentration of diffusible cations is higher, and that of the diffusible anions is lower, on the protein side than on the opposite side. Electroneutrality is preserved on both sides, and the requirement of Eq. (9) is also met.

In the practically protein-free ultrafiltrate, because of the Donnan factor the concentrations of the univalent cations (e.g., Na^+ and K^+) are about 5% lower than in the plasma water, and the concentrations of the univalent anions (e.g., Cl^- and HCO_3^-) are about 5% higher. Because the Donnan factor and the protein correction factor are of about the same order of magnitude, for the univalent cations they approximately cancel out. For the univalent anions, however, they add, so that the ultrafiltrate concentration of these ions is about 10% less than the plasma concentration (see Table 30-1).

Structure of the glomerular filter. The partition between the lumen of a capillary and that of Bowman's capsule is made up of three layers. As shown in Figure 30-8, the thin **capillary endothelium** is extensively fenestrated. These pores, ranging in diameter from 50 to 100 nm, hold back the cellular elements of the blood.

The next layer is formed by a continuous **basement membrane**. It consists of a three-dimensional network of glycoproteins bearing a strong polyanionic charge, which is embedded in a matrix that appears homogeneous in the electron microscope. The basement membrane evidently acts as a sieve to retain the larger protein molecules in the plasma.

The densest filter, and hence the barrier that most sharply separates the plasma components, appears to be reserved for the third layer, the **epithelium of Bowman's capsule**. Where this epithelium contacts a glomerular capillary its cells are modified into *podocytes*, cells with multiple "feet". These processes are interleaved with those of adjacent cells, from which they are separated by a *"filtration slit"* 20–50 nm wide. The slits are filled with sialoprotein, a polysaccharide mate-

Table 30-1. Concentration of important ions in plasma, plasma water and ultrafiltrate

	Plasma mmol/l	Plasma water mmol/l	Ultrafiltrate mmol/l
Na^+	142	151	144
K^+	4	4.3	4
Ca^{2+}	2.5[a]	1.4	1.3
Cl^-	102	110	114
HCO_3^-	25	27	28

[a] Including the calcium bound to plasma proteins

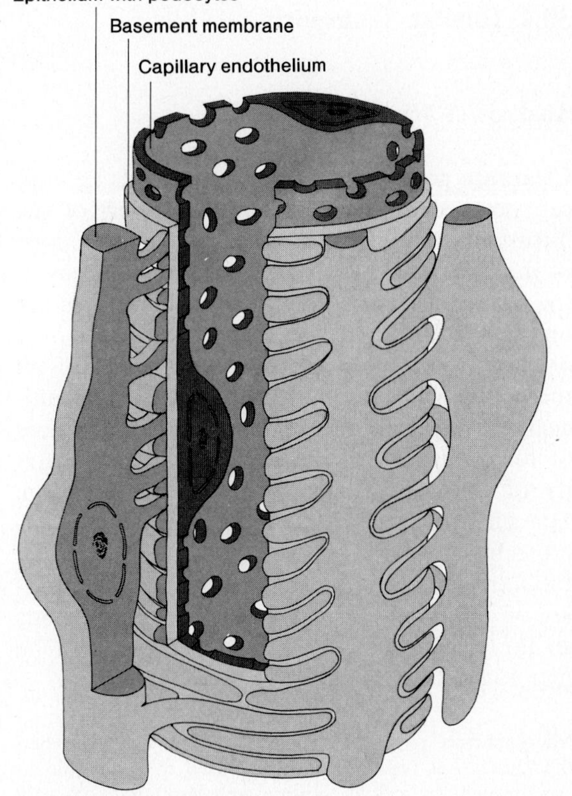

Fig. 30.8. Diagram of a glomerular capillary leash. Glomerular filter: epithelium of Bowman's capsule with podocytes, which are covered with a glycocalyx of strongly anionic sialoproteins; basement membrane with network of glycoproteins carrying a strongly polyanionic charge *(red)*; capillary endothelium with fenestrations. (Modified from [39])

rial, and closed off from the basement membrane by a delicate skin [26]. The slit system, called a *glycocalyx*, makes passage increasingly difficult for macromolecules with an effective radius of 1.5 nm or more, and is practically impermeable to those as large as 4.5 nm.

Permselectivity. In the critical region of molecular diameter, between 1.5 and 4.5 nm, *polyanionic plasma proteins* (albumins) are *much more severely hampered* in passing the glycocalyx than equally large neutral or positively charged macromolecules. The reason is the predominantly anionic charge of the proteins in the basement membrane and the filtration slits. That is, the steric configuration of the structural elements in the glomerular sieve is supplemented by an electrical filter. As a consequence of this "permselectivity" of the filter, the traces of protein that appear in the ultrafiltrate differ considerably from the protein pattern of the plasma [34].

30.4 Tubular Transport

Analysis of Transport Processes

Clearance procedure. Clearance methods (p. 740) can be used to obtain a good overview of the filtration, secretion and reabsorption functions of the kidneys. All that is required is analysis of the blood and urine; the kidneys themselves are untouched. What one learns, however, gives only a general indication of the performance of all the active nephrons. This information is insufficient for localization of functional disturbances or for evaluation of the extremely varied activity of the individual sections of the nephron. For such purposes, experiments employing microtechniques are required. Our knowledge of tubular function is based on experimental studies of this kind. Of the multitude of methods so far developed, only a few examples can be mentioned here.

Micropuncture techniques. In many animal species, when the kidney has been surgically exposed it is possible to see through the kidney capsule well enough to identify convolutions of the proximal and distal tubules as well as peritubular capillaries, and sometimes even glomeruli. Under microscopic observation a sharply pointed glass capillary moved by a micromanipulator can be inserted into these structures to *sample fluid for analysis* (Fig. 30-9A). Conversely, micropuncture capillaries can be used to inject radioactively labeled material or other easily measured substances into the tubular fluid and take samples further downstream, for studies of *transport in the intervening section* of the nephron. One way to measure quantitatively the transport rate in a given nephron segment is to isolate this segment with oil blocks and perfuse it with a precisely controllable microperfusion pump (Fig. 30-9B). Such *tubule perfusion* can also be performed with pieces of nephron dissected out of the kidney. In this case, by varying both the perfusion solution and the composition of the external bath, the conditions for transport of a great variety of substances can be set up as desired [56].

Electrophysiological techniques. Most of the renal transport processes involve the transport of electrically charged

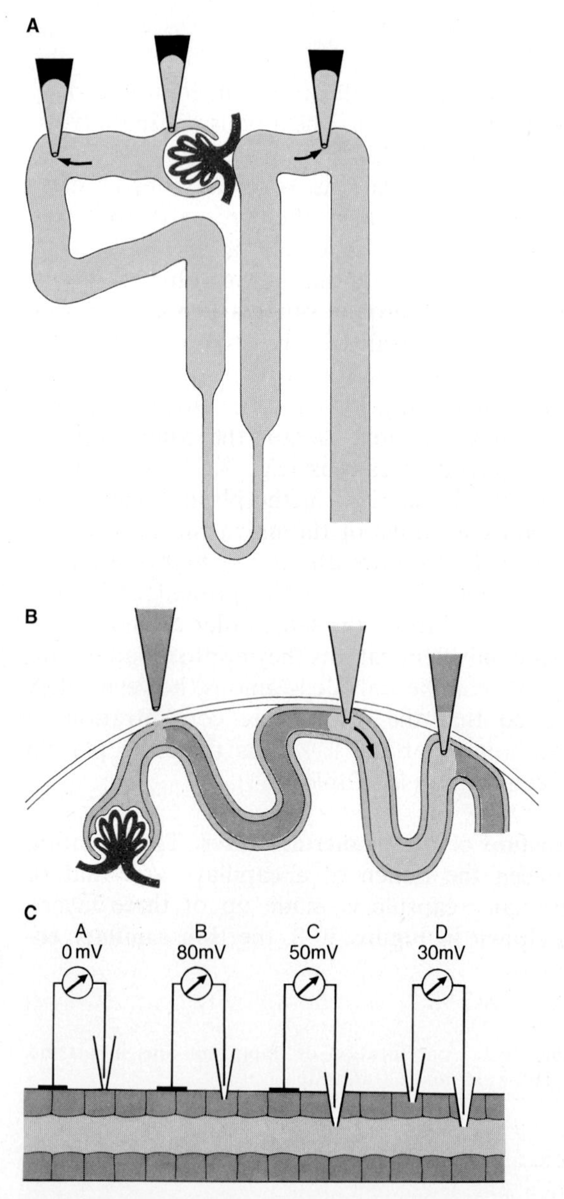

Fig. 30-9 A-C. Examples of application of the micropuncture technique: **A** Collection of tubule fluid in Bowman's capsule and the proximal and distal convolutions; **B** microperfusion in vivo of a tubule segment isolated by oil blocks; **C** measurement of transmembrane electrical potential differences in a distal convolution

particles across charged interfaces. The *electrical potential differences* across the cell membranes can be measured with microelectrodes (Fig. 30-9C). Furthermore, *electrometric determination of the activities* of H^+, Na^+, K^+, Cl^- or Ca^{2+} ions is possible with microelectrodes made of special glass. Such measurements reveal the transport conditions for each kind of ion at the individual membranes.

Patch clamp technique. The ionic currents in the membranes mostly flow through protein windows embedded in the lipoid structures of the membrane. By virtue of their steric configuration and charge distribution, the protein molecules quite selectively allow the passage of particular species of ions; they act as *ion channels.* When a small patch of membrane is brought into close contact with a microelectrode by suction, an individual ion channel can be isolated and the currents through it, or the alternating opening and closing of the channel, can be recorded with highly sensitive, computer-assisted methods.

Membrane vesicles. From homogenized cells, one can obtain isolated pieces of membrane that form vesicles after suitable treatment. Often such vesicles retain most of the transport properties of the membrane in situ. They can be used, for example, to study differences in transport function between brush-border membranes and membranes of the basolateral surface of the cell.

Cell cultures. In recent years it has become possible not only to keep cells taken from various parts of a nephron alive in nutrient media but also to allow growth and cell division. Such "established" cell lines retain the basic features of the original cell even after many generations. Because the functions of cultured cells are independent of influences present in the whole organism or intact organ – in the form of neural activity, hormones or other mediators – these cells can be used for biochemical and electrophysiological studies of the basic processes of life under precisely defined conditions.

The Reabsorption of Fluid

Volume reduction along the tubule. Of the 170 l of ultrafiltrate produced by the glomeruli per day, only about 1.5 l appear in the urine. 99% of the filtrate is reabsorbed in the tubular system. The various sections of the nephron participate to very different degrees in this reabsorption process. As Fig. 30-10 shows, most of the task is accomplished at the beginning of the nephron; in the *proximal convolution* 65% of the filtrate volume is returned to the circulation. Reabsorption continues in the descending limb of *Henle's loop* but comes to a halt in the ascending limb, which is nearly impermeable to water. At the beginning of the *distal convolution* about 20% of the original filtered volume is still present, and half of this is reabsorbed by the time the collecting duct is reached; an approximately equal volume is reabsorbed as the fluid passes through the *collecting duct system.*

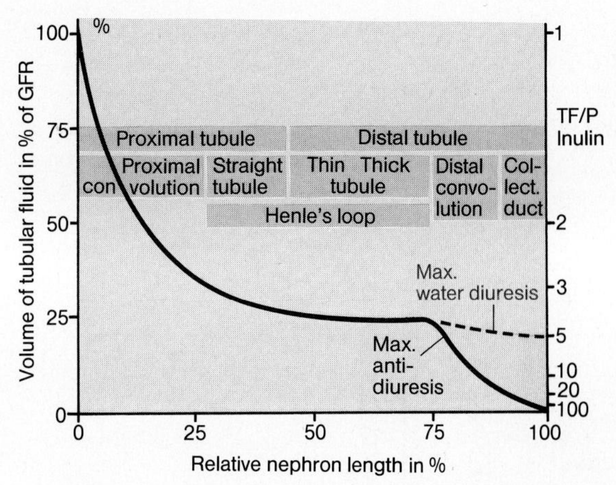

Fig. 30-10. Degree of water reabsorption at various sites along the nephron. The percentage of the filtrate volume remaining in the tubule *(left ordinate)* can be determined from the ratio of the concentration of the test substance inulin in the tubular fluid (TF) to its concentration in the plasma or ultrafiltrate (P) (TF/P, *right ordinate*). In the distal convolution and collecting tubule the degree of water reabsorption varies *(red region)*: In antidiuresis, with ADH action maximal, almost complete reabsorption *(continuous line)*; in water diuresis, with ADH blocked, hardly any reabsorption *(dashed line)*

Antidiuresis and water diuresis. In the proximal part of the nephron the fluid volume is reduced by the same amount regardless of the functional state of the kidney – i.e., whether it is in the "normal" state of *antidiuresis*, producing an osmotically concentrated urine, or in a state of *water diuresis*, in which the urine is less concentrated than the blood plasma in order to eliminate water that has been consumed in excess. The degree to which water is eliminated is determined by adjustment of the rate of reabsorption in the *distal part of the nephron*, under the control of the hormone ADH (p. 757).

Electrolyte Transport in the Proximal Convolution

Sites of the transport processes. The *proximal tubule* also dominates in the reabsorption of dissolved substances, in that the greatest amounts of electrolytes and other solutes are reabsorbed here. It is also the chief site of secretion of hydrogen and ammonium ions, and it alone is capable of secreting weak organic acids and bases. Although the quantities reabsorbed in the *distal sections* of the nephron are much smaller, it is here that the *fine adjustment* of reabsorption or secretion of the most significant electrolytes occurs. This process is controlled by mediator

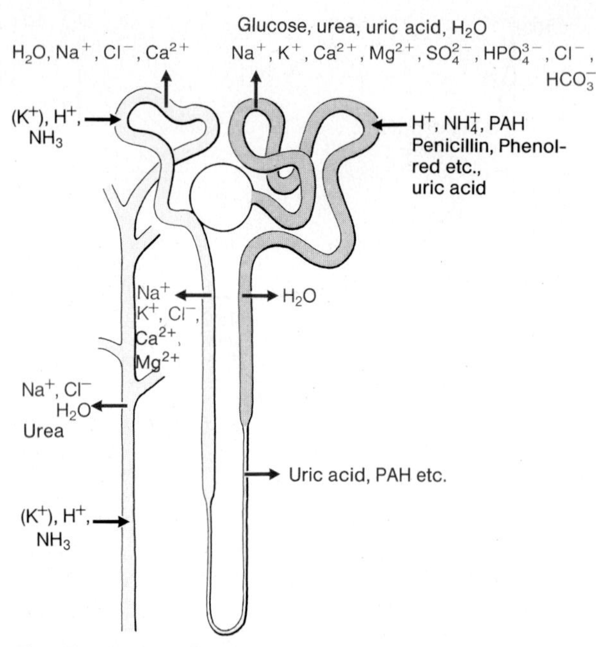

Fig. 30-11. Sites of the various transport processes in the nephron; *red:* reabsorbed substances, *black:* secreted substances

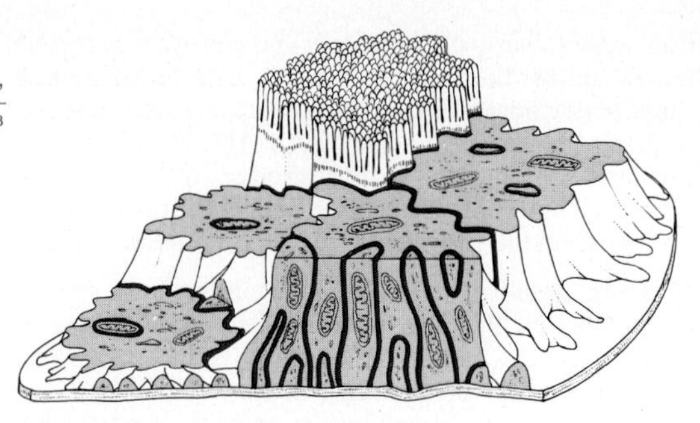

Fig. 30-12. Schematic drawing of proximal tubule cells, with intact cells at the back and those in front cut in different planes. The basal processes of the cells interdigitate. The gaps between them are marked in *red* in the various planes of section. (From [52])

substances formed in the kidney itself and by hormones produced and regulated extrarenally; the most important of these come from the hypothalamus, pituitary, thyroid and parathyroid glands, heart and adrenal cortex.
The diagram in Figure 30-11 gives a rough indication of the parts of the nephron in which the major transport processes occur.

Reabsorption of sodium salts. Sodium salts account for four-fifths of the amount of solute in the ultrafiltrate. Therefore the *reabsorption of sodium* is the greatest task performed by the kidney. But at the same time it can be regarded as the driving force for almost all the other tubular transport processes. Of the filtered sodium, the so-called *sodium load*, two-thirds is reabsorbed in the proximal tubule, 70% as NaCl and 30% as $NaHCO_3$. Because water follows in equivalent amounts (Fig. 30-10), the tubular fluid remains *isotonic* along the proximal convolution; that is, its osmotic pressure remains the same as that of the blood plasma and the remaining extracellular fluid of the body.

Structure of the tubule cells. Like all epithelial cells capable of transcellular electrolyte and water transport, the tubule cells are *asymmetric in structure* [32]. This asymmetry is especially pronounced in the proximal cells, which have the highest transport performance of all the cells in the body. On the luminal side they are covered with a dense *brush border*, which enlarges the surface in contact with the tubular fluid by about a factor of 40. The opposite surface of the cell is similarly enlarged by numerous basal processes, which interdigitate with the neighboring cells to form a system of fairly large channels (Fig. 30-12). Below the brush border the cells are connected by so-called tight junctions. This term, based on histological appearance, is somewhat misleading, because these junctions provide an entrance from the tubular lumen into the basolateral channel system. This route is called the *paracellular shunt*. A striking feature of the basolateral part of the cell is the large number of mitochondria, shaped to correspond with the shape of the podial processes.

Active transport. The mitochondria provide the energy for the **Na^+-K^+ ATPase** in the neighboring basolateral membrane. By splitting adenosine triphosphate, this enzyme liberates the stored metabolic energy and thus directly fuels a *Na^+-K^+-exchange pump* [25]. This active transport keeps the Na^+ concentration inside the cell low and simultaneously raises the K^+ concentration to about 35 times that in the extracellular fluid. Because the cell membrane is somewhat permeable to K^+, the tendency of K^+ to diffuse outward produces an electrical *potential difference of ca. 70 mV*, with the cytosol negative with respect to the extracellular space.

Transport mechanisms. The electrical potential and the low intracellular Na^+ concentration provide the *driving force for the inflow of Na^+* from the tubular fluid, by either of two routes (Fig. 30-13). One takes the form of **coupled transport** (also called cotransport or symport) with anions, mainly phosphate, sulfate, chloride and amino acids. A larger amount of Na^+ is brought into the cell by **Na^+-H^+ exchange** (also called countertransport or antiport). Having entered the cell, the Na^+ is sent on into the interstitial space by the Na^+-K^+ ATPase in the basolateral cell membrane. The H^+ secreted into the tubular fluid is buffered by the **bicarbonate** present there, and the resulting carbonic acid is converted to H_2O and CO_2 by the enzyme *carbonic anhydrase*, which is abundant in the brush border. The CO_2 diffuses into the cell and can be converted back to H^+ and HCO_3^- ions by the intracellular carbonic anhydrase. Whereas the H^+ ions recirculate by way of Na^+-antiport at the luminal membrane, bicarbonate is sent out of the cell through the basolateral membrane by a Na^+-coupled carrier system, probably in the ratio 3:1.

By the mechanism of preferential bicarbonate transport through the cells, the "neglected" **chloride** in the tubular fluid undergoes a slight increase in concentration. Hence it becomes possible for chloride to diffuse through the paracellular shunt [38]. A diffusion potential builds up, forming an electrical field within which Na^+, as well as **Ca^{2+} and Mg^{2+}**, can also migrate. The electrolyte flow in turn generates a flow of water, by osmosis. But the water current carries additional dissolved substances with it, by the principle of "solvent drag"; the main solute so transported is, of course, the most abundant, NaCl.

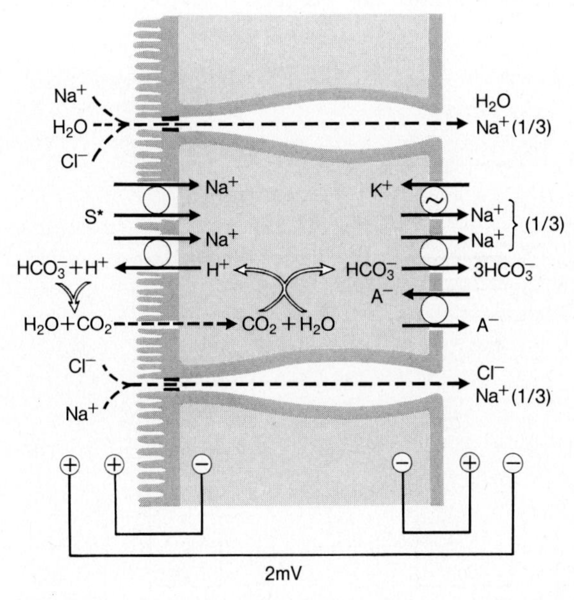

Fig. 30-13. Transport processes in the proximal tubule, schematic. Ion pumps are marked by *circles* and *solid arrows*, paracellular transport by *dashed arrows*. S* = substrate

Solvent drag is the process whereby a stream of water sweeps a certain amount of a solute through a barrier. This amount (Jis) is given by the formula

$$Jis = J_v \cdot c_i (1 - \sigma_i) \tag{17}$$

where J_v is the volume flow, c_i is the mean concentration of the substance *i* at the barrier (the tubule wall), and σ_i is the reflection coefficient of the substance *i* at the barrier (the proportion that is "reflected" and not allowed through).

Energetic aspects. On balance, then, *active metabolic energy* is required for only about *one-third of the reabsorbed sodium.* Renal structure and function are optimally adjusted so that most of the sodium that is reabsorbed follows this fraction passively. Given the stoichiometry of the Na^+-K^+ ATPase, 3 Na^+ per molecule ATP, the end result is the extraordinarily economical transport of 9 Na^+/ATP. Furthermore, because the tubular transport of most substances is *coupled to sodium*, these transport processes require no additional energy. Although such **secondary active transport** comes to a halt when the energy supply is interrupted, it is not driven by its own (primary) ATPase. Examples include the absorption of glucose or amino acids, as well as the exchange of Na^+ for H^+. Various ions such as Ca^{2+}, Mg^{2+}, HCO_3^- and H^+, which are moved to a great extent by secondary active transport, appear in addition to undergo primary active transport, by their own, specifically activatable ATPases. Quantitatively, however, the latter are practically negligible in comparison with Na^+-K^+ ATPase.

It follows that the **renal energy turnover**, measured by O_2 consumption, is clearly correlated with the reabsorption of Na^+. As long as no filtrate is produced, so that no reabsorption work need be done, the kidneys have a low basal metabolic rate. *With rising Na^+ load, and hence an increasing Na^+ reabsorption rate, renal energy consumption rises linearly* (Fig. 30-14), ultimately surpassing even that of the myocardium [14].

Glomerulotubular balance. In the *proximal tubule*, the part of the nephron in which most of the glomerular filtrate is reabsorbed, the transport processes are subject to only a slight degree of control. In the distal convolution and collecting duct, by contrast, various hormones bring about a fine adjustment of reabsorption that allows precise regulation of salt and water balance.

It is characteristic of the proximal tubule that the amount reabsorbed is always *a certain percentage of the filtrate* – about 65% for NaCl and water – rather than a constant amount per unit time.

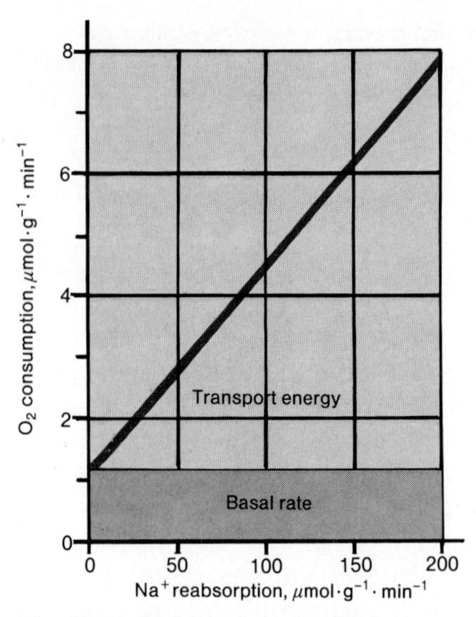

Fig. 30-14. Relation between Na^+ transport and O_2 consumption in the kidney. (Modified from [14])

That is, tubular reabsorption is proportional to glomerular filtration. The **fractional reabsorption** remains the same regardless of whether the GFR is high or low.

This property of the proximal tubule, known as **glomerulotubular balance**, is significant for renal function in several respects. For instance, it ensures that when the GFR is low the tubular fluid is not completely reabsorbed in the proximal nephron, which would give the regulatory processes situated in the distal sections no chance to operate. On the other hand, when the GFR is high the distal sections do not receive all the additional filtrate but only about one-third of it, so that their limited capacity for regulation is not overloaded. The mechanism underlying glomerotubular balance has not yet been satisfactorily explained. Luminal factors such as bicarbonate concentration could be involved, as could the facts that the reabsorption of the filtrate into the peritubular capillaries depends on the hydrostatic and oncotic pressure as well as the rate of plasma flow, and that these parameters are in turn dependent on the filtration rate [28].

Electrolyte Transport in Henle's Loop

Transport in the descending limb. The loop of Henle begins with the **straight part (pars recta) of the proximal tubule**. Its transport properties correspond to those of the proximal convolution, though with a distinctly reduced capacity. Along the proximal tubule, beginning at the glomerulus, there is a gradual decrease in the density and height of the brush border and of the basolateral infoldings of the cells. Corresponding to this morphological gradient, there is a progressive decrease in the ability to transport large amounts of electrolytes and water. Conversely, the capacity for secretion of weak organic acids and bases (p. 756) rises, reaching a peak in the pars recta.

Transport processes in the thick ascending limb. Another key region for renal function is the *thick ascending limb of Henle's loop*. The epithelium here is distinguished by *very effective transcellular Na^+ transport* but almost complete *impermeability to water* at the tight junctions. Na^+ enters the cell by passive cotransport; one K^+ and two Cl^- ions travel together with each Na^+ ion (Fig. 30-15). Because the conductance (see below) of the luminal membrane for K^+ is quite high, most of these ions diffuse back into the lumen of the tubule; as a result, the membrane on this side of the cell is more strongly polarized than the basolateral membrane. This asymmetry produces a net potential difference across the tubule cell, with the *lumen positive to the interstitial space* [20, 21].

Cations, Ca^{2+} and Mg^{2+} as well as Na^+, can be reabsorbed passively by following the paracellular route down this potential gradient. Some of the K^+ ions that have entered the cell by cotransport leave it through the basolateral membrane in symport with Cl^-. There also seem to be specific Cl^- channels here, at which the driving force is the electrical gradient across the basolateral membrane. On balance, then, K^+ and Cl^-

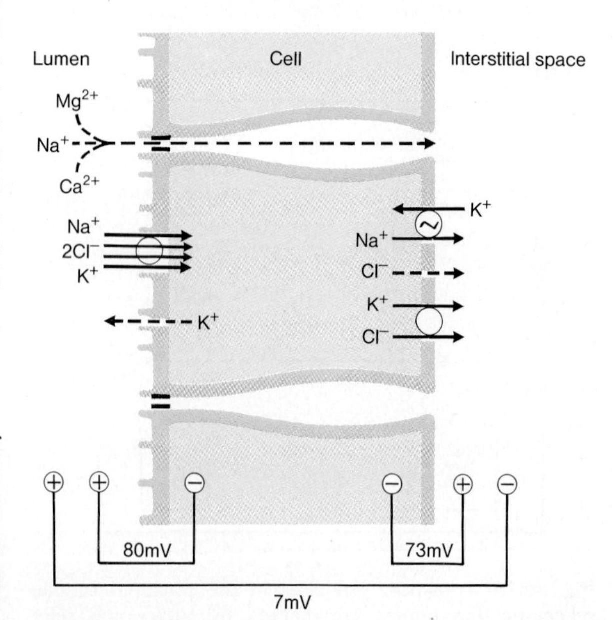

Fig. 30-15. Diagram of transport processes in the thick ascending limb of Henle's loop

perform a major service in assisting very effective sodium transport, the primary energy for which is provided by the basolateral Na^+-K^+ ATPase. The combination of massive electrolyte reabsorption with no water reabsorption makes the tubular fluid *hypotonic*; that is, the osmotic pressure falls below that of the plasma and at the end of Henle's loop is only about one-seventh the osmolarity of the plasma.
On the other hand, the reabsorbed substances make the interstitial fluid hypertonic. This *osmotic dissociation in the renal medulla* is the prerequisite for the kidney's ability to excrete either osmotically concentrated or osmotically dilute urine, as required (p. 757).

Ionic conductance. In physics, conductance (G) is defined as the reciprocal of resistance (R). According to Ohm's law (V=R·I), therefore, the conductance is the ratio of current (I) and voltage (V).

$$G = \frac{I}{V} \quad (18)$$

The ionic conductance of a membrane thus describes the electrical current driven through the membrane by a particular ion at a given voltage difference.

Electrolyte Transport in the Distal Tubule

Distal transport of univalent ions. The final sections of the nephron are the site of *fine adjustment of renal excretion*, by which the volume and chemical composition of the extracellular fluid are kept in precise balance. Although the individual segments of the distal tubule differ in details of transport, the following discussion of general properties applies to all of them. Here, again, the primary motor is the Na^+-K^+ ATPase in the basolateral membrane, which creates a Na^+ concentration gradient. Na^+ moves out of the lumen down this gradient, in part by way of *Na^+-Cl^- symport*. But it can probably also diffuse directly into the cell, and in addition can be taken up by *luminal Na^+-H^+ antiport* (Fig. 30-16). In any case, Na^+ absorption so far exceeds that of Cl^-, the dominant anion, that the lumen becomes negatively charged with respect to the interstitial space. This transcellular electrical potential difference increases continuously along the distal convolution and can reach 70 mV (lumen negative to interstitial space). Because passive sodium absorption is prevented by the strong transcellular electrical field, here all the Na^+ must take the active route through the cell, driven by metabolic energy.

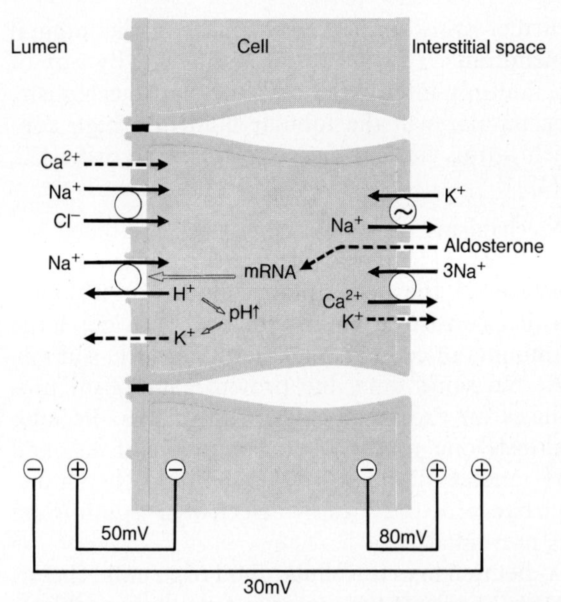

Fig. 30-16. Diagram of transport processes in the distal tubule

Extrarenal control of distal transport. The distal reabsorption of electrolytes is controlled by extrarenal factors. The influence best understood so far is that of **aldosterone**. When the extracellular volume becomes too small, as well as when the kidney is in danger of losing too much NaCl, *renin* is released from the macula densa in the juxtaglomerular apparatus, which initiates the formation of *angiotensin II* (p. 737). The latter stimulates the release of aldosterone from the adrenal cortex. Aldosterone *enhances Na^+ absorption in the distal nephron*, probably by stimulation of a messenger RNA, which in turn induces the synthesis of membrane proteins on the luminal side of the cell. These proteins either drive a Na^+-H^+ antiport (in the thick ascending limb of Henle's loop) or function as specific Na^+ channels (in the distal convolution and collecting tubule). The resulting augmented Na^+ flow into the cell seems to stimulate the basolateral Na^+-K^+ ATPase, so that now the active Na^+ transport can proceed at a greater rate. In this situation more Na^+ is transported out of the cell than K^+ is simultaneously brought in, in a ratio of about 3:2. That is, the *pump is now electrogenic*; its activity increases the polarization of the basolateral cell membrane and, therefore, the overall transcellular electrical potential difference.
The aldosterone action also has other consequences. Due to the stimulation of the Na^+-H^+-exchange pump, more H^+ ions enter the tubular fluid. Retained there by buffers, they can be eliminated in the urine (p. 752). This increased H^+ secretion leads to *intracellular alkalosis*, which

further *raises the K^+ conductance* of the luminal membrane. The end result is that K^+, by way of a multiply interlinked amplification mechanism, accumulates in the tubular fluid in a high concentration and can be excreted in the urine [23, 24].

Mechanisms of homeostasis. The combined actions of aldosterone help to maintain homeostasis of the extracellular fluid. For instance, a diet consisting mainly of meat provides large amounts of cellular potassium and little sodium. At the same time, the protein catabolism produces an excess of acidic equivalents. Because aldosterone promotes the secretion of K^+ and H^+ and simultaneously acts to retain Na^+, a disturbance of the sensitive electrolyte equilibrium is prevented.

A diet rich in extracellular fluid (e.g., milk, cheese, blood) presents the opposite regulatory problem: more Na^+ must be eliminated and the excretion of K^+ and H^+ must be restricted. The latter is achieved by reducing the rate of aldosterone release. The enhancement of Na^+ excretion, natriuresis, is under additional hormonal control. Although the existence of a "natriuretic hormone" from the hypothalamus has long been postulated, it has not yet been convincingly demonstrated. But it has been established that a *peptide hormone* synthesized in the atria of the heart has a natriuretic action; it is called **ANF (atrial natriuretic factor)**. ANF *raises the GFR and slows Na^+ absorption at the end of the nephron.* ANF is stored in vesicles in the atrial tissue, and is released either neurally or directly by atrial stretching. Because the extracellular volume is very much dependent on the sodium content of the organism (p. 766), ANF also plays an important role in the regulation of extracellular volume and hence of blood volume.

In experiments a number of additional hormones – for instance, ADH, angiotensin II, bradykinin, and prostaglandins – have been found to influence the transport of Na^+ and Cl^-. Their practical significance in homeostasis, however, is not yet certain.

Distal calcium transport. Calcium is also closely related to the renal management of Na^+. Only about half of the calcium in the plasma is free, rather than bound to proteins, and hence can be filtered in the glomeruli. In the proximal tubule and in Henle's loop calcium and sodium are absorbed about in proportion. Ca^{2+} follows the paracellular routes discussed above and can also be absorbed transcellularly; in the distal part of the nephron the latter seems to be the only route, as is the case for Na^+. At the luminal cell membrane Ca^{2+} transfer is entirely passive, but there appear to be two ways for it to pass through the basolateral membrane. One is based on primary active transport by a *Ca^{2+} ATPase.* The other, which seems to be more important quantitatively, is the result of a secondary active transport by a *Na^+-Ca^{2+}-exchange pump.* Here the driving force is the influx of Na^+ into the cell down its electrochemical gradient. Because the intracellular Ca^{2+} activity is smaller than the extracellular by four orders of magnitude, the outward transport of Ca^{2+} occurs against a very steep electrochemical gradient. In the process, Na^+ ions are exchanged in the ratio 3:1 [13, 51, 59].

As in the case of Na^+, the fine adjustment of the distal absorption of Ca^{2+} is accomplished by hormones. The most important of these is parathyroid hormone (PTH). By a mechanism not understood in detail, it *promotes distal Ca^{2+} absorption.* Other substances with a direct action are vitamin D_3 (1,25-dihydroxycholecalciferol), which increases Ca^{2+} absorption, and calcitonin (p. 770), which inhibits it [49].

Hormonal Disturbances

Most of the hormones that affect the kidneys act mainly on the distal tubule. Therefore the chief symptoms of renal disorders of hormonal origin are associated with distal-nephron malfunction, as illustrated by the following examples of typical syndromes.

Diabetes insipidus. When the *production of ADH* by the hypothalamus is restricted or eliminated (e.g., after accidents in which the base of the skull is fractured, though the condition can also be congenital or caused by tumors and metastases in the pituitary/hypothalamus region), large amounts of hypotonic urine are excreted continually. In rare cases such *polyuria* is due to a defect of the distal tubule that prevents it from responding to ADH. Because 25% of the glomerular filtrate remains unreabsorbed at the end of Henle's loop and flows, as a hypotonic solution, into the final, ADH-sensitive section of the nephron (Fig. 30-10), in the absence of ADH the volume of urine can exceed 20 l/day. The consequence is hyperosmolarity of the extracellular fluid with hypernatremia. The patient is always thirsty and drinks constantly. This *polydipsia* is a compulsive behavior; if no water is available, the patient will drink anything he can find – the contents of vases, or even his own urine.

Hyperaldosteronism. The situation in which the adrenal cortex produces more aldosterone than is currently required to maintain the Na^+-K^+ balance is called hyperaldosteronism. It is *primary hyperaldosteronism* when the cause of the overproduction lies in the adrenal cortex itself (as in Conn's syndrome with aldosterone-producing adenoma) and *secondary hyperaldosteronism* when the cause is external to the adrenal cortex (e.g., renin overproduction in the kidney, hyponatremia, hyperkalemia, overproduction of ACTH, etc.).

The excess aldosterone acts on the distal nephron to increase both the retention of sodium and the excretion of potassium, magnesium and hydrogen ions. The consequences are hypernatremia, hypokalemia, magnesium deficiency and alkalosis. The resulting clinical symptoms, often more conspicuous in primary hyperaldosteronism, take the following forms. The hypernatremia causes hypertonia, hypervolemia and edemas, among other things. The hypokalemia leads to muscular weakness, constipation, EKG changes and loss of the kidney's ability to concentrate urine, and tetany is produced by the hypomagnesemia and alkalosis.

Hypoaldosteronism. Here, again, there are primary and secondary forms. Aldosterone deficiency due to adrenal insufficiency is found in Addison's disease, in the Waterhouse-Friedrichsen syndrome and where there are congenital defects in the enzymes for steroid biosynthesis. Secondary hypoaldosteronism can result from suppression of the renin-angiotensin system, ACTH deficiency, misuse of mineralocorticoid-containing medicines or licorice abuse. Na^+ is lost continuously because of the aldosterone deficiency; therefore the extracellular volume diminishes, producing tiredness, headache, low blood pressure and tachycardia. The simultaneous retention of K^+ and H^+ results in hyperkalemia and acidosis, the symptoms of which are cardiac arrhythmia and muscle cramps, and hyperventilation and impaired consciousness, respectively.

30.5 Special Tubular Transport Mechanisms

Transport of Threshold Substances

In the proximal tubule about 2/3 of each of the main components of the filtrate – water and the most abundant electrolytes, such as Na^+, K^+, Ca^{2+} and Cl^- – are reabsorbed. Not only is this ratio constant despite a fluctuating GFR (glomerulotubular balance, p. 745), it also persists if the concentration changes. For such substances, within the range of physiologically tolerable concentration increases, the transport rate can increase accordingly. But the transport of other substances reaches a limit when the concentration has risen to a certain maximum, called the **renal threshold**. Among these substances are glucose, phosphate, sulfate, amino acids and bicarbonate.

Glucose. Glucose is freely filtered in the glomeruli and is most efficiently reabsorbed in the *first third of the proximal convolution* (Fig. 30-17). At the end of the proximal convolution its concentration has fallen to about 1/10 of the plasma concentration, and this concentration is maintained until the end of the nephron.

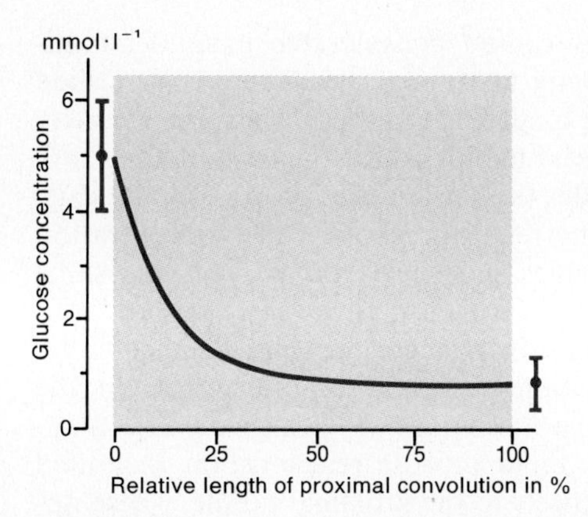

Fig. 30-17. Decreasing concentration of glucose in the tubular fluid along the proximal convolution. For the glucose concentrations in plasma and urine both mean and range are shown

However, water is also being reabsorbed, so that the volume of the solution is reduced by 65% at the end of the proximal convolution and by 99% at the end of the nephron. It follows that a total of 99.9% of the tubular glucose load is reabsorbed, 96.5% proximally; the urine ultimately excreted is almost *glucose-free*.

When the plasma concentration rises, in the first instance almost complete reabsorption of the glucose continues, until at a concentration of about 11 mmol/l (2 g/l) the renal threshold is reached. With a further increase in concentration, the amount of glucose excreted in the urine increases proportionally (Fig. 30-18), producing *glucosuria*.

The term **transport maximum** (TmG) has been introduced for this limitation of reabsorption,

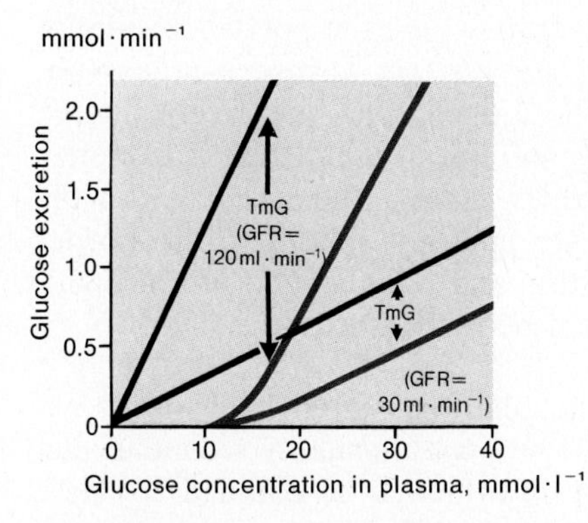

Fig. 30-18. Glucose excretion as the plasma concentration rises above threshold. The difference between the amounts of glucose filtered *(black line)* and excreted *(red line)* per unit time gives the rate of reabsorption. Above the threshold this rate reaches a maximum *(TmG)*, the magnitude of which is proportional to the current glomerular filtration rate *(GFR)*

but it has caused considerable misunderstanding. In many textbooks the kidney is described as having a specific maximal transport capacity for glucose, but this is not the case. If the GFR rises or falls, the TmG varies proportionally (Fig. 30-18). The renal threshold – the concentration beyond which glucosuria occurs – is the same regardless of GFR, but above the threshold glucose remains in glomerulotubular balance [10]. This situation becomes comprehensible in the light of the mechanism by which glucose is reabsorbed. Since glucose reabsorption is limited almost entirely to the proximal tubule, where uptake into the tubule cells is *coupled to the uptake of sodium* (see Fig. 30-13), glucose transport is necessarily subject to the laws governing Na^+ reabsorption. At the brush-border membrane, within the protein molecule responsible for the cotransport, glucose can form a transport complex with Na^+. When the glucose concentration is so high that all the receptor sites are occupied, the *threshold concentration* has been reached. The glucose reabsorption rate cannot be raised by a further increase in glucose concentration. On the other hand, the turnover rate of the cotransport can be raised by an increase in the tubular Na^+ load (see glomerulotubular balance). Then, *even though the glucose threshold has been reached, the maximal glucose transport rate rises in proportion to the Na^+ transport.* This transport behavior offers a great physiological advantage. Because the glucose threshold is twice as high as the normal plasma glucose concentration, there is no danger of a loss of glucose when glucose-containing food is consumed. Moreover, the coupling to Na^+ reabsorption minimizes the loss of glucose associated with increased GFR.

Other carbohydrates. Like the polyfructoside inulin (p. 739), *sucrose and lactose* escape reabsorption in the kidney; they are freely filtered and the entire amount in the filtrate is excreted. The disaccharides *maltose* and *trehalose*, on the other hand, are split by specific brush-border enzymes (maltase and trehalase) to produce glucose, which can be reabsorbed.

Phosphate. Phosphate is reabsorbed almost exclusively in the *proximal tubule* by secondary active transport in which it is coupled to Na^+, probably in the ratio 1:2. This is another transport system with a typical *threshold characteristic*. In the case of glucose, the threshold is far above the normal plasma concentration; the kidney normally plays no role in adjustment of the plasma concentration, and all the hormones that can influence the plasma glucose level (e.g., insulin, glucagon, adrenalin) have no direct influence on renal glucose transport. Phosphate is in a different situation. Its threshold concentration is in the range of normal plasma concentrations, so that the kidney makes a crucial contribution to regulation of the plasma phosphate concentration. This renal function is under hormonal control, by *parathyroid hormone* (PTH) in particular. This hormone not only mobilizes phosphate from the bone matrix but also increases renal phosphate excretion by *inhibiting the proximal reabsorption* of phosphate, a process mediated by cyclic adenosine monophosphate (cAMP). The net effect is to lower the phosphate threshold of the kidney [27, 33].

Sulfate. Sulfate is also reabsorbed *in the proximal tubule* by means of cotransport. However, its affinity for the transport protein is low, so that there is a *low renal threshold* (0.8–1.2 mmol/l). Hence the amount of sulfate in the extracellular fluid can be kept small, which is a significant factor in acid-base balance. Sulfate is derived from the sulfuric acid produced as a breakdown product in protein metabolism; as soon as it is formed, the acid is buffered. The kidney excretes sulfate in the form of a neutral salt, simultaneously eliminating the superfluous H^+ ions and retrieving the bicarbonate that had been used for buffering (p. 752).

Amino acids. Amino acids are handled very much like glucose in the kidney. Their reabsorption is almost entirely limited to the *proximal tubule*, and takes the form of *secondary active transport by coupling to Na^+ transport*. The transport proteins in the luminal brush border exhibit *stereospecificity at the receptor sites* for various amino acids. Amino acids with identical or very similar steric molecular configurations have affinity for the same receptor sites and hence can be transported by the same "carrier". So far seven different transport systems have been distinguished, as follows.

"Acidic" amino acids: glutamic acid, asparaginic acid

"Basic" amino acids: arginine, lysine, ornithine

"Neutral" amino acids

- cystine, cysteine
- proline, oxyproline, glycine
- glycine
- phenylalanine, leucine, isoleucine, tryptophan, methionine
- taurine, γ-aminobutyric acid, β-alanine

An innate or acquired defect in one of these specific transport systems causes an increased urinary excretion of the amino acids in the associated group *(hyperaminoaciduria)*. When the plasma concentration of one amino acid rises, saturation of the specific transport system results in increased excretion not only of this amino acid but also of all the others belonging to the same group [46].

Bicarbonate and Proton Transport

Bicarbonate. As illustrated in Fig. 30-13, by far the greater part of the filtered bicarbonate is reabsorbed in the *proximal tubule*, by the **carbonic-anhydrase mechanism** [35]. This process depends on the secretion of H^+ into the lumen of the tubule by way of Na^+-H^+ antiport, driven by the electrochemical potential difference for Na^+ (p. 745). Bicarbonate reabsorption, then, is also *coupled to the active processes of Na^+ reabsorption.* By this active transport, the bicarbonate concentration in the tubular fluid is normally reduced to about 5 mmol/l by the end of the proximal convolution. The situation here is a *dynamic equilibrium*, since the wall of the tubule is to a certain extent permeable to bicarbonate ions; the bicarbonate permeability is about half that of chloride. That is, the active pumping counteracts a "leak" in the form of the passive back-diffusion. The equilibrium is represented by

$$J_{act} = P\,(C_{Pl} - C_{TF}) \quad (19)$$

where J_{act} is the active pump rate, P is permeability, C_{Pl} is the plasma concentration, and C_{TF} is the equilibrium concentration in the tubular fluid.

The *pump-and-leak mechanism* [55] maintains a bicarbonate concentration gradient of ca. 20 mmol/l. Because about 60% of the filtrate volume has been reabsorbed by the end of the proximal convolution, and the bicarbonate concentration in the remaining volume has been reduced to 1/5, only about 8% of the filtered bicarbonate reaches Henle's loop. This residue is reabsorbed mainly in the descending thick limb of the loop. However, the bicarbonate-reabsorbing capacity of this part of the nephron is limited, and that of the distal convolution and collecting duct is even more so. Therefore bicarbonate is always excreted when the tubular fluid at the end of the proximal convolution contains an elevated concentration of bicarbonate. It is fundamentally because of the *combination of*

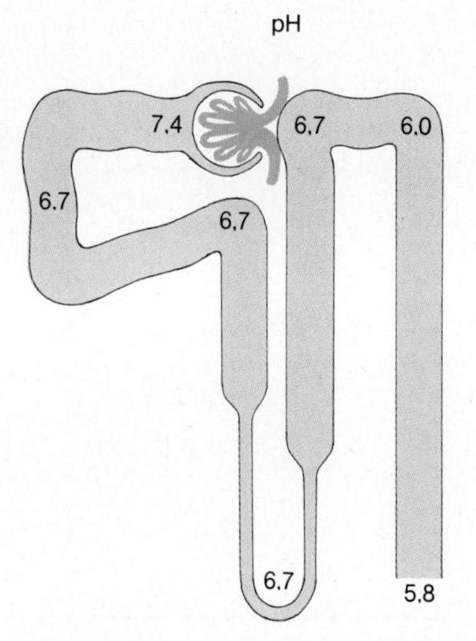

Fig. 30-19. Variation in pH of the tubular fluid along the nephron

gradient-limited reabsorption in the proximal convolution and capacity-limited reabsorption in the subsequent nephron segments that the kidney can act as a regulator when the acid-base balance is upset (see p. 753).

Hydrogen ions. The metabolism of a healthy human produces *60–100 mmol of hydrogen ions* per day. These ions must be eliminated by way of the kidneys, for only trace amounts of free H^+ can be tolerated. As it enters the tubule, the glomerular filtrate has the pH of blood plasma, 7.4. In the beginning of the proximal convolution it is reduced to pH 6.7, and this value is maintained over most of the nephron (Fig. 30-19). Only at the very end of the nephron does the urine pH fall to 5.8 or, in rare cases of extreme acidosis, as low as 4.5. But even this acidity corresponds only to a H^+ concentration of 0.03 mmol/l, which means that only 0.05% of the metabolically generated H^+ can be excreted as free ions. Although the amount of free H^+ excreted is so small, the resulting *acidification of the tubular fluid* is crucial. It is the prerequisite not only for reabsorption of the bicarbonate in the tubular fluid but also for the regeneration of the bicarbonate buffer in the organism as a whole. Furthermore, the acidity of the tubular fluid controls the excretion of acids in neutral form by the ammonia mechanism as well as by way of the so-called titratable acid (see below). Although only 0.1 mol of protons per day is eliminated by the kidney, the capacity for H^+ secretion is quite considerable, especially in the proximal tubule. Most of the bicarbonate is absorbed in buffered form, and for each of these bi-

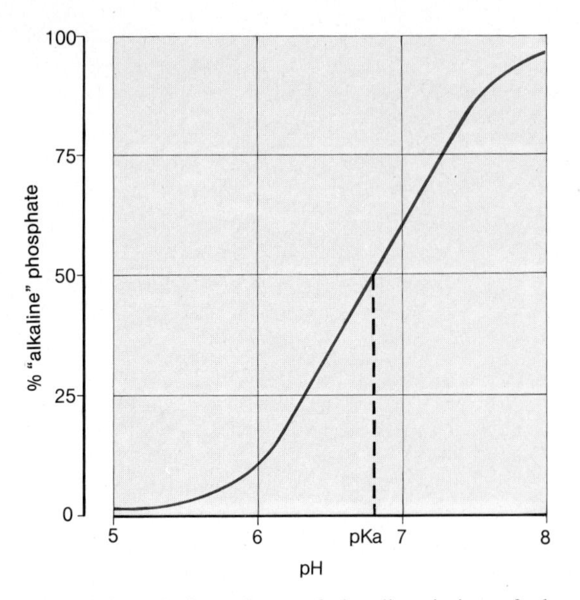

Fig. 30-20. pH-dependence of the dissociation of phosphate. At an acid pH, $H_2PO_4^{2-}$ predominates and at alkaline pH, HPO_4^-. At a pH of 6.8 (pKa) the two stages of dissociation are present in equal concentrations

carbonate molecules a hydrogen ion is required. The kidneys handle 4–4.5 mol bicarbonate per day, which requires proton secretion at a rate about 3 times greater than that of gastric acid production [31, 47, 50].

Titratable acids. The "titratable" acids are those *excreted in pH-neutral form, by means of buffers*. To determine the amount eliminated in this way, it is necessary to *titrate the urine with a base*. The most important buffer substance is **phosphate**. Excess amounts of it are produced in the metabolism of proteins and phospholipids, and because of the low renal phosphate threshold (p. 750) this excess is not reabsorbed from the tubular fluid. At a pH of 7.4 75% of the phosphate is present as HPO_4^{2-} *(secondary phosphate)*. As the pH falls, it is progressively converted to *primary phosphate*, $H_2PO_4^-$, until at pH 5.8 90% is present in this form (Fig. 30-20).

The H^+ buffered by the phosphate is derived from the dissociation of carbonic acid. The phosphate-bound H^+ ions do not simply recirculate, as in the case of bicarbonate reabsorption, but are eliminated in the urine. On balance, therefore, for each H^+ ion excreted a molecule of *bicarbonate is formed de novo*, so that the bicarbonate content of the body is restored (Fig. 30-21).

Ammonia mechanism. Mitochondrial glutaminase in the tubule cells deaminates the basic amino acid glutamine, first to glutamate$^-$ and then to oxoglutarate^{2-} [46a]. In each of these steps one molecule of *ammonium* (NH_4^+) is split off. Some of the ammonium ions are converted to *ammonia* (NH_3) by cleavage of a hydrogen ion. This electrically neutral molecule can readily diffuse across the luminal cell membrane into the tubular fluid. There it is converted back to NH_4^+ by combining with H^+ ions that have been secreted into the lumen by another route (see Na^+-H^+ antiport). Evidently, however, ammonium can also cross the tubule wall without prior conversion. Although the membrane is less permeable to NH_4^+ than to NH_3, the concentration of NH_4^+ in the tubule cells exceeds that of NH_3 by more than two orders of magnitude. The ammonium ions in the tubular fluid can substitute for Na^+ in neutralizing surplus anions such as SO_2^{2-} for excretion.

The glutarate^{2-} combines with two H^+ ions to form CO_2 and glucose. These H^+ ions are derived from the reaction of CO_2 and H_2O catalyzed by carbonic anhydrase, which also produces HCO_3^-. The net result is that **one molecule of bicarbonate is obtained for each ammonium molecule excreted.** The more ammonia moves from the cell into the tubular fluid, and more NH_4^+ is formed

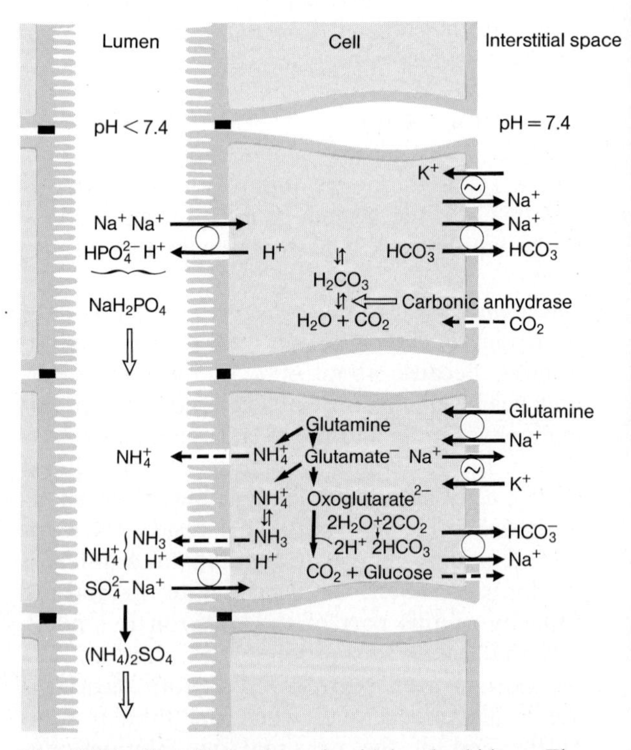

Fig. 30-21. The elimination of acid by the kidney. The *upper* part illustrates excretion by way of titratable acid, and the *lower* part shows the ammonia mechanism

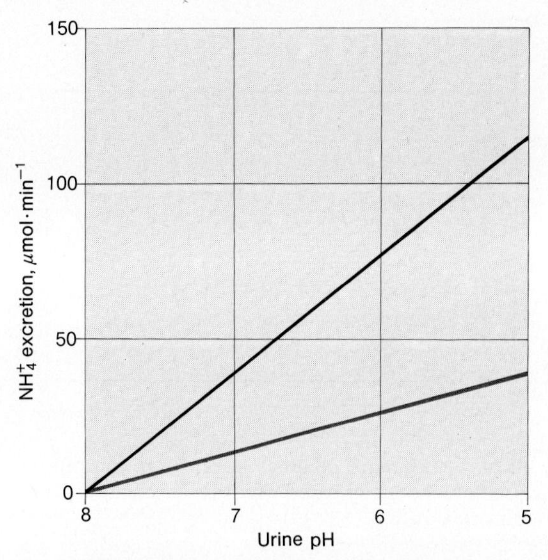

Fig. 30-22. Relation between urine pH and the excretion of ammonia by way of the kidney, in the cases of acid/base equilibrium *(red line)* and chronic metabolic acidosis *(black line)*. (Modified from [5])

there, the more H^+ ions are secreted. But because the H^+ ions also use up the other buffers in the solution, the tubular fluid becomes progressively more acidic. In fact, there is an approximately linear (inverse) relation between the pH of the excreted urine and the amount of ammonium it contains (Fig. 30-22). Normally 30–50 mmol H^+ are eliminated in pH-neutral form per day by the ammonia mechanism [18, 44].

Renal compensation of acid-base imbalances. In case of need (e.g., in diabetic acidosis), the *rate of ammonium excretion can be raised 10fold* (Fig. 30-22). This adjustment is brought about by the pH-dependence of glutamine metabolism, such that in acidosis the glutaminases are stimulated. As the H^+ concentration increases, proportionally more ammonium is produced for *elimination of the H^+ ions*; as an added advantage the body's bicarbonate content, depleted by the acidosis, is simultaneously replenished.

But it is just as important for *bicarbonate reabsorption* to be adjusted in cases of acid-base imbalance. The events by which this is accomplished can be inferred from the basic limitations of transport (p. 751).

For example, if the bicarbonate concentration in the plasma has risen due to **metabolic alkalosis**, the most the proximal tubule can achieve is to maintain the usual concentration difference between tubular fluid and interstitial space. Therefore the fluid flowing into the distal parts of the nephron has an elevated bicarbonate concentration. The limited reabsorption capacity here is exceeded, and *bicarbonate is excreted in the urine* (Fig. 30-23b). Conversely, when the bicarbonate concentration is reduced in **metabolic acidosis**, in the presence of the normal gradient greater amounts of bicarbonate are retrieved from the tubular fluid (Fig. 30-23c). In **respiratory acidosis** the elevated P_{CO_2} produces acidosis in the cells as well, so that more H^+ ions are made available for the exchange pump. The pump can work at a greater rate and maintain a *higher bicarbonate gradient* (Fig. 30-23d). In both forms of acidosis, then, the reabsorption of bicarbonate is enhanced, ensuring that the bicarbonate simultaneously being resynthesized by the elimination of H^+ in the kidney cells (p. 752) cannot be lost. These mechanisms continue to operate until the normal dynamic equilibrium is restored, the acidosis having been compensated.

In **respiratory alkalosis**, finally, because of the reduced P_{CO_2} the interior of the cells is also at an elevated pH. With insufficient H^+ production, activity of the exchange pump is impeded,

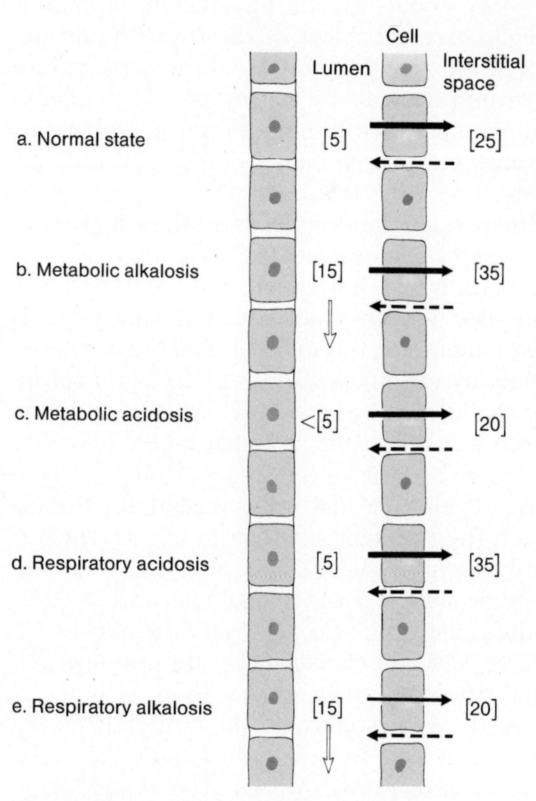

Fig. 30-23. Mechanisms for renal compensation of acid-base imbalances. The bicarbonate concentration gradient maintained by active transport is indicated by *arrows* and the passive backflow, by *dashed arrows*. The figures in *square brackets* give the bicarbonate concentrations in mmol/l

so that only a *reduced bicarbonate concentration difference* can build up. Bicarbonate remains unabsorbed in the tubular fluid and is excreted (Fig. 30-23e).

Transport of Nitrogenous Substances

The body's protein metabolism produces not only phosphate, sulfate and H^+ to be eliminated by the kidney, but also nitrogen-containing end products. Two of these have already been mentioned, *creatinine* (p. 740) and *ammonia* (p. 752). The category also includes various substances with small-to-medium molecular weight; of these, *urea and uric acid* are of the greatest practical significance. Traces of *proteins* also appear in the urine.

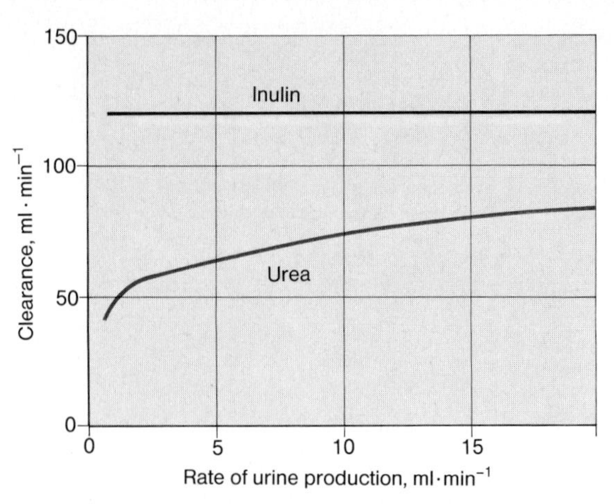

Fig. 30-24. Dependence of urea clearance on the rate of urine production, as compared with the diuresis-independent inulin clearance

Proteins and peptides. As mentioned above (p. 740), **proteins** are mostly retained by the glomerular filter. The protein concentration in the tubular fluid is only about 1% of the plasma concentration. Given the large volume of filtrate, however, this amounts to several grams per day; but only about 1% of the filtered protein is actually excreted. Most of the reabsorption occurs in the proximal tubule. Large proteins are taken into the cells by *endocytosis.* The endocytotic vacuoles then fuse with lysosomes containing enzymes that ultimately break the proteins down.

Peptides (e.g., glutathione, carnosine) and especially peptide hormones (e.g., insulin, angiotensin, parathyroid hormone) – all of which are molecules of such small size that they pass almost unhindered through the filter – are split so rapidly by various *peptidases in the brush border* that the liberated amino acids can almost all be reabsorbed within the proximal tubule [46].

Urea. In humans and most vertebrates the nitrogen from protein metabolism is excreted primarily as urea. As a small, electrically neutral molecule, urea is freely filtered and also so readily diffusible that *in the proximal tubule about 1/3 diffuses back into the blood.* The diffusion permeability to urea is low in the *distal nephron,* as far as the final section of the collecting ducts, but here it can be reabsorbed with the assistance of *solvent drag* (p. 745). Therefore if large amounts of water are being reabsorbed in the distal sections, as happens in antidiuresis, with production of urine having a high osmotic concentration (p. 759), then *an additional third of the filtered urea* can be reabsorbed along with the water. In the case of water diuresis, distal water reabsorption ceases; then correspondingly more urea is excreted. That is, the *excretion of urea varies with diuresis.* In Fig. 30-24 this relationship is explained in terms of the **urea clearance.** Urea passes through the filter at the same rate as the comparison substance inulin (p. 739). However, its clearance is always lower by at least 1/3, because this proportion is reabsorbed in the proximal tubule (regardless of the state of diuresis). An additional third can be reabsorbed in the distal nephron if (in extreme antidiuresis) the distal water reabsorption, and hence the amount of urea dragged with the water, reaches a maximum. As water reabsorption diminishes, with increasing diuresis, more urea is excreted.

Urea is a nontoxic, inert substance. Therefore its concentration in the extracellular fluid is relatively unimportant, and there is *no special regulatory mechanism* to control it. Its plasma concentration depends on protein catabolism and on the magnitude of the GFR (Fig. 30-25).

Uric acid. Only 5% of the nitrogen eliminated in humans is in the form of uric acid. But this compound is significant medically, because it is the *cause of gout and kidney stones,* diseases that have exhibited a stepwise increase in recent decades. Uric acid is an end product of purine metabolism, and therefore it is always produced in larger amounts when a diet rich in the nuclei of cells (animal protein, especially internal organs) is metabolized.

Uric acid is *freely filtered* and, like various other organic acids (p. 756), can also be extracted from the peritubular blood by the *proximal tubule* and *secreted* into the tubular fluid. Simultaneously,

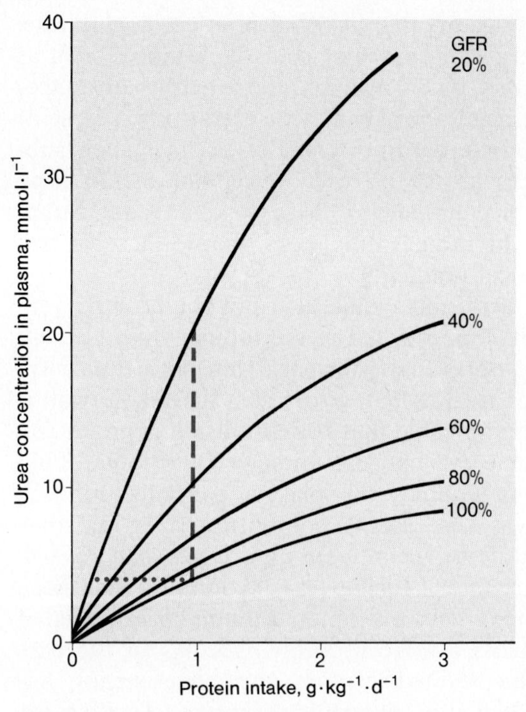

Fig. 30-25. Urea concentration in the plasma as a function of protein intake and GFR. The *red dashed line* indicates that with a constant protein intake the urea concentration rises when the GFR decreases from the norm (100%). The *red dotted line* demonstrates that even when the GFR is reduced a "normal" plasma urea concentration can be maintained if protein intake is lowered appropriately

however, it is *reabsorbed* in the proximal tubule, so that at the end of the proximal convolution there is always as much uric acid present as was originally filtered. In the *descending part of Henle's loop* reabsorption predominates. Only about 10% of the uric acid reaches the tip of Henle's loop, and this amount is ultimately excreted, because the distal parts of the nephron are almost impermeable to uric acid (Fig. 30-26). The fact that the amount of uric acid is reduced before it passes through the nephron structures in the renal papilla is significant for two reasons: the *water solubility* of uric acid is both *limited* and *pH-dependent*. Uric acid has a pKa of 5.8, and at the normal blood pH of 7.4 it is almost completely dissociated, as the urate anion. If the concentration of urate were too high when the fluid reaches Henle's loop, where physiologically the Na^+ concentration is the highest in the body (p. 759), because of the *limited solubility product (L)*

$$L = [Na^+] \cdot [urate^-] \quad (20)$$

there would continually be a risk of precipitation.

In *dissociated form as urate*, however, uric acid is *20 times more soluble than undissociated uric acid.* In its passage through the distal nephron, however, the tubular fluid decreases in volume and at the same time is further acidified (Fig. 30-19); therefore the concentration of uric acid rises, and its dissociation is increasingly suppressed. In the collecting duct, at pH 5.8, 50% of the uric acid is undissociated, and at pH 4.5 this figure rises to 95%. Thus, the reabsorption of uric acid in the descending limb of Henle's loop, before these two dangerous regions are reached, acts as a kind of safety valve.

Kidney stones

Urate stones. In a normally functioning kidney the urine is rarely acidified beyond pH 5.8 (Fig. 30-19). Patients predisposed to develop urate stones often have a distinctly lower urine pH, so that larger amounts of the poorly soluble uric acid are present (see above). Furthermore, deficient removal of the urate reabsorbed in the descending limbs of the loops of Henle seems to play a role in the accumulation and precipitation of uric acid in the renal medulla and the urinary apparatus. The uric acid taken into the vasa recta would become concentrated according to the principle of countercurrent diffusion (p. 738), and accumulate in the tip of the papilla if it were not continually being carried away in the bloodstream. This transport is assisted by binding of some of the uric acid to the erythrocyte membranes. In patients predisposed to urate stones and gout kidneys (deposition of uric acid in the renal tissue), the binding capacity of the erythrocytes is reduced.

Oxalic acid stones. Oxalic acid is another metabolic end product that tends to precipitate and form *concrements* because of its *low water solubility.* Like uric acid, oxalate can be secreted and reabsorbed in the proximal tubule. As a result of these processes, the amount of oxalate present

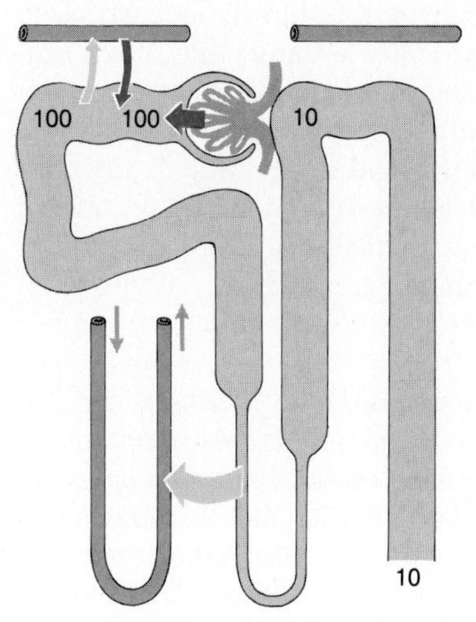

Fig. 30-26. Relative concentrations and directions of transport of uric acid along the nephron

at the end of the proximal tubule is 25% greater than the amount filtered in the glomerulus. Because the distal parts of the nephron are largely impermeable to oxalate, this amount appears in the urine. The tubular oxalate concentration resulting from filtration and secretion is directly dependent on the plasma concentration. Patients predisposed to oxalate stones should therefore limit their consumption of foods rich in oxalate (e.g., rhubarb, spinach, chocolate) and those that increase the amount of oxalate formed metabolically (e.g., vitamin C, theophyllin).

Cystine stones. Cystine is by far the least soluble of the amino acids. Nevertheless, cystine stones very rarely result from a defect in the cystine-cysteine system itself. More commonly, they are caused by failure of the transport system for "basic" amino acids (p. 750). Arginine, lysine and ornithine then become more concentrated in the blood and tubular fluid, though they are sufficiently soluble that they do not precipitate out. But they swamp the cysteine system, for which they also have an affinity, and displace cystine from its reabsorption site. The concentration of cystine rises, and precipitation is the result.

Phosphate stones. Phosphate precipitation is particularly likely to be associated with inflammatory processes in the renal medulla. Phosphate is more soluble, the more acidic the milieu. When direct damage to the distal tubule and collecting tubule abolishes the local pH gradient, so that the tubular fluid can no longer be acidified, and/or when bacterial decomposition releases increased amounts of ammonia (which acts as a base) into the tubular fluid, phosphate can no longer be kept in solution.
Another important factor here is the prevailing *Ca^{2+} concentration*, because calcium salts in general are less soluble than, for example, sodium salts. Therefore both phosphate and oxalate precipitate chiefly in the form of their calcium salts.

Secretion of Organic Compounds of External Origin

Uric acid and oxalic acid are organic acids with the special property of being *secreted in the proximal tubule.* There are a number of other **weak organic acids** not naturally occurring in the body that, evidently because they have similar structural characteristics, can also be secreted by the same mechanism. Among these are p-aminohippuric acid (PAH) and X-ray contrast media such as diodrast, as well as several medicines such as penicillin and various other antibiotics, sulfonamide, diuretics, barbiturates and so on [58].

Mechanisms of secretion. The secretion mechanism is evidently based on one or more *anion exchangers located on the basolateral surface of the proximal tubule cells* (Fig. 30-13). These expel from the cell anions such as bicarbonate and perhaps chloride, supplying the cell simultaneously with substrates necessary for metabolism. The preferred substrates in this part of the nephron are weak organic acids such as α-ketoglutarate, fumarate or free fatty acids. Substances such as uric acid, oxalic acid and the extrinsic substances mentioned above can evidently also make use of these anion-antiporters. But because such substances are of no use for cellular metabolism, they accumulate in the cytosol in equilibrium with the tubular fluid, according to their electrochemical gradients.
Uric acid and oxalic acid do not become very highly concentrated in the tubular fluid because of the opportunity for back-transport. But a substance such as *PAH*, to which the tubule wall is so impermeable that back-diffusion is prevented, can reach a concentration in the tubular fluid that is 5 times the plasma concentration. As long as the plasma concentration is low they continue to accumulate until a *maximal concentration in the tubule* (ca. 3.5 mmol/l) has been reached. This maximum cannot be exceeded if the plasma concentration rises. As in the case of glucose reabsorption, this phenomenon has been called a *"transport maximum (Tm)"*. Here, again, it is a rather unfortunate term, because it is often misunderstood to mean a maximal amount of substance that can be transported. But since the limiting value for secretory transport is not the amount of substance secreted per unit time but rather the *maximal concentration in*

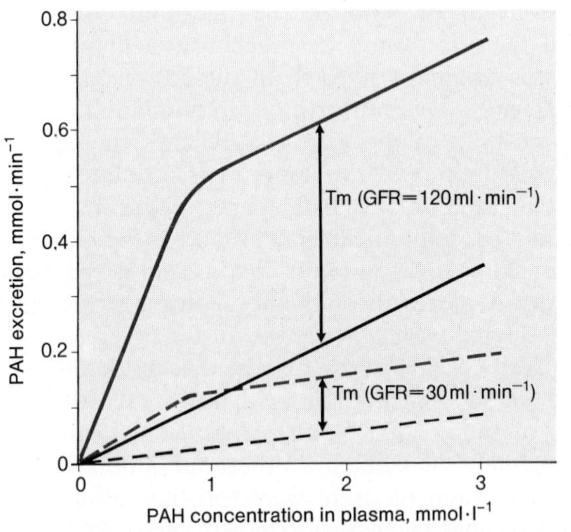

Fig. 30-27. Excretion of p-aminohippuric acid as a function of its plasma concentration and of the glomerular filtration rate (GFR). The difference between the rates of filtration *(black lines)* and excretion *(red lines)* of PAH gives the rate of secretion into the tubule. At a certain plasma concentration the concentration in the tubular fluid reaches a maximum; from that point on, the PAH transport rate can no longer be increased *(Tm)*. When the GFR changes, changing the volume flow into the tubule, Tm varies in proportion

the tubule, here too one finds a *proportional dependence of Tm on GFR*. The greater the volume in which the secreted substance is taken up, the greater the amount accumulated at the maximal concentration (Fig. 30-27).

PAH clearance. Below the maximal concentration, up to 90% of the PAH is extracted from the renal blood by filtration and, in particular, by secretion. Because the clearance (p. 740) of a substance is a measure of the volume of plasma from which this substance is removed, *the PAH clearance corresponds approximately to the renal plasma flow*. Therefore it can be used, in association with the hematocrit, to estimate the *rate of renal blood flow*. In earlier times this was a standard procedure in the diagnosis of kidney function, but it has since been supplanted by technical procedures simpler to carry out.
Whereas the total amount of PAH accumulated in the tubular fluid is excreted in the urine, other organic acids can diffuse back out of the fluid to some extent. Such organic acids often have a *higher lipid solubility in undissociated form*, which allows easy penetration of biological membranes ("non-ionic diffusion"). Because the degree of dissociation of such weak electrolytes depends on the pH of the medium as well as on their pKa, back-diffusion occurs to a greater extent as the tubular fluid becomes more acidic. This situation can be *exploited therapeutically;* for instance, in a case of barbiturate overdose the tubular fluid should be kept as alkaline as possible (by infusion of bicarbonate and simultaneous inhibition of carbonic anhydrase). On the other hand, when treating an infection of the renal tissue with a suitable antibiotic, one should ensure the greatest possible acidity of the tubular fluid, so that the dissociation of the weak acid is largely prevented; thus the amount of the substance in the form to which the membranes are more permeable is maximized, and a high tissue level can build up.

30.6 The Adjustment of Urine Concentration

Water Excretion

The concept of osmolarity. The osmotic pressure of a solution depends on the number of dissolved particles it contains. The unit *1 osmol* is defined as $6.06 \cdot 10^{23}$ dissolved particles (= 1 mole of a non-dissociating substance). When the osmotic concentration is expressed with respect to the volume of the solvent (osmol/l) it is called **osmolarity**, and when with respect to the weight of the solvent (osmol/kg H_2O) it is called **osmolality**.

Osmolarity in the tubule. When too much liquid has been drunk, the surplus water must be excreted. As described on p. 746, the *thick ascending limb of Henle's loop* is capable of reabsorbing NaCl from the tubular fluid while preventing water from following. Therefore the *tubular fluid becomes hypotonic* to the blood plasma; its osmotic concentration has fallen from about 290 mosmol/l to about 1/7 of that value (ca. 40 mosmol/l). At the end of Henle's loop 20–25% of the originally filtered volume is still present (Fig. 30-9). In the extreme case of maximal *water diuresis* this volume can remain almost unchanged until the end of the nephron is reached. Urine can then be excreted at a rate as high as 30 ml/min, and contains a minimum of osmotic substances. Normally, however, the kidney's task is to eliminate osmotically effective substances, so that the degree of water diuresis is much lower.

Action of ADH. The amount of water reabsorbed in the distal nephron, and hence the degree of diuresis, is controlled by the **antidiuretic hormone (ADH)**. ADH is formed in the supraoptic nucleus and in the paraventricular nucleus of the *hypothalamus* and delivered by neuroaxonal transport to the pituitary, where it is stored in the posterior lobe (pp. 743 and 766). In response to signals from *volume receptors in the atria of the heart* and from *peripheral and central osmoreceptors in the liver and hypothalamus* (see Fig. 31-3), ADH is gradually released, always in just the right amount to ensure that the water reabsorbed in the distal convolution and collecting duct is sufficient to keep the water content of the body in the normal range. Only the water surplus to the requirements of homeostasis is excreted [22].

The Urine-Concentrating Mechanism

Substances excreted in the urine. A person on a mixed diet must excrete about *1,200 mosmol of waste materials* (metabolic end products, etc.) daily in the urine. If it were necessary for the urine to be isotonic with the plasma, more than 4 l of water would be needed to dissolve these substances. Our water balance is more economi-

cally managed – and our social life considerably improved – by the production of a urine so concentrated that no more than ca. 1.5 l need to be excreted per day. The concentration of osmotically effective solutes in this urine is about 3 times higher than that in the plasma.
To concentrate the urine, the kidney employs the same mechanisms as to dilute it, *the NaCl pump in the thick ascending limb of the loop of Henle, with ADH as the controlling hormone.*

Countercurrent principle. The hairpin arrangement of Henle's loop, with flow in opposite directions in the closely apposed ascending and descending limbs, provides the structural prerequisite for the urine to be concentrated according to the countercurrent multiplication principle. In the highly simplified model in Fig. 30-28, the fluid becomes more concentrated because NaCl is pumped out of the ascending limb of the loop and into the descending limb. If the partition between the two limbs is impermeable to water, this procedure dilutes the solution in the ascending limb and concentrates the solution in the descending limb. That is, the isotonic saline flowing into the descending limb becomes progressively hypertonic as it approaches the tip of the loop. After the turn it continues as a countercurrent through the ascending limb to the base of the loop; on the way, *at each level there are only slight horizontal concentration differences between the two limbs.* The NaCl pump in the ascending limb can therefore operate in *small single steps* with relatively little energy expenditure, but these single events are *multiplied by the countercurrent effect* so that a very large vertical concentration difference is built up, between the base and the tip of the loop. This gradient is then used to bring the urine to its final concentration, as follows. The solution flowing out of the ascending limb is hypotonic; in the distal convolution water is withdrawn from it by osmosis, making it isotonic and halving its volume. During the subsequent passage through the collecting duct, toward the tip of the papilla, the osmotic removal of water continues as the fluid equilibrates with its progressively more hypertonic surroundings. Here, as in the distal convolution, the *degree of water permeability* of the collecting duct is *controlled by ADH.* Depending on the amount of ADH available, the urine leaving the kidney at the tip of the papilla will be more or less reduced in volume and osmotically concentrated [42, 60].

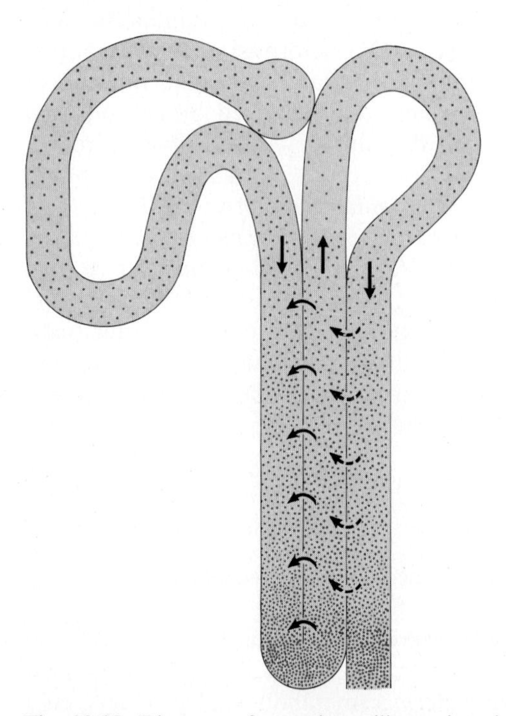

Fig. 30-28. Diagram of a nephron illustrating the countercurrent mechanism in the loop of Henle. The transport of NaCl from the descending into the ascending limb is indicated by the *solid arrows* and the flow of water out of the collecting tubule, by *dashed arrows*

Model of the concentration process. Such a simple model is useful only to describe the basic principle by which the urine is concentrated. The actual situation in the renal medulla is considerably more complicated. For one thing, the *blood flow through the renal medulla* (p. 737) plays a central role. Another factor to be considered is that although the osmotic concentration is maximal at the tip of the papilla, the energy for the concentration process is supplied not over the whole length of the ascending limb but only in the upper, thick part. Finally, the urine ultimately excreted is not a concentrated NaCl solution; its main solute is *urea.*
These considerations are included in the (still greatly simplified) model in Fig. 30-29 [48]. Here it is assumed that the vasa recta are highly permeable to NaCl, urea and water, so that they and the interstitial space together form a single fluid compartment. The *NaCl pumped out of the thick ascending limb of Henle's loop into the interstitial space* draws water, under the influence of ADH, out of the descending limb and also out of the adjacent collecting tubules. Because the latter are relatively impermeable to urea, it becomes highly concentrated in the solution reaching the inner

zone of the medulla. The parts of the collecting tubules in this region are permeable to urea. Therefore urea diffuses into the interstitial space here and can draw water osmotically out of the descending limb. The latter is impermeable to NaCl, so that the NaCl in the tubular fluid becomes progressively more concentrated toward the papilla tip. When it turns into the thin ascending limb, the fluid enters a zone with the opposite permeabilities: low for water, but high for NaCl and urea. Following their concentration gradients, NaCl diffuses out and urea diffuses in. The thick ascending part has a low permeability to urea, as do the distal convolution and the upper section of the collecting duct, where under ADH water is removed. Therefore the urea concentration rises continuously, and urea progressively replaces NaCl, much of which can be reabsorbed in the terminal part of the nephron, especially under the influence of aldosterone (p. 747). That is, some of the urea recirculates in the distal nephron, and in so doing it *transfers the energy for concentration from the thick limb of the loop into the inner zone of the medulla.* The accumulation of urea in the medulla is assisted by the vasa recta, in which, again according to the principle of countercurrent diffusion (p. 738), urea is most concentrated toward the tip of the loop. This effect in turn keeps the concentration gradient between blood and collecting-tubule fluid small. The end result is that the urine leaving the kidney has been *osmotically concentrated by NaCl transport*, but the *NaCl has been replaced by urea*, so that this metabolic end product can be excreted in solution with a minimal amount of water.

Renal Insufficiency

The production of glomerular filtrate is the most important requirement for the overall function of the kidney. If insufficient volumes are filtered, it is irrelevant whether the tubular mechanisms for reabsorption of electrolytes, glucose or amino acids are still intact, or whether the mechanisms for secretion of K^+ and H^+ or ammonia are operative. Without enough filtrate, and without adequate flow through the individual parts of the tubule, all the partial functions sited there are ineffective. A *critical reduction of glomerular filtrate* can appear suddenly (acute renal failure) or develop in the course of a prolonged kidney disease (chronic renal insufficiency).

Acute renal failure. The causes of this functional disturbance are extrarenal. When the circulation breaks down after loss of blood or fluid or due to acute cardiac insufficiency – and often after only a brief circulatory weakness, which transiently diminishes the renal blood flow – the glomerular filtrate can be drastically reduced. Then the

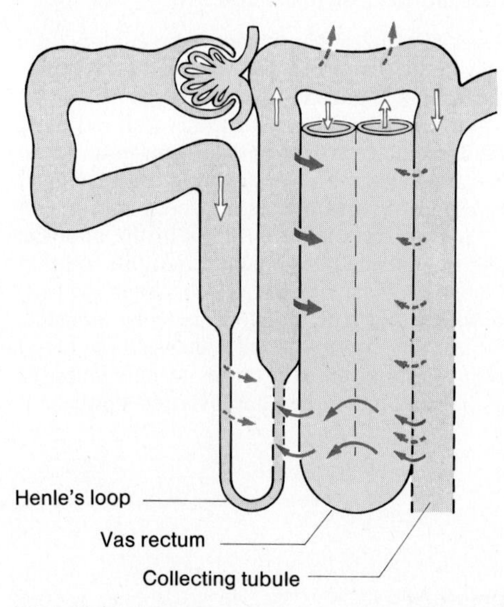

Fig. 30-29. Countercurrent concentrating process in the renal medulla. The vasa recta, highly permeable to NaCl, urea and water, are a fluid space that communicates freely with the interstitial space. NaCl is pumped out of the thick ascending limb into this space, and the concentration of urea in it rises progressively toward the tip of the papilla. The structures permeable to urea are *dashed.* ⟹ active NaCl transport, ⟶ flow of urea, – → flow of water

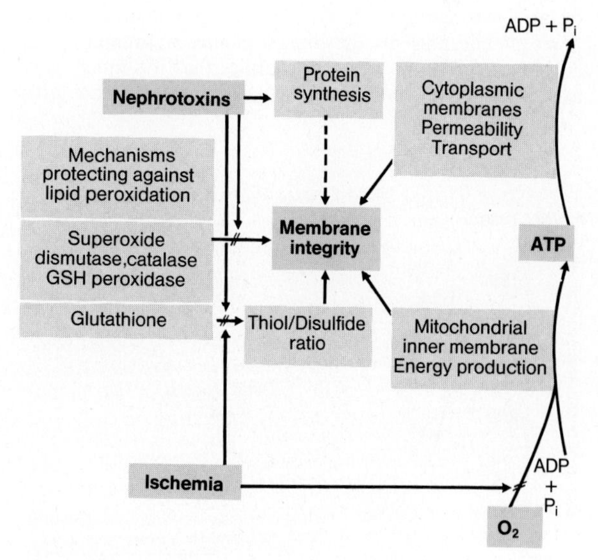

Fig. 30-30. Influences on energy metabolism and membrane functions during oxygen deficiency or exposure to nephrotoxins, due to failure of the mechanisms that ordinarily protect against lipid peroxidation. (Modified from [40])

flow of urine is also severely reduced *(oligiuria)* or ceases altogether *(anuria)*. When the circulation has been stabilized, the renal blood flow usually also soon recovers, but the diminished filtration and the oliguria or anuria can persist. The consequence is a retention of all the substances normally excreted in the urine, until uremia develops (see below). If some residual filtration continues, a condition of *polyuria* often develops; that is, an increased volume of urine is excreted. In this case the kidney is eliminating most of the filtrate and has almost entirely lost its ability to reabsorb and secrete electrolytes. It is also unable to either concentrate or dilute the urine and hence cannot regulate the body's salt and water balance. All these disorders can gradually disappear after several days or weeks, and afterward the kidney is often found to show little or no morphological damage [12].

Acute renal failure can be caused by a number of poisons, called *nephrotoxins* (e.g., aminoglycosides or heavy metals), as well as by circulatory deficiencies. Therefore the basic causes are thought to be disturbances of cellular metabolism [53]. The aerobic metabolism of the kidney cells generates *reactive metabolic intermediates* such as superoxide anions and peroxide, which must be rapidly inactivated. By means of the enzymes superoxide dismutase, catalase and glutathion-SH-peroxidase (GSH), the O_2 intermediates are reduced to alcohols. Blocking of GSH leads to the peroxidation of lipids and thus to disruption and loss of membranes (Fig. 30-30). The affected elements include both the ATP-synthesizing inner membranes of the mitochondria and the cell membranes, with their ($Na^+ + K^+$)-ATPase and the other molecular structures for ion transport [53]. As compared with this *cellular debilitation, which interferes with production and conversion of metabolic energy* to fuel the transport processes, the reduction in glomerular filtrate is initially the lesser evil, as far as supporting life is concerned. Glomerular filtration may be kept low by a mechanism involving feedback from the tubule (see macula densa, p. 737) [11].

Chronic renal insufficiency. When the glomerular filtrate is gradually reduced (e.g., in chronic glomerulonephritis or by an obstruction to flow), a chronic renal insufficiency develops and presents the clinical picture of **uremia**.

Although the word "uremia" signifies that too much urea is present in the blood, the urea itself is not a particularly important problem. Urea is a metabolic end product that is hardly toxic even in high concentrations (see p. 754). But the elevated urea concentration in uremia can serve as an indicator of the simultaneously impaired renal elimination of other substances that are toxic when their concentration in the body fluids rises (e.g., guanidine, phenols, diverse polypeptides etc.). The latter can produce a variety of symptoms and functional disturbances in the CNS, heart, alimentary canal and skeleton, as well as in metabolism and the formation of the blood.

Fortunately, the kidney has a considerable *capacity to adjust* to restricted glomerular filtration. Even in people with healthy kidneys the GFR falls steadily from about age 40 onward, so that between the 80th and 90th years it is only about half the original value. But this deterioration does not cause uremia, nor does removal of one kidney. The remaining kidney or the remaining *intact nephrons hypertrophy*. The individual nephrons produce more filtrate and the tubules become capable of increased reabsorption and secretion. Not until the GFR falls below 40% of normal does progressive renal insufficiency develop. With a further reduction in filtration, the extracellular concentration of substances eliminated exclusively through the glomeruli, such as creatinine, increases exponentially (Fig. 30-31). Then the kidneys gradually lose their ability to excrete waste materials, to achieve osmoregulation and to maintain water and electrolyte balance.

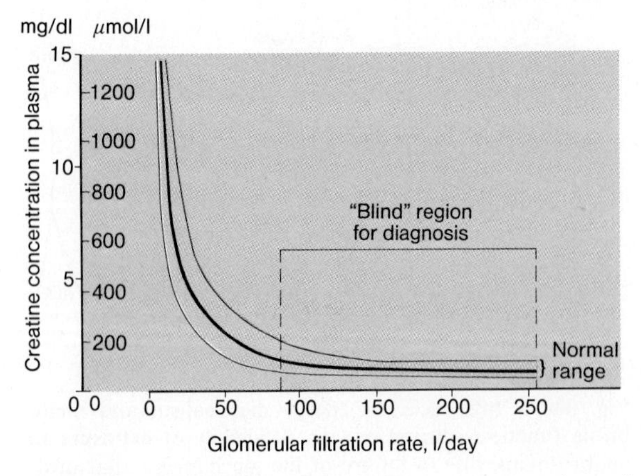

Fig. 30-31. Dependence of the plasma concentration of creatinine on the glomerular filtration rate

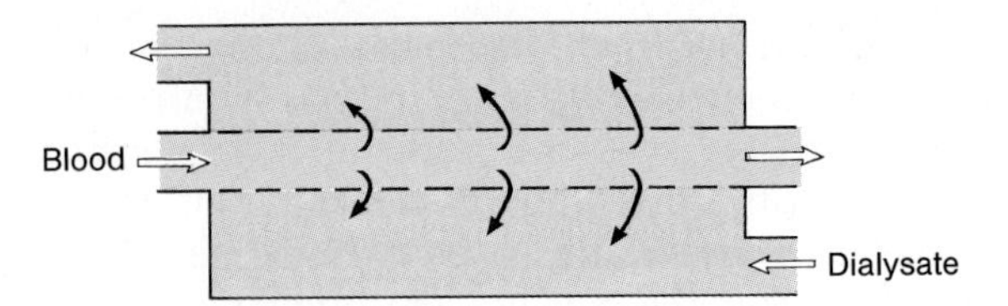

Fig. 30-32. Principle of extracorporeal hemodialysis

Dialysis. In cases of acute or chronic loss of renal function, apparatus is available by which the wastes that accumulate in the extracellular fluid can be removed, as can toxins and excess water and electrolytes. In the oldest and most commonly used method, *extracorporeal hemodialysis*, the patient's blood flows from an artery through a system of artificial semipermeable membranes and back into a vein (Fig. 30-32). An electrolyte solution flows in the opposite direction along the outside of the membrane; this solution contains the most important serum electrolytes in the concentration to which the patient's blood is to be adjusted. Because of the concentration difference between the blood and the dialysis solution, the substances to be eliminated flow into the dialysate until the concentration gradient is abolished.

30.7 References

Textbooks and Handbooks

1. Brenner, B.M., Rector, F.C. (Eds.): The Kidney. Vol. I.II. W.B. Saunders Co. Philadelphia 1976
2. Deetjen, P., Boylan, J.W., Kramer, K.: Physiology of the Kidney and of Water Balance, Springer, New York, Heidelberg, Berlin 1975

3. GREGER, R., LANG, F., SILBERNAGL. S. (Eds.): Renal transport of organic substances. Springer Verlag, Berlin Heidelberg New York 1981
4. MASSRY, S., R. GLASSOCK (Eds.): Textbook of Nephrology Vol. I + II, 2. Ed., Williams + Wilkins, Baltimore 1989
5. ORLOFF, J., BERLINER, R.W.: Renal Physiology, Section 8 in Handbook of Physiology. Am. Physiol. Soc., Washington D.C. 1973
6. PITTS, R.F.: Physiology of the Kidney and of Body Fluids, Year Book Medical Publishers, Chicago 1972
7. SARRE, H.J., GESSLER, H. (Eds.): Nierenkrankheiten 5. Aufl. Georg Thieme Verlag, Stuttgart 1986
8. SELDIN, D.W., GIEBISCH, G. (Eds.): The Kidney, Physiology and Pathophysiology Vol. I, II. Raven Press. New York 1985
9. SIEGENTHALER, W. (Ed.): Klinische Pathophysiology 5. Aufl. Georg Thieme Verlag, Stuttgart 1982

Original Papers and Reviews

10. BAEYER, VON H., DEETJEN, P.: Renal glucose transport. D.W. SELDIN u. G. GIEBISCH (Eds.), The kidney Vol. II, pp. 1663–1675 Raven Press, New York 1985
11. BLAIR-WEST, J.R.: Renin-angiotensin system and sodium metabolism. In K. THURAU (Ed.), Int. Rev. Physiol. Kidney and urinary tract physiology II, Vol. 11, pp 95–143 University Park Press. Baltimore 1976
12. BLANTZ, R.C.: Intrinsic Renal Failure: Acute., D.W. SELDIN a. G. GIEBISCH, (Eds.) The Kidney, Vol. II. p. 1863–1884. Raven Press, New York 1985
13. CARAFOLI, E.: The regulation of the cellular functions of Ca^{2+}. In F. BRONNER and J.W. COBURN (Eds.), Disorders of mineral metabolism, calcium physiology, Vol. II, pp. 1–42. Academic Press, New York 1982
14. DEETJEN, P., KRAMER, K.: Die Abhängigkeit des O_2-Verbrauches der Niere von der Na-Rückresorption. Pflügers Arch., Europ. J. Physiol. *273*, 636–650 (1961)
15. DUNN, M.J., HOOD, V.L.: Prostaglandins and the kidney. Am. J. Physiol., *233*, F 169–184 (1977)
16. DWORKIN, L.D., BRENNER, B.M.: Biophysical Basis of Glomerular Filtration. D. W. SELDIN and G. GIEBISCH (Eds.), The Kidney, pp. 397–426, Raven Press. New York 1985
17. GIEBISCH, G., Renal tubular control of potassium transport. Klin. Wschr. *57*, 1001–1008 (1979)
18. GOLDSTEIN, L.: Ammonia production and excretion in the mammalian kidney. In THURAU (Ed.), Int. Rev. Physiol. Vol. 11, pp. 283–316, University Park Press, Baltimore 1976
19. GOTTSCHALK, C.W.: Osmotic concentration and dilution of the urine. Amer. J. Med. *36*, 670 (1964)
20. GREGER, R.: Ion transport mechanism in thick ascending limb of Henle's loop of mammalian nephron. Physiol. Rev. *65*, 760 (1985)
21. GREGER, R., SCHLATTER, E., LANG, F.: Evidence for electroneutral sodium chloride cotransport in the cortical thick ascending limb of Henle's loop of rabbit kidney. Pflügers Arch. *396*, 308–314 (1983)
22. HANDLER, J.S., ORLOFF, J.: Antidiuretic hormone, Ann. Rev. Physiol. *43*, 611–624 (1981)
23. HIERHOLZER, K.: Sodium Reabsorption in the Distal Tubular System. In D. W. SELDIN a. G. GIEBISCH (Eds.), The Kidney, Vol. II, pp. 1063–1069, Raven Press, New York 1985
24. JAMISON, R.L., HALL, D.A.: Collecting duct function and sodium balance, Ann. Rev. med. *33*, 241–254 (1982)
25. KATZ, A.I.: Renal Na-K-ATPase: its role in tubular sodium and potassium transport. Am. J. Physiol. *242*, F 207–F 219 (1982)
26. KERJASCHKI, D.: Molekularpathologie des glomerulären Sialoglykoproteins Podocalyxin, dem Hauptbestandteil des „glomerulären Polyanions", in der experimentellen und humanen glomerulären Minimalveränderung. Klin. Wschr. *63*, 850–861 (1985)
27. KNOX, F.G., HARAMATI, A.: Renal Regulation of Phosphate Excretion. In D.W. SELDIN a. G. GIEBISCH (Eds.), The Kidney, Vol. II, pp. 1381–1396, Raven Press, New York 1985
28. KNOX, F.G., HAAS, J.A.: Factors influencing renal sodium reabsorption in volume expansion. Rev. Physiol. Biochem. Pharmacol. *92*, 76–113 (1982)
29. KRAMER, K., DEETJEN, P., BRECHTELSBAUER, H.: Gegenstromdiffusion des Sauerstoffs im Nierenmark. Pflügers Arch. ges. Physiol., *274*, 63 (1961)
30. KRAMER, H.J., KRÜCK, F.: Molecular basis of tubular transport and of the action of diuretics. Klin. Wschr. *60*, 1165–1263 (1982)
31. KOEPPEN, B., GIEBISCH, G., MALNIC, G.: Mechanism and Regulation of Renal Tubular Acidification. In D.W. SELDIN a. G. GIEBISCH (Eds.), The Kidney, Vol. II, pp. 1491–1526, Raven Press, New York 1985
32. KRITZ, W., KAISSLING, B.: Structural Organization of the Mammalian Kidney. In D.W. SELDIN a. G. GIEBISCH (Eds.), The Kidney, Vol. I, pp. 265–306, Raven Press, New York 1985
33. LANG, F., GREGER, R., KNOX, F., OBERLEITNER, H.: Factors modulating the renal handling of phosphate. In BERLYNE and THOMAS (Eds.), Renal Physiology, Vol. 4, pp. 1–16 (Karger, Basel, 1981)
34. MAAK, T., PARK, C.H., CAMARGO, M.J.F.: Renal Filtration, Transport, and Metabolism of Proteins. In D.W. SELDIN a. G. GIEBISCH (Eds.), The Kidney Vol. II, pp. 1773–1804, Raven Press, New York 1985
35. MAREN, T.H.: Carbonic anhydrase: chemistry, physiology, and inhibition. Physiol. Rev. *47*, 597–781 (1967)
36. MCGIFF, J.C., WONG, P.Y.: Prostaglandins and Renal Function. Proc. VII Inst. Congr. Nephrol., Montreal 1978, p. 83.91, S. Karger Verlag, Basel
37. MOFFAT, D.B., FOURMAN, J.: The vascular pattern of the rat kidney. J. Anat. Lond. *97*, 543 (1963)
38. MURER, H., BURCKHARDT, G.: Membrane transport of anions across epithelia of mammalian small intestine and kidney proximal tubule. Rev. Physiol. Biochem. Pharmacol. *96*, 2–51 (1983)
39. PEASE, D.C.: Fine structures of the kidney seen by electron microscopy. J. Histochem. *3*, 295 (1955)
40. PFALLER, W., GSTRAUNTHALER, G., DEETJEN, P.: Biochemical Aspects of Cell Injury in Acute Renal Failure. In H.E. ELIAHOU, (Ed.), Acute Renal Failure p. 25–29, John Libley, London 1982
41. QUAMME, G.A., DIRKS, J.H.: Magnesium: Cellular and Renal Exchanges. In D.W. SELDIN a. G. GIEBISCH (Eds.), The Kidney, Vol. II, pp. 1269–1280, Raven Press, New York 1985
42. ROY, D.R., JAMISON, R.L.: Countercurrent System and Its Regulation. In D.W. SELDIN a. G. GIEBISCH (Eds.), The Kidney, Vol. II, pp. 903–932 Raven Press, New York 1985
43. ROOS, A., BORON, W.F.: Intracellular pH. Physiol. Rev. *61*, 296–443 (1981)
44. ROSS, B., LOWRY, M.: Recent developments in renal handling of glutamine and ammonia. In GREGER, LANG, SILBERNAGL (Eds.), Renal transport of organic substances, pp. 78–92, Springer, Berlin Heidelberg New York 1981
45. SCHNERMANN, J., BRIGGS, J.: Function of the Juxtaglomerular Apparatus: Local Control of Glomerular Hemodynamics. In D.W. SELDIN a. G. GIEBISCH (Eds.), The Kidney, Vol. I, pp. 669–697, Raven Press, New York 1985
46. SILBERNAGL, S.: Amino Acids and Oligopeptides. In D.W. SELDIN a. G. GIEBISCH (Eds.), The Kidney, Vol. II, pp. 1677–1702. Raven Press, New York 1985
47. STEINMETZ, P.R.: Epithelial Hydrogen Ion Transport. In D.W. SELDIN a. G. GIEBISCH (Eds.), The Kidney, Vol. II, pp. 1441–1458, Raven Press, New York 1985
48. STEPHENSON, J.L.: Central Core Model of the Renal Counterflow System. Kidney Int., *2*, 85–94 (1972)
49. SUTTON, R.A.L., QUAMME, G.A., DIRKS, J.H.: Transport of calcium, magnesium and inorganic phosphate in the kidney. In GIEBISCH (Ed.): Membrane transport in biology, pp. 357–412, Springer, Berlin Heidelberg New York 1979
50. TANNEN, R.L.: Control of acid excretion by the kidney. Ann. Rev. Med. *31*, 35–49 (1980)
51. TAYLOR, A., WINDHAGER, E.E.: Cytosolic Calcium and Its Role in the Regulation of Transepithelial Ion and Water Transport. In D.W. SELDIN a. G. GIEBISCH (Eds.), The Kidney, Vol. II, pp. 1297–1322, Raven Press, New York 1985
52. THOENES, W., LANGER, K.H.: Relationship between cell structure of renal tubules and transport mechanisms. In K. THURAU a. H. JAHRMÄRKER, (Eds.), Renal Transport and Diuretics. Berlin Heidelberg New York, Springer 1969

53. THURAU, K., MASON, J., GSTRAUNTHALER, G.: Experimental Acute Renal Failure. In D.W. SELDIN a. G. GIEBISCH (Eds.), The Kidney, Vol. II, pp. 1885–1899, Raven Press, New York 1985
54. THURAU, K., WOBER, E.: Zur Lokalisation der autoregulativen Widerstandsänderung in der Niere. Pflügers Arch. ges. Physiol., *274*, 553–566 (1963)
55. ULLRICH, K.J., FRÖMTER, E., MURER, H.: Prinzipien des epithelialen Transportes in Niere und Darm. Klin. Wschr. *57*, 977–992 (1979)
56. ULLRICH, K.J., GREGER, R.: Approaches to the Study of Tubule Transport Functions. In D.W. SELDIN a. G. GIEBISCH (Eds.), The Kidney, Vol. I, pp. 427–496, Raven Press, New York 1985
57. WEBER, P.C., SCHERER, B., SIESS, W., HELD, E., SCHNERMANN, F.: Formation and action of prostaglandins in the kidney. Klin. Wschr. *57*, 1021–1030 (1979)
58. WEINER, I.M.: Organic Acids and Basis and Uric Acid. In D.W. SELDIN a. G. GIEBISCH (Eds.), The Kidney, Vol. II, pp. 1703–1724, Raven Press, New York 1985
59. WINDHAGER, E.E., TAYLOR, A.: Regulatory role of intracellular calcium ions in epithelial Na transport. Ann. Rev. Physiol. *45*, 519–532 (1983)
60. WIRZ, H., HARGITAY, B., KUHN, W.: Lokalisation des Konzentrierungsprozesses in der Niere durch direkte Kryoskopie. Helv. physiol. pharmacol. Acta *9*, 196 (1951)

31 Water and Electrolyte Balance

P. DEETJEN

31.1 Water Balance

Water Intake and Excretion

Volume and distribution of the water in the body. Humans are composed mainly of water. The proportion of water is greatest, 75% of the body weight, in infancy. It falls to about 65% by the time growth has been completed, and in old age is only 55%.
The water is distributed among several fluid compartments (Fig. 31-1). 60% is within the cells **(intracellular space)**, and the rest is **extracellular** water, which is divided between the interstitial space and the blood plasma, and the so-called **transcellular** water in the cerebrospinal fluid, the chambers of the eye, the alimentary canal, the exocrine glands, the renal tubules and the urinary ducts.

Water balance. The body continually accumulates substances that must be excreted by way of the kidneys – about 1,200 mosmol per day, in a person on a normal diet. These include metabolic end products such as urea, creatinine or uric acid, as well as various ions such as ammonium, sulfate and phosphate, also derived predominantly from protein metabolism. Salts consumed in food in amounts greater than required must also be excreted. Because the kidneys are capable of producing urine as much as 4 times as concentrated as plasma, a daily volume of only 1 l of solution suffices to eliminate these substances. In addition to this *obligate water loss by way of the kidneys*, 100 ml of water are lost in the *feces*.
Finally, a not inconsiderable amount of water is lost as *"insensible" perspiration* (p. 631). This is water that leaves the skin unnoticeably by diffusion and evaporation, plus that in the expired air, which is saturated with water vapor. Insensible perspiration amounts to a little more than 0.5 ml per hour per kg body weight, or about 900 ml per day for a 70-kg human. Altogether, then, each day a person loses 2 l of water (Fig. 31-2), which must be replaced from external sources.
Only about half of this must be taken in by *drinking*. Almost an equal amount is supplied in solid food; like humans, the animals and plants that serve as our food are largely composed of water. There are, of course, great differences – for instance, between fat bacon (10%) and a ripe peach (95%) – but on average an ordinary mixed diet can be considered to have a water content of 60%. Finally, the *water of oxidation* produced during decomposition of the foodstuffs also enters into the balance. Each gram of carbohydrate oxidized in the body yields 0.6 g water. Fat, because of its relatively large hydrogen content, actually provides 1.0 ml water/g, whereas protein provides only 0.4 ml. Given a mixed diet, the overall yield of water from oxidation processes is about 300 ml per day. The balance diagrammed in Fig. 31-2 represents only the *minimal water turnover* under average living conditions. It can vary considerably, depending on circumstances. A diet low in salt and protein can cause the production of substances that must be excreted in the urine to decrease to about 200 mosmol/day,

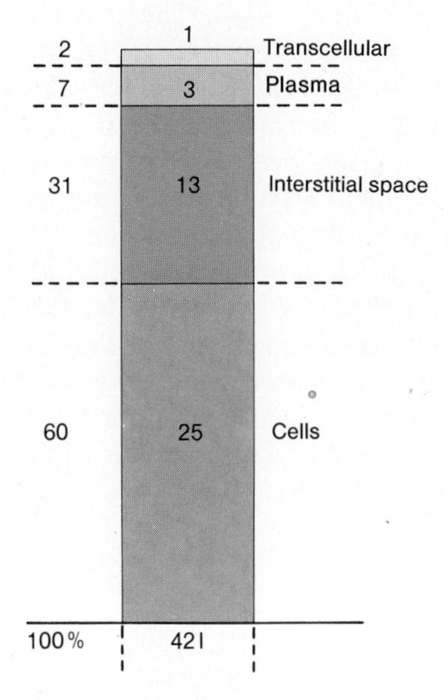

Fig. 31-1. Distribution of the total body water of an adult into the four different fluid spaces

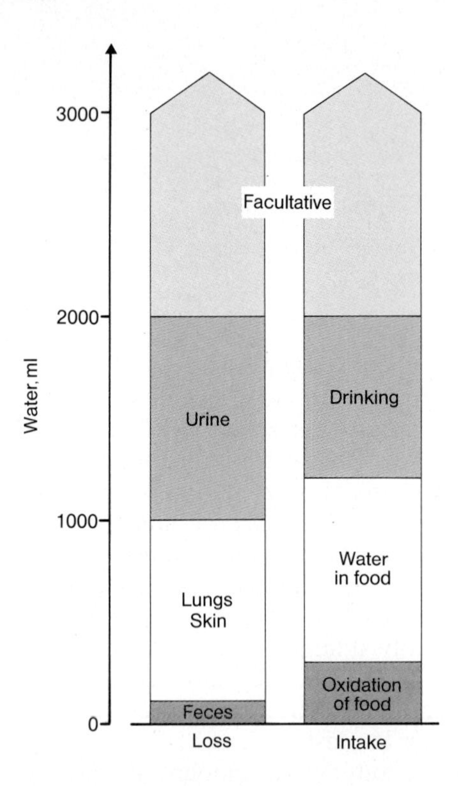

Fig. 31-2. Components of the daily water balance. A certain average water turnover is obligatory; the turnover can be considerably increased by drinking water in excess of the obligatory amount. If this extra consumption was not necessitated by extrarenal water losses (sweating, respiration, vomiting, diarrhea etc.), it is compensated by increased diuresis

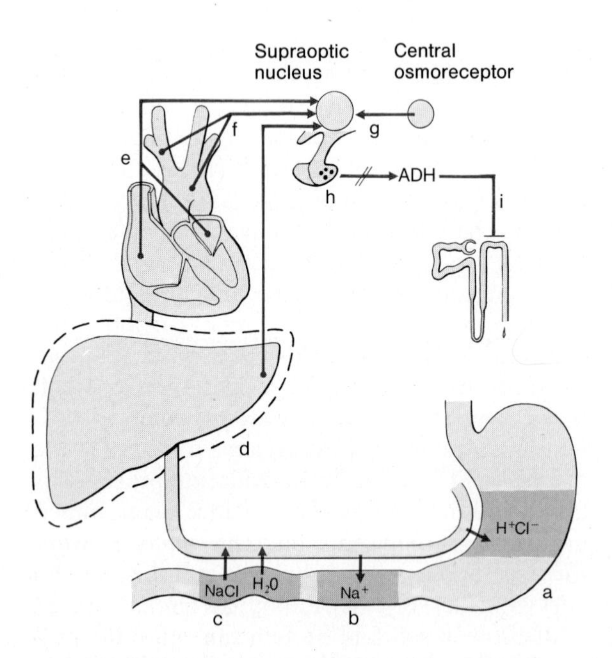

Fig. 31-3. Enteral water absorption and osmoregulation (*a-i:* see text)

so that the amount of water required to carry them in solution for excretion is also reduced to 1/6 and the minimal water intake required is less by about 40%.

On the other hand, when overheated the body can undergo considerable *water loss by sweating*. A person performing hard physical labor in extremely hot surroundings (e.g., working in a blast-furnace) can secrete sweat at a rate as high as 1.6 l/h, requiring the additional intake of as much as 20 l of water per day.

Water Reabsorption from the Intestine

The stomach and small intestine, together with their accessory glands, send *7–8 l of secretions* into the alimentary canal per day (p. 724). Even with a water turnover in the region of the obligate minimum, therefore, about 10 l must be reabsorbed enterally. Of this reabsorption, 2/3 occurs in the small intestine and the rest in the large intestine; only 1% of the water is excreted in the feces.

Even when *pure water is drunk*, only a small fraction is absorbed directly because of the osmotic gradient. There is a very rapid "conditioning", in which the contents of the canal are made *isotonic with the body fluids by an influx of osmotically effective substances*. This process begins in the stomach, with HCl secretion (Fig. 31-3a); the main ions that enter in the duodenum are Na^+ and HCO_3^- (Fig, 31-3b). Most of the water is taken up *in the jejunum by isotonic reabsorption*, involving a mechanism similar to that in the proximal convolution (p. 744). The driving force is the same, the electrochemical Na^+ gradient set up by active transport involving Na^+-K^+ ATPase. The coupling of enteral water reabsorption to an energy-requiring electrolyte transport may, at first glance, appear an unnecessary extravagance. However, it ensures that the *water uptake into the body is slow* and of long duration. If water not osmotically buffered were to enter the small intestine, which is extremely permeable to water, within seconds the water could enter the circulating blood and – if large amounts have been drunk – quite possibly overload the right heart and cause heart failure.

Regulation of Water Balance

Osmoregulation. The osmotic adjustment of water that has been drunk, to make it isotonic with the plasma, is a first response of the organism that simultaneously provides the signal for the next step. Because of the initial (slight) water influx, plus the subsequent outflow of Na^+ and Cl^- from the *portal blood*, the latter becomes *somewhat hypotonic* (Fig. 31-3a,b). It reaches the (isotonic) liver, which now acts as an osmometer and takes water into its cells (Fig. 31-3d). The water content of the liver can increase by as much as 30%. This *physiological hepatic swelling* excites **osmoreceptors** within the liver; the afferents from these cells run to the hypothalamus, where they *restrict the synthesis and release of* **ADH** (Fig. 31-3d).

The reduction in ADH activity results in the *onset of water diuresis* in the kidney (Fig. 31-3i), at a time when enteral water reabsorption is only just coming fully into operation. That is, the liver amounts to a first "outpost" in the homeostatic regulation of water balance.

It is not until the liver's capacity for maintaining a state of equilibrium is exhausted that the osmolarity of the arterial blood begins to fall. This situation is detected by extremely sensitive *osmoreceptors in the hypothalamus* itself (Fig. 31-3g), which respond to changes of as little as 2–3 mosmol/l. They enhance the inhibition of ADH, and bear the main responsibility for determining the duration and extent of water diuresis.

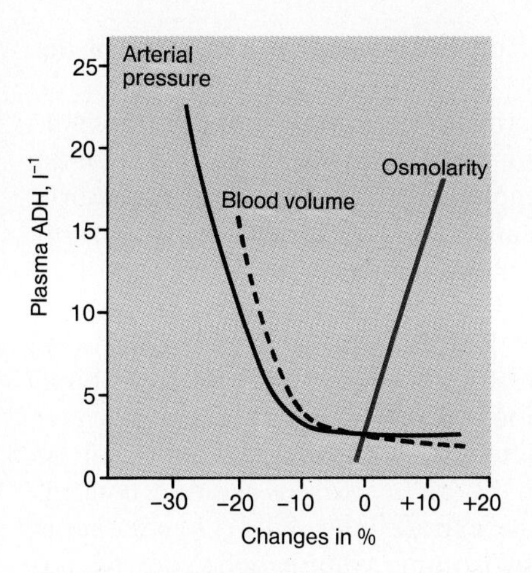

Fig. 31-4. Differential responses of ADH secretion to changes of extracellular osmolarity, blood volume and arterial pressure. (From [15])

Volume regulation. When liquid is consumed not as pure water but as an isotonic solution – for instance, a tastily salted soup – neither the peripheral nor the central osmoreceptors can detect the alteration in the body's water content. However, an increase in the amount of isotonic fluid in the extracellular space is detected by **volume receptors in the low-pressure region of the circulation** (Fig. 31-3e). These are very numerous in the wall of the large intrathoracic veins and expecially in the atria of the heart (p. 515). Their adequate stimulus is the stretching of the wall as the volume of fluid in the lumen increases. Signals from these receptors are conveyed to the supraoptic nucleus of the hypothalamus, where they (like the osmoreceptors) *inhibit ADH production*. However, the volume receptors are much less sensitive than the osmoreceptors (Fig. 31-4). Therefore they have less effect on ADH production, and it takes longer to excrete the isotonic solution and return to normal volume.

Volume loss produces a rather different situation. If the extracellular fluid has become more concentrated because of volume reduction due mainly to water loss (e.g., sweating of a heat-adapted person), the highly sensitive *central osmoreceptors* ensure *high ADH activity*, so that the kidney retains water as effectively as possible. The feeling of *thirst* produced at the same time induces sufficient water intake to restore normal volume and osmotic conditions.

The volume receptors are very insensitive to small decreases in volume (Fig. 31-4). But once the volume loss exceeds a critical threshold (more than 350 ml decrease in blood volume), there is an *exponential increase in the responsiveness of the volume receptors* and correspondingly high ADH production. If there is a distinct drop in blood pressure, this effect is reinforced by an ADH-stimulating action of the **baroreceptors** in the *aortic arch and carotid sinus* (p. 512) (Fig. 31-3f). These receptors, by way of synaptic relays in the nucleus of the tractus solitarius and the area postrema, respectively, also stimulate ADH production in the supraoptic nucleus. When there is an *acute danger of circulatory instability*, the water-regulation hierarchy changes; *volume regulation becomes dominant*, taking priority over osmoregulation. For instance, a person who loses considerable amounts of water and salt (e.g., due to blood loss or severe sweating by a non-adapted person) first replaces the lost volume by drinking water, even though the result may be a marked reduction in the extracellular sodium concentration and in osmotic pressure. In this situation the osmoreceptors are demanding that the release of ADH be stopped, but this demand can be overruled by the much stronger stimulus for ADH production that originates in the volume receptors and baroreceptors. It is more important to prevent the circulatory collapse threatened by the volume deficiency than to take action against the hyponatremia associated with dilution of the blood.

In the long term, however, the optimal extracellular fluid volume can be maintained only with an adequate supply of NaCl. Therefore regulation of NaCl balance (p. 748) is also an important element in volume regulation.

Thirst. Water loss amounting to about 0.5% of the body weight gives rise to a feeling of thirst. This sensation triggers a drive to drink water and has no tendency to adapt. Thirst can be elicited both by an increased osmotic concentration of the extracellular fluid *(hyperosmotic thirst)* and by isotonic volume deficiency *(hypovolemic thirst)*.

In the case of **hyperosmotic thirst** the triggering condition may be either an absolute water deficiency (caused, e.g., by sweating) or a relative water deficiency, which could be caused by eating food that contains too much NaCl (e.g., salt herring). The actual stimulus generated by this condition is thought to be the osmotic shrinkage of cells in the region of the *central osmoreceptors*, near the supraoptic nucleus of the hypothalamus [1] (Fig. 31-5). **Hypovolemic thirst** must be triggered by another mechanism, because isotonic volume loss (e.g., donation of blood) would not cause cells to shrink. There is much evidence that *angiotensin is the signal substance* [14]. An intravenous injection of angiotensin elicits thirst, and injection directly into the hypothalamus is considerably more effective. It is consistent with this finding that in cases of volume deficiency the *renin-angiotensin system* is activated (pp. 737f.) and the plasma concentration of angiotensin is elevated. Furthermore, the enzyme renin, which produces angiotensin, is present not only in the kidney but also in the brain, where it could play a local role in the physiological control of thirst.

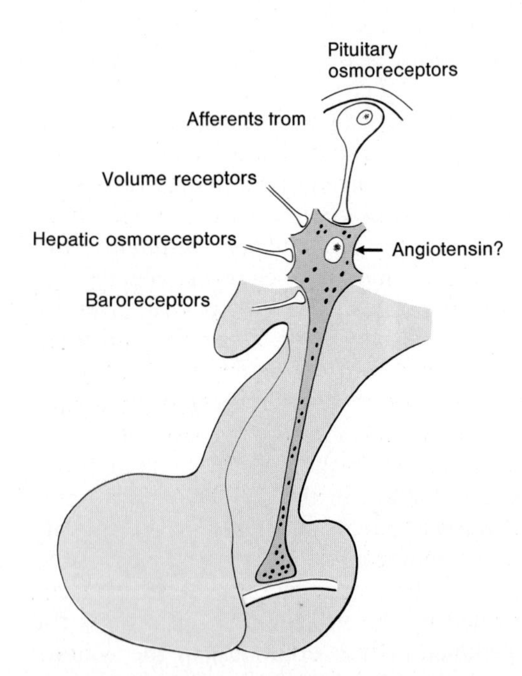

Fig. 31-5. Model of the osmotic and nonosmotic control of ADH production in neurons of the supraoptic and paraventricular nuclei of the hypothalamus

Fluid Compartments

Intracellular volume. As described above (p. 763), the body water is distributed among different compartments. The volume of each compartment is kept constant within a narrow range. The specific system for *regulation of the extracellular space*, discussed in the preceding section, is also largely responsible for *controlling the volume of the intracellular space.* The basic link here is the fact that the cell walls are permeable to water but impede the entrance of sodium (because of their low Na^+ permeability) and prevent its accumulation in the interior of the cell (by way of the Na^+-K^+ ATPase in the membrane, which actively transports Na^+ outward). That is, the cell membrane acts as a semipermeable membrane with respect to Na^+, the most important solute in the extracellular fluid. An increase in the extracellular Na^+ concentration raises the extracellular osmotic pressure and causes water to flow out of the cell, and a decrease has the opposite effect.

In principle, the *low Na^+ permeability of the cell wall* has the same effect as the impermeability of the cell membrane to the intracellular proteins. Both give rise to a *Donnan equilibrium* (p. 740), but in opposite directions. The extracellular Na^+ cancels out the osmotic force of the intracellular proteins, preventing cell swelling or increase of the intracellular hydrostatic pressure because of water influx. But because the cell membrane cannot completely prevent the passive influx of Na^+, the extracellular osmotic force due to sodium persists only as long as the Na^+ slowly entering the cell can be removed by the Na^+-K^+ pump. When the *active Na^+ transport is blocked* by poisons such as ouabain, or when the metabolic processes that provide energy for transport are stopped by O_2 deficiency, substrate depletion, cyanide poisoning or cold, then the flow of Na^+ into the cell continues until its intracellular concentration equals that in the extracellular fluid. At the same time, potassium can no longer be kept at the normal high concentration in the cell;

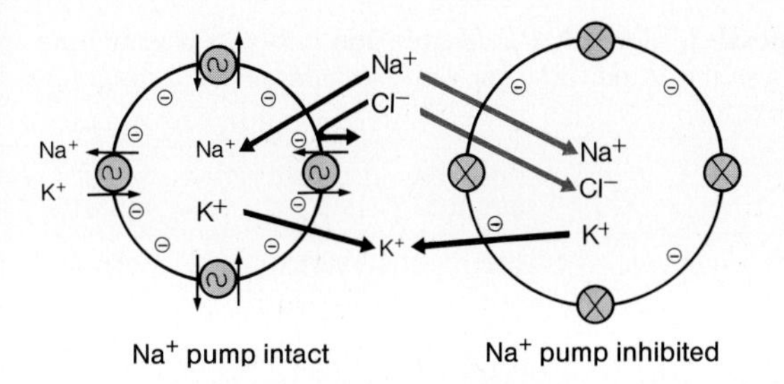

Fig. 31-6. Cellular volume regulation by means of the active Na^+-K^+ pump. Inhibition of the pump by metabolic poisons, O_2 deficiency or cold causes the cell to swell

as the K^+ concentration gradient between the interior and exterior declines, the electrical charge of the membrane is reduced, so that the membrane no longer acts as a barrier to the inflow of Cl^-. The NaCl entering the cell is followed by water, and *the cell swells* (Fig. 31-6).

Measurement of the fluid compartments. The water content of the body as a whole and that of the individual compartments can be determined by way of the *distribution of appropriate test substances.* If a known amount of a substance is introduced into a compartment of unknown volume and time is allowed for the substance to become uniformly distributed, the volume can be calculated from its final concentration. Because a concentration (C) is defined as the quantity (Q) of a substance in the available volume (V), C=Q/V, it follows that

$$V = \frac{Q}{C} \tag{1}$$

Substances suitable for determining **total body water** include *heavy water* (D_2O), *tritium-labeled water* (THO) or a substance to which the cell membrane is highly permeable, such as *antipyrine.* The size of the **extracellular space** can be measured with substances that easily pass through the capillary endothelium but cannot diffuse through cell membranes, such as *inulin* (p. 739) or *thiosulfate.* The **plasma volume** can be found with substances that bind tightly to the plasma albumins (e.g., *radioactive iodine,* ^{131}I, or a dye such as *Evans blue*) and are therefore retained within the vascular space. The **intracellular volume** can then be calculated as the difference between total body water and extracellular volume; the interstitial volume is the difference between the extracellular volume and the plasma volume. Because the distribution spaces of all these substances include the plasma, their con-

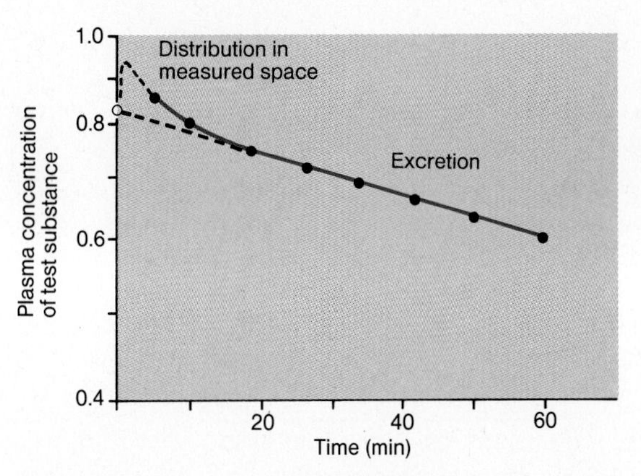

Fig. 31-7. Measurement of fluid spaces by means of a test substance injected at time 0. Each *point* represents the concentration of the substance found in a blood sample taken at the indicated time. The equilibrium concentration that would have been reached if the substance were not excreted is found by extrapolation of the excretion curve to the *ordinate*

centrations can be very simply determined from blood samples. The analysis is complicated by the fact that during the distribution time some fraction is excreted. In practice, therefore, a series of blood samples is taken beginning shortly after injection of the test substance; by analysis of these it is possible to extrapolate the equilibrium concentration that would have been reached if no excretion had occurred (Fig. 31-7).

Water content of individual organs. When a fluid compartment is measured with indicator-dilution methods, the result is an average value for the whole body. Individual organs, however, vary greatly in water content (Table 31-1). **Adipose tissue** has by far the *smallest proportion of water,* only 10%. The average for all the other body tissues, after the fat has been deducted, is 73% –

Table 31-1. Water content of individual organs. (From [16])

Organ	Water %	Body weight %	Amount of water in a human with 70 kg body weight kg
Blood	83.0	8.0	4.65
Kidneys	82.7	0.4	0.25
Heart	79.2	0.5	0.28
Lungs	79.0	0.7	0.39
Spleen	75.8	0.2	0.10
Muscle	75.6	41.7	22.10
Brain	74.8	2.0	1.05
Intestine	74.5	1.8	0.94
Skin	72	18.0	9.07
Skeleton	22	15.9	2.45
Adipose tissue	10	10–50	0.70

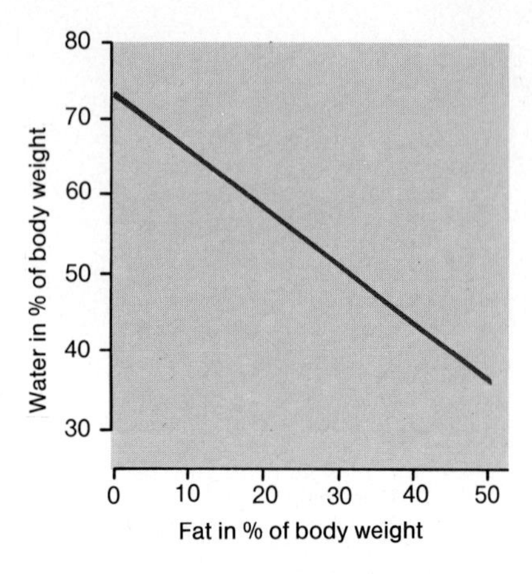

Fig. 31-8. Relation between the proportions of fat and of water in the body. (From [13])

Table 31-2. Electrolyte concentration in blood plasma and intracellular fluid. (Plasma values include normal range of variation)

	Plasma mmol/l		Cell mmol/l
Na^+	142	(130–155)	10
K^+	4	(3.2 –5.5)	155
Ca^{2+}	2.5	(2.1 –2.9)	<0.001[a]
Mg^{2+}	0.9	(0.7 –1.5)	15
Cl^-	102	(96 –110)	8
HCO_3^-	25	(23 –28)	10
HPO_4^{2-}	1	(0.7 –1.6)	65[b]
SO_4^{2-}	0.5	(0.3 –0.9)	10
Organic acids	4		2
Proteins	2		6

[a] Free Ca^{2+} in cytosol
[b] Including organic phosphates

not only in humans but also in other full-grown mammals. This value can be used to find the proportion of fat in the body from the measured total body water, as follows:

$$\% \text{ body fat} = 100 - \frac{\% \text{ body water}}{0.73} \quad (2)$$

This relation is plotted in Fig. 31-8. From that diagram one can see that in a young adult with a total water content amounting to 65% of the body weight, normally about 10% will consist of fat deposits. In the obese it is quite possible for adipose tissue to account for 50% of the body weight, in which case the water content of the body is only 37%.

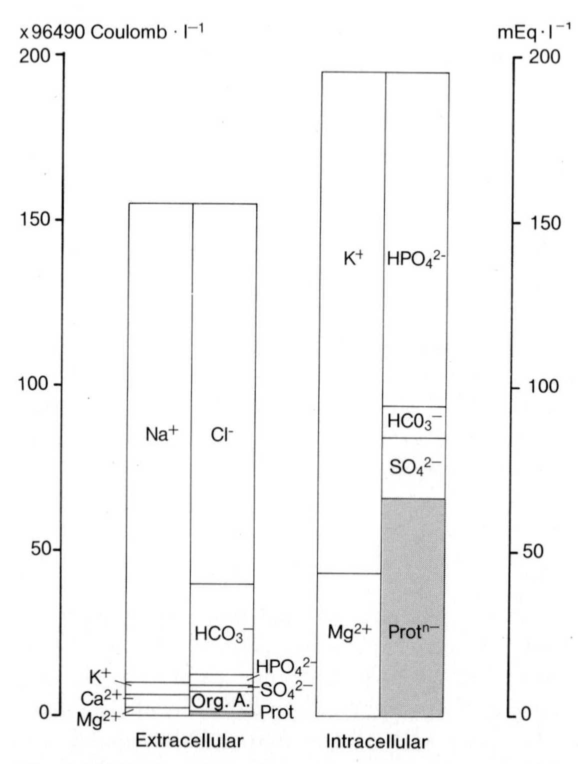

Fig. 31-9. Ionic composition of extra- and intracellular fluid

31.2 Electrolyte Balance

As explained above, the fluid spaces are regulated by way of electrolyte transport. The water and electrolyte balances are therefore functionally inseparable.

Electrolyte Concentrations

Extra- and intracellular concentrations. The osmotic pressures in the extracellular and intracellular fluids are identical under equilibrium conditions. However, the concentrations of the individual electrolytes differ quite considerably (Table 31-2). Because the various fluid compartments differ in protein concentration, the differences in electrolyte concentration are partly imposed by the Gibbs-Donnan equilibrium (p. 740). But a much stronger influence is exerted by the continual activity of the Na^+-K^+ ATPase in the cell membranes, which ensures that the *Na^+ ions* dominating the extracellular space are kept at a low concentration inside the cell, and that in their place potassium is accumulated in high concentrations. The intracellular concentration of *magnesium*, though distinctly lower than that of K^+, is still considerable. Among the anions, *Cl^- and HCO_3^-* are predominant extracellularly

and *phosphate ions*, intracellularly. Both in the plasma and in the cell the cations and anions are in equilibrium; that is, the total numbers of positive and of negative charges are always equal. This electroneutrality is not discernible from the molar concentrations (Table 31-2), because of the presence of polyvalent charge carriers, especially within the cell. To clarify the situation, Fig. 31-9 shows the molar concentrations in terms of equivalents (see below).
The bivalent ions and, to an even greater extent, the polyvalent proteins make a great contribution to the charge equilibrium. At the pH of the body fluids, the proteins are present as polyanions with an average of 10 negative charges per molecule. As shown in Fig. 31-9, the different distribution of mono- and polyvalent electrolytes causes the electrical charge density in the cell to be about 20% higher than in the extracellular fluid, even though the osmotic concentrations are the same in the extra- and intracellular fluids.

Electrochemical equivalent. A monovalent cation or anion transports an elementary charge of $1.6 \cdot 10^{-19}$ coulombs (C). One mol of a monovalent electrolyte thus corresponds to $1.6 \cdot 10^{-19} \cdot 6.06 \cdot 10^{23} = 96,490$ C. This number is called the electrochemical equivalent or 1 faraday (F). The equivalent concentration is then calculated as

$$\text{Concentration} \cdot \text{valence} = \text{mol} \cdot \text{l}^{-1} \cdot \text{F} \cdot \text{mol}^{-1} = \text{F} \cdot \text{l}^{-1} \quad (3)$$

It used to be customary to give all electrolyte concentrations as equivalent concentrations in the units mEq/l. Since the introduction of SI units this practice should be abandoned in favor of molar concentrations, particularly in view of the difficulty often encountered in specifying equivalents precisely (e.g., because of pH-dependent or even concentration-dependent differences in degree of dissociation).

Sodium and Potassium Balance

Sodium. A 70-kg human contains a total of 4,200 mmol of sodium. Only ca. 2.5% of that is in the cells. About 1/3 of the sodium is firmly incorporated in the crystalline structure of the bone and cannot be exchanged. The remainder is in *diffusion equilibrium with the plasma sodium*, permitting the compensation of short-term losses of sodium such as result from profuse sweating in one who is not heat-adapted or from diarrhea. Under the dietary and general living conditions in Central Europe, a person's daily sodium intake averages 160 mmol/day, which corresponds to 5% of the exchangeable sodium. This turnover rate is evidently unphysiologically high and is probably one of the causes of the prevalence of high blood pressure in the industrialized countries. In populations living under primitive conditions, in which this disease is rarely encountered, the sodium turnover is lower by more than half.

Potassium. In contrast to sodium, almost the entire K^+ content of the body, about 3,300 mmol, is freely exchangeable. Only about 2.5% of the total K^+ is in the extracellular space. Because *extracellular losses* (e.g., by diarrhea or overuse of laxatives and diuretics, or in acidosis) are always *rapidly compensated from the intracellular space*, the potassium concentration in the extracellular space often varies very little over long periods. For this reason, a critical K^+ deficiency with the threat of cardiovascular and neuromuscular disturbances can easily be overlooked in routine examinations if only the plasma K^+ concentration is tested.

Calcium and Phosphate Balance

Calcium. Calcium is an important component of bones and teeth, and because of the great mass of the skeleton it is the *most abundant cation in the body*, with 28 mol/70 kg body weight. Only 1/100 of the body calcium is found in the extracellular fluid; of this amount, about half is present as ions and half bound, 5-10% to organic acids and the rest to proteins. The intracellular calcium concentration is 10^{-7} mol/l, about 4 orders of magnitude below the extracellular concentration.
For many cells a change in the intracellular Ca^{2+} concentration is the *signal for important functional changes* [17]. For example, Ca^{2+} controls the excitation-contraction coupling in muscles (pp. 66ff.), influences the Na^+ conductance of excitable cells (pp. 27f.) and of many nonexcitable cells, increases the K^+ conductance of cell membranes, affects ion pumps, enables the release of transmitters at synapses (pp. 54f.), stimulates the secretory activity of exocrine glands, triggers the release of hormones, plays a role in several phases of blood clotting (pp. 419ff.), and regulates the activity of enzymes.
The intracellular Ca^{2+} concentration is kept very low by ion pumps in the cell membrane (pp. 10 and 748). Because of the steep concentration gradient so produced, even slight changes in membrane permeability lead to distinct changes in the amount of intracellular calcium. Such permeability changes are usually triggered by extracellular agents such as hormones. The magnitude of the

calcium influx into the cell is determined by the extracellular calcium concentration as well as by the amount of hormone or transmitter present. Therefore the precision of molecular processes in the cell is critically dependent on the *constancy of the extracellular calcium-ion concentration.* Not surprisingly, there are several elaborate mechanisms to ensure this constancy, a regulatory system rivaled only by that governing hydrogen-ion concentration.

Phosphate. Many molecules of metabolic significance are phosphates (e.g., ATP, cAMP, creatine phosphate, DNA, and phospholipids). However, the intracellular amounts of these substances and the reactions in which they are involved are hardly affected even by wide fluctuations in the concentration of phosphate in the extracellular space. Therefore the extracellular phosphate concentration is less accurately regulated than that of calcium; one consequence is that, if necessary, phosphate can be employed for the elimination of H^+ (p. 752). Most of the phosphate in the body is located in the bone, partly as amorphous calcium phosphate, but mainly in the form of hydroxyapatite crystals.

Regulation of calcium phosphate balance. The *bones* are the most important reservoir from which, when the extracellular calcium concentration falls, *calcium phosphate can be mobilized* at any time. The most rapid and effective mechanism for this mobilization involves **PTH** (see also pp. 750f.), the hormone of the parathyroid gland (Fig. 31-10). Its release is triggered by *hypocalcemia*; in the bone it stimulates the osteoclasts to secrete organic acids (citric, lactic or succinic acid), which dissolve the alkaline apatite and set free calcium and phosphate ions. The effect is optimized by two simultaneous actions of the parathyroid hormone on the kidney: it enhances Ca^{2+} reabsorption in the distal tubule (p. 748), preventing loss in the urine, and lowers the threshold for phosphate (p. 750) in the proximal tubule, so that more phosphate is excreted. It is important that PTH has *opposite effects* on calcium and phosphate. The solubility product of calcium phosphate is quite low, and if the concentrations of both partners were to increase, there would soon be a risk of ectopic precipitation; that is, calcium phosphate could form concretions outside the bone (p. 756). The renal elimination of phosphate avoids this danger and, indeed, is a prerequisite for a maintained increase in the extracellular concentration

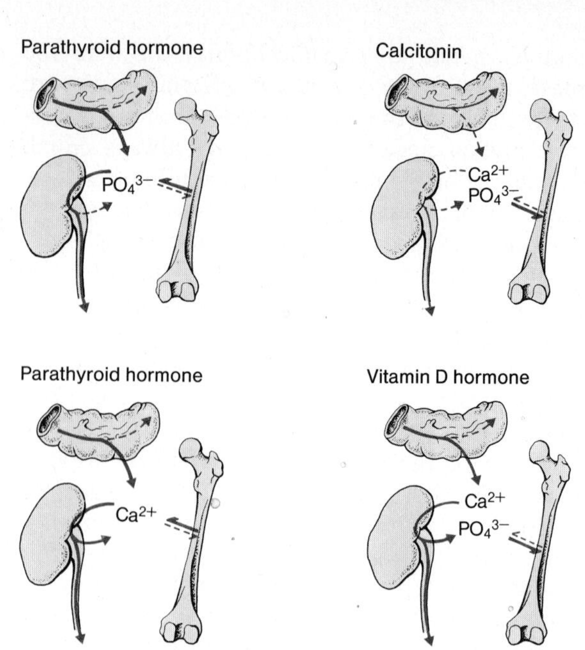

Fig. 31-10. Action of the calcium-phosphate-regulating hormones on kidney, intestine and bone. (From [5])

of ionized calcium. Furthermore, the mobilization of strongly alkaline calcium phosphate from the bones would threaten the *acid-base balance.* The development of metabolic alkalosis is prevented by still another action of PTH, to *inhibit the carbonic anhydrase* in the brush border of the proximal tubule and thereby force the excretion of bicarbonate.

In the long term, however, the highly effective and rapid regulation of the extracellular concentration of ionized calcium by PTH would cause demineralization of the bone. Another mechanism, also involving parathyroid hormone, operates to prevent this outcome; during the brief time when PTH itself is active (half life ca. 10 min) it initiates a long-term stabilization of the calcium phosphate balance by activating **vitamin D hormone** (p. 396). The precursors of vitamin D hormone are derived from food (vitamin D) or synthesized in skin and liver. Conversion to the active vitamin D hormone (1,25-dihydroxycholecalciferol) occurs in the liver and kidneys. The influence of this hormone is exerted to some extent within the kidney itself, where it enhances the *reabsorption of calcium and phosphate.* But its main action is to induce certain effector proteins in the intestine, which enable the long-term *reabsorption of calcium phosphate* whenever food containing it is consumed. Vitamin D hormone also ensures that this calcium phosphate is *incorporated into the bones.*

A third hormone with a specific role in this regulatory process is **calcitonin** (Fig. 31-10). It is released from the thyroid gland under the stimulus of *hypercalcemia* (p. 395) and acts to *reduce the plasma concentrations of calcium and phosphate.* It does so by promoting mineralization of the bone and simultaneously inhibiting the renal and enteral reabsorption of both substances.

31.3 Generalized Disturbances of Water and Electrolyte Balance

The many factors that can upset the equilibrium of water and electrolytes in the body can more readily be surveyed by classifying the various states of imbalance systematically, as follows. If more water is lost than is consumed, the result is a **negative water balance** with *dehydration.* In the opposite situation, with the accumulation of excess water in the body, the **positive water balance** leads to a volume increase and *hyperhydration.* Because the uptake and loss of water and electrolytes always occur by way of the extracellular space, the next level of classification is based primarily on the changes that appear in the extracellular space. The reference point is the normal osmotic concentration of the extracellular fluid, about 290 mosmol/l (p. 757), called the *isotonic* concentration. A lower osmolarity is a *hypotonic* disturbance, and a higher osmolarity is *hypertonic.* The water balance and osmolarity criteria combine to give 6 possible kinds of departure from the equilibrium state.

Dehydration

Isotonic dehydration. This condition always develops when isotonic fluid is lost. There can be either a *loss of extracellular fluid* (bleeding or the seepage of interstitial fluid and plasma from extensive burns) or an excessive *loss of transcellular fluid* (by diarrhea, prolonged vomiting, sweating in someone not adapted to heat, or the use of strong saluretics). Because the relative osmotic concentrations in the extra- and intracellular spaces are unchanged, the latter is not affected. The clinical picture is determined by the abnormally low plasma volume *(hypovolemia)*, which causes circulatory malfunctions (tachycardia, a drop in blood pressure, and a tendency to collapse that can progress to hypovolemic shock).

Hypotonic dehydration. If the thirst produced by isotonic volume loss (see above) is quenched by drinking water alone, only part of this water can be retained in the extracellular space, and the circulatory symptoms persist. The osmolarity of the extracellular fluid has been reduced, producing an osmotic gradient along which *water is taken into the cells.* Symptoms of cell swelling are especially pronounced in the brain, where the increased tissue pressure can cause headache, vomiting, apathy and clouded consciousness or even convulsions and coma.

Hypertonic dehydration. This condition appears, for example, in mountain climbers at high altitudes, where two factors operate: the thirst mechanism no longer functions properly, probably because of cerebral O_2 deficiency, and during hyperventilation in the cold, dry air large amounts of water are lost in the expired breath. A heat-adapted person sweating heavily can also experience this form of dehydration. An increased *action of aldosterone* (p. 747) on the ducts of the sweat glands causes the secretion of a Na^+-poor, hypotonic sweat, so that the water deficit is very much greater than the sodium deficit. The same situation arises in *diabetes insipidus* (p. 748) because of the lack of ADH control, which results in the continual excessive excretion of hypotonic urine. *Diabetes mellitus* presents a similar picture; in this case, the increased excretion of glucose causes osmotic diuresis. Although the urine so produced is isotonic, its osmotically effective constituents comprise mainly glucose and only a little sodium.

In hypertonic dehydration both the extra- and intracellular spaces are diminished. To the symptoms of hypovolemia (see above) are added signs of cellular dehydration, including a reduced flow of saliva, lowered skin turgor, dry mucous membranes and a rise in temperature.

Hyperhydration

Isotonic hyperhydration. An increased retention of water and salt in isotonic proportions leaves the osmotic situation unchanged. Therefore the only effect is an *expansion of the extracellular space*, with no change in intracellular volume. In addition to an enlarged plasma volume, with correspondingly enlarged blood volume *(hyper-*

volemia), the increase in amount of interstitial fluid produces generalized *edema.* The condition can be caused by mechanical factors such as an *increased hydrostatic pressure* in cardiac insufficiency or portal hypertension, or a *decreased oncotic pressure* in cirrhosis of the liver or nephrotic syndrome. But *inadequate sodium excretion* can also result in edema, because the sodium retains sufficient water to maintain isotonicity. This situation arises, for instance, in renal insufficiency and hyperaldosteronism or under the increased influence of other hormones and substances with a Na^+-retaining action (contraceptives, antirheumatics and so on).

Hypotonic hyperhydration. This disorder occurs when renal water excretion is inadequate (e.g., in severe cardiac insufficiency or acute renal failure) and excessive amounts of water are taken in either by drinking or, for example, as a glucose infusion. A state of *"water intoxication"* develops. Because of the osmotic gradient between extra- and intracellular space, the *cells swell*; again, the clinical picture is dominated by symptoms of increased brain pressure (see above).

Hypertonic hyperhydration. This rare disorder can result, for instance, from *infusion of hypertonic NaCl or sodium bicarbonate solution.* Such a condition can also be temporarily produced when shipwrecked people drink sea water. But because the salt content of the oceans is higher than the greatest NaCl concentration that can be excreted in the urine, to eliminate the excess salt the body's own water must be depleted; therefore the hypertonic hyperhydration very soon gives way to hypertonic dehydration.

31.4 References

Textbooks and Handbooks

1. ANDERSEN, B.: Regulation of water intake. Physiol. Rev. *58*, 528 (1978)
2. BRENNER, B.M., RECTOR, F.C. (Eds.): The Kidney, Vol. I and II. W.B. Sanders Co., Philadelphia 1976
3. DEETJEN, P., BOYLAN, J.W., KRAMER, K.: Physiology of the Kidney and of Water Balance, Springer Verlag, New York 1975
4. GAMBLE, J.L.: Chemical Anatomy, Physiology and Pathology of Extracellular Fluids. Harvard University Press, Cambridge Mass., 1954
5. LANG, F.: Pathophysiologie und Pathobiochemie. 2. Aufl., Ferdinand Enke Verlag, Stuttgart 1979
6. LANG, F., DEETJEN, P., REISSIGL, H.: Wasser- und Elektrolythaushalt. Hdb. d. Infusionstherapie Bd.I. S. Karger, Basel 1984
7. PITTS, R.F.: Physiology of the Kidney and Body Fluids, Year Book Med. Publ. Chicago 1963
8. SARRE, H.J., GESSLER, H. (Hrsg.): Nierenkrankheiten. 5. Aufl., Georg Thieme Verlag, Stuttgart 1986
9. SELDIN, D.W., GIEBISCH, G. (Eds.): The Kidney, Physiology and Pathophysiology, Vol. I and II. Raven Press, New York 1985
10. SIEGENTHALER, W. (Ed.): Klinische Pathophysiologie. 5. Aufl., Georg Thieme Verlag, Stuttgart 1982
11. VALTIN, H.: Renal Function: Mechanisms Preserving Fluid and Solute Balance in Health. Little, Brown and Co., Boston 1973

Original Papers and Reviews

12. ANDERSSON, B., RUNDGREN, M.: Thirst and its disorders. Ann. Rev. Med. *33*, 231–239 (1982)
13. BEHNKE, A.R.: Physiologic studies pertaining to deep sea diving and aviation, especially in relation to fat content and composition of the body. Harvey Lectures *37*, 198 (1941/42)
14. FITZSIMONS, J.T.: Physiology and Pathology of Thirst and Sodium Appetite. In SELDIN, D.W. and GIEBISCH, G. (Eds.), The Kidney, Vol. II, pp. 885–902, Raven Press, New York 1985
15. ROBERTSON, G.L.: Diseases of the posterior pituitary. In P. FILING et al. (Ed.), Endocrinology and Metabolism, pp. 251–277, McGraw-Hill, New York 1981
16. SKELETON, H.: The storage of water by various tissues of the body. Arch. Int. Med. *40*, 140 (1972)
17. TAYLOR, A., WINDHAGER, E.E.: Cytosolic Calcium and its Role in the Regulation of Transepithial Ion and Water Transport. In SELDIN, D.W. and GIEBISCH, G. (Eds.), The Kidney, Vol. II, pp. 1297–1322, Raven Press, New York 1985

IX
Reproduction, Pregnancy and Aging

32 Sexual Functions

W. Wuttke

32.1 Sexual Differentiation

Development of the gonads. To understand the physiology and pathophysiology of sexual functions, one should first know how the gamete-producing glands – the ovary and testis – develop in the fetus. The gonads are derived from two different tissues. The somatic *mesenchymal tissue* forms the matrix of the gonads, whereas the *primordial germ tissue* later gives rise to the gametes. The primordial germ tissue migrates into the matrix of mesenchymal tissue in about the third week of pregnancy. At this time it is not yet possible to distinguish male from female gonads; that is, they are still in the indifferent stage.

In about the sixth week of gestation, when the migration of the germ cells has been completed, in genetically male embryos (those with Y chromosomes) vigorous proliferation of the gonadal tissue begins. The *spermatozoa* will eventually develop from the primary germ tissue, and the *Sertoli cells* and *Leydig's interstitial cells*, from the mesenchymal tissue. At this early stage the testes are already clearly identifiable histologically. The female gonads are still relatively undifferentiated at this stage; the primordial germ cells are still proliferating by mitosis, while the *granulosa cells* are developing from the mesenchymal tissue. Later, the primordial germ cells mature to form *oocytes*, and these, surrounded by granulosa cells, constitute the *primordial follicle*.

For a gonad to differentiate in the male direction, a Y chromosome must be present; in the absence of a Y chromosome, female gonads develop. To develop normally, however, they require two X chromosomes. Individuals with *Turner's syndrome* have only one X chromosome and in these, although ovaries develop, the primordial germ cells do not complete their differentiation (a form of *ovarian dysgenesis*). In summary, both X chromosomes are necessary for normal ovarian development, whereas a Y chromosome stimulates testicular development.

Sexual differentiation of the internal genitalia. No endocrine activity is required for the female genitalia to continue to develop, but differentiation of the male structures is induced by two hormones produced in the embryonic testes. The Leydig's cells secrete *androgens*, and the Sertoli cells produce a protein hormone called the *Müllerian duct-inhibiting factor*. The internal genitalia develop from two different primordial structures, the Wolffian duct and the Müllerian duct, both of which are present in each gonad of the early fetus. Androgens *stimulate the Wolffian duct*, causing it to develop into the epididymis, the vas deferens and the seminal vesicle. The Müllerian duct-inhibiting factor causes *regression of the Müllerian duct*. In female fetuses the Wolffian ducts degenerate and the Müllerian ducts develop into the oviducts, the uterus, the cervix and parts of the upper vagina.

Animal experiments have shown that early castration of male fetuses causes female differentiation of the internal genitalia. That is, without androgens the Wolffian duct is not stimulated into development, and because the Müllerian duct-inhibiting factor is absent, the Müllerian ducts develop into the female internal genitalia. This result makes clear that the ovaries play no active role in normal development of the female genitalia.

Sexual differentiation of the external genitalia. In the female fetus the urethral folds do not close but remain as the *labia minora*, and the paired labioscrotal swellings become the *labia majora*; the genital tubercle forms the *clitoris*. Like the internal genitalia, these develop independently of the ovaries. For the indifferent structures to develop into male external genitalia, androgens are required. In their presence, the urethral folds fuse to enclose the urethra, and the labioscrotal swellings close to form the *scrotum*. The genital tubercle grows under the influence of androgens and becomes the *penis*.

During embryogenesis the gonads, originally next to the kidneys, migrate caudally. The ovaries remain in the true pelvis, and the testes descend into the scrotum, surrounded by a membrane that duplicates the peritoneum. There are extremely important physiological reasons for the testes to lie within the scrotum; it is only at the relatively *low temperature* prevailing in this external structure that *normal testosterone production and spermatogenesis* are possible. It can happen that the testes fail to descend into the scrotum and remain in the abdominal cavity. In children with undescended testes, or *cryptorchidism*, normal testicular function does not develop, because the temperature in the abdominal cavity is too high.

Pathophysiological aspects. In the syndrome called *testicular feminization*, genetic males (i.e., individuals with the XY genotype) have a receptor defect that makes the fetal external genitalia resistant to the action of androgens. Such fetuses develop normal male internal genitalia, testes capable of producing androgens and Müllerian inhibiting factor. But because of the defective androgen receptors, the external genitalia develop in the female direction.
Just the opposite disorder can affect genetically female fetuses in which the adrenals produce *no cortisol*. Because there is no feedback effect of cortisol on ACTH secretion, the fetus produces large amounts of ACTH, which stimulates steroid secretion in the adrenals. The adrenal glands metabolize these steroids to form androgens (p. 389), which cause virilization of the external genitalia. Because these fetuses have no Y chromosome, they develop normal ovaries, and in the absence of Müllerian inhibiting factor the Müllerian duct develops into female internal genitalia. This combination of female internal organs with external genitalia of masculine appearance is the *adrenogenital syndrome* (see also p. 389).

Sexual differentiation of the CNS. The brains of males and females also exhibit morphological differences. Under the influence of the male sex hormones the fetal brain is masculinized. It has been shown that patients with the *adrenogenital syndrome* who were discovered to be genetically female soon after birth, so that they were raised as girls, in later life have physiological and behavioral traits that demonstrate such masculinization. A brain not influenced by androgens during embryonic development remains feminine.

32.2 Hormonal Regulation of Gonadal Functions

The functions of the reproductive organs of men and women depend on hormonal regulatory processes. Sexual behavior is also influenced by hormones, to a certain degree. For these reasons the sex hormones are crucial to survival of the species, even though they are not necessary for survival of an individual. Both sexes produce both male and female sex hormones, but in different amounts.

Release and action of the gonadotropins. The pituitary hormones involved in reproduction are **follicle-stimulating hormone (FSH)** and **luteinising hormone (LH)** (p. 379). Both of these are glycoproteins composed of two subunits. Their structure is identical in men and women. It was once thought that in men Leydig's interstitial cells were stimulated by a pituitary hormone with a structure differing from that of LH, which was called *interstitial-cell-stimulating hormone (ICSH)*, but now the two are known to be chemically the same, and only the term LH is used. As far as is known at present, both FSH and LH are released in response to a hypothalamic *releasing hormone*, called **LHRH** or *gonadotropin-releasing hormone (GnRH)*. It is a decapeptide and is now available in synthetic form for diagnostic and therapeutic purposes [10, 19]. LHRH is formed in hypothalamic neurons, the axons of which terminate on the portal vessels in the median eminence. These hypothalamic LHRH neurons have special neurophysiological properties. In sexually mature individuals they discharge phasically, in synchrony with one another, so that they all release their decapeptide simultaneously into the portal vascular system [2, 3]. This *phasically synchronized activation of the LHRH neurons* is essential for normal hypophyseal secretion of FSH and LH [13, 17]. In both sexes, the two gonadotropic hormones FSH and LH stimulate the gonads to *synthesize and release the sex hormones*. All the sex hormones are steroids. The *androgens* are the main products of the male gonads, under the influence of LH. In the woman, FSH stimulates *follicle growth* and *estrogen production*, and LH stimulates the release of *progestins* in the ovary.

Sex steroids. These, like all steroid hormones, are derived from *cholesterol*. The first step is the formation of pregnenolone and progesterone in the gonads, by the side-chain cleaving enzyme system. **Progesterone** is the most important hormone of the *corpus luteum*, which synthesizes and releases it in relatively large amounts during the second half of the menstrual cycle. Considerably larger quantities of progesterone are produced by the *placenta* during pregnancy.
In other steroid-producing cells of the gonads, progesterone appears only as an intermediate in the synthesis of androgens or estrogens. The pathway is diagrammed in Fig. 32-1. The most important testicular androgen is **testosterone**,

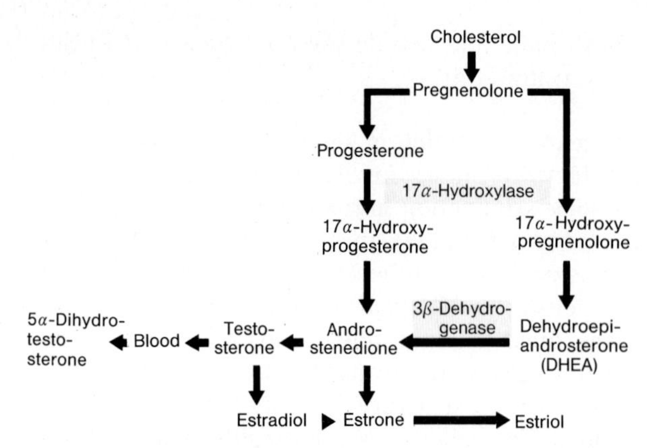

Fig. 32-1. Synthesis pathways of the gonadal steroid hormones. Testosterone circulating in the blood is reduced to 5-α-dihydrotestosterone (5-α-DHT) in certain target organs (seminal vesicles, prostate, cutaneous sebaceous glands and hair follicles)

which is synthesized by the *interstitial cells* and released into the blood. In some cases (e.g., in the CNS) testosterone acts directly on the cells of the target organ, but in others the active hormone is formed within the cells of the target organ by reduction of testosterone at position 5. For instance, the androgenic action on the pattern of hair distribution and on the sebaceous glands occurs by way of 5-α-dihydrotestosterone (5-α-DHT). The active androgen at the accessory sex glands (prostate, seminal vesicle) is also 5-α-DHT.

In the ovaries, *estrogens* are produced and released by the follicle cells prior to ovulation. The most important and most physiologically active estrogen is **estradiol-17-β**. Estrogens can be derived from androgens, by aromatization at the A ring of the androgen and cleavage of a methyl residue.

A major fraction of all the sex hormones in the blood is associated with plasma protein by noncovalent bonding. There is a *sex-hormone-binding globulin* (*SHBG*, see p. 777) with a relatively high affinity for estrogens and androgens. Only the free steroid hormones, not bound to transport proteins, are active.

32.3 Hormonal Regulation of Male Sexual Functions

Regulation of Gonadal Function in the Man

The LHRH neurons in the male hypothalamus release their secretory product simultaneously, at 2- to 4-hour intervals [6]. In many men *LHRH pulses*, and hence *LH and FSH pulses* occur more often at night and in the early morning. As a result, there is a distinct diurnal fluctuation of the testosterone level, which is directly correlated with the level of LH circulating in the blood. In experiments with reversal of sleep phase and in studies of shift workers it has been shown that the secretion of LH and testosterone is determined by sleeping habits and not by the time of day.

LH stimulates the interstitial cells to increase their *androgen production*. Intratesticular androgens are necessary for normal spermatogenesis [2, 5]; the most important of these is *testosterone*. Testosterone also enters the general blood circulation, reaching the pituitary and CNS by this route. There it provides *negative feedback*, suppressing the activity of the LH- and LHRH-producing cells. Castration (removal of the testes) greatly reduces the amount of testosterone in circulation. The low testosterone level is signaled to the hypothalamic LHRH-producing neurons by androgen-sensitive neurons, and as a consequence more LHRH is released. At the same time

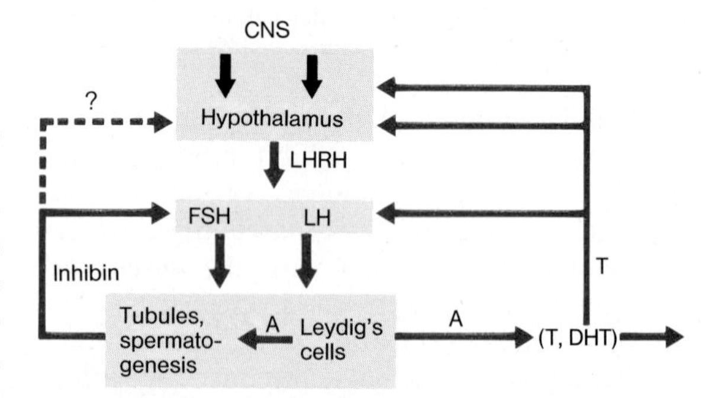

Fig. 32-2. Hypothalamic-pituitary-testicular control system. LHRH neurons in the hypothalamus release their decapeptide into the portal vessels; it stimulates the secretion of LH and FSH. The LH stimulates Leydig's interstitial cells to produce more androgens, which feed back to the pituitary and hypothalamus, closing the circuit. In the convoluted tubules of the testes, spermatogenesis is induced by FSH. At the same time, the Sertoli cells of the tubules release the peptide inhibin, which travels to the pituitary in the bloodstream and there selectively inhibits FSH secretion. It is not clear whether inhibin also feeds back to the hypothalamus. The androgens produced by the Leydig's cells under the influence of LH are also essential for normal spermatogenesis in the tubules. The main testicular androgen is testosterone (T). In the cells of peripheral target organs (cutaneous structures, prostate, seminal vesicles etc.), testosterone is ineffective until it has been reduced to 5-α-dihydrotestosterone (DHT). DHT has no feedback action on the pituitary or hypothalamus. Testosterone-receptive neurons are also present in limbic structures in which sexual and aggressive behavior are stimulated by testosterone

the hypophyseal gonadotropin-producing cells become more sensitive to the phasically released LHRH. The result is an increased *LH production* with an especially conspicuous pulsatile pattern. The *secretion of FSH* in the pituitary is also augmented. After administration of testosterone in physiological doses, however, only the LH level is reduced. On the basis of this finding and other pathophysiological and biochemical observations, it has been postulated that the testes produce a peptidergic factor that selectively inhibits FSH secretion, presumably by acting at a site in the pituitary. The hormones with this effect (it is not yet clear whether there are more than one) are called *inhibins* [5]. As yet, it is not known whether inhibin-receptive neuronal structures exist. The hypothalamic-pituitary-testicular control circuit is illustrated in Fig. 32-2.

Spermatogenesis

Formation and maturation of the sperm cells. Under the influence of FSH and androgens of testicular origin, **spermatogenesis** occurs in the *convoluted seminiferous tubules* [2, 5]. This process can be subdivided into three steps:

1. mitotic division of the spermatogonia,
2. a process of meiosis, and
3. maturation of the spermatids to spermatozoa.

This last step is called *spermiogenesis*. The entire process of spermatogenesis takes about 70 days. The epithelium of the seminiferous tubules consists of *supporting cells* (Sertoli cells) and *sperm cells* in various stages of maturation. The primitive sperm cell is the *spermatogonium*. The *spermatocytes* to which these give rise depend on the Sertoli cells for their development, for the latter provide both the nutritive and the endocrine milieu required for maturation. The Sertoli cells produce an *androgen-binding protein (ABP)* that transports testosterone from the interstitial cells to the Sertoli cells, where it is aromatized to *estrogens*. Both estrogens and androgens are necessary for spermatocyte maturation. Furthermore, it is presumably the Sertoli cells that produce *inhibin*.

The fully formed spermatocytes enter the long ducts of the *epididymis*. Passage through the epididymis is necessary for the sperm to become motile and able to fertilize an oocyte. Sperm cells taken directly from the seminiferous tubules are incapable of locomotion and cannot penetrate the zona pellucida of the oocyte. During passage through the epididymal channels, then, the *final maturation of the spermatocytes* occurs, a process requiring about 5–12 days [5, 7]. The detailed events that bring about this maturation are unknown. A small proportion of the spermatocytes remains in the epididymides, but most of them are stored in the vasa deferentia and the ampullae. Here they remain capable of fertilization for months.

Seminal fluid and sperm motility. Normal sperm cells are able to locomote by bending the long, flagellum-like "tail". This movement is promoted by weakly alkaline surroundings. In an acidic milieu the sperm appear rigid. Because the vaginal secretions are slightly acidic, *alkaline constituents* are added to the seminal fluid. The greater part of the seminal fluid originates, not in the testes, but in the *seminal vesicles* and in the *prostate*. The seminal vesicle contributes to the ejaculate a *fluid rich in fructose, prostaglandins and fibrinogen*, which nourish the sperm and allow the semen to coagulate. The prostaglandins may increase the motility of the female genital tract; the fibrinogen causes fibrin formation and hence coagulation of the seminal fluid after ejaculation. The ejaculate also includes a milky, alkaline secretion from the prostate, which contains enzymes needed for the coagulation and later fibrinolysis of the semen. The ejaculated semen, then, comprises the spermatocyte-containing fluid from the vasa deferentia plus the fluids from the seminal vesicle, the prostate and mucous glands, especially the bulbourethral glands in the urethral sphincter. The seminal fluid is able to make the acidic milieu in the vagina slightly *alkaline*, so that the sperm encounter *optimal conditions for ascension*.

The functions of the epididymides and of the glands along the ducts through which the semen passes are all androgen-dependent. Testosterone from the interstitial cells is reduced to the active form, *5-α-dihydrotestosterone (5-α DHT)* in the cells of the affected organs.

Actions of the Androgens

Anabolic Action. The chief hormone secreted by the testes is **testosterone**. Most of it is coupled to a protein [5] known as *sex-hormone-binding globulin (SHBG)* or testosterone-binding globulin (TBG). Only the free fraction of testosterone, the part dissolved in the plasma, is biologically active. The androgens have various peripheral actions. Throughout the body they are *protein-anabolic*; that is, they stimulate protein synthe-

sis. It is for this reason that the male physique is generally larger and more muscular than the female. Androgens promote *bone formation* by stimulating the protein matrix, and also have a stimulatory action on the *muscle mass*. The latter two effects become especially prominent during muscle training. Testosterone circulating in the blood is reduced to 5-α-dihydrotestosterone (5-α-DHT) in many organs in the skin. Here 5-α-DHT is responsible for the *masculine distribution of hair* (beard growth, etc.) and for an excessive production and secretion of fat in the skin (seborrhea).
All the *anabolics* used in medicine and sport (misused by athletes, but producing a desirable effect in severely emaciated patients) are *androgen derivatives* and therefore have all the virilizing properties of the androgens.

Sexual behavior and aggressive behavior. Sex steroids exert a feedback influence on hypothalamic and limbic structures [8, 15], the elements of the CNS that share responsibility for aggression and sexual behavior. In the hypothalamus they influence the secretory activity of the LHRH-producing neurons. In many male mammals the *androgens* circulating in the blood – again, *testosterone* in particular – are especially significant in determining *sexual behavior*, though they also contribute to *aggressive behavior*. It is quite clear that a certain amount of circulating testosterone, between 1 and 2 ng/ml in the man, suffices to maintain normal male (sexual and other) behavior. Testerone levels above this *threshold* do not intensify these forms of behavior. That is, it is an all-or-none phenomenon.
In all species, *castration* reduces the testosterone level below the threshold, which in most cases diminishes aggressive behavior and libido. Interestingly, however, in humans the sex drive often persists for a long time after castration. The connection between blood testosterone levels and aggressive behavior is of interest in forensic medicine. Removal of the gonads (castration) or treatment with substances that block the action of androgens (antiandrogens) frequently improves compulsive – and often criminal – behavior due to these drives. When a physician prescribes androgens to persons so castrated, of course, there is a risk that their aggression and libido will increase.
The testes remain functional for the entire life of the individual. Although the secretion of testosterone eventually diminishes as one grows older, spermatogenesis often continues normally until a very old age.

32.4 Hormonal Regulation of the Female Sexual Functions

Follicle Maturation

The ovary of a newborn girl contains the primordia of many million *follicles* [5, 9]. Most of these many follicles degenerate as the child develops, so that only a few hundred thousand *primary follicles* are present in a girl at puberty. Human females remain in a state of sexual maturity for at most 40-45 years. In each menstrual cycle one follicle ovulates, and a woman has an average of 13 ovulation cycles in a year; hence no more than *600 follicles ovulate in a woman's lifetime*. Nevertheless, at the end of the reproductive phase of life only a few primary follicles, or none at all, remain in the ovary. It follows that many thousand follicles mature during each cycle; there is a *cohort of maturing follicles*. For unknown reasons, only one among this cohort becomes dominant and reaches the stage of ovulation. As a rule, then, only *one egg per menstrual cycle* is available for fertilization. Only once in 200 cycles do two follicles become dominant, so that two eggs can be fertilized. In every 200th pregnancy, therefore, dizygotic twins develop. The probability that a fertilized egg will divide completely, producing monozygotic twins, is also 1:200. Therefore about *one in every 100 pregnancies is a twin pregnancy.*

Regulation of Gonadal Function in the Woman

Hormonal control system. The hypothalamic-pituitary-ovarian control system is diagrammed in Fig. 32-3. The principles of regulation here are the same as those for the regulation of gonadal activity in the man. There are neurons in the hypothalamus that produce **LHRH** and release it into the blood through axon terminals on the portal vessels. In the pituitary it binds to LHRH receptors of cells that produce LH or FSH. The resulting increase in **FSH secretion** causes a cohort of follicles in the ovary to develop from *primary to secondary follicles*. For unexplained reasons, as a rule only one of these follicles proceeds to become *dominant*, developing into a tertiary and finally a *Graafian follicle* [11].
The fluctuations in hormone levels during the course of the menstrual cycle are illustrated in Fig. 32-4. Below these curves are schematic drawings to show the associated changes in the ovary

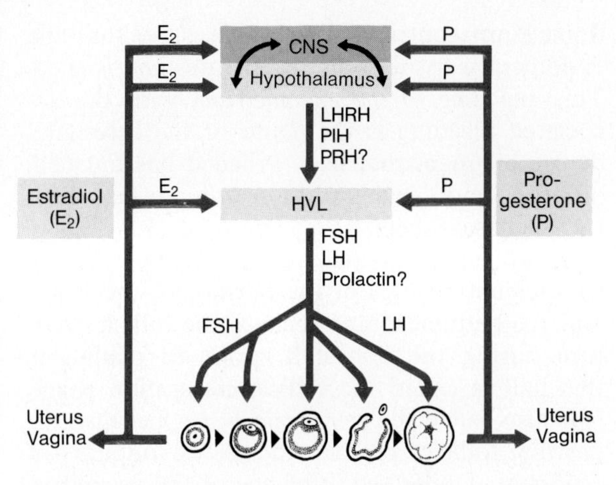

Fig. 32-3. Hypothalamic-pituitary-ovarian control system. The decapeptide LHRH released by hypothalamic neurons stimulates the secretion of both gonadotropins, follicle-stimulating hormone (FSH) and luteinizing hormone (LH). FSH stimulates the maturation of a set of follicles, one (or very rarely two) of which, in humans, mature completely. The maturing follicle produces increasing amounts of estradiol (E_2), which causes endometrial proliferation. The feedback provided to the pituitary and hypothalamus by sufficiently high E_2 levels, in the middle of the cycle, increases LHRH release and raises the sensitivity of the hypophyseal FSH- and LH-producing cells to LHRH. This process enables the mid-cycle surge of FSH and LH. LH brings about ovulation and the luteinization of the follicular granulosa cells. Under the influence of LH, the latter begin to produce and release progesterone (P). Both steroid hormones, E_2 and P, feed back to the hypothalamus and pituitary, reducing FSH and LH secretion in the latter half of the cycle. Both hormones also act in higher central-nervous structures, so that the libido (sexual drive) is regulated in conformity with the cycle. PIH, prolactin-inhibiting hormone; PRH, prolactin-releasing hormone

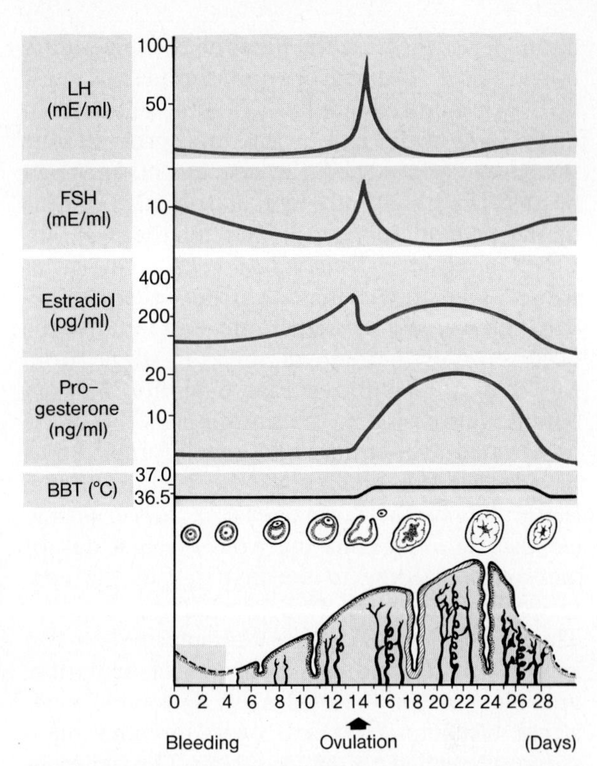

Fig. 32-4. Blood hormone levels during the course of a menstrual cycle. In the follicular phase one follicle matures to a tertiary follicle, producing increasing amounts of estradiol, which causes the endometrium to proliferate. In the middle of the cycle, the pituitary suddenly releases a great quantity of LH and FSH, thereby triggering ovulation. The ruptured follicle becomes the corpus luteum, which produces progesterone in large amounts, converting the proliferating endometrium into a secretory endometrium. Increased progesterone levels also bring about the slight rise in basal body temperature (BBT). Menstrual bleeding (indicated by the *thick line on the abscissa*) is progesterone-withdrawal bleeding

and endometrium. The *maturing follicles produce estrogens*, the most important of which is **estradiol**. The tertiary and Graafian follicles, in particular, produce increasing amounts of estradiol. The hormone travels in the blood to the pituitary, the hypothalamus and higher CNS structures. *Low estrogen concentrations* keep the LH- and FSH-producing cells in a state of *low sensitivity* to the action of LHRH; furthermore, it is likely that little LHRH is released under these conditions. That is, below a certain concentration estradiol provides *negative feedback*, as a result of which the blood levels of LH and FSH remain low. As a follicle matures, the level of estradiol in the blood rises. Just before ovulation it becomes so high (Fig. 32-4) that the LH- and FSH-producing cells in the pituitary suddenly become highly responsive to LHRH; presumably there is a simulataneous increase in the amount of LHRH released by the hypothalamus. Estradiol now provides *positive feedback*, increasing hypophyseal FSH and LH secretion. The **LH** surge brings about *ovulation*; the follicle ruptures as a result of processes initiated by the raised LH level. The granulosa cells in the follicle, which had been producing estradiol, now begin in addition to synthesize and release greater amounts of **progesterone**, the most important gestagen in the woman. This LH-dependent process is called *luteinization* of the granulosa cells, because it converts the follicle to the *corpus luteum*. Although estradiol is still being secreted in relatively large quantities, in combination with the progesterone it has a negative influence on the pituitary and hypothalamus, so that the rates of LH and FSH secretion return to the basal level.

Progesterone acts on thermoregulatory centers of the hypothalamus so as to raise the temperature of the body *(thermogenetic action)*. High progesterone levels increase the **basal body temperature** by ca. 0.5 °C. For reasons not completely clarified, the corpus luteum has a lifetime of about 14 days. Toward the end of this time progesterone secretion declines and the process of *luteolysis* begins. The basal body temperature also returns to the preovulatory level. That is, the cycle involves a *biphasic temperature curve*. The latter serves as an important diagnostic criterion, because an increase in temperature can indicate the occurrence of the preovulatory LH surge; from this it may be inferred that ovulation has occurred. Furthermore, the duration of the phase of elevated temperature can give information as to whether the lifetime of the corpus luteum is normal. In the normal case, a *menstrual cycle lasts 28 days*, counting from the first day of menstrual bleeding to the first day of the next menstruation.

The menstrual cycle is thus characterized by two special events. One is the process of ovulation, and the other is the externally detectable menstrual bleeding. How are ovulation and menstruation related to one another? The neuroendocrine control circuit that has been described, for the regulation of ovarian activity, serves to make pregnancy possible, and pregnancy occurs in the uterus. The interior of the uterus is lined with a mucous membrane, the *endometrium*, the structure of which changes depending on the steroidal milieu [12]. Near the beginning of a cycle only the basal layers of the endometrium are present. As the *estrogen level rises* during the first half of the cycle, *the endometrium proliferates*, so that by the middle of the cycle, at the time of the preovulatory LH and FSH surges, it has become considerably thicker. After ovulation, under the influence of the elevated blood progesterone, cryptlike glands develop in the proliferated endometrium; this event marks the transition from the *proliferation stage* to the *secretion stage*. In this condition, the endometrium is optimally prepared for the eventuality of pregnancy.

At **ovulation** a fertilizable egg is washed out of the ruptured Graafian follicle along with the follicular fluid and enters one of the Fallopian tubes, which connect the two ovaries with the cavity of the uterus. At this time the egg is ready to be fertilized. If fertilization does not occur, the endometrium need no longer be prepared for pregnancy. In the presence of a basal LH level, the corpus luteum survives for ca. 14 days; when it ceases to function, the *progesterone level falls*. Because the endometrium can exist only when the progesterone level is high, it now undergoes regressive changes. The spiral arteries of the endometrium contract at their bases, so that the endometrial tissue soon degenerates and is shed. This *shedding of the endometrium* with the associated bleeding is the cause of the externally detectable **menstrual flow.** When it has finished, all of the endometrium has been removed except for the basal layers.

The two halves of the cycle are named for the characteristic states of the hormones, the ovary and the endometrium. Because the follicles mature during the first half, prior to ovulation, this half is called the **follicle-maturation phase.** It is also called the *estrogenic phase*, because the growing follicles produce increasing amounts of estrogens. Under the influence of the estrogens, the uterine endometrium proliferates, so that the term *proliferation phase* is also used. In the second half of the cycle, after ovulation, a *corpus luteum* has formed; this period can thus be called the **luteal phase**. The corpus luteum secretes progesterone, and because progesterone is a gestagen, the endocrinological name for this phase is the *gestagenic phase*. Progesterone causes the proliferating endometrium to be converted to the secretory form – hence the name *secretory phase* for the second half of the cycle. If conception has not occurred, the entire cycle is repeated: formation of the corpus luteum and its eventual regression with associated menstrual bleeding, which is ultimately a progesterone-withdrawal bleeding.

Pulsatile LHRH secretion. It has been shown that in the woman, as in the man, release of LHRH from the hypothalamic neurons is not a uniform but rather a pulsatile process [2, 3, 11]. That is, the LHRH neurons are also *synchronized* and *phasically active* in the woman. In the first half of the cycle, before ovulation, the pulses occur about every 90 min. During the time after ovulation, under the influence of a high progesterone level, the LHRH pulse frequency of the woman matches that of the man; the pulses are observed at intervals of 3-4 hours. The pulsatile release of LHRH from the hypothalamus is of fundamental significance to the regulation of LH and FSH secretion.

In a series of impressive experiments on monkeys KNOBIL et al. [13, 17] showed that the pulsatile release of LHRH from the hypothalamic neurons acts as a signal to the pituitary. In order to study the physiological relevance of the pulsatile secretion, the hypothalamus (including the LHRH cells) was ablated from female rhesus monkeys. Because the LH and FSH cells in the pituitary were no longer being stimulated by LHRH from the hypothalamus, they stopped secreting LH and FSH. Then the animals were equipped with a pump that *injected a bolus of LHRH into the circulation* through a venous catheter every 60 minutes. That is, this function of the hypothalamus was simulated artificially. Secretion of LH and FSH in the pituitary promptly rose to the normal levels. Then the pulse frequency was varied; with frequencies of 2 or more pulses per hour or less than 1 pulse per hour the rate of LH and FSH secretion was altered, usually reduced. *Constant infusion of LHRH*, at a rate equivalent to the dosage that had caused normal LH and FSH secretion during pulsed administration, resulted in a cessation of hypophyseal LH and FSH secretion. Even when the amount of LHRH was increased, constant infusion did not stimulate the secretion of these pituitary hormones.

Obviously, the pituitary cells that secrete LH and FSH must be exposed to LHRH at particular, regular intervals. When they are, the pituitary releases LH and FSH in amounts that keep the LH and FSH in the blood at the normal basal level. Under the influence of the basal FSH, the follicles maturing in the ovary gradually increase their production of *estradiol*. After one has matured to a Graafian follicle, particularly large amounts of estradiol are released. The high circulating estrogen level *sensitizes the hypophyseal LH- and FSH-producing cells* in such a way that, in experiments on monkeys, a constant pulsatile administration of LHRH can now cause such massive LH release that the process of ovulation is initiated. Under these conditions there is also an *increased FSH* release in the middle of the cycle, so that a new cohort of follicles begins to mature for the next cycle.

These findings in hypothalamectomized monkeys can be applied to humans. There is a disease in which pulsatile secretion of LHRH by the hypothalamus is either absent or occurs at a suboptimal frequency. The results are impaired follicle maturation and failure to ovulate, with a cessation of menstrual activity. This condition is called *hypothalamic amenorrhea*. The inability to bear children often causes these women to consult a physician; the latter, knowing the physiological situation, can easily help the patient with a portable pump that injects pulses of LHRH at the correct frequency. The fact that only an optimal pulse frequency produces optimal LH and FSH secretion can also be exploited to suppress the pituitary secretion of LH and FSH *(bloodless and reversible castration)*. As suggested by the above experiment, in which continuous administration of LHRH abolished the secretion of LH and FSH, the administration of very-long-acting *LHRH analogs* can have the same effect. After an initial increase in the production of LH and FSH, secretion of both gonadotropic hormones stops completely, and ovarian activity is suppressed. Of course, male gonadal activity is also suppressed in this way, because these regulatory hormones operate by the same principles in men. The effect in either case amounts to castration, with the advantage that it requires no surgery and, above all, is reversible. This situation is not uncommonly desired for diagnostic and therapeutic reasons.

The modulating action of estrogens and gestagens on the amplitude and frequency of the LH pulses is illustrated in Fig. 32-5. The pulsatile nature of LHRH secretion by the hypothalamic neurons is particularly clear in *ovariectomized* women; because the *negative feedback* normally provided by low concentrations of estradiol is eliminated, LH is also secreted in large pulses. In the presence of basal estrogen levels, pulsatile release of LHRH from the hypothalamus continues, but the *estradiol* has made the LH-producing cells in the pituitary *less responsive*, so that the amplitude of the LH pulses is much reduced. The amount of LHRH released per pulse is probably also reduced when moderate amounts of estrogen are present. When the estrogen level is high for some time, the hormone acts to provide *positive feedback*. Now each pulse of LHRH secretion elicits a more vigorous response of the LH-secreting cells, culminating in the *ovulation-triggering LH surge* [2]. In this situation, the pulses of LHRH are probably also of larger amplitude. In the *luteal phase*, characterized by moderate amounts of estradiol plus distinctly elevated progesterone, the pulse frequency of the hypothalamic LHRH neurons is reduced, so that LH episodes are observed only every 3–4 h (Fig. 32-5).

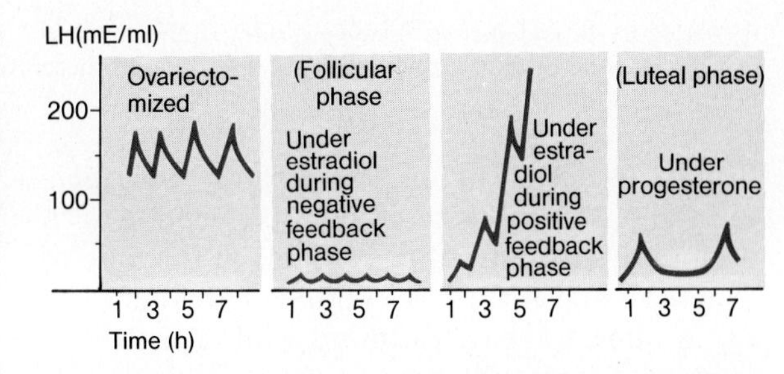

Fig. 32-5. Pulsatile mode of LH secretion in the woman, with various kinds of estrogen and progesterone feedback

Ovarian peptide production. It has been mentioned that the testes produce a protein with a selective FSH-inhibiting action. This hormone, called *inhibin*, is also produced in the ovary; its action is the same in females as in males. The corpus-luteum cells in the ovary synthesize a peptide that has previously been discussed as a hormone of the posterior pituitary, the octapeptide *oxytocin*. It is presumably involved in the process of *luteolysis*. The second neurohypophyseal hormone, *ADH*, has also been demonstrated in the ovary. Furthermore, luteal cells produce a larger peptide called *relaxin*, the ovarian function of which is not well understood. The same hormone is produced by the placenta and uterus during pregnancy, and facilitates the *process of birth* by causing dilation of the uterine cervix and relaxation of the symphysis. In addition to the above peptides, the ovary produces others that so far have been found only in this organ; these are evidently involved in regulation of the complex cycle. Very recently evidence has been accumulating that the gonads also secrete peptides in the category of *endogenous opioid peptides, VIP, oxytocin and vasopressin*. Little is known about the function of these hormones in the ovary.

Female fertility. The oocyte remains *fertilizable* for about 24 h [5]. Therefore, if conception is to occur, the sperm must be available at the time of ovulation and for a brief period thereafter. The egg is almost always fertilized while it is still in the *tube*. Because the time required for the sperm to travel from the vagina to the tubes varies, coitus as long as 48 h before ovulation can still produce conception. It is essentially impossible for an oocyte to be fertilized later than 24 h after ovulation.

It is often not easy to determine the **optimal time for conception**. When ovulation has occurred, the corpus luteum produces larger amounts of progesterone and the body temperature rises. These few hours would be the ideal time for conception, but because the oocyte remains fertilizable for only about 24 h, coitus should actually have occurred prior to ovulation. Therefore a couple desiring a child should be advised to have sexual intercourse shortly before the day on which the next ovulation is predicted.

Contraception

The biphasic body-temperature curve can also be used as a very *unreliable guide to contraception*. Sexual intercourse should be avoided during the 2–3 days before the expected ovulation and for 24 h after the stepwise increase in basal body temperature, if conception is not desired *(Knaus-Ogino method)*.

Hormonal suppression of fertility: the pill. It has long been known that ovulation can be inhibited by the administration of estrogen and/or progesterone. A combination of the two hormones has the same effect, and it is on such a combination that *oral contraceptives* are based. For a long time it was not really clear how such contraceptives act. Today we know that they reduce both the *frequency of pulsatile LHRH secretion* and, presumably, the *amount of LHRH secreted per pulse*. There is an equally important *direct action of estrogens and gestagens on the pituitary*. The unphysiologically high blood estrogen and gestagen levels desensitize the LH- and FSH-producing cells to the action of LHRH. These three effects of an oral contraceptive *completely block the preovulatory surge of LH and FSH*. However, the endometrium is induced to proliferate by the estrogen components in the contraceptives. The gestagens change the proliferated endometrium into a secretory endometrium. When a pill cycle is completed, after 21 days, *hormone-withdrawal bleeding* occurs, as in the normal menstrual cycle without contraceptive pills.

LHRH "superagonists". It has been mentioned that the pituitary secretes FSH and LH optimally only when it is provided with pulses of LHRH at regular intervals. The molecular structure of this decapeptide can be modified so as to produce derivatives that are still more effective. These *LHRH analogs* act both more strongly and considerably longer than the native decapeptide. In their presence, the pituitary is no longer exposed to the optimal endogenous rhythm and the LHRH receptors of the gonadotropic cells become insensitive to the peptide – a process called *down-regulation of the receptors*. The consequence of repeated administration of such LHRH "superagonists" is that, after an initial increase in the production of LH and FSH, the pituitary no longer responds at all. The FSH and LH levels in the blood fall so far as to be practically undetectable, so that follicular maturation and ovulation cannot occur. Because the follicles do not mature, no estrogens are produced; a quasi-ovariectomized condition results. This is of course not the best method of contraception, but it does offer an alternative for cases in which, on medical grounds, ovarian activity should be suppressed (e.g., hormone-dependent carcinomas).

32.5 Puberty and Menopause

Puberty

Hormonal factors. Puberty is the *maturation of reproductive ability*. Very little is known about the signal for the onset of puberty. The hypothalamus appears to release LHRH in pulsatile form even in the newborn, because measurable amounts of LH and FSH are already present in the blood [18]. Consequently, the gonads show signs of activation by the two gonadotropic hormones. But soon after birth pulsatile LHRH secretion ceases, and after the first 3 to 6 months of life LH and FSH are practically undetectable in the blood. Not until the *onset of puberty* (between 9 and 11 years of age in girls, and between 11 and 13 years in boys) do the hypothalamic LHRH neurons resume *synchronized, phasic activity*. At first this activation is sleep-dependent, being limited to the *phases of deep sleep*. Hence gonadotropin secretion is increased at night, when it stimulates gonadal activity. As puberty progresses, the pulsatile LHRH secretion becomes *independent of*

the sleep phases; LHRH pulses are increasingly observed during the day. This condition marks the beginning of adulthood.
In studies of infant female rhesus monkeys with hypothalamic lesions, it has been shown that pulsatile LHRH administration alone suffices to activate ovarian function (p. 780). Evidently the ovary is capable of responding with ovulation to an appropriate hormonal milieu at a very early age. The process of puberty is therefore governed by a purely central-nervous mechanism [3, 5].
Under physiological conditions, the maturation of reproductive ability is preceded, by about 2 years, by a development called the *adrenarche*. For reasons not yet clarified, the zona reticularis of the adrenal cortex develops at this early time and begins to produce androgens in larger amounts. It was once thought that the adrenarche was a precondition for puberty, but we now know that normal puberty can occur with no preceding adrenarche.
The somatic development into an adolescent boy or girl during puberty is a direct consequence of the increased release of sex hormones.

Male puberty. When pulsatile secretion of LHRH begins in the hypothalamus of a male child, it causes a slow increase in LH and FSH secretion. FSH stimulates *spermatogenesis*, and LH stimulates *androgen production*. The androgens virilize the individual both mentally and physically, and the elevated production at puberty brings about the bodily development of a boy into a man. The **action of androgens** can be summarized in general as *protein-anabolic* (pp. 777f.). Under their influence the musculature becomes more massive and more protein is incorporated into the bones. The androgen increase during puberty also induces a *spurt of linear growth*. But after this spurt the elevated androgens cause *ossification of the growth zones (epiphyses)* of the long bones. Once this has occurred, further elongation of the bones is impossible.

An understanding of this initially growth-promoting and subsequently growth-inhibiting action of the androgens is clinically important. In eunuchs or eunuchoid children ossification of the growth zones does not occur, and *eunuchoid gigantism* results. On the other hand, true *pubertas precox*, a condition caused by too-early androgen production, is characterized by a premature androgen-induced spurt of growth. At first, the affected children are larger than normal, but because epiphyseal closure also occurs prematurely, these children later are undersized.

Another characteristic of male puberty is the development of a *deeper voice*, again under the control of the androgens. Here they stimulate growth of the larynx ("Adam's apple", a masculine attribute) and because the vocal cords are thereby lengthened, the pitch of the sound they produce is lowered. The *masculine hair pattern* (beard, chest and pubic hair) is also androgen-induced. The hair-forming follicles reduce testosterone to dihydrotestosterone (p. 778), the androgen that can cause masculine hair growth.
The above-mentioned protein-anabolic action of the androgens is responsible for the enhanced muscle formation in the pubertal boy and the still better developed musculature of the sexually mature man. This androgen action is pharmacologically useful in that asthenic patients can be helped to a more rapid recovery by taking **anabolics**. Without exception, these anabolics are androgen derivatives. *Doping* of athletes with anabolics is now forbidden, in part because of undesirable androgenic side effects. The uncritical use of anabolics by women engaged in physically demanding sports not only develops the muscles, which is desired in order to improve performance, but may also profoundly affect the female hypothalamic-pituitary-gonadal control system.

Female puberty. The onset of phasic, synchronized activation of the LHRH neurons is also a crucial feature of puberty in girls. Under the influence of the rising blood FSH level, a number of follicles begin to mature and to produce larger amounts of *estradiol-17-β*. In early puberty, however, none of these developing follicles progresses to ovulation; all eventually are removed by atresia. As in the male, the pulses of LHRH secretion at first occur only at night; when they extend to the daytime, the *FSH* and *LH secretion* typical of the sexually mature woman begins. Under these conditions one of the follicles in the maturing group becomes dominant and can produce sufficient **estradiol** to provide positive feedback (p. 779). The resulting LH surge causes the dominant follicle to ovulate. However, pubertal girls often have *anovulatory cycles*, in which the follicles mature and produce large amounts of estrogen but, for reasons not entirely understood, ovulation does not occur. Such a cycle ends with pure estrogen-withdrawal bleeding. Not until the late pubertal phase do regular menstrual cycles begin. The relatively *slight protein-anabolic action of estrogens* is responsible for the mild *pubertal spurt of growth* and the subsequent *epiphyseal closure* in girls, so that toward the end of puberty linear growth is completed. The estrogens also induce the somatic changes by which a girl acquires the *secondary sexual characteristics* of a young woman.

Menopause

A woman does not remain capable of reproduction until the end of her life. The time at which the *menstrual cycle stops* is called menopause. The cycles often become irregular for some time preceding menopause, when the woman is in a *premenopausal* state. When the cyclic activity of the reproductive system has stopped altogether, she is *postmenopausal*. Menopause occurs when most or all of the follicles in the ovary have been used up. Because no more follicles are maturing, ovarian estradiol production falls almost to zero, with the effect of quasi-castration.

Because of the altered androgen-to-estrogen ratio, the effects of the androgens produced by the adrenals become more pronounced. Hence a slight virilization of the menopausal woman is entirely physiological.

As a result of the extremely *low estrogen level*, this hormone no longer provides negative feedback to the hypothalamus and pituitary. Estrogen-receptive neurons signal the estrogen deficiency to the LHRH-producing cells, causing them to release more LHRH, which in turn causes an *increased release of FSH* from the pituitary. But the FSH cannot stimulate follicular maturation, because there are not enough follicles remaining. The LHRH also stimulates *LH secretion*, so that the blood levels of both hormones (FSH and LH) rise. Because the LHRH neurons never abandon the pulsatile mode of secretion, the menopausal woman exhibits a typical *pulsatile pattern* of LH and FSH secretion. The same pattern, of course, is also observed following removal of the gonads of a sexually mature woman or of a man (i.e., it is a castration effect; see Fig. 32-5).

Menopausal and postmenopausal women frequently experience typical unpleasant reactions at the beginning of each LH episode, *hot flushes* caused by the increased hypothalamic activation that results from the too-low estrogen level. They can be alleviated by administering small doses of estrogens. Estrogens have a slight protein-anabolic action. Although this effect is not as pronounced as that of the androgens, it is clinically relevant, as follows. When ovarian estrogen production ceases, the protein matrix of the bones may break down, producing the condition called *osteoporosis*. If estrogens are prescribed in time, at the beginning of menopause, this bone degeneration can be prevented.

32.6 References

Textbooks and Handbooks

1. Franchimont, P.: Clinics in Endocrinology and Metabolism. Vol. 15, No. 1. Paracrine Contr. W.B. Saunders Company Philadelphia 1986
2. Johnson, M., Everitt, B.: Essential Reproduction. Blackwell Scientific Publications, Oxford 1980
3. Leyendecker, G., Stock, H., Wildt, L.: Brain and Pituitary Peptides II. Pulsatile Administration of Gn-RH in Hypothalamic Failure: Basic and Clinical Aspects. S. Karger Basel 1983
4. Martini, L., James, V.H.T.: The Endocrinology of Pregnancy and Parturition. Exp. Endocrinology Vol. 3, Academic Press 1983
5. Shearman, R.P.: Clinical Reproductive Endocrinology. Churchill Livingstone Edinburgh London Melbourne and New York 1985
6. Wagner, T.O.F.: Pulsatile LHRH Therapy of the Male. TM-Verlag Hameln 1985
7. Wilson, J.D., Foster, D.W.: William's Textbook of Endocrinology. W.B. Saunders Co. 7th Edition Philadelphia 1985
8. Wuttke, W., Horowski, R.: Gonadal Steroids and Brain Function. Springer-Verlag Berlin Heidelberg New York 1981
9. Yen, S.S.C., Jaffe, R.B.: Reproductive Endocrinology. Saunders, Philadelphia 1986

Original Papers and Reviews

10. Guillemin, R.: Peptides in the Brain: the New Endocrinology of the Neuron (Nobel Lecture). Science *202*, 390–402 (1978)
11. Jaffe, R.B.; Monroe, S.E.: Hormone Interaction and Regulation During the Menstrual Cycle. Frontiers in Neuroendocrinology, Vol. 6. pp. 219–247. Raven Press New York 1980
12. Jensen, E.V.; Greene, G.L.; Closs, L.E.; DeSombre, E.R.; Nadji, M.: Receptors Reconsidered: A 20-Year Perspective. Recent Progress in Hormone Research, Vol. *38*, 1–40 (1982)
13. Knobil, E.: Neuroendocrine control of the menstrual cycle. Recent Progr. Horm. Res. *36*, 53–88 (1980)
14. Leong, D.A.; Frawley, L.S.; Neill, J.D.: Neuroendocrine Control of Prolactin Secretion. Ann. Rev. Physiol. *45*, 109–127 (1983)
15. McEwen, B.S.; Biegon, A.; Davis, P.G.; Krey, L.C.; Luine, V.N.; McGinnis, M.Y.; Paden, C.M.; Parsons, B.; Rainbow, T.C.: Steroid Hormones: Humoral Signals Which Alter Brain Cell Properties and Functions. Rec. Progr. Horm. Res. *38*, 41–92 (1982)
16. Neill, J.D.: Neuroendocrine Regulation of Prolactin Secretion. Frontiers in Neuroendocrinology. *6*, 129–155 (1980)
17. Pohl, C.R.; Knobil, E.: The Role of the Central Nervous System in the Control of Ovarian Function in Higher Primates. Ann. Rev. Physiol. *44*, 583–593 (1982)
18. Reiter, E.O.; Grumbach, M.M.: Neuroendocrine Control Mechanisms and the Onset of Puberty. Ann. Rev. Physiol. *44*, 595–613 (1982)
19. Schally, A.V.: Aspects of hypothalamic regulation of the pituitary gland (Nobel Lecture) Science *202*, 18–28 (1978)

33 Reproduction and Pregnancy

W. Wuttke

33.1 Coitus

The desire for sexual intercourse is called the sex drive or *libido*. Sexual intercourse is the only physiological means by which *conception* can occur; it comprises the act of *coitus*, the insertion of the erect penis into the vagina. The sexual act is associated with particular reaction sequences in both woman and man.

Sequence of Sexual Reactions in the Man

Erection and emission. Thinking about a possibly impending sexual act, in the presence or even in the absence of a sexual partner, can cause the penis to become stiff *(erection)*; the same effect is achieved by mechanical stimulation of *erogenous zones*, especially the glans of the penis. Erection is brought about by the activation of parasympathetic fibers from the sacral cord, which send impulses through the pelvic nerve to the arterioles in the corpora cavernosa and corpus spongiosum of the penis (p. 353). These parasympathetic impulses dilate the arteries, and at the same time the venous outflow from the penis is partially blocked. As a result, the two *corpora cavernosa* are put under arterial pressure and become distended with blood; the penis grows hard and lengthens. The parasympathetic activity also causes the *urethral* and *bulbourethral glands* to increase the production of a mucous secretion. When the sexual stimulus becomes especially intense – for instance, by the massaging of the penis during coitus – a reflex center in the lower thoracic and upper lumbar region is activated and triggers contraction of the vasa deferentia and the ampulla. The contraction transports sperm into the posterior urethra; this part of the orgasm phase is called *emission*.

Ejaculation. Filling of the posterior urethra excites afferent fibers in the *pudendal nerve*, which activate a sacral reflex center to produce rhythmic contractions of the *ischiocavernous* and *bulbocavernous muscles*. The rhythmic contractions of the basal parts of the penis rhythmically expel the semen from the urethra. This process is called *ejaculation*. Some of the trunk muscles also contract rhythmically during ejaculation, driving the penis deeper into the vagina. Emission and ejaculation together characterize the male **orgasm**. After this orgasm phase the sexual responsiveness of the man is greatly reduced. The erect penis subsides, and a pause of several minutes to hours is required before erection again becomes possible. This pause is called the *resolution phase*.

All the events preceding and during coitus are heavily dependent on the level of *testosterone* in the blood. In many men, removal of the testes (orchiectomy) extinguishes the sex drive. Not uncommonly, however, the ability to have an erection persists for a considerable time after castration.

Sequence of Sexual Reactions in the Woman

Libido and orgasm. As in the man, a successful sexual act in the woman depends on mental and local mechanical stimulation. Women, like men, can become sexually excited by erotic thoughts alone. The female *libido* varies in intensity during the course of the menstrual cycle. Sexual desires are particularly frequent and strong around the time of ovulation. As in the man, again, the mechanical stimulation of certain *erogenous zones* causes sexual arousal. Embryologically, the clitoris corresponds to the penis of the man (p. 774); accordingly, it is particularly sensitive to sexual stimuli. The analogy with the man goes further; by way of reflexes involving the *pudendal nerve* and sacral segments of the spinal cord, during sexual stimulation the *clitoris* and other external sex organs become swollen with blood. The entrance to the vagina is narrowed, so that the penis is held tightly and subjected to intense mechanical stimulation during the coital movements. This increase in blood flow is brought about by parasympathetic signals, which also increase the secretion of mucus to lubricate the penis in the vagina. The female *orgasm* is analogous to emission and ejaculation in the man. During orgasm the perineal musculature contracts rhythmically, the cervix of the uterus dilates, and there are rhythmic contractions of the uterus and the tubes, so that conditions are optimal for sperm ascension. It is still unclear whether the *oxytocin* (p. 378) released from the posterior pituitary is a causative factor for the increased motility of the uterus and the tubes in humans. Because of increased tone in the muscles of the pelvic floor, the uterus rises to a more vertical position, so that the *ejaculate* is propelled into the immediate vicinity of the cervix. When sexual stimulation stops, the woman enters a resolution phase, during which the extra blood drains away from the pelvic region. Unlike the man, the woman can experience several orgasms if sexual stimulation continues.

Extragenital reactions. During the orgasmic phases both woman and man exhibit characteristic extragenital reactions. Whereas the genital orgasmic reactions are mainly under *parasympathetic* control, the extragenital phenomena are indicative of elevated *sympathetic tone*. Heart rate and the systolic and diastolic blood pressure rise, the pupils are greatly dilated, blood flow through the female mammary gland increases, and the nipples are erect.

33.2 Pregnancy, Birth and Lactation

Pregnancy

Fertilization. The neuroendocrine control circuit that governs ovarian function serves to make available an egg that is capable of being fertilized and to optimize the conditions for gestation if conception should occur [1, 3]. On p. 780 it was explained that at each ovulation an egg is washed out of the follicle and enters the adjacent Fallopian tube. The egg is *fertilized in the tube* by sperm that swim, by undulations of the tail, up from the vagina through the uterus. After fertilization the egg begins to divide rapidly, reaching the four-cell stage while still moving down the tube.

The **embryo** is transported into the uterus by microperistaltic movement of the tube. As mentioned above, the cyclic alterations of the endometrium serve to provide the developing *trophoblast* with conditions optimal for continuation of the pregnancy. Because the endometrium would be shed if the corpus luteum stopped functioning, the preservation of luteal function is a prerequisite for pregnancy. This is the responsibility of the trophoblast; at a very early stage, the trophoblast produces a hormone that acts like the luteinizing hormone from the pituitary. It *stimulates progesterone synthesis* by the corpus luteum. The hormone from the trophoblast is **human chorionic gonadotropin (HCG).** Because of the LH-like action of HCG, the corpus luteum synthesizes and secretes progesterone in amounts sufficient to ensure endometrial survival and prevent the regression that otherwise occurs on the 10th to 12th day after ovulation. That is, the contraction of the spiral arteries as a consequence of progesterone deficiency is avoided, so that the endometrium does not become necrotic and there is no menstrual bleeding. The absence of an expected menstruation is often the first detectable sign of a beginning pregnancy.

Nidation and placentation. At about the time when menstruation fails to occur, the trophoblast reaches the uterus and finds an endometrium in optimal condition for pregnancy. The trophoblast now begins to secrete *proteolytic enzymes* that break down the tissue and allow it to "eat" its way into the endometrium. This process is called implantation or *nidation* ("nesting").

These proteolytic enzymes are fundamentally involved in the pathophysiology of **extrauterine pregnancy**. Inflammation of the uterine appendages frequently leaves scars on the tubes. This scar tissue can shrink, constricting the tube lumen. The small, mobile sperm can still ascend and fertilize the egg, but a larger, multicellular structure cannot pass the constriction in the direction of the uterus. Retained in the tube, the trophoblast releases its proteolytic enzymes and becomes implanted there. Because conditions in the tube are not optimal, the trophoblast remains hypotrophic; the situation can be detected by the subnormal HCG levels in the blood and urine of the mother. An extrauterine pregnancy can develop rather dramatically if the enzymes eat through the tube wall and the trophoblast escapes into the abdominal cavity, where it can cause considerable irritation of the peritoneum ("acute abdomen"). Furthermore, one of the many periuterine vessels may be eroded, with the possibility of life-threatening hemorrhage.

The implanted trophoblast finds optimal nutritive conditions in the endometrium. Under physiological conditions the trophoblast develops into the *syncytiotrophoblast*, which eventually becomes the *fetoplacental unit*. During the first 8-10 weeks of pregnancy the chorion of this unit produces massive quantities of *HCG*, so that luteal function is increasingly stimulated. Therefore the progesterone level also rises during early pregnancy.

Functions of the placenta. The primary role of the placenta is to permit *exchange of substances between the maternal and fetal blood*, so that the fetus can be nourished and its metabolic end products removed. The thin layer of tissue that separates the intervillous space from the lumen of a villous capillary, known as the **placental barrier**, favors this exchange. O_2 and nutrients are taken up by the fetal capillary blood, and CO_2 and other metabolic end products are given off into the maternal blood. The placental barrier is also permeable to electrolytes, antibodies (e.g., IgG), viruses (e.g., the rubella and measles viruses) and – as we now know – to various medicines (e.g., sedatives and barbiturates) and alcohol, which can damage the embryo. By the 8th to 10th week of pregnancy the placenta is well developed and takes over the *production of progesterone*. From this time on the pregnancy is independent of the function of the corpus luteum and would no longer be terminated by ovariectomy.

Fetal hormone production. When the pregnancy reaches its 3rd month, the fetal adrenal gland is well developed and produces large amounts of the weakly androgenic steroid *dehydroepiandrosterone sulfate (DHEAS)*. It is not entirely clear why the fetal adrenal is so large and active at such an early stage [1, 2]. The DHEAS is converted to *estriol* by the placenta. The estriol enters the maternal circulation and is excreted in the urine. Many measurements during normal pregnancies have shown that from the 10th to the 40th week the estriol level in the blood of the mother rises continuously, and *normal limits* have been established. These norms are an important diagnostic aid to the obstetrician, for they allow evaluation of the *well-being of the fetoplacental unit*. If all is not well with the fetus, its adrenal function is also disturbed and the placenta produces less estriol from the adrenal precursors (including DHEAS; see also p. 389). If something is wrong with the placenta, it cannot convert enough of the fetal DHEAS to estriol. In both cases, the result is a decrease in the amount of estriol in the maternal blood. Because the estriol is excreted in the urine of the pregnant woman, one can monitor the pregnancy endocrinologically by measuring the estriol in urine collected over 24 h.

Another hormone produced by the placenta is **human placental lactogen (HPL).** Because this hormone also has actions like those of somatotropin, some authors refer to it as human chorionic somatomammotropin (HCS). Very little is known about its actions in the fetus and/or on the mother. Probably it stimulates fetal growth. There is some evidence that HPL also acts by stimulating insulin-like growth factors (somatomedins; see p. 381).

Preparation for lactation. Under the influence of the rising estrogen levels in the maternal blood, the pituitary of the mother is stimulated to secrete *prolactin*. The prolactin level is also very high in the amniotic fluid. Both HPL and prolactin prepare the mother's mammary glands for imminent lactation. The reason why the high prolactin and HPL levels do not already cause lactation during the pregnancy is not completely understood; probably the very high blood estrogen level has a direct inhibitory, and hence prolactin-antagonistic, action in the breasts.

Duration of pregnancy. The duration of pregnancy is calculated on the basis of the length of a normal menstrual cycle (i.e., 28 days). *On average* pregnancy lasts for ten menstrual cycles – that is, *280 days or 40 weeks*.

Birth

Initiation of labor. Essential hormonal aspects of the process of birth (parturition) have been treated previously in the discussion of the posterior-pituitary hormone oxytocin (p. 378). In the present context, it is important to know that as pregnancy progresses the estrogen and progesterone levels in the maternal blood rise. **Estrogens** *sensitize the uterus to oxytocin*, the hormone that elicits labor. High levels of progesterone antagonize this action. After almost exactly 40 weeks of pregnancy (280 days) the uterus, which has reached its maximal size, with the external orifice barely closed, becomes extremely sensitive to the action of oxytocin. It is not yet quite clear why *labor*, the uterine contractions to expel the fetus, begins on the 280th day of pregnancy; perhaps the high blood progesterone level falls briefly, or substances are formed that inhibit the progesterone action. *Prostaglandins* and other substances not yet identified chemically cause the external orifice to relax and gradually become wider.

Expulsion of the fetus. Eventually the posterior pituitary releases oxytocin in amounts sufficient to cause *contraction of the myometrium*, which exerts concentric pressure on the amniotic sac. The only open route away from this pressure is through the cervix of the uterus, which is stretched by the amniotic sac and the head of the child, low in the pelvis. The abundant mechanoreceptors in the cervix and vagina are strongly stimulated, and the stimulation is signalled neuronally to the CNS (see Ferguson's reflex, p. 378). When the information reaches the oxytocin-producing cells they are phasically activated in synchrony, so that boluses of oxytocin are released into the bloodstream (p. 378). At the myometrium, the oxytocin bolus causes a new contraction. In this way labor is maintained until the fetus and then the placenta are expelled from the mother's body. It is likely that other hormones of diffuse origin, as well as the peptide hormone *relaxin*, are involved in bringing pregnancy to a normal end.

Lactation

Initiation of lactation and milk ejection. After the placenta has been expelled, the progesterone and estrogen levels in the maternal blood rapidly decline, because the cells producing these hormones are no longer present. The *prolactin level* remains high and can now initiate milk synthesis in the mammary glands, because the antagonistic action of a high estrogen level has been eliminated. The process of *lactation* begins. When the infant is brought to the breast, it begins to suckle the nipple, which is well equipped with mechanoreceptors. The mechanical stimulus is signaled by these receptors to the prolactin- and oxytocin-regulating neurons in the hypothalamus, triggering the *milk-ejection reflex* (p. 378).

Maintenance of lactation. When the prolactin-regulating cells are informed about the mechanical stimulation of the nipple, they probably cause a *reduced secretion of dopamine* into the portal vessels. Because the lactotropic (prolactin-producing) cells of the pituitary are very readily inhibited by dopamine, reduced hypothalamic dopamine release results in *disinhibition* of the lactotropic cells and hence *increased prolactin secretion* [4, 5]. Probably the suckling stimulus also causes the release of one or more *prolactin-releasing hormones*, though little is known about their chemical nature. In any case, suckling raises the prolactin level in the maternal blood, which maintains the state of lactation. High prolactin levels can be detected by prolactin-receptive neurons in the hypothalamus, which raise the rate of hypothalamic dopamine release. This is the *autoregulatory principle* discussed in the section on prolactin (p. 383).

Postpartum amenorrhea. As was illustrated in Fig. 17-11, an increased intrahypothalamic dopamine release not only inhibits prolactin secretion in the pituitary but also has a *direct or indirect inhibitory action on the hypothalamic LHRH cells.* Hence a high prolactin level reduces the activity of the hypothalamic LHRH cells, so that the hormone reaches the pituitary in smaller amounts and, still more importantly, not in pulsatile form. The consequence is that no follicle matures and *cyclic menstrual activity is abolished.* This mechanism underlies the phenomenon of postpartum amenorrhea, also called lactation anestrus in animals (see p. 383).

33.3 References

Textbooks and Handbooks

1. Martini, L., James, V.H.T.: The Endocrinology of Pregnancy and Parturition. Exp. Endocrinology Vol. 3, Academic Press, New York 193
2. Wilson, J.D., Foster, D.W.: William's Textbook of Endocrinology, W.B. Saunders Co. Philadelphia 1985
3. Yen, S.S.C., Jaffe, R.B.: Reproductive Endocrinology. Saunders, Philadelphia 1986

Original Papers and Reviews

4. Leong, D.A., Frawley, L.S., Neill, D.J.: Neuroendocrine Control of Prolactin Secretion. Ann. Rev. Physiol. *45*, 109–127 (1983)
5. Neill, J.D.: Neuroendocrine Regulation of Prolactin Secretion. Frontiers in Neuroendocrinology. Vol. *6*, 129–155, Raven Press, New York 1980

34 Aging and Old Age

R.K. Zahn

34.1 Basic Features of the Biological Aging Process

Aging and Life Expectancy

Definition of biological age. The term "age", when used as a synonym for the advanced stage of life, denotes a condition of reduced adaptation to physical and mental demands that is characteristic of these later years. In this strict sense, the term can be applied only to humans, to higher primates or to social organisms. Age starts around mid-life, with the decline of the ability to reproduce, and progresses until the death of the organism.

Life expectancy. During the entire history of the human race there have been old people; indeed, there have always been some individuals who reached the oldest age attainable in modern times. But as the average life expectancy has risen, the percentage of old people has steadily increased. In 1980 the *mean life expectancy* was 913 months (76.1 years) for women and 832 months (69.5 years) for men [16]. Fig. 34-1 shows the age composition of the population resident in Germany. Irregularities in the characteristic pyramidal shape [8] of the diagram result from wars and crises (as indicated in Fig. 34-1), and recently have also been introduced by the presence of a subpopulation of immigrant workers with a particular age composition.

Studies of skeletal remains from the Stone Age indicate that at that time the mean human life expectancy was 20 years. By the Middle Ages it had risen to 30 years, and by 1880, to 36 years. Around 1900 the mean life expectancy was still only 46 years, but since then it has steadily increased, except for wartime and postwar periods.

The difference in male and female life expectancy was formerly attributed mainly to the greater occupational demands made on men. At present the differences in smoking habits of the two sexes are also thought to contribute. The greater tobacco consumption of men increases their risk of dying early of circulatory and respiratory diseases. This hypothesis is supported by the finding that among the adherents of nonsmoking religious sects, women have the same life expectancy as men [11].

The *maximal human life expectancy*, about *115 years*, is reached by very few. The earlier death of most individuals is brought about by various endogenous and exogenous influences, including

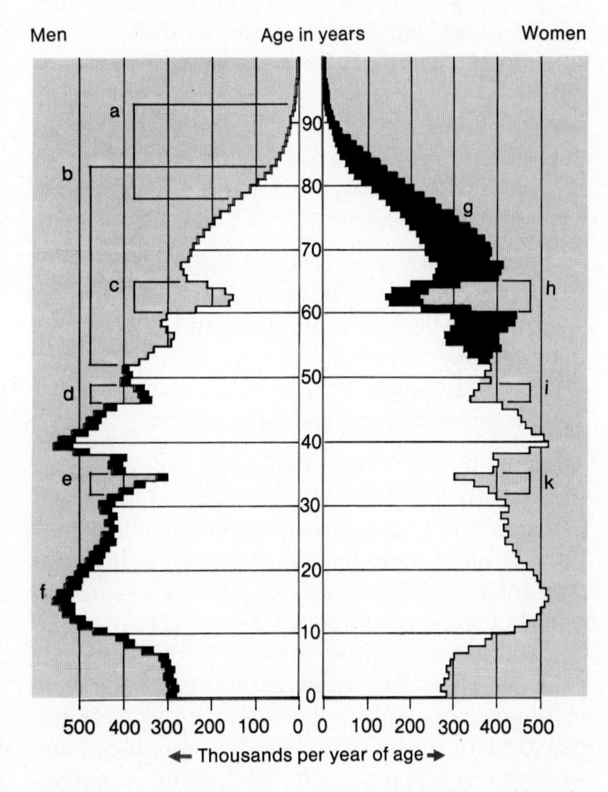

Fig. 34-1. Age composition of the population resident in Germany on December 31, 1979. (a) Casualties of the First World War; (b) casualties of the Second World War; (c) reduced birth rate during the First World War; (d) reduced birth rate during the depression, around 1932; (e) reduced birth rate at the end of the Second World War; (f) more men than women; (g) more women than men; (h) reduced birth rate in the First World War; (i) reduced birth rate during the depression, around 1932; (k) reduced birth rate at the end of the Second World War. (From [16])

hereditary factors, accidents and *diseases.* People whose parents reached a very old age are more likely to come close to the maximal life expectancy themselves.

The Aging Process

Whereas (old) age is a condition specific to one's later years, the *biological process of aging* begins at birth and continues, irreversibly, throughout life. At first increasing age is associated with an enhancement of physical and mental performance capacity. After a certain level has been reached, new abilities can be acquired only if others are given up. Eventually overall performance capacity begins to decrease, and this deterioration proceeds until death.

Aging used to be regarded as the progressive replacement of physiological functions by pathological processes. But since modern gerontology has come into being, it has become increasingly clear that aging is probably a *multifactorial biological event*, which is modified to different degrees by pathological factors.

Theories of aging. There is no consensus about the mechanisms involved in aging; indeed, theories abound [2]. Most of them can be assigned to two basic classes:

- the *non-genetic (epigenetic) theories*, in which structural changes of cells and tissues are regarded as the cause of aging, and
- the *genetic theories* [4], in which the responsibility for aging is attributed to changes in the transmission of genetic information.

Theories in the two groups often arrive at very similar conclusions, but by different logical steps (i.e., different cause-and-effect relationships).

In the older non-genetic theories, aging was thought to occur as parts of the body *wore out* [5, 10, 15] or accumulated *toxins* [1]. In other theories the aging process is ascribed to a *change in the degree of hydration and solvation of macromolecules* [20], as a result of which the mechanical strength of the tissues would be reduced and various cell functions disturbed. More recently a causative role of the *genetic component* has been under discussion, since the cellular apparatus for the transmission and expression of information, including DNA, is always found to be involved in the aging process. However, it remains controversial whether the DNA changes are themselves the cause of aging or whether they are simply side effects.

Nucleotide and protein changes as a cause of aging. According to a theory proposed by SZILARD [18], *radiation damage to the chromosomes* produces aging and eventually, when the damage has become extensive, leads to death. Well-founded objections have been raised to this theory, in its various modifications [17]. Radiation is only one of the factors injurious to the genetic information carriers; many other influences (including smoking), most of them at a much lower energy level, can damage the genetic material during the course of a lifetime.

This viewpoint is taken into account in the **error catastrophe theory** of ORGEL [12, 13], which also provides a link between the genetic and non-genetic causes of aging. The proposal here is that various kinds of damaging influences alter molecules of ribonucleic acid (RNA), so that after transcription *the wrong proteins are synthesized.* If these are proteins that themselves form part of the programmed biosynthesis chain, as in the case of the DNA-dependent RNA polymerase, the error is propagated. The altered copies induce the synthesis of other erroneous ribonucleic acids. Theoretically, once a critical error magnitude is exceeded, the process grows like an avalanche; an error catastrophe would have occurred. However, when experiments showed that the development of error avalanches is prevented by a self-inhibiting process, the theory had to be revised. In the new version, a steady-state level of erroneous synthesis ultimately becomes established.

The protein modifications that accompany aging were subsequently examined more closely, and it was found that the *specific activity of certain enzyme proteins decreases sharply* as one grows older [7]. That is, the change in the proteins has reduced their enzymatic activity. In old age, more enzyme proteins must be synthesized to achieve the necessary enzymatic effects. The significance of this finding with respect to the aging process is limited, however, in that certain groups of enzymes do not deteriorate with age and others actually show an increase in their specific activities. Furthermore, it has not been possible to isolate or produce pure samples of the altered proteins.

In summary, the aging process is probably a multifactorial phenomenon at the cellular level, in which alterations of the genetic apparatus play an important role.

34.2 Age-Related Functional Changes

As as person grows older, the organs undergo certain changes, none of which is lethal. At an advanced age, however, the probability that pathological changes will occur increases. As shown in Table 34-1, the major causes of death in the last stage of life are heart disease, strokes and neoplasms (tumors). The aging process itself is never the cause of death; life is brought to an end by the *diseases of old age* [3, 6, 14].

Blood. The age-related changes in the blood primarily affect the cell-producing system. The active bone marrow has a total volume of about 1,500 ml in a young adult. In the presenium (40–60 years) noticeable amounts of it are replaced by fat and connective tissue, and in still older people this process continues. The bone marrow in the sternum of a 70-year-old has a cell density only half that found in the young. This reduction affects *erythropoiesis* (p. 411) more than *leukopoiesis* (p. 414). Accordingly, with advancing age there is a slight decrease in erythrocyte count, total hemoglobin and hematocrit. The life span of the erythrocytes, however, is hardly changed. Metabolic changes are indicated by the decrease in the ATP and 2,3-diphosphoglycerate content of the erythrocytes.
Of the leukocytes, the *lymphocytes* – the T lymphocytes, in particular (p. 427) – decrease in number by 25% after the 40th year of life. The *reduced immunological competence* may be due in addition to the involution of the thymus in old age [9].

Heart. In healthy elderly people the weight of the heart remains constant in relation to the body weight, but the muscle fiber mass decreases and is partly replaced by connective tissue. There are characteristic degenerative changes in the muscle fibers, with the deposition of *lipofuscin* near the nuclei of the cells. The endocardium becomes thicker with age. Chief among the clinically significant morphological changes in the hearts of those over 70 is *coronary arteriosclerosis.* which can cause insufficient blood flow through the myocardium.
Functional disturbances of the heartbeat often result from changes in the conducting system, which is partially replaced by collagen. As a result, the *transmission of excitation is impaired* to a greater or lesser degree. Alteration of the membrane permeability to the ions involved in excitation can produce *ectopic foci,* which disrupt the heart rhythm (pp. 445, 459ff.). Such functional disturbances, reflected in the ECG, affect 50% of the older population.

Vascular system. The ways in which aging affects the arterial system are well known, but relatively little information is available about the venous and lymphatic systems. The dominant characteristic in the arteries is a progressive *decrease in elasticity.* Elastic fibers and smooth musculature disappear and are increasingly replaced by collagen. Arteriosclerotic changes in the vessel walls, which qualify as pathological changes, are ascribed to genetic factors as well as to diet and other aspects of life style. They are the basis of many of the diseases of old age, such as thromboses, embolisms and strokes.
The loss of arterial elasticity is often considered to be responsible for the statistical *rise in blood pressure* with aging (p. 525). In about 30% of the population, however, such a rise does not occur. Therefore some epidemiologists contend that the increased blood pressure is not part of the normal aging process but rather is an artefact produced by the inclusion of asymptomatic hypertensives in statistical analyses.

Table 34-1. Major causes of death ranked by frequency, for various age groups in 10 highly industrialized countries. (WHO 1974)

Age group: Rank	0–4 years	5–14 years	15–44 years	45–64 years	65 years and over
1	Accidents	Accidents	Accidents	Neoplastic diseases	Heart disease
2	Congenital disorders	Neoplastic diseases	Neoplastic diseases	Heart disease	Stroke
3	Neoplastic diseases	Congenital disorders	Heart disease	Stroke	Neoplastic diseases
4	Pneumonia	Pneumonia	Suicide	Accidents	Pneumonia
5	Intestinal infections	Heart disease	Stroke	Infections of airways	Chronic infections of airways

Respiratory tract. Even in healthy nonsmokers, the respiratory apparatus exhibits typical changes during aging. The alveoli become several times larger, and some of the alveolar septa disappear. There is a decrease in the number of pulmonary capillaries and of elastic fibers.
These morphological changes limit pulmonary function to a certain extent. Because of the reduced elasticity of the lung parenchyma and the increased rigidity of the thoracic skeleton, the *vital capacity and compliance decrease* (pp. 555f.). Because the tension produced by the elastic fibers is necessary to expand the smallest bronchioles, loss of these fibers is associated with an *increased resistance* (pp. 556f.). The relative forced expiratory volume decreases to the same degree (pp. 559f.). In the course of time, the increased airway resistance leads to an *increase in functional residual capacity* (p. 549). Finally, because of the reduced respiratory surface area the *diffusing capacity* (p. 565) is diminished.

Gastrointestinal tract. Beginning in middle age, *esophageal peristalsis* is more commonly disrupted, by the occurrence of nonpropulsive contractions instead of coordinated peristaltic waves. In the over-sixty age group a progressive *atrophy of the gastric mucosa* can eventually give rise to atrophic gastritis. The mass of the small intestine is reduced, and regeneration of its mucosa proceeds more slowly. The net result is a *diminished reabsorption* of certain substrates. The characteristic age-related changes of the large intestine are hypertrophy of the muscularis mucosae and atrophy of the muscularis propria. The elderly often suffer from *constipation*, but this can be prevented by a high-fiber diet and physical activity. In extreme old age, there is an increasing tendency to insufficiency of the sphincter muscles.

Liver. The liver, the most important gland in the human body, also undergoes distinct age-dependent changes. Beginning in the 5th decade of life, the weight of the liver and the blood flow through it both decrease. There is a clear decline in some *enzymatic activities* as well as in the processes that lead to *enzyme induction*. As a result, *in senescence many drugs are broken down more slowly*. In treating an old person with such medicines, care must be taken to allow for this change in pharmacokinetics.

Kidneys. The progressive structural and functional changes in the kidneys of an older person are based on the *loss of nephrons*. In the 8th decade of life the kidney comprises only about 70% of the original number of nephrons. Although this loss is partly compensated by enlargement of the remaining nephrons, the total weight of the kidneys decreases, and the *glomerular filtration rate* (p. 739) is reduced accordingly.

Skin. The changes in the skin are the most obvious signs of aging. It is here that the environmentally induced alterations of the genetic information carrier are most clearly revealed; clones of mutant cells appear as pigmented spots in parts of the skin that are exposed to light *(dermatohelioses)*. In addition to this variegated pigmentation, the skin exhibits proliferative changes – wrinkles, sagging, dryness and so on. The *hairs* lose their pigment and become more sparsely distributed. Often the head hairs fall out and are replaced by a fine, downy growth, forming a bald spot.

Reproductive organs. Opinions regarding the *sexual functions* in old age vary widely, in part because of the difficulty of obtaining a broad data base. But the evidence suggests that there is no biological end point for sexual interest or competence, in either men or women, although the frequency of sexual activity decreases as one grows older. The decisive factors here seem to be the individual's situation in life and hormonal status.
In **men**, for reasons partly still obscure, after the 55th to 60th year of life *enlargement of the prostate (prostate adenoma)* frequently occurs. It is produced by a benign growth of the paraurethral glands, which push the actual prostate tissue outward. The expanding glands compress the urethra, causing some degree of difficulty in urination.
In **women** a major change occurs at about age 50, the *climacteric*, when the gonads cease to function. The first sign is that menstrual bleeding becomes weaker and less regular; then ovulation stops and no corpus luteum is formed. As the levels of estrogen and progesterone in the blood fall, for a few years FSH production is greatly increased and that of LH, somewhat less so (p. 775). *Menopause* is the time when the final bleeding occurs. Unpleasant symptoms of the climacteric include hot flushes, sudden sweating, confusion and depressive moods. Pathological developments characteristic of aged women are uterine tumors (myomata) and atrophy of the vulva, vagina and urethra.

Central nervous system. Probably the most significant of the processes of aging, both subjectively and objectively, are those affecting brain function. In a healthy old person *cerebral blood flow* is only slightly reduced, and CO_2 responsiveness (p. 607) is fully retained. A major decrease in brain perfusion, statistically more common in those over 50 than in younger people, as a rule is the result of arteriosclerosis and should be regarded as pathological. An additional danger in these cases lies in the possibility of a *stroke* (apoplexy), caused by either cerebral hemorrhage or a cerebral infarct.

Contrary to popular opinion, the *intellectual functions* are not necessarily impaired in old age. But there is considerable individual variation in this respect, one of the main factors being the rate of cerebral perfusion. Disturbed sleep, reduced motor activity, difficulty in concentrating, diminished sensory abilities, emotional shallowness and modification of endocrine functions are all ascribed to age-dependent *alteration of neurotransmitter levels.* In the *EEG* (pp. 135ff.) of older people the relative abundance of low-frequency waves increases.

The *DNA content* of the aged brain is unchanged, as a rule, but *DNA damage* becomes increasingly widespread, perhaps because repair proceeds at a lower rate. Occasionally hyperploidy is observed. The methylation rates of DNA and histones are reduced; the metabolic activity of the chromatin-bound histones declines with advancing age. The rate of phosphorylation, and hence genetic activity, also decreases. The change most clearly correlated with aging is an increased lipofuscin production.

Sense organs. As they grow older, people **hear** less well. The ability to perceive high frequencies declines progressively (*presbycusis*, p. 289) and speech also becomes harder to understand, probably because the tuning curves of the auditory nerve fibers change (pp. 292f.). The causes of these sensory losses are stiffening of the basilar membrane, atrophy of the organ of Corti, and metabolic deficits due to atrophy of the stria vascularis. A progressive *loss of neurons* reduces the capacity for auditory information processing.

The **sense of sight** also deteriorates in various ways during senescence. Because the lens becomes less elastic, the range of accommodation is reduced, to less than 2 D in those over age 55 (*presbyopia*, p. 245). The lens also becomes less transparent, and under pathological conditions (*cataract*) can be nearly opaque. Changes of the lipids in the cornea can cause an *arcus senilis* to develop. Occasional disturbances of aqueous humor circulation can be caused by alterations in the canal of Schlemm. The *retina* is very likely to undergo age-related changes that can be interpreted as phototoxic effects. In people over 75 there is progressive degeneration of the pigment epithelium, hyalinization of Bruch's membrane and finally, in extreme old age, the formation of new vessels. These structural changes are associated with a *decreased acuity of long-distance vision*, so that the visus (visual acuity as measured with a Landolt ring) falls to about 0.6 in 80-year-olds and to only 0.3 at age 85.

Somatovisceral sensibility is impaired in very old people by a progressive loss of *Pacinian* and *Meissner's corpuscles* (pp. 199f.), amounting to as much as 30% at age 90.

Nutrition in senescence. With respect to the nutritional requirements of people over age 50 it should be kept in mind [19] that

- the *energy requirement is reduced*,
- there is an *increased protein requirement*, necessitating a daily intake of 1.2–1.5 g/kg body weight of high-quality protein containing the essential amino acids,
- fats with *polyunsaturated fatty acids* are to be preferred,
- the proportion by weight of *carbohydrates* should be *reduced to 40%*, and mono- and disaccharides should be avoided,
- although the absolute *vitamin requirement* is hardly altered, when less food is eaten vitamin deficiency can easily result and must be prevented by a suitable selection of food or by vitamin supplements,
- an *adequate supply of Ca^{2+}* should be ensured (e.g., by adding plenty of milk and milk products to the diet), to prevent the development of osteoporosis.

34.3 References

1. Barbour, H.G. and Hammelt, F.S.: Heavy water and longevity. Science 96,538–540 (1939)
2. Bürger, M.: Altern und Krankheit, Leipzig: Thieme 1960
3. Cape, R.D.T., Coe, R.M., Rossman, I.: Fundamentals of Geriatric Medicine. New York: Raven Press 1985
4. Curtis, H.J.: Das Altern. Die biologischen Vorgänge. Jura: Fischer 1968
5. Darwin, C.: quoted from Bürger, M.: Altern und Krankheit, Leipzig: Thieme 1960
6. Finch, C.E., Hayflick, L.: Handbook of the Biology of Aging. New York: Van Nostrand Reinhold Comp. 1985

7. GERSHON, H. and GERSHON, D.: Detection of inactive enzyme molecules in aging of organisms. Nature *227*, 1214–1217 (1970)
8. GOMPERTZ, B.: On the nature of the function expressive of the law of human mortality and on a new mode of determining life contingencies. Phil. Trans. Roy. Soc., London *1825*, 513–585
9. MAKINODAN, T.: Immunity and Aging. In FINCH, C.E. and HAYFLICK, L. (Eds.), The Biology of Aging, New York: Van Nostrand Reinhold Cy., 1977
10. MEDAWAR, P.B.: The uniqueness of the individual. London: Methuen 1957
11. MILLER, G.H., GERSTEIN, D.R.: The Life Expectancy of Nonsmoking Men and Women. Public Health Reports *98*, 343–349 (1983)
12. ORGEL, L.E.: The maintenance of the accuracy of protein synthesis and its relevance to aging. Proc. Nat. Acad. Sc. USA *49*, 517–521 (1963)
13. ORGEL, L.E.: The maintenance of the accuracy of protein synthesis and its relevance to aging: A correction. Proc. Nat. Acad. Sc. USA *67*, 1476 (1970)
14. PLATT, D.: Geriatrics. Berlin-Heidelberg-New York: Springer Vol. *1*, 1982, Vol. *2*, 1983, Vol. *3*, 1984
15. SELYE, H.: The Future for Aging Research. In SHOCK, N.W. (Ed.), Perspectives in Experimental Gerontology, Springfield (Ill.): Thomas Publ. 1966
16. Statistisches Bundesamt: Statistisches Jahrbuch 1981 für die Bundesrepublik Deutschland. Stuttgart, Mainz: Kohlhammer 1981
17. STREHLER, B.L.: Time, Cells and Aging. New York: Academic Press 1977
18. SZILARD, L.: On the nature of the aging process. Proc. Nat. Acad. Sc. USA *45*, 30–42 (1959)
19. THEWS, G., MUTSCHLER, E., VAUPEL, P.: Anatomie, Physiologie, Pathophysiologie des Menschen. Stuttgart: Wissenschaftl. Verl. Ges., 1982, p. 326
20. VERZAR, F.: Experimentelle Gerontologie. Stuttgart: Enke Verlag 1965

X
Appendix

Physiological Units

G. THEWS

International system of units. In recent years various international societies and organizations have recommended that a new system of units be introduced to standardize the physical and chemical quantities used in physiology, as in other branches of science. Many countries have followed this recommendation, passing laws that require the use of the new system. This *International System of Units (SI,* for *Système International d'Unités)* is based on the seven units listed in Table 1.

Table 1. Names and symbols of the SI base units

Quantity	Name of unit	Symbol
Length	meter	m
Mass	kilogram	kg
Time	second	s
Electric current	ampere	A
Thermodynamic temperature	kelvin	K
Luminous intensity	candela	cd
Amount of substance	mole	mol

These base units are defined as follows:

Meter (m) – The meter is the length equal to 1,650,763.73 wavelengths in vacuum of the radiation corresponding to the transition between the levels $2p_{10}$ and $5d_5$ of the krypton-86 atom.

Kilogram (kg) – The kilogram is the unit of mass; it is equal to the mass of the international prototype of the kilogram.

Second (s) – The second is the duration of 9,192,631,770 periods of the radiation corresponding to the transition between the two hyperfine levels of the ground state of the cesium-133 atom.

Ampere (A) – The ampere is that constant current which, if maintained in two straight parallel conductors of infinite length, of negligible cross section, and placed one meter apart in vacuum, would produce between these conductors a force equal to 2×10^{-7} newton per meter of length.

Kelvin (K) – The kelvin, unit of thermodynamic temperature, is the fraction 1/273.16 of the thermodynamic temperature of the triple point of water.

Candela (cd) – The candela is the luminous intensity, in a given direction, of a source that emits monochromatic radiation of frequency 540×10^{12} hertz and that has a radiant intensity in that direction of (1/683) watt per steradian.

Mole (mol) – The mole is the amount of substance of a system which contains as many elementary entities as there are atoms in 0.012 kilogram of carbon-12.

The units of all the other quantities can be derived from these base units. Some of them are listed in Table 2.

The numerical values of the quantities in Tables 1 and 2 often contain powers of ten as factors. To simplify specification of numerical data, certain commonly used powers of ten have been assigned special prefixes (Table 3) which are combined with the names of the units in question.

The conventional units listed in Table 4 can continue to be used along with the SI units.

Table 2. Names and symbols of some derived SI units

Quantity	Name of unit	Symbol	Definition
Frequency	hertz	Hz	s^{-1}
Force	newton	N	$m \cdot kg \cdot s^{-2}$
Pressure	pascal	Pa	$m^{-1} \cdot kg \cdot s^{-1}$ ($N \cdot m^{-2}$)
Energy	joule	J	$m^2 \cdot kg \cdot s^{-2}$ ($N \cdot m$)
Power	watt	W	$m^2 \cdot kg \cdot s^{-3}$ ($J \cdot s^{-1}$)
Electric charge	coulomb	C	$s \cdot A$
Electric potential difference	volt	V	$m^2 \cdot kg \cdot s^{-3} \cdot A^{-1}$ ($W \cdot A^{-1}$)
Electric resistance	ohm	Ω	$m^2 \cdot kg \cdot s^{-3} \cdot A^{-2}$ ($V \cdot A^{-1}$)
Electric conductance	siemens	S	$m^{-2} \cdot kg^{-1} \cdot s^3 \cdot A^2$ (Ω^{-1})
Electric capacitance	farad	F	$m^{-2} \cdot kg^{-1} \cdot s^4 \cdot A^2$ ($C \cdot V^{-1}$)
Magn. flux	weber	Wb	$m^2 \cdot kg \cdot s^{-2} \cdot A^{-1}$ ($V \cdot s$)
Magn. flux density	tesla	T	$kg \cdot s^{-2} \cdot A^{-1}$ ($Wb \cdot m^{-2}$)
Inductance (magn. conductance)	henry	H	$m^2 \cdot kg \cdot s^{-2} \cdot A^{-2}$ ($V \cdot s \cdot A^{-1}$)
Luminous flux	lumen	lm	$cd \cdot sr$[a]
Illuminance	lux	lx	$cd \cdot sr \cdot m^{-2}$ ($lm \cdot m^{-2}$)
Activity of a radioactive substance	becquerel	Bq	s^{-1}

[a] sr (steradian) = SI unit of solid angle

Table 3. Prefixes and symbols of frequently used power-of-ten factors

Factor	Prefix	Symbol	Factor	Prefix	Symbol
10^{-1}	deci	d	10	deca	da
10^{-2}	centi	c	10^{2}	hecto	h
10^{-3}	milli	m	10^{3}	kilo	k
10^{-6}	micro	μ	10^{6}	mega	M
10^{-9}	nano	n	10^{9}	giga	G
10^{-12}	pico	p	10^{12}	tera	T
10^{-15}	femto	f	10^{15}	peta	P

Table 4. Units not belonging to SI but currently retained

Name of unit	Symbol	SI equivalent
Gram	g	$1\ g = 10^{-3}$ kg
Liter	l	$1\ l = 1\ dm^3$
Minute	min	1 min = 60 s
Hour	h	1 h = 3.6 ks
Day	d	1 d = 86.4 ks
Degree Celsius	°C	t °C= (T–273.16) K

Conversion among units. Within the provisions of the SI system, concentrations can be given as amount of substance per unit volume (mol/l, mmol/l, μmol/l) or as mass per unit volume (g/l, mg/l). It is recommended that the *substance concentration* always be used for chemically uniform substances of known molecular weight (relative molecular mass). The *mass concentration* is a useful measure in the case of mixtures of dissolved substances – for example, total plasma protein. The conventional concentration units g% (g/dl), mg% (mg/dl) and meq/l can be converted to SI units by reference to the relations summarized in Table 5.

The new system will probably not be used consistently in medicine until a fairly long transition period has elapsed. Time is required not only for new equipment to become generally available, but also for the modification of unit-dependent norms to conform to the new system. Not until the most important norms in the new units have become as natural a part of the physician's store of knowledge as the old ones are now will the practicability of the proposed new system have been established. In particular, objections have been raised with regard to the replacement of the traditional unit of pressure, mm Hg, by the less easily visualized pascal. On the other hand, the joule is being increasingly accepted as the unit of energy, in place of the conventional calorie. To help the reader become accustomed to the new units, in this book they are usually used together with the conventional units.

Some of the frequently required conversions between SI and earlier units are given in Table 6.

Table 5. Conversion from conventional concentration units (g%, mg%, meq/l) to SI units of mass concentration (g/l) and substance concentration (mmol/l or μmol/l)

	1 g% =	1 g% =
Plasma protein	10 g/l	
Hemoglobin	10 g/l	0.621 mmol/l[a]
	1 mg% =	**1 meq/l =**
Sodium	0.4350 mmol/l	1.0 mmol/l
Potassium	0.2558 mmol/l	1.0 mmol/l
Calcium	0.2495 mmol/l	0.5 mmol/l
Magnesium	0.4114 mmol/l	0.5 mmol/l
Chloride	0.2821 mmol/l	1.0 mmol/l
Glucose	0.0555 mmol/l	
Cholesterol	0.0259 mmol/l	
Bilirubin	17.10 μmol/l	
Creatinine	88.40 μmol/l	
Uric acid	59.48 μmol/l	

[a] The molar hemoglobin concentration is based on the relative molecular mass of the hemoglobin monomer (see p. 582)

Table 6. Conversion between SI units and conventional units

Quantity	Relationships	
Force	$1\ dyn = 10^{-5}$ N	$1\ N = 10^{5}$ dyn
	1 kgf = 9.81 N	1 N = 0.102 kgf
Pressure	1 cm H_2O = 98.1 Pa	1 Pa = 0.0102 cm H_2O
	1 mm Hg = 133 Pa	1 Pa = 0.0075 mm Hg
	1 atm = 101 kPa	1 kPa = 0.0099 atm
	1 bar = 100 kPa	1 kPa = 0.01 bar
Energy (work) (amount of heat)	$1\ erg = 10^{-7}$ J	$1\ J = 10^{7}$ erg
	1 m·kgf = 9.81 J	1 J = 0.102 m·kgf
	1 cal = 4.19 J	1 J = 0.239 cal
Power	1 m·kgf/s = 9.81 W	1 W = 0.102 m·kgf/s
	1 HP = 736 W	1 W = 0.00136 HP
(heat flow)	1 kcal/h = 1.16 W	1 W = 0.860 kcal/h
(energy	1 kJ/d = 0.0116 W	1 W = 86.4 kJ/d
metabolism)	1 kcal/d = 0.0485 W	1 W = 20.6 kcal/d
Viscosity	1 poise = 0.1 Pa·s	1 Pa·s = 10 poise

Subject Index

R. F. Schmidt, University of Würzburg (Ed.)

Fundamentals of Sensory Physiology

Translated from the German by M. A. Biederman-Thorson

Springer Study Edition

3rd revised and expanded edition. 1986. 143 figures, mostly in color. XI, 300 pages. Soft cover
ISBN 3-540-15870-7

Contents: General Sensory Physiology, Psychophysics. - Somatovisceral Sensibility. - Neurophysiology of Sensory Systems. - Nociception and Pain. - Physiology of Vision. - Physiology of Hearing. - Physiology of the Sense of Equilibrium. - Physiology of Taste. - Physiology of Olfaction. - Thirst and Hunger: General Sensations. - Suggested Reading. - Answer Key. - Subject Index.

The basic aim of this highly-acclaimed work remains unchanged: it gives students with physiology as either a major or minor subject a superb introduction, based on neurophysiology, to the fundamental physiological mechanisms underlying human sensations.

From the reviews:

"This updating of an already excellent standard textbook on sensory physiology is most welcome. This edition retains the best features of its predecessors, most notably the carefully constructed outline organization matched to an extraordinarily complete index.

Contemporary Psychology-Medicine

Springer-Verlag
Berlin Heidelberg
London Paris
Tokyo Hong Kong